Alan Burt Overstreet

McGraw-Hill Series in History

Ralph E. Turner, *Consulting Editor*

JAPAN SINCE PERRY

McGraw-Hill Series in History

Ralph E. Turner, *Consulting Editor*

JAPAN SINCE PERRY

by

CHITOSHI YANAGA

Associate Professor of Political Science
Yale University

FIRST EDITION

NEW YORK   TORONTO   LONDON

McGRAW-HILL BOOK COMPANY, INC.

1949

JAPAN SINCE PERRY

To the Memory

OF

WALLACE M. ALEXANDER

Preface

The past century of Japan's development has been clearly an integral and inseparable part of world history. Important events within Japan itself were influenced, if not induced, by what happened in other parts of the world. The events of the nineteen thirties which led almost inexorably to the Pacific War have demonstrated that developments within Japan could have severe repercussions and far-reaching consequences on the rest of the world. It is now being demonstrated that the future of Japan depends more on what other nations do than what the Japanese people themselves can or will do. In the last few years we have become increasingly aware of the fact that Japan's future role in the fast-shifting scenes of world politics must be evaluated in the light of her past developments and achievements. The present volume attempts to present the events, personalities, and policies which contributed to Japan's emergence from a feudal nation. This was achieved through unremitting and undeviating efforts by her leaders who followed a carefully worked-out blueprint.

Almost a century ago Japan was impelled by world conditions to abandon, not without considerable misgivings, her centuries-old policy of seclusion and isolation. But once the decision was reached, the nation went about transforming itself into a modern power to a degree sufficient to gain admittance into the family of nations in a space of less than fifty years. The price paid for the achievement was high. What Japan achieved was not so much the enhancement of the dignity of the individual as the creation of a strong state capable of coping with nineteenth-century nationalism and expansionism. Westernization and modernization, which were carried out vigorously, were more material than spiritual and more in the techniques of production than in the advancement of the well-being of the people. Impelling needs for national economic and military strength set the course of the nation.

In the feverish effort to adopt and assimilate the ideas and institutions of Europe and America, the leaders showed little inclination to change the nation's traditional concepts, mores, thought patterns or institutions except when they stood in the way of progress. This resulted in an incongruous juxtaposition of Oriental and Occidental ideas and ideals as well as of old and new, and gave rise to inconsistencies, anachronisms, anomalies, and serious conflicts which could not easily be resolved. Japan is only now beginning to show signs of assimilating and digesting some of the elements of Western civilization which were first introduced three quarters of a century ago, but the process is painfully slow.

So far there has not appeared any standard work, either in Japanese or in any other language, which covers the recent history of Japan's development, that is, the period since the arrival of Commodore Perry. This period is not only the most interesting but also is unsurpassed in the inexhaustible store of materials it possesses. However, the difficulty of writing a comprehensive history is accentuated by the fact that many of the source materials still lie hidden and scattered among family papers in out-of-the-way private archives and storehouses throughout Japan.

In writing the present volume, the author utilized a considerable portion of the latest available researches of Japanese scholarship. However, he has given much greater emphasis to cultural, intellectual, social, and economic aspects of national development than has been customary among Japanese historians writing on the period. Official documents and sources have been used but due emphasis has been given also to informal, unofficial sources and especially the behind-the-scene activities of various groups and individuals which heretofore have not received sufficient attention.

While in general a chronological order is followed, each chapter has been written practically as a unit in itself, dealing with an aspect or phase of national development. The bibliography including works in both Japanese and Western languages is provided as an aid to the reader who desires additional references for more extensive study. The Oriental practice of giving family names first has been followed consistently in both the text and bibliography except where Christian given names are involved. Romanization is after Kenkyūsha. Long vowel pronunciation marks have been used throughout as an aid to correct pronunciation of Japanese words.

This volume would not have been possible without the cumulative output of numerous scholars, both Japanese and non-Japanese. The author is indebted especially to those who have specialized in the various aspects of Japan's development in the recent period. To Professor Edwin O. Reischauer of Harvard University, the author makes grateful acknowledgment for the arduous task of reading the entire manuscript and making corrections and valuable suggestions. The author wishes to thank Dean William C. DeVane of Yale College for providing the opportunity to complete the work. The author is also happy to acknowledge the debt he owes both former and present colleagues and students who, by their interest, response, and reactions, helped in the writing of the volume. Finally, he wishes to acknowledge the debt to his wife, especially for her interest and patience as well as her constant help and encouragement.

CHITOSHI YANAGA

NEW HAVEN, CONN.
June, 1949

Contents

Chapter 1. The Eastward Advance of Western Expansion

Marco Polo, the thirteenth-century Venetian adventurer who had served at the court of the great Mongol ruler Kublai Khan, pictured Japan as a land of unbelievable wealth where the entire roof of the Emperor's palace was "covered with a plating of gold." "So vast, indeed, are the riches of the palace," he wrote, "that it is impossible to convey an idea of them." [1] His glowing and tantalizing, though highly inaccurate, account of the "inexhaustible supply" of the precious metal excited the imagination of his contemporaries and sent Europeans of succeeding generations, particularly of the fifteenth and sixteenth centuries, upon hazardous voyages over uncharted seas in quest of the Oriental El Dorado. Irrepressible forces of colonial and commercial expansion were reflected in the voyages of discovery and exploration that were undertaken with the blessings of the crowned heads of Europe.

The Age of Exploration was opened by Portugal under Prince Henry the Navigator early in the fifteenth century. Vasco da Gama's voyage around the Cape of Good Hope to the Indian Ocean from 1497 to 1499 blazed the first maritime trail to Asia, which was soon thereafter exploited fully by the Portuguese explorers and traders. What riches were in store for the traders could be seen by the fact that the sale of the spices and other East Indian goods that Da Gama brought back netted sixty times the expenses of the voyage. Between 1510 and 1515 the Portuguese under Alberquerque seized Goa, Malacca, Ormuz, and the island of Socotra. By 1519 they had explored Java, Sumatra, Borneo, and the Celebes and had acquired fortified bases of operation throughout the East Indies from Malacca to Amboina in addition to the Indian ports of Chaul, Bombay, Bassein, Daman, and Diu. At the very height of their power, which lasted from 1511 to 1641, the Portuguese possessed a chain of fortified trading posts extending from Zanzibar to Malacca.

Spain was not far behind Portugal in her program of expansion, although at first it was not so well planned. The discovery of the New World by Columbus in 1492 marked the beginning of Spain's expansionist career. In anticipation of serious competition, the Pope issued his Bull of Demarcation in 1493 dividing the world into Spanish and Portuguese spheres. The discovery of the Pacific

[1] Marco Polo, *Travels*, p. 324, E. P. Dutton & Co., Inc., New York, 1926.

1

Ocean by Balboa in 1513 started Spain on her career as the dominant colonial power in the Western Hemisphere. The round-the-world voyage of Magellan from 1519 to 1521 aroused Spain's interest in the Far East. It was only a matter of time before the full impact of Spanish and Portuguese expansion came to be felt in Japan.

Beginning with the conquest of Mexico by Cortez and the subjugation of Peru by Pizarro thirteen years later, the adventurous conquistadores laid a strong foundation for Spain's vast colonial empire in the New World. With Mexico as their base of operations they began to extend their activities to the lands across the Pacific. In 1542 an expedition led by Villalobos was sent with instructions to establish permanent settlements in the Philippines. Twenty-two years later the Legazpi expedition was sent out, and in April, 1565, the first permanent Spanish colony in East Asia was founded at Cebu. By 1571 the Spaniards had captured the flourishing commercial town of Manila, which was ruled by a Mohammedan prince, and made it the capital of their new island empire. Ten years later the bishopric of Manila was created. From Manila, Spanish Franciscan missionaries were sent in 1592 for the first time to Japan, where Portuguese Jesuits had monopolized the missionary activities. The rivalry which developed between the two orders, and the aggressiveness and lack of circumspection on the part of the Franciscans, were to contribute toward the banning of Christianity in a matter of few years.

In 1517, even as Spain and Portugal were intensifying their efforts at empire building, Martin Luther set off the Protestant Reformation with his theological radicalism. The spiritual upheaval quickly spread to Switzerland, France, and England, resulting in the creation of a large number of independent sects. It was only natural that the Roman Catholic Church should view the vigorous attack launched by Luther with something less than equanimity, for it was a challenge hurled in the face of Catholicism. A vigorous defensive reaction took the form of the Catholic Counterreformation. As part of this movement an aggressive Catholic order, the Society of Jesus, dedicated to controverting Protestantism and preventing its spread, was founded by a zealous Spanish Catholic, Ignatius Loyola, in 1540. This new anti-Protestant movement had the support of Philip II of Spain, the most vigorous royal protagonist of Catholicism in his day. Within his realm the Inquisition was most active in persecuting and checking Protestantism. The Jesuits were not content, however, to rest with the mere preservation of Catholicism; they began vigorous and aggressive missionary efforts, which soon extended to India and the Far East.

Soon after the accession of John III in 1521, the Portuguese embarked on a systematic campaign for the extension of Christianity to the peoples of India and the Far East. In 1538 they established at Goa a bishopric, which was later raised to an archbishopric. In his boundless zeal and misdirected effort to impose Christianity upon the Indians, the Portuguese monarch instructed the viceroy to discover and destroy all the idols, thereby succeeding in antagonizing all non-Christian faiths. In 1560, the Portuguese established the Inquisition at Goa.

Only nine years after the founding of the Society of Jesus, Francis Xavier arrived in Japan to begin the work of propagating Christianity. Unlike the advent of Buddhism nine centuries earlier, the introduction of Christianity was not accompanied by violent political strife or bloodshed. Although there was considerable opposition, the missionary efforts of Xavier during his two-year sojourn bore considerable fruit. Thirty years after his arrival there were in Japan some 50 Jesuit missionaries, 200 churches, and 150,000 converts. In 1582, at the instance of the Jesuit provincial, Valegnani, who was anxious to show the Pope the results of missionary work, the influential Christian *daimyō* of Kyūshū were prevailed upon to send a good-will mission to the Papacy. Though not a diplomatic mission, this was the first embassy ever to be sent by the Japanese to the Occident.

It was one of the ironies of history that the intrepid European explorers bent on finding a short route to the land of fabulous wealth should be denied the satisfaction of "discovering" Japan. By a trick of fate, Portuguese sailors aboard a Chinese junk driven off its course by storm were the first to reach Japan in 1542,[2] exactly a half century after Columbus's memorable voyage of discovery. From the Portuguese, the *daimyō* of the island of Tanegashima, where the sailors had landed, secured firearms and had his men learn the art of manufacturing guns and gunpowder.

Although their arrival was quite unintentional, the Portuguese became the harbingers of Western civilization, passing on to the Japanese the spirit as well as the forces and instruments of European expansion and imperialism. The impact of European civilization set into motion inexorable forces which were to affect profoundly the course of Japanese history. No longer was the island empire to remain unaffected by the developments in Europe and America, for Japan was thrown willy-nilly into the current of world history. The introduction of firearms greatly changed, or even revolutionized, the traditional concept as well as the art of warfare. By 1555 a considerable number of guns had been turned out, and in that year they were used for the first time in the encounters between Takeda and Uesugi. Musket companies were organized and formation fighting came into vogue, although it did not completely supersede single combat for some time. The innovation necessitated modification in the planning and construction of castles. Foot soldiers became a very important component of the fighting force, enabling even an ordinary foot soldier of ability to rise from the ranks to a position of leadership, without regard to his social background. The introduction of gunpowder thus contributed toward the shifting and perhaps the undermining of the preexisting power relationships and affected even the social structure of the period. Even more far-reaching, however, was the effect of inter-

---

[2] Some historians give the year 1543 as the time of arrival of the Portuguese.

course with Europe on the economic and cultural developments of the nation.

The last quarter of the sixteenth century was punctuated by the activities of the English freebooters who were intent on destroying Spanish commerce wherever it was found. Hawkins, Drake, Frobisher, and other daring Elizabethan sea dogs wrought havoc on the Spanish galleons. By the 1580's Dutch and British ships appeared in the waters of India and Asia determined to break the hundred-year East Indian trade monopoly of the Portuguese. Philip's attempt in 1588 to retaliate against the English privateers preying upon Spanish commerce by destroying English naval power and carrying out the invasion of the island kingdom in order to drive out Protestantism ended disastrously. The disastrous consequence was the virtual annihilation of the mighty Armada and the destruction of Spanish supremacy on the seas. The overwhelming victory bolstered English nationalism and greatly strengthened the foundations of England's maritime power. Following the defeat of the Spanish Armada, John Lancaster was sent with an expedition to make contacts for commercial activities in the Far East. However, the Dutch actually preceded the English by several years in establishing themselves in the East Indian trade.

Four Dutch ships under Cornelius van Houten left Amsterdam in April, 1595, for the Indies and returned in August, 1597. So profitable was the trade that within a few years many rival companies had been organized, and the danger of ruinous competition among themselves haunted the Dutch. To avoid such a disastrous eventuality, a single joint stock company was given a charter with a twenty-one year monopoly of Far Eastern trade. This company was empowered to enter into treaties and agreements with the rulers and peoples of the Indies, to build forts, appoint governors, and maintain troops as well as courts of law for the preservation of peace and order. Thus, the Dutch set the pattern for the colonial exploitation of the Far East. In 1602, they were impelled to organize the Dutch East India Company to cope with English competition. The company did an incredibly lucrative business even during the uncertain years of its early existence. For the five-year period, 1606 to 1610, the annual dividends paid by the company to its stockholders ranged from 20 to 75 per cent, giving an average of 52 per cent return annually on their investment.

The appearance of the Dutch in Japan in 1600 was as much an accident as the arrival of the Portuguese more than a half century earlier. The Dutch ship *de Liefde,* blown off its course, was stranded on the coast of Bungo in northeastern Kyūshū. Since the Dutch were totally unprepared at the time, it was not until the summer of 1609 that they returned to enter into commercial relations with the Japanese. This was followed next year by the opening of a factory at Hirado in northern Kyūshū, which antedated by three years the establishment of the trading post by the Dutch on Manhattan island.

Dutch expansion in the East Indies, which was going on simultaneously with her colonization in North America, proceeded quite rapidly. In 1602, the year the

Dutch organized the East India Company, they drove the Portuguese out of Ceylon. Three years later, they seized the entire island of Amboina and by 1619 they assumed territorial sovereignty over Jacatra, which they renamed Batavia. Moving gradually northward, the Dutch in 1622 established a commercial and naval base on Pescadores, followed by another on the island of Formosa itself two years later.

Anglo-Dutch competition took a violent form on the island of Amboina, where the Dutch massacred English residents. Meanwhile, in Japan the Dutch subjected the English to terrific competition and forced them to withdraw "voluntarily." Thus, by the time Peter Minuit bought Manhattan island from the Indians for twenty-four dollars and founded the settlement of New Amsterdam, the Dutch traders in Japan were free of English competition. After the Portuguese and Spanish traders were banned by the Japanese authorities, the Dutch were the only Europeans permitted to remain behind and trade. In 1641, the Dutch captured Malacca and destroyed Portuguese power in the East Indies completely. For the next 157 years, from 1641 to 1798, the Dutch East India Company dominated the East Indies, having acquired a direct overlordship of Java, which served as the base of commercial operations in the Far East, and particularly in Dutch trade with Japan. Once more, the Dutch found themselves in a position to set the price of East Indian spices in the European market.

The English East India Company, founded on the last day of the year 1600, was the reply of the London merchants to the Dutch traders' boosting the price of tea and represented an effort to secure an English monopoly of the East Indian trade. However, it was not until two years after the Dutch arrived that English ships appeared in Japan to begin trade relations. This was due very largely to the efforts of the Englishman Will Adams, who arrived in Japan in 1600 as pilot major aboard the Dutch ship *de Liefde* and became the Shogun's adviser. Adams kept telling his friends and London merchants of the lucrative trade with Japan until he finally succeeded in interesting them. England soon began to make inroads into the Dutch commercial empire in East Asia. However, England's serious efforts at achieving commercial supremacy did not begin until after she was forced out of Japan by the Dutch. In 1639, she acquired the first piece of Indian soil and established the town of Madras. The acquisition of Bombay from Portugal as part of the dowry of Catherine of Braganza, who married Charles II, strengthened England's hold on India. In time, Bombay, Madras, and Calcutta became the three main centers of commercial activity for the English East India Company.

France was not far behind England in her vigorous efforts to seize commercial opportunities in Asia. In 1664, Louis XIV granted a French company the exclusive right to navigate and trade in the regions of the Far East from the Cape of Good Hope east as far as the Strait of Magellan. Four years later, a factory was established at Surat. In 1674, the company bought the town of Pondicherry, only 70 miles south of Madras. It was not until 1745, however, that the Anglo-French duel for supremacy was started between the agents of the two countries, who intrigued to secure disputed thrones for princes friendly to their respective interests. Indian rulers allied with or subsidized by foreign groups fought the battles which determined whether the control of India should fall to the French or to the English. Although the Frenchman Dupleix devised the technique by which European domination was eventually established in India and other parts of Asia, it was Robert Clive, a clerk in the employ of the English East India Company, who proved to be the consummate master of that technique. He laid the foundation for England's empire building in Asia. After 1761, France ceased to be an influence in the political affairs of India. By 1789, with the Dutch as well as the French out of the running, England was virtually in a position of undisputed supremacy in the East Indian trade.

POLICY OF NATIONAL SECLUSION

All might have been well for the Europeans but for the awakening of the feudal authorities to the possible danger of European aggrandizement. The Portuguese merchants had lost no time in establishing themselves in trade, and by the time the Spanish traders arrived on the scene they were firmly entrenched at Nagasaki. Hideyoshi, the political master of Japan, was a mercantilist at heart and an enthusiastic supporter of foreign trade as long as it held for him the promise of wealth and power without any threat to his position of supremacy. However, a specter of European imperialism began to haunt him before long, especially after he learned of the events in the city of Nagasaki. There, the Portuguese merchants had succeeded in forcing the *daimyō* to offer the revenues of the city as security for the loan they had made him. What alarmed Hideyoshi was the fact that the Portuguese were insisting that they be given the right to administer the city, threatening the withdrawal of trade in the event of refusal. In Hideyoshi's eyes, this was no less than a naked display of the land hunger of the Europeans about which he had been hearing.

The arrival of the Franciscan missionaries in the 1590's caused considerable complications because of sectarian differences and rivalry, and also because the newcomers were obviously not so circumspect or judicious as had been the Jesuits and thus unduly antagonized the authorities. Yet Hideyoshi's attitude toward the Christian missionaries was far from irreconcilable, though he had already issued as early as 1587 a decree prohibiting the dissemination of Christianity. After the *San Felipe* affair of 1596, there was no doubt in Hideyoshi's mind that the proscription of Christianity was necessary for his own security. Infuriated by the officious and high-handed treatment of the officials who had confiscated the cargo of the Spanish galleon, a member of the crew boasted defiantly that Spain's method of empire building consisted of sending out missionaries and traders to the new lands followed by troops who rapidly conquered and annexed them to her vast world empire. The apprehension of the officials as well as that of Hideyoshi regarding the danger of European aggression was heightened by this incident to a point where drastic steps followed as a natural consequence.

Perhaps because of the influence of his adviser, Will Adams, Ieyasu, successor to Hideyoshi, evinced a strong interest in foreign trade, an interest obviously based on mercantilistic thinking. His attitude toward the Portuguese was most cordial. In 1608, after an encounter at Macao between the Portuguese and the ships of Arima Harunobu, he complied with the Portuguese request and forbade Japanese ships to call at the port. Moreover, when he subsequently received a courteous communication from Goa, he gave the Portuguese permission to resume trade at Nagasaki.

Commercial intercourse with Spain, which had temporarily been suspended, was resumed at the instance of the Shogun in 1603 when ships from Luzon began to call at Uraga every year. Ieyasu was desirous of carrying on direct trade with Mexico. In 1609, when the ex-Governor of Luzon Don Rodrigo de Vivero was shipwrecked and his ship *San Francisco* completely destroyed, Ieyasu not only received the Spaniard cordially but sent him on to Mexico the following year in the ship *Santa Buena Ventura,* which had been built for him by Will Adams. On this occasion an agreement was reached for the opening of trade relations with Mexico, and Ieyasu promised the opening of a port, a grant of land for a trading post, and protection of Christianity, although he refused to grant Vivero's request that the Dutch be expelled.

Ieyasu selected Alonzo Munoz, a Franciscan missionary, as his personal envoy to Philip III of Spain and sent him along with Vivero. On board the little 120-ton ship manned by a crew including some Japanese sailors was a Kyōto merchant, Tanaka Katsunosuke, who was the first Japanese to set foot in Mexico and for that matter the North American continent as well.[3] After being royally received in Mexico, the ship returned to Uraga in 1611, bringing Sebastian Vizcaino, an envoy from the viceroy of New Spain.

In Mexico, a rumor was current that there were islands off the Japanese archipelago that contained an inexhaustible supply of gold and silver. On the pretext that it was a necessary preliminary to the opening of trade relations between Japan and Mexico, Vizcaino secured the permission of the Shogunate to survey the northeastern coast of the country. When the authorities discovered that he was searching for the hidden El Dorado, he was sent back to Mexico in 1613 in company with the embassy that was being sent to the Pope by Date Masamune, a *daimyō* of Sendai, who was anxious to open trade relations with Mexico.

[3] N. Murakami, "Japan's Early Attempts to Establish Commercial Relations with Mexico," in Panama-Pacific Historical Congress, *Pacific Ocean in History,* pp. 467–480, The Macmillan Company, New York, 1917.

Attempts by both Hideyoshi and Ieyasu to preserve foreign trade by its complete separation from religion or politics were unavailing. Moreover, strong suspicion was engendered by the intense rivalry among the Europeans, who intrigued and curried favor in order to maneuver themselves into the most advantageous position. In 1611, the Dutch divulged to the Shogunate a plot to overthrow the regime by the converted *daimyō* of Kyūshū with the help of the Portuguese, who were to furnish both ships and troops needed. This came at a time when the Shogunate was obsessed with fears that *daimyō* malcontents might enlist foreign aid in plotting its overthrow. Impelled by a strong desire to preserve its own power, the Tokugawa Shogunate adopted the policy of banning Christianity in 1612 and ordered converts to renounce their faith. Because of the practical impossibility of drawing a line between religious and commercial activities, particularly as carried on by the Portuguese at Nagasaki, the authorities came to the conclusion that it was best to exclude all Europeans except the Dutch, who alone had not shown any interest in the propagation of Christianity. In 1636, individuals as well as ships were prohibited from going abroad on pain of death. By 1639, all the Europeans had been expelled from Japan except the Dutch, who, with the Chinese, were allowed to carry on trade under extremely restricted conditions. For the next two hundred years, the Dutch were the purveyors and intermediaries in the limited importation of European civilization into Japan.

Denial of intercourse with the nations of the West was not only unnatural, but it could not be maintained indefinitely in the face of strong determination by the excluded powers to enjoy the benefits of trade that was much too lucrative to be ignored. It was to the advantage of the Japanese policy of seclusion that the intense colonial rivalries of the European powers kept them preoccupied and prevented them from taking effective measures to break down the seclusion. However, the overflowing energy of European expansion, which advanced relentlessly to the Far East, could not be stemmed by the mere refusal to recognize the realities of world events. Nor could Japan escape the full force of nineteenth-century imperialism without being caught in its rip tides and crosscurrents or at least in its backwashes.

RUSSIA AND ENGLAND TURN TO THE EAST

Russia's steady eastward march across the steppes of Siberia, which had its inception in the early sixteenth century under Ivan the Terrible, gained speed in the early seventeenth century and was beginning to reach the peaceful shores of Japan just as she was entering into a period of self-imposed seclusion that was to last more than two centuries. In 1636, a band of Cossacks pushing eastward from Yakutsk reached the Shilka, the northern tributary of the Amur River, and two years later they reached the Pacific at Okhotsk. On the heels of the pillaging expeditions of Cossacks, who were neither traders nor settlers, came the traders, followed by agricultural settlers. Before long, settlements sprang up at various points. By 1643, Yakutsk had its imperial governor, and in 1658 Nerchinsk was founded. Peasants were sent out in 1672 to colonize the place that later became Aigun, and the work of colonizing eastern Siberia was started in earnest by the Russian Imperial Court. The Treaty of Nerchinsk in 1689, while acceding to Chinese demands, gave concrete evidence of Russian influence as well as her intentions in the Far East. Before the end of the seventeenth century, permanent settlements had been established in Kamchatka, and the Amur was already being used advantageously for trading by the Russians. By 1711, they had occupied part of the Kuriles.

Beginning in 1739, the Russians made repeated, though unsuccessful, attempts to pry open the tightly closed doors of Japan by utilizing the convenient device of repatriating shipwrecked Japanese sailors and seizing the opportunity for negotiations. Many of the shipwrecked sailors had been pressed into service to teach Japanese to the Russians and to give information regarding their country. Some of them were taken all the way to the Russian capital, where they taught in the Japanese language school. The first official Russian attempt to open trade relations with Japan was made in 1792 by Lieutenant Laxman, who was sent by Catherine II. Officials of the Shogunate were adamant in their refusal to relax the seclusion law then in force. The closing years of the eighteenth century saw frantic efforts on the part of the Shogunate to strengthen the defense of Yezo against possible Russian encroachments from the north. In 1799, the Russian American Company, a Russian counterpart of the chartered colonization companies of Europe, was greatly expanded and given the right to engage in fisheries, fur trade, and in the colonization of the Pacific Coast of North America, as well as of Kamchatka, south of the 55th parallel. Russian colonization activities were intensified in North America, and a trading post was established at Fort Ross in Spanish California in 1816, only to be withdrawn in 1845 in the face of American advances on the Pacific Coast.

It was Count Nicolai Resanov, a son-in-law of the founder of the company, who as director of the powerful organization arrived in Nagasaki in 1804, escorted by Captain Krusenstern of the Russian Navy. His demand for the opening of the country to commercial intercourse was met once more by the adamant attitude of the officials. Frustrated by the refusal, and in retaliation, Captain Krusenstern sent two small ships in 1806 and 1807 to ravage the coast of Sakhalin and the island of Iturup. The raiding parties intimidated the natives, carried out plunder, burned down houses and ships, and threatened the inhabitants with even bigger raids if their demands were not met. This technique was quite in keeping with the methods the company employed in Alaska in dealing with the natives there. In 1811, the Russian sloop of war *Diana,* under the command of Captain Golovnin, was seized by the Japanese while the Russians were surveying the coast of

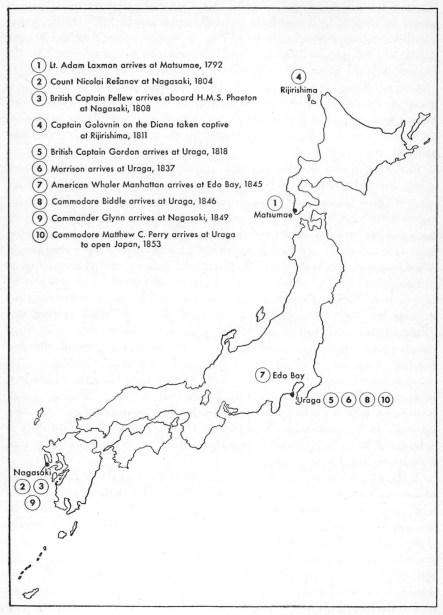

1. Lt. Adam Laxman arrives at Matsumae, 1792
2. Count Nicolai Rešanov at Nagasaki, 1804
3. British Captain Pellew arrives aboard H.M.S. Phaeton at Nagasaki, 1808
4. Captain Golovnin on the Diana taken captive at Rijirishima, 1811
5. British Captain Gordon arrives at Uraga, 1818
6. Morrison arrives at Uraga, 1837
7. American Whaler Manhattan arrives at Edo Bay, 1845
8. Commodore Biddle arrives at Uraga, 1846
9. Commander Glynn arrives at Nagasaki, 1849
10. Commodore Matthew C. Perry arrives at Uraga to open Japan, 1853

Western Attempts to Open Japan, 1792–1853.

Yezo and the Kuriles. Golovnin and several other officers were detained as prisoners for two years. Other Russian ships continued to call at the northern islands for a time thereafter, but preoccupation with the Napoleonic Wars prevented the Russians from carrying out their threat and forced them to abandon for the time being their persistent efforts to open Japan.

The closing years of the eighteenth century were a period of active geographical exploration for England. Captain James Cook of the Royal Navy, who discovered the Hawaiian Islands in 1778, was under orders from the Earl of Sandwich to explore the coast of the Japanese archipelago, but his untimely death prevented the execution of the order. In 1791, Captain George Vancouver surveyed Alaska and the California coast. Six years later Commander William R. Broughton, in command of the *Providence,* appeared in Japanese waters and, on September 15, dropped anchor in Muroran harbor in southern Yezo (Hokkaidō). The following year he sailed north along the coast of Hokkaidō into the Straits of Sōya, exploring the west coast of Sakhalin but without ascertaining that it was an island separated from the Asiatic mainland. He sailed southward, surveying the coast of the maritime province, following the eastern coast of Korea. After returning to Amoy, he started north again, going as far as Muroran, charting the eastern coast of Japan on his map, confirming the location of Edo Bay.

The temporary cessation of Russian attempts to open Japan did not afford the Japanese even a brief respite, for the British soon superseded the Russians. Even in Japan, repercussions of the Napoleonic Wars were felt. For a time the Dutch factory at Deshima in Nagasaki was the only place in the world where the Dutch flag was still flying. The annexation of the Netherlands to France by Napoleon had temporarily taken away Dutch sovereignty. In 1808, the British frigate *Phaeton,*[4] under its nineteen-year-old Captain Pellew, engaged in raiding and destroying Dutch commerce between Japan and Batavia and entered Nagasaki on suspicion that a Dutch merchant ship was in port. Pellew threatened to burn the Japanese and Chinese junks in the harbor if he was not supplied with provisions and water.

When English traders voluntarily withdrew from Hirado early in 1624, the director of the factory was looking forward to the time when trade could be resumed. In 1673 the English ship *Return* entered Nagasaki, and the officials interrogated the captain for information but did not permit the unloading and disposal of the ship's cargo. When the Macartney mission was sent to China in 1792 to smooth out the ruffled Anglo-Chinese relations, England was desirous of opening trade relations with Japan in order to buy tea and silk and to encourage trade competition with a view to lowering the price of Chinese products. Although the mission was equipped with "dormant credentials" and could have proceeded to Japan to negotiate the opening of trade relations, the report of an

[4] G. W. Aston, "H.M.S. *Phaeton* at Nagasaki in 1808," *Transactions of the Asiatic Society of Japan,* Vol. 7, p. 324, 1879.

impending clash between England and France prevented the mission from taking any action. It was not until two decades later that England began to attempt the reopening of Japan.

In 1813, Sir Stamford Raffles tried to open trade with Japan, but the director of the Dutch factory frustrated the attempt by threatening to expose British intrigue to the Japanese. Five years later, Captain Peter Gordon of the British Navy stopped in Edo Bay in the 65-ton trading brig *Brothers* on his way from Bengal to Okhotsk but failed to open Japan. The acquisition of Singapore in 1819 marked the beginning of more vigorous activities by the British in East Asia. The frequent appearance of British vessels in the subsequent period alarmed the Shogunate, resulting in the issuance in 1825 of a decree for the forceful expulsion of foreign ships that appeared in Japanese waters. At the same time it prohibited Japanese merchant ships and fishing vessels from approaching and contacting foreign ships. At the time of Gordon's visit, the Japanese had shown their irrepressible curiosity. Crowds flocked to inspect the ship, and a large number of people managed to barter goods. The efforts of the authorities to restrain the people were not entirely successful.[5]

The expulsion decree, however, was relaxed in consequence of the vigorous opposition on the part of enlightened scholars of Dutch culture, and particularly as a result of the humiliation suffered by China in consequence of her defeat in the Anglo-Chinese War of 1839–1842. Although English ships appeared in Japan several times, their attempts to open the country were not successful. It remained for the United States to make serious attempts and finally to succeed in opening the country to Western intercourse.

AMERICA'S EXPANSION AND INTEREST IN JAPAN

At the close of her war of independence, the United States found ships that had returned from privateering lying idle in the Atlantic seaports and most of the sailors unemployed, in spite of the fact that there was a market in America for the produce of Asia, which had formerly been brought over in British bottoms. At the same time there was a rich market in China for such American products as ginseng and fur. Moreover, there was the urgent need of replenishing the empty coffers and putting the financially exhausted nation back on its economic feet. These were impelling reasons, indeed.

John Ledyard, a native of Connecticut, who had joined the British Navy and had served as a corporal of the marines aboard H.M.S. *Resolution* in the last expedition of Captain James Cook to the Pacific in 1776–1781, was impressed by the limitless possibilities of trade with Asia. He had seen fur skins that had been bought on the northwest coast of North America for sixpence a piece sold in

---

[5] Peter Gordon, "An Account of a Short Visit to Japan in 1818," *Indo-Chinese Gleaner*, Vol. 2, No. 7, pp. 53–54, April, 1819.

Canton for one hundred dollars. In 1882, the year after the Cook expedition returned to England, Ledyard deserted the British Navy and made his way back to America, where he took upon himself the task of convincing American merchants of the profits which awaited them in the China trade. His efforts bore fruit, and in February, 1784, the first ship, *Empress of China,* a 360-ton clipper, owned and fitted out jointly by Robert Morris of Philadelphia and a group of New York merchants represented by the firm of Daniel Parker, was sent to Canton. In a few years clipper ships were plying regularly between the Atlantic seaports of the United States and Canton. With almost unbelievably favorable protective measures extended by the Federal government to the China trade, Atlantic ports like Salem, Boston, Providence, New London, New Haven, New York, Philadelphia, and Baltimore were launched on their way to commercial prosperity.

The lucrativeness of the China trade can be seen by the twenty-three-month voyage of the 93-ton *Betsey,* which set sail from New York in 1797 to Canton by way of Cape Horn and returned in 1798 by way of the Cape of Good Hope. The net proceeds of the voyage were more than $120,000 on an initial outlay of only $7,867, which covered the cost of vessel, outfit, insurance, and interest. After deducting customs duties, shares of the captain, the officers, and the crew, and the capital invested, there was a clear profit of $53,118 to the owners.[6] Such a high percentage of return on investment was a more than adequate incentive to the expansion of the China trade.

America's entry into the East India trade was only a partial manifestation of the lively expansionist spirit which grew out of the successful war of independence and which was soon manifested in the search for produce, trade, capital, and wealth all over the world. With President Jefferson's acquisition of the vast Louisiana territory from Napoleon Bonaparte in 1803, the westward expansion of the United States was on, as the trans-Mississippi West was opened up to the trappers, traders, and explorers who relentlessly pushed the frontier westward. The Lewis and Clark Expedition of 1804–1806, which charted rivers and fertile meadows and recommended locations for forts, was a carefully planned prelude to the opening of the West for migration and settlement. Going up the Missouri River and over the Rocky Mountains, the expedition reached the mouth of the Columbia River in 1805. Simultaneously, Captain Zebulon Pike started out on the exploration of the newly acquired Louisiana Territory. Between 1810 and 1812, the Astor party busied itself in establishing trading posts for the purpose of extending the fur business into the new territory. Although the War of 1812 temporarily slowed down the westward movement, the tide of expansion flowed with even greater force after the end of the conflict.

Once more the irrepressible force of expansion pushed back the frontier, as the course of empire made its way ever westward. The first American settle-

[6] Tyler Dennett, *Americans in Eastern Asia,* pp. 11–12.

ment on the Pacific Coast had been established by John Jacob Astor on the Columbia River in 1811. The Santa Fe Trail from Independence, Missouri, to Santa Fe, New Mexico, was opened in 1822 and continued until the Civil War as a caravan route to the Southwest. It was obvious when the Monroe Doctrine was enunciated in 1823 that it was directed against Russia as much as against any other power, since her colonization activities had been extended almost as far southward as the San Francisco Bay with the establishment of Fort Ross in 1816. The Oregon Trail, the western part of which had been traversed first by the overland expedition of the Astor party in 1811–1812, was reestablished in 1824 and came to be generally known. In 1832, the first wagon was taken over the trail. The first immigrant train made its way over it in 1841, after which immigrants poured into the Oregon country in increasingly large numbers; by 1846 there were some 10,000 Americans.

The seriousness of the government's intention with regard to the Pacific Coast was first evinced by the dispatch in 1831 of Captain Bonneville, who went into the Oregon country disguised as a fur trader to scout on the activities of the British and the Hudson's Bay Company. John C. Frémont's explorations of the Nevada, California, and Oregon country in 1843–1844 were the immediate prelude to the actual acquisition of the Pacific Coast by the United States.

In the second half of the 1840's, under the expansionist President James K. Polk (1845–1849), whose courage coupled with good fortune contributed greatly to spectacular successes in American diplomacy, a period of vigorous territorial expansion unfolded. "Manifest Destiny" characterized the mood of the Americans of the forties, and there prevailed a widespread popular conviction that the young republic was destined to expand by peaceful process over the whole of the North American continent. No wonder then that Polk's election in 1844 to the presidency should have been taken as a virtual mandate from the people for the annexation of Texas. A joint resolution of Congress for annexation was signed by President Tyler on March 1, 1845, just three days before he relinquished the presidency to Polk.

The following year, President Polk scored a diplomatic victory over Great Britain, the greatest power in the world. By the treaty of 1846, the United States secured the Oregon country. In the same year, Frémont incited five hundred Americans in California to insurrection and under his leadership they declared the Bear Flag Republic. Two years later, in the Treaty of Guadalupe Hidalgo which marked the end of the Mexican War, Mexico gave up all claim to Texas, with the Rio Grande as the boundary, and ceded to the United States the provinces of New Mexico and Upper California (comprising California, Nevada, and Arizona), an area of some 522,955 square miles for the price of 15 million dollars. But for the small area acquired five years later by the Gadsden Purchase from Mexico, the territorial expansion of southwestern United States had, for all practical purposes, come to an end.

Westward expansion was accompanied by a strong demand for improved means of transportation. In 1845, Asa Whitney, a New York merchant engaged in the China trade, memorialized Congress urging the construction of a railroad from Chicago to the Pacific, which, he hoped, would draw the trade of the Far East to the United States. The following year, George Wilkes of New York presented a memorial to Congress proposing the construction of a national railroad from the Missouri River to the Pacific Ocean for the purpose of obtaining a short route to Oregon and the Indies. Farsighted and patriotic Americans had come to regard the construction of a transcontinental railroad as an urgent necessity, not only in opening up the interior regions to agricultural settlement and turning the wide expanses of the prairies into golden fields of grain, but also in gaining access to, if not pre-emption and command of, the markets of Asia. Vast countries that still lay in the voluptuous regions of the East, and whose productions and resources were scarcely known, awaited the benefits of commercial intercourse and the civilizing influences of the West. Wilkes was particularly interested in "the opulent empire of Japan" whose "single trade is capable of the enrichment and aggrandizement of an empire and it should not be considered as too much for American diplomacy and American enterprise to illustrate the measure of its value in favor of the United States." [7]

An internal improvement convention held in Chicago in 1847 with Horace Greeley as chairman passed resolutions and went on record as favoring a transcontinental railroad. October, 1849, saw the holding in St. Louis of the first convention to discuss ways and means for a transcontinental railroad. The discovery of gold in California furnished the necessary spur to the settlement of the Pacific Coast. Miners, traders, and settlers poured into the West by the thousands so that within a year there were nearly 300,000 Americans on the Pacific slope. Increased population necessitated better transportation and the discussions of transcontinental railroad projects were invariably related to the East Asia trade.

What first brought Japan within the interests of American merchants was the rapid growth of the Pacific Northwest fur trade, which flourished until about 1820. Two American ships on their way to Canton in 1791 visited a southern Japanese port and tried unsuccessfully to dispose of sea otter pelts. At first, however, little active interest was shown by the American merchants, for these early incidents were soon forgotten. Shortly after the War of 1812, Commodore David Porter proposed to Secretary of State James Monroe the sending of an expedition to open Japan. No action was taken on the proposal, however. The Pacific Northwest fur trade gave way to whaling activities in the North Pacific in the 1820's, and American interests extended to the islands of the Pacific as

[7] George Wilkes, "Proposal for a National Railroad to the Pacific for the Purpose of Obtaining a Short Route to Oregon and the Indies" (New York: D. Adee, printer, 4th ed., 1847), reprinted in *Magazine of History*, Vol. 36, No. 1, pp. 55–75, 1928.

well as to the lands of Asia. In 1820, exactly two centuries after the arrival of their forefathers, New England missionaries arrived in the Hawaiian Islands to minister to the needs of the natives at a time when more and more whaling ships were beginning to visit the islands.

Desirous of extending American trading rights in the region of the Indian Ocean by opening commercial relations with some of the countries, President Andrew Jackson, in 1832, commissioned Edmund Roberts, a wealthy shipowner of Portsmouth, New Hampshire, to negotiate treaties. Although he succeeded in concluding treaties with Muscat and Siam, he did not get to Japan, as had been planned. In 1835, the United States Senate having ratified the treaties, Jackson sent Roberts back to exchange ratifications, handing him a communication written in Dutch and Latin, as well as a gold watch, small arms, swords, maps, paintings, cloth, and other gifts to be presented to the Emperor of Japan. While en route to Japan, Roberts became ill and died at Macao in 1836, and the plan came to naught.

The first actual attempt to open Japan was privately undertaken by the firm of Olyphant and Company of Canton in 1837. Seven shipwrecked Japanese sailors at Macao were taken aboard the company's ship *Morrison* to be repatriated and at the same time to seize this opportunity to open negotiations for missionary work as well as for trade. When the *Morrison* arrived at Uraga in July and made known the purpose of the visit, the Shogunate refused to have any dealings with the Americans, ordered her away, and then opened fire on the vessel. The Japanese officials interpreted the withdrawal of the *Morrison* as a sign of weakness on the part of the Americans and deluded themselves into thinking that they had repelled the American ship by superior force. Although the attempt failed, the Americans thereafter never allowed the subject of opening Japan to drop out of sight.

When Caleb Cushing successfully negotiated a treaty with China in 1844, American missionaries and merchants in Canton urged him to take necessary steps to open Japan next, which was regarded as a fruitful field for trade and missionary efforts. Cushing communicated this to President Polk who remained somewhat dubious of the possibility of concluding a treaty with Japan. When Secretary of State John C. Calhoun, after deliberating on the matter, sent instructions commissioning Cushing with full powers to negotiate a treaty, it was too late, for Cushing had already left China to return to the United States.

On February 15, 1845, following the publication of the Cushing correspondence on the China treaty, Congressman Pratt of New York introduced a resolution in the House calling for immediate measures to effect commercial arrangements with Japan and Korea, but it passed unnoticed. The time was not yet ripe for such an undertaking. When the American whale ship *Manhattan* visited Edo Bay in April, 1845, to return shipwrecked sailors, it was accorded hospitable treatment, although it was permitted to remain only a few days. When the ship left, some Japanese stowaways seized the opportunity offered to go abroad to study and observe the Western world.

The application of Manifest Destiny to Asia was voiced by United States Senator Thomas Hart Benton of Missouri, father-in-law of John C. Frémont, who, in May, 1846, eloquently expressed his belief that "the arrival of the van of the Caucasian race upon the border of the sea which washes the shore of Eastern Asia" promised a greater and more beneficent change upon the earth than any human event past or present "since the dispersion of man upon the earth." The Caucasian race "must wake up and reanimate the torpid body of Asia. . . . The moral and intellectual superiority of the White race will do the rest: and thus the youngest people, and the newest land, will become the reviver and the regenerator of the oldest." [8]

Alexander H. Everett, the first American Commissioner to China under the Cushing treaty, sailed for China early in June, 1845, carrying with him a commission to negotiate a treaty with Japan, but he became ill en route and was forced to return. He was unable to reach China until October, 1846. Meanwhile Commodore James Biddle, to whom Everett had delegated his duties, arrived at Uraga on July 20, 1846, in command of two ships, *Columbus* and *Vincennes*. The American envoy refused to comply with the Japanese demand that guns and weapons be dismantled. Biddle tried to show Chinese translations of the treaties concluded by England, France, and the United States with China, but the officials refused to accept on grounds that the American envoy had no authority. Negotiations were not even begun, although the Japanese supplied Biddle with provisions and other needs. Although Everett was again given full plenipotentiary powers to treat with Japan, he was unable to accomplish his mission because of his untimely death in Canton in May, 1847.

From 1846 on, the subject of a treaty with Japan came more and more to engage the attention of Americans. An increasing number of ships came within Japanese territorial waters as American shipping at Shanghai increased and the whale fisheries in the North Pacific increased rapidly. Due to rough weather and unfamiliarity with conditions prevailing in those waters shipwrecks were not uncommon. Moreover, the treatment of the shipwrecked American sailors in Japan left much to be desired. Severe treatment was common, and repatriation was necessarily slow as it had to be carried out through the Dutch at Nagasaki.

In January, 1849, Commander James Glynn of the United States Navy proceeded to Nagasaki in the sloop *Preble* to rescue the survivors of the crew of the whaler *Lagoda,* which had been shipwrecked in the Japan sea the year before. Although the release of the imprisoned sailors was effected after considerable difficulty, there was no attempt made to urge trade relations upon the Japanese

[8] Ralph H. Gabriel, *The Course of American Democratic Thought,* pp. 343–344.

authorities, who were beginning to suspect espionage because of the increasing number of Americans who appeared in Japan.[9]

In the summer of 1850, Joseph Levyssohn, director of the Dutch factory at Deshima, received through the Dutch chargé in Washington a letter and papers from his friend, Aaron Haight Palmer, director of the American and Foreign Agency in New York, pertaining to Palmer's proposal made in 1849 to the United States Senate and Secretary of State John M. Clayton for the promotion of trade relations with the countries of the Far East. The letter indicated his hope that the United States would send an expedition to Japan in an attempt to make her conform to the prevailing civilized standard of justice in the treatment of shipwrecked Americans and to open her ports to trade. For the projected steamship line between San Francisco, Shanghai, and Canton, coaling stations were to be opened at Matsumae, Tsushima and Ryūkyū.

Palmer pressed the matter in January, 1851, urging President Fillmore to send a special envoy to Japan escorted by a strong naval squadron. Secretary of State Daniel Webster discussed the matter with Palmer. Meanwhile, Commander Glynn returned to New York and reported the existence of many good harbors, which could be used for shelter from storm, and of large supplies of high-quality coal, for he recognized the need for establishing coaling stations in Japan. In June, Glynn himself urged on the President the need for negotiating a commercial treaty with Japan, in view of the projected opening of a steamship line between California and the Orient. This, he argued, had to come eventually, and if it could not be achieved peacefully, it would have to be achieved by resorting to force, if necessary. He emphasized, however, that it should be made clear to the Japanese that the United States entertained no intention of interfering in their internal politics or religion and that she was interested only in freedom of trade.

On February 21, 1851, the American bark *Auckland* put into San Francisco with seventeen Japanese sailors who had been rescued at sea. Commodore John H. Aulick, who had also seen the need of opening Japan, suggested to the State Department that the repatriation of these sailors would provide an excellent opportunity for the opening of relations with Japan. President Fillmore called a meeting of his Cabinet and Aulick was appointed special envoy to Japan in May. While the Commodore was en route, he was relieved of his assignment because of a diplomatic problem he created in South America. He was not informed of this, however, until he arrived in Far Eastern waters.

In late March, 1852, Commodore Matthew Calbraith Perry was appointed commander in chief of the East India Squadron and special envoy to Japan. At the request of the new commander in chief, the squadron was doubled in size. Although Secretary of State Daniel Webster had died before issuing instructions to the special envoy, Acting Secretary Charles M. Conrad, then Secretary of War,

[9] "Cruise of the U.S. Sloop of War *Preble*," *Chinese Repository*, Vol. 18, No. 6, pp. 315–332.

issued instructions on November 5 that not only became the basis of Perry's negotiations but also reflected American policy vis-à-vis Japan. Significantly enough, the instructions contained the first comprehensive statement of the basis of an American policy for the Pacific.[10]

Recent events—the navigation of the ocean by steam, the acquisition and rapid settlement by this country of a vast territory on the Pacific, the discovery of gold in that region, the rapid communication established across the Isthmus which separates the two oceans—have practically brought the countries of the east in closer proximity to our own; although the consequences of these events have scarcely begun to be felt, the intercourse between them has already greatly increased and no limits can be assigned to its future extension.

Tremendous energies unleashed in the process of the westward extension of the American frontier had resulted not only in spanning the wilderness, the prairies, the rivers, and the mountains of the American continent but also the expanse of the Pacific, and they were now making their impact felt on the hermit empire of the East.

[10] Dennett, *op. cit.*, pp. 262–263.

Chapter 2. The Resumption of Intercourse with the West

Japan was by no means in a state of peaceful slumber during the more than two centuries of self-imposed seclusion. News of the outside world trickled into the island empire through the Dutch factory at Deshima in Nagasaki harbor, which was the gateway to the West. Although news was sifted and screened for the authorities, the Japanese were in a general way kept informed of the latest and most significant events in the Western world. It is certain that repercussions of world events were felt in Japan, though perhaps never their full impact or their immediacy. Government officials therefore could not possibly have been completely ignorant of what was transpiring in the outside world.

In 1844, William II of the Netherlands addressed to the Shogun a personal letter in which he cited the Anglo-Chinese War (1839–1842) and expressed anxiety for Japan. He explained how the introduction of steam navigation had reduced distances and emphasized that a nation which continued to remain in seclusion could not avoid incurring the hostility of other nations. Once again in 1847 the Dutch monarch advised the Shogun of the march of world events and pointed out that they made the policy of seclusion anachronistic, unwise, dangerous, and untenable.

The director of the Dutch factory at Deshima informed the authorities in 1850 of the westward expansion of the United States which had been gaining momentum after the Mexican War, particularly as the result of the discovery of gold in California, the steady stream of migration into the Pacific Coast states, and the completion of the Isthmian railroad. When the United States decided early in 1852 to send an expedition to Japan, Secretary of State Webster informed the American Minister at The Hague who transmitted the information to the Dutch Foreign Minister in July together with the assurance that the American mission was to be a peaceful one. In due time the Japanese received from the Dutch all the available information on the projected expedition. The warnings, advice, and information given by the Dutch were carefully noted by the Shogun's officials and filed away but nothing was done about them.

On a midsummer's day in 1853, Commodore Matthew Calbraith Perry appeared off Uraga with his squadron of four "black ships." Perry's plan was to enter Edo Bay with a large squadron of twelve ships but when he left Naha, he had only four ships, the flagship *Susquehanna,* the frigate *Mississippi,* and the sloops *Plymouth* and *Saratoga*. Bearing in mind the treatment received by the *Morrison* in 1837 and the capture of the Russian Captain Golovnin in 1811, Perry took every caution and ordered the decks cleared for action and the guns loaded as the squadron sailed up Edo Bay.

Although the Dutch had predicted and forewarned the Japanese of the impending arrival of an American expedition, the Shogunate was taken completely by surprise and thrown into confusion and the officials were panic-stricken. High-ranking officials were hurriedly summoned to the Shogun's castle in Edo for an all-night conference, but they were unable to devise ways and means of effectively coping with the grave situation. The news of Perry's arrival spread fast into the countryside and terrified residents, fearing for their safety, took flight into the hills and refused to come out until they were assured that the danger was past.

The officials who were in charge of Perry's reception tried to shunt him to Nagasaki as a method of delaying, if not discouraging, the presentation of President Fillmore's message to the Shogun. The Commodore not only insisted on making the presentation, but threatened that if a suitable person was not appointed to receive the communication, he would go ashore with a sufficient force and deliver it himself. While the Japanese were deliberating, he began to take soundings of the bay and harbor. Failing in the dilatory tactics of sending Perry to Nagasaki, the Shogunate finally dispatched two commissioners of Uraga to receive the American envoy at Kurihama. After receiving President Fillmore's message, the Shogunate requested time to deliberate on the serious matter of concluding a treaty. Perry consented and left with the promise to return early the following year with a larger force. In his report to the Secretary of the Navy James C. Dobbin, Perry stated that he had to consent to the Japanese demand for time to deliberate until next spring, because he could not stay and wait for the reply in the face of lack of provisions.

Immediately, the Imperial Court at Kyōto was notified of Perry's arrival and the purpose of his visit. Simultaneously, the Shogunate embarked upon a program of military preparedness, which included the construction of forts in the Bay of Shinagawa, granting permission to *daimyō* in the different feudatories for the building of large ships (which previously had been banned), purchasing men-of-war and guns from Holland, and giving the feudatories the freedom to construct fortifications. The Shogunate then ordered the *daimyō* to submit their views on the question of opening the country, an issue which was now being forced upon the nation for a speedy decision. A translation of President Fillmore's message was submitted to them. This was an unprecedented step for the Shogunate which had always arrived at any decision in a dictatorial manner. This procedure would have been unthinkable under normal circumstances. The Shogunate was in a serious dilemma and had no other alternative, for it had neither the strength nor will to exercise arbitrary power.

Most of the *daimyō* recommended the continuance of the policy of seclusion. Those who favored the opening of the country suggested it only as a temporary expedient or a dilatory measure to gain time while rushing the strengthening of national defense. However, they were practically unanimous in their strong desire to avoid hostilities. Knowing its own weakness too well, the Shogunate decided on the dilatory policy which it had been pursuing for some time and which was quite in keeping with the traditional feudal concept of strategy.

Meanwhile, the Russians, who had known for some time that the United States was sending an expedition to Japan to open the country, were determined not to be left behind in treaty negotiations, especially in view of the fact that they had already made several unsuccessful attempts. The sudden arrival in Nagasaki of Admiral Putiatin, in command of four naval vessels, took the Shogunate by surprise. Coming as it did, right on the heels of the demands made by Commodore Perry, who was then in the China Sea, it posed a diplomatic problem that the feudal authorities did not relish. The Russians pressed a demand for boundary settlement as well as for the opening of trade relations. Two of the ablest officials, Tsutsui Masanori and Kawaji Toshiakira, were ordered to Nagasaki to deal with the Russian envoy. In October, while still waiting for the Bakufu representatives to arrive from Edo, Putiatin received by way of Shanghai the disquieting news that his country was on the verge of war with Great Britain and France over the Turkish question. He hurriedly left for China, but returned in December and started negotiations with the officials, who proposed that the boundary question be deferred to a later date when surveys would have been made on the spot by a boundary commission. As to the opening of trade relations, the Japanese officials informed Putiatin that it was impossible as it would be a contravention of the age-old seclusion law which was still in force. Although hardly any progress had been made in the negotiations due to the dilatory tactics of the Bakufu officials, the Russian envoy reluctantly weighed anchor and left Nagasaki in January, 1854, without having achieved his mission, for the Crimean War was now in full swing and he could not prolong his stay any further.

When Perry received word of the arrival of Putiatin in Japan, he lost no time in hurrying back to resume negotiations for a treaty. He returned on January 16, 1854, with a greatly reinforced squadron of nine ships, sailed up Edo Bay and dropped anchor off Kanagawa to await the Japanese reply to President Fillmore's message which he had delivered in the summer of the preceding year. The Bakufu was by this time thoroughly convinced of the futility of discouraging the Commodore who showed unswerving determination to accomplish his mission. In March, only a few weeks after his return to Japan, Perry secured the Treaty of Kanagawa, a treaty of amity and friendship by which the ports of Shimoda and Hakodate were opened in addition to Nagasaki which had been open in fact for some time.

With its coffers depleted, its defenses so woefully weak that it lacked even a token standing army, and having few loyal supporters, the tottering feudal regime under the Tokugawa was in no position to prevent or even delay the opening of Japan. It had bowed to the inevitable as graciously as the circumstances permitted. But in so doing, it had released the irresistible forces as well as a chain of inexorable events which were in the end to lead to its own destruction.

While the Crimean War was in progress, in August, 1854, Admiral Sterling of the British Navy, in command of four warships, entered Nagasaki and requested the authorities' permission to enter Japanese ports freely in pursuit of Russian ships. The Shogunate informed the Admiral that it would be impossible to give favored treatment to any of the belligerents, but that it would open the ports of Nagasaki and Hakodate to enable British ships to take on fuel, water, and provisions. Admiral Sterling accepted the Japanese offer and in August signed a treaty of amity and friendship.

In the following month, Putiatin once again surprised the Japanese with his unexpected appearance, this time in Ōsaka. The authorities instructed him to proceed to Shimoda where he was received by the same officials with whom he had unsuccessfully negotiated the year before. In December a treaty was signed, and the ports of Shimoda, Hakodate, and Nagasaki were opened to the Russians. The boundary question relating to Sakhalin and the Kuriles was also discussed and an informal understanding was reached. That portion of the Kuriles including the Iturup and the islands to the south of it was to be Japanese while the boundary in Sakhalin was to be left undetermined. The following year, the Bakufu notified the Dutch government of the conclusion of treaties with the United States, Great Britain, and Russia, lifted the restrictions on the Dutch which had been in effect throughout the period of seclusion, and formally concluded a treaty of friendship. Treaties with other powers followed and the same ports were thrown open to them.

By the Treaty of Kanagawa the American government was entitled to diplomatic representation at the port of Shimoda eighteen months from the date of the treaty. In fulfillment of this stipulation the United States sent as its first representative to Japan, a man of outstanding ability and character, who won completely the confidence of the Japanese officials and people alike to a degree attained by no other foreign representative. Arriving in the summer of 1856 in an atmosphere charged with strong suspicion and explosive antiforeign sentiment, Townsend Harris immediately set out to achieve his objective. No better representative than this former New York merchant could have been selected by the American government for the difficult mission that lay ahead. A less stout heart would have foundered; a less sympathetic soul would have antagonized the Japanese.

The Bakufu was fearful of the difficulties that would arise from the stationing of foreign representatives in the country. It was determined, therefore, to force

Harris to give up and return home in disgust. To this end, the Bakufu used every conceivable method of persuasion and dilatory tactics; no stratagem was overlooked. But the new consul was not to be outdone in his determination to stay on to accomplish his mission regardless of the odds so plainly against him. The Treaty of Kanagawa which Perry had negotiated made no provision for commercial intercourse between Japan and the United States. Furthermore, Harris was determined to have his name occupy a place in history. Overwhelmed by the persistence and dogged perseverance of the man, the Shogunate yielded and permitted Harris to set up a temporary consulate in a Buddhist temple, Gyokusenji, in Shimoda. Here in this out-of-the-way village, the first American consul, the first representative of an Occidental power, was to live in complete isolation for more than a year. At first, his request to go to Edo for an audience with the Shogun to present his credentials and to conduct negotiations with the Senior Minister fell on deaf ears.

In the meantime, the officials of the Shogunate who were in charge of foreign relations were coming in frequent contact with foreigners. This led inevitably to the understanding of foreign affairs on the part of the officials, who then became favorably disposed towards foreign trade. When Hotta Masayoshi was made the Senior Minister in charge of foreign relations in October, 1856, he assigned Kawaji Toshiakira and Iwase Tadanari to make a study of foreign trade. In February, 1857, the antiforeign seclusion laws were relaxed to permit American merchants to live in Nagasaki, Shimoda, and Hakodate. As a result, the way was opened for Inoue Kiyonao, the Commissioner of Shimoda, to confer with Townsend Harris from time to time. In the course of their conversations, Japanese officials learned from Harris the elements of economics as well as the rudiments of international law and the intricacies of diplomatic relations and procedure.

When Hotta Masayoshi took complete charge of foreign relations, the policy of the Shogunate became favorable to foreign trade. To the persistent demands of Townsend Harris, Hotta finally acceded and secured the necessary authorization from the Bakufu to enable the American consul to visit Edo. On October 21, 1857, the opportunity finally was given Harris to enter the Shogun's castle to present his credentials. A few days later, he conferred at length with Hotta and explained that the United States entertained no territorial designs, that the existing world situation would not permit Japan to continue much longer her policy of nonintercourse, and that under the circumstances it would be far better to enter into trade relations voluntarily than to be coerced by the nations which were prepared to use force if necessary. Harris warned the Shogunate that danger, such as confronted China in the Anglo-Chinese War of 1839–1842, would face Japan unless necessary steps were taken immediately to avert it. Sincerity and sympathetic attitude had won the day for Harris, as Hotta Masayoshi made up his mind to enter into trade relations with the United States. While Harris ably represented his country in dealing with Japan as well as the other powers, he was always supporting the Japanese in their dealings with the powers of Europe, especially when the Shogunate officials were pitted against the shrewd and experienced diplomats of the European nations.

Convinced of the inevitability of trading with the powers, Hotta requested the views of the various *daimyō* regarding Harris' advice to open trade relations voluntarily. Several, including Matsudaira Yoshinaga (Shungaku), Lord of Echizen, expressed their views regarding the inevitability of commercial intercourse, but practically all suggested that, even if a provisional treaty were to be negotiated, it would be advisable to obtain imperial sanction before signing it, since such a treaty was a serious matter.

While the number of leaders who recognized the inevitability, if not the desirability, of trade had increased noticeably since the advent of Perry, there was still a considerable number of persons including Tokugawa Nariaki, former Lord of Mito, who advocated an unmitigated antiforeign stand. Consequently, Hotta started out to secure imperial sanction for the treaty by going to Kyōto himself, only to find that the antiforeign, anti-Shogunate movement had brought about the stiffening of the attitude of the Imperial Court. Failing to secure the approval of the Emperor, he returned to Edo, completely at a loss to decide what the next move should be. In an attempt to work itself out of this difficult situation, the Shogunate elevated to the position of Senior Minister Ii Naosuke, one of the *daimyō* who had boldly advocated the opening of Japan at the time of Perry's arrival. This resulted in the further straining of the already delicate relations between the Bakufu and the Imperial Court. Meanwhile, the deadline set for the signature of the treaty had arrived, and the Bakufu was obliged to request its extension until July 27.

When the news of the signing of the new Treaty of Tientsin, which strengthened the position of the treaty Powers in China, was brought to Shimoda in June by an American ship, Townsend Harris promptly relayed it to the authorities at Edo. The Shogunate lost no time in dispatching Inoue Kiyonao and Iwase Tadanari to confer with Harris. Utilizing the opportunity presented him, Harris told them that it would not be long before the British and French warships, flushed with the latest diplomatic victory over China, would be arriving in Japan to demand the opening of her ports. He gave assurance that, if the treaty were signed with the United States, he would stand by the Japanese and exert every effort to prevent the powers from making excessive or unreasonable demands. In the face of the urgency of the situation and acting on the recommendation of the two officials whom he had sent to confer with Harris, Ii Naosuke signed the treaty on June 20, 1858, without waiting for the imperial sanction which he had vainly sought to obtain. Thus, the United States was instrumental in bringing Japan's two-hundred-year-old national seclusion policy to an end by opening her to commercial intercourse with the rest of the world.

To Townsend Harris' infinite patience, understanding, and consummate tact and skill in negotiating with the Japanese officials must be attributed the successful conclusion of the Treaty of Amity and Commerce between the United States and Japan. The first commercial treaty with the West in more than two hundred years provided that (1) ministers and consuls were to be exchanged between Japan and the United States; (2) in addition to Shimoda and Hakodate, the ports of Kanagawa, Nagasaki, Niigata, and Hyōgo were to be opened by stages, Shimoda was to be closed six months after the opening of Kanagawa, while Edo and Ōsaka were to be opened to residence; (3) customs were to be imposed on both exports and imports; (4) extraterritoriality was to be recognized for United States nationals; (5) freedom of religious worship was to be accorded Americans; (6) the treaty was to take effect in June, 1859; and (7) the treaty could be revised after July 4, 1872.

Of particular significance was the stipulation (Article II) contained in the treaty that the "President of the United States at the request of the Japanese government will act as a friendly mediator in such matters of difference as may arise between the Government of Japan and any European power." Townsend Harris also included a provision that the Japanese government could purchase or construct in the United States ships of war, steamers, merchant ships, whale ships, cannons, munitions of war and arms of all kinds, and any other thing it might require. Another stipulation (Article X) gave the Japanese government the right to engage in the United States scientific, naval and military men, artisans of all kinds, and mariners to enter into its service. Every possible help was to be given by the United States in the development of Japan.

Harris was strongly opposed, in principle, to extraterritoriality. Consequently, it was with the greatest reluctance that he decided on its inclusion in order to ensure the acceptance of the treaty by the powers. He realized too well that the chances were almost nil of a treaty with an Oriental power which did not contain the extraterritoriality clause being passed by the United States Senate or the British Parliament, particularly in view of the precedent that had already been firmly established in the Chinese treaties with the powers. The old view that the law of nations applied only to Christendom and not to the pagan countries still persisted.

On July 10, Captain Curtius, on July 11, Putiatin, on July 10, Lord Elgin, and on September 3, Baron Gros signed treaties of commerce with Japan for the Netherlands, Russia, Great Britain, and France, respectively. All these treaties were based on the United States treaty, in the drafting of which Townsend Harris had practically a free hand, since he enjoyed the implicit confidence of the Japanese authorities. Keeping constantly in mind the interests of the Japanese as well as the most-favored-nation principle, the American consul succeeded in producing a treaty that was eminently fair. It protected Japan against any power bent upon taking advantage of the ignorance and inexperience of a nation that had just emerged from isolation and seclusion.

Article XIV of the American-Japanese Treaty of Commerce of 1858 provided that ratifications were to be exchanged in the city of Washington. Harris was eager to see the Japanese send their first embassy to the United States rather than to any other country. He became even more determined when he learned that Lord Elgin was applying pressure to have the Japanese send an embassy to Britain first. The authorities finally decided on an embassy to the United States and appointed Shimmi Masaoki, Lord of Buzen, as the chief envoy. Townsend Harris personally made the necessary arrangements through the Department of State even to the working out of an itinerary to ensure the arrival of the Japanese in Washington at the most pleasant season of the year. At his behest, the Congress appropriated $50,000 to defray the expenses of the mission.

The U.S.S. *Powhatan*, under the command of Commodore Tatnall, which had formerly served as Commodore Perry's flagship and on which the treaty of 1854 had been signed, was made available by the United States to transport the Japanese embassy across the Pacific. The embassy arrived in San Francisco by way of Honolulu in late March, 1860, and reached Washington in the middle of May via the Isthmus of Panama, which the emissaries had crossed by rail. At the American capital, the Japanese were given a royal welcome and lavish entertainment. They were given the opportunity to observe the Congress in session, the first time any Japanese had witnessed a national legislature at work. The Americans reciprocated the curiosity of the Japanese by flocking to the hotel, the theaters, and various functions to get a glimpse of the strangely attired and exotic-mannered visitors from a distant land. Nothing was left undone to make the visit of the Japanese as pleasant as possible. There were no secrets, not even military, where the visitors were concerned. They were taken to military installations, naval yards, arsenals, factories, public and private institutions and were shown anything and everything in which they showed the slightest interest. They were given all sorts of gifts by the government, business firms, and individuals. They left New York on the American steamer *Niagara* and arrived back in Edo in November by way of the Cape of Good Hope after having completely circumnavigated the globe. In a short space of a few months, they had seen the wonders of Western civilization and more specifically, American life and civilization of the turbulent ante bellum period. They had the unique opportunity of observing American political, economic, and social institutions, and technological advances, and gaining a not inconsiderable understanding and appreciation of the West. Interesting too was the fact that the Japanese arrived in Washington just as the Republican National Convention was meeting in Chicago to nominate Abraham Lincoln for the presidency. It was this group of Japanese who, in the years following their return, began to put into practice some of the things they had learned, thus setting into motion the process of westernization and modernization which was to reach its climax a quarter of a century later.

In the face of violent antiforeign outbursts which began while the Embassy of 1860 was visiting the United States, the Shogunate decided in 1862 to negotiate for the postponement of the opening of the two ports of Hyōgo and Niigata and the two cities of Edo and Ōsaka for residential purposes, after consulting with Harris and securing his assent to the plan. Sir Rutherford Alcock, the British Minister, was favorably disposed too; although he felt that, inasmuch as an embassy had already been sent to the United States, it was only right that the next mission should be sent to Europe. Accordingly an embassy with Commissioners of Foreign Affairs Takeuchi Yasunori and Matsudaira Yasunao as chief envoy and vice-envoy, respectively, was appointed to go to Europe, accompanied by Fukuchi Gen'ichirō, Fukuzawa Yukichi, Mizukuri Shūhei, and Terashima Munenori, all of whom were to become leaders in their own fields in less than a decade. Minister Alcock was instrumental in obtaining passage for the embassy on H.M.S. *Odin*. After visiting the treaty Powers and securing assent to the postponement of the opening of the two ports and two cities for a period of five years until January 1, 1868, the embassy returned in 1863. The embassy was also successful in achieving its secondary mission of observing and studying manufacturing, trade regulations, military installations, residential zoning, and the methods of renting and leasing land and buildings.

The mounting dissatisfaction of the displaced *samurai* or the *rōnin* at the existing state of affairs was reflected in the acts of violence against the foreigners and their own officials as well. Overt acts by this relatively large discontented element worried the officials considerably. Violence, when directed against the representatives of foreign governments, complicated the none-too-easily managed foreign relations of the Shogunate and added to the difficulties and embarrassment of the feudal authorities. Some of these outbursts were deliberately planned to aggravate the already difficult, if not untenable, position of the tottering Shogunate by arousing the indignation of the foreign powers. Moreover, antiforeignism was fanned by those who attributed the social and economic ills of the nation to the opening of the country and the coming of the foreigners. There was some truth, of course, in their assertion that gold was rapidly being drained out of the country and that as a result prices had risen sharply to increase the cost of living and aggravate the economic distress and social insecurity of the people. It came to be felt generally that it was the patriotic duty to rid the country of the foreigners, and the displaced *samurai* or free lances took upon themselves the task of harassing both the foreigners and the authorities.

Beginning with the slaying of three Russian naval officers under the command of Admiral Muraviev at Yokohama in 1859, antiforeign violence flared up with disturbing frequency and regularity. In 1860, Heusken, the Dutch interpreter of the American legation serving under Townsend Harris, was cut down in Edo as he ventured out at night. Not long afterwards, fourteen *rōnin* led by a former *samurai* of Mito attacked the temporary British legation and wounded the newly arrived legation secretary, Laurence Oliphant, and Consul Morison,

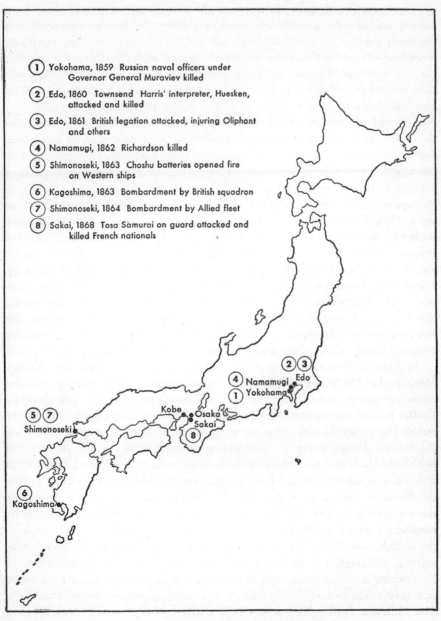

1. Yokohama, 1859 Russian naval officers under Governor General Muraviev killed
2. Edo, 1860 Townsend Harris' interpreter, Huesken, attacked and killed
3. Edo, 1861 British legation attacked, injuring Oliphant and others
4. Namamugi, 1862 Richardson killed
5. Shimonoseki, 1863 Choshu batteries opened fire on Western ships
6. Kagoshima, 1863 Bombardment by British squadron
7. Shimonoseki, 1864 Bombardment by Allied fleet
8. Sakai, 1868 Tosa Samurai on guard attacked and killed French nationals

Antiforeign Outbursts, 1859–1868.

who had accompanied the British Minister to Edo from Nagasaki where he was
stationed.

There were no signs of abatement of the hostile feeling; instead there were
ominous rumors of impending attacks on foreigners. The foreign representatives,
therefore, decided to withdraw from Edo to Yokohama for safety, as it was
quite evident that the Shogunate was unable to cope with the situation or provide
the necessary protection. Harris alone among the foreign diplomatic representatives refused to withdraw. In complete disregard of his own personal safety he
remained behind in Edo and represented the other powers whose legations had
been moved to the port city of Yokohama. He also offered his good offices in
the settlement which was made by the Shogunate in the slaying of his interpreter
and in transmitting the apology of the Bakufu to the foreign representatives for
the repeated outrages. In settlement of Heusken's murder, the Shogunate paid
$50,000 to the victim's mother.

Antiforeign outbursts continued without any appreciable letup and on February 1, 1863, the new British legation, nearing completion, was destroyed by fire
started by antiforeign *samurai*. By far the most serious incident of this period
from the diplomatic point of view was the Namamugi Incident or the Richardson Affair of September, 1862. Richardson and three fellow Britishers, one of
whom was a woman, were out on horseback in Namamugi just outside of Yokohama, where they came upon the procession of Shimazu Hisamitsu, *daimyō* of
Satsuma. Not knowing the strict etiquette required on such an occasion, the
foreigners invited the ire of the *daimyō*. Richardson was attacked and mortally
wounded while his two companions were seriously wounded.

In March, 1863, the British Government dispatched Admiral Kuper from
Hongkong to Yokohama and presented an ultimatum to the authorities early the
following month, demanding that (1) the Shogunate pay an indemnity of
100,000 pounds and make a formal apology; (2) the Shimazu family of Satsuma
punish the perpetrators of the crime and pay 10,000 pounds to the survivors of
the victim. Although the Shogun was away in Kyōto, the officials met the
British demands and paid the indemnity in June. In spite of the advice of the
authorities to the contrary, the British decided to take the matter up directly with
the Shimazu family. In August, the British Government sent a squadron of
seven ships into Kagoshima Bay and presented its demands. While negotiations
were under way, the British ships were fired upon. In the battle which ensued,
the British sank several Satsuma ships and silenced the shore batteries before
retiring. Although the British suffered some losses in the bombardment of
Kagoshima, it was demonstrated to the Japanese beyond any shadow of doubt
that they could not effectively oppose the superior armaments of the West.
The Shimazu family later sent representatives, one of whom was Shigeno
Yasutsugu, who subsequently distinguished himself as professor of history in the
Tōkyō University, to negotiate with the British Minister. In the settlement,

Satsuma paid an indemnity of 25,000 pounds and agreed to execute the culprits in the presence of the British representatives. Interestingly enough, it was at this time that the British Minister offered to assist Satsuma in the procurement of warships. The naval encounter with the British stimulated the interest of Satsuma in naval affairs to such an extent that in the years that followed the clan furnished practically all the leading naval officers, including Admiral Tōgō.

In a strategic move, the Imperial Court forced the hand of the Shogun, resulting in setting June 25, 1863, as the date on which a decree for the expulsion of the "Western barbarians" was to take effect. Notices were sent to the foreign representatives informing them that the ports of Hakodate, Yokohama, and Nagasaki would be closed on that date. The Imperial Court was fully aware of the rashness as well as the impossibility of even attempting to close the ports in utter disregard of treaty agreements, for such an act would constitute a flagrant violation of international law. But it was a deliberate plan to force the Shogunate into a vulnerable and untenable position.

On June 25, the *daimyō* of Chōshū decided to take upon himself the responsibility of enforcing the barbarian expulsion decree since the Shogunate showed no inclination to do so. Early on June 26, the armed vessels of Chōshū opened fire on the American ship *Pembroke,* bound from Yokohama to Shanghai, as she lay at anchor near the entrance to the straits of Shimonoseki. On July 8, the Chōshū ships and batteries fired upon a French gunboat passing through the straits, and three days later, the Dutch sloop *Medusa* was subjected to a similar shelling.

Alarmed at the recalcitrance of Chōshū, the Shogunate promptly dispatched an official envoy to rebuke those who were responsible for the rash act. To this Chōshū replied that it was acting on orders from the Imperial Court and, in defiance of the Shogun, executed the envoy and seized the ship on which he had arrived.

When the news of the attack on the American ship reached Yokohama, the U.S.S. *Wyoming* was ordered to proceed to Shimonoseki to capture the vessels that had fired upon the *Pembroke*. When the American warship arrived in the straits of Shimonoseki, it was fired upon. Commander McDougal, the commanding officer, destroyed the guilty Chōshū ships and returned to Yokohama. On the heels of McDougal came the French Admiral Jaurès, who landed a small force, destroyed one of the shore batteries, burned a village, and withdrew after avenging the insult to the French flag. These individual acts of retaliation proved inadequate to impress upon the Japanese the sanctity of treaties. It came to be felt by the treaty Powers that it would be necessary to retaliate in kind and in concert if they were to uphold successfully their treaty rights. With the tacit approval, if not the support, of the Shogunate, which was unable to control effectively the Chōshū feudatory, four Western powers organized a joint punitive expedition back of which was the strong hand of Sir Rutherford Alcock, the veteran British Minister.

In late August of 1864, an allied fleet comprising nine British, four Dutch, three French warships, and one small American armed vessel left Yokohama and, arriving on the scene in early September, bombarded Shimonoseki, sent landing parties ashore, and silenced the troublesome shore batteries. Soundly beaten, Chōshū entered into negotiations. On September 14, an agreement was reached (1) to open the straits to the ships of all nations and to allow the ships to purchase supplies or stop at Shimonoseki; (2) not to fortify the straits, and (3) to pay a ransom for the town and defray the expenses of the expedition. As a punitive undertaking, the joint expedition was a success, but it imposed a heavy burden on the Bakufu, which was forced to pay an indemnity of $3 million to the allied powers. By an Act of Congress in 1883, the United States returned her share of this indemnity, and Japan used it for the construction of the breakwater in the harbor of Yokohama. The effect of the Shimonoseki expedition on Chōshū was similar to that of the bombardment of Kagoshima upon Satsuma. A burning desire to learn the secret of the military power of Western nations was manifested by the young men of Chōshū, many of whom devoted themselves to the study of military arts and affairs. It was not a mere coincidence that Chōshū led the nation in the building of a modern army and for many years monopolized the important positions in the newly organized national army.

Although the antiforeign movement was broken, antipathy against the foreigners did not subside for a considerable period thereafter. As a matter of fact, it continued well into the Meiji period to harry the officials of the new government. Early in March, 1868, some Tosa *samurai* on guard duty at the port of Sakai attacked and killed or wounded fourteen French nationals. The French Minister demanded and obtained (1) an apology from the Japanese government; (2) an indemnity of 150,000 yuan; (3) extreme penalty for the *samurai* who perpetrated the attack, and (4) the exclusion of sword-carrying Japanese from the foreign residential quarters. At Sannomiya in Kobe some Englishmen cut across a *samurai* procession and were attacked; three persons were killed. As a result of this incident British and American warships landed troops to guard the entrances to the Sannomiya station.

Antiforeignism, which was deliberately fostered for more than a decade between the arrival of Perry and the end of the feudal regime in 1867, had to be promptly disavowed by the new government. An overnight about face from the "expulsion of foreigners" to the "opening of the ports" which entailed the welcoming of foreigners with open arms was simple enough to proclaim to the nation, but it was very difficult to change individual sentiments and attitudes. Violence which had been directed against the foreigners by the reactionaries was later turned upon their own leaders, resulting in the assassinations of Yokoi

Shōnan, Ōmura Masujirō, Hirozawa Maomi, Mori Arinori, and Ōkubo Toshi-michi, who were strong proponents of Western ideas and institutions.

As we have already seen, antiforeignism became noticeable from 1859 when the ports were opened for the first time and the rise in prices came to be felt by the people who were in a less favored position economically. Large volumes of export led to a scarcity of goods, particularly consumer goods, thereby increasing the cost of living. In the eight-year period, 1859–1867, the price of raw silk trebled, tea doubled, cotton quadrupled, and kelp trebled. In the seven-year period, 1860–1867, the price of rice increased twelvefold, salt tenfold, soybean fivefold, and wheat threefold. The rise in price was also attributed to the large outflow of gold during the period which was induced by the disproportionately high price of silver in Japan. The Shogunate had set the ratio of silver to gold at anywhere from 6 to 1 to 10 to 1 when it was 15 to 1 in other countries. When the Comstock Lode was opened in Nevada and the production of silver spurted there was a steep drop in the price of silver, bringing the ratio to 20 to 1 in the international market. Still there was no attempt by the Shogunate to readjust the price of silver. This unnatural situation enabled foreigners to bring in cheap silver from the outside, especially from China, and exchange it for Japanese gold, realizing in the simple transaction profits ranging all the way from 50 to 140 per cent. Even members of the foreign diplomatic corps in China and Japan could not successfully resist the temptation of such a lucrative business entailing so little effort. It has been estimated that in the brief space of about six months from the opening of the ports in June, 1859, to the end of that year, something like a million *ryō* of gold was taken out of the country. This outflow continued until it was checked in April, 1860, when the Shogunate tardily adjusted the ratio so that it corresponded more nearly to that prevailing in the world market.

When, through direct contact and actual demonstration of power, it was clearly shown that Japan was no match for European powers, efforts were begun for the absorption of Western civilization. Even as early as 1855, the Bakufu had established a naval training school in Nagasaki, where instruction was given in navigation, seamanship, gunnery, naval science, and shipbuilding under competent instructors from the Dutch Navy. Virtually all the warships of the Shogunate were built in Holland. Western learning, however, was not confined to military subjects, as students came to Nagasaki from all parts of the country to study medicine which was taught by Dr. Siebold, a German physician who first came to Japan in the employ of the Dutch but became an adviser to the Bakufu in 1861. Dr. Guido Verbeck, who arrived in Nagasaki as a missionary of the Dutch Reformed Church of America, became a teacher of English at the request of the Shogunate. Later he counted among his students such men as Ōkuma, Soeshima, and others who studied the rudiments of international law under him. Thus, Nagasaki, which had been the center of Dutch learning during the greater part of the Tokugawa period, began to attract students of English and international law as well as medicine even before feudalism came to an end.

However, it was not long before students began to leave the country for Europe and America in pursuit of learning. This was done in spite of the seclusion law which prohibited Japanese subjects from leaving the country on pain of death. Niishima Jō, the earliest of Christian leaders in Japan, went to Hakodate and boarded an American whaling ship whose captain befriended him and took him back to New England where he attended Amherst College and Andover Theological Seminary. Upon his return to Japan as an ordained Congregational minister, he founded a school which later became the Dōshisha University.

To the Netherlands in 1862 went Enomoto Takeaki, Itō Gempaku, Tsuda Shindō, Nishi Amane, and others who studied either naval science or political science and political economy. In May, 1863, the Shogunate ordered Inoue Kaoru and Itō Hirobumi [1] to England to study, but this was done virtually in secret, for the ban on foreign travel had not yet been lifted. Satsuma [2] and Chōshū too sent considerable numbers of students abroad especially after their grievous encounter with the British and the allied bombardment of Shimonoseki. By 1868, when the new Meiji Government adopted the policy of encouraging study abroad, studying abroad was no longer an innovation, for there was already a considerable number of persons who had been abroad.

[1] Among those who were sent to England a little later by the Shogunate were Toyama Masakazu, Kikuchi Dairoku, Hayashi Tadasu, and others whose names occupy a prominent place in the history of new Japan.

[2] Satsuma students who went to Europe to study included Terashima Munenori, Godai Tomoatsu, Sameshima Naonobu, Mori Arinori, Yoshida Kiyonari, and Tōgō Ainosuke, all of whom distinguished themselves later in the service of their country.

Chapter 3. The Collapse of Feudalism

Decadence was the inevitable sequel to the maturity of feudalism. For nearly four centuries after its establishment in the late twelfth century, feudalism continued in its decentralized form with the power firmly in the hands of local barons. In the sixteenth century the ruthless struggle for supremacy among the powerful *daimyō* plunged the country into an "epoch of wars." But out of the chaos emerged a politically unified Japan. It remained for Tokugawa Ieyasu and his successors to perfect the feudal system through the achievement of a high degree of centralization.

When Ieyasu became Shogun in 1603, he was determined to make the Shogunate secure for the Tokugawa family. In an attempt to ensure permanence of power for his posterity he drew upon the recorded experiences of the regimes which preceded his. However, even the feudal structure which he and his successors so carefully built up contained defects which were bared in the course of time.

All the policies of the Tokugawa Shogunate were pointed toward the ultimate goal: the preservation and perpetuation of its power. Ironically enough, it is in the imperfections, irrationalities, and ineffectiveness of these policies that the historian will find the causes of the downfall of the regime.

In order to make it impossible for anyone to challenge the supremacy of the Shogunate a unique system of distributing the *daimyō* was devised. The trusted ones were placed between those of doubtful loyalty to exercise strict vigilance over them. The loyal *daimyō* were concentrated in the Kantō region and the approaches to Kyōto, while those of doubtful loyalty were concentrated in western Japan. This arrangement provided the western *daimyō* with the opportunity to carry out effective opposition against the Shogunate, once the control and vigilance over them were relaxed because of the decline in the authority of the feudal government.

The unduly harsh punishment imposed on recalcitrance in the *samurai* class gave rise to an element of society which gave the authorities no end of trouble. When a *daimyō* was found guilty of conspiring against the Shogunate, the penalty imposed was death, confiscation of his holdings (fief), and extinction of the house. As a consequence, his retainers were deprived of their means of livelihood and were forced into a life of wandering. Another factor which was responsible for the increase of these *rōnin* was the family system. Under the system of primogeniture that was prevalent only the oldest son enjoyed security, and the other sons were doomed to a life of discontent and frustration, unless they were fortunate enough to be adopted into other families. In a peaceful society their opportunities were limited, although a few of them went into the arts, literature, and even business. Most of them chose a life of debauchery and turned into ruffians who sought trouble as eagerly as they pursued pleasure. These homeless, wandering *samurai* were always to be found where trouble was brewing. This element was the thorn in the side of the Shogunate as it participated in harassing activities which were as embarrassing to the authorities as they were destructive. Peasant uprisings and other acts of defiance against authority were frequently inspired and led by the *rōnin,* the free-lance troublemakers. Without the solid support and active participaton of this aggrieved element bent on vengeance on the Shogunate, the overthrow of feudalism would have been vastly more difficult, if not impossible, to achieve.

By keeping the different classes in their proper places the Shogunate hoped to ensure its security. For this purpose the system of class distinction, first introduced by Hideyoshi in the sixteenth century, was perfected by the Tokugawa Shogunate. At the top was the *samurai,* the privileged ruling class; next came the farmers, who were indispensable as a producing class, followed by the artisans, who were also makers of useful goods. At the very bottom of the social scale was placed the mercantile class, regarded as the nonproductive class. It was a rigid occupational caste system which based the individual's social position on birth and permitted no change whatever in status. This system worked well enough in the beginning as a device in preserving the social, political, and economic *status quo* and in the maintenance of peace and order. Its effectiveness, however, could not continue unimpaired in the face of rapidly changing conditions over which the feudal regime had no control.

Over two and a half centuries of peace made the very existence of the military class not only anomalous but superfluous. The *samurai* as a class lost their *raison d'être.* Their special function became unnecessary in a peaceful era, and the Shogunate encouraged them to devote their energies to learning and the ways of peace. With the growth of commercial cities around the feudal castles of the *daimyō,* the *samurai* became urbanized and lost the virility which characterized them in their original rural setting. They soon acquired the extravagant tastes of the townsfolk but without the necessary wherewithal to indulge in expensive pleasures. Financial distress became acute among the *samurai.*

Furthermore, it was the calculated policy of the Shogunate to keep the *daimyō* and *samurai* impoverished. *Daimyō* were required under the system of *sankin kōtai* to alternate residence between Edo and their fiefs. This involved the maintenance of residences befitting their station in two different places. The journeys back and forth between the two places were a drain on the treasury of the *daimyō,* but the Shogunate also ordered other expensive undertakings, such as public works, to be carried on at the expense of the *daimyō.* The extravagance plus large forced expenditures left the *daimyō* little or nothing with which to start any effective opposition against the regime. The peasants and merchants were squeezed harder and harder as the financial plight of the *samurai* class increased. By allowing them only limited financial resources, the Shogunate effectively checked the *daimyō*. However, this policy boomeranged before long. The financial plight of the *samurai* class was more than equaled by the desperate situation of the Shogunate.

Although Ieyasu had laid a sound financial foundation for the Shogunate through astute planning and management, by the middle of the seventeenth century financial difficulties began to appear as a result of unsound policies, inept management, and unbridled extravagance. The attempt to improve the situation through a series of tax increases and profits from coinage did not help matters. Nor was the Shogunate successful in keeping agricultural population and production from declining in the face of crop failures and famines. Earthquakes, fires, and floods added to the difficulties. In spite of the very limited volume of foreign trade, large amounts of gold and silver were drained out of the country. All the sumptuary laws, which were issued continuously towards the end, had no visible deterrent effect on the rapidly deteriorating finances or the declining power and prestige of the harassed government. So desperate was the condition of the Bakufu finances that in 1813 the Shogun was impelled to levy on the wealthy merchants of Ōsaka money contributions which were voluntary only in a euphemistic sense. When Perry arrived forty years later, the Shogunate was virtually in a state of bankruptcy.

By the end of the seventeenth century money had penetrated into the rural areas. As the land tax was paid in rice, which constituted the basis of Tokugawa finance, the economic well-being of the feudal regime was dependent on the amount of revenue derived from the land. The financial condition of the Shogunate as well as the *samurai* class as a whole was determined by the amount of production and the price of rice. As commerce developed, the mercantile class came into possession of large accumulations of money. Furthermore, the merchants became the indispensable agents of the *samurai* class in the process of converting their rice income into money. In the transaction the *samurai* were at the mercy of the merchants who were in a position to manipulate the price of rice at will. With the power of money the merchants were more than able to match the political power of the *samurai* class. Even the Shogunate became dependent on the economic power of the mercantile class.

Economic developments soon undermined the structure of the class system. Farmers left the unrewarding drudgery of the farm for the greener pastures of lucrative business or trade in the cities. Impoverished *samurai* condescended to engage in business to ensure a livelihood for themselves and their families. Sons of wealthy merchants joined *samurai* households as adopted sons for a consideration. Many a *samurai* sold his family stock to the highest bidder. It soon became impossible for the feudal authorities to preserve the rigid class system which was rapidly disintegrating under the impact of economic necessity.

The Tokugawa regime based its political structure on military power and implemented its military policies with a rigid social structure. Its forced disarmament on the *daimyō* and insistence on strict observance of precedents, conventions, and formal etiquette stifled initiative, resulting in a highly formalized and devitalized society. Moreover, with the attainment of political stability, Tokugawa rule rapidly lost its military characteristics and by the time of the eighth Shogun, administration had become thoroughly civilian in nature and the military controls had all but disappeared. The Shogunate officially undertook the task of encouraging learning, which at first consisted almost entirely of Confucianism. This was an attempt to give refinement to the machinery of government and to propagate the official philosophy.

As one means of effectively preserving the *status quo,* the policy of national seclusion was adopted in the 1630's. While it is true that this elimination of the greater part of foreign intercourse afforded the nation the time and opportunity to develop its own culture, it is equally true that the self-imposed isolation eliminated Japan from the international scene, causing her to fall far behind the Western powers in economic, cultural, scientific, and technological developments, to say nothing of overseas expansion.

Fearful of possible consequences, the Shogunate prohibited the importation of all Western learning. The resultant lack of information and understanding of international developments and the ignorance of international law and diplomacy were responsible at least partly for throwing the Shogunate into a state of consternation and panic when Commodore Perry arrived in 1853 with his squadron of four "black ships." Furthermore, the ignorance, indifference, and impotence of the authorities who had completely neglected defenses aggravated their fears and the feeling of helplessness at the sight of the American ships.

From the very beginning, the Shogunate took great pains to keep out ideas which were inimical and dangerous to the regime. Learning was encouraged by the authorities as a means of diverting and deflecting the thinking of the military as well as of other classes. In this deliberate endeavor, even the Shogun themselves became interested in literature and the peaceful arts. Confucianism of the Chu Hsi school was adopted as the official political philosophy of the regime and used for the enlightenment and guidance of the people. Although the philosophy itself was mild, the encouragement of Chu Hsi philosophy brought about results which had not been anticipated or intended and were quite incompatible with the feudal regime itself.

Arai Hakuseki, the outstanding historian of his day and the philosopher-statesman who served as the highest adviser to two of the Shogun, caused the Shogunate to reconsider and reappraise Christianity. The policy of seclusion was calculated to avert the danger of European aggrandizement through the proscription of Christianity and the exclusion of Europeans. In the early eighteenth century Hakuseki discovered to his own satisfaction that there was not necessarily a connection between Christianity and the conquest of Japan and prevailed upon the Shogunate to modify its attitude. As a result, by the first quarter of the eighteenth century, the ban on Western literature was relaxed and the policy of encouraging the study of Dutch was adopted at the same time. This led to the introduction of Western learning, embracing such subjects as astronomy, medicine, mathematics, military science, and other useful sciences.

Inevitably the encouragement of learning led to the study of classical and historical works of the earlier periods, resulting in the intense admiration if not worship of the heroes of Japanese history. The emergence of the Mito school of historians and the compilation of the *History of Great Japan* (*Dai Nihon Shi*) under the auspices of Tokugawa Mitsukuni, one of Ieyasu's grandsons, awakened the national consciousness of the people. Native classical scholars and Confucianists alike helped to strengthen the feeling of loyalty to the Emperor by pointing out that the Shogunate had originally come into existence through the usurpation of political powers which rightfully belonged to the Emperor. The popularity of Wang Yang Ming philosophy, which emphasized action, began to push the mild, *status quo* ideas of the Chu Hsi school into the background from the end of the eighteenth century on. With the appearance of Takeuchi Shikibu and Yamagata Daini, who fearlessly advocated direct action, the ideological foundations of the Shogunate began to totter. Thus, the Confucian scholars, Shintō theorists, native classicists, political economists, and historians stimulated the people into thinking, and that was definitely dangerous to the feudal regime. In the intellectual ferment which started, national consciousness was awakened as never before. All that was necessary now to start in motion the irresistible forces which would lead to the collapse of the feudal regime was a major event. Such an event was furnished by the arrival of Commodore Matthew Calbraith Perry in the summer of 1853.

POLITICAL EVENTS LEADING UP TO THE COLLAPSE OF THE TOKUGAWA REGIME

By signing the Treaty of 1858 on his own responsibility without waiting for imperial sanction, Ii Naosuke, the Senior Minister of the Bakufu, brought on himself scathing denunciations from the court nobles, *daimyō, samurai,* and royalists who regarded his action as a contempt of the Imperial Court. In the midst of this hostile atmosphere, there arose the problem of selecting a successor to the Shogun who was ill and without an heir.

Keiki (Yoshinobu) of the Hitotsubashi branch of the Tokugawa had the strong support of an influential group which included the *daimyō* of Echizen, Owari, and Satsuma, who were convinced that the selection of a right successor could retrieve the situation and help the Shogunate to regain prestige and power. However, Naosuke had never been able to get along with Keiki's father, Nariaki of Mito, who was an outspoken advocate of antiforeignism. Furthermore, Nariaki had never been popular with the Shogun's wife or her ladies-in-waiting. Consequently Keiki, as the son of Nariaki, was not acceptable.

The Shogun's choice was his thirteen-year-old cousin, Iemochi, of the Kii branch of the Tokugawa. Brushing aside all the advice to the contrary, Naosuke invited Iemochi to become the fourteenth Shogun. Angered by the Senior Minister's arbitrary action, royalists and advocates of antiforeignism joined together in roundly denouncing the Bakufu.

In order to preserve the prestige of the Bakufu in the face of this unhealthy situation, Naosuke resorted to a drastic measure of ordering the disciplinary confinement of the *daimyō* of Mito, Owari, and Echizen. He then ordered the punishment of the ministers and nobles at the Imperial Court on the grounds that they had opposed the policies of the Shogunate. At the same time he arrested scores of patriots, including Hashimoto Sanai and Yoshida Shōin, who were executed, while others were exiled, imprisoned, or placed in disciplinary confinement. This wholesale punishment of those who dared to oppose Naosuke, known as the Purge of the Ansei Era, was the beginning of the end of the Bakufu. It was symptomatic of the rapid deterioration and disintegration which Naosuke had tried desperately but unsuccessfully to arrest, if not to prevent, by the use of force.

Such a ruthless policy could not achieve even a temporary measure of success, for it served only to strengthen the hands of the opposition. The resentment of the Mito group, which had suffered the most from the oppressive policy, could not be held in check. In the spring of 1860, a small band of *samurai,* most of whom were from Mito, assassinated Naosuke. Fearful of repercussions and the adverse effect this action might have on the public, the Bakufu concealed his death for nearly a month, after which it issued an announcement relieving Naosuke of his official position and observed mourning. Naosuke's reactionary measures brought about not only his untimely death but an irreparable loss of Bakufu prestige. Advocates of the policy of "reverence for the Emperor and the expulsion of the barbarians" increased their clamor and redoubled their efforts in their unrelenting attack on the Shogunate.

After the death of Naosuke, the post of ranking Minister went to Kuze who, with Andō, managed the affairs of state. The two ministers carefully avoided the high-handed measures of their predecessor and endeavored by their moderate, if not conciliatory, policies to restore confidence in the Bakufu. Their goal was to achieve a union of the Imperial Court and Bakufu by having Princess Chikako, a younger sister of the Emperor, become the consort of the Shogun. Although the marriage was successfully consummated toward the end of 1861, it contributed little, if anything, to the achievement of harmony between the Court and the

Shogunate. Rather, it was interpreted by the hostile, antiforeign royalists as a Bakufu stratagem to obtain imperial sanction for the treaty. Furthermore, rumors spread to the effect that the Bakufu was scheming to force the Emperor to abdicate in the event it failed to secure imperial sanction. The upshot of all the confusion was the unsuccessful attempt on the life of Andō early in 1862, and he retired from office only a few months later.

Beginning about the autumn of 1861, royalists and free lances began to stream into Kyōto from all parts of the country to take part in the anti-Bakufu activities in close cooperation with the court nobles and court officials. Especially numerous were those from Satsuma, Chōshū, and Mito who advocated an extreme form of "reverence for the Emperor and the expulsion of the foreigners." But there were two factions. The extremists, organized around the Chōshū clan, openly advocated the expulsion of foreigners and condemned the Bakufu, while they secretly planned the overthrow of the regime by supporting the Imperial family. The moderates, led by the Satsuma clan, endeavored to unify national sentiment through the achievement of a coalition of the Court and the Shogunate. In the spring of 1862, Shimazu Hisamitsu of Satsuma arrived in Kyōto and, at the request of the Imperial Court, pacified the extremists who were getting out of hand. His proposal for the coalition of the Court and the Shogunate was adopted and an imperial envoy was sent to Edo to institute a reform of Bakufu administration along the lines suggested by Shimazu, who accompanied the envoy as official escort and adviser. The Shogun accepted the imperial advice and appointed Keiki to serve as his assistant and tutor and Matsudaira Shungaku as his Senior Minister in charge of general administration. He also relaxed the age-old system of alternate residence (*sankin kōtai*), required of all the *daimyō,* by reducing the period of residence in Edo to one hundred days every three years and permitting their wives and children to return freely to their homes in their own fiefs. In addition, those who had run afoul of the Bakufu laws since the Ansei purge were pardoned.

Shimazu's departure from the capital for his native province in the early fall of 1862 was a signal for renewed activities by the extremists. The Imperial Court, now under the influence of the extremists, dispatched Sanjō and Anegakōji, two of the leading anti-Bakufu extremist nobles, to the Shogun to compliment him for the reform which had been put into effect, and at the same time to demand that, inasmuch as the matter of expelling the foreigners had not been settled yet, the method be determined and the date be set for its enforcement.

Chōshū, at first, seemed to be in agreement with Satsuma on the policy of opening the country as a means of effecting the coalition of the Court and the Shogunate. But the prominent part which the Satsuma clan played in having the Emperor dispatch an envoy to effect administrative reforms in the Bakufu apparently brought about a reversal in attitude on the part of the Chōshū clan which took offense at what it considered to be a deliberate slight. Chōshū henceforth furnished leadership to the extremists, who now held sway at the Imperial Court. With their leader gone, the moderates were overshadowed. Thus began the friction between the Satsuma and Chōshū clans, which flared up time and again in the years which followed.

When Shogun Iemochi entered Kyōto in the early spring of 1863, he found the capital saturated with antiforeignism and the extremists in virtual control. Political bullies (*sōshi*) were active in the work of harassing the authorities. The Shogun found it impossible to achieve what he had been hoping would be possible: to rally the moderates, who favored the Court-Shogunate coalition, and to overcome the opposition of the extremists. To make matters worse, he suffered indignities and loss of prestige. No attempt was made to conceal the existing attitude of hostility towards the Bakufu. That the extremists were advocating the overthrow of the Shogunate was already quite apparent.

By late summer, the extremists had succeeded in convincing the Imperial Court that, inasmuch as the Satsuma and Chōshū clans had already engaged in hostilities with foreign powers, the Court should proceed with the expulsion of the foreigners. The Emperor announced subsequently that he would hold a military council to make preparations for an expedition to expel the foreigners. What was being considered was in reality an expedition against the Bakufu and not against the foreigners.

Disturbed by the turn of events, the Satsuma clan worked with Matsudaira, Lord Protector of Kyōto, and succeeded in convincing the Emperor of the folly of such an expedition. The troops furnished by the Chōshū clan and assigned as Imperial Palace guards were summarily dismissed and replaced by the troops of Satsuma and Aizu while the two extremist nobles, Sanjō and Sanjō-Nishi, were suspended from their court positions. The Emperor then ordered all the Chōshū men out of the capital. With them went the seven nobles who had been working closely together with Chōshū.[1] Back in their own province, the Chōshū men bided their time until an opportunity presented itself.

In the summer of 1864, the Chōshū clan was unsuccessful in its appeal to the Imperial Court for the pardon of their *daimyō* and the seven court nobles. Whereupon it decided to overpower the moderates by force in order to secure reconsideration of their appeal. In this audacious attempt they also failed. The Shogunate replied by sending a punitive expedition. Opinion within the Chōshū clan was divided, but the *daimyō* and his son followed the counsel of the peace faction and submitted to Bakufu orders. Although the expeditionary force returned to Kyōto in triumph early in 1865, strong criticism arose within the Bakufu that the Chōshū clan had been dealt with much too leniently.

Meanwhile, the war party in Chōshū, of which Takasugi Shinsaku was one

---

[1] The seven nobles were Sanjō-Nishi Suetomo, Sanjō Sanetomi, Higashikuze Michitomi, Mibu Motonaga, Shijō Takauta, Nishikōji Yoritomi, and Sawa Nobuyoshi.

of the leaders, liquidated the opposing faction and mobilized a force for an armed clash. Toward the end of that spring, the Shogunate organized a second expedition against Chōshū. The Shogun, in personal command of the loyal troops of his bannerets, proceeded to Ōsaka to supervise the operations. In the fall, while the expeditionary force was waiting for the Chōshū clan to surrender without a fight, a serious diplomatic problem arose.

The representatives of Great Britain, France, the Netherlands, and the United States came to Ōsaka, backed by a squadron of nine warships, and demanded the opening of the port of Hyōgo. In 1861, the Bakufu Minister in charge of foreign relations had secured the assent of the treaty Powers to the five-year postponement of the opening of the port. However, the representatives were anxious to hasten its opening if possible. They made it clear to the authorities that if they were refused, they would go directly to the Emperor for his approval. The Bakufu Ministers, Abe and Matsumae, nearly acceded to the demand without waiting for imperial sanction. For this meditated but unaccomplished act the Imperial Court ordered their immediate dismissal. This direct intervention by the Court in the affairs of the Shogunate impaired the power and prestige of the Shogun, who promptly submitted his resignation to the Emperor. Through the adroit management of affairs by Keiki, the Shogun finally succeeded in obtaining imperial sanction for the treaty in the late fall of 1865. Although the immediate opening of Hyōgo was not approved, the foreign representatives were satisfied and the warships of the four powers were withdrawn. Having obtained imperial sanction for the treaty, the Shogun withdrew his resignation and the difficulties in foreign relations were resolved, at least for the time being.

But after nearly half a year, the Bakufu had made no progress in the punitive expedition against Chōshū. In fact, no troops had yet engaged the enemy in the field. In the summer of 1866, a Bakufu envoy was sent to Hiroshima to inform the representatives of the *daimyō* of Chōshū of the penalties to be imposed for the act of recalcitrance against the Shogunate. This attempt at intimidation did not work. Having no other alternative, the Shogunate sent troops by land and sea, only to be defeated again and again by the superior, well-trained forces of Chōshū.

By this time the Satsuma and Chōshū clans had composed their differences and had concluded a secret agreement to work together for the overthrow of the feudal regime. Among those who were instrumental in bringing the two clans together were Saigō Takamori, who had long since given up any hope of rescuing the Shogunate, Ōkubo Toshimichi, Kido Kōin, and Sakamoto Ryūma. The Satsuma clan openly defied the Bakufu by refusing to heed the order to furnish troops for the punitive expedition against Chōshū.

In the early fall, the Shogun died a natural death at Ōsaka Castle, his temporary military headquarters. The Imperial Court seized the opportunity to order the Bakufu to demobilize the troops out of respect to the deceased Shogun. The

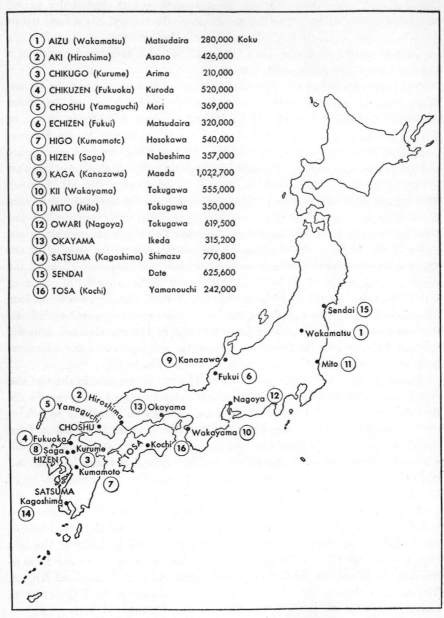

①	AIZU (Wakamatsu)	Matsudaira	280,000 Koku
②	AKI (Hiroshima)	Asano	426,000
③	CHIKUGO (Kurume)	Arima	210,000
④	CHIKUZEN (Fukuoka)	Kuroda	520,000
⑤	CHOSHU (Yamaguchi)	Mori	369,000
⑥	ECHIZEN (Fukui)	Matsudaira	320,000
⑦	HIGO (Kumamotc)	Hosokawa	540,000
⑧	HIZEN (Saga)	Nabeshima	357,000
⑨	KAGA (Kanazawa)	Maeda	1,022,700
⑩	KII (Wakayama)	Tokugawa	555,000
⑪	MITO (Mito)	Tokugawa	350,000
⑫	OWARI (Nagoya)	Tokugawa	619,500
⑬	OKAYAMA	Ikeda	315,200
⑭	SATSUMA (Kagoshima)	Shimazu	770,800
⑮	SENDAI	Date	625,600
⑯	TOSA (Kochi)	Yamanouchi	242,000

Leading Daimyō and Their Fiefs, 1865.

Bakufu complied promptly as it gave an opportunity to recall the unsuccessful punitive expedition without suffering too great a loss of face. The dismal failure of the expedition further exposed the utter impotence of the Shogunate, which was by this time unable to control even a single *daimyō*.

Upon the death of Iemochi his adviser and tutor Keiki became the fifteenth and last Shogun. Less than a month later Emperor Kōmei passed away and his fifteen-year-old heir ascended the throne to begin his long period of eventful rule which lasted for forty-five years. Having suffered irretrievable loss of power and prestige, the Bakufu was no longer in a position to manage effectively the affairs of state.

Convinced that the time was now ripe, Iwakura worked secretly with Saigō, Ōkubo, Kido, Sanjō, and others to plan the overthrow of the Shogunate. Opinion among the *daimyō* was still divided as some advocated overthrow while others were loyal to the Bakufu. In some of the fiefs there was no agreement as to the course to be followed. Yamanouchi Toyonobu (Yōdō), the ex-*daimyō* of Tosa, sent two of his trusted retainers, Fukuoka and Gotō, to Iwakura and his group in an attempt to dissuade them from carrying out their plans, but was met only with a rebuff. Still hoping for a peaceful method, he presented a memorial to the Shogun urging him to surrender his political powers to the Emperor for the sake of national unity. The astute Shogun had been watching the irresistible trend of events and had realized the impossibility of saving the Bakufu in the face of pressures from both within and without. As a matter of fact, he had already, at the time of his appointment as Shogun, made up his mind to surrender his powers at an opportune time.

The opportunity came in the fall of 1867, and the Shogun announced his decision to relinquish his powers. Although the unexpected announcement took the country by surprise, no one questioned the wisdom of the decision. The Emperor forthwith accepted the Shogun's petition requesting permission to surrender the political powers to the Throne. Thus, 265 years of Tokugawa rule came to an end, and with it almost seven centuries of feudalism passed out of existence.

Iwakura's efforts in the meantime had borne fruit, and a secret imperial rescript for an expedition against the Bakufu was issued, only it came too late, on the day the Shogun surrendered his powers. Reluctantly, plans for the expedition had to be dropped. However, the leaders, especially Saigō and Ōkubo, were convinced that a spectacular military operation against the Bakufu was necessary to capture the imagination of the nation and to facilitate the initiation of sweeping changes.

Early in January of 1868, the Emperor issued the Restoration Rescript. Immediately, all the offices which had functioned under the feudal regime were abolished and a provisional machinery was set up with those who had actively participated in the Restoration in charge. This small group included Saigō, Ōkubo,

Gotō, the court nobles, *daimyō,* and a few princes of the blood, but the real power was in the hands of one man, Iwakura, a court noble.

Immediately following the ceremony for the promulgation of the Restoration Rescript, a conference was held in the Imperial Palace in the presence of the Emperor to decide the method of disposing of the Tokugawa family. Keiki was to resign from his official court position as well as from the post of Shogun and surrender the fiefs to the Throne. The Aizu and Kuwana clans, whose *daimyō* had been summarily dismissed from their official positions at the capital, and the old faithful vassals of the Bakufu saw the hand of Satsuma in the decision reached by the provisional government.

At the residence of the *daimyō* of Satsuma in Edo a large number of *rōnin* had been assembled by Saigō, who employed them to provoke the residents of the city. These troublemakers plundered and terrorized the populace. When a part of the Edo Castle burned down early in 1868, the Satsuma *samurai* were suspected of starting the fire. In retaliation, the adherents of the Bakufu attacked and burned the residence of the *daimyō* of Satsuma. Bakufu warships opened fire on Satsuma warships and put them to flight. When news of these clashes reached Ōsaka, Keiki decided on a punitive action against Satsuma. Accordingly, in February, 1868, a Bakufu force of 30,000 troops began to move on Kyōto from Toba and Fushimi, but was badly beaten by the combined forces of Satsuma and Chōshū.

Keiki's hereditary *daimyō* and bannerets were far from unanimous in their views. Some advocated resistance, while others were equally firm in advocating submission to imperial authority. Edo residents, who had been outraged by the acts of terrorism instigated by Satsuma, expressed sympathetic sentiments toward the Tokugawa.

When the Emperor appointed Prince Arisugawa to head the expedition against the Bakufu, the Tokugawa followers knew that Satsuma and Chōshū were behind the move. Many of them were ready to fight Satsuma with all the help they could get from France. Napoleon III, in his eagerness to extend his influence to the Far East, was making an effort to secure the good will and support of the Bakufu. The French government, through its Minister Léon Roches, had already given its assistance in the construction of the Yokosuka shipyards and in the training of Bakufu troops. The British Minister, Sir Harry S. Parkes, on the other hand, made no secret of supporting Satsuma and Chōshū. The visit of the British representative to Satsuma in the summer of 1866 was the beginning of the Anglo-Satsuma friendship. In the fall of the same year, the friendship between England and Chōshū was cemented.

Soon after Keiki returned from Ōsaka, Léon Roches called on him and urged him to make a stand against the government, promising material assistance in the form of warships and munitions. The ex-Shogun, however, declined the offer of help, thereby averting the danger of intervention by two rival European powers, Britain and France, in the settlement of an internal political struggle which might well have ended in the loss of political independence for the nation.

In February, 1868, the Imperial Court stripped Keiki of his court rank and a month later the punitive expedition was on its way to Edo. The loyal supporters of the Bakufu were determined to fight, but Keiki succeeded in restraining them sufficiently so that resistance was necessarily limited. He then retired to a temple in Ueno to await imperial orders while his trusted retainers, Katsu Awa and Ōkubo Ichiō, conferred with Saigō, the chief of staff of the expedition, to arrange for surrender. The terms imposed by the Imperial Court on the ex-Shogun included the surrender of the Edo Castle, warships, and guns, the removal of Bakufu vassals from Edo, and the punishment of those who conspired with the Bakufu against the Emperor. Keiki's penalty was commuted from death to a life of sequestration in Mito. At the same time, Tayasu Iesato, a member of one of the branch houses, was designated by the Imperial Court to carry on the main Tokugawa house and was awarded the fiefs of Suruga, Tōtōmi, and Mutsu with a combined revenue of 700,000 *koku* of rice.

Although the ex-Shogun calmly accepted the penalty imposed on him, resentment flared up among his loyal followers, who were determined to fight, as they felt that a great injustice had been done. A resistance group was organized in Edo while Enomoto, who was in command of the Bakufu navy, slipped out of Edo Bay bound for Hakodate in order to put up stiff resistance there. Ōtori Keisuke, former Bakufu Chief of Infantry, also led a group against the government forces. At the Wakamatsu Castle, the Aizu troops put up the stiffest resistance against the imperial forces for months, but in mid-autumn they were forced to surrender.

Enomoto, in the meantime, had succeeded in driving out the governor and capturing the stronghold outside the city of Hakodate. With the support of those under him, he proceeded to administer Hokkaidō. He then displayed his audacity by calmly petitioning the Imperial Court to appoint a member of the Tokugawa family to take charge of the development and administration of Hokkaidō with a view to providing a bulwark against possible aggression from the northern approaches to the island. The government responded to this request by dispatching troops in the spring of 1869. After putting up a fierce fight against impossible odds, Enomoto surrendered in early summer, bringing to a close all hostile opposition to the government. With the end of resistance, the government turned its energies to the task of laying the foundations for a modern state.

Chapter 4. Establishment of the New

Government

In the spring of 1868, while battles were still raging, the young Emperor Meiji announced the Charter Oath of Five Articles to the nobles, *daimyō,* and officials assembled at the Imperial Palace in Kyōto. This document furnished the fundamental principles and charted the course for the new ship of state. It formed the basis of a strong centralized state, and for the modernization and Westernization of almost every important aspect of national life, thus enabling the nation to take its place in the family of nations in the brief space of three decades. The five articles were as follows:

1. Deliberative assemblies shall be established and all matters be decided by public opinion.

2. The whole nation shall unite in carrying out the administration of affairs of state.

3. Every person shall be given the opportunity to pursue a calling of his choice.

4. Absurd customs and practices of the past shall be discarded and justice shall be based on the laws of heaven and earth.

5. Wisdom and knowledge shall be sought all over the world in order to establish firmly the foundations of the Empire.

The Charter embodied the progressivism of Yuri Kimmasa who had been strongly influenced by the democratic ideas of Yokoi Shōnan, the liberalism of the Tosa school, and the antifeudal ideas of Kido Takayoshi. Its significance was clearly brought out by Emperor Hirohito in his New Year's Day Rescript of 1946, when he called on the nation to make the Charter Oath of Five Articles the basis of national policy in the building of a new and peaceful Japan.

The promulgation of the Charter was followed by the announcement of a new governmental structure which was based on the doctrine of the separation of powers. Fukuoka and Soeshima, who had been entrusted with the planning of the Charter, followed closely a treatise on American government. The legislative branch was divided into the upper and lower chambers, the former in charge of policies, laws, regulations, and diplomatic matters, including the questions of war and peace, while the latter was entrusted with military affairs, currency, taxation, trade, transportation, and matters pertaining to foreign relations. The administrative branch was divided into the Departments of Administration, Shintō, Finance, Military Affairs, Foreign Affairs, and Local Government. The Department of Criminal Law was the judicial branch. Separation of powers was carried out scrupulously in the beginning, since administrative officials were prohibited from holding legislative offices. However, when officials entrusted with legislative functions began to encroach upon administrative functions, the legislative branch was abolished and the members of the upper chamber were made administrative officials, and the doctrine of separation of powers was all but abandoned. Even allowing for the fact that the architects of the new government could not possibly have grasped the full significance of all the features of American government, the new form was nevertheless too radical a departure for a nation that had only recently thrown off the shackles of feudal tyranny, and that had not yet been completely unfettered in its ideology. Furthermore, turning over the fiefs to the Throne in 1869 necessitated another change in governmental organization.

Accordingly, in the summer of 1869, a reorganization was effected. However, it actually represented a reverting back to the governmental structure of the Taihō Code of the eighth century. The administrative branch was designated the Council of State (*Dajōkan*), under which were placed the Ministers of the Left and the Right. Placed above and outranking the Council of State and all the administrative departments of the government was the Office of Shintō Worship (*Jingikan*). This preferred position given to Shintō affairs over the administration of state was in line with the policy of disestablishment of Buddhism, and the enhancement of state Shintō was meant in turn to increase the prestige of the Imperial family. Under the Council of State were created six departments, namely, Civil Affairs, Finance, Military, Justice, Imperial Household, and Foreign Affairs. Several changes were effected before stability and permanence were achieved in 1885 with the establishment of the cabinet system which has come down to the present without any major changes with the exception of the abolition of the War and Navy ministries following defeat in the Second World War in 1945.

No problem was more pressing or difficult than the establishment of a sound financial basis for the new government. When the new government took over the administration of the affairs of state, the Treasury was empty. As a temporary expedient the policy of confiscating the old fiefs under Bakufu control was decided upon. But this could not be carried out fast enough to meet the immediate needs. Expenditures incurred in the forming of a new administrative structure, the enforcement of laws, and the sending of expeditionary forces to Edo and Hokkaidō had to be met promptly; yet there were no funds. In January, the government, in desperation, resorted to levying on the wealthy merchants of Ōsaka, Kyōto, and Edo a forced loan of three million *ryō*, which became the Treasury fund. At the same time the Mitsui-gumi (the House of Mitsui) was entrusted with the work of transacting the business of the Government Treasury.

Acting on the proposal of Yuri Kimmasa and using the total (*koku*) rice production of the nation as a basis, the Government decided in early 1868 to issue paper currency to the amount of 48,973,973 *ryō* to be redeemed in legal tender in thirteen years. Although it was announced that the issuance of paper money was for the relief of the fief and of the people through the development of industries, it was actually to relieve the financial plight of the Government. How desperate this plight was can be seen by the fact that the House of Mitsui made an outright gift of 1,000 *ryō* to the Government, the first instance of a money contribution to the new Government. This example was followed by other wealthy merchants. By such acts the financiers were able to put themselves in an advantageous position vis-à-vis the Government.

Largely because there was no clear statement as to the amount to be issued or the way it was to be called in, the value of paper money dropped to a point where its ratio to silver reached three to ten, and smooth circulation could not be achieved. Complaints were heard everywhere as poor circulation led to the stagnation of trade and to business failures. But from about the middle of the 1870's circulation improved, and by 1871 paper currency came to be accepted as readily as specie and the difference in value became negligible as the confidence in the government increased. In the spring of 1871, a government mint was established in Ōsaka to coin metallic money. The yen was made the unit of coinage. The Mitsui-gumi was designated the government's fiscal agent to handle the exchange of old for new coins and the collecting and forwarding of gold and silver bullion. This was soon followed by the establishment of the Bureau of Printing and Engraving in Tōkyō to print paper money and bonds.

In the face of nearly insurmountable financial difficulties it was impossible to carry out an effective administration, as long as the 273 fiefs remained under the control of the former *daimyō,* who continued to take the revenues for their own use. The Government had control only over the former holdings of the Bakufu which it had confiscated. This comprised only eight cities (*fu*) and twenty-one prefectures which were being administered directly by the central government rather than by the ex-*daimyō* governors, as was the case with the remainder of the country.

The return of the land and the people to the Throne was therefore imperative, not only for the financial well-being of the Government, but also to make certain that no political complications developed to disrupt or wreck the work of the Restoration. Kido and Ōkubo were among those who had been gravely concerned over this serious problem. After having convinced the *daimyō* of Chōshū and also of Satsuma, Kido and Ōkubo proceeded to convince the *daimyō* of Tosa and Hizen. This resulted in the four *daimyō* presenting, in early 1869, a petition to the Imperial Court offering the surrender of their fiefs to the Throne. Other *daimyō* followed the example. The Government then ordered all the *daimyō* to surrender their fiefs and offered in return an income equivalent to one-tenth of their current revenues and an appointment as governors of their old fiefs.

It was hardly to be expected that the mere return of the fiefs to the Throne would liquidate the legacy and particularly the evils of feudalism, when the ex-*daimyō* continued to function as chief administrative officials of their former fiefs. The lord and vassal relationship, which was the basis of feudalism, was carried over into the relationship between the fief governor and his subordinate officials, while the people continued to act and be treated as if they were still part of the old feudal organization. Conspicuous was the tendency of the administration of the fiefs to lag behind that of the prefectures; and the relationship between the central government and the fiefs was neither smooth nor satisfactory. To make matters worse, there developed in some of the fiefs a movement to oppose the reforms which had been instituted by the Restoration. This incipient opposition had the possibility of getting out of hand and developing into a large-scale uprising.

Leaders of the Chōshū and Satsuma clans including Kido, Inoue, Yamagata, Ōkubo, Saigō, and Ōyama met secretly with Sanjō and Iwakura and decided to carry out the abolition of the fiefs, which were to be superseded by prefectures throughout the nation. As a safeguard against any untoward incident in the execution of the plans, the assistance of Chōshū, Satsuma, and Tosa was obtained in the form of troops, which were organized early in 1871 into the Emperor's Guard (*shimpeitai*), comprising infantry, artillery, and cavalry units, numbering 10,000 men.

In the late summer of 1871, the Emperor summoned the ex-*daimyō* governors of seventy-six fiefs and proclaimed to them the establishment of prefectures to take the place of the fiefs. Three years elapsed before the modernization of administration could be achieved, but further changes were made in the succeeding years until the system of local government attained stability when the number of prefectures was reduced to forty-six exclusive of Hokkaidō. The abolition of the fiefs was a necessary step in the modernization of political and social institutions, but dissatisfaction was expressed by individuals and groups opposed to changes. For example, when the Emperor was on an inspection tour of Kyūshū in the summer of 1872, Shimazu Hisamitsu, the reactionary younger brother of the ex-*daimyō* of Satsuma, Nariakira, requested the sovereign to remove Saigō and Ōkubo, who had been instrumental in the abolition of the fiefs.

In order to ensure the security of the nation a modern, efficient military organization was regarded as an absolute necessity. This fact had been impressed upon the leaders even before the Restoration. Furthermore it was thought no less imperative for the complete liquidation of the feudal system. Military service as a monopoly of the *samurai* class was not merely a relic of feudalism, it was a serious obstacle to the complete liquidation of the feudal class system. A modern army could not possibly be based on class privilege or a caste system.

Ōmura Masujirō, who had foreseen this soon after the Restoration, became a strong advocate of a national conscript army and had already drawn up plans for the training of officer personnel. However, before he could put his plans into effect, his career was cut short in 1869 by a reactionary assassin who resented his introduction of European ideas and methods in the military organization of Japan.

In 1870 the Government sent Yamagata and Saigō to Europe to study Western military organization. Upon his return, Yamagata devoted his attention to the planning of a modern military organization for Japan. In 1871 garrisons were established in Tōkyō, Sendai, Ōsaka, and Kumamoto. In the following year, the administration of military affairs underwent a change, as separate departments were set up for the army and the navy. Yamagata was appointed the first War Minister under this new plan. By the end of the year, the universal military conscription ordinance was completed and in January, 1873, it was promulgated.

The army, during the early Meiji period and the closing years of the Shogunate, was patterned after the French military system; but after the defeat of the French Army in the Franco-Prussian War, the German Army became the model and continued to be until the defeat in 1945. The navy, on the other hand, received its training and guidance during its early stages of development from the Dutch. However, in later years, it turned to Britain and the United States for advanced naval training, and by the time the Russo-Japanese War had started there were several high-ranking admirals who had been trained in the British Navy and at the United States Naval Academy.

Immediately after the announcement of the establishment of prefectures in 1871, a new organization for the central government was adopted. This was the work of the Committee for the Study of Political Institutions (*Seido Chōsa In*), of which Saigō, Kido, and Ōkubo were members. Under the new arrangement, three chambers were established as component parts of the Council of State. The Main Chamber (*Shōin*), presided over by the Minister President (*Dajōdaijin*), was the supreme chamber, whose function it was to deliberate and to render final decisions on the most important matters of state in meetings held in the presence of the Emperor. It had over-all supervision of the affairs of state, held powers of diplomacy, religious rituals, declaration of war, conclusion of peace, making of treaties, and command over the armed forces. Next to the Minister President were the *Dainagon* (later changed to the Ministers of the Left and the Right) who were assisted by an undetermined number of Councilors (*Sangi*), whose functions were those pertaining to policy making. Although the Left Chamber was theoretically charged with legislative functions, in actual practice it was no more than an advisory organ. The Right Chamber was a body comprising the executive heads and deputy heads of the various departments which drafted departmental ordinances and regulations, handled the business of the departments, and discussed the problems of actual administration. Independence of judicial powers was stressed, and the Department of Justice was newly created to exercise judicial functions.

In spite of the intention of Etō Shimpei and others to effect the separation of powers, actually there was no separation of executive and legislative powers. The latter were completely absorbed by the former. The Office of Shintō Worship (*Jingikan*) which had been placed in 1869 above the Council of State was made into an ordinary department in the reorganization of 1871 and placed on the same level with all the other administrative departments. This was the result of the policy of deemphasizing Shintō and is significant as a reversal of the earlier policy of the government. This reorganized government was dominated by the four leading clans: Satsuma, Chōshū, Tosa, and Hizen.

Disagreement and clashes among the leaders began to assume serious proportions while Iwakura, Kido, Ōkubo, and Itō were away on a tour of Europe and America. These leaders, who were the key figures in the government all through the 1870's, were gravely concerned about the political situation which might arise at home in their absence. They were fearful that the powers of government would fall into the hands of Saigō, Itagaki, Etō, Gotō, Soeshima, and Ōki, who constituted the force of opposition within the government. To provide against such an eventuality, they secured before they left a pledge from each of those who were remaining behind to manage the affairs of the state not to institute any major reforms or to make new appointments on the higher levels. If either should become imperative, they should act only after consultation with Iwakura and his group. It was agreed that changes were to be kept to the minimum for the time being, inasmuch as a great many important changes would have to be made upon their return from the important mission.

Feudal influences, which were still very much in evidence within the government, prevented the achievement of complete harmony and cooperation. Principles and political views became hopelessly confounded in the heated arguments which took place in the Council of State, and disagreements on important issues soon developed into personal clashes. Sanjō Sanetomi, the Minister President, revealed his impotence time and again by his utter inability to control the situation. Had Sanjō possessed firmness, he might have averted some of the clashes. Departmental frictions and jealousies as well as personal ambitions and animosities aggravated the difficulties.

In flagrant disregard of the pledge not to institute any reforms during Iwakura's absence, those who remained behind instituted several major reforms. Government reorganization, appointment of additional councilors, educational reforms, land tax reform, the adoption of the Gregorian calendar, military conscription law, the banking law, and the family registration law were among the innovations introduced. The feudal socioeconomic class system was abolished, and the ban on the nobility and the *samurai* entering the occupations was lifted. Thus, more than half of the reforms which Iwakura had hoped to institute upon his return were put through in his absence, but not without creating difficulties and animosities which could not be resolved by ordinary means.

Minister President Sanjō, who had been reporting the developments at home to Iwakura, wrote on January 13, 1873, asking him to instruct Ōkubo and Kido to hasten back. The situation had gotten out of hand and the presence of the two men in the Council of State was desperately needed. Ōkubo was the first to return, followed by Kido. An unexpected development in the personal relationship of the leading members of the Iwakura Mission during the trip had a far-reaching effect on the course of events which followed. Due to the clash of views as well as of personality, Ōkubo and Kido drifted apart and were no longer as friendly during the trip as they might well have been. Itō, who had always regarded Kido as his mentor, became quite intimate with Ōkubo. This was a blow to Kido, whose feelings were visibly affected. However, neither Kido nor Ōkubo allowed their personal feelings to influence their decisions on important matters of state. Yet the effect of the drifting apart of Kido and Ōkubo on subsequent developments is unmistakably clear. It led to a closer relationship between Ōkubo and Itō, which virtually placed the latter in line of succession for the ranking position in the government after Ōkubo.

A government scandal was brought to light in the summer of 1872, implicating some of the officers of the Imperial Guard. A merchant, Yamashiroya (Nomura Michizō), purveyor to the government, embezzled funds which belonged to the government. As Yamagata was then in command of the Guard, the Satsuma military men seized upon the scandal as a rare opportunity to attack Chōshū. Saigō who had been in attendance on the Emperor at Kagoshima was ordered back to Tōkyō to straighten out matters. For this assignment, the Emperor elevated him to the rank of Field Marshal and appointed him Commander of the Imperial Guards. As the relationship between Satsuma and Chōshū became strained, Saigō recommended Yamagata for the post of War Minister and, for the time being, he succeeded in preserving a balance between the two rival clans.

Kido, however, resented strongly the elevation of Saigō to the rank of Field Marshal, for he saw in the move an opening wedge enabling the military to sway the deliberations in the councils of state. The Chōshū statesman was opposed to the idea of giving the military undue influence over matters of state, but at the same time he was influenced in his attitude by the struggle for power which was being waged between his own clan and Satsuma.

THE KOREAN QUESTION

The most crucial issue of domestic politics in 1873, if not of the first decade of the Meiji era, was the question of how to deal with Korea. Several attempts were made immediately following the Restoration for the resumption of normal relations with Korea, but without success. In the spring of 1872, the Foreign

Office sent Hanabusa Yoshimoto and Moriyama Shigeru to negotiate with the Korean government, only to be met by a rebuff. In the following year open hostility against the Japanese reached its peak as the result of the violent anti-foreign policy of Taiwunkun. Leaders were aroused to a point where some of them were advocating war against Korea.

Minister President Sanjō submitted the matter to a meeting of the Council of State. Itagaki was convinced that, inasmuch as it was the duty of the government to protect its resident nationals, troops should be dispatched without delay and negotiations begun with a view to concluding a commercial treaty. Saigō proposed that an envoy with plenipotentiary powers be sent to negotiate with Korea and, if she still persisted in treating Japan with contempt, the world should be notified of the fact before any troops were dispatched. He then asked to be designated the head of the mission, which would almost certainly be insulted or attacked, thereby providing a good cause for war. Although the majority of the Councilors supported Saigō, the Minister President did not express approval until he was forced to do so reluctantly by Saigō's well-executed maneuvers. In the Council meeting of August 17, 1873, an official decision was reached that Saigō was to be appointed envoy to Korea. The Emperor's approval was secured on the condition that the announcement was to await Iwakura's return.

Discontent among the former *samurai* had been mounting rapidly since the abolition of the fiefs in 1871, and those who were dissatisfied with the attitude of Satsuma and Chōshū began to show opposition against the government. Saigō was gravely concerned over the unhealthy state of affairs which was developing at home, the demoralization of the military men in particular, and sought to correct the situation. One effective method, he believed, was to channelize and divert their energies to activities overseas and at the same time achieve national expansion. He had early turned his eyes northward with the idea of strengthening the defenses in the northern regions. In the fall of 1871 he had dispatched Major General Kirino to Hokkaidō on an inspection tour. Subsequently, he made an attempt to establish and personally command a garrison at Sapporo, since he was convinced of the inevitability of war with Russia. It was his strong conviction that the defense of Hokkaidō by itself was not sufficient; the Korean question had to be settled in view of the necessity of pushing out into the Maritime Province. Thus, in the fall of 1872, in the execution of a plan he had formulated earlier with Foreign Minister Soeshima and Councilor Itagaki, he dispatched two army officers to Korea and two officials of the Foreign Office to Manchuria to survey conditions, and in 1873, he dispatched similar missions to South China and Formosa.

Saigō regarded the Korean question as an integral part of Japan's long-term policy of national expansion and viewed Russia as her antagonist in the not too distant future. He was certain that if he failed in his mission to Korea, he could not return alive. Yet, he rejoiced over his appointment as official envoy to negotiate with Korea. But his rejoicing was short-lived; it soon turned into disappointment and dejection.

In the midst of confusion and agitation on the domestic political scene, Iwakura returned from Europe in September, 1873, in company of Itō and Yamaguchi, two of the four vice-envoys. Ōkubo had already returned at the end of May followed by Kido two months later, in July. The members of the Iwakura Mission had seen with their own eyes how pitifully backward Japan was in her national development as compared with the nations of Europe and America. After what they had seen, Japan's future course was crystal clear to them.

The Council meeting of October 14, held at the insistence of Saigō, ended in violent disagreement. In the meetings that followed on succeeding days the government could not arrive at any decision. A hopeless deadlock developed and Sanjō was powerless. Though a son of an illustrious father, he was not gifted with administrative ability, power of decision, forceful character, or the political acumen so indispensable to high statesmanship. The terrific strain of responsibility made Sanjō critically ill and incapable of carrying on. There was only one person with the stature and ability necessary to take the helm of the ship of state through the worst storm. Thus, Iwakura was appointed acting Minister President to carry on the work with the able assistance of Ōkubo. In spite of the earlier clashes, Kido, who was now bedridden, wrote Iwakura highly recommending Ōkubo and at the same time urging him to use Itō, his onetime protégé, who was still comparatively obscure and untried.

Saigō's vigorous and unrelenting efforts were unavailing, as Iwakura was adamant in his determination that his first duty to the nation was to put into effect the policy of internal reforms and improvements. He had not the slightest doubt that the development of national power should take precedence over foreign relations and that the nation was in no condition to undertake a military expedition against Korea or any other nation. In late October, Iwakura was received in audience by the Emperor, who accepted his recommendations and ordered him to proceed with the program of extensive domestic reforms. Seeing that his cause was lost, Saigō resigned from the government in indignation and went into retirement in his native prefecture of Kagoshima. Soeshima, Itagaki, Etō, and Gotō, who had given unwavering support to Saigō on the Korean issue, also resigned their posts and continued active opposition against the government.

The split in the government over the Korean question was the first major political tragedy of the Meiji period. It heralded the beginning of an eventful period, punctuated by outbursts of fury against the constituted authorities. It was the parting of the ways for Saigō and Ōkubo, who were born on the same street in Kagoshima, had grown up together as bosom friends, and had worked closely together with selfless devotion in the Restoration. Once the break occurred, there was no attempt made by either to effect any compromise or reconciliation. Remarkable is the fact that no evidence can be found of any personal feeling of bitterness or enmity between the two great leaders.

Saigō's resignation from the government nearly wrecked the Imperial Guard as an efficient military organization. Many of the officers, who were Kagoshima men entertaining a strong sense of personal loyalty to Saigō and at the same time were in favor of "chastising Korea," resigned and returned to their native prefecture. However, under orders from Kido, War Minister Yamagata and his assistant, Torio Koyata, reorganized the Imperial Guard around the Chōshū military men, thereby preparing the way for the domination of the army by the Chōshū clique for the next several decades. The supremacy of the Satsuma clique in the navy, however, continued unimpaired by the event.

Clearly, the split over the Korean question was the result of the struggle for supremacy between the military-minded Saigō faction and the civilian-dominated Iwakura faction. The immediate issue was not whether or not relations with Korea should be placed on a satisfactory basis; it was a question of priority between domestic problems and foreign relations. The clash was an inevitable product of the difference in thinking between the civilian party and the military party.

To Saigō, the Korean issue was a test of strength to see how he stood in the struggle for power that he was carrying on in behalf of the old *samurai* class, whose cause he consistently championed. Iwakura, Kido, and Ōkubo represented the forces of progress which could not be checked by the reactionary chauvinism of the discontented *samurai*. Feeling was widespread among the disillusioned *samurai* that the evil forces of the West were responsible for the moral degeneration of the people and the sad plight of the *samurai,* who had shamelessly turned into urban civil officials and who feared death and loved wealth and luxury more than honor.

That the government in the first two decades following the Restoration should be an oligarchy was perhaps inevitable. The new government was dominated by a small group of outstanding men who had furnished active leadership in the overthrow of the feudal regime, had launched the new regime, and laid the foundations for the emergence of a new Japan. Minister President Sanjō and Minister of the Right Iwakura, who were members of the old nobility, and Saigō, Ōkubo, and Kido, the "triumvirate of the Restoration," who were representatives of the lower *samurai,* constituted the pillars of early Meiji Government. This oligarchy consisted of, and was supported and assisted by, men from Satsuma, Chōshū, Tosa, and Hizen, the four clans that contributed most to the overthrow of the Tokugawa Shogunate. Noteworthy is the fact that the *daimyō* class was not included in the oligarchy. It was the deliberate policy of the lower *samurai* to exclude the influence of the upper class *samurai* just as much as to liquidate the Shogunate, which represented the apex of the feudal hierarchy.

In terms of clan influence, the oligarchy was built around the Satsuma and Chōshū, which alternated in dominating the government in the beginning. The first decade of the Meiji era was dominated by Satsuma, since Saigō and Ōkubo were in control; in the next decade, control passed on to the Chōshū, which provided leadership through Itō, Inoue, and Yamagata.

In May, 1877, Kido, whose ideals, foresight, and political acumen were of inestimable value to the oligarchy as well as to the nation as a whole, died at the age of forty-five, in the prime of life. Less than six months later, Saigō, the military genius of the Restoration, gave his life to a lost cause. Ōkubo alone of the "triumvirate" was left to carry on the unfinished work of the new government. In his hands he held, unchallenged by any other person, the powers of government, military as well as civil. Although he was officially only Home Minister and Councilor, he exercised the powers of a premier. It remained for him to complete the work of pacifying and unifying the country and of setting up a strong central government. In this work, he was ably assisted by Ōkuma Shigenobu and Itō Hirobumi who were to occupy, in a few years, the center of the stage.

The first step in the program of internal development was the creation in January, 1874, of the Department of Home Affairs. Ōkubo, to whom internal reforms had become a consuming passion, became the first head. At every opportunity, he planned and executed policies which were aimed at the improvement of internal administration, particularly sound public finance, the increase of national wealth, and the advancement of public welfare. To these ends he instituted administrative reforms and innovations. To encourage industry he ordered government offices to use domestic products, and to pay off foreign debts he planned a program of foreign trade.

In an attempt to point the way for private industry to follow, he established model government enterprises, which were later turned over to private ownership. Experiment stations, laboratories, and technical schools were established to give the necessary training, assistance, and encouragement to the industries. The Home Minister gave more than his share of attention to the development and improvement of agriculture.

To Ōkubo goes the credit for the first exposition in Japan, which was opened in the summer of 1877 while the Satsuma Rebellion was in progress. Although the government was vigorously prosecuting the war, Ōkubo felt that the work of encouraging the industries should go on uninterrupted. He had demonstrated his faith in an exposition as a means of stimulating trade and industry by his decision to have Japan participate in The Centennial Exhibition in Philadelphia. Until his career was cut short by an assassin, he worked tirelessly toward the increase of national power. Although he was a statesman of the highest caliber and of unswerving loyalty and determination, his achievements in the administration of internal affairs were in no small measure due to the experiences, convictions, and inspiration he derived from his visit to Europe and America as a member of the famed Iwakura mission. Great as his achievements were, his methods of getting things done were not infrequently autocratic. Historians, however, give him full credit for having started the industrialization and modernization of Japan's national economy.

THE COLONIZATION AND DEVELOPMENT OF HOKKAIDŌ

Until recently, the northern regions have always constituted the undeveloped, undefended frontier of Japan. It was quite natural that the attention of the leaders should be directed to the north in the creation of a strong Japan. In the spring of 1868, the Emperor personally attended a meeting of the Council of State and sought its advice regarding the development of Yezo land. Most of the Councilors, feeling uneasy over the encroachment of Russia from the north, regarded the establishment of a court (*saibansho*) as an urgent need. The decision of the Council was followed by the establishment of the Hakodate Court, which was almost immediately changed to the Hakodate Office. Iwakura considered the development of Yezo as one of the three most urgent tasks confronting the government in 1869, the other two being foreign relations and public finance.

With the establishment of the Office of the Commissioner of Colonization and Development of Hokkaidō in the summer of 1869, the work of developing the northernmost island began in earnest. Yezo was renamed Hokkaidō. The importance of the undertaking may be seen by the fact that the Commissioner was given cabinet rank and the Deputy Commissioner the rank of vice minister. For more than ten years, until its abolition in 1882, the Office carried on an extensive program of developing the resources of the island and of encouraging settlements to strengthen the defenses on the northern frontier. The development of this northern frontier was induced and accelerated not so much by economic necessity as by impelling strategic considerations.

Sapporo was selected as the seat of the Office of Colonization, and the program of developing the agricultural and mineral resources was launched on an ambitious scale when Kuroda Kiyotaka assumed the post of Deputy Commissioner. Early in 1871, he visited the United States to secure specialists as advisers, to purchase machinery and equipment, and to make arrangements for students to study in America. With the help of Chargé Mori in Washington, he secured the services of General Horace Capron, U.S. Commissioner of Agriculture who became adviser to the Commissioner in Japan, Thomas Antisell, Chief Chemist of the U.S. Department of Agriculture who became Director of the Geological, Mining, and Engineering Department, and Benjamin Smith Lyman who became general geologist and mining engineer in Japan.

At the suggestion of Capron an agricultural school was founded early in 1872.

This became the famous Sapporo Agricultural College in September, 1875, and Dr. William Clark, President of the Massachusetts Agricultural College, was invited to become its head. It was under Clark that outstanding men like Nitobe Inazō and Uchimura Kanzō received not only scientific and agricultural training but also came under strong Christian influence.

In the development of Hokkaidō more than seventy foreign teachers and advisers were employed. As American advisers predominated, American influences have left an indelible imprint on Hokkaidō. One observes a striking resemblance between the agricultural landscape of this part of Japan and that of rural America. The experiences gained in the development of Hokkaidō, particularly in the installation and operation of various facilities and the management of government enterprises, were put to use years later in the colonization and development of Formosa, Korea, and Manchuria.

In the opening up of Yezo, voluntary settlement was not the method used by the government. Nor was it an individual migration. It was group migration, a virtual transplanting of communities undertaken by the different fiefs that were assigned different districts which they had to manage and finance as well. In a few instances individuals as well as Buddhist temples were allotted districts for settlement.

This particular method was decided upon with the idea of achieving two purposes at the same time. By carefully distributing the able-bodied of the different fiefs, defense plans could be worked out without the expense of maintaining regular military organization, while at the same time the rehabilitation of the displaced *samurai* could be accomplished. But such a policy was doomed to failure, particularly as adequate consideration was not given to geographic factors. Inhabitants of the southern and southwestern parts of the country, who were not familiar with actual conditions in the northern regions, could not or would not adapt themselves to the vastly different climatic conditions and environment. By the fall of 1870 the fiefs had requested and obtained release from the responsibility of managing the districts assigned to them because of financial and management difficulties. In August, 1871, the entire island was placed under the direct jurisdiction and administration of the Commissioner of Colonization and not long thereafter all restrictions were removed and settlement of Hokkaidō was put on a voluntary basis.

In September, 1871, Kuroda urged upon the central government the necessity of providing a defense against possible Russian encroachment. More than two years later, in December, 1873, he proposed the establishment of a system of agrarian militia (*tonden nōhei*) to be formed by able-bodied farmers. This time, his proposal was promptly approved, and on June 23, 1874, Deputy Commissioner Kuroda was made Lieutenant General and placed in charge of agrarian militia affairs.

Under this system, started October 30, able-bodied persons between the ages of eighteen and thirty-five were to be recruited and organized into regiments, battalions, and companies as in the regular army and given military training when not engaged in farming duties. They were to serve as dismounted military police and in peacetime to perform police duties. In exchange for this service to the Government, the family of a recruit was given 5,000 *tsubo* of land and necessary arms as well as farming implements, household goods, and provisions for a period of three years. Although at first only the ex-*samurai* were eligible, the policy was changed, beginning in 1891, to allow anyone to serve in the agrarian militia. The War Ministry began to take interest in the militia in 1885 and made a study of the Russian Cossack organization in an effort to improve the system. But in 1896, the militia was superseded by the Seventh Division of the Army. In September, 1903, the system was abolished. However, the success of colonization of Hokkaidō owed a great deal to this system, which was responsible for building towns and villages in various parts of the island.

RESISTANCE AGAINST THE GOVERNMENT

Hostility flared up against the new regime in different parts of the country, as peasants staged local uprisings in which officials and wealthy individuals were made the targets of attack. Thousands of persons participated in violent outbreaks against those in authority, causing considerable casualties and damages. But this was a resistance against changes brought into the peasants' lives and not in any sense a political movement intended to overthrow the government. The peasants were much too unconcerned with politics.

Social and economic changes that came abruptly and in unending series were not only disturbing to the almost changeless mode of life to which they had been accustomed for centuries but economically they were also very painful. The conservative and unenlightened farmers could not understand and much less appreciate the purpose of the Restoration. They would have been content to be left alone. They received every change with suspicion and misgivings and not infrequently misunderstood the intentions of the government. Military conscription was taken literally as a blood tax, the introduction of Western subject matter in the schools as the propagation of a false religion and sorcery, and the enforcement of the family registration system as a preliminary to the selling of women and children into bondage. In a great many instances the new land tax system, instead of giving relief to the farmers, actually increased their financial burdens. It was quite natural therefore that the demands made by the peasants in their uprisings included the lowering of prices, especially of rice; abolition of schools, teaching of English, military conscription; abandoning of the Gregorian calendar and the Western haircut; a ban on Christianity and against foreigners, and the *eta* becoming commoners.

The opposition, carried on for the most part by the peasants, decreased as the confidence of the people in the government grew with the establishment of a strong authority and the reduction of land taxes, which ameliorated to some degree the sufferings of the peasants. Peasant uprisings practically disappeared after 1877. For the first decade of the Meiji era some two hundred peasant uprisings are on record. However, to the authorities they were less of a problem, even at their height, than the opposition which came from the discontented ex-*samurai*, who were led by influential leaders.

Resistance of the most violent and persistent type directed against the government came from the disillusioned members of the dissolved *samurai* class, whose efforts at readjustment to new conditions were not altogether successful. After the overthrow of the Shogunate they had entertained hopes of prosperous days ahead as a reward for the valuable services they had rendered to the new government. But this was not to be. The collapse of the feudal regime was soon followed by the abolition of fiefs, the abolition of the *samurai* class itself, and finally the loss of even their meager and insecure source of livelihood. The majority of the ex-*samurai* found themselves out of employment without either funds or skill to earn a livelihood under new and altogether strange conditions. Troubled by insecurity and uncertainty, many of them looked back to the good old days of feudalism with more nostalgia than they could conceal and wished for their return. Only a handful of them were rewarded with positions of power and prestige in the government. This was a patent injustice to the less fortunate *samurai*, who began to give vent to dissatisfaction and resentment by criticizing the policies of the government. Some advocated the policy of chastising Korea and ignored the urgency of internal reforms which they were willing to sacrifice for an undertaking designed to restore the prestige of the ex-*samurai* and possibly even to restore the class to power. Others rejected the policy of friendship with the foreign powers and the adoption of European civilization in favor of chauvinistic nationalism and antiforeignism. Still others denounced the absolutism of clan oligarchy in government and advocated the establishment of a system whereby decisions on important matters of state were to be made on the basis of public opinion. These men organized themselves into groups to carry on active resistance against the government and put up a stubborn fight against changes instituted by the government without regard to merits.

Against this backdrop must be viewed the constant struggle for power that was going on among the different factions of the government itself. The attempts by the Tosa clique to dislodge both the Satsuma and Chōshū cliques from power and the friction between the military clique and the civilian group that came to a head over the Korean question provided the stage for a series of hostile outbreaks against the government beginning in 1874. These conflicts were the outward manifestations of the struggle for power which had been going on under the surface between the various opposing factions: the progressives and the conservatives, those in power and those outside of the government, those who favored rapid changes and those who wanted gradual changes, the military men and civilians, the urban interests and agrarian interests. Earliest of a series of explosions came in 1874.

Stung by the defeat over the Korean question in 1873, Etō Shimpei resigned his position as Councilor and, at the invitation of an organization in favor of chastising Korea (*Seikantō*), returned to his native prefecture, Saga, where he found Shima Yoshitake, former governor of Akita prefecture, heading another faction comprising dissatisfied *samurai*. The two factions joined hands and with some twenty-five hundred members, Etō started a rebellion on February 1, 1874, thinking that Saigō in Kagoshima and Itagaki in Kōchi would respond by starting armed opposition against the government. When the news of the revolt reached the capital, the Emperor appointed Home Minister Ōkubo to take over personally the direction of a punitive expedition. Although Ōkubo had no military background, he had requested that he be assigned the task for which he felt responsible because he was the most powerful member of the government and had incurred the animosity of the discontented elements outside the government since the split over the Korean question. Under Ōkubo's able direction of the troops the rebellion was quelled in short order. Etō escaped to Kagoshima, where he vainly sought Saigō's protection. He then entered Tosa to seek Itagaki's protection, only to be turned down. He was captured and executed as was Shima Yoshitake. This rebellion, the first attempt of its kind by malcontents to overthrow the government by force, ended unsuccessfully but did not dampen the spirit of other dissatisfied ex-*samurai*.

In Kumamoto, which had been for some time a center of Confucian scholars, there was a group known as the *Shimpūren* (*Keishintō*), which opposed the Westernization policy of the government. It believed in a conservative, if not reactionary, policy of nationalism and chauvinism. The members wore topknots, feudal headdress, and long swords, and they looked down disdainfully on those who advocated Westernization. Efforts were made by the prefectural governor to keep this group under control. But the government's announcement of March 28, 1876, of the order banning the wearing of swords was almost too much for them to endure. This was soon followed by the government's decision to pay the former *samurai* in pension bonds (*kinroku kōsai*), virtually the final act in the liquidation of the *samurai* class. This was the last straw. On October 24, some two hundred members of the *Shimpūren* swiftly carried out a surprise attack on the prefectural office and the Kumamoto garrison, killing the commanding general and fatally wounding the governor. The rebellion was put down in short order, but not before it had stirred other groups into action elsewhere.

Four hundred discontented *samurai* of Akizuki fief in the neighboring prefecture of Fukuoka responded to the action of the Kumamoto group by starting a rebellion three days later. While it was an antigovernment outbreak synchronized with the *Shimpūren,* the leaders were advocates of expansion of national

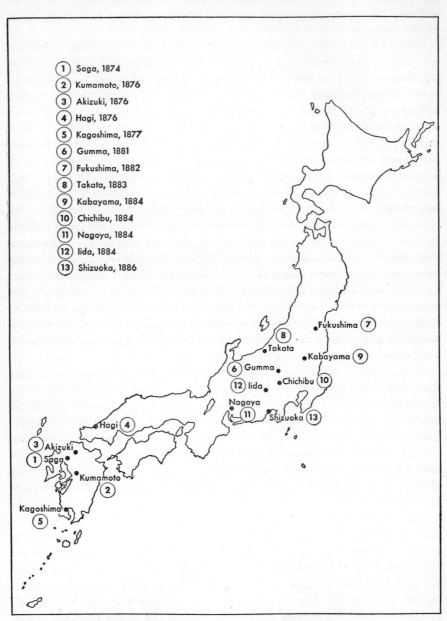

Rebellions (1874–1877) and Disturbances (1881–1886).

power beyond its own borders and had denounced the government policy of deferring the Korean question.

In Yamaguchi, Maebara Issei, a former Councilor and Vice Minister of Military Affairs, had been in retirement after resigning from the government as a result of a clash of views. He was critical of the government on the Korean question, the land tax reform, the exchange of Karafuto and the Kuriles with Russia, and the disposition of the *samurai* problem. He had been working closely with the groups in Kumamoto and Akizuki and had come to an agreement about starting revolts simultaneously in different parts of the country. When he learned that the Kumamoto group had started a rebellion, he assembled some two hundred followers and started out to attack Yamaguchi, the seat of the prefectural government, on October 26, two days after the outbreak at Akizuki. Less than two weeks later, this rebellion was also put down and the leaders were executed.

Thus ended the last of a series of comparatively small-scale rebellions. None of these involved much more than four hundred participants. The leaders had been confident that the discontented elements in Satsuma would rise in arms the moment a minor revolt broke out and that the rebellion would spread rapidly to all parts of the country. Fully awake to such a possibility, the government had made thorough preparations to cope with any eventuality. Secret agents were at work gathering information for the government, and in the case of the Hagi Rebellion, Maebara's intentions were correctly known to the authorities well in advance, so that the government was ready when it broke out.

Meanwhile, all was not quiet in southern Kyūshū. After returning to Satsuma, Saigō started a private school (Shigakkō) in June, 1874, in the city of Kagoshima for the training of the youth of the prefecture. In this work he was assisted by able lieutenants, who had served in the Imperial Guard but had resigned their commissions and followed Saigō back to Kagoshima. An infantry school and an artillery school were operated while instruction was given in the Chinese classics. Pupils flocked to Kagoshima to study under the great Saigō who had become a national idol, and soon branch schools had to be established within the prefecture to accommodate the pupils. Before long there were 124 branches in the outlying areas in addition to about twelve in the city itself. It was Saigō's plan to train promising young men for future service with the government, as he seemed to think that the government then in power would automatically collapse of its own weaknesses. When that happened he hoped to step in and to reorganize the government to carry out his own ideas in the administration of the affairs of state with the aid of those trained under him. It is likely too that he had in mind a possible venture on the Asiatic continent for which the exacting and rigorous training given to pupils in his private school could be used to advantage.

The administration for Kagoshima prefecture at the time was unique in that the government had appointed natives of the prefecture exclusively to all the

positions, from governor down to minor officials. The governor appointed those
who had studied in Saigō's private school as heads of districts and villages as well
as policemen. Saigō's reputation and Governor Ōyama's hearty cooperation spread
the influence of the school to a point where the Shigakkō faction was in virtual
control of prefectural administration. Although Saigō's presence in the prefecture
was responsible for this situation, he held no official position in the prefectural
government. The power of the central government did not extend into the prefecture, which enjoyed a *de facto* condition of extraterritoriality. To correct this
situation which was fraught with danger, Home Minister Ōkubo, himself a
native of Kagoshima, summoned Ōyama to the capital in an attempt to revamp
prefectural administration. But the governor succeeded in postponing action on
the matter with the plea that conditions were unfavorable for such a move.
Meanwhile, rebellions broke out in Kumamoto, Akizuki, and Hagi and the government was unable to accomplish anything in the way of reforming prefectural
administration in Kagoshima.

Upon receipt of the disquieting news from Kagoshima in the wake of the
Kumamoto Rebellion, the government sent Hayashi Tomoyuki, a high official of
the Home Ministry, to undertake the reform of prefectural administration. But
after two months he returned without having achieved his objective; he had
been prevented from doing anything. It was imperative that Kagoshima be
brought under the control of the central government if its authority were to be
firmly established and recognized. The government therefore sent several hand-
picked inspectors from the Tōkyō Metropolitan Police Board to Kagoshima to
keep close surveillance over the movements of the Shigakkō faction and at the
same time to make every effort to dissuade any rebellious action by persuasion
of friends and relatives of incipient rebels. However, the arrival of the police
officials was suspected as a government scheme to dissolve the faction and
liquidate the leader, Saigō. Almost simultaneously, as a precautionary measure,
the War Ministry ordered the removal of arms and munitions from the Kagoshima Branch Arsenal to Ōsaka, a step which was interpreted as preliminary to
using them against the Shigakkō faction. Saigō's followers decided to seize the
initiative.

From the very outset there had existed a considerable number of faithful and
unquestioning followers of Saigō, who misunderstood or misinterpreted his intentions and began to entertain the idea of attempting the reorganization of the
central government by forceful means or a *coup d'état*. This element urged the
acquisition of stores of ammunition, encouraged the return of former members
of the Satsuma clan to their homes in preparation for the impending conflict,
and hurled challenges and inflammatory words at the government.

Beginning on the night of January 29 and for three days afterwards, they attacked the Army Munitions Depot and the Navy Yard and succeeded in carrying off sizable quantities of rifles and ammunition. Later they took possession

of the yard, changed its name back to the one which had been used by the fief, and started turning out weapons and ammunition. When the news of the seizure of arms reached Saigō, who was out on a hunting trip in the mountains of Ōsumi, he hastened back to Kagoshima. At first it was decided in a meeting of the leaders that Saigō was to head a delegation to the capital to make representations to the government, but this plan was abandoned in favor of more drastic action. Things in the meantime had gone too far for any last-minute attempt to check the violence which had been unleashed. There remained no alternative for the leaders but to cast their lot with those who had already released the inexorable force. Bowing to the inevitable and resigning himself to fate, Saigō resolved to sacrifice himself for the cause.

From February 15 to 17, the Satsuma army of 150,000 under Saigō and his lieutenants Kirino and Shinohara left Kagoshima ostensibly to make demands upon the government. The governor, who idolized Saigō, as did most of the people of Satsuma, turned over government money to help defray the expenditures of the military undertaking; furthermore, in his official capacity as governor, he sent word to the governors and garrison commanders on the route of march requesting them to permit Saigō and his troops safe passage through their respective jurisdictions and explaining that General Saigō was on his way to Tōkyō to discuss matters with the government. When the communication was received at the headquarters of the Kumamoto garrison, Colonel Kabayama and Major Kodama assumed the responsibility of rejecting it.

On February 22, the Satsuma forces, after clashing with advance scouts of the government forces, reached the Kumamoto Castle, which was held by a garrison under the command of Major General Tani Tateki, and immediately laid siege. Meanwhile Prince Arisugawa was appointed Commander in chief of the government expeditionary forces. Serving under him were General Yamagata and Admiral Kawamura, Ministers of War and Navy respectively. After more than fifty days of siege, aid came to the Kumamoto garrison just in time to prevent its surrender to the enemy. Defeat would have otherwise been inevitable as food and ammunition were nearly exhausted.

In an early vanguard engagement with the enemy, Major Nogi (General Nogi of Port Arthur fame in the Russo-Japanese War), then in command of a regiment, suffered a reverse and lost his regimental colors to the enemy. The government forces were unable to advance much until heavy reenforcement under Generals Nozu and Miyoshi were brought up. After the middle of March the tide of war turned in favor of the government, and by the first of June Satsuma forces were on flight. The issue had been decided by the beginning of August. After a series of disastrous defeats, the rebel forces were put to rout. Remnants numbering no more than several hundred headed for Kagoshima where they took their position on Shiroyama. Here Saigō made his last stand with less than four hundred men out of the original 150,000 who had started out only six months earlier. On the dawn of September 24, the government troops launched a general attack. In the encounter, Saigō was critically wounded and had one of his faithful lieutenants, Beppu, deliver the *coup de grâce*. Kirino, Shinohara, Murata, and others who had stood by the leader either died in action or took their own lives rather than surrender. Not many more than two hundred lived to surrender to the government as the rebellion came to an end.

In spite of the resistance by force he carried out against the government, Saigō was regarded with respect and worshipped as a hero. History has not relegated him to a position of infamy, indicted him as a rebel, or even stigmatized him for the role he played. Instead, it has accorded him a position of high honor.

With superior generalship and equipment, coupled with the excellent training and discipline of the new conscript army, the government successfully put down the largest rebellion in modern Japan. It had lasted eight months and cost some forty-five million yen. The enemy, whose troops numbered 40,000 effectives at maximum strength, suffered over 20,000 casualties, of which 5,000 were deaths. The government troops, more thon 60,000 strong, suffered casualties of 16,000, of which 6,000 were deaths. The navy contributed its share by putting 11 warships, 44 transports, and 2,280 officers and men into service, but there was no naval action. All the fighting was on land.

So decisive and conclusive was the victory achieved by the government forces that no more attempts were made to overthrow the government by a resort to arms. Even the most skeptical could no longer doubt the effectiveness of the conscript army as a fighting force; it had proved its mettle. There was no question that the sons of peasants and merchants made fighters as good as the former *samurai* and their sons. The war served as a training ground for young army and navy officers who were later to distinguish themselves as field and fleet commanders in the Sino-Japanese War and the Russo-Japanese War.

It is necessary to note here an incident which was completely overshadowed by the Satsuma Rebellion, but which was nevertheless significant as a closing chapter in the agitation for representative government and which was carried on persistently by the militant followers of Itagaki. The Tosa clan had always been in the vanguard of the fight to bring about popular government based on public deliberation. This was true even in the years preceding the Restoration. During the early Meiji period, it maintained its own military force which could be used if necessary in checking the power of the Satsuma and Chōshū clans. The role of Tosa's leaders in the Korean question was to try to reject the dictatorial decisions of the government dominated by Iwakura, Ōkubo, and Kido.

Immediately following the split in the government in January, 1874, the champions of popular rights presented a suggestion for the establishment of a popular representative assembly. Seeing that no immediate action would be forthcoming, Itagaki established three months later a society, Risshisha, for the dissemination of the concept of liberty and popular rights in his native province. This organization, deriving inspiration from the ideas of Voltaire and Rousseau, emphasized that governments were instituted for the protection of the rights of the people and existed for the people. The society pointed out as its goal the establishment and extension of popular rights, the securing of a livelihood for all, the advancement of public welfare, the preservation of national independence, and the encouragement of industries. It established an institute of legal affairs to study jurisprudence and to handle suits and a commercial bureau to engage in the buying and selling of products. It also founded a school for the training of youth for leadership in the movement.

After the Ōsaka Conference, Itagaki rejoined the government but soon left in disgust when he found it impossible to carry out his cherished ideals. Thereafter he became more determined than ever to fight for popular rights, but he scrupulously insisted on achieving his ends only by legal means and particularly by using the power of public opinion to destroy the absolutism he found in government. However, there were among his followers Hayashi Yūzō, Ōe Taku, and others who apparently believed that the end justified the means and proceeded to achieve their aims by force. To them, the Satsuma Rebellion was an unequaled opportunity. They made plans to purchase arms. Mutsu Munemitsu was drawn into this plot without difficulty, since he was determined to break the power of the Satsuma-Chōshū clan oligarchy, which was then running the government.

It was ostensibly a plot to force the government to institute reforms thought to be necessary for securing popular rights and establishing a representative assembly. While it was an attempt which was unmistakably antigovernment in nature, its avowed objective was the establishment of a popular assembly. It was quite different from the ideas of the Satsuma Rebellion leaders, who were not interested in popular rights as such, although Saigō himself was not opposed to modernization or Westernization within what he considered reasonable limits. The plot was nipped in the bud, and the leaders were arrested and imprisoned. Among those who were incarcerated but released and pardoned later were Kataoka Kenkichi, who served as Speaker of the House of Representatives, and Mutsu Munemitsu, who consistently fought against clan bureaucracy, and who, as one of the most enlightened statesmen of the Meiji period, occupied the position of Foreign Minister at the time of the Triple Intervention.

Chapter 5. Adoption of Western Science and Learning

Japanese leaders turned increasingly toward the ideas and institutions of the West in their search for the basis of Westernization and modernization of their country. Those branches of learning which would furnish the foundations of a new national state attracted their attention first. Practical knowledge was placed before theoretical studies. Economic ideas and institutions, production techniques, financial machinery, and trade structures that were prevalent in the advanced nations of the West were urgently needed to bring Japan quickly up to a level where she could eventually build up her national strength to compete successfully in the markets of the world. These subjects came to be the objects of intensive study.

In the spring of 1862, two students in their middle thirties, Tsuda and Nishi, were sent by the Shogunate to study in Holland, where they remained for four years. At the University of Leyden, they studied, among other subjects, natural law, the law of nations, constitutional law, economics, and statistics under Professor Simon Vissering, a strong opponent of the English corn laws and an advocate of free trade, who leaned heavily toward the views of Frédéric Bastiat, the eminent French economist. After the opening of the country Japanese students of Western learning were thus exposed first to the ideas of laissez-faire and free-trade economists. Names of English political economists like Adam Smith, Ricardo, Malthus, and Mill soon became familiar to the Japanese.

The cradle of social science research at the time was the Shogunate's Institute for the Study of Barbarian Literature (*Bansho Torishirabejo*) which, from 1865, specialized in the translation of foreign works and the teaching of foreign languages. This institute was the forerunner of what later became the Tōkyō Imperial University. One of the earliest exponents of economic liberalism was Kanda Kōhei, a professor in the Institute.

In 1867, Kanda published the *Rudiments of Economics* (*Keizai Shōgaku*), which was a translation of William Ellis's *Outlines of Social Economy*. Five years earlier, in his *Discussions on Agriculture and Commerce* (*Nōshōben*), he set forth his mercantilistic views and urged that Japan should build herself up by foreign trade. His reason was that nations based on trade would always prosper while those based on agriculture would remain poor. He explained the poverty of Oriental nations and the prosperity of the Occident with this theory as a basis. He also pointed out that, as a source of revenue, trade was far superior to agriculture and expressed his conviction that Japan could achieve prosperity through commerce and industry. Later, his mercantilistic ideas were put into practice by the Meiji Government.

Laissez-faire and free-trade concepts were introduced into Japan through the writings of English and American economists. Fukuzawa Yukichi was instrumental in introducing American works. In 1868, even as battles were raging in Edo between the government forces and the die-hard followers of the Shogunate, Fukuzawa was lecturing at Keiō to a class in political economy, using Francis Wayland's *Elements of Political Economy* as a text.

In 1869, the government's newly established Translation Bureau published the *Principles of Economics (Kampan Keizai Genron)*, which was no more than a translation of *Elements of Political Economy* by Arthur Lay Perry, professor at Williams College. The *Treatise on Corporations (Kampan Kaisha Ben)* by Fukuchi Gen'ichirō, published by the Finance Department in 1871, represented an effort to encourage and enlighten the public in commercial enterprises. It was based largely on the chapters in Wayland's *Elements of Political Economy* that dealt with banks. John Stuart Mill's *Principles of Political Economy* was made available in translation in the late 1870's by Hayashi Tadasu, who later distinguished himself as a diplomat. Thus, by 1880, the study of economics and law had become the main pursuit of ambitious young government officials as well as university students. Colleges and universities were founded to specialize in the teaching of these two important fields.

The government became involved in the study of the economic systems of the West as part of a program to adopt the best features of organization, production methods, and techniques. However, it was reluctant to throw overboard the good preservable features of the old system. In order that some of the desirable features might be preserved and harmonized with the best that the West had to offer, the government set out to make a thorough study of Japan's economic past. Researches were made of the development of the various industries as well as of the origins of economic institutions and practices. This resulted in such valuable studies as the *History of Japanese Currency* (1876–1883) and the *History of Japanese Taxation* (1882) by the Department of Finance, as well as the *History of Japanese Agriculture* (1891) and *Materials on Japanese Agricultural Administration* (1897) by the Agriculture and Forestry Ministry.

As free trade versus protectionism became a lively issue among policy makers and students of economics, books on the subject began to appear. In 1877 the work of the English jurist, Sir John Barnard Byles, *Sophisms of Free Trade and Popular Political Economy Examined,* was published in a Japanese translation by Wakayama Giichi as an appendix to his *Discussions on Protective Trade.*

By 1878, Fukuzawa, erstwhile champion of free trade, had abandoned this theory in favor of protectionism, as he veered toward nationalistic policies. His *Discussions on National Power* (*Kokken Ron*) clearly indicated his new position. About the same time, Bastiat's *Economic Sophisms* (*Sophismes économiques*), an attack on the English corn laws, was brought out in translation. In 1882, Adam Smith's *Wealth of Nations* was translated in parts, but it was not until later that it became available in its entirety. In 1880 was introduced a partial translation of *Free Trade and Protection* by Henry Fawcett, the economist-statesman and professor of political economy at Cambridge, who played an important role in the radical politics of the day as a member of Parliament. His *Manual of Political Economy* became very popular later.

The coming of Erasmus P. Smith as legal adviser to the Foreign Office in 1871 was directly responsible for the popularity of the ideas of Henry Charles Carey, the first American economist and strong protectionist who, like his father, opposed the English classical economists, particularly Ricardo and Malthus. His *Principles of Social Science,* regarded as the first significant American work in the field, gained wide following among the Japanese through the work of his student Kate McKeen, who condensed the work in the *Manual of Social Science*. The protectionist ideas of Carey, which had been developed in the period of expansion and "Manifest Destiny" in the United States, appealed to Japanese leaders, who used them as a basis for the building up of a modern Japan.

By far the staunchest advocate of free trade was Taguchi Ukichi, who in 1878 published a *Discussion of Japanese Economics* to uphold his stand. The following year he founded a publishing firm and began the *Tōkyō Journal of Economics* (*Tōkyō Keizai Zasshi*). He also fathered the Tōkyō Economic Association to advocate free trade in practice as in theory. This group opposed the National Economic Association, which stood for protectionism. Until the very last, he consistently championed free trade, even long after the time the nation had accepted nationalism and its corollary, protectionism. In order to put into practice his laissez-faire ideas, he founded a railway company, a foreign trade company, operated a mine, and participated in the management of a number of banks and corporations. His publishing firm pioneered in the compilation of source materials, a field in which the government had had virtually a monopoly. He was successively a member of lawmaking bodies on all levels: ward, municipal, prefectural assemblies, and finally, the Diet.

FUKUZAWA'S ROLE IN THE DEVELOPMENT OF ECONOMIC IDEAS

Fukuzawa, the greatest publicist of Westernization and economic liberalism of the early Meiji period, wrote *Foreign Intercourse* (*Tōjin Ōrai*) in the early

1860's to rid Kanda's maidservant of her antiforeignism. In it he stated, after pointing out the rather disastrous consequences of China's antiforeignism, that to abstain from intercourse with foreign nations was a contravention of the laws both of nature and human nature. An eloquent discourse on the benefits of foreign trade, it was one of the earliest works advocating free trade. Toward the end of 1874, he expressed his belief, in the *Chōya Shimbun,* that foreign relations, especially foreign trade, were the most important problem of the day. He had advocated in his *Outline of Civilization (Bummeiron no Gairyaku)* that the economic theories of the West could not be applied directly to Japanese conditions and that modifications and adaptations were necessary because of the different conditions obtaining in Japan. Early in 1875 he called the attention of the public to the fact that the Japanese were not reaping the profits of their trade, because the foreign merchants were getting them.

He was spurred on by the niggardly progress he witnessed to concentrate on business education, through which he hoped not only to change the traditional concepts but to help build up the country economically. Thus, the Keiō University, which he founded, came to emphasize the training of business and industrial leaders. It was Fukuzawa who introduced bookkeeping and undertook the dissemination of the economic ideas and business practices of the West. Between 1877 and 1882 he published his *Discussions on Popular Economics (Minkan Keizairoku)* as a textbook for the education of the public.

In 1884, Fukuzawa published his *Discourses on Wealth and Poverty (Himpu Ron),* in which he recognized the sacred right of property but deprecated the high concentration of wealth among a small number of people. He wryly observed that the poor would contend that poverty was the cause of ignorance in reply to the economist's assertion that ignorance was the cause of poverty. He accepted the disparity of wealth as a fact but failed to go a step further in suggesting measures to relieve poverty. Although by 1891 he had become gravely concerned, if not alarmed, over the ever widening chasm, he was vastly more concerned with the urgency of increasing the nation's wealth and strength through successful competition in the world market than with bettering the lot of the economically underprivileged at home.

INFLUENCE OF GERMAN ECONOMISTS

After 1885, in keeping with the increasing popularity of German ideas in the realm of politics, students of political economy and policymakers began to show their interest in German ideas. Particularly attractive to the Japanese were the ideas of Friedrich List, author of the *National System of Political Economy,* a book that had been embraced by German commercial and governmental circles, and which had become the basis of national economic policies under Bismarck. His advocacy of free trade in the early stages of industrialization, followed by a change to protectionism as a necessary measure for protecting and aiding an expanded industry to compete successfully in the world market, appealed to the leaders in government, business, and industry.

The Japanese government began to send students to Germany for study. Among them was Dr. Kanai Noburu, who went to the University of Berlin. For a short period he studied at Halle under Johannes Conrad, an authority on agricultural policy and statistics. At Berlin, in 1888, he came under the influence of Gustav von Schmoller, founder of the Verein für Sozial Politik, and of Adolph Wagner. Returning in 1890, after three years of study, he emphasized the socioeconomic problems in his country, advocating social legislation in the form of relief to the poor and protection of labor. He pointed out that those who still clung to John Stuart Mill and Henry Fawcett were behind the times, since even in conservative England changes were taking place and the classical school was on the decline.

Deriding Gustav Boissanade for his antiquated eighteenth-century economic theories and legal ideas and calling Bastiat's banal, Kanai vigorously disseminated the ideas of the newest school: the cathedral socialists. Cathedral socialism had first been introduced into Japan in 1888 by Professor Wadagaki Kenzō. Professor Kanai's chief contribution to the subject, *Social Economics (Shakai Keizaigaku)*, was the outstanding work in the field of economic theory of this period in Japan.

The Association for the Study of Social Policy, founded in April, 1895, at the instance of Kuwata Kumazō, member of the House of Peers, was directly inspired by the ideas of cathedral socialism. In explaining the aims of the Association, Kuwata stated that this organization was opposed to *laissez faire* because the mobilization of extreme selfishness and unrestricted competition would only serve to widen the gap between wealth and poverty. It was also opposed to socialism because of the resulting destruction of existing economic structure and the liquidation of capitalists that would impair national progress. It was the aim of the Association to study social problems with a view to preserving the existing structure of private enterprise and ensuring harmony in society through individual and governmental efforts, hoping that this would prevent class struggle.

Interest in Japanese Economic History. Interest in economic history in general was first stimulated in 1879 by the government publication of the *History of British Commerce and of the Economic Progress of the British Nation, 1763–1870* by Leon Levi, an English economist and statistician. This was part of the government's promotion work, a means of encouraging trade and business activities. At first Japanese economists, who had been nourished by the English classical school which had developed economics as an abstract deductive science, neglected the study of their own economic history. It was not until the middle of the 1890's that the conditions became favorable to the serious study of Japanese economic development. Professor Yokoi Tokifuyu pioneered in the field with his *History of Japanese Manufacturing* (*Nihon Kōgyōshi*), *History of Japanese Commerce* (*Nihon Shōgyōshi*), and the *History of Commerce since the Restoration* (*Ishingo no Shōgyōshi*). Pioneer studies of more specific topics than Yokoi's were made by Uchida Ginzō, a graduate of the Tōkyō Imperial University, who began teaching at his alma mater in 1899. His course has generally been regarded as the first one on Japanese economic history ever to be taught. Professor Uchida was profoundly influenced by Sir William James Ashley, who in 1892 introduced at Harvard the first course on economic history ever to be taught in any university. He was also influenced by Dr. Gustav von Schmoller and William Cunningham who also taught economic history at Harvard.

One of Yokoi's students, Fukuda Tokuzō, went to Germany and studied at Leipzig and later at Munich, where he studied under Lujo Brentano. His inaugural dissertation in German, which was published in 1900, was the first systematic attempt at the socioeconomic interpretation of Japanese history in terms of European scholarship. This epochal work remained untranslated into Japanese for seven years after its first appearance. In 1902 Professor Uchida published his *Economic History of Japan,* which set forth the meaning as well as the methods of economic history. Stimulated by the rapid strides made in the industrial development of the nation after the turn of the century, Japanese economic historians began to concentrate on the study of special aspects of the nation's economic life. Their studies in time completely superseded the government's research activities.

The favorable conditions which prevailed during the period of the First World War gave Japan an undreamed-of prosperity followed by an economic collapse, accompanied by unrest and backwashes of a world revolutionary movement. Existing social conditions served to stimulate interest in and growth of the social sciences, and economic history came into its own. Economic history assumed a position equal to that of traditional history which emphasized political developments almost to the exclusion of others. The advent of Marxism was followed by the appearance of works colored by historical materialism, which reflected the awakening consciousness of the propertyless classes. Outstanding among them was Sano Gaku's *Outline of Japanese Economic History* (*Nihon Keizaishi Gairon*) and his *Introduction to the Social History of Japan* (*Nihon Shakaishi Joron*).

Inspired by the agrarian crisis and the widespread distress among farmers, the decade of the 1920's unfolded unprecedented activity among historians, who devoted their energies to the study of the peasantry, agrarian movements, labor movements, special villages or communities of social outcasts, and even peasant uprisings. At the same time, the development and maturing of capitalism came to command historians' attention as the decade wore on. In 1928 Itani Zen'ichi interpreted the history of Japanese capitalism in the light of the new economic liberalism in his *Japanese Capitalism* (*Nihon Shihon Shugi*), while Takahashi Kamekichi gave his own special interpretation in his *History of the Development of Japanese Capitalism* (*Nihon Shihon Shugi Hattatsushi*). Noro Eitarō, a young Keiō graduate, came forth with a Marxist interpretation in his *History of Japanese Capitalism*. Discussions by Marxian economists were brought together in the lectures on the *History of the Development of Japanese Capitalism* (*Nihon Shihon Shugi Hattatsushi Kōza*) by Noro, Hirano, Ōtsuka, and Yamada.

The publication in 1928–1930 of the *Nihon Keizai Taiten* [1] was an event of tremendous import in the study of the economic thought and institutions of the last 250 years of the Japanese feudal system. This veritable treasure house of source materials of the Tokugawa period was an enlarged version of the collection first published between 1914 and 1918. Source materials of various types for the social and economic history of Japan have become available since, and the study of Japan's social and economic development has made rapid progress.[2]

INTRODUCTION OF WESTERN PHILOSOPHY

John Stuart Mill's influence in shaping the philosophy of the early Meiji period was far reaching.[3] His chief work, *System of Logic*, was adopted as early as 1873 in the government's Kaisei Gakkō, the forerunner of the Tōkyō Imperial University, and furnished the basis of English empiricism in Japan. Jeremy Bentham became well known among the Japanese through his *Principles of Morals and Legislation*, which was made available in translation in 1876. Herbert Spencer gained an even greater following than Mill. Two scholars, a Japanese and an American, were responsible for the widespread popularity of Spencerianism in Japan. In 1876 Toyama Masakazu returned from the United States as a convert to Spencerianism after having spent several years at the University of Michigan, where he did both undergraduate and graduate work. Upon assuming his chair at Tōkyō University, he began his lectures dealing with Spencer's ideas on biology, psychology, and sociology. Ernest Fenollosa, professor of philosophy at Tōkyō University, expounded religion in terms of Spencer's sociology. So popular did Spencer become that his views and advice were sought eagerly even by the government on various and sundry problems.

---

[1] This monumental fifty-four volume compilation by Professor Takimoto Seiichi is indispensable to the study of socioeconomic life in the Edo period, to which we must turn for the many antecedents of present-day Japan.

[2] Professors Honjō Eijirō, Nomura Kentarō, Hori Tsuneo, Kada Tetsuji, Tsuchiya Takao, Kokushō Iwao, and Ono Takeo are but a few of the scholars who have contributed greatly to the study of Japanese economic history.

[3] Other works of Mill which were made available to Japanese readers were *Considerations of Representative Government* and *On Liberty*.

The most notable example perhaps was in the matter of advocating inter-marriage, which was being seriously considered by the government as a means of securing recognition from the West. Spencer advised strongly against any sort of planned miscegenation by the state for the improvement of the race. Darwinism, which was introduced in the early 1880's through the *Origin of Species,* had a great impact on Japanese scholarship, leaving an impression not only on the scientists but on social and political theorists of this period.

German idealistic philosophy began to make inroads into the intellectual development of the nation from about 1880, when Professor Cooper began to lecture at Tōkyō University on Kant's critical philosophy. Fenollosa lectured on philosophical theories from Descartes to Hegel, using the philosophical works of Schlegel as references for the students. From about 1885, when German influence came to be felt in the various spheres of national life, German philosophy gained ascendancy, and the works of Nietzsche, Schopenhauer, and Hegel became very popular. It was in this period that Dr. Inoue Tetsujirō returned from his studies in Germany to begin his lectures on European philosophy with a strong emphasis on Wundt and Kuno Fischer, the Hegelian philosopher. The popularity of German philosophy continued for more than a decade and well into the closing years of the nineteenth century.

Psychology was first introduced into Japan in 1876 as part of philosophy by Professor Syle, who was the first to lecture on the subject, using Mark Hopkins's *Study of Man* and Haven's *Mental Philosophy.* Professor Toyama's lectures on psychology at the University, beginning in the same year, were based primarily on the works of Alexander Bain and Herbert Spencer, particularly on the latter's *Principles of Psychology.* Professor Motora's return from Johns Hopkins University marked the beginning of an experimental psychology which reflected the influence of Wundt. It was at this point that the works of the Danish philosopher, Harald Hoeffding, particularly his *Outlines of Psychology,* gained a following. In 1900 George Trumbull Ladd, Professor of Mental and Moral Philosophy at Yale University, visited Japan and lectured on psychology and philosophy. Subsequently, his *Philosophy of Knowledge* and *Philosophy of Conduct* were translated into Japanese to stimulate the scholars in the new field of study. William James's works were translated, read and regarded highly by psychologists after the Harvard professor's visit to Japan.

Professor James Summers gave the first lectures on logic at the Kaisei Gakkō in 1873, using as textbooks Fowler's *Deductive Logic* and John Stuart Mill's *System of Logic.* Three years later when Professor Toyama started teaching the subject at the University, he used W. Stanley Jevons's *Pure Logic.* Interest in ethics started considerably earlier through the efforts of Nakamura Masanao who translated *Self Help* and *Character* by the Scotch author Samuel Smiles, who had written them for the moral education of the people. Wayland's *Elements of Moral Science* attracted the attention of Japanese students, though not nearly as much as his *Elements of Political Economy*. Leaders of thought, like Nakamura and Fukuzawa, strove to encourage the development of individualism and the concept of property rights as a controlling element in society. Without such rights, they felt, there could be no industry and no progress. This resulted in the popularity of such works as Mark Hopkins's *Lectures on Moral Science* and the *Law of Love and Love as Law*. Also widely used in the study of ethics were the works of Henry Sidgwick, Thomas Hill Green, John Muirhead, George Trumbull Ladd, and Friedrich Paulsen.

Jurisprudence. Western jurisprudence was first introduced by Tsuda Mamichi, who published in 1868 *A Treatise on Western Public Law* (*Taisei Kokuhō Ron*), which was an expansion of the notes he had taken on the lectures of Professor Vissering at the University of Leyden. When the Kaisei Gakkō was reorganized into Tōkyō University in 1876, the College of Law was set up, together with the Colleges of Science and Literature, to conform to the prevailing practice in England and America. Instruction in the Law College at first was limited to Anglo-American law. At the same time, the Law School of the Department of Justice started the training of judicial officials in the field of French law. Professors of law were English, American, and French. They lectured not in Japanese, but in either English or French. Consequently, even the Japanese who were appointed to the law faculty after their period of study abroad lectured at first in English, as for instance Dr. Hozumi Nobushige. This was due largely to the lack of legal nomenclature in Japanese. Instruction at first was confined to private law, contracts and torts being the main subjects in Tōkyō University. At the Department of Justice Law School civil and commercial law constituted the main fields of study.

When the Tōkyō Imperial University came into existence in 1886, its Law College set up three fields of specialization: English, French, and German law. It was not until the time of the promulgation of the Constitution, that public law came to be a field of study. Dr. Hozumi Yatsuka, the first scholar to teach in the field of public law, pioneered in constitutional and administrative law, which subjects remained for many years his private preserve as he was the only authority in the country. Dr. Ariga Nagao, whose contributions in the field of international law are well known to Western students, first became interested in public law while in Vienna, where he heard the lectures of Dr. Lorenz von Stein. A milestone in the progress of public law was the appearance in 1895 of the first systematic treatise on Japanese administrative law by Dr. Oda Yorozu, who subsequently served for a number of years as a judge of the Permanent Court of International Justice at The Hague, and who was well known to the jurists of America and Europe.

In the drafting of the legal codes, the government set great store by the French system. In 1870, the government initiated a project of translating French legal codes to aid in the thorough study which was carried on preparatory to the setting up of judicial and legislative systems. In 1877 the French jurist, Dr. Gustave Boissanade, was asked to Japan as legal adviser to draft the criminal code and the code of criminal procedure. Although the criminal code was revised later, it remained in force until 1908 as a monument to the efforts of the French jurist. In the code of civil procedure, the drafting of which was started by the Senate (*Genrōin*) the year before his arrival, Boissande's advice and criticism were sought from time to time.

Emphasis gradually shifted, however, from the French to the German legal system. In 1884, the drafting of the code of civil procedure was entrusted to a German legal expert. In March of the same year, when the work of drafting the Constitution was started, Dr. Herman Roessler, a German professor at Tōkyō University, was appointed adviser and consultant to the Committee for the Drafting of the Constitution. The ordinances for the organization of municipalities, towns, and townships, which were promulgated in 1888 at the instance of Home Minister Yamagata, were based on the outline drawn up by Dr. Albert Mosse, who had based it on the Prussian system of local government. In Tōkyō University and the law schools, Anglo-American law, as well as French law, came to be overshadowed by the popularity of German law. Promising students looking forward to a career in the government almost invariably elected a course in German law.

Historical Studies. The advent of Western civilization brought in its wake a keen interest in the history of that civilization. People were eager to probe into the mysteries of Western civilization in order to examine not only the workings of Western institutions, but also to discover the reasons for the advanced state of the civilization. The introduction of historical writings together with the historiography of the West stimulated the study of history.

In the period following the Restoration works of Guizot and Buckle attained popularity. Guizot's *General History of Civilization in Europe,* which reflected his efforts to reconcile the interests and ideologies inherited from the *ancien régime* with the growing forces of democracy, seemed to provide a case which was applicable to the situation in Japan. It appealed particularly to Fukuzawa, who was influenced by the French historian as much as he was by Buckle.

Thomas Henry Buckle's *History of Civilization in England* was read avidly by those of a progressive turn of mind, to whom the attack on conservatism carried a strong appeal, particularly as it provided justification for the fight against old ideas and institutions. Buckle's emphasis on a true inductive science of history, as well as his insistence on the study of the masses rather than of the exceptional individual, was to find application in the historical works of Japanese scholars within a few years.

Fukuzawa's *Outline of Civilization,* published in 1875, was the earliest work to be written under the influence of Guizot and Buckle, although it was written for the enlightenment of the people, a necessary prerequisite to the modernization of the country. In his *Short History of Japanese Civilization,* Dr. Taguchi Ukichi attempted a reexamination and reinterpretation of Japanese civilization in the light of Buckle's ideas from an economic point of view and with a progressive but decidedly bourgeois view of society. His work reflected the materialism which dominated the thinking of the people of the middle class and above. The significance of this little work lies in the fact that it was the first concrete manifestation of historical consciousness in a period of transition from a feudal state to a modern capitalistic state, and as such its influence was far reaching. Guizot's influence was even more noticeable in the author's economic view of society, which his contemporary, Fukuzawa, did not grasp completely.

The popularity of studies on the history of civilization in the decade 1878 to 1888 was mirrored in the number of works on the history of Japanese civilization which appeared. Among them was Fujita Mokichi's *History of the Eastward Advance of Civilization,* published in 1884, which was an attempt to trace the development of Japanese civilization under the impact of Western civilization.

The creation of the Historical Compilation Bureau in the Council of State in 1873 for the compilation of records of the Restoration period was followed by the publication of the *History of the Restoration (Fukkoshi),* which had the effect of stimulating historical studies. After successive changes, this bureau became part of the Tōkyō Imperial University in 1888, becoming finally the Historiographical Institute (Shiryō Hensanjo) in 1929. In response to a request from the French authorities in charge of the Paris Exposition, a volume on Japanese history was prepared by Professors Shigeno, Kume, and Hoshino of Tōkyō University. This work was revised and amplified to serve as a textbook when a course on Japanese history was first introduced at the University in 1888. Another development during that year was the organization of a group that, in 1911, became the Society for the Compilation of Historical Materials of the Restoration Period (Ishin Shiryō Hensan Kai) in the Ministry of Education.

In 1886, Professor Ludwig Riess, graduate of the University of Berlin, assumed a newly established chair in history and taught the historical methods of Leopold von Ranke, under whom he had studied. Largely through his efforts, the first course on Japanese history was introduced two years later in the University. Seeing also the need for an organization to stimulate the study of history, Riess persuaded his students and colleagues to organize the Historical Science Society (Shigakukai) in the winter of 1889.

MEDICAL SCIENCE

From the very beginning of their contact with the West, the Japanese have shown a keen interest in medicine. During the Edo period, two Dutch doctors, Carl Thunberg (1776–1777) and Philip Franz von Siebold (1823–1829), brought the medical science of Europe to Japan.[4] Von Siebold, a German doctor in the employ of the Dutch, began lectures on clinical medicine soon after his arrival in 1823 and also opened a school where he taught medicine and botany. He introduced ophthalmology and obstetrics in which the Japanese had not gotten beyond book knowledge. It was their eagerness to master Western science and medicine that had led a great many of them to study the Dutch language. Dr. J. L. Pompe van Meerdevoort, remembered as the second Siebold, contributed greatly to the development of Japanese medicine in the closing years of the feudal regime. During his seven years' stay in Japan from 1856 to 1863, he taught at the Nagasaki Medical College.

In the early 1860's, some English medical works that had been translated into Chinese by an English physician, Benjamin Hobson, were brought to Japan. These works included surgery, internal medicine, and obstetrics, and helped to establish the popularity of English medicine. Thus, after the collapse of feudalism, the popularity of Dutch medicine soon gave way to English and American medicine. Before German medicine came into vogue, English medicine had taken firm root in Japan. American medicine became known with the publication of a Japanese translation of Dr. Henry Hartshorne's *Theory and Practice of Medicine*.

Dr. William Willis, a graduate of Edinburgh University, came to Japan in 1862 as a medical officer of the British Legation. Six years later, at the suggestion of Sir Harry Parkes, the British Minister, he offered his services to the Japanese government and treated the wounded Satsuma troops at the Battle of Toba-Fushimi, and also the government troops in the campaigns in the northeast. He was the first to teach aseptic surgery to the Japanese. In recognition of the invaluable services he rendered in the field, he was placed in charge of a large government hospital which was built in Tōkyō after peace was restored. He was also instrumental in setting up a medical school for the Japanese government.

When the Shogunate dispatched the Embassy of 1860 to the United States to exchange ratifications of the Treaty of 1858, there was a Dutch-trained physician, Makiyama Shūkei, in the entourage, whose main duty was to observe the progress of medical science in the West. The United States government provided medical books for the embassy. In the same year, Dr. J. C. Hepburn, the first American medical missionary to Japan, arrived at Yokohama, where he opened a dispensary. A little later, Dr. Alexander E. Vedder, an American naval surgeon, opened practice in the treaty port after resigning his commission.

In the meantime, Japanese medical men had discovered that most of the medical works available in the Dutch language were translations of original German works. These doctors had become strongly inclined towards German

---

[4] Other doctors whose names are well known were Mohnike who was a resident of Japan from 1848 to 1852, and Baldwin who lived there from 1861 to 1866.

medicine and launched a movement for its official adoption. After obtaining confirmation from Dr. Guido F. Verbeck, an American political and legal adviser to the Japanese government, that German medicine was far in advance of most other countries, it was officially decided to develop Japanese medical training along German lines.

Accordingly, in the fall of 1871, two German military medical officers, Dr. Mueller, a surgeon, and Dr. Hoffman, a specialist on internal medicine, joined the medical faculty of Tōkyō University. In the ensuing years, other German doctors followed, occupying virtually all the chairs in the medical schools until the turn of the century. Among them were Dr. Baelz, who remained twenty-three years until 1900, contributing immeasurably to internal medicine, and Dr. Scriba, a surgeon, who devoted twenty years to the training of Japanese doctors.[5] Because of the immense popularity of German medicine, it became a regular practice for medical students to go to German universities for advanced work, just as did American graduate students in the eighties and the nineties.

Even after the official adoption of German medicine, English and American doctors, most of whom were medical missionaries, were practicing in various parts of the country, while at the same time engaging in educational work. Dr. William Willis left Tōkyō in 1870 for Kagoshima, where he set up a hospital and trained medical students. An English physician, Dr. W. Anderson, was at one time on the faculty of the Navy Medical School. Some of the graduates of medical schools were sent to England and America. Consequently, Anglo-American medical influence continued, and medical works in English were popular.[6] American influence has been particularly noticeable in dentistry ever since the first American dentist began his practice in Yokohama in 1872. Most of the dentists of the Meiji era were graduates of American dental schools.

In 1876, an International Medical Conference was held at the Philadelphia Centennial Exhibition. This was the first conference attended by Japanese doctors, Dr. Nagayo, the official delegate, utilized the opportunity to study the progress of medicine and sanitation in the United States. Japanese medicine came into its own in the twentieth century, as it began to make contributions through such outstanding scientists as Doctors Noguchi Hideyo, who made valuable contributions especially in yellow-fever prevention as a member of the staff of the Rockefeller Institute for Medical Research, Takamine Jōkichi, who made adrenalin and diastase available, and Kitasato Shibasaburō, who contributed to the study of the bubonic plague, which was for many years the scourge of Asia.

[5] Other German doctors who taught in Japan were Wernich, Disse, Schulz, and Denitz.

[6] Gray's *Anatomy,* Flint's and Dalton's *Physiology,* Lindel's, Gross's and Sane's *Surgery* were among the popular medical works in English which were widely used by Japanese medical students.

THE SCIENCES

In the development of mathematics, Kanda Kōhei was a pioneer. He gave a course in Western mathematics in the Kaiseijo in 1863 when it was still under the Shogunate. In due course arabic numerals were adopted and arithmetic, algebra, geometry, trigonometry, and other branches of mathematics were introduced. However, for a decade following the establishment of the Meiji government, little progress was made and mathematics was taught only in conjunction with astronomy and physics. The textbooks were no more than translations of foreign works.

It was not until Kikuchi Dairoku returned from Cambridge University that mathematics began to show progress. From 1877, when he was appointed to the faculty of Tōkyō University, until 1898, when he assumed its presidency, Dr. Kikuchi contributed to the development of mathematics through teaching and research. The founding of the Tōkyō Mathematics Society in 1877, the introduction of a course of study in mathematics at the University in 1881, and the publication of textbooks and popular works were some of Kikuchi's many achievements.

Astronomy commanded the attention of the Japanese as early as the seventeenth century because of its importance in navigation. An astronomical observatory was established by the eighth Shogun, Yoshimune, and meteorological observations were made. However, progress in scientific studies was necessarily slow during the period of seclusion. After the Restoration, the study of astronomy was renewed with vigor under French tutelage, resulting in the establishment of the Tōkyō Astronomical Observatory in the summer of 1888.

In keeping with the Occidentalism of the new age, the government abandoned the old lunar calendar which had been in force for over twelve centuries since it was first introduced from China in the seventh century. In its place, it adopted the Gregorian calendar, and the third day of the twelfth month of the fifth year of Meiji (1872) was officially designated January 1, 1873. Eleven years later, Japan sent Dr. Kikuchi to the International Conference held in Washington, D.C., for the purpose of determining the prime meridian. In accordance with the agreement reached, Japan adopted the 135th meridian, which gave a time difference of nine hours between her and Greenwich.

The role played by Kikuchi in the advancement of mathematics was closely paralleled by Yamakawa Kenjirō in the field of physics. His appointment to Tōkyō University was preceded by a period of study in the United States. After a quarter of a century of teaching, he succeeded Kikuchi to the presidency of the Tōkyō Imperial University in 1901. Physics received a great impetus through the efforts of three distinguished American physicists who were on the faculty of the University, Professors Ewing, Knott, and Mendenhall. These men trained

Japan's outstanding physicists as, for instance, Tanakadate Aikitsu and Nagaoka Hantarō, who distinguished themselves particularly in the field of magnetics. In 1903, Nagaoka made public his studies on atomic theory and became one of the earliest scientists to explore this new field.

For the advance made in the field of chemistry in the pioneering period, credit goes to Professor R. W. Atkinson, an Englishman who was invited in 1874 to become a professor in the University. There, for seven years, he taught organic chemistry, theoretical, applied and analytical chemistry, as well as metallurgy. In the same year another Englishman, Dr. S. Divers, took charge of lectures on inorganic chemistry and remained on the faculty for twenty-five years until 1899, exerting his influence on the development of chemistry in Japan through his effective teaching and investigations. He emphasized successfully the prime importance of studying science for its own sake. After Atkinson's departure, his place was taken by Professor Matsui Naokichi, who had returned from the United States in 1880, and Dr. Sakurai Jōji, who returned from England the following year.

Owing to the fact that the country afforded such excellent natural facilities for the study of earthquakes and the apparent need for their scientific investigation, the study of seismology made amazing progress in a relatively short time. This branch of science was introduced in the 1870's by three American physicists, Professors J. Milne, J. A. Ewing, and T. Gray. Milne was instrumental in the founding of the Japan Seismological Society in 1880; Ewing devised a seismograph to record horizontal vibration, while Gray developed one to record vertical vibration. Sekiya Kiyokage, who improved on Ewing's bracket seismograph and collected and studied all available seismological data from the fifth century down to recent times, was the first incumbent of the chair of seismology created in 1886. His successor, Dr. Ōmori Fusakichi, gained international renown as one of the world's outstanding seismologists. With the highly sensitive seismograph he devised for recording pulsatory oscillations, he made it possible to predict an earthquake within ten to twelve hours before its actual occurrence. Through his studies, data were obtained to enable the determination of the best forms of structure in a strong earthquake zone like Japan. Professor Tanakadate Aikitsu designed both the parallel-motion seismograpth for indicating strong earthquakes and the spiral seismograph for recording vertical motion, both of which are now largely in use in Japan.

Geological studies date back to 1862 when William P. Blake of Yale and Raphael Pumpelly of Harvard were invited by the Shogunate to study the mineral resources of the country. When the opening of Hokkaidō was decided upon in the 1870's, the government secured the services of Lyman and Monroe, who undertook the survey of coal and other mineral deposits on the island. Later Lyman engaged in the geological survey of other parts of the island empire, as well as in the survey of mineral and petroleum deposits. These activities, which originated in Hokkaidō and were extended to other parts of the country in the years between 1876 and 1879, laid the groundwork for the development of the geological sciences. Teaching of geology at Tōkyō University was at first in the hands of foreign experts, particularly German professors, among whom were K. Schenck, H. S. Monroe, Edmund Naumann, David Brauns, and Carl Gootsche. Best known among them was Naumann who arrived in 1875 and proposed the establishment of a Geological Survey Bureau and the making of a detailed geographical map. When the Geological Survey Bureau was created in 1878, he was made its head and in this capacity he covered the entire country thoroughly. His work on the structural geology of the various regions of Japan was a valuable contribution to the subject. By 1889 more than a beginning had been made in geology and mineralogy, and courses on lithology, paleontology, and even theoretical geology were being taught by Japanese professors who had studied under European scientists both at home and abroad.

Botany was pioneered by Yatabe Ryōkichi who, like Toyama Masakazu, was an American-trained scientist on the faculty of the University. Both these teachers were also endowed with poetic gifts. They collaborated with a colleague on the *Anthology of New Style Poetry,* which was published in 1882. On his return from Cornell University in 1876, Yatabe joined the faculty and engaged not only in teaching but in collecting botanical specimens. His protégés made one of the greatest discoveries in plant morphology in 1896, when they discovered spermatozoids in the pollen tubes of the gingko and the cycad.

The study of modern zoology began in 1877 with the arrival of Professor Edward Sylvester Morse, an eminent zoologist from Harvard. Although he remained only two years, he left an indelible imprint on the biological sciences of the period, particularly through the emphasis he placed on the influence of Darwinism. He was succeeded by Professor C. O. Whitman, subsequently of the University of Chicago, who developed the modern technical method and inspired students in the field of zoology. The establishment of the Marine Laboratory at Misaki in 1887 gave a strong impetus to the study of marine life. In later years such eminent American scientists as Dr. David Starr Jordan, President of Stanford University, and Professor Bashford, Dean of Columbia University, inspired and stimulated the work of Japanese zoologists.

ANTHROPOLOGY AND SOCIOLOGY

Anthropology had its origin in the arrival of Professor Morse. One of the first incidents upon his arrival in Japan was the discovery of a prehistoric shell heap in Ōmori, which he noticed from the window of a train on his way to Tōkyō. After a thorough investigation of the site, he published the results, which stirred the interest of Japanese scholars. Men like Professors Tsuboi, Koganei, and

Torii developed their interest in anthropology as a result of this discovery and began a thorough search and study of these prehistoric sites. They also carried on studies of the savage and primitive races in other parts of Asia. Studies in the origins of the Japanese people were started from about 1886. The monumental study of the Ainu by Batchelor and the archeological studies of Neil Gordon Munro contributed greatly to the understanding of Japanese primitive life.

Importers of Western learning were the first to adopt the social view of civilization, which had been developed under the influence of nineteenth-century liberalism in England and was dominated by the ideas of John Stuart Mill. The writings of Guizot and Buckle influenced the Japanese to start the study of social development, as did Carey's *Principles of Social Science.* In 1875, Fukuzawa furnished a theory of social progress to the Japanese in his *Outline of Civilization,* which defined civilization as progress in human relations, or intellectual and moral progress. The following year, Toyama began teaching sociology at Tōkyō University and became one of the pioneers, if not the founder, of sociology in Japan. It was Toyama who coined the Japanese equivalent of the name which August Comte first gave to that social science.

The year 1883 was appropriately enough the starting point in the development of Japanese sociology. That year represented the fruition of the efforts at importing and assimilating sociological ideas and methods from the West. This was marked by the publication of the translation of Herbert Spencer's *Principles of Sociology* and the appearance of the first Japanese book in the field. *Sociology* by Dr. Ariga Nagao was an ambitious attempt to establish a systematic sociology, using evidences obtained from Japanese, Chinese, Korean, and Asiatic experiences and tracing social evolution. Of the projected six volumes, he finished three, *Social Evolution* (1883), *Religious Evolution* (1883), and the *Evolution of the Family System* (1884), all of which were based on the organismic theory of society. In 1886, Nishimura Shigeki attempted to establish the positive philosophy of August Comte.

In the late 1880's, Lester F. Ward's *Dynamic Sociology* became the favorite of Japanese students of that science. Gumplowicz and Franklin H. Giddings were held in high regard some years later. In spite of the auspicious beginning in the effort to establish a solid foundation for the study of sociology, progress was slow and little was achieved except in the sociological interpretation of politics, law, and ethics. This state of affairs was due perhaps to the political conditions of the time and particularly to the existence of a strong bureaucratic government. However, the first chair of sociology was created at the Tōkyō Imperial University in 1893.

Before the nineteenth century was over, the intellectual and scientific developments of the nation had reached a stage of progress which enabled the leaders in the various fields to keep informed, if not abreast, of the developments in the

West without too great a difficulty. Scientifically, the Japanese were still far behind the nations of Europe and America, but the foundations had been laid. The First World War gave the nation an unexpected opportunity to push science and technology ahead at a much greater speed than it had been thought possible. By the decade of the 1930's, the Japanese had achieved scientific progress which compared favorably with some of the countries of the West.

Chapter 6. Acceleration of Modernization and

Westernization

Even after the political powers were restored to the Emperor, the social and economic foundations of feudalism were still intact in 1868. It was imperative that relics of the feudal age be liquidated before an effective program of modernization and Westernization could be instituted. Japan was working toward the recognition and approval of the Occident, which she was trying hard to emulate. Only thus could she hope to win a position which would place her within the pale of international law. In other words, her passion was acceptance by the Occidental powers as a civilized nation worthy of being accorded equality. To this end the nation and its leaders directed all their efforts.

One of the greatest obstacles that stood in the way of progress and that demanded immediate attention was the feudal class system, the legacy of the Tokugawa regime. Obviously such a system was not merely a stigma but an obstacle to a nation striving for international recognition.

Ieyasu, the founder of the Tokugawa Shogunate, had instituted the caste system as a means of preserving the *status quo* in the hope of perpetuating the power of his own family. It was his belief that, by rigidly defining the status of individuals and freezing them in the particular station to which they belonged, the supremacy of his family could be ensured indefinitely.

This feudal social system comprised the following distinct estates: the nobility and the clergy, the ruling *samurai,* the commoners (including the peasants), the artisans and merchants, and the social outcasts made up of pariahs (*eta*) and beggars (*hinin*). The nobility and the clergy together were numerically a very small group and therefore were not the object of administrative concern; neither were the social outcasts, who were entirely outside the scope of administration, since they were allowed autonomy. The estates over which the Shogunate showed primary concern were the *samurai,* the farmers, and the townsfolk, comprising the artisans and merchants. In determining the position of these castes, the criterion was the usefulness of the functions they performed in feudal society. The *samurai,* being the ruling class charged with the protection and administration of the nation, was assigned the highest sociopolitical status. The farmers came next as they were the indispensable producing class on which the *samurai* depended for their economic existence, although as individuals they were never treated with respect or even consideration. The townsfolk comprised two types, the craftsmen and the merchants, but the former was ranked higher, for as makers of weapons and builders of castles, they followed the farmers closely in their usefulness. Those craftsmen who were producers of nonmilitary goods were regarded as not much better than the merchants, who were regarded as not only unproductive money-changers and profit-makers, but also as parasites living off the fat of the land.

The *samurai* class comprised approximately 400,000 families with a population of two million, ranging all the way from the Shogun at the top to the *rōnin* at the very bottom of the scale. Next to the Shogun came his close relatives and the *daimyō*, followed by his vassals and those of the *daimyō*. There were the *samurai*-farmers (*gōshi*) who received land and stipend from the *daimyō*, engaged in agriculture in peacetime, and took up arms in times of war. At the very bottom of the scale were the masterless, incomeless, dispossessed, displaced *samurai* who belonged to the class socially, but were actually outsiders in an economic and political sense. They were estimated to have numbered anywhere between 100,000 and 200,000. During most of the Tokugawa period, particularly during the closing years, they proved to be the thorn in the side of the Shogunate.

As early as the beginning of the eighteenth century, the *daimyō* and their retainers had become dependent on the merchants' loans for the management of their straitened finances. They found themselves constantly in the embarrassing position of not only having to humor, but also having to kowtow to the wealthy merchants. Furthermore, it became necessary to allow the merchants to use family names and to wear swords, and even to grant stipends. This conferring of *samurai* privileges was granted in exchange for the financial services the merchants rendered and was tantamount to the sale of *samurai* status to them.

In time, however, the actual selling of family stock became a common, if not a regular, practice. Even as early as 1661, the Shogunate found it necessary to issue a decree forbidding the bannerets from adopting sons who brought gift money with them. In extreme cases, *samurai* families resorted to adoption, regardless of the presence of a male heir because of their desperate need for money. As the result of this surreptitious practice, standard rates existed for adoption. The amount paid was proportionate to the size of the rice stipend received by the *samurai* family. The rate in 1853, the year of Perry's arrival, for instance, was computed on the basis of 50 to 100 *ryō* for each 100 *koku* (5 bushels to a *koku*) of stipend rice.

By far the largest number of the *samurai* belonged to the lower brackets, receiving rice stipends from their lords. The Bakufu retainers averaged 28 *koku*, while the *daimyō* retainers averaged only 16 *koku*. As a rule this income remained constant for generations, though the cost of living in the city rose steadily. However, when the *daimyō* suffered from financial difficulties, the stipends to the retainers were invariably reduced. In order to make up the difference between the small income and the ever-increasing expenses the *samurai* were forced to engage in handicraft manufacturing, which was usually carried on as subcontract work under the merchant-entrepreneurs. To the large majority of them, homework became a necessity and the only means of supplementing the meager and wholly inadequate family income. Thus many of them became makers of fans, parasols, toys, *tabi,* paper lanterns, rattan ware, fish nets, toothbrushes, toothpicks, writing brushes, etc. Some of them turned merchants, tenant farmers, day workers, and even coolies, while others went into fishing, horticulture, poultry raising, and the like.

Toward the end of the Tokugawa period, the feudal production system had reached a state where it could not sustain the large number of *samurai.* As an inevitable consequence, homework became a new form of production for the absorption of the heretofore unutilized manpower of the *samurai* class. Thus, the *samurai* became a part of urban life, not only as consumers, but also as producers, bringing about a radical change in their outlook, attitude, and ideas. This situation nurtured a rebellious spirit against an order of society which could not support them or improve their station in life, contributed to a decline in *samurai* consciousness, and brought the gradual assimilation of the *samurai* by the townsfolk in thought and action as well as mores. It gradually and finally led to opposition and resistance against the upper class *samurai,* whose conservative and uncompromising thinking and attitude had brought on an impasse in the political, social, and economic life of the nation.

Class distinction was also a consideration among the townsfolk who were divided into three classes: the monied class, the middle class petty bourgeoisie, and the small merchants, craftsmen, and workers. Wealth was concentrated in the monied class who controlled banking and exchange as well as buying, selling, and storage of rice and other commodities. The "ten men exchange" (*jūnin ryōgae*) had the monopoly on exchange and handled the Treasury business of the Shogunate. The main exchange houses (*hon ryōgae*) numbered more than a hundred, of which over fifty had capital exceeding 200,000 yen each. These houses were engaged in the buying and selling of gold and silver, in making loans, drawing drafts, and taking deposits. There were also the *kakeya,* that made loans to the *daimyō,* usually with rice as security. Of this group, Kōnoike of Ōsaka was the largest. In addition, there were about one hundred *fudasashi,* who handled the storage and sale of rice for the bannerets and served as their bankers. The middle class comprised the independent merchants, artisans, and the managers and clerks employed by the big merchants. By far the largest group numerically was the lowest class, comprising small merchants, artisans, hucksters, clerks, apprentices, and day workers.

The rise of a money economy and the growth of the commodity market enhanced and strengthened the position of the mercantile class, particularly of the monied class. Through the power of money, they were able to exercise control over the *samurai* class. As a matter of fact, the *samurai* class was at the mercy of the merchants, many of whom became landowners, while others elevated their social and cultural position by turning Confucian scholars, physicians, writers, poets, philosophers, artists, and masters of the tea ceremony. Not a few of them achieved *samurai* status through the purchase of family stocks or through adoption.

As in the case of other classes, the farmers were also divided into several grades according to their position or economic status in the villages. At the very top was the village head, who was invariably one of the leading residents economically as well as politically. He was assisted by heads of associations (*kumigashira*) in the administration of the village. They in turn were supervised by the *hyakushōdai*.

Most numerous among the farmers were the small-holders (*jisaku nōmin*) who were given the right by the *daimyō* to cultivate the land in return for taxes paid and labor services rendered. They were tied down to the land, however. Next came the tenant-farmers, followed by the farm hands, who were actually semi-slaves and who could be bought and sold. The landowners included farmers, farmer-merchants, or merchants, who rented out land to tenant farmers from whom in turn they collected tenancy fees.

The keystone of the feudal economy on which the welfare of the *samurai* class rested was the farmers' land tax. Any large-scale change of occupation by the farmers naturally weakened, if not threatened, the economic structure. The authorities, therefore, made it a policy to prohibit a change of occupation and the free movement of the farmers. The farmers' plight resulted from the fact that, as the economic difficulties of the *samurai* class increased, they had to bear the brunt of the economic burden. Even in normal times they were allowed only a bare existence and left with no surplus of any kind. It was not uncommon for their lands to be confiscated by the *daimyō* who found themselves in straitened circumstances.

Unable and unwilling to tolerate the extremely trying conditions, farmers in large numbers deserted the soil and went to the cities. To the three big cities, seaports, and the castle towns they went, to engage in small business, work as day laborers, servants in *samurai* and merchant families, or as coolies or carriers. Natural increase in population was stopped by infanticide, and the farming population decreased with the area of land under cultivation also decreasing. The influx of rural population into urban centers created a social problem since it greatly increased the number of the poor in the cities.

For a decade beginning with the Restoration, extensive changes were introduced in an effort to reshape the nation's social structure. The concept of equality, which had gained ground during the twilight years of the feudal regime, contributed much to the eventual breakdown of the caste system. This development had come as a reaction against the rigid system of social distinction which existed in feudal society and was implemented by the determination of the lesser *samurai,* farmers, townsfolk, and priests, who had taken an active part in the Restoration in order to break down the distinction. As a result, the first decade of the Meiji era was devoted to the overhauling of the social system and the establishment of fundamental human rights, the concept of equality, and the recognition and respect of individual worth. These changes involved the abolition and revocation of special privileges on the one hand and the conferment of new rights on the other.

In the summer of 1869, the old court nobility and the *daimyō* were given the designation of peers while those of the *samurai* class from the bannerets down received the new designation of *shizoku* (gentry). By the end of the year the gentry had been divided into eighteen different grades. To straighten out the resulting confusion, the government decreed in the fall of the following year that there would be only two classes: the *shizoku* and the *sotsu.* Finally, early in 1872, the upper half of the *sotsu* was given *shizoku* status, while the lower half was absorbed into the *heimin* (commoner) category which had been created to embrace the farmers, merchants, craftsmen, priests, and the social outcasts, whose identity as *eta* and *hinin* had been abolished. The three designations, peers, gentry, and commoners, were adopted for use in the system of family registration on a historical genealogical basis of identification, rather than as a distinction conferring legal privileges. Actually the *shizoku* was no higher in status than the *heimin* and did not enjoy any special privileges.

Although the government was pressed for time, it was careful not to rush, but to effect gradually, the radical changes which were needed. Some idea of the technique as well as the speed can be seen by the revocation of the special privileges of the *samurai* class. In 1869, Mori Arinori proposed that the abandonment of the feudal custom of wearing swords be made optional. However, since there was considerable opposition, the government waited until the fall of 1871 to issue a decree making the wearing of swords and cutting of hair optional. A few days later the government revoked the feudal *samurai* prerogative of cutting down a commoner for real or fancied insults. Meanwhile, early in 1872, the universal military conscription system was instituted, opening military service to all classes, thus taking away the special privilege which the *samurai* had come to regard as their monopoly. Then, in 1873, the government abolished the time-honored feudal practice of vendetta.[1] The discontinuance of sword wearing, which had been made optional in 1871, was finally made mandatory in 1876, after an ample lapse of time to allow the *samurai* to abandon the practice voluntarily, thereby giving them a chance to save their face.

As a first step toward the elevation of the commoners' position, the government allowed them to assume family names in the fall of 1870. Under the

---

[1] Duels were banned in 1889.

Tokugawa regime, only those who had special permission from their feudal lords could use them. But it was five years before the use of family names was made compulsory, not only for the peasants and townsfolk, but also for the priests. In the spring of 1871, the farmers were allowed to travel on horseback on public highways. In the fall, the commoners were permitted to wear costumes previously reserved exclusively for the *samurai* class and were even allowed to intermarry with members of the nobility.

Social outcasts numbered some 382,000 in 1871, when they were absorbed into the *heimin* class. The identity of the social outcasts, particularly of the *eta,* was established during the Muromachi period, and when demand for leather goods increased during the period of continuous internecine warfare in the fifteenth and sixteenth centuries, the *daimyō* competed with each other in getting them to come to their castle towns. Furthermore, they were given special protection, since their services were regarded as indispensable. As they were exempted from labor levies and other assessments they thrived and their population increased. During the Tokugawa period, however, the demand for leather goods and arms declined, and their services were not so greatly in demand. It was then that segregation in special villages was begun. They were given administrative autonomy and engaged in highly specialized economic functions. Leather goods still continued to be their most important product, although they made other goods such as bamboo bark slippers, lamp wicks, tea whisks, etc. They rendered services as slaughterers, executioners, handled the dead and the offals, and performed menial tasks which were shunned by the people in general as unclean. In their status of degradation, they were not even allowed to work as domestics in the homes of farmers and merchants. Obviously, this caste was made to serve the function of mitigating psychologically the lot of the farmers by making it more bearable and to deflect and soften their opposition and resistance to the oppressive rule of the feudal authorities.

When social outcasts as a class were abolished, they were legally absorbed into the category of commoners and charged with the duties of paying taxes and serving in the armed forces while their special feudal economic privileges were revoked. They were legally free to engage in any occupation they chose. Actually, however, their social and economic status remained unchanged, and by 1873 a new name was widely used to identify the former outcasts: they were called the "new commoners." Socially they were not conceded equality, as intermarriage with them was frowned upon and social functions were closed to them. Their economic opportunities were limited to handicraft, tenant farming, peddling, and day labor. "Special villages," which were legally dead, continued their physical and social existence.

In the spring of 1870, the government banned a custom according to which the court nobles blackened their teeth and shaved their eyebrows, which dated back to the Heian period. Married women, who had for centuries followed the same custom, also took the cue and abandoned the absurd custom, especially after March 3, 1873, when the Empress personally set the example for the whole nation to follow. A year later, the government issued an order permitting Buddhist priests to eat beef and also authorizing them to marry. Early in 1872 the Emperor partook of beef, thereby assuring the nation that it was respectable to eat the meat of a "four-legged" animal. Prefectural governors extolled the high nutritive value of beef in a vigorous, concerted effort to overcome the centuries-old aversion to beef, which had been started and kept alive by Buddhism. Furthermore, the fact that beef-eating was practiced in the West and was regarded as a sign of an advanced state of civilization was responsible in no small measure for the enthusiasm with which the official propaganda was pushed.

Few things were as symbolic of the process of Westernization as the introduction of the haircut into Japanese life. Since the dawn of history, the Japanese had worn their hair long, although the style of hairdress underwent changes and modifications from age to age. Furthermore, throughout history, hairdress had been a distinguishing mark between classes, just as clothing and other features of the national costume had been. During the Tokugawa period the style of hairdo identified the rank and position of the wearer.

The earliest effort to adopt the Western style of haircut came, interestingly enough, like the wearing of Western costume and the use of bread, as a by-product of the adoption of Western military training. For some time after the Western style of military uniform was adopted, the troops continued to wear their long hair in topknots or some other form. However, when it was discovered that long hair was a hindrance to both military efficiency and bearing, the haircut was adopted.

As early as 1867, some of those who had been to Europe returned with the Western-style haircut. In 1873, most of the members of the Iwakara Mission had done the same. Scholars of Western studies and soldiers were the first to have their hair cut. In the fall of 1871 the government decreed that the haircut was optional, but there followed no rush to get rid of the topknots. After Emperor Meiji set an example in March, 1873, the people followed more willingly the tonsorial innovation. Cropped hair, in time, came to symbolize progress and enlightenment whereas long hair was regarded as anachronistic and unprogressive. But the tonsorial renovation of the nation proceeded rather slowly, in spite of the prodding by the government; for after a whole decade, 20 per cent of the population still preferred to keep their hair long. Such was the force of tradition and habit. It was not until the time of the promulgation of the Constitution that topknots disappeared, except from the heads of professional wrestlers.

From 1869, when the suggestion was first made that sword wearing be discontinued, there was strong resistance to that proposal by the former *samurai*. The sword had been regarded for centuries as the very soul of the *samurai*. But even this had to give way to progress. In the fall of 1871, the optional discontinuance of sword wearing was encouraged by the government. Resistance was still so strong that the government allowed a lapse of fifteen years before it finally issued an order, on March 28, 1886, liquidating the last visible physical vestige of feudalism.

An attempt to adjust the nation to the moral standards of the West and the presence of foreigners in the country necessitated effecting, at an early date, several modifications in customs and manners which might prove offensive and abhorrent to non-Japanese eyes. Among the earliest changes introduced in 1869 was the prohibition of lotteries, which had been practiced extensively even by the Buddhist temples and Shintō shrines, abortion, which had been as common a practice as infanticide during the Tokugawa period, and mixed bathing, which had survived the feudal regime. The year 1872 saw the ban on selling of persons into bondage, the sale of pornographic pictures and objects, mixed wrestling, tattooing and other repugnant relics of feudalism. Simultaneously positive steps were taken to encourage the adoption of Occidental customs, particularly those which would contribute substantially to the spirit of progress and be helpful in the modernization of national life. Earliest of these was the adoption by the government of the Gregorian calendar on January 1, 1873. This was followed three years later by the adoption of official holidays, making Sunday a government holiday and Saturday a half holiday.

The position of women in Occidental countries became the subject of discussion by the press as early as the second year of Meiji. Japanese women enjoyed a relatively high position, though perhaps not equality, before the introduction of Chinese civilization and the teachings of Buddhism. However, Confucian morality and Buddhist taboo degraded the position of women, which has been low ever since. Such a state of affairs was neither helpful nor conducive to the building of a progressive nation. Nor was it likely to elicit the respect of Occidental countries. A change that would elevate the position of women to a point acceptable by Western standards was much needed.

One of the earliest advocates of feminine rights was Fukuzawa, who fought tirelessly for equal educational opportunities for women. In 1872, he startled his relatives and friends by championing monogamy and advocating respect for women. In the spring of the same year, the government issued a decree abolishing the long-standing ban on women entering holy places, particularly the Shintō shrines and Buddhist temples. An amusing, though not a significant, upshot of the famous *Maria Luz* affair was the issuance in late 1872 of an order by Justice Minister Etō for the liberation of all the geisha. All contracts were canceled and nullified, but the effect was only temporary. In 1873 the wife was given the legal right to initiate divorce action against her husband, a right which previously had never been hers.

From about this time feminists began to attract public attention. In February, 1875, Mori Arinori, one of the outstanding exponents of Westernization and a strong feminist, set a novel precedent by signing with his wife a marriage contract witnessed by Fukuzawa. At the conference of prefectural governors three years later, the question of woman suffrage was raised for the first time by Hirayama Yasuhiko, who argued that, inasmuch as women had been given the legal right to become heads of households and were required to pay taxes, they should be given the franchise on the same basis as men. Although nothing concrete emerged from the prefectural governors' conference, the event was of great significance as the beginning of the discussion of feminine suffrage rights.

The increasing emphasis on the position of women in a new age led naturally to an awareness on the part of the gentler sex of the need of preparing for the day when they would have to take their rightful places in the political life of the nation. The traditional concept of feminine accomplishments which had been cherished for centuries was tossed out of the window without so much as a second thought. To be a good wife and wise mother as the mistress of her home and hearth was no longer emphasized as the most important function of womanhood. No longer was she to be a home body. Rather it became the primary duty of a lady to be a genial companion and social asset to her husband.

Feminine education in the middle of the eighties, under the impact of Westernism and carried out by Education Minister Mori, emphasized vivaciousness rather than refinement, intellect over gentility, social graces in preference to domestic arts, and academic learning over utilitarian arts. Incredible as it may seem, the mastery of a foreign language, particularly English, the ability to trip gracefully the light fantastic, and the acquisition of an Occidental mode of life came to be the avowed objectives of a girl's high school education.

Flurried efforts at the adoption of Western costumes was the logical result of the fanatical worship of the West. So great was the urge to adopt everything that the Occidental costume was officially adopted by the Imperial Court and the members of the peerage. Men and women in the upper strata of society adopted costumes which were not always appropriate or becoming. Even after some three-quarters of a century they have not completely assimilated themselves to Occidental costume.

Symbolic of the age and the process of Westernization, which went on feverishly and quite blindly, was the Rokumeikan, a pretentious social hall erected by the government in 1883 at a cost of 180,000 yen. The government staged dazzling social functions in the rather naive belief that the complete Westernization of Japan's elite society was a necessary prerequisite to, and a logical step toward, her admission into the family of nations. Superficially stimulated sophistication and gaiety which permeated the Rokumeikan all but overshadowed the government's feeble and unsuccessful attempts at treaty revision. Dancing was held every Sunday evening from the summer of 1884 on. Members of the elite society gathered and mixed with the foreign diplomatic corps in a conscious effort calculated to develop social graces through dancing, card games, and other pastimes indulged in by ladies and gentlemen in the best traditions of Occidental society. The 1880's was indeed the gilded age for the elite society at the Japanese capital.

The grand masquerade ball held at the Rokumeikan on April 20, 1887, was the logical culmination of the officially inspired craze for Westernization. It was an unprecedentedly gala event which went down in history as the most talked of event of the period. Undoubtedly, it was a ludicrous exhibition of what the well-meaning but misguided "Dancing Cabinet" of Premier Itō and Foreign Minister Inoue erroneously regarded as the finest concrete demonstration of the progress of Westernization. The dignitaries appeared in fancy costumes, which, although they must have been novel to the foreign representatives present, were nevertheless as outlandish as they were comical. The occasion was glossed over by those who were responsible because of the unsavory scandals which were the inevitable by-products of the elaborate social function.

The span of half a decade from 1883 to 1888 was a phenomenal period. It saw the eruption of a veritable rash of improvement societies of every imaginable type. An almost universal feeling developed among the sophisticated urbanites that everything Japanese fell far short of Western standards and that improvement was the crying need in every phase of life. No aspect, social, economic, political, religious, intellectual, or moral escaped this fetish of improvement. Its objectives ranged all the way from a better style of hairdress to eugenics advocating intermarriage with Caucasians for the improvement of the racial stock. Charitable organizations, temperance societies, ladies' societies, art, drama, novel, and language-improvement societies mushroomed overnight. Intense as the passion was for improvement, which was synonymous with Westernization, it began to subside from the eve of the constitutional era. But while it lasted, it was a phenomenon perhaps without parallel in modern history.

The advocacy of intermarriage with Occidentals as a sure means of improving the racial stock of the Japanese, begun in 1883 by Takahashi Yoshio, did not easily die out. It was seriously considered by the leading statesmen of the period, including such notables as Itō and Inoue. The question had become a subject of such heated discussion and agitation among scholars and politicians that Herbert Spencer's advice was sought in 1892. In his reply, Spencer was emphatic in stating that intermarriage should be positively forbidden on biological grounds. He argued that miscegenation inevitably produced bad results in the long run. Any thought of encouraging intermarriage seems to have been abandoned after 1892 although it was not banned for individuals.[2]

Obviously, times had changed, for beef, which was regarded as unfit for human consumption and was eaten only by the social outcasts, was now highly

[2] A letter from Herbert Spencer to Baron Kaneko Kentarō was published in the London *Times* of January 18, 1904.

recommended, not only as food for the enlightened and the civilized, but also as effective in curing those who were afflicted with vacillation or addicted to old customs and other absurdities and anomalies. Milk was first made available in 1868, when an Englishman started a small dairy in Yokohama. Two years later, a Japanese started a dairy with twenty head of milk cows and supplied consumers who were mostly high officials and members of the foreign legations. By the 1880's butter, milk, and cream became available on a commercial basis.

Alcoholic beverages were known to the Japanese people during the late feudal period, but not to the extent that they were used by upper class society in the 1870's. As the demand for wines of all kinds, champagne, whisky, gin, brandy, and beer developed, manufacture of some of the beverages was started. The most notable success was achieved in the manufacture of beer following the development of Hokkaidō. The opening of the first beer hall in Tōkyō on July 4, 1899, to celebrate the taking effect of the revised treaties with the Western powers introduced a feature of Western life which had been unknown to the Japanese.

There were visible changes in the daily life of the people, brought on by the importation of Western civilization and technology. By 1874, the photograph had become so popular that it all but drove out of competition the more artistic *nishikie*. Lantern slides were the marvel of the seventies and the people were fascinated by the still imperfect, but wonderful, talking machine. As the decade wore on, other marvelous inventions of the West were brought into Japan. Thomas A. Edison's kinetoscope, which was exhibited at the Chicago Columbian Exposition in 1893, reached Japan before the year was over. Means of mass communications were gradually being improved as the telephone, telegraph, motion pictures, and the press came to occupy an important place in the daily life of the people. Thus, the technological importations from the West were effective in implementing and accelerating the social and economic changes that were taking place.

The courier service of eighteen round trips a month between Edo and Ōsaka, which was maintained during the closing years of the feudal regime, was discontinued early in 1871 when the twelve fiefs and six prefectures along the Tōkaidō were ordered by the government to set up facilities for the collection of letters and sale of postage stamps. Before the end of that spring, a postal service modeled on those of the countries of Europe and America was introduced between Tōkyō and Ōsaka. It was not until 1873, however, that the government took over the postal service. Since the public was skeptical and distrustful at first, the post office authorities were obliged to issue a receipt for every letter posted until confidence in the new system was established.

The foreign powers, Great Britain, France, and the United States, established post offices in Yokohama, Kōbe, and Nagasaki in 1872 to handle their own mail. Three years later, Japan exchanged mail directly with a foreign power for the first time when the United States withdrew her post offices; the following year she joined the International Postal Union. By 1880 both Great Britain and France had followed the example of the United States and withdrawn their post offices, leaving postal service in the hands of Japanese authorities, who inaugurated foreign postal money order and parcel post service before the year was up.

The telegraph dates back to Commodore Perry's arrival, when a present was made to the Shogun of a set of apparatus. Four years later, Shimazu Nariakira, *daimyō* of Satsuma, set up telegraph lines in his castle for his personal use. The telegraph was first actually used in the fall of 1869, when connection was made between the Court House and the Light House Bureau in Yokohama, a distance of less than half a mile. This was soon followed by the linking of Tōkyō and Yokohama. International telegraphic communication was inaugurated in 1871 when cable lines connecting Nagasaki with Shanghai and Vladivostok were opened. The following year, the government took over the ownership and operation of telegraph service. Telegraphic communication was greatly stimulated by the Satsuma Rebellion of 1877, which put the system to a real test.

A trial telephone line was set up between Tōkyō and Yokohama in 1877, eleven years after Alexander Graham Bell invented it and only a few years after it was first put to successful commercial use in the United States. As in the case of the telegraph, the government took over its operation.

Gas, kerosene, and electricity gradually took the place of rapeseed oil, whale oil, and candles, not only to revolutionize the method of illumination but also to furnish a new type of fuel and motive power heretofore unknown in Japanese industry. The gaslight era opened auspiciously in the fall of 1872 on the dark and narrow streets of Yokohama, where huge crowds gathered to watch the spectacle. Three years later, the streets of Tōkyō were lighted with gas manufactured by the company which had been organized by the prefectural government. This company was turned over to private ownership in 1885 to become the Tōkyō Gas Company.

A memorable event was the lighting of a 2,000-candle-power arc light in front of the Ōkura-gumi store on the Ginza on November 1, 1882. Night after night, people came from far and near to witness with their own eyes and to marvel at the wonder of civilization. In February of the following year, the government authorized the formation of an electric company. Incandescent lights made their appearance in Tōkyō for the first time in 1885; and beginning in January, 1887, the Tōkyō Electric Company made electricity available to the consumers. In a matter of a quarter of a century a network of electric power lines covered the entire nation, and there was hardly a hamlet, however remote, to which electricity had not penetrated to provide a new method of illumination for even the humblest of the farmhouses.

Chapter 7. Reorganization of Education

Educational opportunities for the people had been rigidly circumscribed through-out the more than two and a half centuries of Tokugawa rule. The general policy of the Shogunate was to keep the masses in a state of ignorance and il-literacy, partly as a means of more effectively controlling them. There were clan schools in the feudatories and the official Tokugawa school, the Shōheikō, in Edo, but they existed for the education of the sons of the *daimyō* and *samurai*. No com-parable facilities were available to the townsfolk who, if they could afford it, sent their children to the temple school (*terakoya*), where they were taught the rudiments of reading, writing, and the abacus. Opportunities were even more meager for the peasants in remote rural areas where no temple schools existed. Such a system of education, inadequate as it was, did not constitute a serious obstacle as long as conditions were stagnant. But the end of feudalism brought the nation face to face with a stupendous task of modernization.

In the creation of a new state along modern Occidental lines, an effective modern educational system was a prime requisite. An educational system capable of giving speedily and efficiently such training to the entire citizenry as would accelerate national development was the pressing need. Ignorance and illiteracy could no more be allowed to stand in the way of progress than the other obstructive institutional legacies of feudalism. It became clear that what was urgently needed to meet the exigencies of the time was a highly utilitarian and practical system. Perforce, education was to emphasize training in the useful arts and sciences with a strong concentration on the materialistic aspects of Western civilization, even at the expense of its theoretical aspects and intangible values. Unfortunately for the country, the spiritual concomitants of Western civilization were pushed into the background in the terrific haste to assimilate the scientific and technological developments. If emphasis on producing an educated individual or the "whole man" was noticeable at times, it was most certainly not the consistent or persistent policy of the government. Its ultimate objective was the achievement of an efficient citizenry as a foundation for a strong Japan.

The Education Department was created in 1871, with Ōki Takatō as its head, to eradicate illiteracy. In order to achieve this, it put into effect a system of compulsory education the following year. The highly centralized organiza-tion of the French educational system was taken as a model, and the country was divided into eight university districts, which were subdivided into thirty-two sec-

100

ondary school districts. Each secondary school district comprised 210 elementary school districts, thereby giving the country one elementary school district for every six hundred persons. School attendance became compulsory for children upon attainment of the age of six years. In the very beginning the period of compulsory education was only sixteen months, but this was extended to three years in 1880 and to four years in 1886. It was finally extended to six years and this has continued until the present. Although in 1940 a law was enacted by the Diet extending the period of compulsory education to eight years, its enforcement was suspended indefinitely by the outbreak of the war in the Pacific in 1941.

While the over-all administrative organization was patterned after the French model, the elementary school and its curriculums followed the American model. Tanaka Fujimaro, an Education Department official, who as member of the Iwakura Mission had studied the educational organization and practice of the United States and of European countries, was impressed most favorably by what he saw in America. With Mori Arinori, the resident Minister in Washington at the time, he worked out plans to adopt those features of American education that could be applied to advantage in Japan.

In the spring of 1872, when the Tōkyō Normal School was opened, an American educator, Marion M. Scott of Honolulu, was invited to become a teacher and educational adviser to the Minister of Education. Entrusted primarily with the work of teacher training, he used American textbooks, teaching materials, equipment and classroom methods. His classes were conducted in English with the aid of interpreters. This resulted in a very marked American influence throughout the country. Textbooks in the normal schools, which were later established in different parts of the country, and even the books used in the elementary schools were at first outright translations of American books and readers.

Upon becoming Vice Minister of Education in 1873, Tanaka embarked upon a vigorous program of transplanting American educational practices to Japan and invited Dr. David Murray of Rutgers College to the post of educational adviser to the Minister of Education and superintendent in charge of educational administration. Arriving in the summer of 1873, Dr. Murray devoted his energies during his six-year tenure of office to the organization of a system which was not only in harmony with Japanese national characteristics, but adapted to the special needs of the nation. He also helped to lay the foundation of female education which both Tanaka and Mori promoted vigorously. It was then that English was adopted as the required foreign language in the secondary schools and higher institutions of learning. In the 1880's the Education Ministry carried this a step further by introducing English into the elementary schools. At the same time, the needs of business and industry were met by the establishment of a system of business and vocational training, and schools multiplied as the nation concentrated on industrial expansion during the 1890's.

Normal schools, which had been established and administered originally by the central government, were turned over in 1877 to the prefectural governments, placing the teacher-training institutions under the jurisdiction of local authorities. Two years later, the Education Department, on the basis of Tanaka's proposals, remodeled education along American lines, thus recognizing the principle of local autonomy in educational administration. However, a rapidly changing domestic scene forced a change in another direction and, in 1886, Education Minister Mori effected a far-reaching educational reform, which reflected a strong German influence. The highly nationalistic system of education which came into being remained in effect for the next sixty years without substantial changes.

In 1877, Tōkyō University emerged as a result of the merger of three separate educational institutions which had been in operation since the government took them over from the Shogunate at the time of the Restoration. However, it was not until the promulgation of the University Ordinance, in 1886, that it attained full university status with its component departments of law, medicine, engineering, sciences, and literature under a single administration. It was renamed the Tōkyō Imperial University in June, 1897, when the Kyōto Imperial University was opened.[1]

For many years, the graduates of the Tōkyō Imperial University have virtually monopolized the field of higher civil service by filling most of the important posts in the executive and judicial branches of the government and the diplomatic service as well, leaving only the legislative branch open to graduates of other universities. This was in keeping with the traditional concept of the principal function of a government university, which had come down from the seventh century when the first university was founded. However, the special privilege conferred on universities goes back to the 1880's, when regulations for the appointment of officials were first put into effect. At the time, Itō ruled that the graduates of Tōkyō University were eligible for appointment without examination, a ruling which was an expedient, motivated by, and based on, his political ambitions.

In 1880, the French system of educational organization gave way to the American system with the organization of local elective education boards. This innovation was short-lived, and Mori abolished it in 1885, when he became Education Minister. In its place was set up a strongly nationalistic system patterned after that of Germany, a step which was consonant with the prevailing mood of looking to Germany for inspiration. A new philosophy as well as a system of higher education was effectuated in March, 1886, by an imperial ordinance which defined the function of the Imperial University as "the offering of in-

---

[1] The third imperial university at Sendai was opened in 1907, the fourth at Fukuoka in 1910, and the fifth at Sapporo in 1918. The last one was founded in Ōsaka in 1931. In the meantime, two others had been founded outside Japan proper, one at Keijō in 1923, and the other at Taihoku in 1928.

struction and carrying on thorough investigations in the arts and sciences to meet the needs of the state." One of the most conspicuous results produced was the strong awareness engendered among the Imperial University students that they were being trained to become leaders rather than followers. The Imperial University obtained official sanction as the training school for the bureaucracy. At the same time, a significant change was brought about in teacher training which placed great stress on discipline and the cultivation of virtues, required the teachers and students to live together in dormitories, and prescribed compulsory military drill for the students.

To implement the new philosophy of education, the government brought Professor Hausknecht to the Tōkyō Imperial University, in 1887, as lecturer on Herbartian pedagogics and educational doctrines that had a wide following and dominated the thinking in German educational circles. Herbartian ideas in time also came to dominate the educational philosophy of the Japanese for the next two decades or so, largely as a result of Mori's initiative. Inoue Ki, who succeeded Mori, pushed the nationalistic trend a step further by placing a greater emphasis than before on instruction in morals, language, and the Chinese classics, through which he endeavored to strengthen the basis of national morality. At the same time, however, he did not lose sight of the increasing needs in vocational and business education.

The appearance of private universities reflected the unprecedented demand for men trained in politics, law, and business in the early years of the Meiji era, when there was a paucity of trained personnel. Oldest among the private universities is the Keiō University, which dates back to the private school started by Fukuzawa in the late 1850's to teach the Dutch language at first and the English language later. Owing to the emphasis placed by the founder on practical education, and particularly on the training of leaders in trade and industry, Keiō University has produced a large number of eminent men in those fields.[2] Almost all other universities that were founded during this period existed for the express purpose of teaching law, a subject which had the greatest appeal to ambitious young men.[3]

Unique among the institutions of higher learning, especially because of its conception, is the Waseda University, founded in 1882 by Ōkuma Shigenobu,

[2] Among the early outstanding graduates of Keiō were Nakamigawa Hikojirō, who, as the pillar of the Mitsui economic empire, placed a large number of Keiō graduates in key positions; Shōda Heigorō and Toyokawa Ryōhei of the Mitsubishi; Watanabe Kōki, President of the Tōkyō Imperial University; Takamine Hideō, head of the Tōkyō Women's Higher Normal School; and Naka Tsūsei, historian and head of Tōkyō Girls' Normal School.

[3] The first law school was founded by the Department of Justice in 1872. Hōsei University was founded in 1879 as the Franco-Japanese Law School. The promulgation of the Criminal Code in 1880 stimulated the appearance of law schools. Senshū University in 1880, Meiji Law School in 1881, and the English Law School (later Chūō University) in 1886 were some of the institutions of learning which appeared.

who was then not in the government. As Tōkyō College, it was founded as an institution of higher learning which would be free from the domination and influence of the government. Its avowed aim was to produce capable leaders, needed for the building of a new Japan. It is not surprising, therefore, that the emphasis given should have been on politics, law, and economics. True to its tradition, it has since its founding trained more men for active life in politics, journalism, and letters than any other private university.

Mention should be made here also of some of the universities which were originally founded as Christian denominational schools. Rikkyō University was opened in Ōsaka in 1871 as a school for the teaching of English by Rev. C. M. Williams, an American Presbyterian minister, who was one of the earliest missionaries to arrive in Japan in 1858. After its removal to Tōkyō, it grew rapidly, later achieving the status of a university. Dōshisha University, which was started in Kyōto as the Dōshisha English Language School, was the first institution founded by a Japanese to offer Christian training.[4] It was founded by Niishima Jō, perhaps better known to the West as Joseph Hardy Neesima, an ordained Congregational minister, who was educated at Amherst College and Andover Theological Seminary and came under the influence of J. H. Seelye and Mark Hopkins.

Although Niishima never looked down upon practical utilitarian education, his goal was the making of cultured gentlemen of faith and character. Like the New England clerics of his day, he recognized the importance of money but never condoned its worship. His constant reminder to the students was that money was a faithful slave but a dangerous master. He devoted a great deal of attention to female education and founded a girl's high school in 1876, the same year in which he established his theological school. He was firm in his belief that the improvement and elevation of the family was basic to the building and progress of a new Japan. And in the elevation of the family he envisioned women in the role of spiritual leaven.

By the end of the nineteenth century, the foundation of the Japanese educational system had been fairly well laid, though it was by no means completed. In 1894, the higher schools (*kōtō gakkō*) were established by the government to offer professional training as well as preparatory education for entrance to the imperial universities. With the promulgation of the ordinance for the establishment of colleges in 1903, they were made exclusively university preparatory institutions while the professional schools were separated and given independent status. This resulted in the establishment of separate colleges of agriculture, forestry, engineering and technology, mining, sericulture, fisheries, medicine,

---

[4] Christian training and also theological training soon were given in a number of other denominational institutions of collegiate level which were established. Among them were the Aoyama Gakuin, Meiji Gakuin, Kantō Gakuin, Kansai Gakuin, Tōhoku Gakuin, and Chinzei Gakuin.

pharmacy, dentistry, commerce, fine arts, music, and others. Secondary education underwent a notable development in 1899, when middle schools were created and girls' high schools were provided for all the prefectures.

EDUCATION OF WOMEN

Education for women constitutes an interesting as well as an important chapter in the development of modern Japan. Feudal society had relegated women to a position of obscurity and subservience to men. Their function was limited solely to the narrow precincts of the home. Consequently, education of women was restricted to those types of training which fitted a woman to perform the dual role of good wife and wise mother. Her life was one of obedience to men virtually from the cradle to the grave: first as a child to her father, after marriage to her husband, and as a widow to her adult son, the head of the household. The sort of training received by the women of the middle class during the Tokugawa period consisted of the minimum essentials of reading and writing. Education went no further except that they were taught the necessary household arts and domestic skills such as spinning, weaving, sewing, and cooking. For the well to do, there was usually additional training intended to give graceful manners and refinement. These usually included tea ceremony, flower arrangement, and music, and dancing.

Obviously such training was out of date and a hindrance to the progress of modern Japan. Fukuzawa had been one of the earliest to see this. But in the actual work of educating women for the new age Christian missionaries were the real pioneers. One of the very first of the mission schools for girls was the Ferris Seminary, founded in Yokohama in 1870. In the first two decades of the Meiji era no less than forty-three schools were founded by the mission boards to advance the education of women.

One of the earliest government officials to take a genuine interest in educating women was Kuroda Kiyotaka. As Vice Commissioner of Colonization of Hokkaidō he visited the United States in 1870 and was impressed by the freedom and intelligence of American women. The upshot of this was that in the following year five girls were sent to the United States by the Colonization Office for a period of study. This was followed, in 1872, by the founding in Tōkyō of the first public school for girls, open to all girls between the ages of seven and fourteen years, regardless of family status, *samurai* or commoner. Two years later, the first girls' normal school was founded. Although a number of such teacher-training schools for girls came into being in various parts of the country, it was not until 1882, when the girls' high school attached to the Tōkyō Girls' Normal School was opened, that secondary education became generally available.

One of the five girls sent by the government to the United States for study was Tsuda Umeko, who was then only seven years old. Ten years' sojourn in the United States so thoroughly Americanized her that when she returned to her native land in 1881 she had to relearn her mother tongue. When the Peeresses' School was founded by the Empress four years later, Miss Tsuda became a teacher of English. But in 1889 she returned to the United States for a college education and entered Bryn Mawr from which she was graduated four years later. Her long-cherished dream of a women's college became a reality when she established in 1900 the school which later became the Tsuda English College. In the same year Dr. Yoshioka Yayoi, one of Japan's first women doctors, founded a medical college for women. The following year, the Japan Women's College was founded.[5] But equal opportunities in education for women were slow in materializing. In 1913, the Tōhoku Imperial University at Sendai opened its doors to women for the first time on a restricted, experimental basis and admitted three students. Three years later, two of them were graduated with the degree of bachelor of science, the first time women were granted a degree by an imperial university. However, ten more years had to elapse before two women students were graduated with the degree of bachelor of arts from the same university. However, higher education for women on a basis of absolute equality with men was still a thing of the distant future. The 92nd Diet, the last under the old Meiji Constitution, which dissolved on March 31, 1947, passed a basic education law providing not only nine years of free compulsory education, but also removing all administrative barriers to coeducation. This, together with the equality for women provided in the new Constitution, which went into effect in May, 1947, paves the way for equal opportunities in education for women on all levels.

MUSIC EDUCATION

The introduction of music into the educational curricula was achieved in much the same manner as the introduction of art. A committee for the study of music education was appointed by the Education Department in 1879 to look into ways and means of introducing into the schools songs which would inculcate "noble sentiments, moral character, and refinement." Educational authorities were not introducing music merely for music's sake. It was in pursuance of a definite policy directed toward the attainment of a national morality that this subject was being introduced into the schools.

Izawa Shūji, the chairman of the committee, who had studied in the United States, invited his former professor, Dr. Luther Whiting Mason, as adviser and director of a group of educators and musicians who were commissioned to compose songs for use in the schools. *A Collection of Elementary School Songs* was the result. This was followed by collections of songs for normal schools and

---

[5] The year 1918 saw the founding of Tōkyō Women's College, a private Christian institution of higher learning.

middle schools. The songs which were composed and compiled combined the good features of both Occidental and Japanese music, but they were sentimental and didactic in substance. They praised the beauty of the land, extolled its unique "national polity," emphasized the enormity of the debt of gratitude to the sovereign, parents, and teachers, and dwelt on didactic themes intended to develop a strong sense of duty and patriotism more than just music appreciation or aesthetic taste.

Music education received a tremendous impetus in the late 1880's when the Tōkyō School of Music was established to offer instruction for the first time in piano, organ, violin, voice, musicology, musical theory, and the teaching of music. Although the school was conducted at first along American lines by Izawa, German influence gradually became predominant as instructors came in increasingly large numbers from Germany and Austria. By the last decade of the century, the growth of army and navy bands as well as the increase in the number of those with the appreciation of Western music brought about a noticeable change in attitude and taste. No longer was Western music the monopoly of the elite society; it had become popular enough to be appreciated and enjoyed by the people in general.

EDUCATIONAL PHILOSOPHIES AND PRACTICES

For nearly seventy-five years from its beginning in 1871 to the collapse of the Empire in 1945, the Japanese educational system was geared to the policies of the nation. It was as effective an instrument of national policy as the army or the navy, and, though in a different way, it was as much an auxiliary organ of the state. The contents of education from the kindergarten through the university had been prescribed and regulated by the government. Thought control was exercised in, and through, the school system, notably during the late 1920's and through the 1930's. The ultimate objective of education as conceived by the authorities had been the training of individuals capable of rendering the maximum of service to the state without any thought of their own rights or privileges and only incidentally the turning out of well-rounded intelligent individuals capable of, and accustomed to, independent thinking. The effects of such a system have been far reaching and telling, for it has produced a high degree of regimentation and unquestioning, almost blind, obedience to authority.

That educational philosophies and practices of the West should gain wide currency in Japan was quite natural inasmuch as the basis of the educational policy of the government was derived from the last article of the Charter Oath of Five Articles which stated that "wisdom and knowledge shall be sought after in all parts of the world." The history of the three-quarters of a century, beginning in the 1870's, could very well be characterized as a continuous process of adoption and adaptation of European and American educational philosophies, theories, techniques, methods, organization, and administration within the framework of broad national policies.

Until the last decade of the nineteenth century, French, English, and American ideas dominated the Japanese educational scene. Educational ideas of the West were first introduced by a magazine started by the Education Department in 1873. American ideas were dominant between 1873, when the Iwakura Mission returned, and 1885, when Mori became the first Education Minister under the newly instituted cabinet system. The appointment of Tanaka as Vice Minister of Education in 1876 marked the beginning of a vigorous effort to adopt American educational practices. This was aided by the return in 1878 from the United States of Izawa Shūji and Takamine Hideo, who were instrumental in making American educational ideas and practices tremendously popular. Izawa was a graduate of a normal school in Bridgewater, Massachusetts, from where he went on to Harvard for further study. Takamine was a graduate of the Oswego Normal School in New York State. Their influence on Japanese educational leaders of this period was profound. Izawa's *Pedagogics,* which was a work incorporating his studies at Bridgewater, and Takamine's translation of Johonott's work, which was on the educational ideas of Herbert Spencer, Louis Agassiz, and Pestalozzi, achieved great popularity.

Until the publication of Izawa's *Pedagogics* in the early 1880's slight attention was paid to teaching methods. Little, if any, progress had been made since the Tokugawa days when the learning process consisted of reading and storytelling, relying almost completely on rote memory. The educators' knowledge of the learning process was negligible and research in this field was practically unknown, for only a precious few recognized its importance. Nearly a decade after Dr. David Murray had tried with scant success to put across Pestalozzi's natural method, Izawa's work caught the imagination of the educators and stimulated their thinking and research efforts. So popular did his work become that any elementary school teacher who was not acquainted with the developmental method was thought unworthy of his profession.

The utilitarian philosophy of education, which Fukuzawa vigorously expounded, was traceable to English and American educators, notably to the ideas which President Francis Wayland of Brown University had expressed in the mid-nineteenth century. In the 1880's, however, its theoretical basis was derived from Herbert Spencer's *Social Statics* as well as from his *Education, Intellectual, Moral and Physical,* which placed emphasis on scientific knowledge as the chief aim of education, and from the works of Bain and Johonott. What appealed particularly to the Japanese was the fact that Johonott put equal emphasis on the complete life of an individual as the ultimate aim of education and the aesthetic values of the arts and literature, without in any way minimizing the importance of scientific education. Utilitarianism and empiricism in education reached their height of popularity in 1887, when Takamine published his *New Pedagogics*. Pestalozzi was popular for a time, but his influence was not lasting, for his ideas were regarded as incompatible with the then popular Lockean empiricism, and his method not equal to the task of giving essential knowledge to the students. The inadequacy of Spencerian educational theory in the matter of morality led the policymakers to discard his philosophy in favor of the Herbartian theory.

Education Minister Mori was emphatic in his belief that the aim of education lay in the building up of national power. Having spent his youth in England as one of the students sent by the Satsuma fief, Mori was an unmitigated exponent of Westernism up to 1879. In that year, he toured Europe and came in contact with the intense nationalism which was rampant on the continent. As a result, his attitude underwent noticeable change. Reacting against the doctrine of freedom and popular rights, he became converted to nationalism and assumed the view that it was proper to sacrifice the individual for the state. If he still believed in Westernism, he had certainly veered to the right to the extent of upholding absolutism. When he became Education Minister in 1885 he promptly set out to turn the educational system into an instrument for the nourishing of nationalism. As we have already noted, teacher training became the center of this program for the inculcation of strong nationalism. The dormitory system in the normal schools was a means of keeping students under strict supervision and control and of preventing outside contacts which might prove distracting. As a matter of fact dormitories became semimilitary barracks for the carrying out of rigid discipline and the inculcation of unquestioning obedience.

Herbartian ideas were introduced at first by students who had studied in Germany and through English translations of German sources. However, it was not until Professor Emil Hausknecht began his lectures on pedagogy at Tōkyō University in 1887 that they obtained wide following as well as official sanction. The adoption of German educational theories was in line with the general trend which developed from about the mid-eighties: the adoption of German ideas, institutions, and practices in many fields, including government administration, military organization, science, medicine, police, philosophy, history, and even literature. The popularity of Herbartian pedagogy rested on its emphasis on moral character as the aim of education, a concept which was in consonance with the government policy of encouraging nationalism.

Government leaders began to feel that educational philosophy and practices favored practical education to the extent of neglecting, if not actually holding in contempt, the old traditional concepts and ideals. It was clear that in the 1870's liberalism and equalitarian ideas had gained ground at the expense of time-honored moral concepts. Consequently, in 1882, the Education Department felt impelled to place the course on morals at the head of the list of elementary school subjects to offset what it regarded as the baneful effects of Western ideas. Meanwhile, the craze for westernization gained momentum, reaching its height in the 1880's. Educational authorities decided that there was urgent need for a policy as well as a philosophy which would give direction and stability to a nation which was in ideological confusion. The policy was to furnish at the same time a basis for strong nationalism. The result was the promulgation on October 30, 1890, of the Imperial Rescript on Education which set forth clearly the moral objectives of education by combining Shintō ideology with the ethical concepts of Confucianism. Interestingly enough, Shintoists insisted that the Rescript reflected the traditional ideals and "national morality" as developed by Shintō during more than twenty-five hundred years of national existence, while the Confucianists were certain that it was the embodiment of Confucian philosophy, and the Buddhists claimed that the teaching of Buddhism constituted its source. According to this document, loyalty and filial piety were made the cornerstone of Japanese national morality. The Rescript came at a time when reaction was setting in against the trend of westernization, which for a time appeared to the government to be exceeding the bounds of propriety, and it was obviously intended to be a brake to prevent extreme westernization. While it had a sobering effect on those who tended to go to extremes, there is little doubt that it served to strengthen the position of the conservative elements and even of the reactionaries.

The movement for the preservation of "national virtues" developed into an advocacy of strong nationalism after Mori succeeded in making it the basic concept in education. This reactionary trend was aided by the promulgation of the Constitution in 1889 and the Rescript on Education the following year. Thus, Japanism became the battle cry of those opposed to Westernism. In this period of reaction, Professor Kume Kunitake was forced out of the Tōkyō Imperial University for a statement that Shintō was an ancient ritual of the worship of heaven. However, the prophets of chauvinistic nationalism, like Takayama Chogyū and Nishimura Shigeki, were opposed by Tokutomi and others who denounced superficial Westernism and advocated democracy. Saionji, on assuming the post of Education Minister in January, 1898, expressed his view to an editor of the *Kokumin Shimbun* that the regulation and control of national morality on the basis of narrow, intolerant, and reactionary ideas would bring ruin to the country and that the State alone as an ethical basis was too narrow a concept. He stressed that if Japan were to take her place among the powers of the world, she would have to keep in step with world trends and not to go against them.

If the German influence was considerable, the influence of American ideas and methods was stronger and more enduring. The empiricism, individualism, and activism of William James left their imprint on educational thought and practice in the closing years of the nineteenth and the early years of the twentieth century. Also, the visit of George Trumbull Ladd, Professor of Mental and Moral Philosophy at Yale, in 1900, stimulated Japanese interest in educational philosophy, psychology, and pedagogics. Toward the end of the First World War and in the period immediately following, the pragmatism of John Dewey exerted a strong influence on Japanese educators through his *Democracy and Education,* which became the bible of liberal and progressive leaders in education. The Gary and Winnetka systems, the platoon plan, the Dalton plan, the project method, and other similar theories have all been given a trial in the schools at one time or another and many of the good features were adopted and incorporated into the Japanese educational system. Even progressive education has had its day, although the obstacles which stood in its way were indeed great. In short, Japan has tried to benefit from the educational experiences of the West, and particularly of the American people, by experimenting on novel ideas and theories.

Chapter 8. A New National Defense Structure

That the problem of national security should be the obsession of the leaders of the Meiji government was more than understandable in view of the circumstances under which Japan was forced to open her doors in 1854. The pathetic state of affairs in which the nation found itself especially in regard to national defense at the time of Perry's arrival was enough to make the leaders shudder. Lacking any sort of standing army, the Shogunate was compelled to issue orders to the fire brigades along the coast to stand by. Because of the utter unpreparedness of the Shogunate, it would have been relatively simple for any of the Western powers to overrun Japan with a relatively small force. Only the intense rivalry which existed among the powers precluded such an ignominious fate for Japan.

In analyzing the development of Japan's national defense system and her military organization, it would be well to take into full account the initial psychological impact of Western military might as well as her centuries-old military traditions. What happened to China after the Anglo-Chinese War was well known to the Japanese leaders of the Restoration period.

Although a strong national defense force was needed, a standing army could not immediately be provided for. The government was forced reluctantly to make use of the troops of the various fiefs, which constituted the only available forces, although they were none too effective. The general reorganization of government, effected early in 1868, provided for a Bureau of Military Defense to take over the administration of the garrisons stationed in several parts of the country. These garrisons were made up of *samurai* furnished by the fiefs, which were required by the government to furnish for every 10,000 *koku* revenue ten regular troops for duty in the capital and fifty reserve troops in the fief, and a military assessment of 300 *ryō*. There was an urgent need for unification of military organization, as each of the fiefs had its own system of organization and training, modeled on the French, Dutch, or English system. When the Department of Military Affairs was created in the summer of 1869, Vice Minister Ōmura Masujirō adopted the French system as a model and proposed the establishment of a military school to train the officer personnel, the abolition of the *samurai* class, and the institution of a conscription system by which recruits were to be obtained from all walks of life. Although the military school was actually started, Ōmura unfortunately fell at the hands of an assassin and did not live to see the realization of his dream of a conscription system. It remained for one of his protégés, Yamagata, to translate it into reality.

The return of Yamagata Aritomo from Europe in the summer of 1870 after a study of the military systems of France and Prussia marked the beginning of a thoroughgoing military reorganization. When he was offered the post of Vice Minister of Military Affairs, he accepted on the condition that he be authorized to carry out the unification of the military. Yamagata embarked on his program of introducing necessary changes at a time when the Prussian army was demonstrating its prowess to the world by pushing back the French army at Sedan just before the siege of Paris. Although Yamagata had become a great admirer of the German military system, his views did not prevail in the Council of State at first. In the fall of 1870, the Council of State, in disregard of Yamagata's recommendations, chose the French army as the model for the Japanese army and organized the navy along British lines.

Before the year 1870 came to a close, regulations were issued and conscription attempted on an experimental basis in the Kyōto region, but the project had to be abandoned. This was followed in February, 1871, by the organization, by Saigō Takamori, of the Emperor's Own (*Goshimpei*), which was later renamed the Imperial Guard. Two months later, two garrisons, one in the East and the other in the West, were created. By summer, the garrisons were increased to four, and all the troops of the fiefs were ordered disbanded, many of them being absorbed into the new garrisons. This step marked the beginning of a national army whose strength at the time was only slightly in excess of twenty battalions, comprising the Imperial Guard and the four garrisons. At this stage, military strength was altogether inadequate for national defense although the army was satisfactory as an internal police force.

Itagaki advocated a volunteer army, like the one in England and the United States, as more suitable to the needs of Japan, which, he claimed, could not afford a large standing army. Saigō supported Itagaki but for different reasons. However, in a move preliminary to the attainment of a strong national defense force, the Department of Military Affairs was divided into two separate departments: the War and Navy Departments, in February, 1872. This was preparatory to the institution of a universal military conscription system. Under the new organization, which represented a triumph for Yamagata, the nation's military strength was to be made up of the following three components: the regulars, the reserves, and the national army. All able-bodied males twenty-one years and over were to be conscripted for compulsory military service for a period of three years, after which they were to remain in the reserves for another four years and would be liable to service until they reached the age of forty. The conscription ordinance, which went into effect at the beginning of 1873, was liberal in its provisions inasmuch as it exempted from service certain categories of persons such as heads of households, government officials, heirs, only sons, only grandsons, and acting heads of households. In addition, anyone who paid 270 yen was exempt from service. This system of exemption was abolished later when it was found to be unsatisfactory.

Under the conscription system, military service ceased to be the exclusive privilege of the *samurai* class as in the days of old. Instead, it became the duty of all persons in whatever stations or walks of life. This change, however, was not greeted with enthusiasm, as has been frequently supposed. The ex-*samurai* were outraged by the "injustice" done them in taking away a privilege which they had enjoyed for centuries. And to add insult to injury, they were forced to serve in the armed forces alongside their former inferiors, the sons of peasants, merchants, and artisans. The farmers, on the other hand, felt that the new system was harsh and unjust to them in that it deprived them of the much needed manpower on the farms. Moreover, peasants, fearing the "blood tax," as it was called, not only put up resistance against the authorities, but also evaded military service. For a time, it was impossible for the government to secure the necessary quota of conscripts for the army, a fact which proved to be of serious embarrassment to the authorities. This situation was corrected only after an intensive nationwide educational campaign had been carried on by the government through the prefectural government offices.

Conscription was admittedly the only method of building up a strong military organization and at the same time of breaking down the barriers of class, which had long existed under feudalism. If the *samurai* were dubious of the fighting ability of the new conscript army, the military leaders were confident of its effectiveness. General Yamagata, like Ōmura, entertained not the slightest doubt of the fighting qualities of the common people, for he had seen how the Chōshū clan had built up in the pre-Restoration days an effective fighting unit, the Kiheitai, out of raw recruits taken from all walks of life and had used it with telling effect against the Shogunate. Furthermore, he had also seen at first hand the efficient military organizations of European powers, which were based on the conscription system.

Simultaneously with the institution of the military conscription system, the country was divided into six military districts, with a garrison in each: Tōkyō, Sendai, Nagoya, Ōsaka, Hiroshima, and Kumamoto. The authorized peacetime strength of a garrison was set at 40,000 and wartime strength at 70,000. This provided a standing army of about 400,000, a force which was considered adequate to put down any civil disturbance.

The first test for the new army came in the spring of 1874, when it was used effectively against Etō Shimpei's Saga Rebellion. On this occasion it was significant to note that a civilian official, Home Minister Ōkubo, was invested with full military powers for the purpose of restoring peace and order. A month later, the army was employed in an overseas expedition to Formosa. However, the real test for the conscript army did not come until the Satsuma Rebellion of 1877, during which the sons of peasants and merchants acquitted themselves creditably, displaying excellent fighting spirit and courage under fire and proving themselves to be easily the equal of the vaunted ex-*samurai* soldiers. The expectations of the military authorities were more than fulfilled while the prejudice of the ex-*samurai* was dissipated.

The General Staff Office, modeled on that of Germany, was created by an imperial ordinance in December, 1878, at the instance of Yamagata. This marked the beginning of the separation of military command function from military administration. A complete separation was finally achieved in the spring of 1886 with the reorganization of the General Staff Office. With the creation of the Office of Inspector General of Military Education in 1879 the central machinery of military organization was rounded out. Meanwhile, organization and training methods were changed over from the French to the German system. With the establishment of the military academy in 1882 a modern system of officer training was instituted. In January of the same year, the Emperor had issued the Rescript to the Soldiers and Sailors which provided a strong moral basis for the education, training, and indoctrination of the officers and men of the armed forces.

In a modernization move in January, 1886, the garrisons were superseded by divisions which now numbered seven, two in Tōkyō and one each at the five former garrison headquarters, The period following the Sino-Japanese War saw an expansion of the army by six more divisions. After the Russo-Japanese War, the army was expanded by another six divisions. In 1915, the year after the outbreak of the First World War, two more divisions were created, both in Korea, bringing the total to twenty-one divisions and a standing army of 290,000. In the 1920's, in the face of public clamor for retrenchment as well as for the modernization of the army, four divisions were abolished, resulting in reduction by some 90,000. However, the Manchurian Incident in 1931 occasioned the beginning of rearmament, and by 1937, the army comprised seventeen divisions aggregating 250,000 troops.

Through two successful wars, the Sino-Japanese War and the Russo-Japanese War, the military machine achieved high reputation for efficiency abroad as well as at home, where it was credited with achieving national security and enhancing Japan's international position. By the turn of the century, the army had ceased to be a mere internal police force and had developed into a formidable factor in the world of power politics. The military leaders were neither blind to its potentialities nor reluctant to use it as an instrument of national policy. Nor were they above using it to enhance their own power and prestige in the realm of domestic politics. It is pertinent to note also that the international acclaim given Japan for her successful prosecution of wars helped to increase the prestige of the military and contributed to the rise of militarism at home.

The growth of Japanese sea power since the advent of Perry was no less spectacular than the appearance of the army. Japan's navy dates back to 1855, when the Shogunate first secured Dutch naval officers as instructors in naval science and tactics, navigation, naval architecture, and naval ship construction. At the time of the Restoration, the Shogun's navy was able to give a good account of itself in fighting the Emperor's men-of-war. It was a source of considerable pride to the Japanese to be able to take the *Kanrin Maru* on a cruise to San Francisco and back in 1860 with a Japanese captain and crew. This trip was in the nature of a return call for Perry's visit seven years earlier. Few years were to elapse before the Japanese were to appreciate fully the value of sea power.

The demonstration of naval might on two separate occasions, the bombardment of Kagoshima by a British squadron in the summer of 1863, and the bombardment of Shimonoseki by Allied ships in the early autumn of the following year, convinced even the most skeptical of the importance of naval power. It was no accident, therefore, that Satsuma was the first to see the tremendous possibilities a strong navy offered and begin to take steps to build up a naval force of its own. As a result, when the new navy was organized, Satsuma men were in a position not only to furnish leadership, but also to monopolize the important positions.

In 1867, the Shogunate had secured the services of an English naval officer, Commander Tracy. Two years later, when a naval training school was established in Tōkyō, the government staffed it with English naval officers under Lieutenant Commander Douglas. In the early stages of the development of the Japanese navy, the cadets at the Naval Academy received instruction, not in their mother tongue but in a foreign language, English. In the training of naval personnel, Japan first received tutelage from the Dutch, then from the British and Americans. Many of the naval officers of the early days were not only British trained but actually put through a period of apprenticeship in the British Navy. The most distinguished of them, Admiral Tōgō, was schooled in the best traditions of Lord Nelson aboard British men-of-war. Some of the other officers, like Admiral Uryū, were trained at the United States Naval Academy at Annapolis. It was natural therefore that navy men in England and the United States looked upon the Japanese victory over the Russian Baltic Fleet as the triumph of their naval tradition as well as their naval science over that of the Tsar's navy.

Following the creation of the Navy Department in 1872, Katsu Awa, who was captain of the *Kanrin Maru* on its cruise to San Francisco and back in 1860, became its head and the program of naval building was begun in earnest. By 1875, the Japanese had made sufficient headway in naval construction to build their first warship at the Yokosuka Shipyards. The 900-ton ship *Seiki* made a voyage to Europe three years later, manned by an all Japanese crew. However, the Japanese Navy relied on foreign shipyards for its warships for some time thereafter. By 1882, the government was able to dispense with all foreign naval instructors except teachers of foreign languages.

From a force of seventeen ships totaling slightly over 13,000 tons in 1873, the navy had expanded to twenty-eight ships totaling 57,600 tons and twenty-four torpedo boats in addition, on the eve of the Sino-Japanese War. The naval battles of the war with China were fought almost entirely with foreign-built warships. In the clamor for naval expansion which came after the war, the navy succeeded in getting through the Diet, in 1896, a building program for a fleet built around six battleships and six armored cruisers. By the end of 1903, the year before the Russo-Japanese War, the navy comprised seventy-six warships aggregating 250,000 tons exclusive of its seventy-six torpedo boats.

Perhaps the greatest single stimulus to naval expansion immediately after the turn of the century was the conclusion of the Anglo-Japanese Alliance, in 1902, which called for joint consultation and planning between the naval authorities of the two powers. It envisaged the maintenance by the signatories of a combined naval force equal to the naval strength of any two powers in Far Eastern waters. In 1911, under the Saionji Cabinet, plans for an eight-eight fleet took shape. However, it was not until 1919 that the government succeeded in securing the authorization of the Diet to push the plans to completion. Before the program, which provided for the largest navy ever planned by Japan, became a reality, the Washington Conference was called. This meant the scrapping of the projected eight-eight fleet, but Japan had already attained third place among the navies of the world.

NATIONAL DEFENSE STRUCTURE, GOVERNMENT, AND POLITICS

It was apparent even to the layman that the new national defense structure was modern and that it incorporated the newest developments in organization and administration as well as in military science and tactics. What was not so apparent was the fact that, psychologically and ideologically, the new army and navy did not represent a new departure. Nor was the role the military decided to play in the affairs of the nation a new feature, although the techniques which it employed were more refined and effective than those used by the military class of the feudal period.

With the abolition of the fiefs and the establishment of prefectures in 1871, the administration of national affairs changed hands from the feudal ruling class to the capable and ambitious scions of the lower caste *samurai* who, as insignificant underlings and underdogs, never had been given the opportunity to develop their talents or achieve positions of importance. These young men, who had been awakened and aroused to the new opportunities for service and fame opened to them by their contact with Western civilization, became bold thinkers who dared to act. Increasingly large numbers of them began to occupy important positions in the government.

That a considerable number of them should go into the new military organization to make a career of soldiering was very natural, especially for those with *samurai* background, particularly at a time when effective national defense was recognized by all to be an absolute prerequisite not only to the security of the nation but even to its very existence. Yet, in the initial stages of the development of the system of national defense, the brilliant minds of the army and navy were found devoting their energies to purely civilian activities, such as working on the most pressing problems of law codification, local administration, police administration, and even education. This was possible because early governmental organization utilized talents regardless of the branch in which they were found, military or civilian. Army and navy officers on active duty status performing nonmilitary duties produced no adverse criticisms as there was no line of demarcation between the military and civilian functions of government.

The absence of even an attempt to distinguish between civilian and military functions in the government is best illustrated in the handling of the Saga Rebellion in 1874. Home Minister Ōkubo was invested with full military powers for the restoration of peace and order, including the command of troops. The military took orders from a civilian Home Minister, a fact which seems almost incredible in the light of subsequent developments. Even during the Satsuma Rebellion three years later, the power of military command was still in the hands of the same official, Ōkubo.

In the achievement of a strong central government, the organization of a unified national army was an absolute and urgent prerequisite. Without it, no government could possibly have survived the civil disturbances and rebellions which were directed at its destruction. It was natural that the central figures in the new national defense structure should come to assume an important role in the planning and execution of national policies, not only in military matters but in all other matters of state. That Yamagata, as architect of the Japanese military structure, should have become the core and backbone of the military bureaucracy which emerged later was not surprising at all.

Yamagata was interested in making the position of the military unassailable, especially after he had seen the Prussian system in operation. With this objective in mind, he had the General Staff Office created on December 5, 1878, by an imperial ordinance. This marks the beginning of a series of successful attempts at the separation of military command functions from military administration as well as from the general affairs of state. The reorganization of the General Staff Office in March, 1886, brought about an almost complete separation of military command from administrative functions. The Imperial Rescript to the Soldiers and Sailors issued on January 4, 1882, made it unequivocally clear that the power of supreme military command was vested in the Emperor. All the members of the armed forces were under the direct personal command of the Emperor.

The power of the military was strengthened greatly by the creation of the Privy Council in 1888. Although the Council was organized ostensibly for the purpose of deliberating upon the Constitution, its political purpose was to make it serve as a means of accommodating powerful remnants of feudal forces, particularly the five clans—Satsuma, Chōshū, Tosa, Hizen, and Higo, the old Bakufu group—and the court nobility. Gradually, the Council became the stronghold of bureaucrats and militarists whose conservative and not infrequently reactionary views were imposed upon the government. The Elder Statesmen also became a powerful force which more often than not supported the military, particularly when this group was dominated by Yamagata.

Steadily the military pushed ahead towards its objective of a position of independence in the control and management of military affairs. The Ordinance for the Organization of the Cabinet, promulgated on December 24, 1889, and revised in 1907, assigned to the Cabinet the duty of advising the Emperor on all those matters which do not pertain to military secrets or functions of military command. For these strictly military matters, the Chief of General Staff was empowered to report directly to the Emperor without having to go through the Cabinet.

The most memorable, if not the most auspicious, session of the Diet, the First Diet, opened under the government headed by Yamagata, the arch enemy of political parties and champion of the military. By the end of 1889, when he first assumed premiership, he was a seasoned bureaucrat. His career as an administrator began in 1883, when he assumed direction of the Department of Home Affairs and he continued uninterrupted for six years in the same capacity. He was Home Minister in the first two Cabinets of Itō and Kuroda, relinquishing the post only after he became Premier. Thus, the internal affairs of the nation were managed by a military man during the most crucial period in the development of parliamentary government. What sort of influence he exerted on the Home Ministry during his tenure of office and in the subsequent period can readily be deduced.

An irreconcilable clash developed between the Diet and the Matsukata Cabinet in the Second Diet, which was convened in 1891. The fight over the budget was vengeful. Navy Minister Kabayama, in the course of his effort to prevent the deletion of the expenditures for new naval construction, showed the arrogance as well as the contempt of the military bureaucracy for the members of the Diet and boasted that Japan owed her progress to the Satsuma and Chōshū clans. Dissolution of the Diet, which came in the midst of the deadlock over the budget, was a convincing demonstration of the power of the military clique, which would not tolerate a recalcitrant act or the defiance of the legislators.

The extent to which the military clique was beginning to impose its will on the government, even by the use of terroristic methods, was demonstrated again during the Matsukata Cabinet. In the general election, which was held on February 15, 1892, following the dissolution of the Second Diet, the government carried out wholesale interference, employing not only the police but also the gendarmerie and the regular army. Home Minister Shinagawa (Yajirō), reputedly the faithful henchman of Yamagata, instructed the police to interfere. In Saga, the native prefecture of Ōkuma, one of the two strongholds of the opposition forces (the other was Itagaki's Kōchi prefecture), a battalion of regular troops was mobilized in addition to the gendarmes. Men like General Takashima, the War Minister, and Admiral Kabayama, the Navy Minister, were the claws of the military clique upholding the free use of force at any time to suppress the people and stamp out political parties, and, if necessary, they were ready even to resort to the drastic step of suspending the Constitution.

Understandably enough the Triple Intervention which divested Japan of one of the fruits of victory detracted nothing from the glory and acclaim won by the military. On the contrary, it enhanced the position of the military even more than the victorious war itself. The leaders, both civilian and military, were convinced that military power was absolutely essential for the safeguarding of national interests. The upsurge of nationalism and the expansionist activities of patriotic societies only served to strengthen the hand of the military.

Another development that pushed the military to the fore in national affairs was the great increase in military expenditures. The national budget for 1896 was nearly twice that of the preceding year and the greater part of the increase was in military expenditures. In the following year, military expenditures took up 49 per cent of the entire national budget. Because of the direct control it exercised over such a large proportion of the national expenditures, the military achieved, before the close of the nineteenth century, the position of a large stockholder with a strong voice in the management of national affairs. As both the army and navy worked increasingly toward self-sufficiency in the manufacture of munitions, the military began to assert itself more and more in the economic and industrial policies of the nation as well as in diplomacy. This was particularly true in regard to policies related to the Asiatic continent.

By 1897, the military bureaucracy, headed by Yamagata, became the core of the newly risen military clique which was to be further nourished and strengthened by the Boxer Rebellion and the Russo-Japanese War. So powerful had Yamagata become that he was able to challenge his strongest opponent, Itō. At the meeting of the Elder Statesmen in 1898, following the dissolution of the Diet, Yamagata strenuously opposed Itō's suggestion that the next Cabinet be based on political parties, going so far as to advocate the suspension of the Constitution, if necessary, to check the political parties and the movement for popular rights. He had no scruples about disregarding the will of the Cabinet or the wishes of the Diet and the people to advance the interests of the military. To him, the military came before the people. Finally, in the same year in which Itō, following his resignation as Premier, recommended that the Ōkuma-Itagaki coalition be given the task of forming the next Cabinet, an open break occurred between him and Yamagata.

Itō abandoned the bureaucracy and the old clan bureaucrats and approached the financial world, bidding for support through Shibusawa's help. Thus, after 1897, the struggle for power was no longer between the clan bureaucrats and the political parties as in the past. It had become a struggle between the military bureaucrats headed by Yamagata and the political parties, which had in the meantime become the front of the civilian bureaucrats supported by the financial interests. An entirely new alignment had come into being in the arena of politics.

Yamagata did not minimize the strength which Itō could muster against him and, in anticipation of such an eventuality, made thorough preparations to meet it. Up to this time, the War and Navy Ministers and Vice Ministers had been active generals and admirals only in practice and without legal sanction. Yamagata therefore worked during his second premiership with his protégé, War Minister Katsura, to have the practice given the force of law by having an imperial ordinance issued in May, 1900. This ensured absolute supremacy of the military clique in one aspect of national affairs by excluding civilians entirely. It was a clever move calculated to safeguard the vested interests of the military clique of which Yamagata never lost sight. The new ordinance had the effect of investing the military with the power of making or breaking the Cabinet at will.

The founding of the Seiyūkai Party by Itō in September, 1900, was a challenge hurled at Yamagata and was intended as a check against the increasing power of the military bureaucracy. Itō succeeded in forcing Yamagata out almost immediately after the launching of the party and assumed the premiership himself for the fourth and last time. This was Yamagata's farewell to active political life. Although he was never to appear in the active arena of politics, his days of political activity were far from over. He worked from behind the scenes much more effectively in the capacity of Prince, Field Marshal, Elder Statesman, President of the Privy Council, and the undisputed leader of the military clique. In fact, he wielded far greater power behind the scene than he had as Premier. Moreover, his influence lasted longer and was far greater than that of Itō.

After his retirement in 1900, he concentrated his energies on building up a solid clique to oppose the political parties, which he could not tolerate. In June, 1901, he succeeded in having his protégé, General Katsura, assume the premiership. It was a move intended to protect the military bureaucracy from the encroachments of the political parties. The Katsura Cabinet lasted four years and seven months, the longest ever to remain in power, owing largely to the outbreak of the Russo-Japanese War. The victory over Russia strengthened the position of the military and contributed to the resurgence of nationalism and further expansion of military and naval armaments.

Interestingly enough, military power underwent a temporary decline in 1913 under the Third Katsura Cabinet, which was the shortest on record, lasting only two months. The frontal attack of the political parties forced Katsura to resort to the organization of a political party with which the military clique attempted vainly to parry the thrusts of the opposition. But with Yamagata still in the background, the military clique was still to have another round or two. General Terauchi, whose Cabinet was formed in the fall of 1915, headed the war cabinet of the First World War, just as the Katsura Cabinet had ruled during the Russo-Japanese War. Through the various activities in China and in Siberia, it earned for Japan the distrust of the powers.

Death finally removed in February, 1922, the pillar of the powerful military bureaucracy, which had been built systematically over a period of several decades. For a half century, from the time he put into effect the military conscription system in 1872 until his death, Yamagata wielded power as Home Minister, Premier, acting War Minister, Chief of General Staff, Supreme War Councilor, Privy Councilor, and Elder Statesman. At the height of his power, even a man of Prince Saionji's caliber had to bow to his will. No other high-ranking official held so many important positions as did Yamagata. Having tasted power early in his career as Home Minister, he found the exercise of power fascinating. Except for the brief period of service in the Sino-Japanese War as commander in chief of the First Army, practically his entire active career was spent in administration and in policy making. With his unswerving devotion to the military and his equally unremitting and irreconcilable opposition to political parties and parliamentary government, Yamagata spurred himself on to forge the army into an efficient war machine and to make it, at the same time, into a powerful factor in Japanese politics. Without his careful planning, clever stratagems, chicanery, and skillfully executed maneuvers and manipulations the military could not have achieved the power it did. The solid foundations laid by Yamagata also enabled the military to reassert itself in the decade of the 1930's and eventually to assume the complete direction of national affairs, leading the nation to the brink of disaster.

Chapter 9. Religious and Intellectual Awakening

Spiritually and ideologically the Meiji Restoration was of a dual nature which was bound to give rise to conflicts. In the restoration to the Emperor of the political powers which had been in usurpation by the Shogunate and the reaffirmation of the monarchical principle through the reestablishment of the imperial sovereignty both in name and in fact, this period represented a reversion to the ideals of ancient Japan. This harking back was reflected unmistakably in the new administrative organization patterned after that of the Taihō Code of A.D. 701. In the liquidation of feudalism and the modernization and westernization of institutions and ideas, a renovation of national life occurred on a scale hitherto unknown and unattempted in Japan. It was inevitable that such a contradiction should give rise to strong clashes between the conservatives and the progressives who represented the opposite poles of the dualistic reform.

These clashes were at first frequent, but even the conservatives eventually came to the realization that progress was not only necessary but could not even be stopped under the impact of Western civilization, particularly in the face of the aggressive and irresistible power of the West. Slowly but surely the ranks of the vigorous opponents of modernization became thinner and many of the antiforeign conservatives of an earlier period became the enthusiastic supporters of a new civilization. As a consequence, the ten years preceding the promulgation of the Constitution witnessed the most unremitting efforts at the Occidentalization of the country, which at times appeared to have gone completely beyond the bounds of reason and propriety. Before long, a reaction set in, as leaders both within and without the government became alarmed at the extremes to which the movement was going. Preservation of national heritage and virtues became the concern of leaders in virtually every field of endeavor and stimulated the rise of nationalism in the decade of the 1890's, particularly after the war with China.

Let us now see how the restoration of the imperial authority was implemented. In the reaffirmation of the concept of imperial sovereignty, the government decided on the policy of reestablishing and revitalizing Shintō. This had for its natural corollary the disestablishment of Buddhism, which had dominated the religious scene all through the Tokugawa period under the special aegis of the feudal regime. Prior to the Restoration, the Buddhist priests had entrenched themselves in the Shintō shrines as intendants or chief priests, wielding power over the Shintō priests, whom they oppressed and held in contempt. In order to correct this unfavorable situation the government decreed early in 1868 the separation of Shintō from Buddhist domination and ordered the return of Buddhist priests and nuns who had been serving in the Shintō shrines to laity.

The government went a step further to enhance the position of Shintō. It placed the newly created Office of Shintō Affairs above the Council of State, thereby giving Shintō a primacy it had enjoyed only in ancient Japan. Buddhist temple holdings which had been the gift of the Shogunate were confiscated by the government. All the measures for the disestablishment of Buddhism had the effect of degrading the position of Buddhism as well as of its priests and indirectly engendered a feeling of hostility against Buddhism. This was aggravated by the fact that leadership in the anti-Buddhist feeling was furnished by Shintō priests, who had long chafed under the humiliating treatment of the Buddhist priests. The upshot of it was a nationwide anti-Buddhist outburst during the years 1869 and 1870, leading to wanton destruction of temples and unwarranted attacks on Buddhist institutions as well as the denunciation of Buddhism itself as an obstacle to progress.

The disestablishment of Buddhism was clearly a step toward the reestablishment of the governmental organization and political ideals of the Taika Reform of the seventh century. It had reverted to the period in the ancient past when Shintō occupied the highest place in the governmental organization. This was quite natural as the ideological bases of the Restoration were furnished by the Confucian, Shintō, and nationalist scholars, who were not by any means sympathetic to Buddhism. It is also a significant fact that there was no one among the high government officials of the Restoration period who was close to the Buddhist church or its leaders. Little wonder then that Buddhism did not fare so well.

In spite of the disestablishment of Buddhism, the faith of its devotees remained unshaken. Once the separation of Shintō and Buddhism was effected and the attacks on Buddhism had subsided, Buddhism was able to regain strength and with the competition coming from Christianity, it was able to inject some vitality into its own organization. Thus, Buddhism was shaken out of the lethargy and degeneration into which it had fallen during the Tokugawa period. The anti-Buddhist atmosphere had the effect of awakening and stimulating the priesthood into activity, and men of ability and promise were soon joining their ranks. Since the government had from the very outset no intention of letting the separation of Shintō develop into an anti-Buddhist movement, it endeavored to bring about harmony between them. The Iwakura Mission afforded the Buddhists an opportunity to have their representatives join in the tour of inspection of the conditions in Europe and America and to carry out a survey of the religious systems of the West. Upon their return they were instrumental in getting Buddhism to adopt some of the results of their observations.

Subsequent to the conclusion of the treaties of commerce in 1858, the Powers succeeded in getting the Shogunate to abandon the practice of "picture treading" (*fumie*) which had been in force in the Nagasaki region as a method of forcing apostasy on the native Christians. Although this was undoubtedly a step toward the eventual establishment of freedom of religion, the ban on Christianity remained unrevoked, continuing on until a few years after the Restoration.

Early in 1862, a French Catholic missionary started a church in Yokohama and began preaching sermons in Japanese. When the governor of Kanagawa jailed those who heard his sermon, the missionary lodged a protest with the Japanese government through the French Minister. Through the adroit handling of the case by Katsu Awa, the preaching of sermons in Japanese was suspended, those who had been jailed were released, and possible diplomatic complications were averted.

In the spring of 1867, when the Christians of Uragami village in Nagasaki province gathered at their Catholic church to worship, the officials were alarmed and began arresting them. However, before the offenders could be punished, the feudal regime came to an end and the new Meiji Government came into existence. Early in the following year, the government sent Kido Kōin to Nagasaki to dispose of the problem. Three thousand Catholics were forced to renounce their faith and were dispersed to twenty-one feudatories. The treaty Powers saw in this a threat to the freedom of worship and advised the government to release them. Accordingly, in the spring of 1873, after considerable delay, they were released, returned to their native village, and were aided by the government in their rehabilitation. Signs that had been posted in public places announcing the existing ban on Christianity were taken down after word was sent back by the Iwakura Mission advising the lifting of the ban. Thus, in 1873, the prohibition of Christianity, which had been in effect for more than two centuries, came to an end.

Christian missionaries began to come into the country in considerable numbers. Even the Greek Orthodox Church sent its priests over to start a church in Tōkyō. In contrast to the missionary activities of the latter half of the sixteenth century and the early years of the seventeenth, which were carried on exclusively by Roman Catholic missionaries chiefly from Spain and Portugal, the missionaries who began to come into Japan in the latter part of the nineteenth century were mostly Protestants from England and the United States. The popularity of Townsend Harris and of American teachers was responsible for the welcome the Japanese gave to American missionaries after the ban on Christianity was lifted. By 1873, the number of foreign missionaries in Japan had increased to fifty-five from a mere thirteen in 1869.

The first seeds of Christianity after the reopening of the country were sown by foreign teachers who were invited to teach in the various schools. Among the earliest of these were William E. Griffis at Fukui, Guido F. Verbeck at Nagasaki, Thompson and Veeder at Tōkyō, Clark at Sapporo, and Brown at Yokohama. Most of them were missionary teachers, but even in the case of laymen, like Dr.

Clark and Captain Janes, their Christian influence was profound. Dr. Nitobe Inazō and Dr. Uchimura Kanzō became Christians under the influence of Dr. Clark, while several of the students of Captain Janes at Kumamoto became prominent Christian leaders in Japan.

Dr. Niishima Jō's return from the United States marked the beginning of Christian educational work by a native Christian. His founding in 1875 of the Dōshisha English School in Kyōto, which later became the Dōshisha University, was one of the outstanding events of the period both educationally and religiously, as it laid the foundation of Christian training. At the age of twenty, Niishima decided to go to the United States in quest of education. At Hakodate he shipped himself aboard an American vessel as a "boy" and proceeded to Shanghai. From there he sailed to Boston on a ship owned by Captain Alpheus Hardy, a wealthy New England merchant engaged in the China trade. Hardy took a personal interest in the young man and sent him through Amherst. Upon graduation he returned to Japan and joined the Iwakura Mission as an interpreter. But he returned to New England later to finish his theological education. It was after he had been ordained a Congregational minister that he returned to Kyōto in 1875 to begin his educational work.

Out of the Kumamoto School, where young Japanese students sat at the feet of Captain Janes, an American layman, came a number of outstanding leaders of the nation. When the school was discontinued in the summer of 1876, the young students who were leaving for Dōshisha to continue their education dedicated their lives to the spiritual reformation of Japan. Among the outstanding students who later distinguished themselves were Kozaki Hiromichi, Yokoi Tokio, Ebina Danjō, Ukita Kazutami, and Tokutomi Iichirō.

Spurred by the success of Dōshisha several other Christian schools were founded beginning in the 1880's—Aoyama College (1883), Meiji Gakuin (1886), Tōhoku Gakuin (1886), Kansai Gakuin (1888), and Rikkyō.

The decade of the 1880's was a period of gratifying progress for the missionaries since the enthusiasm for Western ideas and institutions was at its peak. Christianity, however, had to compete against the rising popularity of English empiricism and the utilitarianism of Jeremy Bentham and John Stuart Mill, the ideas of Spencer, Buckle, and Guizot, not to mention Darwinism. The middle 1880's saw a considerable number of young men joining the Christian church at a time when the government was pushing its policy of Europeanization vigorously with the support and encouragement of Premier Itō and Foreign Minister Inoue.

It was in March, 1882, that in his speech at Kōfu, Itagaki Taisuke, president of the Liberal Party, denounced Shintō, Confucianism, and Buddhism as detrimental to national progress and openly asserted his sympathy for Christianity at a time when the people were hurling the epithet "Christian" at their political opponents. Itagaki's stand brought the Christians close to the Liberal Party with which they cooperated in political matters.

In 1887 the Japanese translation of the Old Testament was completed, followed by the New Testament three years later. In 1889, the year of the promulgation of the Constitution, the number of Christian converts had passed the 100,000 mark.

However, the success achieved by the missionaries in gaining converts invited attacks from Shintoists and Buddhists. The rise of nationalism, which developed as a reaction against extreme Europeanization, made the work of propagating Christianity increasingly difficult for a time. But the real enemy of Christianity was neither Shintoism nor Buddhism. It was English empiricism and utilitarianism whose followers had their stronghold in Tōkyō University and which expounded the theory of evolution and agnosticism. Against those ideas the Christians fought, pointing out that the Copernican theory, the Baconian philosophy, and modern science, rather than undermining Christian faith, had helped to purge it of all forms of superstitions. They carried on their fight against skeptics, empiricists, and utilitarians as well as against the agnostic thinkers. Theological controversies which developed within the ranks of Christian leaders reduced the effectiveness of their work. This was aggravated by Foreign Minister Inoue's failure at treaty revision, which caused antipathy against Westernism to manifest itself openly.

In adhering strictly to their faith, some of the Christians aroused the ire of anti-Christians, who regarded the refusal to show reverence towards the imperial portrait as unpatriotic. In November, 1890, on the occasion of the Emperor's birthday, Dr. Uchimura Kanzō, then professor in the First Higher School in Tōkyō, and a devout Christian, hesitated to bow before the imperial portrait. This brought on him the charge of *lèse-majesté* and summary dismissal from his position. The public, which had long suspected the attitude of Christians, made accusations of disloyalty against the followers of the foreign faith. Increasing anti-Christian attitude found expression in an article by Dr. Inoue Tetsujirō in 1893 entitled "The Conflict between Religion and Education." He argued that Japanese educational principles must be based on the Imperial Rescript on Education, the cornerstone of which was nationalism and loyalty to the Emperor and to one's parents. Inasmuch as Christianity was cosmopolitan and placed Christ above the sovereign and parents it was incompatible and in contravention of the educational principles set forth in the Rescript. This view was subscribed to by others, most of whom were Buddhists, and eventually it came to be supported by a large segment of the public. Exponents of Japanism like Takayama Chogyū took a similar stand by branding Christianity as un-Japanese. In the face of such onslaughts a temporary decline in the work of Christian missionaries was inevitable. With theological controversies raging within, the Christian church of Japan fell into a state of inactivity from about 1892 on, and nothing of note occurred for the next few years. There was yet another factor which contributed to the decline in Christian activities. The lucrative promises in business and industry beckoned many a promising young man into those activities and fewer persons considered the ministry as their lifework.

The turn of the century saw Christianity regaining its popularity and strength and a new period of progress unfolded. In 1901, the foreign missionaries were given the right to own land. By 1905, the Congregational Church of Japan had achieved a status of independence as it no longer needed financial help from the outside. In the period of moral and spiritual decline in the wake of the Russo-Japanese War, a large number of young men and women turned to Christianity for spiritual help.

Christian missionary activities brought the Shintoists and Confucianists closer together to meet the competition more effectively. The Christian threat also caused the Buddhists to take stock of themselves and to revitalize their religious program with a view to achieving better results. They adopted Christian methods and techniques by extending the religious work into the factories, prisons, slums, and in the armed forces, organized young men's and women's associations, and even adopted hymns and the Sunday school. They also founded orphanages, hospitals, schools for the blind, and extended their religious activities to foreign fields in China, Siberia, Malaya, Hawaii, and North and South America, wherever there were Japanese residents.

IMPORTATION OF WESTERN THOUGHT

Reforms are invariably accompanied or followed by a certain amount of confusion and disorder. We have just seen what transpired in the religious and intellectual life of the nation. Other disturbances, such as peasant uprisings in opposition to the abolition of fiefs and the establishment of prefectures, attacks on the social outcasts as the protest against the abolition of that particular social class, and outbursts against the adoption of Western costumes and haircut, and the abolition of sword wearing were the natural accompaniments of the radical changes effected in the mode of national life. Those were the violent reactions of the conservatives who could not bear to see the long-cherished customs swept away with so little regret. In time, however, progressivism triumphed over conservatism. We shall now turn to the survey of the ideas that were brought in during this period as part of the process of modernization.

The impact of Perry's arrival in 1853 on the thinking of the Japanese was great indeed. Almost instantaneously the nation turned its eyes to the West, and a thirst for the knowledge of Western civilization became irrepressible. In 1855, only two years after Perry's first arrival, the Shogunate established a Bureau for Western Learning (Yōgakusho) to collect information and carry on the translation of foreign works. A number of fiefs soon started to send students abroad secretly to study, in spite of the prohibition of foreign travel on pain of death. Needless to say, it became necessary to lift this ban before many more years had elapsed.

As the first nation to conclude a commercial treaty, the United States played a leading role in helping the Japanese to import Western civilization. Beginning with the indefatigable efforts of the first American diplomatic representative, Townsend Harris, in 1856, Americans have continuously influenced the thinking of the Japanese. Earliest of all influences were the Protestant missionaries, who began to arrive in the late 1850's immediately after the conclusion of the Treaty of Commerce. Brown, Williams, Hepburn, and Verbeck were among the earliest to respond to the call. After having taught such subjects as English and international law at Nagasaki for several years, Dr. Guido F. Verbeck, in 1869, became a professor in the Kaisei Gakkō, the forerunner of the Tōkyō University, and served simultaneously as political, legal, and educational adviser to the government. Dr. Hepburn's contribution to Westernization was the system of romanization which the Japanese adopted officially and used until a few years ago. The contributions to the modernization of Japan by these men of the cloth, who were primarily teachers, and the large number of technical experts, professors, and advisers, the majority of whom were Americans, were as invaluable as they were numerous and variegated.

The goal of the Restoration was the establishment of a strong state capable of ensuring the security of the nation. When the Shogunate was liquidated the moral, political, social, and economic principles on which it was based were swept away. Once the policy of modernization of national life was decided upon, the nation turned to the West for guidance. Occidental civilization became the standard as knowledge was eagerly sought after in the countries of Europe and America. The craze for Occidental civilization, which developed as a result in the first two decades of the Meiji period, became almost a pathological phenomenon, perhaps without parallel elsewhere in the modern world. European civilization was by no means new to the Japanese. During the Tokugawa period, the study of Dutch gained tremendous popularity, causing scholars who had been brought up in the traditions of Chinese classics to change to Dutch studies. However, after the reopening of the country to Western intercourse in the late 1850's Dutch was soon surpassed by English in popularity, since two of the most important treaty Powers were English-speaking countries. Many of the scholars took up the study of English after they had already studied Dutch or Chinese or both. So great was the demand for those who possessed a knowledge, however meager, of the Occident that at first even a smattering of English was a sure passport to an official position in the government.

One of the earliest of the Japanese to begin the dissemination of Western ideas was Nakamura Masanao (Keiu), who, immediately upon his return from England in 1868, made available through translation the Constitution of the

United States, Washington's Farewell Address, and the essays of Ralph Waldo Emerson. While devoting his energies to the dissemination of American ideas, he founded in 1873 a private school, the Dōjinsha, where he offered an English type of education. This school ranked as one of the three great private schools in Tōkyō, the other two being Fukuzawa's Keiō Gijuku and Seki Shimpachi's Kyōritsu Gakusha. In an attempt to inculcate the spirit of independence which he considered essential for the new age, he translated in 1870 Samuel Smiles' *Self Help,* which soon came to be regarded as the "bible of the Meiji era" and exerted such a profound influence on the thinking of his day that even plays were written around it. In 1872 he translated John Stuart Mill's essay, *On Liberty.*

The idealistic and spiritual aspects of the new bourgeois culture which was emerging found its able exponent in Nakamura, whose humanitarianism was a combination of Confucian philosophy and Christian idealism. He provided the spiritual aspects of life in support of Fukuzawa's utilitarianism, placing it on a higher plane. What he sought to disseminate through the translation of Smiles' *Character* was a morality suitable for the rising bourgeoisie. If Fukuzawa was an exponent of bourgeois culture, Nakamura was a prophet of bourgeois morality, which he would predicate upon independence and self-reliance. In addition, however, Nakamura contributed to the propagation of the ideas of freedom and the rights of the individual.

It was the return of the Iwakura Mission in 1873 that gave a tremendous impetus to and accelerated the dissemination of Western ideas necessary for the modernization program. In that year a concerted effort in this direction was launched by the leaders of thought including Nakamura, Fukuzawa, Mori Arinori, Kanda Kōhei, Tsuda Shindō, and Nishimura Shigeki, who founded the Meirokusha and started its fortnightly organ, *Meiroku Zasshi.* This became the medium for the introduction, discussion, and dissemination of new knowledge and ideas which were eagerly sought by young students as well as highly placed government officials. Feminism, romanization, freedom of the press, as well as the leading issues of the day in economics and politics found expression in the pages of the earliest magazine before they were taken up and discussed seriously by the public. For almost two years, the magazine performed the unique function of leading and molding the thinking of its readers. But by the end of 1875, when a great majority of the members of the Meirokusha had either entered or reentered government service and the increasing encroachment of the government on the freedom of the press became oppressively apparent, the publication was voluntarily discontinued.

Fukuzawa Yukichi continued as the outstanding leader of thought by refusing persistently to go into government service. Born of a minor *samurai* family, Fukuzawa had early taken up the study of Dutch, first in Nagasaki and later in Ōsaka. On moving to Edo later, he realized keenly the need for a knowledge of English. In 1860, he visited the United States as a member of the party accompanying the Embassy which was dispatched by the Shogunate at the suggestion of Townsend Harris to exchange ratifications of the treaty of 1858. This trip abroad was a turning point in his life although he got only as far as San Francisco. Two years later, he was chosen to accompany another mission to Europe and America. In 1867 he visited the United States for the third time. These trips brought him in direct contact with the ideas and institutions of Europe and America and he became the best-informed person of his day on conditions in the Occident. He became convinced that Japan's progress could be achieved by following Western examples.

In 1860, he had brought back with him a copy of Webster's English dictionary as a memento of his visit to the United States. This marked the beginning of his study of English. Five years later he opened in Edo a private school for the instruction of young men in English and Western studies. At the time of the Restoration, when the battles were raging in Edo and most of the public places including amusement houses were closed, Fukuzawa continued to lecture to a handful of students, who listened to him expound the economic ideas of Francis Wayland as expressed in his *Elements of Political Economy,* a work which advocated free trade. This school was moved to a new site in 1871 and named the Keiō Gijuku, later becoming the Keiō University, known for its tradition of pragmatic education and utilitarianism.

After witnessing the wonders of the Occident, Fukuzawa felt impelled to enlighten his countrymen who were eager for information on the ideas, customs, manners, laws, and institutions of Europe and America. In 1869, he published *The Conditions in the West (Seiyō Jijō),* which created a sensation. Thousands of copies were sold. Covering the history, government, finance, military organization, and other important political and economic aspects of the Western Powers, this work exercised a far-reaching influence on the policy-makers in the government as well as individuals of the post-Restoration period. English and American institutions were naturally given the most detailed treatment. Fukuzawa carefully explained that there were three forms of government: monarchy, aristocracy, and republic. He went on to discuss the scope of government functions. His discussion of the rights and duties of individuals was predicated on the doctrine of the natural rights of man. Through this work, he furnished the liberalism of the opening years of the Meiji period. He concluded that a government which assured freedom was the best ruling body, and he believed that this ideal form was to be found in parliamentary government as it existed in England. He had no doubt that the English government was the best in the world.

Fukuzawa carried on the work of educating and enlightening the people to the responsibilities of a new age. His unique role was the liquidation of feudal Japan and its vestiges and to build up a new Japan unfettered by old customs, manners, morality, and old concepts of politics and economics. The realization of equality, freedom, and independence was his goal. He introduced the study of economics in which he strongly advocated *laissez faire* and preached utilitarianism in the best traditions of Jeremy Bentham and John Stuart Mill. His advocacy of a new culture for Japan reverberated through all his writings, particularly *The Outline of Civilization,* published in 1870. His pragmatic philosophy was amply reflected in *The Encouragement of Learning* (1873–1876) which emphasized useful, usable knowledge to the exclusion of impractical, theoretical education, unsuited to the actual needs of the individual and society. His unmitigated opposition to impractical book learning was well known. He recognized the profit motive as a necessary incentive in economic activity and advocated noninterference by the government. There was no doubt in his mind that wealth constituted the indispensable foundation of a strong state and worked to get rid of the feudal Japanese attitude of disdain for money.

Freedom, independence, and equality of the individual he conceived to be the cornerstone of the new civilization. "Heaven does not create a man above a man, or a man below a man. All men are equal, without distinction as to high or low, noble or humble." With these words he opened *The Encouragement of Learning,* published in installments from 1873 to 1876, a book which was without doubt the best seller of the period. Upwards of seven hundred thousand copies are said to have been sold, "causing a rise in the price of paper in the capital." Fukuzawa gained nationwide following by this work, in which he advocated the institution of an educational structure based on Western models and equality for women in the form of educational opportunities.

In order to popularize more effectively the knowledge of the Occident, he developed a simple style of language which was understood even by his housemaid. He contended in his *Moji no Oshie* (1873) that two or three thousand Chinese characters should suffice for ordinary purposes, thus becoming perhaps the earliest exponent of the limitation of characters. Not the least of his contributions was the introduction of public speaking and the study of the English language.

His writings numbered more than a hundred items in books, pamphlets, and articles. The role he played in the post-Restoration period bore a striking similarity to that of the encyclopedists of eighteenth-century France. With a view to intensifying his efforts at the dissemination of ideas, he founded the newspaper *Jiji Shimpō* in 1882. Fukuzawa contributed immeasurably to the development of Meiji ideas and institutions in his multiple role of critic, publicist, journalist, educator, businessman, feminist, and philosopher. In the intellectual life of the nation, no other person of his day contributed as much as the "Sage of Mita" to the liquidation of the old and the building up of the new Japan in the early years of Meiji.

Chapter 10. New Economic and Financial

Policies (1868–1893)

The Meiji Restoration was an economic revolution which was accelerated by the impact of Western capitalism, resulting in the liquidation of the feudal economy and the emergence of a modern capitalistic system. In the 1850's Japan's economy had not yet reached the stage where it was ready for a full-scale industrial revolution. The government found it necessary to lay the foundations for the rapid acceleration of industrial development. It initiated and supported industries and services necessary for the achievement of political and economic objectives.

In the formulation of its economic policies, the new government was confronted from the very outset with several vexing problems. Foremost of these was the financial problem which demanded immediate attention. When the Shogunate relinquished its political powers, it did not turn over anything to the new government except an empty treasury. The old regime had virtually pumped the sources of revenue dry and was in a state of insolvency. Consequently, new sources of revenue had to be found. Government leaders decided to adopt the policy of finding the new sources in the commercial and industrial enterprises that as yet had to be created and developed.

Political and military considerations demanded the achievement of national unity through centralization of control, not only in political administration, but also in economic and financial spheres as well. Development of manpower and occupational skills became the necessary prerequisites not only to a sound national economy, but also to national defense plans. The adoption of the new weapons of the West and the building of military power entailed the organization of a system of universal military conscription and the encouragement of strategic industries and munitions production with government aid. Competition from Western capitalism, the leaders decided, could be met only by increasing the industrial and commerce capital. Under the circumstances, the adoption of capitalistic policies became inevitable, if not imperative, in the discharge of treaty obligations that were based, after all, on the needs of the capitalistic nations of the West.

However, before a strong and sound national economy could be secured, numerous obstacles standing in the way of economic progress had to be removed.

This resulted in the government carrying out policies of paternalism in the development of commerce and industry more than in almost any other aspect of national life. During the feudal period the occupations or economic pursuits in which a person could engage were regulated and restricted by his status, rank, or special privileges. The class distinction based on occupation which divided society into the four major classes of *samurai*, farmer, artisan, and merchant was abolished soon after the Restoration and freedom of choice of occupations established. Also, the guilds (*kabu-nakama*) in manufacturing and business, that were of feudal origin, were abolished, and by the beginning of 1872 the *samurai* class was given freedom to engage in farming, manufacturing, business, or whatever occupation they preferred. Farmers too were allowed, for the first time, complete freedom in the choice of occupations.

No less urgent in the acceleration of industrial progress was the removal of obstacles to the freedom of trade. With the abandoning of the seclusion policy immediately after the Restoration, foreign trade and travel abroad were permitted once more. Under the feudal regime various types of trade barriers existed; some fiefs imposed export duties (*tsudome*) to prevent goods from being exported outside their jurisdiction, while others imposed import duties as well. These duties were all abolished in 1869, permitting the free movement of goods between the provinces. The practice of imposing port duties (*tsuzei*) on goods which came into the ports of their jurisdiction was terminated with the abolition of the fiefs. The third major change was the lifting of the ban on the individual's freedom of movement and choice of residence, both of which had been restricted, and in some cases prohibited, during the Tokugawa period. This change included the removal in 1869 of barriers or passes (*sekisho*) that had been set up at fief boundaries to control and restrict the freedom of movement.

REHABILITATION OF THE SAMURAI CLASS

One of the major socioeconomic problems tossed into the lap of the new government was the rehabilitation of the *samurai* class that numbered approximately two million. For the greater part of the feudal period, the *samurai* had performed the political and military functions of society virtually to the exclusion of the other classes. They were the "chosen," the ruling class of society. The end of feudal society meant, however, the end of the centuries-old class system and the abolition of the special privileges they had long enjoyed. It was no longer possible nor necessary to permit the continuance of the *samurai* as a class entrusted exclusively with the administration of the affairs of state. The sudden changes necessitated in the nation forced them into an anomalous existence, and they came to be regarded as an anachronistic, if not a superfluous, element of society.

Because the Meiji Restoration was achieved with the help of a number of powerful *daimyō* families, it was impossible for the government to abolish suddenly the fiefs and take over their land and people. Consequently, for a very brief period, the leading *daimyō* enjoyed membership in the aristocracy with the court nobles at Kyōto. In 1869, when the fiefs were surrendered to the throne, 262 former *daimyō* were appointed governors of their old fiefs. Two years later, when the fiefs were abolished and superseded by prefectures, the fief governors were recalled to Tōkyō.

The *daimyō* class fared quite well as their huge debts to the wealthy merchants of Kyōto and Ōsaka were automatically canceled in the general confusion arising in the wake of the Restoration. Furthermore, they had the good fortune of having their private residences in Edo recognized by the new government as their own private property. As a result many of them became wealthy landowners, particularly those who had their residences in the choice sections of the city. In 1875 the government reimbursed the *daimyō* with large amounts of pension bonds. When the new Peerage Ordinance was promulgated in the summer of 1884 they were all made members of the new nobility along with the court nobles and others who had rendered meritorious services to the state.

The lesser *samurai*, that is, those below the *daimyō* class, such as the bannerets (*hatamoto*) and the retainers of the *daimyō*, did not fare as well, except for those who had actively participated in the Restoration. Very few of them were given peerage. Most of them were included in the new category of *shizoku*, or the gentry. *Samurai* of the lowest status became either *shizoku* or commoners (*heimin*). Many of these former *samurai* tried their hand at business or farming but most of them failed and lost everything, including the pension bonds. These unsuccessful *samurai* went into a variety of activities. A considerable number of those who were disgusted with the existing state of affairs became political bullies (*sōshi*) for the Liberal Party to give vent to their displeasure against the government. Some of them adopted the auxiliary occupations they had been carrying on for some time as their main economic activity, while others degenerated into tailors, laundry operators, egg dealers, masseurs, paper lantern makers, peddlers, and similar humble occupations. In extreme cases they were forced by circumstances to sell their daughters into bondage in the "gay quarters."

But the great majority of those who were in the category of "the intellectual proletariat" were assisted by the government's policy of rehabilitation. The government appointed large numbers of them to positions in both the central and local governments. At one time, more than 80 per cent of the government employees were former *samurai*. A large number of them became teachers in the elementary schools, but an even larger number of them became policemen. In fact, a large majority of the police force consisted of former *samurai* and so many of them were from the Kagoshima prefecture at first that their dialect was for a time the standard vernacular of the police. The officiousness of the police in dealing with the people, then and now, can be attributed to the fact that the officers who were once *samurai* set the standard of conduct based on the traditional feudal attitude of contempt toward the common people.

In addition to positions in the government, every other possible assistance was given through the land development program to help the *samurai* establish themselves in agriculture. The development of Hokkaidō, where thousands of them were transplanted, was the greatest undertaking of its kind during the period. Furthermore, the government gave them employment preference in the recruitment of officers and skilled workers in the government's model enterprises, the railways, and the factories. Training centers were established in various sections of the country to teach occupational skills. Last but not the least, the government made loans on exceedingly favorable terms to those who would engage in some business or industry. Perhaps those who were most successful in rehabilitation were the *samurai*-squires (*gōshi*), who were given title to the land they had been cultivating under the old regime. Economically they were in a favored position and they became successful farmers.

The government encouraged and the samurai preferred to go into the transplanting of economic institutions, industrial organization, and production techniques of the West. For this purpose the government took the lead in establishing and operating enterprises to serve as models and to give the necessary stimulus and assistance, both technical and financial. For these enterprises, the traditional merchant and industrialist of the old school, steeped in feudal business practices and outlook and conservative in his operations was, more often than not, found wanting in the aggressive spirit of enterprise so essential in the new economic age. On the other hand, many of the *samurai* who were faced with the problem of finding a suitable enterprise did not care to go into the traditional types of business or industry in competition with the old established merchants. Many of them did not relish the idea of becoming associated with or employed by merchants they had looked down upon or even of going into the kind of economic activity traditionally associated with the townsfolk of the feudal period.

The fact that the ex-*samurai* were imbued with the adventurous spirit of enterprise and were looking for new fields to conquer without shying away from risks contributed immensely to the success they achieved in fields heretofore untouched by the traditional merchant-industrialist, such as shipping, mining, tea manufacturing, silk reeling, cotton spinning, printing, newspaper publishing, etc. There were, of course, some who went into the traditional business enterprises such as banking and merchandising. Ex-*samurai* businessmen like Nakamigawa Hikojirō, the genius of the House of Mitsui, Shibusawa Eiichi, Yasuda Zenjirō, Iwasaki Yatarō of Mitsubishi, and Ōkura Kihachirō were the luminaries of the new bourgeois class that adorned the pages of the recent economic history of Japan. They were the leaders who were instrumental in laying the firm foundations of the capitalistic economy of modern Japan.

GOVERNMENT'S FISCAL PROBLEMS

Since the new government inherited an empty treasury from the Shogunate, it was impelled by necessity to levy a forced loan to raise funds on which it could operate.

Readjustment of the currency was next on the order of business. The monetary system of the last days of the Tokugawa regime was based on the one that was instituted back in A.D. 1600 and had been in effect since, with very little change except that the successive debasement through recoinage had brought about confusion. What existed at the time of the Restoration, in 1868, was a sort of bimetallism, although the outflow of large amounts of gold coins had caused almost a depletion of gold, and silver had become virtually the standard.

In other words the new government inherited the feudal monetary system which had all but broken down. There were two types of money—metallic and paper. The Shogunate had minted gold, silver, copper, brass, and iron coins of various denominations, shapes, and sizes. There were actually 1,694 varieties of paper money that had been issued, either with or without the permission of the Shogunate, by the *daimyō* and bannerets for circulation in their own fiefs, and that consisted of various and sundry types such as gold, silver, rice, and silk certificates.

Yuri Kimmasa, who had been instructed by the government to begin recoinage on European and American models and to increase the intrinsic value of coins, submitted his views to the government in the spring of 1868. A year later Ōkuma proposed the adoption of round coins to replace the square ones then in circulation and the use of the decimal system in keeping with the practice in virtually all of the countries of the world. The proposal was adopted and the yen was made the standard unit of value, a yen being 100 sen. Early in 1871, after it had been decided to make the one yen silver the standard unit and gold the subsidiary coin, Itō, who was then in the United States studying the currency system, sent back a memorandum. He expressed the view that, in the establishment of a new currency system, the gold standard should be adopted inasmuch as this was the general practice the world over. He emphasized that to adopt a silver standard would be going counter to world trends.

Whereupon the government reversed the decision it had already made and adopted the gold standard, notifying the foreign representatives of the fact in the early summer of 1871. The one yen gold was made the standard unit of value and the silver coin subsidiary, placing a limit of ten yen as the amount acceptable as legal tender, while a limit of one yen for copper coins was imposed. At the same time a foreign trade silver yen was issued for exclusive use in the treaty ports for trade purposes. The value of the trade yen was set slightly higher as it was equivalent to 1.10 standard yen.[1] The Ōsaka Mint was opened in 1871, and the government appointed the Mitsui Company to be the fiscal agent of the Mint to exchange new coins for old and to collect and forward gold and silver bullion.

After the government took over the feudal notes, it issued Dajōkan gold notes at the suggestion of Yuri Kimmasa in 1868. These notes were made convertible into specie the following year when the Civil Affairs Department (*Mimbushō*) notes were issued to remedy the prevailing shortage of money of small denominations. In the autumn of 1871 the Finance Department convertible notes were issued, followed by the Colonization Office convertible notes early the following year. By 1872–1873 all four kinds of government notes were in circulation.

The issuance of the Dajōkan notes in the spring of 1868 was not met with any enthusiastic response on the part of the public which had little confidence, if any, in paper money. Consequently smooth circulation could not be obtained and prices dropped. No sooner had they come into their hands than the people took the government gold notes to the exchange companies and exchanged them at a discount for the gold coins which they preferred. In the summer, the government issued an order prohibiting the practice but with little success. It then made the payment of taxes and other obligations to the government in gold notes mandatory. Still, the value of the notes continued to fall. Finally, realizing that the condition could not be corrected by legal coercion, the government decided to recognize the 20 per cent discrepancy of value between the gold notes and specie. The notes finally obtained smooth circulation after 1871, when the amount of issue was limited to 32,500,000 yen and when they were made convertible into money which had been newly coined.

Out of necessity, the government revised the national banking regulations in the summer of 1876, enabling a national bank to issue notes without any specie reserve. The revised regulations required the holding of government bonds to the amount of 80 per cent of the capital instead of a gold reserve. In 1875 and 1876, there was hardly any discrepancy between paper money and specie. In fact, the value of paper money was slightly higher than that of foreign silver in the fall of 1876.

But inflation set in with the Satsuma Rebellion in 1877 as the result of the government's issuance of paper money to meet the military expenditures. The revising of the national banking regulations greatly facilitated the issuance of bank notes. In January, before the outbreak of the Rebellion, the amount of

---

[1] In May, 1888, the restriction on the use of the trade silver yen was abolished, making it in effect legal tender like the standard gold yen without any limit as to the amount and permitting its use for all purposes. This caused the monetary system to change over to the bimetallic standard.

money in circulation was 106,000,000 yen of which 104,000,000 were in the government notes and the remainder in bank notes. Two years later, at the end of December, 1878, the total had reached the enormous amount of 120,000,000 yen of which the increase in bank notes alone amounted to more than 11,000,000 yen.

In January, 1880, the amount of inconvertible paper money in circulation had reached the unprecedented total of 170,157,477 yen, causing the skyrocketing of prices, excess of imports over exports, the draining-off of specie, extravagant habits, and wild speculation in business. Interest rates hit a high of 18 per cent and a low of 12 per cent for the year 1880. The skyrocketing of prices was reflected in rice which was 4.60 yen per *koku* (approximately 5 bushels) in January, 1877. It had risen to 7.00 in 1878, 8.99 in 1879, and a record high of 12.11 in December, 1880. By the end of 1880 the market price of government bonds had dropped to a new low, as pension bonds sank to 58 per cent of the face value.

Establishment of Banks. One of the most serious obstacles to the development of commerce and industry was the lack of capital. In order to remove this obstacle and to ensure the circulation of money and stimulate economic activities, the government turned its attention at an early stage to the setting up of banking facilities. In 1869 wealthy merchants were prevailed upon to form exchange companies (*kawase kaisha*), which were authorized to issue gold, silver and foreign silver certificates as well as handle deposits, loans, and exchanges. All the exchange companies were dissolved when the National Banking Ordinance was promulgated in 1872, except the Yokohama Exchange Company, which was reorganized into the Second National Bank.

The national banking system was instituted in response to the urgent need for commercial banking facilities and to replace government paper money with convertible bank notes. It was based on the American system, which Itō had carefully studied in 1870 and 1871. Contrary to expectations, there was no rush to open banks when the new regulations were promulgated. Only four opened for business between 1872 and March, 1874. The first to be established was the First National Bank in Tōkyō. This was followed by the Second National Bank in Yokohama, the Fourth National Bank in Niigata, and the Fifth National Bank in Ōsaka.[2]

Business had hitherto consisted of small enterprises and transactions because the public was ignorant of the advantages of conducting business on the joint-stock basis. Even after strong prodding by the government, very few came forward to start new enterprises. In fact, the government practically had to order the Mitsui and Ōno interests to form the First National Bank. Of the 2,500,000 yen capital the two firms subscribed to 2 million, leaving only half a million

[2] The Third National Bank received its charter but never did see the light of day.

for the public to subscribe. The response was poor and only the sum of 440,000 yen was subscribed. It was difficult enough to collect capital but it was even more difficult to find men of ability to conduct banking business or, for that matter, any type of business enterprise.

The national banks were given the exclusive right of issuing bank notes to an amount not exceeding 100 million yen on the condition that 60 per cent of the capital would be held in government fiat money, which was to be on deposit with the government and for which 6 per cent interest-bearing government bonds were given. With these bonds as security, they were given bank notes printed by the government. The remaining 40 per cent of the capital had to be held in specie as reserve to meet the demand for conversion. To overcome the general lack of knowledge pertaining to banking among businessmen as well as government officials, an Englishman, Shand, who was a member of the Oriental Bank in Yokohama, was appointed in the Bureau of Currency to handle the work of supervising banking and offering instruction in money and banking.

Lack of public confidence in the bank notes soon caused the value to drop to 98 per cent of the specie while the increase in the volume of paper currency in circulation caused inflation and price rises, and the increasing volume of imports caused the constant outflow of gold. Banks suffered losses in meeting the demand for conversion of government paper money into gold, and even the gold reserves were soon depleted. The Second National Bank at Yokohama wisely refrained from issuing a single note since this was not profitable. The notes came back to the banks of issue so speedily that the volume in circulation was never large. In June, 1876, for instance, the total amount in circulation did not exceed the small sum of 62,000 yen. Thus, in so far as the main purpose of the National Banking Ordinance was concerned, it was a failure because the government fiat money could not be put into circulation. Upon receipt of a petition from the four national banks for a change enabling them to simply exchange the bank notes for currency, the government decided to revise the regulations.

By the revision, in 1876, of the National Banking Ordinance the provision requiring the conversion of bank notes into specie was dropped and in its stead it provided for conversion into currency, safeguarding the banks from the possibility of loss resulting from a rise in the price of gold. Bank notes were now on the same basis as government currency, both being inconvertible. At the same time, the banks were authorized to issue a larger amount of notes and required to have on reserve only one-third of their value in government currency instead of the gold reserve.

The revision made it sufficiently advantageous to the banks so that the number of applications increased greatly. As a matter of fact, the government found it necessary to stop granting licenses after December, 1879, when the 153rd National

Bank at Kyōto was authorized. By the end of 1882 failures had decreased the number of banks to 143 with a total capitalization of 44,206,000 yen. By a further revision of the National Banking Ordinance in 1886, the note-issuing power was to be surrendered to the Bank of Japan, and after twenty years, these banks were to be allowed to continue business as private institutions.

After the revision of the National Banking Ordinance in 1876, private banks came into existence, the earliest of which was the Mitsui Bank, capitalized at 2,000,000 yen as an institution, much like a French *societé anonyme,* with unlimited liability. Until the establishment of the Bank of Japan in 1882, the Mitsui Bank acted as fiscal agent for the government. Thereafter, it ceased to handle the Treasury business and engaged itself mainly in general commercial banking.

It was not until July, 1893, that the banking ordinance went into effect to give a well-planned system of regulations for ordinary banking activities. Finance Minister Matsukata's policy was to develop commercial banks to collect the savings of the people and to make the funds available for commercial and industrial enterprises. Inasmuch as banking was closely related to the public interest, the government would exercise special supervision over the banks. That the character of ordinary banks was determined largely by the structure of Japanese industry is evident. Numerous small- and middle-scale industrial and commercial enterprises were in need of both short- and long-term capital. This need was met by small, local, independent banks. Large city banks affiliated with the great industrial houses like Mitsui, Mitsubishi, and Sumitomo, and carrying on a wide range of commercial and industrial activities closely related to national policies mobilized the nation's capital, directing it into those enterprises under their control. The Finance Ministry's Deposit Bureau and the private savings banks came into existence to collect and direct the savings of the poor to proper channels. In order to carry out a rationalization of banking, which underwent a period of indiscriminate competition in the period after the Sino-Japanese War, the government promulgated a law for the merger of banks in April, 1896. This law, although rescinded in 1900, became the basis for the law for the amalgamation of corporations, as embodied in the new Commercial Code, promulgated just before the abolition of extraterritoriality.

The first bank to specialize in savings was the Tōkyō Savings Bank established in 1880. Until then the national banks and ordinary banks handled savings business on the side. In 1893, the Savings Banks Law went into effect, giving legal recognition to the banks operating exclusively for savings deposits. Postal savings were initiated in May, 1875, under a system patterned after the English Postal Savings Act and actually antedated those of France, Germany, and the United States. Until 1877 the postal savings deposits were kept at the First National Bank, from where they were transferred to the Ministry of Finance when the Deposits Bureau was created in 1885. Greatest care has been exercised in the investment of postal savings that represent the combined resources of the lowest income groups who can least afford to lose them.

GOVERNMENT ENCOURAGEMENT OF INDUSTRY AND COMMERCE

Even while sporadic fighting was in progress in the period immediately following the Restoration, the government was taking steps to encourage business by establishing, in 1868, the Business Bureau (*Shōhōshi*), which was superseded by the Trade Bureau (*Tsūshōshi*) during the next year. This bureau was in charge of national revenues and the promotion of trade and production through the granting of loans at low interest. Its purpose was to help increase government revenues through the development of domestic and foreign trade. Under the bureau's control, commercial companies (*Tsūshō Kaisha*) were established to engage in foreign and domestic trade, and the exchange companies (*Kawase Kaisha*) were organized to render financial aid to the commercial companies and to facilitate the general circulation of money.

At the same time, the government wanted exchange brokers to form general stock companies to engage in the same activities as the exchange companies. To encourage them, the Department of Finance published in 1870 and 1871 two pamphlets, "A Description of Corporations" and "Rules for the Organization of Corporations," edited by Fukuchi Gen'ichirō and Shibusawa Eiichi for general distribution. It was an attempt on the part of the government, in the absence of a commercial code, to make the public understand the nature of corporations and instill in businessmen the spirit of cooperation with a view to accelerating the establishment of much needed enterprises.

As a concrete method of stimulating industrial activities, the government set up model enterprises for private industry to follow. These enterprises were set up to manufacture those goods which were being imported from abroad to meet the increasing demands created by the establishment of the new government and the resultant policy of Westernization. The government enterprises included silk filatures, cotton and woolen mills, tea factories, shipyards, cement and glass factories, clothing factories, paper mills, printing shops, and breweries. At first, the quantity of goods produced was not adequate to meet all the demands, and foreign goods had to be imported for a considerable period thereafter, though production increased gradually. Through these manufacturing activities, the Japanese mastered the industrial skills and techniques of the West with the help of foreign experts. Some of the enterprises were turned over to private operators as soon as takers were found. The Ashio Copper Mining Company, in 1871, was one of the earliest to become a private enterprise. Five years later, the Ishikawajima Shipbuilding Company too became a private establishment.

Meanwhile, the government's policy of encouraging private corporations began to show results. One of the earliest of these to be organized was the Ōji Paper Company in 1872. This was followed by the Tōkyō Gas Company. An important development was the appearance of the insurance companies. Particularly significant was the founding of the Tōkyō Marine Insurance Company in 1879 by a group of ex-*samurai* capitalists at the suggestion of Shibusawa, who perhaps more than any other person contributed immeasurably to the development of commercial and industrial corporations of the early Meiji period. The Japan Railway Company, which was organized two years later, was also an enterprise employing capital owned by the ex-*samurai*. Once the spirit of enterprise caught, private corporations appeared in rapid succession. In 1885, the aggregate capital of private corporations totaled 50,000,000 yen. This amount was nearly quintupled in five years as total capitalization in 1890 jumped to 225,000,000 yen.

After the Satsuma Rebellion, the government raised a loan of 12,500,000 yen for the purpose of encouraging industrial enterprises. This was the first time the government issued domestic bonds to be subscribed to by the public. The idea was entirely foreign to the people, who at first showed skepticism, if not real resistance, believing it to be a forced contribution to the Treasury. At the request of the government, the Mitsui Bank, in collaboration with the First National Bank, floated the loan. It was a success. The loan was oversubscribed, the Mitsui Bank alone subscribing to 12,470,000 yen.

The question of stock exchanges had to be decided by the government, but no unanimity of opinion existed among the leaders. There was apprehension on the part of some that exchanges would encourage and spread the evils of gambling and speculation, while others insisted that they were indispensable to the nation's economic development because of the functions they performed in setting market prices. Commodity exchanges were first to be set up. The Grain Exchange Regulations were issued in 1876 and rice exchanges were set up the following year in Tōkyō, Ōsaka, and other places. In 1878, Stock Exchange Regulations were promulgated, and the Tōkyō and Ōsaka Stock Exchanges were established soon thereafter. The Foreign Silver Exchange, which was established in 1879 in Yokohama, was somewhat different in its objective. It was intended to prevent speculative transactions in silver.

THE AGRARIAN POLICY

Agrarian reforms of the early Meiji period were conditioned by two important factors, namely, the projected tax reform which the government was in the process of carrying out, and the prevailing idea of *laissez faire* which dominated the economic thinking of the time, both in and out of government. The land reform, which was instituted beginning in 1872, was based on the government's desire to stabilize revenue, the main source of which was the land tax. Under the old feudal system, the land tax was assessed on the yield of the land. This had the serious disadvantage of not only making its administration cumbersome, but causing it to vary from year to year according to the size of the harvest as well as the fluctuations in the price of rice. It was imperative that the land tax be modernized, if the government were to know in advance, for budget-making purposes, the amount of revenue to be expected.

The first step in land reform was taken in 1872 by the removal of the ban on the sale of land. This ban had been in effect since 1643 when the third Shogun, Iemitsu, decreed it with a view to preventing the annexation of land by the landowners and safeguarding the farmers from being dispossessed as a result. This restriction was deemed necessary for assuring an adequate supply of food under a policy of seclusion and also for keeping the farmers in agricultural production. However, in spite of the ban, annexation of land went on surreptitiously during the Tokugawa period, and the evasion of the law by such methods as mortgaging or placing in custody became quite common.

As the ban had never been really effective, the new government did not hesitate to recognize private ownership. It issued deeds, in 1872, giving legal title to the owners, who were given, in the following year, the right to sell or mortgage their land. At the same time, the restriction on the amount of land any one individual could hold was removed. Restrictions on the sale of agricultural products were also abolished in 1873. Even the export of rice to foreign markets was now permitted, as the government itself took the initiative and set an example by exporting its holdings of rice in 1872 to China, Hongkong, Sidney, Melbourne, and even to London and San Francisco.

All these steps were merely preliminary to the institution of a new system of land tax in 1873. Payment of tax in kind, that is, in rice, was abolished in favor of money payment at the rate of 3 per cent. Assessment was henceforth to be based on the value of land and not on the actual harvest. This contributed to the commercialization of farming in subsequent years.

While these changes were beneficial to the government and to the landowners they actually worked great hardships on the small farmers whose holdings were rarely sufficient to produce more than a bare subsistence. The burden of land tax fell squarely on the farmers who usually paid the landowner in kind and invariably suffered from the fluctuations in the price of rice, while the large landlords could turn these fluctuations to their advantage. The reform had the effect of facilitating the penetration of capital into the rural farming areas where annexation of land became a common practice.

Although the planners of the reforms were aware of the possibility that the gap between the wealthy landlords and the poor farmers would widen, they were so imbued with the doctrine of *laissez faire* that they thought it unwise to interfere with free competition by encouraging "the idle and wasteful poor" and penalizing the "industrious and thrifty rich." If they had the desire to prevent the annexation of land, they certainly made no attempts to translate it into action.

Their main concern was the organization of a system which would encourage industrial development and assure stable revenue for the government.

In the early years of the Meiji era the government pursued a consistent policy of encouraging the development of agriculture. First as a councilor and later as Minister of Home Affairs, Ōkubo Toshimichi devoted a great deal of his time and energy to giving every possible assistance and protection. The government furnished the necessary capital for agricultural enterprises, established experimental farms and agricultural colleges, published agricultural information bulletins, and issued regulations helpful to the industry. The agricultural developments and activities of the period were affected by the wave of Westernism which swept across the country. European and American agricultural experts, farm implements and machinery, farming methods, crops, and livestock were imported in a well-planned program which would improve the technique of farming and thereby increase production.

The government set up various sorts of facilities and enterprises and carried on a variety of agricultural experiments. Starting with the inspection of silk for export begun in 1868 and the introduction of cattle raising the following year, every conceivable type of agricultural activity was tried out during the next ten years. These activities included the experimental cultivation of American cotton, wheat, barley, pasture grass, sugar beets, turnips, olives, fruits, such as grapes, oranges, lemons, California walnuts, and peanuts, and Java coffee.

With the untimely death of Ōkubo in 1878, the policy of active protection and guidance came to an end. Fortunately, however, the rapid expansion of both domestic and foreign markets for agricultural products brought prosperity to agriculture. Although the Department of Agriculture and Commerce was established as an independent department in the spring of 1881, the government pursued a policy of *laissez faire,* choosing to let those engaged in agriculture take the initiative in its development. This policy was continued for nearly a decade until the opening of the Diet in 1890. During this period the government let the experienced farmers assume the leadership in organizing local committees for the improvement of agricultural affairs, issued regulations for the development of trade associations (*dōgyō kumiai*) for rice, silk, and tea producers, and remained in the background. The trade associations concerned themselves with inspection of commodities, issuing certificates of quality.

There was a minor temporary reversion to the policy of government assistance after the opening of the Diet. The government undertook the establishment of a national agricultural experiment station in 1891 with six branches in different sections of the country, and also encouraged the prefectures to institute land reforms (boundary—*denku kaisei*) with a view to increasing the yield and improving the quality of rice. Although the laissez-faire policy was somewhat relaxed, the picture remained substantially unchanged until the Sino-Japanese War.

MATSUKATA'S POLICY OF FINANCIAL STABILIZATION

Upon becoming Minister of Finance in October, 1881, Matsukata reestablished the system of convertible notes, and began calling in paper money. The total amount then in circulation was 154 million, of which 120 million were in government notes and only 34 million in bank notes. Matsukata was instrumental in the change of fiscal policy requiring local government expenses to be met by local taxes. At the same time he effected a retrenchment in the expenditures of the central government, bringing an end to government operation of model enterprises, many of which had been operating at considerable loss. The profitable ones were turned over to private industry while others which could not be operated at a profit were abandoned completely. Government retrenchment took another form: the reduction in the number of foreign advisers and technical experts and the sharp reduction of the number of students who were being sent abroad by the government to study.

Thus, by exercising rigid economy in government expenditures and applying surplus revenue to the redemption of notes and increasing the specie reserve, Matsukata succeeded in reducing the volume of paper money and restored its value almost to par within a period of five years. Impelled by the necessity of encouraging the export trade and the manufacturing of goods for export purposes, the government initiated the policy of assisting in the improvement of manufacturing, not only in its technical aspects but also in putting management on a scientific basis. Rationalization of industry was undertaken as an indirect aid to the solution of the government financial problems. As a means of stimulating the export of domestic goods, the government undertook to lower the prices. Thus, in the period after 1880 and until about 1895 the policy of the government was to protect and assist private industry through various means such as subsidies, technical advice and guidance, and the furnishing of capital. Under this system the greatest strides were made in the fields of banking and ocean transportation. Silk reeling and cotton spinning also showed phenomenal development in the period preceding the Sino-Japanese War. On the whole, it was in the realm of light industries that the greatest advances were made. It was in this period that the domestic market came to assume an increasingly important place in the nation's economy.

On March, 1882, the Finance Minister presented to the government a memorandum giving the blueprint for a central bank. In presenting his plan, the Finance Minister noted that the financial and economic ills from which the country was suffering could be attributed to (1) the unequal distribution as well as the restricted circulation of the currency, (2) the increasing shortage of liquid capital, and (3) the virtual depletion of specie. He emphatically pointed out that the prosperity of the nation, the happiness of the people, the development and stimulation of industrial enterprises and commercial activities were all dependent on a sound financial policy. The establishment of a central bank such as was in existence in the principal countries of Europe, he believed, would correct the financial difficulties and contribute materially to the achievement of national prosperity. It would help to equalize rates of interest in different parts of the country, make capital available by loosening the money market and keeping interest down, and ensure smoothness of circulation.

The government approved the memorandum and issued the regulations for the Bank of Japan in June. Four months later, on October 10, 1882, the Bank of Japan opened for business. Matsukata believed that the Bank of Belgium was the best model to follow. Consequently, its regulations were copied with such modifications as were necessary to meet peculiar Japanese needs. The Bank was capitalized at 10 million yen, 50,000 shares at 200 yen each, the government subscribing to one-half of the total and the public invited to subscribe to the balance. As the nation's central bank, it was given the following functions: (1) to exercise the sole right of issuing convertible bank notes; (2) to be the supreme organ for the regulation of currency; (3) to discount foreign bills of exchange to regulate the influx and outgo of specie and bullion; (4) to simplify the business of the Government Treasury; (5) to furnish capital to national banks, trading companies, and industrial enterprises, and (6) to lower and keep down the rate of interest.

Simultaneously with the establishment of the Bank of Japan, the government took steps to increase its revenues. It levied for the first time stamp duties on patent medicines, license tax on rice exchange and stock exchange brokers, and revised *sake* and tobacco taxes. In 1885, taxes were levied for the first time on soy and confectionery. One-half of the surplus of revenues thus obtained was earmarked for the redemption of inconvertible paper money, while the other half was added to the reserve fund for the importation of specie from abroad. The government found the importation of specie an absolute necessity because of the low output of gold and silver from domestic mines, which amounted to no more than 500,000 yen annually. For this purpose, consulates were established in London, New York, and Lyons, the three greatest foreign markets for Japanese goods, and to encourage foreign trade at the same time.

Preparatory to the resumption of specie payment, the Bank of Japan began to issue convertible notes in May, 1885. On January 1, 1886, the government began to pay specie in exchange for government paper money. As a consequence, the rate of interest dropped, the commercial and industrial enterprises expanded, and the volume of foreign trade increased, contributing to a marked improvement in the economic conditions of the country. Within a few years, both the government paper money and the national bank notes were exchanged with the convertible silver notes of the Bank of Japan. The replacement of inconvertible paper money with convertible silver notes actually placed the country on a silver standard.

While the economic conditions were improved, the fluctuations of the price of silver in the world market began to exercise immediate influence on Japan's economic and financial condition. Therefore, the Coinage Investigation Commission was appointed in the fall of 1893 to look into the situation. The Commission submitted its final report and recommendation to the Finance Minister in July, 1896. Although the adoption of the gold standard was recommended by the Commission, the difficulty of creating a large gold reserve at once prevented the government from taking steps to put it into effect. However, the war indemnity paid by the Chinese government was made available the following year. As a result, on March 26, 1897, with the promulgation of the Coinage Law enacted by the Diet, the gold standard became a reality and Japan's monetary system was placed on a firm footing.

Chapter 11. Struggle for the Establishment of a

National Assembly

After resigning from the government, Itagaki demonstrated his political acumen and astuteness by deciding to oppose those in power with an appeal to public opinion instead of resorting to force as Saigō, Etō, and some other malcontents were trying to do. He gathered his followers in Tōkyō for the work ahead, and at the same time he even tried unsuccessfully to induce Saigō to forswear violence. Undaunted by the defeat he suffered in the Council, Itagaki together with seven others including Etō, Gotō, Soeshima, and Yuri[1] presented to the government in January, 1871, a memorial for the establishment of a popular representative assembly. The document denounced the despotism of those in power and advocated strongly the need for a popularly elected national assembly. This was the starting signal for the movement for freedom and popular rights which culminated in the organization of constitutional government less than two decades later.

To spearhead the movement for the establishment of a national assembly, a political organization called the Aikoku Kōtō or the Patriotic Public Party was founded. It was emphatically presented as a public party to distinguish it from the numerous private factions and cliques that existed primarily for the purpose of securing political power for themselves. A declaration outlining the program of the party was issued simultaneously. Although in the strict sense of the term the new group could not be called a party, it was one of the earliest of such organizations.

Following the Saga Rebellion, led by one of the signers of the Memorial, Etō, and the attack on Iwakura perpetrated by some of the hotheaded young followers of Itagaki, a drastic policy calculated to liquidate political opposition was initiated by the clan-dominated government. Itagaki foresaw difficulties and disbanded the party in March, 1874, returning to Tosa where he founded the Risshisha in order to concentrate his efforts on disseminating liberalism. Under him gathered a group of keen and eager youths as well as his staff of workers, who became his loyal followers.[2] Tosa soon became the stronghold of liberalism.

[1] The Memorial was signed by Itagaki Taisuke, Etō Shimpei, Gotō Shōjirō, Soeshima Taneomi, Yuri Kimmasa, Komuro Nobuo, Okamoto Kensaburō, and Furusawa Shigeshi.

[2] Prominent among those who became Itagaki's faithful followers were Kataoka Kenkichi, Hayashi Yūzō, Furusawa Shigeshi, Ueki Emori, Ōishi Masami, and others.

The political ideas of the French Revolution formed the main ideological basis of Itagaki's liberalism and that of his followers. Rousseau's *Social Contract* became perhaps the most important literature for the early leaders of this group. So popular did the Risshisha become that hundreds of persons found their way to Tosa, the mecca of liberals. For a time Tosa was known among the liberals as the "cradle of freedom."

Kido was perhaps the first among those high in the government to propose the establishment of constitutional government. As an enlightened statesman with insight and political sagacity, he early foresaw the need, as well as the inevitability, of permitting the people to participate in the political affairs of the nation. Immediately upon his return from Europe he proposed the adoption of a constitution and the opening of a national assembly. This was in 1873, a year before Itagaki and his group presented the Memorial. Although his proposal was not adopted by the government, he worked indefatigably and succeeded in starting the annual conference of prefectural governors. This he regarded as a necessary preliminary to the establishment of a national assembly as well as a means of softening the popular demand for immediate action, which could not longer be ignored.

Highly displeased with Kido's success, Ōkubo set out to counteract the former's gains. He hit upon the Formosan Expedition as a means of checking the advocates of popular rights and of appeasing the militarists who had been clamoring for armed clashes. This operation was conceived as a device for diverting both groups' grievances and energies to an overseas undertaking which would at the same time enhance national prestige. In spite of strenuous opposition from Kido, he threw his weight to the pro-expedition faction in the Council, which decided in his favor. Kido had no alternative but to resign.

The arbitrary behavior of the Satsuma clique continued to goad many leaders in and out of government to oppose the policies of the government. However it reached a new high when Ōkubo took over completely the reins of government. The Formosan Expedition, of which he was the prime mover, did little to increase his popularity. It actually turned out to be a major headache for him. When the British Minister, Harry S. Parkes, lodged a protest, Ōkubo was frightened and had an imperial order issued to Ōkuma, then Director of the Formosan Expedition Office, in an attempt to stop the sailing of the troops from Nagasaki. Saigō Tsugumichi, the commander in chief, refused to heed the order, and when Ōkubo himself arrived to stop it, the expedition had already embarked from Nagasaki. The expedition and the negotiations with China which followed were failures. As a consequence the prestige of the government suffered, and public opinion became increasingly hostile.

To straighten out the unsatisfactory state of affairs within the government, Inoue Kaoru, then out of the government, enlisted the aid of Itō in planning the reconciliation and cooperation between Ōkubo, Kido, and Itagaki. With this as an objective, the Ōsaka Conference met in January, 1875, when the conferees resolved to effect the following:

1. That the Senate (*Genrō-in*) be established to provide for a regular legislative process and to make the necessary preparations for the establishment of a national assembly.

2. That the Supreme Court be established and a reform in the Justice Department carried out to ensure the independence of the judiciary and strengthen the basis of the judicature.

3. That a conference of prefectural governors be called to enable the Government to keep accurately informed of the conditions among the people and together with the Senate lay the foundations for the opening of a national assembly.

4. That concurrent tenure of the offices of Councilor and Minister be discontinued by separating the two offices, making the Councilor a member of the Cabinet responsible for advising the Throne, while placing the Minister in charge of the administration and management of a department.

The conference produced a semblance of unity in the Cabinet, but actually it was still a clan government, built around and dominated by two personalities, Iwakura and Ōkubo. Although the study of constitutional systems kept Kido, Ōkubo, Itagaki, and Itō well occupied, there was no visible improvement in their relationship. It was the same cabinet as before, with neither unity nor harmony. Only the struggle for power unfolded with even greater intensity. In the fall Itagaki clashed with Ōkuma, who was supported by Ōkubo, and, seeing that his proposal to separate the functions of Councilor-Minister did not stand a chance of being adopted, resigned once more from the government.

Kido worked tirelessly at translating his own proposal at the Ōsaka Conference into reality, and succeeded in having the first conference of prefectural governors convened in June, 1875. On this occasion he served with distinction as chairman of the conference, which was characterized by lively, fearless discussions and debates by the governors who were not in the least inhibited or fazed by the presence of high officials of the central government.

In spite of the efforts made at the Ōsaka Conference, the government soon lapsed back into the same despotic oligarchy dominated by clan leaders as before and renewed its ruthless policy of suppressing public opinion. Giving up hope that his proposals would ever be carried out, Itagaki had returned to Tosa, where he devoted his energies to the Risshisha in the fight for freedom and popular rights.

Although Ōkubo was eminently successful in laying the foundations for a strong centralized state, the policies he instituted and the methods he employed in carrying them out made strong enemies for him. In May, 1878, he was assassinated by Shimada Ichirō and others for having "obstructed public discussion, suppressed popular rights, and exercised political powers of the government as if they were his own private prerogatives, erred in the conduct of foreign relations and caused a decline in national power and prestige." The government immediately launched a vigorous program of prosecuting the advocates of popular rights. Itagaki and his supporters responded by fighting back with grim determination.

Undisturbed by the implication of Risshisha members in an unsuccessful plot at the time of the Satsuma Rebellion of 1877, Itagaki remained in Tosa to carry on his work, all the while thinking of starting the Patriots' Society (Aikokusha) which he was just about to launch in 1875, when he was asked to rejoin the government. Finally, in the spring of 1878, he prepared a prospectus and sent a deputation of speakers to different parts of the country to explain the aims of the new organization.

In September, the first meeting was held in Ōsaka and the Patriots' Society was formally launched. Members of local chapters were to be sent to the central headquarters in Tōkyō, where they were to meet several times a month to observe and discuss political developments and to send reports back periodically to their own chapters. The second meeting was held in Ōsaka the following spring, followed by the third in the fall. It was decided unanimously at the third meeting to petition the Emperor for the opening of a national assembly. As representatives of more than one hundred thousand signers, Kataoka Kenkichi and Kōno Hironaka took the petition to Tōkyō for submission to the Council of State and the Senate, but neither body would accept it. Although the petition was met with a rebuff, the attempt succeeded inasmuch as it aroused public opinion against the authorities. Itagaki was spurred to go on a nationwide speaking tour to take the issue directly to the people. This move was acclaimed by newspapermen, businessmen, and even by the bureaucrats, who gave tremendous moral support by tendering a huge reception in Tōkyō.

When the government promulgated the Newspaper Ordinance and the Libel Ordinance (*Zambō Ritsu*) in June, 1875, it could hardly anticipate the intensity with which the proponents of freedom and popular rights would fight back, using every available means including the press and public gatherings. With the object of rigidly controlling, if not suppressing, public discussion, the reactionary leaders in government promulgated in April, 1880, the Public Gatherings Ordinance (*Shūkai Jōrei*). This new ordinance required police permission for public meetings and police approval for political organizations, forbade members of the armed forces, police officials, and students to listen to political speeches, and prohibited communication between political organizations.

Within the government, which was controlled by a clan oligarchy, the struggle for power was between Itō and Ōkuma. With the death of Ōkubo in the middle of the year 1878, control of the government passed from Satsuma to Chōshū. After the death of Kido, Itō had succeeded to the leadership of the Chōshū clique and got along well with the Satsuma group. Ōkuma, who had deliberately refrained from getting involved in the Sat-Chō struggle for power, found himself in need of solidifying his position. This he proceeded to achieve with the backing of Fukuzawa, whom he greatly admired, and Gotō Shōjirō. He also brought into government service the most promising graduates of Keiō University. He planned for the speedy adoption of a constitution and an early opening of the national assembly, whereby he hoped to liquidate the clan oligarchy and personally assume leadership in the new constitutional regime. As part of the general plan, he worked out his own draft constitution which he tried to have adopted as the basis for constitutional government.

Needless to say, there were differences of opinion within the government itself on the question of establishing a national assembly. Although the conservatives opposed it vigorously, the enlightened leaders like Itō and Ōkuma saw its inevitability and advocated the necessity of making preparations. With these two leaders taking a favorable stand, the course of the government was set and the remaining problem was to determine what kind of national assembly was to be set up, when, and how.

Disregarding an earlier pledge to Itō to work together in the important undertaking, Ōkuma secretly prevailed upon Iwakura and Prince Arisugawa for their support of his plan to convoke in 1881 a national assembly in accordance with his own draft constitution. Upon learning this, the Cabinet was shocked. Ōkuma's action was branded highly irregular, since he had consulted neither Itō nor the Cabinet. As a consequence, a movement immediately developed to oust Ōkuma from the Cabinet. Resentment was strong, especially among the Satsuma and Chōshū leaders, who saw in it a plot to dislodge them from power.

Ōkuma was not entirely to blame, however. As discussed in detail elsewhere, a government scandal in connection with the disposal of the installations and enterprises of the Hokkaidō Colonization Office was uncovered in the fall of 1881. Ōkuma as Councilor objected to the disposal, which was virtually a free gift, of government property that had cost 22 million yen and that was to be sold for a mere 300,000 yen payable in thirty annual installments without interest. By this strong stand the Councilor from Hizen became *persona non grata* to the other Councilors.

Sanjō, Itō, Saigō (Tsugumichi), Yamada, and others met with Iwakura and prevailed on the Emperor to call a conference to ask for Ōkuma's resignation. Even before this resignation had been secured, the government had completed a list of those who were to be dismissed from service for being supporters of the discredited Councilor. Among those who left the government were men who distinguished themselves later, such as Yano Fumio, Ozaki Yukio, Inukai Tsuyoshi, and Ono Azusa.[3]

---

[3] Others who resigned with Ōkuma were Agriculture and Commerce Minister Kōno Togama, Maejima Hisoka (Mitsu), Ushiba Takuzō, Nakamigawa Hikojirō, Mutaguchi Gengaku, Komatsubara Eitarō, Shimada Saburō, Nakano Buei, and Tanaka Kōzō.

Although he was forced to leave the government, Ōkuma had the satisfaction of having won a dual victory—the fight to stop the irregular sale of government property and the fight for constitutional government. On October 11, 1881, an imperial rescript was issued canceling the disposal of Hokkaidō Colonization Office property and enterprise. On the following day a momentous announcement was made in an imperial rescript promising the opening of a national assembly in 1890. This was the culmination of the movement for a popularly elected national assembly started by Kido quietly within the government in 1873, which was launched by Itagaki and his group outside the government in 1874, and fought for by countless numbers of people. The efforts of the government's opposition forces were crowned with victory.

After October 12, 1881, the date of the Imperial Rescript for the Establishment of the Diet, the movement for constitutional government entered the second and final stage. Prior to this, the movement had been primarily an agitation to force the government to agree to the establishment of a popular assembly. Once this was achieved, the work of stirring up public opinion in the demand for liberty and popular rights gave way to the serious work of preparing and educating the public for the responsibilities of constitutional government.

Liberal Party (Jiyūtō). On October 18, 1881, less than a week after the Imperial Rescript was issued, an organization meeting of the Liberal Party was held in Tōkyō with Gotō Shōjirō as chairman. By the end of the month its organization was completed and Itagaki was chosen its first president. The aims of the party, as they were set down in the articles of organization, were the realization of a constitutional government, the extension of freedom, protection and extension of popular rights, the advancement of the happiness and welfare of the people, the improvement of society, attainment of equality with other nations, and the achievement of national progress.

Besides Itagaki, the leading men of the party included Numa Morikazu, Kōno Hironaka, Matsuda Masahisa, Ueki Emori, Baba Tatsui, and Gotō Shōjirō. Although the party ideology was patterned after the ideas of Rousseau and Montesquieu, there were extremists who resorted to violence, and some of them helped to earn for the party the undesirable name of Jacobins.

At Ōsaka, Furusawa Shigeshi, Kusama Tokifuku, and others assembled the advocates of popular rights and organized the Constitutional Party (Rikken Seitō) which had the appearance of a branch of the Liberal Party.

Reform Party (Kaishintō). Ōkuma, who had resigned from the government in October, 1881, gathered together his former colleagues, Kōno Togama, Maeshima Hisoka, Inukai Tsuyoshi, Ozaki Yukio, and others to organize the Reform Party (Kaishintō) on March 14, 1882. Its membership was drawn largely from the middle class intelligentsia of moderate views. Numa Morikazu, one of the leading spirits of the party, had been a follower and coworker of Itagaki up to the time of the founding of the Liberal Party, but when he clashed with Baba

Tatsui he left and joined Ōkuma. As editor of the Tōkyō *Mainichi,* he played an important role in awakening the political consciousness of the reading public.

Yano Fumio was the leader of the second group comprising chiefly the graduates of Keiō University, founded by Fukuzawa, whose stronghold was the *Yūbin Hōchi,* among whom were Inukai Tsuyoshi, Ozaki Yukio, Fujita Mokichi, Hatano Shōgorō, and Minoura Katsundo, who had strongly advocated a national assembly. This group advocated the ideas of British parliamentarism. The third group led by Ono Azusa was an organization of Tōkyō University graduates, (Ōtokai) interested in political problems, and counted among its membership persons like Takata Sanae, Amano Tameyuki, Yamada Ichirō, and others.

The Reform Party considered it a responsibility to include persons of means, scholars, and those already well established in life, as contrasted with the Liberal Party, which brought in the rural farmers as well as the young impatient malcontents and showed definite leanings toward the nonpropertied and small-propertied classes. In opposing the government it was no different from the Liberal Party against which it had no intention of competing. On the contrary, the founders hoped for an eventual merger. The differences lay, therefore, not in the objectives but in the techniques, ideas, temperaments, and the general atmosphere within the organization, which gradually led them to drift farther apart and to oppose each other.

Specifically, the Reform Party listed the following objectives:

1. Maintenance of the dignity and prosperity of the Imperial family and the welfare of the people.

2. Improvement of internal administration and increase of national power.

3. Abolition of interference by the central government and the building up of local self-government.

4. Extension of the rights of suffrage in accordance with the progress of society.

5. Keeping political relations with foreign powers to the minimum and increasing trade relations as much as possible.

6. Maintenance of a "hard-money" policy in regard to currency.

If the successful attainment of political freedom and popular rights was the main objective of the parties opposing the government, it would appear that one party would have been sufficient and more effective than two. However, there was an unbridgeable temperamental gap between Itagaki and Ōkuma.

Imperial Party (Teiseitō). Having witnessed the enthusiasm with which the new political parties were received by the public, the government concluded that the rising popularity of the Liberal Party and the Reform Party could no longer be offset by the exercise of police powers alone. It was decided therefore to sponsor a government party to counteract the influence of the popular parties. Thus the Imperial Party was launched on March 18, 1882, at the insistence of the government and under the leadership of Fukuchi Gen'ichirō, Maruyama Sakura, Mizuno Torajirō, and others. Tani Tateki, Sasaki Takayuki, and others joined the party which derived its membership chiefly from the ranks of the rising bureaucracy including officials of prefectural, municipal, town, and township government offices as well as Shintō and Buddhist priests, public school teachers, and businessmen with government connections.

Although its membership was small compared to that of the other two parties opposing the government, its influence was not to be underestimated, because the power of the government stood behind it. The party's program was to make certain that the government's decisions regarding the establishment of the Constitution and the Diet were faithfully carried out. It was also to be used in giving necessary assistance to the government in carrying out its policies and program and to engage in a counterpropaganda campaign against the Liberal and Reform parties. For this purpose it had at its command several newspapers. Among them were the Tōkyō *Nichi Nichi, Meiji Nippō, Tōyō Jihō,* and the *Daitō Nippō* which not only defended the clan-oligarchy, but praised it, while at the same time conducting a smear campaign to make the opposition parties appear treasonable.

Each of the three political parties made vigorous efforts to spread its political ideas and programs and to bring about the adoption of the form of constitutional government it favored. The Liberal Party contended that the state existed not for the ruler or a small minority but for all the people, and the sovereign ruled not for himself but for the people. It maintained that sovereignty resided in the people and that the Constitution would have to be drafted and adopted by a constitutional convention which was truly representative of the people. The Imperial Party advocated ideas which were diametrically opposed to those of the Liberal Party. It argued that since the land and people belonged to the Emperor, sovereignty too belonged to the sovereign and that the Constitution must be his gift to the people. Between the two stood the Reform Party which maintained that a national assembly represented both the sovereign and the people. In it therefore resided sovereignty as in the case of the English parliamentary system.

Debates were carried on regarding details of the parliamentary structure to be set up. The Liberal Party insisted on a unicameral legislature, while the Reform and Imperial parties believed in the bicameral system. While the public did not possess sufficient background for understanding the political theories involved, there is no doubt that the parties helped to stimulate public interest in political ideas and institutions.

The announcement of the establishment of constitutional government was received with rejoicing by those who had been fighting for freedom and popular rights. Although the period of agitation was now over, the more arduous task of preparing the nation for new political responsibilities was still ahead. At the same time, the leaders of different groups and parties found it necessary to continue fighting against the high-handedness of the authorities. Unfortunately, the government's policy of suppression, aimed at the stamping out of liberalism, gave rise to revolutionary literature and stimulated young minds to violent action, and, at the same time, encouraged reactionary officials to retaliate mercilessly, as they gave vent to their dislike, if not hatred, of liberal groups and individuals.

In the spring of 1882, Itagaki made a speaking tour of the country and received ovations everywhere. In his stirring speeches he denounced the high-handed actions of the central government officials and sounded a warning against indolence in public affairs. At Gifu, after finishing his speech at the gathering, he was attacked and stabbed by a would-be assassin, who turned out to be an elementary school teacher who had been a faithful reader of the *Tōkyō Nichi Nichi*. Unmindful of his wounds, he cried out, "Itagaki may die, but liberty never!"

The attention of the whole nation was focused on this event, and sympathy was expressed everywhere. Members of the Liberal Party indignantly laid the blame on the government for allowing papers like the *Tōkyō Nichi Nichi* to publish inflammatory editorials. Under pressure, the *Nichi Nichi* and *Daitō Nippō* retracted their editorials and wrote letters of apology to the headquarters of the Liberal Party.

Widespread public indignation was reflected in the increasing intensity of attacks on the government. Unable to cope with the situation the authorities tightened the laws and, by the use of police power, began the further suppression of antigovernment parties. In June, 1882, the already drastic Public Gatherings Ordinance was revised to give it more teeth. This was an attempt to ban political organizations, public meetings, and political discussions. The police was empowered to watch over and disband any meeting when it was deemed necessary for the preservation of public peace and order. Kabayama Sukenori, Superintendent-General of the Metropolitan Police Board, directed the exercise of police power with little regard for the rights of the people and vigorously enforced the government's policy of suppression and terrorization of parties.

The ruthlessness of the authorities in the carrying out of suppressive policies can be seen in the numerous clashes between the officials and the outraged people in the 1880's. Typical of the method employed by many a reactionary government official was the famous Fukushima Incident. In the spring of 1882, Mishima Michitsune was appointed governor of Fukushima prefecture, which was one of the strongholds of the Liberal Party. The new governor, who was later rewarded with appointment as Superintendent-General of the Tōkyō Metropolitan Police Board in the First Cabinet in 1885, vowed publicly that arson, burglary, and the Liberal Party would not be tolerated in his jurisdiction. One of his first official acts was to replace close to a hundred prefectural officials with men of his choice. He then built an elaborate official residence and started highway construction which was not urgent. He decreed that the residents of the districts through which the highway ran must bear the cost of 370,000 yen. Furthermore, he ordered all the residents between the ages of fifty and sixty to donate a day's labor each month for a period of two years. This labor levy was commuted to 15 sen a day for men and 10 sen for women who could not provide actual labor.

The prefectural assembly led by the Speaker, Kōno Hironaka, one of the prominent leaders of the Liberal Party, opposed the governor, voted down every bill submitted by him, and refused to appropriate the requested expenditures. In utter disregard of the action of the assembly, Mishima went ahead with his program and collected more taxes from the people whose tax burden was already heavy. Incensed by the actions of the governors, members of the Liberal Party aroused the people. This resulted in clashes with the police.

Despite the fact that Kōno was in no way implicated in the disturbances, Mishima was determined to find something to incriminate him. In December, 1882, the police descended upon the headquarters of the Liberal Party and took Kōno and a score of others into custody. The police could find no incriminating evidence in the raid and were ordered to find something. Whereupon they dug up a written oath signed by the members of the Liberal Party in the summer of 1880, in which they had pledged to "overthrow the despotic government in order to establish a government by public discussion." This was seized upon as proof of subversive action and was used as incriminating evidence. Kōno Hironaka and his colleagues were tried and sentenced to imprisonment on the grounds that they had plotted the overthrow of the government.

Not content with the policy of suppressing the political parties, the reactionary element in the government sought to shut off completely the channel for the expression of public opinion by abolishing the prefectural assemblies. In December, 1882, Iwakura Tomomi submitted his views proposing the suspension of prefectural assemblies. As a great leader of the Restoration period, Iwakura's contribution to the nation was immeasurably great, but his aristocratic background and temperament did not permit him to view the development of popular rights with equanimity. He was a firm believer in an enlightened despotism, regarding the government as the special preserve of a privileged class. To him the people existed merely as a class entirely subordinate to the government and not entitled to meddling in the affairs of state. He abhorred the political parties which, so far as he was concerned, devoted their energies solely to opposing and obstructing the policies and activities of the government.

In harmony with his firm belief in absolutism backed by military power, he entertained the calamitous idea that a nation could best be governed by intimidating the people into obedience by the use of military and police power. He was convinced that the existence of prefectural assemblies and the establishment of a Constitution would imperil the security of the state. Fortunately, the reactionary and retrogressive policy advocated by Iwakura was rejected by the progressively minded leaders in government.

As president of the first major political party to be organized in the country, Itagaki decided at the persuasion of Gotō Shōjirō to go abroad and observe conditions in the countries of Europe in order that he might better discharge his duties in the future. Baba Tatsui, Ōishi Masami, and Suehiro Tetchō, thinking the move unwise, urged Itagaki to give up the trip, which could only weaken the party and perhaps even cause its collapse. When they were met with a rebuff, they started attacking the Liberal Party president and, at the party meeting of September 17, they succeeded in passing a resolution censuring him and threatening his dismissal from the presidency. Undaunted by the dissension in the party, Itagaki left for Europe in November, 1882, accompanied by Gotō Shōjirō. Simultaneously, Baba, Suehiro, and Ōishi left the party.

Taking advantage of the dissension within the enemy camp, the Reform Party launched a vigorous attack on Itagaki and the Liberal Party. Schemers within the government were giving aid in the attack which lessened the prestige and influence of the oldest party. Unable to strike back, the Liberal Party was biding its time for a chance to even the score. That opportunity was provided by the intimate connection which developed between the Mitsubishi interests and Ōkuma, president of the Reform Party.

At the time of the Formosan Expedition, the Mitsubishi Company was engaged in shipping with eleven small ships. The government at the cost of $1,400,000 bought thirteen large ships, which it turned over to the company for the transportation of troops and supplies. After the expedition was over the ships were given outright to the company. Needless to say, Ōkuma, who was the Finance Minister, was responsible for this arrangement. As the company prospered and enjoyed a practical monopoly in the field of maritime industry, it invited the resentment of the public. Newspapers began to criticize Mitsubishi. The Liberal Party saw in this situation an excellent opportunity for revenge and started attacking Ōkuma and Mitsubishi. The government was also alert to the opportunity which was presented. It decided to organize a quasi-governmental Mutual Transportation Company to oppose the Mitsubishi Company. This was done because the government had been suspicious for some time that the Mitsubishi Company was providing Ōkuma with funds to carry on his political activities.

The Liberal Party vengefully carried on its attacks on Mitsubishi and the Reform Party, labeling it the spurious party, and contending that in reality it was a profit-making organization parading as a political party. Meanwhile the connection between the *Jiyū Shimbun* (Liberal Party organ) and the Mutual Transportation Company was exposed—to the embarrassment of the Liberal Party. The editors-in-chief of the *Jiyū Shimbun*, Furusawa Shigeshi and Wada Hikojirō, who had been attacking the Reform Party and the Mitsubishi Company without mercy, had been taken in completely by the government and had become its tools in a calculated maneuver to weaken the parties. Public confidence in the political parties reached a new low and the Liberal Party as well as the Reform Party barely continued to exist for they had practically lost their *raison d'être*.

In August, 1883, Itō Hirobumi returned after spending almost a year studying the constitutional systems of Europe. Like Ōkuma, he had first been introduced to English political ideas, but his stay in Germany and his intimate contact with Bismarck changed his views completely. He returned a convert to Prussian ideas and institutions, to advocate bureaucracy and militarism which he had seen in action in Germany in the flush of victory in the Franco-Prussian War. He started out immediately on a campaign to stamp out the political parties and to place the government outside them. He notified Fukuchi Gen' ichirō that the government no longer needed the Imperial Party. On September 24, 1883, the termination of the party was announced.

It was not a pleasant situation which greeted Itagaki on his return from a trip abroad in June, 1883. The nation was a virtual political cauldron boiling over with violent actions against the government. There was an ugly political battle in progress between his party and the Reform Party. Itagaki saw that conditions were adverse to the existence and healthy development of political parties and decided to disband the Liberal Party. On October 29, 1884, on the third anniversary of its founding, a disbanding ceremony was held in Ōsaka with the members vowing to carry on the work despite the liquidation of the organization. That the spirit of the Liberal Party did not die but continued even more aggressively thereafter was reflected in the activities of the former members as outbreak after outbreak occurred.

In October, 1883, the Home Ministry appointed Mishima concurrently governor of Tochigi prefecture. Here he practically repeated what he had done earlier in Fukushima. He removed the prefectural capital from the city of Tochigi to Utsunomiya and constructed a magnificent prefectural office building. Voices of condemnation arose against him and members of the Liberal Party began coming into the prefecture to give moral support to the suffering people. A group drew up plans to go to Tōkyō to assassinate en masse the newly created peers at their celebration on September 19, 1884. As this was postponed indefinitely, the group decided on an alternative plan to start a revolution. The starting signal was to be the wholesale massacre of the ministers and councilors at the ceremony celebrating the completion of the prefectural office building in Utsunomiya. This too was postponed indefinitely when the government became suspicious. The leaders established their headquarters at Kabayama on September 23, 1884, and sent out a call to the revolutionaries, but they were forced to disband after two days when they failed to get anyone to join them. The plot was nipped in the bud, and the conspirators were sentenced to death or imprisonment.

Several unsuccessful attempts to dislodge the autocratic government were made even after the dissolution of the Liberal Party. The Chichibu Uprising of October, 1884, called for plans to gain popular support by proposing land tax reduction and revision of military conscription. After this the rebels were to tear down the Maebashi prison in the manner of the storming of the Bastille, overpower the military garrison at Takasaki, and from there they were to march triumphantly on to Tōkyō. The mob, composed largely of farmers, fishermen, and others, attacked government offices with considerable success but the troops dispatched from Tōkyō quelled the disturbance in short order.

Of all the attempts the Iida Incident came closest to showing the earmarks of a revolution, although it did not go much beyond the planning stage. Muramatsu Aizō, a newspaper editor and staunch advocate of freedom and popular rights, was infuriated by the government's suppression of the liberal movement and of public opinion. Although he had been carrying on a fight against the tyranny of the oligarchy through his paper, he came to the conclusion that fighting for popular rights by appealing to public opinion was much too circuitous and slow. As a result he planned to overthrow the government by force and printed five million copies of a manifesto condemning the tyranny of the despotic government and enumerating the specific crimes of the Sat-Chō oligarchy. He urged revolution on the people as a means of correcting the evils. The plot was uncovered by the police before the copies of the manifesto could be distributed and necessary preparations, including the raising of funds, had been completed. In December, 1884, Muramatsu and others were imprisoned.

Disunion plagued the Reform Party, and President Ōkuma was weary of his ineffective organization. So he had Kōno Togama, the Vice President, propose its dissolution, but he was met with opposition. In December, 1884, Ōkuma and Kōno withdrew from the party and were followed by Maejima Hisoka, Kitabatake Harufusa, Ono Azusa, Mutaguchi Gengaku, and others, leaving the opposition, led by Numa Morikazu and including Shimada Saburō, Ozaki Yukio, Minoura Katsundo, Nakano Buei, Fujita Mokichi, Koizuka Ryū, and others, to keep the party going. But its days were numbered.

The policy of Europeanization pursued vigorously by the Itō Cabinet in the 1880's as a means of hastening acceptance by the treaty Powers induced a reactionary movement within and without the government. Criticisms leveled at the government by the chauvinists as well as by the liberals became more scathing than ever. Home Minister Tani expressed strong opposition to Foreign Minister Inoue's draft treaty revision and resigned in protest. Gustave Boissanade, the legal adviser to the Home Minister, also showed disapproval of the treaty by pointing out its defects. In the attack on the government, the proponents of freedom and popular rights joined hands with the rightists. Itagaki, in an eighteen-thousand-word memorial, pointed out the evils of the day, roundly denouncing the government for suppressing the forces of liberalism. Gotō Shōjirō was active in stirring up the antigovernment forces and factions, while at the same time he sought to secure an imperial audience to present to the Emperor a document denouncing the government. Demonstrations became common everyday occurrences, while memorials demanding reductions in taxes, freedom of speech, press and assembly, and self-respecting diplomacy poured into the government in endless stream.

Faced with a threatening situation, the Home Ministry on September 29, 1887, issued an ordinance intended to check demonstrations against the government, which were beginning to assume serious proportions. Premier Itō summoned the prefectural governors to a conference and defended the administration's policies pertaining to the projected constitution and foreign relations as well as domestic affairs. At the same time, however, he admonished the governors to enforce the policy of muzzling public opinion. The high-handed policies of the government boomeranged, and the agitators appeared ready to go into violent action. An extremely tense situation prevailed in the capital. Plots to assassinate cabinet ministers en masse and to burn the city were rumored. Fearing that the situation might get out of control, the government resorted to extraordinary measures. On December 26 the Peace Preservation Ordinance was promulgated in an extra edition of the *Official Gazette*. In accordance with its provisions some 570 persons were deemed dangerous to public peace and order and were told to quit Tōkyō immediately. In this group of "dangerous" persons were Hoshi Tōru, Ozaki Yukio, Nakae Tokusuke, Nakashima Nobuyuki, Kataoka Kenkichi, and Hayashi Yūzō, whose names are prominently identified with the liberal movement of the period. As a precautionary measure, troops were assigned to guard the Imperial Palace and the official residences of the cabinet ministers. Thus the year 1887 was ushered out in the midst of a tense political situation, with the government distraught with fear and anxiety, while the work of drafting the Constitution was nearing its end.

Chapter 12. Setting Up of Parliamentary Government

A deliberative assembly was stipulated in the Charter Oath of Five Articles, but at the time of its issuance it was not the popularly elected assembly that the leaders had envisaged. In 1868 the Kōgisho was established, permitting representatives of the fiefs, government offices, and schools to meet six times a month to deliberate on laws and problems of administration. This was the extent of deliberation that the leaders were willing to concede. The following year, a bureau was created for the purpose of eliciting the views of the people. After successive changes in the governmental structure, the Left Chamber was given legislative functions in 1871.

Early in 1869, Iwakura had pointed out the urgency of appointing capable persons to office to ensure efficiency in government. Etō Shimpei was interested in a constitution as a means of bringing order out of the confusion which followed the Restoration. Although a progressive thinker and astute statesman, Kido's thinking on constitutional government did not go much beyond the practical goal of achieving national stability in a period of confusion that had arisen from the abolition of fiefs and the establishment of prefectures. Ōkubo's main concern was the firm establishment of the sovereignty of the Emperor. Thus, to the leaders of the early Meiji period, constitutional government was primarily a means of achieving a strong centralized government.

However, several outstanding leaders in the government resigned following the clash over the Korean question in 1873. These men comprised a group which was determined to break the power of the Satsuma-Chōshū oligarchy. In the same year, Komuro Nobuo and Furusawa Shigeshi returned from England, greatly impressed by the workings of the English parliamentary system and determined to see it adopted in Japan. They succeeded in convincing Itagaki Taisuke and Gotō Shōjirō, leading to the presentation in January, 1874, of the Memorial for the Establishment of a Popularly Elected National Assembly.

Immediately after the publication of the Memorial, Dr. Katō Hiroyuki, an official in the Imperial Household Department, sent a negative reply, arguing that the time was not yet ripe for a popular assembly. Fukuchi Gen'ichirō and Suematsu Kenchō also voiced their opinion to the effect that the establishment of a popular assembly was premature. Ōi Kentarō and Suehiro Tetchō took

163

up the fight and advocated the immediate opening of a national assembly. Public interest was aroused and discussions were carried on through the press and in public meetings on the pros and cons of the establishment of a popular assembly.

By the spring of 1875, when the Senate (*Genrō-in*) was created, the government apparently had come around to the view that it would eventually have to yield to the demand for the establishment of constitutional government. Meanwhile demands were being made by business interests for an administrative system adapted to the structure of capitalistic production that would enable a rational increase of wealth. The popular rights movement by the masses, the agrarian and urban proletariat, and poor farmers, joined by the landowners and the newly risen bourgeoisie, gained strength in the late 1870's. The government could no longer ignore the movement.

That the government was weakened in 1873 by the split over the Korean question was all too apparent. The urgent need was for a unified leadership. Differences between Home Minister Ōkubo and Councilor Kido, who had resigned and retired to his native prefecture of Yamaguchi, had to be composed if the ship of state were to weather the gathering storm. Inoue Kaoru, who had also resigned from the government earlier over a disagreement regarding financial policies, was gravely concerned over the course of events and offered his services in smoothing the way for cooperation among the leaders. This resulted in the Ōsaka Conference of February, 1875, which was attended by Ōkubo, Kido, Itagaki, Inoue, Itō, Komuro, Furusawa, Hayashi Yūzō, and others. This was an attempt to achieve a united front in the face of the strong agitation for a popularly elected national assembly and to make necessary preparations for the eventual establishment of a national legislature.

This compromise accelerated the establishment of a constitution and the opening of a national assembly, since it resulted in the Imperial Rescript of April 14, 1875, announcing that constitutional government would be established by gradual stages. It achieved also the coalition of all the opposing forces with the exception of Saigō, who refused Itagaki's urging to rejoin the government. Kido and Itagaki rejoined the government with the assignment to investigate political systems and to work closely with Ōkubo and Itō. The outline of the organization of national assembly which came out of their efforts called for an upper house composed of artistocrats, learned persons, and those who had rendered meritorious services to the state, and a lower house comprising the conference of prefectural governors.

It was chiefly, if not entirely, through the efforts of the farsighted statesman, Kido, that the government agreed at the Ōsaka Conference to call a meeting of prefectural governors as a preliminary step in the government's preparation for a national assembly. The Imperial Rescript of April 14 announced that the Senate and the Supreme Court would be established and a conference of prefectural governors would be called to pave the way for the gradual establishment of constitutional government. Thus, the government definitely committed itself to the program of constitutional government.

The first conference was held in Tōkyō from June 20 to July 17, 1875, with Kido as its presiding officer. Its opening and closing sessions were favored by the presence of the Emperor. The agenda for the conference included public works, police affairs, local expenditures, local assemblies, poor relief, and elementary education. The question of popular representative assemblies produced a lively discussion, making it necessary to extend the conference period by several days. It was decided by majority opinion to establish first prefectural assemblies with officials as members. In officially closing the conference, the Emperor assured the members that he would act on their recommendations after referring them to the Senate for advice. Although it was a conference of prefectural governors, it was held with the solemnity of a national assembly.

It was not until 1878 that the government could manage to hold the second conference, although these meetings had been planned as annual affairs. As Ōkubo was at the pinnacle of his power, rumors had started that he would have the Imperial Rescript of April, 1875, revoked. Naturally, when the conference was actually opened on April 1, 1878, the public was surprised, and when the conference decided to put into operation a system of local representative assemblies public amazement was even greater. In February, 1880, the third and last conference was held. Thereafter, such meetings were held in the Home Ministry as routine administrative conferences of prefectural governors.

The ordinance creating the Senate was promulgated on April 25, 1875,[1] and on July 5 the Senate was officially opened in the presence of the Emperor. This body was entrusted with the work of drafting ordinances and regulations and making preparations for the establishment of a constitutional government. In May the Supreme Court was set up, and the regulations for the organization of the courts were promulgated. This was to establish clearly the independence of the judiciary.

On September 6, 1876, the Emperor made his appearance in the Senate and commanded its President, Prince Arisugawa, to begin the study of constitutional systems, preparatory to the drafting of a constitution. Accordingly, the Bureau for the Study of Constitutional Systems (*Kempō Seido Torishirabe Kyoku*)

---

[1] Appointed immediately to membership were Yamaguchi Naoyoshi, Torio Koyata, Miura Gorō, Tsuda Izuru, Kōno Togama, Katō Hiroyuki, Gotō Shōjirō, Yuri Kimmasa, Yoshii Tomozane, Mutsu Munemitsu, and Matsuoka Tokitoshi. The members elected Gotō Shōjirō to the position of Vice President. On July 2, three days before the opening, additional appointments were made: Prince Arisugawa, who became President, Yanagihara Sakimitsu, Sano Tsunetami, Kuroda Kiyotaka, Hase Nobuatsu, Akizuki Taneki, Mibu Motonaga, Sasaki Takayuki, Saitō Toshiyuki, and Ogiu Yuzuru.

was created within the Senate and a committee was appointed to begin the study.[2]

Prefectural assemblies were sanctioned for the first time by an ordinance promulgated on July 22, 1878, providing the basis for constitutional government that became a reality twelve years later. By this ordinance, prefectural assemblies were empowered to deliberate on the budget and the method of collecting taxes. All males, twenty years of age and over, paying not less than five yen in land tax were qualified to vote for their representatives to the prefectural assembly. At the same time an ordinance was issued setting up the smaller administrative units of districts (*gun*), wards (*ku*), cities, towns, and townships. It was not until January, 1880, however, that an ordinance for the establishment of assemblies for wards, towns, and townships was promulgated.

After the assassination of Ōkubo leadership passed to Ōkuma and Itō, with Iwakura still in the background. Until 1873, Iwakura had been the link between the Imperial Court and the Sat-Chō coalition of Saigō, Ōkubo, and Kido. After 1873, however, he gave full support to Ōkubo in the suppression of rebellions and civil strife and in the control of peasant disorders and the popular rights movement. It was also he who engineered the ouster of Ōkuma Shigenobu from the Council of State in 1881 in a purge of liberally inclined bureaucrats and who ensured a conservative nationalistic policy in the creation of a constitutional system. Iwakura consistently fought for the establishment of a strong monarchical principle.

In June, 1879, when popular agitation for a national assembly was being carried on vigorously, former United States President Ulysses S. Grant arrived on his world tour. The Japanese lost no time in seeking his views on various and sundry questions. In August, Emperor Meiji received him in audience at the Hama Detached Palace and posed several questions. Grant said that a government based on the people, whether it be a republic or a monarchy, was the strongest and that a popularly elected assembly should eventually be established in Japan. However, he emphasized that once a popular assembly was established it could never be taken away from the people; therefore, caution must be exercised in avoiding the confusion that would result from its premature establishment. Slow and gradual progress toward constitutional government was advisable, he said, as it would allow ample time for the education of the people. Grant pointed out the important functions of political parties under a system of constitutional government.

At the suggestion of Iwakura, the government had requested the Councilors in 1879 to submit their views on the Senate draft of the Constitution. All the Councilors[3] except one agreed that the creating of a constitution and open-

---

[2] Appointed to the committee were Nakashima Nobuyuki, Yanagihara Sakimitsu, Hosokawa Junjirō, Fukubane Bisei, and Kanda Kōhei.

[3] The Councilors were Yamagata, Kuroda, Yamada, Inoue, Itō, and Ōki.

ing of a national assembly at that time would be quite premature and advised a policy of slow and gradual adoption. Ōkuma, the ranking Councilor, was alone in advocating the immediate opening of a national assembly and the adoption of party government patterned after the English parliamentary system. His schedule called for the adoption of a constitution by the end of 1881, a national election in 1882, and the opening of a national assembly in 1883. This proposal was criticized by Itō as too radical. Seven months after the submission of his proposal, Ōkuma found himself involuntarily relieved of his position of leadership in the government.

On July 6, 1881, Iwakura revealed his grave concern over the question of a national assembly, which he conceded as inevitable. In his communications to Sanjō Sanetomi and Prince Arisugawa, President of the Senate, he set forth clearly what he regarded as an acceptable constitutional system for Japan.[4] He rejected the English parliamentary system and party government and favored the Prussian system.[5] It is quite understandable why Iwakura rejected the Senate draft as being incompatible with Japan's national polity since it gave a great deal of power to the legislative branch of the government.

The policy of the government regarding the Constitution and the Diet, derived from Iwakura's outline of July, was set forth in the joint statement of the Councilor written at the meeting on the night of October 11, when the ouster of Ōkuma was decided. Popular assembly was to be instituted but not to affect in any way the prerogatives of the Emperor. The bicameral system of legislature was to be created with the Upper House occupying a more important position as its membership was to include imperial princes, the nobility, and the former *samurai* class as well as the highest taxpayers. Thus, the shape of things to come, so far as the constitutional system was concerned, had been determined by the Sat-Chō-dominated oligarchy. Itō was the man designated to carry out the policy set down by Iwakura.

Iwakura had, for a considerable time, served as an effective brake in preventing Itō from trying to transplant Prussian and German ideas and institutions to Japan. He was convinced of the importance of adapting them to the special conditions and needs of the Japanese people. Yet, Prussian ideas triumphed over English ideas in 1881 as the dominant philosophy of the government leaders. On the other hand, liberalism, which was emphasized by the leaders of the opposition forces and incorporated in the numerous private draft constitutions, did not find its way into the Constitution. Instead, this philosophy was lost completely with the suppression of violent outbreaks against the government in 1882 and 1883. Consequently, French liberalism made no imprint on the Japanese Constitution.

---

[4] *Iwakura Kō Jikki,* Vol. II, and Ōtsu Jun'ichirō, *Dai Nihon Kensei Shi,* Vol. II, p. 410.

[5] Iwakura was strongly influenced by Inoue Ki, who in turn was influenced by Dr. Herman Roessler and Prussian ideas.

A thorough study and observation of the constitutional systems of the West were considered an indispensable preparation for the successful drafting of a new constitution. Therefore, in March, 1882, Itō was sent to Europe accompanied by Itō Miyoji, Hirata Tōsuke, and Saionji Kimmochi to study the leading constitutional systems. However, even before his departure, Germany had been selected as the country to be studied thoroughly as a model, inasmuch as her political structure under the monarchy, her ideas, and her practices were closest to those of the Japanese. Itō heard lectures by Rudolf Gneist in Germany and also spent some time in Vienna with Lorenz von Stein. Itō was more profoundly influenced by Gneist, who favored a bicameral legislature, property qualification for voting, the reservation of diplomatic, military, and economic powers and prerogatives to the Throne, and who rejected a party government which made the legislative body the center and source of political power.

In July, 1883, while Itō was on his way back from Europe, Iwakura died. Although his death was a great loss to the nation, his usefulness in his later years had been very limited, as he had become quite reactionary. Although actual leadership was firmly in the hands of Itō, it was nevertheless very difficult for him to express his views frankly or to carry out necessary measures in the face of opposition from Iwakura. Consequently, the death of the reactionary elder removed the obstacle and Itō was now free to go ahead with his program of progressive reforms.

Itō returned from Europe in the summer of 1883 after an absence of more than a year, showing visible signs of change. He had become so enamored with the German Chancellor and developed such a worship of him that he affected the mannerisms of Bismarck, imitating even the way he smoked his cigar. He was convinced that Prussia offered a fitting model for Japan. Thus Prussian nationalism, militarism, and bureaucracy became the basis of Japan's national organization. Itō invited German teachers and advisers, whom he placed in the various government departments. In March, 1884, he established the Bureau for the Study of Institutions to begin preparations for the drafting of a constitution and also to review draft ordinances submitted by the administrative departments and to institute reforms in the administrative structure. He became its President, while holding concurrently the post of Minister of Imperial Household.

As a preliminary step to the revamping of the governmental structure, Itō set up a new system of peerage, which became effective with the promulgation of the peerage ordinance on July 7, 1884. The new peerage, modeled on the German system, comprised the five ranks of prince, marquis, count, viscount, and baron, which were distributed to the members of the old court nobility, the former *daimyō,* and those of the lower *samurai* class who had rendered meritorious services to the state as bureaucrats. The new aristocracy counted more than 500 members, but some prominent individuals were omitted from the honors. Gotō Shōjirō, Itagaki Taisuke, Ōkuma Shigenobu, and Katsu Awa were among those who had been overlooked. Needless to say, Itō and other members of the Sat-Chō oligarchy rewarded themselves for their services to the clan-dominated government. Plainly, it was a political maneuver to create a new privileged class whose support Itō needed, especially since the lesser *samurai* class had withdrawn support from the bureaucratic clan-government. At the same time, the new aristocracy was expected to furnish membership to the Upper House as a check on the power and actions of the Lower House. In a sense, the institution of the peerage was a contravention, if not a negation, of the principle of equality which was espoused by the government at the time when the feudal class system was abolished. It was a retrogressive step which set back the hand of time in the final achievement of true equality and popular rights.

By creating a privileged class, Itō succeeded in absorbing the conservative elements both in and out of government into his orbit of power. Itō was lauded by the new peers whom he had won over. He had not only satisfied his own desire for honor by becoming a count himself, but had dissolved the suspicion and distrust of the court nobility and former *daimyō*. Not the least of the achievements was the securing of control over the Sat-Chō oligarchy. The political power for which he had been working with such singleness of purpose was now firmly in his hands.

The next step toward the establishment of the constitutional system came on December 12, 1885, when the Council of State was superseded by a modern cabinet system, which closely followed the Prussian model. Separation was effected also between general state affairs and imperial household affairs. The vestiges of feudalism in the form of respect for status were swept aside and merit came to be emphasized for appointment to the cabinet. The system also provided for the specialization of the administrative functions of the ministers while at the same time bringing about a greater centralization of powers.

Nine Ministries, Foreign Affairs, Home Affairs, Finance, War, Navy, Justice, Education, Agriculture and Commerce, and Communications comprised the Cabinet which was headed by the Prime Minister. Itō, then only forty-five years old, was appointed Premier while holding concurrently the post of Minister of Imperial Household. Significant was the fact that the cabinet members were comparatively young, ranging in age from thirty-nine to fifty-one years old, the average age being slightly over forty-six years. As was expected, Satsuma and Chōshū dominated the Cabinet, and the members were all colleagues of Itō and of lesser *samurai* origin, who had worked together in laying the foundations of the Meiji Government. Not a single member of the old court nobility was included. It was the first time that a man of humble origin, a virtual commoner, had risen to the highest position open to a subject. As such the Cabinet was, indeed, precedent-setting and significant.

Clearly, Itō's aim was to replace the clan oligarchy with an efficient bureaucracy and to improve the administrative machinery. As an initial step toward the achievement of the goal, he issued regulations governing the appointment of officials. This was the forerunner of civil service, which was instituted some years later. Although Itō succeeded in increasing administrative efficiency and in ending the clan-dominated oligarchy, he paved the way for a bureaucratic government dominated by a different type of official. Itō gave preference to graduates of the Tōkyō Imperial University by appointing them without examination. Furthermore, he appointed professors of his own choice to the University. In so doing, he practically turned the University into a training school for bureaucrats.

The two years 1884 and 1885 had to be devoted primarily to the reorganization of the administrative structure as a whole. During the next two years, efforts were concentrated on the drafting of the Constitution. Itō, who was entrusted with the responsibility of drafting the fundamental law of the land, had in Inoue Ki an able bureaucrat to take actual charge of a committee of three consisting of himself, Itō Miyoji, and Harvard-educated Kaneko Kentarō.

Dr. Herman Roessler, protégé of Rudolf Gneist, professor of jurisprudence and authority on English and German constitutional law, served as adviser to the Committee. Invited originally by the Foreign Office to serve as adviser on civil law and commercial policy, Roessler arrived in 1878 and in the subsequent years influenced Inoue. Even more conservative and Prussian in his ideas than his teacher, he was regarded highly by Itō, Inoue, and Iwakura. In 1884, when the opposition forces were resorting to violence reminiscent of the techniques of the French Revolution, Roessler's short work, *The French Revolution,* was translated into Japanese and published.[6]

As Prime Minister Itō was too busy to devote much time to the actual drafting of the document. He merely provided a broad outline of principles, leaving the details to the members of the drafting committee. Inoue was the principal drafter, who assumed direct responsibility for the Constitution; Itō Miyoji for the Laws of the Houses, and Kaneko for the Law of the Organization of the House of Peers and the Law of Election.

The members of the drafting committee worked in utmost secrecy at the summer villa of Prince Itō on the little island of Natsushima off Yokosuka. They were under oath not to breathe a word even to the members of their own families. Strict secrecy was maintained to preclude any adverse criticisms or interference that might come from premature or unfavorable publicity. No outsiders were consulted. Dr. Roessler, the adviser, was consulted frequently on technical points, but it appears that he too was sworn to secrecy. It was in an atmosphere of reaction incompatible with the ideas of popular rights and liberty and in utter disregard

---

[6] In this work, Roessler attributed the violence in the French Revolution to the dangerous doctrines and inflammatory words of Voltaire, Montesquieu, Diderot, Helvetius, and others. See Itō Hirobumi, *Kempō Shiryō* (2 vols.), Vol. I, pp. 310*ff.*

of public opinion that the Constitution was drafted. Instead of the work being done in the Senate, which was the properly constituted body charged with the function of drafting ordinances and regulations, it was placed in the Imperial Household Ministry, where it was virtually immune to outside influence or adverse criticisms.

After two years of strenuous work, the draft Constitution was completed in the spring of 1888. A method for the adoption of the Constitution had to be found. Ōkuma and Itagaki were among those who advocated ratification by a constitutional convention of delegates duly elected by the people. Officials were of the opinion that, inasmuch as it was to be a grant from the Emperor, acceptance by him alone would be sufficient. However, a sort of compromise between the two methods suggested by Itō was adopted and a special organization to deliberate upon the draft Constitution was created.

Thus, on April 28, 1888, the Privy Council came into being for the express purpose of deliberating upon the drafts of the Constitution, Laws of the Houses, the Imperial Household Ordinance, Law of Election, and the House of Peers Ordinance. Its membership was highly selective, if not exclusive, for it was a galaxy of distinguished statesmen and members of the peerage. The Council, as the highest advisory body to the Emperor, was in time entrusted with the important function of giving advice to the Emperor on the following:

1. Interpretation of the Constitution and laws based on it.

2. Disputes over doubtful points in budgetary matters and accounts.

3. Drafts of constitutional amendments.

4. Drafting of new laws, rescinding of laws, drafting of law revisions, treaties with foreign powers, and plans on administrative organization.

5. Important imperial ordinances.

6. Other important administrative and fiscal matters that would require the special deliberation of the Council.

Itō Hirobumi, who had just turned over the premiership to Kuroda, became the first President of the Privy Council. As a matter of fact, he arranged for this before relinquishing the premiership, which was becoming untenable because of the political situation. He had actually sought and found a political haven in his new creation and had made certain by special dispensation of the Emperor that he had a voice in the Cabinet.

Deliberations on the Constitution were started by the Privy Council in May, 1888, behind closed doors in the Imperial Palace and neither the public nor the press was admitted.[7] The draft was considered carefully article by article and discussed in the presence of Emperor Meiji who showed deep interest in the proceedings by attending all the meetings but one. The work of deliberation was

[7] This method is said to have been suggested by Kaneko, who had derived inspiration from the accounts of James Madison and Thomas Jefferson of the Constitutional Convention, that met at Philadelphia in 1787.

finished in January, 1889, and the Constitution was promulgated on February 11, 1889,[8] in a solemn ceremony at the Imperial Palace in the presence of foreign diplomatic representatives, high government officials, and the presiding officers of prefectural assemblies.

The Constitution was an instrument, not so much for the granting of political rights to the people, as for the establishment of a strong centralized government. It was actually a document for the enhancement of the monarchial tradition, although it gave the people the opportunity to participate, in a limited way, in the administration of the affairs of state. We must not overlook the fact that it was also an integral part of the government's program to achieve treaty revision. Japan felt that until she had a constitution, legal system, and courts of law comparable to those of Occidental countries, the treaty Powers would not regard her as sufficiently civilized to deserve serious consideration in the matter of treaty revision.

Even a cursory examination reveals the fact that the Constitution was quite Japanese in concept. Such a concept as "The Emperor is sacred and inviolable" (Article 3) could hardly be regarded as appropriate for inclusion in a constitution of any Western power. It was essentially a document embodying both spirit and substance that were distinctly Japanese in character but neatly put up in a Western garb.

The Constitution provided a bicameral system of legislature in which the Upper House was definitely aristocratic and intended as a check against the Lower House. While the separation of powers was carried out in form, the executive branch of the government was more powerful than the legislative. The doctrine of judicial review was not adopted, and the Privy Council rather than the Supreme Court was entrusted with the function of passing on the constitutionality of laws and administrative actions.

Although Itō and others maintained that national government should be organized before undertaking the institution of local self-government, Home Minister Yamagata had disagreed and had gone ahead with his plans. Toward the end of 1884, he set up in the Department of Home Affairs the Committee for the Study of Local Government and in June, 1885, had a draft law on the organization of municipal and town governments finished. As it was not adequate, Dr. Albert Mosse, a German authority on local government and protégé of Rudolf Gneist, was requested to prepare a draft outlining municipal and town government. Although his draft was completed in February, 1887, it was revised to suit Japanese conditions and needs, and approved a year later by the Senate. In the Cabinet a heated discussion developed about the method of selecting the mayor, and the Senate's recommendation of government appointment came very close to being discarded in favor of popular election. However, popular election

---

[8] The anniversary of the founding of the Japanese empire by Emperor Jimmu in 660 B.C.

was recognized only in principle, with the actual passing of a compromise providing for the election of three candidates, one of whom was to be appointed by the Emperor. On April 17, 1888, the system of local self-government went into effect nearly a year ahead of the Constitution.

The reorganization of local self-government, which materialized in the spring of 1888 with the promulgation of the Law of Municipalities and Towns, made it necessary to set up self-government on the prefectural level too. In May, 1890, the Law of the Organization of Prefectures based on the German system of local government went into effect. Simultaneously, intermediate administrative units between the prefecture and the municipality were set up in the form of districts (*gun*).

In February, 1889, the Law of the Houses of the Diet and the Law of Election were promulgated simultaneously with the Constitution. The former set down the organization and structure of the two houses of the Diet and defined their powers, while the Law of Election provided the regulations for the conduct of elections for the lower house. The Law of the Organization of Courts became effective in the same month, setting up the Supreme Court, the Courts of Appeal, District Courts, and Local Courts. In October the Court of Administrative Litigation was established to handle litigation arising from administrative actions. Prior to this, the ordinary courts had jurisdiction over disputes involving violations of rights of individuals by administrative officials.

The Board of Audit provided for in the Constitution was established in May, 1889, independently of the government and placed directly under the Emperor. This was a necessary step in the tightening of control over the accounts. Auditing of government accounts was first started in 1871 by the Department of Finance. Ten years later, the Board of Audit, which was in the Council of State, was given the power to review as well as formulate departmental budget estimates. However, in the following year, 1882, this power was revoked, leaving to it only the function of auditing the final accounts of the government.

In December, 1889, cabinet regulations were revised, resulting in the strengthening of the Cabinet and also in giving the position of quasi-independence to the War and Navy Ministers, who were given direct access to the Emperor on strictly military matters. Thus, the government had now completed all the necessary preparations for the opening of the Diet in 1890, which would mark the beginning of the Constitutional period.

Chapter 13. Diplomatic Struggle for Equality

In the intervening years between the arrival of Perry and the Meiji Restoration, Japan learned a great deal from the West in the field of diplomacy and international economics, especially under the painstaking and patient tutelage of the great American, Townsend Harris. Yet, in spite of Japan's astonishing willingness and capacity to learn, what she had mastered was still woefully inadequate to carry her unscathed through the vicissitudes of international affairs. Especially the art of diplomacy was not to be mastered overnight; it had to be learned through constant practice and unremitting efforts in solving difficult problems. To some extent these shortcomings, that were inherent in a newly established and inexperienced foreign service, were offset by the securing of experts, mostly Americans, as diplomatic advisers. It was not until the last decade of the nineteenth century that Japan could regard her conduct of foreign relations as anywhere near the level of skill that existed in the countries of the West.

One of the earliest acts of the newly established Meiji Government was to set up on January 9, 1868, an office to handle its foreign relations. A few days later, an imperial announcement of the Restoration was made, proclaiming to the sovereigns and peoples of all the foreign powers that permission had been granted to Shogun Tokugawa Yoshinobu to surrender his political powers to the Emperor, and that the Emperor himself was henceforth to exercise supreme authority in foreign relations as well as in the internal affairs of the nation. It also declared that the title of Emperor was to be substituted for that of Tycoon, which had been in use in the existing treaties that were to be continued in force.

This proclamation made unequivocally clear the location of sovereignty, a question that previously had not always been clear to the foreign representatives. Then, in March, the Emperor granted an audience to the diplomatic representatives of France, the Netherlands, and Great Britain at the Imperial Palace in Kyōto. This was the first time in the history of Japan that foreigners were admitted to the presence of the Emperor. It was an unprecedented act, symbolic of the new role the Emperor was to play in the conduct of foreign relations. At the same time, it was a convincing demonstration of the fact that he had come out of the seclusion in which he had been kept all during the almost seven centuries of feudalism.

In the armed clashes that were taking place between the die-hard supporters of the Shogunate and the government the representatives of the powers came out with a declaration of neutrality on January 28, 1868, as had been requested by the

174

Japanese. Instead of putting the rebels at a disadvantage by demanding neutrality, as the government had hoped, it found itself with its own hands tied. In transporting troops and supplies by sea to the northeastern provinces, the government discovered much to its chagrin that it could not secure the much needed assistance of the foreign powers, who were now committed to the observance of strict neutrality. What was even more vexing to the government was the complication which developed to prevent the use of an armored ship. The S.S. *Stonewall Jackson,* which the Confederacy had originally purchased from France, was bought by the Shogunate after the end of the Civil War. On April 2, 1868, Lieutenant George Brown of the U.S. Navy brought the ship into Yokohama, but the American Minister, Van Valkenburgh, in strict observance of neutrality, refused to turn it over to the government, which was anxious to use it against Enomoto, the Shogun's naval officer, who had the control of the seas at the time.

When the northeastern provinces were completely pacified in September with the capture of the Aizu Castle, the government made an overture to the foreign representatives for the termination of their neutrality declaration, but the powers would not easily agree to such an action. Finally, on December 28, after Iwakura Tomomi had negotiated with the foreign representatives in Yokohama, the neutrality declaration was withdrawn by the powers and the United States turned the armored ship over to the Japanese government. By using the armed vessel to spearhead the attack on Hakodate, the government was able to force the surrender of Enomoto.

An international complication nearly arose when the Japanese government discovered that some French army and navy officers and noncommissioned officers had been fighting under Enomoto. Among them were artillery Captain Brunet and three noncommissioned officers who had originally been invited by the Shogunate to serve as military instructors, but who were suspected of participating in the fighting at Hakodate under secret orders from Léon Roches, the French Minister. A few days before the fall of the city, they were quietly whisked away aboard a French warship and taken to Saigon. When, in May, 1869, the government demanded an explanation, the French Minister Outrey gave assurance that the participants would be court-martialed for their violation of neutrality, and the incident was closed.

The Franco-Prussian War, which soon followed, provided Japan with the first opportunity for a declaration of neutrality. When diplomatic relations between France and Germany were severed, the representatives of the two powers requested and obtained a formal declaration of neutrality from Japan, on July 28, 1870. The government thereafter prohibited such discussion of the war as might be construed an unneutral act, declared the region within a three-mile limit from the shore as its territorial waters, and sent warships to the treaty ports on patrol duty to enforce strict neutrality.

From early 1868 to the summer of 1869, the machinery for the conduct of foreign relations was in a constant flux, as the government groped in its attempt to find a satisfactory system. The name of the office as well as its structure was changed at least twice during this period. Finally in the summer of 1869, it acquired a semblance of stability and adopted the name that has come down to the present: the *Gaimushō*, or the Ministry of Foreign Affairs. Sawa Nobuyoshi was appointed Foreign Minister. Toward the end of 1871 consuls and consul-generals were appointed for the first time and representatives were sent abroad. Among the first to be sent to represent Japan abroad were Sameshima Naonobu, who was accredited concurrently to Great Britain, France, and Germany as resident minister to those powers, and Mori Arinori, who was stationed in the United States as first resident minister at Washington.

That the first treaties with the Western powers concluded by the Shogun's government should have been somewhat disadvantageous to Japan was inevitable in view of the attitude of the West toward the nations of Asia. The feudal government soon began to feel the practical disadvantages and the stigma of inferiority to which the nation was subjected and began thinking seriously of revision, although it was unable to take any concrete steps. It remained, therefore, for the new government to initiate the process of treaty revision, a task which had been handed down by the Shogunate as unfinished business. Needless to say, the leaders of the Meiji Government were not altogether blameless for the stigma of unequal treaties, since it was through the government's ignorance of international law and diplomacy that the nation came to suffer further indignities and disadvantages. The most notable case in point was the negotiation of a treaty of commerce with Austria-Hungary in 1869. At the time, Austria-Hungary was represented by Sir Harry Parkes, the British Minister, who was the dean of the diplomatic corps in Tōkyō. By skillful negotiation, the provisions of the treaty were made far more specific and precise than had been the case in any of the earlier treaties. Furthermore, Austria-Hungary had been given additional rights and advantages. Through the application of the most-favored-nation clause, all the other treaty Powers were automatically given the same advantages.

Except for some of the problems of internal development, there was no issue of greater importance in Japanese politics than treaty revision during the first twenty-five years of the Meiji period. As a matter of fact, it was more spectacular and effective in arousing the imagination of the public. Successive cabinets devoted their energies to the removal of the stigma of unequal treaties. Many a foreign minister was forced to resign for the failure in treaty negotiation.

THE IWAKURA MISSION

It was stipulated in the Treaty of 1858 with the United States that a revision of the treaty could be effected after July 4, 1872. The government decided, therefore, to send an embassy to the treaty Powers considerably ahead of time to inform them of the progress made in domestic reforms and, if possible, to start preliminary negotiations. At the same time they could observe and study conditions of progress in the countries they were to visit.

Foreign Minister Iwakura Tomomi was designated Ambassador Plenipotentiary and Envoy Extraordinary. Councilor Kido Takayoshi, Finance Minister Ōkubo Toshimichi, Vice Minister of Industry Itō Hirobumi, and Assistant Minister of Foreign Affairs Yamaguchi Yoshika were designated vice envoys.[1] In order to carry out as effectively as possible the mission of study and observation, the entire group was divided into three sections. One section was entrusted with laws and political institutions; another was held responsible for public and private finance and fiscal matters and was to pay particular attention to taxation, bonds, currency, bills of exchange, fire and marine insurance, trade, public works, railways, telegraphs, postal systems, gold and silver smelting, industrial plants of all types; and the third section was entrusted with matters pertaining to educational systems and laws, social welfare, public health, and eleemosynary institutions.

The mission, comprising forty-eight members, left Yokohama in late December, accompanied by the American Minister Charles De Long, who, without the authorization or knowledge of the Secretary of State, joined the party as the official guide. Aboard the ship were fifty-four young students, mostly children of the nobility and *samurai* families, who were being sent to America and Europe for study. There were six girls among them, Ueda Teiko, Yoshimatsu Ryōko, Yamakawa Sutematsu (later wife of Field Marshal Ōyama Iwao), Nagai Shigeko (wife of Admiral Uryū Sotokichi, a graduate of Annapolis), and Tsuda Umeko who was only seven years old. From among these students later came a number of outstanding leaders and builders of the new Japan, Count Kaneko Kentarō, Count Makino Nobuaki, and Baron Dan Takuma, to mention only a few.

Before the Iwakura Mission left Japan, the consensus of opinion among the leaders of government was that the time was not yet ripe for the revision of treaties. Therefore, the undertaking was regarded to be more in the nature of a good-will mission to the treaty Powers. It was decided that the greater part of the time and energy of the mission was to be devoted to the study and observation of political, economic, social, and legal institutions, industrial and scientific installations, in short all those aspects of Western civilization that would be of material help in the modernization of Japan. Evidently, Dr. Guido Verbeck had advised Ōkuma in 1869 that the government should send an embassy to the

---

[1] Others who made up the party included Grand Chamberlain Higashikuze Michitomi, Justice Vice Minister Sasaki Takayuki, Major General Yamada Akiyoshi, Tanaka Mitsuaki, Tanaka Fujimaro, Hida Tameyoshi, who were ranked as commissioners, and Tanabe Taichi, Watanabe Kōki, Ga Noriyuki, Shiota Atsunobu, and Fukuchi Gen'ichirō, who were secretaries. Several of these men in subsequent years distinguished themselves in public life.

United States and the countries of Europe for the purpose of observing and studying Western civilization and institutions.

After twenty-two days at sea, the Iwakura Mission arrived in mid-January of 1872 in San Francisco where the members were received with enthusiasm. The Japanese remained in the city for fifteen days, enjoying hospitality showered on them by the state as well as the city. They even attended the session of the California legislature at the state capital as honored guests. Unlike the Embassy of 1860, the mission traveled overland since by this time the Union Pacific Railroad had been in operation for several years. However, at Salt Lake City, they were forced to wait half a month, as the transcontinental rail service was disrupted by a very heavy snowfall. After passing through Chicago, which still showed the scars of the great fire, the party arrived in Washington on March 2.

Ambassador Iwakura and the vice envoys were received by President Grant and Secretary of State Hamilton Fish. Shortly thereafter, Iwakura was informed by Secretary Fish that there was no point in conducting negotiations and arriving at verbal agreements. The Secretary of State emphasized that unless some written record of the negotiations could be preserved for a succeeding administration and Secretary of State, any talks would be futile. When asked to produce a draft treaty and also the necessary credentials investing him with full powers to negotiate a treaty, Iwakura was unable to show either. He had not come prepared for negotiations. He hurriedly sent Itō and Ōkubo back to Japan to secure the necessary documents.

Three months later, Itō and Ōkubo returned with an additional member, Terashima Munenori, as well as the credentials giving plenipotentiary powers to Iwakura. However, the Japanese government had made up its mind to carry on negotiations for treaty revision in Tōkyō. Consequently, it did not wish to press treaty revision at this time. Meanwhile, the German Minister von Brandt had stopped over in Washington on his way back to Germany and advised the Ambassador of the disadvantages of carrying on separate negotiations. Moreover, two students, Ozaki Saburō and Kawakita Toshisuke, who had been studying in England, arrived in Washington and argued convincingly that treaty revision was premature. The draft treaty which Iwakura submitted to the Secretary of State was not acceptable to the United States. By this time, Iwakura had been thoroughly convinced of the futility of attempting any further negotiations with the powers. President Grant's opinion that it was not advisable to negotiate separately and his suggestion that revisions could best be taken up in Tōkyō after their return confirmed the wisdom of the decision of the Japanese government. Furthermore, the President assured Iwakura that in the event negotiations were started in Tōkyō, he would respond heartily and promptly. It was extremely gratifying to the Japanese at this time to learn that the government of the United States was planning to return the Shimonoseki indemnity to Japan.

The mission left Boston for England, where they were received in audience by Queen Victoria at Windsor Castle in December. On the day after Christmas they arrived in Paris, where they met President Thiers. After being received in audience by Leopold II, the King of the Belgians, and Wilhelm III of the Netherlands at The Hague, they went to Germany where they were received by Kaiser Wilhelm. Then, a few days later, on March 15, 1873, Bismarck invited Iwakura, Ōkubo, Itō, Kido, and Yamaguchi to dinner at his residence. The far-reaching effect of this event upon subsequent Japanese developments cannot easily be gauged, but certainly it cannot be overemphasized.

With the perhaps pardonable pride of a person who is conscious of having written history, the Iron and Blood Chancellor explained to the eagerly attentive Japanese how Germany had achieved strength and power in face of the almost overwhelming odds which she had to overcome. He told them that nations could not be trusted, and that there was only one way open to a country like Japan: to strengthen and protect herself with her own power and without reliance on other nations. He warned the Japanese that international law was looked upon by the powers as an instrument for the preservation of their rights under conditions of normal intercourse between nations, but that once clashes of interests occurred between nations, the observance of international law was usually insisted upon by those who found it to their advantage. When it was clearly not to their advantage they ignored it and resorted to arms.[2] It is quite obvious that such an eloquent expression of *Machtpolitik* by Bismarck did not help the Japanese to form a very favorable impression of international politics or the sanctity of international law. Even if the Japanese were not convinced then of the ruthlessness of a power bent on achieving its national ambitions, they recalled what Bismarck had said when the Triple Intervention came years later with Germany as an active instigator.

From Germany, the Iwakura Mission went to Russia, where they were received by Tsar Alexander II in St. Petersburg in April. They were subsequently received by the rulers of Denmark, Sweden, and Austria-Hungary. Even little Switzerland was not omitted in their tour. Thus, the mission visited practically all the major countries of Europe except those of the Balkan and Iberian peninsulas. To say that the tour was educational is to underestimate the effect it had on the individuals who comprised the mission and on the developments in Japan in the decades that followed.

BEGINNING OF POSITIVE DIPLOMACY

Two important developments were responsible for the noticeable change in the attitude of those who directed Japanese foreign relations in the 1870's. Iwakura, who relinquished his post as Foreign Minister, was superseded by Soeshima

[2] Ōmori Kingorō, *Gendai Nihon Shi,* pp. 207–209.

Taneomi, a firm believer in positive diplomacy. In April, 1871, Sir Harry S. Parkes, the British Minister, returned to England on furlough. This provided Soeshima with the long-awaited opportunity to do away with the meek and weak-kneed attitude in the conduct of foreign relations. When the British Chargé R. G. Watson sought an interview with the Foreign Minister, the request was turned down since the British representative insisted on the customary etiquette of having the Japanese representative stand throughout the interview, with which Soeshima's predecessors had complied. But Soeshima refused to submit any longer to a practice which he regarded as undignified.

The new Foreign Minister was not only a man of strong will but also of ability. Moreover, he was well versed in international law and diplomacy, which he had studied as a student in Nagasaki under Dr. Verbeck. As a necessary prerequisite to the strengthening of Japanese diplomacy, he devoted considerable energy to giving a thorough training to the personnel of the Foreign Office. Charles De Long, the American Minister, after seeing the Japanese diplomats outmaneuvered and humiliated by foreign diplomats because of their insufficient grasp of international law and diplomacy, had earlier urged the government to secure foreign legal experts as diplomatic advisers. Acting on this suggestion, Foreign Minister Sawa had instructed Mori Arinori in Washington to request Secretary of State Hamilton Fish to recommend a suitable person. This resulted in the appointment of Erasmus Peshine Smith, Examiner of Claims in the U.S. Department of State, who in 1871 became the first foreign adviser to the Japanese Foreign Office. It was he who was instrumental in bringing about the end of a humiliating period in Japan's foreign relations by initiating a positive, self-assertive foreign policy which did not sit well with the British Minister, who tried to have the American legal expert dismissed. However, as Smith enjoyed the absolute confidence of Soeshima, the strong pressure applied by Parkes proved unavailing. By the skillful handling of the difficult *Maria Luz* case, Smith not only demonstrated his ability, but also helped to enhance tremendously Japan's prestige in international affairs.

Maria Luz Affair. In the summer of 1872 a Peruvian ship, the *Maria Luz,* engaged in coolie traffic, put into Yokohama for repairs. On board were two hundred Chinese coolies, two of whom escaped and took refuge on H.M.S. *Iron Duke,* the flagship of the British China Squadron, which was in port. The British Chargé Watson called the attention of the Foreign Minister to the alleged ill-treatment of Chinese coolies. Under orders from the government, a special court was set up at the Kanagawa Prefectural Office to try the case. Smith, the Foreign Office adviser, and George Wallace Hill, legal adviser to the Kanagawa Prefecture, assisted in the prosecution of the case. Lieutenant Ricardo Hereiro, the master of the ship, was found guilty but no penalty was imposed on him by the court. The coolies were freed and taken back to China by Chinese commissioners who had been sent specially for the purpose. Early in 1873, the

Peruvian government sent Captain Aurelio Garcia, a naval officer, as special envoy to demand an indemnity for the *Maria Luz* affair. The matter was submitted to Tsar Alexander II for arbitration. Two years later, on May 29, 1875, the Tsar handed down a decision upholding Japan's humanitarian action. Thus, the Japanese government helped to deal a heavy blow to the coolie traffic, which declined soon afterwards. But in so doing, she won the hearty approval of the powers.

The Formosan Expedition. Towards the close of 1871, Ryūkyūans were shipwrecked on the eastern coast of Formosa, where fifty-four out of the sixty-six survivors were massacred by the wild head-hunting aborigines. Only twelve were rescued and returned to Ryūkyū by a Cantonese. In the spring of 1873, Soeshima arrived in China, escorted by two war vessels and accompanied by General Le Gendre as counselor. Ostensibly, the mission was to exchange ratifications of the Treaty of 1871 and to convey felicitations to the Emperor, but the real purpose was to obtain an audience with the Emperor and demand satisfaction on the Formosan outrage. In Peking Soeshima succeeded in forcing the issue of audience with the Emperor and established a precedent for an imperial audience without the usual kowtow which the Chinese Court had been insisting upon. Moreover, as Ambassador, he was accorded precedence over all the ministers of the other powers whom he outranked. It was evident that Soeshima was asserting equality vis-à-vis not only China, but also the other powers. The reply given by the *Tsungli Yamen,* the Office in charge of Foreign Relations, was vague and evasive. It was noncommittal on the question of whether or not China actually exercised sovereignty over Formosa. However, Soeshima himself concluded that the Formosan aborigines were outside the control of the Chinese government, and upon his return to Japan, he began to advocate a punitive expedition against Formosa for the outrage. In this, he was supported by Ōkubo.

General Charles W. Le Gendre had been secured by Soeshima at the suggestion of De Long as adviser to the Foreign Office, primarily on the strength of his knowledge of Formosa. As American Consul at Amoy since 1862, Le Gendre had taken an active part in the American expedition to Formosa following the wreck of the bark *Rover.* It was his contention that the Chinese government did not exercise sovereignty over that part of Formosa where the aborigines had massacred shipwrecked Ryūkyūans.

In the spring of 1874, the government decided to send an expedition to Formosa. The explosive situation that had been developing at home as the result of the violent clashes and split over the Korean question had reached dangerous proportions, and the leaders felt that an overseas expedition would serve as a safety valve in releasing the pent-up energies and grievances of the discontented ex-*samurai*. In April the government set up the Office of Formosan Affairs with Ōkuma as its Director. Late in the following month the expedition commanded by Lt. General Saigō Tsugumichi landed in Formosa. Simultaneously, Minister

Yanagihara Sakimitsu was dispatched to Shanghai and thence to Peking where he formally notified the *Tsungli Yamen* of the Formosan Expedition. Whereupon the *Tsungli Yamen* demanded the prompt and unconditional withdrawal of troops from Formosa and attempted to forcibly enforce the demand.

Ōkubo Toshimichi, Councilor and Home Minister, was sent at his own request to China with full powers to negotiate a treaty for the settlement of the Formosan dispute. He arrived in Peking on September 10, accompanied by Gustave Boissanade, the French legal adviser, who held that sovereignty over a territory could be recognized only where the power claiming it actually exercised the functions of government. Ōkubo carried on negotiations with Prince Kung and others in the *Tsungli Yamen,* reiterating constantly the principle of international law emphasized by Boissanade. In the face of a hopeless deadlock, Ōkubo broke off negotiations and prepared to leave. At this point Sir Thomas Wade, the British Minister, offered his good offices. As a result, the Peking Treaty was signed on October 21, 1874, and the Chinese government recognized the Formosan Expedition as a proper action on the part of Japan and paid indemnities to the victims, the Ryūkyūans. By this act of indemnifying Ryūkyūans the Chinese government weakened, if not virtually forfeited, its earlier claims of suzerainty over Ryūkyū.

Settlement of the Ryūkyū Question. In the year 1609, Shimazu, the *daimyō* of Satsuma, brought Ryūkyū under his control by conquest. But even after that, the islanders continued the practice of sending tributes to the Ming and Ching Courts. More than two hundred and fifty years elapsed with the status of the islands remaining vague and anomalous. Then came the Restoration and the end of feudalism. In 1872, the year following the abolition of old fiefs and the establishment of prefectures, Shōtai received a title of nobility and was invited to take up residence in Tōkyō. At the same time the Foreign Office established a branch office at Naha to manage the foreign relations of the islands. In 1874, the jurisdiction of the islands was transferred from the Ministry of Foreign Affairs to the Home Ministry. Finally, in 1879, the islands became the Okinawa Prefecture.

When General Grant visited Peking on his trip around the world, the Chinese government proposed to submit the Ryūkyū question to his arbitration. After conferring several times with Chinese authorities including Prince Kung and Li Hung-chang, the ex-President arrived in Tōkyō on July 3, 1879. During his two months' stay, he made a thorough review of the question in conference with Home Minister Itō Hirobumi, War Minister Saigō Tsugumichi, and Minister to the United States Yoshida Kiyonari. Then, on August 18, he wrote to Prince Kung suggesting that China withdraw certain threatening dispatches addressed to Japan, that the two countries each appoint a commission to confer on the matter, and if unable to reach an agreement, they might submit the dispute to arbitration, but under no circumstances should they bring any foreign power into the negotiations.

Accordingly, the two commissions met in Peking on October 21, 1880, and a settlement was agreed upon, namely, the dividing of the islands between the two powers. This agreement, however, was not put into effect. In 1882, Li Hung-chang appeared willing and ready to go to war with Japan to settle the question, but John Russell Young, the American Minister, urged him not to start hostilities. Confronted with more serious problems at home, China did not revive the Ryūkyū question. In the meantime, Japan's actual administration of the islands over a period of years had established *de facto* sovereignty over them. After the Sino-Japanese War, the residents of Ryūkyū discontinued their tributary relationship with China. Thus the issue was decided by default on the part of the Chinese government.

Karafuto Boundary Settlement. Russo-Japanese relations became a matter of grave concern to the Shogunate from about the middle of the Edo period. When the Russians advanced into the Kuriles, the Bakufu Minister Tanuma Okitsugu ordered a survey of Hokkaidō, then known as Yezo. In the 1770's the Shogunate brought Yezo under its direct administration and in 1785 began to explore the Kuriles and Sakhalin. The Russians had laid claims on Sakhalin as early as 1804.

In 1855 the Shogunate negotiated with Russia a treaty by which the boundary in the Kuriles was fixed between the islands of Iturup and Urup, but Sakhalin was left in joint occupation. Four years later Count Muraviev, the Governor-General of the Maritime Province, arrived in Edo with a naval force and demanded the cession of the entire island, but the Japanese refused to yield to the demand. In 1862, the two powers agreed in principle to dividing the island at the 50th parallel, but the agreement was not formally effectuated because of the pressure of domestic affairs which preoccupied the Shogunate. In 1866 the Shogunate sent an envoy to St. Petersburg in an attempt to reach a settlement, but nothing was accomplished.

When William H. Seward arrived in Tōkyō in October, 1870, on his round-the-world tour, Foreign Minister Sawa sought the good offices of the former Secretary of State to secure the mediation of the United States in the boundary dispute. Seward suggested that Japan purchase the island just as the United States had purchased Alaska, a negotiation in which he himself had taken an active part only a few years earlier. Acting on this suggestion, Foreign Minister Soeshima proposed the purchase of Russian claims to Sakhalin (north of the 50th parallel) to the newly arrived Russian minister. Since the Russian representative could not agree, the matter was dropped. Meanwhile, the boundary question was lost completely in the serious debate which raged on how to deal with Korea, an issue which threatened to destroy the unity of the government.

A few years later, Kuroda Kiyotaka, the then Deputy Commissioner of Colonization and Development of Hokkaidō, submitted his views to the government, pointing out the great difficulties of administering Karafuto and proposing the abandonment of the island altogether. His recommendation was based on his eagerness to remove every possible cause of friction which might lead eventually to a clash with Russia and at the same time concentrate all the energies on the development of Hokkaidō. This proposal was accepted by Sanjō, Iwakura, and Ōkubo, who were advocates of a policy giving priority to internal developments as opposed to a policy of actively promoting foreign relations, which, they believed, would dissipate the energy of the nation. Thus, a plan for the disposition of Sakhalin was decided upon arbitrarily by the small oligarchy in power and without consulting the views of other officials.

In January, 1874, Admiral Enomoto Takeaki was appointed Minister to St. Petersburg for the express purpose of negotiating the boundary question. The Russian government appointed the Director of the Asiatic Bureau of its Foreign Office as plenipotentiary. Discussions were begun on August 29 and a treaty was signed on May 7 of the following year. According to this treaty, Japan surrendered all her claims to Sakhalin in exchange for all the islands of the northern Kuriles, beginning with Urup, which had been occupied by Russia. This island had been Russia's reimbursement for the money expended on public works in Sakhalin, and for fishing rights in the Okhotsk Sea and around Kamchatka. Settlement of the boundary question, which had been the subject of repeated negotiations over a long period of time, was finally achieved. However, the public was highly critical of the treaty as a diplomatic defeat on the part of the short-sighted government. Contrary to Kuroda's hope, the treaty did not contribute to the building up of harmonious relations between the two nations, although it cannot be denied that it relieved the tension for the time.

OGASAWARA ISLANDS RECOGNIZED AS JAPAN'S POSSESSION, 1875

In 1861, the Shogunate formally notified Townsend Harris, the American Minister, of its intention to reoccupy the Ogasawara Islands, which it claimed by right of discovery in 1593 by Ogasawara Sadayori, a claim which was not conclusive by any means. Because of the great distance from the homeland, the islands had never been settled by a large number of people, owing partly, of course, to the policy of seclusion which was in effect. Matters were complicated as there were other claimants.

An English sea captain touched the islands in 1827 and planted the Union Jack. A quarter century later, in 1853, Commodore Perry claimed the islands for the United States on the basis of Commodore Kelly's act of taking possession of the Coffin group; and at one time there were several Americans on the islands. Thus, three powers, Japan, Great Britain, and the United States claimed the Bonins.

Active colonization efforts were begun in earnest in 1861, when the Bakufu decided to station a regular official to administer the islands, and immigrants were sent out to settle there. Commissioner of Foreign Affairs Mizuno Tadanori went to the islands in person for this purpose. In 1873, Secretary of State Hamilton Fish formally ruled that the possession of the islands had never been expressly sanctioned by the United States government and therefore those citizens who had gone there were to be regarded as having expatriated themselves.[3] Two years later the United States exerted efforts in Japan's behalf and succeeded in getting the powers to recognize the islands as a Japanese possession. Thus, the Japanese came into undisputed possession of the islands which were incorporated in October, 1880, into the Tōkyō metropolitan prefecture, and an official was sent out to look after its administration.

KOREAN RELATIONS

Immediately following the Restoration, in 1868, the Japanese government informed the Korean government of the end of the Shogunate through Sō Shigemasa, *daimyō* of Tsushima, with whose family the relations with Korea had been conducted during the entire Tokugawa period. Since the form of the diplomatic correspondence was at variance with that which had been used previously and the term "Emperor" was used throughout, the Korean government construed this as the initial step in an attempt on the part of Japan to place the peninsula in a position of subservience, if not suzerainty, and flatly refused even to accept the communication.

The Foreign Office in 1870 sent one of its officials to explain to the Korean government the political changes that had been effected with the restoration of political powers to the Emperor by the Shogunate. Still the attitude of the Korean government showed no visible signs of change. Upon his return from the unsuccessful mission, Sada advocated the conquest of Korea. In this he was supported by Kido Takayoshi, Itagaki Taisuke, and Gotō Shōjirō. Later in the year Yoshioka Kōki was sent for the same purpose and was met with the same attitude.

As we have already seen, the appointment of Soeshima as Foreign Minister on November 4, 1871, brought about a visible change in the government's conduct of foreign relations. On August 18, 1872, Hanabusa Yoshimoto, Moriyama Shigeru, and Hirotsu were dispatched to Korea, to prevail upon the Korean government to reopen friendly intercourse but all of them returned without having made any progress.

Since the Korean King was a minor, his father, known by his title Taiwunkun, was acting as Regent. An incurable and unremitting reactionary, he banned Christianity, and persecuted Christians, ruthlessly massacring them. He carried

[3] U.S. Department of State, *Foreign Relations of the United States,* 1874, pp. 635, 637.

out an antiforeign policy, including the Japanese in the category of "Western barbarians." By 1873 anti-Japanese violence had reached alarming proportions. Threatening demonstrations were held near the Japanese legation (*Sōryōkan*) in Fusan and blistering denunciations and epithets were hurled at the Japanese for having yielded to the Western barbarians and adopted their ways. To the antiforeign Koreans the Japanese were the Oriental renegades who had sold their soul to the hated Westerners. Incensed by the difficult and arbitrary behavior of the Korean government, sentiment among the Japanese leaders and the public was roused to a high pitch and a punitive expedition against Korea became a topic of heated discussion both in and out of government. In 1873 the Korean question had become one of the gravest political issues before the nation. A decision to send Saigō as special envoy to Korea to demand satisfaction had been given imperial sanction in the summer of that year, only to be reversed in the fall upon the return of Iwakura and his group from an extensive inspection tour of America and Europe.

Taiwunkun Retires. In the fall of 1873, about the time the violent discussion of the Korean question was coming to an end in Japan, the King attained majority and Taiwunkun retired. The Queen's family, the Min, anxious to exercise power, had planned the retirement of the Regent. In an attempt to secure the good will of the foreign powers and establish popularity at home, it reversed the antiforeign policy which Taiwunkun had been pursuing and took steps to improve relations with Japan. But the supporters of Taiwunkun planned a return for the former Regent.

An attempt to remedy the unsatisfactory relations was made again in February, 1875, when Moriyama was sent to Korea, this time bearing a communication from the Foreign Minister to the Korean government. But this mission ended in failure, as the friction within the Korean government precluded any sort of agreement. Convinced of the effectiveness of a demonstration of force, the government decided to dispatch warships from time to time to the Korean coast ostensibly to engage in coastal survey.

Kanghwa Treaty. In September a warship on a survey mission, which had put in at Kanghwa to take on fuel and water, was fired upon by a Korean shore battery. A battle ensued on September 21, and the Japanese captured the fort. The government dispatched Kuroda Kiyotaka, who was instructed to obtain a commercial treaty in lieu of an indemnity. The negotiations were not proceeding satisfactorily because of dissension within the Korean government, but when an ultimatum was presented, the opposing factions got together and a treaty of commerce, the Treaty of Kanghwa, was signed on February 27, 1876. The treaty stated with unmistakable clarity the independence of Korea and emphasized her equality with Japan, while at the same time it contained a provision recognizing consular jurisdiction. Two ports in addition to Fusan were to be opened and ministers and consuls were to be exchanged. Detailed provisions for commercial intercourse were to be negotiated within six months. However, it was not until December, 1880, that an agreement was reached on the opening of the ports of Fusan, Jinsen, and Gensan to trade, and on the exchange of ministers.

JAPAN'S TREATY OF 1876 WITH KOREA PAVES THE WAY FOR COMMERCIAL RELATIONS

The treaty which Japan succeeded in concluding with Korea in 1876 resulted in the opening of several ports to Japanese trade. The European powers and the foreign diplomats in China were most reluctant to recognize, as America had already done, the fact that Japan was rapidly assuming leadership in Eastern Asia, a fact which became more apparent after General Grant's visit to Japan in 1879. The favorable impression which the General formed regarding the Japanese seemed to have been an important factor in the bringing about of American Far Eastern policy favorable to Japan. De Long, who was recalled from Tōkyō for his indiscretions, had long maintained that Japan held the key with which to unlock the East, a view toward which the American government seemed to incline more and more as time passed.

The signing of the Treaty of Kanghwa occasioned the renewal of struggle between the two factions, the reactionaries supporting the Taiwunkun and the progressives rallying around the Min family. At this time discontent had developed among the Korean troops because of the corruption of officials who appropriated army provisions for themselves and failed to turn over the rice allotments to the soldiers. Furthermore, the troops resented the presence of a Japanese military instructor in their midst. Utilizing this discontent, the Taiwunkun incited the troops and mobs to action in late July of 1882. In the flare-up of violence several government officials as well as Lt. Horimoto (Reizō), the Japanese military instructor, and three foreign office Korean-language students were murdered and the Japanese legation was attacked. Minister Hanabusa fled with his staff to Jinsen, where he was taken aboard a British survey ship and escorted back safely to Nagasaki.

Warships were immediately dispatched to Fusan to protect Japanese nationals and Minister Hanabusa was ordered back to his post in Seoul. But this time he was accompanied by an infantry battalion and two warships, *Kongō* and *Nisshin*, under command respectively of General Takashima and Admiral Nire. Four demands were made on the Korean government: an official apology, punishment of the perpetrators of the crime, an indemnity to the families of the victims, and an indemnity for damages to Japanese property. The Chinese government offered to mediate, but the Japanese authorities declined the offer. Meanwhile, Li Hung-chang invited Taiwunkun to a banquet and whisked him away to Tientsin in protective custody.

Treaty of Chemulpo. On August 30, 1882, the Treaty of Chemulpo was signed between Minister Hanabusa and the Korean representative. The Korean government met all the Japanese demands. In addition, the treaty authorized the stationing of Japanese troops to guard the legation, the Korean government bearing the expenses of building and maintaining the barracks. China also secured the right to station troops in the Korean capital.

Following the outbreak of 1882, the opposition between the two factions within the Korean government was greatly intensified. The progressives were pro-Japanese, while the conservatives were pro-Chinese. The stake in the violent struggle that raged was the control of the Court and the administration of national affairs. Conservative leaders made attempts to destroy the progressive faction by exiling its leaders, Bok and Kim, who were seeking the support of the Japanese Minister Takezoe and urging him that the best method was to employ troops to liquidate the conservatives. The political situation was becoming increasingly serious.

Outbreak of 1884. Before Minister Takezoe had time to receive instructions from Tōkyō on the critical situation, the explosion came. On December 4, 1884, on the occasion of the opening of the Post Office at Seoul, the followers of Bok and Kim set fire to nearby buildings and, in the resulting confusion, assassinated several cabinet ministers of the conservative faction. They rejected the Min family and, with the King on their side, issued a proclamation announcing a political reform. A new Cabinet was formed by the progressives and simultaneously a request for protection was made to the Japanese Minister in the name of the King. In response, a company of Japanese troops was dispatched to guard the Palace. The Min family countered by appealing to Yuan Shih-k'ai, the Chinese Resident. Some 2,000 Chinese troops were dispatched to the Palace where they clashed with the Japanese troops. The King managed to slip out of the Palace and sought Yuan's protection. Minister Takezoe fled to Jinsen while Kim and Bok escaped to Japan.

Early in January, 1885, Foreign Minister Inoue Kaoru arrived in Seoul under guard and concluded a treaty by which the Korean government indemnified the Japanese for the loss of life and property suffered in the outbreak. But since the clash was actually between Chinese and Japanese arms, it was imperative that tension between the two powers be relieved. For a time at least the deterioration of Sino-Japanese relations was arrested. In the spring of 1885, Imperial Household Minister Itō Hirobumi arrived in China in an attempt to improve the relationship between the two countries. After negotiations with Li Hung-chang in Tientsin he concluded the Tientsin Convention (also known as the Li-Itō Convention). By this agreement, troops of both countries were to be completely withdrawn from Korea within four months, and in the event of any disturbance necessitating the dispatch of troops, notice was to be given in writing in advance. Upon settlement of the matter, troops were to be withdrawn without delay. It also provided that neither Chinese nor Japanese were to be employed as instructors in the organization and training of the Korean army.

While the ostensible aim of the progressives was to achieve independence by shaking off Chinese domination, the real purpose of Kim, Bok, and their followers was to take over the power and influence which were being exercised by the Min family. In other words, while advocating reforms on the one hand, they were intent on realizing their own ambitions on the other. Unable to see through the ulterior motives of the progressives, Minister Takezoe was completely taken in and used by a faction which was trying to gain power in the name of independence and progress.

SINO-JAPANESE RELATIONS

In the summer of 1870, the Foreign Office sent Yanagihara Sakimitsu and Hanabusa Yoshimoto to China to start preliminary negotiations for the opening of trade relations. At first the Chinese government was adamant, but when Li Hung-chang warned the *Tsungli Yamen* that there was no good reason for refusing Japan trade relations which had already been accorded the nations of Europe and America by treaty, it indicated its willingness to negotiate.

Accordingly, in 1871, Finance Minister Date negotiated with Li Hung-chang and concluded a commercial treaty which recognized the equality of the two countries and provided for reciprocal extraterritoriality, but without the most-favored-nation clause. It also expressly prohibited the importation of opium into Japan. Foreign Minister Soeshima himself went to China and, after exchanging ratifications with Viceroy Li in Tientsin on April 30, 1873, he proceeded to Peking, where he was received in audience by the Chinese Emperor on June 29. On this solemn occasion, communications from the Japanese Emperor and the Chinese Emperor were exchanged. For the first time in history the diplomatic relations between the two countries were placed on a basis of equality, in the language as well as in the etiquette of diplomacy. In 1876 China sent a diplomatic representative to Tōkyō, the first ever to be stationed in a foreign country.

Yuan Shih-K'ai's Role in Korea and Sino-Japanese Relations. In recognition of the services he had rendered to his country, Yuan Shih-k'ai was appointed in 1883 Chinese Resident in Seoul, where he wielded enormous influence over the Korean Court as representative of the suzerain power. The Min family, however, began to cultivate the friendship of the United States and Great Britain and even secretly approached Russia. Yuan saw the need of checking the Queen's family as well as the Russian influence. After three years of virtual exile in China, Taiwunkun was returned to Korea on orders from Viceroy Li. With this maneuver, China's influence, which was beginning to show signs of decline, got a new lease on life. This move was calculated to preserve the suzerain power of China over the peninsula by offsetting the influence of the Min family and reducing, if not removing, Russian influence. The beginning of Russian influence in Korea was made possible by the Li-Itō Convention, which stipulated the complete withdrawal of troops by Japan and China and the ban on furnishing of military instructors by either. After the Convention went into effect, attempts were made by the Min family to secure Russian military instructors for the training of Korean troops.

Kim Ok-kiun, who was in voluntary exile in Japan, was making plans to return to Seoul to attempt a *coup d'état* once more. Li Hung-chang correctly figured that, if Kim carried out his plans, a clash of Chinese and Japanese troops would be inevitable. This would have the effect of further strengthening Russia's influence in Korea. He therefore ordered Yuan Shih-k'ai to discuss with Minister Takahira plans for putting down any disturbance and at the same time instructed the Minister to Tōkyō to secure the cooperation of Foreign Minister Inoue. Kim's sympathizers, including Ōi Kentarō and other members of the Liberal Party who were planning to give aid in starting a civil war in Korea, were arrested. This removed a threat to the Korean government and the power of the Min family continued to grow.

Yuan Shih-k'ai spread reports of Kim's plans for a *coup d'état* and succeeded so well in his attempt that he actually had the Korean government believing that Kim's arrival in Seoul was imminent and that the only safe course was to seek Chinese assistance. This scheme worked and the Korean government came increasingly under the domination and control of Yuan. Kim was lured to Shanghai, where he was assassinated under mysterious circumstances on March 29, 1894, and a potential threat to the Korean government was thus removed. However, this incident stirred up public opinion in Japan, resulting in a feeling of hostility toward China.

Before long the Korean government found Chinese domination unpleasant, if not intolerable, particularly the high-handed and arbitrary actions of Yuan Shih-k'ai. In order to counteract Chinese influence and terminate the *de facto,* if not *de jure,* status of dependency, it made an attempt, following the signing of a treaty with the United States, to conclude additional treaties with Great Britain, Germany, France, Russia, and Italy and to exchange diplomatic representatives. However, it was met with a rebuff and reprimand from Yuan who pointed out that the conduct of foreign relations independently was not a function of a dependency. Furthermore, he emphasized that there was no need of sending diplomatic officials anywhere, except to Japan. The high-handed actions of the Chinese Resident had become, by this time, a matter of common knowledge among the representatives of the foreign powers in Seoul.

After the signing of the Li-Itō Convention in 1885, Japan assumed an inactive policy with regard to Korean internal politics. China, however, through her aggressive resident, Yuan Shih-k'ai, redoubled her efforts and established her influence firmly over the Korean government. In 1889 at the instigation of

Yuan, the Korean government promulgated a law forbidding the sale of rice to Japanese merchants in contravention of Article 37 of the Treaty of Commerce and in spite of the abundant harvest that year. Although this action was later rescinded in face of strong representations from the Japanese government, it nevertheless contributed toward the further deterioration of Sino-Japanese relations.

Tonghak Rebellion. The incident that became the immediate prelude to the outbreak of hostilities between China and Japan was rebellion of the Tonghaks in Korea. The Tonghaks were a group of reactionaries intent on driving out foreign influence as well as foreigners from Korea. Its origin has been traced back to 1860, when efforts were begun to combine the teachings of Confucianism, Buddhism, and Taoism to form a single faith as a means of preserving Oriental learning or "Eastern Learning" and expelling the alien Western civilization of which the Japanese had imbibed so freely and shamelessly. This group regarded the Japanese as "Oriental renegades" who had lost their Oriental souls and therefore were unfit to associate with. Politically, this group was the enemy of the government and the Min family and had the backing of Taiwunkun. In June, 1894, the disturbance broke out in the southern part of the peninsula and spread rapidly northward.

Although Chargé Sugimura reported the outbreak from Seoul, he did not think the Tonghaks were strong enough to overthrow the government. However, he added that troops might be needed to protect Japanese nationals and diplomatic and consular establishments. Foreign Minister Mutsu was not disposed to view the outbreak lightly, for he was of the opinion that developments in Korean internal political affairs were at best unpredictable. Although he felt that the discussion regarding a dispatch of troops was premature, he decided to take precautionary steps. The Diet was at the time in session following an election, but it was at odds with the government, which had on June 1 decided on dissolution. Upon receipt of the news that the Korean government had requested the Chinese government's military assistance, Mutsu immediately secured Cabinet approval for the dispatch of troops to Korea. But even as war clouds were gathering in one corner of the Far East, negotiations were going on between the Japanese Foreign Office and the powers for the termination of unequal treaties.

TREATY REVISION

One of the consuming desires of the Japanese government between 1858 and 1894 was the removal of the stigma as well as the disadvantages of unequal treaties. Every foreign minister gave his best for the achievement of this end. Early in 1870 Foreign Minister Sawa notified the foreign representatives of the government's desire to take up the question of treaty revision. This was followed by Itō's letter from Washington urging the government to take a definite step to open negotiations for treaty revision. In the spring of that year Vice

Minister Terashima made some overtures, but failed to get any response. How-ever, the interest and concern of the public as well as the government were heightened and in the fall of 1871, Finance Minister Ōkubo and Vice Minister Inoue jointly submitted a concrete proposal to the government regarding treaty revision.

The first attempt at treaty revision by the new Meiji Government was made through the Iwakura Mission in the United States. But even before the mission left the country, the government had decided that domestic reforms should precede negotiations if efforts at treaty revision were to succeed. Consequently, treaty revision was never the primary mission of Ambassador Iwakura. Rather, it was to make a thorough observation and study of the political, economic, financial, industrial, and educational institutions of Europe and America as a preparation for the wholesale institution of necessary domestic reforms.

In February, 1874, at the instance of Foreign Minister Terashima, the Bureau for the Study of Treaty Revision was created and preparations were pushed ahead. Meanwhile, Finance Minister Ōkuma advocated the need for a restoration of tariff autonomy and an increase in rates as a means of increasing national revenues. Accordingly the government instructed Terashima in January, 1876, to open negotiations with the United States in order to revise the tariff provisions. After first securing the understanding of the American Minister, John A. Bingham, the negotiations were carried on by Minister Yoshida Kiyonari in Washington. This resulted in the signing of a treaty in Washington on July 25, 1878, completely restoring tariff autonomy, but with a clause which made the approval of the other powers a condition for its taking effect. Since the raising of tariff rates would have been most disadvantageous to Great Britain, Sir Harry Parkes, the British Minister, raised an objection, which was supported strongly by the other foreign representatives. This automatically invalidated the treaty, although ratifications had already been exchanged in April, 1879. As Terashima's draft did not include the abolition of consular jurisdiction it drew violent attacks from the press and the public, and the Foreign Minister was forced to resign in September.

Inoue Kaoru, who succeeded Terashima as Foreign Minister, resumed the work of treaty revision. A draft treaty in which Councilor Ōkuma also had a hand was completed early in July, 1880, and circulated among the foreign representatives in Tōkyō. On July 16 and 17, the Japan *Herald* published the main points of the draft to which the government had tried so hard not to give premature publicity. The Dutch government recalled its Minister who was responsible for the leak and made an official apology for the incident. The British Government expressed its disapproval of the draft in a communication dated October 25, 1881, on the grounds that it represented a complete overhauling of the provisions rather than a revision of the articles, thereby resulting in the attenuation of the extraterritorial rights for British subjects residing in Japan.

It also objected to the change in the tariff provisions and suggested that a conference of foreign representatives be held to discuss the matters involved. In January of the following year, the Foreign Minister met the foreign representatives in a conference which continued for six months, during which time twenty-one separate meetings were held, without any visible progress. The foreign representatives were adamant in their refusal to take up the question.

For nearly two years treaty revision was at a standstill. Then came an important development. On April 10, 1884, the new British Minister, F. R. Plunkett, submitted a memorandum stating that the unequal treaties would automatically be abolished when Japanese laws attained the standard which existed in the various countries of the West. This spurred the government to concentrate its efforts on the compilation of laws and codes, resulting in the hiring of a number of foreign legal experts among whom were Boissanade, Roessler, Mosse, and others. The Japanese responded immediately to the insistence of the powers on the modernization of the legal and political institutions of the country to a point comparable to those of Europe and America as condition to the granting of equal treaties.

Inoue's Attempt. In December, 1885, a modern cabinet system was set up with Itō Hirobumi as the first Premier. Inoue, who became Foreign Minister in this new Cabinet, lost no time in starting work on a new draft. In April, 1886, he was authorized to begin negotiations with a view to concluding equal treaties with the powers. At the same time he pushed ahead the work of drafting the Civil and Criminal Codes by establishing in August the Bureau for the Study of Legal Codes in the Foreign Office and assumed its directorship. On May 1, a conference to consider the revision of treaties was opened in the Foreign Office with the foreign representatives. Altogether twenty-eight meetings were held between May 1, 1886, and April 22, 1887, during which the most hotly debated issue was consular jurisdiction.

The Inoue draft, prepared by the Committee for the Study of Treaty Revision which formed the basis of the discussions, was modified by the draft submitted jointly on April 2 by the British Minister Plunkett and the German Minister von Halleben. This Anglo-German draft called for the opening of the entire country to foreigners two years after the date of the treaty. In the intervening period civil, criminal, and commercial codes, laws of civil and criminal procedure, and police regulations were to be promulgated and courts of law set up in accordance with Occidental standards. For three years after the opening of the country to unrestricted residence, consular jurisdiction was to be retained as previously in Tōkyō, Yokohama, Kōbe, Ōsaka, Nagasaki, Niigata, and Hakodate, and in civil cases elsewhere. Where foreigners were involved, foreign judges and procurators were to be appointed. In regard to tariff, import duties were set at 10 per cent *ad valorem* for most commodities, but ranging from the old rate of 5 per cent to as high as 25 per cent for luxury goods, while export duties were to be 5 per cent.

As in the Terashima draft, the provision regarding the appointment of foreign judicial officials became a serious issue within and without the government. Opposition unexpectedly developed within the government only two months after negotiations were opened by the Foreign Minister. Agriculture and Commerce Minister Tani Tateki submitted a memorial to the government denouncing the draft as a national disgrace and resigned his position in protest. Katsu Awa, a palace adviser, also voiced strong opposition. Even the Home Ministry legal adviser, Boissanade, submitted a memorandum criticizing the draft and pointing out its undesirable features.

Nationalistic groups as well as individuals voiced indignation at the government for attempting to bring on a national disgrace. Even the liberals joined in the denunciation of the government. When the public learned of the provisions permitting unrestricted residence to foreigners, indignation ran high. After twenty-nine meetings, negotiations were suspended in July, 1887. The Foreign Minister subsequently notified the representatives of the powers that the government had decided to concentrate its energies first on the compilation of laws and codes and that upon their completion, it would resume negotiations for the revision of treaties. Having failed in his attempt, Inoue resigned and Premier Itō assumed concurrently the post of Foreign Minister. But the hostility of public opinion against the government showed no signs of subsiding; it became increasingly worse. Consequently, Itō resorted to the drastic method of wholesale expulsion from Tōkyō of those who were thought to be responsible for leading the strong opposition against the government through the effective use of a powerful weapon, the press. This was carried out in December, simultaneously with the promulgation of the Peace Preservation Ordinance which was intended to suppress, if not stamp out, effective opposition.

Itō relinquished his concurrent post to Ōkuma Shigenobu, his onetime political adversary, on February 1, 1888, chiefly on the strength of Inoue's recommendation. The new Foreign Minister was determined to succeed where his predecessors, including Inoue, had failed. Ōkuma decided, while abiding by the treaties which were in effect, to pursue the policy of making the foreign powers wish for revision. That his attitude was much firmer and more positive than that of any of his predecessors was quite evident. When there was a complaint against the infringement of a trade-mark, Ōkuma rejected the protests of the British and German Ministers, pointing out that there was no good reason for protecting a trade-mark which was not registered with the Japanese Patent Office. He also reversed Inoue's method of negotiating collectively with the powers and began separate negotiations. Through Mutsu Munemitsu, Minister in Washington, he had an equal treaty signed with Mexico on November 30, 1888. By this treaty Mexico surrendered completely her extraterritorial rights in Japan. In return she was accorded more rights and advantages than those which had been given to the other treaty Powers. Obviously, this was intended to be a tempting invitation to the other powers to open negotiations, but none of them came forth with an offer to negotiate. Ōkuma, therefore, opened negotiations with the United States and succeeded in agreeing on a treaty with Minister Hubbard in Tōkyō in February, 1889. This was followed by another between Saionji and Bismarck in Berlin in June, and one with Russia in August. The British Government objected to the draft but later an understanding was reached through the efforts of the Japanese Minister to the Court of St. James.

Strict secrecy was maintained throughout the negotiations, since the government was fearful lest any leak of information might obstruct the successful conclusion of the new treaties. The government's fears were well founded, for on April 19, 1889, the London *Times* carried a story of the pending treaty with its provisions. Beginning on May 31, the Tōkyō newspapers carried the item from the *Times*. Public resentment flared up in spite of the fact that Ōkuma's draft was a vast improvement over the Inoue draft. It was obvious that political capital was being made of the draft, as all the political parties except Ōkuma's own Reform Party opposed it vigorously. Nationalists like Generals Tani Tateki and Miura Gorō were joined by the Liberal Party element in Gotō Shōjirō's Great Coalition, the Daidō Danketsu, in common opposition to the government. More than three hundred memoranda were received by the government. Nearly 57,000 signers urged the abandonment of the unfavorable draft, while only 6,700 persons expressed approval. Strong opposition developed within the government itself on the grounds that the provision pertaining to the appointment of foreign judges was an infringement on the Constitution. Inoue Tsuyoshi (Ki), Director of the Cabinet Bureau of Legislation, resigned in protest. Three months later, in October, Itō resigned from the presidency of the Privy Council after issuing a public statement.

The upshot of this was the Imperial Conference of October 15, 1889, at which Ōkuma defended his position with an eloquent explanation of the reasonableness of the proposed draft. Premier Kuroda and Justice Minister Yamada were among those who supported the Foreign Minister. Home Minister Yamagata led the opposition, which included Communications Minister Gotō Shōjirō, Agriculture Minister Inoue Kaoru, Finance Minister Matsukata, and Councilors Terashima, Soeshima, and Torio. The long-drawn-out conference lasted four days and tempers rose as the issue of treaty revision had been inextricably and hopelessly tied in with politics and personalities in the highest government circle. Premier Kuroda saw that with the opposition in such large majority Ōkuma's cause was hopeless. Then, on October 18, before the issue was settled, the nation was shocked to learn of the attempt on the life of the Foreign Minister by an impetuous youth. As Ōkuma's carriage approached the Foreign Office, one Kurushima, a member of the Black Ocean Society, hurled a bomb at the Foreign Minister, who was returning from the imperial conference. Assuming responsibility for the failure of treaty revision and the unfortunate attack on the Foreign Minister, the Kuroda Cabinet resigned en masse a few days later. Once again the attempt at treaty revision foundered on the treacherous rocks of domestic politics. Forces opposing the government were too strong to be muffled. Aoki Shūzō, who succeeded Ōkuma as Foreign Minister, seemed to be making satisfactory progress, but he resigned in consequence of the unfortunate attack on the Russian Crown Prince at Ōtsu by a policeman, which for a while it was feared might precipitate an international incident.

Soon after Mutsu Munemitsu assumed the portfolio of Foreign Minister in the Second Itō Cabinet in August, 1892, he assigned Henry Willard Denison, a foreign office adviser, and one of the departmental secretaries, to draft a treaty which differed from the Aoki draft in at least one important respect. Aoki wanted the treaties to go into effect immediately while deferring the abolition of extraterritoriality and restoration of tariff autonomy for five years. Mutsu wanted to have the treaties go into effect five years later, all the provisions becoming effective simultaneously. He believed that it would require that much time to complete what still remained to be done to put the new civil and commercial codes into final form. Moreover, he made no move until the Premier brought up the subject of treaty revision, and only then did he launch the program, thereby not only ensuring full support but precluding the possibility of censure from above. Negotiations were begun in November, 1892, not through the foreign representatives in Tōkyō, but with the foreign offices of the powers through the Japanese Ministers. From the very outset, Mutsu rejected secrecy in favor of open diplomacy which kept the nation informed on the progress of the negotiations.

Mutsu was convinced that if and when Great Britain and the United States signed a new treaty, all the other powers would follow suit. On this assumption, which ensuing events proved to be correct, he instructed the veteran diplomat, Aoki Shūzō, his immediate predecessor, the Minister to Germany, and by far the ablest representative of Japan in Europe, to negotiate with Number Ten Downing Street. The fact that Aoki was of sufficient stature and experience as well as the fact that as Foreign Minister he had already achieved some measure of success with the British Minister, Frazer, contributed immensely toward his success in negotiating with Foreign Secretary Kimberley. In July, 1894, the British Government agreed to the Japanese draft and on the 16th a treaty was signed to take effect five years later, on July 17, 1899. For a time it appeared that the tense situation in Korea might hold up the signing of this treaty as unfavorable reports were being sent back to London by the British Minister. How far Sino-Japanese relations had deteriorated by this time can be seen by the fact that only two weeks later Japan formally declared war on China.

On November 22, Minister Kurino in Washington and Secretary of State

Gresham signed a revised treaty and, while that was before the Senate, a situation developed which threatened to hold up the signature. The New York *World* carried a Shanghai dispatch under date of November 28 to the effect that Japanese troops had carried out an indiscriminate and wholesale slaughter of Chinese civilians after the capture of Port Arthur. Foreign Minister Mutsu immediately wired an official denial to the *World* to prevent any unfavorable public reaction. Finally, in February, the United States Senate ratified the treaty which it had held up so long.

Once the treaties were signed with Great Britain and the United States other powers soon followed. With the signing on December 5, 1897, of the treaty with Austria-Hungary, the last unequal treaty was removed and the long struggle for diplomatic equality had come to an end. Although the stigma of extraterritoriality was thus removed in 1899, tariff autonomy was not restored until the signing of the Treaty of Commerce and Navigation with the United States on February 21, 1911.

Chapter 14. Rise of the New Literature and the

Arts (1868–1898)

In literature and the arts the early years of the Meiji were merely the extension of the Edo period. Consequently, there was little that was new or original at first. The early attempts at creating something new did not go beyond the pouring of old wine into a new bottle, resulting in an appreciable change in form but not in substance. That there should be a period of borrowing, particularly in literature and thought, was inevitable and even necessary in a period of planned transformation. This began with the translations of European and American works in the 1870's and continued well into the next decade, when creative efforts began to show concrete results.

Even as the process of sweeping away the old was getting under way, a group of humorous writers, tracing their literary lineage back to the famous humorists of the Edo period,[1] managed to gain considerable popularity. Outstanding among them was Kanagaki Robun, who demonstrated his ability to exploit the humorous situations arising out of the violent social changes, clashes between the old and new, the confusion and incongruities in customs and manners, and the prevalence of superficial knowledge and sophistication brought on by the over-acceleration of westernization. His best-known work, *Journey on a Shank's Mare in the West* (*Seiyō Dōchū Hizakurige*) (1870–1876), was a satire on the superficiality of the blind imitation of the West. Although Robun was never the equal of his Tokugawa predecessors, his works enjoyed popularity, for he cleverly parodied some of the more popular writings of Fukuzawa, the best-known writer of the age. By skillfully weaving together the materials obtained from works on world geography, travel guides, accounts of expositions, and Fukuzawa's *Conditions in the West,* he narrated humorously the experiences and countless *faux pas* of two ignorant individuals who were taken to an exposition in London by a wealthy Yokohama merchant.

However, as the changing conditions demanded a new type of literature adapted to the new age, the humorists were barely able to survive the first decade of the Meiji era. Quick to detect the trend of the times and seeing the disad-

---

[1] Santō Kyōden, Kyokutei Samba, and Jippensha Ikku were the outstanding humorists of the Edo period.

vantages of continuing as a writer of the old school, Robun turned journalist and started the newspaper *Kanayomi Shimbun* in 1875.

If Robun was the representative novelist of the post-Restoration decade, Narushima Ryūhoku was easily the outstanding miscellanist. Originally a Confucian scholar of the Bakufu, well versed in Chinese as well as in native classical literature, he later became a fairly proficient student of English, following his visit to Europe in 1872. Yet in spite of his contact with Western civilization, he never ceased yearning for the past and lamented over the passing of the old culture of Edo, and especially the culture which had developed around the gay quarters. His lamentations found literary expression in 1873 in the *Ryūkyō Shinshi,* in which he mirrored the tone of society, the customs, manners, and life in a period of confusion. He deplored the deterioration of public morality and the license and self-indulgence of some of the clan leaders. His contemporary, Hattori Seiichi, a champion of popular rights, wrote of the new civilization that was unfolding. The *Tōkyō Shin Hanjōki* (*The New Prosperity of Tōkyō*), which he published in 1874, was received enthusiastically. It depicted the gay quarters as well as the life of the lower strata of society.

The failure of the Satsuma Rebellion brought to an end all attempts to resort to force in opposing the government. But the fight against the autocratic government was waged relentlessly, as the movement for liberty and popular rights spread throughout the nation, supported by the newspapers, which carried on withering attacks on the clan oligarchy. When the government struck back with repressive measures, writers resorted to the novel as a means of expressing their political views. These political novels were not the work of professional novelists but rather of politically ambitious young men who aspired to be leaders and had already dabbled in the translation of European political novels, particularly those with revolutionary themes.

The appearance in 1878 of an abridged translation of Lord Lytton's novel *Ernest Maltravers* literally created a sensation. That a work by an English writer should have been translated and published first was not surprising, for the English language as well as English ideas were most popular in the years following the Restoration. Through this novel the readers learned of English life, customs, and manners, political struggles and connivances, social intrigues, the intimate relationship between parents and children, the love of husband and wife, and the gap between the rich and the poor. Appearing as it did at a time when the public was thirsting for fresh reading material, it had a tremendous appeal to the readers. Its immense popularity was due also to the fact that it conformed to the Japanese ideal of fiction, namely, a happy ending for the deserving hero and heroine, a skillful combination of romance and reality. It satisfied the craze for Western things besides. It has been stated that this social novel by Lord Lytton set the keynote of the new literature of the Meiji era. This was followed by translations of *The Last Days of Pompeii* in 1879, *A Strange*

Story in 1880, *Rienzi* in 1885, and *Kenelm Chillingly,* a satire on the fads of the period, which appealed tremendously to the readers, as it was more political in substance than *Ernest Maltravers* and at the same time introduced the realities of English social life.

The political interest of the readers of the period was reflected in the popularity of Disraeli's *Coningsby,* which appeared in 1884. Two years later, when Ozaki Yukio published the life of Disraeli, it was received with enthusiasm. Although imperialism as such did not crystallize for another decade, its germs were already beginning to appear. It is not difficult to understand the keen interest shown in Lord Beaconsfield and his concepts of Tory democracy and English conservatism, which were brought out in *Endymion* and *Henrietta.* These books were made available in translation in 1886 and 1887, respectively.

When freedom and popular rights became the center of the liberal movement in the decade of the 1880's, Alexandre Dumas' works were made available by the members of the Liberal Party. Although the originals were historical novels, the translators introduced a sufficient amount of their own ideas so that they became political novels that could be used for the propagation of liberalism. Even Schiller's "Wilhelm Tell" was translated and offered to the public as an inspiration in the fight for freedom and popular rights. Shakespeare's "Julius Caesar" in translation also reflected the spirit of the time, as its translator, Tsubouchi Shōyō, could not resist giving it a new title, "The Final Blow of the Sword of Freedom."

Along with the translations of European political novels, original works were offered by Japanese writers. Yano Fumio, Suehiro Tetchō, and Sudō Nansui were the best-known political novelists of the decade. They were received enthusiastically, because they wrote on those themes which captured the imagination of the public on the eve of the constitutional period. These political novels served the useful function of working up an enthusiasm for the innovations which were due, and of convincing the public that fiction writing was not a leisure time preoccupation of writers of melodrama, that reading them was not an escapist pastime, and that literature or literary expression could make its influence felt on society.

While an increasing interest in political matters was being manifested, a new literary development was in the making. The appearance of *An Anthology of New Style Poems* (*Shintai Shishō*) in the summer of 1882 was a milestone in the development of Meiji literature as it gave application for the first time to a new colloquial style of language, which was being advocated by progressive leaders. A joint compilation by three Tōkyō University professors, Toyama Masakazu, Inoue Tetsujirō, and Yatabe Ryōkichi, the anthology consisted of nineteen selections, out of which five were originals by Toyama and Yatabe, both of whom were American educated. This fact could very well have determined the selection of the translated poems, which comprised the remainder.

Represented among these poems were the works of Thomas Campbell, Robert Bloomfield, Tennyson, Kingsley, Gray, Longfellow, and Shakespeare. Tennyson's "Charge of the Light Brigade" provided the sort of tempo in perfect cadence with the march of Western civilization, while Gray's "Elegy in a Country Churchyard" gave the serenity in harmony with the calm which prevailed after the Satsuma Rebellion. This collection was followed four years later by another anthology of new style poems and songs compiled by Takeuchi Setsu, entitled *New Style Poems and Songs* (*Shintai Shika*), which included songs for school children as well as selections like Komuro Kutsuzan's (Shigehiro) "Song of Freedom" and "Song of Diplomacy." [2]

This new colloquial style, which was first used in poetry, exerted its influence on prose, as it was immediately taken up by such eminent writers as Tsubouchi Shōyō and Futabatei Shimei.

Nearly two decades of the Meiji period elapsed before any work in the field of literature appeared, which presaged a new epoch. Tsubouchi's *Essence of Fiction*, published in 1885, was a landmark in the development of Japanese literature and the starting point of Meiji fiction. Tsubouchi was the first to explain the "what and how" of fiction, having arrived at his ideas as a result of a thorough comparative study of English and Japanese literatures, which he first began while he was a student of English literature at Tōkyō University. In this monumental work he strongly deprecated the artificial morality of the writers of the old school, particularly that of Takizawa Bakin of the Edo period, and the expediency of political fiction of his time, and emphasized that the function of the novel was the accurate, uncolored delineation of life. There was no place for didacticism, morals, or political views in fiction, which must be based on human nature. The work exerted such a profound influence on the writers of the day that the author has been called the father of the modern Japanese novel.

In the same year, on the heels of the publication of the theory of fiction, followed a series of short sketches of student life in fiction form in *The Spirit of Present Day Students* (*Tōsei Shosei Katagi*), which won immediate acclaim, although the stories that were written while Tsubouchi was still a student at the University were not necessarily meant to be illustrations of his theory. It is particularly significant as a work which set the pattern of the new fiction. However, Fukuzawa's progressive newspaper *Hōchi Shimbun* responded by blasting the work and declaring that, not only was it beneath the dignity of a university man to engage in novel writing, but it also impaired the dignity of educated

[2] Although the beginnings of this new colloquial style can be traced back to the *Collection of Elementary School Songs* (*Shōgaku Shōkashū*), published in 1881 by the Department of Education, and Fukuzawa's *Nations of the World* (*Sekai Kunizukushi*), published in 1869, Yamada Bimyō deserves the distinction of having used it first in his *Summer Trees* (*Natsu Kodachi*), a collection of verses in the vernacular.

persons. Even the *Tōkyō Nichi Nichi,* edited by Fukuchi Gen'ichiro, who later became a novelist and playwright himself, declared emphatically in a righteous attitude that valuable newspaper space could not be wasted for fiction. These were the reflections of the traditional disdain for novelists that had survived the Restoration. But the number of educated persons going into the field of fiction writing increased, and before long, in fact before the end of the century, novelists were to be recognized as respectable and upstanding members of society.

Although *The Spirit of Present Day Students* was the turning point in Meiji literature, it was not by any means a work of great literary merit. For a work worthy of being the model of new fiction, we must turn to another writer. The realistic novel which Tsubouchi set down as the goal of fiction writing in his *Essence of Fiction* was first achieved in 1887 by Futabatei Shimei in *The Drifting Cloud (Ukigumo),* which was acclaimed as a masterly work. Influenced by Russian writers including Dostoevski, Goncharov, Belinsky, Gogol, and especially Turgenev, the novel set a precedent in prose writing by employing the vernacular style for the first time. Although it had no plot to speak of, it contained faithful delineations of character along with the common everyday occurrences of life. Penetrating observations of human nature and psychology characterized the work, which has come to be regarded as the forerunner of the humanistic writings that flowered in the two succeeding decades, culminating in the naturalism of the closing years of the nineteenth century.

Of special significance was the beginning of a literary movement started in the mid-eighties, which subsequently exerted a profound influence in the development of literature. Early in 1885 a literary coterie was formed by a group of young students in the preparatory course of Tōkyō University, including Ozaki Kōyō, Ishibashi Shian, Yamada Bimyō, and Iwaya Sazanami for the purpose of studying literature "for fun." The Ken'yūsha, as the group was called, began to publish their works from May, 1888, in their organ, *Garakuta Bunko (A Collection of Odds and Ends),* which had the distinction of being the first literary magazine. This undertaking was merely an enjoyable pastime without any thought of profit. Their works were well received, and the membership increased in proportion to their popularity, but they scrupulously avoided becoming interested or involved in politics. This group produced a considerable number of literary luminaries and practically monopolized the literary world for the next ten years until 1896.

In the summer of 1886, the Ken'yūsha, under the leadership of Yamada, published an anthology called *A Selection of New Style Poems (Shintai Shisen),* in competition with the Tōkyō University professors' group headed by Toyama Masakazu, which had published *An Anthology of New Style Poems* four years earlier. This was the first publication of the group, as it actually preceded *A Collection of Odds and Ends.*

Needless to say, the few years before and after the beginning of the Constitution was the period in which the literary movement mirrored the trends of the times. This was a period in which efforts were being made for the integration of Westernism and nationalism. The appearance of the literary magazine *The Nation's Friend* (*Kokumin no Tomo*) in 1887 aided the westernization movement. Its founder, Tokutomi Sohō (Iichirō), the most distinguished journalist of modern Japan, was a graduate of Dōshisha, who had been educated as a Christian. He began his literary career in 1881 when he translated Macaulay's essays and a biography of Cromwell. He first attracted the attention of national figures in 1885 with an essay entitled "The Japanese Youth of the Nineteenth Century and Their Education," which was published in Taguchi Ukichi's *Tōkyō Journal of Economics* (*Tōkyō Keizai Zasshi*). His essay "The Japan of the Future" won for him high literary fame which virtually launched him on a magazine publishing venture. Seventy-five hundred copies of the first number of *The Nation's Friend* were sold, and the new literary undertaking was a success from the beginning. The fortnightly magazine, which was inspired by the American magazine *The Nation,* became a public forum, as it carried articles on politics, economics, and social problems, as well as on literature and religion. Its avowed aim was the building of a peaceful, commercial, and democratic Japan. It assailed the unequal distribution of wealth, inequality of educational opportunities, and sexual inequality, while at the same time it worked for the propagation of socialism. It was the first to advocate the formation of a labor union.

True to its reputation as "the great phenomenon of new Japanese literature," it provided the necessary medium for the publication of representative works of the new literary movement, which was now well under way. And with its moderate middle of the road policy, it was looked up to as the bright hope of the new era. In its endeavor to interpret Occidental literature and to help in the development of a new literature, it published translations, original works, and literary criticisms, as well as discussions of literary problems and controversies. Translations of Victor Hugo's *Les Miserables, Jubel, the Detective,* and *The Blind Messenger* were brought to its pages and vernacular versions of the shorter works of Turgenev, Byron, Daudet, and Shakespeare were also introduced. Among the original works of Japanese writers that first saw the light of day in the magazine were Tokutomi Roka's *Green Mountains and White Clouds* (*Seizan Hakuun*), Kunikida Doppo's *The Plains of Musashi* (*Musashino*), and Miyazaki Koshoshi's *Homecoming* (*Kisei*). A superb translation by Futabatei Shimei of a selection from Turgenev's *Sportsman's Sketches,* a charming and sympathetic picture of the downtrodden Russian peasants, was first introduced to the Japanese readers through Tokutomi's literary magazine in 1888.

As the "lighthouse of the political world" and the "bell that heralds the dawn of reform" *The Nation's Friend* enlightened and informed the reading public. Its phenomenal success stimulated the appearance of numerous magazines the following year. Among them by far the most outstanding was *The Japanese* (*Nihonjin*).

A group of conservatives including Miyake Setsurei, Shiga Jūkō, Inoue Enryō, and Shimaji Mokurai, who had formed the Seikyōsha, began the publication of *The Japanese* in 1888, the year following the appearance of Tokutomi's *Kokumin no Tomo*. The purpose of the magazine was to advocate the preservation and enhancement of national values and Japanese heritages. Naturally it emphasized Oriental culture and personages, and its literary scope was restricted to essays and articles to the exclusion of light reading such as fiction. This was an attempt to check the blind imitation of the West and represented the conservative, if not reactionary, force of nationalism as against the progressive Occidentalism of *The Nation's Friend*.

Meanwhile, success crowned the efforts of the coterie of young student writers who had launched a literary movement through the Ken'yūsha. Several of the members became distinguished novelists of the day. Yamada Bimyō created a sensation with his novel, *The Butterfly* (*Kochō*), a tragic story of conflict between love and loyalty to the master. When it appeared as a supplement to *The Nation's Friend* for January, 1889, with a nude picture of the heroine as an illustration, it not only occasioned widespread public discussion but raised a storm of controversy. The colloquial style, which the author used in his works, was a distinct contribution to the development of literature.

Stimulated by the success achieved by Bimyō, his former colleague, Ozaki Kōyō came out with his first work, *The Love Confessions of Two Nuns* (*Ninin Bikuni Irozange*), in 1889. In keeping with the general trend of casting off the influence of Occidental literature and returning to Japanese letters, Kōyō found his literary model in the outstanding writer of the Genroku period, Ibara Saikaku, whose style he adopted with remarkable success. His imitation of Saikaku reached its high water mark in the depiction of life in nightless Yoshiwara.

Practically overnight Ozaki achieved literary fame. In 1896, the newspaper *Yomiuri* published serially another of his works, *Much Love, Much Hate* (*Tajō Takon*), which was acclaimed as a superb piece of writing. However, the work for which he gained undying literary fame was his unfinished masterpiece, *The Golden Demon* (*Konjiki Yasha*), which was started as a serial in the same newspaper in 1897 and continued into 1903, when he died virtually in the prime of his literary career. Using a combination of classical and colloquial styles and showing Occidental influence, he depicted the changing social order of the period following the Sino-Japanese War, bringing out clearly the increasing conflicts in life caused by economic prosperity and materialism, particularly the havoc that wealth had wrought in the romantic life of two young people.

If Kōyō could not equal the penetrating observation of life and human psychology which was Saikaku's, he amply reflected the realism and style of his model. His works were strongly objective and characterized by an abundance of common sense, philosophy, and morality. As a man of letters, Kōyō commanded the high respect of society, as his writings had universal appeal and were read by all classes and persons in every walk of life. He gave to the novel the prestige it lacked in the past and elevated the social position of literature as well as that of the writers.

Among the other well-known members of the famous coterie, regarded as the earliest group of writers in the development of bourgeois literature, Hirotsu Ryūrō stood out in his understanding and accurate portrayal of human nature and psychology. Although one of his works was a political novel published serially in a newspaper, he achieved literary renown as a writer of tragic novels. There was also Kawakami Bizan, who, like Kōyō, was noted for his elegant style of writing in both prose and verse. Iwaya Sazanami, who specialized in juvenile romances, was responsible for pioneering in fairy tales and children's stories and has been credited with the distinction of being the originator of juvenile literature in modern Japan.

Beneath the elaborate embellishments of prose, the products of the writers of the Ken'yūsha school were realistic novels of predominantly Edo taste. In sharp contrast to this group and quite independent of it was Kōda Rohan, who, like Kōyō, adopted the style of Saikaku. While Kōyō's style was brilliant, scintillating, flowery, and fluent, Rohan's was characterized by calm, astringent, and masculine traits. His idealistic novel, *The Graceful Buddha* (*Fūryūbutsu*), strongly tinged with Buddhist philosophy, was published in 1889, the same year as Kōyō's *Love Confessions,* and was promptly acclaimed as a great masterpiece of fiction in the Meiji period. His monumental work, *The Five Storied Pagoda* (*Gojū no Tō*), portrayed the powerful faith and the indomitable will of a craftsman to achieve his goal, both of which grew out of his own experiences and his unshakable belief in the permanence and indestructibility of art, and demonstrated the power of faith in creative art.

In Saitō Ryokuu the literary world found a genius who exhibited amazing versatility. After a period of study under Kanagaki Robun, he wrote melodramatic novels, but he distinguished himself more as a satirist than a novelist, and his best works were short occasional writings.

A group led by Mori Ōgai published a collection of poems, both translations and originals, as a summer supplement to *The Nation's Friend* in 1889. Through this medium were introduced the works of English masters like Byron and Shakespeare; but even a larger number of German poets were included, such as Goethe, Heine, Hoffmann, Scheffel, and Korner. Although Mori started as a translator of poetry, he won recognition in the field of fiction in 1890 with his first effort, *Danseuse* (*Maihime*), a reminiscence of the days he spent in Berlin. This work has been regarded as a milestone in Meiji literature, as it was the first short story written by a Japanese author using European fiction technique. He followed this with two others, *A Fleeting Account* (*Utakata no Ki*) and *A Letter Bearer* (*Fumizukai*), stories about his days in Munich and Dresden.

Mori's contribution to poetry was great, but his activities also included literary criticism and playwriting. He regarded himself as the "Lessing of Japan" and hoped to bring about a revolution in Japanese letters. Using Hartmann's aesthetics as his standard, he discussed and criticized the literature and arts of the period. He was generally recognized as the most outstanding literary and art critic of the Meiji period. Mori's influence on the literature of the period was all the more remarkable as his literary activities were extracurricular efforts during his army medical career, in which he was prominent, serving for a time as the surgeon-general of the Japanese army. His achievements in the translation and introduction of European, and particularly German, works covered a wide range, for in 1903 he translated Clausewitz's work *On War*.

Opposing Mori in literary criticism was Tsubouchi, who founded the *Waseda Bungaku* in October, 1891. Through this journal, which became the medium of expression for the literary great of the age of naturalism, he introduced the masterpieces of English literature, particularly the tragedies of Shakespeare, of which he became the foremost authority in the country. With amazing skill he translated most of the plays into Japanese without losing the flavor of the originals.

Interest in science and technology was stimulated tremendously as a natural consequence of the introduction of the mechanical civilization of the West. Scientific knowledge was eagerly sought after by the public. Scientific novels satisfied the curiosity as well as the craving for adventure. The first of these novels to appear was Jules Verne's exciting adventure story *Around the World in Eighty Days* in 1878–1880. This was followed in 1884 by his *Twenty Thousand Leagues Under the Sea.*

When mystery stories became popular in the late 1880's, Wilkie Collins' *The Woman in White* was received with enthusiasm. Kuroiwa Ruikō, who founded the newspaper *Manchōhō*, in 1893 was instrumental in stirring the interest of the reading public in mystery stories. He introduced detective and adventure stories serially in his newspaper, including Alexandre Dumas' *Count of Monte Cristo*, and Victor Hugo's *Les Miserables* at the turn of the century.

The public tired of realistic and romantic novels and began to crave historical novels when the last decade of the nineteenth century began. In 1894, the *Yomiuri*, which prided itself on being the only truly literary newspaper, published a prize-winning historical novel, *Takiguchi Nyūdō* by Takayama Chogyū, who is said to have written it in twenty days while he was a student at the Tōkyō Imperial University. Contemporary as well as historical biographies became a vogue as a by-product of the interest in historical materials. In the five years from 1893 to 1898 a series of biographical sketches of foreign and native men of letters was published. Included were Carlyle, Macaulay, Wordsworth, Emerson,

Byron, Shelley, Johnson, Goethe, Hugo, Tolstoi, Ogyū Sorai, Chikamatsu Monzaemon, Arai Hakuseki, and Rai San'yō.

DEVELOPMENT OF DRAMA

Drama followed the pattern of development similar to the other fields of literature. In 1886, the year after the publication of Tsubouchi's *Essence of Fiction,* and the same year that Okakura and Fenollosa went on a European tour of inspection to study the systems of art education, the Drama Improvement Society was founded. Suematsu Kenchō, the son-in-law of Premier Itō, was the prime mover, and Toyama Masakazu, who was one of the university professors instrumental in starting new-style poetry, was one of the strong supporters. Among the promoters were men prominent in government like Inoue Kaoru and Mori Arinori, businessmen like Shibusawa Eiichi and Nakamigawa Hikojirō, journalists like Fukuchi Gen'ichirō and Yano Fumio, and educators like Kikuchi Dairoku, Mizukuri Rinshō, and Sakurai Jōji.[3]

The proposals for the improvement of drama included among other things (1) conformity to Occidental stage construction by the elimination of peculiarly Japanese features such as the outer passage, revolving stage, and other peculiarities; (2) elimination of musical accompaniment and concentrating on acting and the lines; (3) discontinuing the unnatural makeup, acting, and lines; (4) discontinuance of the practice of assigning feminine roles to male actors and using actresses to play feminine roles. It was an attempt to make the theater as realistic as possible and also to help establish the profession of playwriting as a dignified pursuit.

On April 26, 1887, Foreign Minister Inoue, one of the members of the Drama Improvement Society, utilized the occasion of the Emperor's presence at his residence to present *kabuki* plays with a cast of the best known actors of the period. This command performance had the effect of elevating the position of drama to a position of respectability. Imperial patronage made drama more than acceptable to even the highest stratum of society. It enhanced the social position of the actors, who until then had been looked down upon as a very low caste not worthy of association with the common people, let alone the socially elite.

The Drama Improvement Society faded out in the face of reaction against the craze for Westernization. In the fall of 1889 the Japan Drama Association was organized with Imperial Household Minister Hijikata as its president, and Okakura Kakuzō, Tsubouchi Shōyō, Mori Ōgai, and Takata Sanae as members of the literary committee. The plan of drama improvement was changed from Westernization to the preservation of the good points of the traditional classical

[3] Among the patrons of the Drama Improvement Society were prominent leaders in government, including Prince Saionji, Itō Hirobumi, Ōkuma Shigenobu, and Mutsu Munemitsu.

Japanese drama. The proposals that had been made earlier were dropped, and efforts were made to improve while preserving Japanese characteristics. The opening of the *Kabuki* Theater in Tōkyō in November was a notable event, which signalized the launching of a program to encourage classical drama. This movement resulted in the unfolding of a heyday of the *kabuki* drama which extended over a period of a decade and a half.

REVIVAL OF NATIONAL LITERATURE

Advocates of westernization were overshadowed by the conservative, if not reactionary, forces that became increasingly active following the promulgation of the Constitution in 1889. Emphasis shifted from westernization to the preservation of national virtues and values. This trend was aided by advances in the art of printing which stimulated the publication of reprints of the old classics. Novelists and poets alike looked back to the past for literary models and found inspiration in the old masters. Some of the prose writers came under the strong influence of Chikamatsu and Saikaku, while some of the poets went as far back as the Man'yōshū of the eighth century for inspiration.

The first to launch the movement for the revival of national literature was Ochiai Naobumi. Deprecating the extreme westernization movement of his time, he eloquently upheld the great value of a national language and literature and contributed to the rise of national consciousness in literature. Together with Konakamura Yoshikata and Hagino Yoshiyuki, he compiled and edited in 1890 *A Complete Collection of Japanese Literature* (*Nihon Bungaku Zensho*), which made accessible to the public for the first time the masterpieces of Japanese literature, hitherto unavailable to all but a few of the specialists in the field.

It was not without reason that the *tanka* or *waka,* the traditional thirty-one-syllable short poem, was chosen as a vehicle for the revival movement. Although the poets had adopted the new subjects in such Occidental objects and ideas as the telegraph, the locomotive, the steamship, freedom, popular rights, and equality, they were unable to break away from the traditional spirit, expressions, and forms of poetry. It was to break through this impasse that Ochiai assembled a group of promising young poets with a view to injecting a new spirit into poetry. The efforts of this group, known as the Asakasha, bore fruit several years after Ochiai's death, and a new school of poetry emerged.

A similar movement in the field of the seventeen-syllable *haiku* was started by Masaoka Shiki (1867–1902), a contemporary of Ochiai. After tasting bitter defeat in fiction writing, Shiki turned his energies to verse. In the summer of 1892 he contributed a series of articles in a newspaper championing a reform in *haiku*. In the next seven years, his efforts bore fruit and a golden age of Meiji *haiku* unfolded with Shiki winning acclaim as the peerless *haiku* poet of his age. Not only did he develop outstanding protégés, like Takahama Kyoshi and

Naitō Meisetsu, but he elevated the position of *haiku* to a point where it was given a place in the literature of a new Japan. His special contribution was the elimination of exaggeration and fancy in favor of accurate and realistic portrayal in verse. In 1898 he threw in his weight to help in the movement to reform the *tanka*.

ROMANTICISM OF THE 1890'S

The appearance of the literary magazine *The Literary World* (*Bungakukai*) in January, 1893, marked the launching of a new literary movement, and furnished the crucible for the fire and enthusiasm of the young poets who loved beauty and yearned to live in a world of idealism. Although the works of these young poets were tinged with pessimism and melancholy, it was through them that romanticism was introduced. This in turn helped the ferment resulting in the development of naturalism.

Kitamura Tōkoku (1868–1894), one of its founders, who greatly influenced the tone of the magazine during the first few years of its existence, was sorely troubled by the irreconcilable chasm between ideals and realities. His great disillusionment forced him into finding consolation in romanticism and transcendental idealism. His thinking and outlook were influenced by both Byron's *Manfred* and Goethe's *Faust,* more perceptibly by the former. His works reflect strongly the romanticism which he developed in the course of his struggles against adversity and misfortune. To his dismay, he discovered that the more he intensified his idealism and aspiration for his ideals, the more acutely he felt the inconsistencies between what he strove for and what he had to accept. In the end, exhausted in mind and body, he was driven by despair to take his own life. It was a turbulent life for the young poet, who found himself in a period not dissimilar to the *Sturm und Drang* of the age of romanticism in Germany. Although his life was short, his influence on the writers of the nineties was incalculably great. Most profoundly influenced by him was Shimazaki Tōson.

THE NEW POETRY

Throughout the Sino-Japanese War, *The Literary World,* of which Shimazaki Tōson was one of the founders, transcended the events of the war and stoutly maintained that there was little, if any, value in war literature. It urged upon the world of letters a kind of transcendentalism in an effort to uphold art for art's sake. Tōkoku had maintained that the Creator was the manifestation of the spirit of the universe, while man was a manifestation of his inner self. It was the function of the poet to discern his inner self and express the result of his observation in a realistic and concrete form. To do this inspiration was necessary, which meant that a true idealist had to be an inspired poet.

In Shimazaki Tōson (1872–   ) was to be found the first concrete manifestation of an inspired poet and true idealist after Kitamura's heart. Tōson's first poems, which were published in *The Anthology of Young Greens* (Wakanashū) in 1897, were the sentimental and individualistic echoes of youth's new-found freedom and its joys. Reflecting naive enthusiasm for life and full of the hope and vigor of youth, these verses were the products of Tōson's springtime of youth. But with the passing of youth, there came a change in his views and attitude, and after he published his last collection in 1901, he forsook poetry and turned his talents to prose. From the world of romanticism he passed on to the world of realism once he came face to face with the realities of life. By the close of the century he was singing praises of those who lived and worked in the world of reality. The world of letters too was gradually changing from romanticism to realism as the nineteenth century was drawing to a close. Shimazaki Tōson deserves the credit for being the first to perfect the new poetry, although he himself abandoned verse writing at the turn of the century. With the style he developed he exerted a far-reaching influence on poetry, for there was hardly any poet who came after him who was not influenced.

MUSICAL DEVELOPMENT

Musical development during the greater part of the period since Perry consisted of the importation and assimilation of Western music. Earliest to be imported was military music. In 1853 the Japanese were impressed by Perry's military band and the various feudatories began the training of drum and fife corps under Dutch instruction. Following the bombardment of Kagoshima by a British squadron, when Satsuma decided to establish a navy, the plans included a navy band. In 1869 Satsuma sent some thirty members of the drum and fife corps to Yokohama, where they were trained as bandsmen under John William Fenton, a bandmaster attached to the British troops stationed at the treaty port.

Through Fenton the Japanese learned to their surprise and chagrin that Occidental nations had national anthems which were used on ceremonial occasions. Ōyama Iwao, later a field marshal, then an artillery commander, submitted a verse of ancient origin in the *Wakan Rōeishū*. Using the tempo and tune of ancient Japanese ceremonial music, a German musician, who was employed as Fenton's successor, set the verse "Kimigayo" to music. The result was something which sounded quite English, since the German musician had had some training in England, and his standard was the English national anthem. On the Emperor's birthday in November, 1880, it was officially played in the presence of the sovereign. It was adopted by the navy and later by the army, but it was not until 1888 that it was officially adopted as the national anthem and the treaty Powers formally notified.   ,

By the end of the century, the growth of army and navy bands and the increase in the number of those who had studied Western music and developed appreciation for it brought about a change in the attitude of the public. Western music was no longer the monopoly of the upper classes of society but had become the common possession of the people.

During the Sino-Japanese War, the burning patriotism of the populace was fanned to unprecedented heights. Martial spirit was running high as the nation rejoiced over successive military victories. Military bands enjoyed enormous popularity. This was the heyday of war songs, which resounded across the length and breadth of the nation. Intended primarily for the stirring up of martial spirit and the bolstering of morale, these war songs extolled the heroism and exploits of the fighting men, gave vivid descriptions of battles, or told news of home and the home front. Some of them even expressed the undisguised feelings of the soldiers who were at the front. One of the earliest of these songs was that of Yamada Bimyō, written in 1887 to extol the courage of fighting men. Two years later a collection of war songs was published. Although war songs began to appear with the rising tide of nationalism it was not until the war with China broke out that they were on everybody's lips.[4]

The advent of the motion picture in 1896 was followed by the phonograph the next year, which enormously increased the popularity of Western music. By the end of the century sufficient interest had been created in orchestral music so that the Meiji Music Society was organized to popularize it. In 1900 a serious study of the opera was started, and three years later Gluck's "Orpheus" was presented, the first time an opera was produced by the Japanese. This was the occasion for the debut of the opera singer Miura Tamaki who later achieved international fame as "Madame Butterfly."

DEVELOPMENTS IN THE PICTORIAL ARTS

Perhaps in no field was the attempt to destroy the old and adopt the new carried to greater extremes than in the field of the pictorial arts. In Tōkyō, it was proposed that the pine trees surrounding the Imperial Palace be cut down; in other places there were attempts to tear down famous historic buildings and temples so that the lumber and metal might be sold as scrap, and even the famous five-storied pagoda at Kofukuji in Nara was almost sold for only a few yen by the priest. Things Japanese were considered worthless in the face of the unbelievable popularity of imported foreign goods. Native paintings and art objects were sold for a song, and many priceless treasures were practically given to foreigners.

Great painters like Kano Hōgai and Hashimoto Gahō found it difficult to earn enough to keep their body and soul together. Hōgai was obliged temporarily to abandon painting to try his hand at silk-raising, which also ended in failure.

---

[4] One of the most popular songs was "The Brave Sailor" (*Yūkan naru suihei*).

For a time he found himself in extremely straitened circumstances. Gahō managed to keep his wife and three children alive with his meager earnings as drafting instructor at the naval training school. Literati-painting alone managed to retain its popularity for the time being. Painters of the Shijō-Maruyama school in Kyōto found themselves eking out a bare existence by drawing designs for printed mousseline.

Western painting at first could not make any headway, although there were artists like Kawakami Tōgai, trained as literati-painter, trying to apply to his landscape paintings the perspective and the technique of light and shade, which he borrowed from the West solely through self-study. Toward the end of 1876, the government established an art school in the Department of Public Works, headed by Itō. Italian art teachers, Fontanesi, Ragusa, and others were invited as instructors to the newly established school. Fontanesi was a well-known painter of the French Barbizon school, specializing in landscape and pastoral scenes. However, the outbreak of the Satsuma Rebellion in 1877 interrupted temporarily the program of art education.

Interestingly enough the inspiration for the new Meiji art development came from a Bostonian, Professor Ernest F. Fenollosa, who was invited in 1878 as professor of philosophy to Tōkyō University. Soon after his arrival he took up the study of the art of appraising painting under Kano Eitoku, a painter of the Kano school. In May, 1882, he talked of the decided superiority of Japanese painting and sculpture and pointed out the folly of imitating Western art. At the same time he advocated the establishment of a new Japanese art based on national traditions and history, and offered a three-point program for its realization: (1) the establishment of a school of fine arts, (2) the encouragement and assistance of artists, and (3) the development of the appreciation of art on the part of the people through such means as art exhibits. During his eight years' stay in Japan, Fenollosa was able to witness the establishment of his three-point program.

Okakura Kakuzō, who served as Fenollosa's interpreter at the University while still a student, became the outstanding protégé of the Bostonian. In 1884 they were appointed to serve together on the Committee to Study Art Education, which was organized in the Department of Education. Two years later the government sent Fenollosa and Okakura to Europe to study the condition of art education in the leading countries. They were joined in Europe by Hamao Arata, Director of the Bureau of Colleges of the Education Department, who was already in Germany studying her educational system. Upon their return the following year they submitted a report recommending that, inasmuch as the Western countries were endeavoring to bring out the best in their own national art instead of imitating other countries, the policy of the Japanese government should be to bring out and develop the good points of Japanese art first, and with this foundation the good features of foreign art might be adopted to good advantage later.

This resulted in the founding of the Tōkyō School of Fine Arts in February, 1889, almost simultaneously with the promulgation of the Constitution. The program of art education at first was strongly nationalistic, as it offered training in Japanese art only. In the founding of the School and in the conscious effort to establish a new art and a new ideal of art for modern Japan, Fenollosa, Okakura, Kano, and Hashimoto worked tirelessly. Kano and Hashimoto were the artists, and Fenollosa and Okakura were the theorists and the motive power in the movement. Hashimoto in particular boldly applied the Occidental technique of perspective, light, and shadow to his works to give a new life to Japanese painting. He was also eminently successful as a teacher, who brought out the best in the student and helped to develop their talents. His protégés, Yokoyama Taikan, Shimomura Kanzan, and Hishida Shunshō have adorned the world of art of the contemporary period as well as the latter half of the Meiji era. Okakura stands out prominently in the pages of art history through his invaluable services as a promoter and theorist, although he never wielded a brush. Together with Fenollosa, he planned and founded in 1888 the *Kokka,* a learned journal devoted entirely to the study of classical art. For seven years he guided the growth and development of the Tōkyō School of Fine Arts as its head. In 1898 he founded the Japanese Academy of Art, the crowning achievement of his life.

It was natural that the revival of Japanese painting should retard and eclipse the progress of Western painting. But artists like Kawakami Tōgai and Koyama Shōtaro kept working hard at popularizing Occidental painting under adverse conditions. The rare opportunity for the development and popular acceptance of Western painting was provided by the Sino-Japanese War. Viscount Kuroda Kiyoteru, after having studied for ten years (1884–1894) in France under Raphael Colin, returned with Kume Keiichirō and introduced a combination of *plein-air* and impressionist painting with the academic style which had been the only type known up to that time. The fresh and lively style gave new life to Western painting, and Kuroda commanded the attention of the art world as well as that of the public. Beginning with a nude, exhibited for the first time in the Fourth Industrial Exposition held in Kyōto in the spring of 1895, his reputation grew. Although painting of the nude stirred up considerable discussion of the pros and cons of such a subject, it served as a beginning in the understanding of Western painting, which, unlike native painting, was characterized by realism. The growing popularity of Western painting occasioned the establishment of a course in Western painting in 1896, when both Kuroda and Kume were appointed professors in the Tōkyō School of Fine Arts. So popular did it become that the number of students taking it far exceeded that of those who were studying Japanese painting.

Sculpture was given in the art school at the Engineering College under the

Department of Public Works under Itō in 1876. This subject was taught by Ragusa, who trained Ōkuma Ujihiro and Fujita Bunzō. However, when emphasis on native art increased from about 1888 the blending of the East and West in sculpture was achieved by the new sculptors, Takamura Kōun, Takeuchi Kyūichi, and Ishikawa Kōmei, all of whom were professors of the Tōkyō School of Fine Arts. Kōun was by far the best known of the three, for through the Meiji, Taishō, and Shōwa eras there was hardly anything of importance in the field of sculpture in which he did not have a hand in some way.

Chapter 15. Parliamentary Government in Action: Party versus Bureaucracy (1890–1898)

Constitutional government in Japan was ushered in by the first national election held on July 1, 1890. The first election was carried out with a far greater degree of earnestness as well as success than those which followed. Inexperienced as the government was, it showed circumspection and assumed a cautious attitude, lest foreign powers should comment unfavorably on the conduct of the election. The voters and candidates were in earnest too, but they naively expected the opening of the Diet to overthrow the clan autocracy immediately, to remove oppressive government, and to lighten the tax burden.

In 1890 eligible voters numbered 450,865 out of which only 27,630 persons failed to exercise their franchise. Competition among the candidates was especially keen as they were all eager to have the honor of being elected to the first national assembly in history.

Total membership in the House of Representatives was set at 300, a ratio of one representative to every 120,000 population. Voters had to be at least twenty-five years of age. The candidates had to be at least thirty years. They also needed a record of having paid not less than 15 yen in direct national tax, and they should have resided in the prefecture in which they were voting or running for the Diet. The franchise was limited to men. Only one out of every hundred persons had the right to vote.

Following the election of the members of the House of Representatives, the House of Peers was organized with a total membership of 250, consisting of peers, imperial appointees for meritorious services, scholars, and high taxpayers.

THE FIGHT IN THE FIRST DIET

As a bitter struggle against the government was anticipated in the Diet, it was difficult to find a person who was willing to undertake the formation of a new cabinet to succeed the Kuroda Cabinet, which fell subsequent to its failure at treaty revision. Clan bureaucrats hesitated to accept the responsibility of heading a cabinet which was bound to run into difficulties in treaty revision, a subject

215

that still remained one of the major problems. Finally, however, Yamagata was called on to form a cabinet, but the acting Premier in the interim had managed to effect a few important changes in the organization of the cabinet. The power of the Premier was restricted a little, the countersignature of the Minister was required for statutes and ordinances, and Ministers were required to attend cabinet meetings.

Upon assuming his premiership Yamagata issued directives to the prefectural governors on how to deal with the political parties. His instructions were similar to those that had been issued by his predecessors, Kuroda and Itō. The gist of the instructions was that the governors, as administrative officials, should stand above, and not be influenced by, the political parties in governing the people under their jurisdictions. It was Yamagata's belief that political power should remain permanently in the hands of the government and the bureaucracy.

Opposition parties which had been suffering under the oppressive, high-handed policies of the government were now given the opportunity to attack the authorities on the floor of the Diet, where freedom of speech could be exercised without restrictions.[1] In the first session of the Diet, which opened on November 29, withering criticisms were directed against the policies of the government, particularly in regard to treaty revision. However, after seeing that the attack on the diplomatic problem was not very effective, the opposition shifted the emphasis to the problem of finances as a more effective point of attack. They emphasized the necessity of economy in government expenditures in order to give relief to the people, who were suffering from the heavy tax burden. The Appropriations Committee, which was dominated by the members of the opposition parties, slashed the budget drastically by more than 10 per cent.

In the pre-constitution period it was a simple matter for the autocratic clan government to forcibly suppress any opposition by invoking existing ordinances or by issuing new ordinances. Such a method was not feasible in dealing with a hostile Diet. Naturally the government was forced to modify its attitude and tactics toward the political parties. Outwardly, the government brandished the threat of dissolution while secretly it exerted every effort to placate the members of the Diet. Thus, Yamagata found himself disregarding, and going counter to, the instructions he had issued to the prefectural governors to stand above and ignore the political parties. While endeavoring to placate and to win over some of the parties, Yamagata was simultaneously trying to split and thus to cause the disintegration of the Liberal Party. Unable to achieve its ends, the government was virtually about to dissolve the Diet. To this, the Agriculture and Commerce Minister Mutsu Munemitsu strenuously objected on the grounds that such a drastic step in the very first Diet session was bound to bring adverse criticisms

---

[1] Rikken Jiyūtō had 130 seats and the Rikken Kaishintō 41 seats, giving a combined strength of 171 to the opposition, which commanded a majority.

from the foreign powers. The government finally succeeded in having 2½ million yen restored to the slashed budget only through the betrayal of some twenty-nine members of the Liberal Party members in the Diet. The Yamagata Cabinet discovered, much to its chagrin, that it not only could not ignore, or remain completely outside, the political parties in its dealings with the Diet, but it also set the bad precedent of luring the parties into sordid and questionable practices and giving them an unsavory reputation.

Matsukata Cabinet. Although the Yamagata Cabinet safely weathered the storm in the 1st Diet, the Premier had had enough troubles, in fact more than he could stand, and handed in his resignation. On May 6, 1891, Finance Minister Matsukata was called on to form a new cabinet.

The 6 million yen slash in the budget, which the opposition put through in the 1st Diet, had no adverse effect on the government, and the revenues of the government were in excess of the expenditures. Seeing this, the Matsukata Cabinet advocated further government spending and planned the strengthening of national defense, nationalization of railways, establishment of steelworks, flood control work, etc. However, the government's inept explanation and justification of the new expenditures included in the budget estimate, and particularly Navy Minister Kabayama's self-righteous and haughty attitude in justifying expenditures of the naval expansion program, aroused the antagonism of the 2nd Diet.[2] The navy shipbuilding program and government steelworks were promptly voted down, as was the nationalization of railways a little later. The House had finished its voting on the slashed appropriations bill on December 25, when the government suddenly ordered its dissolution. It was apparent that the first dissolution in the annals of Japanese constitutional government was not in harmony with the spirit and intention of parliamentary government, as it was not carried out for the purpose of ascertaining whether or not the action of the Diet was in accord with the wishes of the people who had elected the members. It was a retaliatory act on the part of the government for an alleged intransigence of the Diet. Part of the blame must be placed on the Diet for its unjustifiable action in increasing the budget revenue estimate by 500,000 yen and slashing expenditures merely to spite the government. Rascality was evident on both sides.

Interference in Election. In accordance with the constitutional provision requiring an election after the dissolution of the Diet, the government announced a special election to be held on February 15, 1892. Outraged by the highhandedness of the Matsukata Cabinet, which was concretely demonstrated by its dissolution of the 2nd Diet, the opposition parties swore vengeance. The government too was making plans to smash the opposition of the political parties. Two sessions of the Diet had convinced the government that without the support of the majority of the members it could not carry out its policies.

[2] Convened November 21, 1891.

Home Minister Shinagawa Yajirō, who regarded the Diet and political parties as harmful to the State, planned with his Vice Minister Shirane to carry out a systematic interference in the election by sending secret instructions to the prefectural governors. In spite of opposition to such a method within the government itself and among the Elder Statesmen, Premier Matsukata gave his blessings to the scheme. The government invoked the Peace Preservation Law to suppress the opposition parties, while at the same time it used bribery in an effort to ensure the election of those candidates endorsed by parties that were supporting the government. Ambitious governors obliged their superiors by ordering their subordinates and police officials to interfere with the election in every possible way. Election interference was greatest in the prefectures of Kōchi, Saga, Fukuoka, Toyama, Ishikawa, and Kumamoto, where the opposition parties were the strongest. In some of the prefectures uniformed policemen with drawn sabers intimidated the voters, leading to open clashes. In Kōchi the officials called out the gendarmerie in the name of preserving peace and sent troops, who fired cannons at the people, burning the houses and killing innocent persons. A total of 25 persons was killed and 388 persons wounded during the encounters throughout the country which resulted from government interference in the special election. Such was the tyranny of the government dominated by the clan bureaucrats.

Even the normally sympathetic House of Peers deplored the outrageous act of election interference, which resulted in bloodshed. Itō, who was then the President of the Privy Council, censured the government and even started a movement within the Imperial Court to institute remedial measures. In the face of adverse reaction Matsukata was forced to bring about the resignation of the Home Minister. Agriculture and Commerce Minister Mutsu, outraged by the attitude of Premier Matsukata and Home Minister Shinagawa, left the Cabinet.

In spite of the vigorous interference by the authorities, the result of the election was unfavorable to the government, for it secured only 95 supporters while the opposition force won 152 seats, not counting the independents or nonpartisan members. However, it set the precedent for vote buying and other corrupt electoral practices. Those who were elected with government backing were dubbed "the illegitimate children of election interference."

The 3rd Diet, which opened on May 6, 1892, denounced the Cabinet at the very outset as incompatible with national prosperity and the welfare of the people. After considerable argument regarding the proper procedure to be followed, the House of Representatives passed a no-confidence resolution censuring the government for election interference. Instead of assuming the responsibility and resigning his position, Premier Matsukata intimidated the Diet by proroguing it for seven days. As a result, opposition against the government stiffened. When the government submitted a supplementary budget bill for warship construction, steelworks, and flood control asking 2,815,000 yen, the House of Representatives slashed one-third and sent it to the House of Peers where all the deleted items were restored. This resulted in a controversy between the two Houses on the question of whether or not the House of Peers had the power to restore items deleted by the House of Representatives. The dispute was submitted to the Emperor, who referred it to the Privy Council for advice. In ruling that it was within the powers of the House of Peers to amend or restore items in the bill sent from the other House, the Privy Council had assumed the function of interpreting the Constitution. This became the precedent for referring questions of constitutionality to the Privy Council, since there was no provision in the Constitution for the doctrine of judicial review, and the Supreme Court was not competent to pass on such questions.

Collapse of the Matsukata Cabinet. The new Home Minister Kōno, who replaced Shinagawa, set out to restore the confidence of the public in the government. As a first step he transferred or dismissed the governors of those prefectures where election interference had been carried out with the greatest intensity. Some of the governors who had been disciplined resented the action of the Home Minister and enlisted the aid of War Minister Takashima and Navy Minister Kabayama. When Home Minister Kōno turned deaf ears to the War and Navy Ministers' urgings to drop the matter of punishing the governors, the two ministers resigned, and Matsukata tendered his resignation on the grounds of disunion within the Cabinet.

Recommending a successor to Matsukata was no easy task, particularly in the face of the hostility that the political parties and the general public felt against the government. In an attempt to find a capable person and to retrieve the situation Kuroda, Yamagata, Inoue, and Itō met to discuss ways and means of restoring confidence in the government. This is the origin of the conference of Elder Statesmen that was called for the purpose of recommending a new premier. The Elder Statesmen were not necessarily in sympathy with Matsukata's interference in the election, but they were nevertheless anxious to keep and preserve political power in the hands of the clan bureaucrats. Consequently, they had been watching with an uneasy feeling the increasing strength of political parties, which were carrying the fight to the stronghold of the bureaucrats. Their decision was based on their determination to stem the rising tide of opposition against clan bureaucracy. Rotation of the premiership, or rather its alternating between Satsuma and Chōshū, had become an established practice. After Matsukata it was now Chōshū's turn. The result was the formation of the Second Itō Cabinet, including all the veteran statesmen of Chōshū and Satsuma except Matsukata. What was foremost in the minds of these veteran statesmen was not the advancement of constitutional government based on popular opinion, but the retrieving of the prestige lost by the clan bureaucrats through Matsukata's election interference and the further strengthening of their influence. This was betrayed by Itō in his instructions to the prefectural governors, in which he pointed out the disadvantages and unprofitableness of election interference, and in which he emphasized that the ministers of state should not bend to the wishes of political parties.

However, Itō fully realized the impossibility of coping successfully with the Diet without being able to control the majority of members. Even Shinagawa had organized the Kokumin Kyōkai, a social club in name, but a political party in fact. More amazing was the fact that Saigō Tsugumichi, conservative as he was, resigned from the Privy Council to join Shinagawa. Insurmountable opposition confronted Itō in the Diet which convened on November 25, 1892. The House of Representatives addressed a memorial to the Throne censuring the government of Itō. Neither dissolution nor resignation offered any promise of settlement of the difficulty. Dissolution would have enraged the parties and incensed the people, while resignation would not have enhanced the prestige of the bureaucrats. In desperation Itō secured the intervention of the Emperor, who summoned the Ministers, Privy Councilors, and the presiding officers of both Houses to the Palace and issued a rescript admonishing them to compose their differences and to work harmoniously for the good of the nation. Thus another precedent, that of invoking the imperial rescript to overpower the opposition, was put in the way of a healthy development of responsible government. Undoubtedly through Itō's clever stratagem, the Emperor offered 300,000 yen annually for six years, taken out of Court expenses, to be used for the construction of warships by the navy and instructed the officials, both civilian and military, to turn over one-tenth of their salaries for a similar period for the same purpose. The effect of the rescript was as magical as it was instantaneous for the Diet completely reversed its stand and passed the appropriations bill for 1893 with only minor reductions. The successful maneuver of Premier Itō gave the clan bureaucrats another weapon that could be and was used in political crises to overrule and overpower public opinion. While the blame rests primarily on Itō, the ignorance and the lack of firm views and principles on the part of the political parties contributed to the vindictive struggles that went on between them and the government and were in no small measure responsible for the countermeasures devised by the clan bureaucrats.

Expulsion of Speaker of the House Hoshi. All the clashes were not between the government and the political parties. An interesting incident in the history of constitutional development was the expulsion of the presiding officer of the House of Representatives in the 5th Diet. A no-confidence resolution was passed by the House of Representatives, requesting its Speaker, Hoshi, to resign from his position. Keen, resourceful, and ambitious, the President of the Liberal Party was a politician who believed that the end justified the means. As he was also arrogant and presumptuous, he had made political enemies. It was rumored that he had made huge profits by utilizing his official position in connection with the establishment of the stock exchange. Hoshi displayed his stubbornness by refusing to heed the no-confidence resolution and, arguing that such an act was improper and detrimental to constitutional government, continued to occupy the chair. After several unsuccessful attempts, the Chamber ordered a week's suspension. But at the end of the period, he reappeared to assume the chair. This infuriated a large number of Diet members who finally expelled Hoshi by a two-thirds majority vote. Had Hoshi graciously relinquished the speakership, he would have been permitted to retain his seat in the Diet as the original intention of the House of Representatives had not been to expel him.

The successful expulsion of Hoshi intensified the fighting spirit of the 5th Diet, which was now determined to embarrass the government by censuring the Minister and Vice Minister of Agriculture and Commerce, who were rumored to have been involved in the stock exchange deal. Premier Itō accepted the challenge with a belligerent attitude, and the matter was referred to the Privy Council by the Emperor. The Privy Council supported Itō, and the government was vindicated. At the time, Itō was the center of power in the Cabinet as well as in the Privy Council and at the Palace. That the stand of the Privy Council was favorable to Itō was no surprise. Failing in the attempt to discredit the government, the Diet shifted its attack to the treaty question. Finally, after having prorogued the Diet twice, the government ordered its dissolution on January 30, 1894.

Itō made no attempt to give the reasons for dissolution, but it was evident that the refusal of the Diet to respond readily to the bidding of the government was at the root of the Premier's action. Soon after the dissolution Itō replaced the Agriculture and Commerce Minister Gotō, who was under fire, with Enomoto. This was to placate inflamed public opinion. At the same time, however, the government stiffened the regulation of public gatherings and, by enforcing police regulations, suspended newspapers that were critical of the government, dissolved political organizations, suppressed the freedom of speech, and hampered the activities of political parties.

A special general election was held on March 1, 1894, as war clouds were gathering over Korea. Instructions were given in advance to the prefectural governors, chiefs of prefectural police bureaus, and gendarmerie commanders, who were summoned to the capital before the event and instructed to aid in carrying out a fair election. In view of the failure of Matsukata's election interference, the government endeavored to make the election completely free of interference. As a result it was carried out with fairness, although the intensity of competition among the candidates was responsible for casualties of one dead and over one hundred injured. Unexpected results were the increase in the number of Liberal Party members and the reelection of Hoshi, who had been expelled. When the 6th Diet met in May Premier Itō explained the reasons for the dissolution of the preceding Diet and outlined the policies of the government. As the Diet persisted in opposing the government for spite rather than in pursuance of any constructive policy, Itō dissolved the 6th Diet on June 2, 1894. Motivated by a burning hatred of the clan bureaucrats over a period of years, reenforced by the resentment against the government for the dissolution of the 5th Diet, the political parties had lost sight of the larger issues of the nation; they were only bent on the overthrow of the clan-dominated autocratic government. Party members had been carried away by their feelings and were guilty of rash and unreasonable actions.

Itō, on his part, was guilty of setting a precedent with dangerous implications. He was responsible for the Emperor's rejection of the memorial presented by the lower chamber, which at the time came the closest to representing the will of the people. While historians do not begrudge him the many contributions he made as the outstanding statesman of the Meiji period, his ambitions, at times, plagued him and nullified some of his good works.

EFFECT OF THE OUTBREAK OF HOSTILITIES ON DOMESTIC POLITICS

When hostilities with China commenced the hostile atmosphere that had prevailed in domestic politics vanished. The political parties, that were bent on revenge for the government's dissolution of the 6th Diet and its policy of suppression, suddenly dropped their belligerent attitude and joined hands with the government parties in supporting the war policies of the Second Itō Cabinet. The election was carried out quietly without any criticisms against the government. In the name of national unity all differences of opinion were buried.

The 7th Diet was convened on October 15, 1894, in Hiroshima, where the Imperial Headquarters had been established. This session, which lasted for a week, was undoubtedly the most uneventful one in Japanese history. War expenditures, amounting to 150 million yen, were approved unanimously practically without discussion, and all other bills submitted by the government were also passed. Still another session, the 8th Diet, was convened during the war, and the appropriations bill which had always been the center of controversy between the government and the Diet was passed without revision.

That the Sino-Japanese War impeded the progress of constitutionalism and responsible government cannot be denied. To a certain extent this was inevitable, inasmuch as the political parties and particularly the opposition forces refrained from active opposition in times of national emergency. Yet, they must assume the responsibility for the abandonment of constitutional processes and legitimate criticisms of the government. This was undoubtedly the result of the inexperience and ignorance of the political parties. The upshot of the situation was that the progress of constitutionalism was retarded. Thanks to the Sino-Japanese War, the clan bureaucracy, which was beginning to show signs of tottering, gained a new lease on life, enabling it to revitalize its autocratic rule without interference from the political parties.

By cleverly diverting the attention of the nation to the war with China, Itō's government succeeded in concluding a new treaty with Britain on July 16, 1894, without drawing any criticism. Obviously the treaty was not equal, inasmuch as it did not recognize tariff autonomy. Neither did it reciprocate Japan's concession of rights to British nationals to engage in coastwise shipping. Despite such indisputable evidences to the contrary, the government broadcasted it as an equal treaty to magnify its achievement. Naively the people and even the political parties accepted the government's word and praised the authorities for the success. Heretofore the people had shown no hesitation in sacrificing anything for the achievement of treaty revision. In fact their consuming passion for equal treaties had accelerated the establishment of constitutional government and had given impetus to the development of freedom and popular rights. But now, with the achievement of equality, though it was more apparent than real, there was a noticeable letdown in their efforts at reform and progress, thereby paving the way for the resurgence of conservative and even reactionary thought and attitude as well as of nationalism and chauvinism.

Jubilant voices echoed throughout the nation as celebrations were held to rejoice over the military victory. The people were satisfied with the conditions of the peace treaty that had been signed at Shimonoseki. But even before the shouting died down the rejoicing turned into indignation when three great European powers intervened to force the retrocession of Liaotung. To the public, which had been kept in the dark as to what had been transpiring in the major capitals of Europe, the Triple Intervention came as a bolt out of the blue. It was a surprise to the government too, although officials had an inkling of what was going on in the major capitals of Europe. The government was in a terrible dilemma but, as related elsewhere, it reluctantly acceded to the demands of the three powers.

In an attempt to mollify enraged public opinion, an imperial rescript was issued, and the government explained the situation on the domestic as well as the international scene, emphasized the overwhelming superiority of the military might of the intervening coalition of powers, and originated the slogan *"gashin shōtan"* (suffer privations for revenge). But public opinion was not to be so easily pacified. Although the retrocession of Liaotung under the circumstances was unavoidable, the parties nevertheless carried on a vigorous campaign in the press as well as in public meetings to expose the real state of affairs and to criticize the foreign policy of the government. Once again the government resorted to suppression, suspending newspapers, disbanding public meetings, and prohibiting liaison between political organizations.

Only the Liberal Party showed signs of changing its attitude. In fact, beginning with the 6th Diet, it had come to the defense of the government when opposition parties attacked the authorities. Publicly it began to support the government, especially with regard to the Liaotung question. When in the face of unrelenting attacks the government took the initiative through Mutsu in approaching the Liberal Party in a move to gain its backing, this party threw off its mask and publicly announced in November its support of the government. The Liberal Party, which had been from the opening of the Diet the chief opponent of clan government, capitulated to Itō's government to become the supporter of the most bureaucratic Cabinet. Such a complete reversal of policy was as unexpected as it was distasteful to some of its own members as well as to other opposition parties. Obviously, it was not a coalition born of the identity of principles or policies, but rather an expedient by which the Liberal Party sought to increase power, and the government hoped to carry out its policies. It was definitely a marriage of convenience.

With the support of the largest political party the government virtually sailed through the 8th Diet. As reward for services rendered, Itagaki, President of the Liberal Party, was invited to join the Cabinet as Home Minister. But the unity of the Cabinet was impaired by a move which drew fire from the other opposition parties and finally led to the collapse of the Second Itō Cabinet.

THE MATSUKATA CABINET AND THE PROGRESSIVE PARTY

Even to the party-hating Matsukata, the political parties had become a force to be reckoned with. His attempt to smash the power of the political parties through election interference and bribery was more than a failure. Furthermore, he had seen what success Itō achieved in pushing his policies through the 9th Diet with the support of the Liberal Party. Although his ideas regarding the parties had not undergone much change, there was a radical change in his method of dealing with them. He saw the wisdom of utilizing the parties instead of antagonizing or fighting them. It was on the basis of this new policy that he asked Ōkuma to join the Cabinet which he was called upon to form.

Ōkuma was the *de facto* head of the new Progressive Party, which had been launched on March 1, 1896, by the merger of several parties, including the old Reform Party, which had carried on vigorous opposition against the government. The merger had been forced on them by the suppressive measures of the government. The new party was not averse to supporting the government to advance its own aims. It was merely following in the footsteps of the Liberal Party. Unprincipled as such an action may seem, it was not at all surprising. Party principles in Japan have seldom, if ever, stemmed out of, or been based on, strong convictions, but have more nearly been expedients for unifying the sentiments within the party organizations.

Due to the enthusiastic support of the Progressive Party, the Second Matsu-

kata Cabinet [3] enjoyed the confidence of the public at the time of its formation. Among other things the new government pledged respect for such constitutional guarantees as freedom of speech, press, and assembly, the adjustment
of finances, the strict enforcement of official discipline, and the perfection of
national defense. It showed progressive tendencies and intentions. It also appointed high-ranking officials from among the people, particularly from among
the members of the Progressive Party, such as the Chief Secretary of the Cabinet,
Director of the Bureau of Legislation, Vice Ministers, Bureau Chiefs, Counselors, and prefectural governors.

However, the *Twenty-sixth Century* affair evoked widespread public dis-
cussion, which redounded to the disadvantage of the government. In January,
1897, in the midst of the Diet session, a dispute arose between the Imperial
Household Ministry and the Cabinet over the question of jurisdiction of the
Empress Dowager's funeral. The Cabinet's yielding to the Imperial Household
Ministry touched off an explosive denunciation of the latter. Chief Cabinet
Secretary Takahashi Kenzō, an ex-*Asahi* newspaperman and one of the pillars
of the Progressive Party, criticized in his magazine *Twenty-sixth Century* the
attitude of the Imperial Household Ministry and the indiscriminate handing
out of titles of nobility. He also exposed the unsavory relationship between Itō
Hirobumi and the Imperial Household Minister Hijikata Hisamoto. Public
opinion seethed as corruption in the Ministry was brought to light. The antigovernment parties demanded that the Matsukata Government resign. The
pro-Itō members of the Cabinet regarded the action of Chief Secretary Takahashi
highly improper and demanded his punishment, but the government refused
to take action, insisting that freedom of speech and press was its declared policy.
In the face of increasing pressure from the Chōshū clique and the wavering of
some of the members of the Cabinet, the government had to suspend the publication of the *Twenty-sixth Century* and other newspapers that were implicated
in the severe criticism.

Although the government did manage to get through the Diet safely, it
had actually lost the confidence of the people and disunion began to plague
its own ranks. Furthermore, the achievements of the Cabinet fell far short of
the sanguine hopes and the lofty and progressive policies announced at the
beginning. In diplomacy it had bungled its relations with China and Hawaii,
while in finance hardly anything was achieved. The vacillation of Premier
Matsukata made it increasingly difficult to preserve unity within the Cabinet,
particularly after the *Twenty-sixth Century* affair. Chief Secretary Takahashi
and Director of the Bureau of Legislation Kōmuchi Tomotsune, who were the
link between the Satsuma clique of Saigō and Takashima and the Progressive
Party, resigned together when their proposals were not heeded. In November,

[3] The Cabinet is often referred to as the Shōwai Cabinet or the Matsukata-Ōkuma Cabinet.

when the coalition between the Progressive Party and the Satsuma clique foundered, Ōkuma resigned and was followed by other officials who belonged to the same party. The attempt to deal a staggering blow to the Chōshū clique by exposing the relationship between Itō and Hijikata ended in failure. The scheme backfired and broke up the shaky Matsukata-Ōkuma coalition.

After the Progressive Party deserted the government, the cabinet members resorted freely to bribery and bought out some of the members of the Liberal Party, but they did not succeed in gaining control of the party itself. Confronted with the united opposition of all the parties and a no-confidence resolution in the 11th Diet, which convened late in December, the government struck back with the only weapon at its disposal, dissolution. That this was retaliation pure and simple can be seen by the fact that Premier Matsukata followed it up with his own resignation. Such an irresponsible act was plainly in contravention of the principles of constitutional government, but Matsukata never displayed any understanding or appreciation of constitutional government or even the desire to aid in its sound development. In a sense it was a confession on the part of the government of its utter inability to untangle the confusion in the financial administration of the postwar period, although it was perhaps more of an act of retaliation against the political parties.

THIRD ITŌ CABINET DISSOLVES
THE 12TH DIET

Upon the recommendation of the Elder Statesmen, one of its members, Itō, was called on to form the next government. This was the third time for the veteran statesman. Knowing that he could not possibly manage the Diet without the support of political parties, he invited Ōkuma, head of the Progressive Party, to join the Cabinet as Foreign Minister. The Progressive Party, however, demanded that Ōkuma secure three additional portfolios for its members. This caused negotiations to break down. Having failed in the attempt to secure the support of the Progressive Party, the Premier-designate tried to reach an agreement with the Liberal Party by bringing Itagaki into the Cabinet. But this too ended in failure. As a result, the Cabinet which emerged on January 12, 1898, was overwhelmingly dominated by the Chōshū clique.

On the following day Premier Itō invited the members of the Liberal Party to an elaborate banquet at his official residence. On this occasion, after praising the strength and aims of the party and expressing the hope that it would contribute in cooperation with the government to the achievement of truly constitutional rule, he declared that he was not averse to acceding to the wishes of the party. In the sixth general election, which took place two months later on March 15, the Liberal Party captured over 100 seats, and on the strength of this showing, it demanded that Itagaki be appointed Home Minister. Because of strong opposition within the government, particularly of Inoue, this did not materialize. Whereupon the Liberal Party concluded that it had been betrayed by Itō and began active opposition against the government.

The scramble for concessions that was going on in China and attendant diplomatic problems engrossed the attention of the government, which found no time to devote attention to the handling of the political parties. Voices criticizing the government as incompetent and devoid of policies came to be heard increasingly as public opinion was aroused. The Progressive Party organized an effective opposition by criticizing the Asiatic policy. Moreover, it introduced a no-confidence resolution at the very beginning of the 12th Diet. Although the resolution was defeated by the successful opposition of the Liberal Party, the government encountered the stiffest resistance against the appropriations bill. When the Diet defeated the government's most crucial land tax increase bill by an overwhelming vote, Itō retaliated with dissolution. The land tax increase bill was the most unpopular bill in the House of Representatives, where approximately 70 per cent of the membership represented the farming population, particularly the middle class farmers and above.

Although the life of the 12th Diet was cut short by dissolution, at least one outstanding achievement must be credited to it. After a decade of abuse and misuse, the Peace Preservation Ordinance, which was issued by the government in 1888 with a view to smashing the political movements and parties, was brought to an end by the action of the Diet. The question of its termination had been a perennial problem ever since the 1st Diet, having been brought up in virtually every session thereafter. What had long been regarded as the nemesis of political parties and the development of responsible government had at last been removed.

Chapter 16. Labor Problems and the Beginning

of Socialism (1882–1912)

It was in 1882, only a year after the emergence of the first political party, that Sir Thomas More's *Utopia* [1] and Theodore D. Woolsey's *Communism and Socialism* appeared in translation. At the time of its founding in 1881 the Liberal Party declared social reform as one of its objectives. From as early as 1877, Itagaki had devoted his energies to the dissemination of liberty and popular rights in his native province of Tosa. Through the Risshisha, which at one time had more than a thousand members, he carried on the work of studying and propagating the political and legal ideas and institutions of the West. It was natural that, in the process, the French Revolution should be idealized, and the Russian revolutionaries praised particularly by radical followers.

When the reign of terror unfolded in Russia in the years 1878 to 1881 the Japanese followed the developments closely through the press, which devoted considerable space to it. Although the Japanese press did not condone the actions of the revolutionaries, it showed sympathy for the Russian people for the deplorable conditions which gave rise to the disorders, and at the same time advised the Japanese government of the necessity of establishing a definite policy on social problems. The newspapers, however, made it a point to emphasize the dangers of socialism. When the news of the assassination of Tsar Alexander II was received in the spring of 1881, many Japanese showed considerable satisfaction, not at the tragic fate of the Tsar, but at the victory won by the revolutionaries over the oppression and tyranny of the Czarist regime.

The first party to carry the socialist label was the Oriental Socialist Party organized in May, 1882, at Shimabara in Kyūshū by Tarui Tōkichi, chiefly around the tenant farmers of Hizen province, who were more conscious of the gap between wealth and poverty than those in other parts of the country. Its avowed aim was to achieve morality, equality, and the greatest good of the public. It proposed to correct the evil practices of the past by putting an end to the inheritance of wealth or property and by an equitable distribution of land. On July 7, the party, which had over four thousand members, was dissolved by order of the Minister of Home Affairs who deemed its existence preju-

[1] Notice of More's *Utopia* was contained in the *Encyclopedia* compiled by the Department of Education in 1875.

dicial, if not dangerous, to public peace and order. If the meteoric existence of the party precluded any real activity, it certainly inspired a lively discussion of socialism. The newspapers had pointed out the evils of socialist parties and clamored for measures which would nip them in the bud. The government lost no time in suppressing the Oriental Socialist Party, as it was quite fearful of the power of socialism, if allowed to grow.

A union of rickshaw men in Tōkyō was organized in 1883 by Okumiya Kenji, Ueki Emori, and other young leaders of the Liberal Party to oppose the newly established horse tramway company which had driven a number of rickshaw men out of employment. A violent movement developed from the attempt of the union to force the horse tramway out of business. The union was promptly disbanded by the government. This was the first time socialistic ideas were translated into an actual proletarian movement directed against capitalistic enterprise. While it may not have been a labor movement as such, it was a resistance by the workers against the introduction of machinery, which threatened to deprive them of their means of livelihood.

One of the earliest labor disturbances occurred in the Takashima Colliery in northern Kyūshū as the result of the inhuman treatment of miners.[2] In June and July, 1888, two articles appeared in the magazine, *Nihonjin* (*The Japanese*), exposing the incredibly inhuman treatment of workers in the mines. Three thousand miners were working under conditions no better than imprisonment or slavery with a twelve-hour working day, which included no rest periods and no provision for holidays or Sundays. The wages were so low and arrangements for room and board were such that miners were in a state of perpetual indebtedness to the mine owner. Sticks were used freely on those who took any time out for rest, while disobedience brought speedy punishment in the form of beating and stringing from a beam in the mine.

A solution was proposed by the editor, Dr. Miyake Yūjirō, who suggested the following:

1. Revision of government rules and regulations for the operation of mines, investigation of the working and living conditions of the miners, and the punishment of mine officials responsible for violations.

2. Establishment of employer-employee harmony.

3. Shortening of the twelve-hour working day.

4. Provision for holidays and days of rest to the miners.

5. Payment of the miners at the end of every month.

6. Allowing the miners the freedom of correspondence with the outside.

7. Allowing miners to go out freely outside of working hours.

8. Permit miners to have amusement and entertainment, except those pastimes which are harmful to morals.

[2] The following year witnessed labor trouble in a tea factory operated by a foreign resident.

9. Release of miners when they have paid up all their debts to mine owner.

10. Release of miners upon reaching the age of 50 years.

11. Recruitment of miners by fair and open methods.

12. Ending of the cruel treatment of workers.

13. Establishing ways and means of helping miners to save a part of their earnings.

The public took a very sympathetic attitude toward the stand taken by the *Nihonjin,* as the press of the country gave publicity to the labor disturbance. As a result, the government could not ignore the matter and carried out an investigation with Kiyoura Keigo, Chief of the Police Affairs Bureau of the Home Ministry, in charge. While there was no doubt that the deplorable conditions were the cause of public criticism, the fact that the colliery was owned by the Mitsubishi interests brought on denunciation from the nationalistic element which did not relish the idea of capitalists accumulating wealth under government protection and at the expense of the helpless working class.

In striking contrast to the inhuman treatment of workers in the colliery, there was one capitalist who was not only concerned with labor problems, but actually took a sympathetic attitude toward the working class. In his own printing shop Sakuma Teiichi put into effect a nine-hour working day, after having experimented with an eight-hour day, a week's vacation for employees at the beach, and a system of employee training. This reflected a very enlightened attitude toward labor. In 1892 Sakuma published his views on trade unionism in the *Nation's Friend.* It was his belief that the strike was a legitimate weapon of the laborer for protection against any unnatural forcing down of wages by the employer. He was convinced that not only did labor deserve adequate wages to raise the standard of living, but that this was a necessary part of industrial development, inasmuch as higher wages helped to increase the purchasing power of the workers, thereby creating a larger demand for industrial goods. As the first capitalist friend of labor Sakuma was called the Robert Owen of Japan by his biographer.

Before socialism became a full-fledged movement, a number of periodicals performed the important educational function of disseminating and popularizing the ideas of socialists and the theories of socialism. Outstanding among them was the *Nation's Friend,* founded by Tokutomi to help the country toward political and economic democracy through political liberty, economic equality, and Christian morality. In 1887, in the first number of the *Nation's Friend,* he published a translation of one of the writings of Henry George. He used the term "socialism" constantly and helped to popularize it. Accurate and detailed reports from Paris on socialist movements in Europe by Sakai Yūsaburō, a protégé of Nakae Chōmin, were particularly good, and aroused the interest of the reading public. In 1893 the magazine introduced Edward Carpenter's *Civilization, Its Causes and Cure.* This was followed by its own book, *Present*

Day Socialism, which traced the historical development of socialist thought, beginning with Christianity and bringing it down to the modern period, discussing Thomas More, Saint-Simon, Carlyle, Fourier, Louis Blanc, Mill, Lassalle, Marx, and others including the Russian Socialists. It was through this work that Nishikawa Kōjirō first learned of socialism, to which he later became an ardent convert.

An epoch-making event in the history of the labor movement was the appearance, in the summer of 1890, of the Association for the Formation of Labor Unions (Rōdō Kumiai Kisei Kai) in San Francisco. Organized by Jō Tsunetarō, Takano Fusatarō, Sawada Hannosuke, and a few others, its purpose was to study labor problems in Europe and America preparatory to launching a labor movement in Japan. Most of the members of this group were back in Japan by 1897, when Sawada and Jō formed the Workmen's Society (Shokkō Giyūkai) in Tōkyō. Katayama Sen who was actively propagating socialist doctrines and Takano, who was working on an English language newspaper in Yokohama, joined the workmen's movement. The organization was formally launched in July, 1897, with a membership of some 70 persons, which increased rapidly so that in 1900 its membership was more than 5,400 persons. This was the first labor union with a constitution and bylaws, which were borrowed from American labor organizations. Simultaneously, Katayama launched a monthly magazine, *The Labor World* (*Rōdō Sekai*), which was the sole organ of the labor movement at the time.

The increase in the number of factories with its attendant labor disputes in the late 1890's caused the government to recognize the need of enacting a law to bring about harmonious relationship between capital and labor. Some of the government leaders were anxious to see the enactment of factory legislation. Although the government drafted a factory law in the summer of 1898, it was never submitted to the Diet because of the opposition of the big interests, who were shown the draft by the Chambers of Commerce to which it had been submitted by the Agriculture and Commerce Minister Mutsu Munemitsu.

A systematic study of social problems was started by various groups that were alert to the needs of the time. The Association for the Study of Social Problems was organized in 1890 by Miyake Yūjirō, Katayama Sen, Sakuma Teiichi, Tarui Tōkichi, and the Rev. Charles E. Garst, an ardent follower of Henry George, who styled himself "Single-Tax Tarō." This was followed by the formation of the Association for the Study of Social Policies, led by Professors Kanai Noburu and Kuwada Kumazō, and which counted a number of graduates of the Tōkyō Imperial University among its members. The objective of this group was to study ways and means of putting a stop to class conflicts through the concerted actions of individuals and the state, but without disturbing the existing system of private property.

The opening years of the last decade of the century found the government gravely concerned with the problem of agrarian distress and devising measures for its relief and amelioration. The study of social reform received strong impetus from the appearance in 1892 of Henry George's *Social Problems, Progress and Poverty,* and *The Land Question* and William H. Dawson's *Bismarck and State Socialism.* William Stanley Jevon's *The State in Relation to Labor* and Edward Carpenter's *Civilization, Its Cause and Cure,* both of which appeared in the following year, were useful to the government. A grim picture of the struggle for existence among the underprivileged in the slums of Tōkyō was graphically painted in 1893 in *Darkest Tōkyō (Sai-ankoku no Tōkyō)* by Matsubara Iwagorō, an account of personal experiences extending over a period of more than a year among the poor in the slums of Tōkyō.

Together with the Iron Workers' Union, the Kyōseikai, organized in 1898 by railway engineers and firemen of the Nippon Railway Company, did much to advance the cause of labor. Early in 1898 circulars were distributed to the engineers and firemen pointing out their unreasonably low wages and urging all to unite in demanding higher pay. Instead of openly organizing and making themselves vulnerable, they sent anonymous letters of complaint to the company directors. When the company summarily discharged the ten persons who were suspected of being the ringleaders, more than four hundred engineers and firemen threatened to walk out and completely paralyze the railroad. The strike was averted by the company, when it yielded to the demands of the workers, including the reinstatement of the ten discharged leaders. Having seen a practical demonstration of the power of organized labor, the engineers and firemen formed the Kyōseikai in March to protect themselves from oppressive and arbitrary treatment by the employers.

The Kyōseikai required each member to contribute a day's wage every month toward the funds out of which illness and death benefits were paid. The society grew under the influence of its Christian members and soon even a temperance society was organized within it. However, the Nippon Railway Company later succeeded, with the help of police authorities, in forcing the dissolution of the society, administering one of the severest blows to the labor movement.

Dissatisfied with the attitude of the Liberal Party, which had gone over to the support of the government, Ōi Kentarō organized in November, 1892, the Oriental Liberal Party, which gained the distinction of being the first political party to work for the protection of the working class.[3] The aim of the new party was to readjust public finance in order to lighten the tax burden of the farmers and to promote the public welfare, particularly the relief and protection of the underprivileged workers. It organized shoemakers, carpenters, masons,

---

[3] Economic ideas which formed the basis of the Oriental Liberal Party were set forth in Ōi Kentarō's *Jiji Yōron,* published in 1886.

and rickshaw men and fought for the abolition of the rickshaw tax. A weekly, *The New Orient,* which Ōi had started in October, was made the party organ, and a translation of Edward Bellamy's *Looking Backward* was published in it. As auxiliary organizations of the party, Ōi formed the Japan Labor Association (Dai Nippon Rōdō Kyōkai), the League for the Attainment of Universal Suffrage (Futsū Senkyo Kisei Dōmeikai), and the Association for the Study of Farm Tenancy Legislation (Kosaku Jōrei Chōsakai). Although the party was short-lived, it succeeded in making a beginning in wrestling with the agrarian problems and paving the way for a labor movement through the unionization of workers.

During the last decade of the nineteenth century socialist politicians, noting the disparity of wealth, engaged in muckraking by condemning the industrialists and businessmen with political connections, who, by means of special favors from high government officials, succeeded in accumulating great wealth in short order. Stimulated by such events, radical thinkers like Kojima Ryūtarō and Sakai Yūsaburō organized the Society for the Study of Social Problems to delve into the problems of wealth and poverty.

The labor movement received a tremendous impetus from the rapid industrialization in the years immediately following the war with China. The growth of the spirit of enterprise, the establishment of huge factories, and the tremendous increase in the number of wage-earning factory workers all brought on a sudden awakening of class consciousness on the part of the laboring class. At the same time the increasing burden of taxation aggravated the poverty of the laborers. In 1897, exactly ten years after the introduction of Henry Fawcett's *Pauperism, Its Causes and Remedies* and John A. Hobson's *Problems of Poverty,* an inquiry into the industrial condition of the poor made its appearance at a time when there were indications of a growing concern over poverty. Recognizing the need for a systematic effort at the education of labor, the Association for the Formation of Labor Unions published the pamphlet *What the Laborer Should Know.* Kawakami Kiyoshi, a graduate of Aoyama College, contributed to the literature on labor with his work, *The Protection of Labor.* Tajima Kinji's *Social Problems of Present Day Japan* was probably the first systematic treatment of Japanese social problems.

The depression of 1897 brought in its wake a wave of shutdowns and unemployment as well as government suppression of the labor movement. On the occasion of a cherry blossom picnic in the spring of 1898 the members of the Iron Workers' Union were prohibited from marching through the streets of Tōkyō. In January of the following year the police broke up the first anniversary gathering of the same union at Ueno Park. In the meantime the labor movement was making progress.

The appearance in the fall of 1898 of the Association for the Study of Socialism (Shakai Shugi Kenkyūkai) was a concrete manifestation of the mounting interest in social problems. It represented also the joining together of the left wing of the Liberal Party and the Christian Socialists. The members of the Association met regularly in the hall of the Unitarian Society in Tōkyō and studied socialism by discussing the lives and works of the outstanding Socialists of Europe like Saint-Simon, Proudhon, Fourier, and Marx. As a result of disagreements within the group between those who favored socialism and those who opposed it, the Association decided after two years to take up active work. Thus, at the end of 1900, the nonsocialist members withdrew and the name was changed to Socialists' Association (Shakai Shugi Kyōkai). However, it became too small and weak to launch any political movement, as the membership shrank to only between thirty and forty. Before the year 1899 ended, however, a cooks' union and a furniture workers' union had been organized in Tōkyō and Yokohama respectively.

Industrial accidents that were caused by the negligence of industrial operators as much as by natural hazards intensified the feeling of labor against the capitalists. In the summer of 1899 the tragic death of some two hundred miners who were burned alive and left to die at the Hōkoku Colliery in Kyūshū caused feeling to run high. Shortly afterward, thirty-one girls employed in a cotton mill were burned to death in the company dormitory which was locked from the outside, apparently to prevent the girls from leaving their jobs and returning to their homes. Public sentiment was aroused to the point where the policy of the *Labor World* was being received with general public approval.

A short work on socialism, written by Murai Tomoyoshi, who had studied under William J. Tucker at Andover Theological Seminary and under Professor Heron at the University of Iowa, was banned by the authorities in 1899. However, other works appeared to focus public attention on the problems of labor and poverty. *Japan's Lower Strata of Society* by Yokoyama Gennosuke, who had actually lived among the urban working class, depicted the squalor and poverty in the slums of the industrial poor, and emphasized the disparity of wealth as the cause of class hatred and as a possible threat to peace and order. *Capital-Labor Harmony* by Toyohara Matao was an attempt to urge the need for a harmonious relationship between capital and labor. The posthumous publication of the writings of Rev. Charles E. Garst under the title *Economics of the Single Tax* was in keeping with the prevailing interest of the time.

Utilizing the sympathetic attitude of the public, the Japan Labor Association, headed by Ōi Kentarō, began the publication of its organ, *The Ōsaka Weekly,* in the autumn of 1899. The Association's aim was the protection of the working class through the institution of a definite program involving the (1) training of workers and their sons; (2) protection of discharged prisoners; and (3) providing of dormitories, free dispensaries, free baths, life, sickness, and accident insurance, free or low cost employment service, savings banks, and relief or aid in case of death or accident involving miners, factory workers, and fishermen.

The inaugural editorial of the *Ōsaka Weekly,* which appeared in the first issue dated October 22, noted the increasing population, the intensification of the struggle for existence, and the disappearance of morality and deplored the degeneration of society. It observed that conditions had reached a sad state when the poor could not possibly avoid enslavement by the rich, and that there was no liberty, equality, philanthropy, or justice, but only oppression, rapacity, greed, and deceit. The rich were becoming wealthier, while the poor could not help becoming poorer. All these conditions, it contended, were the product of existing social structure and their remedy was to be found in social reform. The salvation of society was indeed contingent on the carrying out of socialism. Ōi pointed out that heretofore leadership of the workers had been left completely to the laborers themselves, who were without many intellectual attainments, and no scholar, clergyman, or politician had provided any leadership for the working class. This he felt to be the cause of the confusion among the workers and their inability to improve the working conditions prevailing in industry.

A momentous decision was made by the Japan Railway Workers' Union, when it passed a resolution at the annual meeting in March, 1901, proclaiming that socialism provided the only means for solving labor problems and instructed its executive committee to join in the universal suffrage movement. Encouraged by the support of the workers, particularly by the members of the Kyōseikai, the Social Democratic Party was launched in the spring of 1901 by Katayama Sen, Kōtoku Denjirō, Kinoshita Naoe, Kawakami Kiyoshi, Nishikawa Kōjirō, and Abe Isoo, who were the leading lights of the Association for the Formation of Labor Unions. A declaration was issued on May 22, setting forth the objectives of the party to be (1) the extension of the principle of universal brotherhood; (2) disarmament with a view to the attainment of world peace; (3) the abolition of the existing system of class distinction; (4) the establishment of public ownership of both land and capital; (5) the establishment of state ownership of means of communications such as railways and shipping; (6) the equitable distribution of wealth; (7) the establishment of equality of political rights, and (8) the establishment of a system of free education at the expense of the state. As the eight-point program was thought to be impossible of immediate realization, the party listed twenty-eight other items that were to be put into effect as soon as possible, if not immediately.

Home Minister Suematsu Kenchō, son-in-law of Premier Itō, taking a leaf out of the Bismarckian policy of suppression, ordered Katayama and Kinoshita to dissolve the party within three hours of its launching. The authorities confiscated the copies of the *Labor World* in which the party declaration had been published. In addition, they banned the circulation of three other newspapers, *Yorozu, Mainichi,* and *Hōchi* for having published the declaration and imposed a fine on each of them. A month later, when the Itō Cabinet collapsed and was succeeded by the Katsura Cabinet, the Socialists planned to revive the party under the new name of Japan Commoners' Party, but their application was turned down by the authorities.

Despairing of success in any political movement, the Socialists turned their energies to educational and propaganda work. In this they received help from some men who were not in the movement. Tokutomi Roka, the eminent novelist brother of the founder of the *Nation's Friend,* in 1901 and 1902 published serially in the newspaper *Kokumin* his socialist novel, *Black Current,* exposing and decrying the corruption and degeneration of the peers, the upper class, and the clan bureaucrats.

The first year of the twentieth century witnessed a flood of socialist literature, written by those in the thick of the movement. Kōtoku attacked imperialism and the tide of expansionism in his *Imperialism, the Twentieth Century Monster;* Katayama championed the cause of universal suffrage; Abe interpreted the social problems of the day and explained that socialism was neither communism nor anarchism. Shimada, Nishikawa, and Sakai too contributed to the propaganda activities of the Socialists.

Of great significance to the cause of socialism was the appearance of *The New Society* by Yano Fumio, a graduate of Keiō Gijuku, who served in the Department of Finance under Ōkuma until 1881, when he left the government and helped the latter in the organization of the Reform Party. As a journalist he was with the newspaper *Hōchi* until 1896, when he was appointed Minister to China by Ōkuma, who became Foreign Minister in the Matsukata Cabinet. Three years later he resigned, retired from political life, and began to take interest in social problems. The culmination of that interest was a utopian novel, which appeared in July, 1902, a work reminiscent of the new society envisaged by Edward Bellamy. Influenced by Thomas More and Ferdinand Lassalle as well as Bellamy, Yano advocated eliminating the evils of competition by state ownership and operation of the means of production, including land and forests while also leaving some room for private property. He emphasized particularly the equality of educational opportunity and the democratization of government and laws.

In 1903, when diplomatic relations between Russia and Japan became strained, Kōtoku and Sakai, who had been disseminating the socialist doctrine through the newspaper *Yorozu,* and Uchimura Kanzō, who had been propagating Christianity through the same paper, joined together in a protest against war. As an upshot of this action, all three were forced to sever their connections with the newspaper. Kōtoku, Sakai, Nishikawa, and Ishikawa organized the Heiminsha and started their own weekly, *Heimin Shimbun* (*Commoners' News*) on November 19. From the very beginning until it was forced to discontinue on January 29, 1905, it took a strong antiwar stand.

The Heiminsha was a group whose ideological lineage could be traced back to the liberal school (liberty and popular rights) but which was now centering more around the social democratic ideas of the German Socialists, tempered somewhat by the humanism of Tolstoi and with a slight touch of the philosophical anarchism and communism of Kropotkin.[4] In its declaration, the group proclaimed that liberty, equality, and philanthropy were the three great principles for which humanity existed and, in order to achieve liberty for mankind, it proposed to uphold democracy and the rights of the common man by breaking down class distinctions which were based on social status, wealth, and sex and by removing tyranny and oppression.

In order to secure equal blessings to all mankind, it advocated socialism through which the public ownership of the means of production, distribution, transportation, and communication would be carried out. It favored pacifism, which was to be achieved by a world-wide disarmament without regard to race or color or differences in the political systems of nations, and the prohibition and abolition of war.

In its first issue the *Heimin Shimbun* repudiated the existing social order, which, it feared, would cause a few millionaires to bring destruction to several million poor people unless reorganized. It strongly deplored the power of wealth and the manifestation of a warlike spirit in the nation. It set out to study and examine the different interests involved, weigh the advantages and disadvantages, and to devise solutions for such issues as the nationalization of land and railways, graduated income tax, property inheritance tax, abolition of peerage, industrial legislation, labor legislation, universal suffrage, prison reform, schools for the poor, and free hospitals for the underprivileged. It hoped to eradicate inequality and injustice resulting from the disparity of wealth, thereby bringing about harmony in society. However, it emphatically rejected the techniques and tactics of the Communists and the social democratic parties of Europe.

Immediately after the sea engagement off Port Arthur on February 10, 1904, the day of the formal declaration of war with Russia, the editors of the *Heimin Shimbun* grew vehement in their denunciation of war and held public meetings as demonstrations against the government. The first Socialist antiwar meeting had been held in the Y.M.C.A. hall in Tōkyō early in October of the preceding year, and the antiwar movement had gained considerable momentum. The movement was encouraged and inspired by a letter from Count Tolstoi himself to the *Heimin Shimbun*. When Tolstoi's essay on the Russo-Japanese War appeared in the London *Times* of June 27, 1904, it had the effect of spurring on the Japanese Socialists.

The Socialists opposed war on the grounds that it increased the sufferings of the downtrodden working classes regardless of its outcome. When hostilities

[4] In the office were prominently displayed pictures of Marx, Engels, Bebel, William Morris, Zola, and Tolstoi.

commenced in spite of their desperate efforts to prevent the war, they decided to appeal to the International Congress of Socialists, which was scheduled to meet at Amsterdam in August of that year. The Japanese Socialists declared in the resolution which they sent to the conference that the war was a conflict between two capitalistic governments and inflicted great harm on the working classes in both countries. They besought each of the members to urge on the government of his country to take steps to bring the war to a speedy close. Katayama Sen, who was then in Europe, was designated as a delegate to represent the Japanese Socialists.

The antiwar campaign by the Socialists continued with increasing vigor even after the commencement of hostilities. When the *Heimin Shimbun* came out strongly against the increase in taxation necessitated by the war, the authorities prosecuted Sakai, its editor and publisher. This marked the beginning of the government's persecution of the Socialists, which became increasingly severe, until finally the circulation of the paper was banned.

On November 13, 1904, the *Heimin Shimbun,* in commemoration of its first anniversary, published the "Communist Manifesto" of Marx and Engels. A garden party was to be held on the same day for the Socialists and their families, but the authorities forbade it and simultaneously banned the circulation of the newspaper.

The socialist movement during the war years became more and more intellectual, radical, and international, as the government intensified its policy of suppression. Meetings were held for the study of socialism, debating clubs were set up, and social as well as public meetings were held to keep socialism alive. Undaunted by their abortive attempts at the organization of a political party, the Socialists intensified their efforts in the propagation of socialism. Teams were organized to sell socialist tracts and literature in the vicinity of Tōkyō and in other parts of the country, in the northeastern region in particular. Some of them went as far west as Kyūshū. Students utilized their summer and winter vacations to go on the errand of selling socialist propaganda literature.

In the summer of 1905 Yamaji Aizan, Shiba Teikichi, Yamane Goichi, and Nakamura Tahachirō organized the State Socialist Party (Kokka Shakaitō), the purpose of which was to check the tyranny of the rich with the help of the Imperial Family, who, they claimed, had from ancient times practiced socialism. Mob violence, that flared up in September, 1905, as a protest against the Katsura Government and the Portsmouth Treaty, brought on martial law and suppression of socialist activities. In November the government ordered the dissolution of the Socialists' Association.

Following dissolution, the group split into three different groups. The Christian Socialists decided to disseminate socialism among the Christians. Kinoshita Naoe decided to effect a merger of Christian idealism with socialism. After graduation from Tōkyō College in 1888, Kinoshita practiced law for a while, but in 1899 he joined the Tōkyō *Mainichi* and began a crusade against the social evils of the time, such as political corruption, licensed prostitution, and the deplorable working conditions in the Ashio copper mines. His ideas underwent change during this period, shifting from democracy to socialism, resulting in his joining the socialist movement in 1901. When the *Commoners' News* was launched in the winter of 1903, he assisted Kōtoku and Sakai, since he agreed with their strong antiwar stand.

While actively participating in the movement, he utilized his literary talents in writing socialist novels on the side. *The Pillar of Fire,* which appeared early in 1904 and went into ten editions in a few months, was the most powerful socialist novel, far surpassing the *New Society,* which had appeared two years earlier. *The Confessions of a Husband,* which appeared in the same year, also influenced the thinking of thousands of readers. In Kinoshita, the outstanding novelist of socialism, the socialist novel reached its high-water mark. However, the magazine *New Era,* which he launched, was unable to reach its goal, and Kinoshita had to admit the failure of the movement in November, 1906, exactly a year later. Just as he had opened the initial issue with a prayer, he ended the publication with a confession of shame and repentance. Realizing the sham and hypocrisy of his own life, he thereafter withdrew completely from active life into a life of piety and repentance.

A fortnightly, *The Light,* was started by Nishikawa Kōjirō and Yamaguchi Yoshizō about the time the *New Era* made its appearance. It endeavored to awaken the working class through education, to inform those interested in social problems on the conditions among the lower strata of society, to work for universal suffrage, and to report accurately on labor and social movements at home and abroad. The third group of Socialists published the *Home Magazine.*

The Japan Socialist Party, under the leadership of Katayama, Sakai and Nishikawa, appeared in February, 1906, with a membership not exceeding two hundred. Although it published no declaration, its objective was to effect socialism within the limits of law. Through public meetings, speaking tours into the rural districts, study meetings, and discussion groups, it carried on an intensive, aggressive movement for the dissemination of socialism. One of its first activities was the unsuccessful campaign to raise electric tramway fares in Tōkyō. This campaign also had the support of the state Socialists.

In 1906 Miyazaki Tamizō published a work advocating the equitable distribution of land, which, he pointed out, was a gift of Providence and intended to be the common property of mankind. The book was immediately banned by the government; but he carried on his campaign through the Association for the Restoration of Land (Tochi Fukken Kai), which he founded for the purpose. Like Henry George, under whose influence he found himself, he was convinced that evils and injustices of all kinds, including poverty, could be abolished by a reform of the land system. Charity and relief he denounced as a prostitution of justice and insisted that they could not be more than a temporary expedient at best. Giving peace of mind to the poor through religion was no solution.

A turning point in the socialist movement was the great riot which broke out at the Ashio copper mines on February 14, 1907, and continued for three days. It was put down only after troops were called out. The riot spread all over the mines, resulting in the destruction of a large portion of the mining properties and a loss estimated at approximately 2 million dollars. More than 200 miners and labor leaders were arrested. This was the first instance of violence on a large scale in the history of the Japanese labor movement. Although it was a spontaneous uprising of the miners against the outrageous ill-treatment and exploitation by the mine owners, the authorities and the press blamed the Socialists and the *Daily Heimin* for contributing to, if not actually fomenting, the labor trouble.

There is little doubt, however, that, with the riot as the turning point, the socialist movement went through a very noticeable change, taking on an extremely radical and revolutionary tone. At the same time the clash between the two opposing factions of the Socialists developed into a bitter feeling of animosity. So intense was the animosity that the socialist leaders neglected the cause of socialism and even lost sight of the interests and welfare of the working classes, whose rank and file did not share in the bitterness and showed little interest in the question of tactics.

At the first anniversary meeting of the Socialist Party in Tōkyō on February 17, 1907, the executive committee under the leadership of Sakai proposed the combined use of parliamentary methods and direct action in advancing the socialist cause. Kōtoku offered an amendment advocating direct action to the exclusion of all other methods, including universal suffrage, while Tazoe Tetsuzō proposed the disavowal of all but parliamentary methods. The resultant conflict was resolved by the adoption by a majority vote of the original proposal by the executive committee. When the proceedings of the conference appeared in the *Daily Heimin,* the government ordered suspension of the paper on the grounds that it had printed matter conducive to disorder, and forced the dissolution of the Japan Socialist Party. For more than a decade following the dissolution the socialist movement was without a party.

Once again the Socialists concentrated their efforts on propaganda activities through the *Daily Heimin* but were forced to discontinue the paper in April, as the government banned it on the grounds that it had published subversive literature, especially Kropotkin's *Appeal to the Young.* The depression added to the woes of the Socialists. It placed the workers in a defensive position, making it difficult for them to carry on an aggressive labor movement.

Dismissal of leaders who had called a meeting which voted to ask a 30 per cent increase in wages brought some 200 miners into conflict with the company officials at the Besshi Copper Mines on June 4, 1907. At the peak of the disturbance over 15,000 miners who participated in the rioting secured control of the mines. Although the disturbance was quelled by government troops, and the owner acceded to the miners' demands, it exposed the working conditions in the mines.

No less than ten books were banned in 1907, which was a banner year for works on socialism. Among them were *Sixteen Years in Siberia* by L. G. Deutsch, leader of Russian Socialists, who spent years in exile in the wastes of Siberia but succeeded in escaping, and an autobiography of Priest G. Gapon, the leader of a Russian workers' organization, who on January 22, 1905, led a huge crowd of workmen to the Winter Palace in St. Petersburg to appeal to Tsar Nicholas II, resulting in the famous "Bloody Sunday." Writings of Sakai, Kōtoku, Morichika, and novels by Kinoshita were all banned.

Meanwhile, the direct actionists had rallied around the *Ōsaka Heimin Shimbun,* which was published by their organization, the Friday Society. Under the leadership of Kōtoku, Yamakawa, and Sakai, they fought in defense of their convictions, not only against the oppressive policy of the government, but also against the Ōsaka capitalists. On June 22, 1908, the direct action group and their rival Marxists held a joint meeting in Kanda, Tōkyō, in honor of a comrade who had just been released from prison. After the meeting the members of the Friday Society paraded on the street waving red flags and singing their revolutionary song, "The Shackles of Wealth." The police bore down on them and arrested scores of them. Ten were sent to prison for a period of from one year to two and a half years. Sakai, who was not in the demonstration, was sentenced to two years in prison. The "Red Flag Incident," as this event was called, was the beginning of the government's all-out policy of ruthless suppression of the socialist movement. However, in spite of the fact that most of the radical Socialists were already behind bars, revolutionary literature, such as writings by Kropotkin [5] and works of Tolstoi,[6] Marx, and Engels were secretly printed and distributed.

Public opinion was aroused by the press, which denounced the Socialists as the worst enemies of society. Encouraged and emboldened by the support given by the press, the government relentlessly pursued the Socialists and exercised the strictest surveillance over every known Socialist, who was hounded by policemen and detectives by day and by night.

The uncovering by the authorities of a plot by Kōtoku and his anarchist followers to harm the Emperor in the summer of 1910 came as a shock to the nation and virtually sounded the death knell of the socialist movement. Kōtoku, a native of Tosa province, had studied under Nakae Chōmin and become a champion of popular rights. After leaving the Liberal Party in disgust, he

---

[5] Among Kropotkin's works were: *The State, Its Historic Role; Anarchism, Its Philosophy and Ideal; The Conquest of Bread; Law and Authority; An Appeal to the Young; Mutual Aid.*

[6] Tolstoi's *The Meaning of the Russian Revolution* was banned by the authorities.

became one of the founders of the Association for the Study of Socialism. In 1898, after joining the staff of the newspaper *Yorozu,* he published *The Decay of Society, Its Cause and Cure.* In the fall of 1905 he visited the United States to regain his health and to organize the Japanese Socialists. Upon his return in the summer of 1906, after being caught in the San Francisco earthquake and fire, he began to advocate direct action as he became more militant and anarchistic under the influence of Kropotkin.

While awaiting trial in prison Kōtoku wrote *The Refutation of Christianity,* a work he intended to be his farewell opus, a culmination of a decade of writing for the cause of socialism. Although there is no denying that Kōtoku believed the state to be unnecessary, it was quite apparent that his unremitting fight against the government was motivated by his hatred for the tyranny of the bureaucratic clan oligarchy and the plutocracy, which showed little or no concern for the welfare and happiness of the great masses of people.

The "anarchist trials" for Kōtoku and twenty-three others were held in secrecy, and the special court found them all guilty of violating Article 73 of the Criminal Code. Kōtoku and eleven others, including a woman, were hanged only three days after sentences were pronounced on January 19, 1911. The speed with which the sentences were carried out was unprecedented, as a period of sixty days usually intervened between the time of the sentence and its execution.

Whatever other significance future historians may attach to the high treason trials one fact will always stand out. The execution of Kōtoku and eleven others was an effective demonstration of the government's ruthless policy of suppression, which led to the disappearance of the socialist movement. Nishikawa, one of the leaders of socialism, disavowed socialism in his *Confessions,* which he published soon after his release from prison in 1911.

The Tōkyō streetcar strike, which began on the last day of 1911, tied up traffic in the city of two million people so completely for five days that the strikers got what they wanted and obtained a bonus totaling 100,000 yen. It was a great victory for labor, but there was no marked activity thereafter. The outbreak of war in Europe two years later was soon followed by unprecedented economic activities. Labor forgot its woes, and socialism was completely overshadowed by prosperity for the time being.

Chapter 17. The Sino-Japanese War and Its Aftermath

Information regarding the Korean government's request for Chinese troops to quell the Tonghak Rebellion was received by the Foreign Office on June 4, 1894, from Chargé Sugimura at Seoul. Wires from the Tientsin consulate and from the military attaché at the Peking Legation received on the 5th gave further information on Chinese military preparations under way in Tientsin. Several days later, the Chinese Minister in Tōkyō was informed that his government was sending troops into Korea and, in accordance with Article III of the Li-Itō Convention, he was instructed by a communication dated June 7 to give notice to the Japanese government.

Upon receipt of the notice, the Foreign Office immediately sent a telegram to Chargé Komura in Peking, instructing him to notify the Chinese government that Japan was also sending troops to Korea in accordance with the provisions of the Li-Itō Convention of 1885. Several exchanges of communications followed. Meanwhile, Li Hung-chang sought the mediation of the powers in vain. Premier Itō suggested the sending of a joint Sino-Japanese Commission to Korea, but the Chinese government rejected the proposal on the grounds that there was no need for joint action inasmuch as the uprising had already been put down and troops would be withdrawn when the matter was settled. The Chinese government's reply also emphasized the fact that since the Japanese government had recognized the independence of Korea, any domestic reform should be left to the Koreans themselves to carry out.

Frustrated by China's refusal of joint action, the Japanese government abandoned the idea of working together in favor of independent action and notified the Chinese government that it could not withdraw its troops from Korea. Hitrowo, the Russian Minister in Tōkyō, interceded and proposed the simultaneous withdrawal of Chinese and Japanese troops to Foreign Minister Mutsu, who replied that his government was unable to accept the proposal. Again, on June 30, the Russian Minister repeated the proposal and added that, if Japan did not withdraw her troops when China did, she would be assuming a grave responsibility.

The Chinese government was seeking Britain's mediation at the same time. O'Conor, the British Minister to Peking, offered to mediate, but the Japanese government declined the proposal and proceeded with its preparations for an armed clash, which it regarded as inevitable. In June, Minister Ōtori arrived in Korea accompanied by a mixed brigade of troops and was received in audience by the King on the twenty-sixth. He proposed among other things the clarification of the powers and duties of officials, the eradication of corruption among local government officials, the appointment of officials on the basis of merit, assurance of fairness of trials, the adjustment of finances, reforms in military organization and the police, reform in currency, and the establishment of an educational system. Ōtori insisted that these reforms could not be instituted as long as Chinese influence remained in Korea. Shortly thereafter, the King, under pressure, proclaimed the abandonment of the treaty with China and requested the Japanese to help drive the Chinese troops out.

In spite of the firm attitude of the Japanese government, Li was still hopeful that hostilities might be averted. This hope he held out to the very last. Within the Chinese government itself opinion was divided on the question of peace or war. However, both Li and Yuan Shih-k'ai, the Chinese resident in Korea, were inclined to underestimate Japanese determination and ability to go to war, particularly in the face of internal difficulties. The Japanese government was faced with hostile opposition from the Diet, which had been dissolved three times within the brief space of less than three years, immediately preceding the outbreak of hostilities. The last dissolution, carried out on June 2, was taken as an unmistakable sign of national disunion and weakness, which precluded any possibility of Japan going to war. Both events proved that Li and Yuan, like so many others, had erred in the appraisal of the domestic political situation in Japan.

On July 25, three Japanese warships, steaming toward Korea, were fired upon by three Chinese warships that were convoying the transport *Kowshing* carrying 1,200 troops to Korea. In the ensuing battle the transport was sent to the bottom, and one of the warships was captured. The sinking of the *Kowshing* brought a protest from the British Government, as the ship was British although it had been leased to the Chinese government. This protest was withdrawn when two eminent British authorities on international law, Holland and Westlake, held that the Japanese had acted in accordance with the rules of international law and therefore were blameless.

Acting on the request of the King for the expulsion of the Chinese troops, Minister Ōtori instructed Major General Ōshima to proceed with the execution of the request. Four days after the initial naval encounter, the Japanese troops engaged and defeated the Chinese troops on Korean soil. Hostilities had actually started, but there was still no declaration of war.

Formal declaration of war by Japan came on August 1, followed by China's. The powers promptly declared neutrality. Although Russia, France, and Austria-Hungary made no declarations, they proclaimed that they would observe strict neutrality in fact. On the 26th, a defensive alliance was concluded between Japan and Korea.

In mid-September, Emperor Meiji proceeded to Hiroshima where he established his Imperial Headquarters. The Diet moved to the same city where it deliberated on the affairs of state for the duration of the war. On September 16, the city of Pyongyang (Heijō), the stronghold of the Chinese forces, fell to the Japanese. At sea the combined fleet under Admiral Itō intercepted and defeated the Chinese fleet under Admiral Ting in the battle of the Yellow Sea at the mouth of the Yalu River. With this victory, the Japanese navy secured control of the sea and maintained naval supremacy throughout the remainder of the war.

General Yamagata, now in command of the First Army, landed in Korea in October, crossed the Yalu River into Manchuria, and captured the Chinese strongholds of Kiuliencheng and Fenghuangcheng. By the middle of December he had taken Haicheng. In Antung province he established a military government office to look after the administration of civil affairs. The Second Army under General Ōyama landed on the Liaotung Peninsula and by the end of November had captured Dairen, Port Arthur, and Chinchow. Contingents of the Second Army from Port Arthur effected landings on the Shantung Peninsula and captured Weihaiwei on February 2, 1895. The Chinese Admiral Ting, who was defending Liukungtao desperately with the remnants of his battered fleet, could not hold out in the face of powerful attacks from land and sea; on February 12, he surrendered to Admiral Itō and, after turning over the warships and arms, committed suicide.

The First and Second Armies effected a junction in March and advanced toward Peking after capturing Newchwang, Yinkow, and Tienchuangtai. In the south, an army contingent, with the support of naval units, captured and held the Pescadores. China suffered defeat after defeat with no prospect of turning the tide of war to her advantage, and Li Hung-chang sought the mediation of both Russia and Great Britain to terminate the war. But he was unsuccessful in his attempt to enlist their help.

While the attack on Port Arthur was in progress, Li dispatched Detring, a German in the employ of the Chinese Customs Service at Tientsin, to Japan to sue for peace. Bearing only a personal letter from Viceroy Li to Premier Itō, the emissary arrived towards the end of the year. The Japanese government refused to deal with him on the grounds that he brought only a private communication from Li and was invested with no power to negotiate a treaty; furthermore, he was only a foreigner in the employ of the Chinese government and without the status or prestige befitting a peace emissary. Detring's return to Tientsin demonstrated to the Viceroy the necessity of appointing an envoy with full powers to negotiate, as the Japanese had insisted. But he was unwilling to put himself in a disadvantageous position in face of the uncertainty of the Japanese demands. Li had been trying to ascertain in advance what Japanese conditions for peace would be. On December 12, he finally transmitted to the Japanese government through the American Minister Denby his desire to hold a peace conference in Shanghai. The Japanese government, in reply, demanded that the names and ranks of the Chinese envoys be made known in order to enable the appointment of its own envoys, and that the conference to negotiate peace be held in Japan.

The Chinese envoys arrived in Hiroshima on January 31, 1895, and on the following day the first meeting was held in the Prefectural Office Building. It was discovered, however, that the Chinese delegates, although they had credentials, had not been invested with full authority to negotiate a peace treaty. The Japanese government accused the Chinese of lack of good faith and emphasized that only persons of the caliber of Li Hung-chang or Prince Kung would be acceptable as plenipotentiaries in the negotiation of a peace treaty.

Finally, the Chinese government decided to appoint the Viceroy as the peace emissary, and on February 18 information to this effect was relayed to the Japanese government by American Minister Denby. The Japanese telegraphed back to the Chinese government for confirmation of Li's appointment and received a reply indirectly through the American Minister confirming not only the appointment but also the fact that the envoy was invested with full powers to negotiate.

Li arrived in Shimonoseki on March 19 and held the first meeting with Premier Itō, the Japanese plenipotentiary, on the following day. Four days later, a would-be assassin fired on the Viceroy. Fortunately, the Chinese envoy was not seriously injured and negotiations were continued at his bedside without interruption. The unwarranted attack on the person of the peace emissary stirred public sympathy throughout the nation, and placed the government in a disadvantageous position, for the Viceroy could easily have broken off negotiations in indignation. Official regret was expressed, and the Emperor personally sent the Surgeon General of the Army Satō as an attending physician to Li. On March 30 the Japanese government agreed to an unconditional armistice. There had been an almost hopeless deadlock until the attack on the Viceroy, when Itō's attitude softened. On April 17, less than a month after negotiations were first started, the Shimonoseki Treaty was signed and peace was restored between China and Japan.

At Shimonoseki Americans were serving as advisers on both sides. John W. Foster, Secretary of State in the Harrison Administration and legal adviser to the Chinese Legation in Washington, was adviser to Li Hung-chang during the peace negotiations. The Japanese were advised by Henry W. Denison, a veteran legal adviser to the Foreign Office.

By the Treaty of Shimonoseki, China recognized the complete independence of Korea, ceded the Liaotung Peninsula, the island of Formosa, and the Pescadores, paid an indemnity of 200 million taels of silver, and opened the four cities of Shashi, Chungking, Suchow, and Hangchow to Japan for commercial and industrial purposes.

Hardly any of the powers had conceded Japan the slightest chance of winning the war. But the Japanese forces moved swiftly on land and sea, and after eight months of fighting administered such complete military defeat to the enemy that the Chinese government sued for peace. The surprise at the outcome of the war was complete, as it was so unexpected. In the words of one of the leading authorities on the Far East, "The largest, the oldest, the most populous country in the world, a huge continental empire long accustomed to esteem itself the sole repository of national strength and substance, was defeated in war and invaded by the armed forces of a little insular neighbor." [1]

The war exposed China's military weakness, her lack of national consciousness, and the corruption of the Manchu Court. It revealed the lack of integrity on the part of officials and their inefficiency in the face of modern conditions. The foundations of the dynasty were so badly shaken by the defeat that in less than two decades it was destined to come to an inglorious end. Japan, on the other hand, discovered that her stock had risen suddenly. Foreign military observers gave nothing but the highest praise to her army and navy, at whose exploits they marveled, little realizing that they were helping to raise military prestige to unprecedented heights. She was now in the ascendancy, and the world welcomed her into the family of nations. The powers acknowledged the new fact that Japan was now a factor which could not be disregarded in Far Eastern politics.

No less far reaching were the changes which were brought about by the war on the domestic scene. The sizeable indemnity she received subsequently and the territories ceded to her, the commercial and industrial rights acquired, all gave tremendous impetus to national activities. In the flush of victory, an extensive program of expansion of armaments was launched with a view to placing the nation among the leading military powers of the world. Militarism and expansionism followed almost as a natural consequence of victory. Economic, industrial, and financial activities received greater stimulus than in any period since the Restoration.

Important as these effects were, they were overshadowed by the change which had taken place in the attitude of the European powers toward China. Until 1895, there had been no large scale war against China which provided the opportunity to test her real strength. No nation had cared or dared to arouse the wrath of the "Sleeping Dragon." However, Japan's victory over her neighbor had revealed the impotence of China, which had long been suspected, and had encouraged the European powers to press demands for territorial privileges. In the years immediately following the Sino-Japanese War, there unfolded a

[1] Stanley K. Hornbeck, *Contemporary Politics in the Far East*, p. vii.

period during which European powers vied with one another in a scramble for concessions, which threatened a virtual dismemberment of China, and which was arrested only somewhat by the Open Door notes of John Hay, the United States Secretary of State.

THE ATTITUDE OF THE POWERS DURING AND AFTER THE WAR

What worried the Japanese government most at the time of the declaration of war was whether or not Britain would come to the aid of China, notwithstanding the fact that, when the relations between China and Japan took a turn for the worse after the Tonghak Rebellion, she interceded in an attempt to prevent the outbreak of hostilities. British Minister O'Conor at Peking had urged on the *Tsungli Yamen* the advisability of making a final effort at peaceful negotiations to avert war. However, when all attempts to forestall war appeared futile, Britain obtained in July, 1894, an assurance from the Japanese government that the Shanghai area would not be turned into a war zone. By this action the Japanese government learned that Britain had no treaty promising military assistance to China. When Japan's victory became certain, Britain made an attempt to bring the powers together for a concerted action for the preservation of the *status quo* in the Far East, primarily for the purpose of checking Japan's expansion and Russia's unrestrained actions. Both Russia and Germany objected and nothing resulted.

On February 12, 1895, the British Government, at the request of China, offered to mediate through its Minister in Tōkyō. Public opinion in Britain had become friendly toward Japan by this time. Even the London *Times,* which had been carrying anti-Japanese items regularly, had changed its tune and on March 15 featured an article favoring Japan's taking possession of the Liaotung Peninsula. British public opinion had come to accept the attitude that it was expedient to aid Japan's northward expansion in order to check Russia's southward expansion. In Europe the efforts on the part of Germany to establish closer relations with Russia made the British see the need of strengthening their own position. This realization, in turn, made the British Government begin to see the advantage of working together with Japan.

Russia, urged on by her age-old quest for an ice-free port, turned eastward and renewed her activities in the Far East with French support. Simultaneously with the announcement of her plans to build the Trans-Siberian railway in 1891, she sought and obtained necessary financial assistance from France. Utilizing this occasion, France and Russia concluded an agreement which developed into the Dual Alliance. This arrangement proved mutually beneficial, as France obtained an ally to provide against Germany. Russia was released from the fear of attack from the rear while she turned her attention to the Far East.

In the realization of Russian plans for expansion in the Far East, Korea was regarded as the main obstacle. Consequently, after the conclusion of the Tientsin Convention between China and Japan, when the latter's influence in Korea was at its lowest ebb, Russia sought the lease of Port Lazareff. As a countermove, British naval forces occupied Port Hamilton, an anchorage in a group of islets off the southern tip of the Korean Peninsula and remained there until February, 1887, when the British Government was satisfied that Russia had abandoned the idea of occupying Port Lazareff. In August, 1888, Russia concluded a treaty of commerce and, by currying favor with the Korean Court, attempted to introduce policies calculated to advance her own aims at the expense of Korea. But China stepped in and foiled Russia's plans.

On July 21, on the eve of the Sino-Japanese War, the Russian government, in a vaguely threatening manner, informed the Japanese Foreign Minister that it could not countenance any agreement which would violate Korean independence. Yet, when the war broke out between China and Japan, Russia did nothing to interfere with its progress. Contrary to expectations she came out with the statement that she had no objection to Japan's taking possession of Formosa. On February 14, 1895, the Russian Minister made an attempt to obtain information on conditions of peace, while at the same time emphasizing the inadvisability of Japan's expansion on the Asiatic continent.

It was apparent that Russia was anxiously watching developments which might possibly affect her interests. While outwardly giving the impression that the guarantee of Korean independence was her primary concern, she was exercising as unobtrusively as possible close vigilance over Japan's continental aims and moves.

A month before the Triple Intervention, Minister Kurino submitted a confidential report from Washington to the Foreign Office, which was based on the telegraphic report to the Secretary of State from the American Minister at St. Petersburg. It disclosed Russia's grandiose plans for the annexation of Manchuria and North China and her determination not to allow Japan to take over any part of those regions or to become the protector of Korea. It also contained the fact that there were already 30,000 Russian troops in the northern parts of China.

On April 2, the day after Japan made known to Viceroy Li at Shimonoseki the conditions of peace settlement, the German government obtained and transmitted them to the Russian government. Russia suddenly showed activity and on the eighth, she proposed to Great Britain, France, and Germany the need for friendly intervention to advise Japan to retrocede the Liaotung Peninsula to China in the interests of peace. Count Serge Witte, the Finance Minister, whose influence overshadowed that of the Minister President, was the prime mover of this policy. Witte contended that the preservation of the *status quo* in China would work to the greatest advantage of Russia and therefore, no nation, however powerful, should be permitted to carry out territorial expansion at China's expense. Foreign Minister Lobanov was moderate in his views and the Russian government hesitated in arriving at a final decision. However, the Finance Minister's views prevailed in the end, and the decision to intervene was reached in an imperial conference presided over by Tsar Nicholas II. Russia informed the French and German governments that in the event Japan refused to heed the advice, she was prepared to carry out a naval blockade to isolate the Japanese troops in China and, after joining forces with the other two nations, to conduct a combined operation against Japan.

Prime Minister Rosebery informed the German Ambassador in London on April 8 that no provision of the peace treaty could so affect British interests as to necessitate undertaking an intervention which would involve the use of force. A similar reply indicating lack of interest in the Russian proposal of intervention was given by the British Government to France. However, no attempts were made to oppose actively the intervention, for fear that a strong stand might jeopardize Britain's position in Europe.

THE TRIPLE INTERVENTION

Before the signatures on the Treaty of Shimonoseki were dry the Triple Intervention came. On April 23, less than a week after Viceroy Li and Premier Itō concluded the treaty, the representatives of Russia, France, and Germany called on Vice Minister Hayashi at the Foreign Office and delivered orally the instructions from their home governments advising the Japanese government to retrocede the Liaotung Peninsula to China. It was pointed out that Japan's possession of the peninsula would not only be a threat to China, but would also render the independence of Korea meaningless and, furthermore, would disturb the peace of the Far East.

Although the intervention came suddenly, it did not come as a complete surprise except to the man on the street in Japan and the rest of the world. The major capitals of the world were informed. Neither the Foreign Minister nor the Premier was taken by surprise. They had a considerable amount of information regarding events in the capitals of Europe. Furthermore, the government was already in receipt of intelligence that the Russian fleet units in Far Eastern waters were under secret orders and standing by and that reserves were being called up at Vladivostok.

Without losing any time, Hayashi telegraphed the Premier, who was in Hiroshima, and Foreign Minister Mutsu, who was convalescing at Maiko. On the following day, an imperial conference was hurriedly called at the Imperial Headquarters. In attendance besides the Premier were only the Ministers of War and the Navy, Yamagata and Saigō, and some high-ranking army and navy general staff officers.

Premier Itō explained that there were three alternatives: first, to reject the advice at the risk of war; second, to call an international conference to which several powers would be invited to settle the question of retrocession of the Liaotung Peninsula; and third, to accept the advice to retrocede the peninsula to China. The first alternative was regarded as impossible under the circumstances as the nation was close to exhaustion both in military and financial resources and was in no position to fight the Russian fleet, let alone the combined forces of the three intervening powers. The third alternative was thought to be fraught with danger, as it might cause violent reaction not only among the military but in the nation generally and might even lead to serious disturbances. The conference, therefore, tentatively decided on the second alternative of calling an international conference.

From Hiroshima, Premier Itō hastened to the bedside of the Foreign Minister at Maiko, where he was joined by Finance Minister Matsukata and Home Minister Nomura. The Foreign Minister strongly opposed an international conference on the grounds that it would not only delay the final peace settlement through the injection into the conference of the powers' own interests, but would also invite further intervention of European powers leading ultimately to the complete undoing of the Treaty of Shimonoseki. Mutsu's well-founded apprehension was based on his knowledge of the Treaty of San Stefano of March 3, 1878, which was practically nullified by the Congress of Berlin. The four cabinet ministers agreed that, inasmuch as the imperial conference had decided against action which would antagonize any power, the government would have to accept the "advice" either completely or partially, if the three powers persisted. They decided against prolonging the negotiations with the intervening powers, as there was the possibility that China might take advantage of the delay and refuse the exchange of ratifications. The ratification of the treaty and the question of intervention were to be dealt with separately and independently of each other.

Since the date of exchange of ratifications was still more than ten days away, the government decided to see if the demands of the intervening powers might not be modified. Feelers were sent out to ascertain if any assistance could be expected from two or three powers, which might desire to check Russia, France, and Germany. Thus, Japan was by force of circumstances willy-nilly projecting herself into the orbit of European power politics.

Russia flatly refused to reconsider or modify the terms of the advice, stating that there was no good reason for any démarche. Minister Nishi in St. Petersburg telegraphed the Foreign Office informing of Russia's immovable determination. Minister Katō in London sent back a reply to the effect that, although Foreign Secretary Kimberley was friendly to Japan, the Rosebery Government had decided against any kind of intervention.[2]

Minister Kurino reported from Washington that the Secretary of State had

---

[2] Samuel H. Jeyes, *The Earl of Rosebery*, p. 164.

assured him that the United States would instruct its Minister in Peking to advise the Chinese government to carry out the exchange of ratifications without any delay. The attitude of the Italian government was as surprising as it was gratifying to the Japanese. Not only had it already agreed to treaty revision before any other power, but now it expressed its willingness to try to enlist the cooperation of Britain and the United States in opposing the intervening powers.

Convinced of the futility of relying on other powers for assistance, the government bowed to the inevitability of accepting the "advice." What Bismarck had taken the trouble to explain to the Japanese back in 1873 was now actually being demonstrated in a practical lesson in power politics, and ironically enough Bismarck's own country was a party to the demonstration of "might makes right" policy.

On May 2, using the Triple Intervention as the reason, but actually at the instance of Russia, the Chinese government proposed a delay in the exchange of ratifications of the Treaty of Shimonoseki. Since the indefinite postponement of the settlement of two major problems could well militate against the achievement of even a modicum of success, the Japanese government reached its final decision on May 5 to yield completely to the three powers but to stand pat against China's proposal. Accordingly, the Foreign Minister telegraphed instructions to the Ministers in St. Petersburg, Paris, and Berlin to transmit to the three powers the government's decision to accept their advice not to take possession of the Liaotung Peninsula. In acknowledgment of this notification, the representatives of the three powers called on the Foreign Minister on May 9, to offer congratulations for the high-minded action taken by the Japanese government in the interests of world peace. The exchange of ratifications of the Treaty of Shimonoseki was carried out as scheduled at Chefoo, China, on May 8, by the representatives of the two nations.

The Triple Intervention was a bitter pill for the Japanese to swallow. It has been referred to as one of the most tragic chapters in the history of modern Japan. In the face of overwhelming odds there was nothing else to do but to yield. The people did not allow themselves or the government to forget the national humiliation for the next ten years, during which the whole country worked and lived for one consuming passion—namely, to even the score at an opportune moment. The intervention demonstrated to the Japanese that the course of their own national development could no longer be planned and followed independently of and unaffected by external factors and developments on the international scene. That Japan was being drawn inexorably into the vortex of European power politics had become unmistakably clear.

There were at least two factors which were responsible for Germany's active participation in the Triple Intervention. First, she was following Bismarck's formula for dealing with Russia, namely, the diverting of her neighbor's energies to the Far East to relieve the pressure on her own borders. Secondly, she hoped to collect her share of the reward in the form of a foothold in the Far East for her participation in the intervention.

When Britain attempted to bring the powers together to mediate on the eve of the Sino-Japanese War, Germany preferred to be a bystander as she fully expected a clash between Britain and Russia. Kaiser Wilhelm suggested in his letter of November 17, 1894, to his Chancellor Hohenlohe that, in the event of a scramble for territories in China by European powers, Germany should seize Formosa. Because of the opposition of Foreign Minister Mareschal, nothing was done about this plan. The German Minister to China had proposed the seizure of Kiaochow Bay and the Pescadores as bases for commercial activities in the Far East, but this too was turned down by the Foreign Office. Aoki Shūzō, the Japanese Minister in Berlin, learned in his conversation with a counselor of the German Foreign Office that the German government had tried to establish a foothold in one of the provinces of southeastern China.

Germany's policy was to refrain from participating in concerted action which gave benefits to other powers, but to be on the alert to participate in any action which would help to provide against any shift in the balance of power in Europe. On March 23, 1895, she notified the Russian government of her willingness to participate in a joint action for the solution of the Far Eastern problem. In a letter of April 26, the Kaiser offered assistance to the Tsar in the securing of territory, but in exchange he asked that support be given Germany in the securing of a seaport. German policy toward France concerned itself with bringing about diplomatic isolation by undermining the Dual Alliance and weakening the Russian position in Europe through dissipation of her energies elsewhere, particularly in the Far East. Consequently any action involving diversion of military and financial resources to the Far East was most welcome, as it relieved pressure from both the Russian and French frontiers.

France, on her part, was relatively unconcerned with the developments in North China, as her interests were centered in the south. It was primarily the obligation arising out of the Dual Alliance that brought her into the Triple Intervention. This was made clear in the explanation given by Foreign Minister Hanotaux in the Chamber of Deputies. However, when the scramble for concessions started in earnest, France was not far behind in claiming the reward for her part in the intervention.

In the period following the Sino-Japanese War, East Asia and China in particular constituted a low pressure area of power politics. With imperialism in Africa at an impasse after the middle of the 1890's, the European powers were casting their eyes about for new fields to conquer. In the wake of China's defeat, European powers rushed in with demands for concessions, leases of ports and territories, trade privileges, mining and railway rights, and proffer of loans. For a while it seemed as if the only thing which could save the Celestial Empire from complete dismemberment might be the jealousies and quarrels of the "predatory" nations who would partition her.

Taking advantage of the immediate need of money for the payment of a huge indemnity to Japan, the powers began to proffer loans to China. At the time of the Triple Intervention, Russia had already promised a loan to the Chinese government. At the suggestion of Sir Robert Hart, Chief of the Chinese Imperial Maritime Customs, the Chinese government was negotiating a loan from Britain. Meanwhile, the Russian government, fearful of the influence Britain might wield in China's financial affairs in the future, outstripped Britain in making jointly with the French on July 1, 1895, a loan of 400 million francs to enable China to meet the first installment of her indemnity. This Franco-Russian diplomatic triumph caused the British Government to lodge a strong protest with the *Tsungli Yamen* for the bad faith shown in the negotiations for a loan. It also brought Britain and Germany into closer cooperation. The two powers succeeded in arranging joint loans to China in March, 1896, and in March, 1898, of 16 million pounds each, enabling China to pay the indemnity to Japan according to schedule. These loans were arranged through the Hongkong-Shanghai Bank and the Deutsche Asiatische Bank and secured by the maritime customs and the salt gabelle.

That the Triple Intervention was not motivated solely by altruistic considerations was quite apparent. If it were, the general debacle in the Celestial Empire would not have followed. As an initial step in the achievement of her aims, Russia inveigled China into concluding a secret agreement in 1896. This agreement enabled her to embark on a well-planned program of expansion. On the occasion of the coronation of Tsar Nicholas II in May, the Chinese government sent Li Hung-chang as a special envoy. His selection was based on the recommendations of the Russian Minister Cassini. Count Witte, the Minister of Finance, pointed out to Li that China ought to provide against any possible danger, and that Russia was desirous of giving effective aid in the event China's territory were menaced. He emphasized that it was advisable, therefore, to give Russia the means to carry this out. Witte's convincing arguments resulted in the signing of the Li-Lobanov Treaty, a defensive-offensive military alliance directed against Japan, which provided the following: (1) Mutual assistance through the use of military and naval power of the two parties in the event of Japanese aggression against Chinese, Korean, or Russian territory in the Far East; (2) conclusion of a peace treaty with the enemy only with the approval of the other party; (3) throwing open all the ports of China to Russian warships and merchant vessels during the period of hostilities; (4) approval by China of the construction of a railroad through the Heilungkiang and Kirin provinces to Vladivostok; entrusting the construction and development of this railway to the Russo-Chinese Bank; and concluding of contract between the Chinese Minister at the Russian capital and the Russo-Chinese Bank; (5) free use of railway for transporting troops and supplies in times of peace and war. This treaty was to take effect on the date of the contract as provided above, and to continue in force for a period of fifteen years.

By the terms of this agreement, the Chinese Eastern Railway, or the Manchurian section of the Trans-Siberian Railway, was to be financed by the Russo-Chinese Bank in which China was allowed to invest 5 million taels. The Bank, which was established under Russian Charter, was only nominally a joint undertaking. Actually it was purely a Russian concern in its incorporation and control and, ironically enough for the Chinese government which subscribed to its capitalization, set up as an instrumentality through which Russia was to effect the penetration of Manchuria. The Chinese Eastern Railway Company carried on a variety of activities, such as mining, manufacturing, and commercial activities, in addition to the operation of the railroad. Later, the Russian government secured the right to construct a southern extension of the railway which became the Manchurian Railway linking the Chinese Eastern with the port of Dalny. The Russo-Chinese Bank soon extended its banking activities over a wide area of China. Thus, Russia forged ahead in laying the groundwork for the political and economic penetration of the Far East which she pursued unrelentingly until the war with Japan.

For over thirty months after the end of the war between China and Japan, the Kaiser's government tried vainly to wrest a concession from the former. Finally, on November 1, 1897, an opportunity presented itself. Two Roman Catholic priests were murdered by a band of armed men in the village of Yenchow in Shantung province. Bishop Anzer, the German bishop of Shantung, immediately telegraphed the Kaiser asking protection for his mission. This was the moment the Kaiser had been waiting for. It also gave him the opportunity to demonstrate to his Catholic supporters that he had their welfare at heart. On the fourteenth the German East Asia Squadron steamed into Kiaochow Bay and landed a force at Tsingtao. At the same time the Kaiser's younger brother, Prince Heinrich, was sent to the Far East in command of two warships.

Without losing any time, the German Minister to China made the following six demands on the Chinese government: (1) The erection of monuments for the murdered priests; (2) the payment of indemnities to the survivors of the victims and reparations for the destroyed church and the two other churches to be built, and the granting of land on which the churches were to be constructed; (3) the dismissal of the governor of Shantung, Li Ping-hêng and barring him forever from holding a government position; (4) the payment of indemnity for defraying the military expenditures incurred in the occupation of Tsingtao; (5) the granting of exclusive mining and railway rights to Germans in Shantung province; (6) the leasing of Kiaochow Bay to Germany for use as a naval base.

The insistence of the *Tsungli Yamen* on the withdrawal of troops as a condition to the opening of negotiations was met with a rebuff from the German Minister. China had been hoping for assistance from a third power in softening Germany's demands, but no such help was forthcoming. France was preoccupied with the Dreyfus Affair and the Fashoda Incident, Great Britain had her own troubles in South Africa, while the United States was in the midst of the Cuban problem. Russia was not in the least interested in preventing the establishment of the much-needed precedent for her own future actions. Furthermore, the Li-Lobanov Treaty of 1896 was directed specifically at stopping aggression on the part of Japan but not of any other power. China had no altertive but to accede to all the demands, and on March 6, 1898, the Sino-German Treaty was signed. This treaty gave to Germany the following: (1) a 99-year lease on Kiaochow Bay with complete sovereignty to Germany and a 50-kilometer belt of neutral zone surrounding the Bay totaling some 200 square miles; (2) railway rights in Shantung province; (3) rights to coal mining and other enterprises and necessary public utilities within a zone of 30 Chinese miles on either side of the railway; (4) preference to Germans in economic activities in Shantung so that when foreign aid was needed in the form of capital, personnel, or materials, the Chinese government had the responsibility of calling first upon the German industrialists and merchants to supply them.

Germany immediately set out to transform Kiaochow into not only a naval base but also a center of commercial activities in North China.

Russia was not to be outdone by Germany in the competition for concession-wresting. Spurred on by Germany's success in obtaining a lease on Kiaochow, she moved ahead with her plans, which had long been in the making. In December of the preceding year, she had already dispatched five warships to Port Arthur, ostensibly for wintering, at a point which would enable them to protect China. Immediately thereafter negotiations were begun with the Chinese government to lease Dalny and Port Arthur under the same conditions as the German lease of Kiaochow. The Empress Dowager vigorously opposed the lease, but the Chinese representatives yielded in the face of bribes,[3] an ultimatum, and the presence of the Russian squadron at Port Arthur. On March 27, 1898, the treaty was signed, and Russia came into possession of the territory. Port Arthur became exclusively a naval base, open only to Russian and Chinese vessels, but Dalny was to be kept partially open as a foreign trade port. Russia was given the right to construct military installations on the leased territory. Furthermore, on July 6, she secured the extension of the original concession granted in 1896 through a supplementary agreement whereby the Chinese Eastern was authorized to construct a line linking leased territory with Dalny

---

[3] Li Hung-chang received from the Russian government a gift of 500,000 rubles and Chang Yin-huan 250,000 rubles. *Krasny Arkhiv*, Vol. II, pp. 287–293.

and, if necessary, to construct lines to other points as well. In addition, the Chinese government, by the supplementary convention of May 7, pledged not to grant in the neutral zone any rights to nationals of other powers, or to open Chinese cities on the eastern or western coast of the neutral zone to the foreign trade of other powers, or to relinquish highways, mining rights, commercial or industrial rights without Russia's approval.

French interests had always been in South China where the government concentrated its efforts. Less than two months after the Triple Intervention France secured her first reward. On June 20 a treaty was signed by Minister Gerard and the Chinese government for "rectifications" of the Annam-Chinese frontier. Then, in the spring of 1898, anti-missionary disturbances in the province of Kwangtung provided a suitable pretext for the landing of French troops at Kwangchowan. When China showed astonishment at the size of the demand and made signs of balking, France sent a fleet in a demonstration of power. In April, a month after Germany gained a foothold in Kiaochow, France obtained a leasehold on Kwangchowan, including an area of some 200 square miles. The treaty which was signed for this purpose gave the following rights to France: (1) a 99-year lease on Kwangchowan and the nearby islands to be used as a naval base and coaling station with exclusive jurisdiction; (2) the right to construct defense installation; (3) same accommodation to vessels of China and of powers having treaty relations with China, as is given in China's treaty ports; (4) railway rights, including the construction of railroad from the Tongking frontier to Yunnanfu; (5) China's promise not to alienate to another power the provinces of Kwangtung, Kwangsi, Yunnan, or the island of Hainan.[4] By this treaty, France hoped to prevent the penetration of South China by a third power through Annam and nearby regions and at the same time to provide a base of operation against Hongkong and Formosa.

Britain, in the face of the rapidly shifting balance of power in the Far East, could not remain indifferent or inactive. The course of events following the Triple Intervention had not been such as to give comfort or permit optimism or relaxation of vigilance. Seeing that Russia's leasing of Port Arthur and Dalny would seriously affect, if not threaten, British interests, and that countermoves were necessary, the British Government convinced the Chinese government of the advisability of granting a leasehold on Weihaiwei for as long a period as the Russians were to have theirs, and as soon as the Japanese withdrew her troops. As an understanding had already been reached in advance with both Germany and Japan the negotiations were completed in short order. When the Japanese troops evacuated on May 23, following the payment by the Chinese of the last installment of the indemnity, the British moved in, although the formal lease was not signed until July 1.

---

[4] *Foreign Relations of the United States* (1898), p. 191.

Because of the rights already granted to Germany in the Shantung province the lease on Weihaiwei did not include any commercial or industrial rights. The British Government made a formal declaration to Germany that it had no intention of injuring or contesting German rights and interests in Shantung, or of creating difficulties for her. As already stated above, the acquisition in April of a French leasehold on Kwangchowan constituted a possible threat to Hongkong, and the British Government demanded an extension of holdings on the adjacent peninsula, or Kowloon, to protect the colony. On June 9, 1898, the British Government secured a 99-year lease on the Kowloon Peninsula. Earlier in the same year, it had secured a pledge from China that no part of the Yangtze Valley would be alienated to another power.

Encouraged by China's declarations of nonalienation of territory to Britain and France in February and April respectively, Japan asked for a similar assurance for the province of Fukien. The *Tsungli Yamen* gave its assurance on April 26, 1898. Eleven months later Italy demanded the cession of a naval station on Sanmen Bay on the east coast of Chekiang province. Japan held that it was a district lying within the territory which came under the nonalienation promise. Although the demand was given lukewarm approval by Britain, Germany, and France, the Italian government abandoned its claim in face of Chinese resistance.

In November, 1900, following the Boxer Uprising, Secretary Hay, author of the Open Door notes, instructed, at the instance of the Navy Department, the United States Minister in Peking to take steps to obtain a naval base and territorial concessions at Samsah Bay.[5] As it was located in the area claimed by Japan as her sphere of interest, Washington consulted Tōkyō. When the Japanese declined to approve the lease, the matter was dropped.

[5] *Ibid.* (1915), pp. 114–115.

Chapter 18. The First Attempt at Party Government

The defeat of the land tax increase bill was the result of the close cooperation in the Diet between the Liberal Party, which had unsuccessfully attempted to reap the benefits by supporting Itō, and the Progressive Party, which had vainly tried to further its own objectives by allying itself with Matsukata and the Satsuma clique. Both parties had been awakened to the full realization that the power of the clan-dominated government could be checked through effective cooperation. As a result they liquidated their long-standing differences and rivalry and decided to effect a merger. On June 22, 1898, the Kenseitō was born as an effective step toward the attainment of responsible party government.

Clan bureaucrats as well as the government were as amazed as they were alarmed and lost no time in calling an imperial conference on the following day to discuss countermeasures to cope with the threat, or rather the challenge, which was explicit in the merger of the two parties. At this conference Itō underscored the impossibility of maintaining a super-party government under a system of representative rule and proposed three alternatives: (1) that he would remain in government to organize and lead a large government party and to carry out the administration of the affairs of state; (2) that he would leave the government to organize and head a political party to support the policies of the government; or (3) that he would turn over the government to the newly formed Kenseitō and let Ōkuma and Itagaki form a cabinet.

Yamagata expressed violent opposition to these ideas on the grounds that the proposals were not only in contravention of the spirit of the Constitution, but in conflict with "national polity," inasmuch as the government would necessarily be based on political parties. As a solution he advocated that the Constitution be suspended temporarily and the Diet be divested of financial powers, if necessary. A heated argument developed between Yamagata, the leader of the military clique, and Itō, the leading civilian bureaucrat. When his proposals were not accepted, Itō retired from the meeting after stating that there was no alternative but to recommend the head of the Kenseitō as his successor. Early on the following morning, Premier Itō tendered his resignation, for he had clearly seen the handwriting on the wall.

It fell to the lot of the Elder Statesmen to find a suitable successor to Itō.

259

No one among their number would dare accept the responsibility at such a difficult time.[1] Even Yamagata, who had strongly opposed Itō's proposals, could not muster enough courage to take the helm of state. In the end, however, they adopted Itō's third proposal and called on Ōkuma and Itagaki to form a new government. Upon learning of the decision, Itō, who was absent from the conference of Elder Statesmen, which was held in the presence of the Emperor, summoned the two co-leaders of the Kenseitō and requested them to take over the government. At this meeting, which was held on the night of June 25, Itō asked the leaders to bury their hatchets and work together in the new government. It was clear that by this time the ex-Premier had been convinced of the indispensability of Diet support, which meant the backing of the majority party. So surprised were Ōkuma and Itagaki at the unexpected turn of events that they were unable immediately to give a reply of acceptance. They had to collect themselves first.

The Ōkuma-Itagaki Cabinet[2] thus came into being on June 30, 1898. All the members, with the exception of the War and Navy Ministers, belonged to the Kenseitō. While some historians have called this the first party cabinet, that was true only in a loose sense. The Kenseitō was less than a week old when it was called on to form a cabinet, and at best it was still a shaky organization which had just come into existence by the merger of two parties, brought together by a common grievance against the oppressive policy of the clan-dominated government. Obviously it was not a union born of the identity of principles or political platforms but rather of political expediency. Moreover, those who joined the cabinet were not members of the Diet at the time, since this body had just been dissolved.

In spite of the fact that this cabinet fell far short of the requirements of a true party cabinet, its significance in the development of responsible government cannot be overemphasized. It was indeed a revolutionary step. At the time of the opening of the Diet in 1890, Yamagata, Itō, Kuroda, and others regarded the maintenance of intimate relation or cooperation between administrative officials and political parties as a serious offense and a desecration of imperial authority. Only a few years earlier Ōkuma had been eased out of his position as member of the Privy Council for having conferred with Itagaki, who was president of a political party. When Itagaki was rewarded with a cabinet post for supporting Itō, he was obliged to sever his connections with the party of which he was president. Now, less than a decade after the opening of the Diet, the clan bureaucrats, who once regarded the cultivation of friendly relations with political parties as tantamount to criminal offense, had actually

---

[1] Yamagata, Kuroda, Inoue, Saigō, and Ōyama were all asked, but all the Elder Statesmen declined to undertake the formation of a cabinet.

[2] This Cabinet was referred to by the Japanese as the Waihan Naikaku.

been persuaded to select a party leader as head of the government. While it was evident that the bureaucrats had come to the realization that successful administration of state affairs could not be carried out by excluding the political parties, it was equally evident that they had also lost the fear and suspicion of political parties, that they entertained in the beginning.

Members of the Kenseitō, who had starved for political power for years, were now determined to make full use of the opportunity presented to reward themselves with government positions. One of the concrete manifestations of this desire was the introduction of parliamentary administrative positions which were to be filled by party members. The invasion of government positions by party men gave rise to apprehension among the bureaucrats, who feared for their security. The administrative retrenchment policy advocated by the Minseitō included proposals to abolish the Ministries of Education and Justice as well as the Metropolitan Police Board, a reduction in the number of courts and the size of the army and navy, all of which aggravated the feeling of insecurity among the bureaucrats and the military. This was the beginning of the intensification of opposition against the party by both the bureaucrats and the military clique. Intensive office hunting developed and those who felt they were not properly rewarded began to stir up internal strife. Party disunion developed as cleavages widened within the organization which had been held together by both parties' common enemy, the bureaucrats. When the bureaucrats were overpowered, the party in power began to fall apart, and the old Liberal Party faction and the old Progressive Party faction began to fight.

The sixth general election was held on August 10, 1898, a little over a month after the formation of the Ōkuma-Itagaki Cabinet. The Kenseitō captured an absolute majority of 260 seats, divided almost evenly between its two factions. The jealousy and antagonism that smouldered between the two factions blighted party solidarity, and they fought against each other over such issues as the abolition of the Metropolitan Police Board, the appointment procedure in the civil service, and the nationalization of railways. Into this strife and confusion entered Hoshi Tōru, a former speaker of the House of Representatives, who had been expelled from its membership. In spite of Foreign Minister Ōkuma's disapproval, he had taken a furlough from his post as Minister to the United States in order that he might take an active part in politics at home. Indignant at not being included in the new Cabinet formed by the Kenseitō, he caused his followers to stir up unrest within the party in an attempt to wreck the Cabinet and to achieve his own ends.

As if this were not enough, another incident took place to add to the difficulties of the Kenseitō. On August 21, 1898, Education Minister Ozaki Yukio delivered an address before the Imperial Education Association in which he warned the educators against the spreading menace of rank materialism reflected in the "worship of money." After emphasizing that there was no possibility of Japan ever adopting a republican form of government, he gave a hypothetical example of how, if a republican form of government were to come into being, a Mitsui or an Iwasaki might aspire to become president. This utterance was immediately seized upon by the *Tōkyō Nichi Nichi,* mouthpiece of the clan bureaucrats, who intensely disliked the Kenseitō Cabinet, to launch violent attacks on the Education Minister, who, it declared, should be dismissed for disrespect to the Throne. The ambitious and conniving Katsura, then War Minister, contrived to have Ozaki ousted by spreading false reports of mutinous conditions in the army, while Home Minister Itagaki made the prefectural governors submit fabricated reports that placed the Education Minister in a very unfavorable light. In the face of strong attacks from the clan bureaucrats, the Liberal Party faction, and hostile public opinion Ozaki was forced to resign, although his conscience was clear, and he felt that the entire cabinet should assume responsibility if anyone needed to be censured.

The dissension within the party came to a head in the fall of 1898. The Liberal Party faction succeeded in wrecking the Kenseitō and then reorganized itself as the new Kenseitō toward the end of October, while the Progressive Party faction reorganized itself as the Kenseihontō early in November. Thus the marriage of convenience came to an inglorious end after less than six months of unstable existence. By the end of December the clash of views between Ōkuma and Itagaki had reached a point where reconciliation was impossible, and the latter felt he could no longer put up with the former. Consequently, on December 28, Itagaki tendered his resignation. Having made a pledge at the time of the formation of the Cabinet to act together in everything, Ōkuma followed with his resignation, giving as his reason the disunion of the Cabinet. The Emperor was greatly disturbed and ordered Saigō and Katsura to endeavor to restore a harmonious relationship between the two estranged statesmen. The Kenseitō Cabinet, which was enthusiastically hailed by party members as the beginning of responsible party government, and on which high hopes were placed by the public, collapsed even before it could meet the test of a Diet session, not because of external opposition but because of the selfishness and lack of principles and convictions on the part of the rank and file as well as the leaders. By its failure and loss of prestige it provided the clan bureaucrats once again with the welcome opportunity to attempt a political comeback. For the setback suffered in the progress of constitutional government, Ōkuma and Itagaki and their followers must share the blame.

THE SECOND YAMAGATA CABINET

With a suavity rare among military men and exhibiting consummate skill in political craft and wiles, Katsura bent his energies to aggravating the cleavages within the Kenseitō. Outwardly, he made a gesture of working for the reconciliation of warring factions, but secretly he was using every means at his command to disrupt the party. Divide and conquer was his strategy. He was working with the clan bureaucrats to overthrow the Ōkuma-Itagaki Cabinet and to restore clan bureaucracy to power. Moreover, Katsura was anxiously waiting to realize his long-cherished ambition of demonstrating his political ability.

When the collapse of the Ōkuma-Itagaki Cabinet became imminent, the Elder Statesmen met frequently to plan their next moves. At the time, Itō, who had antagonized some of the clan bureaucrats by giving Ōkuma and Itagaki an opportunity to form a cabinet, was on a tour of China to get away from the unpleasant political atmosphere that hung over the capital. Following the resignation of Itagaki, Ōkuma telegraphed Itō, urging him to return immediately, as he needed the help of the veteran statesman. Knowing that Itō would not welcome a super-party cabinet, Yamagata and the other Elder Statesmen rushed the formation of the new government, completing the investiture ceremony on November 8, the day after Itō arrived back in Nagasaki from his trip to China.

For years Yamagata had been an extreme advocate of the nonparty cabinet and of all the clan bureaucrats, he showed the strongest antipathy for political parties. However, even he could not successfully resist the inexorable current of the times. From his own bitter experiences he too had come to realize the impracticability, if not the impossibility, of trying to maintain political power without the support of the political parties in one form or another. As the new Premier, he therefore approached Itagaki, the leader of the Kenseitō, and reached an understanding with him. Although the party's initial demand for the appointment of Kenseitō members to the Cabinet was turned down by Yamagata, it agreed to support the government on the conditions that (1) the government issue a declaration to the effect that it was not assuming an attitude of aloofness, but rather was working closely together with the Kenseitō; (2) the government was in agreement with, and was adopting, the policies of the Kenseitō, and it would introduce bills in the Diet in order to carry them out, and (3) the government would assist in the extension of the powers of the political parties, and that cooperation with the Kenseitō would not merely be regarded as a temporary expedient, but would continue into the future.

Yamagata's abandonment of his earlier attitude of hostility in favor of cooperation with the leading political party was prompted by the necessity of seeing through the tax increase of 44 million yen, which was absolutely essential for the vastly expanded postwar finances, and was also made necessary by the state of general confusion which existed at the time. Of the fiscal problems the most unpopular one was the proposed increase of the land tax, which had been chiefly responsible for the collapse of the second Matsukata Cabinet. Even Itō did not succeed in surmounting this obstacle. The backbone of public opinion at the time was the rural farming population. Naturally the increase in the land tax was distasteful to the farmers, who put up strenuous opposition. The political parties capitalized on this situation and, by opposing the government's program for a tax increase, enhanced their popularity.

In spite of the support from the Kenseitō, the second Yamagata Cabinet was not to have too smooth sailing on the tax increase bill. The Kenseihontō organized all the opposition parties and formed the Anti-Land Tax Increase Federation under the leadership of Ōkuma, Tani, and Miura. Although the government ordered the disbanding of the Federation, opposition against increase in the land tax became more vociferous instead of subsiding. As a countermeasure, the government banned public addresses, disbanded public meetings, prevented local leaders from coming to the capital, and bribed members of the Diet to organize the Association for Land Tax Increase. Finally, by reducing the rate of increase from 4 per cent to 3.3 per cent and limiting it to a period of five years, and also by resorting to more bribery, the government managed to get the bill through the Diet. With the successful passage of the appropriations bill, the government rewarded the Kenseitō by increasing the salaries of the presiding officers of both houses from 4,000 to 5,000 yen, their deputies from 2,000 to 3,000 yen, and those of the members from 800 to 2,000 yen.

Confronted by the persistent office-hunting of the party members who expected reward, Yamagata revised the regulations for the appointment of civil officials, and by passing the Ordinance Pertaining to the Status of Civil Officials and the Ordinance Pertaining to the Discipline of Civil Officials closed the door to party office seekers and protected the tenure of civil officials. Before this revision, although officials of *sōnin* and *hannin* ranks had to meet certain requirements for appointment, there were no such requirements for *chokunin* officials. Since the change was made without consultation with the Kenseitō, the action was regarded as an insult and a challenge hurled at the party by the government. Yamagata met the threat to withdraw party support by dismissing the Vice Home Minister and Chief Cabinet Secretary, who had drafted the new Civil Service Ordinance, and explained that it was unable to rescind what had already been published, even though it was not what the government really wanted. This step had the effect of appeasing the party, at least for the time being. When it became apparent that the support of the Kenseitō could no longer be counted on, the Yamagata Cabinet decided to organize an out-and-out government party. Accordingly, on July 5, 1899, the Imperial Party was organized by a score of members,[3] but it was unable to become even a feeble political factor.

[3] The group that organized the party Teikokutō included Motoda Hajime, Ōoka Ikuzō, Sassa Tomofusa, and Saitō Shūichirō.

NEW ELECTION LAW

One of the by-products of the working coalition between the Kenseitō and the government was the enactment of a new election law. The first election law of 1889 required the payment of 15 yen in direct national tax for voters as well as for candidates. This property qualification kept the number of voters down to about 450,000 out of a total population of more than 40 million, and disqualified a considerable number of capable persons from candidacy. There were other disadvantages, such as the smallness of the election districts, which enabled politicians of small stature to be elected, and the open vote, which made it possible for voters to be influenced unduly by personal considerations.

Because of the obvious shortcomings of the electoral law, reform bills were submitted repeatedly to the Diet beginning in 1894, but each time the House of Peers voted them down after they were passed by the House of Representatives. The bill submitted by the third Itō Cabinet was by far the most liberal, reducing the tax requirement to 5 yen, the age requirement for voters to 20 years and for candidates to 25 years, and giving one representative for every 100,000 population in the rural sections, and one representative for every 50,000 population in urban independent election districts. However, this bill died with the 12th Diet, which was dissolved before the House of Peers had a chance to take it up.

The Yamagata Cabinet was obligated, in spite of its wishes, to carry out at least a portion of the legislative program of the Kenseitō, to which it was committed. Furthermore, public opinion was clamoring for the election reform which was long overdue. The revised election law, which it succeeded in passing, provided for a secret ballot, reduced the tax qualification to 10 yen, made the whole prefecture an election district, and a year's residence a prerequisite to voting. Cities of 30,000 population and over were made into separate election districts. This increased the total number of representatives to 369, giving one representative to every 130,000 population in cities and rural areas alike.

Despite some concessions to the Kenseitō and some apparent, but not altogether successful, efforts to win over public opinion to his side, Yamagata was all the while doing everything in his power to strengthen the foundations of clan bureaucracy and particularly that of the military. The Civil Service Ordinance, described elsewhere, was promulgated for such a purpose. As the first Home Minister under the newly established cabinet system in the 1880's Yamagata laid the foundations of bureaucracy. From 1883 until the end of 1889 he gathered under him in local and central government administration young officials, both civilian and military, who served him with unswerving loyalty in subsequent years. The large following he had built up was truly amazing but understandable in view of the fact that he had served before the end of the century in practically every important position in the country. He had served as Home Minister, Prime Minister, Justice Minister, Chief of General Staff, Elder Statesman, Privy Councilor, and had attained the rank of Field Marshal in 1898. His influence was equally strong among Chōshū men and non-Chōshū men, and civilians as well as military men.

Yet another ordinance with far-reaching consequences in the course of Japanese political and constitutional development was promulgated by the Yamagata Cabinet without so much as attracting the attention of either of the political parties or the public. As a matter of fact, it was known only after it had become an accomplished fact. No other legal provision so strengthened the position of clan bureaucracy and the military and so retarded constitutional progress as the Imperial Ordinance of May, 1900, which provided that only generals and lieutenant generals on the active list might hold the post of War Minister and only admirals and vice-admirals on the active list might become Navy Minister.[4] This gave the army and navy the power of life and death over the government since either one could wreck any existing cabinet or prevent the formation of a new one by withdrawing its Minister or by refusing to recommend one. It gave the military the power to manipulate the exercise of sovereignty, inasmuch as no cabinet could exist without the consent and cooperation of the military. The head of the War or Navy Ministry had been from the beginning an administrative official, although there was no reason why it could not be filled by a civilian. However, since there had never been a civilian War or Navy Minister, it was taken for granted by all that he should be a military man. If the political parties and public opinion had successfully fought the ordinance originated by Yamagata and prevented the military-dominated clan government from solidifying its position, the growth of militarism and military supremacy might well have been nipped in the bud.

Although the achievements of the Yamagata Cabinet were not inconsiderable, the methods which were employed were often questionable. The militarist-bureaucrat Premier acted on the belief that the end justified the means. He showed little, if any, concern for responsible government; in fact, he did his utmost to prevent the political parties from gaining ascendancy. The expansion of the powers of the Privy Council, which he successfully engineered on the eve of his resignation from that body, the revised regulations for the appointment of officials, and the requirement that Ministers of War and Navy had to be general officers on active list were all intended to check the political parties and to strengthen the position of the military. Perhaps more than any other person of his day he was responsible for the obstruction and retardation of normal and

---

[4] This provision was modified in 1913 by the Yamamoto Cabinet, making reserve officers eligible for the posts of War and Navy Ministers. In 1936, under the Hirota Cabinet, it was changed back to the original form as promulgated by Yamagata.

healthy growth of political institutions, leading toward responsible government.

In spite of the loyal support given by the Kenseitō in getting the tax increase bill through the Diet, Yamagata made no attempt to reward the party. On the contrary, his underlings were inclined to show openly their dislike and contempt for party members. It was natural that a rift should develop. At this point, Itō, who was no longer on friendly terms with Yamagata, whose policies and actions he abhorred, began to attack the financial policies of the government while at the same time advocating the need of improving political parties. Borrowing the political and constitutional ideas of Edmund Burke and Thomas B. Macauley, he eloquently argued that a model political party was urgently needed to realize parliamentary government in the true sense. Seeing the wisdom of forsaking Yamagata and allying itself with Itō, the Kenseitō presented to the former a demand which it knew would not be met, and after satisfying itself that it was rejected, went over to Itō.

It was quite clear that Itō was preparing to secure political power through leadership of a new party. Realizing the difficulty of taking over an existing party and wishing to avoid further antagonizing Yamagata and his powerful military clique, he decided not to become involved with the Minseitō. He therefore proposed first the disbanding of the party before organizing a new political party, which he would then be free to shape as he saw fit. Before he embarked on the actual formation of the party, however, he secured in advance the approval of the Elder Statesmen as well as of the Emperor, thereby precluding the possibility of interference from any quarter. An organization committee of twelve, including such notables as Prince Saionji, Baron Kaneko, Hoshi Tōru, Hara Takashi, and Ozaki Yukio, launched the new party, Seiyūkai, on September 16, 1900, and a declaration and a prospectus were issued in the name of Itō Hirobumi.

In founding a new political party and heading it, Itō was giving concrete expression to his belief that political parties were important and necessary in the effective administration of the affairs of the state. At the same time, by this act, he was trying to even the score with Yamagata, who had opposed him when he recommended that the majority party, Kenseitō, be given the task of forming a new cabinet. However, Itō was not quite ready for party government in the true sense of the term, as he stood his ground in denying the party members any right to participate in the selection of cabinet members or in the formulation of government policies. As President of the Seiyūkai, he exercised almost absolute power, following the policy of ordering the members to follow his commands without question. The newspaper *Hōchi,* in commenting on the position and attitude of Itō with regard to the Seiyūkai, referred to him as the "Louis XIV of Japanese political parties."

THE FOURTH ITŌ CABINET

Almost immediately after Itō launched the Seiyūkai, Yamagata recommended Itō as his successor and promptly resigned his position as Premier. Although Itō entertained ambitions of capturing political power, he hesitated to accept immediately the imperial command to form a cabinet, inasmuch as he detected signs of antipathy in Yamagata's resignation. However, on the insistence of the various fellow Elder Statesmen, he conferred repeatedly with Yamagata and, after securing the retiring Premier's pledge, accepted the command to form a new government. Thus the fourth Itō Cabinet came into being in October, 1900. All the members except the Army, Navy, and Foreign Ministers were members of the newly founded Seiyūkai, a fact which led to the extravagant and erroneous claim that it was a party government.

With the Seiyūkai controlling a safe majority of the total membership of 300, it was an easy matter for the Itō Cabinet to get bills through the Diet. Even the then unprecedently large appropriations bill of 250 million yen virtually breezed through the House of Representatives. Unexpectedly, however, it met with stiff resistance in the House of Peers, where conservative statesmen and bureaucrats resented Itō's leadership of the Seiyūkai as well as his heading a cabinet of party members. The conservative upper chamber was also outraged by Itō's inclusion in the Cabinet of Hoshi Tōru, whom the House of Peers loathed.

As Hoshi was one of the leaders of the Seiyūkai, he was made Communications Minister in Itō's Cabinet. Concurrently, he was President of the Tōkyō Municipal Council, a position he utilized to manipulate municipal administration at will. Municipal assembly and council members under him were arrested one after another on suspicion that they had accepted bribery, misappropriated public funds, obtained money by fraud, even though Hoshi himself had once been indicted for accepting a bribe. Even the Privy Council had been moved by the increasing clamor against Hoshi's remaining in the Cabinet. Finally the indignant members of the House of Peers advised the Premier to oust Hoshi. With the assurance from Justice Minister Kaneko that no legal proceedings would be taken against him, Hoshi retired from the Cabinet late in December, 1900.

Hoshi's resignation from the Cabinet, however, did not stop the House of Peers from attacking the government. On the contrary, it stimulated its attack on the appropriations bill. Premier Itō appeared personally before the Special Committee on Appropriations of the House of Peers and, setting aside his pride and dignity, humbly pleaded for the passage of the appropriations bill. However, his efforts were unavailing. The peers insisted that the Lower House did not represent the people and therefore had no right to pass the appropriations bill, which included the increase in excise taxes on sake, sugar, and tobacco. In an attempt to break the deadlock, Itō sought vainly the aid of the Elder Statesmen, but Yamagata was not friendly, while Matsukata regarded Itō's policy of increasing taxes as ill-advised. The Premier, therefore, summoned the Elder Statesmen in the name of the Emperor and prevailed upon them to mediate in the dispute between the government and the Upper House, but even this could not break the deadlock. As a final resort, which he had used before, he had the President of the House of Peers summoned to the Imperial Palace to receive an imperial rescript instructing the Upper House to pass the tax increase bill which had already been passed by the Lower House. The rescript had a magical effect on the peers, who immediately reversed their stand and passed the bill. This incident brought out clearly the fact that imperial rescripts and decrees were issued at the specific request of the Ministers of State who were responsible for them.

After a long and difficult struggle the Itō Cabinet succeeded in getting the appropriations bill for the fiscal year 1901 through the Diet. However, the increase in revenue for 1901 was not sufficient to balance the budget. Furthermore, the expenditures incurred in connection with the Boxer Rebellion had to be made up, and 30 million yen were needed for enterprises to be defrayed by the prearranged issue of bonds in 1901. As a result, the government attempted, after the adjournment of the Diet, to change its already established financial plans. With Premier Itō's approval, the Finance Minister proposed the suspension of government enterprises for the fiscal year 1901, such as those pertaining to railways, telephone, and others. But in a cabinet meeting five ministers who were all members of the Seiyūkai, Suematsu Kenchō, Matsuda Masahisa, Kaneko Kentarō, Hara Kei, and Hayashi Yūzō, and who had entertained a dislike for the Finance Minister from the outset, vigorously opposed the proposal to suspend government enterprises. Foreign Minister Katō, War Minister General Kodama, and Navy Minister Yamamoto, who constituted the neutrals in the dispute, endeavored to reconcile the opposing groups, but in spite of their efforts, by the middle of April, the feuding parties had passed the stage of reconciliation. On May 2, without consulting the members of the Cabinet, Itō proceeded to the Imperial Palace and submitted his resignation, giving as his reason the disunion of the government.

The fourth Itō Cabinet, which was based on a political party, ended in failure, not because of an opposition from the outside, but because of an internal squabble which impaired its unity beyond repair. Itō was without doubt the ablest bureaucratic statesman of his time. In regard to experience in official life, the extent of power wielded, and the confidence he enjoyed in government as well as court circles, he was without peer. He displayed consummate skill and political acumen in commanding the respect and obedience of his subordinates. However, he had no experience in leading party members and was found wanting in the tact, perseverance, and energy necessary to control and harmonize the conflicting elements within the party. As a bureaucrat Itō was eminently successful, but as a party politician he was a failure.

No sooner had Itō submitted his resignation than the Elder Statesmen swung into action, but they could not find a suitable person to recommend. They therefore strongly urged Itō to remain, but he refused. For a month they looked for a candidate, but nobody would assume the responsibility of forming a cabinet as long as Itō controlled an absolute majority in the Diet as President of the Seiyūkai. Even Saionji, the acting Premier in the interim, had no desire to take on the responsibility. Finally, the Elder Statesmen, reversing their policy, decided to recommend a young obscure statesman for the Premiership. General Katsura Tarō, an ambitious military protégé of Yamagata, who had been working hard to ingratiate himself with the Elder Statesmen, was given the assignment.

In a sense, the Katsura Cabinet, which emerged on June 2, 1901, was a reaction against party government as it did not include a single party member. However, since the new Premier was not one of the Elder Statesmen or the clan bureaucrats, it could be regarded as a progressive step in the direction of constitutional government. Up to this time every government, with the exception of the Ōkuma-Itagaki Cabinet, had been headed by, and organized around, an Elder Statesman or a clan bureaucrat. Although Katsura was a Chōshū man and member of the military clique, his Cabinet was not dependent on the Elder Statesmen.

By the skillful handling of the political parties, Katsura managed to get the appropriations bill passed. This was facilitated to a considerable extent by the eagerness of the Seiyūkai to support the government, although it was suffering from lack of unity since the assassination of Hoshi on June 21 and particularly since Itō was away on a European tour. The Katsura Government, which, at the time of formation, had been branded as second rate, gained considerable prestige by the successful conclusion of the Anglo-Japanese Alliance in January, 1902.

The seventh general election was held on August 10, 1902, as the term of office of the representatives elected on August 10, 1898, expired. This was the first election to be held in accordance with the new Election Law of 1900. Since the Katsura Cabinet did not have a special relationship with any of the political parties, there was no interference, and the election was run off smoothly and without any untoward incidents. The Seiyūkai members captured absolute majority in the Diet, as they won 191 seats.

Although the Katsura Cabinet steered its legislative program through the Diet by befriending all the political parties and favoring none, such a policy was bound to end without having made any friends on whom the party could rely in a crisis. That was precisely what happened in the next session of the Diet, when the government had to fight the united opposition of all the political parties.

In the face of threatening developments in the wake of the Boxer Rebellion, the Katsura Government outlined a plan of national defense providing for an eleven-year (1903–1913) naval expansion program, and involving the construction of approximately 80,000 tons of new battleships, cruisers, and destroyers. The expenses were to be met by the repeal of the limit imposed upon the Land Tax Increase Law. When the government announced the program of naval expansion and increase in land taxes, Seiyūkai President Itō expressed strong disapproval, advocating a radical change in the nation's financial policies, which included the deferment of all new government enterprises, readjustment of administration, and disarmament, as a means of relieving the people of the heavy burden. The Kenseihontō joined the Seiyūkai in its opposition to the government.

Undaunted by the opposition, Katsura submitted the appropriations bill without any changes. When the Appropriations Committee of the Lower House disapproved the Land Tax Increase Bill and referred it to the Committee of the Whole, Katsura made a personal appearance on the floor of the Diet to explain and uphold the bill. But in spite of his efforts, it appeared that the House would disapprove it. Whereupon Katsura prorogued the Diet for five days, during which time the government bribed and abducted party members in an attempt to break the united front of the parties. When these methods failed, it tried mediation by requesting General Kodama Gentarō and President of the House of Peers Konoe to step in between the government and the parties. This also having proved futile, the government dissolved the Diet. In this head-on clash, Itō, as President of the Seiyūkai, spearheaded the attack on the government, but the victory was Katsura's, at least for the time being.

Immediately after the dissolution was ordered, the leaders of the Seiyūkai and Kenseihontō met and pledged to work together for the reelection of the same representatives. In the election that followed on March 1, 1903, the Seiyūkai captured an absolute majority. In view of the splendid showing the government desired, if possible, to effect a reconciliation with the Seiyūkai. Yamagata was pressed into service as a mediator to effect a reconciliation with Itō. Realizing the disadvantages of persisting in opposing the government, particularly in view of the latest dissolution, the Seiyūkai indicated its willingness to work with the government, provided it were given the opportunity to save the honor of the party with regard to the stand it had taken on the tax increase bill.

Accordingly, the government submitted the bill for the extension of the tax increase to the Diet which was given the opportunity to vote it down. This was merely a device to save the face of the Seiyūkai. After withdrawing the defeated bill, the government effected an economy through administrative retrenchment and diverted to naval expansion expenditure the funds which had previously been allocated to improvements and telephone and railway enterprises. The additional funds necessary for the expenditures were to be raised by a bond issue with the approval of the Diet. Thus, the Katsura Cabinet succeeded in putting through the naval expansion program together with the necessary legislation to raise the funds through the issuance of bonds.

Two sensational scandals were brought to light during the special session of the Diet in May, 1903. At the time the compilation of elementary school textbooks was in the hands of private book publishers. However, once they were approved by the Ministry of Education, their adoption in the schools was decided by the Elementary School Textbook Committees in the different prefectures. As keen competition developed among book publishers in their energetic efforts to have their textbooks adopted as widely as possible, bribes were offered freely to governors, school inspectors, prefectural council members, and principals of middle, normal, and elementary schools. Corruption in the educational associations of nearly every prefecture was exposed, and several hundred persons, including prefectural governors and members of the Diet as well as prefectural assemblies, were taken into custody. The other scandal was bared in connection with the issuance of an imperial ordinance pertaining to the stock exchanges. In June, 1902, the government promulgated an imperial ordinance requiring the approval of the Minister of Agriculture and Commerce for certain types of transactions. However, when the regulation met with opposition from those in business, the government countermanded the provisions of the imperial ordinance with a ministry ordinance. This action was severely criticized as an unconstitutional act and drew a resolution censuring the irresponsibility of the government. In spite of the censure by the Lower House in both of the scandals, the Katsura Cabinet showed little, if any, embarrassment. No attempt was made, however, by the political parties to follow up their attack on the government, thus missing an excellent opportunity to strengthen their position.

Although the Katsura Government managed to weather the special session of the Diet with the support of the Seiyūkai, the Premier was nevertheless greatly harassed by Itō, who was at the same time President of the party and Elder Statesman. By virtue of his dual position, Itō moved around in governmental and court circles, as well as in political ones, and managed to have a hand in the determination of all major government policies. Through Yamagata, Katsura demanded that Itō make his position clearer by choosing either the party presidency or his membership in the group of Elder Statesmen. Itō flatly refused the demand, and on July 1 Katsura indignantly submitted his resignation, giving as his reason the recurrence of a chronic ailment, a standard face-saving excuse which has come to be accepted in Japanese politics as legitimate.

Yamagata and Matsukata, who were summoned by the Emperor, emphasized the inadvisability of changing the Cabinet in a period of stress and strain both at home and abroad and advised the urgency of pulling Itō out of the Seiyūkai and installing him in the Privy Council as President. This was Yamagata's scheme to tear Itō away from the Seiyūkai, thereby weakening its political activities which were not to his liking. Itō suspected this move to be the calculated plan of Yamagata, Matsukata, and Katsura; he therefore hesitated for a while to accept the new post.

Meanwhile, disunion had seriously weakened the Seiyūkai. Itagaki, Ozaki, Hayashi Yūzō, and Kataoka Kenkichi had dropped out, and the Seiyūkai no longer commanded a majority in the Diet. On July 12, Itō accepted the presidency of the Privy Council and turned over the presidency of the Seiyūkai to his political protégé, Prince Saionji, who was retiring as head of the Privy Council. It was actually an exchange of positions.

Simultaneously with Itō's departure from the Seiyūkai, Katsura withdrew his resignation and set about to bolster the Cabinet by filling the portfolios in Education (Kikuchi Dairoku) and Agriculture and Commerce (Hirata Tōsuke), which had been vacated by the resignation of the two incumbents who had been implicated in the textbook and stock exchange scandals. In the face of the maneuvers of Katsura and Yamagata, even the great Itō suffered a miserable defeat, after which it was impossible for him to recoup his political power, which was in the firm grip of the military clan bureaucrats, Yamagata and his cohorts.

Indignant at the political trickery perpetrated by Katsura, the Seiyūkai and Kenseihontō came together in a determined effort to smash the Cabinet. On December 10, at the formal opening of the 19th Diet by the Emperor, Speaker of the House of Representatives Kōno Hironaka departed from the established practice of reading a formal reply and read instead one which he himself had drafted casually though in a dignified manner, befitting the solemn occasion. The unsuspecting Diet approved it without giving it a second thought. However, it created a furore when it was discovered by the members on careful perusal that it contained expressions of no-confidence, censuring the government. Flustered by the unexpected and unorthodox form of attack, the government moved fast and through hurried arrangements with the Imperial Household Ministry, prevented the Speaker from appearing at the Imperial Palace to present to the Emperor the Diet's reply, which was highly offensive and derogatory to Premier Katsura. The Diet was immediately dissolved. Thus, the 19th Diet was dissolved before it had the chance to begin its deliberations, an action which could hardly be justified from the point of view of responsible government.

It was not until March 1, 1904, almost a month after the commencement of hostilities between Japan and Russia, that the general election was held. Much to the surprise of foreign observers and particularly to that of the Russians, the election was carried out in an atmosphere of unity and national solidarity. The political parties, which only a few months before had been determined to overthrow the government, now supported Katsura wholeheartedly and without reservation, passing every bill and appropriating the war expenditures requested without even so much as scrutinizing the items. The Diet existed in name only, as absolute control was exercised by the Katsura Cabinet, which strengthened its position at the expense of the political parties. Although the Russo-Japanese War enhanced national power and prestige in the eyes of the world, it set back by several years the development of responsible party government toward which the nation had seemed to be moving rather rapidly at the turn of the century.

Chapter 19. Prelude to Russo-Japanese Conflict

Immediately after the commencement of hostilities with China in 1894, a provisional agreement was signed between Minister Ōtori and the Korean Foreign Minister. This agreement stipulated that the Korean government would carry out the needed domestic reforms in accordance with the advice of the Japanese government; that the two governments would appoint commissions to meet and discuss problems pertaining to the strengthening of Korea's independence; and that Japanese troops guarding the Palace would be withdrawn at an opportune time.

On August 26 a military alliance was concluded with a view to securing the independence of Korea, furthering the interests of the signatories, and expelling Chinese troops from Korean soil. By this treaty, which was to expire simultaneously with the conclusion of a peace treaty between China and Japan, Korea was to facilitate the prosecution of the war by aiding in the movement of Japanese troops and in procuring supplies and provisions.

Meanwhile, the July 23 attack on the Palace had purged the Court of the influence of the Min faction, and Taiwunkun was brought back into the government to serve once more as Regent. Under his watchful eyes the King proclaimed domestic reforms, the punishment of the Min faction, and the renunciation of the Sino-Korean Treaty. Unfortunately, the *coup d'état* developed into a personal revenge on the Min family, which Taiwunkun had long been planning. Although power was now completely in his hands, the Regent was anxious to restore public confidence, which had been badly shaken. Accordingly, he gathered together the leaders of the moderate faction and ordered the formation of a cabinet. The progressive pro-Japanese faction, which had staged a comeback as a result of the elimination of the Min faction, was now given the task of planning the reforms. The planners were radical and impatient, but wanting in experience and judgment, while the Regent himself was an ultra-conservative, if not a downright reactionary. Consequently, clashes were frequent and endless. The Cabinet, a group of moderate leaders caught between these two extreme elements, was unable even to initiate necessary reforms.

Until the Japanese captured Pyongyang (Heijō), the Korean government as well as the people were uncertain as to the outcome of the war. Many believed that ultimate victory would be China's. The Cabinet and Taiwunkun endeavored to remain on good terms with both countries. On the surface the Korean government made a show of trying to carry out reforms in conformity with Japanese advice, but at the same time it could not very well ignore Li Hung-ch'ang's orders not to follow Japanese advice. The net result was that the program of reform remained virtually at a standstill. Furthermore, the northern part of the peninsula was at first under the complete domination of Chinese troops, while the southern half was busily occupied in supplying the needs of the Japanese troops. This left the Korean government with a small area, including Seoul and its neighboring regions, over which it actually exercised authority. An additional obstacle in the way of effectuating reforms was the fact that the Japanese government did not have a clearly defined policy.

Because of the tremendous importance of Korea to Japan's defense, and since the question of reform in Korea affected her prestige, the Japanese government decided to take definite steps to effectuate necessary changes. The failure of the reform program was attributed to Minister Ōtori's ineptness by both Saionji and Suematsu, who urged Premier Itō to send over a statesman of experience and high caliber. General Yamagata, who was then in command of the First Army in Korea, concurred. Itō, therefore, chose Home Minister Inoue Kaoru, who had requested that he be given the difficult but challenging assignment. The new Minister arrived in Seoul toward the end of October and began a careful study of the situation. He promptly concluded that it was necessary to bring about the removal of Taiwunkun before a progressive policy could be instituted. Early in November he conferred with the Korean Premier and Foreign Minister to plan ways and means of effecting reforms. At the same time he censured the actions of the Regent, who, a few days later, appeared at the Japanese legation and apologized for his past misdeeds and gave a solemn pledge not to meddle any more in the affairs of state. Inoue endeavored to distinguish between the affairs of Court and government and worked energetically in the face of almost insuperable odds. The Triple Intervention had created an extremely difficult, if not an impossible, situation for the Japanese Minister. The Queen and the anti-Japanese factions began to rely more and more for help on the Russians, who had gained prestige through the Intervention and were achieving results in the intrigues of the Korean Court.

Meanwhile, the behind-the-scenes activities of the Court increased and the Cabinet wavered, while the struggle between the progressives and the conservatives increased in intensity. In May, 1895, the progressives succeeded in forming a Cabinet. Assuming this to be an opportune moment to take up the discussion of future policies with the government, Minister Inoue returned to Tōkyō in late June. In his absence, the Queen set out to retrieve her lost power. In an effort to regain power, she became increasingly friendly to the Russian Minister. Her attitude toward the Cabinet and particularly Home Minister Bok became cold. Influenced by the Queen's change of attitude, the King stiffened his attitude toward the Cabinet. It soon became evident that Russia was working with the

Queen to oust the Premier. She finally did succeed in ousting him, but Taiwunkun was determined to get rid of her in turn.

The Court received word from an informer on July 6 that ex-Home Minister Bok was plotting against the Queen. This forced Bok to seek asylum in the Japanese legation, whence he went to Japan to remain in exile. On learning of the turn of events, Inoue hurried back to Seoul and helped to organize the Kim Cabinet. He made the King and the Cabinet pledge to carry out the long-projected reforms in administration. The statesmanlike Inoue, who enjoyed the confidence of the Queen, was soon succeeded by General Miura Gorō, whose direct but injudicious actions drove Korea into the arms of Russia.

On the very day Inoue landed in Kōbe, the Korean Court issued an imperial ordinance reversing the reform which had been promulgated only four months earlier in May. This was done without so much as getting the advice of the Cabinet. This action was followed in October by bringing pro-Russian leaders into the government and dismissing Premier Kim. The leader of the Min faction, who had just returned from Chefoo, attempted to set up a pro-Russian faction with the assistance of Russian Minister Weber. Miura, who was anxious to prevent this, worked together with Taiwunkun with a view to wrecking the plans of the pro-Russian faction. Early in the morning of October 8, the Regent led Japanese-trained Korean soldiers, supported by a heavily armed group of Japanese political bullies (*sōshi*), forced his way into the Palace, and cut down the Queen. After taking the leaders of the Min faction prisoner, Taiwunkun organized a new Cabinet. Miura succeeded in forcing the King to sign documents guaranteeing cabinet rule and appointing officials who were friendly to Japan. For four months after the murder of the Queen the King was virtually a prisoner of the Cabinet and in constant fear for his life.

However, the King and the Crown Prince escaped from the Palace and obtained asylum in the Russian legation on February 11, 1896, remaining there exactly a year, after which they returned to take up residence in the Palace. During this period imperial decrees and orders were issued from the Russian legation. On the very day the King took refuge there, he issued an imperial decree announcing the dismissal of the pro-Japanese Kim Cabinet as well as the severe punishment of those responsible for the Queen's murder. In the blood purge which followed, the dismissed Premier and several Ministers were murdered.

Henceforth, Russia superseded Japan in exercising control over the Korean government. The Japanese-trained army was disbanded and the Japanese resident merchants as well as fishermen along the coast left Korea and returned to Japan. The special position which Japan had secured in consequence of the victory over China was nullified by the advent of the Russians on the Korean political scene, following the successful intervention of 1895.

YAMAGATA-LOBANOV PROTOCOL

Premier Itō, who was anxious to attend the coronation ceremonies of Tsar Alexander II in May, 1896, sent Yamagata in his place, entrusting him with the responsibility of concluding an agreement with Russia. A protocol was signed by Yamagata and Foreign Minister Lobanov on June 5, 1896, which placed the two contracting powers on an equal footing as regards rights and privileges in Korea. Both parties agreed that their troops should be withdrawn in order to let Korea police as far as possible her own territory, and that all should work together in pressing financial reforms on the Korean government. Shortly after the signing of the protocol the Russian government proceeded to ignore the terms of the agreement by sending military advisers and instructors to help organize the Korean army along Russian lines. Not content with the concessions she had wrested from Korea earlier, the timber concession on the Yalu River and the mining concessions along the Tumen River, she attempted to secure control of Korean finance.

Russian policy toward the Korean Court was at first based on ingratiation and gentle persuasion, but as soon as she was in the ascendancy her methods underwent a considerable change. After her supremacy was established in October, 1896, her tactics changed from persuasion to threat, and it appeared as if she would take over completely the management of Korea. As a result Koreans both in and out of government were goaded into resistance by the high-handed attitude of the Russian government. The Korean Independence Society was organized, and a pro-American party emerged to add variety as well as intensity to the political activities at the troubled, if not bedeviled, Korean capital. Russian influence began to meet with resistance when it became known to the public that the pro-Russian faction was yielding easily to Russian demands.

Nishi-Rosen Convention. At a time when the Russian government was showing a more conciliatory attitude than had been customary, Foreign Minister Nishi signed on April 28, 1898, a convention with the Russian Minister Rosen in Tōkyō. This agreement, which came when Russia was satiated at least temporarily by the securing of the lease of Liaotung Peninsula, reiterated and strengthened the principles embodied in the Yamagata-Lobanov Protocol. It was in effect a redefinition of the positions of the two powers in Korea. The signatories recognized the sovereignty and independence of Korea and agreed not to assist Korea in the reorganization of the army and her finances without previous consultation and agreement. In agreeing not to impede the development of Japanese commercial and industrial interests, the Russian government virtually recognized Japan's paramountcy of interests. Although this agreement reflected the temporary eclipse of Russia by Japan, it did not settle the Korean question by any means. Russia's relaxation of efforts in Korea was more than compensated by her vigorous activities in China and, more specifically, in Manchuria, where she launched an ambitious program and proceeded to ignore her pledges with impunity.

THE OPEN DOOR POLICY

No one could safely predict in 1898 when or where the competitve game of concession-wresting from prostrate China would stop. It was a disturbing situation, to say the least. American merchants viewed the debacle with apprehension. The British, who had a far greater stake in the foreign trade of the Far East, were even more concerned. On March 8, 1898, two days after Germany secured her lease on Kiachow, the British Ambassador in Washington suggested to Secretary of State Sherman that the two nations work together to ensure equal commercial opportunity in China. Coming as it did barely three weeks after the sinking of the *Maine* in the harbor of Havana, when the country was in the grip of a war hysteria, the United States could not work up much enthusiasm for the Open Door on the other side of the globe especially in the face of gathering war clouds over the Cuban question.[1] When the British renewed the Open Door proposal in January, 1899, the United States refused to take it up on the grounds that it was inconsistent with traditional American policy.

However, a series of speeches given in the United States by Lord Charles Beresford and popularizing the concept of equal commercial opportunity stimulated public interest in the Open Door, which began to meet with increasing favor. Finally, the pressure from American business and missionary interests became too strong for the State Department. A British subject, A. E. Hippisley, who was a staunch advocate of the Open Door, working with and through W. W. Rockhill, his old friend and former special agent of the State Department in China, brought to the attention of Secretary of State John Hay and President McKinley the importance of equal commercial opportunity in China. The President was convinced, and the diplomatic notes drafted by Rockhill were adopted by Secretary Hay. On September 6, 1899, Secretary Hay sent identical instructions to the United States representatives in Berlin, London, and St. Petersburg, asking them to secure formal declarations from the respective foreign offices to the following points: First, that it would not interfere with any treaty port or vested interest within any "sphere of influence or leased territory." Second, that the Chinese tariff should apply within such spheres of interest, and that duties should be collected by the Chinese government. Third, that it would not discriminate in favor of its own nationals in the matter of harbor dues and railroad charges within its sphere of interest.

Although the propositions were not entirely acceptable to any of the powers,

---

[1] On March 9, 1898, Congress unanimously voted $50,000,000 for war preparations. On April 19 it passed a joint resolution, which was signed by President McKinley on the twentieth, and a state of war was recognized as having existed on April 21.

they were given prompt attention. Britain agreed to the declaration on November 30 (excluding Kowloon, which Lord Salisbury regarded as part of Hongkong), followed on December 4 by Germany, who stated that she would not object if the other powers agreed. France, which was not approached until late in November, replied on December 16, while Russia gave an evasive reply which was equivalent to a polite declination. Japan was approached after the other powers but agreed promptly on December 26.

The news of the negotiations was not released to the press until January 3, 1900. On March 20, Secretary Hay announced that he regarded as "final and definitive" the declaration of the powers that the Open Door would be maintained, and that China would continue to collect the customs. In this announcement was implicit the fact of China's exercising the rights of sovereignty in the various spheres of interest. But the Open Door was merely an enunciation of Secretary Hay's policy, which did not have any binding power so far as international law was concerned. Furthermore, it applied only to relatively small leaseholds and spheres of influence and did not in any way guarantee the territorial integrity of China. Nor did it refer to mining or railway concessions or to capital investments. Vested interests were to be left undisturbed. Needless to say, it did not result in a completely open door. What the Open Door succeeded in achieving was the averting of the immediate partitioning of the Celestial Empire, which had appeared to be imminent. However, the antiforeign outburst, culminating in the Boxer Uprising, which followed almost immediately on the heels of the Hay notes, threatened to nullify what Secretary Hay had so laboriously achieved.

THE BOXER UPRISING

Antiforeign upheaval in China was the inevitable culmination of the chain of events which followed the humiliating defeat of 1895. The tottering Manchu dynasty was incapable and unwilling to institute the badly needed reforms which might have prolonged its life a little. Officials were corrupt and incompetent, funds needed for national defense were used for private purposes, and court pleasures and offices were openly bought and sold. The people were writhing under the heavy burden of taxes, and the officials were obliged to make forced contributions, which had been ordered by the Empress Dowager.

Convinced of the need of instituting far-reaching reforms to save the Empire from dismemberment and the fate met by India, Egypt, Burma, Annam, and other dependencies, Chinese leaders from the Yangtze region and the southern provinces urged changes. Reform societies were organized, and the reform movement gained momentum and spread. Under the strong pressure of the reformers, Emperor Kuang Hsu issued a number of reform edicts in the summer of 1898. Among the innovations undertaken were changes in the educational and examination systems, establishment of a translation bureau, encouragement of railroad building, reorganization of the military forces, and abolishment of numerous sinecures. These reforms were instituted by the Emperor with the advice of K'ang Yu-wei, whose views were moderate and far from radical. However, opposition developed and the Empress Dowager, who had been in retirement, was moved by the events to interfere. The reformers urged on the Emperor to act against the Dowager, but through the betrayal of Yuan Shih-k'ai, who outwardly appeared to be sympathetic to the reformers, he was seized and kept in virtual imprisonment until his death ten years later. With the help of Chargé Hayashi and Itō Hirobumi, who was visiting in Peking at the time, K'ang Yu-wei found asylum in Japan, from where he carried on a campaign for the establishment of constitutional government in China. Liang Ch'i-ch'ao, who had assisted K'ang, was aided by the Japanese legation in his flight to Japan. Thus, the one hundred days of reform came to a sad end as most of the edicts issued by the Emperor were promptly rescinded. The conservatives reacted violently against the innovations as well as the ideas of the reformers whom they had purged, and in an attempt to stave off the swelling tide of discontent, they diverted popular hostility against the "foreign devils." Reorganization and reform along Western lines having been rejected, the reactionary government dominated by the Empress Dowager and her supporters reverted to the old traditional policy of isolation supported by force.

In 1899 an eruption of antiforeign outbreaks in all parts of China began. Antagonism was directed at first against the native Christians, who were looked upon as renegades who had forsaken the ways of the past and shown scant respect for the teaching of the sages. Bitter feelings against missionaries and converts were aroused, as Christianity disturbed old cherished customs and ideas. Particularly objectionable to the local officials, the gentry, and to the masses was the disturbing influence of the missionaries on the indolent and corrupt practices of the officials, the rejection by the converts of ancestor worship, and their refusal to share the expenses of supporting the native faith. Added to this were the aggressions of the powers and the unrest and sufferings brought about by famines in Kansu and Chekiang provinces and floods in Shantung, Chihli (Hopei), and Anwhei provinces all of which aggravated antiforeign feelings.

In Shantung province, where a group known as Righteous Harmony Fists (*I Ho Ch'uan*) or Boxers had gained a large following, the antiforeign movement reached serious proportions. Its antiforeignism was expressed in the motto: "Preserve China and Destroy the Foreigners." In 1899, they began seriously to annoy Westerners, whom they wanted to drive out. Soon the movement spread in Chihli, resulting in attacks on Christians. Encouraged by their success and emboldened by their belief that the charms and occult practices they employed rendered them invulnerable to the weapons of the enemy, they carried out attacks with increasing vigor. In April, they struck at Tientsin, where they destroyed the railway station and tracks, cut telephone wires, murdered foreigners, and cut off communications completely between that city and Peking. From the very beginning the movement had the blessings of the reactionary Court. With the starting of the siege of Peking the Court finally threw its support to the Boxers.

The legations in Peking were under a siege, during which the German Minister Baron von Ketteler and a chancellor of the Japanese Legation, Sugiyama, were murdered by the Chinese, who were now openly supported by the imperial troops. A *de facto* state of war existed between China and the foreign powers. The siege continued from June to August, when the Allied expeditionary force relieved the beleaguered foreign residents and members of the legations. The desperate situation at Peking demanded the immediate dispatch of troops, but the troops available on the spot were woefully inadequate. It became evident that no Western power could send troops fast enough to meet the emergency. Japan alone was in a position to do so because of her proximity to the area of disturbance. However, she held herself back, for she knew too well the distrust some of the European powers had begun to show as a result of her policies and rapid rise to power. Any display of armed strength was bound to redound to her disadvantage; so she waited. The powers debated and hesitated, but as there was no time to be lost, they were impelled to request Japan to dispatch troops.[2] Japan responded promptly by dispatching a division, which arrived in Tientsin in mid-July. The Peking Relief Expedition comprising a force of some 18,800 troops moved out of Tientsin on August 4, reached Peking ten days later, broke the siege, wrested the city from the Boxers, and rescued the foreign residents.[3] In October, two months after the rescue of Peking, Field Marshal Count von Waldersee arrived in the Chinese capital and assumed command of the Allied forces.

Japan's part in the expedition was significant as it had an important effect on the developments that followed. Nearly half of the troops used in the rescue of Peking were furnished by her. The discipline, efficiency, and conduct of the troops, who fought under the close observation of military commanders and competent military critics of the major European powers and the United States, greatly enhanced her reputation. The Japanese troops were under instructions to be on their best behavior, as they were to be under close scrutiny of other powers. By withdrawing half of the forces immediately after the relief of the legations and by cooperating heartily with the powers in the negotiations which ensued, Japan allayed their suspicions.

[2] The London *Times* carried Lord Salisbury's plea to Japanese Chargé d'Affaires Matsui requesting dispatch of Japanese troops at once on humanitarian grounds.

[3] The relief expedition was made up as follows:

Japan (General Yamaguchi in command)	8,000	United States (General Chaffee)	2,100
Russia (General Linievitch)	4,800	France (General Frey)	800
Great Britain (General Gaselee)	3,000	Austria	58
		Italy	53

In the negotiations for settlement with China, which began in late December of 1900, the powers demanded large indemnities. The Emperor appointed the wily, crafty Li Hung-chang and Prince Kung to conduct the negotiations. In order to formulate demands commensurate with China's capacity to pay, the diplomatic representatives formed a committee to study Chinese financial resources, the apportionment of the indemnity, and the method of payment. As a result, the total amount was set at 450 million taels or the equivalent of $333,900,-000. Its apportioning involved a great deal of jockeying among the powers, and considerable time passed. Agreement was not formally reached until June 14, 1902, when signatures were finally affixed by the representatives of the powers.

By the settlement contained in the Boxer Protocol, signed on September 7, 1901, China paid a high price for her unsuccessful attempt to forcibly expel the foreigners. She was saddled with a large additional debt as well as further restrictions to her sovereignty. Over and above the payment in thirty-nine annual installments of an indemnity of 450,000,000 taels, which was secured by maritime customs, salt tax, and local native customs, the Chinese government agreed to the following: (1) the punishment by the Chinese government of some of the officials responsible for the attacks on foreigners; (2) offering apologies for the murder of Baron von Ketteler, the German Minister, and payment of an indemnity for the murder of Sugiyama, a chancellor in the Japanese legation; (3) the prohibition of the importation of arms, ammunitions, and materials for their manufacture for two years, to be extended by two-year periods if and as long as the foreigners deemed necessary; (4) the quartering of troops by each power in the capital as legation guards; (5) the military occupation of certain points to keep open communication between Peking and the sea; (6) the dismantling of the Taku forts to ensure free communication from Peking to the sea; (7) the suspension for five years of the official examinations in towns where foreigners had been massacred or persecuted; (8) the publication of edicts to discourage antiforeign outbreaks; (9) the amendment of existing treaties of commerce and navigation with the powers; (10) the improvement of the river channels leading to Tientsin (Peiho) and Shanghai (Whangpu), and (11) the establishment in place of the *Tsungli Yamen,* of a Foreign Office to take precedence over all the other ministries of the government.

That Japan emerged from the Boxer incident with enhanced national prestige was quite evident. Her participation in the military expedition against the insurgents, as well as her close and willing cooperation in the settlement, secured for her not only international recognition but also an opportunity to work closely with Great Britain and the United States in a concerted action to frustrate Russia's ambition in the Far East.

RUSSIA OCCUPIES MANCHURIA

Russia found in the preoccupation of the powers in the Boxer Uprising a golden opportunity to further her Far Eastern plans. When the disturbance broke out, she lost no time in pouring troops into Manchuria, where unrest had developed and bandits had become active. This she carried out in the name of preserving peace and order and the protection of her rights. As antiforeign outbursts spread northward, some of the Boxers invaded the three northeastern provinces after overflowing first in Chihli. Russia sent a comparatively small force of 4,800 troops for the Allied expedition in order that she might use the bulk of her troops in Manchuria.

Early in July, the Chinese government demanded the turning over of the Chinese Eastern Railway and the evacuation of its Russian employees from Manchuria. When the demands were refused, the Chinese regulars forced the Russian railway guards and opened fire on Blagoveshchensk. This action brought prompt reprisal and thousands of resident Chinese were massacred. Russian troops drove the Chinese troops out in short order and mopped up the Boxers. By mid-October order was restored along the railway lines. In September the Russian government explained the reasons for the dispatch of troops into Manchuria and pledged their withdrawal upon the restoration of peace and order.

In spite of the solemn pledge to withdraw the troops, the Russians continued actions which betrayed their announced intentions. In November while the negotiations for the settlement of the Boxer Rebellion were in progress, General Tseng, Viceroy of Mukden, and Admiral Alexiev signed a convention which, although it was never ratified, revealed Russia's designs. If carried out, it would have reduced Manchuria to the status of a Russian protectorate. The publication of this agreement caused a stir abroad as well as in Peking. The Chinese government appealed to Britain, the United States, Japan, and Germany for joint intervention. Russia abandoned the agreement, repeating her denial of any aggressive designs in Manchuria. But the actions that followed her denial were highly contradictory, since she endeavored to tighten her grip on Manchuria.

As the United States was committed to upholding the Open Door, the independence and territorial and administrative integrity of the Chinese Empire, she protested against the Russian occupation of Manchuria and against the acceptance by China of conditions of evacuation as unfavorable to her as those provided in the Tseng-Alexiev agreement. While outwardly professing friendship for China, Russia continued to promote her interests at the expense of the former. She demanded and obtained the lion's share of the Boxer indemnity, an amount more than three and a half times that of Japan and four times that of the United States. Moreover, she insisted on the powers evacuating North China before the signing of the Boxer Protocol and on absolute nonintervention in the internal affairs of China. Yet, at the same time, she vigorously maintained that the Manchurian settlement was the concern solely of herself and China.

In Russia the Bezobrazov group, which advocated strong measures in carrying out a positive, aggressive policy, was on the ascendancy in 1901, while Witte's influence was practically in eclipse. The Tsar had, with the counsel of men like War Minister Kropotkin and Admiral Alexiev, modified his attitude to favor aggressive policies. In February Foreign Minister Lamsdorff opened negotiations for a second secret agreement with Chinese Minister Yang. This agreement included (1) the restoration of the three provinces to China; (2) the temporary stationing of Russian troops as railway guards; (3) rendering assistance to China in case of sudden and serious developments; (4) the Chinese refraining from stationing of troops between the time of the completion of the railroad and the operation of trains (in case troops were to be stationed later, Russia was to be consulted first); (5) a ban on the importation of arms and ammunition into Manchuria by the Chinese; (6) reform of military organization with exclusive Russian help; (7) promise not to grant mining or railway rights in Manchuria, Mongolia, and Sinkiang to foreigners without Russia's approval; (8) the payment of indemnity to Russia for the damages and military expenditures incurred in the restoration of peace and order in Manchuria; and (9) the granting of railway rights to Russia.

The acceptance of the conditions stipulated would have resulted in the reduction of Manchuria to the status of a protectorate, as they enabled Russia to meddle in the internal affairs of China. When the secret agreement was divulged in the London *Times,* the British Government lodged a strong protest, to which Foreign Minister Lamsdorf replied with a denial of the existence of such an agreement. Secretary Hay sent a note to China pointing out the danger as well as the inadvisability of concluding such a special agreement affecting her territorial integrity. Even the German government filed a protest with the Chinese government, urging it to reflect seriously on the matter. On April 6 China and Russia announced the dropping of the secret agreement. Still another attempt was made in October of the same year, when the Russian Minister started discussions with Viceroy Li but nothing came of it as the latter died early in November.

It became all too apparent that Russia had no intention of withdrawing from Manchuria until and unless she succeeded in imposing her own terms on China. She was confident that no power would care or dare to make an issue of the matter, much less to challenge her to a test of arms. With the assurance and support of the three powers, Britain, the United States, and Japan, who had been drawn closely together by the developments, China flatly refused to accept the conditions laid down by Russia in 1901 for the evacuation of Manchuria.

Slightly over two months after the Anglo-Japanese Alliance was signed, Russia concluded an agreement with China pledging the evacuation of her troops from Manchuria in eighteen months in three different stages. For a time, it appeared as if it might well be the beginning of a satisfactory solution of the Manchurian problem. But the failure on the part of Russia to carry out the promise led ultimately to the clash of arms between Russia and Japan.

RUSSIA AND FRANCE COUNTER THE ANGLO-JAPANESE ALLIANCE

Immediately following the announcement of the Anglo-Japanese Alliance on February 11, 1902, Russia and France countered the challenge which was implicit in it by issuing a statement to the effect that the scope of the Dual Alliance had been extended to include the Far East. This was followed by Russia's signing in April, less than two months later, the Manchurian Convention with China, pledging the complete evacuation of Manchuria in eighteen months (October 8, 1903). The withdrawal of troops was to be carried out in three stages, namely, South Manchuria at the end of six months (October 8), Central Manchuria at the end of twelve months (April 8, 1903), and the whole of Manchuria at the end of eighteen months. Upon completion of the withdrawal, the control of the entire region was to be restored to China. However, the agreement contained a proviso which was tantamount to an escape clause. Withdrawal was to be carried out "provided that no disturbance arise and that the actions of other powers furnish no obstacles." The first stage, the evacuation of southwest Manchuria, was carried out according to schedule, but instead of withdrawing the troops from Manchuria, Russia transferred them to other points. The second six months went by without further evacuation as pledged. Protests were lodged by Japan, Great Britain, and the United States. When the United States showed strong opposition to Russia's action, she received assurances that the rights of the powers would not be violated or interfered with.

When Russia failed to carry out the second stage of evacuation the deadline of which expired on April 8, 1903, Japanese public opinion was aroused. On June 1, seven professors of the Tōkyō Imperial University pressed Premier Katsura for a war on Russia.[4] In the midst of hostile public opinion Russian War Minister Kuropatkin arrived after his Manchurian tour of inspection. The purpose of his visit was to assess as accurately as possible the general conditions and the state of public opinion in the island empire in order that he might more effectively plan and execute Russian policies in the Far East. Until it was squelched by the Premier, speculation was rife that his arrival was related to the negotiation of some sort of a *quid pro quo* regarding Russian rights in Manchuria and Japanese rights in Korea. From Japan Kuropatkin proceeded to Port Arthur, where he called a conference of Russian civil and military officials in the Far East and pronounced confidently that there was no need to fear Japan as an antagonist. On

---

[4] The seven professors were Tomii, Tomizu, Onozuka, Kanai, Takahashi, Nakamura, and Terao.

July 15, almost immediately after the Port Arthur conference, the Russian Minister to Peking called on Prince Ch'ing and informed him that in view of existing conditions in Manchuria, Russia could not withdraw her troops unconditionally even at the risk of inviting intervention by the powers. He stated that Russia had no alternative but to go ahead with her plans, even if such a course led to an armed clash with Japan.

As we have already seen, Russia's Far Eastern policy assumed an aggressive pattern in 1903. The group headed by Bezobrazov and Plehve had come into power and advocated taking over Korea as well as Manchuria. The Tsar, who had become convinced that Japan could not possibly offer effective opposition, decided to launch an aggressive program with the assistance of Viceroy Alexiev. Even as early as May 20, while Kuropatkin was in the Far East, an imperial conference had been held and the decision made to abandon the Manchurian Convention of 1902, to reinforce the troops in the three provinces, and to bring the Korean territory on the left bank of the Yalu River into her sphere of influence.[5]

In the face of such developments, the Japanese government was impelled to make a fateful decision. The decision reached in April, 1903, by the Elder Statesmen was of tentative nature and did not provide for any contingency. It did not go beyond the *quid pro quo* arrangement for a free hand in Korea in return for Russian liberty in Manchuria. Moreover, opinion was still divided on the question of the methods to be used. But the imperial conference of June 23, held in Tōkyō, changed all this. It was decided that, while Manchuria might be left in Russian hands, Korea was to be a completely Japanese sphere of influence, admitting no interference from any power. On the basis of this decision, Foreign Minister Komura telegraphed Kurino in St. Petersburg, instructing him to present a memorandum to the Russian government. Negotiations were opened on August 12 with a view to relieving the existing tension between the two powers by a clear definition of interests.

Japan proposed to Russia that (1) both countries agree to respect the independence and territorial integrity of China and Korea; (2) the principle of the Open Door and equal opportunity be maintained in China and Korea; (3) Russia recognize Japan's special interests in Korea, and Japan in turn recognize Russia's special railway rights in Manchuria. Each concede to the other the right to develop the interests so recognized within the limitations of the first stipulation; (4) Russia recognize the exclusive right of Japan to give advice and aid to the Korean government in the interest of reform and good administration; and (5) Russia give assurance to Japan not to obstruct the extension of Korean railways into southern Manchuria for the purpose of linking them with the Chinese Eastern, Shanhaikan, and Newchwang lines.

[5] Witte, *Memoirs,* p. 120.

On the day following Kurino's presentation of the Japanese proposals, the Russian government instituted a radical change in the administrative organization in the Far East. The Amur territory and the Kwantung province were unified under a new Far Eastern Viceroy, who was vested with extensive military and diplomatic powers. Alexiev, who was appointed to the post, was freed from all control, civil, military, and even that of the Ministers at St. Petersburg, only taking orders directly from the Tsar.[6] The Foreign Office no longer made any decisions without first consulting the Viceroy. Simultaneously, the Committee of the Far East was created at the capital, with the Tsar as its nominal head, but actually dominated by Abaza. Thus there were three separate uncoordinated agencies which were involved in the carrying out of Russia's Far Eastern policies. The Foreign Office, though the legitimate organ of foreign relations, was the weakest, as it did not enjoy the confidence of the Tsar. On the other hand, the Committee of the Far East, which was closest to the Tsar, wielded the greatest power. The Viceroy of the Far East was the authority on the spot who took orders from the Committee in carrying out the policies.

Early in September Foreign Minister Komura opened formal conversations in Tōkyō with Rosen, the Russian Minister. Meanwhile, Viceroy Alexiev convened a conference of officials at Port Arthur and at the same time carried on demonstrations of armed might on land and sea. Fortifications were erected and houses were built on the banks of the Yalu River. It was obvious that evacuation was actually remote from the minds of the Russians. Rosen returned from the Port Arthur Conference on October 3 and presented to the Japanese government Russian counterproposals, which provided for (1) mutual agreement to respect the independence and integrity of Korea only, and not that of China or Manchuria; (2) Russian recognition of Japan's superior interests in Korea and her right to assist in the reform of civil administration only; (3) Russian agreement not to interfere with the development and protection of Japanese commercial and industrial interests in Korea; (4) agreement not to fortify the coasts of Korea to menace the freedom of navigation in the Straits of Korea; (5) designation of the portion of Korea north of the 39th parallel as a neutral zone; (6) recognition by Japan of Manchuria and its littoral as entirely outside her sphere of interest.

According to this counterproposal Japan was to allow Russia a free hand in China, while Russia was to allow Japan to develop only industrial and commercial interests in Korea while denying political or strategic interests, which meant the whittling down of Japanese rights and privileges. Minister of the Interior Plehve had joined forces with the Yalu concessionaires for the purpose of encouraging a foreign war to stem the rising tide of revolution at home.[7]

The Japanese government presented on January 13, 1904, a final revised pro-

[6] *British and Foreign State Papers, China,* No. 2 (1904), pp. 85, 92.
[7] Witte, *op. cit.,* p. 250.

posal to the Russian government, which was in its nature an equivalent of an ultimatum. By this time national feeling against Russia had reached an explosive state. On the following day the Supreme War Council was created, war finance measures were adopted, defense and transportation ordinances were promulgated, and the Japanese government entered the final stage of preparations to provide against the rupture of diplomatic relations. In spite of the fact that the essential justice of the Japanese demands was recognized by the Russian leaders, they kept on systematically protracting the negotiations.[8] Four weeks elapsed, and still there was no reply from the Russian government. On February 6 Minister Kurino was instructed by his government to inform the Russian government of the severance of diplomatic relations and to demand the recall of Rosen from Tōkyō. Only a month earlier Russians had been informed that Japan was at the end of her patience and that if no reply was forthcoming within a few days, hostilities would break out, but they had not taken it seriously.[9] Four days after the notice of severance of relations, Japan formally declared war on Russia.

[8] Witte, *op. cit.*, p. 126.
[9] *Ibid.*

Chapter 20. The Anglo-Japanese Alliance

By the end of the nineteenth century shifts in the balance of power could not occur in Europe without profoundly affecting power politics in the Far East. Until the Sino-Japanese War, Great Britain had regarded China as the nation to work through, if not to rely on, in advancing and safeguarding her interests in East Asia. Her attitude, however, began to undergo noticeable modification even before the Sino-Japanese War. After China's defeat in 1895 there remained little doubt among Britain's leaders that Japan, the newly risen power in the Far East, would be the one most likely to offer effective resistance against Russian advances in that part of the world.

Japan was well aware of the increasing threat to her security in Russia's ambitious expansionist policy. In the newspaper *Jiji Shimpō* of May 28, 1895, only a few days after the Triple Intervention, Vice Foreign Minister Hayashi advocated the need for a positive foreign policy. Less than a month later the same newspaper, amplifying Hayashi's views, editorialized on the necessity as well as the practicability of an Anglo-Japanese alliance.[1] It was apparent that a similar sentiment was growing in some circles in Britain. On June 23, the day the Rosebery Cabinet bowed itself out after its defeat, Foreign Secretary Lord Kimberley summoned Minister Katō to Downing Street and expressed his desire that, inasmuch as Britain and Japan had a community of interests, the two nations should always maintain friendly relations.[2] At that time, however, the expression remained no more than a desire as nothing actually came out of it. Significantly enough, the new Prime Minister Lord Salisbury reassured the British people in his speech at Guildhall on November 11, 1895, that they need not show any unnecessary fear or anxiety regarding the situation in the Far East, inasmuch as Britain was fully capable of meeting any challenge on the field of battle or in commercial competition anywhere.[3] Such exuberant optimism and confidence were short-lived, indeed, for the tone of British leaders changed to that of anxiety in a space of less than two years.

From the time of Queen Victoria's second jubilee in 1897 the military weakness of the British Empire had become increasingly apparent to continental Europe and particularly to Russia and Germany, the two powers that were in the best position to exploit such vulnerability. Yet, it was not until after the outbreak

---

[1] *Jiji Shimpō*, August 21, 1913.
[2] M. Itō, *Katō Takaaki*, Vol. I, p. 251.
[3] London *Times*, November 11, 1895, p. 6.

of the South African War that Britain was made to feel keenly, and perhaps even perilously, the dangers of isolation, for a small but well-armed Boer nation put the military forces of Britain to an unexpectedly severe strain.

At the outbreak of hostilities in South Africa in October, 1899, Great Britain was technically at peace with all foreign powers, but she could not look to any of the great powers for anything more than strict neutrality and not always friendly neutrality.[4] In most countries, public opinion was extremely hostile to the British, to say nothing of the policies of the foreign governments, which were coming into conflict with hers. Even in the United States, the Irish and German-Americans showed undisguised hostility, although it did not affect the atmosphere of good will and friendship which obtained officially in Anglo-American relations. In Germany, more than anywhere else, public opinion was solidly and deeply anti-British, as the middle class Germans, bent on industrial and commercial expansion, regarded Britain as their chief and most objectionable rival, who obstructed at every turn Germany's path to empire and world dominion.

Simultaneously with the outbreak of the Boer War, the government-controlled press of Germany began a vitriolic campaign of hatred against the British. The German people saw in Britain's South African difficulty their heaven-sent opportunity. However, the Kaiser's government saw Germany's opportunity in a somewhat different light, as it preferred to exact concessions gracefully from Britain in several of the pending questions and to lure her into a network of alliances which had been set up round the German Empire by Bismarck. The advantages of an alliance with Britain had become quite obvious to Germany, especially in the face of the growing intimacy between France and Russia.

Salisbury, through his long experience in foreign affairs, had come to perceive clearly how poorly organized and prepared the British Empire was to meet the crucial strain to which it might be subjected at any time. In spite of the vast resources at its command, it was not altogether unlikely that the Empire might find itself in an extremely precarious position in trying to cope with the growing menace presented by the ambitions of rival powers. Shortly after the commencement of hostilities, Salisbury's powerful colleague, Colonial Secretary Joseph Chamberlain, who was *de facto* Vice Premier, also visualized the dangers with which the British Empire was confronted. He saw that the traditional policy of "splendid isolation" had placed Britain in a position where she might have to meet unaided and alone an assault on any one of the many vulnerable points of her vast Empire. To Chamberlain, the pressure steadily applied by France and Russia on Britain's position in West Africa and Asia appeared to be a more formidable menace than the German threat. He was convinced that there existed a deep-seated and irreconcilable antagonism be-

[4] *The Cambridge History of British Foreign Policy*, Vol. III, pp. 263ff.

tween Britain's interests and those of France and Russia, whereas there were no serious differences between Britain and Germany which did not lend themselves to satisfactory and amicable solution.

During the first two years of the South African War, negotiations were carried on between London and Berlin for a formal alliance, despite the aggressively hostile anti-British sentiment which existed in Germany. In November, 1899, Kaiser Wilhelm visited Windsor Palace in response to Queen Victoria's invitation. During his visit he and his Foreign Minister, Count von Bülow, held long conversations with Colonial Secretary Chamberlain on the possibility and desirability of an alliance. On November 30 Chamberlain, who was enthusiastic over the prospects of an alliance, delivered at Leicester a memorable address in which he paid an eloquent tribute to the fine qualities of the Germans, "a people of the same stock as ourselves," and declared that an Anglo-German alliance would be based not only on interest but on sentiment as well. He even expressed his sanguine hope that the United States might form with Great Britain and Germany a new triple alliance for the peace of the world.

However, much to the astonishment and outrage of the British Minister, less than two weeks later, on December 11, Count von Bülow delivered a speech in the Reichstag virtually disavowing the Windsor conversations with Chamberlain and emphasizing instead the Triple Alliance between Germany, Austria-Hungary, and Italy and the maintenance of friendly relations with Russia. Not content to stop there, he went on to emphasize the prime and urgent need of strengthening the imperial navy to make Germany a world power. This sudden change of attitude, which was no less than a betrayal, was induced undoubtedly by the news of military reverses suffered by British arms in South Africa, but at the same time it was the Kaiser's method of getting out of the alliance he had proposed through Eckardstein.[5] The method worked so well in rousing British public opinion and official circles to such a high pitch of indignation that it was now unthinkable for the British to ally themselves with Germany. In a letter dated December 28, Chamberlain notified Berlin that under the circumstances all further negotiations must be dropped for the present.

Anglo-German relations were severely strained all through the South African War. Admiral von Tirpitz was grim in his determination that every Anglo-German incident be exploited in supporting the new German Navy Bill of 1900, which was to double the naval strength that had been authorized two years earlier. The preamble to the bill emphasized that "Germany must have a fleet of such strength that war with the mightiest naval power would involve risks threatening that power's supremacy." It left no room for doubt that it was a direct challenge hurled at Britain's naval supremacy. Introduced on February 3, the bill was adopted by the Reichstag on June 12 with the aid of a wave

[5] K. Ishii, *Gaikō Yoroku,* p. 51.

of anti-British agitation, which was allowed to subside thereafter but only temporarily.

Meanwhile, developments in the Far East once more brought home to the German government the value of friendly relations with Britain, whose naval supremacy still remained unchallenged. The outbreak of the Boxer Uprising in the summer of 1900, while giving the Kaiser a chance to display his military might in North China, demonstrated convincingly at the same time his dependence on British good will as well as British naval stations for the transport of troops. Moreover, the Kaiser could not view with equanimity Russia's unblushing exploitation of the disorder in China to advance her own ends in Manchuria.

Thus, Russia's aggressive action in Manchuria brought Great Britain and Germany together once more in a concerted attempt to cope with the menace. On October 16, 1900, only a few months after the Boxer outbreak, an agreement was concluded between Foreign Secretary Salisbury and German Ambassador Hatzfeldt, upholding the principle of the Open Door and disavowing any territorial designs in China. Other powers were invited to adhere to the pledge (1) to maintain the territorial *status quo* in China; (2) not to take advantage of the disorganization of the Empire to advance their own interests; (3) to work for the opening of the Empire to the trade and legitimate economic activities of all nations; and (4) to work together in carrying out necessary measures for the protection of their interests in the event anyone attempted to change the territorial *status quo* in his own interest.

Japan received an invitation for adherence to the agreement from the British Government on October 24, and after receiving assurances from both signatories that she would be given equal footing, Foreign Minister Katō announced his government's adherence five days later. Austria-Hungary, France, Italy, and the United States followed suit, but Russia signified her adherence by shrewdly appending a statement, tantamount to a reservation, to the effect that the Convention had not perceptibly modified the situation or the *status quo* established in China by existing treaties. Shortly afterwards, Germany virtually nullified the effect of this agreement, which was intended to check Russian advances in Manchuria.

Although the Anglo-German agreement was, in a sense, a variation of the Open Door policy, it was by no means motivated solely by altruism. It was the crystallization of the desires of the trading powers to maintain their rights and interests through the preservation of the territorial integrity of China. By her adherence to the agreement Japan was drawn closer to Great Britain. As a matter of fact, Japanese leaders regarded this as the forerunner of the Anglo-Japanese Alliance. Ironically enough, this was the fruition of the efforts of the German government to bring Japan and Britain together to checkmate Russia in the Far East.

At the turn of the century, there were impelling reasons for Britain's frantic search for an ally. The Boer War had exposed, much to her distress, the weakness in her imperial defenses, among which one of the most glaring was the lack of a genuine friend among European powers. There was more than a faint prospect that Britain would soon have to reckon with not only an aggrieved China, an indignant and hostile Russia, an unfriendly France, but with an ambitious Germany, which was intent on challenging British supremacy on the seas, to say nothing of challenging her aggressive policy of colonial expansion.

The Anglo-German Agreement paved the way for the resumption of conversations regarding the possibility of an alliance. Early in 1901 Baron von Eckardstein notified his government that the Colonial Secretary and his friends in the Cabinet had been forced finally, by the renewal of Russian pressure in the Far East and French activities in Morocco, to recognize that Britain would have to come to terms with France and Russia or join the Triple Alliance, but that they had shown preference for an agreement with Germany and would do everything to promote it. Protracted negotiations were carried on spasmodically for nearly two years between Berlin and London in a most curious sort of secret diplomacy, which was as unreal as it was without many parallels. The attempt foundered, in the end, on the rocks of Anglophobia and passionate jealousy on the part of Germany. The British ministers satisfied themselves once and for all that, if Empire security could no longer be found in the old policy of "splendid isolation," it certainly was not going to be sought in an alliance with Germany. Britain thus turned her eyes to the new power in the Far East and concentrated her efforts on the negotiation and conclusion of an alliance with Japan.

NEGOTIATIONS FOR THE ANGLO-JAPANESE ALLIANCE

The year 1898 was the turning point in Anglo-Japanese relations though for Britain it opened with an increasing anxiety over Russia's aggressive actions in the Far East. This anxiety was clearly reflected in the British note to the Chinese government on February 2, 1898, demanding the noncession of the Yangtze valley to any foreign power. On March 1, Sir Ellis Ashmead Bartlett declared on the floor of Parliament that Britain could maintain her position in the North Pacific and expel Russia from China only with the assistance of Japan. This marked the beginning of a favorable turn in British public opinion regarding Anglo-Japanese cooperation. Then came the momentous Chamberlain-Katō conversations on March 17, in the course of which the Colonial Secretary showed grave apprehension of Russia's possible southward advance from Manchuria into North China, which might lead to the partition of China. His concern was all the greater because of the absence of British troops on the spot to check the Russian forces. Chamberlain underscored the identity of interests of Japan and

Britain and expressed surprise at Japan's not having approached the British Government on the subject of cooperation in the Far East.[6]

That Russia's advance, if unchecked, would involve the annexation of Manchuria and the eventual absorption of North China was a foregone conclusion. Even Witte, the Tsar's Finance Minister, who was regarded as a comparatively mild expansionist, did not hesitate to tell the British Ambassador that Chihli, Shansi, Shensi, and Kansu provinces were within the Russian sphere of influence.[7] Britain's fears were reenforced by the absence of natural barriers between North China and the region of the Yangtze valley. Needless to say, Britain's position in the Far East had a direct relationship to the security of the Empire. China's territorial integrity and administrative independence were essential for the protection, not only of British commercial intersts, but also of the colonies, Hongkong, the Malay Peninsula, Burma, and even India.[8]

Japan was drawn towards Great Britain for the first time when Lord Rosebery's government led all the powers in agreeing to abandon consular jurisdiction, thereby helping her to free herself from the many servitudes which had been imposed on her by the Western powers since 1858. Again in 1895, she was drawn towards Britain when the British Government refused to join with Russia, France, and Germany in coercing her into the retrocession of the Liaotung Peninsula to China. Consequently, Japan welcomed British occupation and the leasing of Weihaiwei after her withdrawal to counterbalance, if not to offset, Russian occupation of Port Arthur.

Positive Anglo-Japanese cooperation grew out of Britain's securing of the leasehold of Weihaiwei. Japan had occupied the Yellow Sea port after its capture during the Sino-Japanese War. In the conversation between Chamberlain and Katō on March 17, 1898, the British Colonial Secretary not only acknowledged Japan's prior claim on the seaport if she desired a leasehold, but went so far as to offer support. However, he expressed the possibility that Britain might wish to secure it in the event Japan was not interested. Three days later, in Tōkyō, the British Minister approached Foreign Minister Nishi on the subject and inquired whether the Japanese government had any objection to his government's leasing Weihaiwei on identical terms as Russia's leasehold on Port Arthur. In spite of the fact that the army and the Foreign Office were desirous of retaining a hold on Weihaiwei, the Cabinet decided with the concurrence of the Elder Statesmen to withdraw, for fear that it might cause complications with Russia and also because of the eagerness of the government to leave and get the indemnity from China, which was contingent upon withdrawal.

The decision having been made to withdraw, Nishi replied, in a memoran-

---

[6] Itō, *op. cit.*

[7] *British Documents on the Origins of the War,* Vol. I, p. 8.

[8] *British Parliamentary Debates,* 4th series, Vol. LVI, p. 279, April 5, 1898; Vol. LXIV, p. 782, August 10, 1898; Vol. XCII, p. 165, March 28, 1901.

dum on the twenty-second, to the effect that the Japanese government had no objection to Britain's occupying the Chinese port. On April 2 Vice Foreign Minister Komura notified British Minister Sir Ernest Satow that the Japanese government actually desired British occupation of Weihaiwei, as it would ensure China's territorial integrity.[9] On the same day acting Foreign Secretary Balfour telegraphed the British Ambassador, Sir Frank Lascelles, in Berlin to inform the German government that Britain had asked China for the lease of Weihaiwei with the object of preserving a balance of power in the Gulf of Pechili, now menaced by the Russian occupation of Port Arthur.[10] It was made clear that Britain had no intention of encroaching upon German rights in Shantung. On the following day, the Russian Minister proposed to Foreign Minister Nishi that Japan and Russia jointly intervene to prevent Britain from securing Weihaiwei, but it was too late. Japan turned over the buildings and installations at Weihaiwei intact to the British and helped the British troops in taking over the port. The hearty and active cooperation of the Japanese government earned the thanks of the Salisbury Government and the Prime Minister expressed his warm appreciation to Katō.[11] The two governments were now well on their way to close collaboration for the safeguarding and advancement of their common interests.

When Anglo-German negotiations proved unsuccessful in mid-April of 1898 through the strong opposition in the German Foreign Office,[12] Colonial Secretary Chamberlain, in casting about for a possible ally, saw that Britain and Japan possessed common interests in the Far East. Consequently, the Salisbury Cabinet began to make efforts toward the consummation of an alliance between the two powers, but this plan did not receive the serious attention of the Japanese government and had to be dropped.

In late April, Foreign Secretary Balfour was able to strike a note of optimism, although by then Germany had leased Kiaochow (March 6) and Russia had secured Liaotung (March 27). He asserted with confidence that, in the past few months, Britain had placed herself in a far more powerful position, both commercially and strategically, than heretofore, enabling her to face the future with a feeling of greater confidence and security.[13] On May 14, in his Birmingham speech, Chamberlain advocated the conclusion of a triple alliance of England, the United States, and Japan as a means of handling the Chinese problem. Only four days later in the House of Lords, Lord Kimberley, the leader of the opposition, questioned Salisbury regarding the possibility of an Anglo-Japanese agreement. Although Salisbury carefully avoided committing himself, this was

[9] Itō, *op. cit.*, pp. 306, 307.

[10] *British Documents on the Origins of the War*, Vol. I, p. 31.

[11] Itō, *op. cit.*, pp. 307–308.

[12] Dugdale, *German Diplomatic Documents*, Vol. III, p. 21.

[13] London *Times*, April 29, 1898.

the first time the question of Anglo-Japanese cooperation was mentioned by the British Government. Lord Beresford, a staunch advocate of the Open Door in China, was one of the earliest advocates of an alliance between England and Japan.

Minister Katō, who was the staunchest advocate of Anglo-Japanese cooperation, felt that he was not making sufficient progress in bringing it about largely because of the attitude of his own government. When he returned to Japan in 1899, he was succeeded by Hayashi Tadasu, who devoted his energies toward the conclusion of an alliance. However, the matter came to a standstill temporarily when the Itō Cabinet fell.

In January, 1901, Iswolsky, the Russian Minister in Tōkyō, who had been a persistent advocate of Russo-Japanese cooperation, proposed the neutralization of Korea under the joint protection of the two powers. Premier Itō appeared to evince some interest in the proposal, but Foreign Minister Katō and Hayashi Gonsuke, Minister to Korea, promptly squashed it.

At the turn of the century, Germany presented a sort of enigma in the Far Eastern situation. On March 6, Inoue, Minister to Berlin, was assured by the German Vice Foreign Minister that the German government would not recognize Russia's actions in Manchuria, and that no secret Russo-German agreement regarding the Far East was in existence. The German official also stated that his government could promise to maintain friendly neutrality in the event of a Russo-Japanese clash and ventured the opinion that Britain would very likely give aid to Japan.[14] Foreign Minister Katō immediately informed the British Government of the conversation and inquired whether or not the word of the German official could be taken at face value. At the same time, he sought to ascertain the extent to which Britain would give aid. It was disclosed that Britain desired neutrality above all, but that she recognized the need for giving aid to Japan in order not to drive the latter to a *rapprochement* with Russia.[15] Obviously, Japan, at the time, was most apprehensive of a possible repetition of the kind of intervention which came in 1895 "to wrest the legitimate fruits of victory." In this connection, Britain rendered valuable service to Japan by instructing her ambassadors in the European capitals to ascertain what the attitude of the French government would be in the event of a conflict between Russia and Japan.[16]

Japan's objective in her diplomatic offensive was to secure a free hand in Korea and to regain all that had been wrested from her by the Triple Intervention. There were two ways of attaining these aims. Opinion within the government itself was divided, one group favoring *rapprochement* with Russia, the

[14] *British Documents on the Origins of the War*, Vol. II, p. 41.
[15] *Ibid.*, p. 43.
[16] *Ibid.*, pp. 45, 46.

other advocating close cooperation with Great Britain. The former, led by Itō Hirobumi and Inoue Kaoru, believed that in carrying out a long-term policy it was impossible to drive out Russian influence from the Far East; consequently a *rapprochement* with Russia to preserve the independence of Korea, the first line of Japan's defense, was worth conceding Russia's paramount interests in Manchuria. The latter, whose proponents included Katsura and Yamagata, maintained that, Russia having already bared her ambition of bringing both Manchuria and Korea under her domination, agreement with her would be at best a temporary expedient, which would prove utterly ineffective in preserving peace in the Far East; Japan would eventually have to come to grips with Russia, and to provide for such an eventuality Japan should work closely with Britain as an ally, inasmuch as she was eager to conclude an alliance.

In Tōkyō, a cabinet meeting was called on March 12 at the instance of Foreign Minister Katō for the purpose of formulating clearly the government's policy toward Russia. Katō pointed out, in a carefully studied written statement, that the British Government was not prepared to oppose Russia because of its preoccupation with the South African question; Germany's action would be quite restricted though she had expressed sympathy toward Britain and Japan. Three days later, however, von Bülow stated in his speech to the Reichstag that Manchuria was outside the scope of the Anglo-German Agreement. This virtually blasted the last hopes of securing Germany's active cooperation against Russian moves in the Far East, while at the same time bringing Japan and Britain closer together than ever before.

During the months of March and April, von Eckardstein called frequently on the Japanese Minister Hayashi. In the course of his conversation, he privately proposed a five-year triple alliance of Britain, Germany, and Japan to provide against a future emergency and a balance of power in the Far East. It was to be a Far Eastern counterpart of the Triple Alliance, giving Japan a free hand in Korea, and providing that, in the event of war involving one of the allies, the others were to maintain neutrality except when a third power came to the assistance of its enemy. In that event, the two remaining allies were to intervene. Chamberlain, Balfour, Lansdowne, and later Salisbury were all in favor of such an alliance. Kaiser Wilhelm and von Bülow also favored it, although German public opinion was unmistakably and violently anti-British.[17]

Toward the end of March, a secret conference was held in the Japanese War Ministry following receipt of intelligence reports on Russia's military strength in Manchuria. This was followed on April 5 by a meeting of the Board of Field Marshals and a cabinet meeting after which the second protest was made to the Russian government on the delay of the troop evacuation from Man-

[17] M. Kashima, "Nichiei Dōmei," *Kokusaihō Gaikō Zasshi*, Vol. XXXI, pp. 52–54, May, 1932.

churia. Regarding the triple alliance proposed by Eckardstein, Katō informed Hayashi in London that the government was not yet in a position to express its views, but authorized him to proceed with a preliminary exploration of the views of the British Government. It was evident that, at this point, the British Government was not quite ready to consider an Anglo-Japanese agreement. On April 17, Hayashi conferred with the Foreign Secretary Lord Lansdowne, who gave him every encouragement. With the approval of Lord Salisbury and King Edward, cordial conversations followed and the idea of a formal alliance was received favorably by both sides.

In his visit to Downing Street a month later, Minister Hayashi explained to Lansdowne that the aims of Japan's foreign policy were the maintenance of the Open Door, the preservation of China's territorial integrity, and the protection of her rights in Korea. Since England and Japan possessed a community of interests in China, the two powers should work together to prevent the coalition of those powers intent on violating those interests. Subsequently, Eckardstein confided in Hayashi his certainty that his government was also giving serious consideration to the same problem. Germany was apprehensive of Russo-Japanese *rapprochement,* which would permit Russia to divert her energies from the Far East to Europe and which would adversely affect German aims and activities. It was with a view to averting such an eventuality that the German government was devoting its energies in London to bringing Britain and Japan together.

In mid-July, Sir Claude MacDonald, British Minister to Tōkyō, then home on furlough, confided in Hayashi his view that the British Government ought to form an alliance with Japan in order to cope with the situation in the Far East, but that, because such an alliance was contrary to traditional policy, it would require some time. He stated emphatically the hope that the Japanese government, in the meantime, would not conclude an agreement with Russia. This was the first intimation to the Japanese government that Britain was practically ready to enter into formal negotiations. However, the British Government had not yet abandoned hope that Germany could be brought into the alliance.

Foreign Secretary Lansdowne notified Hayashi on July 30 that the time had come for the consideration of a permanent agreement and asked what Japan's demands would be in such an agreement.[18] In Tōkyō, on August 3, Premier Katsura conferred with Itō, the leading Elder Statesman, who was dubious of Britain's serious intention to form an alliance with Japan. Itō gave his approval, which was contingent upon Britain's recognition of Japan's rights and wishes and her willingness to conclude an agreement that would confer advantages on Japan as well as on Britain.[19] The Premier lost no time in calling

[18] *British Documents on the Origins of the War,* Vol. II, pp. 90–91; Lord Newton, *Lord Lansdowne,* p. 220.

[19] Ishii, *op. cit.,* p. 53.

a meeting of the other Elder Statesmen, Yamagata, Saigō, Matsukata, and Inoue and obtained their approval of the proposed alliance. The Foreign Office, in the meantime, had made a thorough study of Britain's record in diplomatic dealings and satisfied itself that there was no instance of a breach of diplomatic commitments on the part of Britain or failure to live up to her obligations as an ally.[20] On August 14, Lord Lansdowne suggested that the Japanese government prepare a draft agreement, inasmuch as Japan's interests were greater than those of Britain. Needless to say, this had a salutary effect on the negotiations for the alliance.

Having prepared the grounds at home for the alliance, the new Foreign Minister Komura gave Minister Hayashi on October 8 full powers to negotiate. On October 16 negotiations entered the final stages. On November 1, Foreign Minister Komura requested the British Government to submit its draft, which was handed to Hayashi two days later in London. For the next ten weeks the negotiations were carried on smoothly, most of the time being spent on revisions, which were necessary to satisfy both sides. It is of significance that no serious disagreements arose during the entire period of negotiation.

Although Itō had given his approval, though conditionally, for an Anglo-Japanese agreement, he was still skeptical as to its success. He had not abandoned the possibility of an agreement with Russia, which he really preferred, as did Inoue, his long-time colleague. Itō had been selected as one of the recipients of an honorary doctor of laws degree by Yale University[21] on the occasion of its bicentennial celebration in October, 1901. Seizing this opportunity for foreign travel and welcome respite from a strenuous and not-too-happy political life, he decided to continue on to Russia in a private capacity to initiate preliminary negotiations with a view to arriving at a *rapprochement*. The one-time Premier arrived in Washington early in October and paid his respects to President Roosevelt. After receiving the degree from Yale, he left for France. Upon reaching Paris, he was shown the draft of the treaty of alliance submitted by the British Government, which had been brought over by Minister Hayashi. The document surprised Itō, who thought that the chances of a successful conclusion of an alliance with Britain were very slim. He was even more surprised to see Japan's special position in Korea and mutual interests in China recognized.[22] There were no longer grounds for opposing the alliance. From Paris Itō proceeded directly to the Russian capital. He had deliberately avoided stopping over in England, as he was fearful lest he be drawn into conversations in progress, thereby inviting the suspicion of the Russian government and ruining the chances of successful negotiations. Apparently, Itō was intent on securing a

[20] Asahi Shimbun, *Nihon Gaikō Hiroku*, p. 105.
[21] Ishii, *op. cit.*, p. 53.
[22] *Ibid.*, p. 54.

treaty with Russia to defeat the pro-British faction, which was dominated by the two leaders of the military clique, Yamagata and Katsura. It was not so much his hostility against the British as a smouldering political antagonism which had been growing over the years and which made Itō determined. Yamagata and his group, though opposed to Itō's policy of "vacillation," were more anxious not to afford Itō the opportunity of retrieving his lost political power and prestige. Itō, on the other hand, was afraid that the control of the affairs of state might fall completely into the hands of a group dominated by the military if not a military bureaucracy.

Itō was received in audience by the Tsar, who awarded him the highest decoration, on November 28. He subsequently conferred with Foreign Minister Lamsdorf and Finance Minister Witte, discussing the details of a possible Russo-Japanese agreement. Itō's proposals, which were very liberal, included: (1) reciprocal guarantee of the independence of Korea; (2) reciprocal obligation not to use any part of Korean territory for strategic purposes; (3) reciprocal obligation not to take military measures on the Korean coast which would hamper the freedom of passage in the straits of Korea; (4) Russia's recognition of Japan's freedom of action in political, industrial, and commercial matters in Korea; (5) Russia's recognition of Japan's exclusive right to assist Korea with advice and aid in the carrying out of engagements which fall upon every well-organized government and to dispatch troops whenever necessary.[23] As a *quid pro quo,* Itō was prepared to concede to Russia complete freedom of action in China. Although Witte was favorably disposed, Lamsdorf was not willing to concede so much to Japan. Having made little headway in the talks, Itō left early in December for Berlin, from where he quietly watched the progress of negotiations in London. In the middle of the month he received from Russia the revisions made to his draft by Lamsdorf, which stipulated a free hand for Russia in Chinese territory contiguous to the Russian border. Lamsdorf asked Japan not to use any part of Korean territory for strategic purposes and not to take military measures on the Korean coast which would hamper the freedom of passage in the straits of Korea, but without imposing corresponding restrictions on Russia. Itō could not accept the revisions, inasmuch as they gave overwhelming advantages to Russia at the expense of Japan.

Although Itō's attempt was not successful, his visit to Russia stimulated the British into action and actually hastened the conclusion of the treaty of alliance. Britain was very uneasy over the possibility of a Russo-Japanese alliance, which would have been disastrous to British interests not only in China, but in the Pacific, and would have freed Russia from her fears in the Far East, enabling her to attempt further advances in Afghanistan, Persia, and the Near East.

[23] Kashima Morinosuke, *Teikoku Gaikō no Kihon Seisaku,* p. 158.

From Berlin, Itō sent back to Tōkyō a detailed telegraphic report of his conversations with the Russian government together with advice that the signing of the Anglo-Japanese Alliance be postponed pending further negotiations with Russia, and that both England and Japan should together make every effort to bring Germany into the alliance.[24] The Cabinet met on December 9 to discuss Itō's report but decided that it would be the height of folly to risk the Anglo-Japanese Alliance, which was virtually a *fait accompli,* merely to give Itō an opportunity to revive negotiations with the Russians in the hope that an agreement might be reached. Success was extremely dubious in view of the excessive demands of the Russians. Premier Katsura and Foreign Minister Komura lost no time in getting to the Palace to report the decision of the Cabinet to the Emperor, who immediately sought the advice of the Privy Council. Meanwhile, Itō, having given up hope for a Russo-Japanese agreement, wired on December 14 from Paris expressing his approval of the Alliance. He had decided not to stand in the way of what was clearly the desire of the government and the majority of the leaders. The Emperor sanctioned the conclusion of the Anglo-Japanese Alliance upon receiving a favorable report from the Privy Council. Itō arrived in London shortly thereafter and explained that his visit to Russia had been made in a strictly private capacity and voiced strong support of the Alliance.[25] On January 30 signatures were affixed to the Anglo-Japanese Alliance in London by Lord Lansdowne and Minister Hayashi. Its simultaneous announcement in London and Tōkyō on February 11 was received with mingled feelings in the capitals of the world.

Within only a few months of the abandonment of the Anglo-German negotiations, Great Britain, the greatest empire and strongest naval power in the world, became an ally of Japan, the newest addition to the family of nations and latest to appear on the stage of world politics. The German government, which had been instrumental not only in supporting enthusiastically but actually in engineering this alliance, promptly heaped denunciations upon Great Britain, whom it accused of a treacherous betrayal of the white race to the lowly, aggressive yellow race.

Such a radical departure on the part of Britain as breaking with tradition and abandoning the policy of "splendid isolation" to conclude an alliance with a non-Occidental, non-Christian power could be justified by British leaders only on the grounds of extraordinary urgency. Indeed, those were urgent times and the exigencies of the situation demanded action and immediate action.

The preamble of the agreement affirmed that the contracting parties were actuated solely by a desire to preserve the *status quo* and the general peace of the Far East. Both powers were deeply interested in maintaining the inde-

[24] William L. Langer, "The Origins of the Russo-Japanese War," published in *Europäische Gespräche,* Hamburg, 1926.
[25] Ishii, *op. cit.,* p. 56.

pendence and territorial integrity of China and Korea, and in securing equal opportunities in these countries for all nations. They further declared that they had no aggressive intentions against China or Korea, but that each might take the measures necessary for safeguarding its interests, if threatened by the aggressive action of any power or disturbances in China or Korea. It was emphasized that British interests were primarily in China while Japan, in addition to her interests in China, was particularly interested in Korea. In case of war with a third power, the nonwarring party would maintain strict neutrality, and would endeavor to prevent the other belligerent from securing outside aid. In case any other power joined the enemy of one of the contracting parties, the other agreed to come immediately to the ally's assistance. In such an event, peace was to be made only by mutual agreement. The Alliance was to run for a period of five years, at the end of which it could be denounced. But if either ally was engaged in war at the time of expiration, the Alliance was to continue until the conclusion of peace.

In the annals of international relations the Anglo-Japanese Alliance was no less than the merger of Japanese and European politics. Of special significance was the fact that it was the first and last bilateral alliance between an old, established Occidental power and an Oriental state that was a newcomer on the international scene. It also marked the beginning of a new era in world politics, for it was tantamount to a seal of British approval on Japan's aspirations and efforts toward recognition as a world power, and consequently it constituted, although indirectly, an endorsement of her program of expansion, which was launched in the last decade of the nineteenth century. Although the Alliance did not prevent war with Russia, it enabled Japan to plan and prosecute a war against Russia without any fear of interference from a third power. Moreover, it was an effective guarantee that there would be no repetition of a coalition of powers against Japan, such as had occurred after the Sino-Japanese War. Needless to say, its advantages were not one-sided; it was of great value to Great Britain, to whom the policy of isolation had become not only untenable but also dangerous to the security of the Empire. In the opinion of Japanese leaders, it came closest to being an ideal alliance, because it protected the interests of both contracting parties while helping to maintain peace in East Asia after the Russo-Japanese War.[26] There is little doubt that without the help of the Alliance, Japan could not have possibly achieved the international position that she enjoyed for the next forty-five years.

[26] *Ibid.*, pp. 41–42.

Chapter 21. The Russo-Japanese War

During the last stages of the protracted negotiations, which extended over a period of nearly six months, the autocratic Tsar of All the Russias confidently assumed that the decision for war or peace rested entirely in his hands, and that the Japanese government would accept any condition or concession he chose to make rather than run the risk of war. Obviously, he was not well posted as to Japan's determination, military strength, or preparedness.

It must not be forgotten, however, that an internal conflict raging in St. Petersburg at the time helped to further complicate matters. There were at least three different factions, each maneuvering and scheming to gain the favor of the Tsar in an undisguised attempt to impose its own policies and programs on the government. Witte, who was an exponent of peaceful economic penetration of Manchuria and China through the investment of capital and the railroad enterprise, wielded powerful influence for a time. But after 1898, there appeared a group dominated by the adventurer, Captain Bezobrazov, who advocated a program of economic penetration backed by force. Still another group, comprising army and navy officers, was interested in securing a port in Korea and gaining military control of Manchuria. This last group was responsible for utilizing the confusion following the Boxer disturbance to pour troops into Manchuria.

After 1902 the Bezobrazov group secured a position of undisputed supremacy in the councils of state and launched vigorous activities along the Yalu and Tumen Rivers in the months immediately preceding the outbreak of the war. Ambitious schemes were pushed ahead ruthlessly by Bezobrazov, who had a direct and personal stake in the Yalu Timber Company. Supported by the Grand Dukes and the military, this clique favored an aggressive policy calculated to put Russians in complete control of Manchuria. They proposed to build a screen on the Yalu River, from which they could threaten Japanese interests in Korea while at the same time developing the huge lumber concessions along the river, and also to use native brigands in Manchuria in such a way as to drive out the Chinese and all other foreigners except themselves. The plan won the enthusiastic support of the Tsar, and Bezobrazov himself went out to the Far East. While at Port Arthur, he was in close touch with the Viceroy of the Far East, Admiral Alexiev. In St. Petersburg he was completely successful in 1903 in a bitter contest to control policies. That the Russian government, which was completely dominated by the Bezobrazov clique, never intended to evacuate

Manchuria was borne out by the events that followed. In the event of quick victory, Russia's plans were to carry out the annexation of all of northeast China and Korea, placing Peking under her tutelage and working gradually for the eventual absorption of the whole of the Chinese government.[1]

A few days before the year 1903 came to a close Prime Minister Balfour wrote the King revealing his view that a war between Japan and Russia in which Britain was not actively concerned and in which Japan did not suffer serious defeat would not be an unmixed curse, as it would make Russia much easier to deal with both in Asia and in Europe.[2] He added, however, that he would do everything to maintain peace short of wounding the susceptibilities of the Japanese people. The Prime Minister seems to have entertained a personal conviction that Russia would not be able to crush Japan, a view which was by no means universally accepted at the time. Admiral Sir John Fisher of the Admiralty was of the opinion that Russia would be victorious. He is said to have actually pointed out to Foreign Secretary Lord Lansdowne on the map the exact spot where Japan would be annihilated.[3]

Unlike Prime Minister Balfour, Foreign Secretary Lord Lansdowne was not so bold a backer of Japan. Consequently, he attached a much greater importance to averting war. He saw a threefold risk in the event of war, namely, (1) the possibility of Japan being crushed by Russia, (2) the possibility of becoming implicated, not by treaty obligation but because the British public would not stand idly by while Japan was being defeated, and (3) the aggravation of Britain's already grave financial difficulties. Although he succeeded in convincing His Majesty's Government that Britain should try the role of a mediator, the Japanese government indicated clearly that mediation would not be acceptable, though it hinted that a loan of 20 million pounds would indeed be helpful. But since such a loan would be practically an "act of war," which might drag Britain into the conflict, His Majesty's Government took no action.[4]

If Britain could not view Russian actions in the Far East without concern, the United States could not view the development with indifference. It was not to American interests to allow Russia to consolidate her position in the Far East. The American government looked upon the loosening of the Russian grip on Manchuria as a distinct service to the United States. As American interests toward Russia at the time almost coincided with those of Britain and Japan, the United States showed a benevolent attitude toward Japan throughout the war. Roosevelt's policy was to lend Japan whatever support he could, short of an alliance.[5]

[1] Letter from Cecil Spring-Rice to Theodore Roosevelt, January, 1905, in Tyler Dennett, *Theodore Roosevelt and the Russo-Japanese War.*

[2] B. E. C. Dugdale, *Arthur James Balfour*, Vol. I, p. 281.

[3] Lord Newton, *Life of Lord Lansdowne*, p. 307.

[4] Dugdale, *op. cit.*, pp. 282–284.

[5] A. Whitney Griswold, *The Far Eastern Policy of the United States*, p. 104.

President Roosevelt's sympathies were unofficially, though unmistakably, on the Japanese side. He entertained a strong distrust, engendered in him by his advisers, of the Russian government, which he regarded as "insincere and arrogant." [6] As soon as war broke out, he notified Germany and France in the most polite and discreet fashion that he would promptly side with Japan in the event that they combined against Japan as they did in 1895.[7] American bankers worked with their British colleagues in financing Japan's war expenditures and the bulk of Japan's war financing was carried out through loans floated in London and New York.

No sooner had diplomatic relations been severed on February 6 than a Russian force crossed the Yalu River into Korea. The Japanese government immediately dispatched the first expedition to the theater of operations. Almost simultaneously with the severance of diplomatic relations, the combined fleet under Admiral Tōgō left Sasebo and steamed towards Korea. A fleet under the Annapolis graduate Admiral Uryū convoyed transports to Chemulpo, where the army's Twelfth Division was safely landed on the eighth. That night a flotilla of torpedo boats struck at Port Arthur. On the following day Uryū engaged a Russian cruiser and a gunboat outside the harbor of Chemulpo and put them out of action. By the time the formal declaration of war was made on the tenth, units of the Russian fleet at Port Arthur and Chemulpo had suffered severe enough damage so that the Japanese naval command felt it was safe to resume the transport of troops from Nagasaki to Chemulpo.

An imperial rescript, proclaiming the existence of a state of war between Russia and Japan, was issued by the Japanese government on February 10, two days after the actual commencement of hostilities. The rescript pointed out that the integrity of Korea had long been a matter of the gravest concern to Japan and that the separate existence of Korea was essential to Japan's national security. It accused Russia of bad faith by pointing out that, notwithstanding her treaty pledges to China and repeated assurances to the powers, she not only continued to occupy Manchuria, but had also consolidated and strengthened her hold upon it and was bent on its final absorption. It declared further that, although the possession of Manchuria by Russia would compel the abandonment of all hopes for peace in the Far East, the Japanese government had hoped for a peaceful settlement through negotiations, which were carried on for nearly half a year. But Russia had never met Japan's proposals in a spirit of conciliation nor had she shown any sincere desire for peace. Consequently Japan was placed in a position where what she once sought to secure by peaceful negotiation she could now seek only by an appeal to arms.

To the Japanese government this was a struggle to recoup the fruits of

---

[6] Letter from Roosevelt to Rockhill, August 29, 1905, in Dennett, *op. cit.,* p. 110.

[7] *Ibid.,* p. 2, Roosevelt to Spring-Rice, July 24, 1905; and Stephen Gwynn, *Letters and Friendships of Sir Cecil Spring-Rice,* Vol. I, p. 478.

victory which had been forcibly wrested from it a decade earlier by the power-ful European coalition. The whole nation had been preparing for this inevitable conflict, which was in a sense a revenge, but was even more a means of vindicat-ing the policies pursued by the Japanese government. It was also a war to make secure her strategic position by preventing Russia from using Korea, "the dagger pointed at the heart of Japan," as a base against her.

Europe, no less than the Tsar, was taken by surprise when Japan declared war on Russia, as no one had been fully aware of Japan's determination to go to war to settle the issues. To the very last, the Russian, German, and French Foreign Offices were asserting confidently that there would be no war. On the day following the formal declaration of war by Japan and Russia, the United States declared her neutrality. China followed with her declaration despite the fact that she was secretly allied with Russia.

Japanese naval strategy was directed at crippling the main strength of the Russian fleet concentrated at Port Arthur. To this end night attacks were car-ried out repeatedly by destroyers, while at the same time mines were laid and indirect attacks were made whenever possible. A bold plan was executed to block the narrow channel forming the entrance to Port Arthur by sinking old merchant vessels. Three attempts to accomplish this were made beginning in late February. Although the third attempt in early May was quite successful, the channel remained partially open at high tide even to large vessels. It was found necessary to further cripple the Port Arthur Squadron before armies could be transported to Manchuria with absolute safety. On April 13 the Japanese navy lured Admiral Makarov's squadron out of the harbor for an engagement. In the retreat back toward the harbor the Russian flagship *Petropavlovsk* struck one of the Japanese mines and went down with the Admiral and some six hundred men.

On land, General Kuroki's First Army advanced northward from Seoul and met and defeated an advance Russian force at Pyongyang. In late April the battle of the Yalu River commenced. Less than a week later, on May 1, Kiuliencheng fell to the Japanese onslaught, and five days later Fengcheng also fell. The Second Army, under General Oku, which landed at Pitzewo on the northeastern coast of Liaotung Peninsula on May 5, captured Chinchow three weeks later and Dalny at the end of the month. Meanwhile, the newly organized Third Army, under General Nogi, was given the task of capturing Port Arthur, the mightiest Russian stronghold in the Far East, which was reputed to be impregnable. Nogi captured the 203 Meter Hill on May 30, after which the Japanese could direct their fire on the harbor below and on the Russian fleet at anchor with telling results.

By the summer of 1904 Russian troops in southern Manchuria had been driven north to the Liaoyang region, which constituted a strong point for the Russians. With Field Marshal Ōyama in command of the Japanese forces in Manchuria, a general offensive was launched in late August. After ten days of fighting, on September 4, Liaoyang fell, and the Russian forces retreated towards Mukden; but General Kuropatkin was determined to retake the stronghold. The contest was resumed and the battle of Shaho was fought from the 5th to the 17th of October, but the Japanese lines held against the savage onslaughts and the Russian attempt failed.

After six months of fierce fighting, Port Arthur finally fell on January 1, 1905. General Stoessel, the Russian commander, surrendered and turned over the forts, 25,000 men, and 500 guns to General Nogi in a dramatic meeting amidst devastated ruins in a spirit not unlike that of Generals Grant and Lee at Appomattox forty years earlier. The siege had cost Japan the lives of 20,000 men, an exceedingly high price, a fact that preyed on the mind of General Nogi for the rest of his life. The veterans of Port Arthur, numbering some 50,000 to 60,000, moved north to join Ōyama's army on the plains of Manchuria, where a decisive clash was already in the making.

The battle of Mukden, one of the decisive battles of history, raged for more than three weeks, from February 20 to March 16, 1905. Five army corps aggregating sixteen divisions under Ōyama, numbering at least 400,000 troops, and occupying a front of nearly a hundred miles were pitted against Kuropatkin's Russian forces of no less than 350,000. The Russians were confident that the Japanese would not be able to withstand their assault and that they could turn the tide of war. After more than two weeks of incessant fighting, on March 10, the Japanese captured Mukden. A week later, the Tsar relieved Kuropatkin of his command and placed General Linievitch over him as the new commander-in-chief. The Russian casualties in killed and wounded numbered approximately 150,000, while the Japanese casualties numbered no less than 50,000. By this overwhelming defeat of the powerful Russian army, the issue of war was no longer in doubt. However, the *coup de grâce* was still to be administered two months later, not on land, but on sea.

Early in the war, the Russians had lost the control of the sea to the Japanese. Their hope of regaining it lay in the dispatching of a fleet to Far Eastern waters. Towards the end of August the Russian government decided to dispatch a fleet in an attempt to turn the tide of war. After its departure had been announced several times, the Baltic Fleet finally started out from Kronstadt in mid-October of 1904 under Vice Admiral Rozhestvenski.

In a state of high nervous tension, induced by rumors that Japanese torpedo boats were lurking in European waters, some Russian officers imagined detecting some of them among the British fishing boats at Dogger Bank in the North Sea on the night of October 21. They fired upon them, sinking a trawler, killing two fishermen, and injuring several others. This incident brought Russia perilously close to war with Britain. Feeling in Britain ran high in the days that followed until the Russian government, through French efforts at mediation, agreed to an international inquiry on a basis satisfactory to the British Government. How close Britain came to war can be seen by the fact that the Prime Minister, who was scheduled to give a speech, had actually prepared the text to announce either the relief of tension or the fact that the British Empire had come to grips with Russia. It was not until his train reached Southampton on October 28, the day he was to deliver the speech, that he received a telegram announcing that an agreement had been reached.

Earlier the British Government had denied the Russian fleet coaling facilities en route to the Far East. This, of course, did not help the progress of the Baltic Fleet. Near the French island of Madagascar the fleet drilled its raw crew, thence went on to the French Indo-China coast, and remained near Saigon and Camranh Bay. After being joined by another section of the fleet, which did not leave Libau until February 15, 1905, the Baltic Fleet headed toward its final destination and unsuspected doom in late May.

Admiral Tōgō was convinced that, in an attempt to reach Vladivostok, the Russian fleet would make a dash through the Korean Straits rather than take the circuitous route via the Tsugaru (Le Perouse) Straits. On the morning of May 27, Tōgō's scouts telegraphed that the Russian ships were sighted near Quelpart Island. Early in the afternoon of the same day and during the first hour of fighting the issue was decided. Admiral Voelersam had been killed in action and Rozhestvenski wounded, forcing Admiral Nebogatov to assume command. By sunset, the flagship, *Kniaz Subarov,* and three other battleships had been sunk. Before noon of May 28 Admiral Nebogatov surrendered. In the two-day running battle the Russians lost six battleships, five cruisers, one converted cruiser, five destroyers, four special service vessels, and one coast defense ship. Two battleships, two coast defense ships, and a destroyer were captured by the Japanese. It was estimated that out of the 18,000 Russian sailors, nearly 12,000 went down with the ships. The Japanese lost three torpedo boats, 116 men killed, and 538 wounded. Only the cruiser *Almaz* and two destroyers reached Vladivostok after escaping destruction or capture. Those ships which escaped to Shanghai and Manila were dismantled.[8]

Peace talks continued throughout the war and almost never ceased from the commencement of hostilities. The war was never popular in Russia, inasmuch as it was undertaken by the Tsar and the Committee of the Far East, which supported the Yalu timber concessionaires headed by Bezobrazov. Initial negotiations were opened in London in the summer of 1904, when Baron von Eckardstein of the German Embassy acted as the intermediary in the peace overture made by Witte to Japanese Minister Hayashi. But, at the time, when there was still a hope of victory, the Tsar would not listen to any talk of peace. Witte resumed his overtures in February of the following year, but this time Japan

[8] The *Aurora, Oleg,* and *Jemchug,* which sought asylum at Manila, were interned on June 8. Moore, *Digest of International Law,* Vol. VII, pp. 992–994.

was not inclined to give serious consideration so soon after the fall of Port Arthur, when the tide of war was rapidly turning in her favor.

Early in April, the French Premier Delcassé informed Minister Motono that he was prepared to intercede to bring Russia and Japan together for a peace talk, if Japan would agree to eliminate certain conditions unacceptable to Russia. These included the cession of Russian territory and the payment of indemnity, which were regarded as too humiliating for the Russian government to even consider. However, the Japanese government, speaking through Henry Willard Denison, Foreign Office adviser, expressed preference for American over French good offices and laid the matter before President Roosevelt in April. The onetime Rough Rider, who was on a hunting trip in Colorado, cut short his vacation and hastened back to Washington to await further developments. On the last day of May the Japanese government formally requested the President to invite the two belligerents to come together for direct peace negotiations. This was the opportunity President Roosevelt had been waiting for. He had expressed earlier to Secretary of State Hay that he could not permit Japan "to be robbed a second time of the fruits of victory." [9]

Meanwhile, in Russia indignation against the bureaucracy as well as the pressure for reform in the government had reached threatening proportions by early June. Even the Kaiser saw the danger to the Tsar's authority and strongly urged him to make peace. Kaiser Wilhelm had written to Roosevelt on June 4, expressing his deep apprehension that the news of the disastrous Russian naval defeat, suffered at the hands of the Japanese navy, might cause a revolution, if not an attempt on the Tsar's life.

Roosevelt instructed Ambassador Meyer in St. Petersburg to see the Tsar personally to urge on him the dire necessity for peace and to secure his consent to make arrangements for direct negotiations with Japan. The Tsar expressed his eagerness to have a meeting arranged before the enemy set foot on Russian soil, but emphatically insisted that the fact of his consent be kept secret until Japan's consent had been secured. Having completed the necessary preliminaries, Roosevelt extended on June 8 a formal invitation to the belligerents to meet for a peace talk, and two days later he released the news to the press.

By the summer of 1905 none of the neutral powers wanted the war to continue any longer. All the powers most directly interested had good reasons to want peace. France wished that Russia would be free to discharge her obligations to the Dual Alliance. Germany was now satisfied that her purpose of weakening Russia had been achieved. Furthermore, the Kaiser and his autocratic circle feared that the spread of the Russian Revolution would threaten their own position. Britain saw that her interests could not be served by the continuance of a war whose effects appeared uncertain. Russia was faced with the ominous threat

[9] John Hay's diary of January 1, 1905, in Thayer, *Life of John Hay,* Vol. II, p. 361.

of revolution and with no assurance that financial assistance would be forthcoming. Despite her victories on land and sea, Japan was on the verge of financial exhaustion and her manpower had reached a dangerously low point. Finally, the American people wished fervently for peace, as they felt that a further sacrifice of lives served no useful purpose.

Agreement as to the place of meeting was not reached immediately. Russia proposed Paris, the capital of her ally, which to her offered definite advantages, while Japan's choice was Chefoo, China. President Roosevelt suggested first The Hague and later Washington. However, since Washington was not considered a very satisfactory place for a conference in the month of August, the final choice fell on Portsmouth, New Hampshire, where the government possessed a navy yard and ample conveniences.

Remembering her experience in the selection of peace envoys after the Sino-Japanese War, Japan had decided not to appoint her most distinguished statesmen until and unless she could ascertain who the Russian envoys were to be. It was felt that such a step was necessary to safeguard her national dignity. The Russians appointed Witte and Rosen; the Japanese government then selected Foreign Minister Komura and Baron Takahira, Minister to Washington.

On August 10, almost two months to the day after Roosevelt extended formal invitations to the belligerents, the peace conference opened. In spite of the fact that both Japan and Russia desperately desired and needed peace, each imagined that the other was in a more desperate plight. This attitude was reflected in the actions of the plenipotentiaries at every stage of the conference. At the beginning of the conference, the Japanese presented the following demands: (1) the recognition of Japanese supremacy in Korea; (2) the transfer of Russian interests in South Manchuria including the leasehold and the railroad; (3) the surrender to Japan of all Russian war vessels interned in neutral ports during the war, and the limitation of Russia's naval strength in the Far East; (4) the payment of an indemnity to cover the cost of war; (5) the granting of fishing rights to Japanese subjects in the waters off the coast of Siberia, and (6) the cession of Sakhalin.

Russia acceded to some of these demands but absolutely refused to consider the demand for indemnity, which was considered humiliating, the turning over of interned war vessels, the limitation of her naval power in the Far East, and the cession of Sakhalin. In the deadlock that developed it became necessary for President Roosevelt to intervene. The Tsar stubbornly refused to make peace unless Japan's demands for territory and indemnity were dropped. Through Ambassador Meyer in St. Petersburg, the President succeeded in getting the Tsar to agree to the division of Sakhalin and the payment of a "substantial sum" for the return of the northern part to Russia. Meanwhile, Roosevelt warned the Japanese government of the folly of insisting on an indemnity, and finally secured its assent to taking Sakhalin and relinquishing all demands for indemnity.

On August 28 it appeared that Witte, under instructions from his government, might break off negotiations and sail for home. Russia was now convinced, by confidential reports received in the meantime, that Japan had no alternative but to make peace because of her dire financial plight; consequently her government refused to consider even the "substantial sum" to which the Tsar had agreed earlier. This shift and stiffening of Russia's attitude were reported immediately to the Japanese government. An imperial conference was hurriedly called in Tōkyō and the government decided to yield and accept the Russian "ultimatum." Thus, the Treaty of Portsmouth was signed on September 5. In the diplomatic poker game the seasoned and veteran diplomat Witte, aided by Dr. E. J. Dillon's skillful handling of publicity, easily won over the less experienced and less publicity-wise Komura. From the very outset the peace conference had been to an extraordinary degree a publicity duel between the Russian and Japanese plenipotentiaries. If publicity had been as skillfully handled by the Japanese as it had been during the progress of the war, the outcome at Portsmouth might have been quite different.

In February, immediately after an Imperial Conference decided to go to war with Russia, Itō, the then President of the Privy Council, prevailed upon Harvard-educated Baron Kaneko, member of the House of Peers, to serve as publicity agent in the United States. Itō saw clearly the crucial importance of favorable American public opinion in the successful prosecution of the war and even more in the successful conclusion of a peace treaty with Russia.

Kaneko arrived in New York where, following his interview with President Roosevelt at the White House, he established his headquarters. As the President and Baron Kaneko had known each other at Harvard during their student days, their meeting in the spring of 1904 was more in the nature of a reunion.[10] Roosevelt confided in Kaneko his hope for a Japanese victory and assured him of every possible aid.[11] At the time of Kaneko's arrival, the American press was far from friendly to Japan, though a little later Kaneko felt reassured by the words of the President, who stated that the attitude of army and navy men was sympathetic to the Japanese cause. In the face of the open hostility of prevailing public opinion, Kaneko was able to help create, through public speeches and articles in periodicals, a pro-Japanese attitude in America.[12] It must be added, however, that he owed his success, to a considerable extent, to the willing aid given him by American businessmen, financiers, the press, and above all, the President himself.

[10] The influence of the old school tie in international relations seems to be demonstrated in the relationship between Roosevelt and Kaneko as revealed in the latter's account of his activities in the United States during the war. Although written with his own personal bias and from a Japanese point of view, the account throws light on an interesting aspect of the Russo-Japanese War. *Kokushi Jiken Ronshū*, p. 489.

[11] *Ibid.*, pp. 489*ff.* See also Griswold, *op. cit.*, p. 104.

[12] *Ibid.*

This advantage, which was on Japan's side throughout the war, was lost to the Russians at Portsmouth. By the skillful handing of newspapermen, Witte succeeded in gaining their good will and had them "eating out of his hand." The Japanese envoy, Komura, on the other hand, alienated and even antagonized the press by the inept handling of the newspapermen. He was further handicapped by the policy of secrecy which his government pursued, thereby making it impossible to promote an American public opinion favorable to Japan. Thus, while Japan scored a decisive victory on the field of battle, she suffered a miserable defeat at the bar of public opinion and at the peace table.

Within Japan itself, the government clamped on a rigid press censorship immediately after the outbreak of hostilities on the grounds of military necessity. The public had not been given an accurate or well-balanced picture of the war or even of conditions on the home front. They were given only stories of heroism on the battlefield and news of successive victories. Victory seemed more complete to them than was actually the case. They were not aware of the severe economic, financial, and manpower strains that the war had placed on the nation almost to the breaking point. While the Portsmouth Conference was in progress the public was kept from learning what was going on.

When the terms of the peace treaty were published in Japan, the people felt that they had been betrayed by the government, which had concluded a "soft" peace. They had been led to expect a big indemnity for the great sacrifices they had made and the complete military victory they had scored over Russia. Yet, Russia did not pay even a ruble of indemnity. A huge public demonstration to express indignation was held at Hibiya Park in Tōkyō, denouncing the government's weakness and demanding the rejection of the treaty. Mob violence broke out and the newspaper *Kokumin,* which had supported the policies of the government, was attacked and its offices were not only torn down, but also burned. As a result, the government was forced to proclaim martial law in an attempt to restore order. The government's inept handling of the press and publicity backfired and invited blistering attacks. An enraged public turned its wrath upon the Katsura Cabinet, which had successfully prosecuted the war, and forced its collapse in January, 1906.

President Roosevelt's successful mediation efforts had restored peace in the Far East in September. For a while, however, it seemed as if peace negotiations might collapse. Roosevelt's determination and statesmanship forestalled such a tragic eventuality. The conditions by which the Treaty of Portsmouth restored peace between Japan and Russia included: (1) recognition of Japan's paramount political, military, and economic interests in Korea; (2) transfer to Japan of Russian rights in the Liaotung Peninsula; (3) ceding of the southern section of the Manchurian Railway to Japan; (4) ceding to Japan of the southern half of Sakhalin, that is, south of the 50th parallel; (5) withdrawal by Russia and Japan of troops from Manchuria, except the railway guards, which were to be retained; (6) noninterference by Japan and Russia in any measures China might take for the commercial and industrial development of Manchuria, and (7) exploitation of railways purely for commercial, and not strategic, purposes, except in the Liaotung Peninsula.

Thus, there appeared in the Far East a new power, a little Oriental power, which had not only dared to challenge a mighty European nation but had also succeeded in inflicting a humiliating defeat. Russia was driven out of Korea and her position in the Far East was reduced temporarily to one of minor importance. China was amazed as much as Europe at what had happened and began to probe for the reasons of Japan's surprising rise to power. At the same time the war awakened and stimulated nationalism in China. For the first time China turned seriously to Japan for tutelage and inspiration and her students, in a constantly increasing stream, went to Japan to study.

The repercussions of the Russo-Japanese War were no less real in Europe. Even while the war was in progress, the Russian people had opposed the absolutism of the Tsarist regime. The increasing demand for the establishment of a national assembly gained so much momentum and became so powerful that finally, in September, a constitution was promulgated and a national assembly was convened. The Russian Revolution, which was to come later, was already in the making. Also a shift in the power alignment resulted in Europe. The Russian defeat was instrumental in enabling Great Britain to establish a cordial relationship with the Dual Alliance, leading to the Triple Entente in 1907.

A phenomenal expansion of Japanese foreign trade, industry, and finances followed in the wake of the Russo-Japanese War, as recounted elsewhere. Militarism flourished, as unstinting praises were heaped upon the military for the victory it achieved for the nation. The military, riding on the wave of popularity, succeeded in getting huge appropriations for the expansion of armaments. But far more important than these was the effect of the war on Japan's international position.

In the eyes of the world, Japan had by her triumph over her adversary Russia earned her right as a full-fledged member of the family of nations, to which she had been admitted only a few years before. Her prestige as well as her position in the Far East was enhanced far beyond her fondest expectations. Moreover, she secured a firm foothold on the Asiatic mainland as a continental power. Her dream of continental expansion, which had vanished a decade earlier, had become a reality.

The powers applauded Japan for the overwhelming victory, but only momentarily. They were suddenly awakened to the realization of the full significance of the event. Some of the powers began to view the emergence of a strong Japan with considerable apprehension and uneasiness. Public opinion in the United States was no longer what it used to be before and during the Russo-Japanese War.

President Roosevelt was quick to see that the balance of power in the Pacific had been altered. Although he welcomed the elimination of Russian tyranny, he was not willing to see her complete collapse, which would create disequilibrium, if not a vacuum. He wanted to see a peace settlement reasonably favorable to Russia [13] by which a balance of power between Japan and Russia might be reestablished as a safeguard against further territorial expansion by Japan. The interests of Japan and the United States began to come increasingly into conflict over immigration and policies regarding China and Manchuria, blighting American-Japanese relations which had been on the most cordial terms for fifty years immediately preceding the war.

[13] *Ibid.*, p. 105.

Chapter 22. Political Parties on the Ascendancy

By the conclusiveness of the military victory scored over Russia the people had been led into thinking that Japan was entitled to very favorable terms of peace. Thus, to a large segment of the nation, several billion yen indemnity, the cession of the whole island of Sakhalin, the entire Chinese Eastern Railway, the transfer of the leasehold of Liaotung Peninsula, and Russia's relinquishing of all her special rights in Korea and Manchuria appeared to be the minimum conditions of peace. Naturally, when the terms were revealed, the nation reacted violently against the treaty as humiliating and denounced the incompetence of the plenipotentiaries as well as of the government. Public opinion seethed, and on September 5, the very day on which signatures were affixed to the treaty, a huge demonstration meeting at Hibiya Park passed a resolution demanding official apology to the nation by the Cabinet as well as the peace plenipotentiaries, the rejection of the peace treaty, and the resumption of hostilities in order to crush the enemy forces in Manchuria.

Attempts by the Metropolitan Police Board to keep the enraged mobs out of Hibiya Park led to clashes, and in the ensuing violence mobs attacked and tore down the newspaper *Kokumin,* the mouthpiece of the government, and set fire to the Home Minister's official residence. Several companies of infantry were called out to protect government officers and the residences of Elder Statesmen and to put down the disorder. The disturbance continued into the night as mobs, under cover of darkness, burned street cars, demolished police boxes, and raided police stations. With the situation completely out of hand, the government proclaimed martial law and ordered the suspension of all newspapers except those which were friendly to the government. When order was restored the toll stood: 169 police substations burned or wrecked, 550 persons killed or wounded, 38 homes burned, 10 Christian churches destroyed, 471 police officials killed or injured. About a thousand persons were arrested on suspicion of inciting mobs to violence. The dissatisfaction at the conditions of the peace treaty and the hostility engendered against the highhanded method of the government in suppressing the freedom of expression fanned public resentment to an unexpected intensity.

In an attempt to mollify enraged public opinion, the government relieved the Superintendent General of the Metropolitan Police Board as well as the Home Minister. When Premier Katsura saw that the public was not to be appeased, he tendered his resignation prior to the opening of the Diet, thereby denying to the political parties the satisfaction of passing a no-confidence resolution and forcing the collapse of his government. Although at the time of its formation it was branded a second-rate Cabinet, the embattled Katsura Cabinet held its position and survived in the face of uncompromisingly hostile public opinion for nearly five years, owing largely to the Premier's wile and craft in handling the political parties and also to the fact that it gained a new lease on life by the outbreak of the Russo-Japanese War in 1904. Yet, as if by retribution, it was the immediate aftermath of the war that brought on its downfall.

As soon as he had reached the decision to resign, Katsura summoned Prince Saionji and asked him to accept the responsibility of heading the next cabinet and to continue the policies he had initiated. Saionji consented without consulting the Seiyūkai, for it was Katsura's wish to avoid giving the impression that his choice had anything to do with the Prince's being president of that party. Katsura's selection of Saionji as a person to whom he wished to hand his baton was motivated by his desire to solidify his own position and to provide for his political future. This is borne out by the fact that from that time on the premiership passed back and forth between the two until 1913. In recommending Saionji, Katsura was making certain that the Elder Statesmen did not get a chance to recommend his successor. It was the practice at the time for the Elder Statesmen to recommend a successor in the event the outgoing premier failed to recommend one.

The Saionji Cabinet, which came into being on January 6, 1906, included only two leading members of the Seiyūkai, the rest being those of the Yamagata faction. At the very outset, Saionji issued a statement to the effect that he was succeeding to all the policies of his predecessor. In forming the Cabinet, Saionji took the greatest care not to displease Yamagata, but to win his good will instead. The Saionji Cabinet sought on the one hand the good will of Yamagata, and on the other endeavored to open the way for the successful steering of the political parties. With the unconditional and unswerving support of the Seiyūkai, the Saionji Cabinet had no trouble getting the appropriations bill passed by the Diet. Even the nationalization of railways was approved by the Diet in spite of the opposition of the Kenseitō. This resulted in the resignation of Foreign Minister Katō, who was unalterably opposed to nationalization.

Ever since the Kaishintō days, the Kenseihontō had been led and controlled by Ōkuma, Inukai, and others, and it had endeavored at every opportunity to strengthen its unity by faithful adherence to its principles and policies. However, in the face of adversity discontent developed within its ranks and a reform faction emerged to advocate the abandonment of its established policy in favor of collaboration with the government. This faction supported the government's financial plans and the expansion of military armaments. In an attempt to persuade this faction to consider its action further, Ōkuma pointed out the importance of holding to high principles and refusing to be tempted by temporary power or temporary advantages. When his efforts proved unavailing, Ōkuma resigned, taking the blame for his failure to inject a new spirit into the party.

In relinquishing the leadership of the party, he declared that, although he was leaving the important position of the presidency of a party, he was not forsaking politics, which were his very life. At the same time he attributed the political confusion to the Elder Statesmen and declared emphatically that he had no desire to join their ranks. If it was a sad exit for a great political leader, it was an even sadder commentary on the existing condition of deterioration in politics and government. Political parties and individuals were engrossed in advancing their own selfish interests. Although they loudly and freely lauded those who championed worthy causes, they were not always ready to lend support, cooperate with, or fight side by side with them unless their own interests could be served, and served adequately.

In the process of formulating the budget for the fiscal year 1908, a deficit of 150 million yen appeared, which the Saionji Government hoped to cover partially with a bond issue, surplus Treasury funds, and money received from Russia as reimbursement for the expenses of maintaining prisoners of war; the difference was to be made up through the issuance of convertible notes. When the plan was submitted to the Elder Statesmen for their approval, Matsukata and Inoue disapproved of what they regarded as a makeshift financial policy, which would impair the financial basis of the government. In its place, they recommended retrenchment and postponement of new undertakings and, if necessary, a tax increase.

Although the government and the Seiyūkai had been advocating a nonincrease of taxes and nonissuance of bonds, it had to scrap its own financial plans to accept the advice of the Elder Statesmen. A balanced budget was worked out by increases in the price of monopoly tobacco, a liquor tax, a sugar excise tax, and a new tax on petroleum. What was actually passed by the Diet, therefore, was the financial policy of the Elder Statesmen, rather than that of the Saionji Government. As a result, in January, 1908, Finance Minister Sakatani and Communications Minister Yamagata resigned. Because of the crisis precipitated in the Cabinet by the disagreement, Saionji also tendered his resignation, but was prevailed upon by the Emperor to remain in office.

In the tenth general election, held on May 15, 1908, following the adjournment of the 24th Diet, the Seiyūkai increased its strength to command an even larger absolute majority. However, less than two months after the election, Saionji submitted his resignation, naming Katsura as his successor. Saionji was luckless in carrying out the financial plans which were imposed on him by the Elder Statesmen. When it came to executing the postponement of some of the government undertakings, War Minister Terauchi and Navy Minister Saitō stubbornly refused to comply with the wishes of the rest of the Cabinet. Furthermore,

Inoue and Matsukata continued to be critical of the government in financial matters.

Public opinion welcomed the formation of the second Katsura Cabinet, for the Saionji Cabinet had become quite unpopular. However, the relinquishing of the government by a party leader who still commanded an overwhelming majority in the Diet to a person without any party connection appeared highly irregular, to say the least. The public suspected the existence of a deal between Saionji and Katsura to hand the premiership back and forth between them. In turning over the premiership to Katsura, Saionji had not even consulted his own party.

With the support of the absolute majority held by the Seiyūkai, Katsura managed to sail through the 25th, 26th, and 27th Diets without any difficulty. Such smooth sailing was possible since this was the period in which political strife existed among the parties, which regarded the government with perhaps some degree of tolerance, if not magnanimity, certainly with far less hostility than they did the other rival political parties. The Katsura Cabinet steered a course of calculated aloofness, if not impartiality, in dealing with the parties and was successful in not incurring their enmity.

The Japan Sugar Refining Company (Dai Nihon Seitō Kaisha) which had been formed by a merger of several companies with a capital of 12 million yen in the period following the Russo-Japanese war was able to pay dividends of 64, 20, 17.5, and 15 per cent beginning almost immediately after its incorporation. Toward the end of 1908 rumor had it that the large dividends had been made possible by defrauding the government of customs duties. The failure of the Fujimoto Bank, where the company had its account, unexpectedly brought to light the fact that the corporation owed the government 4 million yen in customs duties. It was also revealed that the officials and directors of the company had bribed members of the Diet to effect legislation that would be favorable to the enterprise. The legislation included the extension of the system of drawbacks on raw sugar imports and the introduction of bills in the Diet for the government operation of the sugar-refining industry. This scandal exposed the corruption in business and political circles as well as the evils of corporations and enterprises directly or indirectly protected by the government or by a protective tariff.

Involved in the scandal were scores of Diet members. At least twenty were arrested including eleven who were members of the Seiyūkai and seven members of the Kenseihontō. Public confidence in the members of the Diet was badly shaken as a result. But more significant was the fact that it gave the clan bureaucrats the necessary ammunition for the attack on parties and party members, thereby helping indirectly to increase their own prestige.

Under a political system that provided for a weak Diet that found itself constantly at the mercy of the Cabinet, the Elder Statesmen, the military, and the bureaucrats, the Diet members could little hope for the advancement of their position and power by ordinary means. They soon found out that the only effective means of strengthening their own position and increasing their influence was through the power of money. For the businessmen, intimacy with the authorities and legislators paid dividends and was a short cut to success. As a matter of fact, businessmen who achieved great success were almost invariably those who had government connections and received direct or indirect government aid or protection. It has been practically impossible to carry on large business enterprises in Japan without maintaining some sort of connection with the government as government control has been the rule. Consequently, businessmen cultivated intimate relations with government officials, and this could be done effectively through the members of the Diet. Ambitious Diet members who were struggling to increase their affluence as well as influence through the power of money and businessmen seeking favors from the government through Diet members made it almost inevitable for some kind of improper relationship to develop.

As the Seiyūkai continued to command absolute majority in the Diet to support the government and reap the benefits therefrom, all the other parties quietly planned to merge in opposition against the leading political party. This resulted in the birth of the Kokumintō on March 13, 1910. This new development made it necessary for the Seiyūkai to change its former attitude and also secure its relations with the government. Consequently, it took a stronger stand in the 27th Diet and began to criticize the government. Katsura, finding it necessary to form a more intimate relationship with the Seiyūkai if he were to get through the Diet session safely, was obliged to make a personal call on Saionji, the president of the party. This was followed in January, 1911, by a banquet given for Seiyūkai members by the Premier, who officially declared coalition with the party.

By the summer of 1911 public confidence in the Katsura Cabinet had declined sharply, financial conditions had become tangled, and the prospects of formulating the budget for 1912 had become very dubious. In late August, before work was begun on the 1912 budget, Katsura submitted his resignation, recommending Saionji as his successor. The public had come to expect the alternating of premiership by this time. On August 30, the second Saionji Cabinet was formed but there was no indication that either the Elder Statesmen or Katsura were consulted in the process of its formation.

Saionji's Finance Minister Yamagata made a thorough study of the financial situation and arrived at the conclusion that a policy of retrenchment was imperative if the government's finances were to be placed on a sound basis. On his recommendation the naval expansion program, the creation of two additional army divisions, and harbor improvements were deferred in the face of strenuous objection by the War and Navy Ministers. The appropriations bill, as drafted and submitted by the Cabinet, was passed by both Houses of the Diet.

In the formulation of the budget for 1912 the bureaucrats and militarists, who rallied around the Chōshū clique, emphasized the urgency of establishing two additional army divisions and were determined to force the Saionji Government to carry out the expansion program. Yamagata, who regarded Saionji's formation of his Cabinet without consulting him as a personal slight, seized upon the issue as a means of retaliating against the Premier and encouraged his subordinates and henchmen to harass the Cabinet. The War Minister insisted that it was the decision of the army as a whole and therefore the plan could not be withdrawn. A cabinet meeting with the rest of the members was held and they decided unanimously against the creation of two additional divisions. Thereupon, War Minister Uehara called on Yamagata, Ōyama, and Katsura and, after securing their approval, handed his resignation to Saionji on December 2. Saionji called on Yamagata to obtain his recommendation for a new War Minister but was met with a rebuff. This left no alternative for Saionji but to resign.

On December 5, 1912, the Saionji Cabinet fell, although it held an absolute majority of seats in the Diet won in the May election. Its downfall was not due to loss of public confidence, nor was it due to any impasse or maladministration. It was the military clique, which, by refusing to recommend a successor to the War Minister just resigned, made it impossible for Saionji to continue. Yamagata's strategy, which had been worked out with keen foresight years earlier to check the influence of the political parties, found effective application.

Saionji made no recommendation for a successor when the military forced his resignation. The task of selecting a successor, therefore, fell on the Elder Statesmen, Yamagata, Ōyama, Matsukata, and Inoue. Although they urged Saionji to reconsider his resignation and remain in office, he was adamant. Matsukata, Hirata Tōsuke, Yamamoto Gombei, and Terauchi Seiki were asked, but they all declined. They were unwilling to assume the responsibility of heading a government under extremely difficult conditions. After nine conferences had been held by the Elder Statesmen without success, they finally decided to call back Katsura, who was in retirement from political life since his acceptance, on Yamagata's recommendation, of the position of Lord Keeper of the Privy Seal and who was concurrently the Chief Aide-de-Camp to the Emperor.

Public opinion was aroused at the formation of the third Katsura Cabinet. Strong indignation was expressed at Katsura's reappearance in the political arena after having virtually renounced political life by becoming Lord Privy Seal, and especially at the manner in which imperial rescripts had been misused to effectuate his political comeback. All the political parties, with the exception of the Chūō Kurabu (Central Club), which was headed by Home Minister Ōura, with the help of the newspapermen led by Ozaki Yukio and Inukai Tsuyoshi organized the Federation for the Protection of Constitutional Government in determined opposition to the Katsura Cabinet. A vigorous movement for the preservation of parliamentary government and the smashing of clan oligarchy was launched with public meetings and social gatherings all over the country.

Katsura convoked the 30th Diet on December 24 and after the opening ceremonies he ordered a recess until January 20. Meanwhile, he hoped to organize a strong political party around the Kokumintō and Chūō Kurabu as a nucleus and to bring in a part of the Seiyūkai. Since his plans did not materialize as he had hoped, he prorogued the Diet on January 21 for fifteen days on the grounds that the printing of the budget bill had not yet been finished.

Although the Kokumintō lost more than half of its membership to the government, this strengthened the remaining membership and intensified its hostility against the government, resulting in the banding together with the Seiyūkai in an "offensive-defensive alliance" to smash the clan oligarchy and preserve parliamentary government. On February 5, they introduced a no-confidence resolution, backed by 299 members. Ozaki who introduced the resolution appeared on the rostrum and denounced the tyranny and irresponsibility of the Cabinet. At the same time he delivered a blistering attack on Premier Katsura. The government thereupon prorogued the Diet for another five days.

It became evident that the Cabinet could not weather the storm. On February 8, Katsura, through his Foreign Minister Katō, called on Saionji for help. On the following day, Saionji was summoned to the Palace and was handed a rescript by the Emperor. Katsura's act of invoking an imperial rescript aroused public opinion to the boiling point. On the tenth, a meeting of Seiyūkai members in the Diet was held and Saionji addressed them in an effort to pacify them. Instead of being pacified, the party members were stirred to action and started for the reopening of the session, saturated with a spirit of vengeance. Alarmed at the situation, Katsura prorogued the Diet for another three days without waiting for the reconvening.

On this day tens of thousands of people milled around the Diet building in anticipation of trouble, shouting epithets at the government, denouncing the unconstitutional acts and giving moral support to the antigovernment parties. As a precautionary measure, the Metropolitan Police Board stationed some 2,200 uniformed police officers, 200 plainclothesmen, and 30 mounted policemen, a total of more than 2,500 to guard the Diet building to prevent the mob from getting near the Diet session. Crowds clashed with the police. When the news of prorogation came from the Diet building, the assembled crowd could not contain their indignation. They denounced the highhandedness of the government and gave vent to their feelings by hurling bricks at the policemen. They attacked the *Miyako,* setting fire to it, and stormed the *Kokumin, Yomiuri, Hōchi,* and *Niroku,* and other newspapers that had given support to the government. The storming of the *Kokumin* was a bloody affair, in which the mob clashed with the employees of the newspaper, producing casualties in dead and wounded. The government mobilized troops to protect the newspapers and to guard the official and private residences of Premier Katsura. Mob action did not abate as had been hoped, and with nightfall further violence broke out. The mob attacked and burned police boxes in various parts of the city, producing scenes reminiscent of the outbursts at the time of the announcement of the Portsmouth Treaty.

With the situation completely out of hand, Katsura resigned on February 11, 1913, after only fifty-three days in office. There is little doubt that Katsura was one of the most skillful bureaucrats in the art of manipulating political parties, far more refined than Itō. But even so, he found it impossible to control the situation and was forced to resign. With this the power of the bureaucrats began to show signs of slipping, while the political parties appeared definitely to be on the ascendancy. The collapse of the Katsura Cabinet was an indication that the era of the clan bureaucrats, who managed the affairs of state with the collaboration of political parties, had come to an end. Although responsible party government was still rather a thing of the future, it had become increasingly clear that it was no longer possible for anyone to form a strong government without the direct support of the political parties.

In view of the hostile attitude of the political parties and the public, it was impossible for any cabinet to weather the Diet sessions without the support of the Seiyūkai, which commanded an absolute majority. However, Saionji was not in a position to accept the responsibility because of the imperial rescript he had received at the instance of Katsura. After long and careful deliberation, the Elder Statesmen recommended Admiral Yamamoto Gombei, who agreed to accept the premiership on condition that the Seiyūkai give him the necessary support. Members of the Seiyūkai hesitated to express immediate approval of Yamamoto so soon after their successful fight against Katsura, when they were still fired with their enthusiasm for the smashing of clan oligarchy and the preservation of parliamentary government. Not only did Yamamoto belong to the Satsuma clan but he was an admiral on the active list. Furthermore, he was regarded as the outstanding representative of the navy, just as Yamagata was the acknowledged and outstanding representative of the army. Several of the Seiyūkai members insisted that Yamamoto resign from active service and join the party as a condition for the support. However, satisfactory agreement was reached, and the Seiyūkai pledged support on the condition that all the cabinet members except the Premier, Foreign, and Army and Navy Ministers be party members.[1] Thus, although the Yamamoto Cabinet was not a party government in the true sense of the term, it was based on Seiyūkai support and represented considerable improvement, in a parliamentary sense, over the preceding Katsura Cabinet.

Strong opposition to the formation of the Yamamoto Cabinet was voiced by the Kokumintō, which had worked together closely with the Seiyūkai in over-

[1] Three were members while the other three joined the Seiyūkai at the time of their appointment.

throwing the Katsura Government. When the Seiyūkai went over to the support of Yamamoto, the Kokumintō terminated its cooperation. At the same time, a vigorous faction within the Seiyūkai, numbering twenty-four members and led by Ozaki Yukio, broke off and organized a small group called the Seiyū Club. With the loss of twenty-four members, the Seiyūkai lost the absolute majority which it had long enjoyed in the Diet. The Kokumintō and the Seiyū Club under the leadership of Ozaki and Inukai launched their attack on the government with a movement for the overthrow of clan rule and the preservation of constitutional government.

Meanwhile, on February 7, just before he resigned, Katsura had formed a new party, the Rikken Dōshikai, which was made up of the former members of the Chūō Club, the Kokumintō, and the bureaucrats, numbering altogether ninety persons. However, the new party announced neither a declaration nor a platform, since it was a group formed around the person of Katsura and was hardly deserving of the name "party." Two weeks after Katsura's resignation from the premiership, the party announced its principles and platforms, which were so vague and general that almost anyone belonging to any party could subscribe to them, and therefore were of little significance. Such a party, however, was not exceptional or rare, for there have been other political parties that have been launched without any principles or platforms.

In spite of the Seiyūkai's loss of majority, the Yamamoto Cabinet managed to sail through the 30th Diet, and no one suspected that it would collapse during the next session. The most important program of the government was that of naval expansion which was generally approved even though dissension had been expressed regarding the increase of the army strength by two divisions. Paying little attention and showing even less concern over the question of two additional army divisions, which had proved to be the undoing of the Saionji Cabinet, Admiral Yamamoto went right ahead with his plans for a large naval expansion program. This aroused the antagonism of some of the army leaders, who resented the Premier's partiality to the navy. On January 21 the Naval Replacement Expenditures Bill, giving the Navy a huge sum of 160 million yen for a six-year period, came up before the Diet. Two days later Shimada Saburō attacked the government, using a Berlin news dispatch exposing a scandal in which Japanese naval officers were implicated in accepting commissions, an act tantamount to accepting bribery.

For some years, the public had suspected some corruption within the Navy Ministry but it was impossible to look into its affairs, for even the Diet had no power of supervision or investigation over either the army or the navy. The corruption in the navy was exposed quite accidentally in a German court, where a former employee of the Siemens Schuckert Company was on trial for stealing secret documents. This provided excellent ammunition to the opposition parties for an attack on the Yamamoto Cabinet. There was a group in the House of

Peers, which was regarded as the stronghold of the Chōshū clique, and which had been dissatisfied with the national defense program of the Premier, who favored the navy and Satsuma at the expense of the army and Chōshū. This group was successful in their agitation, and the House of Peers slashed 70 million yen from the budget, giving as its reason (1) the overemphasis on naval program and neglect of army needs in defense plans, and (2) the need for house cleaning in the Navy. The conference committee met to discuss the slash but could not reach an agreement. Meanwhile a no-confidence resolution was introduced in the Diet and the opposition parties held a mass meeting at Hibiya Park. This resulted once more in the clash between the people and the police, in the course of which a *Tōkyō Nichi Nichi* newsman was wounded by a policeman, and public opinion was incensed, resulting in the censure of the Home Minister. Newspapermen, who were infuriated by the government's highhanded action, held an All Japan Newspapermen's Convention, at which they passed a resolution roundly denouncing the Yamamoto Cabinet. On February 26, the Yamamoto Cabinet resigned, even before it could get the appropriations bill through the Diet.

The Siemens Affair brought out in sharp focus the real cause of the downfall of the Yamamoto Government. Among a multitude of causes were (1) popular indignation against the Navy; (2) antagonism within the Navy itself against Yamamoto for the special position he occupied; (3) army-navy cleavage; (4) jealousy between the Satsuma and Chōshū cliques; (5) indignation at the Seiyūkai's arbitrary behavior over the years; (6) a movement started by the Dōshikai against the government; (7) popular outbursts against the government; and (8) disapproval of the appropriations bill by the House of Peers.

As usual, Elder Statesmen Yamagata, Matsukata, and Ōyama met to find a successor. Their first choice was Prince Tokugawa, for they had learned that Saionji was not interested. This move was calculated apparently to restore confidence in the government, which had been badly shaken. However, Tokugawa declined to leave the respectable and relatively secure position of President of the House of Peers in exchange for an insecure one. Finally, Kiyoura Keigo, who had no party connections, was called on to form the new cabinet, though from the very outset public opinion was against him. Newspapers joined the political parties in carrying on demonstrations against the formation of a cabinet by Kiyoura, on the grounds that it would be the revival of the Chōshū clan and the establishment of a nonparty government. As Kiyoura was an adopted member of the Chōshū clique and did not have any intimate friend within the navy, his efforts to secure a navy minister proved abortive. This was the immediate cause of his failure to complete the formation of a cabinet, although, by this time, it had become clear that a nonparty cabinet stood a very small chance of survival under normal conditions.

The public greeted the news of Kiyoura's abortive attempt with open satisfaction. The three Elder Statesmen, Yamagata, Matsukata, and Ōyama, who had recommended Kiyoura were so sure that the Premier-designate would succeed in his attempt that they had scattered to different parts of the country. When Kiyoura's attempt failed, the Elder Statesmen were confused and chagrined. Inoue was called in and the four Genrō met to decide on their choice. They knew that they could not err for the second time. Following Inoue's proposal, which required courage, they decided to ask Ōkuma to join the Genrō meeting at Inoue's home where they discussed plans for the formation of the new cabinet. Ōkuma made it a point to obtain in advance the understanding of the Elder Statesmen as a condition for the acceptance of the premiership.

Thus, on April 16, 1914, the second Ōkuma Cabinet emerged in the midst of a display of public enthusiasm surpassed only perhaps by the reception given the Ōkuma-Itagaki coalition Cabinet sixteen years earlier. It commanded an absolute majority and even the hostile Seiyūkai refrained from any criticism in the beginning. In spite of great odds and circumstances of political adversity, Ōkuma had fought consistently against the Elder Statesmen, defied the bureaucracy, advocated the crushing of clan oligarchy, and championed the cause of constitutional government.

However, as it actually turned out, the Ōkuma Cabinet was no more than a puppet cabinet, manipulated by the Elder Statesmen and the military clique, under whose influence it remained. When the bill for the expansion of the army by two divisions was rejected by the Diet, the government ordered its dissolution on December 25, 1914. In the general election held on March 25 of the following year, Home Minister Ōura, who was out to defeat the opposition party, Seiyūkai, at any cost, carried out an effective interference. With the generous financial assistance of the Mistubishi interests, with which Ōkuma had intimate connections as well as the support of popular opinion, the government parties succeeded in capturing 241 seats in the Diet.

In the three-week special session, which opened on May 20, 1915, the Seiyūkai attacked the foreign policy of the government, especially on relations with China. It denounced the Twenty-one Demands as a disgraceful blot on Japanese foreign relations, which not only impaired friendly relations with China, but also had invited the suspicion of the entire world. It also succeeded in forcing the resignation of Home Minister Ōura, who was found guilty of bribing a score of Seiyūkai members.

The Ōkuma Cabinet lasted for approximately two and a half years, and as cabinets go, it was rather long-lived. However, public disappointment was great, since hopes had been so high at the time of its formation. Too much had been expected of it. Unable to withstand the pressure from the Elder Statesmen, Ōkuma resigned in October, 1916, less than a week before the new party, Kenseikai, the merger of three supporting parties, was to be effected. The achievements of the Cabinet were not altogether the things that Ōkuma had been championing, nor were they up to his high standards, and they fell far short of his expectations.

On the eve of the resignation of the Ōkuma Cabinet, the party leaders and cabinet members came to the conclusion that a strong political party was imperative to make effective their participation in politics and especially in their relentless fight against the antiparliamentary, oligarchic forces of the military and the Elder Statesmen. Accordingly, the Kenseikai was launched on October 10, 1915, with Foreign Minister Katō Takaaki as its president. Efforts at the formation of the party had been started in June by Dr. Takata Sanae, the then Education Minister and colleague of Katō. When it became known in August that Yamagata was planning to recall General Terauchi from Korea with a view to grooming him for the premiership, the movement received impetus. The platform of the party emphasized (1) the strengthening of national defense; (2) strengthening of financial and economic bases of national power; (3) promotion of friendly relations with the powers with a view to achieving world peace; (4) extension of education and dissemination of ideals of constitutional government; (5) encouragement of industries with a view to increasing national wealth; (6) improvement and encouragement of local self-government; and (7) raising the nation's standard of living through the institution of necessary social policies.

On the very day the Kenseitō was born, Katō unleashed a powerful attack on the Terauchi Cabinet and made the first anti-Genrō declaration in history. Only three days earlier, he had already issued a political ultimatum to the Terauchi Government and the Yamagata faction of the Elder Statesmen. Directing the attention of the audience to the forces opposing the growth of parties, he called on the public to rise and eradicate the malignant growth of antiparliamentarism in the body politic.

Ōkuma's recommendation of Foreign Minister Katō for the premiership was neatly ignored by the Elder Statesmen, especially by Yamagata, who had already selected his own protégé, Terauchi, for the post. On October 5, when the official acceptance of the resignation of the Ōkuma Cabinet was still pending, the command to form the Cabinet was handed down to General Terauchi. This was clearly a stratagem on the part of the powerful military Elder Statesman to circumvent the plans of Ōkuma and the party leaders and to obstruct the healthy development of political parties and responsible government. Yamagata summoned Katō to his home and tried vainly to seek the latter's acquiescence and cooperation. Katō firmly resolved to challenge the power of the Elder Statesmen and to bring an end to the usurpation of power by the extralegal body of imperial advisers.[2]

Katō had already abandoned the practice of showing secret documents to the Elder Statesmen and made no secret of the indifference with which he received

[2] M. Itō, *Katō Takaaki*, Vol. II, pp. 235–238.

their gratuitous advice. Moreover, he refused to curry favor with the Elder Statesmen, as had been customary, for the purpose of securing or preserving political power, and openly resisted their meddling in the affairs of state. In November, he delivered at the city of Yamagata a pointed attack on the Elder Statesmen for their arbitrary and unconstitutional act of turning down the recommendation of a retiring premier. He gave as example the British practice, which respected the recommendation of the incumbent (Salisbury recommending Balfour and Campbell-Bannerman recommending Asquith). He characterized the Terauchi Government as the reactionary representative of the bureaucracy and the oligarchy, which looked upon political parties as subversive. It was a declaration of war against the Elder Statesmen in order to put the nation back on the "Normal Path of Constitutional Government."

In rejecting Ōkuma's recommendation, the Elder Statesmen claimed that they did not regard it necessary for the prime minister to be the president of the party commanding an absolute majority in the Diet. They emphasized that to set a precedent that the command to form a cabinet must fall on a person because he is the president of the majority party would be contrary to the spirit of the Constitution and would have the effect of restricting the imperial prerogative. It was not a wise policy, they argued, to favor one party and antagonize the others in a period of unprecedented emergency created by the European War, when national unity was so greatly desired. They claimed that Viscount Katō was suspected of being in favor of throwing the Russo-Japanese Agreement into discard and emphasized that the apprehension and suspicion of the Chinese had not been dissipated. Consequently, for the sake of satisfactory relations with Russia and China and for the termination of the European War, Count Terauchi would be more desirable than Viscount Katō. It was the consensus of opinion among the Elder Statesmen that this was not quite the time for Katō to assume the premiership.

It was apparent that the Genrō had been motivated by a strong apprehension that their position might be completely undermined unless they took a resolute stand. From the inception of the cabinet system this small extralegal, extraconstitutional body of advisers to the Emperor, comprising both the military and the bureaucrats, had exercised the prerogative of recommending premiers, and now they were jealously guarding against any possible encroachments. Ōkuma's recommendation of a successor without consultation of their views was taken as a direct assault on their prerogative. For nearly half a century, they had held the political powers as well as the nation's destiny in their hands, and they had come to believe that, unless their will was carried out, the security of the nation would be in jeopardy. They had come to attribute the rapid progress of the nation to their astute statesmanship. The establishment of constitutional government, the successful prosecution of two wars within a decade, the revision of treaties, the abolition of extraterritoriality, and all the major achievements of the nation were, they believed, the fruits of their wise and careful planning and execution. To them, the Diet was a mere sounding board of public opinion. The Elder Statesmen were therefore reluctant to relinquish their powers to any other group, particularly to the political parties.

The Terauchi Cabinet was confronted by the united front of three opposition parties that threatened with an absolute majority to pass a no-confidence resolution. As Ozaki of the Kenseikai was about to give a speech censuring the government, Terauchi dissolved the Diet in a surprise move. The election that followed gave a majority to the government, while at the same time stabilizing the domestic political situation to some extent. Problems of diplomacy urgently in need of readjustment, however, were not to be easily solved.

The inept handling of relations with China by the Ōkuma Cabinet had created a crisis. At the suggestion of Miura Gorō, the government set up, within the Imperial Palace, the Provisional Committee on Foreign Relations to bring together Hara Takashi, Katō Takaaki, and Inukai Tsuyoshi, the presidents respectively of the three leading parties, Seiyūkai, Kenseikai, and Kokumintō in the formulation of policies. Miura apparently was reluctant to see foreign relations and national defense turned into a political football. It was his hope that through the Committee national opinion might be unified for the renovation of diplomacy as well as the establishment of responsible party government. Needless to say, the immediate purpose was to obtain for the government the much-needed support of the three parties.

The Committee, which was headed by Premier Terauchi, included the Ministers of Foreign Affairs, War, Navy, and Home Affairs, and the representatives of the Privy Council, the bureaucrats, the Satsuma clique, and the presidents of the Seiyūkai and Kokumintō. Only the Kenseitō was not represented as Katō refrained from participating. He was convinced that a coalition cabinet would be more appropriate for the unification of public opinion.

Meanwhile, the unprecedented industrial and economic activities brought on by the war in Europe produced inflation and the skyrocketng of prices. Beginning with the imposition of the gold embargo by the Finance Ministry in September, 1917, the government issued a series of ordinances in an attempt to control runaway inflation. In April, 1918, the government promulgated an emergency ordinance to control the price of rice and hoped that together with the antiprofiteering ordinance, it would check the spiraling price of rice; but to no avail. On August 6 voices of discontent raised by the housewives of a fishing village in Toyama prefecture reverberated throughout the nation. Rice riots broke out and spread to 24 prefectures and 103 cities, towns, and townships. In 42 of the cities and towns the rioters were put down only after troops had been called out.

In confusion and despair, the government suppressed the news of riots and attempted to put down the nationwide disturbance by the use of force. Realizing its utter impotence in the face of mounting public dissatisfaction, the Terauchi Cabinet resigned on September 15, about a month and a half after the outbreak of the rice riots. The Elder Statesmen met to deliberate on the choice of a successor to Terauchi. With Inoue and Ōyama gone, there were only three survivors, Yamagata and Matsukata from the original group, and Saionji, who was included in the group shortly after his relinquishment of the Seiyūkai presidency to Hara. Although the command to form the new cabinet was actually given to Saionji, he declined it and recommended Hara Takashi, the president of the Seiyūkai. This definitely marked the end of an era, and the beginning of a new one. A commoner was placed for the first time in history at the head of the government.

Chapter 23. Expansion on the Asiatic Continent

Japan's urge to expand suffered only a temporary setback by the Triple Intervention at the hands of Russia, Germany, and France. It was kept alive for the next ten years by a burning national desire for revenge. True, the expansionists were forced for the time being to abandon any attempt to translate their desires into action, but they were merely biding their time. Spurred on rather than deterred by the Triple Intervention, ultranationalist, expansionist societies like the Black Ocean Society (Gen'yōsha) and the Amur Society (Kokuryūkai), better known as the Black Dragon Society, renewed their aggressve efforts, while the nation was solidly united in a firm resolve to prepare for the expected clash with Russia.

Repercussions of the ideas and utterances of the prophets of expansionism in other parts of the world, including the United States, Great Britain, Russia, Germany and others, were felt in Japan, where the leaders began to think and plan in terms of their own counterpart of "the White Man's Burden" and "Manifest Destiny." Their avowed goal was the hegemony of Asia. The writings of Captain Alfred Thayer Mahan of the U.S. Navy, particularly *The Influence of Sea Power Upon History,* exerted a not inconsiderable influence on the Japanese leaders, of whom Admiral Tōgō was one. Neither did the formation of the German Naval League in 1898 and the passage of the Naval Bill of 1900, which was intended to overcome British supremacy of the seas, pass unnoticed in Japan. The naval race that soon developed between England and Germany in the early years of the twentieth century stimulated the naval building program of the Japanese, giving the island empire the third largest navy in the world in a matter of two short decades.

It was no accident that the energies of the nation were directed toward the achievement of a place in the family of nations. Japan had learned well her lesson in power politics even before the nineteenth century had come to a close. In the attainment of national power the Boxer Uprising, the Anglo-Japanese Alliance, and the war with Russia were but milestones on the way.

By the Treaty of Portsmouth, Russia acknowledged Japan's paramount political, military, and economic interests in Korea and agreed not to obstruct or interfere with the measures of guidance, protection, and control which the Japanese government might find necessary to take in Korea. Manchuria was to be restored completely to the exclusive administration of China, except for the Russian leasehold on the Liaotung Peninsula, the South Manchuria Railway and its railway zone, and the coal mines, all of which were to be transferred to Japan.

Following the ratification of the Portsmouth Treaty in November the Japanese government dispatched Baron Komura to Peking to negotiate a treaty to secure Japan's newly acquired position on the Asiatic continent. In a formal treaty of December 22, 1905, China agreed to all the transfers of rights and privileges assigned by Russia to Japan in the peace treaty with the proviso that Japan conform so far as circumstances permitted to the original agreements concluded between China and Russia. At the same time, Japan succeeded in obtaining China's consent to the opening of important cities and towns in Manchuria to international residence and trade. She was also granted the right to improve for commercial use the military rail line which she had constructed between Antung and Mukden during the war. Japan agreed to withdraw her troops and railway guards when China became capable of affording full protection to Japanese lives and property in Manchuria. In a secret statement of intention by the Chinese plenipotentiaries, who negotiated with Komura, Japan was assured that the Chinese government would not construct any main line in the neighborhood of or parallel to the South Manchuria Railway or any branch line which might be prejudicial to the interests of the same.

By succeeding to the rights and special position Russia enjoyed through the leasehold on the Liaotung Peninsula, the railway from Port Arthur to Changchun, and mining and other rights, Japan entrenched herself firmly on the Asiatic continent to become in reality a continental power. Because the Triple Intervention had divested Japan of the fruits of victory in 1895, a foothold on the Asiatic continent was obtained a decade later than the expansionists had originally counted on.

RENEWAL OF THE ANGLO-JAPANESE ALLIANCE

While the Japanese and Russian peace envoys were meeting in the United States, the Anglo-Japanese Alliance was renewed in London for a term of ten years. Although it was actually signed on August 12, nearly a month before the conclusion of the Portsmouth Treaty, it was kept a secret until after the peace treaty was signed for fear that it might be prejudicial to Japan's cause. In place of the pledge of Korean independence the recognition of Japan's paramount political, military, and economic interests in the peninsula was written into the agreement. For the protection of those interests, Japan was accorded the right of guidance, control, and protection. This provision, which was contained in Article 3, was repeated almost verbatim in Article 2 of the Portsmouth Treaty. That it was a mutual defense pact was apparent from the assertion that it was intended for the "maintenance of the territorial rights of the High Contracting Parties in the regions of Eastern Asia and of India and the defence of their special interests in the said regions." In the event of "unprovoked attack or aggressive action . . . on the part of any power or powers" on either contracting party, the other party was obliged "at once to come to the assistance of the ally and conduct the war in common and make peace in mutual agreement with it."

American reaction to the renewal of the Anglo-Japanese Alliance was on the whole favorable. A month before the alliance was renewed Secretary Taft called on Premier Katsura in Tōkyō and effected the Taft-Katsura agreement of July 30, 1905, which included (1) a disclaimer by Japan of any hostile intentions as regards the Philippines; (2) a proposal for an informal understanding with the United States, which would make her in certain respects a silent friend of the Anglo-Japanese Alliance, and (3) the view expressed by Secretary Taft that Japanese troops might set up suzerainty in Korea in such a fashion that Korean foreign affairs would be under Japanese control.[1]

On November 22, the Japanese government declared that "relations of propinquity have made it necessary for Japan to take and exercise, for reasons closely connected with her own safety and repose, a paramount interest and influence in the political and military affairs of Korea." [2] The United States promptly withdrew her legation from Seoul and transferred diplomatic representation in Korea to the American legation in Tōkyō.

Public opinion in England gave unstinted praise when the treaty was announced in September. Sir Edward Grey, representing the opposition, gave it his complete approval, hailing the treaty as one of the three cardinal features of British foreign policy, the others being the growing friendship and good feeling for the United States and the friendship with France. It was regarded by the English public as an integral part of the Empire policy in the Far East and a bulwark of peace.

The Japanese public received the news of renewal with a great deal of satisfaction, as it helped to offset to some extent their frustration over the Portsmouth Treaty. The Russians were as chagrined as they might have been over a resounding military defeat. However, the calling of the first Duma and the subsequent internal developments caused them to find consolation in the fact that the defeat administered by Japan had contributed directly to the securing of the first assembly for Russia. Not only that, the way was paved for better relations between Japan and Russia, for the Anglo-Japanese Alliance furnished, indeed, the new starting point for a Russo-Japanese understanding, which became a reality two years later.

With a firm foothold on the Asiatic continent, Japan began to build up systematically her sphere of influence. On August 1, 1906, the Government General of Kwantung Territory was established to administer the newly acquired area.

---

[1] A. L. P. Dennis, *Adventures in American Diplomacy,* pp. 416–417.
[2] *Foreign Relations of the United States,* 1905, p. 613.

Its head, the governor-general, was to exercise concurrently civil and military powers and was appointed from among generals and lieutenant-generals, indicating the close relationship between the military and diplomacy in the formulation and execution of the policy of expansion on the Asiatic continent. For the management of the railway lines, the South Manchuria Railway Company, a quasi-governmental joint stock company, was organized with the government holding one-half of the shares of capital stock and the right to appoint its principal officers, the president and the vice-president. Wide powers were given the company, which was authorized to engage not only in transportation but also in mining, public utilities, especially electric power, and the sale of goods transported by the lines. It was even invested with civil administrative powers, for it collected taxes, established local government, and carried on educational administration. It was a twentieth-century counterpart of the East India companies of former times, but definitely an agency recognized at home and abroad as an effective instrument of national policy and expansion.

No sooner had Japan set about to consolidate the special position she inherited from Russia, than forces of international politics began to converge upon Manchuria. The mood of American businessmen in the post-Rooseveltian era was soon to be reflected in that corner of the world. In the autumn of 1905, E. H. Harriman, an American railway magnate, visited Japan and met Premier Count Katsura. Exemplifying the spirit of enterprise of the Taft-Knox era as well as that of "Dollar Diplomacy," Harriman was attempting to work out a scheme for a globe-encircling railroad and steamship service. He had come to the Far East to obtain trackage rights over the Trans-Siberian and to buy the Chinese Eastern and the South Manchuria railways. The plan called for a syndicate which would share equally with the Japanese government in ownership and operation of the railways. Katsura was favorably disposed and in October concluded a preliminary agreement for the sale of the Port Arthur-Changchun line. The return of Komura from the peace conference during the month occasioned a popular outburst against the government for the humiliating Treaty of Portsmouth. In the face of hostile public opinion, Katsura became convinced that the Harriman plan would not be acceptable, inasmuch as the railroad represented one of the few tangible financial rewards of the war. The government, therefore, decided against the sale of the South Manchuria Railway, which the Premier had already agreed to earlier in a preliminary negotiation.

Meanwhile, Japan's attempt to establish a profitable market for her domestic products in Manchuria before admitting foreign competitors brought charges of violation of the Open Door. Many of the Russian practices to which the Japanese had strongly objected and against which they had protested they themselves were now blandly carrying out. Rebates on the railroad were given to Japanese goods and Dairen at first was closed to all but Japanese goods and vessels. Goods were transported over the railway to the interior, when the transportation facilities were supposedly being used only for the evacuation of troops and for other military purposes, as stipulated in the agreement with China. In March, 1906, Secretary of State Root found it necessary to call the matter to the attention of the Japanese government.

Even as the plenipotentiaries of Japan and Russia were wrestling with the terms of peace, Secretary of War Taft, then on a mission to the Philippines, negotiated in Tōkyō on July 29, 1905, a secret memorandum with Premier Katsura, whereby the United States approved Japan's paramountcy of interest in Korea in return for her disavowal of any aggressive intentions toward the Philippines. Needless to say, the understanding had the effect of allaying, though temporarily, the fears of Theodore Roosevelt, who had long since the annexation come to regard the Islands as the Achilles' heel of the United States. The Japanese government proceeded with its plans to carry out a protectorate over Korea. On December 21, it issued a declaration of protectorate without protest from either the United States or Great Britain.

FRANCO-JAPANESE AGREEMENT

Uneasiness prevailed in high quarters of the French government in the period immediately following the conclusion of the Russo-Japanese War. The assistance which France had given her ally by permitting the Baltic fleet to use the facilities at Madagascar and Camranh Bay in French Indo-China was regarded by neutral observers as an act constituting a violation of neutrality and was resented by the Japanese. There was even a rumor that General Kodama, then Governor-General of Formosa, was making military preparations for the seizure of French Indo-China as an act of retaliation. The renewal of the Anglo-Japanese Alliance on August 12, 1905, rudely awakened the French to the realization that a clash with England was not altogether inconceivable in the event of resumption of hostilities between Japan and Russia. It had become quite evident that a *rapprochement* between Japan on the one hand and France and Russia on the other was an absolute requisite for bringing England and Russia together in Europe.

Foreign Minister Pichon, who was stationed in Peking at the time of the Boxer Uprising, informed Minister Kurino that there should be an agreement between France and Japan for the maintenance of peace in the Far East and the preservation of the rights and interests of the two powers in that part of the world. When Foreign Minister Hayashi Tadasu consulted the leaders, including Baron Komura, one group held that such an agreement was unnecessary, inasmuch as Japan entertained no designs on French Indo-China; and what was more, France could not offer any satisfactory *quid pro quo* for Japanese assurances. Others expressed the belief that an agreement would be helpful in ensuring the successful flotation of a loan in the French capital. The Cabinet arrived at a decision in favor of *rapprochement* and instructed Kurino to open negotiations with the French government.

At that time the Japanese government was in the midst of an attempt to float a 5 per cent loan of 23 million pounds sterling to convert a 6 per cent loan, floated during the war with Russia. Baron Takahashi Korekiyo, who was entrusted with the negotiations for the loan, arrived in Paris in March, 1907, and conferred with French leaders in government and in the financial world. Russia unexpectedly raised an objection for fear that Japan's success in floating a loan in Paris would lessen her own chances of borrowing from the French. However, as Russia was then in the process of negotiating a secret agreement with Japan, her attitude changed from opposition to support, although, in the meantime, Takahashi had gone to England, where he succeeded in floating the loan.

Because France was an ally of Russia, and Japan was carrying on treaty negotiations with both governments, France was given the opportunity to come forward as an intermediary when the Russo-Japanese negotiations were impeded and also to facilitate the process by having her own treaty with Japan serve as a pattern for Russia to follow. The Havas dispatch of May 5, 1907, informing the world of the impending Franco-Japanese agreement was followed the next day by the statement of Foreign Minister Pichon, proclaiming enthusiastically the advantages of the treaty. Formal signatures to the document were affixed in Paris on June 10. In addressing the national assembly, Pichon represented this agreement as supplementing the Russo-Japanese Agreement, which was then in the process of negotiation, the Anglo-French Agreement, and the Franco-Russian Alliance and in harmony with the China policies of the United States, Germany, Austria, and Italy. In strongly urging its approval on the assembly, he uttered a truism which had been evident for sometime, that European politics had become world politics. The Japanese had seen a convincing, though unpleasant, demonstration of this fact more than a decade earlier, when France herself was party to the Triple Intervention.

RUSSO-JAPANESE AGREEMENT

That an atmosphere of suspicion and apprehension should exist in the relations between Japan and Russia in the period immediately following the war was no more than natural. Indignant public opinion in Japan assailed the weak-kneed government of Katsura for having failed to take full advantage of the decisive military victory to wrest the most favorable terms of peace from Russia. For a considerable period of time thereafter the Japanese found it difficult to reconcile themselves to the fact that a golden opportunity had been lost forever. Russian public opinion too reflected strong dissatisfaction at the premature suing for peace during a time when Japanese forces were being slowly ground down in what might have developed into a war of attrition. But there were also those in Russia who feared Japan's attempt to strike back while others clamored for a war of vengeance and predicted that the treaty of peace would end as an armistice, since hostilities would be resumed soon.

It was in the midst of an atmosphere of strain and uncertainty that Izvolsky assumed his post as Foreign Minister in the new Russian Cabinet, which was intent on restoring peace and order in the country. The new government decided to pursue the policy of healing the wounds of war and rebuilding the strength of the nation. Accordingly a *rapprochement* with Britain was being effected with the good offices of France, while in the Far East Russia was desirous of maintaining peace through an understanding with Japan. As the year 1906 was drawing to a close the new Russian Foreign Minister divulged to Japanese Minister Motono in St. Petersburg the desire of the Russian government to strengthen the bonds of friendship with Japan and to ensure peace between the two nations by removing the irritants that stood in the way of friendly relations.

With an attitude of hopefulness mingled with skepticism and wariness, the Japanese government received the Russian proposal. How to take the Russian overture coming so soon after the end of hostilities was the question that bothered the Japanese leaders. Could the Russians be sincere? Or was it merely a scheme intended to relax Japan's vigilance in order to facilitate Russia's vengeance on Japan? Foreign Minister Hayashi accepted the Russian proposal in good faith; he was favorably inclined, but he also consulted the leaders. Baron Komura, the chief negotiator of the Treaty of Portsmouth, was convinced that for at least ten years Russia would be in no position to resume her aggressive policy in the Far East. However, Itō, then Resident General in Korea, was strongly in favor of an early understanding with Russia.

Negotiations were started secretly between the Japanese Minister and the Russian Foreign Minister and by February, 1907, a draft of the agreement was ready. The obstacle encountered by the Japanese at this point was Article 5 of the Anglo-Japanese Alliance, which provided that "neither of the High Contracting Parties will, without consulting the other, enter into separate arrangements with another power to the prejudice of the objects described in the preamble." Japan was apprehensive lest the *rapprochement* with her former enemy cool the cordial relationship existing between her and Britain, her ally. In order to obviate such an eventuality, the Japanese government consulted the British Government. The problem was solved easily enough, as Great Britain expressed approval, for she too was trying to arrive at an understanding with Russia through the good offices of the French government.

On June 13 an agreement regarding the Chinese Eastern Railway and the South Manchuria Railway was signed at St. Petersburg, followed on July 28 by the Fisheries Convention, defining Japanese fishing rights in the Japan Sea, Bering Straits, and the Sea of Okhotsk, and the Treaty of Commerce and Navigation. Two days later the representatives of the two powers, Isvolsky and Motono, signed the treaty, reaffirming the provisions of the Portsmouth Treaty and the special treaties concluded between them, as well as the independence and territorial integrity of China, and enunciating the principle of the Open Door and equal opportunity.

The announcement of the treaty sent repercussions to the far corners of the world. Comments and speculations filled the newspapers of Europe and America as well as of Japan and China, for astonishingly enough the erstwhile enemies had forsworn enmity in favor of mutual cooperation for the protection of their interests in the Far East. In a separate secret protocol they made boundary settlements. With the conclusion of the treaty, Japan became in a sense a partner sharing in the political fortunes of the Triple Entente formed by Britain, France, and Russia, and ironically enough allied herself with two of the former members of the Triple Intervention, only to become deeply and hopelessly enmeshed in European power politics, from which she could not extricate herself.

WORLD CRUISE OF THE UNITED STATES FLEET

An unprecedented era of good feeling between Japan and the United States came to an abrupt end with the termination of the war with Russia. This deterioration in American-Japanese relations continued unchecked until it ended in war thirty-six years later. For fifty years, since the arrival of Townsend Harris as the first diplomatic representative of a Western power, relationship between the two countries had been most cordial, almost incredibly cordial, and unmarred by any unpleasant incidents. Americans in large numbers gave unstintingly of their time and knowledge in offering tutelage to a willing nation, eager to bring itself abreast of the West in science and technology as well as in government and economics.

With the victory over China and the participation in the Boxer Uprising, both of which impressed the Western nations as proof of the progress she had made, Japan entered the twentieth century with confidence. She had been accepted as one of the great powers of the world. The alliance with Great Britain elevated her to a position never before attained by a non-Christian Asiatic power. But it was the defeat she administered to Tsarist Russia that placed her in the position of the foremost Asiatic power. This was achieved, however, at a heavy cost in good will, particularly in the United States.

Throughout the Russo-Japanese conflict, American public opinion was favorable, and even partial, to Japan. However, the military collapse of Russia on the battlefields of Manchuria brought home the realization that Japan might soon be in a position to challenge Western powers and threaten their interests in the Far East. As a result of the highly effective public relations of the Russian delegation at Portsmouth, American attitude began to change noticeably in favor of Russia. Americans, who had first looked on Japan with curiosity and then with admiration, began to look upon her with suspicion. This was reinforced by a group of American newspaper correspondents who returned in 1905 and began to inflame the antipathy of the public against Japan.

The anti-Japanese agitation, which started in earnest in May, 1905, with the formation of the Japanese and Korean Exclusion League in San Francisco by Mayor Schmidt, did not attract much public attention, as it was overshadowed by the war. When the city by the Golden Gate was visited by the earthquake and fire in April of the following year, the Japanese were among the first to send relief to the stricken. That the anti-Japanese antics of some of the San Franciscans had not yet caused any resentment in Japan was clear from the prompt and generous response and sympathy shown the city by the Japanese. Only six months after the disaster, a near international crisis was precipitated by the San Francisco School Board. On October 11 a resolution was passed by the Board directing the school principals in the city to carry out the segregation of Chinese, Japanese, and Korean children in the public schools. This brought an immediate protest from the Japanese government which deplored the discriminatory action. Although the segregation order was later rescinded as a result of the intervention of President Roosevelt, this marked the beginning of the progressive worsening of American-Japanese relations.

Despite the temporary respite afforded by the Taft-Katsura Agreement, relations between Japan and the United States showed no marked improvement. Deterioration continued and war talk became so persistent and frequent, not only in the Hearst papers, but even in the press of the European capitals, that President Roosevelt was alarmed. In fact, he was alarmed to a point in July where he was impelled by developments to send instructions to General Wood for the defense of the Philippines against an expected Japanese attack. Taft was again dispatched from Manila to Tōkyō, from where he sent a reassuring cable to the President stating that the Japanese government was anxious to avoid war. Still war talk in the United States continued without any signs of abating.

By July of 1907, Roosevelt had reached the decision to impress upon the Japanese that he had nothing but the friendliest possible intentions toward them, but that he was not afraid of them and "that the United States will no more submit to bullying than it will bully." He was convinced that the only thing that would prevent war was the realization by the Japanese that they could not defeat the United States. His decision to send the American battle fleet around the world was a gesture calculated to impress the Japanese with the naval strength of the United States as a possible antidote for their "very, very slight undertone of veiled truculence" which he had come to sense.

On December 16, 1907, sixteen battleships weighed anchors at Hampton Roads for their destination, San Francisco. On March 12, 1908, the fleet reached Magdalena Bay, Lower California, after an unhurried cruise along both the Atlantic and Pacific coasts of South America. The next day, Secretary Metcalf announced that the fleet would return home by way of Australia, the Philippines, and the Suez Canal, confirming the widely believed rumors of a world cruise. Five days later, on the eighteenth, Ambassador Takahira in Washington delivered to the Department of State an official invitation from the Japanese government for the fleet to visit Japan. Satisfaction was expressed by the Japanese people when the invitation was accepted by the United States.

Seven months to the day since the Japanese government extended the invitation, the American battle fleet, under the command of Admiral C. S. Sperry, dropped anchor in Tōkyō Bay and received an overwhelming reception, which was as unexpected as it was sincere and spontaneous. The hospitality shown by the Japanese people made a profound impression on the officers and men of the United States Navy and the reaction of the American press was highly appreciative. Ambassador O'Brien reported the visit of the fleet as an extraordinary success and the tone of the Japanese press universally favorable. At the same time, he expressed the view that the good effects of the visit would be material and far reaching. British Minister Macdonald echoed a similar sentiment by characterizing the visit as an unqualified success, which produced a marked and favorable impression on American officers and men and "put an end to all nonsensical war talk." No untoward incident marred the visit and the splendid behavior of the men of the fleet was matched and reciprocated by the cordial attitude of the Japanese populace. The visit also had the salutary effect of quieting the yellow press, and the tension which had previously existed between the two nations seemed to be relieved, though the effects were not lasting, as later events proved.

While wielding the "big stick," Roosevelt did not neglect to "speak softly" for in May, 1908, he signed with Japan a five-year arbitration convention. Six months later, he took the biggest step toward the elimination of conflict of Japanese and American interests in the Far East by easing the tension between the two powers. In an exchange of notes between Secretary of State Root and Ambassador Takahira on November 30 it was declared that the policies of the two governments consisted of the maintenance of the *status quo* in the region of the Pacific Ocean and the Open Door in China. Each would respect the territorial possessions of the other and support "by all pacific means at their disposal the independence and integrity of China and the principle of equal opportunity." Thus, the United States indicated her choice not to embroil herself in a war by openly challenging Japan's special position in Manchuria. Another crisis was weathered. To Japan, the Root-Takahira notes appeared tantamount to American acceptance of the interpretation of her position given by the Portsmouth Treaty, the Anglo-Japanese Alliance, and the agreements of 1907 with France and Russia.

RAILWAY POLITICS IN MANCHURIA

A challenge to Japan's policy in Manchuria regarding railway construction came late in 1907, when a British firm undertook to build for the Chinese government a railroad over a distance of some fifty miles from Hsinmintun near Mukden northward to Fakumen. The funds were to be provided to the Chinese government by a loan from the British and Chinese corporation. The Japanese government vigorously protested against the construction of the line on the grounds that it would violate the Sino-Japanese agreements of 1905. When the British financial and construction interests appealed to the British Government, the Foreign Office refused to come to their aid against the Japanese government. Japan's success in preventing the construction of the projected Hsinmintun-Fakumen line strengthened her claim of a monopoly in railroad building in South Manchuria although it invited severe criticisms both in England and the United States.

Simultaneously with the Hsinmintun-Fakumen project the Chinese government invited E. H. Harriman to finance a Manchurian loan of 20 million dollars. Although the financial panic of 1907 in the United States prevented the acceptance of the invitation, Harriman's interest in the purchase of Manchurian railroads was reawakened. For a time it appeared as if a Manchurian loan would be concluded without any difficulty, and even a triple entente of China, Germany, and the United States might be formed. But neither materialized.

Late in the summer of 1909, Willard Straight, a former American consul general in Mukden, who was a proponent of "Dollar Diplomacy" as was his superior, Secretary Knox, returned to China as an agent of a banking group including J. P. Morgan and Company, Kuhn, Loeb and Company, the National City Bank of New York, and the First National Bank, intent on securing a concession for a Manchurian railway that would provide a broad field for the investment of American capital, and at the same time help to smash Japan's special position in South Manchuria. The Chinese government readily granted the necessary concession in October, and the Chinchow-Aigun Railway was to be constructed. However, as the line would cut directly across the Japanese and Russian spheres of influence, Straight's profitable plan to use American capital as an instrument of China's political salvation threatened serious international complications.

In an attempt to find a much broader basis for the solution of the complex Manchurian railway problem, Secretary of State Knox suggested in January, 1910, the purchase by China of the Manchurian railroads from Japan and Russia with the funds provided by those powers which had pledged to uphold the Open Door. This so-called "neutralization" proposal called for the operation of the railroads by an international board of management until China repaid the large international loan. Its purpose was obviously to "smoke Japan out," as she was developing a sphere of influence in South Manchuria which threatened to overthrow the spheres that Germany, Russia, England, and France had planned for themselves earlier.

The European powers accepted the Knox proposal in principle but would not go any further. To both Japan and Russia the plan was obviously unacceptable. In replying through United States Ambassador O'Brien on January 21 the Japanese argued that it was too much at variance with the Treaty of Portsmouth and the subsequent agreements made with China. They said that they could not see the need in Manchuria for an exceptional system, not considered necessary in other parts of China. Furthermore, they not only expressed doubt that international management would add to the efficiency of their railroad operations, but they also felt that international control would be conducive to political friction. While expressing approval of the principle of the Open Door and equal opportunity in Manchuria, as did Japan, Russia insisted that the proposal would injure her interests and refused to accept it.

Russo-Japanese Treaties of July 4, 1910. The efforts of Harriman, Straight, and Knox to finance Manchurian railroads came to naught after five years of maneuvering. Instead of checking the activities of Japan and Russia, the unsuccessful attempts produced exactly the opposite results. They served only to strengthen the determination of the two countries to hold on to their spheres of influence, whatever the cost. As an immediate consequence, the two powers were brought together more closely than ever before, and a secret convention was signed in St. Petersburg on July 4, 1910, thereby strengthening their respective spheres in Manchuria by the reaffirmation of the agreements of 1907 and the *status quo,* as well as by forswearing of all harmful competition, particularly between Dairen and Vladivostok. This agreement was motivated by the common desire of the two powers to prevent the other powers from hampering their activities in Manchuria and to eliminate the possibility of clashing in the Far East at a time when Russia was desirous of concentrating her entire energies on the more vexing European problems.

The new Russo-Japanese agreements reflected a definite shift from the negative attitude shown in the agreements of 1907 to one of cooperation, if not collaboration, in the protection and advancement of their special interests. An obligation arising out of the secret convention of July 30, 1907, was now made public, serving notice on the powers that the signatories agreed to "engage mutually to lend each other friendly cooperation with a view to the improvement of their respective lines of railroad in Manchuria and to the perfecting of the connecting service of the said railways, and to refrain from all competition unfavorable to the attainment of this result."

Japan and Russia mutually assumed the obligation to undertake common action, after agreeing on measures, or to give support to each other. The 1907 convention provided in Article 2 that the parties were to engage to "sustain and defend the maintenance of the *status quo* and respect for this principle by all pacific means in their reach." However, in the new treaty, they were to use "whatever measures they may judge it necessary after consultation together to take," making the agreement assume the nature of defensive alliance for the preservation of the *status quo* which had, according to the interpretation given by the signatories, come to mean the protection of their special interests in Manchuria. This paved the way for Japan's next step.

ANNEXATION OF KOREA

In the remaining years of the nineteenth century following the Sino-Japanese War, when the mad scramble for concessions began in China, Japan found it impossible to remain calmly on the sidelines as a disinterested bystander; she was drawn into the scramble with the Western powers. In 1902, the community of interest between her and England and the fear of a common enemy led to the conclusion of an alliance which lasted two decades.

Shortly after the outbreak of hostilities against Russia, Japan secured the consent of the Korean government to an arrangement whereby Korea would accept Japanese advice in the improvement of administration. In return Japan guaranteed the independence and territorial integrity of Korea and promised to take necessary steps in case her security were threatened by the action of other powers or by internal disorders. Six months later this agreement was implemented by the engagement, on the recommendation of the Japanese government, of a Japanese financial adviser and a foreign diplomatic adviser who happened to be an American, Durham White Stevens.

In the eyes of the Japanese leaders, the stability of Korea was the key to the peace of the Far East. They reasoned that the stability of Korea could be ensured only by annexation. The first step taken toward this objective was the establishment of a protectorate over Korea late in 1905. This act met with no opposition from Western powers, inasmuch as it was a formal declaration of what had already been approved in the second Anglo-Japanese Alliance and the Treaty of Portsmouth. The United States raised no objection, as the Taft-Katsura memorandum had already conceded Japan's paramountcy of interest in Korea. Furthermore, for some years, there had existed a feeling in diplomatic circles that there must be a policy of give-and-take in international dealings.

Prince Itō, then president of the Privy Council, was the negotiator of the agreement of November 18, with the Korean King establishing a full protectorate over Korea. Japan, by virtue of this agreement, was given control of Korean foreign relations and the right to appoint a resident-general at Seoul. Foreign relations were to be conducted through the Foreign Office in Tōkyō, which fell heir to Korea's treaty obligations, and the Korean nationals abroad were to be protected by Japanese diplomatic representatives and consular officials. The resident-general was entrusted exclusively with the management of matters pertaining to foreign relations. Treaties and agreements in effect between Japan and Korea, which did not conflict with the provisions of the agreement, were to continue in force.

Appointed to be the first Resident-General in December, 1905, Itō took up his duties at Seoul the following February. One of his first acts was to propose a comprehensive program of internal reforms including the improvement of agriculture, encouragement of industry, construction of roads and waterworks, building of schools and hospitals, and the reorganization of the courts, the police, and the judicial system. But the powers of the resident-general were advisory and the reforms proceeded slowly in the face of opposition.

In June, 1907, the Korean King dispatched a secret mission to the Second Hague Conference in an unsuccessful attempt to secure the intervention of the powers in her behalf to free the country from Japanese control. This resulted in forcing the abdication of the King in favor of his son and also in an agreement, on July 24, which placed all matters of internal administration as well as foreign relations under Japanese control. The Korean government was henceforth to accept the guidance of the resident-general in matters of administrative reform and the enactment of laws, while important administrative actions were to receive his prior approval. Judicial functions were separated from the administrative. The power of appointment and dismissal, even in the case of foreign advisers, was to be exercised with the approval of the resident-general, who was given virtually the power of appointing Japanese to official positions, as the acceptance of his recommendations was made mandatory.

Itō sponsored the founding of the Oriental Colonization Company in 1907 as part of the general program. In spite of the powers he enjoyed, the Koreans found ways to nullify or circumvent his advice. Itō was confronted on every hand with stubborn Korean opposition to his plans, and by July, 1909, when he resigned and returned to his old post of president of the Privy Council, he was finally, though reluctantly, convinced that it was impossible to bring about efficient administration or preserve Japan's special interests by any method short of annexation. Thus, the man who at first strenuously opposed annexation was now convinced that there was no other alternative.

However, Itō realized perhaps better than any other person that the understanding of both Russia and China was a strong desideratum, if not an absolute necessity, in ensuring not only the success of annexation, but also of Japan's entire continental policy. By arrangement of Baron Gotō Shimpei, former president of the South Manchuria Railway Company, he was to confer at Harbin for the purpose of arriving at an understanding on Manchurian problems with the Russian Finance Minister Kokovstev, who was coming out all the way from St. Petersburg on an inspection tour of the Far East. On October 26, soon after his arrival in Harbin, Itō was assassinated by a Korean fanatic. His untimely death aroused public sentiment in Japan, where demands for immediate annexation were heard among the people at large as well as in high government circles.

In May, 1910, following the resignation of Sone, who had succeeded Itō the year before, War Minister Terauchi was appointed concurrently resident-general. Upon his arrival in Seoul, he promptly took over police powers and placed the entire country under the strict control of the gendarmerie. A condition of virtual martial law was in effect, as preparations were rushed for the final step. On August 22, within a month of his arrival in Korea, General Terauchi succeeded in concluding a treaty of annexation, which transferred all rights of sovereignty to the Emperor of Japan. In the announcement which followed, Japan declared that her own treaties would apply in Korea. Thus, *finis* was written to another chapter in the international struggle for the control of Korea, but only temporarily. Exactly thirty-five years later, in August, 1945, Korea was liberated from Japanese rule, although it was thrown into the anomalous status of being independent, but not autonomous, and divided into two zones of occupation, with the 38th parallel as the line of demarcation.

THIRD ANGLO-JAPANESE ALLIANCE (JULY 13, 1911)

The renewal of the Anglo-Japanese Alliance in 1905 had been greeted with enthusiasm by the British public. Even the members of the opposition party, including Asquith and Grey, expressed hearty approval of Lansdowne's diplomatic achievement. Not so the second renewal of the Alliance in 1911, for the intervening years had brought developments that affected the attitude of the British people. The Anglo-Russian and Russo-Japanese *rapprochements* of 1907 seemed at least for the time being to have removed the hypothetical enemy envisaged in the Anglo-Japanese Alliance. Furthermore, the tension that developed in Japanese-American relations gave rise to anti-Japanese and pro-American sentiments in the British dominions. And there was also the additional matter of clash of economic interests between the Japanese and the British in China.

Postwar developments led to unprecedented activities in Japanese trade and industry, and the finished products of Japan's industries began to flow into the markets of East Asia, particularly the Chinese market, and gave severe competition to the more expensive British goods. At the same time the efforts of the Japanese financiers to keep British capital out of Manchuria in the Hsinmintun-Fakumen and Chinchow-Aigun railway projects did not sit well with private British interests and led to the accusation that Japanese were violating the Open Door and the principle of equal opportunity in Manchuria and Mongolia. The London *Times'* Peking dispatches tended to inflame public opinion against Japan. Such developments aggravated the feeling that existed in England in and out of Parliament that British interests in China were being threatened by Japan.

Furthermore, the unfavorable publicity given the trials and execution of Kōtoku and other alleged anarchists created the impression that Japan was a semi-barbaric nation unworthy as an ally of a culturally superior Great Britain.

By 1911 British public opinion had become noticeably frazzled, if not hostile, towards Japan. The Manchester *Guardian* repeatedly opposed the renewal of the Alliance while the *Daily News* commented at the time of the renewal that, if anyone had predicted the continuation of the Alliance a year ago, he would have been laughed into silence. Anti-Japanese sentiment in New Zealand, Canada, and particularly Australia increased as apprehension was felt that England might be drawn into a war aginst the United States in support of the Alliance, if it were to be renewed.

Notwithstanding the hostile attitude of public opinion at home and in China and the dominions, the British Government had to consider the Alliance carefully and seriously from a broader point of view, taking into account the security of the Empire as well as the preservation of its overall and long-term interests. Germany at the time was in the midst of a huge naval construction program intended to overcome England's naval supremacy. Anglo-German commercial rivalry and competition in colonial expansion brought discomfiture to Great Britain. In order to effectively encircle Germany, the Anglo-Japanese Alliance was as indispensable as the Triple Entente. Although Russo-Japanese policies were encroaching upon British commercial interests in the Far East, they were not nearly as serious or threatening as the aggressive imperialism of Germany nearer home, which was threatening the very existence of the British Empire. The choice was unmistakably clear to the British Government, which had as early as 1907 refused to back Pauling and Company in the construction of a railway line from Hsinmintun to Fakumen in the face of Japan's objection. A further incentive to the British Government for the renewal of the Alliance was furnished by the Potsdam meeting of the Tsar and the Kaiser in November, 1910, which resulted in an understanding, though only a temporary one, between the two monarchs on Persia and the Berlin-Bagdad Railway and noticeably improved Russo-German relations. It appeared to the British leaders that the abandonment of the Anglo-Japanese Alliance at this point could conceivably bring about a *rapprochement,* if not an alliance, of Germany, Russia, and Japan, a situation that would be at best intolerable and at worst disastrous for British diplomacy. Such an eventuality could not be allowed to come to pass.

The decline in the popularity of the Anglo-Japanese Alliance was noted also in Japan, where public opinion reflected the irritation caused by the anti-Japanese attitude of the Britons in China. "Why should Japan act as Britain's watchdog for the security of India in view of the unfriendly British attitude?" they asked. But the Japanese government regarded the continuation of the Alliance as necessary to the peace of the Far East and her policy of economic penetration of the Asiatic continent. Government leaders were satisfied with the friendly attitude of the British Government and could afford to overlook the hostile public opinion. Although the Elder Statesmen and some other leaders who were influenced by the unpopularity of the Alliance favored an agreement with Russia as an alternative, Ambassador Katō Takaaki was determined that the Alliance should be renewed. He was supported by Premier Katsura and Foreign Minister Komura. The Elder Statesmen were won over, as even Prince Itō, who had originally favored an alliance with Russia over the Anglo-Japanese Alliance, had expressed hearty approval of its continuation to the British Ambassador Macdonald in Tōkyō as early as May, 1909.

As renewed on July 13, 1911, the Anglo-Japanese Alliance, which was to continue in effect for another ten years and for the last time, had for its objectives (1) the consolidation and maintenance of general peace in the regions of Eastern Asia and India; (2) preservation of independence and integrity of China and the principle of equal opportunity for the commerce and industry of all nations in China; and (3) the maintenance of the territorial rights of the two powers in Eastern Asia and India and the defense of their special interests in those regions. As regards the method of carrying out the purport of the treaty, the two governments were to communicate with one another fully and frankly and to consider in common the measures to be taken to safeguard menaced rights or interests. If either party should, by reason of unprovoked attack or aggressive action on the part of any power or powers, be involved in a war in defense of its territorial rights or special interests, the other party was obliged to come to the assistance of its ally, and to conduct the war together. Neither power was to enter, without consulting the other, into separate arrangements with another power to the prejudice of the objectives of the Alliance.

As was expected, the renewed Alliance helped to ease the existing tension in Japanese-American relations through the exclusion of the United States from the application of its provisions. Both President Taft and his Secretary of State expressed satisfaction at the provisions (Article 4) that made it easier for the conclusion of the general arbitration treaty, which was in the process of negotiation between Great Britain and the United States at the time. Nearly all the European powers, and Germany in particular, characterized the new alliance as considerably weakened and favoring Britain at the expense of Japan. Russia, however, received the news with calmness, while China expressed surprise at the renewal.

THE CHINESE REVOLUTION

Japan had furnished a haven for Chinese political offenders ever since K'ang Yu-wei and Liang Ch'i-ch'ao sought asylum after the unsuccessful one hundred days of reform. Sun Yat-sen, too, had found political refuge in the late 1890's, after an unsuccessful attempt to start a revolt against the Manchu dynasty.

Chinese students in increasing numbers found their way to Japan in search of education and to learn how the island neighbor had brought about the modernization of the country in such a short space of time. Tōkyō soon became the center of Chinese political refugees, revolutionaries, and students.

In July, 1905, on the occasion of Sun Yat-sen's return from the United States, the Chinese revolutionaries then residing in Tōkyō, including among others Huang Hsin, Sung Chia-jen, and Wang Ching-wei, met in the headquarters of the Black Dragon Society and organized the Tung Meng Hui, or the Alliance Society. From its headquarters in Tōkyō and its branch headquarters in Hongkong, the members carried on the movement for the establishment of republican government by means of vigorous propaganda campaigns in the various provinces. They launched a program of revolution based on Sun's *People's Three Principles* (*San Min Chu I*) and adopted the name Chunghua Minkuo for the new republic that they planned to establish. When the Tung Meng Hui staged an unsuccessful military revolt in China in 1907, the Japanese authorities asked Sun to leave Japan.

When the revolution broke out in Wuhan in October, 1911, the Japanese government was alarmed. Conservatives, including the Elder Statesmen, were of the opinion that, since the revolutionary outbreak was bound to have in the long run an adverse, if not a dangerous, effect on Japan, every possible aid should be given to the Court at Peking. However, the government hoped for a joint action with Great Britain because of the existence of the Alliance and the possibility of the Chinese revolutionaries stirring up a serious international controversy as well as the anti-Japanese attitude. While the matter was being discussed with the British, the Japanese leaders unobtrusively attempted to soften the attitude of the revolutionaries with a view to effecting a compromise settlement within the framework of the constitutional monarchy, which they favored.

The British Government was reluctant to take any action against the revolutionaries that might provoke actions prejudicial to British interests, as the insurgents were in control of the Yangtze valley. When the leaders, including Yuan Shih-k'ai, who were supporting the monarchy, began to show signs of wavering, the Japanese government began to question the wisdom of supporting even a constitutional monarchy at the expense of British friendship and cooperation. Late in December, Sun Yat-sen returned from exile abroad and was elected President of the Provisional Republic, established at Nanking by the revolutionaries.

With the abdication of the child Emperor, Pu Yi, on February 12, 1912, Manchu rule came to an end. A few days later, Yuan was elected President of the Provisional Republic of China, taking the oath of office the following month, when the provisional constitution was promulgated. By this act the union of the North and South was effected and a republic was established at least in name, if not in reality. Sun Yat-sen withdrew from the presidency of the Nanking government, to which he had been elected a short time before. In April Yuan signed an agreement for the reorganization loan of 25 million pounds sterling with the Six Power Group, including Japan. The southerners, under the leadership of Sun, claimed that the conclusion of the loan was in defiance of the Assembly and that Yuan had exceeded his powers. In May, 1913, an insurrection against Yuan broke out in the Yangtze valley. The uprising was ruthlessly suppressed, and Sun Yat-sen found himself taking asylum once more in Japan, where he and other Kuomintang leaders received encouragement from unofficial quarters.

Japanese public opinion was generally sympathetic to the cause of the southern revolutionaries and was strongly critical of the government's attitude, which was looked upon as partial to Yuan. Because of strong public criticism, the government was compelled to issue a long statement in the Tōkyō newspapers on June 9, 1913, clarifying its impartial and nonpartisan attitude regarding the Chinese situation and maintaining official neutrality. However, assistance to the revolutionaries was made available through the formation of a Sino-Japanese corporation with Sun Yat-sen and Shibusawa Eiichi as joint presidents, and the former Vice Foreign Minister as vice president. This was not the first time aid was given, as Sun had already been given considerable material assistance in 1911.

Opportunities presented by the chaotic conditions which resulted from the Chinese revolution did not go unnoticed by the powers intent on extending their spheres of interest. Russia was busily engaged in promoting her interests in northern Manchuria, Mongolia, and Turkestan. Taking advantage of the unsettled conditions, she gave aid in the achievement of independence in the fall of 1911 to Outer Mongolia, bringing it within her sphere of influence. Great Britain was active in Tibet, achieving a position almost analogous to that of Russia in Outer Mongolia. Japan too was busily engaged in her program to advance her position on the continent.

The murder by the Chinese of Japanese nationals in Nanking in 1913 occasioned the opening of negotiations by the Japanese government for the settlement of the railway question in Manchuria and Mongolia. In response to the ultimatum delivered in early October, the Waichiaopu informed the Japanese Minister in Peking that the Chinese government would like to have the cooperation of the Japanese government in the matter of railway bonds. This opened the way for the investment of Japanese capital in railway enterprise, as the Chinese government agreed to give priority to Japanese financiers in inviting foreign capital.

RUSSO-JAPANESE SECRET TREATY

In the cabinet meeting of December 2, 1910, the Tsar's government arrived at a conclusion that the annexation of northern Manchuria was an absolute requisite to the protection of Russian territory in the Far East. However, the immediate carrying out of such a program was out of the question, for it could invite the opposition of the United States, Great Britain, and even Japan and might even precipitate a war. The views of Prime Minister Kokovtsov, Foreign Minister Sazonov, and the Finance Minister prevailed and the Cabinet decided that, in view of the danger of international conflict and the fact that annexation was economically unsound, it would be best for the time being to concentrate all the efforts on the protection of treaty rights.

Foreign Minister Sazonov was aware that, in order to carry out Russia's program, it would be necessary to take precautionary steps, which would preclude the opposition of both England and Japan. Accordingly, in a neatly executed diplomatic maneuver, involving the withdrawal of an earlier protest against Britain's "scientific expedition" into Tibet and the recognition of the Russian right to take necessary actions to safeguard special interests in pursuance of the provisions of the secret convention of 1910, Sazonov ascertained to his own satisfaction that the two powers would not oppose Russian actions. On December 23 the Russian government declared that, in view of the unsatisfactory reply of the Chinese government, rejecting the request for the establishment of additional consulates in North Manchuria, Mongolia, and West China, it had been forced to resort to more positive action. Troops were mobilized and concentrated at Djarkend and Ussin to demonstrate Russian determination. China subsequently complied with all the Russian demands.

A loan agreement was signed on April 15, 1911, by the Chinese Imperial government with the Four Power Group representing a syndicate of American, English, French, and German bankers. The 10-million-pound loan was to be used for currency reform and industrial development in the three eastern provinces of China. The Consortium came into direct conflict with the special interests of Japan and Russia, who were completely left out, in spite of the fact that they were the two most interested powers. Japan protested on the grounds that the loan agreement left her out of the Consortium, which was given priority in furnishing capital to China. Russia objected on the grounds that it tended to obstruct the development of her special interests in Manchuria and other regions. Russia and Japan exchanged views with each other on the problem, as they had agreed to do in the Convention of 1910.

Although Russia's attempt to break the Consortium by urging French withdrawal did not meet with success,[3] France supported Russia's stand and backed

---

[3] Friedrich Stieve, *Isvolsky and the World War*, p. 29.

her demands regarding Manchuria, Mongolia, and Turkestan. As a result of exchange of views, it was revealed that the participation of both Japan and Russia was favored by China as well as the four powers. In March, 1912, Japan indicated her willingness to participate on the condition that her special rights in the regions of South Manchuria and the eastern part of Inner Mongolia would not be impaired in any way.[4] Russia's attitude softened and in April she agreed to join, provided her special rights and interests in North Manchuria, Mongolia, and West China were respected.[5] In June the Four Power Consortium, which had made the reorganization loan to the Provisional Republic of China under President Yuan, was enlarged into the Six Power Consortium with the inclusion of Japan and Russia. Thus, the successful united front presented by the two powers against the Four Power Consortium brought them closer together perhaps than at any other time since 1905. Cooperation and collaboration between the two powers reached a new high.

The summer of 1912 saw for the first time a mention in an official communiqué, of the maintenance of the "balance of power" in Europe. This occurred on the occasion of the meeting of Kaiser Wilhelm and Tsar Nicholas at a Baltic port in June. Sazonov, the Russian Foreign Minister, found an opportunity to converse with the Kaiser, who reminded him that he was the first to foresee the Yellow Peril and to direct the attention of the European powers to the new menace in the Far East. The Kaiser pointed out that the conclusion of the Anglo-Japanese Alliance, which enabled Japan to fight and defeat Russia, was a "great sin against the solidarity of the white races," and had caused the center of gravity in the Far East to shift suddenly toward Japan, a new great power. There was only one course to pursue, namely, to build up the military strength of China to make her a bulwark against the Japanese onslaught; and Russia alone could assume this task to which she was forcordained. The Kaiser warned that unless Russia undertook this, Japan would undertake the reorganization of China, causing irrevocable loss of Russian possessions in the Far East as well as her access to the Pacific Ocean.

Upon his return to St. Petersburg Sazonov, who regarded the Kaiser's proposed line of action as unnecessary and dangerous, took Viscount Motono, the Japanese Ambassador, into confidence and repeated the substance of the astonishing conversation. Motono telegraphed the conversation to Tōkyō and soon afterwards he was recalled to assume the post of Foreign Minister. It is quite possible that the information given by Sazonov had considerable influence on Japanese leaders in coming to the decision to declare war on Germany in 1914. But the more immediate effect was the conclusion of the Russo-Japanese treaties the following month.

[4] *Foreign Relations of the United States,* 1912, p. 137.
[5] *Ibid.,* p. 111.

It became evident to the Japanese and Russian governments that the reservations or conditions they attached to the Six Power Consortium needed clearer definition. This realization took concrete form in the treaty signed in St. Petersburg on July 8, 1812, by Sazonov and Motono, the purpose of which was to make precise and complete the provisions of the secret conventions of July 30, 1907, and July 4, 1910, and to avoid all causes of misunderstanding concerning their special interests in Manchuria and Mongolia. A clear line of demarcation was drawn, dividing Manchuria into northern and southern parts, and Inner Mongolia into western and eastern parts.[6] Russia claimed North Manchuria and Western Inner Mongolia as her spheres of interest while Japan claimed South Manchuria and Eastern Inner Mongolia. On November 1 Russia concluded a treaty with Mongolia, recognizing the latter's independence, but actually reducing her to the status of a Russian protectorate.

[6] For texts of all the treaties between Russia and Japan, see Ernest B. Price, *The Russo-Japanese Treaties of 1907–1916 Concerning Manchuria and Mongolia*, 1933.

Chapter 24. Diplomacy of the First World War

Events moved with kaleidoscopic rapidity in Europe following the assassination of Archduke Francis Ferdinand of Austria at Sarajevo on June 28, 1914. Less than a month later, on July 24, came Austria's twenty-four-hour ultimatum to Serbia. Frantic efforts to prevent a general war were made in the days that followed by such men as England's Viscount Grey, France's Cambon, and Germany's Prince Lichnowsky, but to no avail. The course of events was not to be changed. Then, on July 28, came Austria's declaration of war on Serbia, touching off the conflagration that soon enveloped most of the world. Russia made a strong protest against Austria's action and proceeded at the same time to mobilize her troops. On August 1 Germany declared war on Russia. Two days later France came to the aid of her ally with a declaration of war on Germany. At midnight on August 4 Great Britain declared war on Germany for the violation of Belgian neutrality. Thus, within a week of the outbreak of hostilities, all the major powers of Europe with the exception of Italy had been drawn into the holocaust. Before the month was over Japan too became a belligerent against Germany and Austria.

At no time after the outbreak of the war in Europe did the Japanese government feel that it could long remain neutral. Its actions therefore were governed accordingly. British Foreign Secretary Sir Edward Grey at first hoped that it would not be necessary to call on Japan for help. It was obvious that Britain wished to keep Japan out of the war if possible. But after her declaration of war, she found it necessary to modify her attitude in the face of developments that altered her strategic needs.

On August 4, British Ambassador Greene called on Foreign Minister Katō and requested Japan's aid in the event the war spread to the Far East, and Hongkong or Weihaiwei came under enemy attack. Katō assured the British envoy that in such an event the Alliance would be invoked automatically, but suggested that consultations be held between the two governments in doubtful cases. Three days later, the British Ambassador called again, this time presenting a formal memorandum from the British Government, stating that "it is most important that the Japanese fleet should, if possible, hunt out and destroy the armed German merchant cruisers who are now attacking our commerce. If the Imperial Government," the memorandum continued, "would be good enough to employ some of their men-of-war thus, it would be of the greatest advantage to His Majesty's Government. This, of

353

course, means an act of war against Germany, but this is, in our opinion un-avoidable." Foreign Minister Katō was convinced that the destruction of German vessels alone was not a sufficient justification for Japan's entering the conflict.

That very night a fateful cabinet meeting was held at Premier Ōkuma's private residence at Waseda. The Foreign Minister explained the diplomatic situation, dwelling at length on Anglo-Japanese relations, but made it clear that the conditions which would make Japan's entry into the war mandatory had not yet materialized. He emphasized that the Japanese government was not as yet obliged, under the terms of the Alliance, to go to Britain's aid. Katō expressed the view, however, that it would be to the best interests of the nation to enter the war as a friendly gesture in compliance with Britain's request and also for the twofold objective of liquidating German influence in the Far East and enhancing Japan's international position.

Deciding the issue of peace or war was a difficult task, as there was no unanimity of views among the government leaders. There were three alternatives, namely, to remain neutral, to join on the Allied side, or to join on the German side. Considerable hesitancy, if not reluctance, was shown by the leaders in coming to a decision for fear that they might choose the wrong side, and also because of the uncertainty regarding the sharing of the fruits of victory. Some cabinet members who were in doubt as to the final outcome of the war questioned whether it would not be possible to find a solution short of war. But Katō's convincing arguments and unshakable confidence in the ultimate victory of the Allied Powers dissipated doubt and convinced the Cabinet of the wisdom of entering the conflict in fulfillment of the moral, if not the legal, obligations of the Anglo-Japanese Alliance, and also in retaliation against Germany for the leadership she assumed in forcing the retrocession of the Liaotung Peninsula. A second cabinet meeting was held the following evening, attended also by the four Elder Statesmen, Yamagata, Matsukata, Ōyama, and Inoue. Some of the Elder Statesmen were still worried about the possibility of a German victory, but Katō allayed their fears, pointed out the advantages which would accrue to the nation, and succeeded in securing the final decision to go to war. Thus, within thirty-six hours of the receipt of the British request, the Japanese government had made up its mind.

Foreign Minister Katō promptly notified the British Government of Japan's decision to go to war. Britain responded to the notice by requesting that Japan restrict her activities to the protection of commerce on the high seas and hold the declaration of war in abeyance, lest a declaration give the impression that hostilities would spread to China and thereby adversely affect her. Having arrived at a decision and obtained imperial sanction for it, the Japanese government was in a position where it was virtually impossible to reverse itself. Katō presented a memorandum to the British Government expressing confidence that Japan's decision to enter the war would be met with approval. On

August 11, Grey requested postponement of military action pending further developments. This was in effect the withdrawal of the earlier request for assistance made through Ambassador Greene. Katō stood his ground and insisted that, since the preparations for military action were completed and the nation was poised for war, the government could not now back down. Grey finally yielded and agreed to Japan's declaration of war but demanded the limitation of the war zone. However, he was unable to secure Japanese agreement to the limitation and resorted to issuing a statement to the press to the effect that it was "understood that the action of Japan will not extend to the Pacific Ocean beyond the China Seas, except in so far as it may be necessary to protect Japanese shipping lines in the Pacific, nor beyond Asiatic waters westward of the China Seas, nor to any foreign territory in German occupation of the Continent of Eastern Asia." Katō disavowed any such commitment by his government, and in so doing, nullified the effort of the British Foreign Secretary.

FRENCH AND RUSSIAN OVERTURES FOR ALLIANCE

On August 4 the French Ambassador called on Foreign Minister Katō and proposed out of a clear sky a treaty of alliance. Coming as it did before the news of British declaration of war had reached Japan, the Foreign Office was in the midst of considering possible courses of action in the event of Britain's involvement in the war. Katō's response was cautious and noncommittal, if not evasive; he refrained from discussing such an alliance. Three days later, however, the French Ambassador returned with instructions from his government to ascertain the views of the Japanese government regarding the possibility of France joining the Anglo-Japanese Alliance. The French Ambassador disclosed that the inquiry as to the possibility of an alliance was motivated by the anxiety to preserve the territorial integrity of French Indo-China.

Within a week of the French overture, the Russian Foreign Minister transmitted to Minister Motono the Russian desire to conclude a treaty of alliance with Japan for the "lasting peace of the Far East and the permanent securing of Japanese and Russian interests." On August 2, the day on which she declared war on Germany, Russia had approached the British Foreign Secretary regarding her desire to join the Anglo-Japanese Alliance. Immediately upon Japan's declaration of war later in the month, the Russian Ambassador in London advised Sir Edward Grey that the opportune moment had come for the conclusion of the tripartite alliance. Grey dismissed the whole matter by stressing that Britain, Japan, and Russia were now allies in fact, a common war on the enemy making unnecessary the concluding of any formal alliance.

Katō, like Grey, wanted to avoid the inclusion of France and Russia in the Anglo-Japanese Alliance, inasmuch as such an arrangement would have the effect of weakening, if not emasculating, the effective bipartite defensive alliance. He was reluctant to turn the alliance into a general entente. But France and Russia were far from discouraged by the lack of enthusiasm on the part of the Japanese and the British. Instead of abandoning their efforts, they approached Grey early in January, 1915, this time urging the conclusion of a four-power alliance. As an alternative, they proposed bringing Japan into the Declaration of London of September 4, 1914, by which France, England, and Russia had agreed not to conclude a separate peace.

In the meantime, the unfavorable turn of events on the Eastern Front bared the weakness of the Russian army and caused considerable apprehension in London, where grave doubts were entertained as to the ability of Russia to weather the ominous internal storm that was fast gathering. The situation called for the lending of every political support to Russia without any loss of time. In the face of alarming developments, Sir Edward Grey reversed his former attitude and took the initiative in securing Japan's adherence to the Declaration of London. Although there was considerable opposition in the Diet, the Cabinet succeeded in overcoming it. As a result, Japan adhered to the Declaration of London in October, 1915, largely through the efforts of Foreign Minister Ishii, who saw the need of securing a voice for Japan at the peace conference which would place her on equal footing with the other Allied Powers.

Only a few days before Japan sent an ultimatum to Germany, Russian Foreign Minister Sazonov had urged her to enter the war. The Japanese government by this time had already made up its mind. For a week after the decision had been made, the Foreign Minister and his intimates, including the Navy and Finance Ministers, held daily secret conferences, devising painstaking plans to achieve their war aims with the minimum of risk and cost to the nation. It was on August 10 that the German Ambassador informed the American Ambassador in Tōkyō that the "elimination of Germany from the Far East and the transfer of her possessions to Japan would be prejudicial to American interests." It was obvious that Germany was trying to prod the United States into action against Japan. In the meantime, China, too, had sought American support in an attempt to exclude the area of hostilities from the Far East.

Finally, on August 15, Vice Minister of Foreign Affairs Matsui handed an ultimatum to the German Ambassador. Simultaneously, it was cabled to the Japanese Ambassador in Berlin for transmission to the German Foreign Office. Copies were sent also to the Japanese diplomatic representatives in London, St. Petersburg, Rome, The Hague, Berne, and Stockholm to ensure delivery of the ultimatum. Instead of the customary twenty-four- or forty-eight-hour limit for the reply, the Japanese government allowed Germany a full week. Using a language reminiscent of the "advice" received nearly two decades earlier, the Japanese government advised the Imperial German Government to (1) withdraw their men-of-war and armed vessels from Japanese and Chinese waters and to disarm at once all that could not be so withdrawn, and (2) deliver to the Japanese authorities not later than September 15, without condition or compensation, the entire leased territory of Kiaochow, with a view to its eventual restoration to China.

During the period of the ultimatum, on August 20, the Chinese suggested that German rights at Tsingtao be ceded to the United States for immediate transfer to China. This step, which was intended to deflect Japanese resentment against the United States, was recognized as such by Secretary of State Bryan, who replied promptly to the Chinese authorities that the course of action suggested would provoke rather than avert war. It became apparent to the State Department that the Chinese had deluded themselves into thinking that the United States government was going to act in opposition to the interests of the Japanese in China. Furthermore, they were hoping that the United States would undertake to guarantee China's independence and territorial integrity.[1] To counteract this unwarranted assumption, acting Secretary of State Lansing made clear to the Chinese government that, although the United States would be glad to exert any influence to further by peaceful methods the welfare of the Chinese people, "it would be quixotic in the extreme to allow the question of China's territorial integrity to entangle the United States in international difficulties."[2]

On the very day the Japanese ultimatum was handed to Germany, Katō invited the representatives of France, Russia, the Netherlands, and the United States to assure them that the Japanese government entertained no territorial ambitions and that their interests would not be violated. When, on this occasion, the perturbed Dutch Minister asked point blank whether the Japanese government entertained any thought of annexing the Dutch colonial possessions in Asia, he drew from Katō a reassuring reply to the negative. There is little doubt that this incident reflected accurately the suspicion and anxiety with which Japan's moves in the Far East were watched by European powers. The Japanese knew that such fears were not unfounded, for there were those who were advocating the annexation of the Netherlands East Indies. It was not strange that suspicion and fear of Japan's motives and actions should spread in time to the British dominions in the Pacific and even to the Pacific Coast of North America.

DECLARATION OF WAR

If Germany had complied with the demands of the ultimatum and if Yuan Shih-k'ai had not been engaged in a negotiation with the Kaiser's government, looking to the retrocession of German holdings at Kaiochow and special rights

---

[1] *Foreign Relations of the United States,* 1914 (Supplement), pp. 186–187.
[2] *Ibid.,* p. 190.

in Shantung, Japan might have exerted her efforts to remain out of the war at least until treaty obligations forced her into it. The attitude of the military clique and the Elder Statesmen toward Germany was far from hostile or irreconcilable; on the contrary, it was rather sympathetic. However, having received no reply at the expiration of the seven-day period, Japan declared war on the Imperial German Government on August 23, within three weeks of Britain's declaration.

Four days later, the Japanese Navy announced the blockade of Kiaochow. On September 2, the 18th Division, under the command of General Kamio, landed at Lungkow for a thrust at Tsingtao from the rear. A general offensive was launched on the last day of October and the German stronghold fell a week later, on November 7. While the land operations were proceeding, the navy mobilized four separate fleets in the Pacific, and between October 3 and 19 naval forces captured German bases on Yalut, Yap, the Marshalls, Marianas, and Carolines. From then on they were engaged in hunting down and destroying German ships, particularly commerce raiders, which were wreaking havoc on Allied commerce, and in convoying Australian troopships. In 1917 the entire ocean area between Australia and South Africa was in charge of Japanese naval forces.

Although the Japanese leaders emphasized that Japan's participation in the war was motivated by her desire to preserve freedom and justice, to discharge the moral obligations of the Alliance, and to settle the score with Germany, ensuing events bore out the fact, with unmistakable certainty, that they expected to be fully rewarded for the services rendered as an ally. The First World War was in no way a defensive war for Japan, and it was not fought as such. It was quite different from the war against Russia a decade earlier, when her national security appeared to be threatened. Needless to say, the government was influenced, if not motivated, by the desire to take over Germany's sphere of interest and special rights in Kiaochow and Shantung provinces, thereby advancing further the policy of expansion on the Asiatic continent.

On August 19 a British fleet shelled the radio station on Yap, and by the middle of September it became known that Australian troops would be sent to take possession of the island. Foreign Minister Katō approved the move, but when he learned of plans to occupy the neighboring island of Angaur as well, he lodged a strong protest, which caused the British Government to abandon the plan. It was Katō's belief that Japan was entitled to the German islands north of the equator in return for her part in the war.

In September Britain requested Japan to dispatch naval units to the Mediterranean, but Katō replied that the Japanese Navy, which was built around a defensive strategy, already had its hands full with operations against Tsingtao and the protection of commerce in the Pacific, and could not undertake a further increase of responsibilities. At the end of October, when Britain was planning a thrust in the Baltic, she again sent for help. The following month brought another request, this time a request for a fleet to participate in the blockade of the Dardanelles. But it was not until May, 1917, that the Japanese government responded to the final British request, made in January, for a destroyer force for convoy and anti-submarine duty in the Mediterranean. On January 17, a full week before the United States severed diplomatic relations with Germany, Japan initiated negotiations for a *quid pro quo* for her aid.

In a secret exchange of notes during February and March the Japanese government secured from Great Britain, France, Italy, and Russia a pledge for their support, at the peace table, of Japan's claims to Germany's rights in Shantung and possessions in the islands north of the equator. The British, on February 16, promised Japan the necessary support in return for the dispatch of the destroyer force to the Mediterranean and Japan's support of British claims to the German islands south of the equator. French support was a *quid pro quo* for Japan's supporting the plan to force China to break off diplomatic relations with Germany. Although the secret agreements were not recognized at the Peace Conference, the islands were mandated to Japan.

Immediately following Japan's entry into the war France and Russia urged through the British Government the dispatch of three Japanese army corps to the theater of war in Europe. Again, in October, when Turkey joined the German side, Britain joined the two powers in another appeal for military assistance. This was followed by the third request, which emphasized the need of military aid on the Western Front, where Japanese troops would fight alongside the British on the French border. Katō, who had persistently declined to send troops to Europe as a matter of principle, turned down the Allied request for the third time. He emphasized that to throw in a decisive weight no less than ten army corps would be necessary, which would make the homeland vulnerable. Although other requests subsequently came from Belgium, France, and even Serbia, the Foreign Office was adamant. Thus, no Japanese land troops participated in the European theater of war.

THE TWENTY-ONE DEMANDS

After the fall of Tsingtao early in November, Japan's part in the war was reduced to naval convoy duty and furnishing her Allies with munitions and supplies. For the remainder of the war her activities were more in the political and economic spheres than in the military. In foreign relations she concentrated her efforts on scoring political gains, while at home she devoted her energies to the expansion of trade and industry. Her "irrepressible urge" for expansion found concrete expression in her activities on the Asiatic continent, while her Allies were preoccupied with the prosecution of the war in Europe.

Immediately after the fall of Tsingtao, Foreign Minister Katō consulted the

Elder Statesmen and recalled Minister Hioki from Peking to prepare a final draft of demands to be made on China. But the attacks on the Foreign Minister in the Diet caused a delay in the opening of negotiations with China. The "Twenty-one Demands" were presented to China on January 18, 1915. Negotiations, which got under way in Peking on February 2, were hampered by several factors, not the least of which was the apt handling of publicity by China. The contents of the demands were known to the world as soon as they were presented. Yuan Shih-kai was apparently quite confident that the powers would intervene on China's behalf. Furthermore, he believed that if public opinion were sufficiently aroused, the Japanese demands could be rejected. Japan's attempt to withhold the demands of Group 5 from the rest of the world by insisting on absolute secrecy had engendered the suspicions of the powers. At the same time the Japanese government felt the stricture of the Elder Statesmen from above and a critical public opinion, mobilized by the opposition parties, from below.

Altogether twenty-five meetings were held over a period of three months without any noticeable results. In the face of the impasse, the Japanese government submitted a revised draft, which was considerably milder. On May 7, an ultimatum was delivered with the demands minus Group 5, giving the Chinese government two days in which to reply.

Arranged in five groups, the demands were aimed at the establishment in China of a dominant economic position. They were a sequel to the Russo-Japanese agreement of 1912 and an implementation of the continental policy of the Japanese government, which was supported by Russia in the secret protocol.

In the treaties signed and notes exchanged between the governments of China and Japan on May 25, 1915, China made concessions to Japan although the most obnoxious features had been dropped in the final demands. The Shantung Treaty covering Group 1 demands provided that (1) China should "give full assent to all matters on which the Japanese government might hereafter agree with the German government relating to the disposition of all rights, interests, and concessions which Germany by virtue of treaties or otherwise possesses in relation to the province of Shantung"; (2) Japanese capitalists have the right to build the Chefoo-Weihsien railway; and (3) additional places should be opened in the province for trade and foreign residence. China further agreed, in a note, not to alienate any territory within the province or islands along its coast to any foreign power under any circumstance. The Japanese government indicated its intention to restore the leased territory of Kiaochow Bay to China after receiving it from Germany, provided China open the whole of the Bay as a commercial port and set aside an area as a residential concession under exclusive Japanese jurisdiction and also an international settlement for other foreigners, if they so desired.

The treaty regarding South Manchuria and Inner Mongolia (Group 2) provided for (1) the extension to 99 years of the lease of Port Arthur and Dalny and the South Manchuria and Antung-Mukden railway agreements; (2) the right of Japanese to reside and travel in South Manchuria, engage in business and manufacturing, and lease land outside of treaty ports for trade or agricultural purposes; (3) the granting of permission by the Chinese government to any joint Chinese-Japanese enterprise; (4) the amenability of Japanese subjects to Chinese local law but the retention of the system of extraterritoriality in the trial of offenders; (5) the opening of suitable places in Eastern Inner Mongolia to foreign trade and residence, and (6) the revision of the Kirin-Changchun railway loan in favor of Japan. In addition, the Chinese government conceded, in separate notes, (1) the right of Japanese subjects to open mines in certain areas specified by the Japanese, (2) priority to Japanese capital in the event foreign financial assistance is needed for railway construction in Manchuria in the future, and (3) that the Japanese supply financial, military, or police advisers in South Manchuria when needed.

With respect to Group 3 demands centering around the Hanyehping Company, the Chinese Foreign Office stated in a note that permission would be given, if the Japanese capitalists and the company agreed upon cooperation in the future. Also the Chinese government agreed not to confiscate the company or convert it into a state enterprise without the consent of the Japanese capitalists, or cause it to borrow and use foreign capital other than Japanese. As to that part of Group 5 dealing with the Fukien province, the Chinese government stated that no permission had been given to foreign nations for the construction of dockyards, coaling stations for military use, or naval bases, and that it had no intention of borrowing foreign capital. Although Japan was forced to beat a retreat in the face of adverse world opinion, she did succeed in getting from China quite a substantial gain, which helped to push her policy of expansion on the Asiatic continent a step further.

RUSSO-JAPANESE CONVENTIONS OF JULY 3, 1916

Russia was forced by the outbreak of war in Europe in 1914 to abandon for the time being her plans for the further development of her interests in the Far East. The Tsar's government was already demonstrating by 1915 and 1916 growing irresolution, vacillation, and reactionary tendencies. As a matter of fact, reactionaries were coming into power. At the same time, inadequately equipped troops were being slaughtered on the field of battle. By the late spring of 1916 the military campaign in Galicia was in full swing along a vastly extended front. Supplies were barely trickling in by way of Archangel and Murmansk and the pitifully small quantities were wholly inadequate to meet the demands of the troops, who were literally crying for guns and ammunition. In her desperate plight Russia looked to her Far Eastern ally, Japan, for aid.

Japan immediately turned over to Russia all the guns and ammunition she could spare to buttress the weakening ally. At the same time she put the two government arsenals in Tōkyō and Ōsaka on a twenty-four-hour schedule to produce munitions for the hard-pressed Russians. In addition to some 600,000 to 700,000 guns, machine guns, and artillery pieces Japan furnished clothing, shoes, and other military needs, aggregating over 300 million yen. Whatever Japan might ask in return for the aid she was rendering, Russia was in no position to bargain, much less to refuse, for the Tsarist regime was already in the throes of a death struggle. Japanese leaders had been concerned for some time with the possibility that Russia might sue for a separate peace, despite her adherence to the Declaration of London. It was with a view to preventing such a dire eventuality and also to safeguard further the interests of Japan and Russia in the Far East that negotiations were started by Foreign Minister Sazonov and Minister Motono in Petrograd. What had been secured by the Twenty-one Demands on China, the Japanese government now wished to have Russia recognize at least in part, if not in its entirety.

By the agreements of July 3, 1916, Russia recognized Japan's considerably strengthened position in South Manchuria and Eastern Inner Mongolia. In a public convention, each of the signatories pledged not to be a party to any arrangement or political combination directed against the other. In the event the territorial rights or special interests of either were menaced, the two powers were to confer on measures to be taken to safeguard those rights and interests. A secret convention, which was signed at the same time and which was to last for five years, set up a defensive alliance. The two powers recognized that their vital interests made it imperative that China should not come under the domination of any third power hostile to either of them. Should such a threat materialize, they were to confer and to take such steps as might be agreed upon. In the event a war was precipitated in defense of these vital interests, each was bound to come to the aid of the other on demand and to undertake not to make peace without a previous agreement with the other. Thus, the agreement with Russia achieved, there remained only one other power whose understanding was necessary for the advancement of the expansionist policy of the Japanese government. That power was the United States, with whom negotiations were begun the following year.

LANSING-ISHII AGREEMENT

Developments in the Far East following the outbreak of the war in Europe as well as their policies toward China made Japan and the United States view each other with mutual suspicion and growing uneasiness. Germany was missing no opportunity to aggravate the irritations and discord that were known to exist between the two allies who faced each other across the Pacific. The

Zimmermann telegram of January, 1917, proposing bringing Mexico into the war against the United States and seeking the Mexican President's mediation between Germany and Japan, could not help but create deep suspicion in the United States.

In response to the demand in the Diet for a better understanding with the United States, the Terauchi Cabinet announced in June, 1917, the appointment of Viscount Ishii Kikujirō as Special Ambassador to the United States. Ostensibly, his mission was similar in nature to that of Lord Balfour for England and Justice Minister Vivani for France, namely, to express gratitude to the United States for her entry into the war as an ally. The Ishii mission arrived in Washington on September 1, and unlike the other missions, it was taken on a visit to the Atlantic Fleet, which had been assembled on the northern shore of Long Island, where it was awaiting orders to put out to sea. This was planned to give the Japanese visitors a very good idea of the naval might of the United States.

Viscount Ishii was willing to accept the abolition of spheres of influence in exchange for American recognition of Japan's special position in China. However, in Tōkyō, when the question was submitted to the Provisional Committee on Foreign Relations set up by the Terauchi Cabinet, the members could not agree, although the majority expressed disapproval. In the face of the deadlock in the advisory body, Ishii had no alternative but to proceed with the conversations with the Secretary of State in Washington without waiting for instructions from Tōkyō.

A difficulty was encountered during the negotiations on the use of the words "paramount interest," which Ishii suggested as having been first used by Secretary Seward and also by Frelinghuysen in describing American interests in Mexico. A compromise was reached and the expression "special interests" was substituted to the satisfaction of both Lansing and Ishii. Agreement was reached after less than two months of actual negotiations. By the exchange of notes on November 2 the United States recognized "that territorial propinquity creates special relations between countries, and consequently, the Government of the United States recognizes that Japan has special interests in China, particularly in the part to which her possessions are contiguous." Reiterated once again were the preservation of the independence and territorial integrity of China, the maintenance of the Open Door and the principle of equal opportunity. The impression created in the foreign capitals as well as in China was not what the United States had hoped. But it was precisely the effect which the Japanese government could use to good advantage in pushing its continental policy.

Nishihara Loans. Japan utilized every opportunity to advance her special position in China, though not without opposition. She pushed ahead with her plans, employing economic and diplomatic means. Following up the partial success of the Twenty-one Demands, the militaristic government of General

Terauchi engineered the Nishihara loans to the Chinese government of Premier Tuan and his Anfu clique as a leverage for further economic and political gains. The decision was based on the views of the China experts in the army. The series of loans aggregating 145 million yen were arranged between September 28, 1917, and September 28, 1918, by a certain Nishihara under instructions from the military and without the knowledge of the Foreign Office. Furthermore, the loans were not secured by anything more substantial than promissory notes, and a considerable portion of the loans helped to line the pockets of the officials. The greater part of the loan was never accounted for.

Coming as it did at a time when China was politically inert and corrupt and the great powers unable to do anything about it, this bold and reckless action was looked upon with suspicion as the baring of the designs of the militaristic Terauchi Cabinet on the Asiatic continent. Japanese critics regarded the loan, which involved the largest sum in Sino-Japanese relations since the Chinese government paid a war indemnity in 1897, as an unjustifiable undertaking carried out in gross ignorance, if not utter disregard, of elementary principles of international relations by those who were lacking in accurate appraisal of the Chinese situation. Consequently, the entire amount, with the exception of only 5 million yen that were repaid, was lost by default. The Bank of Taiwan, Bank of Chōsen, and the Industrial Bank found themselves in an extremely difficult position, necessitating the Bureau of Deposits of the Finance Ministry to assume the obligations arising from the Nishihara loans. All that the Terauchi Government reaped from the gratuitous loans was the antipathy of the Chinese and an unsavory reputation for Japanese policies. The loans blighted Sino-Japanese relations further and the disadvantages and distrust that accrued to Japan were great. At the same time they helped to call the attention of the world to the existence of dual diplomacy.

Siberian Expedition. Czechoslovak troops, who were fighting on the Galician Front with the Russians, were crossing the expanse of Siberia in order to join the Allied forces on the Western Front. Their object was to fight against Austria for the achievement of an independent Czechoslovakia under Masaryk. Approximately 200,000 of them had made their way into Russia, and for a time there were 120,000 in Vladivostok alone. But the outbreak of the revolution in 1917 led to the separate conclusion of the Treaty of Brest-Litovsk. Subsequently, Czech troops, who were being subjected to cruel treatment, began to fight against the Bolsheviks with the encouragement of the Allies. In June, they captured Vladivostok and, in their attempt to rescue their comrades scattered from Irkutsk to the west, sought the assistance of Allied Powers. In response, the United States in July, 1918, proposed the sending of a joint expedition to rescue the beleaguered Czechs. The aims as set forth by the American government were (1) to help the Czechs consolidate their forces; (2) to help efforts at self-government or self-defense in which the Russians themselves might be willing to accept assistance, and (3) to guard military stores which might be needed subsequently by the Russians.

In the first days of August, the Terauchi Government issued a declaration announcing the dispatch of troops to Siberia. The Japanese General Staff wanted to intervene in order that Japan might control Eastern Siberia against the Bolsheviks and dominate the Chinese Eastern Railway in Manchuria. An army division was promptly dispatched to Vladivostok, followed immediately by a second division. On September 3 the Japanese troops captured Khabarovsk and by the end of October they had mopped up Eastern Siberia as far west as the Baikal region. The Czech troops that had been cut off in the west rejoined the rest of their comrades. Japan supported Admiral Kolchak, a former officer in the Tsar's navy, who established his government at Omsk with the backing of the British and the French. Kolchak's cause was lost when the white Russian armies were defeated in the Ural region in the summer of 1919. By November Soviet armies reached Omsk, and the Allied attempt to save Siberia from Bolshevism collapsed. The Allied interference in Russian affairs in an attempt to profit both economically and politically ended in failure.

The United States announced the withdrawal of her troops and railway experts in January, 1920, under pressure of domestic public opinion. British, French, and Canadian troops were also withdrawn promptly soon thereafter. All the powers except Japan washed their hands of the unsuccessful Siberian intervention. In Washington, Japan's Ambassador Shidehara read in the newspapers the announcement of the pending withdrawal of American troops and hastened to the State Department. He was of the opinion that, inasmuch as the Siberian expedition had been undertaken as a joint venture, the Japanese government should have been consulted before a decision was reached to withdraw troops. Secretary Lansing expressed no objection to Japan's exercising her freedom of action with regard to the Siberian expedition. Meanwhile, in Tōkyō, War Minister Tanaka decided to dispatch additional troops, disregarding the views and advice of the civilian ministries. The military authorities were not only working at cross-purposes with the Foreign Office, but also went ahead with their plans without so much as consulting it. Dual diplomacy was in full operation, with the Foreign Office playing not even second fiddle.

Premier Terauchi issued on March 31 a public statement that was an attempt to justify the continued occupation of Eastern Siberia on the grounds that, because of its geographic position, chaotic conditions there would adversely affect the regions of Manchuria and Korea and endanger the lives and property of Japanese residents. He emphasized that he would withdraw the troops as soon as conditions were stabilized, dangers to Japanese life and property were removed, and the freedom of movement and transportation assured.

Approval had been given originally by the Advisory Committee on Foreign Relations on the basis that the Siberian expedition was being undertaken for the rescue of Czechoslovak troops from the Bolsheviks, as proposed by the United States. However, by March 31, 1920, after American troops were withdrawn, the aims of the Japanese government had expanded to include political stability in Siberia, the removal of any threat to Manchuria and Korea, the safety of Japanese life and property, and a guarantee of freedom of movement and transportation. From the original plan calling for 7,000 troops, it had expanded to an expeditionary force of close to 75,000 troops at its peak, involving a vast military expenditure of 100 million yen and 3,500 casualties in dead and wounded. In return for the costly armed intervention, Japan earned for herself the suspicion, distrust, and ill will of the powers and the antipathy of the Russians. As a naked manifestation of the imperialistic designs of the military this action stands out as a monument to the naiveté and ineptitude, if not the duplicity, of military authorities in handling the complex problems of diplomacy.

The government's Siberian policy was subjected to withering attacks by the opposition and particularly by Katō Takaaki, president of the Kenseikai, on June 27, 1920. Characterizing it as a mistake from the very outset for having exceeded the scope of cooperation agreed to by the Allied Powers, he criticized the government for the unilateral action taken in sending troops deep into the interior regions. Although the opportunity to withdraw was presented more than once, the government chose not to heed it and disregarded public opinion. Katō pressed Premier Hara for immediate withdrawal of troops and demanded his resignation. As pointed out by Katō in an hour-long interpellation on the floor of the House of Peers on January 24, 1921, there was neither the need nor the right to preserve peace and order in Russian territory by the use of force. It was apparent that the spread of communism or any other idea could not be effectively checked by force. An attempt to forcibly impose any type of government could not possibly succeed. Once more a diplomatic blunder of the first order, the result of dual diplomacy, arising from the military domination of foreign relations, earned for Japan an unenviable reputation, which lingered long after the troops were finally withdrawn from Siberia in October, 1922.

Chapter 25. Versailles and the League of Nations

With the second battle of the Marne in the summer of 1918 the tide of war turned, as the Allied offensive gained momentum and German morale began to show signs of cracking. After Bulgaria's armies collapsed and she sued for peace early in October, Austria-Hungary weakened and soon asked Italy for an armistice. In the following month German morale finally collapsed, and on November 8 the German delegation met the Allied representatives in the forest of Compiègne and received the terms of armistice, which the German government accepted two days later. At eleven o'clock on the morning of the eleventh the firing ceased. Although the roar of the cannons and the rattle of the machine guns came to an end, the long and difficult task of reshaping a broken world and erecting a durable peace structure still lay ahead.

That the greatest war in history should be followed by the greatest peace conference as well as a tremendous political and social upheaval was not surprising. In January, 1919, hardly before the signatures on the armistice agreement were dry, delegates from twenty-seven countries gathered at Paris to begin deliberations on the conditions of peace. After agreement was reached on the terms of peace, formal negotiations with the German representatives were started in May. Although at first the Germans balked, the presentation of an ultimatum on June 15 left them no alternative but to accede to the demands of the Allied Powers. On June 28, Germany signed the peace treaty, the consequences of which no statesman at that time could foresee.

At the very outset of the Versailles Conference the four major powers, the United States, England, France, and Italy, decided that they would choose only one additional associate, Japan, to participate in the preliminary deliberations on the terms of peace. Japan's practical political influence was thus recognized by the responsible directors of the Big Four with her inclusion as one of the Five Great Powers of the world. Each of the powers sent two representatives to the Council of Ten, which for more than two months was recognized as the official source of authority of the Conference. It was the Council which called the Plenary Assembly into being, regulated its activities, reviewed the action of that body when necessary, and created commissions to study special subjects in detail to prepare them for the consideration of the Conference.

For Japan participation in the Peace Conference was the realization of her long-standing dream. It meant the attainment of the position in international affairs toward which she had been working for decades. The government saw

367

in it the opportunity to impress the nations of the West and to make Japan's voice heard in world affairs. Naturally, her delegates were chosen with the utmost care. Prince Saionji, the chief delegate, lent the Japanese delegation the dignity and prestige as well as the connection it needed, for he was not only a distinguished nobleman and statesman but also an old friend of Clemenceau from his student days in Paris in the 1870's. The chief delegate rarely, if ever, left his suite in the Hotel Bristol and was not seen in public, never attending the meetings at Versailles. He was virtually inaccessible to the press, including the Japanese newspapermen, who traveled on the same ship all the way from Japan to the French capital. This started speculation and the French press raised the question of whether or not Prince Saionji was really in Paris.[1] Western-educated Makino and Chinda attended the meetings diligently, no matter how tedious the proceedings. To one of the observers the Japanese "with features immobile as the Sphinx" appeared as "enigmatic as the Mona Lisa." [2] They spoke seldom but perhaps were listened to more attentively and with greater interest on that account.[3] It was obvious that they were not so interested in European questions, which constituted most of the business. However, Japan had a seat on all those commissions in which she felt a particular interest. The delegates expressed themselves only when questions of immediate interest to Japan were under discussion.[4] Their interests were directly affected in three questions, two of which were imperialist claims to economic and territorial rights. The former concerned the Shantung question and the latter was a claim to the German island possessions north of the equator. The third was a claim to equality of treatment in the League of Nations.

One of the crucial problems of the Peace Conference revolved around the Shantung question. In the Sino-Japanese exchange of notes on September 24, 1918, Japan promised that after the transfer of German holdings to Japan by the Peace Conference, she would restore them to China except that certain economic interests would be retained by her. Discussions were begun at the meeting of the Council of Ten on January 27 on the Japanese proposals relating to the transfer of former German interests in Shantung and in the South Seas. Baron Makino insisted that the Japanese demands regarding Shantung were based on treaties and agreements concluded between China and Japan. China's able and eloquent delegate, Dr. Wellington Koo, maintained, however, that the Sino-Japanese Treaties of 1915 could not have binding power, inasmuch as they had been signed under duress and that therefore they should be canceled. He contended that China's participation in the war had released her from any treaty

---

[1] Stephen Bonsal, *Suitors and Suppliants*, pp. 227, 229.

[2] As described by Charles Seymour in E. M. House and Charles Seymour, *What Really Happened at Paris.*

[3] D. Hunter Miller's observation in *ibid.,* p. 409.

[4] Ray Stannard Baker, *Woodrow Wilson and the World Settlement*, Vol. I, p. 145.

commitments to Japan. Makino held fast to his original demand for direct cession to Japan, emphasizing that what should take place afterwards had already been the subject of discussion between China and Japan.[5] To further strengthen his stand, he issued on February 12 and 13 a lengthy statement to the press refuting the Chinese stand, which he characterized as preposterous. It was evident that the issue involved the validity of the Sino-Japanese agreements of 1915 and 1918, by virtue of which Japan was gradually working herself toward the attainment of hegemony in East Asia. Obviously, Japan's desire was to establish the right to freedom of action in China without interference from third parties. That the militarists were back of this was more than evident.

Japan had a strong legal case, not only in her agreements with China but also in the assurance of unqualified diplomatic support from Great Britain, with whom a *quid pro quo* agreement regarding former German rights in Shantung and the Pacific islands had been reached secretly in February, 1917. However, Wilson was emphatic in his assertion that all spheres of influence in China ought to be abandoned, and he tried an appeal to sentiment and principle to move the powers. Makino expressed Japan's readiness to cooperate fully in any general renunciation of special advantages in China. Japan was on safe ground, for she knew full well that to urge her to act upon the principle of China's right to abrogate all the unequal treaties signed under duress was to raise the whole question of the validity of the treaty rights of the powers in China. Thus, her position was practically invulnerable from a moral as well as a legal and diplomatic standpoint.

Early in March, the Japanese delegation suffered a considerable loss of prestige, when the Council of Ten, composed of the ministers of foreign affairs, was superseded by the Council of Four, better known as the Big Four, namely, Wilson, Clemenceau, Lloyd George, and Orlando. Although this change was based on a mere technicality, the exclusion of the Japanese was regarded as unwise by Colonel House, the confidential adviser to President Wilson.[6] Realizing the possible implications, President Wilson authorized House "to assure Makino that the work of the Four will be submitted to him before its final adoption and that then the Big Four will be expanded into the Big Five."[7]

On the twenty-second Makino proposed an amendment to Article 12, providing for the suspension of military preparations while a dispute was under examination. The text of the amendment ran:

From the time a dispute is submitted to arbitration, or to inquiry, by the Executive Council, and until the aforesaid term of three months shall have elapsed, the parties to the dispute shall refrain from making any military preparations.[8]

[5] Baker, *op. cit.,* Vol. II, pp. 228–231.

[6] Bonsal, *op. cit.,* p. 228.

[7] *Ibid.*

[8] Bonsal, *Unfinished Business,* pp. 144–145.

On April 11 Lord Robert Cecil called the attention of the Commission to Draft the Covenant of the League of Nations and to the difficulties that would arise if the Japanese amendment were adopted. He felt that the amendment would "impose obligations too great for human nature and put tremendous advantages into the hands of unscrupulous states." [9] Others were of the opinion that it would compel states to increase the number of their effectives and to maintain throughout a period of peace the maximum possible military force. President Wilson explained why he had welcomed the adoption of the Japanese amendment at an earlier meeting. The amendment was withdrawn by Makino, however, and the matter was closed.

On April 22 Makino presented his demands officially to the Supreme Council of the Peace Conference. Both he and Chinda successfully answered every attack on their position. On the same day, the Supreme Council held a discussion with the Chinese delegation, and Wilson expressed his frank view that their legal and diplomatic position was weak, adding that he was impelled to agree with the Japanese contention that China's declaration of war against Germany could not possibly have invalidated the Sino-Japanese Treaties of 1915. He even warned Wellington Koo that it would do little good to entertain the idea that there was injustice in the treaty arrangements entered into with Japan, inasmuch as "unjust treatment of China in the past has been by no means confined to Japan." [10] The implications were clear.

The Shantung question was taken up in the Council of Foreign Ministers during April. The United States Secretary of State Lansing suggested the cession of former German rights in Shantung to the five great powers for eventual restoration to China, while Prime Minister Lloyd George proposed the assignment of Shantung as a mandate under the projected League of Nations. Both proposals were successfully vetoed by the Japanese delegates. Although Wilson and his Secretary of State favored the Chinese claims, both Lloyd George and Clemenceau were bound by the secret agreement of 1917 pledging support to Japan's claims.

The encounters between the Chinese and Japanese delegates were not limited to the halls of Versailles, for the fight was carried on in the press as well. Although scurrilous articles about the Japanese, written by Chinese newspapermen, helped to focus public attention on China's case, these stories were regarded as unwise by observers, who felt that it was a serious tactical mistake, which made matters difficult for those who were working for China's cause. [11] A Chinese manifesto in many languages was circulated, according to Colonel House's adviser "with the connivance and perhaps even with the authorization of Mr. Koo and the delegation." [12] Because of the adverse effect it was having on the

[9] *Ibid.*
[10] D. Hunter Miller, *Diary,* Vol. XIX, p. 176.
[11] Bonsal, *Suitors and Suppliants,* pp. 235, 238.
[12] *Ibid.,* p. 239.

progress of the whole question, the American delegation found it necessary to advise restraint through Dr. Morison, who was serving as adviser to the Chinese delegation.

On April 24, the day the Italian delegation suddenly walked out of the Conference, following an open breach with Wilson over the Adriatic claims of Italy, Saionji pressed for a definite settlement of the Shantung question with the least possible delay. Anxious lest Japan's following in Italy's footsteps might reduce the "world congress" to the impotence of a "rump parliament," Clemenceau, Lloyd George, and Wilson met to consider the problem, and on April 30 they reached the decision to uphold Japan's claims. On Makino's word of honor that the withdrawal from Shantung would be carried out as soon as it could be done with dignity, the League averted the danger of a collapse.

When the experts' report to the Supreme Council made it clear that the Sino-Japanese agreement of September 24, 1918, gave Japan rights far in excess of what Germany had ever enjoyed, President Wilson felt that it would be impossible to consent to the terms for the retrocession of Shantung. A complete deadlock ensued. Colonel House felt strongly that it would be a mistake to reach any decision likely to drive Japan out of the Peace Conference. In an effort to get the Japanese to cede all rights in Shantung directly to the Allied and Associated Powers, who would act as trustees, Wilson sounded out Lloyd George on the proposal that all the powers forego special rights in China. The British Government, however, could not agree to such a proposal.

Meanwhile, Chinda reported receipt of instructions from his government not to sign any treaty that failed to incorporate Japanese demands. Makino called on Balfour on April 27 and promised not to make a public row of the race question at the plenary session scheduled for the following day, provided Japanese demands regarding Shantung were met. At a hurriedly called meeting of the Supreme Council, Wilson yielded to Balfour in the face of a possible open clash with the Japanese in the plenary session that afternoon. Before the meeting convened, however, the Japanese delegation had a message from Balfour expressing general approval of the Shantung articles from the Supreme Council. On April 29 the Japanese agreed to the declaration of a pledge to return Shantung in full sovereignty to China, retaining only economic privileges. The following day agreement was reached and the Shantung question was settled, but not to the satisfaction of the Chinese delegation.

To Wilson, the settlement was the "best that could be had out of a dirty past." [13] His desire was to prevent the defection of Japan, which might break up the Conference and destroy the League of Nations. He was fearful lest Japan's withdrawal from the Conference might lead to a Russian-German-Japanese alliance and a return to the old balance of power system in the world. Through

---

[13] Baker, *op. cit.*, Vol. II, p. 266.

the League of Nations he hoped "to secure justice for the Chinese, not as regarding Japan alone, but England, France, and Russia all of whom had concessions in China." [14] But it was clearly a defeat for Wilson, inasmuch as he had to yield to Japan, in whose behalf the British had interceded.

Thus, by the Treaty of Versailles [15] all former German rights in Shantung were transferred to Japan. Makino declared that it was Japan's policy "to hand back the Shantung Peninsula in full sovereignty to China, retaining only the economic privileges granted to Germany and the right to establish a settlement under the usual conditions at Tsingtao." On May 6 all German islands in the Pacific to the north of the equator were assigned to Japan under the newly established mandate system of the League of Nations.

A copy of the original text of the peace treaty was brought back to Japan in August and was placed under careful scrutiny of the experts of the Foreign Office and other ministries concerned. Privy Council President Yamagata appointed a special subcommittee to examine carefully the provisions of the treaty with a view to ascertaining the possible effects of the League Covenant on the Constitution and the Anglo-Japanese Alliance. As the treaty had already been ratified by Great Britain, France, and Italy, the cabinet of Premier Hara requested the speeding up of deliberations. Accordingly, the Privy Council adopted the favorable report of the special subcommittee and, on October 27, recommended to the Emperor the ratification of the peace treaty without any reservations. Imperial sanction was given three days later.

THE LEAGUE OF NATIONS

The Allied delegates to the Versailles Conference officially agreed on January 25, 1919, to create a League of Nations "to promote international cooperation and ensure the fulfillment of accepted international obligations and to provide safeguards against war." [16] A committee, later known as the League of Nations Commission, was appointed to work out the details of the constitution and functions of the League. The Commission held its first meeting in Paris on February 3. Various drafts of the Covenant were submitted by the various delegations. The Japanese, however, did not submit any. Baron Makino had stated at the meeting of the Council of Ten on January 30 that his government was ready to participate in the work of setting up the important world organization although it had no official plan of organization to submit. In the course of the deliberations, the Japanese delegation proposed several amendments. They also took an interest and an active part in the discussion of disarmament, arbitration, and particularly the question of racial equality.

[14] *Ibid.*
[15] Treaty of Versailles, Articles 156–158.
[16] Miller, *Drafting of the Covenant*, Vol. I, p. 183, and Baker, *op. cit.*, Vol. II, p. 234.

On February 7 Makino presented a proposal to the League of Nations Commission to include a racial equality clause in the Covenant to read:

The equality of nations being a basic principle of the League of Nations, the high Contracting Parties agree to accord as soon as possible, to all alien nations of States, members of the League, equal and just treatment in every respect, making no distinction, either in law or fact, on account of their race or nationality.[16a]

Makino indicated clearly that the racial equality clause was not intended to encroach upon the internal affairs of any nation, but rather should serve as a declaration setting forth a guiding principle in the conduct of international relations in the future. Dr. Wellington Koo went on record expressing hearty approval of the principle, which he hoped the Commission would see fit to adopt. This was perhaps the only issue on which the Chinese and Japanese delegations saw eye-to-eye. The Chinese delegate's stand was supported by Orlando of Italy, Bourgeois of France, Venizelos of Greece, Kramar of Czechoslovakia, and Dmowski of Poland, who felt it would be difficult for the Commission to reject the Japanese proposal.

The Japanese delegates, particularly Makino, felt that they were more than justified in insisting that, if the League of Nations meant anything, it meant full equality of member states. Both President Wilson and Colonel House were hopeful of finding some formula that would meet the Japanese demand and avoid offending their sensibilities. As a matter of fact, House advised Makino and Chinda to prepare two resolutions, one of which they desired, and another that they would be willing to accept as a compromise measure. On February 5, when Makino and Chinda brought their two draft resolutions, Colonel House showed them to President Wilson. The preferred draft was rejected at once, but the President thought the compromise draft might do with slight revision. By next evening Colonel House found himself in a position of having to inform them that even the compromise draft would not be acceptable, despite the fact that it could not be more than a general, vague, and pallid formula, endorsing the principle of racial equality without giving it any legal effect.

The sudden turn to the disadvantage of the Japanese and to the detriment of Colonel House's efforts was attributable to the obstreperous Australian Premier Hughes, who demonstrated his intransigence by objecting to every solution that Wilson's adviser and the Japanese delegates had proposed.[17] Hughes bellowed at Lloyd George morning, noon, and night "that if race equality is recognized in the preamble or any of the articles of the Covenant, I and my people will leave the Conference bag and baggage."[18] Lord Balfour detested the Australian Prime Minister while Lord Robert Cecil characterized him as an inveterate trouble-

[16a] *Ibid.*
[17] Seymour, *op. cit.,* Vol. II, p. 313.
[18] Bonsal, *Suitors and Suppliants,* p. 229.

maker.[19] Even President Wilson, who usually showed restraint in his expressions, branded Hughes "a pestiferous varmint." [20] All the British Empire delegations were willing to accept the form agreed to by Wilson, Makino, and Chinda, but Hughes opposed them vigorously and succeeded in blocking the agreement.

Meanwhile, Colonel House had sent to Elihu Root the draft of the racial equality provision and received an emphatic reply: "Don't let it in, it will breed trouble. In any event, you're going to have a hard sledding, but with the racial provision, you will get nowhere in the Senate. . . . On the Pacific Coast, at least, they would think there lurked behind it a plan for unlimited yellow immigration." [21] The domestic politics of a participant at the Peace Conference were injected into another issue, the consideration of the advisability of inserting the principle of racial equality into the League Covenant. It was now apparent that the racial equality provision stood no chance of approval.

Upon Lord Cecil fell the unenviable task of rejecting the Japanese proposal on behalf of the Empire delegation. Hughes had the effrontery to give the Japanese delegates the impression that the real source of opposition to the racial equality proposal was the American delegation.[22] He made it unmistakably clear to his British colleagues that, if they and the Americans agreed to even the mildest formula of racial equality, he would not only publicly raise the whole question at the plenary session of the Peace Conference, but would also appeal directly to the racial prejudices in the Dominions and in the western part of the United States.

At the final meeting of the League Commission on April 11 the Japanese delegation decided to avail itself of the last opportunity to amend the completed draft of the Covenant. In a renewal of the plea, first made in February, Baron Makino made a long statement that impressed the listeners.[23] In asking for the insertion in the preamble to the Covenant of the words "by the endorsement of the principle of the equality of nations and just treatment of their nationals," he referred to the League as the highest court of justice, intended to be a world organization for enforcing justice and defeating force. He underscored its function "to regulate the conduct of nations and peoples toward one another according to a higher moral standard than has obtained in the past, and to administer justice more fairly throughout the world." After touching upon the fact of the sentiment of nationalism, which has been awakened by worldwide reawakening, and the existence of wrongs of racial discrimination, which have

[19] Miller, *op. cit.,* Vol. I, pp. 123, 178.

[20] Bonsal, *Suitors and Suppliants,* p. 229.

[21] Bonsal, *Unfinished Business,* p. 154.

[22] Miller, *op. cit.,* Vol. II, p. 258.

[23] David Hunter Miller considered it as one of the most impressive speeches he had ever heard. See "The Making of the League of Nations" in House and Seymour, *op. cit.,* p. 415.

stirred the deep resentment of a large portion of the human race, especially among oppressed nationalities, he stated that it is "only reasonable that the principle of equality of nations and the just treatment of their nationals should be laid down as a fundamental basis of future international relations in the new world organization."

Lord Cecil stated that, although he was in personal agreement with the Japanese proposal, he was not in a position to vote for the amendment. President Wilson wanted to accept the amendment, and House had to intervene actively to prevent him from doing so. He knew that if the amendment were adopted, Hughes would carry out his threat to deliver an inflammatory speech at the plenary session. And this was no time to raise the race issue throughout the world.

When the vote was taken on the amendment at Baron Makino's request, eleven out of seventeen members, representing Japan, France, Italy, Brazil, China, Greece, Yugoslavia, and Czechoslavakia expressed approval. Actually no one voted against it, as only affirmative votes were taken. The British and American delegations refrained from voting. Neither Wilson nor House voted. Although the majority voted in favor of the amendment, Wilson ruled that decisions were not valid unless they were unanimous. Thus, the amendment was lost. Lord Robert Cecil declared formally that he had been instructed by his government to refuse to accept the Japanese proposal. The views of the Dominions had triumphed.

There was one more opportunity for the Japanese to press their demands, when the plenary session of the Peace Conference was held on April 25 to approve the final version of the League Covenant. Baron Makino relieved the anxiety and tension on this occasion by stating that no attempt would be made by the Japanese delegation to press for the adoption of their proposal. Then he went on to state "that the Japanese government and people feel poignant regret at the failure of the Commission to approve of their just demand. . . . They will continue in their insistence for the adoption of this principle by the League of Nations." [24]

When the Treaty of Versailles became effective on January 10, 1920, the League of Nations began its legal existence and the long struggle to find a *modus vivendi* to ensure world peace. By virtue of her position as one of the "Five Great Powers," Japan secured a permanent seat in the Council, the executive committee of the League, which was charged with settling disputes, summoning conferences, and supervising the observance of mandates and of minority agreements. At the same time, she was represented in the Assembly, the sovereign body, whose chief function was to provide opportunity for the full expression of the wishes and ideas of all League members with a view to ascertaining policies

[24] Miller, *op. cit.*, Vol. II, pp. 702–703.

acceptable to all and determining the guiding principles to govern the relationship between the member states. This body also selected Council members and judges of the Permanent Court of International Justice.

Japan played an active role in the activities of the Council. Her able representative in the Council, Viscount Ishii, submitted a report on the free city of Danzig, which was adopted by the Council on November 17, 1920.[25] When the Upper Silesia question came up, he was the presiding officer. In the Corfu crisis, affecting Italy and Greece in 1923, he functioned effectively once more.[26] As President of the Council in 1926, Viscount Ishii played a decisive role, while at the same time endeavoring to bring Aristide Briand and Stresemann to an agreement.[27]

In the Secretariat, the international civil service and administrative agent of the League, which operated under the direction of the Council, Japan also took her place alongside the other powers. One of the positions of Under Secretary General was reserved for a Japanese. From the inception of the League until 1926 Dr. Nitobe Inazō served as an Under Secretary General and concurrently as Director of the Section on International Bureaus. In December, 1926, he was replaced by a career diplomat, Dr. Sugimura Yōtarō, who at the same time became Director of the Political Section, which was the most important section and regarded virtually as the "Foreign Office" of the Secretariat.

Even before the Covenant of the League of Nations took effect on January 10, 1920, it was contemplated that a committee of jurists should be appointed to draft a plan for a world court. Thus, in February, 1921, the Council appointed a committee of leading jurists to formulate the scheme of organization and to draft the statute. Adachi Mineichirō, Japan's Minister to Brussels, a onetime professor of international law and diplomatic history, and a judge of various prize courts during the Russo-Japanese War, sat on the committee with Elihu Root of the United States and Lord Phillimore of Great Britain. The Protocol of the Permanent Court of International Justice, drafted by the committee of jurists, was ratified by a sufficient number of states in 1921, and the World Court came into being at The Hague. Japan signed the Protocol on November 16, 1921,[28] and became an active participant.

At the first election of judges for the newly created international tribunal in September, 1921, Dr. Oda Yorozu, who had been professor of administrative law at the Kyōto Imperial University, was elected to sit with such eminent jurists as Dr. John Bassett Moore of the United States and Viscount Robert B. Finlay of Great Britain. In September, 1930, Dr. Adachi, who had been regarded as one

[25] Felix Morley, *The Society of Nations*, p. 245.

[26] League of Nations, *4th Year Official Journal*, pp. 1274–1316.

[27] See *The New York Times*, March 15, 1926.

[28] Sweden was one of the first to sign, on February 21, 1921. Siam signed on February 27, Great Britain and the British Empire on August 4, Italy on June 20, France on August 7, and China on May 13, 1922.

of the best rapporteurs the Council ever had,[29] was elected judge, and on January 16 of the following year he was elevated to the presidency of the high tribunal, thus becoming the fourth person on whom this high honor was conferred since its creation.[30] For nearly three years, until he was succeeded by Sir Cecil Hurst of Great Britain, who was elected on December 2, 1933, Dr. Adachi presided over eleven sessions, from the twentieth through the thirtieth, during which time many important decisions and opinions were rendered. In 1932 he found himself in the most difficult position of heading a committee in the Council for the investigation of the Sino-Japanese dispute. Having held most of the important posts in the League, such as delegate to the Assembly, representative on the Council, member of the 1920 committee of jurists, representative on the Governing Body of the International Labor Organization, and president of the Fifth International Labor Conference at Geneva in 1923, Adachi enjoyed unique prestige among the representatives of the various member states of the League. The last judge, Nagoaka Harukazu, was elected on September 15, 1935, and continued to serve until long after Japan's withdrawal from the League, as his resignation did not become effective until January 15, 1942. Japan's representatives participated in the Court elections of 1936, 1937, and 1939, both in the Council and the Assembly, as permitted by the Assembly's resolution of October 3, 1936.[31]

In the nonpolitical category, labor problems attracted perhaps the most serious and interested attention of the members of the League of Nations. An organizing committee for an international labor organization first met in Paris on April 14, 1919, with representatives of the various member states in attendance. Japan was represented by Dr. Oka Minoru, an official of the Ministry of Agriculture and Commerce, who worked together with distinguished representatives like Professor James T. Shotwell of the United States, Sir Malcolm Delevingne of Great Britain, Arthur Fontaine of France, and Professor William E. Rappard of Switzerland. H. B. Butler, Assistant Secretary of Labor, formed a secretariat in London, where the committee met later and the necessary structure was erected.

The International Labor Organization was based on the recognition that international peace and social peace were bound together inseparably and that there could be no peace between states if there were class war within the states themselves. It was conceived as a fundamental and integral part of the system of world cooperation and conciliation set up by the Peace Conference, and as such, it was provided for in both the Treaty of Versailles (Part 13) and the Covenant of the League of Nations (Article 23). It was created to deal with such questions affecting labor as hours, wages, unemployment, child labor, old

[29] Morley, *op. cit.,* p. 412.
[30] Dr. Adachi received the largest number of votes of any, 49 out of 52.
[31] Manley O. Hudson, *The Permanent Court of International Justice,* pp. 254–256.

age pensions, sickness benefits, migration, and the freedom of association. The twofold aim of international labor legislation was to raise the workers' standard of living in "backward countries" and to protect manufacturers in "advanced countries" from the unfair competition of backward countries. These objectives were to be achieved through the International Labor Office and an annual conference, to which each member state sent two government representatives, one employer representative and one labor representative.

When the first International Labor Conference, called by President Wilson, met in Washington from October 29 to November 29, 1919, Japan sent her delegates [32] in spite of her labor conditions and in spite of the fact that the stage of development in the trade-union movement was far behind that of the nations of the West. Because conditions differed considerably, a number of exceptions were made in the case of Japan in the enforcement of the agreements that were arrived at in Washington. Through the International Labor Office in Tōkyō, Japan cooperated in the work of the International Labor Organization, even after she had withdrawn from the League itself.

It was clearly to Japan's interests to participate actively in the League, in spite of the serious handicaps, such as the great distance to the center of the World Organization, linguistic barrier, and cultural differences. Her security was not threatened, as in the case of some of her European allies. The pacific settlement of disputes was inapplicable to Russia or to the United States, the two major powers with whom serious clashes of interests could have developed. The financial burden placed on Japan was not inconsiderable, for in 1928 she was assigned sixty units or approximately $290,000 which was as large as Italy's share, and next only to Great Britain's, France's, and Germany's; this was in addition to the expenses of maintaining the League of Nations office and the International Labor Office. The direct benefits arising out of her participation were rather limited. However, from the point of international prestige and having a voice in international affairs, Japan gained vastly more than what she put into the League.

[32] The government's representatives were Dr. Kamada Eikichi, member of the House of Peers and President of Keiō University, and Dr. Oka Minoru, ex-Director of the Bureau of Commerce and Industry, Ministry of Agriculture and Commerce; employers' representative, Mutō Sanji, President of Kanegafuchi Spinning Company; labor representative, Masumoto Uhei.

Chapter 26. Economic Developments of the

First World War and After

The initial impact of the European War on Japan was the dislocation of foreign trade and international exchange, resulting in extreme business gloom. It further aggravated the financial difficulties with which the nation had been grappling. When stock exchanges and commodity markets in London, Berlin, Paris, and Vienna suddenly slumped or collapsed, interest rates skyrocketed, and a moratorium had to be declared, while the carrying trade declined so sharply that international trade seemed to come almost to a dead stop.

Repercussions of the critical situation in Europe and America were felt immediately in Japan, as the more important channels of trade were interrupted and her arrangements for financial settlements through London were disrupted. Her national bonds held abroad dropped and the Tōkyō Stock Exchange suffered the consequences. In the resulting breakdown of stock and commodity exchanges, the business world was thrown into a state of confusion. Particularly hard hit were raw silk and rice, although they were not the only commodities to suffer.

Agriculture as a whole received its gravest blow within a few months of Japan's entry into the war, as both the rice and raw silk markets collapsed. Before 1914 agriculture had barely been able to hold its own, and it took very little to put it in a difficult position. The depression in agriculture that followed was a combination of various factors, among which were the smallness of the average farm holding, not exceeding two and a half acres, the farmers' lack of business or marketing information, inflation in the cost of production, shortage of labor supply, inadequate credit facilities, antiquated methods of production, and the heavy burden of taxes.

The slump in the rice market that began in September, 1914, brought together the Imperial Agricultural Society and other organizations of growers to press the government for the regulation of the price of rice. In January, 1915, the Cabinet had an emergency ordinance promulgated for the regulation of the price of rice. The ordinance empowered the Finance Minister to buy, sell, or exchange rice and enter into any and all such contracts as might be called for whenever he deemed necessary. In the same month the Minister of Agriculture and Commerce outlined a program calculated to bail agriculture out of its plight. This included the opening up of additional arable land, improvement of drainage, land improvement and intensive cultivation, use of high grade seeds, improvement in cultivation methods, as well as the making available of larger working capital. In addition increased diligence and frugality on the part of farmers, greater consumption of domestic products, increasing production of simple homemade fertilizers as a method of improving the financial position of the farm household, building up of export trade in fruits, vegetables, and livestock, and the establishment of markets and warehouses were proposed.

On March 20, 1915, the government organized the Imperial Raw Silk Company, capitalized at 2 million yen, with nearly all the leading raw silk merchants of Tōkyō and Yokohama as stockholders. With a subsidy of 5 million yen, it gave the much-needed boost to the silk industry during its brief existence of a few months. In the fall, the government created also the Rice Commission in an effort to devise ways and means of giving relief to the rice market and particularly to cope with the falling price of rice. This investigative commission of seventy members was placed under the authority of the Agriculture and Commerce Minister to report on matters pertaining to the regulation of the price of rice. When prices began their upturn in August of 1916, the commission was relieved of the work of trying to restore the rice market to normalcy. In a matter of only a few months, the situation was so completely reversed that the government was confronted with the even more difficult problem of how to curb the ever-spiraling price of rice that seemed to know no bounds.

In an effort to spur industry in the months immediately following the outbreak of the First World War, the Japanese government hurriedly made loans to manufacturers and producers of the most important export commodities and substitutes for import commodities needed for domestic consumption. Funds were made available for the encouragement of the export trade and the import of gold. As imports disappeared completely after the outbreak of the war, which cut off their sources, the shortage of drugs and chemicals was most acutely felt, and their prices became exorbitant. Other items such as steel, machinery, glass, paper, and woolens were also extremely short. Consequently, a nationwide campaign followed for the encouragement of domestic manufacture to meet the needs, resulting in the organization by the government of the Association for the Promotion of Domestic Products in October, 1914. Under its auspices the first public exhibition of domestic manufactures was held in Tōkyō, followed by a number of other exhibitions in the various prefectures. The association was successful in its aim to encourage the manufacture of various products, to increase their use, and also to extend their sale in foreign markets.

The dislocation of the normal channels of trade, which was brought on by the war, induced the Japanese government to investigate industrial conditions and particularly the effect of the war in the principal foreign markets. Late in November, officials of the Ministry of Agriculture and Commerce, accompanied by a group of some forty businessmen, visited successively North, Central and South China, British India, Netherlands East Indies, Australia, the United States, Canada, and Asiatic Russia. This was followed in the summer of the following year by another group, which added South Africa, Central Europe, and Scandinavia to their itinerary.

A special bureau was created in February, 1917, in the Agriculture and Commerce Ministry to study and recommend measures necessary to meet the conditions in trade and industry during and after the war. The bureau took over the business of investigating economic conditions abroad and sent its officials in 1917 and again in 1918 to the United States, Canada, South America, Southeast Asia, Netherlands East Indies, the Philippines, India, China, Australia, Asiatic Russia, and Europe.

By the spring of 1915, the nation had emerged from the initial setback, as markets were thrown open to her, especially in East and Southeast Asia, where the former suppliers, preoccupied with the war, were unable to export their manufactures. Moreover, munitions contracts began to be placed with Japanese manufacturers by the governments of the Allied Powers and soon strong demand became apparent for Japanese shipping as well. Since Japan was an active belligerent only during the first few months of the war and was far removed from the theater of war in Europe, she was not only spared the ravages of war but was free to devote practically all her energies to manufacturing for the needs of her allies as well as her nonindustrial Asiatic neighbors. An unprecedented industrial boom resulted as important new enterprises were launched in many branches of industry, while existing ones underwent tremendous expansion. This caused a phenomenal increase in the volume of trade characterized by an unexpectedly favorable balance of trade for the first time in the nation's history.

For over half a century after the opening of the country to trade, Japan's volume of trade remained insignificantly small. When commercial relations with the West started in 1859, only a little trade was carried on through the three ports of Yokohama, Nagasaki, and Hakodate. Even after three additional ports, Kōbe, Ōsaka, and Niigata were opened in 1868, the volume of trade did not show much increase. From 1868 to 1885, the annual per capita volume of export trade was was less than one yen, except for the year 1882, when the amount actually exceeded three yen. This was the period when the national economy was still based an agriculture and industrialization had barely started.

An attempt was made in 1876 by Japanese businessmen to capture their share of the profits of foreign trade. The Mitsui and other firms, including Ōkura, Morimura, and Takata companies set up offices in the principal foreign cities. In 1877, however, 94 per cent of the exports and 95 per cent of the imports were carried in foreign bottoms, as they were handled by foreign business houses in the treaty ports. The establishment of the Yokohama Specie Bank in 1880 to facilitate foreign exchange transactions, the founding of two steamship lines, the

Ōsaka Shōsen in 1884 and Nippon Yūsen in 1885, helped to provide the much-needed facilities for foreign trade. Still, in 1887, all of 87 per cent of the exports and 88 per cent of the imports were handled by foreign merchants. By 1894 the position of Japanese merchants had shown some improvement, for foreign merchants handled 81 per cent of the exports and 70 per cent of the imports.

When Japan first entered the field of foreign trade, her national economy was practically self-sufficient for there was hardly any demand for Western manufactured products. Consequently, imports were made only in small quantities and exports comprised a few varieties of raw materials. This was the situation until the Sino-Japanese War. In 1894, foreign trade began to show notable development, as both exports and imports were in excess of 100 million yen for the first time. Five years later, they each exceeded 200 million yen. Contact with Western civilization and the progress of modernization produced a demand for foreign goods, and manufacturing made rapid strides. Demand developed for raw materials, machinery, and other materials needed for the building of a modern business and industrial structure.

Several factors were responsible for the phenomenal growth of foreign trade in the period following the Sino-Japanese War. The victory over China gave the nation both the confidence and the means to carry out a program of economic expansion overseas. Industrialization within the country had proceeded at a very rapid rate during the war and in the period following it. To encourage economic development, particularly in the field of foreign trade, the government enacted in 1896 a law for the subsidization of ocean transportation and, at the same time, abolished import duties on cotton. Three years later Japan did away with export duties altogether. Private enterprise responded promptly to the government's positive policy of encouragement by extending and expanding commercial activities abroad. For instance, the Yokohama Specie Bank, which before the Sino-Japanese War had branches in New York, Lyons, London, San Francisco, Honolulu, and Shanghai, expanded its activities to other parts of China, India, and Southeast Asia.

The establishment of the gold standard in 1897 reduced the risks involved in foreign exchange and removed the element of speculation from foreign trade, thereby contributing materially to its healthy development. Although the abolition of extraterritoriality in 1899 did not restore tariff autonomy to the Japanese, it placed them in a more favorable position than ever before. The whole country was thrown open to residence to foreign nationals, resulting in a sharp decline in the treaty port foreign trade. By 1900 the Japanese merchants were handling 37 per cent of the exports and 39 per cent of the imports.

It was in the period immediately following the Russo-Japanese War that the nation plunged into large-scale business and industrial enterprises, as well as foreign trade. The war, in addition to enhancing Japan's international position, enabled her to expand her market for manufactured goods not only to China and Korea, but also to other Asiatic countries and to Southeast Asia. Expansion of trade and industry was carried out vigorously under government encouragement. The importation of foreign capital and the development and improvement of transportation led to the amazing growth of enterprises of all types. Exports rose from 300 million yen in 1904 to 400 million yen the following year, and in the year preceding the outbreak of the First World War had reached 632 million yen.

Tariff autonomy, which was restored to Japan by the Treaty of Commerce and Navigation of 1911, enabled her to pursue a protective policy, helping her nationals to capture a much more substantial share of the foreign trade. Of the total volume of trade passing through the port of Kōbe in 1911, Japanese merchants handled 52 per cent of the exports and 64 per cent of the imports, while the foreign merchants handled 48 per cent and 36 per cent respectively. This represented a significant shift from the early years of Meiji, when practically all the foreign trade was handled by foreign merchants in the treaty ports. By 1913, the nation's foreign trade had reached the total of 1,360 million yen, more than double the 1903 volume.

Japan enjoyed unprecedented economic prosperity from 1915 to 1920. Since the import of goods from the belligerent nations had stopped completely, the nation was forced to accelerate domestic production and to begin the manufacture of goods that had formerly been import items. As the needs of the Allied Powers increased with the progress of the war, Japan not only furnished more and more of their needs, but also supplied the needs of China, India, and other countries of Asia. Foreign trade stimulated shipping and revenues from the carrying trade, charterage, and insurance reached enormous proportions, creating an unprecedentedly favorable balance of international payments, which caused a specie inflow of 1,180 million yen in the period from 1916 to 1922. The favorable balance of trade for the four-year period, 1915 to 1918, aggregated 1,480 million yen, and the combined foreign specie holding of the government and the Bank of Japan at the end of 1919 reached 1,343 million yen. The total specie holding both at home and abroad at the end of 1920, the year that marked the beginning of recession, showed an all-time high of 2,178 million yen. Almost overnight, the country had changed from a debtor to a creditor nation enjoying undreamed of prosperity. The large banking houses underwrote governmental loans and helped to float Allied loans.

While the war continued to drain heavily the financial resources of the Allies, Japan was accumulating immense quantities of gold through foreign trade. It was felt that the gold, which was rapidly piling up, should be invested in foreign bonds, thereby giving financial aid to the Allies and putting the money to practical use. By the latter part of 1916 this policy was in operation, as Japan was making loans to Russia in addition to supplying her with badly needed goods and munitions. She also made loans to Great Britain, France, and China.[1]

During the war an important change occurred in the structure of trade, as processed or manufactured goods came to comprise 90 per cent of the exports, while raw materials and foodstuffs dropped to a mere 10 per cent. Of the imports, raw materials comprised 66 per cent, partly processed goods 14 per cent, while manufactured goods dropped to 20 per cent. Before the Russo-Japanese War, 50 per cent or more was in processed goods and 33 per cent comprised completely manufactured goods; exports were made up of partly manufactured goods and raw materials.

The tremendous expansion that took place in trade and industry was reflected in the increase of aggregate paid-up capital of corporations in the five-year period, 1915 to 1920, which was eight times that of the ten-year period, 1905 to 1915. Banks and corporations, whose capital outlay in 1914 for new organization and expansion had been 251 million yen, increased it over tenfold in 1918 to 2,677 million yen. The industrial boom was accompanied by a tremendous increase in the number of laborers. The number of workers in factories employing five or more persons jumped from 948,000 in 1914 to 1,612,000 in 1919. Shipping tonnage had doubled from 1½ million tons in 1914 to 3 million tons in 1918, while the net income from freight jumped in the same period from 40 million to 450 million yen a year. Accompanying the quantitative expansion was a conspicuous change in the structure of enterprise. Until the First World War period, individual proprietary enterprise made up a very substantial proportion. But corporate enterprise began the systematic absorption of individual enterprises and the mergers naturally led to a high concentration of capital.

Because of the intensive German submarine warfare a total of over 12 million tons, or about 30 per cent of world shipping, was lost by the Allied Powers. Japan herself lost in excess of 120,000 tons. This naturally brought about an acute shortage of bottoms and the skyrocketing of freight rates. For large ships the charterage fee, which was 2.10 yen in 1913, jumped to 45 yen in 1918, an increase of twenty times in the seven-year period. As the profits of ocean transportation reached unbelievable heights, shipping companies multiplied. Paid-up capitalization of 79 million yen at the end of 1914 had more than quadrupled to 335 million yen only three years later. Shipping tonnage, which stood at 1,593,000 tons at the end of 1914, had reached 3,050,000 tons, or doubled in six years. The year 1918 represented the peak of the shipbuilding boom for during the second half of the year, shipyards paid dividends ranging from 25 to 110 per cent. Mitsubishi paid 25 per cent while the Kawasaki and Ishikawajima shipyards paid 40 per cent return on investments. Because of the abnormal ex-

---

[1] Kobayashi Ushijirō, *The Basic Industries and Social History of Japan*, p. 260.

pansion carried out during the war the heaviest blow fell on the shipbuilding industry in the period of economic recession after the war.

For the purpose of maintaining her commercial position in Siberia, China, India, and Southeast Asia, which had been newly acquired during the war, the Japanese government established commercial agencies and consulates in those countries. In Harbin and Singapore, beginning in the summer of 1918, commercial agents were stationed who studied economic conditions and promoted the introduction of Japanese-manufactured products. The creation of new markets was accompanied simultaneously by the increase of the resident Japanese population. To protect her nationals abroad and to expand further her commercial activities, consulates were established in the key cities of China, Asiatic Russia, South America, and even South Africa.

Tendencies toward economic planning appeared while the war was still in progress. An Economic Commission of sixty-five members, under the chairmanship of the Premier and charged with the function of investigating and advising the government on wartime and postwar economic policies with a view to putting the nation's economy on a firmer footing, was created on April 5, 1916. The committee functioned until November 30 of the following year, when it went out of existence. One section of the commission in charge of foreign trade recommended a system of inspection of export commodities to ensure uniform standards of goods produced in small factories. Accordingly the government instituted in December the inspection of matches, glassware, and enameled iron manufactures through associations of manufacturers and exporters. This inspection was carried out at the source, that is, at the place of production and by the method of sampling. Of the total cost of inspection 10 to 30 per cent was borne by the government. It was through this system that the credit and reputation of Japanese products were maintained.

One of the most critical shortages faced by Japanese industry early in the war was iron and steel. When Great Britain, the main source of supply, placed a ban in April, 1916, on the export of iron, steel plates, structural steel, wire, pipes, tubing, and ingots, Japan found herself in difficulty. This ban was a severe blow, especially on her shipping and shipbuilding industry. The result was a clamor for making the nation self-sufficient in iron and steel. In response to this demand the government created, in May, 1916, the Iron and Steel Commission which, though short-lived, made several recommendations that formed the basis of the policy adopted subsequently. When plans for the expansion of the government's Imperial Steel Works at Yawata proved unsatisfactory, the government introduced a bill in the Diet providing for government aid to nongovernmental enterprises. In July, 1917, a law was enacted, exempting from business and income taxes mills producing a specified minimum tonnage of pig iron.

Critical shortages occurred also in drugs and dyestuffs when the war cut off the import of these basic raw materials for which Japan had been entirely dependent on Germany and Great Britain. Before the year 1914 came to an end, the government created an emergency committee to study methods of regulating the supply and promoting the manufacture of drugs. Two large pharmaceutical companies, the Naikoku and the Tōyō, were given financial aid by the government in its program to boost production. In February the Japan Dyestuff Manufacturing Company was organized in Ōsaka with a capital of 8 million yen, which was open to public subscription. Although applications totaled more than 800 times the amount of issue, the government, in an ordinance for the encouragement of the manufacture of dyestuffs and drugs promulgated four months later, guaranteed the company an annual 8 per cent dividend on the investment. In the seven years following its establishment, the government paid out in subsidies a total of approximately 15 million yen, nearly twice its capitalization. The company produced dyestuffs in quantities sufficient to export to China. In 1920 the government raised import duties to protect the industry from American and English competition, and four years later further import restrictions were placed as a protective measure.

Government encouragement of industry took another form that was indirect in method. In March, 1917, the Institute of Physics and Chemistry was established in response to the demand for a research laboratory to carry on studies for the development of chemical industries, a field that was still in its infancy. The origin of the idea dated back to the return of Dr. Takamine Jōkichi shortly before the war from the United States, where he had achieved international fame as the scientist whose name was inseparably connected with adrenalin and diastase. Takamine urged Baron Shibusawa to fill the crying need for a national chemical research institute that would aid in the industrial development of the nation. The idea materialized under wartime conditions which convinced the leaders of the need of such an agency. Since its establishment the Institute has served as the beacon light of Japanese research in physics and chemistry.

The second half of 1917 witnessed a phenomenal growth of foreign trade, accompanied by inflation and an enormous rise in commodity prices. The spiraling price of rice and other necessities was threatening to undermine the standard of living. It was clear that the high cost of living was the result of a dislocation in the relationship between supply and demand. Goods were scarce but demand was high. Every possible measure had been devised in an effort to correct this unhealthy situation but without success. The Anti-Profiteering Ordinance of September 1 represented the government's desperate and determined efforts to curb profiteering by prohibiting hoarding or cornering the market in cereals, iron and steel, coal, cotton yarns and fabrics, paper, dyestuff, drugs, and chemicals. The Minister of Agriculture and Commerce was empowered to order any person to cease and desist hoarding or cornering specified commodities, or if necessary, to arrange for the sale of hoarded commodities. The Price Adjustment Ordinance, promulgated also on September 1, was intended to keep prices down.

During the war period, Japan's economic well-being and particularly her monetary policy became closely tied to developments abroad as well as to her trade-promotion policy. Although for a short while after the outbreak of the war, the United States took the place of Britain as a free market for gold, she became alarmed at the large specie shipments of Mexico, Spain, and Japan. Consequently, on September 7, 1917, President Wilson, acting on the advice of the Federal Reserve Board, decided to place an embargo on the export of gold and silver except by special permission of the Secretary of the Treasury. Tōkyō soon found itself impelled to follow in America's footsteps. On September 12, only two days after America's embargo went into effect, the Minister of Finance placed a ban on the export of gold except under official license, and at the same time rendered illegal the collecting and melting of gold coins for sale as bullion. The ban on silver had preceded the gold embargo by almost a week, as the Finance Minister, alarmed at the rapid outflow of the metal, prohibited the export of silver coins on September 6.

By 1918 the Japanese price structure was completely out of gear as a result of a combination of increased purchasing power, short supply of commodities, inflation of currency, and profiteering by dishonest and unscrupulous merchants. The government's frantic efforts at price stabilization were producing no visible results. In March, 1918, the government placed an export ban on rice, wheat, and wheat flour in the hope of curbing the rising price of rice. The Agriculture and Commerce Minister repeatedly warned brokers who were suspected of illegal transactions. But since this accomplished nothing, he prohibited speculation in deliveries, for the current as well as the succeeding month, in all the grain exchanges throughout the country. In late April, with the promulgation of the Rice Import Control Ordinance, he designated the Mitsui, Suzuki, Yuasa, and Iwai companies as rice importers.

As a measure intended to ameliorate the difficulties caused by the soaring cost of living, the government established public markets in the large cities beginning with Ōsaka and followed by Tōkyō, Kōbe, Yokohama, and Nagoya in April, 1918, following the abnormal advance in the price of rice. Later public markets were established throughout the country. These markets were managed by the municipalities and local authorities. The commodities sold there, which included the daily necessities such as food, cloth, clothing, fuel, and others, were from 5 to 50 per cent lower than in the regular markets. People of the middle and lower classes took full advantage of the markets in the desperate fight they waged against the high cost of living.

On June 14 the government revised the Exchange Law to prevent brokers from reselling or buying back rice ordered by their clients without specific instructions from the latter. The government's attempt to check the skyrocketing price of rice by increasing its supply through imports and suppression of market speculations was not effective, and the situation went from bad to worse.

Early in August housewives of a little fishing village in Toyama prefecture protested against the exorbitant price of rice. This became the starting signal for a nationwide outbreak of riots that kept the nation and the government jittery for a month. On August 8 a riot broke out in the city of Toyama, where residents organized a parade, marched to the city hall, and demanded that rice be sold at lower prices. By August 12 the situation in Ōsaka, Kyōto, and Nagoya had reached such serious proportions that troops had to be called out to preserve order. In Kōbe, the rioters set fire to a number of establishments, including the warehouse of the Suzuki Company and newspaper offices, necessitating the mobilization of troops to patrol the streets. In Tōkyō, when crowds began to mill around Hibiya Park, the usual place for all types of demonstrations and meetings, the municipal authorities saw that this boded ill and, after conferring with the government, decided to hold a sale of Korean rice at prices lower than those in the regular market. On August 13 rioters gathered in Tōkyō, and gendarmes had to be used to preserve order. Incendiarism was reported from Ōsaka and Okayama. In Maizuru, Kure, Shizuoka, Toyohashi, and Sakai the serious situation required the presence of troops. On August 18, an emergency imperial ordinance was promulgated for the expropriation of rice stocks by the government.

Impelling forces led to the creation, in September, 1918, by the harassed Terauchi Government, of the National Economic Commission, which was charged with the task of making investigations into the causes of the alarming rise in the cost of living, suggesting remedies, and recommending policies for coping with the rapidly changing and unstable social and economic conditions in the country that were fraught with danger. Its first session was held in the latter part of December to discuss bills for the regulation of the price of rice. Although bills were introduced into the Diet, they were withdrawn when the Terauchi Cabinet, unable to cope with the situation, resigned on September 21. The Commission, however, continued to function under the succeeding Hara Cabinet.

Convinced of the seriousness of the rice riots, the chambers of commerce of Tōkyō, Ōsaka, Kyōto, and four other cities joined in presenting a memorial to the Hara Government on December 4, 1918, pointing out the urgency of government regulation of the price of rice. This was followed by the appointment, by all the chambers of commerce, of a Food Committee which was entrusted with the investigation of the food situation. The members of the Committee called on Premier Hara on March 16 of the following year and laid before him their recommendations, which included the government purchase of foreign rice to increase the supply, the curtailment of sake brewing as a conservation measure, all possible encouragement for the increase in the production of substitute food crops, and the encouragement of the use of substitute foods.

Although these recommendations were adopted by the government, the rice market seemed to be completely out of control and instead of prices dropping, they continued their steady rise.

In May, 1919, Premier Hara issued a statement setting forth the basic policies of the Cabinet based on the recommendations of the National Economic Commission. The statement covered the whole range of the food problem, including the rice problem. The specific recommendations of the Commission constituted virtually a blueprint for the rehabilitation, if not the reconstruction, of Japan's agriculture. The basic long-term proposals included measures for increasing production, facilitating distribution, the improvement of the conditions of consumption, and the regulation of prices. Production was to be boosted through the increase of acreage and further development of intensive farming and better farming methods. To be made readily available were agricultural education, agricultural credit, cheap and adequate supply of fertilizers. Improvement in the social and economic status of the tenant farmer was to be an integral part of the program. Protection as well as migration of farm labor, measures facilitating shipment of rice between Japan proper and other parts of the empire, and migration of Japanese farmers to rice-producing areas abroad were among the suggestions made as means of increasing the supply of food. As methods of improving the distributive system, the further establishment of spot markets, public markets, and cooperatives, better transportation facilities, government monopoly of food, and improvement in the methods of transaction on the exchanges was advocated. Prices were to be regulated by setting both a ceiling and a floor, the establishment of rice warehouses, supervision of rice exchanges, and the control of currency and credits.

Among the emergency measures proposed were: the increase of food supplies through larger imports; restriction or prohibition of exports; speeding up of deliveries of new crops; restriction of consumption through a ban on the use of rice for other than food; improved methods of cooking and preparing cereals, and increasing the supply and promoting the use of substitutes; ensuring of more efficient distribution through a greater number of spot markets as well as public markets; distribution of staples by public bodies or the government; facilitation of rice shipments, and the prevention of rice market collapse through government stockpiling of grain reserves; dispensing with the middlemen; prohibition of wholesale buying and cornering with the intention of profiteering; holding down commodity prices in general by means of price ceilings for rice and other staples; and increases in wages and salaries commensurate with the rising cost of living.

The signing of the Armistice in November, 1918, brought an end to the demand for munitions and a gradual restoration of the industrial productive capacities of Europe and America. The effects were felt soon on Japanese trade and industry. The second half of 1919 began to show a marked decline in Japan's foreign trade and by the early spring of 1920, the prosperity bubble had vanished. The war boom came to an abrupt end and recession set in. Industry as a whole began to feel the effects of abnormal overexpansion. In its wake came a rash of labor and tenancy disputes on a nationwide scale, as discontent and insecurity were intensified among the laborers and tenant farmers, neither of whom had shared to any extent the prosperity of the war period.

Throughout the war the rural villages appeared to have suffered little from its effects and outwardly appeared as quiescent as ever. But actually the changes wrought by the war were far reaching. Owing to the unprecedentedly high price of rice, the landed class amassed large fortunes with which they increased their holdings greatly. At the same time, the manufacturing activities in the big cities had lured both capital and labor away from the country to devitalize and even impoverish the rural agricultural communities. The plight of the tenant farmers was thus aggravated rather than mitigated by the war.

Beginning in 1917 and 1918, tenancy disputes began to crop up in different parts of the country. These were not temporary or local outbursts; they were widespread and concerted efforts on the part of the aroused tenant farmers to improve their social and economic status, especially in relation to the landlord. Disputes that started in isolated parts of the country soon spread to all sections, developing into a nationwide movement. In 1917 there were only 85 cases, but the following year there were 256, and in 1920 there were 408. A year later, the number suddenly increased to 1,680. Thereafter, the farm tenancy problem became the crucial agrarian issue. The year 1921 marked a turning point, as tenant farmers began to band together to protect their interests. The Tenancy Fee Non-Payment League and the Farmers' Union emerged, while the landowners countered with the Landowners' Federation. More and more, tenancy disputes began to take on the character of class struggle.

In April, 1922, the Japan Farmers' Union was organized with the tenant unions as its core. This was the beginning of an agrarian movement designed to improve the lot of the peasant class as a whole. The Union advocated among other measures the socialization of land, enactment of laws to protect the tenants, minimum wage for agricultural labor, universal suffrage, and the revision of police regulations. In 1926 the All Japan Federation of the Farmers' Unions was formed to cope with the landowners, who had formed the Association of Landowners of Japan the year before.

Gravely concerned over the developments, the government had established in 1920 the Tenancy Problem Investigation Committee. Three years later, on the recommendation of the committee, the government submitted to the Diet a bill aiming to apply the principles of prevention as well as to mediate tenancy disputes. The Tenancy Dispute Mediation Law took effect on December 1, 1924, and tenancy officers were assigned to prefectural offices to make surveys of local tenancy practices and to keep in close touch with developments in landlord-tenant relations with a view to preventing disputes before they developed.

Labor unrest was as natural and conspicuous in the postwar period as was agrarian discontent. The runaway inflation brought acute economic distress to the working classes in the cities, for wage rises never kept up with price increases. The high cost of living was more than a threat to the security of livelihood, while the fear of unemployment plagued the workers, and their resentment against the capitalists and profiteers aggravated class consciousness and antipathy. For all the feeling of insecurity and indignation, the working classes found inspiration and encouragement in the successful revolution in Russia and the social upheavals in Germany.

During the early part of the war, disputes that were settled by capital-labor efforts at harmony did not, as a rule, last more than two or three days. Moreover, 40 per cent of the strikes ended in defeat for the workers, since they were usually carried out by unorganized labor. Labor unions in the true sense were nonexistent except for such groups as Yūaikai or the Friendly Society and Shinyūkai, which were in reality not much more than company unions.

The Factory Law, enacted in March, 1911, was the first piece of labor legislation in Japan, although it did not go into effect for more than five years, in September, 1916. The year 1919 marked the turning point in the labor movement, for the number of laborers topped 2 million, having almost doubled since 1914,[2] and sixteen labor unions were organized in that year alone, whereas only one or two unions had been coming into existence annually previously to that. Also in 1919 labor abandoned the policy of submission in favor of militant, aggressive action. This was reflected in the general strike on September 19 by more than 16,000 workers at the Kawasaki Shipyards in Kōbe, demanding a wage boost. On October 1 the factory workers of the Ōsaka-Kōbe area walked out in a demand for an eight-hour day. During the month of November strikes were called by workers at the Asano Shipyards, Ōsaka Municipal Railway, Yokohama Municipal Railway, and the Ashio Copper Mines. Strikes began to occur with increasing frequency and violence.

With a view to finding a satisfactory solution to the vexing labor problem, Viscount Shibusawa[3] conceived the idea of organizing the Kyōchōkai, or the Society for Capital Labor Harmony, in the summer of 1919. As early as the spring of 1911, soon after his return from a tour of Europe and America, Shibusawa expressed his strong conviction that social problems and particularly labor problems could not be solved by legislation alone. He had been favorably impressed by the employer-employee relationship that he had witnessed at the

---

[2] In 1919, the workers totaled 2,077,148, of whom 1,611,990 were factory workers and 465,158 were miners; while in 1914, the 1,148,377 workers were made up of 853,964 factory workers and 294,413 miners.

[3] Shiraishi Kitarō, *Shibusawa Eiichi Ō*, pp. 739–750.

Waltham watch works in Massachusetts. The Society,[4] which was founded on December 22, 1919, and which was composed of capitalists and supported by the government, was an attempt to create and maintain harmonious relations between capital and labor by preventing through fair mediation such labor strife as plagued industry in the West. To Viscount Shibusawa, a lifelong devotee of Confucianism, capital-labor harmony constituted the cornerstone of industrial and social peace. Moreover, the "Grand Old Man of Japanese Business" was anxious to hasten the government's recognition of trade-unions and also the abolition of Article 17 of the notorious Police Peace Law,[5] which stood in the way of freedom of association, particularly labor organization. Interestingly enough, there were far-sighted and liberal individuals among the capitalists, who were ready at this stage to see workers participate in management.

A profound impression was made upon the Japanese working classes by the first meeting of the International Labor Conference in Washington in the fall of 1919 because of the recognition given labor by the leading nations of the world. It spurred Japanese labor in its efforts to improve its status and make its voice heard. Considerable criticism was directed at the Japanese delegation by labor representatives of other nations on the grounds that there was no real Japanese labor representation. This, needless to say, strengthened the position of labor in Japan, inasmuch as it was an indirect criticism of the Japanese government and its labor policies. The Japanese labor delegate, Masumoto Uhei, took the opportunity to lay the case of Japanese labor before the bar of world opinion.[6] He pointed out that the Japanese government as well as its delegates were not only lacking in sincerity, but were also unsympathetic to labor, and he decried the government's antilabor police regulations, which were invoked freely in the name of public peace and order in its autocratic suppression of labor organizations and their activities. Although his protest against special treatment in the form of exemption of Japan from the application of the eight-hour day and forty-eight-hour week was not adopted since the Conference made allowances for Japan's backwardness, Japanese labor scored a point, though it did not immediately reap the benefits.

On February 5 and 6, 1920, 24,000 workers at the government's Imperial Iron Works at Yawata struck, attacked the steel furnaces, and clashed with the gendarmerie even as the Japan Federation of Labor Unions and the Federation of Kantō and Kansai Labor Unions for Universal Suffrage were being organized. Later in the month, the employees of the Tōkyō Municipal Railway

---

[4] In addition to Viscount Shibusawa, the prime mover, the sponsors included Prince Tokugawa Iesato, President of the House of Peers, Ōoka Ikuzō, Speaker of the House of Representatives, and Kiyoura Keigo, Vice-President of the Privy Council.

[5] The *Chian Keisatsuhō* was first promulgated as Law No. 36, on March 10, 1900.

[6] League of Nations, *The International Labor Conference, First Annual Meeting*, pp. 159, 161.

walked out. The government's grave concern over labor problems was reflected in the creation, on August 24, of the Social Affairs Bureau in the Home Ministry and the Labor Section in the Bureau of Industries of the Agriculture and Commerce Ministry.

After the recession of 1920 there was a marked decrease in the number of labor disputes, and demands for higher wages gave way to an even more determined opposition against wage cuts. While the number of disputes actually decreased, the problems of labor revealed more basic and intensive conflicts in the face of liquidation, retrenchment, mergers, and nationalization of industrial enterprises. At the same time, labor began to demonstrate more efficient organization and tactics as well as greater skill and intelligence in opposing capital in defense of their rights. Demands were made by labor for changes in labor regulations to defend themselves against unreasonable discharges, revision of dismissal procedures, and retirement allowances, and the improvement of working conditions. In their appeal to public opinion, the unions were able to emphasize more and more the public interest involved in labor disputes.

The ever-growing clamor for the enactment of universal suffrage and the nation's participation in the international labor conferences brought out the incontrovertible evidence of the growing strength of labor and led eventually, though none too soon, to the government's recognition of labor unions. At the end of 1925 there were 214 labor unions in the country, of which 94 per cent had been organized since 1919, and over 58 per cent had been organized in the last two years, 1924 and 1925. The government enacted, in 1926, the Labor Disputes Mediation Law, which was soon followed by the National Health Insurance Law, giving concrete evidence of the government's concern over labor problems, which were growing in magnitude as well as in complexity. The abolition of Article 17 of the Police Peace Law was decided by the government of Premier Katō on January 15, 1926, at the cabinet meeting which approved the Labor Disputes Mediation Bill. By the middle twenties, the agrarian and labor movements had merged for political purposes, as proletarian parties appeared and carried on the fight against capital and its constituted organs, the existing regular political parties.[7]

In 1921 the workers of both the Kawasaki and Mitsubishi Shipyards in Kōbe went on a general strike, which lasted forty-five days and necessitated the calling out of troops. There was another strike in the Ashio Copper Mines, which were constantly plagued by strikes. In 1925 the Besshi Copper Mines, owned by the Sumitomo interests, suffered from a protracted strike, extending over a period of 108 days. This was topped, however, by the 217-day strike at the Noda Soy Company, which began in September of 1927 and lasted until

[7] Imanaka Tsugimaro, *Nihon Seijishi Taikō*, p. 395.

the following spring. The Japan Seamen's Union, organized in December, 1920, scored an important victory over the Japan Shipowners' Association in 1928, when it succeeded in securing the establishment of a minimum wage system on an industry-wide basis. This was achieved at least partially as a result of the appeal it made to the International Labor Organization against the government, alleging that the government was not applying the Geneva Convention of 1920 regarding employment offices for sailors. The Director of the Labor Office informally communicated the appeal for comment to the representative of the Japanese government on the Governing Body. The appeal was dropped when the Governing Body was satisfied that the Japanese government was carrying out the provisions of the Convention, but it forced Japanese authorities to recognize the grievance of the sailors' union. Significantly, this was the only case up to that time in which the system for putting pressure on a government had been invoked.[8]

The end of the war found Japanese business and industry gripped by a fear of reaction. Businessmen were in a cautious mood, in spite of the fact that during the period immediately following the cessation of hostilities Japan enjoyed an even greater boom than she had during the war. Speculative activities flourished, the prices of necessities kept on spiraling, and unsound expansion still continued in industry for a while.[9] The inevitable finally came, however, in March, 1920, in the form of a financial panic, which was accompanied by widespread business paralysis. Corporations, both old and new, went by the board. Collapse was particularly pronounced in raw silk and rice. The silk industry took a terrific beating as the price, which had reached its peak in January, dropped to one-fourth of that peak six months later.

Advantages that had been gained during the war disappeared, but the high cost of labor, high prices, and high cost of living continued. Foreign competition returned, and exports declined while imports increased. However, by 1922, Japan was beginning to climb out of the depression, except that those industries which had overexpanded during the war (such as shipbuilding and coal mining) failed to rally. Then came unexpectedly the disastrous earthquake of 1923, which set back recovery by destroying the means of production as well as wealth and manpower, necessitating foreign loans and increased imports of goods and machinery to meet reconstruction requirements. In 1924 the government floated for reconstruction purposes a loan of 150 million dollars in the United States, which was underwritten by a syndicate of Wall Street banks including J. P. Morgan, Kuhn, Loeb, and the National City Bank of New York.

Reconstruction needs boosted imports in 1924 to 2,597,602,000 yen, a record figure, and the following year to 2,734,535,000 yen, an all-time record. Exports

---

[8] C. Howard-Ellis, *The Origin, Structure and Working of the League of Nations*, p. 230.

[9] Yamasaki Kakujirō and Ogawa Gōtarō, *The Effect of the World War upon the Commerce and Industry of Japan*, p. 105.

achieved a new record of 2,377,897,000 yen because of the drop in the yen to $0.385 and the rising economic prosperity in the United States. However, the balance of trade was unfavorable due to large imports for reconstruction. After the mid-twenties the specie holdings and foreign exchange were practically exhausted. Notable was the fact, however, that in 1926, the total volume of export was 131 times that of 1868, while import was better than 222 times.

In the years immediately following the great earthquake of 1923 Japanese industry turned to the United States for much-needed funds for reconstruction and rehabilitation. This resulted not only in the importation of American capital, but also in the working out of combinations with American firms, especially in the electrical industry. Earliest of these was the 50-million-dollar Japanese-American Engineering and Contracting Company, organized in 1923 with control shared by American and Japanese capitalists.[10] The General Electric Company combined its Japanese interests with the Shibaura Electric Works, while the Western Electric Company combined with the Nippon Electric Light Company and the Tōkyō Electric Light Company, which had absorbed nine competing firms in 1923. Westinghouse Electric Company of Japan began the direct distribution of the products of its parent American corporation.

American investment banks including Dillon, Read, Guaranty Trust, Lee Higginson, National City Bank of New York, and Harris, Forbes and Company furnished in the period from 1923 to 1925 capital funds in excess of 120 million dollars to four of the "Big Five" of the electric power companies, the Industrial Bank of Japan, and the Oriental Development Company.[11] American firms extended their activities by establishing plants and subsidiaries. The Ford Motor Company, for instance, set up a new plant in Yokohama, while property investments were made by corporations like the Radio Corporation of America, Libby-Owens Sheet Glass Company, which operated a plant and subsidiary, Robert Dollar Company, International Banking Corporation, International Oil Company, a Standard Oil subsidiary, and Aluminum Company of America, which owned 60 per cent of the shares of the Asia Aluminum Company.

One of the most significant developments of the 1920's was the change in the structure of Japanese enterprise. The rapid growth of stock exchange securities transactions was greatly facilitated, leading to the growth of enterprises. Especially after the enactment, in 1905, of laws permitting mortgages on railways and factories and the trust laws, permitting the issuance of debentures with collateral, the accumulation of capital became much easier. However, up to the end of the First World War expansion almost invariably took the form of an increase in capitalization. In 1905 corporations with a capitalization of 1 to 5 million yen numbered 155 with an aggregate capital of 99,470,000 yen, but by

[10] Robert W. Dunn, *American Foreign Investments*, pp. 164–165.
[11] *Ibid.*, pp. 40–41.

1914 they had doubled in number with 308 firms and a total capitalization of 194,110,000 yen. During the same period corporations with 5 million and over increased from 23 to 64 while their capitalization increased from 353,400,000 yen to 797,720,000 yen.

Beginning in 1919, the concentration of capital became apparent as monopolistic tendencies began to develop. The increase in paid-up capital in the five-year period, 1915 to 1920, was eight times that of the ten-year period, from 1905 to 1915. In 1920 there were 30,000 corporations with a capitalization of 8,238,-000,000 yen; by 1926, the number had increased to 36,000 with a total capitalization of 12 billion yen. In this same year, close to 66 per cent of corporate wealth was held by corporations capitalized at 5 million yen or over. This trend was reflected markedly in the electrical power industry, 36 per cent of which was controlled by the "Big Five," [12] The cotton industry was dominated by two, Kanegafuchi and Tōyō; banking by the five great banks, Mitsui, Mitsubishi, Sumitomo, Yasuda, and Dai Ichi, which held more than 3,200 million yen or 34 per cent of the total deposits, which exceeded 9,200 million yen. Life insurance was securely in the hands of its "Big Five," Nippon, Chiyoda, Meiji, Dai Ichi, and Teikoku, which in 1929 held approximately 44 per cent of the total amount of life insurance in force. The high concentration of capital in the enterprises gave the financial clique, or the *zaibatsu*, particularly the Mitsui, Mitsubishi, Sumitomo and Yasuda, control of 75 per cent of the nation's total corporate wealth. The Mitsui economic empire, comprising 120 corporations and subsidiaries with an aggregate capital of 1,600 million yen, comprised the largest single unit for it controlled 15 per cent of Japan's entire corporate wealth and was as nearly self-sufficient as an economic organization could be.

Hand in hand with the concentration of capital went cartelization on a large scale. With the onset of business recession, demand fell and caused a large surplus in practically every commodity and service. In shipping, which was depressed more substantially than most other activities, the situation was serious, for charterage fee had dropped by 1926 to 1.8 yen, which was somewhat below the prewar level. Adverse economic conditions brought about close voluntary co-operation in the industries which made agreements to regulate supplies and prices to protect their mutual interests. Although the earliest instance of what could be regarded as a cartel agreement was effected in the summer of 1890 by the Japan Cotton Spinners' Federation, which reduced the working week to eight days per month for a three-month period, it was not until the period of depression following the Russo-Japanese War that the trend toward cartelization became noticeable.

Cartelization, which was achieved in the 1920's in all the major industries,

[12] The "Big Five" were the Tōkyō Electric Light, Tōhō, Daidō, Nihon, and Ujigawa Electric Companies.

was an inevitable consequence of the war and its resultant depression. At the same time, it was a development that was closely related to the rationalization of industry. Cartels were formed in mining, iron and steel manufacturing, chemicals, textiles, foodstuffs, paper, cement and others, and even in banking and insurance. These agreements for the control of production, distribution, and maintenance of price levels, which were encouraged by the government, played an important part in the economic development of the period between the First and the Second World Wars.

Chapter 27. The Emergence of Responsible

Party Government

Immediately following the resignation on September 21, 1918, of the military-dominated Cabinet of General Terauchi, the three surviving Elder Statesmen, Yamagata, Matsukata, and Saionji, conferred on the choice of a new premier. Although Saionji was the choice of the group as the person most suitable for the formation of a new cabinet, he declined the honor and recommended in his stead Hara Takashi, who, on September 29, formed the first party government in Japanese history. Both Yamagata and Matsukata were at first reluctant to see a commoner[1] and member of the Lower House become head of the government. Even after he had become reconciled to the idea of having Hara as Premier, Yamagata desired the coalition of the Seiyūkai and the bureaucrats, but the new Premier was adamant in his determination to form a truly party government that did not include any bureaucrats. Thus to Hara went the distinction of becoming the first commoner to organize the first responsible party government. He was also the first Premier to hold a seat in the Lower House. Although this was a definite step forward, it was not responsible government in the true sense since the military continued to wield powerful influence with the backing of Yamagata as well as through the service ministers and the chiefs of army and navy general staffs.

Premier Hara announced immediately upon the formation of his Cabinet its four-point program, namely, the strengthening of national defense, the expansion of higher educational facilities, the encouragement of industries, and the development of transportation and communication. At the same time, Hara aimed at the achievement of popular participation in the judicial process through the institution of a jury system and the extension of participation in administration through a reform in local government organization.

Most urgent in the eyes of the Premier was the increase in the number of higher institutions of learning. The lack of colleges and universities was denying thousands of young men the benefits of higher education. Competitive entrance examinations had reached a point of intensity where unsuccessful candidates were committing suicide to say nothing of the alarming increase in the number of nervous breakdowns. The gravity of the situation called for speedy relief.

---

[1] Hara persistently refused the peerage that was offered to him and remained a commoner to the very last.

In less than three months after assuming office, Premier Hara had succeeded in putting through necessary changes to remove the blight on the nation's higher educational system. Next in the order of achievement was the modification in colonial administration. The then existing system required that the governors-general of Korea, Formosa, and the Kwantung territory be admirals, vice-admirals, generals, or lieutenant-generals. This was changed to make civilians also eligible to the posts, and Hara lost no time in appointing civilians as governors-general of Formosa (Den Kenjirō) and the Kwantung territory (Hayashi Gonsuke).

While the Hara Cabinet was successful in instituting administrative reforms, including the field of higher education, it achieved little in the solution of vexing economic problems. The phenomenal rise in the cost of living led to distress, which in turn produced ideological changes and heightened social insecurity. The swelling tide of democracy during the war years and the revolutionary and socialistic ideas from Russia and Germany had left their impact particularly upon the intelligentsia. The shortage of consumer goods and the insecurity of livelihood, which plagued the victors as well as the vanquished and aggravated the strained relations between capital and labor, were producing a rash of strikes and lockouts in Japan as in other parts of the world.

The *nouveaux riches* had achieved wealth overnight through the various wartime enterprises, often at the expense of the working class. Politicians had become subservient to the wealthy class, whose all too often unrestrained exhibition of extravagance, wantonness, acrimony, highhandedness, and haughtiness served to antagonize the exploited and to accentuate the already existing cleavage and antipathy that separated capital and labor. In an attempt to correct the conditions born of the war the Hara Cabinet created the Bureau of Social Affairs in the Home Ministry and took concrete steps for the establishment of public markets, construction of small housing units, encouragement of consumers' cooperatives, reduction of transportation costs, and made capital readily available at low interest rates. However, it failed to get at the root of the evil, and labor troubles continued as the feeling of insecurity mounted.

Taking advantage of the impotence of the government, the opposition parties launched an attack, which was reinforced by a warning issued by the House of Peers. The question of universal manhood suffrage, which had been taken lightly as the mumblings of a small segment of publicists and scholars, soon developed into a major political issue. Political parties could no longer remain indifferent to the strong clamor that developed with the termination of the European war. The Kenseikai under Katō Takaaki and the Kokumintō both submitted in the 42nd Diet bills for the removal of the tax qualification for voting.

Immediately upon the opening of the Diet on December 24, 1919, the government submitted a bill that provided for an allotment for the fiscal year 1920–1921 of 100 million yen defense expenditure, looking toward the completion of the "eight-eight fleet" program for the navy and the increase of the army's fighting strength. In addition, it requested appropriations for the construction and improvement of railways, highways, and telephonic and telegraphic installations. Necessary funds for these items were to be secured by an increase in taxes. Hara was prepared to take the drastic step of dissolving the Diet, if opposition materialized against the budget and the tax increase bill. However, contrary to expectations, the House of Representatives put up no resistance, thereby depriving the Premier of the excuse for dissolving the legislative body.

On February 26, 1920, immediately after Hara's speech and before any vote could be taken on the universal manhood suffrage bill, the Diet was dissolved. The imperial rescript for the dissolution came as a bolt out of the blue to the opposition parties and even to the members of Hara's own Seiyūkai, except for the party's inner circle. The Premier's lame explanation left the public bewildered and cold. While carefully pointing out that the extension of suffrage had always been the policy of the government, having undertaken it twice, in 1900 and again in 1919, he declared that to attempt the revision of an electoral law that has not been tried out since its enactment the year before would impair the dignity of the legislative process and contribute nothing to the healthy development of constitutional government or the public's confidence in the Diet. His utterance underscored his belief that the bill for electoral reform was not only hastily and lightly conceived and drafted without due consideration of existing conditions, but also contained disturbing ideas that threatened the nation's social structure.

While there is no doubt that the opposition parties used the issue as a political weapon, it is equally certain that Hara hoped to extend the strength of his party by introducing a system of small election districts. Deplorable as it was for such an important issue to be exploited for political gains, it had the salutary effect of educating the public regarding the question of universal suffrage and stimulating its interest. However, five years had to elapse before universal manhood suffrage could become a reality.

The May 10 election, which followed the dissolution of the Diet, not only vindicated Hara but it strengthened his position greatly, as the Seiyūkai returned 279 members to the Diet, giving the government close to a three-fifths majority. This triumph for the government was all the more remarkable in view of the adverse effects of the economic crisis that was precipitated in March. The opposition parties redoubled their efforts, particularly the Kenseikai. President Katō opened a relentless attack on the Hara Cabinet, at whose door he laid the blame for obstructing the passage of the suffrage bill, sacrificing national interests for the welfare of the party, bringing on financial confusion through its mistaken economic policies, lacking a definite policy with regard to Siberia, and inviting through incompetent handling of foreign relations the Nikolaevsk affair, in which Japanese residents were massacred. Accusations of corruption were leveled at Seiyūkai party members. Although Hara was secure with the command of an overwhelming majority in the House of Representatives, he extended his influence into the House of Peers, where he was able to control two groups, the Kenkyūkai and the Kōyū Club. Those who belonged to the bureaucratic faction joined forces with those leaning toward the Kenseikai, headed by Katō, who was a member of the House of Peers, and attacked the government. Mud-slinging became the preoccupation of both the Seiyūkai, the government party, and its opposition, the Kenseikai.

In spite of the strong opposition, the Seiyūkai more than held its own and Hara was in his heyday of political power. However, because of the influence of the party there were members who engaged in shady activities to mar the reputation of the Seiyūkai. As a result, Hara was regarded with suspicion in some quarters and soon voices arose demanding that he be ousted. On November 4, 1921, in the midst of increasing clamor against the Seiyūkai president, Premier Hara fell at the hands of an assassin, a railway switchman at the Tōkyō Station. As great as his loss was to the Seiyūkai, it was an irreparable loss to the political world, for it had an adverse effect on the course of subsequent political developments.

Apprehensive of the adverse effect it might have on the Washington Conference, which was only a week away, the Elder Statesmen sought to find a successor who would pursue the principles and policies for which the deceased Premier had fought. Saionji was firm in his belief that to allow an untoward incident to cause a major political dislocation would not only impede the progress of parliamentary government, but would also cast a dark shadow over the nation's political future. He therefore recommended Finance Minister Takahashi to head the next government. The resignation en masse that had been submitted was rejected, and the Takahashi government emerged on November 13. Simultaneously, Takahashi became the fourth president of the Seiyūkai. Later in the same month, a regency was established for the first time under the Constitution and the Imperial Household Law, as Crown Prince Hirohito assumed the reins of government in place of his invalid father, Emperor Yoshihito.

From the beginning it was clear that the Takahashi Cabinet was faced with a difficult situation. It was too much to expect Takahashi to cope with the political situation, much less to solve the difficult problems, by pursuing his predecessor's policies that he was under obligation to carry out through the Cabinet that he headed, but in whose formation he had had no part. With considerable difficulty he succeeded in getting through the Diet the appropriations bill and the railway construction bill and secured approval for most of the major government policies. However, he failed to get the enactment of the jury system, which had been a major objective of Premier Hara, his predecessor.

As soon as the Diet session was over Takahashi began the much-needed reorganization of the Cabinet but ran into opposition that developed into serious strife within the party and that threatened its unity. Early in May efforts at reorganization were abandoned in order to save the Cabinet as well as the party. But the breach could not be healed nor party harmony restored. By early June matters had gotten completely out of hand and Takahashi submitted the resignation of the entire Cabinet. The Seiyūkai, which, under the leadership of Hara, had gained in membership and power was now threatened with a possible split, if not complete disintegration. With unity, harmony, and discipline gone, the once powerful party was in too precarious a position to make its influence felt.

The normal parliamentary procedure following the fall of the Takahashi Cabinet would have been for the opposition party, the Kenseikai, to form the succeeding government. However, the Elder Statesmen, Saionji and Matsukata, in deliberating upon a successor with Admiral Count Yamamoto and Count Kiyoura, decided to recommend Admiral Katō Tomosaburō, relegating Katō Takaaki to the position of an alternate and second choice. It was apparent that the Elder Statesmen and influential bureaucrats were of the opinion that, in view of the unhappy political situation brought on by sharp clashes and unfavorable public opinion, a party cabinet would be inopportune, and that someone who could retrieve the situation by easing the political tension should be selected as Premier. Such a decision was clearly a contravention of the principles and practices of responsible party government.

The choice fell upon Admiral Katō, apparently for the ability he was supposed to have demonstrated at the Washington Conference, and also for his special qualification in handling the problems arising out of this Conference. Moreover, he was regarded by the most powerful men as the person most likely to succeed in retrieving the domestic political situation. When Admiral Katō hesitated to accept the premiership, the Seiyūkai, out of fear that its political rival, the Kenseikai, might capture the coveted post, came forth and offered the admiral unconditional support in utter disregard of party prestige, public opinion, and the principle of responsible party government. It was all too apparent that the Seiyūkai was bent on preserving and even increasing, if possible, its power by allying itself with a nonparty government headed by a military bureaucrat. The unprincipled action of the Seiyūkai was aptly described by Katō Takaaki as "unconditional surrender to irresponsible government." Needless to say, the formation of the Cabinet by Admiral Katō was an about-face from the responsible party government that first came into being with the Hara Cabinet in the fall of 1918.

In a truly bureaucratic and dictatorial fashion and without so much as consulting anyone, Admiral Katō completed the formation of his Cabinet overnight. It was a nonparty cabinet, organized around members of the House of Peers. It fell to the lot of the Cabinet to carry out the program of naval disarmament, including the scrapping of the "eight-eight fleet" in accordance with the Washington naval agreement. Significantly, too, it carried out an initial program of slashing army expenditures which was as much the upshot of the proposal by

Inukai Tsuyoshi for economy in military expenditures, appropriated by the preceding Diet session, as it was the execution of the Washington Agreement. In spite of the serious illness of Premier Katō, the government was able to get the necessary legislation for the jury system through the Diet. Katō, who, as a member of Admiral Tōgō's staff, had faced fearlessly the Russian Baltic Fleet in the Battle of Japan Sea two decades earlier, found himself more than once confronted by a difficult maneuver in his political encounters with the Privy Council and the Diet.

Toward the end of August, 1923, Admiral Katō died in harness, and another admiral, Yamamoto Gombei of the Siemens naval scandal fame, was called back from retirement to form a cabinet for the second time. This turn of events was so unexpected that not even the newspapers had wind of it. It was obvious that the Elder Statesmen were deliberately holding out against Katō Takaaki, who had entertained misgivings about his chances of heading a government, although he was the most logical person to receive the mantle. Although Yamamoto's efforts were interrupted by the great earthquake and fire of September 1, he succeeded in completing his Cabinet on the following day. Curiously enough, this cabinet, whose birth was shrouded in secrecy, was short-lived, lasting only four months and five days. Although it busied itself with plans for reconstruction, it achieved little and was unable to cope with the unrest and ideological rumblings in the post-earthquake confusion. It dealt with Socialists and Koreans highhandedly, suppressing them and causing the murder of Ōsugi Sakae and others. The Toranomon Affair of December 27, in which Naniwa Daisuke made an attempt on the life of the Regent Crown Prince, shocked the government into submitting its resignation, which was rejected. However, it proved to be only a temporary reprieve, for Premier Yamamoto resigned before the end of the year.

On January 1, 1924, Count Kiyoura Keigo, member of the House of Peers and adopted member of the Chōshū clique, received the imperial command to form a new cabinet but declined it the next day. However, he changed his mind and accepted the command on the third, forming a cabinet that drew its membership from the Kenkyūkai group of the House of Peers. It was rightfully dubbed the "special privilege Cabinet" for the Ministers were ex-bureaucrats who had been rewarded for their services to the state with membership in the Upper House. Thus, the three successive governments during the two years from June, 1922, to June, 1924, were headed by bureaucrats and composed of members drawn, not from the political parties, but from the ranks of the bureaucracy, and were "super-party" cabinets, which were not in any sense responsible to the electorate.

Only four days after the formation of the Kiyoura Cabinet, that is on January 11, Tōkyō newspapermen joined the members of the House of Representatives who had decided on a three-party coalition cabinet and launched a movement for the preservation of the parliamentary system. This was avowedly a "holy war"

against bureaucratic tyranny. Viscount Miura, whose name had been inseparably bound with the court intrigues of the Korean Queen Min and of Taiwunkun
in the 1880's, offered his good offices in bringing together the heads of the three
opposition parties to effect a working coalition against the government with the
purpose of unseating the Kiyoura Cabinet. A united front was achieved and the
leaders arrived at an understanding on the following points: repudiation of the
Kiyoura Government, establishment of responsible government, and checking
the power and tyranny of groups enjoying special privilege, such as the Kenkyūkai of the House of Peers.

Katō Takaaki, president of the Kenseikai, who was himself a member of
the Upper House, directed blistering attacks on the conservative, if not reactionary, half of the Diet, especially the Kenkyūkai, accusing it of lording over
the affairs of the nation as if they were its private preserve. The Cabinet began
to show increasingly its uneasiness over the gathering strength of the opposition.
On January 31 the government dissolved the Diet, and the fight for the preservation of parliamentary government entered its decisive phase. Confident of victory,
Katō intensified his campaign, giving his all and speaking as often as fourteen
times a day on one occasion in the Aichi region in May of that year. As a result,
in the election of May 10, 1924, the Kenseikai scored a 50 per cent gain in the
Diet to become the leading, though not a majority, party after nine lean and
trying years. A less stout-hearted and persistent leader than Katō would have
given up the seemingly hopeless struggle. The Kenseikai victory, scored despite
government interference, was hailed by the public as a triumph over bureaucratic
tyranny. The government and its supporting party, Seiyūhontō, had tried unsuccessfully all sorts of stratagems, including the luring away of opposition party
members in the Diet, stirring up dissension within the three-party coalition,
calumny, and the spreading of false rumors of coalition and reconciliations to
weaken, if not to disintegrate, the opposition.

Having lost the confidence of the public completely and seeing that it was
impossible to retrieve even a semblance of cabinet prestige, Kiyoura submitted
resignation en masse on June 7, relinquishing reluctantly the premiership to the
opposition after only six months of office. There was little, indeed, that the
short-lived Cabinet could show in the way of achievements aside from the
feeble efforts at the reconstruction of Tōkyō. Saionji, who had recommended
Kiyoura, was more shocked and disgusted than disappointed and could not
help but recognize his error of judgment. If in the first place Saionji had more
carefully and accurately appraised the political situation, he might have avoided
the nonparty Cabinets of Admiral Yamamoto and Count Kiyoura, which were
anomalies or anachronisms, if not both.

Public opinion was solidly behind Katō for the next premiership, and Saionji
was aware of this fact. He was more than anxious to rectify his past errors. Thus,
at long last, the opportunity came to Katō, the leader of the three-party coalition,

to restore constitutional government to its normal path. Immediately upon being designated Premier Katō called on Takahashi, the president of the Seiyūkai, to ask him to join his Cabinet, citing precedents of ex-premiers accepting ordinary portfolios. Thus, the three-party coalition Cabinet, drawing its membership from the Kenseikai, Seiyūkai, and Kakushin Club, holding 284 seats in the Diet, emerged on June 11, 1924, under the premiership of Katō. The Cabinet comprised four future premiers as well as an ex-premier and a galaxy of superior political talent.

The 50th Diet, which the Katō Cabinet confronted, was perhaps the most memorable one in the development of Japanese parliamentary history. Retrenchment in government expenditures, which the Premier regarded as the most important of his three major policies, was put through over the strenuous opposition of the armed forces. The able War Minister General Ugaki carried out the reduction of army strength by four divisions [2] involving the release of more than 2,000 commissioned career officers as well as the shortening of the period of compulsory military service. The actual amount of money saved from the reduction of army strength was not as great as one might suppose, since considerable expenditure was necessary for the modernization and mechanization of the army, which were achieved by the addition of an air corps, motor transport and tank units, chemical warfare units, and modern weapons of war to keep abreast with technical progress in the art of warfare. Government economy was achieved also by the dropping of 40,000 persons from its payrolls. This was coupled with the encouragement of thrift and savings. The Cabinet sponsored the first "Thrift Week" in history. From a budget estimate of 1,524,000,000 yen, including the reconstruction of the devastated areas of Tōkyō and Yokohama, Katō succeeded in slashing 256,000,000 yen, an unprecedentedly large cut. No less important and urgent than economy was the revamping of political morale and house cleaning to rid the government of corruption. At the same time rigid official discipline was enforced. In August the Committee to Investigate Tariff Revision was appointed with the Finance Minister as its chairman to study the possible revision of tariff rates. The Committee for the Study of Emigration was set up with the Foreign Minister as its chairman to devise ways and means of coping with the population problem.

Katō's greatest single achievement during his premiership, if not of his entire career, was the enactment of the Universal Manhood Suffrage Law, which stands out as a prominent landmark in the development of popular rights in Japan. Immediately after the end of the First World War, Katō began the fight for the extension of suffrage. Demand for universal suffrage dates back to February, 1902, when a bill was first introduced into the 16th Diet. The issue

---

[2] The four divisions abolished were the 13th at Takata, the 15th at Toyohashi, the 17th at Okayama, and the 18th at Kurume.

was revived at every session of the Diet until 1911, when the bill was passed by the House of Representatives by an overwhelming majority, only to be defeated in the House of Peers. The outbreak of war in Europe overshadowed the issue temporarily, but with the swelling tide of democracy the demand for universal suffrage swept through the country and reverberated in the halls of the Diet. The discussion of the issue was resumed in the 40th Diet, which was convened in December, 1917, and the government succeeded the following year in pushing through the Diet its draft bill, lowering the tax qualification to 3 yen.

On February 11, 1919, the thirtieth anniversary of the promulgation of the Constitution, 3,000 university students in Tōkyō held a mass meeting at Hibiya Park and submitted a petition to the House of Representatives demanding that all males who had attained majority be given the right to vote. In no time voices demanding universal suffrage were heard even in remote villages and hamlets, as even the farmers and laborers, who had previously been indifferent to political matters, began to echo the demands started by the students. Roused public opinion clamored for action. But the next session of the Diet was unable to pass any of the three bills that had been submitted, as it confronted the opposition of the Seiyūkai and was dissolved by Premier Hara.

The Kenseikai and the Kakushin Club, headed by Inukai, both favored universal manhood suffrage, unrestricted by any tax qualification. In spite of the known opposition of the ultra-conservative Privy Council and the rightist Seiyūhontō, the Universal Manhood Suffrage Bill made its appearance on the floor of the Diet at the plenary session of the House of Representatives on February 21, 1925, in the midst of a tense atmosphere, supercharged with anxiety and excitement. Katō had to contend with the strong opposition of the Seiyūhontō, the House of Peers, and the Privy Council. The opposition in the House of Representatives was too weak to delay the bill, while the strong opposition anticipated in the House of Peers failed to materialize in the face of overwhelming public opinion that favored the bill. Because of the deadlock in the conference committee of the two Houses, it was necessary to extend the period of the Diet session three times. Katō was fully prepared to go to the extent of dissolving the Diet in the event the bill failed to pass. Finally, on March 29, the conference committee reached a compromise and a favorable report was made. With the promulgation of the law on May 5, on the auspicious and appropriate occasion of the Boys' Festival Day, the electorate was quadrupled from 3,300,000 to 14,000,000 as the tax qualification, the barrier of economic discrimination, was removed. Although this was an achievement unsurpassed by that of any other cabinet, it was marred by the enactment of the Peace Preservation Law, which took effect on May 12 and brought severe public condemnation as a piece of reactionary legislation. It had the effect of offsetting, to a considerable extent, the good achieved by universal manhood suffrage.

The Katō Government was particularly successful in carrying out a reform of the House of Peers by limiting the number of hereditary members and introducing a new category of members representing the Imperial Academy. Soon after the close of the 50th Diet the government divided the Agriculture and Commerce Ministry into two separate administrative departments, the Ministry of Agriculture and Forestry and the Ministry of Commerce and Industry in response to the need for greater stress on commerce and industry. This showed clearly that the government had shifted from a national economic and financial structure centered on national defense to the policy of basing its finances on commerce and industry.

Early in April Takahashi, who was concurrently Commerce and Industry Minister and Agriculture and Forestry Minister, decided to withdraw from the Cabinet and retire from the presidency of the Seiyūkai. In order to preserve the working coalition, Premier Katō urged Takahashi to reconsider his decision and to remain in the Cabinet, but without success. His efforts to get General Tanaka Giichi, before and after he succeeded Takahashi on April 10 as party president, to come into the Cabinet as the Seiyūkai representative were also unavailing. Neither were the efforts of Communications Minister Inukai and War Minister Ugaki to urge Tanaka to accept a portfolio successful. However, the new Seiyūkai president, in an exchange of memoranda with Katō, pledged to continue his support of the existing coalition. Katō had no choice but to be content with an alternative of securing the Seiyūkai vice-president, Noda Utarō, for the Commerce and Industry portfolio.

Determined to realize the ambition of forming a cabinet by breaking the coalition government, the Seiyūkai plotted secretly to effect a reconciliation with the Seiyūhontō. The Kenseikai, on the other hand, was trying hard to get itself in a position to form a cabinet without having to rely on the troublesome coalition with the scheming Seiyūkai. The behind-the-scene intrigues came out into the open in the clash over the tax issue, and the coalition was irreparably breached in the last cabinet meeting of July 30. On the following day, Katō, who was confident that he would again be commanded to form a cabinet, decided to submit the resignation of the entire Cabinet.

Intent on recapturing power, the members of the Seiyūkai and the Seiyūhontō appeared to have forgotten their differences. However, each party was hoping and scheming to use the other party in seizing power. As soon as they received the news of the resignation of the Katō Cabinet, they held a joint celebration at the Imperial Hotel in their wishful anticipation that political power was coming their way. They sent a telegram to Prince Saionji informing him of the reconciliation they had effected and at the same time they started a diversionary movement with a view to grasping the chance to form the next cabinet. But neither the public nor the Elder Statesmen could be so easily deceived by the façade they presented.

Much to the disappointment and chagrin of the Seiyūkai party, Katō was designated Premier on August 1, 1925. On the following day he completed his Cabinet based on a single party, the Kenseikai, which held but 165 seats. As this was far short of a majority and insufficient to control the Diet, he won over the Seiyūhontō, which preferred to go along with the government. This gave an absolute majority of 252 seats. The Seiyūkai was weakened greatly by the retirement of Takahashi, the illness of Noda, the vice-president, and the departure of Inukai, but even more by the lack of experience of the new president, General Tanaka, who was only an "adopted son" and did not yet command the confidence of the party members.

An unexpected opportunity came to Premier Katō to effect an improvement in the Privy Council when its President, Dr. Hamao Arata, onetime President of the Tōkyō Imperial University, suddenly died. The likely candidates for the vacancy, as seen or desired by some in the Privy Council, political circles, and general rumors, were Count Kiyoura Keigo, Count Itō Miyoji, and Admiral Count Yamamoto Gombei. However, Premier Katō was determined to elevate Baron Hozumi, who was a legal scholar of the highest caliber and integrity, but without political color or ambition. With the concurrence and support of Prince Saionji, as well as Lord Keeper of the Privy Seal Makino and Imperial Household Minister Ichiki, he succeeded in putting the appointment through on October 1.[3] This step had the effect of minimizing the practice of attaching a great deal of significance to the political views and experience of a candidate as necessary prerequisites to appointment to the Privy Council presidency, thereby deemphasizing the political significance of the role of the highest advisory body to the Emperor.[4]

In the field of personnel administration, Premier Katō demonstrated special talent. With the exception of Foreign, War, and Navy Ministers, who were career men, he selected party men for all the portfolios. At the same time, he endeavored to keep out party men from positions that required a high degree of administrative ability above all other considerations.[5] He succeeded to a remarkable degree in drawing a line of demarcation between party policies and state affairs. He strengthened the system of parliamentary officers in the Cabinet for achieving smooth liaison between the executive and the legislative, a system that he had originated in 1914–1915 as the Premier's right-hand man in the Ōkuma Cabinet. In the interests of fairness and efficiency of administration, Katō put an end to the practice of shifting prefectural governors, a form of the

[3] Itō Masanori, *Katō Takaaki,* Vol. II, pp. 656–658.

[4] Both the Tōkyō *Asahi* and *Jiji Shimpo,* in their editorials of October 1, 1925, expressed strong approval of the Premier's choice of the Privy Council President and lauded the appointment as an act of statesmanship.

[5] Among the posts that were reserved for experts were the Chief Secretary of the Cabinet, Superintendent General of the Metropolitan Police Board, Director of the Police Bureau of the Home Ministry, Director of the Cabinet Bureau of Legislation, and the Governors-General of Korea, Formosa, and Kwantung Territory.

spoils system designed to reward party members on the waiting list or inactive status by putting them back into circulation. This system had been regarded traditionally as the safety valve of a party cabinet. In the delegation of powers and responsibilities to the members of his Cabinet, he went all out and brooked no interference or meddling by others.

Social legislation occupied a prominent place in the program and achievement of the Katō Cabinet. A health insurance law, a factory law, a labor dispute mediation law, a labor union law, and others were enacted. Relief was given to the unemployed in the form of reconstruction projects in devasted Tōkyō as well as in the stimulation of various municipal enterprises. In diplomacy, a conciliatory attitude toward China characterized the activities of the Foreign Office under the direction of Baron Shidehara Kijurō. On January 28, 1926, only a week after he delivered his address to the Diet, he was overtaken by illness and suddenly died, bringing to a close a political career that was dedicated to the fight against the military and a struggle to broaden the basis of government through the extension of the franchise. In its morning edition on the same day, the London *Daily Mail* carried the news of Katō's death, while the London *Times*, in its editorial the next morning, eulogized him. Leading American papers, including *The New York Times,* Baltimore *Sun,* Philadelphia *Public Ledger* and others, paid tribute to the role Katō had played in the affairs of his nation.

On the day following the death of Premier Katō, Home Minister Wakatsuki, who had been acting Premier in the last days of Katō's illness, was made president of the Kenseikai. Almost simultaneously the imperial command to form a cabinet fell on him. On January 30 the Wakatsuki Cabinet emerged much to the chagrin of the Seiyūkai, the opposition party. Public opinion regarding the political situation was practically unanimous in supporting the continuance of Katō's policies. The Tōkyō newspapers *Jiji, Asahi, Nichi Nichi, Hōchi, Kokumin,* and *Chūgai* agreed that all the draft bills that had been prepared by Premier Katō should be submitted to the Diet for deliberation and eventual enactment. Leaders in the financial and business world, including Ikeda Seihin of the Mitsui interests and Kushida Manzō of the Mitsubishi interests, supported the concretization of Katō's policies, particularly the retrenchment policies.

The Wakatsuki Cabinet, which was made up of holdovers from the second Katō Cabinet, secured the collaboration of the Seiyūhontō as well as reconciliation with the Kenkyūkai of the House of Peers. It managed to reduce land tax by 1 per cent, increased the national treasury grant for compulsory education by 10 million yen, and increased import duties on grains to protect agriculture. Political rights were extended in consequence of the newly enacted electoral law of 1925, and restrictions that had existed in municipal election laws were removed. The provisions of the national electoral law were made the basis of prefectural elections. However, the Diet, which represented the propertied classes, readily reenforced the Peace Preservation Law in 1928, which became a powerful instrument for the suppression of the proletarian movement in general and communism in particular. Although the government recognized the need for social legislation, the labor union bill that it submitted was a mere excuse, if not a pretense. In spite of its weakness the Diet, which had turned noticeably to the right, regarded it as too radical and promptly quashed it. As a compensatory factor, in the drift toward the right, the Labor Disputes Arbitration Law was enacted.

Although the Wakatsuki Cabinet weathered the storm of the 52nd Diet without resorting to the drastic step of dissolution, an unexpected development that followed left it no alternative but to resign. During the Diet session two proposed bills intended to liquidate the earthquake bills furnished the subject of stormy and animated discussions. The earthquake bills had become the scourge of the financial world, a drug on the money market. National Treasury Bonds were to have been given in exchange for the 207 million yen of the earthquake bills, half of which were held by ordinary banks and the other half by the Bank of Taiwan and the Bank of Chōsen. Submitted to the House of Representatives on January 26, 1927, the bills were approved by the committee in spite of strong opposition and were sent to the House of Peers. The bills became an issue, as the government rejected the Diet demand that the names of the banks holding the bills as well as the amount, the debtors, and the amounts held by each of them be revealed to the public. There was widespread suspicion on the part of the public that the proposed bills were intended to save the Bank of Taiwan, which held these bills in enormous amounts, and to give relief at the same time to the financially wobbly Suzuki Company of Kōbe. In the House of Peers the government yielded a little by disclosing in a secret meeting at least part of the true state of affairs. In spite of the strict secrecy insisted on by the government, information leaked out and the public learned of the names of some of the banks that held the bills. Consequently a minor run on those banks developed.

The Seiyūkai members of the House of Representatives attacked the government for its discriminatory treatment in withholding the facts from them, while disclosing them to the Upper House. On March 14, at the afternoon plenary meeting of the Appropriations Committee of the House of Representatives, Finance Minister Kataoka, in reply to a general hypothetical question on what measures the government intended to take in the event of bank failures, inadvertently and carelessly mentioned that at noon the Watanabe Bank closed its doors. This statement was as incorrect as it was ill advised, since the bank had merely appealed to the Finance Ministry for help, without which it felt that there was no alternative but to close. But the slip of the tongue on the part of the Minister of Finance left no alternative for the Watanabe Bank but to close the following day.

Confused and agitated by the critical situation, the government virtually ordered the city banks to cease and desist in their withdrawal of the call loans to the Bank of Taiwan. The Mitsui Bank not only ignored the appeal of the government and called in the entire amount of the loan, but criticized strongly the action of the government. Between March 16 and 23 call loans totaling some 120 million yen had been withdrawn. On March 27, the Bank of Taiwan, whose loan to the Suzuki Company was reported to be in excess of 350 million yen, decided to discontinue making further loans. When Finance Minister Kataoka notified both the Bank of Taiwan and the Suzuki Company on April 1 that the government was not going to save the latter, the insolvency of the Kōbe firm came to light. No sooner had the news leaked out than a run developed on the Sixty-Fifth Bank, an affiliate of the Suzuki Company. The run spread to the Bank of Taiwan and threatened its ruin. By April 12 all hopes of retrieving the situation had vanished. An emergency cabinet meeting was hastily called the following night and the government reached the decision to invoke Article 8 of the Constitution, providing for emergency ordinances, and also Article 70, pertaining to emergency financial measures. It was the government's intention to issue an emergency ordinance to save the Bank of Taiwan by making good its loss to the amount of 200 million yen in the hope of clearing the atmosphere and dispelling the uncertainty that was casting a gloom over the entire financial world. When the draft emergency ordinances were submitted to the plenary session of the Privy Council on April 17, they met with strong opposition. Privy Councilor Itō Miyoji directed a withering attack on the domestic and foreign policies of the Cabinet in general and excoriated the weakness and failure of Shidehara diplomacy in the presence of the Emperor. The drafts were rejected on the grounds that circumstances did not warrant the invocation of Articles 8 and 70 of the Constitution. It was unmistakably clear that the Privy Council was determined to force out the Cabinet, which went down in defeat by a 19 to 11 vote, only the cabinet members casting votes of approval. In the face of critical public opinion, which clearly reflected the lack of confidence in the financial policies of Kataoka and in the foreign policies of Shidehara and the adamant stand of the intensely hostile Privy Council, the government lost its will to fight and capitulated without making even the gestures of fighting back.

On April 18, the day after the resignation of the Wakatsuki Cabinet, the Bank of Taiwan and all its branches, both at home and abroad, were closed. This touched off a nationwide run on banks and brought on a financial panic of unprecedented proportions. Ironically enough, it was brought on by the Mitsui and Mitsubishi interests in their attempt to force their competitor, the Suzuki Company of Kōbe, out of business by calling in their loans to the Bank of Taiwan and other banks affiliated with the Suzuki Company. With the onset of nationwide economic distress, it appeared for a while as though the gains made in the preceding several years would be wiped out completely. The future prospects of the nation were gloomy indeed.

The Seiyūkai Cabinet of General Tanaka Giichi emerged on April 20 on the heels of a mounting financial panic. In forming the government, Premier Tanaka successfully warded off the attempt of the Kenkyūkai group of the House of Peers to foist themselves on the Cabinet. With the exception of the two service ministers and the justice portfolio, which were given to career men, all the Cabinet posts, including parliamentary vice ministers and counselors, were filled by members of the party. Although Tanaka was very successful in the initial stages of his administration, the remainder of his term of office was plagued with inept selection of personnel as well as haphazard planning and execution of policies.

Immediately after he assumed the premiership, Tanaka declared a three-week moratorium, which began on April 22 and lasted until May 13. On May 4 he called an extraordinary session of the Diet, which voted 200 million yen for the Bank of Taiwan and a special fund of 500 million yen for the Bank of Japan. The 200 million yen were used for the relief of the *zaibatsu* and 150 million was used to call in the bill holdings of the banks, including the Mitsui Trust, Yasuda, Daiichi, Fujita, Hayakawa, Teikoku Asahi, and Chōsen Shokusan. But the 180,000 depositors throughout the country who had suffered losses through bank failures were not indemnified. Through the utilization of the 500 million yen special fund of the Bank of Japan, those banks that had connections with the political parties were rescued from financial ruin, while banks that had been forced against the wall were absorbed by the Shōwa Bank, which was operated jointly by the five great *zaibatsu*. Thus, the three laws enacted by the political parties between January and May, 1927, for the purpose of ameliorating financial distress and involving an amount of 1½ billion yen brought immediate relief to the *zaibatsu,* but saddled the people with additional burdens. In his policy to give succor to financial circles, Premier General Tanaka took particular pains. By securing Takahashi as Finance Minister, he raised the hopes of the financial leaders. At the same time, he appointed a Mitsui man, Inoue Junnosuke, as Governor of the Bank of Japan and succeeded in bringing about the stabilization of financial conditions.

The Tanaka Cabinet was by nature reactionary, as it was made up of those who leaned to the right and who lacked the understanding of the trend or thought of the time. Consequently, it regarded as dangerous all those who were even slightly to the left in relation to them, and carried out a policy of suppression. This was amply reflected in their attitude toward the proletarian parties. In an effort to root out communism, it spared no pains and employed every conceivable method at its command. It revived the draft to revise the Peace Preservation Law, which had been squashed by the extraordinary session of the Diet, and enacted it in the form of an emergency imperial ordinance. This was clearly a negation of responsible parliamentary government. Such arbitrary action could not help but arouse suspicion in view of the fact that the ultra-conservative Privy Council questioned the appropriateness of the method as well as the substance of the proposed emergency ordinance. After two days of discussion, Tanaka succeeded in pushing it through on the plea of absolute urgency. Because of the naïve assumption that leftist ideas could be rooted out by suppression and intimidation, it made no attempt to get at the causes. The reactionary attitude of the Tanaka Cabinet only served to aggravate the thought problems and the entire political situation. In international relations this took the form of an aggressive militaristic policy toward China, earning for Japan nothing but the enmity of her neighbor.

A cycle of a whole decade, which started in a hopeful mood under the commoner Premier Hara, came to an end with the reactionary cabinet of General Tanaka, which cast a heavy gloom over the country, which was accentuated and aggravated by a severe economic depression.

Chapter 28. The Washington Conference

The end of the First World War found the power relationships in the world greatly changed. Although the Paris Peace Conference solved temporarily, though not altogether satisfactorily, some of the major problems of Europe, it did little to settle the outstanding issues in the Far East and the Pacific. On the contrary, it added considerably to the complexities of the difficult problems. As we have already seen elsewhere, the preoccupation of the Allied Powers in the European War was a marvelous opportunity for Japan to advance her economic interests in China and other parts of East Asia. It was clear that, unless the existing clashes of interests could be resolved promptly, they were bound to develop into potential causes of war. The immigration problem on the Pacific Coast of the United States and Canada was contributing toward the deterioration of American-Japanese relations and straining Canadian-American relations. To aggravate the situation, competition in naval armament, which developed after Versailles, gained momentum, and the three-cornered naval race was complicated by the existence of an alliance between Japan and Great Britain.

For some time, the United States had looked upon the Anglo-Japanese Alliance as a political instrument, harmful to her traditional policies in East Asia. It was a source of anxiety for the United States, as there was the possibility that the Alliance might be invoked against her. When Anglo-Japanese negotiations for the renewal of the treaty of alliance were rumored in the spring of 1920, the United States Department of State made inquiries in London,[1] and by May it believed the renewal of alliance likely. The United States was anxious to see modifications made in the Alliance, which would be an aid to Anglo-American cooperation in the Far East and be agreeable to American public opinion. It was hoped that it would be shown clearly that the Alliance was not aimed at America but would include provisions safeguarding the principle of equality of opportunity and the Open Door as well as a guarantee of the independence and territorial integrity of China. In June the British Foreign Office assured the United States that in the event of renewal of the Anglo-Japanese Alliance it would be made clear that it was not aimed at the United States.[2]

On July 8, 1920, Foreign Secretary Curzon and Ambassador Chinda signed

[1] *Foreign Relations of the United States,* 1920, Vol. II, pp. 679–680.
[2] *Ibid.,* p. 682.

and communicated to the League of Nations an agreement[3] to the effect that the governments of Japan and Great Britain had reached the conclusion that the existing Anglo-Japanese Alliance, while in harmony with the spirit of the League Covenant, was not consistent with its letter, and that, if the Alliance should be continued after July, 1921, it should be in a form not inconsistent with the Covenant.

In the United States, Senator William E. Borah introduced on December 14, 1920, a resolution in Congress inviting the President to call a conference for the purpose of achieving an understanding or agreement by which the naval expenditures and building programs of the governments concerned would be reduced during the next five years.[4] The original intention was to limit the conference to the three leading naval powers, the United States, Great Britain, and Japan, and its purpose confined solely to disarmament.[5] Senator Borah's proposal for the limitation of armament met with immediate and widespread approval. President Harding gave it enthusiastic endorsement in his inaugural address the following March. The British Admiralty promptly responded with an expression of a strong desire to prevent a naval race with the United States. As a matter of fact, Lord Lee of Fareham, the new First Lord of the Admiralty, went so far as to propose a naval understanding with the United States based on the principle of parity.[6] The strong public demand for definite action in the United States led to the Senate adopting the Borah Resolution on May 26, 1921, some six months after its introduction. The House of Representatives passed it the following month.

By the beginning of June, 1921, the British Government knew where the United States stood. She favored international disarmament and opposed renewal of the Anglo-Japanese Alliance. But in the event the Alliance was to be renewed she wanted it to be redrafted in a manner more consistent with her Far Eastern policy and exempting her from the application of the military obligations.[7]

The British Imperial Conference opened in London on June 20, and shortly thereafter a spirited debate developed over the question of the renewal of the Alliance as a result of Dominion pressure and particularly Canada's determination. To Canada even the remote possibility of taking up arms against the United States was most abhorrent.[8] However, Lloyd George, supported by Foreign Secretary Curzon, Privy Council President Lord Balfour, Lord Lee,

[3] Carnegie Endowment for International Peace, *Treaties and Agreements with and Concerning China, 1919–1929*, p. 29.

[4] *Foreign Relations of the United States*, 1921, Vol. I, p. 27.

[5] Raymond L. Buell, *The Washington Conference*, p. 147.

[6] E. J. Young, *Powerful America*, pp. 53–54.

[7] A. Whitney Griswold, *The Far Eastern Policy of the United States*, pp. 285–286.

[8] *Ibid.*, pp. 286–288.

Austen Chamberlain and Winston Churchill, had decided to renew and keep the Alliance as a means of safeguarding India as well as the vast British territorial and economic interests in East Asia and the Pacific. Moreover, they looked upon Japan as a bulwark against the spread of communism to China and India. Even Australia's Prime Minister Hughes, the staunch advocate of the "white Australia" policy, who had successfully waged a one-man battle against the Japanese delegation at Versailles on the insertion of the racial equality clause in the League Covenant, insisted strongly on renewal. However, Canadian Prime Minister Arthur Meighen succeeded in the face of overwhelming odds in persuading the Imperial Conference to accept the idea of relinquishing the Anglo-Japanese Alliance, which was to be superseded by a multilateral treaty of general understanding.[9]

On June 23 Secretary Hughes learned that the Alliance, due to expire on July 13, would probably be renewed for another year. The American Secretary of State suggested to the British Ambassador "that if it were true that the policies of Great Britain in the Far East were like our own, there should be cooperation between Great Britain and the United States," and "that this was not an attitude antagonistic to Japan, but would be in the interests of the peace of the world." [10] He went on further to state that he had been advised that a resolution for the recognition of the Irish Republic would be introduced in Congress and that should Great Britain indicate her desire to support United States policy in the Far East, it would strengthen the position of those opposing such a resolution.

Slightly more than a week before the expiration of the Anglo-Japanese Alliance, Ambassador Hayashi called on Foreign Secretary Curzon and obtained an assurance that the British Government had decided to continue the Alliance in a manner not inconsistent with the spirit of the League Covenant. Curzon went on to explain that, inasmuch as the situation had changed completely since the Alliance was first concluded and considerable suspicion would be aroused by its renewal, it would appear that a Pacific conference to discuss outstanding issues would be highly desirable. Evidently, the legal opinion given by Lord Birkenhead [11] that a decision on the matter was not immediately urgent since the Alliance would continue automatically in effect until denounced had influenced the decision of the British government.

The White House, on July 10, announced that the American government had approached the governments of Great Britain, France, Italy, and Japan

[9] An excellent account of Canada's role in the termination of the Alliance is J. Bartlet Brebner's "Canada, the Anglo-Japanese Alliance, and the Washington Conference," *Political Science Quarterly,* March, 1925.

[10] Memorandum of a conversation between the Secretary of State and the British Ambassador, June 23, 1921. *Foreign Relations of the United States,* 1921, Vol. II, pp. 314–316.

[11] London *Times,* July 11, 1921.

as to the advisability of holding a conference on the limitation of armament and the problems of the Far East and the Pacific.[12] The American press received the news with enthusiasm. The London *Times* regarded the proposal as timely and momentous but issued a sober warning that "the task of the proposed Conference will be as delicate and unless discerningly approached, as dangerous as any conference essayed to discharge. Not even the Peace Conference at Paris had to face issues vaster or fraught with greater possibilities of good and evil to the world." [13]

Formal invitations were issued by President Harding on August 11, to the four powers, Great Britain, Japan, France, and Italy, after having secured their expression of approval the month before. Meanwhile, the United States government had arrived at the conclusion that the limitation of armament itself, if unrelated to the other outstanding issues, would be of little avail, and that the eradication of the actual causes of war was imperative. It decided therefore to include the problems of the Pacific and the Far East, and invitations were issued also to China, the Netherlands, and Portugal to participate in those questions affecting their interests in those regions.

That Japan should view the intentions of the Conference with considerable misgivings, if not suspicion, was not surprising in view of the position she occupied in 1921. At the Paris Conference she was successful in securing Allied recognition of her program of continental expansion, which had been aided and accelerated by the First World War, and had progressed to a point where she was practically within reach of hegemony over Asia. When the invitation to the Conference was received a feeling of tension seized both official and non-official circles. Some papers declared that it created a national crisis.[14] Not a few persons immediately jumped to the conclusion that it was a plot on the part of the United States and Great Britain to divest Japan of her special rights in Manchuria and Mongolia, wreck the proposed "eight-eight fleet" naval expansion program, which was already under way, and, in short, deprive her of all the advantages that had been won at great expense and sacrifice. They believed that the powers intended to supersede Japan in her role of leadership in the Far East in order to advance their own national interests. In this confusion Baron Katō's counsel was most reassuring. He admonished the nation against hasty conclusions, attitude of apprehension, and unnecessary constraint, since the Conference was intended to achieve lasting peace.[15]

The Japanese government, in its communication of July 26, indicated that it was averse to discussing special problems between nations or *faits accomplis*.

[12] U.S. Senate Document No. 126, 67th Congress, 2d Session, p. 783.
[13] "The Arms Conference at Washington," *Outlook*, August 31, 1921, pp. 678–681.
[14] Ashida Hitoshi, *Saikin Sekai Gaikōshi*, Vol. III, pp. 742–743.
[15] Tōkyō *Asahi*, July 20, 1921.

This meant that it did not wish the Conference to touch upon such matters as the Twenty-one Demands or the Siberian Expedition.[16] After preliminary conversations with Great Britain and the United States, the topics to be discussed were clarified, and in spite of the outspoken opposition from several quarters, the government of Premier Hara accepted the invitation to participate in the Conference on the condition that its scope be limited to the discussion of problems leading to "a common understanding in regard to general policies in the Pacific and the Far East" and that "introduction . . . of problems such as are of sole concern to certain particular powers or such matters that may be regarded accomplished facts should be scrupulously avoided." [17] It was obvious that the Japanese government was anxious to keep what it regarded as *faits accomplis* off the conference agenda. When the United States submitted on September 12 the draft agenda of the Conference, the Japanese government was reassured. Although the military was unalterably opposed to anything that might divest Japan of any gains secured during the war, it was not in a position powerful enough to prevent the government from sending a delegation to Washington.

Japanese opinion was divided on the desirability of the Conference. One view was that the advantageous position of Japan should be maintained at all costs. The other view favored international cooperation that would contribute toward peace and the reduction of the heavy burden of armament without endangering national security. The latter view prevailed among the majority of newspapers, which were as well informed on world situation as on domestic economic conditions. It is to the credit of the press that it successfully mobilized national opinion favorable to the idea of disarmament to such a degree that even army and navy men admitted public opinion was solidly in support of disarmament.[18]

The importance attached to the Washington Conference by the powers was reflected in the caliber and eminence of the delegates they sent. The United States was represented by Secretary of State Charles Evans Hughes, former Secretary of State Elihu Root, Senator Henry Cabot Lodge, Chairman of the Senate Foreign Relations Committee, and Senator Oscar Underwood, ranking Democratic member of the Committee. Great Britain was represented by President of the Privy Council Lord Balfour, First Lord of the Admiralty Lord Lee, and Ambassador to the United States, Sir Auchland Geddes. The French delegation included Premier Aristide Briand, former Premier Viviani, and Ambassador to the United States Jusserand. China sent Dr. Wellington Koo, Ambassador to the United States Sao-ke Alfred Sze, and former Justice Minister Wang.

Japan sent her Navy Minister Admiral Baron Katō, House of Peers President Prince Tokugawa, Ambassador to the United States Baron Shidehara, and Vice Foreign Minister Hanihara. In the selection of delegates the Japanese govern-

[16] Ashida Hitoshi, *op. cit.,* pp. 742–743.
[17] *Foreign Relations of the United States,* 1921, Vol. I, pp. 43–45.
[18] Mizuno Kōtoku, "Iaku Jōsō to Tōsuiken," *Taiyō,* May, 1922, pp. 44–52.

ment did not depart from the pattern it set a few years earlier at Versailles. With the possible exception of Baron Shidehara, the Japanese plenipotentiaries were not the match of those of the United States, Great Britain, and France.[19] They were inexperienced in conference diplomacy and lacked the keen sensitivity, so essential in keeping tab on the pulse of the Conference and world opinion, and the ability to express themselves spontaneously and fluently in the give-and-take of the discussions. Moreover, they failed to utilize to any appreciable extent the excellent opportunities that were presented to them throughout the conference period. Although with Balfour and Hughes, Katō comprised the "Big Three" of the Washington Conference, he was far from successful in making full use of his position of prestige. The work of the Japanese delegation was rendered less effective because of the lack of cooperation and coordination within its own ranks.

While the Japanese delegates were apparently aware of the importance of press relations and permitted interviews to foreign correspondents, they revealed ineptitude in establishing a smooth working and effective liaison with them. They failed to make themselves easily accessible to the members of the press, including those of their own nationality. Representatives of the Japanese press showed irritation at what they regarded as a slight and took a critical attitude throughout. When compared to the organization of the British delegation, which had the services of a public relations expert not only to effect liaison with the delegates of other powers but to establish smooth working relations with the British correspondents, whose favorable dispatches influenced and led British public opinion, the Japanese delegation was pathetically ineffective.[20]

THE FOUR POWER PACT

First of the agreements to be concluded at the Conference was the Four Power Pact, a quadripartite treaty that in a sense superseded the bipartite Anglo-Japanese Alliance of January 20, 1902. To the United States and other powers, there appeared to be little doubt that the Anglo-Japanese Alliance had aided and abetted in no small measure Japan's program of continental expansion. Moreover, in the face of an increasingly worsening anti-Japanese attitude in the United States following the Russo-Japanese War, Englishmen, particularly in the Far East, did not relish the possibility, however remote, of having to go to the aid of Japan in the event of an American-Japanese War. There was an increasing desire on the part of many Englishmen for the termination of the

[19] Prince Tokugawa, in commenting on the Conference, expressed his personal opinion that the Japanese delegates were in education and experience not the equals of the distinguished plenipotentiaries of some of the powers. Tokugawa Iyesato, "Kafu Kaigi ni Taisuru Yoron," *Taiyō,* March, 1922, pp. 98–99.

[20] Mochizuki Kotarō, "Kafu Kaigi ni Okeru Gaikō no Shittai," *Taiyō,* February, 1922, p. 60.

Alliance, not only because of the possibility of war against the United States, but also because it actually constituted an obstacle to the extension of British economic interests in China.

Anticipating the important role that his London *Times* would be playing in the coming conference at Washington, Lord Northcliffe made a tour of the United States with his editor, H. Wickham Steed. After visiting Seattle, Portland, San Francisco, and San Diego, as well as Vancouver and Victoria, Steed gained a very definite impression of the American-Japanese problem.[21] He was able to ascertain the attitude of British Columbia and the western provinces of Canada toward the renewal of the Anglo-Japanese Alliance. The tour of the Pacific Coast had convinced him of the need for a reconsideration of the prospective policy of the British Empire at the Washington Conference. It was clear to him that unless the Anglo-Japanese Alliance could be abrogated or merged painlessly into some sort of more general agreement, the people of British Columbia and of western Canada generally would be likely to side with the United States in any conflict that might arise between Japan and the United States.

Upon his return to Washington from the tour, Steed discussed his outlook with Secretary of State Hughes, and also very frankly with Ambassador Shidehara, asking him to inform Viscount Makino, Count Chinda, and other friends in Japan of his belief that Japan would be wise to accept the transformation of the Anglo-Japanese Alliance into a larger and more general agreement and to come to Washington with such a policy of peace as to ensure the success of the Conference. When he returned to London in late September, Steed put his conclusions confidentially before the Admiralty, Foreign Office, and Balfour, after he had been appointed chief British delegate to the Conference. It is more than likely that the views presented by Steed had considerable influence on the decision made by the British Government.

Japan would have wanted to continue the Alliance with the understanding of the United States, if that had been possible. Baron Katō Takaaki, who was instrumental in arousing the interest of Britain in the Alliance in the late 1890's, was anxious to see it kept up but felt that, if there were serious obstacles, it would be better to terminate it.[22] Public opinion as well as the government regarded the abandonment of the Alliance as undesirable. It was felt that in a period of Anglo-Saxon dominance the Alliance would help Japan in her difficulties with other powers, particularly in checking the growth of anti-Japanese sentiment, and would preclude the necessity of Britain's keeping a strong fleet in Far Eastern waters. Furthermore, it was felt that the Alliance would go a long ways toward ensuring peace in the Far East.[23]

[21] H. Wickham Steed, *Through Thirty Years, 1892–1922*, Vol. II, pp. 369–370.
[22] Itō Masanori, *Katō Takaaki*, Vol. II, pp. 391–392.
[23] Kashima Morinosuke, *Teikoku Gaikō no Kihon Seisaku*, pp. 351–352.

Conversations were begun between Admiral Katō and Lord Balfour in Washington on November 22 on the question of renewal of the Alliance. After the Cabinet meeting of December 6, the Japanese government, fully aware of the situation, communicated its willingness to accept a tripartite agreement in lieu of the Anglo-Japanese Alliance and instructed the delegation to submit Shidehara's draft to Balfour. Four days later, when Balfour showed the draft to Elihu Root and Senator Lodge, both expressed satisfaction. Secretary Hughes, who also expressed general approval of the draft as revised by Lord Balfour, suggested a few days later the inclusion of France, particularly in view of the existence of anti-British and anti-Japanese sentiment in the United States.

Discussions by the "Big Three" began at the State Department on December 7. At the first meeting Hughes submitted the American draft. On the second day, the group was joined by M. Viviani, the French delegate. Negotiations proceeded with unexpected smoothness and speed. The only disagreement that arose was over the interpretation of the terms "insular possessions" and "insular dominions." Some Japanese were inclined to view the inclusion of Japan proper as an affront to Japan's dignity, since it would obligate the other contracting powers to extend military assistance in the safeguarding of the territorial integrity of Japan itself. The Japanese government insisted on the exclusion of Japan proper, in opposition to the stand of the United States. However, the matter was settled to Japan's satisfaction when a supplementary treaty was signed in January of the following year.

Agreement was reached in record time on December 9, and the following day, at the fourth plenary session of the Conference, Senator Lodge read the entire text of the Four Power Pact. The public was taken completely by surprise, for there was not even a suggestion of such a subject in the conference agenda. As a matter of fact, most other delegations were unaware of the negotiations, which were going on quietly, if not secretly. Signatures were affixed on the document on December 13.

The main feature of the four power agreement was the imposition on the signatories of general consultative obligations. In case a dispute arose between any of the high contracting parties out of any Pacific question that was not satisfactorily settled by diplomacy and was likely to disturb harmonious relations, a joint conference was to be called for the consideration and adjustment of the difficulty (Article 1). If the rights of any nation were threatened by aggressive action of another, full and frank discussions were to be held "to arrive at an understanding as to the most efficient measures to be taken, jointly or separately, to meet the exigencies of the particular situation" (Article 2). The agreement was to remain in force for ten years, but a contracting power had the right to withdraw upon twelve months' notice. Although the Anglo-Japanese Alliance was terminated on August 17, 1923, Japan did not find herself in a position of diplomatic isolation, for she was protected by the Four Power

Pact. Moreover, her security was actually enhanced by the Naval Treaty, which followed within less than two months of the signature of the quadripartite agreement.

FIVE POWER NAVAL TREATY

Central to the problem of security in the Pacific, as well as to the whole world, was the question of naval armament. No sooner had the fighting come to an end in Europe in 1918 than a naval race began. The United States resumed her naval building program, authorized by the Naval Service Appropriations Act of August, 1916, and started by Secretary of the Navy Daniels, which had been interrupted by her entry into the European conflict in 1917. In 1919 the United States embarked upon a three-year naval building program, which would give her a navy second to none. This had been planned to offset Japan's ambitious "eight-eight fleet" program, outlined in 1915 by the Defense Affairs Conference. Appropriations for the completion of this program were made in 1920, and Japan was spending annually a total of 800 million yen in military expenditures. By 1920 a three-cornered naval race was on between the United States, Great Britain, and Japan.

That Japan was not altogether averse to the idea of naval disarmament was indicated as early as March, 1921, when Navy Minister Admiral Katō, in an interview with an Associated Press correspondent, stated that if the naval powers of the world agreed to stop the construction of ships, Japan would be willing to abandon her "eight-eight" program. At the Washington Conference Japan was particularly concerned over the size of fleets that would operate in the Pacific in the event of hostilities. The Four Power Treaty in itself would give Japan little security if the Pacific outposts of the powers were to be fortified and used as bases of operations of their powerful navies. Naturally, the Japanese delegation, though eager to hold down the other major Pacific powers to a binding agreement on naval strength, was even more determined to have the question of fortifications in their Asiatic possessions and colonies settled to Japan's satisfaction.

In officially opening the Conference as its unanimously elected presiding officer Secretary of State Hughes virtually threw a bombshell by proposing a sweeping reduction of naval armament and the establishment of a ratio in capital ships. The timing as well as the daring nature of the proposal electrified the Conference, making the opening session perhaps the most memorable part of the entire session. The proposal called for the scrapping of sixty-six battleships aggregating 1,876,000 tons by the three leading naval powers and the fixing of a naval ratio of 5:5:3 for the United States, Great Britain, and Japan, respectively, and 1.75 for France and Italy.

The United States was to scrap a total tonnage of 845,740, comprising thirty ships, which included nine battleships and six battle cruisers under construction as well as fifteen old battleships. Great Britain was to abandon the four new "Hood" type battleships, whose keels had not yet been laid, and scrap nineteen older battleships totaling 411,374 tons, or a grand total of 581,375 tons. Japan was to abandon four battleships and four battle cruisers in the planning stage, scrap three new capital ships, one already launched and two under construction, four battle cruisers not yet completed, and ten old ships, or a total of seventeen ships, aggregating 448,928 tons.

Japan persisted at first in her demand for a 10:10:7 ratio, on the grounds that it was not only fair but that it was necessary for her defense. This appears, however, to have been done at the insistence of her naval experts rather than of the high-ranking policy makers in the government. Great Britain and the United States were adamant in their stand that the ratio was adequate for Japan. Finally, as a condition for Japan's acceptance of the 5:5:3 ratio, they acceded to her demand to retain the newly built post-Jutland battleship *Mutsu,* and scrap instead the older ship *Settsu.* At the same time, they agreed to maintain the *status quo* with respect to fortifications in their Pacific possessions (Article 19), excepting Hawaii, Australia, New Zealand, the islands along the coast of the United States and Canada, and the islands comprising Japan proper. This nonfortification clause made it virtually impossible for the United States or Great Britain to wage effective naval warfare against Japan and gave Japan a strong feeling of security. At the same time, it made the Philippines, Guam, and the British colony of Hongkong vulnerable to Japanese attack, but did not enable Japan to carry on a successful offensive war against the continental United States or even Hawaii.

By denying herself the right to fortify Guam, Pago Pago, the Philippines, and the Aleutians the United States ruled out the possibility as well as the intention of conducting offensive naval operations against Japan in her own waters. It meant that in case of war with Japan the United States would have to conduct her operations from the Hawaiian Islands. Japan was thus protected against a possible Anglo-American attack by the Four Power Pact, which was in effect a pledge of nonintervention in the Far East.

The treaty as finally signed fixed the capital ratio at 5:5:3:1.75 and provided for a ten-year naval construction holiday. Capital ships and aircraft carriers were to be limited in tonnage to 35,000 and 27,000 tons respectively and gun calibers to 16 and 8 inches respectively. It required also the scrapping of specified ships that were already completed or still under construction.

NINE POWER TREATY

At the very outset of the discussion on China, the Chinese delegation submitted at the request of the American government a statement of China's needs. However, instead of supporting the adoption of the Chinese propositions known also as the Ten Points, the American delegation introduced its own statement of principles to be applied to China, in the form of a resolution presented by Elihu Root. These principles were adopted by the Conference and incorporated into the Treaty, signed on February 6, 1922, in the form of a pledge by the signatories excepting China:

1. "To respect the sovereignty, the independence, and the territorial and administrative integrity of China.
2. "To provide the fullest and most unembarrassed opportunity to China to develop and maintain for herself an effective and stable government.
3. "To use their influence for the purpose of effectually establishing and maintaining the principle of equal opportunity for the commerce and industry of all nations throughout the territory of China.
4. "To refrain from taking advantage of the present conditions in order to seek special rights or privileges which would abridge the rights of the subjects or citizens of friendly states, and from countenancing action inimical to the security of such state."

The powers agreed not to enter into any treaty, agreement, arrangement or understanding with any power or powers which might in any way infringe or impair the principles regarding China. In order to apply more effectively the principles of the Open Door and equal opportunity, the powers forswore any agreement calculated to establish a favorable position, and any monopoly or preference that would deprive nationals of other powers of a fair opportunity. They also agreed not to support any agreements, made by their nationals, designed to create spheres of influence or provide for mutually exclusive opportunities in China. In return for these, China was to refrain from exercising or permitting unfair discrimination. It was provided that when a situation arose which involved the application of the provisions of the treaty, full and frank communication should be made between the contracting parties.

China's plea for the termination of extraterritoriality was received by the delegates with a sympathetic attitude. However, they all agreed that the best procedure was to adopt the suggestion of Secretary Hughes to appoint a subcommittee to inquire into the facts of the case. On November 29, the subcommittee submitted its recommendations in the form of resolutions which were adopted. As a result a commission was appointed to inquire into the existing practice of extraterritorial jurisdiction in China, the laws, the judicial system, and the methods of judicial administration, with a view to making recommendations to improve the administration of justice and assist China in effecting such legislation and judicial reforms as would warrant the powers to relinquish their extraterritorial rights. Actual investigations were postponed until 1925 because of political conditions and at the request of the Chinese government.

China demanded the abolition of foreign post offices on her soil on the grounds that their maintenance constituted a direct violation of her territorial and administrative integrity and that the system had no legal or treaty rights. Dr. Sze pointed out also that the Chinese postal system was deprived of the revenue that it would otherwise have. The resolution, which was adopted, provided for the abolition, not later than January 1, 1923, of foreign postal agencies, except those operating in leased territories or with China's consent. As for the Chinese demand for the withdrawal of armed forces, including police and railway guards in China to protect the lives and property of foreigners, a resolution was passed declaring the intention of the powers to withdraw their armed forces on duty without the authority of a treaty or agreement whenever China guaranteed the protection of the lives and property of foreigners.

Efforts by the Chinese delegation for the regaining of tariff autonomy were no more successful than in the matter of extraterritoriality, in spite of the fact that a nine power customs tariff treaty was signed on February 6, two days after the Shantung settlement with Japan. The treaty gave China a substantial increase in revenues as a result of a rise in duties. At the same time, it also set up a commission to effect reforms in the Chinese tariff administration. However, this was only the very first step in the long and difficult struggle toward tariff autonomy, for which the Chinese delegates were clamoring.

With regard to the cancellation of the Twenty-one Demands, the Japanese rejected, as they had at Versailles, the Chinese contention that the Sino-Japanese treaties of 1915 were invalid because they were signed under duress. They knew too well that Great Britain and France could not afford to undermine the Versailles Treaty by the general acceptance of the Chinese contention. Moreover, these two European powers were not willing to relinquish their spheres of interest and leaseholds any more than was Japan. Consequently, in spite of Hughes' efforts, Japan's special rights and privileges in Manchuria were left unimpaired and intact. As a consolation, three nominal concessions were made by the Japanese delegation, namely, the throwing open to the consortium of her railway loan options in South Manchuria and Inner Mongolia, the disavowal of the use of Japanese military, financial, or political advisers in South Manchuria, and the withdrawal of Group 5 of the Twenty-one Demands.

THE SHANTUNG SETTLEMENT

China was very successful in her demand for the return of Shantung. Ever since Versailles, the Shantung question had been the sore spot of Sino-Japanese relations. At Washington, the Japanese indicated their willingness to restore the province to China, but only according to the terms of the 1915 and 1918 treaties and strictly on the basis of independent negotiations between the two powers. The Chinese insisted on unconditional restoration. Balfour and Hughes, realizing the dangers inherent in the situation, succeeded after considerable exertion in bringing the Chinese and Japanese together for a series of meetings, beginning on December 1, 1921. With two British and two American observers in attendance to ensure fair play, thirty-six meetings, not including those for the drafting of the treaty, were held, during which time their success was threatened with rupture twice. But on February 4, 1922, they signed a treaty by which Japan restored Shantung in full sovereignty to China, though Japan's economic supremacy and political influence in the province were left practically intact. The reassertion of Chinese sovereignty, however, was a considerable victory for China, especially in view of the fact that President Harding had warned the Chinese delegation that their alternative to the settlement of the Shantung question might be the loss of the province.[24]

With regard to Siberia, the American Secretary of State succeeded in obtaining from Baron Shidehara a disclaimer of designs on Russian territory and a statement to the effect that Japanese troops would be withdrawn from Siberia and northern Sakhalin before long.[25] The Yap question, one of the most vexing problems so far as American-Japanese relations were concerned, was settled on February 11, a few days after the close of the Conference. A treaty was signed between the United States and Japan whereby American citizens were granted equal cable, radio, and residential rights, and facilities on the island on identical terms with the Japanese. In return for this, the United States gave consent to Japan's mandate over the Pacific islands north of the equator, which she had obtained at Versailles.

Japan agreed on December 27, 1922, to cancel the Lansing-Ishii Agreement, choosing to do so rather than to consent to the publication of the secret pledges respecting China that had been a part of the executive agreement. Thus, the ambiguous agreement, which was one of the most controversial subjects in American diplomatic history, was brought to an end without ceremony.

In a brief space of less than three months the Washington Conference achieved noteworthy success. It checked a ruinous naval competition in battleships, especially between the two greatest naval powers, and sealed their friendship. It relieved American-Japanese tension at least for the time being and recognized the military supremacy of Japan in the Far East. It also impressed upon China the painful but undisguised fact that her national salvation depended very largely upon herself alone.

Reactions in Japan to the achievements of the Conference were varied. Indignation was expressed in some quarters at the failure to achieve naval parity with the United States and Great Britain. Japanese leaders had no illusions about the fact that the nation with its limited wealth and resources could not vie effectively against Great Britain or the United States in a naval building program. How-

---

[24] Griswold, *op. cit.,* p. 327.

[25] *Conference on the Limitations of Armament,* U.S. Senate Document No. 126, 67th Cong. 2d Sess., Proceedings of Plenary Sessions, p. 853.

ever, to some of them, it was a matter of face and to others a question of military strategy. One of the members of the naval advisory committee attached to the Japanese delegation, Commander Katō Kanji, who by the time of the London Naval Conference had risen to the position of Chief of the Naval Board, is said to have indignantly stated that, as far as he was concerned, American-Japanese war began on the day the naval ratio was adopted.[26] In some quarters there was a feeling that Japan had been divested of her World War gains in China.[27] But the general feeling was that the exchange of views resulting from the meeting of the leading statesmen of the world had helped to clear the atmosphere of misunderstanding, fear, and suspicion, which had cast a dark shadow over the three great naval powers. It was felt that the Conference helped to unfold a new era of international cooperation and good will.[28] No one had the slightest doubt that it had lightened the burden of armament and helped to promote the cause of peace in the Pacific and the Far East.

From the point of her national policy and, more specifically her naval strategy, the Washington Conference was quite a success for Japan, as she stopped America's first line of defense at Hawaii and Britain's at Singapore, leaving the vast expanse of the Pacific between the two points practically within her control, and also virtually controlling China's fate. The elevation of Admiral Baron Katō to the post of Premier in June, 1922, almost immediately after his return from the Washington Conference, was hailed by the American press as a triumph of internationalism in Japan.

[26] Mori Shōzō, *Sempū Nijūnenshi,* Vol. I, p. 41. Lt. Commander Suetsugu, who later became Chief of Naval Board was also a member of the naval committee.

[27] Kashima, *op. cit.,* p. 478.

[28] Ashida, *op. cit.,* pp. 760–761.

Chapter 29. Immigration and Exclusion

Seldom in the annals of modern diplomacy has there been an international issue of local origin that so impaired the friendly relations of two nations as did the Japanese immigration problem in the United States. Nor has there been another issue more exploited for political purposes. For nearly a quarter of a century it constituted one of the basic irritants in American-Japanese relations. It finally came to a head in 1924, resulting in the enactment by the United States Congress of a law containing the provision for the exclusion of Japanese immigrants. Involving as it did the question of national pride and sensibilities of Japan on the one hand and the difficult Federal-state relations of the United States on the other, it was perhaps even more explosive and fraught with greater danger than the problems of naval politics in the Pacific.

Japanese immigration had a very late start. As a late-comer on the international scene, Japan was far behind the European countries and even China in sending immigrants to the lands beyond the seas. When German immigrants began crossing the Atlantic to the New World after the unsuccessful revolution of 1848, the Japanese were still clinging tenaciously, if precariously, to their self-imposed policy of national seclusion, which was first adopted in the 1630's. When the news of the discovery of gold in California spread to all corners of the world, adventurers, dreaming of quick fortune, began converging upon California from all climes and lands, but there were no Japanese among them, although a considerable number of Chinese had joined the rush of the forty-niners and found their way to the mining camps and towns of the West. Nor did the Japanese laborers join, as did the Chinese, the construction gangs that worked on the western sections of the transcontinental railroads in the 1860's.

Even after the opening of the country in 1854 there was no rush to go abroad, for the seclusion decree was still in effect, prohibiting people from leaving the country on pain of death. Those who felt the irrepressible urge to see the foreign countries were those scholars, like Yoshida Shōin, who wanted to see with their own eyes what was taking place in the West, and young students who were eager to acquire Western learning. By the decade of the 1860's there were some Japanese abroad, chiefly those who had been sent to Europe by the Shogunate and the fiefs to study and a few shipwrecked sailors who had been rescued by American ships and landed on American soil as early as 1850.

For a number of years after the Restoration of 1868, the Japanese government gave little, if any, thought to emigration, for it was much too preoccupied with

428

urgent problems demanding immediate attention if not solution. However, in 1868 an American businessman, Eugene Van Reed, residing at Kanagawa and acting as an agent of the Hawaiian government, recruited some 300 contract laborers for a three-year period at $5.00 a month for the sugar planters and shipped them on the British ship *Scioto* to Hawaii, in spite of the protest of the new government. Some of the immigrants were brought back by the special envoy Ueno Kagenori, who was dispatched to Hawaii in the fall of the following year.[1] Consequent to the complications and difficulties that developed subsequently between Japan and the Hawaiian kingdom emigration was suspended for many years, in spite of the fact that a treaty of amity and commerce had been signed in the fall of 1871.

When King Kalakaua visited Japan on his voyage around the world in 1881 he broached to the authorities the subject of resumption of Japanese emigration to Hawaii. The importation in 1878 of Portuguese contract laborers by the Hawaiian sugar planters to cope with existing labor shortage had not worked out well because of the great distance and high cost, and the planters as well as the government turned once more to Japan as a source of labor supply. After much delay an agreement permitting voluntary emigration of laborers to Hawaii was concluded early in 1885, and that only after a special emissary had been dispatched to Japan by the Hawaiian government. Under the terms of the Emigration Convention signed in Tōkyō on January 28, 1886, the flow of Japanese contract laborers to Hawaii continued until the last of the three years' contracts expired in June, 1897. By 1890 there had been admitted into Hawaii 12,360 Japanese, and in 1900 the number was in excess of 61,000.

In the United States there were only fifty-five Japanese in 1870. During the decade that followed some students entered, but the number had increased to only 148 in 1880. By 1890 the number had increased to 2,039, which was insignificant when compared to the Chinese population, which had reached the peak of 132,000. However, by 1900, the number had jumped to 24,326, an increase of over tenfold in the ten-year period. This sudden increase was brought about by the annexation of the Hawaiian Islands by the United States in 1898, after which Japanese laborers left the Islands for Canada and the continental United States, where labor shortages existed and more favorable economic conditions prevailed. In the year 1900 alone, 12,000 entered the United States and attracted the attention of the Californians, who began to regard the influx with uneasiness, if not alarm. By 1910 the Japanese population in the United States had nearly trebled, now totaling 72,157. Ten years later it reached 111,000.

By far the greatest number of Japanese emigrants were motivated by economic gains, although not an inconsiderable number left the country to evade military service. In April, 1896, the Diet enacted the Emigrant Protection Law

[1] Sashihara Yasuzō, *Meiji Seishi*, Vol. I, p. 34.

(effective June 1), which required that a responsible party at home, who could be compelled to provide for his care during illness and if necessary even for his return, put up a guarantee. As the procurement of laborers for foreign employers became a very profitable business, emigration companies were organized to furnish the surety required by law as well as transportation and a job at the destination. These companies worked closely with labor contractors in the United States and other countries where labor was in great demand. In March, 1897, less than two months after the signing of an immigration agreement with the Mexican government, Japanese emigration to Mexico began. Two years later Peru also became a destination of Japanese laborers. From 1908, when emigration to the United States, Hawaii, and Canada was restricted, the government encouraged emigration to other countries such as Brazil [2] and Peru. Subsidies were granted to steamship companies to make inexpensive transportation available to the emigrants.

Next to the United States, the country that received the largest number of Japanese immigrants was Canada; consequently, she experienced considerable difficulty. When Great Britain and Japan signed a treaty of commerce and navigation on July 16, 1894, subjects of each country were granted "full liberty to enter, travel, and reside in any part of the dominions or possessions of the other contracting party." The treaty, however, did not apply to Canada, Australia, and South Africa except upon notice by the British Government to be given within a period of two years. It was not until September 25, 1905, that Canada decided to adhere to the treaty "absolutely and without reserve." [3] A supplementary convention was signed in Tōkyō early the following year by the British and Japanese governments, whereby the treaty was extended to Canada. On January 30, 1907, the Canadian Parliament approved it. At the time there were some 7,500 Japanese in Canada, but in the next ten months 4,429 entered, part of them coming from Hawaii.

Alarmed at the sudden increase, the Canadian government negotiated with Tōkyō and concluded a Canadian Gentlemen's Agreement in which the Foreign Minister stated that, while the existing treaty between Japan and Canada guaranteed to Japanese subjects full liberty to enter, the Japanese government would not insist upon these rights and would take measures to restrict emigration to Canada. Subsequently, in May, 1910, Canada passed an Immigration Act empowering the Governor-General to exclude whatever national or racial groups he deemed "unsuited to the climate or requirements of Canada, or of immigrants of any specified class, occupation, or character." [4] When a new treaty of com-

---

[2] On September 12, 1913, 1,800 Japanese emigrants to Brazil sailed in response to the third call by the Oriental Immigration Company.

[3] *Report of Committee of Canadian Privy Council*, Sessional Paper 74*b*, p. 287, September 26, 1905.

[4] Sec. 38, Act of May 4, 1910, pp. 9–10, *Edw. VII*, Chap. 27.

merce and navigation was concluded between the British Empire and Japan on April 3, 1911, Canada expressed her willingness to adhere to it, provided the treaty should not be deemed to repeal any of the provisions of the Immigration Act of 1910. This proviso followed the reservation made by the United States to the treaty of 1911 with Japan. Thus, aliens, including the Japanese, have enjoyed the right to acquire, hold, and dispose of real and personal property of every description in the same manner in all respects as a natural-born British subject. Furthermore, Canadian law provides for no racial qualification for citizenship.[5]

Australia early decided on a policy of Japanese exclusion through the application of a dictation test, as suggested by Colonial Secretary Chamberlain. This policy was implemented by the Immigration Restriction Act of 1901, which has helped to carry out successfully a "white Australia" policy, but care was exercised not to effectuate specific legislative discrimination in favor of or against any race or color. Although no Asiatic could be naturalized in Australia, there have been no federal restrictions upon landholding by Asiatics. New Zealand followed the example of Australia and adopted the Immigration Restriction Act in 1908, providing for a dictation test similar to the one worked out successfully by Australia.[6] This was repealed in 1920 when the Governor-General was given full power to admit or exclude whatever nations or peoples he liked.[7] Since the Governor-General may grant letters of naturalization to any applicant he thinks fit, no racial bar to naturalization has existed. Because of the non-discriminatory legislative methods employed by Canada, Australia, and New Zealand, Japanese exclusion was achieved effectively without precipitating diplomatic crises of any kind in these countries. In contrast, the Japanese problem in the United States assumed alarming proportions.

The spectre of anti-Japanese agitation began to raise its ugly head in March, 1900, as symptoms of the bubonic plague appeared in San Francisco. Only four months earlier, the plague had made its way from the Orient to Honolulu, where the Board of Health, frightened at its spread and resulting deaths, set fire to the infected houses in a section of Chinatown on January 20, 1900, in the hope of checking it. Mayor Phelan and the San Francisco Board of Supervisors lost no time in ordering a quarantine of the Chinese and Japanese quarters in the city.[8]

Two months later, on May 7, the San Francisco Labor Council passed a resolution urging the extension of the Chinese Exclusion Laws to include the Japanese, after having heard the addresses by Mayor Phelan and Professor E. A.

---

[5] Naturalization Acts of 1914 and 1920.

[6] *Statutes of New Zealand*, Sections 14 (1) and 42 (a), No. 78, 1908.

[7] *Ibid.*, Immigration Restriction Act, 1920, No. 23, 1920.

[8] San Francisco *Chronicle*, March 7, 1900.

Ross of Stanford University.[9] That the initiative for the anti-Japanese campaign came from the working classes was unmistakable. Ever since Dennis Kearney, the Irish-born labor leader, harangued labor into opposing Chinese immigration at the sandlot meetings in San Francisco and organized the Workingmen's Party of California with the slogan, "The Chinese Must Go!", labor had been in the forefront of the movement to exclude first the Chinese and later the Japanese immigrants.

Official recognition of the existence of the "Japanese problem" was given by Governor Henry T. Gage, who called the attention of the California legislature to the problem in his message of January 8, 1901.[10] In November of the same year, a Chinese Exclusion Convention was held under the auspices of the San Francisco Board of Supervisors to urge upon Congress the necessity of reenacting the Chinese Exclusion Laws, which were soon to expire. It also adopted a resolution pointing out that the rapidly increasing numbers of Japanese and other Asiatics constituted "a menace to the industrial interests of our people." This was a reflection of the increasingly important role that labor was beginning to play in state as well as local politics.

From 1898 to 1901 San Francisco underwent a period of unprecedented prosperity, which resulted from the annexation of the Hawaiian Islands, the opening of the Klondike gold mines in Alaska, and the Spanish-American War. This greatly strengthened the position of labor, which felt strong and confident enough to challenge the employers. In January, 1901, the California State Federation of Labor was organized by labor leaders to fight against the employers who had established open shops and lower wages in the period of depression preceding the era of prosperity. The struggle which thus unfolded in 1901 between the San Francisco Employers' Association, which had been organized in 1888, and the Union Labor Party, which had just been organized, was on the issue of unionism and nonunionism. The fight culminated in the San Francisco teamsters' strike of July, 1901, which further strengthened the hand of labor.

The Union Labor Party became powerful enough to carry the municipal election of November 1, 1901, putting Eugene E. Schmitz in the mayor's chair after ousting Mayor Phelan for his allegedly antilabor stand. For the next six years there unfolded in the municipal administration of San Francisco an era of corruption seldom equaled anywhere, which made the notorious Tweed Ring appear insignificant, if not innocuous, by comparison.[11] Corporations ruthlessly exploited the rich resources of the state for their own selfish interests, telephone companies struggled for franchises, the city water supply was vested in a private monopoly, the United Railroads strangled San Francisco's transportation facili-

[9] *Ibid.,* May 8, 1900.

[10] *Ibid.,* January 9, 1901.

[11] For an excellent account of the graft that was rampant in San Francisco see Robert G. Cleland, *California in Our Time, 1900–1940,* pp. 9–25.

ties by bribing the supervisors to the tune of $200,000, while the Southern Pacific Railroad retained legislators and subsidized newspapers to make certain the political control of the state.[12] Gamblers shared their ill-gotten gains with the onetime orchestra leader mayor, while houses of ill-fame had a fixed schedule of prices by which to bribe police officials, from the chief of police down to the policeman on the beat. The corrupt municipal regime, with Abe Ruef as the brain and Eugene E. Schmitz its figurehead, cleverly concealed its crimes at least temporarily by utilizing the diversionary tactics of directing the attention and ire of the public, and particularly of its labor constituents, to the anti-Japanese program.[13]

In November, 1904, the American Federation of Labor, at its annual convention in San Francisco, demanded that the exclusion laws be applied to Japanese immigrants, thus elevating the problem to the level of a national issue. Anti-Japanese agitation was predicated on the economic grievances of California labor, which was aroused particularly by the increasingly large number of Japanese laborers coming from Hawaii. It was characterized by racial denunciations that were not infrequently quite vehement and manifested themselves in acts of physical violence by irresponsible elements. Beginning in 1905, even before she had scored a decisive military victory over Russia, Japan came to be pictured in the United States as a political menace, just as her immigrants had been represented as a threat to American institutions and the economic security of Americans.

On February 23, 1905, shortly before the Japanese armies under Field Marshal Ōyama in Manchuria began the siege of Mukden, the San Francisco *Chronicle* launched an effective anti-Japanese campaign in California with a blazing headline and a nine-column article extending over nearly two pages, emphasizing in no uncertain terms the dangers of Japanese immigration. Needless to say, this aroused the state legislators and needled them into action. On March 1, the California Senate adopted unanimously a resolution declaring against the unrestricted immigration of the Japanese and asking immediate protection from the Federal government.[14]

With 1905 as the dividing line, American-Japanese relations entered a period of friction and irritation. Leadership of the anti-Japanese movement now passed definitely into the hands of union labor. On March 10, 1905, the Labor Council of San Francisco, at the time the largest labor organization west of Chicago, held a meeting, and the campaign against the Japanese was opened under the leadership of Olaf Tveitmoe, a Swedish labor leader with a dubious record from

[12] Fremont Older, *My Own Story,* is an account of San Francisco's municipal corruption by one who participated in its house cleaning.

[13] Raymond L. Buell, "The Development of Anti-Japanese Agitation in the United States," *Political Science Quarterly,* Vol. 37, p. 612.

[14] Senate Joint Resolution No. 10, California Statutes, 1905, p. 1060.

Minnesota. On Sunday, May 7, a mass meeting was held and from it emerged the Japanese and Korean Exclusion League. It was this League that supported, if not actually suggested, the policy of segregating Japanese from white children in the public schools of San Francisco.

Meanwhile, Representative James Livernash, a San Francisco lawyer-journalist member of the Union Labor Party, was sponsoring a bill in Congress to exclude the Japanese. In a characteristically Rooseveltian manner, the President wielded the big stick and declared that he "would veto the bill even if it passed unanimously and deport Livernash." Speaker Joe Cannon of the House of Representatives expressed similar and nearly as violent sentiments to one of the sponsors of the bill.

San Francisco was visited by a disastrous earthquake and fire during the Schmitz regime. While the disaster of April 18, 1906, caused a loss of only 500 lives, the damage was estimated to be well in excess of 350 million dollars. Japan demonstrated her good will toward the city of San Francisco by contributing to the relief of stricken victims through the Red Cross more generously than all the other nations of the world combined. But the act of sympathy and generosity mattered little to the exclusionists. Visiting Japanese scientists studying the earthquake were stoned in the streets of San Francisco, just as the laborers had been and were still being treated.[15] There were no signs that either the earthquake or the smouldering ruins had dampened in any way the spirit of the Exclusion League for, on September 16, it held a mass meeting, which was addressed by congressional candidates. It announced on this occasion that its membership had reached 78,500 and its program had been endorsed by independent organizations whose aggregate membership reached nearly $4\frac{1}{2}$ million. In the political campaign of the fall of 1906 the Japanese question became a popular issue as both the Republican and Democratic state conventions declared for the exclusion of the Japanese.

Little did the Ruef-Schmitz-controlled San Francisco Board of Education realize that it would precipitate a diplomatic crisis between the United States and Japan when it passed, on October 11, a special resolution ordering the school principals to carry out the segregation of Chinese, Japanese, and Korean children, forcing them to attend the Oriental school in Chinatown after the fifteenth. Since the Chinese children were already under segregation, it was evident that the school order was aimed at the Japanese. It was alleged that the Japanese children were not only overcrowding the schools, but were vicious, immoral, and unfit to associate with white children. President Roosevelt sent Secretary of Commerce and Labor Victor H. Metcalf to San Francisco to investigate the affair. It was found that there were only 93 Japanese children of whom 68 were born in Japan and 25 were American born. The drastic action of the school board

[15] Thomas A. Bailey, *Theodore Roosevelt and the Japanese-American Crisis,* pp. 16–27.

was denounced in various quarters, particularly by the press in the eastern part of the country, as a gratuitous affront to a sensitive nation.

A considerable number of influential Californians deplored the action of the school board. Chambers of commerce, churches, missionaries, and educators deplored it. Among the prominent educators of the state who expressed disapproval were President David Starr Jordan of Stanford University, President Benjamin Ide Wheeler of the University of California, school superintendents in various parts of the state, and the school principals of the city of San Francisco itself. A London *Times* correspondent on the scene wrote that if one-quarter of the current reports could be believed, conditions in San Francisco were worse than any other American municipality had ever experienced. Mayor Eugene Schmitz and his brains, Abe Ruef, had both been indicted by a grand jury for extortion shortly before the school board issued the segregation order. Every member of the Union Labor Party Board of Education owed his appointment to the corrupt regime, and the entire body was regarded as a rubber stamp for the Schmitz-Ruef political machine.

The discriminatory action of the San Francisco School Board brought immediate and strong protest from the Japanese government, which regarded it as a deliberate affront. Japan was now in a self-confident, if not belligerent, mood, and more than ever eager to defend her national honor, since she had just been victorious in a struggle for international recognition and had won for herself a new position in the Far East. In some quarters the action was interpreted as tantamount to war. The Japanese press was greatly agitated. One of the influential Tōkyō papers, *Mainichi,* stated on October 21 in an inflammatory tone that Japan should send a navy to chastise the Americans. However, on the whole, the tone of the press was moderate and calm. The press in Europe criticized the United States for what was regarded an entirely unwarranted provocation of a sensitive and proud nation. "The insult was naturally felt keenly," editorialized the London *Times* on October 30, "in Japan, whose people justly consider that they have abundantly proved their right to equal treatment among civilized nations." Germany went so far as to predict that an American-Japanese war was imminent.

American newspapers in general demanded the immediate revocation of the school order and a redress of injury inflicted on Japanese pride. California's reaction to the feeling aroused in Japan as well as to the attitude of the rest of the country was an intensification of anti-Japanese sentiment. So loud and persistent did war talk on both sides of the Pacific become for a time that Roosevelt thought war possible, if not imminent. The incident was, by his own admission, the greatest diplomatic crisis of the Roosevelt administration.[16] The President was "horribly bothered" by the event and censured the Californians. "The infernal

16 A. Whitney Griswold, *The Far Eastern Policy of the United States,* p. 350.

fools in California," he wrote to his son, Kermit, on October 27, "and especially in San Francisco, insult the Japanese recklessly, and in the event of war, it will be the Nation as a whole which will pay the consequences."[17]

While the yellow press incited public opinion to hostile outbursts, the Japanese government entertained no thought of going to war with the United States over the immigration controversy. In the first place, the financial condition of the nation in the period following the expensive Russo-Japanese War did not permit any such undertaking. Government bonds had dropped and no reduction in war debts had been achieved. Japan's position from the point of naval power and war potential was by no means superior to that of the United States. Moreover, a war with the United States would have been an invitation to both China and Russia for revenge. Japan had no inclination to risk the position she had just attained in the Far East at great sacrifice. The government, therefore, was desirous of strengthening American-Japanese friendship by solving the immigration problem through diplomatic negotiations.[18] Accordingly, on September 29, 1908, Foreign Minister Komura instructed Ambassador Takahira in Washington to start negotiations with a view to reaching an agreement with the United States. This resulted subsequently in the Root-Takahira Agreement.

On December 4, after studying the Metcalf report,[19] the President delivered a message to Congress in which he characterized the segregation order as a "wicked absurdity" and bluntly warned that he would use the United States Army, if necessary, to protect the Japanese in California from further violence. At the same time, he reminded Congress of Japan's remarkable progress, her generosity to the San Francisco earthquake victims, the traditional friendship, and the cultural ties between the two nations, and advocated legislation conferring the right of naturalization on the Japanese.[20]

The efforts of the President and the Secretary of State to urge the reflection of the California state legislature and the pressure brought to bear upon the mayor of San Francisco produced no appreciable improvement in the situation. On the contrary, the intervention of the Federal government was resented as an infringement upon local authority, and anti-Japanese agitation was carried on with even greater vigor by the Hearst group and ambitious politicians, who saw in the situation an excellent opportunity to make political capital by exciting prejudice against the Japanese and securing labor support for themselves. The *Chronicle* supported the agitators who contended that the Japanese laborers were not only unassimilable, but also were thwarting the work of the labor unions by

17 Roosevelt to Kermit Roosevelt, quoted in Bailey, *op. cit.,* p. 83.

18 Kashima Morinosuke, *Teikoku Gaikō no Kihon Seisaku,* p. 238.

19 Victor H. Metcalf, *Japanese in the City of San Francisco,* U.S. Senate Document No. 147, 59th Congress, 2nd Session.

20 For the text of the message, see *Foreign Relations of the United States,* 1906, Vol. I, pp. vii*ff.*

their low wages and thus were lowering the American standard of living. The Japanese immigrants had become the victims of the same racial prejudice that had been the product of the mining camps and railway construction gangs of mid-nineteenth century California and that until only a few years before had been directed entirely against the Chinese. This prejudice soon spread into Canada, and the entire Pacific Coast became the center of anti-Japanese agitation.

As expected, the San Francisco *Chronicle* scored the presidential message, calling Roosevelt "an unpatriotic President, who united with aliens to break down the civilization of his own countrymen," and in Washington, California congressmen demonstrated their belligerency by again introducing exclusion bills. In the face of strong antagonism, which increased proportionately with presidential chiding, Roosevelt decided to lay down the "big stick" and speak softly. In the latter part of January, 1907, he asked the San Francisco Board of Education to come to Washington to work out a settlement that would be agreeable to all. Mayor Schmitz waited a week to decide whether or not to permit the Board to go, and then decided to go along with them. Ironically enough, Schmitz had presided over a protest meeting against the President just before Christmas of the preceding year, a meeting held supposedly under the joint auspices of the Union Labor Party and the Exclusion League.

The president of the Exclusion League, Tveitmoe, telegraphed Schmitz in Washington telling him not to desert the laboring man and pointing out that "California is the white man's country, not the Caucasian graveyard." The Exclusion League ignored the President's request to keep silent while negotiations with Japan were in progress, lest unfriendly remarks might be prejudicial to the conclusion of a satisfactory agreement. Neither did the California legislature heed the request that the agitation cease temporarily. Consequently, a mass of anti-Japanese bills appeared in the 1907 session at Sacramento.

On February 29 President Roosevelt signed an amendment to the Immigration Act of 1907,[21] by virtue of which he was empowered to exclude from the United States immigrants holding passports to any country other than the United States, its insular possessions, or the Canal Zone and attempting to use them to enter the United States. This successfully stemmed the flow of Japanese labor from Hawaii, Mexico, and Canada to the United States. As a *quid pro quo,* the San Francisco Board of Education on March 13, upon its return from Washington, rescinded the objectionable resolution insofar as it applied to the Japanese.

On the very heels of President Roosevelt's signature of the amendment to the immigration law of 1907, Foreign Minister Hayashi, in a note dated February 24, responded favorably to Secretary of State Root's proposal that Japan herself voluntarily undertake to impose restrictions on labor immigration. Although this note was the basis, it was not until the following year, on February 18,

[21] *Congressional Record,* 59th Congress, 1st Session, p. 2809.

that the Gentlemen's Agreement was concluded. By this agreement, the Japanese government pledged not to issue passports to laborers, skilled or unskilled, except to those who were domiciled in the United States, or to their families, namely, parents, wives, and children. Nonlaborers were exempt from its provisions. The executive agreement served to alleviate anti-Japanese sentiment in California, at least for the time being, while restricting immigration by a method that did not tread upon Japanese sensibility. However, this marked only the beginning, rather than the end, of difficulties between Japan and the United States, which came perilously close to explosion many times. The Canadian Gentlemen's Agreement was concluded between Japan and Canada in December, 1907, only a few months after the outbreak of riots in Vancouver directed against the 7,500 Japanese residents in the city.

An entirely unexpected development was injected into the complicated immigration controversy to aggravate the already delicate situation that obtained between the United States and Japan. As in the case of most, if not all, immigrant groups arriving in the United States, the number of married men was disproportionately small. In 1900, out of a total Japanese population of 24,326, there were only 410 married women. By 1910 the number had increased to 5,580, but the total population had reached 72,157. Assuming that half of the population comprised those of marriageable ages, the ratio of men to women was better than six to one. As the immigrants settled down in a few years, the demand for women for economic as well as social reasons became great. In California, where antimiscegenation legislation forbade marriage between Orientals and whites, it was practically impossible for the Japanese immigrants to find mates. As a result, they began to send for their wives to whom they were married by proxy in Japan. This gave rise to the "picture brides," a practice not at all inconsistent with their age-old custom of arranging marriages through go-betweens. These "picture brides" were admitted to the United States under the Gentlemen's Agreement. This procedure, which invited the strenuous objection of Californians, was continued until the Japanese government agreed to stop issuing passports after February, 1920, at the request of President Wilson. By 1920, the number of married women had increased to 22,193 out of a total population of 110,010, which was still out of proportion, in spite of the admission of a considerable number of "picture brides." [22]

In February, 1908, even as final negotiations were in progress for the carrying out of the Gentlemen's Agreement, the Exclusion League met at Seattle in its first annual convention and adopted a memorial addressed to Congress declaring against any executive agreement stipulating the class or number of persons to be

---

[22] It was not until the 1930's that a semblance of balance was achieved between male and female population among the Japanese residents in America.

admitted to the United States as immigrants from foreign countries.[23] It left no room for doubt that this was directed against President Roosevelt.

The number of anti-Japanese measures introduced into the California legislature in the 1909 session numbered seventeen. These comprised the Drew Alien Land Bill, compelling every landowner to become a citizen within five years or dispose of his holdings, effectually excluding alien Japanese from land ownership; the anti-Japanese school bill for the segregation of Japanese children in public schools, a revival of the old agitation which precipitated an international crisis only three years earlier; the municipal segregation bill authorizing municipalities to segregate within certain prescribed districts "undesirable, improper, and unhealthy persons" in order to "protect the health, morals, and peace of their inhabitants." At the intervention of Governor Gillett and of President Roosevelt, these bills were dropped.[24]

What aggravated California's apprehension was the renewal in 1911 of the Treaty of Commerce and Navigation of 1894. Article 1 of the new treaty provided that "The citizens or subjects of each . . . shall have liberty to enter, travel, and reside in the territories of the other. . . ." The elimination of the exclusion provision of 1894 alarmed the California legislature. While the 1911 treaty was still pending, the California Senate passed by an overwhelming majority of 29 to 3 a land bill denying to aliens ineligible for citizenship the right to own land. But the measure was dropped at the intercession of President Taft, who gave assurance that the Treaty of 1911 would continue the exclusion of Japanese laborers. The only safeguard against immigration was a declaration, signed by Ambassador Uchida, that Japan would continue to enforce the Gentlemen's Agreement.

The election of 1912 placed a Democratic President in the White House, but the California legislature became Progressive and Republican. This change in American domestic politics was highly significant and was to be reflected inevitably even in foreign relations, particularly in American-Japanese relations. The cleavage between the State of California and the Federal government became more pronounced, as the former assumed a belligerent and perhaps an intransigent attitude. About forty anti-Japanese measures were introduced in the California legislature in the 1913 session. The Senate drafted an antialien land law, applicable to all noncitizens, regardless of nationality or eligibility. Secretary of State Bryan telegraphed his preference for the Senate bill over the Assembly bill, which was to be applied specifically to aliens ineligible to citizenship. The Senate, however, under tremendous pressure brought to bear upon it from certain quarters, amended the bill so as to exempt practically all European and Canadian aliens.

[23] U.S. Immigration Commission, *Reports,* Vol. 23, p. 170.

[24] Theodore Roosevelt, *An Autobiography,* pp. 382–384, 416. Japanese Immigration and Colonization, Senate Document No. 55, 67th Congress, 1st Session, p. 62.

President Wilson protested against the discrimination in the proposed California land law, emphasizing that "invidious discrimination will inevitably draw in question the treaty obligations of the Government of the United States." In an attempt to prevent the passage of a bill that would discriminate against the Japanese, he sent Secretary Bryan to Sacramento in April, 1913. The President's message was delivered to the executive session of the legislature, held behind closed doors. Although the legislature was satisfied that Bryan had come to consult with them and not to wield a club, the efforts of the Secretary of State were in vain. The Senate refused to acquiesce, feeling no need for tolerating the intervention of a Democratic president in a Republican state legislature. The upshot was the Webb-Heney bill, which conformed to the treaty obligations of the United States by leaving to aliens ineligible for citizenship all the rights to real property given by treaty, but no other except the right to lease land for a three-year period. In May the bill became law over the opposition of President Wilson, the Panama-Pacific Exposition, and the Asiatic Exclusion League, whose members believed that the enactment of the law would impede the fight for exclusion. The law, however, did not deprive the Japanese of the land that they already owned.

Comparative quiet prevailed during the war years, particularly after America entered the war and became an ally of Japan. The year 1919 saw a national election approaching, and the American Legion, which had been just organized, entered the picture in California to back Senator Phelan, as the Japanese again became a target of attack in which the exclusionists exaggerated the increase in acreage owned by Japanese through subterfuge and evasion of the law. In April Secretary of State Lansing wired from the Paris Peace Conference that "it would be particularly unfortunate" to have an anti-Japanese law passed by the California legislature, as this would be prejudicial to the interests of the Conference. The signature on June 28, 1919, of the Versailles Treaty removed the diplomatic restraints that had been holding back anti-Japanese talk and agitation for fear that they might seriously affect the signing of peace.

The old Exclusion League, which had been dormant since 1909, was revived in September, 1919, and secured the affiliated membership of such organizations as the American Legion, the State Federation of Labor, and the Native Sons and Daughters of the Golden West. It adopted a five-point program of Japanese exclusion, namely, (1) the cancellation of the Gentlemen's Agreement, (2) the exclusion of "picture brides," (3) the rigorous exclusion of all Japanese as immigrants, (4) the confirmation and legalization of the policy that Asiatics shall forever be barred from United States citizenship, and (5) an amendment to the Federal Constitution providing that no child born in the United States shall be given the rights of an American citizen unless both parents are of a race eligible for citizenship.[25] The Hearst papers joined forces with the Exclusion League

[25] Los Angeles *Examiner,* September 18, 1919.

and the American Legion in leading the movement. The Legion sponsored a propaganda movie, entitled "Shadows of the West," as part of an intensive campaign calculated to rouse public sentiment against the Japanese.[26]

At its national convention in San Francisco in 1920 the American Legion adopted a resolution demanding the cancellation of the Gentlemen's Agreement. The American Federation of Labor, at its forty-first annual convention in Denver, Colorado, in June, 1921, pronounced that "the Japanese peril is not only a serious condition for California but it is a positive menace to the entire nation." [27]

Through an initiative measure, Californians in 1920 passed by a 3 to 1 majority a new alien land law that removed even the right to lease land, a right that had until then been enjoyed by aliens ineligible for citizenship. The new land law recognized the right to lease or acquire real property only as provided for in a treaty; this meant that it was no longer possible for a Japanese to lease land for agricultural purposes.[28] Between 1921 and 1925 alien land laws similar in purpose to that of California were enacted in Washington,[29] Arizona,[30] and a dozen other states, namely, Oregon, New Mexico, Nevada, Idaho, Montana, Nebraska, Kansas, Missouri, Texas, Arkansas, Louisiana, and Delaware.[31]

That the California Alien Land Law was clearly within the purview of the state's rights was recognized by one of the leading Japanese authorities.[32] The subject of legislation was one of those matters in which the state enjoys exclusive jurisdiction and in which the Federal government has no right to intervene. Professor Yoshino emphasized that the limitation of the right of landholding in California to those eligible to citizenship, although an exception to the rule of equal rights for all, did not constitute a violation of the Constitution. He held that a discriminatory feature does not of itself render the law unconstitutional. Moreover, there was no violation of treaty obligations, inasmuch as the right conferred by the treaty on Japanese nationals was restricted to residential, commercial, and industrial uses. There was no provision for the right to lease land for agricultural purposes. Finally, the most-favored-nation treatment was recognized in commerce and navigation, but did not concern agricultural pursuits. Thus, the legality of the California Alien Land Law was beyond question.

On April 27, 1921, the California legislature passed a resolution urging Con-

---

[26] Buell, *op. cit.,* p. 37.

[27] American Federation of Labor, *Report of Proceedings,* Vol. 41, 1921.

[28] *Foreign Relations of the United States,* 1920, Vol. III, pp. 1–2; 1921 California Statutes, pp. 87–90.

[29] 1921 Washington Session Laws, Chap. 50.

[30] 1921 Arizona Session Laws, Chap. 29.

[31] Japan Consulate General, San Francisco. *Documentary History of Law Cases Affecting Japanese in the United States,* Vol. II, pp. 1014–1039; Griswold, *op. cit.,* p. 369.

[32] Yoshino Sakuzō, "Kashū Tochihō no Gōhōsei," *Kokusaihō Gaikō Zasshi (Revue de droit internationale et diplomatique),* Vol. 19, pp. 223–230, November, 1920.

gress to pass an exclusion law.[33] Two years later, on May 18, 1923, it passed another resolution urging the exclusion of aliens ineligible to citizenship.[34] Beginning in 1921 anti-Japanese sentiment in California became markedly acute, as developments within the state incensed the exclusionists. In July Japanese contractors underbid the American Fruit Workers' Union, an organization of "fruit tramps" in the melon fields of Turlock. White farmers insisted that they could not afford to pay the price asked by the union and continued to employ Japanese. Several hundred irate white men, by means of trucks and with the apparent connivance of the local police, placed the Japanese aboard a freight train, and warned them not to come back.[35] Similar incidents followed in other parts of the state, including Florin, which was the scene of violent anti-Japanese demonstrations.

Fearful of a large influx of immigrants from war-ravaged Europe, Congress enacted the Emergency Quota Act, approved in May, 1921, establishing a quota system. The number of aliens of any nationality to be admitted to the United States in any one year was to be limited to 3 per cent of the number of foreign-born persons of such nationality resident in the United States in 1910. A year later, the act was extended for a period of two years. Thus, in 1924, the United States Congress was faced with the task of enacting a permanent immigration law to supersede the emergency act of 1921. It was in the course of deliberation on the immigration policy that Japanese exclusion became an important issue.

Meanwhile, the U.S. Supreme Court in the case of *Ozawa v. U.S.* (260 U.S. 178) handed down a decision on November 13, 1922, to the effect that the Japanese were ineligible for citizenship by naturalization. On February 19 of the following year the Supreme Court ruling was extended to all Orientals in the case of *U.S. v. Thind* (261 U.S. 204) and the legality of the alien land laws of California and Washington was upheld by the highest tribunal.[36]

The House Committee on Immigration, in making a report entitled "Restriction of Immigration" (House Report 350, 68th Congress, 1st Session) on March 24, 1924, contended that the congressional prerogative of regulating immigration from Japan had been surrendered to the Japanese government by the Gentlemen's Agreement of 1908. Representative Albert Johnson of Washington, Chairman of the House Committee on Immigration and Naturalization, presented the official views of the Pacific Coast that favored the exclusion of aliens ineligible for citizenship. Exceptions were to be made of persons returning from a temporary visit abroad, merchants, clergymen, professors, and students. Obviously, Congress was opposed to the continuance of the Gentlemen's Agreement, which was an executive agreement in which it had no part. On April 12 the

[33] 1921 California Statutes, p. 1774.
[34] 1923 California Statutes, Chap. 60.
[35] San Francisco *Call,* July 22, 1921.
[36] Griswold, *op. cit.,* p. 369; Japan Consulate General, San Francisco, *op. cit.,* pp. 1–180.

House adopted the immigration bill, containing the exclusion clause, by an overwhelming majority of 323 to 71, in spite of the protest by Secretary of State Hughes. In the Senate, the attitude had been rather liberal and Hughes' suggestion to place Japan on a quota basis, as was the case for all European countries, appeared to have a reasonably good chance of adoption, in which case only 146 Japanese would have been admitted to the United States every year. The quota had been fixed at 2 per cent of the 1890 census figures.

While the bill was pending in Congress, the Japanese Ambassador Hanihara, with the approval, if not at the suggestion, of the State Department sent a note to the Secretary of State, stating that the Gentlemen's Agreement was in no way intended to restrict the sovereign rights of the United States to regulate immigration to her shores; rather it had been concluded as an alternative to discriminatory immigration legislation, which would have wounded the national susceptibilities of the Japanese people. After emphasizing that his government had scrupulously and faithfully carried out the terms of the agreement which was a "self-imposed restriction," he expressed confidence that the United States government would recommend to Congress that it refrain from resorting to a measure which would hurt the sensibilities of the Japanese nation. Ambassador Hanihara concluded his note with the assertion that the enactment of the pending measure would inevitably bring "grave consequences . . . upon the otherwise happy and mutually advantageous relations between the United States and Japan."

Secretary Hughes, who concurred with the Japanese Ambassador's interpretation of the Gentlemen's Agreement, forwarded copies of the Hanihara note together with his own reply to the Chairman of the House and Senate Committees on Immigration. As already mentioned, the House promptly adopted the general immigration bill, containing the Japanese exclusion clause. In the Senate, however, in the course of deliberations, Senator Lodge of Massachusetts indignantly declared that the note of the Japanese Ambassador was not only "improper" but contained a "veiled threat" against the United States. Even Senator Reed, who had at first favored the extension of the Gentlemen's Agreement, reversed his stand, as he felt that no nation had the right to stop the United States from exercising the sovereign right of determining who shall come within its gates. Senators who had not made up their minds were no longer in doubt as to what course they should take. The Senate voted without hesitation for the exclusion of aliens ineligible for citizenship. By May 15 the immigration bill had been approved by both houses of Congress. Eleven days later, on May 26, President Coolidge signed the General Immigration Bill, appending to it a statement criticizing the method used by Congress to achieve exclusion and making it clear that, had the exclusion provision stood alone, he would have vetoed it without any hesitation.

Thus, after two decades of unremitting efforts of the exclusionists, on July 1, 1924, when the new immigration act took effect, the organized opposition to Japanese immigration, which had had its origin in San Francisco, crystallized into a national policy. Much of the success of the exclusionist campaign was due to Valentine S. McClatchy of the Sacramento *Bee* and his brain child,[37] the California Joint Immigration Committee, representing such organizations as the American Legion, the State Federation of Labor, the National Grange, the Native Sons and Daughters of the Golden West, and other groups and individuals, including women's clubs, patriotic, civic, and fraternal organizations, aided by the Hearst papers, all of which remained adamant and resolutely opposed to any change in Japanese exclusion when a movement to place Japan on a quota basis was started later. In the words of the official report of the American Federation of Labor, the long-drawn-out movement for the exclusion of Japanese labor was crowned with success "largely through the persistent and well-directed efforts of the American Federation of Labor, the American Legion, and the National Grange." [38]

On May 31, the Japanese government lodged a formal protest through its embassy in Washington. Needless to say, the exclusion law aroused much comment and resentment in Japan. In April, fifteen Tōkyō newspapers published a joint declaration calling the bill "inequitable and unjust." Jingoist papers vehemently denounced the United States for the "grave insult," "arrogance," "persecution," and "deliberate slap in the face." Even the moderate papers regarded the law as "harsh, cruel, and unjust" and as a "glaring breach of international etiquette." Although the point of emphasis in the criticisms was the discriminatory feature, many journals resented rather the method used in achieving the exclusion.

In the United States, criticism was directed against Congress for the method it employed in achieving the exclusion of Asiatic immigration, a policy that was unanimously supported by public opinion. Leading papers like *The New York Times,* New York *Herald-Tribune,* New York *World,* the Washington *Post,* and the *Christian Science Monitor* criticized congressional action as a "shocking disregard of the feeling of the Japanese," "an unnecessary affront to Japan," "a deliberate sabotage of our delicate international relations," and a "highly offensive method."

A large number of organizations passed resolutions criticizing the passage of the exclusion law, and particularly the discriminatory feature. A group of prominent New York business and professional men sent a cable to the America Japan Society in Tōkyō deploring the unjustifiable things said regarding Japan during the exclusion debate in Congress. Thirty presidents and presidents emeriti of leading American universities and colleges sent a telegram expressing regret for

[37] "Facts about Japanese Exclusion," editorial in *The Argonaut,* July 19, 1930.
[38] American Federation of Labor, *Report of Proceedings,* Vol. 44, p. 135, 1924.

the "inconsiderate action of the American Congress, which does not represent the sentiments of the American people toward Japan." [39]

Although anti-American demonstrations took place in some cities, and boycotts of American goods were started, they were soon abandoned as they were hurting the Japanese themselves as much as, if not more than, the intended victim, American business. On July 1, the date on which the exclusion went into effect, both houses of the Japanese Diet passed resolutions protesting against the discriminatory act. While the general public found it difficult, if not impossible, to understand the action of Congress, the Japanese government entertained not the slightest doubt that the subject of legislation was clearly within the rights of the United States Congress. What had not been anticipated, however, was the possibility that the wishes of the State Department as well as the President might not prevail in the face of the strong feeling that existed in Congress that the control of immigration was clearly the right of the legislative branch and not within the purview of the treaty-making power of the executive branch of the government. The exclusion law played directly into the hands of the militaristic elements in Japan and furnished an excellent basis for the advocacy of an aggressive, imperialistic foreign policy.

Before the memorable year 1924 came to an end, the Japanese Diet enacted a new Nationality Law [40] providing for expatriation, enabling those of Japanese parentage, born in the United States, Argentina, Brazil, Canada, Chile, Mexico, and Peru,[41] to renounce Japanese nationality. This legal procedure [42] for the termination of dual nationality on an individual basis was the culmination of the efforts of American citizens of Japanese ancestry as well as a concrete reflection of the liberal attitude of the Japanese government under Premier Katō. It was hoped also that it would alleviate the situation for Japanese emigrants abroad.

The achievement of statutory exclusion of the Japanese did not eradicate completely the anti-Japanese sentiment that had grown and been nourished by demagoguery and political opportunism on the part of ambitious politicians who were not bothered by scruples. In the beginning, that is from 1905 to 1907, anti-Japanese agitation had centered in the cities, especially in San Francisco. But after 1907 there developed a movement of Japanese immigrants away from the city to rural agricultural areas to avoid boycotts and unpleasant outbursts against them as much as to utilize their accumulating capital. This soon brought them into direct competition with white farmers. By the 1930's some of them were in a position to give competition to the shipper-growers in such places as the Imperial Valley and the San Joaquin Valley, particularly in the Salinas area. As war clouds began to gather in the Far East, the anti-Japanese feeling in

[39] *The New York Times,* July 6, 1924.
[40] *The New York Times,* July 16, 1924, Law No. 19, 1924.
[41] Imperial Ordinance No. 262, November 17, 1924.
[42] Home Ministry Ordinance No. 26, November 17, 1924.

the state became intense, though not translated into overt hostile action as in the 1920's.

Even as the exclusionists were carrying on their agitation, efforts were being made by enlightened leaders to counter the anti-Japanese movement. That business leaders should show grave concern was natural, for the agitation was adversely affecting American-Japanese trade. The San Francisco Chamber of Commerce "peace" mission in 1920 was an attempt to increase American-Japanese friendship by assuring the Japanese leaders of the good will of the United States in spite of the antipathy of the California legislature and the exclusionists.[43]

In March, 1929, when the quota system was revised, it was found that under the new national origins quota not more than 185 Japanese would be admitted, should Japan be placed on the quota basis. Americans who had opposed statutory exclusion from the very outset, particularly prominent educators, publicists, and clergymen, joined with business leaders on the West Coast in advocating the application of the quota system to China and Japan. The National Foreign Trade Convention, meeting in Los Angeles in May, 1930, adopted a resolution favoring a revision of the immigration law of 1924. Representative Albert Johnson, Chairman of the House Immigration and Naturalization Committee, announced in Washington that "in due time" he expected to propose an amendment to the Immigration Act that would give Japan a quota and expressed confidence that the House and Senate would accept such an amendment.[44] In 1931 the Immigration Committee of the United States Chamber of Commerce declared itself strongly in favor of a quota system. Most active in pushing the demand for a quota system was the California Council on Oriental Relations, organized in 1931 by prominent business and educational leaders of the state.[45] It is interesting to note that even the San Francisco *Chronicle,* which as the arch enemy of Japanese immigration launched a vigorous press campaign twenty-five years earlier, now advocated the quota system for Japan.[46] Everything seemed to be proceeding smoothly and success seemed almost assured in the fall of 1931, when official circles were confident and optimistic that revision of the Immigration Act would soon become a reality. But the blowing-up of the railroad tracks outside Mukden on September 18 precipitated the Manchurian Incident and not only shattered all hopes of repealing the statutory exclusion of Japanese immigrants, but also led inexorably toward a clash between the United States and Japan, which came ten years later.

[43] San Francisco *Call,* April 26, 1920, carried an interview with Wallace M. Alexander, President of the San Francisco Chamber of Commerce, who headed the businessmen's goodwill mission to Japan.

[44] Ichihashi Yamato, *Japanese in the United States,* pp. 368–369.

[45] Tupper and McReynolds, *Japan in American Public Opinion,* Chap. 7.

[46] San Francisco *Chronicle,* May 24, 1930.

Chapter 30. Diplomacy of the Twenties

Japan's diplomacy of the nineteen-twenties was a combination of idealistic profession of internationalism, expressed and reflected in her adherence to international agreements on the one hand, and the pursuit of expansionist policies, largely economic in nature, but nevertheless accompanied at times by political maneuvers and military actions, on the other. To a considerable extent this was the result of dual diplomacy, which gave rise to inconsistencies, contradictions, and not infrequently even to acts that appeared to be the result of almost calculated duplicity on the part of some segment of the government. The right hand did not always know what the left hand was doing. It was also the consequence of the nation's none-too-successful efforts to establish an equilibrium of internal forces that were locked in the struggle for supremacy and to make necessary adjustments in industry and trade in the process of orienting herself to the new conditions in international relations created by the First World War and the Washington Conference.

In spite of the apparent eclipse of the influence of the military during the twenties, caused by the rising tide of internationalism and antimilitarism, the exponents of expansion were never completely overshadowed by their opponents. Rather the military and reactionary civilians were working together to pave the way for what came to pass in the thirties. The highhandedness exhibited by the domineering military clique under the Terauchi Cabinet in 1918 was to be duplicated, if not exceeded, under the Tanaka Cabinet a decade later.

Less than two months before the opening of the Washington Conference, when Japanese public opinion was unequivocably opposed to war, Premier Hara expressed his views regarding the essential requisites of peace.[1] He was convinced that peace must be predicated upon the realization that no nation has the right to force another people to commit national or racial suicide, the recognition of the basic truth that nations and races do not differ in their desire to live and grow, and the assurance to all the peoples of an equitable distribution of the world's resources and the necessities of life. That this was a plea to the world by a "have-not" nation to open wide the "economic doors and to extend to all peoples free access to what is vital to existence" was apparent. However, it reflected the feeling then shared even by the liberal elements that

[1] Hara Takashi, "Reflections on Lasting Peace," *Living Age,* Vol. 312, pp. 7–11, January 7, 1922. This was taken from the Japanese original that appeared in *Gaikō Jihō* (*Revue diplomatique*) of September 15, 1921.

when Japan came out of her long seclusion, "the powerful nations had already divided up the greater portion of the earth's surface among themselves." In expounding his "live-and-let-live" doctrine, Hara asserted that "if universal peace is to be realized, one race or people must cease to menace the existence of another, that the right of all to live and progress must be guaranteed by establishing international equality of economic opportunity and by subordinating narrow egoism to the general welfare of humanity." [2]

During the Washington Conference Ambassador Shidehara, one of the Japanese delegates, provided an amplification of Hara's doctrine with special reference to Japan's China policy.[3] He emphasized that Japan had reached the stage of development where she had no alternative but to industrialize to preserve her national existence. Continental Asia has the materials for her trade, and Japan demanded the right to equal opportunities there; but in competing with other countries, she needs no advantages beyond her geographical position. She asked only the adoption of the "live-and-let-live" policy by all concerned. "Like England," he continued, "we must obtain our sustenance abroad and our products must go to foreign markets. China's markets and materials mean to other countries only more trade; to Japan they are vital necessities." The conciliatory policy that Baron Shidehara pursued as Foreign Minister a few years later was predicated on his belief that a prosperous and stable China, organized to produce and able to buy, would be a blessing for Japan and that "the Open Door and equal opportunity in China mean economy, if not actual salvation, for Japan."

SINO-JAPANESE RELATIONS

Marked deterioration in Sino-Japanese relations followed in the wake of the Twenty-one Demands in 1915. China retaliated with boycotts, which came to be used increasingly as an effective weapon. Strained relations between China and Japan were further aggravated by the failure of the Versailles Conference to settle the Shantung question. The powers had actually sanctioned, though temporarily, Japan's occupation of the province, which had been formerly exploited by the Germans. China's grievances were not redressed and her dissatisfaction was reflected at home especially among the student population.

Several thousand students held a demonstration in Peking on May 5, 1919, while the Peace Conference was in progress at Paris. A band stormed and burned the home of Tsao Ju-lin, Minister of Transportation, and attacked and seriously wounded Chang Tsung-hsiang, Minister to Japan, forcing him to retire from the diplomatic service. The students also stormed the home of the

[2] *Ibid.,* p. 10.

[3] Baron Shidehara Kijurō, "A Frank Official Statement for Japan," *Current History Magazine,* Vol. 15, pp. 391–392, December, 1921.

Director of the Bureau of Currency, Lu Tsung-yu, who, in 1913, was appointed the first Chinese Minister to Japan under the Republic. Anti-Japanese demonstrations spread rapidly to parts outside of Peking and incited mob action. Agitation continued despite the issuance of a statement by the Japanese Foreign Office on May 17 intended to mollify Chinese opinion. Student agitation was revived in June and anti-Japanese general strikes were called in Shanghai, Nanking, and other cities, where organized bands entered shops handling Japanese goods and looted and burned them.

Although the Washington Conference helped to solve the Shantung question, China was embittered by the continuation of the treaties of 1915. The Peking government in March, 1923, sent a note to Japan demanding the abrogation of the Sino-Japanese treaties of 1915 and the return of the Liaotung Peninsula, the lease of which would have expired on March 27 of that year, had it not been for the treaties. When Japan rejected the demand, China retaliated with a spirited student movement as well as boycotts and demonstrations. The anti-Japanese agitation went far beyond the usual boycott, for it included a ban on the supply of raw materials, dismissal of Japanese employees in Chinese firms, withdrawal of Chinese employed by Japanese firms, refusal to deposit in Japanese banks, and refusal to handle Japanese currency. The movement dealt a severe blow to the Japanese, resulting in a marked decline in trade with China, especially in the carrying trade, sluggishness in banking and financing activities, leading to the withdrawal and closing of Japanese commercial establishments.

In the autumn of 1923 Russian advisers, led by Michael Borodin, who had been invited to Canton by Sun Yat-sen, started to inject new life into the Kuomintang by reorganizing it into a closely knit party of disciplined individuals, held together by a common program of action rather than solely by the bond of personal loyalty to Dr. Sun and modeled on the Russian Communist Party. As the reorganization of the Party was proceeding, dissatisfaction mounted among the Canton merchants and the gentry of Kwangtung province, who had organized the Merchants' Volunteer Corps locally to protect life and property against the militarists of Yunnan and Kwangsi, who were exploiting the city and the province through heavy exactions. As the Party increased the intensity of radical propaganda and brought about the organization of workers' and peasants' unions, the gentry became hostile and organized a movement to expel Sun Yat-sen from Canton. However, in the clash that ensued in the fall of 1924 the Kuomintang forces won a complete victory over the merchants' mercenary forces.

With the death of Sun Yat-sen in March, 1925, an internal struggle for leadership of the Party developed and caused a split among the leaders on doctrinal grounds. The left wing, supported by the communist members and having had the advantage of the initial control of the central machinery of the

Party, gained control of Canton. It had no difficulty in overpowering the right wing represented by the merchants and the gentry.

Student demonstrations were resumed in Peking in May, 1925. Several hundred students attacked the Minister of Education, who had issued an order banning the observation of the National Humiliation Day, a reminder of the Twenty-one Demands. On May 30 students and strike sympathizers held a demonstration in the International Settlement and denounced unequal treaties, imperialism, and the imperialist powers: Great Britain, Japan, France, and the United States. This was soon followed by a wave of anti-Japanese and anti-British feeling in the Yangtze valley as far west as Chungking, in the north to Tsinanfu and Peking, and southward to Foochow, Swatow, and Canton. When the anti-British strike and boycott broke out in June, 1925, in Shanghai, the powers found it necessary to land marines. The Shakee-Shamen affair, in which considerable fighting and loss of life took place, was the most serious incident of the antiforeign movement, which lasted until October of the following year. This period of fifteen months witnessed the greatest unrest and most intensive antiforeign agitation since the Boxer Uprising of 1900.

In the midst of the violent antiforeign movement, a customs conference was opened in Peking on October 26, 1925, in accordance with the provision of the Washington treaty and was continued until July 3, 1926, when it was suspended indefinitely. This brought to an end a long period of cooperation among the powers in China. The failure of the conference reflected strong Anglo-Japanese disagreement. Japan wanted Chinese customs revenues, which had been kept in British banks and provided the British with an annual interest large enough to furnish a working capital, distributed to the banks of the various powers, prorated according to the volume of trade handled. Moreover, Japan proposed the appointment of a Chinese as Deputy Inspector-General of Customs. There was also strong disagreement over the method of using additional customs revenues, resulting from the authorized rise in tariff rates.[4]

Japan's opportunity for active intervention in Manchuria came in 1925, when General Kuo Sung-ling revolted against Marshal Chang Tso-lin with the encouragement of General Feng Yü-hsiang and the support of the Soviets. Additional troops were sent into Manchuria, and in December the headquarters of the Tenth Division was moved from Liaoyang to Mukden, and the Japanese military authorities prohibited Chinese troops from entering within 20 *li* of the South Manchuria Railway zone. Although Japanese troops from Korea and elements of the 18th Division were withdrawn early the following year, in January, a precedent for active intervention had been established. Japan's military action in Manchuria was obviously a deviation from the China policy that had been enunciated by the Foreign Office.

[4] Ashida Hitoshi, *Saikin Sekai Gaikōshi,* Vol. III, pp. 978–985.

As if to underscore this point, Foreign Minister Shidehara, in his address to the Diet on January 21, 1926, reiterated Japan's conciliatory China policy, which he had announced in the preceding session of the Diet. This consisted of absolute noninterference in China's domestic affairs and the protection of Japan's rights and interests by all legitimate means at her disposal. "No doubt complete tranquillity of the whole region of the three Eastern provinces, undisturbed by any scourge of war is highly to be desired," he declared, "in the interest of the native population as well as of the Japanese residents." But he felt that it was a responsibility that rested with China, and that the assumption of that responsibility by Japan without just cause would be "manifestly inconsistent with the fundamental conception of existing international relations, with the basic principles of the Washington treaties, and with the repeated declarations of the Japanese government. Taking such a course, we should forfeit our national honor and pride. Once and for all, in no case, and by no means can we be a party to so ill-advised an action."

Meanwhile antiforeign sentiment in China mounted. The Kuomintang Congress in 1926 decided to launch a "northern expedition" to rid the intraparty opposition of the militarists as a preliminary to the carrying out of a fight against foreign imperialism. The expedition planned by General Blücher got under way in the summer with Generalissimo Chiang Kai-shek as commander in chief, and the government was moved from Canton to Hankow in November. The Wuhan government, now dominated by Russian advisers headed by Borodin, was intent on weakening the dominant position of Chiang and to this end launched an anti-Chiang campaign.

In the spring of 1926, at the instigation of Soviet Ambassador Karakhan, nationalist troops, formerly under the command of General Feng, opened fire on Japanese gunboats and foreign merchant vessels at Taku and obstructed their freedom of navigation in and out of Tientsin. In protest of the violation of the Boxer Protocol of 1901, the ministers of the treaty Powers served an ultimatum on March 16. The Peking government had no alternative but to accede to the terms laid down by the foreign powers.

Students, aroused by radical leaders, both Chinese and Russian, protested against the ultimatum and the acceptance of the terms by the provisional government of Tuan Chi-jui. Thousands demonstrated before the Foreign Office (*Waichiaopu*), demanding the severance of diplomatic relations with the treaty Powers and, in the scuffle that followed, Tuan's guards opened fire and more than thirty of the demonstrating students were killed.

On October 20, 1926, which was the date on which revision of the existing Sino-Japanese treaty could be brought up, the Peking government broached the subject to Japan. In a memorandum of November 10 the Japanese Foreign Office communicated its willingness to negotiate for the revision of tariff rates as well as the Treaty of 1896. China's goal was to free herself from the shackles of unequal treaties by abolishing consular jurisdiction and restoring tariff autonomy. While the Japanese government readily expressed approval of the abolition of extraterritoriality in principle, it felt obliged to refrain from acting alone in disregard of the resolution of the Commission on Judicial Inquiry, which had released its report at the end of November.[5]

NANKING AFFAIR

When the Nationalist forces from the south captured Nanking in late March of 1927, they gave vent to their antiforeign feeling. A systematic and controlled attack was launched against all foreigners without distinction as to nationality, age, or sex. British, American and Japanese consulates were attacked, their nationals were murdered or wounded, and homes and institutions of foreign residents were looted and even burned. To protect their nationals, American and British gunboats found it necessary to drop shells on Nanking from the river as well as to land marines. Diplomatic representatives of the United States, Great Britain, Japan, France, and Italy jointly warned the Chinese government.

In reply, Foreign Minister Eugene Chen issued on April 1 a statement to the effect that the outrage was the work of reactionary, antirevolutionary factions. While expressing deep regret for the affair, he indicated that the Nationalist government would lodge a strong protest with the powers for the shelling of Nanking by British and American ships.

Representatives of Great Britain, the United States, Japan, Italy, and France held a conference a few days later in Peking and presented on April 11, identical notes to Generalissimo Chiang and Foreign Minister Chen demanding (1) the punishment of those responsible for the loss of lives, injuries, and affronts; (2) apology in writing from the Generalissimo himself, as well as the military commanders, and a guarantee of security of life and property of foreign residents, and (3) complete reparation for the loss of life, personal injuries, and material damages inflicted. Chen's reply to the powers attributed the disturbance to the existence of unequal treaties. Separate settlements were made by the United States in April, by Great Britain in August, and France in October of the following year. It was not until two years later, in April, 1929, that Japan reached a settlement as a result of negotiations carried on between Minister Yoshizawa and Foreign Minister C. T. Wang. The arrival of the Kuomintang armies in Shantung after the capture of Hsuchow and Pengpu led Great Britain, the United States, and France, as well as Japan to reinforce their troops in Peking and Tientsin, as had been agreed in Peking by the conference of diplomatic representatives in early April.

The Nanking outrage was partly a reflection of the internal strife within the

[5] The Commission met in Peking from January 12 to September 16.

revolutionary army itself, inspired and encouraged by the communist elements, who were out to foil Chiang's objective of achieving political supremacy by precipitating a serious international incident in Nanking. The leftist group at Wuhan, comprising T. V. Soong, Sun Fo, Hsu Chien, and Borodin, bent on seizing the national government, incited mobs into attacking the British concession at Hankow and succeeded in taking possession of it. Chiang had severed relations with the Wuhan government in April and arrested Communists in the Shanghai municipal government, Shanghai Council, and Shanghai Party headquarters. He succeeded in establishing a new anti-Communist Nanking government.

After setting up his government at Nanking on April 18, 1927, Generalissimo Chiang invited the support of all who were opposed to communism and Russian domination. Chinese leaders had become increasingly aware that Russia was more interested in exploiting the revolution for her own purposes than in helping the Nationalist revolution. The left wing non-Communist members of the Kuomintang were brought closer to the moderates, and the general conclusion was reached before long that the Party must be purged of Communists as well as the Soviet advisers. By the end of 1927 all of the region south of the Yangtze came under the control of the reorganized Nanking government headed by Chiang.

CHANGE IN JAPAN'S CHINA POLICY

Foreign Minister Shidehara once more reiterated his conciliatory China policy before the Diet in January, 1927, emphasizing respect for China's sovereignty and territorial integrity based on the policy of strict noninterference in domestic politics, economic cooperation, predicated upon the policy of coexistence and coprosperity, an attitude of sympathy and good will toward China's legitimate aspirations, a desire to aid in their realization, and protection by legitimate means of Japan's rights in China. But all this was to change in a matter of only three months.

The appearance of the Cabinet of General Baron Tanaka on April 20, 1927, signalled a complete shift from the conciliatory policy of Foreign Minister Shidehara to a firm attitude of the new Premier, who chose to be his own Foreign Minister during his entire tenure. The nationalist movement and the resulting political instability provided a rare opportunity to General Tanaka for the initiation of a positive policy toward China.

In the first few days of January, 1927, the antiforeignism of the nationalist movement had revealed itself at Hankow in the mob attacks on the British concession. Similar attacks followed in Kiukiang, while nationalist troops looted the British concession. As the nationalist troops began to advance toward Shanghai, the treaty Powers decided to dispatch troops. Before the end of

January, foreign troops started arriving, and when Shanghai was taken by the Nationalists in March, foreign military forces defending the International Settlement and the French concession numbered more than 16,000, which included 7,100 British, 4,000 Indian, 1,630 Japanese, and 1,430 American troops. By the end of April, when the Tanaka Cabinet was in control of foreign affairs, there were approximately 40,000 foreign troops in Shanghai.

Premier Tanaka seems to have felt strongly that Shidehara's conciliatory policy was weak and negative and had not achieved any results except to encourage the Chinese to stiffen their attitude. Consequently, he thought it was his duty as head of the government to rectify the error by reversing Shidehara's policy. In the cabinet meeting of May 27 a decision to send troops to Shantung was reached, and before the month was over Japan notified both the Peking and Nanking governments that troops were being dispatched to protect her nationals. Both Nanking and Peking protested but Japanese troops proceeded according to schedule to Tsingtao and thence to Tsinanfu. Tanaka's actions were reminiscent of the doings of the Terauchi Cabinet of the First World War. Following the withdrawal of Chiang's forces after his decision to suspend temporarily the "northern expedition," partly because the presence of Japanese troops in Shantung prevented the passage north of the Nationalists, the Japanese government announced in late August its intention to withdraw by September 8.

The continental policy of the Tanaka Cabinet was outlined by the Eastern Regions Conference, which was convened in Tōkyō by the Premier in the summer of 1927. The meetings, which were held from June 27 to July 6, were attended by cabinet members and high policy-making officials, including the Minister to China, Governor-General of Kwantung territory, President of the South Manchuria Railway, and consular officials from various parts of China. The decision reached at the Conference was to push the policy of peaceful economic penetration of China, which had been advocated by Shidehara, a step further, implemented by the use of military power whenever necessary.

While it is not possible to know the details of the discussions, the broad outlines of the policy adopted are quite clear.[6] It was agreed that although China's political stability and her peaceful economic development were greatly desired, they should be left in the hands of the Chinese people themselves, and since under existing conditions the emergence of a strong central government was not likely, the only alternative for the time being was to work with moderate local regimes and wait for the gradual process of national unification. In a period of political instability and disorder lawless elements were bound to disturb the peace and create international incidents. While the Japanese government desired that the Chinese authorities should maintain peace and order, necessary defensive measures were to be taken whenever Japan's rights and the life and

[6] Ashida, *op. cit.,* pp. 1028–1029.

property of her nationals were imperiled. This included measures to cope with anti-Japanese agitation and boycotts.

Manchuria, Mongolia, and particularly the Three Eastern Provinces, were regarded as having special importance on Japan's defense as well as on her economic development. Consequently she felt her special responsibility in maintaining peace and developing the economic and industrial resources of the region while at the same time making it safe for both Japanese and foreign residents. However, it was quite apparent that the government's prime concern was the protection of Japan's rights and their full utilization in strengthening her position. It was emphasized that should there be a spread of disorder into Manchuria and Mongolia to disturb the peace and threaten Japan's special position and rights, the Japanese government was prepared to take necessary steps to safeguard them.

Tsinan Affair. Having suffered reverses in his military campaigns against Sun Chuan-fang and Chang Tsung-chang, Chiang Kai-shek resigned his position in the Nanking government and retired to Shanghai. From there he went to Japan in August, where he remained until he was recalled to resume his position as commander in chief on January 4, 1928. With the issuance of orders for a general offensive, Chiang's "northern expedition" got under way once more in April. The Japanese government on the nineteenth transferred part of the troops from Tientsin to Tsinanfu, ostensibly to protect the 20,000 nationals residing in Shantung province. This was followed shortly by the dispatch of the Sixth Division from Japan "to protect Japanese nationals residing in Tsingtao and other places along the Tsingtao-Tsinan railway."

Nationalist forces entered Tsinanfu on May 1, followed the next day by Chiang himself, who demanded the withdrawal of Japanese troops, inasmuch as the responsibility for maintaining peace and order in the city fell on him. On May 3, however, fighting broke out between the Chinese and Japanese troops. Through the mediation of the British and American consuls an agreement was reached, and on the following day Nationalists were to withdraw from the city to a point 6 miles from the city.

Some 4,000 Chinese troops were still within the walled city, when on May 7 General Fukuda, the commander in chief of the Japanese forces, issued a twelve-hour ultimatum to the Nanking government demanding a formal apology from Generalissimo Chiang, the punishment of those responsible for the Tsinan affair, suspension of hostilities, cessation of anti-Japanese agitation, and the withdrawal of the nationalist troops from Tsinanfu and from each side of the Kiaochow-Tsinan railway to a distance of 20 *li,* or approximately 7 miles. After the expiration of the twelve-hour time limit, the Japanese troops began to expel forcibly the Chinese troops from the railway zone, and fighting was resumed in Tsinanfu. By the eleventh the Japanese were in control of the city, since by then troops in Shantung reached a total of 25,000.

Throughout the entire affair the provocative attitude of the Japanese military was much in evidence. General Fukuda's belligerent declaration beforehand that drastic steps would be taken against the Southern forces to maintain the prestige of the Japanese empire merely reflected the army's as well as General Tanaka's attitude. Japanese military authorities took the matter completely out of the hands of local consular authorities, who were powerless to do anything about it.

The Nanking government wired an appeal to the League of Nations on May 11, protesting against Japanese actions and requesting the calling of an emergency meeting of the Council to set up in accordance with Article 12, Section 2, of the Covenant a machinery of international inquiry or arbitration to advise Japan's cessation of military activities and withdrawal of her troops. The League took no action since the Nanking government had not yet been given *de jure* recognition by the powers. On the following day, the Nanking government unsuccessfully sought the mediation of the United States. As a result, Chiang Kai-shek on the twelfth acceded to all the Japanese demands.[7] The Tsinan Affair represented a clash between Japan's imperialistic and expansionist continental policy and China's growing revolutionary nationalist movement. Its upshot was strong anti-Japanese sentiment that flared up with great intensity in Canton, Shanghai, Peking, and Tientsin.

Marshal Chang Tso-lin's Death. Final clashes between the Southern forces under Generalissimo Chiang and the Northern armies of Marshal Chang were expected in Chihli, Shantung, and along the Yellow River. Armies of Li Tsung-jen, Yen Hsi-shan, and Feng Yü-hsian joined forces with the Generalissimo's forces to press against the Northern armies. By the end of May, the Southern armies had thrown a semicircular ring around Tientsin and Peking. Suddenly, giving up any attempt at resistance, Marshal Chang ordered a general evacuation to the north and he himself left Peking by a special twenty-car train at 0:55 A.M. on June 3, 1928, and headed for Mukden. As the train, speeding toward Mukden at the break of dawn on June 4 approached the point where the South Manchuria Railway line crossed the Mukden-Peking railroad there was a terrific explosion, wrecking the Marshal's car and injuring him fatally. The Marshal's death ended abruptly and mysteriously the colorful career of the son of a peasant who had worked himself up from banditry to the rank of Field Marshal of the Chinese army and simultaneously Grand Admiral of the Chinese navy. He controlled for a time the vast region between the Yangtze in the south and the Amur in the north.

[7] Together with former gendarmerie Captain Amakasu, managing director of the Manchuria Motion Picture Company, Colonel Kawamoto became influential in political circles as wire-pullers behind the scenes. Shortly before Japan's defeat, he was being considered seriously as the next Director of the General Affairs Bureau of Manchukuo, the key position. Mori Shōzō, *Sempū Nijūnen*, Vol. I, pp. 18–19.

Attempts by the government to dispose of the incident satisfactorily ran into serious difficulties in the Imperial Household Ministry, and the military found itself in an almost untenable position. Elder Statesman Saionji's circumlocutional advice to resign was accepted by General Tanaka, who submitted the resignation of his entire Cabinet on July 2. This came so fast that there was no time to find a person to fill the post of Overseas Affairs Minister which had just been created in April.

For seventeen years the death of Marshal Chang remained shrouded in an impenetrable cloud of secrecy. Not until after Japan's defeat in the Second World War did the truth come out. Colonel Kawamoto Daisaku, a staff officer of the Kwantung army, convinced that the liquidation of Chang, who had shifted from cooperation with Japan to collaboration with Great Britain and the United States, would facilitate and materially aid the execution of Japanese policies in Manchuria and Mongolia, had volunteered to remove the Marshal.[7a] After resigning from the army, Colonel Kawamoto found his way into civilian economic activities, becoming the managing director of the Manchuria Coal Company and later president of the Shansi Industrial Company.

SOVIET-JAPANESE RELATIONS

Russo-Japanese relations, which had been interrupted by the overthrow of the house of Romanov during the Revolution in 1917, were restored in January, 1925, with the signing of a treaty in Peking. This was the culmination of the negotiations that had actually been started late in August of 1921 at Dairen. Even earlier, in April, 1919, the Far Eastern representative of the Soviet government had unsuccessfully approached Matsudaira Tsunco, chief of the political affairs department of the Japanese Expeditionary Force at Vladivostok. In December, 1920, the diplomatic representative of the newly established Far Eastern Republic approached Matsudaira without results. Finally in June, 1921, a secret agreement was signed between the Chita representative and Japanese vice-consul Shimada. This actually became the prelude to Russo-Japanese negotiations, which led to the reestablishment of diplomatic relations.

The Dairen Conference, which was opened on August 26, 1921, between Consul General Matsushima and Foreign Minister Ignatius Yourin of the Far Eastern Republic came at a time when, from an international point of view, conditions were unfavorable to Japan. Less than three months earlier, on May 31, the United States government had sent a strong note to the effect that Japan's continued occupation of strategic positions in eastern Siberia served to increase rather than to decrease disorder in the region, and expressing doubt as to whether the occupation of northern Sakhalin and Nikolaevsk in retaliation

[7a] *Ibid.*

for the Nikolaevsk massacre was justifiable according to international law. The note reiterated Japan's pledge to the Russian people made in the summer of 1918 disavowing any designs and emphasizing that the United States would not recognize any of the demands or claims arising from occupation and control, nor would she countenance Japan's violation of treaty rights or Russia's territorial rights and political integrity.

Apparently, in order to avoid the discussion by all the participating powers of the various Far Eastern problems at the coming conference at Washington, the Japanese government decided to negotiate separately with the Russians to settle the outstanding issues including the Siberian question. Japan's demands, which had the approval of the Cabinet, included the nonenforcement of Communism on the Japanese in the Far Eastern Republic, refraining from Communist propaganda, removal of threatening military installations carried over from the old regime, and the establishment of the Open Door in Siberia, which would prevent commercial and industrial restrictions.[8]

The Russians wanted (1) the commercial agreement and the military agreement pertaining to the evacuation of troops considered together; (2) the holding of a meeting with representatives of the U.S.S.R. in attendance in order to revise the fisheries agreement; (3) the negotiation of the Nikolaevsk affair immediately following the conclusion of the basic agreement; (4) the assurance that in the settlement of the Nikolaevsk affair, Japan did not have the intention of violating Russia's sovereignty and territorial integrity, and (5) the withdrawal of troops from northern Sakhalin immediately upon settlement of the Nikolaevsk affair. Agreement seemed to be in sight in April, when Yourin was replaced by Petrov, who made new demands, insisting on a statement setting the definite date of withdrawal of troops. The Japanese agreed to carry out evacuation within three months but refused to agree to the demand that the Far Eastern Republic troops be allowed entry into Vladivostok prior to the withdrawal of Japanese troops. An impasse was reached and the negotiations, which had been in progress for nine months, collapsed on April 16, 1922.

In the middle of June the Soviet government communicated its desire to reopen negotiations. The Japanese government issued a statement on July 1, announcing that it would voluntarily withdraw troops from the Maritime Province as well as Nikolaevsk by November 1, communicating this fact to the Far Eastern Republic on July 18, and simultaneously accepting the Soviet overture to reopen negotiations at an early date.

Negotiations opened on September 4 in the Japanese consulate in Changchun between Matsudaira, Director of the Europe-America Bureau of the Foreign Office, Soviet representative Abram Adolf Joffe, and the Far Eastern Republic representative. Joffe's presence complicated the negotiations, since the conference was

[8] Kashima, *Teikoku Gaikō no Kihon Seisaku,* pp. 400–401.

to solve outstanding issues between Japan and the Chita government, not requiring the understanding of the Moscow government except in such matters as fisheries rights, navigation rights, and the Nikolaevsk affair, which could not be left to the Chita government for final settlement. Although negotiations were to be limited to Far Eastern problems and based on the Dairen draft, Joffe seized the initiative, pushing the Far Eastern Republic representative into the background and endeavoring to extend the scope of the negotiations to a general agreement embracing the question of recognition of the U.S.S.R. Moreover, he insisted that the conference should not limit itself to Far Eastern problems and opposed using the Dairen draft as a basis for discussion.

On September 26, negotiations foundered on the rocks of disagreement. The Japanese representative stoutly maintained that the evacuation of northern Sakhalin was impossible until a regularly constituted government was set up and a satisfactory settlement of the Nikolaevsk affair could be reached; the Russian representative maintained with no less vigor that there was no connection between the two problems. Moreover, the delegates failed to reach an agreement on the matter of satisfactory remuneration for fishing rights and the disposal of Russian arms and munitions in Vladivostok, then under Japanese occupation. The disappointment of the Soviets, who now saw no chance of persuading Japan to recognize her new government militated against reaching any agreement.

Viscount Gotō Shimpei, mayor of Tōkyō and a staunch advocate of *rapprochement* with Russia, was determined to break the deadlock and to bring about the resumption of diplomatic relations. With the understanding of Premier Admiral Katō he extended an invitation to Joffe to come to Japan for a rest cure. The Soviet diplomat arrived in Tōkyō from Shanghai via Atami on February 1, 1923. In the interim period since the breakup of the Changchun negotiations several important developments had taken place. Japanese troops were withdrawn from Nikolaevsk by September 27 and from the Maritime Province by October 25, on which date the Far Eastern Republic troops entered Vladivostok. Meanwhile, the White armies collapsed, and the whole of Siberia except northern Sakhalin came under the control of Moscow and, on November 15, the Far Eastern Republic was admitted into the Soviet Union by decree at a request made by the former only the day before.

Official negotiations were begun in Tōkyō on June 28, 1923, between the Soviet representative Joffe and Kawakami Toshihiko, Minister to Poland, home on furlough at the time. Discussions centered mainly around the northern Sakhalin question and the Nikolaevsk affair. Japan expressed her desire to purchase northern Sakhalin for 150 million yen, but instead of turning it down, Joffe suggested 1 billion gold rubles, which he raised shortly thereafter to 1½ billion. Japan's request for oil, coal, and timber concessions in northern Sakhalin for a period of fifty-five to ninety-nine years met with no response. On

July 24 and 31 Joffe requested the termination of the negotiations on the grounds that he had received instructions to that effect from his home government.

There was a brief respite of less than two months. On September 22 Soviet Ambassador Leo Karakhan, successor to Joffe, called on Minister Yoshizawa in Peking and transmitted his government's desire to resume the Joffe-Kawakami negotiations. The government of Admiral Yamamoto was then preoccupied with the difficult task of planning reconstruction, following the great earthquake and fire, and was unable to make up its mind on a Russian policy. Japan found herself in a greatly weakened condition financially and economically and could ill afford to continue her heavy expenditures in a policy of hostility and suspicion toward Moscow.

By 1924, Japan began to entertain a strong desire for a settlement of disputes with Russia in order to pave the way for a peaceful economic penetration of northeastern Asia, where military and political methods had failed. The recognition of the Soviet regime by the British and Italian governments in February, 1924, strengthened the position of the Soviets toward Japan and resulted in the stiffening of their attitude. Incident after incident occurred. Soviet officials in Vladivostok refused to recognize the official status of the Japanese Consul, who was notified that he would be treated as a private citizen, issued evacuation orders to resident Japanese merchants, allowing them only three days to dispose of their stocks, and arrested and detained Vice Consul Gunji, an army captain, and more than ten businessmen. The Vladivostok postmaster notified the Japanese postmaster at the port city of Tsuruga that the exchange of mail would be suspended. In Moscow, the government ordered Japanese newspaper correspondents to leave the country. However, the Soviet government was not unaware of the attitude of suspicion and distrust that still prevailed and the fact of its exclusion from the Washington Conference was a concrete demonstration of this. The enactment of the Immigration Law by the United States Congress in April, 1924, only three months after the formation of the Kiyoura Cabinet, caused nationwide resentment and furnished the Japanese government with more than an incentive to find a *modus vivendi* with the Soviet Union.

Early in May, Soviet Ambassador Karakhan approached Yoshizawa on the desirability of opening negotiations. A week later, the Japanese government gave Yoshizawa the authority to negotiate. With the formation early in June of the Katō Takaaki Cabinet, Baron Shidehara assumed the post of Foreign Minister and began earnest efforts to arrive at an agreement with Russia. The treaty and appended protocols were signed in Peking on January 20, 1925, on the eve of the first anniversary of Lenin's death, a date that had been set as the deadline by the Soviet authorities. Soviet Russia ratified it on the same day; Japan five days later, when ratifications were exchanged in Peking.

Most significant of the provisions was Article 1, which provided for the resumption of diplomatic relations and the exchange of diplomatic and consular officials. The Soviet Union recognized the continuing validity of the Portsmouth Treaty of 1905, but other treaties, agreements, and conventions concluded under the Tsarist regime were to be revised or abandoned, and the secret treaties and agreements concluded between 1907 and 1917 were canceled. The agreement further provided for the revision of the fisheries agreement of 1907, the recognition of the most-favored-nation treatment in a treaty of commerce and navigation, as well as the freedom of entry, residence, travel, and the security of life and property, and the mutual prevention of propaganda, agitation and aiding of secret plots.

In the attached Protocol A, in addition to arrangements regarding embassies and consulates and the question of debts due Japan from the former Russian governments, Japan agreed to withdraw her troops from northern Sakhalin by May 15, restoring the area to full Russian sovereignty. Each party declared that there existed no agreement that constituted an infringement of or a menace to the sovereignty, territorial rights, or national security of the other. Provided in Protocol B was the granting of oil and coal concessions in northern Sakhalin to Japan five months after the complete withdrawal of her forces, for a period of from forty to fifty years.[9] There was included also a stipulation that Soviet labor laws were to be observed, making it mandatory for Japan to employ half of the technical staff and three-fourths of the unskilled labor from among Soviet citizens.

Adhering to the stipulations of the treaty, Japan completed the withdrawal of her troops from northern Sakhalin by May 15, 1925. The following month, Ambassador Tanaka Tokichi arrived in Moscow as the first Japanese diplomatic representative to the Soviet Union, accompanied by representatives of the North Sakhalin Concessions Company. Contracts for a forty-five year concession on petroleum [10] and coal were signed on December 14, and Japan obtained a timber concession in the Maritime Province the following year.

When the Karakhan-Yoshizawa agreement was signed, rumors arose of a Soviet-Japanese alliance, which were promptly squashed by Theodore Rothstein, a member of the collegium of the Commissariat of Foreign Affairs, who characterized them as "utter rubbish." [11] Foreign Minister Shidehara, in his address to the Diet on January 22, only two days after its signing, attached great significance to the treaty, which he regarded as an important achievement. On February 9

---

[9] In addition to an annual rental of 4 per cent of production, the concessionaires were to pay the Soviet government royalty ranging from 5 to 15 per cent, depending upon the total annual output. Gusher oil called for the payment of money fee equal to 45 per cent of value, while on gas royalty ranged from 10 to 35 per cent, according to gasoline content. Coal required the payment of 5 to 8 per cent royalty.

[10] The Far Eastern Republic granted on May 14, 1921, and ratified on January 22, 1922, a concession granting the Sinclair Exploration Co. the right to exploit the petroleum resources of northern Sakhalin and to construct two ports on its eastern coast. However, this was canceled subsequently, as the United States did not recognize the Soviet Union.

[11] *The New York Times,* June 22, 1925.

the Chinese government protested against Article 2, providing for the recognition of the Treaty of Portsmouth, as harmful to China's territorial rights and sovereignty and in conflict with Article 4 of the Sino-Soviet Treaty of May 31, 1924. The Soviet-Japanese Treaty of Commerce was ratified on February 25, and Premier Katō released an official statement on the full resumption of relations between the two countries.

After an interval of seven years, diplomatic and commercial relations were resumed between Japan and the Soviet Union. This was the result of the change in Japanese attitude toward Russia and Russian foreign policy, aided in no considerable measure by international developments. At the time of the massacre of Japanese residents by partisans in Nikolaevsk in May, 1920, Japanese public opinion was so inflamed that it seemed unthinkable to have the matter settled by a mere expression of regret on the part of the Soviet government. Moreover, the chaotic conditions that prevailed immediately after the Revolution were corrected to a large extent in the next few years, while the Japanese fear and apprehension regarding communism had been allayed by an upsurge of confidence that the Bolshevization of Russia need not and could not lead to the engulfing of Japan by the alien ideology. By 1924, Communist leaders, and particularly Zinoviev, had come to regard *rapprochement* with France, England, Japan, and the United States as desirable in carrying out Russia's foreign policy.[12] This was a modification, if not reversal, of his stand at the Baku Congress, when he emphasized the importance of destroying British imperialism in a program of world revolution.

ACTIVE PARTICIPATION IN INTERNATIONAL CONFERENCES

In the nineteen twenties, Japan, by virtue of her position as a charter member of the League of Nations and as one of the great powers, participated in every major international conference and agreement in which her interests were involved. She was particularly interested in trimming her enormous military expenditures, but without impairing her security or economic opportunities. Her military expenditures during the 1920's amounted to more than one-fourth of her total national expenditures, a ratio that was far in excess of that of the United States and nearly twice that of Great Britain.[13] It is not difficult to see, therefore, that public opinion was behind any international undertaking that would lighten the nation's economic burden.

Three Power Geneva Conference. Japan was one of the participants in the Three Power Conference at Geneva, called in the summer of 1927 at the instance of President Coolidge for the purpose of negotiating and concluding an agree-

---

[12] Michael T. Florinsky, *World Revolution and the U.S.S.R.,* p. 108.
[13] Figures of the Japanese Cabinet Bureau of Statistics in Ishii, *Gaikō Yoroku,* p. 216.

ment that would further limit naval armament, supplement the Washington Treaty, and would cover the classes of vessels not included at Washington. Since the French and Italian governments declined the invitation, it turned out to be a conference of the three great naval powers. The clash of ideas was wholly between Great Britain and the United States instead of between Japan and the United States, as it had been five years earlier at Washington. Japan's role, therefore, was that of mediator between the two clashing powers.

The failure of the Conference to produce any concrete results was attributable to its inability to devise a mutually acceptable formula reconciling the British claim for numbers of vessels with the American desire for the lowest possible tonnage limitations, and perhaps even more to the fact that the entire Conservative Party in Great Britain was opposed to the acceptance of the principle of Anglo-American naval parity. Winston Churchill, as spokesman of the Conservative Party, expressed this point of view clearly in a speech he delivered in London on August 7.[14] Admiral Saitō and Viscount Ishii, the Japanese delegates, were placed in a difficult position because of their government's instructions to take a strong stand. The failure of the Conference precluded the possibility of Japan's nascent militarism coming to the surface and revealing itself to the world.

The Pact of Paris. Japan became one of the fifteen signatories of the Pact of Paris, which renounced war as "an instrument of national policy." News of the signing of the Kellogg-Briand Pact outlawing war on August 27, 1928, was received by the Japanese public with unrestrained acclaim, reflecting unanimous national approval.[15] Count Uchida, ex-Foreign Minister and Privy Councilor, returned from Paris with justifiable pride for the part he had played in the signing of the pact as Japan's representative. Unexpectedly, however, members of the Minseitō and rightist political commentators opened withering attacks on the government for signing the antiwar pact "in the names of the respective peoples." This was denounced as a flagrant, if unintentional, contravention of Article 13 of the Japanese Constitution, which vested in the Emperor the prerogative of making peace and declaring war. It was obvious that the opponents of the government were making political capital out of the issue. It stirred up a storm of controversy as it was carried to the floor of the Diet and debated. Scholars and publicists took up the discussion pro and con. Dr. Tachi Sakutarō,[16] one of the outstanding authorities on international law, minimized it, while conservatives insisted that it was a violation of "national policy." Even the veteran diplomat, Viscount Ishii, viewed it as a violation of the imperial prerogative.[17]

---

[14] London *Times,* August 8, 1927.
[15] Ishii, *op. cit.,* p. 293.
[16] *Gaikō Jihō,* November 15, 1929.
[17] *Ibid.,* October 15, 1929.

The government's reservation to the pact was set forth clearly in a communication from Foreign Minister Tanaka to United States Ambassador MacVeagh: "The proposal of the United States is understood to contain nothing that would refuse to independent states the right of self-defense and nothing which is incompatible with the obligations or agreements guaranteeing the public peace, such as are embodied in the Covenant of the League of Nations and the treaties of Locarno." [18]

In the Diet, the Tanaka Government carefully evaded touching upon the heart of the antiwar pact and managed to get through the session. However, the Privy Council, the self-appointed guardian of the Constitution, stubbornly maintained that the phrase "in the names of the respective peoples" was unconstitutional and refused to recommend its approval. The Minseitō used this as a political weapon by inciting the Privy Council against the Tanaka Cabinet. However, on June 26, the government humbled itself and acceded to the conditional approval of the Privy Council. On June 27, 1929, ten months after its signing, the Tanaka Cabinet issued a declaration to the effect that it understood the phrase "in the names of the respective peoples" not to apply in the case of Japan. With this qualification, the Cabinet was able to weather the storm, but only temporarily. Ironically enough, the Tanaka Government had not suspected that the signing of the pact should prove to be the sealing of its doom.

Although the Pact of Paris represented distinct progress in international cooperation, its effectiveness was vitiated by its failure to provide measures of enforcement, such as sanction against treaty violators and machinery for arbitration and adjudication of disputes.[19] Moreover, the interpretation given by Secretary of State Kellogg, one of the co-authors, that the pact could not be considered a restriction or impairment of the right of self-defense, enabled the signatories to regard any war as a legitimate and justifiable measure of self-protection. The pact was invoked in the Soviet-Chinese dispute over the Chinese Eastern Railway in 1929 and the Sino-Japanese conflict of 1931, only to be found ineffective.

London Naval Conference. Japan was represented at the London Naval Conference, which opened on January 21, 1930, by Baron Wakatsuki, serving as chief delegate, Navy Minister Admiral Takarabe, Ambassador to Great Britain Matsudaira, and Ambassador to Belgium Nagai. For Japan the naval disarmament parley was fraught with political significance at home. Chief of the Naval Board Admiral Katō Kanji put up determined opposition against the naval agreement. When his name was first proposed as one of the delegates, he

[18] U.S. Department of State, *Notes Exchanged between the United States and Other Powers on the Subject of a Multilateral Treaty for the Renunciation of War* (1928), pp. 28–29.

[19] Viscount Ishii, one of the foremost Japanese diplomats, was of the opinion that the renunciation of war could be effective only when accompanied by machinery for arbitration, such as outlined by Professor James T. Shotwell of Columbia University. *Gaikō Yoroku,* p. 288.

had declined it, stating that his job was not to prevent war but to plan for it. With the support of the admirals, he worked to block the approval of the treaty.

On March 14, when Wakatsuki requested government approval of the treaty, the Naval Board opposed vigorously. However, the government rejected the Admirals' views and signed the treaty on April 21. This was interpreted by the outraged military as a flagrant violation of the imperial prerogative of the "supreme command." The upshot was a frontal clash between the military and the government. As time went on this cleavage widened and came out into the open. The Seiyūkai, which had a score to settle, stood behind the scenes and encouraged the military in its fight against the government. Thus, the question of the "supreme command" became an important political issue within the government.

The three weeks' special session of the Diet, which opened on April 21, the day the London Naval Treaty was signed, gave the Seiyūkai the anticipated opportunity to bear down upon the government on various issues. As if fearful of the military, the government evaded the forthright admission of the responsibility for the signing of the treaty. The Seiyūkai acted more like a cat's paw of the military. In spite of the spirited assault by the Seiyūkai, the government sailed through the Diet session. However, it began to encounter difficulties shortly thereafter. A revenue deficit of 80 million yen, resulting from the financial depression, caused difficulty in the execution of the budget and exposed the weakness of the financial policies of Inoue.

After the return of the Navy Minister from London cleavage developed within the navy itself, and the antipathy between the Navy Ministry and the Naval Board increased. So intensive did the antagonism become that the Chief and Vice Chief of the Naval Board and the Navy Vice Minister had to be relieved in order to preserve the unity and harmony within the navy.

In late July, the question of ratification of the treaty was referred to the Privy Council, whose hostility to the Hamaguchi Cabinet was an open secret. Ever since Nakano Seigō, member of the Minseitō, exposed the conniving of the Privy Council in the special session under the Tanaka Cabinet and strongly advocated the chastisement of the august body, no love had been lost between it and the Minseitō. Furthermore most of the Privy Councilors were proponents of extremely conservative thought and had supported Admiral Katō consistently, while plotting to unseat the Hamaguchi Government. The London Naval Treaty was something that could be used to defeat Hamaguchi.

However, Hamaguchi successfully parried every thrust by the special committee of the Privy Council headed by Itō Miyoji and denied it the opportunity for revenge. As the relationship between the government went from bad to worse, it appeared as though a violent frontal clash was unavoidable. But sane counsel prevailed as some of the Councilors, realizing the dangers of carrying vindictiveness to excess, especially in the face of indignation shown by the public as well as the political parties, urged the unconditional approval of the treaty. The special committee, at its tenth meeting, suddenly decided on unconditional approval. This came as a bolt out of the blue to the Seiyūkai, which was holding a special mass meeting, confident of unseating the government. The party was left in the lurch, causing it to suffer almost a complete loss of face and prestige.

The naval treaty, signed by Great Britain, the United States, Japan, France, and Italy, was to remain in force until 1936, during which time the five powers agreed not to undertake the construction of new ships. Japan's demand for a 10:10:7 ratio was unsuccessful and ultranationalists as well as naval circles were incensed by the "position of inferiority" relegated to the Japanese navy as a result of the "usurpation of the imperial prerogative" by a civilian premier. The sentiment evoked and the resentment stirred up in connection with the London Naval Treaty were echoed and reechoed in subsequent years by rightist, ultranationalist groups, and individuals bent on arousing public opinion against the political parties, politicians, and liberals.

Chapter 31. Mass Awakening of the Postwar

Decade

An outraged and inflamed public opinion greeted General Katsura's reappearance as Premier on the political scene late in December, 1912, for the third and last time in the brief space of a decade. Opposition parties and the press came together in a determined movement, led by Ozaki and Inukai, to overthrow bureaucratic tyranny and safeguard parliamentary government. So effective did this organized opposition prove that, in February, 1913, Premier Katsura beat a hasty political retreat and went into permanent retirement. Thus, the military protégé of Yamagata, who once held the record for the longest-lived cabinet of four and a half years' duration, went down in defeat with the shortest-lived cabinet in history, which was credited with a precarious existence of only fifty-three days. The press and public had challenged the tyranny of the bureaucracy and the fight was on in earnest long before the war clouds began to gather in Europe.

The cause of democratic and liberal elements was helped tremendously by the outbreak of the war in Europe. War against Germany was regarded in Japan as a crusade against an autocratic country and the forces of tyranny and militarism, as it was in the other Allied countries. Understandably enough, by 1917, after America's entry into the European War, the Japanese too had begun to look upon the struggle as a "war to make the world safe for democracy." Moreover, the unprecedented economic prosperity that resulted from the war indirectly aided the popularity of democratic ideas and ideals. Small wonder that the tide of democratic ideas swept across the country, capturing the imagination of the young people, much to the dismay and apprehension of the conservatives, who were by and large of the older generation.

To this upsurge of democratic idealism no one contributed more than Dr. Yoshino Sakuzō, professor of political science in the Tōkyō Imperial University, who championed the cause of democracy all through the war and in the years that followed until his death in 1933. In the *Central Review* of January, 1916, he took up the discussion of constitutional government, and while decrying the evils of arbitrary oligarchic rule, he advocated the immediate adoption of universal suffrage and the restriction of the powers of the House of Peers and the Privy Council. In attacking imperialism and the miliary clique in particular, he emphasized that the goal of politics should be the realization of the highest political values, the most important of which was the respect of popular will. This was promptly branded by the authorities as dangerous thought. But because of the profound effect it had on the thought of the period, the publication of Professor Yoshino's article marked a turning point in Japan's political thinking and development. Democracy thus became the focal point in the discussion of government and politics for the next few years.

The Russian Revolution came in 1917, at a time when the advocates of democracy were gathering strength and voices denouncing militarism were beginning to reverberate throughout the nation. The success of the Bolsheviks in overthrowing the autocracy and tyranny of the Romanovs made a profound impression upon the receptive mind of Japanese youth and had the effect of stimulating leftist thought and movement. Russian literature, which had always had a rather wide following since the closing years of the nineteenth century, now jumped overnight to first place in popularity. Even democracy appeared to be overshadowed temporarily.

Toward the end of 1918, Professor Yoshino and Professor Fukuda, an eminent economist, founded the Reimeikai, a society for the dissemination and popularization of democratic ideas. In the same month a student organization, the Shinjinkai, was founded by the members of the debating society of the Law Department of the Tōkyō Imperial University under the guidance of Professor Yoshino. This was the direct outgrowth of the public debate held in November on the subject of democracy between the ultranationalistic members of the Rōninkai, which was inspired and supported by the Black Dragon Society. The members of the Shinjinkai, including graduates, devoted their time and energy to the study and discussion of democracy and social problems. This student society, which advocated the political, social, and economic liberation of the people through the reconstruction of the nation, produced a number of the outstanding leaders of thought and social movement of the postwar period. Waseda University had similar organizations,[1] which were active in the discussion of democracy and social problems. Thus, in the forefront of the liberal movement were the university students, who became the proponents of democracy and socialism.

The new trend in the intellectual world would not have affected public opinion to any great extent but for the fact that it was reinforced by the economic changes that were taking place. In a period of unprecedented boom, every type of industry and trade flourished. Such prosperity was not only intoxicating; it made men bold. For once, young men were not haunted by the specter of unemployment upon graduation, for jobs were plentiful. Labor ceased to take thought for the morrow. With no fear of losing jobs by free expression, young

---

[1] Waseda University had its Gyōminkai, Sōdai Kensetsu Dōmei, and liberal faculty members.

men began to express themselves both in word and action with a new freedom heretofore unknown and even with a degree of recklessness.

By 1918 the humbler classes had been awakened to the point where they were beginning to see the role that they might play in the existing social and economic order. Labor, which was better organized than ever with the help of the students and intellectuals, began to agitate for recognition and a voice in the government. They had come a long ways from the pliable movement launched by Suzuki Bunji with the organization of the Yūaikai in August, 1912. The principle of capital-labor harmony, which was the basis of the Yūaikai, was by 1919 no longer a prominent feature of the labor movement, which became rather militant and somewhat tinged with radicalism. In fact, so much so that in January, 1919, the magazine *Labor,* the organ of the Yūaikai, was impelled to carry an admonition to labor to return to the fold of trade-unionism.

That democratic ideas had become tinged with radical leftist ideas was evident. Socialism made a strong appeal to the older generation as well as to the young people of Japan, especially in the wake of the recession that followed the boom. For the first time in history, the country found itself in the throes of a serious labor strife. The demands of the workers were at first purely economic in that they involved demands for higher wages, prompted by the workers' desire and necessity to keep pace with the spiraling cost of living. But gradually the workers began to demand recognition of their rights and even some voice in the management of industrial enterprises. The Kawasaki Shipyard strike of July, 1921, was one of the strongest demonstrations of the strength of labor, when well organized and thoroughly aroused. The labor demonstration by 30,000 workers on the streets of Kōbe was the greatest staged up to that time.[2]

In the welter of confusion which prevailed in the world of thought, democracy and socialism became the dominant ideological landmarks of the period. In opposition, there arose rightist organizations to espouse nationalism and conservatism as a counterbalance to the democratic idealism. In the war waged by labor against capital, the youth of Japan gave hearty support. Though more easily impressed and swayed by theory than practical considerations, because of their zeal as well as immaturity, the students had been influenced strongly by the unfavorable economic conditions in arriving at their socialistic view of life. New leaders of thought, particularly socialist writers like Sakai, Yamakawa, and Ōsugi, who belonged to the extreme left wing advocating violent measures for the attainment of their objectives, increased their grip on impressionable youth. In the shops and on the streets books on socialism sold by the thousands, as leftist writers and socialists vied with one another in expressing their views in the new

---

[2] An interesting sidelight of this labor dispute was the welcome given Bertrand Russell by the striking shipyard workers, who turned out in force at the Kōbe pier when the English pacifist-philosopher arrived for a visit.

magazines for the masses, which appeared during and after the war. More than 100,000 copies of Kautsky's analysis of Marx's *Capital* are said to have been sold secretly within a matter of a few days.

Government surveillance became strict, especially during the war. Premier Terauchi, the military bureaucrat, regarding democracy as dangerous, pursued a vigorous policy of suppression. Offending publications were suspended and individuals subjected to severe penalties. Academic freedom was trampled upon, as university professors were indicted and punished for scholarly articles that were deemed subversive by the authorities. According to the report of the Ministry of Education of October, 1920, more than 194 books were published clandestinely in 1919 as compared with only 21 the year before. Among the works suppressed by the government were Edward Bellamy's *Looking Backward* (1887) and William Morris' *News from Nowhere* (1892), both of which had been permitted circulation two decades earlier.

Perhaps the best known case of suppression of academic freedom in the period immediately following the war was that of Professor Morito Tatsuo, whose article on the social ideas of Kropotkin was pronounced subversive by the authorities, who felt that it presented communism and anarchism in a favorable light. For writing the offensive article, which appeared in January, 1920, in the learned *Journal of Economics,* the organ of the Department of Economics of the Tōkyō Imperial University, Professor Morito was convicted and sentenced to two months' imprisonment in addition to a fine and dismissal from the university faculty. Professor Ōuchi, the editor of the journal, was also held responsible and sentenced to a month's confinement and a fine. In handing down the decision, the court declared that while it was the function of the scholar to discuss the merits and demerits, advantages and disadvantages, of institutions and criticize existing systems and organizations, the publication of any views or conclusions which disturbed the public peace and order could not be tolerated.

The Morito case stirred up a storm of controversy and brought down a scathing denunciation on the government of Premier Hara for its flagrant violation of academic freedom. To this the government retaliated with even more drastic suppression, resulting in more individuals running afoul of the law and the expulsion of university professors who dared to fight for academic freedom and the freedom of expression.[3]

The organization of the Society for the Study of Military Affairs at Waseda University in May, 1923, was met with strong opposition by the students, who objected to militarism. At the inauguration ceremony held on May 10, the students shouted down the president of the society, Professor Aoyagi, who was

[3] In 1924, Professor Yoshino found himself in a position where he felt it was judicious to resign from a professorship in the Tōkyō Imperial University for having written an article in which he took the military to task.

presiding. Vice Minister of War General Shirakawa read the War Minister's message and other officers spoke, but they were drowned out by the students shouting and singing the Waseda school song, and the meeting ended in an uproar.[4] Antimilitaristic sentiment spread rapidly among university students. In January, 1925, the authorities banned student demonstrations against the military and on April 1, military training was introduced into the secondary schools, both public and private.

The Students' Society for the Study of Social Science [5] held its first meeting on September 14, 1924, at the Tōkyō Imperial University under the sponsorship of the Shinjinkai. Several hundred college and university students assembled declared that the time had come for a united front for the liberation of the working classes. They advocated among other things an international movement looking forward to the outlawry of war, an organization to oppose military training for students, concerted opposition against the enactment of the Peace Preservation Law, and a vigorous protest against the ban on discussion groups in the colleges. The meeting of the National Federation of Societies for the Study of Social Science [6] held at the Kyōto Imperial University on July 16, 1925, marked a shift in the student movement from the abstruse discussion of problems to the policy of active participation in the proletarian movement.

In the famous Kyōto Imperial University affair of December 1, 1925, the police raided the homes of more than a score of students and the headquarters of the Students' Federation for the Study of Social Science. Between mid-January and late April of the following year the police took more than thirty students into custody on the grounds that they had violated the Peace Preservation Law, the Publications Law, and were guilty of *lèse majesté*. The police accused them of spreading, among the students and the masses, the social revolutionary ideas of Marx and Lenin in an attempt to overthrow the government and seize power, put in dictatorship, socialize production, abolish private property, and establish communism. As a countermove the Alliance for the Protection of the Freedom of Students was organized to support leftist student organizations and to inject revolutionary ideas into the training of those who would work for the liberation of the working classes. On the tenth anniversary of the Russian Revolution, however, the student movement voluntarily disbanded, turning over the activities to the laborers and farmers themselves.

Radicalism among the students was a natural reaction of young people

[4] As leaders of the Waseda group of liberal professors, Ōyama Ikuo, Sano Manabu, Inomata Tsunao, and Kitazawa Shinjirō were on the black list of the Special Higher Police Section of the Tōkyō Metropolitan Police Board.

[5] All student associations for the study of social science were ordered disbanded on April 19, 1928.

[6] The Federation was organized on May 5, 1924, and was disbanded by the authorities in November, 1929.

troubled by the miserable lot of the workers who were being exploited. Disquieting disclosures of corruption among officials and politicians, whose unholy alliance with Mammon had engendered a general feeling of distrust of the upper classes, also helped the left-wing movement. And this feeling the students shared. The increasing number of university graduates unable to find employment intensified the antipathy against wealth and privilege and the unemployed intellectuals found the road to radicalism very inviting. Goaded by despair and shattered ideals, many traveled swiftly toward communism and anarchism. The literary output of the time, particularly by the intellectuals who were sympathetic to the working classes, stimulated the idealists to learn about the conditions of the proletariat and to do something to improve their lot.[7]

Intimately connected, as it was, with the labor movement, socialism was subject to the same vicissitudes and precarious existence. Just as it was beginning to give promise of developing into a strong political movement, it suffered a setback with the onset of the recession of the spring of 1920 which was followed by a more serious depression. Wages dropped and many factories were shut down. Labor suffered a loss of power, confidence, and the sense of security. As a consequence, in 1921, the laborites, whose faith in socialistic programs had been gradually decreasing, finally parted company with the socialists, and the labor groups from then on took on a distinctly trade-unionist aspect. This changing character of the labor movement coincided with a change in the political attitude of young Japan. In 1920, the eager spirits had shown little patience for the doctrines of a slowly developing liberalism, but less than two years later they began to swing back once more to the earlier ideas of a liberal democracy, which antedated the revolutionary Russian influence.

With this shift in the general trend of ideas came a corresponding change among the intellectual leaders. The bare economic interpretation of life, which never really appealed to the Japanese temperament, gave way gradually to a more idealistic theory, and the more idealistic thinkers began to rise in popular estimation. It was in this period that writers like Arishima, Kurata, and Kagawa reached their quickly won heights of influence, and Professor Yoshino's sane counsels began to be heeded once more by young Japan. One of the outstanding figures of the troubled twenties was Kagawa Toyohiko, an internationally known Christian. As a comparatively young man of thirty, he came into national prominence with the publication of his novel *Beyond the Death Line*, which ran into some three hundred editions in a brief space of two years. Kagawa stood out as one of those who, without professing to be a socialist, was generally recognized as such. As a student of labor problems for many years and an influential member of the Yūaikai, he became an indefatigable

---

[7] A view expressed by a Supreme Court Judge who had tried many communists in *Contemporary Japan*, February, 1932, p. 197.

social worker in the slums of Kōbe as well as a prolific contributor to magazines.

As a result of the intellectual ferment of the period, movements espousing equality came into their own. The feminist movement emerged, as women's organizations of various sorts appeared in increasingly large numbers. A women's section was established in the labor organization, Yūaikai, and women of the working classes began to show interest in working together to solve their common problems. Feminine voices came to be heard as they undertook to be their own spokesmen.

The Water Level movement, intended to emancipate the liberated former *eta* class, also got its start in the twenties and, as in the case of labor problems, the leaders participated in the political movement by becoming a part of the proletarian party. In the spring of 1921 the first Suiheisha was founded at Kashiwara, in Nara prefecture, virtually within the shadows of the hallowed ground where the first Emperor Jimmu had ascended the throne. A year later, the first nationwide convention of the Suiheisha was held in Okazaki Park in Kyōto and passed a resolution demanding an end to social discrimination. Only two weeks later, 700 members of the organization in Nara prefecture clashed with 600 villagers and members of ultranationalist organizations. In addition to 300 policemen regular troops had to be called out before order was restored.

In 1924, as the month of June was coming to a close, members of the Suiheisha in Kyūshū, who had unsuccessfully urged Prince Tokugawa to relinquish his post as President of the House of Peers three months earlier, made an attempt on his life, only to fail again. Feeling against the former outcasts ran high in many communities. In Gumma prefecture residents of the village of Serada on January 18, 1925, carried out an incendiary attack on the members of the Suiheisha, resulting in injury to more than 100 persons. Unfortunately for the movement, its militant actions and terroristic methods not only alienated sympathy, but also actually stimulated public sentiment hostile to them. By 1926 the movement was thought to have reflected some anarchistic tendencies.[8] On December 13, a plot to attack a regiment in Fukuoka by a group led by Matsumoto Jiichirō, chairman of the central executive committee of the National Suiheisha was uncovered. The incident, which attracted the greatest and the most adverse publicity, was the attempt by a second-class private to present a petition directly to the Emperor at a military parade, held at Nagoya during the army maneuvers in the fall of 1927.[9] With this as a turning point the movement became less obtrusive, and in the late thirties organizations began to disband. By the end of 1940 the movement had been disbanded completely.

[8] A federation called the Zenkoku Suiheisha Kaihō Remmei, which was formed in September, 1926, and disbanded in November, 1929, was regarded as tinged with anarchism.

[9] This incident, which took place on November 19, 1927, involved Kitahara Taisaku, who was himself a member of the former *eta* class.

PROLETARIAN POLITICAL PARTIES

The development of proletarian parties was a natural sequel to the degeneration of existing political parties into instrumentalities for the advancement and
preservation of the interests and special privileges of the governing class. They
found their *raison d'être* in the advancement and protection of the interests of
the working classes against the encroachments of the propertied classes.

Ever since the suppression of the Japan Socialist Party in 1907 successive
cabinets had consistently pursued the policy of suppressing proletarian parties.
During the decade that followed the proletarian parties were unable to establish themselves. But after the First World War, with the rise of labor and
agrarian movements, the proletariat began to receive its share of recognition and
attention in the political sphere, though it was somewhat under suspicion at first.

The Labor's Friendly Society (Yūaikai), organized in 1912 by Suzuki
Bunji, was not so much a labor union as a mutual aid society for the workingmen. Since its policy was one of maintaining capital-labor harmony it was
almost never subjected to interference or suppression by the authorities. Consequently, it enjoyed rapid growth and became known outside of Japan, particularly in the United States, as its founder attended regularly the annual meetings
of the American Federation of Labor beginning in November, 1915, when a
convention was held in San Francisco. Suzuki became friendly with the American Federation of Labor President Samuel Gompers. In 1915 the Yūaikai sent
two fraternal delegates to the California Federation of Labor Convention held at
Santa Rosa.

The year 1919 was a banner year for strikes, which occurred on a large scale
and with such frequency in the factories, mines, and transportation systems that
the employers as well as the authorities became gravely apprehensive. These
labor disputes involved workers on the great newspapers of Tōkyō, the Kawasaki
Shipyards in Kōbe, the Municipal Electric Bureau of Tōkyō, the Army Artillery Arsenals of both Tōkyō and Ōsaka, and the mines of Ashio, Kamaishi, and
Hitachi. Thousands of workers and labor leaders were put in prison in the
course of labor disturbances. Workers now began to take an active interest in
political issues and particularly in the question of universal suffrage. This was
amply reflected in the meeting, held in Tōkyō, in December, of the Labor
Federation for Universal Suffrage, formed by twenty organizations in the Kansai
region and composed of workers of the Yūaikai faction.

By 1919 the Yūaikai had a clear-cut program for labor, which included
among other things the freedom to form labor unions, abolition of child labor,
as well as night work and contract labor, minimum wages and maximum hours,
equal wages for men and women for the same kind of work, equality of treat-

ment for native and non-native labor, workingmen's insurance and compensation laws, labor disputes arbitration, government provision of better housing facilities for workers, improvement of the cottage industries, revision of oppressive police regulations, universal manhood suffrage, and the democratization of the educational system and the equalization of educational opportunities.

The awakening of the laborers was reflected also in the observance at Ueno Park of the first May Day in Japan in 1920 with some 5,000 persons participating. The May Day parades became an annual affair in some of the large cities, although on several occasions they were banned by the authorities. In 1932 some 12,000 persons, representing seventy-five organizations, held a parade in Tōkyō. In 1936 and 1937 the Home Ministry issued directives to prefectural governors prohibiting the holding of May Day parades, and the observance was discontinued until after Japan's defeat in 1945.

Premier Hara's dissolution of the Diet early in 1920 was a heavy blow to the group advocating the extension of suffrage. The upshot of it was the decline of the suffragist agitation in the labor unions and the appearance of syndicalist tendencies. The labor movement as a whole thus came under the influence of syndicalism from the latter part of 1920. The heretofore solid Yūaikai was split into two factions on the suffrage issue. At the eighth annual meeting of the organization in the fall of 1920 Tanahashi Kotora and others of the Kantō regional group advocated direct action and rejected parliamentary methods in typically syndicalist fashion, while Kagawa Toyohiko and Nishio Suehiro [10] of the Kansai group opposed anything but parliamentary methods. The following year the Yūaikai became the General Federation of Labor (Rōdō Sōdōmei).

Socialism, which had been dormant as a movement for a full decade, was activated in 1920 with the formation of the Japan Socialists' Union, the brain child of Yamakawa Hitoshi. It was sponsored by a score of well-known persons [11] representing all shades of ideology: trade-unionism, socialism, anarchism, syndicalism, and communism, and embracing all types of labor organizations as well as intellectual groups like the Shinjinkai of the Tōkyō Imperial University and the Gyōminkai of Waseda University. Its composition was remarkable for its heterogeneity. No sooner had the Socialists' Union announced its prospectus, draft constitution and bylaws in August, than the government decided to suppress it. The inauguration meeting, which was held in December, was broken up by the police and scores were arrested. However, the Union helped to bring

[10] Nishio Suehiro served as Chief Secretary in the Socialist Cabinet of Katayama Tetsu, the first government to be formed under the new Constitution of 1947. The Cabinet came into existence in May, 1947, and collapsed in February, 1948.

[11] Among the sponsors of this Union, known as the Shakai Shugi Dōmei, were Arahata Kanson, Asō Hisashi, Akamatsu Katsumaro, Katō Kanjū, Ōsugi Sakae, Sakai Toshihiko, Takahata Motoyuki, Shimanaka Yūzō, Katō Kazuo, Hashiura Tokio, and Iwasa Sakutarō.

socialism and the labor movement closer together, although in May of the following year the government ordered its disbanding.

After the syndicalist influence in the trade-union movement started to decline, the Japan Farmers' Union [12] was organized in February, 1922. In July, 1924, the central executive committee of the union decided to embark on the formation of a political party. In addressing the conference in February, 1925, its president, Sugiyama Motojiro, stressed the urgency of combining political and economic activities and urged upon the members the nomination of as many candidates as possible in the local elections in order to capture seats in the town and village assemblies. As a result, in that year, the Union elected over 330 members in the rural local assemblies. In July, 1925, the members proposed the formation of a proletarian party in cooperation with the working classes in the cities.

With the enactment of universal manhood suffrage law practically in sight, the Association for the Study of Politics [13] was formed in June, 1924, as a preparatory step for the formation of proletarian parties. The purpose of this organization was to study political, diplomatic, financial, economic, industrial, labor and social problems from the point of view of the working classes and to formulate policies for a rational revamping of Japanese society through the organization of a political party based on the interests of the masses. It was in effect a preparatory committee to educate the masses and to devise ways and means of assisting in the formation of proletarian parties.

When the General Federation of Labor split, the resultant leftist Labor Union Council penetrated the Association of the Study of Politics and intensified its communist leanings. The association was a recognized participating unit of the Preparatory Committee for the Organization of Proletarian Parties, proposed by the Japan Farmers' Union in August, 1925. The Preparatory Committee met in mid-August and selected its Central Executive Committee of fifteen members.[14] As the meeting was dominated by the left wing, which rejected the outline of economic policy drafted by Takahashi Kamekichi, it forced his resignation as well as that of Shimanaka Yūzō and others.

No sooner had the Universal Manhood Suffrage Law been promulgated, than the Japan Farmers' Union set up a preparatory committee for the organization of a political party quite independently of, and stealing the march on, the Association for the Study of Politics. The Farmer Labor Party, composed mainly of farmers, which emerged on December 1, 1925, was ordered disbanded by the government within thirty minutes of its inauguration on the grounds

[12] This was the Nihon Nōmin Kumiai.

[13] The Seiji Kenkyūkai was formed by Shimanaka Yūzō, Aono Suekichi, Takahashi Kamekichi, and Suzuki Mosaburō.

[14] Included among the fifteen members were Ōyama Ikuo, Fuse Tatsuji, Kawakami Jōtarō, Ōmori Yoshitarō, and Suzuki Mosaburō.

that it was communist dominated. Although conditions were very favorable for a proletarian party, this first attempt was suppressed by the Katō Cabinet, which decided that the party was committed to the dangerous program of putting communism into effect.[15]

Not to be daunted by government disapproval, the Japan Farmers' Union immediately set out to launch another party that would exclude the communist element. Thus, the Labor Farmer Party [16] was launched in Ōsaka in March, 1926, with a threefold platform, namely, the achievement of political, economic, and social liberation of the working classes, the reform by legitimate methods of the inequitable systems of land ownership, production, and distribution, and the thorough renovation of the Diet through the defeat of existing political parties that represented the interests of special privilege and wealth. The government did not suppress this party, which was to the right of center. However, it was soon plagued with internal strife and acts of sabotage within its own ranks. All its leaders, including Ōyama Ikuo, were arrested in the communist roundup of March 15, 1928. As an aftermath, a month later, it was ordered disbanded by the Tanaka Cabinet together with the Japan Council of Labor Unions [17] and the National League of Proletarian Youth.[18]

The right wing of the Japan Farmers' Union, led by Hirano Rikizō, formed, in October, 1926, the Japan Labor Party [19] as the official political organ of the National Farmers' Union.[20] With the slogan "A Farmers' Party for the Farmers" the new agrarian political party looked to the realization of a new, rational society in harmony with the laws of nature for the achievement of peace and happiness of mankind. Its program included the establishment of social justice, true parliamentary government, sound national industrial policies, agrarian culture, and a strong national foundation. Two months later, it merged with the Social Democratic Party along with the conservatives, who had bolted the Labor Farmer Party, and the right wing of the Association for the Study of Politics.

After the disbanding of the Farmer Labor Party a demand for the revival of a proletarian party came not only from the ranks of working men, but also from the enlightened intellectuals, led by Professor Abe Isoo of Waseda University, Professor Hori Kiichi of Keiō University, and Professor Yoshino of the Tōkyō Imperial University. This led to the organization in November, 1926,

[15] The platform of the party is given in Asahi Shimbun, *Meiji Taishōshi,* Vol. VI, pp. 433–434.

[16] This party was the Rōdō Nōmintō, the Labor Farmer Party, which is the transposition of the banned party, Farmer Labor Party.

[17] Rōdō Kumiai Hyōgikai was the original Japanese name.

[18] Zen Nihon Musan Seinendan was its original name.

[19] Nihon Rōnōtō.

[20] Zen Nihon Nōmin Dōmei.

of a preparatory committee [21] to rally the moderates among the intelligentsia, laborers, and the farmers. Its efforts bore fruit, and on December 5, 1926, the Social Democratic Party was launched with Professor Abe as president.[22] Based on the idea of social democracy, it represented the right wing of the proletarian movement. It was definitely anticommunist and rejected radicalism, which it believed ignored the process of social evolution, which had to be gradual rather than sudden and violent.

The Social Democratic Party declared its goal to be the attainment of healthy national life, secured through a political and economic structure based upon the working classes. This involved the gradual change from the capitalist oriented production and distributive system to one that was built around the working classes. It looked to reforms in the Diet, the military, fiscal and tax systems, administrative organization, education, land system, universal manhood suffrage in the true sense, popular diplomacy, tenancy legislation, social security, socialization of major industries, abolition of legal and economic discrimination against women, laws restricting the freedom of speech, assembly, and association, and the enactment of laws for the protection of laborers and white-collar workers.

On December 9, 1926, Asō Hisashi, who was expelled from the General Federation of Labor, and others came together to form the Japan Labor Farmer Party (Nihon Rōnōtō), which opposed both the radical left wing and the reactionary right wing elements, in an attempt to steer a middle course in the proletarian movement. The party brought in the anti-Communist faction of the Japan Farmers' Union and formed the nucleus for a united proletarian front to become the Japan Mass Party (Nihon Taishūtō) in December, 1928. After going through successive mergers it finally merged with the Social Mass Party in 1932.[23]

In consequence of the wholesale roundup of Communists by the Seiyūkai Cabinet of General Tanaka in March, 1928, the Labor Farmer Party was crippled through the loss of its influential leaders. Shortly thereafter it was banned by the authorities, and the former members went underground, forming in late December an illegal organization.[24] Those who favored the reestablishment of a legitimate political party bolted and devoted themselves to setting up parties on a local or prefectural basis.

Soon after the breakup of the Labor Farmer Party, proletarian parties disin-

---

[21] The committee included Suzuki Bunji, Nishio Suehiro, Akamatsu Katsumaro, Abe Isoo, Katayama Tetsu, Shimanaka Yūzō, Baba Tsunego, Miyazaki Ryūsuke, Shirayanagi Shūko, and Matsunaga Yoshio.

[22] Katayama Tetsu was chief secretary of the Shakai Minshūtō, while Suzuki Bunji and Shimanaka Yūzō comprised the Central Executive Committee.

[23] In July, 1930, it became the National Mass Party (Zenkoku Taishūtō), and in July, 1931, the National Labor-Farmer Mass Party (Zenkoku Rōnō Taishūtō).

[24] This was the National Preparatory Committee of the Labor-Farmer Alliance for the Securing of Political Liberties (Seijiteki Jiyū Kakutoku Rōnō Dōmei Zenkoku Jumbikai).

tegrated as the result of strife and dissension within their own ranks that could not be resolved. It became painfully evident that a united front was imperative for the survival of the movement. In response to this desperate need, a merger of several parties [25] was effected and the Japan Mass Party (Nihon Taishūtō) emerged. Hopes ran high, but in less than a month a purge movement was started to rid the new party of those who had at any time been intimate with either the Seiyūkai or the financial clique. This was a prelude to violent discord and the withdrawals from membership, which wrecked the merger within six months, leaving in its wake the remnants of one of its components, the Japan Labor Farmer Party. However, in the 1928 local elections the Japan Mass Party won 500 seats in the municipal, town, and village assemblies. Through its organs, the *Japan Mass News* (*Nihon Taishū Shimbun*) and the *Mass Liberation*, the party carried on a campaign for the economic and political liberation of the workers, peasants and nonpropertied urban population, for reform in the existing irrational land, production, and distribution systems, and for the thorough revamping of the political system in the interests of the people by wresting it from the control of the propertied classes.

In early August of 1929 Ōyama Ikuo, Chairman of the Central Executive Committee since the old Labor Farmer Party days, succeeded in calling the attention of the membership to the urgent need for forming a legitimate left-wing party. Despite the expulsion of Ōyama and others, including Professor Kawakami Hajime, the new Farmer Labor Party came into being on November 1, 1929. As a radical left wing party it took upon itself the duty of protecting the everyday interests of the oppressed masses, carrying on a vigorous fight to secure political liberties and strengthening and enlarging the labor unions and farmers' unions.

The following month saw a split in the General Federation of Labor, which formed the core of the Social Democratic Party, resulting in the formation of the National Federation of Labor Unions.[26] Those members of the Social Democratic Party who had been fighting against the increasing reactionary trend within the party joined forces in January, 1930, with the National Federation of Labor Unions and formed the National Social Democratic Party,[27] which regarded itself as a transitional group, and started a unification movement which bore fruit later.

The appearance of the National Labor Farmer Mass Party [28] in July, 1931,

---

[25] These seven political parties were the Nihon Nōmintō, Musan Taishūtō, Chūbu Minshūtō, Shinshū Taishūtō, Kyūshū Minkentō, Shimane Jiyūtō, and the Tōhoku Minshūtō.

[26] This was the Rōdō Kumiai Zenkoku Dōmei.

[27] The Zenkoku Minshūtō was formed on January 15, 1930.

[28] The constituent organizations of the National Labor Farmer Mass Party (Zenkoku Rōnō Taishūtō) included the National Federation of Labor Unions (Zenkoku Rōdō Kumiai Dōmei), General Federation of Labor Unions (Nihon Rōdō Kumiai Sōrengō), Tōkyō Gas Workers' Union (Tōkyō Gasukō Kumiai), and the Yokohama Municipal Employees' Union (Yoko-

marked the beginning of the final stages of the merger of socialist parties. It represented the merger of the National Mass Party, Farmer Labor Party, and the Social Democratic Party for the avowed purpose of protecting and extending the rights and interests of the underprivileged masses. By a thoroughgoing revamping of the capitalistic system, it hoped to liberate the masses. Its program therefore consisted of increasing and strengthening labor unions, farmers' unions, and other proletarian organizations.

Proletarian Parties and Practical Politics. The proletarian parties faced their first test in the prefectural elections of the fall of 1927. Preparations, which they started in the spring, produced results and they were successful in placing 28 out of their 204 candidates in the assemblies. The real test came, however, in the first general election under the Universal Manhood Suffrage Law of 1925, when they fought not only against the strength of the established political parties, but also against ruthless government interference, carried out by the reactionary Tanaka Cabinet. Without resorting to illegal tactics such as vote-buying, of which other parties were guilty, they carried on their fight in the press and in public meetings. As a result they won eight seats in the Diet, the first time in the history that proletarian parties secured representation in the national law-making body.[29] As the result of the general election of 1930, proletarian representation in the Diet dropped from eight to five, owing in large part to the lack of cooperation among the parties, most of which were suffering from internal dissensions.[30]

After the poor showing made by the proletarian parties in the national election of 1930, the question of merger came up once more. A start had been made toward merger when the National Social Democratic Party was formed in January, 1930. Six months later, the National Mass Party had resulted from the merger of the Social Democratic Party and the Japan Mass Party. The lamentable failure in presenting a united proletarian front was attributable to the absence of a rational basis. It was felt that there were only two alternatives, namely, social democracy or communism as far as a basis of merger was con-

---

hamashi Jūgyōin Kumiai), General Council of Japanese Labor Unions (Nihon Rōdō Kumiai Sōhyōgikai), Tōkyō Transport Workers' Union (Tōkyō Kōtsū Rōdō Kumiai), Kōbe Municipal Electric Workers' Union (Kōbe Shiden Jūgyō Kumiai), General Federation of Ceramic Workers (Chitsugyō Rōdō Sōdomei), National Farmers' Union (Zenkoku Nōmin Kumiai), National Suiheisha (Zenkoku Suiheisha), Tenants' Association (Shakuyanin Kumiai), and Salaried Workers' Union (Hōkyū Seikatsusha Kumiai), embracing important farmer-labor organizations.

[29] In the election of 1928 the Social Democratic Party elected Abe Isoo, Suzuki Bunji, Kamei Kan'ichirō, and Nishio Suehiro; the Labor Farmer Party elected Yamamoto Senji and Mizutani Chōsaburō; Japan Labor Party chose Kawakami Jōtarō, and the Kyūshū Minkentō elected Asahara Kenzō.

[30] In 1930 the Social Democratic Party captured two seats (Nishio Suehiro, Katayama Tetsu), the Japan Mass Party two (Asahara Kenzō, Matsutani Yosaburō), and the Labor Farmer Party one (Ōyama Ikuo).

cerned. A national council to work on the merger was set up jointly by the National Mass Party, Social Democratic Party, and the Farmer Labor Party. This resulted in the formation of the National Farmer Labor Mass Party, solving for the first time a problem which had been foremost in the minds of the proletarian party leaders for a number of years. But this achievement was short-lived for, in October, came a split within its ranks. Meanwhile, the Sino-Japanese conflict had broken out in Manchuria. The Manchurian Incident of September 18, 1931, increased the anxiety of the proletarian parties, several of which sent their representatives into Manchuria to investigate actual conditions there. The National Farmer Labor Party set up an Anti-War Committee on the very day of the Incident.

Shortly after the Manchurian Incident, Akamatsu Katsumaro and his group bolted the Social Democratic Party, renouncing the social democratic principle and declaring for state socialism. The Japan National Socialist Party, which he and Shimanaka Yūzō organized on April 10, 1932, came to the defense of the Manchurian Incident by asserting that it was an inevitable step in the realization of national socialism, and that it could not be regarded as an action intended for the protection of bourgeois rights and privileges nor as an imperialistic war. After disagreeing with Shimanaka, Akamatsu broke away and founded on May 29 his own Japan State Socialist Party (Nihon Kokka Shakaitō). On the same day, the Shimanaka faction formed the Shin Nihon Kokumin Dōmei. Akamatsu's Japan State Socialist Party looked to the establishment of imperial rule, institution of controlled national economy, and the liberation of the masses as well as of the peoples of Asia. This was to be achieved through the destruction of the capitalistic structure at home, the achievement of an equitable distribution of the world's resources, and the principle of racial equality.

A new direction was given to the proletarian movement early in 1932, when, as a result of the intense nationalism generated in the wake of the Manchurian Incident, the parties turned fascist, while still preserving to a considerable extent their socialistic ideas. Their programs called specifically for the respect of the national Constitution, rejection of the Marxian concept of the state in favor of the concept that unification and socialization comprised the twofold function of the state, denial of Marxian internationalism, which advances only the common interests of the proletariat of the world, bent on carrying on an utterly standardized international struggle in complete disregard of national interests and conditions, the adoption of realistic and up-to-date internationalism with due regard to the national position of the proletariat, and vigorous mass action outside of parliament, but within the framework of the legally constituted government.

Although the proletarian movement continued to be anticapitalistic, it had become increasingly nationalistic. The appearance of the Social Mass Party, resulting from the merger of the Social Democratic Party and the National

Farmer-Labor Mass Party on July 24, 1932, was the culmination of an attempt to effect a working coalition, if not amalgamation, of the proletarian forces, which had started in 1927. It represented also the beginning of the advocacy of state socialism by the proletarian movement, which had been profoundly affected by the rise of nationalism. Among the policies advocated by the Social Mass Party were the nationalization of major industries and financial institutions as well as land, public management of housing and medical facilities, publicly supported labor education, as well as a labor system that would guarantee a livelihood to workers, social insurance, proper balance and equilibrium between urban and rural economy, the establishment of the principle of equality of all peoples, and the ensuring of world peace.

THE COMMUNIST MOVEMENT

The first Communists in Japan were the last of the syndicalists and the anarchists. They were the spiritual descendants of the followers of Henry George and Edward Bellamy. Communism in Japan developed from those general causes and under circumstances similar, if not identical, to those in other countries. It was based on the Marxian doctrine that all would have plenty if only capitalist production for profit did not systematically deprive the worker of the surplus value he creates.

When the Baku Congress of Nations of the Orient, presided over by Zinoviev, organized the communist movement in Asia in 1921, there was no Japanese representation. However, in the same year, a Chinese agent of the Comintern, equipped with funds, visited Japan and invited a number of left-wing socialists to attend the next conference of the Third International in Moscow. Those who attended this conference were converted to communism, resulting in the founding of the Japan Communist Party about 1922. The arrest of the leaders, Sakai Toshihiko, Yamakawa Hitoshi, and Arahata Kanson in the roundup of May, 1923, halted the activities of the party and caused its collapse. The great earthquake of September caused the communist movement to disappear temporarily.

In 1924–1925, efforts were made to revive the Japan Communist Party at the instance of the Far Eastern Bureau of the Third International which was directing its activities from Shanghai. As Japan was about to enfranchise 10 million propertyless voters, the Comintern read wonderful opportunities in the general election, which was less than three years away. A meeting to revive the party was held on December 4, 1926, at the Goshiki Spa in Yamagata prefecture, where Sano Gaku, Fukumoto Kazuo, Shiga Yoshio and other leaders of the Japan Communist Party had assembled. With a nucleus of 150, the group started its activities as the vanguard of the farmer-labor movement. Reenforced from time to time by Moscow-trained workers, the Communists overhauled completely their organization. A central executive committee was set up to direct its activities and regional committees carried on a political program designed to meet local needs. Cells were formed in factories, in trade-unions, and in the newly organized labor groups and parties, which were getting ready for the first general election under the new Universal Manhood Suffrage Law. Through systematic propaganda [31] and instigation of labor strife they attempted to intensify class struggle. Attempts were made to infiltrate into the army in an effort to convert the troops to communism.

In February, 1927, Sano Gaku and others who had been to the Soviet Union returned with instructions from the Third International and opened an active propaganda campaign through their organ, *The Red Flag*. Agents of the illegal Communist Party infiltrated into the unions and left-wing labor groups and hundreds of young laborite politicians came under the influence of communism. The extreme leftist Labor Farmer Party with a membership of 12,000 came virtually under communist control. As communist following increased, the number of parties influenced or dominated by them also increased.[32]

Taking advantage of the flood of election literature that was being circulated, thousands of communist tracts were distributed. The substance of their propaganda ranged all the way from mild radicalism to the advocacy of a full-fledged, bloody revolution. Handbills were distributed advocating among other things mild ideas in slogans, such as "Right to Strike," "An Eight-hour Day," "Government Relief for All" as well as revolutionary ideas like "Parliament without an Emperor," "Confiscation of the Property of the Emperor and the Capitalists," and "Dictatorship of the Workers and Farmers."

Communist Roundups. The suppression of leftist ideas was carried out relentlessly by the government, particularly after the promulgation of the Peace Preservation Law enacted in 1925. In a pre-dawn raid on March 15, 1928, over 100 police officers of the Metropolitan Police Board descended upon the Japan Communist Party headquarters in Tōkyō and arrested more than 100 members of the party. However, the leaders, Sano, Watanabe, and Nabeyama, managed to slip through the police cordon and went underground. In a nationwide hunt extending over thirty-four prefectures the police rounded up 65,000 persons. Involved were nearly 2,500 students of the imperial universities of Tōkyō, Kyōto, and Tōhoku, as well as students of private universities. Sano and Naniwa escaped to Vladivostok, from where they made their way to Moscow.

The general headquarters for the large scale suppression of the leftists was

[81] *The Red Flag*, which was the official communist organ, was at first circulated secretly among reliable party members, who did not exceed 400.

[32] Regarded as peripheral organizations of the Communist movement were the Council of Japanese Labor Unions (Nihon Rōdō Kumiai Hyōgikai) with 20,000 members, Japan Farmers' Union with 50,000 members, Proletarian Youth League with 3,000 members, National (Students') Social Science Federation, Japan Proletarian Artists' Federation.

the Special Higher Police Section of the Metropolitan Police Board in Tōkyō. Specially trained agents, disguised as businessmen, students, laborers, and even hoodlums, infiltrated into the factories and into every conceivable place to spy on the activities of the Communists. The wholesale arrests were a heavy blow, but the movement rallied its strength again. More Japanese graduates were sent back from Moscow to replace the lost leaders, and some of those who had slipped through the police showed greater determination than ever. In the winter of 1928 to 1929 the Japan Communist Party was resuscitated and the propaganda campaign was renewed with greater vigor.

On April 16, 1929, the second large scale roundup of Communists was carried out by the special higher police. The ban on the news of the arrests was not lifted for two years. In February of the next year the police launched the third nationwide roundup, which continued for six months. The arrest of more than 400 persons, including Sano, and the elimination by the authorities of their fund raising network all but checked the communist movement. From this time on the leaders were constantly "on the run" and the party was unable to function effectively, though in 1931 a revival was attempted and 7,000 members were secured. By the early thirties virtually all the known leaders were under arrest, tried and convicted, or under close surveillance, and the movement had been smashed.

Despite the fervor of the Communists and their persistence, they were much too small in number and their influence too limited to make them a real threat to the nation, although the capitalists were terrified. Moreover, the circumstances that gave them their opportunity in Russia did not obtain in Japan, where the police was strong and efficient and much less subject to the influence of public opinion than in some of the other countries. Before the enactment of manhood suffrage in 1925 Japanese labor saw little hope of achieving its ends by constitutional means and might have been an easy prey to communist propaganda. But the extension of suffrage to every laborer and even the remote possibility of labor forming a government brought the trade-unions around to the approval and support of the parliamentary system. The discontented factory proletariat showed preference for trade-unions rather than the Communist Party.

PROLETARIAN CULTURAL MOVEMENT

The growing social consciousness of the postwar period was reflected conspicuously in the appearance in large numbers in 1919 of magazines and periodicals emphasizing or specializing in social ideas and problems as well as in politics. Among the multitude of such periodicals were the *Kaizō* (*Reconstruction*), *Kaihō* (*Liberation*), *Warera* (*We*), and *Shakai Mondai Kenkyū* (*Journal of Social Problems*), which took up the discussion of social and political questions for their awakened readers. The formation in 1920 of the Japan Socialist Union

(Shakai Shugisha Dōmei) was the starting point of the proletarian cultural movement. The conversion of the intelligentsia to socialism, which constituted one of the significant phenomena of the period, was the by-product of the social unrest and turmoil born of the uncertainties, dilemmas, and fears arising out of the holocaust of the First World War.

Japanese liberals in general had viewed the World War as a conflict between militaristic Germany and the freedom loving peoples of Great Britain and the United States, a life and death struggle between the forces of autocracy and democracy. As an ally of the democratic powers, it was as inevitable as it was natural that the cause of democracy should be enthusiastically espoused by all. As the working classes began to assert their right to live, it became quite evident that awakened labor bid fair to become a powerful force in society. The working classes had in the past been led by the educated, the scholars, and thinkers, in whom leadership had been vested as a special trust; their awakening, therefore, presaged to the intelligentsia the eventual and inevitable relinquishment of its position of leadership in society.

Although the Japan Socialist Union, composed of socialist writers and members of labor organizations, as well as student and thought organizations, was dissolved by the government, the publication of its organ, *Socialism,* was continued for a while longer. In the *Journal of Socialism* communism was espoused by Yamakawa Hitoshi and Yamakawa Kikue. Magazines like *Workers' Literature (Rodosha Bungaku)* and *Socialist Arts and Letters (Shakai Shugi Bungei),* as well as works like Miyajima Sukeo's *The Miners (Kōfu)* and Maedakō Kōichirō's *Steerage Passenger (Santō Senkyaku)* were banned by the authorities for their leftist leanings.

It was out of the anguish of the intelligentsia and their growing social consciousness that the proletarian cultural movement emerged. The movement got under way with the publication in Tōkyō in October, 1921, of the *Sowers of Seeds (Tane maku Hito),* which had been started as a little pamphlet in Akita prefecture by Komaki Ōmi, who had returned from France to find his life of falsehood and deceit intolerable. The contributors to the new magazine included the literary talents of the period,[33] representing all shades of thought ranging from Marxism, anarchism, and nihilism to liberalism and humanism. It was inevitable therefore that constant clashes should take place within the ranks of writers of proletarian literature over what should constitute the guiding principles of the movement, resulting in schisms and formation of new groups. As an attempt to disseminate proletarian ideas the *Sowers of Seeds* succeeded in injecting an antimilitarist and international spirit into the literary movement. Although writers like Akita Ujaku and Arishima Takeo endeavored to dis-

[33] Among the contributors were Arishima Takeo, Akita Ujaku, Baba Kochō, Fujimori Seikichi, Hasegawa Nyozekan, Yamakawa Kikue, Hirabayashi Hatsunosuke, and others.

seminate internationalism, they instilled at the same time in the minds of the people the idea that art and literature could be effective weapons of class struggle.

In the great earthquake the *Sowers of Seeds* and other proletarian periodicals went out of existence. In the midst of the chaos and terror that reigned in the wake of the disaster Ōsugi Sakae, one of the most vivid figures in the history of Japanese communism, was strangled to death in Tōkyō by Captain Amakasu of the gendarmerie. In the death of Ōsugi the Communists lost a great champion who, in his brief life, was successively a socialist, syndicalist, anarchist, and finally a Communist. He had been a member of nearly every socialist organization formed in Japan during his time and always became the leader of a disruptive left wing. He had an unshakable belief to the very end in the efficacy of violence. To him, every disturbance was a step forward, if only it set the people to thinking. He possessed a characteristic credulity in the acceptance of doctrinnaire programs and showed impatience and intolerance for constitutional methods. However, he was more of a theorist than a labor or party leader who could operate under systematic organization and planning.

Although the movement, which had been gathering strength and momentum, suffered an almost irretrievable setback by the death of Ōsugi and the abandonment of proletarian publications, the same group of men resumed their class struggle through the medium of literature. In June, 1924, the leftist *Literature and Arts Front* [34] made its literary debut. Toward the close of 1925, the Japan Proletarian Artists' League was formed for the purpose of achieving organizational unity and the expansion of the *Literature and Arts Front* (*Bungei Sensen*), which was a spiritual and literary descendant of the *Sowers of Seeds*. The League, which was the direct result of the prodding of the Fifth Congress of the Comintern, adopted for its principles the recognition of proletarian class struggle, the establishment of proletarian culture, and the struggle against bourgeois culture and its patrons. Under the leadership of able writers [35] the movement made notable progress.

Meanwhile, proletarian groups organized a drama association as part of the new drama movement. In the spring of 1924 Hijikata Yoshi, a scion of the nobility, who had returned from a study of drama in Germany, founded the Tsukiji Little Theater. With Osanai Kaoru, the leader of the new drama movement, as adviser Hijikata launched the little theater movement in opposition to the established commercial theaters. His aim was to make the theater the most pleasant and meaningful gathering place for the new working classes. At the same time the little theater served as a laboratory, where experiments in new drama were carried on during the four years of its existence, which was finan-

---

[34] This was actually a resurrection of the *Sowers of Seeds,* which disappeared in 1923 after the great earthquake.

[35] Writers who furnished the leadership included Akita, Ema, and Nii.

cially unprofitable. Its discontinuance in 1928 came as the result of financial difficulties. In all, more than 100 plays were presented. Emphasis was naturally placed on plays written by left-wing writers. The repertoire included realistic as well as romantic plays ranging all the way from modern plays to classical drama like the *Forty-seven Rōnin*. Presented also were Russian plays by Chekhov, Gorky, Tolstoy, and Turgenev, German plays of Schiller and Hauptmann, English plays of Shakespeare, George Bernard Shaw, and John Masefield, American plays of Eugene O'Neill, Swedish plays by Strindberg, Norwegian plays by Ibsen (*A Doll's House* and *Peer Gynt*), French plays by Romain Rolland, and Belgian plays by Maeterlinck (*Blue Bird*).

At its second annual conference, the Japan Proletarian Literature and Arts League concentrated its discussions on Marxist principles in an effort to unite with the other proletarian movements of the period. The Shinjinkai of the Tōkyō Imperial University, which played an important part in the League, served definitely, though perhaps quite unintentionally, as a training ground for Communists. It had been organized originally by a group of dissenters who had seceded from the University Debating Society in 1917, when the Russian Revolution was in full swing. Students who had started with abstract discussion of social theories and problems were soon impelled to participate actively in the fight to improve the lot of the underprivileged and they soon found themselves in the vanguard of the proletarian movement.

Within the Japan Proletarian Literature and Arts League existed a social democratic element which found itself in conflict with the main objectives of the group. As the League began to take an increasingly active part in political issues, strife and disunion resulted. Following the clash over the issue of radical changes versus gradual reform, Fujimori Seikichi, Yamada Seisaburo, Aono, Maedakō, Komaki, and Kaneko withdrew late in 1927, formed the Farmer Labor Artists' League (Rōnō Geijutsuka Dōmei), and continued to publish the *Literature and Arts Front*. The extreme left wingers, led by Fujimori and advocating illegal tactics, bolted, formed the Vanguard Artists' League (Zen'ei Geijutsuka Remmei) and published its organ, *Vanguard*. Remaining behind to continue the *Arts and Literature Front* was the group espousing social democracy. They secured contributions from such well-known writers as Ema Osamu, Kataoka Teppei, and Kurahara Koreto.

In the spring of 1928 the National Proletarian Arts League (Zen Nihon Musansha Geijutsu Remmei), which came to be known by its Esperanto abbreviation as the NAP, emerged and began the publication of its organ, *Battle Flag* (*Senki*). This was the merger of the Vanguard Artists' League and the extreme left-wing factions of the proletarian literary movement, which had been rejected by the social democratic elements. In October the International Cultural Research Institute was set up to propagandize the NAP abroad. This was superseded, in 1929, by the Proletarian Science Research Institute, which extended considerably its scope of activities.

During January and February of 1929 the NAP brought together the various independent organizations of artists, playwrights, actors, musicians, and motion picture actors to form the National Congress of Proletarian Artists' Organizations (Zen Nihon Musansha Geijutsu Dantai Kyōgikai). The NAP organ *Battle Flag,* which in the beginning had a circulation of 7,000, had reached 13,000 in 1929 and had exceeded 23,000 in 1930. In view of the unrest and unemployment resulting from the world depression and the sad plight of the farmers and agrarian communities in general the conference of the proletarian cultural organizations, in 1930, decided that conditions were favorable for the communization of literature and arts. The formation of the Japan Proletarian Cultural League in November, 1931, designed to establish proletarian culture based on the doctrines of Marx and Lenin, gave unity to the proletarian cultural movement in Japan. But the outbreak of the Manchurian Incident and the fanning of the flame of nationalism contributed directly and speedily to the recession of the leftist movement, which all but disappeared in the middle thirties.

Chapter 32. Nationalism and the Rise of the

Military to Power

Traditional conservative thought in Japan has been a legacy of centuries of feudalism, which had survived the vicissitudes of time. While the advent of Western thought in the late nineteenth century affected the intellectuals and leaders in and out of the government, by no means did it engulf the traditional thought of the people. Even when economic liberalism and the concept of liberty and popular government were at their peak of popularity, conservative and even reactionary ideologies were far from overshadowed. On the contrary, the contact with the nineteenth-century nationalism of the West made possible the development of a modern nationalism, more intense than the vague sort of nationalism which had obtained throughout the feudal period.

THE EARLY ULTRANATIONALISTS

Ultranationalistic societies in the contemporary sense are the product of the late nineteenth century. Earliest of these perhaps was the Gen'yōsha, founded in Fukuoka by Tōyama Mitsuru and Hiraoka Kōtarō in the late 1870's. The society's twofold aim comprised a positive continental expansionist policy and a program of sweeping internal political reforms. In the movement for liberty and popular rights in the 1870's, the Gen'yōsha supported the forces in opposition to the government. However, by the middle of the 1880's, it had abandoned the cause of popular rights in favor of nationalism and turned its attention to the expansion of national power. While it regarded popular rights as desirable, it became definitely and unalterably opposed to promoting them at the expense of national power. It had reached the conclusion that reliance on the military was the best insurance for the development and preservation of national power. Working closely with Sassa Tomofusa and his nationalistic society, Kokkentō of Kumamoto, Tōyama cooperated with the government in trying to stamp out the movement for liberty and popular rights. Both societies opposed the westernization policies of Premier Itō and Foreign Minister Inoue in the mid-eighties as well as Ōkuma's treaty revision efforts. In the notorious election interference carried out by the Matsukata Government in 1892, the Gen'yōsha played an active part.[1]

Before long, the nationalist society came to deemphasize its role in strictly domestic issues and became a vigorous exponent of continental expansion. In line with this new policy, it participated actively in the sending to Korea of a group whose activities provided at least some of the incidents that became the prelude to the outbreak of hostilities between China and Japan in 1894. After the war, in concert with other expansionist and ultranationalist groups, it supported the program of naval expansion, the domination of Asia, and the Pan Asiatic movement.[2] It also had a hand in the Chinese Revolution from its earliest stages before the turn of the century, when it aided revolutionary exiles like Kang Yu-wei and Sun Yat-sen, in the Russo-Japanese War, the annexation of Korea, the Siberian expedition, and the Manchurian Incident.

The turn of the century saw the birth of a new ultranationalist society that dedicated itself vigorously and militantly to promoting domestic reforms and overseas expansion. The Black Dragon Society,[3] launched by Uchida Ryōhei in 1901 under the aegis of Tōyama's Gen'yōsha, was a reactionary organization whose aims included the dissemination of Oriental civilization, the harmonization and integration of Occidental and Oriental cultures, and the uplift of the peoples of Asia. In advocating domestic renovation, it proposed the eradication of legalism, which allegedly hampered efficiency and common sense, while restricting the freedom of the people. It looked to the overhauling of the educational system, which blindly imitated the West, and setting up a national educational system based on ancient ideals, particularly on the Imperial Way.[4] Diplomacy appeared to be in need of a thorough revitalizing to meet the new demands of overseas activities, while social policies were urgently needed to increase the welfare and happiness of the people and to solve some of the social conflicts such as capital-labor strife.

NATIONALISM OF THE FIRST WORLD WAR AND AFTER

Ultranationalism had its devotees in academic circles too. In May, 1913, Professors Uesugi Shinkichi and Kakehi Katsuhiko of the Tōkyō Imperial University founded the Paulownia Society (Dōka Kai) with the avowed purpose of stimulating patriotism and offsetting the "baneful effects" of liberalism. As

[1] See an article on Tōyama in *Taiyō*, February, 1902, p. 36, and also *Gen'yōshashi* (1917), pp. 419–421.

[2] *Gen'yōshashi*, p. 410.

[3] In 1940, the Society was represented by its President Kuzuu Yoshihisa on the preparatory committee for the setting up of the Imperial Rule Assistance Association.

[4] Kada Tetsuji, *Nihon Gendai Bummeishi: Shakaishi*, pp. 336–337.

the advocacy of democracy gained momentum during the First World War movements were launched to oppose militarism, to check the existing chauvinistic trend in education as a necessary step toward the establishment of responsible government, and to liberate the working classes from oppression and exploitation. In the course of a vigorous assertion of the rights of individuals that developed, severe criticisms were directed even against the Emperor.

The *zaibatsu,* who had profited immensely from the war boom, were not slow in utilizing the tremendous popularity of democracy. They set out by systematic and large scale contributions to the political parties to plan the overthrow of the military and at the same time to check the rightist organizations, which supported the military with the ideology of chauvinism. In their campaign they spared no efforts, going even to the extent of enlisting the laborers and peasants in their campaign to discredit and dislodge the military.

The rightists took up the challenge by launching a counteroffensive and branding the democratic and liberal movement as un-Japanese and subversive. The Black Dragon Society came out strongly against democracy and took upon itself the task of chastising the newspaper Ōsaka *Asahi* for the role it played in the popularization of democratic ideas.[5] The Rōninkai, which had been launched in 1908 as an offshoot of the Black Dragon Society, became a united front for antidemocratic, antisocialistic activities and launched a nationwide campaign to stamp out "subversive" ideas by physical violence and intimidation, which were employed freely against scholars, politicians, and financiers who were either exponents or friends of democracy or democratic ideas. With the strong support of the Rōninkai the rightist elements began a systematic effort to combat democratic developments by organizing powerful ultranationalistic groups under the slogan of "clarification of national polity."

In the fall of 1918, the nationalist Rōsōkai [6] was organized by Dr. Ōkawa Shūmei, Professor Mitsukawa Kametarō, and others to oppose and counteract the pro-democratic forces around the Reimeikai of Professors Yoshino and Fukuda. This was a discussion group, embracing those who represented ideologies ranging from the center to extreme right, and it concerned itself with the problem of reconstructing the nation. The following summer, the leaders of the faction led by Mitsukawa and Ōkawa, who had rejected Marxism, were deeply impressed by the work *History of the Chinese Revolution,* brought back its author, Kita Ikki, from Shanghai, and organized on August 1 a new society,

[5] In broad daylight, bullies dragged President Maruyama Ryūhei of the Ōsaka *Asahi* out into the street and tied him to a telephone pole. The Black Dragon Society was also responsible for forcing Hasegawa Nyozekan and Ōyama Ikuo out of the newspaper Ōsaka *Mainichi* as "red" journalists for having opposed the Siberian expedition and incurred the wrath of the Terauchi Government.

[6] Members included Nakano Seigō, Takahatake Motoyuki, Kanokogi Kazunobu, Date Junnosuke, Kasagi Yoshiaki, and Satō Kajirō.

Yūzonsha, which devoted itself to propaganda work until it fell apart in 1923, when Ōkawa and Kita parted company to become irreconcilable rivals.

In his *Outline for the Reconstruction of Japan* [7] Kita set forth a theory as well as a program of social revolution applied to Japanese society. As a theorist of ultranationalism, he advocated the reconstruction of the nation around the military and an awakened citizenry. A prominent feature of his plan was the strengthening of Japan's military power as a means of establishing international justice. It was his contention that an appeal to arms by a "have-not" nation against a "have" nation to rectify injustice could never be construed as an act of aggression. As a matter of fact, he claimed that it was the birthright of a nation to declare war on another that monopolized large areas of land in contravention of the natural law of human coexistence. Kita proposed limitations on private property, land, and private capital.[8] Land in the city was to be owned entirely by the municipality while forests and large farms were to be state-operated. Strikes and shutdowns were to be prohibited.

The Japan Nationalist Society (Dai Nihon Kokusuikai) was formed in 1919 with the blessings of the then Home Minister Tokonami for the purpose of synchronizing its activities with those of the Rōninkai, which was an exclusively operational unit. This society soon developed into a nationwide organization, boasting a membership of a million, and directed a particularly strong opposition against the "Water Level" movement, which was aimed at ending the social and economic discrimination against the social outcasts, who were still technically slaves in spite of the fact that they had been liberated legally. It also opposed the socialist as well as the labor movement. Its offshoot, Yamato Minrōkai, which was formed in 1921 in the Kanto region, and the Dai Nihon Seigidan, formed in the Kansai region in 1926, achieved notoriety by the violent tactics they employed. Members of the latter organization aped the Italian Fascists and adopted black shirts for their uniforms.

In March, 1922, the League for the Prevention of Communism (Sekka Bōshidan) was formed with the avowed purpose of checking and counteracting the radical tendencies of the period. Its members virtually pledged their lives to the eradication of communism, which, they were convinced, threatened to destroy the foundation of society and blight the happiness of mankind. The League worked for the separation of the labor movement from socialism, with which it had been associated, and strongly urged the capitalists to reflect seriously, inasmuch as their highhandedness was contributing to the growth of radical ideas. As a champion of the principle of imperial rule it sponsored the first

[7] This work, *Nihon Kaizō Hōan Taikō,* was published in 1919. As the bible of the ultranationalists, both civilian and military, in the thirties it had a profound effect on the period and its developments.

[8] Private property was to be limited to 1 million yen per household, landholding to 100,000 yen at market price, and capital to 10 million yen.

"Patriotic Day." In pushing ahead its program, it showed no hesitation in resorting to force, especially in coping with the anarchists.[9]

The following year saw the appearance of three more nationalist organizations. The League for the Study of Statecraft (Keiringakumei) sponsored by Dr. Uesugi Shinkichi, ultranationalist professor of law at the Tōkyō Imperial University, and Takahatake Motoyuki, a onetime socialist, converted to ultranationalism. This organization, which was to carry on both ideological propaganda and direct action, disintegrated as soon as it was formed because of ideological differences within its ranks. From the split, however, emerged two groups, the Radical Patriotic Party (Kyūshin Aikokutō) of Tsukui Tatsuo and the Patriotic Workers' Party (Aikoku Kinrōtō) of Amano Tatsuo and Nakatani Takeyo.[10] In the summer of 1923 the National Association for the Study of Military Affairs (Kokumin Gunji Kenkyū Dan) was organized for the purpose of disseminating and popularizing military ideas and knowledge and for the stimulation of nationalism.

When the government began to take stringent measures against the radical leftist movement in 1924, many of the organizations felt that their services were no longer needed in checking the radicals. Yet, two more societies were founded for the purpose of directing and channeling national thought in the "right direction." The Cherry Blossom Society (Ōkakai), which was formed by the segment that broke off the Japan Nationalist Society, advocated the urgency of giving direction to national thought, while the Radical Youth Party (Seinen Kyūshintō) started the publication of its organ *Japanese Thought* (*Nihon Shisō*) for the study and dissemination of nationalist ideas.

In the face of increasing radicalism the urgency of developing sound national thought was keenly felt. Thus, in the spring of 1924, the State Foundation Society (Kokuhonsha) was organized. It was emphasized by its founder, Baron Hiranuma Kiichirō, then vice president of the Privy Council, that the society was neither fascist nor antiforeign in its purpose. As part of its program, it sent lecturers on nationwide tours to revive, cultivate, and nourish the traditional ideas and awaken the people to the spiritual values inherent in Japan's indigenous culture as a means of counteracting the "unhealthy" trend of the time. Although in the beginning students constituted the greater part of the Kokuhonsha membership, the society gradually extended its influence to judicial and military personnel throughout the country, so that by the beginning of the thirties its roster read like a *Who's Who*. The judicial world was represented by such distinguished personages as Dr. Suzuki Kisaburō, president of the Seiyūkai, Dr. Hara Yoshimichi, Privy Councilor, Shiono Suehiko, three times Justice Minister, and Komatsu Matsukichi. Among the outstanding military men were War

[9] This was demonstrated in the fatal shooting of Takao Heisuke on June 26, 1923, in one of the clashes which took place.

[10] The former comprised the Takahatake faction and the latter the Uesugi faction.

Minister Araki, Supreme War Councilor General Mazaki, General Koiso Kuni-aki, and retired Lieutenant General Baron Kikuchi Takeo, member of the House of Peers. The *rōnin* group was represented by Honda Kumatarō, one-time Ambassador to Germany.[11]

Indicative of the growing popularity and strength of the nationalistic movement was the observance of the Empire Foundation Day on February 11, 1926, under the sponsorship of the Tōkyō Young Men's and Women's Associations, Imperial Reservists' Association, and schools interested in the celebration of the national holiday, which had been observed annually by the entire nation for years. Obviously, this celebration was staged in an impressive manner to bolster the patriotism and nationalism of the Japanese people. Its sequel was the establishment of the Empire Foundation Society (Kenkokukai) and anticommunist organization composed principally of students and intellectuals of the right wing. Implicit in the statement of principles and policies were the enhancement of the traditional Japanese spirit based on the ideal of the emperor-centric state, the achievement of leadership among the nonwhite peoples of the world, and the attainment of national unity and equality of the people. The organization looked to the eventual abolition of the parliamentary system, all existing political parties, and proletarian parties in particular. They were regarded as incompatible with Japan's body politic as were all forms of socialism, social democracy, state socialism, and communism.

These rightist organizations that emerged in rapid succession in the postwar period opposed vigorously the rising power of the liberal and democratic elements. As the democratic movement gained momentum and full force, so did the strength of the working classes and the peasantry. By the mid-twenties the cleavage between the working classes and the capitalists had widened, and this had accentuated their awareness of class struggle. The capitalists began to see in the rising power of labor a threat to their own security. Consequently, in their desperate efforts to check the strength of labor, they turned to the rightist organizations which they had previously regarded as their enemy. They did not hesitate in their efforts to preserve their interests to collaborate not only with the bureaucrats but also with the militarists, who were now looked upon as their allies in a common endeavor to stem the tide of dangerous thoughts.

The reactionary character of the nationalistic movement grew out of the highly irrational ultranationalism and chauvinistic patriotism, calling for the free sacrifice of life whenever necessary. Basically, the movement was an emo-

[11] Affiliated with the Kokuhonsha as subsidiary organizations were the Loyalists League (Kinnō Remmei), headed by Lt. Gen. Baron Kikuchi Takeo as president and Gen. Satō Kiyokatsu as vice president, the Institute for the Study of State Science (Kokutai Kagaku Kenkyūjo), directed by Satomi Kishio, Yamato Spirit League (Yamato Damashii Remmei) of Gotō Takeo, and the Society for the Defense of Japan (Dai Nippon Gokokukai) of Kawate Tadayoshi.

tional one, which appealed almost entirely to the sentiments of religious venera-
tion of the Emperor, implicit in the Japanese monarchical creed. Its spiritual
source was the traditional idea that demanded one's incorruptible and unshakable
devotion to the nation. It was partly the legacy of feudalism, which had survived in the midst of twentieth-century modernism, that was mobilized for the
reordering of Japanese society, plagued by chaos and inequity.

In a sense, Japanese fascism was the manifestation of determined opposition
against Western concepts of liberalism and socialism as well as communism and
was directed against Western influences in general, which were thought to
threaten the pattern of Japanese life and culture to the detriment of national
security. It was therefore authoritarian, antiparliamentarian, antidemocratic, opposed to disarmament, and suspicious of the League of Nations. It was also a
Pan-Asiatic movement, unafraid and unhesitant regarding the use of force. The
ultimate goal of all nationalist groups was the achievement of national self-
sufficiency towards which everything had to be geared. The loud and persistent clamor for the equitable distribution of the world's resources and the
establishment of a controlled economy at home were but means to an end.

Difficulties arising out of the growing dependence of national economy upon
foreign markets for the export of manufactured goods and the increasing concentration of ownership and control of commerce and of industry in the hands
of a few big financial combines had served to intensify the effects of economic
depression, which set in with the financial panic in 1927. Even in the midst
of general economic distress, accentuated by widespread unemployment among
the factory workers and agrarian suffering, the *zaibatsu* missed no opportunity
in making profits through large dollar purchases. To aggravate the situation,
the political parties, in full collaboration with the *zaibatsu,* went into a period
of corruption that lasted well into the thirties. One scandal after another was
brought to light to the irreparable harm of the political parties and party government. The confidence of the public in the institution of responsible party
government was badly shaken, if not shattered. The conditions provided a fertile soil for antidemocratic, antiparliamentary propaganda by the military and
the rightist organizations.

General public discontent at the existing state of affairs provided too good an
opportunity for the reactionaries to miss. Every conceivable method was employed in propaganda campaigns to alienate the public from the political parties
and the *zaibatsu.* The fight that developed between the Minseitō and the military over the London Naval Treaty in 1930 gave the latter sufficient cause to
fear that their traditional independence of action, subject only to the will of
the Emperor, might be subordinated to the authority of the head of the Cabinet,
who would more often than not be a civilian. This was one thing the military
was determined to avoid.

The rightist organizations at first functioned on the periphery, merely as auxiliary operating units of the military, the bureaucracy, and even the *zaibatsu*. Theirs was an inconspicuous behind-the-scene role. Behind the extensive communist hunt, carried out by the government in March, 1928, and April, 1929, the rightists were at work, but their activities were not overt. But a change of method of operation took place during and after the London Naval Conference of 1930.

On May 19, 1930, when Navy Minister Admiral Takarabe, one of the delegates to the London Naval Conference, arrived home, he was greeted at the Tōkyō Station by handbills distributed by the members of the Patriotic Workers' Party (Aikoku Kinrōtō) denouncing him as a traitor, who had sold his country. Rightists groups disseminated propaganda accusing the Hamaguchi Cabinet of scheming against the Privy Council in collusion with Privy Seal Makino and Grand Chamberlain Admiral Suzuki and threatened direct action to achieve their aims.

NATIONALISM OF THE EARLY THIRTIES

The first signs of rightist activity in the army were revealed in late September of 1930, when an organization known as the Cherry Society (Sakurakai) was formed by a handful of army officers of field grade, mostly majors and lieutenant colonels attached to the War Ministry, General Staff Office, and the Inspectorate General of Military Education, who became imbued with an irrepressible zeal for national reconstruction.[12] As stated in its prospectus,[13] the Cherry Society had for its chief objective the protection and enhancement of the military, whose position was jeopardized by the encroachments of the political parties, as demonstrated by the conclusion of the London Naval Treaty, and subversive leftist ideologies. It deplored the impotence of the military, which, because of indecision and lack of courage to take definite steps to remedy the situation, could do no better than to rely upon the Privy Council, a gathering of "has beens," to be its spokesmen. This sad state of degeneration of the military the Society attributed to the general decline in morale induced by peace, the lack of definite convictions and policies among the officer class, and the want of a consuming *esprit de corps*. The member officers were absolutely convinced that what had happened to the navy as a result of the London Naval Treaty was sure to happen to the army in the form of some disarmament agreement in the not distant future.

A bill of particulars of the Cherry Society contained a detailed enumeration of the nation's ills and constituted in effect an indictment against those who

[12] The leaders of the Society were Lieutenant Colonels Hashimoto, Sakada, Nemoto, and Major Suzuki, all of whom had been viewing with misgivings the corruption and degeneration of politics and political parties as well as the bureaucracy and the *zaibatsu*.

[13] See Imanaka Tsugimaro, *Nihon Seijishi Taikō*, pp. 400–402.

were at the nation's helm and responsible for the deplorable conditions in the country. Listed were the corruption of the political parties and high-ranking government officials, as well as the self-centered capitalists and the nobility, who were incapable of understanding the masses, the evil influence of the media of mass communication, which was responsible for the decay of national thought, the indescribably acute agrarian distress, general economic depression and resultant unemployment, the appearance of all kinds of unhealthy "thought organizations," the appearance of a decadent culture, the absence of patriotism on the part of the students, and the undisguised passion of the bureaucrats for the safeguarding of their own positions and interests. In view of these conditions, it was felt that the field grade officers, who constituted the backbone of the army, owed it to themselves and to the nation to undertake national reconstruction. In cleaning out the Augean stables of politics, the government, as it was constituted, was ineffectual and could do nothing. It was therefore imperative that the composition of the government be changed to make the reconstruction of the nation possible. Events that followed are an eloquent testimony of the activities of this group and other like-minded organizations.

The signing of the London Naval Treaty in 1930 presented a wonderful opportunity to the ultranationalist organizations, which were bent on inciting public opinion against the government for its weak diplomacy and alleged encroachment on the imperial prerogative of the "supreme command." The Minseitō came under the violent attack of the rightist elements, which were working hand in glove with the military and the bureaucrats. On November 14 the party's president, Premier Hamaguchi, was fatally wounded by a member of a rightist organization that advocated a positive policy of continental expansion. Rightist groups blamed Hamaguchi's retrenchment policies for the prevailing social insecurity in the nation and were bent on overthrowing the Cabinet.

Great confusion reigned at the plenary budget session of the Diet on February 3, 1931. Acting Premier Shidehara, in reply to the interpellation made by a Seiyūkai member of the Diet, Nakajima Chikuhei, defended the London Naval Treaty on the ground that it could not possibly endanger Japan's defenses, inasmuch as its ratification had been sanctioned by the Emperor. This was interpreted by the opposition as tantamount to placing the responsibility on the Emperor, creating such a furore in the Diet that it had the effect of holding up deliberations for an entire week. Casualties were suffered by members as the floor of the Diet turned into an arena where party members resorted to blows as much as to words in an attempt to make their arguments prevail.

DEVELOPMENTS WITHIN THE ARMY

Within the army itself there was a powerful group, including Vice Chief of General Staff Ninomiya Shigeharu, General Koiso Kuniaki, General Tatekawa

Yoshitsugu, Colonels Hashimoto Kingorō, and Shigefugi Chiaki, who felt strongly the need of national political renovation. At the time it was rumored that General Ugaki Kazushige might join one of the political parties, just as General Tanaka Giichi had done several years earlier. Generals Koiso and Tatekawa, however, ascertained that Ugaki had no intention of taking such a step, especially in view of the degeneration and impotence of the political parties. As a result, an agreement to plan the much-needed political renovation was reached by the group including General Ugaki.[14]

In the spring of 1931, the radical elements of the army plotted a *coup d'état* which failed to go beyond the planning stage.[15] The plot was to have been executed, beginning with the blowing up of the headquarters of the major parties, Seiyūkai and Minseitō, as well as the Premier's official residence. Plans drawn up by Ōkawa Shūmei called for a demonstration by a mob of 10,000 members of both rightist and leftist organizations. Mobilized troops were to surround the Diet building under the guise of protecting it and cut off communications with the outside. A lieutenant general, accompanied by either Major General Koiso or Major General Tatekawa and several officers, was to appear on the floor of the Diet and pronounce that, since the people had no confidence in either the Diet or the Cabinet, they should withdraw gracefully and make way for General Ugaki, who enjoyed the complete confidence of the people. Reforms were then to be put into effect, one after another, under martial law.[16] However, on March 18, two days before the plot was to be carried out, it disintegrated. Koiso and Tatekawa both backed down as a result of General Ugaki's change of mind, which had been induced by the overture made by party leaders to back him up for the premiership.

While the plot was called off largely through Ugaki's change of mind, it is significant that there was a faction within the army that opposed the move, not because the members were opposed to political reconstruction, but because they were convinced that the time was not yet ripe for it, and that the same results could and should be achieved through orderly and legal means. Among those who took this attitude were Colonel Okamura Yasutsugu, Colonel Nagata Tetsuzan, Colonel Yamashita Tomoyuki, and Lieutenant Colonel Suzuki Teiichi.

Instead of showing any signs of decline, the army extremists' zeal for national reconstruction was greatly intensified after the unsuccessful March plot.

14 The agreement was reached in a meeting attended by War Minister Ugaki, Vice War Minister Sugiyama, Military Affairs Bureau Director Koiso, Vice Chief of General Staff Ninomiya, and General Tatekawa.

15 Leaders of the plot were Lieutenant Colonel Hashimoto, General Tatekawa, General Koiso, and Colonel Nagata.

16 Explosives to be used in the *coup d'état,* which had been secured and cached in the General Staff Office by the leaders, had already been distributed to those who were to use them.

By the end of July, it became known in well-informed quarters that a section of the army was planning to create an incident in Manchuria and to carry out simultaneously a program of internal political reforms. Some of the young officer extremists argued that, while the high-ranking generals were aware of and even in favor of the need for reform and renovation, they themselves, because of age and circumstances, were not in a position to carry out national reconstruction. Therefore, there was only one method left and that was for the younger officers to lead the generals, who would follow them once the program were launched and they were absolved of any responsibility.

By the end of August, 1931, Ōkawa Shūmei divulged that his group of rightists had plans to create an incident in Manchuria sometime around October that would aggravate Sino-Japanese relations and economic conditions, brought to an impasse by the interruption of trade with China. This was to be followed by inciting the people to riot in Tōkyō and Ōsaka, and after allowing some time to pass the rightists would then hold a national mass meeting in February of the following year, attack the Diet and carry out a *coup d'état*. However, the Kwantung Army went ahead with its own plans and brought about the Manchurian Incident on September 18.

Right on the heels of the Manchurian Incident came the October plot. Army officers who led the March plot and radical members of the Cherry Society, led by Lieutenant Colonel Hashimoto and Major Osa Isamu, knowing the impotence of party government and being reluctant to entrust even domestic administration to it, decided that steps should be taken to solve domestic problems and to rectify the injurious results of "weak diplomacy." The plot was planned with the support of Lieutenant Generals Koiso and Tatekawa, Major General Nagata, and Ōkawa Shūmei. A Reconstruction Headquarters was to be set up in the General Staff Office. The coup was to be carried out on October 24, using eleven infantry companies and one machine gun company, led by some 120 commissioned officers, joined by about ten naval officers from Yokosuka Naval Base, thirteen naval bombers from Kasumigaura Naval Air Base, and three or four planes from Shimoshizu Army Flying School, as well as the Ōkawa group and the Nishi-Kita group of civilian rightists. Details of the execution of the coup called for an aerial attack on the Premier's official residence while a cabinet meeting was in progress to liquidate the entire government in one stroke. The Metropolitan Police Board was to be seized and occupied, while the War Ministry and the General Staff Office were to be surrounded, communications with the outside completely cut off, and high-ranking officers forced into acquiescing, placing under arrest those who refused. Fleet Admiral Tōgō was to be sent to the Imperial Palace to recommend that the Emperor ask the "newly risen power" to form a new government.[17] A whole week before the date of execution, the

---

[17] Significant is the fact that those who planned the coup paid a great deal of attention to the media of mass communication, as their plans called for the seizure of the Central Telephone

plot was uncovered by the gendarmerie, largely because of the strong mutual suspicion that existed between the Ōkawa faction on the one hand and the Kita-Nishi faction on the other. On October 16, the leaders were arrested at their meeting place in Tōkyō and the plot was nipped in the bud.

THE CIVILIAN RIGHTISTS

The advocacy of national economic self-sufficiency, which was emphasized by all rightist organizations in the post Manchurian Incident era, took two distinct forms. One which was based upon centralization, government control, and industrialization concerns us primarily in the discussion of the extremists' activities of the thirties. However, we must also give some attention to the consideration of the opposing school of thought, in order to appreciate fully the complexities of the ultranationalistic developments of the period.

In the same year that Kita Ikki wrote his *Outline for the Reconstruction of Japan,* Gondō Seikyō [18] came out with his *People's Handbook of Self-Government (Jichi Mimpan),* designed to foster the spirit of self-government among the farmers. Gondō was convinced that the autonomous agrarian communities should provide the basis of national strength in the realization of national self-sufficiency. His radical reactionary agrarianism was a combination of physiocratic emphasis on the importance of the soil and a touch of spiritual anarchism with regard to government, opposed to machine civilization, urbanization, industrialization, administrative centralization, and government control. He extolled in a romantic fashion the virtues of a primitive, feudal mode of production.

The cause of agrarian nationalism was espoused after 1931 by Gondō and Tachibana through the Association for Agrarian Self-Government (Nōmin Jichi Kyōkai) and the Aikyōjuku, a private agrarian workers' school, which was founded by the latter in Ibaraki prefecture in April, 1931. The objectives of the Association included, among other things, the shift from profit-motivated economy to welfare economy, attainment of security of agrarian livelihood through local autonomous economic units, and the prohibition of absentee cultivation and ownership of land. The national economy was to be based solidly upon small and middle class farmers. Tachibana was opposed to bureaucratization and centralization of the national economy and administration. He and his Aikyōjuku

---

Office, the Telegraph Office, the Central Radio Broadcasting Office, and the leading Tōkyō newspapers, *Asahi, Nichi Nichi, Jiji, Hōchi, Kokumin,* and *Yomiuri.*

The Cabinet as planned by the group was as follows: Premier and War Minister General Araki, Home Minister Colonel Hashimoto, Foreign Minister Major General Tatekawa, Finance Minister Ōkawa Shūmei, Navy Minister Rear Admiral Kobayashi, and Metropolitan Police Board Superintendent General Major Osa.

[18] Gondō was also the author of *A Treatise on the Self-Sufficiency of a Farming Community* (Nōson Jikyū Ron), published in 1932.

came into the limelight as a result of their implication in the assassination of Premier Inukai on May 15, 1932.

Civilian rightist organizations became active in the spring of 1931. On March 20 the National Council of Patriotic Movements [19] was formed to effect the merger of the proletarian movement and nationalism and at the same time to achieve a close relationship with the military in a program to utilize war to bring about the reconstruction of the internal political structure. This was followed, in the summer, by the formation of the first openly proclaimed fascist party, the Japan Production Party (Nihon Seisantō),[20] which was promoted by Tōyama, the doyen of the ultranationalists and Uchida, head of the Black Dragon Society, for the purpose of effecting a merger of the masses and intellectual fascism. It was not until November, however, that it was formally inaugurated in Tōkyō, where it began the publication of its monthly organ, *Reconstruction Front (Kaizō Sensen)*. It claimed an initial membership of 70,000 which increased to 100,000 the following year. The party was opposed to centralization and concentration of political power as well as to complete *laissez faire,* which could, in its opinion, not infrequently border on anarchism. Its program included the restriction of property inheritance, limitation of government enterprises and the expansion of quasi-governmental undertakings, liquidation of huge landholdings, and the setting of a minimum standard of living to protect the productive classes of society.

The Japan Production Party reflected almost a messianic complex in regarding its mission to be the saving of the whole world and not merely of the people of Japan. In common with all the ultranationalist organizations, it emphasized as its goal the attainment of national economic self-sufficiency and equitable access to or equitable distribution of the world's resources. As expressed by its founder, Uchida Ryōhei, president of the Black Dragon Society, one of the objectives of the Japan Production Party was "to force the big land-owners of the world (the 'have nations') to make an equitable distribution of land in order to ensure happiness to all the peoples of the world."

Acts of terrorism were perpetrated with great frequency during 1932. Ex-Finance Minister and former Governor of the Bank of Japan, Inoue Junnosuke, then Chairman of the Election Committee of the Minseitō, was assassinated by one Konuma Tadashi, a twenty-four-year-old member of the agrarian ultra-nationalist group at the Aikyōjuku in Ibaraki prefecture. Hardly had the public horror at the assassination of Inoue died down when, on March 5, another member of the *zaibatsu,* Baron Dan Takuma, chairman of the Board of Directors of

[19] The Zen Nihon Aikokusha Kyōdō Tōsō Kyōgikai published its organ *Kōmin Shimbun.*

[20] The party was founded by Uchida Ryōhei, president of the Black Dragon Society, in Ōsaka on June 28, 1931, and was joined by eighteen other organizations on November 20, 1931, when it was formally inaugurated in Tōkyō. Tōyama was made the adviser.

the Mitsui Company, fell at the hands of another youth from Ibaraki prefecture, Hishinuma Gorō.

It became known in due course that a Nichiren priest, Inoue Nisshō, was the spiritual leader of the Blood Brotherhood League (Ketsumeidan) and was behind the acts of terrorism. According to the plans of the League, each member was assigned the task of liquidating one of the designated victims.[21] Singled out for assassination were the influential members of political parties, the financial clique, and the privileged class, who were thought responsible for the corruption, the deplorable state of affairs in the nation, ineffectual and weak diplomacy especially with regard to Manchuria and China, and the unspeakable plight of the agrarian communities.

THE MAY 15 INCIDENT

That the reactionary rightist elements were rapidly gaining ascendancy was demonstrated beyond a shadow of doubt on May 15 when Premier Inukai was assassinated in cold blood. An organized group of naval officers and army cadets, with the support of civilian rightists forming detached flying columns, carried out the attack on the Premier and assaults on the Metropolitan Police Board headquarters, the official residence of Privy Seal Makino, the Bank of Japan, Mitsubishi Bank, Seiyūkai headquarters, and electric transformer stations in various parts of the city. Civilian participants in the attempted *coup d'état* included students of Aikyōjuku, one university student, two elementary school teachers, and two farmers.[22]

On the same day, the group had issued a manifesto in the name of young army and navy officers, farmers, and their friends calling the attention of the public to the dangers confronting the nation and urging the people to take up arms, inasmuch as the only way to save the nation from ruin was to resort to direct action and strike down the villains close to the Throne.[23] It exhorted the farmers, the laborers, and the people in general to rise and protect the nation by assisting in the liquidation of the political parties, the *zaibatsu,* and the enemies of the people, the punishment of the arbitrary bureaucrats, the wiping out of traitors and the privileged class, and the establishment of a vigorous new Japan. It emphasized, however, that before constructive efforts could start, a

[21] Marked for assassination by the Blood Brotherhood League were Premier Inukai, Lord Keeper of the Privy Seal Makino, Elder Statesman Prince Saionji, House of Peers President Prince Tokugawa, ex-Foreign Minister Baron Shidehara, ex-Premier Wakatsuki, Privy Councilor Itō, ex-Home Minister Tokonami, Mitsui's Baron Dan, Ikeda Seihin, and Inoue Junnosuke.

[22] Among those who had given direct aid and encouragement to the group were Ōkawa Shūmei, then president of the ultranationalist Jimmu Society, Tōyama Hideo, president of the Tenkōkai, and Homma Ken'ichirō, president of the Shizanjuku, all of whom were acknowledged leaders of the rightists.

[23] Mori Shōzō, *Sempū Nijūnen,* Vol. I, pp. 114–115.

thorough destruction of the abominable *status quo* was imperative. Interesting was the fact that it was stated without equivocation in the manifesto that the group belonged to neither the right nor the left, and that the rise or fall of Japan depended not on the success of the group's program but on the actions of the people themselves. Parties, blinded by their own interests, the *zaibatsu,* who in collusion with the politicians exploited the people, the bureaucrats, who protected the financial clique, and the decadent military were all held responsible for the weak and ineffectual diplomacy that placed Japan in a disadvantageous position internationally, degenerate education, acute agrarian distress, and the distressing state of national morale and thought.

After the plans were executed, all of the twoscore participants surrendered voluntarily to the gendarmerie and the authorities were able to dispose of the incident with speed. Army and navy personnel involved had been tried and sentenced by the following year. The penalties imposed were light, the severest being only fifteen years' imprisonment. The affair brought to light the unmistakable fact that the military was unalterably opposed to the political parties. Two days after the assassination of Inukai, the newspapers reported that Vice Chief of General Staff Mazaki, Gendarmerie Commander in Chief Hata, Vice Minister of War Koiso, and General Obata had called on War Minister Araki and advised him to inform Prince Saionji of the fact that the army was absolutely opposed to the reappearance of a party government. The Minseitō was quick to utilize the situation to the detriment of its opposition. Thus, the dream of Seiyūkai President Suzuki Kisaburō to form a party government was completely shattered and internal bickering and dissension started within the ranks of the party, which was still numerically quite impressive.

Elder Statesman Saionji was thus impelled by forces beyond his control to suspend party government and recommend that Admiral Saitō form a nonparty bureaucratic cabinet. The army's stand was strengthened and aided by the behind-the-scene activities and maneuvers of the bureaucrats, centering around the Home Ministry group of which Izawa Takio, then member of the House of Peers and supported by Yuasa and Ichiki, both of whom were powerful bureaucrats. Minseitō support in the Diet was assured the Saitō Government by Izawa. Saionji had been persuaded to believe that it was no more than a stopgap and a temporary suspension of party government, which could be restored with the return of more favorable conditions. Actually, however, it proved to be a period of transition from a party government to a nonparty military-dominated bureaucratic government.

Thus, the May 15 Incident was the death knell of party government, although Admiral Saitō not only respected the parties, but also desired the smooth functioning of parliamentary government. Although six Cabinet posts were given to members of the two major parties, four to Seiyūkai and two to Minseitō members, it was no more than a feeble gesture devoid of any meaning.[24] Little more than two months after the formation of the Saitō Cabinet, on August 8, 1932, General Mutō Nobuyoshi was appointed Commander in Chief of the Kwantung Army, Governor-General of the Kwantung Territory, and concurrently Ambassador to Manchukuo. These appointments, which placed military, administrative, and diplomatic powers in the hands of one person, a high-ranking military official, was fraught with great significance as it was a reflection of the power of the military in domestic as well as foreign affairs.

The seeming impasse reached by capitalism and the deterioration in foreign relations and selfish opportunism of the *zaibatsu*-dominated political parties had the effect of stimulating fascist tendencies in the nation. On February 11, 1932, the reactionary Jimmu Society was launched by Ōkawa Shūmei.[25] This was followed two months later by a new political party, the Japan National Socialist Party of Shimanaka Yūzō,[26] which brought within its fold both the left and right wing elements for the achievement of imperial rule, liquidation of capitalistic structure, institution of controlled national economy, and a new world order based on racial equality and equitable distribution of world resources. Shortly before the end of the year Adachi Kenzō, a rightist of long standing, launched his party, the Kokumin Dōmei, to advocate expansionism, a strong administrative setup, and a government-controlled national economy. Adachi attacked the Minseitō and Seiyūkai as old-fashioned, outmoded political parties incapable of coping with new conditions and made a strong bid for peasant support by proposing remission of the land tax to relieve their economic distress.

The Japan State Socialist Party, founded on May 29, 1932, by Akamatsu, who had bolted the Social Democratic Party, envisioned the building of a new national structure based on the traditional ideal of the Imperial Way, free of any exploitation. Its program of state socialism included the establishment of imperial rule to supersede the existing rule by finance capitalism, the replacement by legal means of the capitalistic structure with a state-controlled economy, and the liberation of the peoples of Asia on the basis of racial equality and equitable distribution of resources.

[24] The Seiyūkai was represented by Finance Minister Takahashi, Education Minister Hatoyama, Railway Minister Mitsuchi, and Communications Minister Minami, while the Minseitō was represented by Home Minister Yamamoto and Overseas Minister Nagai.

[25] The Jimmukai had for its avowed aims the clarification of traditional Japanese ideals to be effected through educational reform, the liquidation of political parties, and the rejection of capitalist economy to be superseded by controlled national economy.

[26] Advocated by the party were the checking of party politicians, abolition of the peerage, nationalization of major industries and public utilities, guaranteed living wages for workers, system of social security, and limitation on private property.

GOD SENT TROOPS

On July 10, 1933, while the trials of the Blood Brotherhood League members were in progress, a plot by the "God Sent Troops" (Shimpeitai) to liquidate the Cabinet was uncovered on the very eve of its execution.[27] Amano Tatsuo, organizer and head of the rightist Patriotic Workers' Society (Aikoku Kinrōtō), was convinced like all other rightists of the urgent need for radical national reconstruction. He felt that the concept of freedom and individualism, which had been imported along with the materialistic civilization of the West since the Meiji Restoration, had ruined political, economic, legal, and social institutions, debilitated, if not poisoned, Japanese spirit, and jeopardized the future of the Japanese people. He judged that in spite of the warnings of the Blood Brotherhood League and the May 15 Incident, the political parties, the *zaibatsu,* and the privileged class continued to impair Japan's prestige without any thought of national welfare. In order to safeguard the nation from the dangers confronting it and to ensure lasting national prosperity, he believed it was necessary to literally wipe out the Saitō Cabinet, force martial law upon the capital by creating disorder and confusion, and to bring about the formation of a special cabinet that would carry out the Showa Reform, involving basic changes in the constitution, laws, and political and economic institutions.

Plans had been worked out carefully to the last detail. Ground and aerial attacks were to be carried out by some 3,600 persons and an airplane on objectives that included the official residences of the Premier and the Privy Seal, headquarters of the Seiyūkai, Minseitō, and the Social Mass Party, the homes of Seiyūkai President Suzuki, Minseitō President Wakatsuki, and Admiral Count Yamamoto, and the Japan Hypothec Bank, and the Japan Industrial Club. The courthouse was to be stormed to rescue Inoue Nisshō, whose trial was then in progress. Simultaneously, a propaganda drive was to be carried out by distributing leaflets from the air as well as on the ground and by displaying banners, posters, and other signs.

Trials in the Supreme Court opened on November 9, 1937, and during the course of more than 100 sessions, such notables as General Mazaki, Baron Harada Kumao, Shiratori Toshio, Tokutomi Iichirō, Honda Kumatarō, and Inoue Nisshō were called to the witness stand. It was not until March 15, 1941, that sentences were pronounced. Penalties asked by the prosecution ranged from one to five years, but all of the forty-four defendants were acquitted. In handing down the decision, the Supreme Court ruled that, inasmuch as the objective of the plot was to force the change of Cabinet by liquidating its members, it did not

---

[27] It was not until September 16, 1935, after more than two years of investigation, that the Justice Ministry announced the details of the plot. See Tōkyō *Asahi,* extra edition, September 16, 1935.

constitute an insurrection as charged by the prosecution. In other words, it was not an attempt to illegally change the cabinet system or the basic political structure of the nation. The court contended that this fact was amply demonstrated by the defendants, who all emphasized and upheld the Emperor's sovereignty.[28]

INTELLECTUAL RIGHTISTS

Among the civilians were rightist scholars who, like the political bullies and rightist free lances, climbed on the bandwagon, effecting a working relation with the military and advocating "divinely inspired" theories, catering and playing up to the whims and fancies of the military, branding conscientious scholars as "reds" or "traitors," and forcing them out of their positions. Best known among these opportunistic scholars was Professor Minoda Muneki of Keiō University, founder of the Spiritual Research Institute and publisher of its mouthpiece *Genri Nihon,* which was used without scruples to attack liberals and their writings. As head of the National Society for the Promotion of Nationalism (Zen Nihon Kōkoku Dōshikai), an organization inspired by Professor Uesugi, Professor Minoda was preoccupied with liberal-baiting, issuing reactionary pronouncements, and directing vigorous personal attacks against conscientious scholars.[29] Among his victims were Professor Takikawa Yukitatsu of the Kyōto Imperial University and Professor Minobe Tatsukichi of the Tōkyō Imperial University, both of whom he branded as exponents of "dangerous thought." He was unsuccessful, however, in his attempts to discredit Professors Suehiro Izutarō and Makino Eiichi.

The Kyōto Imperial University affair was precipitated by the disciplinary action taken against Professor Takikawa by Education Minister Hatoyama in May, 1933. This was a clear case of suppression of academic freedom and liberal professors on the part of the Education Ministry, which had yielded to the pressure, and perhaps agreed with the views of the military and the reactionary elements. It represented also the defeat of the Law Department of

---

[28] The leader of the Shimpeitai, Amano, was a civilian and the forty-two-year-old son of the president of the Japan Musical Instrument Company of Hamamatsu. A graduate of the Law Department of the Tōkyō Imperial University in 1919, he had come under the strong influence of the chauvinistic Professor Uesugi and was an active member of the Kōkoku Dōshikai. Maeda Torao had been with the South Manchuria Railway from 1910 to 1916 and had actively participated in the Chinese Revolution with Inoue Nisshō, cofounder of the Empire Foundation Society (Kenkokukai). Lieutenant Colonel Yasuda Tatsunosuke, the adviser to the group, was son-in-law of General Fukuda and had been instrumental in raising necessary funds. Commander Yamaguchi Saburō, a naval flier, had been entrusted with the carrying out of the aerial attack on the official residences of the Premier, the Privy Seal, Grand Chamberlain Admiral Suzuki, Baron Wakatsuki, and others. Suzuki Zen'ichi was a director of the extremist Japan Production Party, a Black Dragon Society affiliate.

[29] Mori, *op. cit.,* pp. 143–144.

the Kyōto Imperial University, which had long been the stronghold of liberalism and academic freedom and marked the beginning of the government's systematic attempt to drive out antimilitaristic, liberal professors from the higher institutions of learning.

The affair had its inception in the Diet in January, 1933, when a Seiyūkai member of the Diet, Miyazawa Yutaka, raised the question of "red" professors at the two imperial universities of Tōkyō and Kyōto. Education Minister Hatoyama promptly responded by declaring that he would take disciplinary action against such professors. Hatoyama's determination to dismiss Professor Takikawa was met with the strong resistance of the entire Law Department of Kyōto Imperial University, which submitted resignation en masse. Students backed the professors by holding a mass meeting and issued a public statement condemning the Education Ministry for its reactionary stand. On May 26 the movement to protect the university and liberalism spread to other imperial universities. However, the Saitō Cabinet scored a victory as the leading professors of the Law Department were dropped.

Encouraged by their success in suppressing liberalism at Kyōto, the rightist scholars, with the support of the reactionary civilians and militarists, began a systematic attack on Professors Minobe and Suehiro by pointing out in Professor Minoda's *Genri Nihon* passages in their writings that could be construed as disrespectful to the Throne and went about inciting public hostility against the two scholars. In 1935 they organized the Federation for the Protection of National Polity (Kokutai Yōgo Rengōkai) to carry on a movement to reject the "organ theory" of the Emperor.[30]

On February 18, 1935, the "organ theory" became a political issue when retired General Baron Kikuchi Takeo raised a question in the House of Peers regarding the renovation of national morale and the regulation of publications. Toward the end of the month a Seiyūkai member of the House of Representatives, reserve Major General Etō Genkurō, who belonged to the Minoda group, started a suit in the Tōkyō District Court against Professor Minobe on the grounds that his works on the Constitution contained statements disrespectful to the Throne.[31] This legal action was followed on March 20 by the House of Peers resolution proposing "the renovation of national thought" (*seikyō sasshin*) and two days later by the House of Representatives resolution calling for the

---

[30] The controversy regarding the location of sovereignty in Japan first started in 1912 between Professors Uesugi Shinkichi and Minobe Tatsukichi. The latter held that the Emperor was one of the organs of state, a theory that was challenged and bitterly fought by the former.

[31] On April 9, the Home Ministry banned the sale of three of his works, *Kempō Satsuyō* (*Outline of the Constitution*), *Kempō Teiyō* (*The Essentials of the Constitution*), and *Nihon Kempō no Kihon Shugi* (*Basic Principles of Japanese Constitution*), and ordered the revision of two others, *Gendai Kensei Hyōron* (*Discussions on Modern Constitutional Government*) and *Gikai Seiji no Kentō* (*A Study of Parliamentary Government*).

"clarification of national polity," which had become a euphemism for the suppression of liberals and liberal ideas, which were deemed in conflict with rightist ideologies. Rightist groups simultaneously launched a movement for the rejection of the "organ theory." On April 4 Inspector General of Military Education Mazaki issued directives to all army personnel calling attention to the subjects' duty of loyalty to the Throne and emphasizing that the "organ theory" was incompatible with the concept of "national polity." Then, finally on August 3, the government, which was no longer able to withstand the army's pressure, issued a solemn statement on the "clarification of national polity."

The Minobe case was dropped on September 18 by the Procurator-General, and on the same day Professor Minobe resigned from the House of Peers. Simultaneously with his resignation he issued a statement that brought down the full force of the army's wrath upon himself. While the issue on the surface revolved around the rejection of the theory that the Emperor was an organ of the state, it was in reality a showdown between the forces of liberalism and the forces of reactionary nationalism and militarism, which were bent on destroying the *status quo*, and the political elements that stood for individualism. Needless to say, the antiliberal forces scored a smashing victory in the protracted battle of thought.

On October 1 the Okada Cabinet issued a statement announcing its decision to stamp out the "organ theory." To this end it would investigate the ideas and views of the professors as well as the content of courses on the Constitution, place a ban on the use of books and textbooks that were deemed undesirable from the point of "clarification of national polity," and rigidly enforce the ban on the publication and sale of proscribed books. This was followed a month later by the formation of the Council for the Renovation of Thought.[32] The report and recommendations submitted by this group a year later led to the creation in July, 1937, within the Ministry of Education, of a new bureau[33] that was entrusted with the task of putting into effect, through the nation's educational system, "the clarification of national polity."

THE ARMY'S DETERMINED DRIVE FOR POWER AND ITS FACTIONAL STRIFE

During the 1920's, the heyday of political parties, internationalism, and disarmament, as well as of pacifist tendencies, the military was all but forgotten. Nothing was left undone to undermine the power and prestige of the armed services. As part of the disarmament and retrenchment program to which the government was committed by international agreements War Minister Ugaki

[32] The Kyōgaku Sasshin Hyōgikai was created on November 6, 1935.
[33] This new bureau was the Kyōgaku Kyoku.

was assigned the task of slashing army strength by several divisions. It was adding insult to injury when the public began to look down upon the army as a superfluous, if not a parasitical, element of society in a peaceful world. The best brains of the nation went to the universities and turned to careers in business and industry, while the military and naval academies were barely able to fill their quotas. It became impossible for them to attract the cream of the nation's crop into the military profession. Times were such that even young women showed preference in matrimony for civilians, and particularly those in a business or industry with a future. In the mid-twenties the prestige of the military had reached the lowest point, for officers on active service preferred to don mufti when off duty rather than to be conspicuous in their uniforms to become the object of pity or silent ridicule.

However, the 1930's saw a reversal of the trend of the twenties, due in no small measure to the shifting international scene. As the thirties wore on, everybody, including even the reservists, donned his uniform at the slightest provocation. The military, which had smarted under the humiliation in the twenties, was determined to capitalize on its increased prestige, brought about directly by the Manchurian Incident and increasing tension throughout the world. The increasing prestige of the military was reflected in, and enhanced by, the formation of such nationalistic societies as the Meirinkai, composed of reserve and retired army and navy officers, retired government officials, and businessmen.[34] The Imperial Way Society (Kōdōkai),[35] organized in 1933 and claiming a membership of 100,000 reservists and farmers, hoped for the abolition of the capitalistic economic structure as well as the political parties and the establishment of a state controlled economy and of international justice that would ensure the equitable use of the world's resources. The role played by the Imperial Reservists' Association (Teikoku Zaigō Gunjinkai) throughout the nation cannot be overestimated in the development of nationalism.

An incident that reflected the increasing assertiveness and swagger of the army was the altercation that took place in Ōsaka between a private first class and a traffic policeman, who reprimanded the serviceman for ignoring the traffic signal. This minor incident, which took place on June 17, 1933, was the sort of thing that was happening every day, and it was not even noticed by local papers. The chief of staff of the Fourth Division, however, regarded the incident as an inexcusable affront to the army by the civilian branch of the government. During the five months that followed there took place between the army and the Ōsaka

[34] Retired General Tanaka Kunishige was president of this society, which was formed in 1932.

[35] This society, which had the strongest support from Yamanashi and Fukuoka prefectures, was organized in April, 1933, by Major General Kurozawa Keiichirō, Major Mizutani Kichizō of the Imperial Reservists' Association, and Hirano Rikizō of the Japan Farmers' Union (Nihon Nōmin Kumiai).

prefectural authorities a continuous exchange of charges and countercharges, which showed no signs of terminating. The protracted dispute was settled finally and only by the good offices of the governor of the neighboring Hyōgo prefecture and the procurator of the Ōsaka district.

For obvious reasons an accurate picture of the internal conditions of the army was carefully concealed from the public and even from the army itself. Consequently, apart from a small number of well-informed individuals, the extent or the seriousness of the factional strife that plagued the army was generally unknown. Only a vague apprehension seized the public when violence flared up in overt actions, such as assassinations and abortive *coup d'état* attempts.

After assuming the portfolio of War Minister in the Inukai Cabinet, which came into existence in December, 1931, General Araki cleaned out the remnants of the Ugaki faction and transferred the officers implicated in the March and October plots. In his bid for popularity and support Araki played up to the admiring young officers of company grade who had broken off from the others to form the Kōdōha, a radical, anticapitalistic, antiparliamentarian, direct action group, which was bent on destroying the *zaibatsu* and the political parties.[36] With the Ugaki faction, and especially those who were dissatisfied with the War Minister's handling of personnel shifts as a nucleus, a movement was launched for the expulsion from power of General Araki and those who were behind him. A segment of this anti-Araki group later became the Purification Faction (Seigunha).[37]

There were also those who, though not directly implicated in the October plot, were burning with antipathy against Araki and Mazaki and at the same time they were urged on by irrepressible ambition to become the "new power" within the army by carrying out national renovation. This group, which came to be known as the Control Faction (Tōseiha) and included General Nagata Tetsuzan and General Tōjō Hideki, chose to employ legal, nonterroristic methods in effecting an orderly reconstruction of the nation.[38] Joined by the Seigunha, it sought a gradual change toward a totalitarian setup by bringing the political system and the capitalists under its control through skillful maneuvers and legitimate administrative measures. It aimed at the establishment of political supremacy through the seizure of civilian, political, and administrative machinery. Utilizing its legal authority to let out contracts to munitions industries, it won over the *zaibatsu*. Even those progressive industrialists who were at first wary

---

[36] Those who belonged to this group were Generals Mazaki, Araki, Yanagawa, Hata and Obata, Lieutenant Colonel Aizawa, Lieutenants Muranaka and Isobe and supported by civilian rightists, Kita Ikki and Nishida Zei.

[37] The leaders of this group were Colonel Hashimoto, Lieutenant Colonel Manaki, and Major Osa.

[38] The Control Faction included Generals Minami, Matsui, Itagaki, Tatekawa, Watanabe, Tōjō, and Nagata, who were backed by officers of field grade and the civilian rightist, Ōkawa Shūmei and his followers.

of the radical military soon got over their suspicion and dislike as they became recipients of fat contracts and huge profits, enabling them to carry out their long-awaited opportunity for industrial expansion.

Owing to the fact that General Hayashi was not a member of any of these factions and because of his alleged ability to bring together the various factions, he was appointed successor to General Araki as War Minister on January 23, 1934. In due course, he was converted to the views of the Control Faction through the indefatigable efforts of his Director of Military Affairs Bureau, General Nagata Tetsuzan. It was under Hayashi that the army made rapid strides toward the achievement of political supremacy.

In October, 1934, the Army Press Section issued a propaganda pamphlet *The Essence of National Defense and Proposals to Strengthen It*,[39] which opened with the sentence: "War is the father of creation and the mother of culture." In emphasizing the importance of cultivating the will-to-win as well as the spirit of nationalism, it pointed out that the "stabilization of national livelihood" was the crux of the problem. For the achievement of this basic requirement the security of livelihood of the workers and the relief of the rural agrarian population were considered most urgent.

Given as the basic defects of the existing economic structure from the point of national defense were (1) individualism, which formed the basis of existing economic organization, tended to leave economic activities to individual will and profit motive, (2) aggravation of free competition with the danger of producing class cleavages, (3) existing disparity of wealth, which was responsible for the poverty of the bulk of the people, unemployment, and the decline of small and middle class manufacturers, merchants and farmers, was obstructing the attainment of stability of national livelihood, and (4) the weakness of state control was obstructing complete mobilization and unified management in the development of resources, the promotion of industries and foreign trade, and limiting the appropriations that were absolutely necessary for national defense purposes.[40]

The thesis advanced in the pamphlet was that, inasmuch as the existing economic system had been developed on the basis of individualism, it tended to serve individual interests and did not always harmonize or coincide with the general interests of the state. Moreover, extreme emphasis on free competition presented a serious danger to security, since it aroused class antagonism. Possession of wealth in the hands of a small minority caused distress among the people, failure of small industries and businesses, and labor-capital strife, all of which upset the equilibrium of national life. The army's propaganda was for the abandonment of individualistic economic concepts and the establishment on

[39] The pamphlet contained five parts: "Reconsideration of the Concept of National Defense," "Essential Elements of National Defense," "International Scene and National Defense," "Proposals for the Strengthening of National Defense Policies," and the "Nation's Resolve."

[40] *The Essence of National Defense and Proposals to Strengthen It*, pp. 41–42.

a collective basis of a rigidly controlled national economy. It anticipated the quasi-wartime structure towards which the military led the nation only a few years later.

The army pamphlet rudely jolted the *zaibatsu* and the political parties out of their feeling of complacency that all had been well since the appearance of War Minister Hayashi, who had given the impression that he had restored order within the army and had the situation well in hand. The Minseitō regarded the army's expression of its views on social and economic reconstruction in its bid for the leadership of the nation as gratuitous and regrettable. The Seiyūkai expressed a similar sentiment and regretted the army's meddling in matters entirely outside its scope and jurisdiction as well as competence, and opposed unified control of national defense, which would require the overhauling of existing economic structure. Most aghast of all were the *zaibatsu*. War Minister Hayashi, however, somewhat allayed their fears by assuring them that the proposals were not going to be forced upon them immediately.

THE NOVEMBER AFFAIR

After the army's special autumn maneuvers of 1934, held in Gumma prefecture, were over, a group of twenty to thirty young officers, most of whom belonged to the radical Kōdōha, met at a teahouse in Tōkyō, where they were supposed to have discussed a plot that was outlined by Captain Muranaka, then a student at the Army War College. It was reported at the time that eleven officers, including Muranaka, were planning a military *coup d'état* on the date of the opening of the extraordinary Diet session after assassinating key figures in government and industry.[41]

Upon being questioned by the authorities Muranaka and his associate Isobe insisted that the alleged plot was no more than a figment of their imagination, and that it was a scheme fabricated by the Control Faction to suppress the Kōdōha. Although there was little room for doubt that some sort of plot was in the minds of extremist officers, the case was dropped on the grounds of insufficient evidence. It was more likely that, in view of a threat by Muranaka that he would divulge the truth regarding the March and October plots of 1931, the army authorities, fearful lest they stir up a hornet's nest, decided to drop the whole matter. The immediate upshot was the suspension of Captain Muranaka, First Lieutenant Kataoka, and Intendance First Lieutenant Isobe.

While under suspension, Muranaka and Isobe wrote and distributed a pamphlet *Views on the Housecleaning of the Army*,[42] in which they described

---

[41] Allegedly, the intended victims of this plot were Premier Okada, Home Minister Gotō, Count Makino, Count Kiyoura, Viscount Saitō, Baron Wakatsuki, Izawa Takio, Goh Seinosuke, Ikeda Seihin, and Iwasaki Koyata.

[42] For writing and circulating this pamphlet, *Shukugun ni Kansuru Ikensho*, Muranaka and Isobe were summarily dismissed from the service in August, 1935.

the irreconcilable cleavage within the army itself and outlined the objective of the Kōdōha, which was to set up a military-centered cabinet headed by General Hayashi and assisted by Generals Mazaki and Araki in achieving the renovation of national politics. It accused the opposing group that supported Generals Minami and Matsui, whose marital and financial connections were regarded as not above suspicion.

Repercussions of the document were strongly felt not only within the army, where the officers of the Kōdōha began to show activity, but also among the extremist civilians, including free-lance rightists like Kita Ikki and Nishida Zei. Ominous reports, both true and fancied, poured into the War Ministry. Fearful of the possibility that the War Minister and the Director of Military Affairs Bureau would have to assume responsibility should army discipline suffer in any way, Hayashi decided to relieve his close and loyal friend, General Mazaki Jinzaburō, of the post of Inspector General of Military Education on July 16, 1935.

War Minister Hayashi blamed the Mazaki faction for the army's internal strife and the terroristic outbursts of hot-headed young officers. By exceeding the bounds of authority vested in the War Minister in disregard of the well-established practice of deciding personnel matters pertaining to general officers by the joint consultation of the "Big Three," namely, the War Minister, Chief of General Staff, and Inspector General of Military Education, and by relieving General Mazaki of his post against his wishes, General Hayashi set a precedent for dictatorial decisions by the War Minister. At the same time he paved the way for the collaboration between the military, the *zaibatsu,* and the palace advisers.

The army's official attitude was consistent throughout in condoning the actions of military personnel regardless of the factions to which they belonged. In a press release following the November plot of 1931, which was a reflection of deep cleavages within the army itself, the authorities explained that the plotters were prompted by the anxiety over the future of the nation and the desire to renovate and improve existing conditions. The army attributed their unsuccessful plot to patriotic motives, thereby indirectly condoning, if not defending, them. Such a stand on the part of the army could not help but encourage the rightist elements both in and out of the army. Moreover, the army did not overlook the value of the terroristic activities of the extremists as a convenient and effective instrument for the overcoming or controlling of the opposition, particularly the political parties and the *zaibatsu.* Nor did it neglect to encourage actively rightist organizations to launch patriotic movements that could be utilized to its advantage, especially in pushing ahead its political program. Even when terrorism was the direct outgrowth of the army's internal strife, the authorities defended the young officers *vis-à-vis* the public and condoned their actions in a united front to uphold the honor and prestige of the army.

The removal of General Mazaki from the post of Inspector General of Military Education in July, 1935, was the fruition of General Nagata's efforts.

It represented the victory of the Control Faction over the Kōdōha, which was represented at the time by Mazaki, who alone was occupying one of the highest positions in the army after the retirement of General Araki. It had been rumored that the palace advisers, the Elder Statesman, and the leaders of the *zaibatsu* regarded the Mazaki-Araki faction as a dangerous radical reform group and had brought the Okada Cabinet into being in the middle of 1934 to check the army extremists. Makino, Takahashi, Saitō, Suzuki, Ugaki, and Minami were said to have pressured Hayashi into carrying out a sweeping personnel shift in the army. Supporting Hayashi were Izawa Takio, an influential bureaucrat and member of the House of Peers, Lieutenant General Inagaki Saburō, Military Affairs Bureau Director Major General Nagata Tetsuzan, Home Ministry Police Affairs Bureau Director Karasawa Toshiki, and Baron Harada Kumao, private secretary to Prince Saionji.

By laying the blame on Mazaki for the terrorism of the officers and ousting him, Hayashi created the impression among the military that he had purged the undesirable element in the army and averted in the nick of time the danger of complete collapse of army discipline and morale. At the same time he also gave the impression to the Elder Statesman, palace advisers, political circles, and the financial circles that he had stopped the army extremists and succeeded in winning their confidence and support. The cooperation between the military, palace advisers, and the *zaibatsu* that subsequently developed was based upon the confidence Hayashi engendered in the civilian leaders and palace advisers.

The regular annual personnel shift of August 1, 1935, helped to retrieve lost prestige and inspire confidence in military administration, which had suffered greatly from the November plot of 1934. The Director of Military Affairs Bureau and leader of the Control Faction, Major General Nagata, was the brain behind the sweeping personnel shift. Young officers, thought to be members of the Kōdōha, met frequently at the tea houses in Tōkyō and indignantly voiced their desire to eliminate Nagata. Muranaka and Isobe, who had since their dismissal from the service become civilian rightist free-lances, published and distributed together with Nishida Zei documents in an effort to divulge inside information pertaining to the Mazaki case. Even as early as July 18, 1935, the evening edition of Tōkyō newspapers warned the public of the existence of a highly charged, if not explosive, atmosphere within the army, caused by the indignation of the pro-Mazaki elements.

An explosion came on the hot sultry morning of August 12, as Major General Nagata, Director of Military Affairs Bureau, was receiving a report from Colonel Shimmi, Commander of the Tōkyō Gendarmerie, on the movement and activities of the Kōdōha officers in Tōkyō, who were under strict surveillance. Utmost precaution had been taken against any disturbance. Reports were coming into the War Ministry, and General Nagata was fully aware that he was a marked man. As the hands of the clock pointed to a quarter of ten,

Lieutenant Colonel Aizawa, who had just received orders for transfer to Formosa, entered the office unexpectedly, drew his sword, and cut down Nagata. On the following day, the War Ministry issued a curt announcement attributing the act of violence to Aizawa's believing erroneous rumors. But judging from Aizawa's background and movements preceding the act, there was more to it than the army authorities were willing to divulge to the benighted public. As early as 1929, as a result of acquaintance with Muranaka, Isobe, and Nishida, Aizawa had become a strong proponent of national reconstruction. Because he was stationed at Aomori distance prevented him from participating in the November plot in 1934. Subsequently, during his tour of duty in Tōkyō, he became personally acquainted with General Mazaki. Immediately after the removal of General Mazaki in July, he came out all the way from his station in Fukuyama to Tōkyō and unsuccessfully urged General Nagata to resign from his post. To this advice the Director of the Military Affairs Bureau replied with a transfer to distant Formosa.

The public was shocked by Aizawa's outrageous act of cutting down his superior with impunity in broad daylight and of all places in the administrative nerve center of the army, the War Ministry. It appeared to the press and the public like the action of a madman. But it was part of a well-considered plan on the part of the extremists for purging those who were thought to be standing in the way of national renovation. It also was a clear reflection of some of the inherent defects of military education, which engendered an almost pathological irrationality, delusion, unscientific attitude, "divine inspiration," dogmatic authoritarianism, and fanatic sense of mission among the members of the armed forces. In other words, the army had for once become the victim of its own propaganda and indoctrination efforts.

In the course of the trial, which began on January 28, 1936, Lieutenant Colonel Mitsui, defense counsel for Aizawa, called to the witness stand such notables as General Hayashi, General Mazaki, Marquis Kido, Ikeda Seihin, and Karasawa Toshiki. On February 25, Mitsui went into a lengthy forensic discussion of widespread agrarian distress, the relationship between rural youth and young army officers, and the causes of depression and inequality of economic opportunities. He went on to attack monopoly capitalism and the Big Four of the *zaibatsu,* Mitsui, Mitsubishi, Sumitomo, and Yasuda. He probed and exposed the relationship between the *zaibatsu* and the palace advisers, naming them individually.[43]

[43] See Tōkyō *Asahi,* February 26, 1936.

THE FEBRUARY 26 INCIDENT, 1936

Neither the determination nor the energies of the Kōdōha had been whittled down by the stratagems of the rival group, the Control Faction. Only a little over six months after the Aizawa Affair, the extremist officers made an unsuccessful attempt at a military *coup d'état.* Young army officers who blamed the palace advisers and the *zaibatsu* for the deplorable state of affairs were determined to carry out the Showa Restoration. All were under 33 years of age, except one who was 38, and were of the middle and lower class, many of them being sons of army and navy officers. Several of the participants were civilians who had been dismissed from military service, while not a few were devout followers of the militant Nichiren sect.

The dawn of February 26, 1936, found Tōkyō blanketed with snow, and downtown traffic had come to a dead stop. Soldiers with bayoneted rifles stood guard at the entrances to the Imperial Palace. Curious crowds milled around, wondering what had happened, for all media of communication were dead. Only rumors were flying. Shortly after eight o'clock in the evening the radio broke the silence, and the first official announcement by the War Ministry revealed that a group of young army officers had attacked several objectives including the newspaper *Asahi,* which they put out of order, and had assassinated Premier Okada, Lord Keeper of the Privy Seal Admiral Saitō, Inspector General of Military Education Watanabe, and wounded Finance Minister Takahashi and Grand Chamberlain Admiral Suzuki. Misguided young extremist officers had resorted to direct action in their erroneous belief that they could spare the nation from impending ruin, which they believed was being brought on by the palace advisers, the Elder Statesmen, the *zaibatsu,* the bureaucrats, and the political parties. Only six days earlier, a general election had been held and an unexpected show of strength by the Social Mass Party, which captured more than thirty seats in the Diet, surprised some quarters and alarmed some others. Only a short time before orders had been issued for the dispatch of the First Division to Manchuria. The young officers wanted to carry out their plans before they left for Manchuria.

The Navy Ministry announced that orders had been issued to the First and Second Fleets to guard Tōkyō and Ōsaka, indicating to the public the seriousness with which the incident was regarded by the authorities. In the afternoon of the following day, martial law was proclaimed in Tōkyō. Gradually, however, the city returned to normal activity, as transportation and communications were restored. But gatherings, newspapers, magazines, and advertisements that might adversely affect the situation were banned as were the sale and transfer of arms and ammunition. Radio was now used exclusively by the martial law headquarters for the release of announcements.

For the first time, late in the evening of the 28th, the public got an inkling of the extent of troop participation. Finance Minister Takahashi, Privy Seal Saitō, and Inspector General of Military Education Watanabe were dead. Premier Okada had miraculously escaped assassination through mistaken identity; his brother-in-law, Colonel Matsuo, who bore a striking resemblance to him had been murdered instead by the assassins. At dawn, on the 29th, all rail traffic into the capital was stopped and telephone connections with the outside were suspended by the martial law authorities as they prepared for a showdown with the insurgents.

Evacuation of the danger zone [44] centering around Nagatachō, where the rebels were holding out, was completed by the early morning of the 29th. Preparations were completed for shooting it out with the insurgents, but efforts were continued to avert bloodshed. Tanks appeared in the area occupied by the insurgents with signs urging them to surrender, and several airplanes flew overhead dropping leaflets telling them that it was not too late to return to their barracks. Even an advertising balloon was used in urging surrender. Finally, on the same day, General Kashii, the martial-law Commander in Chief, issued an ultimatum stating that unless they surrendered they would be regarded as rebels defying the authority of the Emperor. At the same time a touching appeal went out over the radio repeatedly at regular intervals emphasizing family honor, filial piety, and loyalty to the Emperor, and admonishing the troops to lay down their arms in obedience to the imperial command and return to their quarters. The appeal worked. In dribbles, the insurgents began to surrender and by two o'clock in the afternoon all had surrendered. Thus, after four days of breathless suspense, the event that shook the nation and amazed the world ended quietly without the firing of a single shot.

The army authorities released on March 6 information revealing that over fourteen hundred troops of the First Division had participated in the unsuccessful *coup d'état*. Their plans called for the assassination of some of the palace advisers then in Tōkyō as well as Saionji and Makino. Trials were started immediately and verdicts were rendered with record speed. Only four and a half months after the incident all those guilty had been brought to justice. Sentences were pronounced on July 7 and the execution of thirteen army officers and four civilians was carried out on the twelfth, only nine days after Colonel Aizawa's execution.[45]

Terrorism had previously been directed mainly against the palace advisers, the *zaibatsu*, and party leaders. But this time, it had been turned upon the army

[44] The insurgents occupied the War Ministry, the Metropolitan Police Board, the New Diet Building, the Peers' Club, and the Sannō Hotel.

[45] Colonel Aizawa was sentenced to death on May 7 and executed on July 3. The February 26 Incident had the effect of speeding up the Aizawa trial, which had been dragging on until the army was shocked into taking drastic steps.

itself for Inspector General of Military Education Watanabe was one of the victims. Moreover, the insurgents were prepared to go into full dress revolt, which could have been disastrous to the army itself. The position secured since the Manchurian Incident by the army was in jeopardy. Therefore, the government and the army authorities were impelled by the threat of catastrophic consequences to deal with the insurgents with extreme severity. It was clear that the February 26 Incident was the culmination of a series of attacks by the extremist Kōdōha, designed to challenge and overthrow the power of the Control Faction. At the same time, the attempted *coup d'état* was a lawless assault against the army as well as the legally constituted civilian authorities. With the disposal of the insurgents, the extremist Kōdōha was virtually liquidated and the Control Faction achieved undisputed and unchallenged supremacy. The army was now in undisputed control of the affairs of state.

Chapter 33. Military Domination of National Affairs

Military control of national affairs, which came about in the latter part of the thirties and continued for a decade until surrender in 1945, could not have been achieved without the collaboration and support of the civilian bureaucracy, which was a more than willing partner of the military. As a matter of fact, the bureaucracy was the instrumentality by which the military carried out the planning and execution of its national policies, particularly in setting up the "wartime structure." This was not, of course, the first instance of the bureaucracy collaborating with the military. Field Marshal Yamagata, General Katsura, and General Terauchi all had had the strong support of the bureaucracy. In the 1920's, however, the bureaucracy was subservient to another element of the body politic, namely, the political parties which were in their heyday.

RISE OF THE BUREAUCRACY TO POWER

In the clash in the early thirties between the military-agrarian radical elements and the *zaibatsu*-party coalition, the bureaucrats found the opportunity to enhance their political position by allying themselves with the military. They were in a peculiarly advantageous position to exploit the situation, since their civil service status assured them security and their administrative, legal, and technical knowledge and know-how constituted virtually an indispensable asset, which the military needed badly but did not possess to any appreciable extent, in the execution of their totalitarian program. The bureaucratic element lost no time in seizing the opportunity to secure a firm grip of the administrative machinery and exercise control over the formulation and execution of economic and administrative policies. They took full advantage of the crisis psychology that prevailed in the wake of the assassination of Premier Inukai. During the Saitō and Okada Cabinets, especially after March, 1933, when Japan gave official notice of her intention to withdraw from the League of Nations, public opinion was permeated with the feeling of impending "crisis," which became the national catchword. The years 1935 and 1936 were to be the years of crisis, for Japan's fate would be hanging in a precarious balance as the abrogation of the London and Washington naval agreements and her withdrawal from the League of Nations were to take effect, resulting inevitably in diplomatic isolation, which even the military dreaded.

The beginnings of collaboration between the bureaucrats and the military go back to the early thirties. The Breakfast Club (Asameshi Kai), founded by Marquis Inoue Saburō, brought together the leading members of the bureaucracy and the army, and had paved the way for close collaboration between them. It was in this organization that the members of the Nagata faction of the army, the newly risen bureaucrats, and the House of Peers politicians established intimate contacts and started planning together to put their ideas into effect.[1] This group was also instrumental in winning the support of palace advisers, Imperial Household Minister Ichiki Kitokurō and Yuasa Kurahei,[2] and in convincing Privy Seal Count Makino and Elder Statesman Saionji that Admiral Saitō was the most acceptable person to succeed Premier Inukai.

The appointment of General Mutō, Commander in Chief of the Kwantung Army and Governor General of the Kwantung Territory to the concurrent post of Ambassador to Manchukuo on August 8, 1932, was an important step in the consolidation of army power in the management of Manchuria. There, bureaucrats who were pliable and amenable to the army's wishes were given a start in their career, which led subsequently to posts of greater importance at home. Two years later, the government set up the Manchurian Affairs Bureau to coordinate the activities in the various offices relating to Manchukuo, to take over the administrative functions of the Kwantung Bureau, to guide and promote colonization and developmental activities in Manchukuo, and to supervise the South Manchuria Railway Company. At the strong insistence of the then War Minister Hayashi, the Okada Cabinet agreed to adopt the policy of appointing a general officer on the active list to head the Bureau and made it a concurrent post for the War Minister. Thus the administration of Manchuria was placed firmly in the hands of the Kwantung Army and the War Ministry.

In the suppression of the Kōdō faction of the army and the ousting of General Mazaki from the post of Inspector General of Military Education the bureaucrats worked closely with the Control faction, headed by General Nagata, thereby ingratiating themselves with the faction in power and solidifying their own position. Although the assassination of General Nagata in August, 1935, brought the Breakfast Club to an end and caused a temporary setback of the bureaucracy, intimate relations with the military were reestablished after the February 26

---

[1] Among the bureaucrats were Izawa Takio, Gotō Fumio, and Karasawa Toshiki of the Home Ministry faction, while the members of the House of Peers included Marquis Kido Kōichi, Viscount Okabe Nagakage, Baron Harada Kumao, and Baron Kuroda Nagakazu.

[2] Ichiki, who had been Imperial Household Minister since 1925 and Vice-President of the Privy Council since 1924, became President in 1934. Yuasa, who succeeded Admiral Saitō as Privy Seal in 1936, was Imperial Household Minister from 1925 to 1933. These two men, who were elders in the Home Ministry faction of bureaucrats, were close to the Throne.

Incident.[3] In this close relationship, there were two well-identified groups of bureaucrats who cooperated in alternating control of the Home and Welfare Ministries.[4] Marquis Kido, who alternated in holding positions between the government and the palace and exerted strong influence in both places, was a leading figure of one group and was one of the strongest supporters of General Tōjō. Izawa Takio, one of the doyens of the bureaucrats, was also a supporter of Tōjō, though mostly behind the scenes and acting as an intermediary between Prince Konoe and General Tōjō in persistent efforts to bring them closer together.

The outbreak of the China Incident in the summer of 1937 and the organization of the Planning Board subsequently provided an opportunity for the emergence and rise of another group of bureaucrats, whose backgrounds included service in Manchukuo government or in the Planning Board.[5] Because of its personnel and the functions it performed, it was natural that the Planning Board should have furnished the logical medium for the collaboration between the military and the bureaucrats. The Military Affairs Bureau and the Naval Affairs Bureau of the War and Navy Ministries respectively were given controlling influence over the organization which drew its personnel from virtually every ministry. Since those who were in the Planning Board had access to secret information regarding national mobilization and resources, they enjoyed greater prestige than other bureaucrats. Entrusted as it was with the function of carrying out war plans made by the military against China, the United States, Great Britain, and the Soviet Union, especially as they touched upon domestic reforms involving changes in economic structure and the formulation of policies and ways and means of carrying out the provisions of the National Mobilization Law, the Planning Board came to occupy a commanding position in relation to other ministries and laid the basis for bureaucratic control of national policies and administration.

There was a third group of bureaucrats, comprising officials of the ministries having jurisdiction over finance, trade, and industry. The Finance Ministry[6] bureaucrats exercised financial control with the collaboration of the

---

[3] The army leaders with whom the bureaucrats became increasingly intimate included Generals Tōjō Hideki, Umezu Yoshijirō, Anami Korechika, Mutō Akira, Tanaka Shin'ichi, Satō Kenryō, and Ikeda Sumihisa.

[4] One group of bureaucrats centering around the Home and Welfare Ministries was led by Gotō Fumio, Karasawa Toshiki, and Aikawa Shōroku, the other by Marquis Kido Kōichi, Hirose Tadahisa, and Abe Genki.

[5] In the growing military-bureaucrat collaboration the army was represented by Generals Suzuki Teiichi, Akinaga Tsukizō, Numada Takazō, Ikeda Sumihisa, Mutō Akira, Satō Kenryō, the navy by Okada Sumitaka, the bureaucracy by Sakomizu Hisatsune, Minobe Yōji, Okamura Kiwao, and Wada Hiroo.

[6] The Finance Ministry bureaucrats were led by Kaya Okinobu, Ishiwata Sōtarō, and Aoki Kazuo. When the Asia Development Board was created at the instance of the army, its officials were drawn mainly from the Finance Ministry. Aoki Kazuo subsequently became the first Minister of Greater East Asia.

leaders of finance,[7] while the Commerce and Industry [8] bureaucrats wielded power over industrial capital with the support of the military. The strengthening of economic control and its extension to almost every area of national life led inevitably to the increase in the power exercised by the bureaucrats, who were not entirely above corruption. The bureaucrats of the Commerce and Industry Ministry and later the Munitions Ministry became intimate and entered into unholy alliances with the munitions companies and particularly the newly risen *zaibatsu,* centering their activities around the industrial development of Manchukuo.[9] In agricultural administration another group centered around those close to the co-operatives [10] came to assume controlling leadership, and extended their influence into the rural areas through their decisive influence in determining the personnel of the agricultural associations and quasi-government food supply companies.

THE ARMY CONTROLLED HIROTA CABINET

No sooner had the insurgents of the February 26 Incident been brought under control than Saionji repaired to Tōkyō in response to the Emperor's summons. In the Imperial Household Ministry, on the Imperial Palace grounds, he deliberated on the choice of a new premier, while the public waited in suspense. On March 4, Prince Konoe, the scion of the oldest and most renowned nobility, was given the imperial command to form a new government, but he declined the honor on the grounds of poor health, which, he explained, made him unequal to the heavy responsibility. It was obvious, however, that there was more to his circumspect refusal than his publicly announced reason; he was sagaciously following the dictates of his judgment. On the following day, the 5th, after consulting with the War and Navy Ministers and ascertaining that they had no candidates of their own to propose,[11] the Elder Statesman recommended Foreign Minister Hirota, a political dark horse.

Upon receiving the imperial command, Hirota [12] announced his determination to bring about national unity in fact as well as in name, to form a strong cabinet, to respect parliamentary government by inviting party members to join his cabinet, and to select as cabinet members not the traditional type but those who could inject new life and spirit into the government.[13] Immediately after he

[7] Leaders of the financial world included Ikeda Seihin, Yuki Toyotarō, and Tsushima Juichi.

[8] The leading figure of the Commerce and Industry faction was Kishi Nobusuke.

[9] Ayukawa Yoshisuke was the President of the Japan Industrial Company.

[10] Arima Rainei, Ishiguro Tadaatsu, and Sengoku Kōtarō.

[11] Tōkyō *Asahi,* March 6, 1936.

[12] Highly significant was the fact that the premier-designate called on Prince Kan'in, Chief of General Staff, and Prince Fushimi, Chief of the Naval Board, within a few hours of his designation as Premier.

[13] Tōkyō *Asahi,* March 6, 1936.

returned from the Palace, Hirota summoned former Ambassador Yoshida Shigeru and asked him to become his Foreign Minister; Justice Minister Obara was to continue in his post and Kawasaki Takukichi was also to remain in the new government as a holdover. That evening the army's "Big Three" met and decided to recommend General Terauchi for War Minister and to propose a four point program, consisting of the clarification of "national polity," stabilization of national livelihood, strengthening and perfecting of national defense, and the renovation of diplomacy.

Hirota succeeded virtually in completing the line-up of his cabinet within twenty-four hours and fully expected the installation ceremony to take place on the second day. But his expectations were rudely upset by the sudden and unanticipated opposition of the army. When the cabinet line-up was released, the army objected strongly on the grounds that it reflected liberal tendencies, which implied either a total disregard of, or a definite and calculated challenge against, the reform program espoused by the army, if not a complete ignorance of the trend of the times. The army insisted that it could not approve Hirota's choice of cabinet members; it was particularly opposed to the Home and Education Ministries falling into the hands of party politicians.

Even as Hirota was in the throes of cabinet formation, War Minister Terauchi had released a statement which left no doubt as to where the army stood in regard to the question of national political renovation. "The new cabinet, charged with the heavy responsibility of seeing the nation safely through the crisis, should possess both the spirit and the vigor to pursue strong positive policies," said the War Minister, "and that it must not have liberal tendencies or continue to persist in negative and conservative policies and compromises which preserve the *status quo*. The renovation of national administration by means of positive policies is the army's unanimous wish. Compromise and conservatism could not be the proper means by which to save the situation."

So adamant did the army's stand appear, that one Tōkyō newspaper [14] reported prematurely that the refusal of General Terauchi to join the new cabinet had left Hirota no alternative but to abandon his efforts to form a government. On the following day the premier-designate's conference with General Terauchi produced a more compromising attitude on the part of the army. After four separate conferences on as many days an understanding was reached between the army and the premier-designate. On March 9 Hirota issued a statement to the press outlining his basic policies, emphasizing that, in view of the existing domestic and international situation, there should be a thorough house cleaning and reform in government, and that diplomacy should be placed on a positive, self-assertive, and self-reliant basis if the nation were to weather the crisis. He made it clear that a sweeping national reform was to be the government's im-

[14] *Hōchi Shimbun,* March 6, 1936.

mediate goal and that, in order to achieve the goal, national policies were to be planned and executed by a nation united and working together as one without any distinction as to political parties, the military, or the bureaucracy. Therefore, the selection of cabinet personnel, he emphasized, would not be influenced by anyone's status or background; "those who are burning with the loyalty to serve the nation" would be chosen.[15]

Hirota's Cabinet Formation Headquarters had capitulated to the army in a public statement accepting virtually all of the army's demands and conditions.[16] The army successfully blocked the appointment of Yoshida Shigeru, son-in-law of Count Makino, as Foreign Minister, the shifting of Education Minister Kawasaki to Home Minister, and the holding-over of Justice Minister Obara for any portfolio.[17]

In the midst of martial law, the Hirota Cabinet, which the public had almost given up as abortive, saw the light of day, but only after bowing to the unbending will of the army. In the face of extreme political exigency, the nation could not afford an abortive attempt. Naturally the public heaved a great sigh of relief when the completion of the Hirota Government was announced. On March 9 the Cabinet was installed ceremoniously in the Imperial Palace, but it was apparent that the army was now firmly in the saddle, as ensuing events bore out the misgivings of the public. After the first cabinet meeting that very evening, Hirota issued a statement expressing confidence that "the government and the military could cooperate closely in coping with the existing situation." That this was merely a euphemism for capitulation by the government to the army was quite apparent.

Meanwhile, the army, on March 6, had launched its own program of house cleaning by placing Generals Hayashi, Abe, Mazaki, and Araki on the waiting list, and a few days later they were put on the reserve list. A week later, Baron Hiranuma was elevated to the presidency of the Privy Council, of which he had been vice president for a full decade, having been kept from promotion because of his known rightist ideas. Significantly, on the same day, War Minister Terauchi asserted the need for the renovation of administration and expansion of armament looking to the creation of a "total national defense structure." The political trend was now unmistakable, as the swing to the right became more pronounced. Before the month was over, Nakano Seigō, who had been for years one of the more outspoken members of the Minseitō, broke away and formed his own rightist political party, the Tōhōkai.

From about this time on the *zaibatsu* began to show a change of attitude and

[15] Tōkyō *Asahi*, March 9, 1936.

[16] *Tōkyō Nichi Nichi* and Tōkyō *Asahi*, March 10, 1936.

[17] The army also blocked the appointment of Shimomura Hiroshi, Nakajima Chikuhei, and Dr. Mikami Sanji, an eminent historian and professor emeritus of the Tōkyō Imperial University, who was being considered for Education Minister.

the National Federation of Industrial Associations began to soften its opposition against the army. The drift toward fascism had started definitely as monopoly capitalism, faced with a critical situation, found itself in need of forceful means of control to retrieve the situation, if not to preserve itself. The financial clique, which had discovered that the political parties had lost their effectiveness and usefulness owing to the loss of public confidence and support, showed no compunction about jettisoning the party cabinet. The *zaibatsu* would now go along with the army's program rather than fight it.

So long as the military extremists were interested in the destruction of political parties and party government, which had brought about an impasse and meant no harm to monopoly capitalism, the financial leaders had no cause for alarm. As a matter of fact, they had actually utilized the May 15 Incident to help put an end to party government. But the February 26 Incident was something else again, for it reflected unmistakably the rapidly intensifying antipathy of the farmers, middle and small class businessmen, industrialists, and workers against monopoly capitalists. The targets of attack were no longer limited to the statesmen; the wrath had been turned upon the representatives of the capitalists as well as the military. Moreover, the fascist plan of national renovation that the insurgents had intended to put into effect after the coup was much too radical for the capitalists to remain complacent.

Without question, the most important single step that put the military on the road to supremacy was the restoration on May 18, 1936, of the active status requirement for service ministers.[18] This was achieved so quietly, efficiently, and even secretly that the public never got wind of it until it was a *fait accompli* and too late to do anything about it. It gave the military a powerful weapon, enabling the army to release the irresistible forces of national reconstruction, which soon swept political parties and responsible government into the discard and made possible the establishment of a totalitarian structure under its aegis.

Before the first Yamamoto Cabinet could alter in 1913 the active status requirement, which had been instituted ten years earlier by Yamagata, it had to overcome the determined opposition of the army as well as the old General himself, for the military clique looked upon the move as a challenge to its supremacy. However, when the change was put through, the army established an informal practice requiring that all matters of personnel affecting general officers should be deliberated upon and decided by the "Big Three," comprising the War Minister, Chief of General Staff, and the Inspector General of Military Education. It was a countermeasure designed to offset the change.

Immediately after the February 26 Incident the army began its campaign to restore the active status requirement, which was thought necessary as an effective

[18] Promulgated as Imperial Ordinances No. 63 for the Army and No. 64 for the Navy under date of May 16, 1936, and effective on May 18, the date of publication in the *Official Gazette*. See *Kampō*, No. 2810, p. 509, May 18, 1936.

device for keeping out the moderate elements and also for preventing those on the reserve list, like Generals Mazaki and Araki, from staging a comeback and gaining control of national affairs. The army argued that since 1913, when reserve officers were made eligible for the service portfolios, not once had the provision been invoked, making it meaningless, and therefore it should be eliminated. Moreover, it argued that by having a general or admiral on the active list heading the service ministries, it would ensure better discipline in the armed forces. It was emphasized not entirely without equivocation that the change was not to be a permanent one and that it could be changed any time necessity dictated.

Four cabinet members,[19] representing the two major parties, had agreed to the change without any opposition. Submitted to the Cabinet early in May, it was approved by the Privy Council and promulgated within three weeks. That this represented a staggering blow to the progress of parliamentary government cannot be gainsaid. It was retrogression in view of the fact that in 1922 an attempt had been made in the Diet to open the service portfolios to civilians.[20] Ironically, but naturally enough, the active status requirement was used almost immediately with telling effect in forcing the resignation of the Hirota Cabinet itself and also in preventing General Ugaki from forming a cabinet after he had been designated Premier. It was also responsible for the fall of the three Konoe Cabinets, as well as the Hiranuma Cabinet, and enabled General Tōjō to form an undisguised military cabinet in October of 1941.

The seven-point program of national political renovation, as announced by the Hirota Cabinet on August 25, 1936, was in effect the army's blueprint, which the successive cabinets were impelled to follow. If there had been any doubts before as to the role of the military in the government and politics of the nation, the developments after February 26 dispelled them. These policies, which the army insisted upon, were the realization of adequate national defense, the renovation and improvement of education, the adjustment of national and local taxation, the stabilization of national livelihood with special emphasis on the improvement of national health, and the amelioration of agrarian distress, as well as the protection and encouragement of middle and small scale business and industry, the expansion of trade and industry, including the control of electric power, the achievement of self-sufficiency in steel and liquid fuel, encouragement and control of foreign trade, promotion of aviation and merchant shipping and of overseas migration, the vigorous execution of Manchurian policies, and the overhauling and improvement of national administrative structure.

[19] They were Maeda Yonezō, Shimada Toshio, Tanomogi Kakichi, and Ogawa Gōtarō.
[20] Those who were behind this move were Inukai Tsuyoshi, Ōoka Ikuzō, Shimooka Chūji, and Ozaki Yukio.

Late in December, 1936, the Diet assembled for the first time in the new Diet Building, which had just been completed. On January 21, 1937, the first day following the customary year-end recess, Hamada Kunimatsu, Seiyūkai member of the House of Representatives, clashed with War Minister Terauchi on the floor of the Diet. In a gathering the day before, the Seiyūkai had declared that dual diplomacy and secret diplomacy, as conducted by the self-righteous bureaucrats, and dictatorial measures foisted on the public under a quasi-wartime structure were stifling industry and threatening the national livelihood. The attitude of superiority and self-righteousness by the military and the bureaucracy and their meddling in the affairs of state were producing oligarchic tyranny, shutting out the popular will, and bringing about the negation of parliamentary government. The members of the Seiyūkai not only opposed vigorously the German-Japanese Anti-Comintern Pact, but also ridiculed the army's blueprint of a national defense structure. Hamada accused the military of styling themselves the "propulsive power" of the Japanese body politic, and asserted that the nation was not unaware of the existence of a political ideology in the army that was aiding and abetting dictatorial tendencies, which threatened to destroy the harmony and cooperation between the military and the people.

Hamada's attack on the army was as blistering as anyone had dared to make since the Manchurian Incident and had the effect of cheering public opinion, though only momentarily. It was the last desperate stand by the political parties to stem the rising power of the military. War Minister Terauchi accused Hamada of holding the army in contempt and demanded an apology. Hamada retorted that if his utterance could be construed as contempt, he would apologize by committing *harakiri* and demanded that, if the War Minister's accusation proved groundless, he commit *harakiri* instead.[21] This verbal broadside irked the army, causing the resignation of General Terauchi and the collapse of the Hirota Cabinet.

The army's carefully worked-out timetable called for the overthrow by January, 1937, of the Hirota Cabinet, which was to be superseded by the government of General Hayashi. War Minister Terauchi's uncompromising stand was only a part of the army's well planned strategy, just as was its effective obstruction of General Ugaki's effort to form a government only a few days later. Army plans had for sometime envisaged the formation of a totalitarian party.

General Ugaki received the imperial command to form a cabinet on February 25, two days after the Hirota Cabinet was forced to resign by the army. On the following day, the premier-designate was completely stymied in his efforts as the army refused to furnish a War Minister to the Cabinet, regarding Ugaki as unacceptable. Ugaki was acceptable to all other elements and his desig-

[21] This incident, which has been referred to as the famous *harakiri* dialogue, excited public opinion.

nation had been hailed in political circles as a commendable move. But to the army he was *persona non grata,* since he was thought to be too close to the political parties, and there was more than a possibility of his compromising in the program of national renovation. On the 29th he was forced to admit his failure to form a government. During the process of formation, the public showed much more than the usual amount of interest. Suggestions were made that Ugaki should request the Emperor to intercede and command the army to recommend a war minister. The soldier-statesman, however, declined to take such an unprecedented step, which would have been constitutional though not politic. General Ugaki's failure to form a cabinet was a naked demonstration of the army's determination to block the formation of any government that it deemed inimical to its program as well as to its interests. It also proved beyond any doubt that the army's power could not be successfully challenged by civilian authorities.

THE HAYASHI CABINET, THE ARMY'S CHOICE

In the wake of Ugaki's abortive attempt to form a government, the Hayashi Cabinet appeared on February 2, 1937, as the choice of the army and supported by the palace advisers, financial interests, and even the Elder Statesmen. General Hayashi decided to take into his Cabinet party members, provided they renounced their party allegiance.[22] He dispensed with parliamentary vice ministers and counselors, who had been used by previous cabinets to maintain effective liaison between the Diet and the government. Although he was virtually forced to admit that they performed useful, if not indispensable, functions, he did not and could not reverse his stand during his extremely brief tenure of office. Whenever he saw the opportunity, Hayashi deliberately struck blows at the parties, hoping to weaken them and their will to resist. His goal was a single party that would not have the power to oppose or censure the government, but would merely support the government as a rubber stamp. His idea of reform was the establishment of an authoritarian form of government under the leadership of the military.

In his statement of policy on February 8 Premier General Hayashi pronounced to a bewildered public the need for the realization of the ancient ideal of *saisei itchi* which emphasized the identity of Shintō worship and administration. The Premier's anachronistic pronouncement could not help but evoke a feeling that it was contrary in spirit to the modern concept and practice of the separation of church and state. Subsequently, however, he did clarify the

---

[22] Both Nagai Ryūtarō of the Minseitō and Nakajima Chikuhei of the Seiyūkai refused flatly to enter the Cabinet under such conditions. As a result only Yamazaki Tatsunosuke joined as Agriculture and Forestry Minister.

meaning considerably, though not entirely, demonstrating that he was thinking as an Oriental who was not disturbed by an absence of preciseness of meaning.

Premier Hayashi was the first to actually use officially the term "renovation" in a government statement, although just what he meant by it was not clear then. Gradually, however, as his program began to take shape it became apparent that his goal was the establishment of constitutional government peculiar to Japan and that he had no intention of going so far as to do away with the Diet, which was the gift of Emperor Meiji to the nation. Moreover, he was not in favor of extremism, although according to his ideas party government as such would not be recognized nor would suffrage be continued in the existing form.

On March 31, the last day of the session, Premier Hayashi dissolved the Diet. The election that followed, on April 30, was tantamount to the repudiation of his action, as the opposition parties returned an absolute majority. It was clear that it was merely a strategic move on the part of the Cabinet to deal a blow through dissolution and to create disorder within the ranks of the two major parties, which were already beginning to show signs of disintegration because of the increasing popularity of the one-party movement. Hayashi was simply putting into practice what some of the militarists and bureaucrats had been asserting since the Saitō Cabinet, namely, that if the Diet were dissolved several times in succession, the parties would soon lose their will to fight. The repudiation by the electorate left no alternative even for the Hayashi Cabinet but to resign. This came on May 31, 1937, less than four months after it was formed, leaving the government no time to put into effect even a single item on its reform agenda.

Hayashi's resignation brought on the same day a statement from the Social Mass Party accusing the outgoing Premier of general mismanagement of national affairs, aggravation of social insecurity, and bringing confusion, particularly among the lower classes. It contained also an expression of strong desire that the next government endeavor to establish firmly freedom of speech, put into effect social legislation such as labor and tenancy laws, stabilize the national livelihood, and clear the political atmosphere of unhealthy conditions.

As soon as the results of the April general election were known, the Elder Statesmen and palace advisers started looking for a new premier who would fulfill three minimum conditions, namely, acceptability to the army and ability to get along with it with the least friction or no friction, good contacts with the political parties, ability to lead in their revamping, and highest caliber leadership, combining astuteness and ability to surround himself with able men. On the list of prospective candidates were Baron Hiranuma, President of the Privy Council, and Prince Konoe, the youthful President of the House of Peers.

THE APPEARANCE OF THE KONOE CABINET

Intense public antipathy, which had developed against the government of
General Hayashi, changed instantaneously to enthusiastic acclaim on the emergence of the first Konoe Cabinet on June 4, 1937. Konoe's acceptance of the
premiership was received enthusiastically [23] by the public, which had been
thrown into a state of political despondency by the unwarranted dissolution of
the Diet by Premier Hayashi. The popularity of the new cabinet was reminiscent
of the reception given in 1913 to the Ōkuma Cabinet, which succeeded the exceedingly unpopular government of General Katsura. Public apprehension over
the growing fascist trend since February 26 and the feeling of social insecurity
accompanied by rising prices were arrested for the time being by the appearance
of the Konoe Cabinet.

In recommending Prince Konoe as Hayashi's successor, Privy Seal Yuasa
broke a precedent. Instead of asking the Elder Statesman to recommend a
premier, Yuasa assumed the initiative and, after consulting the President of
the Privy Council as well as the Elder Statesman, recommended Konoe on his
own responsibility.[24] This was quite in keeping with the wishes of the Elder
Statesman, then already nearing ninety years of age, to relinquish his function
of recommending premiers to the Privy Seal and others close to the Throne.

The forty-seven-year-old Prince Konoe was one of the few men who was
equally acceptable to the military, the political parties, the bureaucrats, financial
circles, and to all factions and shades of opinion, since he had numerous friends
in all quarters and had never taken a partisan stand. No one approached him
in stature, status, or public esteem. The fact that he was the scion of the oldest
and most respected nobility made him an ideal leader to bring together the
various and divers political elements all the way from the right to the left,
especially in view of his nonpartisan reputation. At the time of the May 15
Incident in 1932 he was vice president of the House of Peers. Even before the
Manchurian Incident he used to meet occasionally with military leaders and
journalists, among whom were Generals Tatekawa, Koiso, and Suzuki, and
Dōmei's Iwanaga and Tōkyō *Asahi's* Ogata.[25] After the February 26 Incident,
War Mininster Terauchi was known to have urged Konoe to assume leadership
in the formation of a political party to supersede all preexisting political parties.[26]

If the Hayashi Cabinet had been in several respects the extension of the

---

[23] Tōkyō *Asahi,* June 2, 1937.

[24] Tōkyō *Asahi,* June 2, 1937.

[25] Konoe was introduced by Prince Saionji's private secretary, Baron Harada, to these army
leaders and journalists, who met occasionally at the Sumitomo residence in Azabu Ward,
Tōkyō, which used to be Prince Saionji's headquarters whenever he came to the capital.

[26] After he resigned the premiership in 1939, the formation of a new party became a
lively topic of discussion in political circles.

preceding Hirota Cabinet, the Konoe Government was the extension of both the Hirota and Hayashi governments in policies as well as in personnel. There were three distinct elements composing the Konoe Cabinet, namely, holdovers from the Hirota Cabinet, Hirota and Baba; holdovers from the Hayashi Cabinet, War Minister Sugiyama, Navy Minister Yonai, and Justice Minister Shiono; and the third element comprising Arima, Nakajima, and Nagai, who wanted to set up a pro-military, if not military-dictated, party under Konoe's leadership. All these three elements were held together by the will of the army, which constituted the catalytic agent as well as centripetal force.

Premier Konoe had neither the intention nor the power to ignore the wishes of the army which, though not expressed as sharply as in the formation of the Hirota Cabinet, were nonetheless real. Unlike Hirota, Konoe judiciously settled the service portfolios first before beginning the selection of the civilian members of the Cabinet.[27] At the very outset he announced his intention to lessen existing friction in various quarters and to achieve a united front embracing the military, the bureaucracy, financial interests, and the parties; to continue with the basic policies of the Hayashi Cabinet and hold over personnel where necessary or advisable; and to give due emphasis to financial and economic policies.[28] He assented to the army's fourfold program of clarification of national policy, strengthening of national defense, renovation of administration, and the stabilization of national livelihood. Konoe did not ask the two party members joining the Cabinet to renounce their party affiliations as did his predecessor; he asked them to join as individuals and not as representatives of their parties. In other words, he did not ask the parties for their official support, especially in view of the strong antiparty sentiment that was making itself felt increasingly in national politics.

To ensure the success of formation Konoe accepted the advice of the service ministers in choosing the remainder of his Cabinet. War Minister Sugiyama recommended Dr. Baba Eiichi for Finance Minister and concurrently president of the Planning Office. However, when the newspapers reported that the extremely unpopular Baba was slated to head the Planning Office, stocks and bonds dropped suddenly. The army was therefore forced to acknowledge the fact of Baba's unacceptability to the financial circles and modified its plans to the extent of respecting the *zaibatsu's* wishes and appointing instead as Finance Minister a career bureaucrat, Vice Finance Minister Kaya.[29] Konoe's task was to bring about an effective coalition of the forces which were at loggerheads, namely,

---

[27] Tōkyō *Asahi,* June 2, 1937.

[28] *Ibid.*

[29] Kaya Okinobu accepted the Finance fortfolio on the condition that Yoshino Shinji join the Cabinet as Commerce and Industry Minister, so that he would have the latter's advice and collaboration in the execution of national policies.

the military, bureaucracy, the *zaibatsu,* and the political parties, to prepare the way for an effective "national defense structure."

At the very first meeting of the Cabinet on June 5 War Minister Sugiyama proposed the control of civil aviation as well as the creation of a ministry to safeguard and promote the nation's health and physical well-being. On June 10 the Fuel Bureau was set up as an affiliated organization of the Commerce and Industry Ministry to formulate and execute the nation's vital fuel policy. With the increasing number of matters coming under the ordinance power of the government and the scope of Diet powers contracting rapidly the need became great for smooth liaison and better understanding between the executive and legislative branches. Accordingly, on June 24, Premier Konoe revived the system of parliamentary vice ministers and counselors.[30]

On July 24, slightly more than a fortnight after the Lukouchiao Incident, the Konoe Cabinet announced its six-point program, which was, in effect, an incorporation of the army's major policies since the Hirota Cabinet and which was designed to hasten the nation toward the goal of totalitarian structure. Most significant perhaps was the fact that national policies were now geared to the needs of prosecuting the war with China. These six points were: the creation of an effective "national defense structure" or a wartime structure, the pursuit of diplomacy in East Asia, which was to be distinct and separate from that of the rest of the world; the establishment of an East Asia economic bloc comprising Japan, Manchukuo, and China; the setting up of a new national structure, which was to be totalitarian; the revamping of education to meet the needs of new conditions in East Asia; and the revitalization of national policies relative to foreign trade and transportation.

The army's relentless drive toward totalitarian structure gained momentum as 1937 wore on and was greatly accelerated after the outbreak of hostilities in China. However, even as early as April 1, the government had put into effect the Alcohol Monopoly Law in anticipation of national defense needs. During the month of August, imperial ordinances were issued to begin or step up production in synthetic oil, gold, and steel, while the Military Secrets Protection Law [31] was revised and tightened. This was soon followed on September 10 by the Munitions Industry Mobilization Ordinance. Meanwhile efforts were begun by the government to mobilize the nonmaterial resources of the nation.

The movement for total national spiritual mobilization to whip public opinion into shape for the "holy war" in China was launched in the fall of 1937. The headquarters for the movement, the Central Federation for National Spiritual Mobilization, was set up on October 12, a week after President Roosevelt's

---

[30] This system was first introduced by Premier Katō Takaaki on August 12, 1924.

[31] Revised on August 13, 1937, the Gunki Hogohō went into effect on October 10 and was revised again on December 12, 1939.

"Quarantine Speech," under the joint auspices and supervision of the War, Education, and Home Ministries, and the Cabinet Information Bureau. Nearly one hundred civilian organizations were mobilized to carry on a propaganda program, which proved to be woefully ineffective, never going much beyond turning out slogans that virtually flooded the country.

Impelled by the necessity of mobilizing the entire resources of the nation fully and effectively for the prosecution of the China War, the Konoe Cabinet set up the Planning Board in mid-October.[32] Although this general headquarters for over-all national planning was headed by a civilian president, the army was given charge of the first section, which was entrusted with the task of formulating over-all national policies. In time, it developed into an army organ for national planning. As a means of bringing together the different groups, the Konoe Cabinet also instituted on October 15 the Cabinet Council[33] to which were appointed outstanding representatives of the army and navy, the political parties, bureaucracy, and the financial circles, whose function was to help deliberate upon important national policies.

Of gravest concern to the army was the deplorably poor physical condition of the nation's youth as revealed in the annual physical examinations for military conscripts over a period of years. The army had plans for the establishment of a central health agency for the purpose of improving the physical well-being of the nation from the point of view of national defense. Since the proposal was made by War Minister Sugiyama in the first cabinet meeting of June 5, 1937, plans for organization took shape rapidly and the Privy Council approved the government's plan in December. The Welfare Ministry opened its doors on January 11, 1938, with Marquis Kido as its first Minister. Charged with the responsibility of protecting and advancing the health and physical well-being of the people with a view to strengthening the nation's military potential, the new agency assumed jurisdiction over social welfare, labor policies, and administration, unemployment and employment, and the stabilization of national livelihood. One of the very first achievements of this new Ministry was the National Health Insurance Law, which was enacted by the Diet in spite of the organized opposition of the Japan Medical Association, and became effective on July 1, 1938.

[32] The precursor to this Board was the Cabinet Investigation Bureau (Naikaku Chōsa Kyoku), set up by the Okada Cabinet on May 11, 1935, with Yoshida Shigeru as its first Director. This Bureau was entrusted with the study of national policies and particularly the population problem. In May, 1937, Premier Hayashi expanded it and made it into the Planning Office (Kikakuchō). Premier Konoe merged it with the Resources Bureau (Shigen Kyoku) and expanded it into the Planning Board, which became the headquarters for national mobilization and the nerve center of cabinet activities.

[33] Generals Araki, Hayashi, Matsui, Ōi, Ugaki, Admirals Abo, Nakamura, Suetsugu, prominent party leaders, representatives of financial circles like Ikeda and Gō, and bureaucrats like Hirota and Matsuoka served as counselors (*Naikaku Sangi*) until the Council was abolished by Tōjō.

In the spring of 1938 the wartime structure for which the army had been striving was given legal form by the National General Mobilization Law.[34] Enacted on March 24, the last day of the Seventy-third Session of the Diet, it was a *carte blanche* delegation of wartime legislative powers to the Cabinet, empowering the government to legislate by ordinance even in those areas of individual rights and freedom that were provided by the Constitution. It constituted a statutory suspension, if not a virtual death sentence, of parliamentary government. Henceforth, the will of the electorate could no longer be reflected in the Diet. In effect, the legislative body was superseded by the bureaucracy, which achieved a position of supremacy in the wartime structure created by the General Mobilization Law, which became effective on May 5. This was a great triumph for the military, to whom it was the instrumentality by which the totalitarianization of the nation was to be achieved legally.

In the same month that the General Mobilization Law went into effect, Premier Konoe took an unprecedented step in the conduct of foreign relations by designating General Ugaki as Foreign Minister. Since the creation of the Foreign Office the Foreign Minister had always been a career man. The only exception was the case of Baron Gotō in the Terauchi Cabinet, who was shifted from Home Minister to Foreign Minister, becoming simultaneously the *de facto* vice premier for a short period. Konoe was confident that Ugaki would be particularly effective in bringing about the satisfactory termination of the China War and at the same time instilling a new spirit into the Foreign Office, which was regarded as plagued with stagnation, inefficiency, internal bickerings, and unhealthy rivalries. But Foreign Minister Ugaki achieved neither and was impelled to resign after a little over four months in protest against the army's plan for a central administrative agency to handle the China problem independently of the Foreign Office, resulting in the virtual stripping of the latter's functions as far as Chinese relations were concerned.

Military preparations were greatly stepped up during the latter half of 1938. Effective April 1, military training had been made compulsory in all the schools of the nation. Beginning in July the Navy started giving university students a taste of navy life through training cruises and life aboard warships, while the army embarked upon a program of training fifteen- to eighteen-year-olds as volunteers for the tank corps. In September the Army Press Section, which had been particularly active since 1934 in propaganda work, was reorganized and expanded into a fell-fledged Army Information Bureau in anticipation of ever greater demands upon it. This was followed on October 15 by the War Ministry extending the period of compulsory military service. Significantly enough, the Inspectorate General of Military Aviation was created early in December, and

---

[34] For an excellent discussion of the General Mobilization Law (Kokka Sōdōin Hō), see Charles B. Fahs, *Government in Japan, Recent Trends in Its Scope and Operation*, pp. 50–53.

Lieutenant General Tōjō Hideki was appointed its first head. Military aviation was thus given full recognition as an "important component of a modern war machine. Even more significant was the opportunity given General Tōjō to begin his rapid rise to the posts of Vice War Minister, War Minister, and finally Premier within a space of three short years.

The creation of a central administrative machinery to handle the China problem began to receive serious consideration from the spring of 1938 on, as the Diet session was drawing to its close. As a result of disagreement with the army Foreign Minister Hirota resigned from the Cabinet. By the middle of September the Cabinet Bureau of Legislation had begun drafting a plan based on the army's proposal. However, the Foreign Office under General Ugaki continued its opposition because the army's proposal called for the taking over of political, economic, and cultural affairs for all of China instead of limiting it to only those areas occupied by the armed forces, and because the Foreign Office was convinced that China policy on the highest level should be determined by the five ministers' conference. After strenuously opposing the army's proposal, Foreign Minister Ugaki resigned late in September. A month later Konoe appointed Arita, under whom the Foreign Office reached a compromise with the army. On October 1 the Cabinet approved the plan of organization, and on December 16 the Asia Development Board (Kōa In) also known as the China Affairs Board emerged with Lieutenant General Yanagawa as its first Director. The Premier was its ex-officio President and the Ministers of Foreign Affairs, Finance, War, and Navy were the vice presidents. The Board was entrusted with the jurisdiction of all aspects of China affairs, except strictly diplomatic matters. These included the formulation and execution of policies in political, economic, and cultural matters, the supervision and control of the activities of corporations to be established, as well as individual enterprises in China, and the coordination of administrative functions pertaining to China in the various ministries. In order to coordinate activities liaison offices were established in Peking, Kalgan (Changchiakow), Shanghai and Amoy.[35] The Political Affairs Division of the Board was headed by Major General Suzuki Teiichi, who was entrusted with the duty of giving guidance to the newly established Nanking Government of Wang Ching-wei, while the Economic Division came under the direction of Hidaka Shinrokurō, counselor of the Japanese Embassy, who exercised supervision over the North China Development Company and the Central China Promotion Company. Serving as advisory body to the Board was a thirty-two member Asia Development Committee,[36] headed by the Premier and includ-

[35] These liaison offices were set up in March, 1939, and active generals were placed in charge of them. In the central organization there were in addition to the Secretariat, the Political, Economic, Cultural and Technical Divisions.

[36] *1940 Asahi Nenkan*, p. 123.

ing representatives of the army and navy, business and industry, the press, bureaucrats, and the political parties.

THE HIRANUMA CABINET

Toward the end of 1938, as soon as Konoe had made up his mind to resign shortly, he reached an understanding with Baron Hiranuma, President of the Privy Council, who agreed to accept the premiership. On January 24 Hiranuma had indicated opposition against totalitarianism in the Diet in reply to an inter-pellation by a Seiyūkai member and clarified his stand as an advocate of the *status quo*. However, his earlier activities as head of the ultranationalistic State Foundation Society, which embraced rightists and military men, had given the impression that he was a strong proponent of radical national reform. Contrary to expectations, however, the Hiranuma Cabinet supported parliamentarism and opposed totalitarianism. The Premier stressed the basic differences between totalitarianism and *Kōdō,* or the Imperial Way, of which he was a strong ex-ponent. On February 24, 1939, shortly after he assumed the premiership, he came out with a strong admonition against the "holier-than-thou" attitude of government officials and bade them abandon internal bickerings and friction within their ranks.

Prince Konoe exchanged places with Baron Hiranuma, assumed the Presi-dency of the Privy Council and was made concurrently Minister without Port-folio. This gave the Privy Council representation in the government, and brought about a closer working relationship between the two, precluding the possibility of the Privy Council becoming a stumbling block to the government in the execution of its policies.

In its composition, the Hiranuma Cabinet gave the appearance of a twice-reshuffled Konoe Cabinet, which it was to a considerable degree. Justice Minister Shiono, who functioned as the chief of staff in the formation of the Cabinet, and the Premier had fully intended to have the important Home Affairs portfolio go to the former, who was Hiranuma's right-hand man. However, in the politi-cal maneuverings that invariably accompany cabinet formation, the important portfolio was preempted by Marquis Kido, a career bureaucrat and Konoe's con-fidant and close to Saionji, Yuasa, Makino, and Matsudaira. Kido then got his protégé, Vice Welfare Minister Hirose, the Welfare portfolio.[37]

Premier Hiranuma's avowed policy of enlisting the assistance of all segments of political life in the management of the affairs of state seemed to produce results, as he sailed through the Diet session with the greatest of ease. All of the eighty-nine bills submitted by the government were enacted although none of

[37] As Director of the Social Bureau of the Home Ministry, Hirose Tadahisa had drafted a number of laws in the field of social and labor legislation and was one of the more promising bureaucrats.

the thirty-two private bills saw the light of day. The budget bill was approved in its original form without even a debate or revision.

The emergence of the Hiranuma Cabinet suspended for the time being the new party movement, which seemed to be gaining headway under the Konoe Cabinet. There was no complete agreement, however, even among Konoe's cabinet members, on the question of a new political party. Home Minister Admiral Suetsugu had favored a new party; Justice Minister Shiono was for utilizing existing parties; Agriculture and Forestry Minister Arima advocated a mass party, based broadly on the people; while Education Minister General Araki favored the strengthening of the national spiritual mobilization movement. Moreover, by December, Konoe had little desire to push the new party movement, as he had already decided to resign. When Hiranuma succeeded him, plans for the reform of the parliamentary system, the House of Peers, and the electoral system were also dropped.

Utilizing the second anniversary of the China Incident, the army issued a pamphlet entitled *To the Fighters in the Nation's Total War,* propaganda designed to gird the nation for a protracted war. It emphasized that the China War could not be brought to a successful conclusion in two or three years as long as third powers rendered assistance to the enemy, and that in the light of the Manchurian experience the establishment of peace and order in China would necessitate five to six years of occupation. Moreover, to win China's friendship for both Japan and Manchukuo, which would involve China's abandonment of reliance upon Europe and America, and to create a rejuvenated Asiatic civilization would require efforts extending over a period of anywhere from thirty to fifty years.

Conditions were not particularly favorable to the Hiranuma Cabinet, for on August 29, slightly less than eight months after it was formed, it fell. Its collapse was induced by the untenable situation created by the conclusion of the Soviet-German Non-Aggression Pact, which all but destroyed the basis of the German-Japanese Anti-Comintern Pact. In a statement clarifying the reasons for his resignation, Hiranuma explained that the Soviet-German Pact had made it necessary to abandon all existing foreign policies and formulate new ones to cope with the extremely complex, if not baffling, situation that had arisen in Europe. He emphasized that to reorient diplomacy, to bolster the domestic structure, and to ride out the crisis it would be necessary and wise for the nation to make a fresh start by effecting a change in government.

To add to the difficulties, Japan's internal forces had for some time been divided sharply into two opposing schools of thought: the *status quo* faction, supporting *rapprochement* with Great Britain and the United States, and the army's reform faction, which was pro-German and favoring alliance with the Nazis. The former included Foreign Minister Arita, Finance Minister Ishiwata, and Navy Minister Yonai, while the latter was a military-bureaucratic coalition led by War Minister Itagaki. Premier Hiranuma was caught between these two opposing forces in the Cabinet and was unable either to extricate himself or to compose the differences between the factions without wrecking the Cabinet.

THE GOVERNMENTS OF GENERAL ABE
AND ADMIRAL YONAI

The government of General Abe, which succeeded the Hiranuma Cabinet on August 30, 1939, was weak and unable to seize the initiative or the opportunity to be effective. As in the preceding cabinet, its policies were geared to the termination of the China War and it looked to the achievement of self-assertive diplomacy in the form of a "new order in East Asia," the strengthening of armament through increased production and self-sufficiency in strategic war materials, the strengthening of the trade structure through greater exports and tighter controls, and the overhauling of the domestic politico-economic structure. The Nazi invasion of Poland on September 1, only two days after the Cabinet's formation, aggravated greatly the difficulties of the Abe Government in the conduct of foreign affairs.

In its meeting of September 26 the Abe Government, under ever present army pressure, decided on the establishment of a Trade Ministry, designed to function as high powered machinery for the promotion of trade. The proposed ministry, the brain child of Finance Minister Aoki, concurrently president of the Planning Board, and Cabinet Bureau of Legislation Director Karasawa, two of the leading nondiplomatic career bureaucrats, was to take over all the nondiplomatic functions of the Commercial Bureau of the Foreign Office, certain functions relating to the export of silk, agricultural, forestry and marine products of the Agriculture and Forestry Ministry, all the functions of the Trade and Textile Bureaus and part of the Chemical Bureau of the Commerce and Industry Ministry, and some of the functions of the Bureau of Colonization and Development and the Korea Department of the Overseas Ministry.

Determined opposition developed in the Foreign Office on the grounds that it would impair the efficient conduct and control of foreign relations. Following the example of Commercial Bureau Director Matsumura, the entire staff of the Foreign Office submitted their resignations early in October. The government had no alternative but to back down and on October 13, Foreign Minister Admiral Nomura rejected the resignations of more than 110 foreign service officers, and the dispute was settled with the abandonment of the proposed Trade Ministry.[38]

[38] This was not the first time that the Foreign Office bureaucrats had staged a successful opposition against the government. In 1924, when Premier Kiyoura tried to bring in an outsider, Fujimura Yoshio, member of the House of Peers, to head the Foreign Office, the entire

On September 29 the Abe Government promulgated an imperial ordinance strengthening greatly the Premier's power of issuing administrative directives in matters relating to national mobilization.[39] Premier Abe, however, was unable to reconcile the government's decision of November 16 to raise the price of tobacco, a government monopoly, with the Price Control Ordinance, which pegged prices of all commodities as of September 18. This, together with the muffing of the proposed Trade Ministry and numerous other failures, led to the cooling of the attitude of the army and its withdrawal of support from the government. On December 26, on the very eve of the opening of the Diet, a majority of the members of the House of Representatives decided on a no-confidence resolution. Seeing that its chances of getting safely through the Diet were extremely small, the Abe Cabinet submitted its resignation on January 14, 1940, while the Diet was still in its customary year-end recess.

In the birth of the Yonai Cabinet was demonstrated the decisiveness of the role played by the army in the choice of government. On January 13, Privy Seal Yuasa submitted several candidates for premier to Prince Saionji. The army opposed General Araki and Ikeda Seihin. The "Big Three" of the army decided that an active general should not take over the helm, inasmuch as conditions were not that hopeless, nor the situation so desperate. Therefore, instead of General Hata, whose name had also been proposed, Admiral Yonai was selected to form the next government, without as much pressure from the army as in some of the preceding cabinets. Apparently, the army was now resting on its laurels.

Admiral Yonai's government, which emerged on January 16, followed in the footsteps of its predecessor and gave first priority in foreign affairs to the settlement of the China War. Premier Yonai exerted efforts to improve relations with the powers, especially Great Britain and the United States, but with no tangible results. As Navy Minister in the Hiranuma Cabinet, Yonai had taken an unusually reasonable stand when asked for the navy's views. He stated that, although the navy had its own views regarding national defense in a narrow sense, in the planning and execution of national defense policies in the broadest sense, neither it nor the army should interfere. It was the function of the government, he averred, to determine over-all national policies in the light of domestic as well as international conditions, in which the services were not well informed. Yonai had expressed also his views that economic reforms should be carried out

---

personnel rose as one under the leadership of the then Vice Foreign Minister, Matsudaira Tsuneo, and not only blocked the appointment, but also forced the government to appoint a career diplomat, Matsui Keishirō, who was one of their number.

[39] This ordinance made it obligatory for cabinet ministers, Governors-General of Korea and Formosa, Ambassador to Manchukuo, Governor of Karafuto, and the South Seas Administrative Office to consult the Premier before issuing, modifying, or rescinding orders in the carrying out of the National General Mobilization Law.

gradually and not rushed through, and should be evolutionary rather than revolutionary. Furthermore, economic controls at best could be carried out only in a limited way, he believed. Such views were in strong contrast and contradiction to army views.

The army was irked by the constant flow of statements issuing forth from the Foreign Office, especially when it felt that the government had no clear-cut foreign policy. Foreign Minister Arita was forced to make the broadcast of June 29, not as an outline of the government's foreign policy as he had intended at first, but merely as a discussion of current diplomatic problems, since the army stoutly maintained that there was no foreign policy. The clash that resulted over the issue between the army and the Foreign Office was resolved for the time being by the apology of the Foreign Minister. When War Minister Hata's query regarding the government's policy for the establishment of a high-powered national defense state and a unified national structure went unanswered by the Yonai Cabinet, the army decided to take action. The army's mounting dissatisfaction at the ineffectiveness of the government in carrying out the army's blueprint brought about War Minister Hata's resignation. As a direct result, the Yonai Cabinet was forced to retire in mid-July.

THE SECOND KONOE CABINET

It was in response to the demand for a powerful government that the Second Konoe Government emerged on July 22, 1940. An understanding was reached in advance in regard to national policies, both domestic and foreign, military plans, and political strategy in a conference of Premier Konoe, Foreign Minister Matsuoka, War Minister Tōjō, and Navy Minister Yoshida on July 18, four days before the Cabinet was installed and before the remainder of the members of the Cabinet had been chosen. Needless to say, this unusual procedure, which represented a departure from well established practice, did not escape the notice of the public.

Konoe's responsibility was to carry out sweeping changes in the political structure, particularly in view of the fact that the spiritual mobilization movement had bogged down. In three years it had not succeeded in whipping national morale into shape for the most effective mobilization of the nation's manpower and material resources to meet stringent wartime demands. Talk of a "new structure" was on everyone's lips, for as a national slogan it was echoed and reechoed even in the most remote mountain hamlets and fishing villages. However, the raising of a new political structure, aided by an effective organization for spiritual mobilization, within the framework of the Constitution was a difficult task.

On August 1, 1940, Konoe issued a euphemistic statement of fundamental national policies,[40] outlining the policies for the creation of a new political, economic, and cultural structure at a time when "the nation was faced with the greatest test since the beginning of history." The basic policy was to establish world peace in accordance with the ancient ideal of "all nations under one roof" (*hakkō ichiu*), and in order to achieve this goal, the nation was to forge ahead in the establishment of a "new order in Greater East Asia," founded on an economic bloc comprising Japan, Manchukuo, and China. The domestic goal was to be the perfection of national defense on the basis of total defense structure while diplomacy's goal was to be the termination of the China War. Planned economy, particularly the control of production, distribution, and consumption, was to be the means of achieving self-sufficiency in food, rationalization of trade policies, expansion of chemical and machine industries, promotion of science, increase of population, improvement of national health, and the equalization of sacrifices and services to be rendered by the people to the state were to be achieved.

SELF-LIQUIDATION OF THE POLITICAL PARTIES

Even at the very beginning the dissatisfaction of the military did not go unnoticed by party leaders. Not a few of the party members began to have contacts with military men and some of them even made attempts to bring about party-military cooperation, if not collaboration. Home Minister Adachi in the Wakatsuki Cabinet planned with Seiyūkai leader Kuhara to bring about the formation of a Minseitō-Seiyūkai coalition cabinet, but without success. The upshot of this attempt was the change of government that took place in December of 1931. When the Wakatsuki Cabinet rejected Adachi's proposal, the latter refused to cooperate, thereby precipitating a cabinet crisis, which resulted in its downfall.

One of the Seiyūkai members, Mori Kaku, had plans for setting up a dictatorial regime in which the Seiyūkai would control the Diet and the military would have extraparliamentary control of national affairs.[41] The Minseitō fought desperately to prevent the Seiyūkai from coming into power in alliance with the military. It was in the course of this intense Minseitō-Seiyūkai rivalry that Izawa Takeo and his bureaucratic colleagues succeeded in securing the support of Yuasa and Ichiki, the influential palace advisers of the Home Ministry faction, in setting up the Cabinet of Admiral Saitō in May, 1932, following the assassination of Premier Inukai.[42]

The impact of the May 15 Incident was as great on the *zaibatsu* as on the

[40] U.S. Department of State, *Foreign Relations of the United States: Japan*, Vol. II, pp. 108–111.

[41] Iwabuchi Tatsuo, *Gendai Nihon Seiji Ron*, p. 306.

[42] *Ibid.*, p. 307.

parties. In September Ikeda Seihin, managing director of the Mitsui Bank, retired from active business life, and in November the Mitsui Holding Company (Mitsui Gōmei Kaisha) donated 30 million yen to social work through its own welfare agency, the Mitsui Hōon Kai, to mollify enraged public sentiment. Although in December, 1933, Matsuoka, who had been the chief delegate to the League of Nations at the time of Japan's withdrawal, advocated disbanding of the political parties, there was no response nor was there any indication that the parties had reached an absolute impasse.

The close relationship that had developed between the bureaucrats and the party politicians had been one of the interesting by-products of Japan's political development. In the heyday of political parties in the nineteen twenties many a career bureaucrat and military man sought political fortune by joining one of the major parties. Minseitō counted among its membership such outstanding ex-bureaucrats as Katō Takaaki, Hamaguchi Yūkō, and Wakatsuki Reijirō, all of whom served as premiers. Seiyūkai had General Tanaka Giichi, Suzuki Kisaburō, and Tokonami Takejirō, who were all career bureaucrats. Many a party leader therefore found it impossible to get away completely from his bureaucratic background, experiences, psychology, and attitude as well as the philosophy to which he had become quite thoroughly assimilated over the years.

As a method to combat fascist tendencies a new party movement based on Seiyūkai-Minseitō cooperation became a subject of serious consideration. It took concrete shape after the general election of February 20, 1936, when it came to be advocated by the Nakajima faction of the Seiyūkai. The plan was to make Konoe its president and stage a comeback of the political parties, which were in bad shape. However, the view that parties should work in cooperation with the military came to receive support in various quarters. Minseitō's Nagai was favorably inclined toward the idea of a mass party with a strong nationalistic tendency and viewed the proposal with more than casual interest. The idea of coalition with the bureaucrats or military leaders and the parties was by no means new.[43] Moreover, no existing party was so pure in its principles and motives as to be above considering a coalition with bureaucratic or military elements, especially in the face of abundance of historical precedents and the possibility of gaining power.

Antipathy that had developed against the political parties was by no means confined to the military alone. Among the party leadership this growing antiparty sentiment was viewed with apprehension. After the resignation of the Hayashi Cabinet, which had been repudiated by the parties in the election, the normal procedure would have been to let the parties form a cabinet. But this course was not taken because of the existence of hostile sentiment against parties,

---

[43] Itagaki's Liberal Party (Jiyūtō) became Seiyūkai when Itō Hirobumi and Hoshi Tōru got together. Most of the Kokumintō, originally Okuma's Reform Party (Kaishintō), went over to join Katsura's new party to form the Rikken Dōshi Kai.

which had been increasing steadily. If the repudiation of the Hayashi Cabinet in the general election of April 30 was tantamount to an absolute no-confidence vote by the electorate, it was in no sense an expression of confidence in the political parties..

It was the appearance of Konoe as Premier in June, 1937, which signalled the revival of the new party movement, which had been held in abeyance temporarily. However, one group favored the creation of a single party through the merger of all existing parties; the other favored the formation of an entirely new party built around those members of existing parties who were thoroughly imbued with reform ideology. As Konoe himself was not satisfied with the mere reconstituting of existing parties, he was not unwilling to become its president when a new party came into existence.

There was no doubt that the tremendous welcome given by the public to Konoe's assumption of premiership and the leadership of the nation was an expression of confidence in the person of the Premier, but it was also a reflection of helpless dependence on the part of the people, who had neither the training nor the ability to organize themselves politically and therefore were content to leave the organization and leadership of a new party movement in the hands of a public figure who had their complete trust.

Before the year 1938 came to an end political parties began to show symptoms of impending disintegration. In October the Seiyūkai suffered a serious split over the vital issue of presidency. By May, 1939, the party had been split three ways, the Nakajima and Kuhara factions and the neutral group.[44] Such rifts, of course, did not help to strengthen public confidence in the political parties. There appeared other signs of party and interparty dissidence. In late February, 1939, a proposal for the merger of the Social Mass Party, the Tōhōkai, and the Kokumin Dōmei had been adopted and the date for inauguration set. However, a disagreement over the question of presidency wrecked the proposed merger. Frustrated by the merger attempt, Nakano, who was president of the Tōhōkai, resigned his membership in the House of Representatives in late March. This led to the disintegration of the Tōhōkai, which ended its existence as a party.

Conditions for the appearance of a single party improved steadily during 1939. The spring of 1940 found the country in a mood to support a totalitarian structure. On March 25 over 100 members of the House of Representatives, embracing all the political parties, formed the Federation for the Prosecution of the Holy War (Seisen Kantetsu Remmei) which pledged (1) wholehearted support of the Konoe policy, (2) collaboration with third powers that approved Japan's establishment of a new order in East Asia, (3) overhauling of the economic structure which had been based too long on *laissez faire,* (4) and the

[44] The Reform Faction (Kakushinha) of the Seiyūkai established a separate identity on April 30, when Nakajima Chikuhei became its president, while Kuhara Fusanosuke was named the eighth president of the legitimate or Regular Faction (Seitōha).

stamping out of un-Japanese ideologies such as communism, liberalism, and utilitarianism. The appearance of this organization was a convincing demonstration of the impotence and pliability of the political parties, which had been thrown into despair regarding their ability to resist the trend of the times effectively and to survive in the face of the increasing strength of the one party movement.

Little over a month later, on April 29, the National Federation for the Construction of East Asia [45] was formed with Admiral Suetsugu as president, but without actual government leadership. This was a super-party organization growing out of the federation of political parties and groups such as Adachi's Kokumin Dōmei, Nakano's Tōhōkai, and Colonel Hashimoto's Japan Youth Party (Dai Nihon Seinentō) with the avowed aim of providing the much needed motive power for the construction of a new Asia.[46] In working towards its objectives, which included the revitalization of diplomacy and domestic reform, it adopted the policy of respecting the electoral process. It also stressed the importance of local organization, inasmuch as it regarded itself as a group raised from below and resting on a broad popular basis.

An unsuccessful attempt to inject life into the dying party system was made on the eve of its disappearance. Katayama Tetsu, who had been read out of the Social Mass Party, attempted to form a new party around former President Abe and the remnants of the old Social Democratic Party. Everything was in readiness for the inauguration of the Nationalist Labor Party (Kinrō Kokumintō), which was scheduled for May 12, 1940. Five days before the appointed date, however, the Home Ministry suddenly issued an order prohibiting the launching of the party on the grounds that the formation of a new party was inadvisable and inappropriate in the light of the existing situation. It was obvious that the government had made up its mind not to permit the launching of any new parties that might interfere in any way with the single party movement.

By the end of 1939 the political parties had been completely supplanted in the function of furnishing cabinet members and influencing government policies by several informal study and discussion groups,[47] formed by active business, political, government, and military leaders. One of the more influential of these groups was the Current Affairs Discussion Society (Jiji Kondankai), formed in November of 1937 by some thirty leading businessmen, members of political parties and government officials in Tōkyō, who worked actively to mold, influence, and unify public opinion on domestic and international questions. The

[45] Tōkyō *Asahi,* editorial, May 1, 1940.

[46] The prime movers of this Federation were Cabinet Councilors Admiral Suetsugu and General Matsui, President Adachi of the Kokumin Dōmei, President Nakano of the Tōhōkai, and Colonel Hashimoto of the Japan Youth Party, who had gathered in Tōkyō on December 7, 1939, to discuss plans of organization.

[47] Itō Kinjirō, "Seiken no Botai o Tankyū Suru," *Chūō Kōron,* January, 1940, pp. 370–378.

International Anti-Communist Federation (Kokusai Hankyō Remmei) composed of rightists like Professor Minoda, Baron Kikuchi, and Baron Ida, the Mizuho Club, led by Generals Oi and Tatekawa, and the rightist Meirinkai, made up chiefly of retired army officers, bureaucrats and businessmen, were quite vocal in their attempts to influence government policies. The National Policy Study Society (Kokusaku Kenkyū Kai) and the Kokui Kai, which were made up mostly of bureaucrats, were very influential, the latter having furnished several of its members to the Saitō and Okada Cabinets. Powerful also were the semi-governmental East Asia Research Institute (Tōa Kenkyūjo), established in 1939 with Konoe as president and having an annual budget of 2 million yen, and the Society for the Termination of the China War (Jihen Shori Kenkyūkai), which was also presided over by Premier Konoe.

TOWARD A TOTALITARIAN POLITICAL STRUCTURE

Prince Konoe relinquished the presidency of the Privy Council on June 24, 1940, in order to devote his entire energies to the establishment of a truly unified national political structure, based directly on the people and not on the old political parties.[48] Thus, the movement for the establishment of a new party was launched under the leadership of a man who was just as much the public's choice as the army's. The political parties lost no time in climbing on the "new structure" band wagon. One by one they initiated the process of self-liquidation, beginning with the Social Mass Party, which dissolved itself on July 6. By August 15, when the last party, the Minseitō, voted itself out of existence, all the political parties had disbanded. Within a period of less than six weeks the parties had vanished completely from the political scene after sixty years of extremely checkered and turbulent existence. The political decks were cleared for Konoe to go into action.

While he was in the midst of deliberation and planning, on July 17, Konoe received the call to head the government for the second time. The experiences he had undergone in dealing with the military had made him realize that a new political structure was necessary as a means of controlling the army and terminating the China War. The fact that the army was desirous of having him head the new party facilitated greatly the actual launching of the movement. After arriving at an understanding regarding national policies with the army and navy he proceeded simultaneously with plans for the launching of the new structure. On August 28 he called a meeting of the Preparatory Commission for the New Political Structure, which represented the public at large and in-

---

[48] Earlier, on June 4, Konoe had made a preliminary announcement of his convictions regarding the establishment of a new party.

cluded legislators from both houses of the Diet, academic, diplomatic, and financial circles, patriotic societies, the press, and the self-governing bodies.[49]

The deliberations of the Commission were finished by the middle of September. All the ministries were represented at the deliberations. Particularly powerful was the influence of the army, which was represented by the Military Affairs Bureau of the War Ministry. Significant was the fact also that an absolute majority of the Commission members were actually representing the government's point of view, and even the seven members of the House of Representatives were more accurately representing the government rather than the people. Out of the twenty-five members, four were representatives of ultranationalist groups, the Black Dragon Society, Tōhōkai, Japan Youth Society, and the National Federation for the Construction of East Asia. Decisions were reached not by majority vote, but by a consensus of opinion as determined by the Premier, a practice which was then in effect in arriving at cabinet decisions.

On October 12 the Imperial Rule Assistance Association was formally inaugurated. According to its President, Premier Konoe, the aims of the new organization were the harmonization of the supreme military command and state affairs, achievement of unification and greater efficiency in government, tying together of the different areas of economic and cultural activities through vertical and horizontal organizations, formation of an organization of Diet members, better mutual understanding between the government and the people, and the full participation by the people in the establishment of the cultural and economic policies of the country. As Premier and ex-officio head of the organization, Konoe carefully pointed out that it was not a political party, inasmuch as it did not represent the interests or viewpoints of certain segments of society. In his statement, he emphasized that the new organization should not become a totalitarian party. When the draft was shown to the army, General Mutō, Director of the Military Affairs Bureau of the War Department, deleted this, but Konoe reinserted it and issued it in its original form.[50]

The rules of the Imperial Rule Assistance Association gave its president virtually dictatorial powers in the management of the organization, as he was empowered to make any changes either in its structure or personnel. It was not until Premier Tōjō appeared on the scene, however, that full use of this provision was utilized. From the outset it was intended to be an organization to do the bidding of the government. From the central headquarters in Tōkyō it worked through local branches or chapters in the prefectures, districts, cities, towns, and villages. Paralleling the main organization and its local chapters as an auxiliary

[49] Perhaps the most significant feature of the composition of the Preparatory Commission was the predominance of rightist ideology and its representatives, while there was only a feeble representation of moderates.

[50] Baba Tsunego, *Konoe Naikaku Shiron*, p. 56. For the text of the statement see *Dōmei Jiji Nenkan*, pp. 97–99, 1941.

were the National Central Cooperative Council and its local branches, which reached down into the neighborhood associations. Because the bureaucrats, who placed their own security and advancement ahead of public well-being, developed the organization along totalitarian lines, Premier Konoe discovered before long that instead of bringing the army under control, the army turned around and used it effectively against him.

The powerful group of counselors (*san'yo*), which ran the organization, consisted of all the Vice Ministers, the powerful Directors of the Military Affairs and Naval Affairs Bureaus of the War and Navy Ministries respectively, the Chief Cabinet Secretary, Director of the Cabinet Bureau of Legislation, Vice President of the Planning Board, and the chief secretaries of both Houses of the Diet.

ACCELERATION OF WAR MOBILIZATION

Active war preparations involving military reorganization and scientific mobilization were carried on vigorously during 1940 and 1941. In the light of the experience gained in the Nomonhan Incident in the summer of 1939 and of the sensational results achieved by Hitler's air power, revision of the military plans made in 1937 became necessary. On April 1, 1940, the Army Ordnance Headquarters was set up to unify munitions administration, while the Army Air Arsenal was established to carry on research on aircraft production, experimentation, and aeronautics. Simultaneously, the government's Aviation Research Institute came into being.

Pressed by the urgency of mobilizing the scientific resources of the nation for military purposes, the War Ministry discontinued the practice of producing all its weapons. On May 17 it held a conference of leaders of science and technology from the universities, research organizations, and industry, and appointed them consultants to the Army Technical Headquarters and the Science Research Institute.

In a bold move the army reorganized itself, on August 1, into regional army commands.[51] The distinctive feature of the new organization was the coordination of the operations of the ground and air forces under one commander in chief for each area and the great emphasis placed on air defense in view of the nation's apparent vulnerability to air attacks. The Army Fuel Headquarters also came into being at the same time to administer the army's vital fuel program.

Paralleling the army's program were the activities of scientific groups. The National Federation of Scientific and Technical Societies (Zen Nihon Kagaku

[51] Japan Proper was organized into four army commands, Northern, Eastern, Central, and Western with headquarters at Asahigawa, Tōkyō, Ōsaka, and Fukuoka. Korea, Formosa, and Manchuria had their army commands with headquarters at Keijō, Taihoku, and Hsinking.

Gijutsu Dantai Rengō) was formed on August 8 by 123 scientific and technical
societies to mobilize and pool the scientific resources of the nation. Shortly after
the conclusion of the Tripartite Alliance, on October 1, the government set up
the Total War Research Institute for the purpose of studying the methods and
full implications of total war. Then came, on December 12, the government
sponsored Science Mobilization Society (Kagaku Dōin Kyōkai) headed by
Premier Konoe and assisted by the Planning Board President. Its aim was to
mobilize some 200 organizations to carry on a five-year research program on a
million yen appropriation. Its specific objectives included (1) the encouragement
and assistance for producing scientific books and films to raise the nation's general
level of scientific knowledge; (2) the strengthening of coordination and cooperation between scientists, private and government, and industry; (3) the making
of studies on research conditions and grants to research; (4) distribution and
allocation of materials needed for research; (5) rewarding those who rendered
valuable service in scientific mobilization, and (6) the establishment of regional and local committees to organize living on a scientific basis and to make
practical application of the results of scientific research.

Mechanization of the army had been going on, especially since the border
clashes in Manchuria and Inner Mongolia had demonstrated its need. But it
was not until April 10, 1941, that the army set up its Mechanized Force Headquarters. The Nazi Blitzkrieg technique came to attract the attention of the
Japanese to such an extent that late in December, 1940, General Yamashita Tomoyuki, Inspector General of Military Aviation and Director of the Army Aviation
Headquarters, left for Germany to observe the Nazi Luftwaffe and Panzer Divisions in action on the fighting fronts. The lessons he learned during the six
months' tour found application in the war, which broke out four months after his
return.

Under constant army pressure the government carried on intermittently
its program of administrative overhauling to increase and accelerate war efforts.
Its constant but never attained goal was the unification, coordination, and integration of the administrative efforts of the government in the interests of
greater efficiency in the mobilization of men and materials. On November 6,
1940, the Cabinet Information Bureau was expanded, taking over information
gathering and dissemination, educational and publicity work, and censorship of
the radio, movies, phonograph records, and plays, which before had been scattered
through the various ministries such as War, Navy, Foreign, Home, and Communications with a considerable degree of duplication and overlapping. For the
first time there was a single agency in which the supervision and control of the
media of mass communication were centralized.[52] A month later the govern-

---

[52] With the expansion of its scope, the Board was elevated practically to the level of
ministry and its first head, Itō Nobumi, became a president. Subsequently, the President of
the Information Board was made Minister of State, that is, Minister without Portfolio.

ment strengthened the system of ministers without portfolio,[53] enabling the appointment of three additional ministers of state over and above the regular cabinet ministers entrusted with administrative responsibilities as heads of the departments. Under the new system Baron Hiranuma was made the first Minister without Portfolio, and President of the Planning Board Hoshino was elevated to the post of State Minister.

With a view to bringing about the necessary reorientation of Japanese education to the "new order in East Asia," the government changed the elementary schools into national schools (*kokumin gakkō*).[54] Elementary education, as it existed, was found wanting by the Educational Deliberative Council (Kyōiku Shingikai) which had been appointed in December, 1937. Under the new system no private school on the elementary level could be called a national school, no child could be exempted from compulsory attendance as in the past on grounds of dire poverty, and the school districts, which had been created for the purpose of financing elementary schools, were abolished. Pedagogically, the emphasis was shifted from the mastery of knowledge or subject matter to basic moral training and discipline as well as to physical training, all of which were essential elements of national power. The curriculum was revamped to deemphasize the traditional subject approach in favor of integration and grades as such were abolished as was the relative numerical standing of the pupils in all the classes. The ultimate objective of the national school was to train the youth as citizens of a "nation which destiny had made the leader of the East Asia coprosperity sphere."

Planning and execution of economic and financial policies under wartime conditions became increasingly complex and critical as the year 1941 opened. As a result, on April 2, Premier Konoe prevailed upon Ogura Masatsune, President of the Board of Directors of the Sumitomo interests, to join the Cabinet as Minister without Portfolio. This was followed immediately by the reshuffling of the Cabinet, in which Vice Navy Minister Toyoda superseded Kobayashi Ichizō, former President of the Tōkyō Electric Light Company, as Commerce and Industry Minister, and General Suzuki, acting Director of the Asia Development Board, replaced Hoshino as Planning Board President and Minister without Portfolio.

As security measures had been inadequate, the government took steps to strengthen them. The Defense Security Law,[55] which took effect in May, was designed to prevent the leakage of state secrets in economic, financial, and diplomatic matters and to foil foreign enemy propaganda and espionage. Drastic penalties, ranging from a minimum of three years to death, were provided for in

[53] This change, which was effected on December 6, 1940, by the promulgation of Imperial Ordinance No. 843 extended the scope of Article 10 of the Cabinet Organization Regulations.

[54] The National School Ordinance was promulgated on March 1 and became effective on April 1, 1941.

[55] Promulgated on March 7, the Kokubō Hoanhō became effective on May 10, 1941.

the law, which was intended to stop the leakage of secrets on the highest level, for it applied to confidential information discussed in imperial conferences, Privy Council meetings, Cabinet and Diet meetings.

By the mid-summer of 1941, when Premier Konoe was heading the government for the third time, military preparations and general mobilization had reached quite an advanced stage and the military was apparently satisfied with what they regarded as a high state of preparedness. But Premier Konoe exerted his entire energies, though they proved insufficient, to restraining the military. There were three impelling reasons for Konoe wanting to prevent an American-Japanese war. First, the outbreak of the Soviet-German War in late June increased the possibility of a clash with the United States, an eventuality he did not contemplate with any comfort. Secondly, he was troubled by the attitude of the navy, which actually was opposed to hostilities with the United States because there could be only disaster ahead but which capitulated to the army to the extent of assuming a fatalistic attitude.[56] Thirdly, he was convinced that it was impossible for Japan to achieve complete economic self-sufficiency, inasmuch as her national economy had been and still was dependent upon the United States and Great Britain. Konoe's unremitting efforts were not enough to check the army and to forestall the impending tragedy.

[56] Admiral Yamamoto Isoroku, Commander in Chief of the Combined Fleet, was unalterably opposed to war with the United States and expressed his conviction to Prince Konoe that so far as the navy was concerned, Japan could more than hold her own and even wreak havoc on the American Navy for a year or so, but that he had no confidence in its ability or staying power if the war should last for two or three years. As Vice Navy Minister under Admiral Yonai he had given full support to his chief in opposing the Tripartite Alliance.

Chapter 34. Diplomacy of Surging Nationalism

THE SWEEP TOWARD EMPIRE

The mysterious explosion of a bomb on the tracks of the South Manchuria Railway outside of Mukden on the night of September 18, 1931, sent its reverberations around the world, and Japan's determined drive for expansion on the Asiatic continent had started. The impelling force behind this sweep toward empire was compounded of several factors, psychological, economic, political, and ideological. The pressure of rapidly increasing population, which became a subject of serious concern to Japanese leaders, was reinforced by the feeling of being treated unfairly by the rest of the world in the matter of distribution of land and resources and access to raw materials and markets. Nationalism bordering on religious fervor was fed by developments both at home and abroad, while the Pan-Asiatic mission, fostered by both the proletarian movement and ultranationalist organizations advocating the liberation of the peoples of Asia from Western imperialism under Japanese leadership, fired the imagination of a sizable segment of the nation. The determination of the fighting services to retrieve their prestige and power, which had been lost during the twenties at the hands of the parties and the *zaibatsu,* added fuel to the fire.

Financial panic, unemployment, and the decline of the middle class convinced the military and the capitalists that expansion on the Asiatic continent was the only course open to the nation in riding out the national economic crisis. It was looked upon in some quarters as a means of checking the growing strength of democratic and socialistic movements that seemed to challenge the supremacy of established groups and vested interests. Ultranationalists believed that the seizure of Manchuria, quite apart from its material advantages, fulfilled a pressing need by affording a means of counteracting the debilitating effects of Western ideas on traditional Japanese ideals and arousing the martial spirit of the nation. Manchuria was to serve as the army's proving grounds for experimenting on and perfecting a militarized, regimented, totalitarian social and economic order, which was the goal of the army's planned society. The enthusiasm for Asiatic expansion, which had cooled off during the twenties, was suddenly reawakened and intensified by the incident.

After the death of Marshal Chang Tso-lin, his son Chang Hsueh-liang succeeded as the ruler of Manchuria, but he swung away from Japan and in December, 1928, declared his allegiance to the Nationalist government at Nanking.

551

This act, which was contrary to the desires of the Japanese military, stimulated the growth of nationalism and anti-Japanese feeling throughout Manchuria. Systematic propaganda by the Kuomintang for the recovery of lost sovereign rights, the abolition of unequal treaties with all their stigma and disadvantages, and the expulsion of imperialism awakened the Chinese in Manchuria to the reality of extensive foreign rights and interests.

In 1929 the Nationalist government of China came into dispute with Russia over the Chinese Eastern Railway in northern Manchuria. The agitation in South Manchuria against the Japanese continued with increasing intensity. Systematic pressure brought to bear upon the Japanese and Korean residents put them in a very uncomfortable, if not insecure, position. Liquidation of Japanese rights, including the recovery of the South Manchuria Railway by China, was freely discussed, giving rise to serious and dangerous tension between the two countries.

The Sino-Japanese tension that developed was characterized by political and economic rivalry between Chinese and Japanese interests in Manchuria. Chinese interests, especially the additional railway lines constructed by Chinese capital to tap the rich agricultural sections, came into sharp competition with the interests of the South Manchuria Railway. Disputes arose and incident after incident occurred. By the summer of 1931 their cumulative effects had heightened the feeling of tension to a dangerous point. In this growing economic antipathy neither side seemed to show any inclination to yield or to compromise. This state of affairs led inevitably to the explosion of September 18.

Within forty-eight hours of the incident, the whole of southern Manchuria, not only along the South Manchuria Railway, but also along some of the Chinese built railroads, and strategic cities like Antung, Changchun, and New-chwang, separated by hundreds of miles, had been successfully occupied. The smooth execution of the *coup* amazed even the veteran Kwantung Army Commander in Chief General Honjō. There seemed to have been perfect coordination and smooth teamwork in every detail of staff work between the Kwantung Army Chief of Staff Itagaki on the one hand, and China Section Chief Colonel Shigefuji and Russia Section Chief Lt. Col. Hashimoto of the General Staff Office in Tōkyō on the other. American Secretary of State Henry L. Stimson had shrewdly observed long before the truth was known even to the Japanese themselves, that "the evidence pointed to a deliberate action planned and authorized by the highest Japanese authorities in Manchuria and possibly with the direction from the high military command in Tōkyō. The orderliness, precision, coordination of time and comprehensiveness with which the vital strategic points in Manchuria were seized indicated a perfection of staff work which could hardly have taken place without such authority." [1]

[1] Henry L. Stimson, *The Far Eastern Crisis*, p. 33.

Brushing off the feeble remonstrances of the civilian authorities, the army carried out a complete occupation of Manchuria, bringing under Japan's effective control an area more than three times as large as that of Japan proper and pushing out her military frontier to the Soviet boundary on the Amur River, which had been the goal of Japanese expansionists since the turn of the century.

In the United States the conclusion had been reached by the Department of State by September 21, practically within forty-eight hours of the event, that the Japanese invasion of Manchuria was a *coup* engineered by the military, very likely without the previous knowledge of the civil authorities, who had not acquiesced, but were unable to oppose it effectively. The policy of the Department of State was therefore to give Baron Shidehara and the Foreign Office an opportunity to get control of the situation.[2] At the same time Secretary Stimson was keenly aware that should Shidehara be forced to yield to army pressure "the damage to the new structure of international society provided by the postwar treaties would be incalculable."[3] Consequently, he decided to let Japan know that the United States was watching her actions and at the same time do it in such a manner as to help Shidehara and "not play into the hands of any nationalist agitators."[4] American policy in the beginning was based on the hope that the more liberal elements might gain ascendancy. But it was a vain hope, for the military extended its activities to Shanghai in January, 1932, and the civil authorities were powerless.

CHINA APPEALS TO THE LEAGUE

China formally appealed to the League on September 21 through Dr. Sao-ke Alfred Sze, who had only a few days earlier taken his seat in the Council as China's representative.[5] With the invocation of Article 11 of the Covenant "for the purpose of preventing the further development of a situation endangering the peace of nations and to establish the *status quo ante*," the League of Nations assumed full jurisdiction of the controversy. On the following day dispatches reported that the League was contemplating sending to Manchuria an investigation commission, appointed by itself. Stimson deprecated the idea of sending an investigation commission over and against Japan's objection, preferring the method of direct negotiations between the parties involved. The American Secretary of State was fearful that imposing an investigation upon Japan would invite popular resentment and throw at once additional difficulties in the path of Shidehara's efforts at solution.[6]

[2] *Ibid.*, pp. 33–34.

[3] *Ibid.*, p. 37.

[4] *Ibid.*

[5] China was unanimously elected a member of the Council on September 14 with the special endorsement of Japan.

[6] Stimson, *op. cit.*, p. 43.

The President of the League of Nations sent on September 22 identical telegrams to China and Japan, appealing to them to refrain from any further act of hostility that would be prejudicial to a peaceful settlement and urging them to withdraw their troops at once without endangering the safety of their nationals and property. In support of the League action, the American government sent two days later similar identical notes to China and Japan.

In a long public statement the Japanese government on September 24 asserted that Japan had already taken steps toward the withdrawal of troops and for a solution of the controversy and that she harbored no territorial designs in Manchuria, her desire being merely to protect her nationals engaged in peaceful pursuits for the development of Manchuria. It also pledged its readiness to cooperate with the Chinese government to settle the incident and to work out constructive plans to remove once and for all the causes of future friction.

The Chinese government disclaimed all responsibility for the outbreak, asserting that it had been caused entirely by Japanese aggression, which was still continuing, and also gave assurance of its willingness to abstain from any aggravation of the situation. On September 28, Dr. Sze explained at the Council meeting his government's readiness for the dispatch of a neutral commission to Manchuria to investigate the facts. Japan's representative Yoshizawa was unable to endorse the proposal.

On September 30 the League Council adopted a resolution noting Japan's disclaimer of territorial designs in Manchuria and her promise to continue the withdrawal of her troops as rapidly as possible into their lawful area of the railway zone, China's assumption of responsibility for the safety of the lives and property of Japanese nationals outside the railway zone, and the assurance of both China and Japan "to prevent any extension of the scope of the incident or any aggravation of the situation." It also requested the disputants to do everything possible to hasten the resumption of normal relations and to furnish full information at frequent intervals as to the steps taken to carry out their commitments.

It appeared to the United States Department of State for a time as though the outbreak might be settled and the *status quo ante* restored eventually. However, Secretary Stimson noticed that Baron Shidehara had been compelled to adopt in his communications a position supporting his government, which strained the credulity of Americans,[7] especially since his excuses for Japan's action did not tally with the facts that had already been disclosed.

Early in October, General Honjō, commander in chief of the Japanese forces in Manchuria, announced that the government of Marshal Chang Hsueh-liang would no longer receive Japanese recognition. On October 8 a squadron of Japanese planes dropped bombs on Chinchow without warning, killing and

[7] *Ibid.*, p. 50.

wounding a number of inhabitants. American protests to Tōkyō brought expressions of regret that appeared quite inadequate.[8] It was obvious that the army was proceeding with its plans without regard to the wishes of the civil authorities.

In the latter part of October an expedition was sent to Tsitsihar, capital of the northernmost province of Heilungkiang, and the forces of General Ma Chan-shan were defeated and destroyed. On January 3, 1932, Chinchow was captured by the Japanese army. With the destruction of the last stronghold of the young Marshal and his organized forces, all of Manchuria came under Japanese control.

The army was gathering behind itself the support of a powerful nationalistic feeling among the people, which it encouraged in every possible way. Moreover, as the military moves succeeded, the civil authorities not only found it impossible to check the army's course but, in helpless resignation, they were not altogether averse to profiting by the army's gains. This was particularly true of certain segments of the bureaucracy that began to play an increasingly active and important, if not crucial, role for the army in Manchuria and later in domestic political affairs.

Remembering the success achieved during the Washington Conference in the settlement of the Shantung question through negotiation between the two parties concerned, the United States Department of State telegraphed the suggestion to the League Secretariat. However, when the Council suggested it to the disputants, Japan refused to adopt it.

In mid-October M. Briand, the President of the Council, invited the United States to send a representative to sit at the Council in the deliberations pertaining to the pacific settlement of a Sino-Japanese dispute in accordance with the Pact of Paris. On October 16 Prentiss Gilbert, the American Consul at Geneva, who had acted as the unofficial observer of the United States at the meetings of the League, was appointed to represent the United States.[9] In a memorandum to the Council, the Japanese government protested.[10] Its objection was based on the contention that the United States as a nonmember did not have the right to sit and participate in the deliberations of the Council. It was quite obvious that Japan did not relish the idea of closer cooperation between the United States and the League in the matter of the Manchurian controversy. However, the objection was overruled by other members. As far as the United States was concerned, the acceptance of the Council's invitation to participate in its discussions was to demonstrate publicly the support and cooperation she was giving to the League and to show that it would have her full moral support

[8] Senate Document 55, 72nd Cong., 1st Sess., *Conditions in Manchuria*, pp. 14–16.

[9] W. W. Willoughby, *The Sino-Japanese Controversy and the League of Nations*, p. 103.

[10] For the text of the Japanese memorandum and the reply to it by the President of the Council see the *Official Journal*, December 31, 1931, pp. 2488–2489.

in achieving the general objective of arriving at a peaceful solution in the Sino-Japanese controversy.[11]

On October 24 the Chinese government had announced its willingness to conclude with Japan a treaty of obligation for the purpose of settling the disputes in a peaceful and legal manner, but Japan remained adamant. By the end of October she made clear her unwillingness to withdraw her troops to the limits of the zone authorized by treaty until and unless negotiations on the dispute had taken place. She emphasized that the negotiations should be conducted strictly between the two disputants, without the presence of neutral observers.

Meanwhile American public opinion became inflamed in the face of the defiant attitude of the Japanese army towards the representations made by the League and the United States. On November 19 Secretary Stimson was impelled to transmit his full and frank views of the situation to Foreign Minister Shidehara through Ambassador Debuchi. He stated that he could not but regard Japan's penetration of North China as "a violation by the Japanese army of the provisions of the Kellogg-Briand Pact and of the Nine Power Treaty." [12] For two months the State Department had been keeping the papers and communications that had passed between the governments of Japan and the United States from the public in the hope of a settlement, so that it might not embarrass the Japanese government or lessen the chances of settlement. However, in the face of critical public opinion and in the interest of the American government Secretary Stimson felt compelled to reserve the right to make public the whole matter. This fact was communicated to the Japanese Foreign Office. But the Minseitō Government of Premier Wakatsuki was already in a precarious, if not untenable position, for it collapsed shortly thereafter, early in December.

Secretary Stimson chose Ambassador Charles G. Dawes at London to represent the United States in the Council meeting, which had reconvened on November 16 in a gloomy atmosphere. However, on November 21, the Japanese representative Yoshizawa made known at the meeting of the Council the willingness of his government to have a commission of inquiry sent to the Far East by the League to look into all matters in the controversy, but he pointed out at the same time that assurances be given that this commission "would not be empowered to intervene in the negotiations that may be initiated between the two parties or to supervise the movements of the military forces of either."

On December 10, on the very eve of the resignation of the Wakatsuki Cabinet and three days before the government of Premier Inukai took over, the resolution was successfully carried in the Council with the assent of the Japanese representative.[13] The United States assented to the inclusion of an American,

[11] Stimson, *op. cit.*, p. 67.
[12] *Ibid.*, pp. 73–74.
[13] Willoughby, *op. cit.*, pp. 177–178.

Major General Frank R. McCoy, in the Commission of Inquiry, which was promptly appointed. The Commission was headed by the Earl of Lytton and included General Henri Claudel, Count Luigi Aldrovandi-Marescotti, and Dr. Heinrich Schnee, representing France, Italy, and Germany, respectively. The members of the Lytton Commission, as it came to be known, were not representatives of their governments but constituted impartial, neutral inquirers or investigators. The Commission arrived in Yokohama on February 29, 1932, and the world hoped for a satisfactory formula for the settlement of the Sino-Japanese controversy. Unfortunately, however, subsequent developments proved that, by the time the Commission was set up in mid-January of 1932, the initiative in government and the direction of the course of events in Japan had passed to a large measure, though not yet completely, from the civil authorities to the military and the reactionary direct-actionist elements of the army.

FIGHTING SPREADS TO SHANGHAI

The indignation of the Chinese against the Japanese, which had been growing over a period of years as a result of tension between the two countries since the First World War, was accentuated by the Manchurian Incident and found expression in the extensive boycott of Japanese trade. Shanghai had become the headquarters of this boycott movement, led by the Anti-Japanese Boycott Association. As anti-Japanese feeling heightened, some of the Chinese in their effort to make the boycott effective had been guilty of violence in their attacks on Japanese trade and traders. Japanese residents, after five had been assaulted on January 18, 1932, held mass meetings in protest, and on the twentieth the Consul-General presented demands that included a formal apology, punishment of those responsible, payment of damages and hospital bills, control of the anti-Japanese movement, and the immediate disbanding of all anti-Japanese organizations engaged in promoting hostile feelings and anti-Japanese agitation.[14] The mayor of greater Shanghai, on the twenty-eighth, acceded to the demands, which were backed by Admiral Shiozawa, commander in chief of the Japanese naval forces. On the same day, however, Japanese marines and sailors were landed to enforce law and order in Chapei, where a large number of Japanese residents lived.

Shortly after midnight, in the early morning hours of January 29, the Japanese landing party of some 2,000 came in contact with the Chinese police and later with the troops of General Tsai Ting-kai's 19th Route Army, then quartered in a section of Chapei. The Admiral ordered planes from a carrier, which bombed the helpless civilian native quarter of Chapei without warning. Meeting unexpectedly stiff and effective resistance from the Chinese troops, the

---

[14] By January 24, Stimson had become convinced that Japan's real purpose was to break up the boycott, and that her announced object of protecting her nationals was no more than a cloak. Stimson, *op. cit.*, p. 133.

Japanese brought up all the reenforcements available, but without results. An Associated Press dispatch brought news to the United States on January 31 [15] that Premier Inukai had suggested to the Ambassadors of several powers in Tōkyō to offer their good offices to stop the fighting at Shanghai. On the initiative of Secretary Stimson the governments of the United States, Great Britain, France, and Italy offered their good offices to Tōkyō and Nanking on February 2. The Chinese government accepted the offer, but Japan rejected it.

Japanese war vessels bombarded Nanking for about an hour on February 1. This action was attributed by the Department of State to the misjudgment of an excited and jumpy Japanese naval commander.[16] The League Council, meeting on February 2, recognized the existence of *de facto* war at Shanghai and undertook to forestall the possible collapse of the League Covenant, the Pact of Paris, and the Nine Power Treaty. At the same time the governments of the United States, Great Britain, France, and Italy requested the Japanese Foreign Minister to comply with the following conditions: the suspension of all hostile actions, cessation of any further actions, withdrawal of troops from Shanghai, and the organization of a neutral zone to protect the concessions, the zone to be guarded by troops of neutral powers.

On February 7 the Japanese Twenty-fourth Mixed Brigade landed, and by February 18 the Japanese had in Shanghai 16,000 troops, including the Ninth Division. Ten days later the fresh Eleventh Division arrived from Japan. On March 1 and 2 the entire Chinese army effected an orderly withdrawal to a new line, so that on March 3 the Japanese commander issued orders to cease fire.

The League of Nations, on March 11, adopted a resolution that stated in part that "it is incumbent upon the members of the League of Nations not to recognize any situation, treaty, or agreement which may be brought about by means contrary to the Covenant of the League of Nations or to the Pact of Paris." In the same resolution was provided the appointment of a Committee of Nineteen composed of the President of the Council, the members exclusive of Chinese and Japanese representatives, and six other members to be elected by secret ballot. This committee was given jurisdiction of the controversy in behalf of the Assembly and charged with the duties of following the process of the withdrawal of Japanese forces from Shanghai, the carrying out of the Council's resolutions of September 30 and December 10, 1931, and the conduct of further efforts at conciliation between the disputants.

In late April negotiations based on a successful formula, devised through the efforts of the local mediators representing the four powers, Great Britain, United States, France, and Italy, supported by the League's Committee of Nineteen, were

---

[15] On the same day the entire U.S. Asiatic Fleet was ordered to Shanghai, and on February 13 the U.S. Pacific Fleet, in the course of its regular annual maneuvers, arrived in Hawaii after completing its exercises in the waters between San Francisco and Honolulu.

[16] Stimson, *op. cit.*, p. 145.

begun on May 3. Two days later a truce was signed and the last of the Japanese troops were withdrawn by the middle of the month, except for the quota of 2,500 marines permitted for garrison duty.[17] The Shanghai fighting greatly increased the suspicion of the powers, as they gained the impression that Japan was openly and brazenly challenging world opinion and flouting the treaties and agreements to which she was a party.

THE STIMSON DOCTRINE

Although President Hoover regarded Japan's action as immoral, constituting an "offense against the comity of nations" and an "affront to the United States," [18] he was unalterably opposed to economic sanctions, which had been proposed and supported by the smaller nation members of the League, for he was convinced that they would lead inevitably to war. He believed that "Our whole policy in connection with controversies is to exhaust the processes of peaceful negotiations," and that the United States had "a moral obligation to use every influence short of war to have the treaties upheld or terminated by mutual agreement." [19] He would cooperate with the world so long as cooperation remained in the field of moral pressures but would not go along on war or any of the sanctions, either economic or military, for he was convinced they would lead to war. Moral sanction was therefore decided upon by President Hoover and his Secretary of State Stimson.

After his failure to work out a possible démarche, in which the British Government was reluctant to join, Secretary Stimson hit on the idea of stating his views on the Nine Power Treaty without having them nullified by an expression of the doubts and fears of others.[20] On the day after Washington's birthday, the Secretary of State addressed an open letter to Senator Borah, Chairman of the Senate Foreign Relations Committee, which became the basis of the Stimson doctrine of nonrecognition.[21] Because of its informal nature, the note gave considerable flexibility of expression as well as of purpose to the author, who had intended it for the perusal of at least five unnamed parties. For China, it was to be a message of encouragement; to the American public it was an explanation of policy; to the League of Nations Assembly, a suggestion of possible future action; to the British Conservative Party, a gentle reminder of the fact that the British Government was a co-author of the Open Door and the Nine Power

[17] For the text of the armistice, see Willoughby, *op. cit.*, p. 299.

[18] Ray Lyman Wilbur, *The Hoover Policies*, p. 600.

[19] *Ibid.*, p. 601. "The United States has never set out to preserve peace among other nations by force, and so far as this pact is concerned we shall confine ourselves to friendly counsel."

[20] Stimson, *op. cit.*, p. 165.

[21] The text of the letter is found in Stimson, *op. cit.*, pp. 166–175, and *Congressional Record* (daily edition), February 24, 1932, p. 4718.

Treaty; and to Japan, a reminder that, should she choose to break down one of the Washington treaties, other nations might feel themselves released from some of those treaties that were important to her. In reiterating the formal notification to Japan and China, dated January 7, 1932, the Stimson letter emphasized that the United States "would not recognize any situation, or treaty, or agreement entered into by those Governments in violation of the covenants of those treaties which affected the rights of our Government or its citizens in China."

JAPANESE SPONSORED PUPPET STATE: MANCHUKUO

On September 20, 1931, Colonel Doihara was made mayor of Mukden, and for a full month the army ran the city before turning it over to Chao Hsin-po on October 20.[22] Starting in late October nominal municipal administrations were set up in different cities, and provincial governments were organized in the provinces under pressure of the Japanese army. These local governments were run by Japanese officials, the Chinese being nominal officials who served as the front. On February 18, 1932, the central government with its component local governments declared its independence. Henry Pu-yi, the deposed Manchu Emperor, was invited back from Tientsin, where he had been living in exile in the Japanese concession, to become the chief executive of the republic. On March 9 he was officially installed as Regent of the newly created state. Although the army would have preferred a monarchy, it decided on the republican form of government to make more plausible the claim that it had been created in response to the spontaneous wish of the 30 million people of Manchuria.

The Foreign Minister of the new state of Manchukuo addressed, on March 12, communications to seventeen nations that had consular officials stationed in Manchukuo and also to some thirty-five other countries, announcing the establishment of the new state and expressing the desire to establish formal diplomatic relations. Subsequently, the customs revenues from Manchuria and salt revenues were claimed and forcibly seized by the new government, and Chinese control over them ceased. Two months later General Mutō Nobuyoshi was appointed concurrently Ambassador to Manchukuo in his capacity as Commander in Chief of the Kwantung Army and Governor General of the Kwantung Territory, thus placing in the hands of a single military official the combined administrative military and diplomatic powers.

British Ambassador Sir Francis Lindley secured assurances from Vice Foreign Minister Arita that the government was not likely to recognize Manchukuo before the Lytton Commission left the Far East. But the army had already

[22] Ashida, *Sekai Saikin Gaikōshi,* Vol. III, p. 1226.

made up its mind independently of the civil authorities to give early recognition. Nothing would stand in its way. Actually, opinion was divided in Japan among the leaders on the question of recognition. Those who opposed immediate recognition maintained that to give recognition before the other signatories of the Nine Power Treaty clearly constituted a violation of Article 1 and a breach of international trust. The Elder Statesman, palace advisers, government leaders, and Foreign Office officials did not relish the idea of being forced to withdraw from the League of Nations over the Manchurian question. They were opposed to withdrawal from the League. But when all the preliminary arrangements were completed, the Japanese government recognized Manchukuo on September 15, 1932.[23]

The Lytton Commission. The Lytton Commission arrived in Yokohama on February 29, 1932, and spent eight days there, during which time they met Premier Inukai, Foreign Minister Yoshizawa, War Minister Araki, Navy Minister Ōsumi, and influential private individuals. Optimism prevailed in Japanese circles regarding the attitude of the Commission toward Japan, which seemed to be quite friendly. However, Manchukuo Foreign Minister Hsieh Chieh-shih informed the Commission that the coming of Dr. Wellington Koo would complicate matters and would be inimical to the best intersts of all concerned. This notification was surprising in view of the Japanese Foreign Office telegram to the Commission, stating that it had no objection. It was evident that this move had been inspired by the Kwantung Army, then in control of Manchukuoan affairs. Although the Foreign Office assured that protection would be given Dr. Koo, the army disavowed any responsibility for his safety outside of the guarded zone.

On April 22 the Commission arrived in Hsinking, the capital of Manchukuo and the headquarters of the Kwantung Army. Orders had been issued to arrest Dr. Koo if and when he stepped out of the railway zone. As a result he remained within the zone throughout his stay and, except for occasional walks, he remained in his room in the Yamato Hotel, the headquarters of the Lytton Commission. In the course of the inquiry, the Commission interviewed General Honjō, Ambassador to Manchukuo, four times.

By the time of the arrival of the Lytton Commission the Foreign Office had degenerated into a mere mouthpiece of the army and was referred to sarcastically as the Foreign Affairs Bureau of the War Ministry. General Koiso, Military Affairs Bureau Director, and General Tatekawa, Director of the First Department of the General Staff Office, who had been regarded as the brains behind the Manchurian Incident, worked on the people and the government, especially the Foreign Office, to bring about the settlement of the Manchurian problems in

---

[23] The Lytton Report, which was signed in Peking on September 4, was not made public until after it was presented to the Council on October 1. Thus, Manchukuo was a *fait accompli* by the time the Lytton Report was released to the world.

the army way.[24] The Foreign Ministry official who assumed the role of intermediary in trying to effect a *rapprochement* between the War and Foreign
Offices was Tani Masayuki, Director of the Asia Bureau. On Tani's suggestion
daily luncheon meetings were held. These informal discussions were attended
by Vice War Minister Koiso, General Nagata of the War Ministry, General
Tatekawa of the General Staff Office, Vice Foreign Minister Nagai Shinzō,
and the Director of the Information Bureau. Particularly active in the army-
diplomat collaboration were Shiratori, Tani, and Koiso. The Foreign Office was
no longer in a position to stand up effectively against the united front of the
Kwantung Army and the War Ministry.

The Lytton Report. The unanimous report of the Lytton Commission, which
was made public on October 2, 1932, disposed of Japan's claims adversely. It
denied the claim that China was not an organized state, that Manchuria was
not Chinese and that therefore China was not entitled to titular sovereignty
over it, that Japan's occupation of Mukden and South Manchuria had been an
act of defense, and that Manchukuo's origin was autonomous. The report
pointed out that the new state was created by the presence of Japanese troops
and officials without whom it could not have been formed, and therefore the
regime could not be regarded as having come into existence as a result of a
genuine and spontaneous independent movement. Its verdict was that "without
declaration of war, a large area of what was indisputably Chinese territory has
been forcibly seized and occupied by the armed forces of Japan and has, in consequence of this operation, been separated from and declared independent of the
rest of China." [25]

It left no doubt as to Japan's violation of her obligations (1) under Article 10
of the League Covenant to respect and preserve as against external aggression
the territorial integrity and existing political independence of her fellow member of the League; (2) under Article 2 of the Pact of Paris not to seek the settlement or solution of disputes except by pacific means, and (3) under Article 1
of the Nine Power Treaty (a) to respect the sovereignty, the independence, and
the territorial and administrative integrity of China, and (b) to provide the
fullest and most unembarrassed opportunity to China to develop and maintain
for herself an effective and stable government.

The solution recommended by the Lytton Report was designed (1) to conform with the interests of both China and Japan and also those of Russia;
(2) to conform with existing multilateral treaties; (3) to recognize China's
sovereignty and Japan's legitimate interests in Manchuria; (4) to maintain general order and security against external aggression; and (5) to provide for the
settlement of future disputes. It was to be a solution that would make for

[24] Mori Shōzō, *Sempū Nijūnen*, pp. 120–121.
[25] Chapter IX, paragraph 5 of the Lytton Report.

permanence by encouraging an economic *rapprochement* between China and Japan in place of the economic warfare that had been going on between them for some time. It also contained a provision for extensive international assistance in the reconstruction of China.

On September 24, a week before the report was to be made public and after the recognition of Manchukuo had been completed, Japan asked for and obtained a six-week postponement of the date set for its consideration by the League in order that she might have an opportunity to study it. In the interim period the American electorate voted for a change in administration. President Roosevelt was elected on November 8. This presaged not only a change from a Republican to a Democratic administration for the United States, but also a change from Stimson to Hull in the direction of the foreign relations.

Debate between Dr. W. W. Yen and Matsuoka Yōsuke in the Assembly started immediately upon its opening in December and continued until the 9th. At the December meeting of the Assembly Matsuoka maintained an unbending attitude on all the important issues of the controversy, insisting stoutly that no settlement was possible that did not include the recognition by the powers of the independence of Manchukuo.

While the League was deliberating on the Lytton Report, the Japanese army sliced off Jehol from the main body of China early in January, 1933, incorporating it into Manchukuo with its old Chinese imperial palaces, its coal, and its strategic mountain passes.

On February 24 the Report of the Committee of Nineteen was adopted by a unanimous vote in the Assembly, only Japan dissenting. It adopted fully and without modification the Lytton Report and recommended a solution following the lines suggested by the Report, namely, recognition of China's sovereignty over Manchuria, denial of Japan's claims that her actions were defensive, absolving China of any responsibility for the development of events since September 18, 1931,[26] denial of the assertion that Manchukuo was the result of a spontaneous and genuine independence movement by the people, inasmuch as it was created by the Japanese and not supported by the Chinese population of Manchuria, and the verdict that the recognition of Manchukuo would be incompatible with the spirit of the resolution of the League of Nations of March 11, 1932. It also provided that the member nations of the League in adopting the Report would continue not to recognize Manchukuo either *de jure* or *de facto*.

[26] The Report also declared that the Chinese boycott subsequent to the Manchurian Incident was a legitimate means of reprisal in the light of international law. This had the effect of virtually closing China to Japanese trade, which had to find outlets elsewhere.

JAPAN'S WITHDRAWAL FROM THE
LEAGUE OF NATIONS

The Lytton Report was an unequivocal indictment of the military action in Manchuria and as such it was impossible for the army to ignore it, although War Minister Araki scoffed at it as an Oriental travelogue. The army's attitude was that the recognition of Manchukuo would close the issue as a *fait accompli*. Japanese public opinion had been stirred up by the army, which was able to keep the leading newspapers in line doing its bidding.

Matsuoka Yosuke, American-educated veteran of the diplomatic service, who was chosen as Japan's official representative to sit on the League Council, became the nation's man of the hour. His grandiloquence and air of defiance and fearlessness, which could have been at least partly a camouflage, seemed to have a tremendous appeal to the hero-worshipping proclivities of the Japanese. He was recommended for the post by both Foreign Minister Uchida and Prince Saionji, under whom he had served as an information officer at Versailles. At the Tōkyō Station he was given a rousing sendoff by the admiring public as well as by high-ranking officials, both military and civil, and other notables, including Foreign Minister Uchida, War Minister Araki, Navy Minister Okada, Agriculture and Forestry Minister Gotō, General Minami, and General Honjō, Commander in Chief of the Kwantung Army.

The government's instructions to Matsuoka were to express fully Japan's views but to avoid resorting to such drastic action as withdrawal, since it would lead to diplomatic isolation and worsening of American-Japanese relations. Although Foreign Minister Uchida, who was under army influence, felt that withdrawal might be inevitable, Vice Foreign Minister Arita was firmly opposed to it. Saionji, Makino, and Shidehara, all of whom had had a direct hand in the launching of the League, were naturally opposed to giving up membership in the League of Nations.

The meeting of the League Council opened in Geneva on November 21. Meanwhile, the predominant view in the army turned increasingly toward withdrawal. A petition submitted to the government urging withdrawal and bearing the signatures of high-ranking Kwantung Army officers was a convincing proof of the determination of the army. Influenced by it, the attitude of the government began to stiffen. On February 1, 1933, Foreign Minister Uchida called on the Elder Statesman and gave a report on the unfavorable developments in the League. By the middle of the month Foreign Minister Uchida, War Minister Araki, and Navy Minister Ōsumi had made up their minds on withdrawal.[27] When Premier Saitō called on the 19th, Prince Saionji expressed the inevitability

[27] Ashida Hitoshi, *Saikin Sekai Gaikō Shi,* Vol. III, p. 1318.

of withdrawal. When the decision became known, the Japanese stock market dropped and this cast a gloom over financial circles.[28]

However, the government, the Elder Statesman, and the palace advisers were much more fearful of the dire domestic consequences of nonwithdrawal than the international consequences of withdrawal. By coincidence, on February 23, 1933, the first anniversary of Secretary Stimson's famous letter to Senator Borah, the Japanese delegation walked out of the meeting of the League of Nations. With this dramatic exit, which followed the impassioned address of the chief delegate Matsuoka, Japan plunged herself into diplomatic isolation and the control of foreign affairs passed from the Foreign Office to the military. On March 27 the Japanese government gave official notice of its intention to withdraw from the League of Nations.

WORLD ECONOMIC CONFERENCE

Many nations hoped that the World Economic Conference, which was called in London on June 12, 1933, pursuant to the resolution passed at the Lausanne Conference of July of the preceding year, would bring about agreement on the methods of attacking the causes of world depression as well as the economic and financial problems that were prolonging it. The topics of discussion included monetary and fiscal policy, reflation, the free flow of capital, the breaking down of trade barriers, reduction of tariffs, and international control of export of raw materials. In its broadest terms, the aims of the Conference were to soften economic nationalism by substituting international economic cooperation and to assist in the reestablishment of friendly relations and greater confidence among all nations.

Sixty-six nations sent 168 delegates. Japan was represented by Viscount Ishii, Matsudaira Tsuneo, and Fukai Eigo. In practically no area was there complete agreement. There were conflicting views regarding the question of currency stabilization. The reduction of tariffs and abolition of trade barriers brought out even greater divergencies among the nations represented. Gold standard countries like France, Belgium, Holland, and Switzerland demanded currency stabilization as a condition and prerequisite to tariff reduction.

Japan's policy regarding the Economic Conference, formulated by a joint conference of Foreign, Finance, War, Navy, Commerce and Industry, and Agriculture and Forestry Ministries gave prime emphasis to the establishment of equitable nondiscriminatory trade in view of the fact that Japan's industrial and economic structure was not only based upon, but also completely dependent upon the import of raw materials, the export of manufactured and processed goods and the crucial importance of shipping, because of her geographical location and insular-

[28] *Ibid.*, p. 1319.

ity. She naturally favored the removal of trade and tariff barriers, the stabilization of currency, the restoration of an uninterrupted flow of capital, and the relaxation of restrictions on coastwise shipping and trade. The joint ministers' conference had decided on pursuing a stronger Far Eastern policy, whereby Japan would oppose any peace or security plan that either disregarded the special conditions in the Far East or endeavored chiefly to meet and serve Anglo-American needs and interests.

The Conference broke down on July 20 with only one achievement in the form of a tariff holiday agreement. Even this lost its effect by the end of 1933, when Great Britain, France, Belgium and Holland withdrew from it. Its unqualified failure brought to an end the second and final attempt to solve the problem of economic cooperation by methods of diplomacy. It was not necessary to go far to find the causes of failure. The Ottawa Agreements of the preceding year had committed Great Britain to a system of Empire preference, involving the abandonment of free trade and strengthening of economic nationalism. This reduced materially the chances of successful cooperation in international trade. The inauguration of President Roosevelt and the New Deal policy brought about definite changes in the domestic economic policy of the United States. In his eagerness to bring the country out of the depression, President Roosevelt turned away from the original objective of the Conference, namely, price and currency stabilization. Moreover, the President was confronted by a Congress intent on raising, not lowering, tariffs, and even imposing import quotas.

In October, 1933, the month following Foreign Minister Hirota's assumption of office, War Minister Araki made a proposal for the holding in Tōkyō, before 1935, of a Far Eastern Conference to solve all the outstanding issues that were at the root of the friction and tension existing in that part of the world and to find a *modus vivendi,* which would ensure the peace of the Far East. Those powers with interests in the Far East, the United States, Great Britain, France, the Netherlands, the Soviet Union, China, India, and also Manchukuo were to be invited to participate. The agenda called for preliminary negotiations for the recognition of Manchukuo and the revision of the Washington and London naval agreements, the implementation of the Pact of Paris and the Nine Power Treaty, the signing of a Soviet-Japanese Nonaggression Pact, and the settlement of outstanding Chinese issues and the solution of economic problems toward India. The proposal however was rejected by the Foreign Office, which did not see eye-to-eye with the army on any problem or policy concerning China and the Asiatic continent.

In February, 1934, in a reassuring message to Secretary Hull, Foreign Minister Hirota stated that there existed no question between the United States and Japan that was fundamentally incapable of amicable solution and emphasized that Japan had no intention of making trouble with any other power. Secretary Hull replied that the policy of the United States in the carrying out of her international policies was to rely on peaceful processes and that, if there should arise any controversy between the United States and Japan, his government would examine Japan's position in a spirit of amity with a view to arriving at a peaceful and just settlement. In spite of the exchange of friendly assurances and optimistic views, only two months later the Foreign Office took an attitude inconsistent with Hirota's assurances.

The Amau statement of April 17, 1934, was a reflection of Japan's restiveness at the cumulative effects of foreign activities in China. The Foreign Office spokesman stated that Japan could not remain indifferent to any action that would be prejudicial to the maintenance of law and order in East Asia, for which she had a most vital concern. She therefore opposed any joint operations by foreign powers, even in the name of technical or financial assistance, and frowned upon a foreign power supplying warplanes, building aerodromes, detailing military instructors, or military advisers, or contracting a loan to provide funds for political uses. Amau claimed for Japan the "sole responsibility for the preservation of peace in the Far East." This had come on the heels of the Foreign Minister's assurance to the American Ambassador that Japan had no intention of seeking special privileges in China, or of encroaching upon China's territorial and administrative integrity, or of creating difficulties for the China trade of other powers.[29]

EASING OF SOVIET-JAPANESE TENSION

From the time of Japanese recognition of the Soviet regime relations between the two powers remained satisfactory until the Manchurian Incident of 1931. In December of that year the Soviets proposed a nonaggression pact to the new government of Premier Inukai, which had just been formed. Vice Foreign Commissar Karakhan in Moscow approached Ambassador Yoshizawa, who was on his way home from France to assume the post of Foreign Minister in his father-in-law's cabinet. Yoshizawa replied that he would take the proposal under advisement, but when he returned home he found that the nation was not in a mood to entertain a nonaggression pact with Russia. The Foreign Office was more interested in solving outstanding issues, rather than in negotiating a nonaggression agreement.

Foreign Minister Uchida was cool to the idea and in December issued a statement to the effect that it was not the time for the conclusion of a Soviet-Japanese nonaggression pact. But because of the unexpected reaction, Russia's disappointment and Britain's delight and her stiffening attitude, the Foreign Minister hastened to amend his statement to the effect that the matter was under discussion. Public opinion regarding a nonaggression pact was divided among the civilians as well as the military.

[29] Joseph C. Grew, *Ten Years in Japan*, pp. 128–133.

In September, 1932, as Japan was in the midst of her preparations for the recognition of Manchukuo, Karakhan brought up once more the question of the pact. On this occasion the sale of the Chinese Eastern Railway was proposed for the first time, but the Japanese government evinced no interest. On May 2, 1933, Foreign Commissar Litvinov proposed the sale of the Chinese Eastern to Ambassador Ōta in Moscow as a means of settling the conflicts that were straining the relations between the Soviets and Japan and Manchukuo. Eleven days later Soviet Ambassador Yurenev in Tōkyō approached Foreign Minister Uchida. The result was the holding of the first conference between Soviet and Japanese representatives in Tōkyō on June 26.

Negotiations were continued spasmodically but soon bogged down. In January, 1934, they were resumed, but it was not until September that Moscow accepted Foreign Minister Hirota's offer of 140 million yen, exclusive of some 30 million yen in pensions to former employees. At the end of January, 1935, Hirota expressed his hope that the Chinese Eastern deal would be closed soon, but asserted in almost the same breath that, because of the sovietization of Sinkiang and the activities of the Chinese Red Army, Japan would have to continue to be on the alert.[30] At long last on March 23, 1935, the sale of the Chinese Eastern Railway was consummated. The contract called for the payment in cash of one-sixth of the purchase price at the signing and one-sixth in cash and two-thirds in goods, both to be paid over a period of three years by Japan and Manchukuo. Thus, one of the major sources of Soviet-Japanese friction was removed, relieving the tension at least for the time being.

Japanese Aggression in China. To the Japanese military, who had seen in the growth of Manchukuo, the fruits of aggression on the Asiatic continent, the vast expanse of North China appeared very inviting and tempting indeed. The mission of the Kwantung Army had been to devote itself to the defense of the northern frontiers against possible Soviet aggression. But the sight of weak and helpless North China dangling before their eyes virtually within reach was irresistible. However plausible the argument that an independent Inner Mongolia would create a corridor of defense against communism, to be used effectively in the event of war against the Soviet Union might have sounded, it was too much to expect China, which was forging ahead toward nationalism if not national unity, to submit without a struggle to the aggressive action of the Japanese army, which relied upon the technique of local settlement, a piecemeal acquisition of effective administrative control over Chinese territory.

In August, 1935, by a joint resolution, the United States Congress authorized the President to proclaim neutrality on the outbreak or during the progress of war between or among two or more foreign states, thereby making it unlawful to export arms, ammunition, or implements of war from the United States to

[30] *Contemporary Japan,* March, 1935, pp. 704–705.

any belligerent country. The legislation provided also for the licensing of arms exports, prohibition of the carrying of arms by American vessels to belligerent states, and the restriction of travel by American citizens on vessels of belligerent states. In signing this resolution on August 31, President Roosevelt explained that the Neutrality Act "was intended as an expression of the fixed desire of the government and people of the United States to avoid any action which might involve us in war." Little over a month later, on October 5, two days after the Italian armed forces invaded Ethiopia, the United States invoked the provisions of the Neutrality Act.

In the fall of 1935 an autonomous movement was launched in North China with considerable publicity and in December the East Hopei Autonomous Council and the Hopei-Chahar Political Council were formed with the support of the Japanese army. At home, the removal of General Mazaki from his post of Inspector-General of Military Education on July 16, 1935, was in effect the triumph of the Kwantung Army and the Control faction of the army and was designed to remove those who were in favor of limiting and localizing the Manchurian Incident. As such it was a necessary preliminary to the unhampered activities of the military in North China.

Late in December Ambassador Grew reported to the Secretary of State that things were being constantly said and written in Japan to the effect that it was Japan's destiny to subjugate and rule the world, and that there was a "swashbuckling temper" in the country largely as a result of military propaganda that could lead Japan during the next few years to any extreme.[31] On December 29 Ambassador Saitō in Washington formally handed to Secretary Hull the official notice of his government's abrogation of the Washington naval agreement, which had been decided by the cabinet meeting of December 3.

THE GERMAN-JAPANESE ANTI-COMINTERN PACT

With the expiration on December 31, 1936, of the Washington Naval Treaty and the London Naval Treaty Japan would have been confronted with the possibility of unlimited competition in naval construction from both the United States and Great Britain. This was in effect the junking of the system of collective security in the Pacific and the Far East and would have resulted in Japan's isolation. The initial step had already been taken in March, 1933, when she served notice to withdraw from the League of Nations. However, even the military was very uneasy at the prospect of isolation and began making plans to forestall such an eventuality. This led quickly to closer cooperation with the Nazis because of the army's traditional attitude of admiration and friendliness toward Germany.

[31] Grew, *op. cit.*, p. 148.

A five-year German-Japanese Anti-Comintern Pact was signed in Berlin on November 25, 1936, by Ambassador Mushakōji and Foreign Minister von Ribbentrop. This was an agreement between the signatories for the exchange of information on the activities of the Communist International and consultation and collaboration on necessary preventive measures. It constituted the first step toward Japan's involvement in European politics, leading subsequently to the Tripartite Pact.

When the Hirota Cabinet was formed in March, 1936, there was considerable discussion as to whether cooperation should be with Great Britain or with Germany. The government was not enthusiastic about collaborating with Germany, but the army vigorously promoted closer relations with Hitler. General Ōshima, then military attaché in Berlin, was the prime mover and chief advocate of German-Japanese cooperation. The outbreak of the Spanish Civil War in mid-July was of great help in further arousing anti-Communist sentiment in Japan. By the end of July, 1936, the army had succeeded in prevailing forcefully on the government to accede to their demand for the conclusion of the Anti-Comintern Pact with Germany. Supporting General Ōshima, one of the leading Germanophiles in the army, was Minister Shiratori in Stockholm, who had been working with the army since the Manchurian Incident, at which time he was Director of the Information Bureau of the Foreign Office.[32] By the signing of the Anti-Comintern Pact, Japan served notice on the world that she was joining the fascist camp. At the same time, the Pact strengthened the hand of the faction bent on achieving military fascism. However, it was denounced by the political parties, financial circles, scholars, journalists, and intellectuals as a concrete example of secret diplomacy carried on in utter disregard of popular will.

Moscow was well informed on what was going on, as Soviet intelligence was intercepting and decoding at The Hague the secret messages that were passing back and forth between General Ōshima and Tōkyō. Therefore, as soon as the Pact was concluded, the Soviet government let the fisheries agreement go by the board; as a matter of fact, it was done on the day before the final signature of the document. Soviet Foreign Commissar Litvinov denounced the Pact as having the effect of spreading aggressive war to two continents and underscored the impossibility of achieving Soviet-Japanese amity in the face of it. Great Britain regarded the agreement as not only a threat to the Soviet Union but also to the entire world. China promptly decided to cooperate with Soviet Russia, while at the same time relying upon Great Britain and the United States to check Japan's attempts at further strengthening her grip.

Japanese troop activities were shifted to the northern part of Chahar, which became the army's base of operations for aggressive activities against the province of Suiyuan. The Suiyuan Incident of November, 1935, staged as part of a move-

---

[32] Shiratori was one of the strong advocates of withdrawal from the League of Nations.

ment for an autonomous Mongolia, was engineered under the slogan "Mongolia for the Mongolians" by General Tōjō, then chief of staff of the Kwantung Army. The special army unit employed was organized and led by Colonel Tanaka Ryūichi, subsequently Director of the Military Service Bureau under War Minister Tōjō. Reenforcing the Japanese unit were the Mongolian forces, comprising 30,000 Mongolians and Manchurian bandits. On November 18 Generalissimo Chiang Kai-shek flew out to Taiyuan to encourage the Suiyuan forces, who were resisting the incursion of the Mongolians. Tōjō's plot was foiled by the Suiyuan forces, who put the Mongolians to complete rout, and Colonel Tanaka was forced to escape back to Manchukuo by plane. Subsequently, Tōjō disavowed any connection and explained away the entire affair as the actions of Mongolian troops.

The Sian Incident. During his tour of Suiyuan to encourage the troops fighting the Mongolians and the Japanese, Generalissimo Chiang was kidnapped on December 12 by Chang Hsueh-liang and held at Sian. He was released only after he had pledged an all-out fight against Japan, which the Communists had been demanding for a long time. This marked the beginning of cooperation between the Communists and the Nationalists in their protracted resistance against Japanese aggression.

Negotiations, which had been conducted more than ten times between Japanese Ambassador Kawagoe and Chinese Foreign Minister Chan Chun over a period of two and a half months, came to an unsuccessful end with the Suiyuan Incident. Relations with China showed no signs of improvement, and issues seemed farther than ever from amicable settlement as the year 1936 came to an end. Since it became increasingly evident that a bluff of military pressure was of little use, the military leaders began to consider some other aggressive method of dominating China.

During the interval of little over four years between the Tangku Truce of May, 1933, and the outbreak of the China Incident at Lukouchiao in July, 1937, the Kwantung Army devoted its energies vigorously to the establishment and securing of firm control over Manchukuo. Simultaneously, however, it was busily engaged in paving the way, through numerous underplots in Hopei in Chahar, for the actual invasion of North China. By the Tangku Truce the Japanese troops had withdrawn to the Great Wall, but the creation of a demilitarized zone in northern Hopei actually placed them in a position of firm control to the south of the Wall.

Meanwhile at home munitions industries, which underwent abnormal growth and expansion following the Manchurian Incident, required tremendous supply of raw materials from abroad. Because of the complications, largely political, the utilization of normal channels of trade with the rest of the world had become increasingly difficult since the Ottawa Agreements. As a result, China came to be regarded as the only profitable market for Japan's manufactures and the source of raw materials for her industries. North China contained an abundant supply of iron, coal, cotton, and salt. Furthermore, there was already in North China a corporation backed by the Mitsui, Mitsubishi, and Sumitomo interests working in close cooperation with the army and this had established a bridge-head of economic offensive. Other enterprises, including the Oriental Development Company, Bank of Chōsen, and Kanegafuchi Spinning Mills, followed, as Japanese capital began to flow into China.

THE CHINA INCIDENT

Toward midnight of July 7, 1937, some Japanese troops which were on maneuver clashed with Chinese troops at Marco Polo Bridge (Lukouchiao), which is situated just outside Peiping. The event in itself seemed to be of little significance at the time. Two weeks later Secretary of State Hull offered the good offices of the United States government toward the settlement of the incident. But by the end of the month the original skirmish had developed into full scale fighting between Japanese and Chinese troops. Few Japanese gave any thought at first to the possibility that the Chinese might offer serious resistance. The army was confident that the whole affair could be settled to their satisfaction in a matter of a few months. In the beginning there was no discernible enthusiasm among the Japanese government and people for war with China.[33]

On August 10 Ambassador Grew in Tōkyō, under instructions from Secretary Hull, once more offered informally the good offices of the United States. The military resented and rejected "the intervention of third powers." On August 13 the fighting started in Shanghai, and the next day Chinese planes carried out aerial attacks on Japanese forces. The abandonment of "nonaggression and local settlement of the dispute," to which the people had given wholehearted support, was announced by the government on August 15. Increasingly large numbers of reserves were called up to carry out the "punitive action" against China, and the graveness of the situation soon dawned upon the public.

Unlike the Pacific War, the China War had not been planned by the government, but was precipitated by the local military authorities. Immediately after the initial clash, the military demanded and succeeded in forcing the government to dispatch troops, ostensibly for the protection of Japanese nationals. In its effort to localize the conflict and to prevent its spread, the government authorized a minimum strength for the expedition. However, once military operations had started, the high command went ahead with impunity to carry out its plans in disregard of the government's policies. When the Premier tried to pin down the War Minister on how far military operations would be carried, he got no reply. After the fighting spread to Shanghai, the War Minister declared that, although the operations might be extended to Wuhu, it would be impossible to advance

[33] Grew, *op. cit.*, p. 214.

as far as Nanking. Yet shortly afterwards, in September, the battle for Nanking began. When Premier Konoe attempted to send a personal envoy to China to discuss with Chiang Kai-shek the possibility of settling the dispute, the gendarmerie intercepted and detained him.

The United States Takes a Firm Stand. Recognizing the seriousness of the situation in the Far East, President Roosevelt on September 14 issued a statement [84] to the effect that merchant vessels owned by the government of the United States would not be permitted to transport arms, ammunition, or implements of war to China and Japan, and that any other merchant vessel flying the American flag that attempted to transport such articles to China or Japan would do so at their own risk.

Three weeks later, on October 5, in the famous "Quarantine Speech" in Chicago, Roosevelt declared that the existing reign of terror and international lawlessness had reached the stage where the very foundations of civilization were seriously being threatened and that isolation and neutrality afforded no escape since the international anarchy jeopardized the security of every nation. In the spreading epidemic of world lawlessness he suggested a "quarantine" of aggressor nations. This was a clarion call to all the peace-loving nations of the world to express their will for peace to the end that nations tempted to violate their agreement and trample upon the rights of others would desist. But the Japanese military machine in China rolled on, and there was little visible sign of a letup.[35] A month later, a fruitless effort was made to bring China and Japan together for a discussion of possible bases of settlement.

On the following day, October 6, the League of Nations Assembly adopted a report declaring that Japanese military operations in North China were out of proportion to the incident that had precipitated the conflict, and that Japan's actions were in violation of her obligation under the Nine Power Treaty and the Pact of Paris. On the same day a second report was adopted recommending calling together the signatories of the Nine Power Treaty to initiate discussion, the expression by the Assembly of its moral support for China, and a plan according to which members should consider how far they could go in extending aid to China.

Representatives of nineteen nations met in November at Brussels in accordance with a provision of the Nine Power Treaty to consider peaceable means for hastening the end of the Sino-Japanese conflict. The Conference hoped "to provide a forum for constructive discussion, to formulate and suggest a possible basis of settlement, and to endeavor to bring the parties together through peace-

---

[34] U.S. Department of State, *Press Releases,* Vol. XVII, No. 416, p. 227, September 18, 1937.

[35] Secretary Hull believed that the speech emboldened the aggressor nations. "It was certainly followed," he states, "by the bolder actions of Japan, culminating in the sinking of the United States gunboat *Panay* by Japanese planes two months later." *Memoirs, The New York Times,* February 6, 1948.

ful negotiation." Japan refused to participate, maintaining that the dispute was outside the purview of the Nine Power Treaty. This, of course, precluded any action by the Conference that could bring about peace by agreement.

In Tōkyō the newspaper *Nichi Nichi* reported on November 10 that increasing consideration was being given to the question of Japan's withdrawal from the Nine Power Treaty. On November 16 members of the House of Representatives adopted a manifesto urging the government to renounce the Nine Power Treaty. This was followed two days later by a resolution of the rightist Meirinkai urging the renunciation of the treaty.

On November 15 the Conference adopted a declaration affirming that the Sino-Japanese conflict was of concern to all the signatories of the Nine Power Treaty and the Pact of Paris. In adjourning on the twenty-fourth, it expressed the belief that satisfactory agreement could not be achieved by direct negotiation between the parties to the conflict alone and deemed it advisable to suspend temporarily its sittings and to call the Conference together again at a time when deliberations could be resumed advantageously.[36]

The Panay *Incident.* Less than a month after the unsuccessful Brussels Conference came an incident that inflamed American public opinion and brought the United States and Japan dangerously close to the brink of war.[37] On December 12, the U.S.S. *Panay,* a river gunboat on the Yangtze River that was carrying members of the American Embassy Staff was moving upriver from Nanking together with Standard Oil Company boats carrying American refugees. The ships were being followed by Japanese shell fire for about two miles. Apparently, Japanese batteries were under orders to open fire indiscriminately on all ships. In an unexpected bombing attack the *Panay* was sent to the bottom and its survivors were strafed by Japanese machine gun fire.

The United States lost no time in dispatching a note to the Japanese government reminding it that the American vessels were on the Yangtze River by "uncontested and incontestable right" and were engaged in legitimate and appropriate business. The Foreign Minister immediately sent a note in reply expressing profound regret and desire to present "sincere apologies," promising full indemnities for all the losses, appropriate measures against those responsible for the incident,[38] and stating that it had already issued strict orders to the authorities on the spot to prevent the recurrence of similar incidents.

[36] On October 21, in an interview with the United Press, Salmon O. Levinson, "father of the Kellogg Pact," declared that the Brussels Conference was doomed because it would not be a Nine Power conference and that any attempt by the participating powers to curb Japan would not only be futile but dangerous.

[37] Grew, *op. cit.,* p. 236.

[38] One of the artillery regiments was commanded by Colonel Hashimoto Kingorō, an avowed extremist, who was subsequently disciplined for his unwarranted action in ordering his unit to participate in the attack.

On the very same day Foreign Minister Hirota called on Ambassador Grew and expressed his apology for the regrettable affair. The public demonstration of regret took the form of apology to the American people, as individuals took upon themselves the responsibility of transmitting their apologies to the American Embassy, while people on the streets stopped Americans and expressed their deep regret. Such genuine and spontaneous expressions on the part of the people took the militarists and xenophobes by surprise, since they could neither anticipate nor appreciate such an attitude. What was potentially an explosive and dangerous international incident was settled amicably in a matter of less than a month. This was the result of the forbearance and the coolness of the American government and people. There was little doubt in the minds of peacefully inclined government leaders and the Japanese people that the American government and people were sincere in their desire to preserve peace, although the chauvinists regarded it as a sign of weakness.

Meanwhile, although the capture of Nanking on December 17 was celebrated by lantern parades amidst outbursts of enthusiasm inspired by the military, the government found itself in the difficult position of having to acknowledge the fact that the China War was far from ended. Hope for a short, swift war, which the government had announced to the nation, vanished as the Chinese Nationalist government moved to its new capital, Chungking, to continue its resistance against Japan. The government was therefore forced to change its slogan and to emphasize the need to prepare for a protracted war.

Shortly after the fall of Nanking an attempt was made to open peace negotiations through the good offices of German Ambassador Trautmann in China, and Premier Konoe indicated his willingness to go to China to take up the discussion with the Chinese government. War Minister Sugiyama and others were opposed to such a move. Moreover, no response came from China, and hopes for peace were blasted. In January, 1938, Premier Konoe was impelled, under army pressure, to issue a statement to the effect that the Japanese government would not henceforth negotiate with the Nationalist government. This statement, which was drafted by Foreign Office Asia Bureau Director Ishii, constituted one of the serious blunders of the second Konoe Cabinet, which the Premier tried unsuccessfully to offset in a new statement of November 3. He then stated that he was not averse to dealing with the Nationalist government, provided it abandoned its anti-Japanese attitude. By this time Konoe was preoccupied in his frantic search for an effective means of holding the army in check, if not to control it. In desperation, he even attempted to restore the Kōdō faction of the army as a counterbalance to the Control faction, which was now unopposed and unchecked and was getting out of hand.

American Moral Embargoes. The widespread and indiscriminate bombing of Chinese civilians by the Japanese army incensed American public opinion. On June 11, 1938, Secretary Hull condemned the practice and the indirect material encouragement that was being given by American manufacturers. On July 1 the State Department notified manufacturers and exporters of aircraft that the United States government was strongly opposed to the sale of airplanes and aeronautical equipment to countries whose armed forces were using airplanes for attacks on civilian populations. This "moral embargo" was extended in December, 1939, to include materials essential to airplane manufacture [39] and also to plans, plants, and technical information for the production of high octane gasoline,[40] resulting in the suspension of the export of aircraft, aeronautical equipment, and aviation gasoline. Beginning also in 1938 a policy of informally discouraging the extension of credit by United States nationals to Japan was adopted and put into effect by the American government.

SOVIET-JAPANESE BORDER CLASHES

Soviet-Japanese relations were subjected to a very severe test in the summer of 1938 by a border clash, which took place at Changkufeng, the point where the boundaries of Korea, Manchukuo and Soviet territory converge, which had been claimed by both the Soviets and Manchukuo, but which had remained unoccupied for some time. On July 12 a Soviet detachment occupied the hill that commands the Soviet naval base at Possiet Bay and that was close to the Korean port of Rashin. Artillery, tanks, and planes were thrown into action on July 30, when Japanese forces threw the Soviet troops back and drove them from the heights. This was the first time since the Russo-Japanese War, a third of a century earlier, that a Japanese artillery regiment was pitted against enemy artillery with modern equipment. In spite of propaganda to the contrary, it was not a smashing victory for the Japanese troops, who barely managed to prevent exposing their vulnerability and poor logistics. On August 10 an agreement was reached in Moscow between Ambassador Shigemitsu and Foreign Commissar Litvinov, and the clash was brought to an end without stirring up much animosity between the two nations. There had been other border clashes before, one along the frontier of Outer Mongolia in the winter of 1935–1936, and another on the Amur River between Blagoveschensk and Khabarovsk in July, 1937, though not on as large a scale as at Changkufeng.

A perennial source of friction since 1928 between the two countries cropped up again in January, 1939, as a result of the Soviet declaration of her intention to let the Far Eastern fishing grounds by tender or auction on March 15. Russia and Japan mutually accused each other of violating the spirit of the Portsmouth Treaty. However, as a result of negotiations, an agreement was signed on April 2, extending the existing fisheries agreement of 1928 until December. The Japanese,

---

[39] U.S. Department of State, *Press Release,* December 15, 1939, *Bulletin,* Vol. I, No. 25, p. 684, December 16, 1939.

[40] U.S. Department of State, *Bulletin,* Vol. I, No. 26, p. 714, December 23, 1939.

under the new agreement, were forced to pay a rental 10 per cent higher than she paid in 1938 for a much smaller area. In June and July the question of Japan's conduct of her oil and coal concessions in northern Sakhalin caused some dispute.

Another serious boundary clash occurred in the summer of 1939 on the not too clearly defined frontier between Manchukuo and Outer Mongolia. Sporadic fighting continued through May, June, July, and August, which was characterized by extravagant claims by both sides regarding their military successes, especially in the number of enemy planes shot down. Japanese troops suffered heavy losses, one of the units coming close to decimation. A cease fire agreement was signed on September 16, and an armistice was declared in Moscow on September 20, bringing the Nomohan Incident to a close. A mixed boundary commission, which was then appointed, reached an agreement later on the demarcation of the frontier. On the last day of December, Ambassador Tōgō in Moscow signed the extension for another year of the fisheries agreement for the fourth time since 1936, when it was placed on a temporary annual basis.[41] When the agreement was concluded in 1928, it was for a term of eight years, but on its expiration in 1936, the Soviet government refused to sign a long-term agreement, insisting on a one-year extension.

JAPANESE AGGRESSION GAINS MOMENTUM

Japanese troops landed at Bias Bay, proceeded to push on toward Canton rapidly, and succeeded in capturing the city on October 21, 1938. Four days later Hankow fell into Japanese hands, and a few days later the Japanese army took over the British concession. On December 22 Premier Konoe reiterated the government's resolve "to carry on military operations for the complete destruction of the military power of the Kuomintang Government, which is resisting Japan, and to forge ahead with those far-sighted Chinese who share our ideals and objectives." [42] The welding of Japan, China, and Manchukuo into a unit on the basis of a three-point program of neighborly amity, common front against communism, and economic cooperation was the announced goal of the Konoe Cabinet. The first included the liquidation of the anti-Japanese attitude and the recognition of Manchukuo. The second was the conclusion of an anti-Communist agreement, including the stationing of Japanese troops at specified points and the designation of Inner Mongolia as a special anti-Communist buffer area. With regard to economic relations, it was made clear that Japan had no intention of exercising economic monopoly in China or of forcing China to limit the interests of those third powers that "understood" the meaning of the new East Asia and

[41] Tōkyō *Asahi,* January 1, 1940.
[42] 1940 *Dōmei Jiji Nenkan,* pp. 165–166.

acted accordingly. Japan's demand to China was that she should extend facilities for the development of China's natural resources, especially in North China and Inner Mongolia. Japan not only respected the sovereignty of China, it was emphasized, but was prepared to give positive consideration to the questions of the abolition of extraterritoriality and the return of concessions and settlements.

As interference with the rights of the United States and its nationals by Japanese or Japanese sponsored agents in China became more and more frequent, stronger protests were lodged by the American government. On the last day of 1938, the United States was impelled to present a note declaring that these interferences were not only unjust and unwarranted but also contravened the provisions of several international agreements voluntarily entered into by Japan and the United States, and emphatically stating that the American people and government could not countenance the establishment of a regime that would arbitrarily deprive them of the rights of equal opportunity and fair treatment.

Japan's expected southward move was given concrete expression in February, 1939, when she occupied the island of Hainan in southern China, located within the French sphere of influence. Within a week protests were lodged by France, Great Britain, and the United States. On March 30, the Japanese government incorporated the Spratly Islands into the city of Takao under the jurisdiction of the Government General of Formosa. Japan claimed title to the islands on the basis of right derived from international law, contending that the French claim was invalid, inasmuch as the French government had set up no establishments on the islands to support its intention to occupy and acquire them. On April 18 the Japanese government announced the incorporation of the islands into the Japanese Empire.

Foreign Minister Arita, on April 15, expressed in his statement a deep concern over any development, political or economic, that might affect the *status quo* of the Netherlands East Indies from the standpoint of the maintenance of the peace and stability of East Asia. Negotiations were started in June with the Dutch government to assure exports to Japan.

On May 18 Arita expressed his government's regret to Ambassador Grew [43] at rumors that had spread giving the impression and creating apprehension among interested powers that Japan entertained territorial designs toward the South Seas as a result of the annexation of the Spratly Islands, and he suggested that his government would be willing to enter into conversations with the United States government to dispel any American apprehensions with regard to the Philippines. Developments that followed proved that the taking over of the Spratly Islands was one of the initial moves in the course of Japan's southward advance.

[43] U.S. Department of State, *Foreign Relations of the United States, Japan: 1931–1941,* Vol. II, pp. 4–5.

ANGLO-JAPANESE TENSIONS .

The 1930's was a period of strong economic nationalism and imperialism. The world tended to split up into economic blocs, and international trade was being diverted into certain well defined areas for the attainment of political objectives. Japan was intent on establishing a *yen* bloc, embracing China, Manchukuo, and herself. Nazi Germany was attempting the economic consolidation of Central and Southeastern Europe. Hitler set out deliberately to remodel the structure of industry and finance with the purpose of utilizing it for the advancement of power politics. Great Britain inaugurated an era of bloc economy at Ottawa with a system of Empire preference. Even the Netherlands Indies, the outpost of a colonial power that had been a staunch advocate of free trade, turned protectionist in 1933. Economic liberalism abdicated in favor of economic nationalism and the tendency was for each nation to isolate itself from world markets.

British trade policy toward Japan in the early 1930's was designed, not so much to secure reciprocal concessions or closer balance of trade, as to restrict Japanese competition, which increased with alarming speed from 1932 to 1934, causing a great reduction in Britain's export of cotton textiles and staple fiber fabrics. The Ottawa Agreements of 1932, allowing only British products to enjoy special preferences in the Dominions and the colonies, marked the start of an economic-political offensive against Japanese goods, which were making serious inroads into British markets that had formerly been an exclusive preserve. In April, 1933, the British Government abrogated the Indo-Japanese Trade Treaty in the interests of Lancashire. Japan's reply was the Trade Protection Law, enacted in the same year as a countermeasure. In September an Indo-Japanese Trade Conference was opened at Simla, India, and discussions were begun to prevent cutthroat competition, but progress was necessarily slow and agreement was finally reached in March, 1937.

Early in 1934 representatives of British and Japanese industries met to discuss an agreement for the regulation of trade, but without success. At this point, the British Government intervened and arranged to impose restrictions on imports to various British colonies and protectorates. From May, 1934, a quota system based upon average imports during the years 1927–1931 was applied to all foreign cotton and artificial silk goods imported into these territories, without denouncing the existing Anglo-Japanese Commercial Treaty. Although it was not an infringement of the most-favored-nation clause, the effect was highly restrictive upon Japanese trade, as it was reduced to about one half of the sales during the two preceding years, and the effect of the policy was to increase considerably Lancashire's exports to the areas affected.

Meanwhile, Japan's program of controlling various parts of China, especially the central part, the region of the Yangtze valley, was bound to interfere, if not clash, sooner or later with British interests. The Amau Statement of April 17, 1934, and other pronouncements did not serve to relieve Anglo-Japanese tension. Trade controversies in India, Australia, and elsewhere further aggravated the rapidly deteriorating relationship between the two countries that once had been close allies.[44]

By 1935 the Japanese cotton industry had completed a program of rationalization to meet the competition of Lancashire. The Japan Cotton Spinners' Association comprised 71 cotton spinning and weaving concerns with an average capital of over 7½ million yen, or three times as much as that of English mills. A vertical combination had been worked out to increase the efficiency of the industry. With new machinery, like the Toyoda loom, and more efficient utilization of the mills the Japanese cotton industry had by 1933 attained six times the productive capacity of English spindles. Moreover, the utilization of female workers in the mills helped to keep down the cost of production.[45]

Anglo-Japanese relations went from bad to worse during 1935 and 1936, in spite of the efforts that were made to restore a cordial relationship. During the second half of December, 1935, the Japanese press shifted its customary attacks from the United States to Great Britain. Sir Frederick Leith-Ross, Chairman of the British Financial Mission to China, was generally regarded in Tōkyō as responsible for the financial and political machinations in China, which were disruptive of Japan's "stabilizing influence" in North China. However, hope for improvement was held out in both countries. In Japan many public leaders felt a strong attachment to Great Britain in spite of the propaganda of the army.

British leaders too were desirous of maintaining satisfactory relations with Japan. On April 16, less than three months before the outbreak of the China War, Sir Samuel Hoare asserted at a London banquet that there was no reason why Great Britain and Japan should not resume their satisfactory relations of former years.[46] Although, by this time, the army had succeeded in concluding the Anti-Comintern Pact with Germany, there were Japanese leaders both in and out of government who were eager to be on friendly terms with the British. In July conversations were held in Tōkyō, resulting in Great Britain taking cognizance of Japan's three basic principles of China policy, as announced by the government and the Arita-Craigie agreement.

However, early in August, disagreement arose over the question of preserving peace and order in North China. By the middle of the month negotiations foundered, and the Japanese army representatives returned to their posts in North

[44] In his memoirs, Winston Churchill states that the abandonment of the Anglo-Japanese Alliance was responsible for many of the difficulties that subsequently arose between the two nations.

[45] S. Uyehara, *The Industry and Trade of Japan,* pp. 91–92.

[46] London *Times,* April 17, 1937.

China. Less than a week after the actual breakup of negotiations, on August 26, British Ambassador Sir Hughe Montgomery Knatchbull-Hugessen was wounded between Nanking and Shanghai, when his automobile was strafed by machine gun fire from a Japanese plane. On October 30 a resolution demanding the immediate severance of diplomatic relations with Great Britain unless she modified her "mistaken policy" toward Japan was unanimously adopted by an emergency meeting of the Current Affairs Discussion Group (Jiji Kondankai), composed of members of the House of Representatives.

In spite of steadily deteriorating relations a conciliatory attitude persisted in some quarters in Britain. On June 27, 1938, the British Parliamentary Undersecretary for Foreign Affairs stated in the House of Commons that the British Government stood ready to mediate to end the Sino-Japanese hostilities, provided both sides were agreeable. The Japanese government, then already under the firm control of the army, was unable to avail itself of this favorable situation for the termination of the China War. It also lost irretrievably the opportunity for reconciliation with the British Government.

Early in the summer of 1939 a serious clash occurred in Tientsin between the British and the Japanese. Refusal of the authorities in the British concession of the city to hand over to the Japanese four Chinese accused of having assassinated a Chinese customs inspector in the pro-Japanese administration was the occasion for the flareup. The Japanese army began to blockade the British and French concessions in Tientsin on June 14 and subjected the British to indignities and insults. The army announced that it was determined to obtain British and French cooperation in the establishment of a new order in East Asia, to stop British support of the Chinese currency, and to introduce pro-Japanese textbooks into the Chinese schools in the British concession. Conversations began in Tōkyō between Foreign Minister Arita and British Ambassador Sir Robert Craigie, resulting on July 22 in a joint formula that the Japanese interpreted as British capitulation to Japanese demands, but no positive settlement on currency and economic issues resulted.

The *Asama Maru* Incident of January 21, 1940, in which a British cruiser intercepted the Japanese merchant ship and seized twenty-one German passengers aboard ruffled official circles in Tōkyō. The Foreign Office immediately lodged a protest with the British Government. Two days later another ship of the Nippon Yusen Kaisha, *Tatsuta Maru,* was subjected to similar treatment to further provoke the military. Deterioration in Anglo-Japanese relations continued steadily thereafter until the outbreak of the Pacific War.

ABROGATION OF THE AMERICAN-JAPANESE
COMMERCIAL TREATY OF 1911

As the tempo of military activities in China heightened and evidence piled up of the destruction of American property, the violation of American rights and interests, and the danger to American lives, the United States government felt a need for stronger measures. After diplomatic representations failed to bring about substantial improvement in the situation, the United States gave serious consideration to the possibility of commercial retaliation against Japan. On July 26, the United States gave notice to Japan of the termination of the Treaty of Commerce of 1911, inasmuch as it was not affording adequate protection to American commerce in Japan or in Japanese occupied parts of China and since the most-favored-nation clause of the treaty stood in the way of putting into effect retaliatory measures against Japan's commerce. The treaty was to be terminated at the end of the six months' period as provided. As a result, on January 26, 1940, when the treaty went out of existence, the legal obstacle to an embargo by the United States on the shipment of war materials to Japan was removed.

On August 23, 1939, the Soviet-German Nonaggression Pact was concluded, and the two powers agreed to "refrain from any act of violence, any aggressive action, or any attack against one another, whether individually or jointly with other powers" and not to participate in any grouping of powers. Germany's occupation of Czechoslovak territory and proclamation of a protectorate over Bohemia and Moravia on March 16 left no room for doubt that the Nazis were not going to allow any obstacles to stand in the way of their acquisitive policy to aggressively secure for themselves adequate *Lebensraum*. Hitler's formal assurance of September 26, 1938, that he had no more territorial claims in Europe had been swept into the discard.

Hardly had the ink on the Soviet-German Pact dried, when, on September 1, Nazi troops began pouring into Poland. Two days later Great Britain and France declared war on Germany. On the 5th, the Japanese Foreign Office in a note [47] to the belligerents, Great Britain, France, Germany, and Poland, gave "friendly advice" to withdraw voluntarily their naval vessels and troops from Japanese controlled areas in North China in order to avoid any unfortunate incidents, inasmuch as Japan planned to avoid becoming involved in the war and to devote her energies to the settlement of the China Incident. Copies of the note were also handed to the American and Italian ambassadors for their information.

On October 19 Ambassador Grew, who had just returned from a furlough to the United States, gave frank and friendly advice straight from the "horse's

---

[47] U.S. Department of State, *Foreign Relations of the United States, Japan: 1931–1941*, Vol. II, pp. 9–10.

mouth" to the Japanese leaders in a sincere effort to induce reflection among the leaders and particularly the military leaders.[48] The speech was given with the full understanding and support of the Secretary of State and seemed to have had a salutary effect on some of the leaders, but the military leaders had involved the nation too deeply in the complicated international situation, making it virtually impossible to extricate the government from its plight, unless the army itself was willing to back down.

In Europe, Secretary Hull decided to extend American good offices to Finland and the Soviet Union to compose their differences, and on November 28 sent a message to Moscow and Helsinki. Finland welcomed the American offer, but the Soviet government felt that it did not need any assistance. On the following day Stalin unleashed the attack on Finland after denouncing the existing non-aggression pact. The United States decided immediately to extend to the Soviet Union the moral embargo that was already in effect against Japan. The effect of Stalin's action on Japan was reflected in the *Yomiuri,* which averred: "We have learned a very good lesson from this [Soviet attack on Finland after denouncing the nonaggression pact] that a nonaggression pact is of no value in guaranteeing a nation's security." [49]

Foreign Minister Admiral Nomura gave Ambassador Grew in Tōkyō on December 4 a categorical assurance that there was no intention on the part of Japanese authorities to expel American interests from China, and that incidents and cases of which the United States has complained had been unavoidable accidents, accompanying military operations on an unprecedentedly large scale over extensive areas in China. He emphasized that "Japanese forces had been ordered to pay every possible attention in their power to protect and respect American property and citizens in China." [50]

On the day following Premier Admiral Yonai's address at the reopening of the Diet on February 2 Minseitō's Saitō Takao, in a two-hour interpellation, lashed out at the three basic principles set forth by the government as a condition for the termination of the China War. As a result, he was asked to resign from the Diet, which was no longer able to resist successfully the pressure from the military. When he refused, the House of Representatives in a secret session on March 7, 1940, voted to expel Saitō from its membership.

PUPPET GOVERNMENT AT NANKING

It was in December, 1937, only a few months after the outbreak of the China War, that the "provisional government of the Chinese Republic" was set up

---

[48] Speech before the America-Japan Society in Tōkyō. *Foreign Relations of the United States, Japan: 1931–1941,* Vol. II, pp. 19–29.

[49] *Yomiuri Shimbun,* December 1, 1939.

[50] *Foreign Relations of the United States, Japan: 1931–1941,* Vol. II, p. 40.

at Peiping, the initiative coming from the Japanese. At Nanking, towards the end of the month, the Peace Preservation Committee was formed under similar auspices. The Anti-Communist Autonomous Government of East Hopei followed on January 30, 1938, with Wang Keh-min as chairman of its executive committee. Then, on March 28, the Renovation Government of the Chinese Republic was launched in Nanking with Liang Hung-chih as President of the Executive Yuan. Finally, on July 1, the Autonomous Government of Inner Mongolia was set up with Prince Teh as its head.

The Japanese army wanted to bring these fragmentary regimes together to form a single Chinese government. The search for a head was long and difficult for T'ang Shao-yi and Wu Pei-fu declined the offer of the Japanese army. In December, 1938, Wang Ching-wei began sounding out the Japanese regarding possibilities of working out a peace on the basis of Konoe's statement of December 22. With the constant backing of the Japanese, Wang carried on his peace movement. Finally, after many premature announcements and long delays, the puppet regime was set up in Nanking on March 30, 1940. The Japanese government issued a statement expressing the hope that the powers would come to recognize the existing situation and contribute toward the establishment of peace in East Asia. At the same time it emphasized that it had no intention of excluding such peaceful economic activities of third powers as would conform to the new situation in East Asia.[51]

Secretary Hull, on March 30, remarked that the new regime at Nanking had "the appearance of a further step in a program of one country by armed force to impose its will upon a neighboring country and to block off a large area of the world from normal political and economic relationship with the rest of the world."[52] He noted that the puppet regime would "especially favor the interests of Japan and deny to nationals of the United States and other third countries long-established rights of equal and fair treatment to which they are legally and justly entitled."

JAPAN TURNS SOUTHWARD

Foreign Minister Arita reiterated on April 15 official concern over any development in political, economic, and other matters that might affect the *status quo* of the Netherlands East Indies from the standpoint of the maintenance of the peace and stability of East Asia. The German invasion of the Netherlands on May 10 and its subsequent developments brought about a series of diplomatic soundings and maneuvers by the Japanese government. On June 5 Arita stated that Japan, as a stabilizing force in East Asia, entertained a more than passing

[51] *Ibid.*, p. 61.
[52] U.S. Department of State, *Bulletin,* Vol. II, No. 40, p. 343, March 30, 1940.

interest in the areas to the south, particularly the Netherlands East Indies, because of close economic ties. He indicated anxiety over the economic status of the Netherlands Indies and intimated that, should the normal flow of goods and commodities be impeded by tariff walls, immigration restrictions, and other barriers to commerce and transportation, frictions and conflicts were bound to follow. This was followed on June 28 by a Foreign Office press release to the effect that the governments of the Netherlands and the Netherlands East Indies had assured Japan that they would not take measures that would prevent the export of commodities desired, such as rubber, tin, quinine, copra, and other materials.[53]

Secretary Hull on June 22 had instructed Ambassador Grew to approach Foreign Minister Arita on the possibility of arriving at an understanding with the government of the United States through an exchange of notes for the maintenance of the *status quo,* except as it might be modified by peaceful means, with regard to the possessions and territories of belligerent powers in the Pacific area.[54] Arita expressed doubt regarding the advisability of an exchange of formal notes in the light of Japan's policy of noninvolvement in the European conflict.

In discussing with the British Ambassador and the Australian Minister on June 28 possible steps to check Japanese aggression in the Far East, Secretary Hull declared that the United States had been exerting economic pressure on Japan for a year, and that everything possible was being done "short of a serious risk of actual military hostilities" in order to keep the Japanese situation stabilized. The United States was determined to keep Japan in check and equally determined not to restore peace in the Far East at the expense of China or of the principles of international policy to which she was committed.

Foreign Minister Arita set forth the "regional bloc" idea in his radio broadcast of June 29, 1940. "Countries of East Asia and the region of the South Seas," he declared, "are geographically, historically, racially, and economically very closely related to each other. They are destined to cooperate and minister to one another's needs for their common well-being and prosperity and to promote the peace and progress in their regions." He elaborated on the need "to establish first a righteous peace in each of the various regions and then establish collectively a just peace of the whole world. This system presupposes the existence of a stabilizing force in each region." The destiny of these regions, he emphasized, "is a matter for grave concern to Japan in view of her mission and responsibility as the stabilizing force in East Asia." [55] According to this explanation, Japan's

[53] *Foreign Relations of the United States, Japan: 1931–1941,* Vol. II, p. 289.
[54] *Ibid.,* p. 86.
[55] S. Shepard Jones and Denys P. Myers (eds.), *Documents on American Foreign Relations, 1939–1940,* p. 289. See also *Foreign Relations of the United States, Japan: 1931–1941,* Vol. II, pp. 93–94.

task of establishing a new order in East Asia was an attempt to form a regional sphere of coexistence and coprosperity by the peoples, who are closely related to each other geographically, racially, culturally and economically.

In compliance with the Japanese representation of June 24, the British authorities agreed on July 17 to prohibit transit through the Burma Road for a period of three months, beginning July 18, of arms and ammunition, as well as gasoline, trucks, and railway materials. Two days earlier, in Washington, Secretary of State Hull, in reply to inquiries by press correspondents, had stated that the United States government had a legitimate interest in keeping open arteries of commerce in every part of the world and considered that such action as the closing of the Burma Road, if taken, could constitute unwarranted imposition of obstacles to world trade. British export of arms and ammunition to General Chiang Kai-shek from Hong Kong had been prohibited since January, 1939. In October, when the three month period expired, the British reopened the Burma Road.

Japan Advances into French Indo-China. The months immediately following the outbreak of war in Europe was a period of watchful waiting for the Japanese expansionists. The fall of France in June, 1940, which followed by a little over a month the overrunning of the Low Countries, and the seemingly hopeless position of England were taken as a green light by the Japanese military in planning their moves. French Indo-China and the Netherlands East Indies lay helpless, and the Japanese concentrated for the time being on southward expansion in order to ensure for herself access to the rich natural resources of the region.

Early in August American news agencies carried reports that Japan had made secret demands on France for rights to move armed forces through French Indo-China and to use air bases at certain points in the country for purposes of military operations against China. On August 30 an agreement was signed between Foreign Minister Matsuoka and French Ambassador Arsene-Henry in Tōkyō providing for the movement of Japanese troops through French Indo-China and the use temporarily of airports. Governor General Vice Admiral Jean Decoux was ready to sign on September 6 an agreement implementing the Vichy-Tōkyō agreement but decided to resist Japanese pressure for a while. However, he yielded when General Nishihara presented an ultimatum for the occupation of Hanoi, Haiphong, and five airports by Japanese armed forces. Unless he acceded to the demands, General Nishihara made clear that he would start the invasion of French Indo-China on September 22. On that date Japanese troops disembarked at Saigon to begin the occupation of French Indo-China.

On September 23 Secretary Hull expressed his view that the *status quo* was being upset and that it was being achieved under duress. In late November the American consul at Hanoi reported that merchandise owned by Americans was being refused reexport permits by Indo-Chinese authorities as the result of

Japanese pressure. Interference with American trade increased as the Japanese military tightened its grip on French Indo-China. That the situation was becoming serious and that the worst was expected can be seen by the fact that in late February, 1941, the Japanese government instructed its nationals to make preparations to evacuate. On May 6, 1941, Tōkyō forced an economic agreement upon French Indo-China, while on July 29 it concluded a mutual defense agreement with the Vichy government. Army and navy forces landed at Saigon and other places on the same day. Three days earlier, when the Japanese government announced that an agreement was reached with Vichy, it was met immediately by an announcement by the United States to the effect that Japanese assets were frozen. Great Britain and the Philippines also took similar steps on the same day. Canada had actually led all others in retaliation since she announced it on July 25. Japan countered by announcing the freezing of foreign assets on July 28.

THE TRIPARTITE PACT

Japan joined the Axis as a full fledged partner on September 26, 1940, when she became a signatory to a ten-year alliance in which Germany, Italy, and Japan agreed to assist one another with all political, economic, and military means, if one of the parties was attacked by a power not then involved in the European war or in the Sino-Japanese conflict. The ultimate object of the Tripartite Pact was the establishment of a new order in Europe under joint Italo-German leadership and a new order in Greater East Asia under Japanese leadership. Joint technical commissions were appointed by the respective governments to meet immediately to implement the Pact. The assertion by Ribbentrop that the Pact was not directed against any other people but "aimed exclusively against those warmongers and irresponsible elements in the rest of the world who contrary to the real interests of all nations strive to prolong and extend the present conflict" left no doubt as to which countries it was directed against. Twenty days later the Selective Service Act went into effect in the United States, and the first draft registration was carried out on October 16.

During Foreign Commissar Molotov's visit to Berlin on November 13 the Nazis offered Soviet Russia accession to the Tripartite Pact, but the latter's conditions for adherence were unacceptable, since they involved the sacrifice of German interests in Finland, the granting of bases on the Dardanelles, and strong influence on conditions in the Balkans, especially in Bulgaria, and also Japan's renunciation of oil and coal concessions in northern Sakhalin.[56] The attempt to bring Russia within the Axis camp thus failed.

Final Moves in Southeast Asia. In mid-September of 1940 conversations were started by special envoy Kobayashi, Minister of Commerce and Industry, and

[56] U.S. Department of State, *Nazi-Soviet Relations, 1939–1941*, pp. 258–259.

the Netherlands East Indies authorities for some sort of agreement regarding economic relations. Japan presented twenty-two demands which, if granted, would have placed her in a privileged position in the Indies. These included demands for more oil, tin, and rubber, an increased immigration quota, an increased import quota for Japanese products, mining and prospecting facilities, and the opening of direct air and cable service between Tōkyō and Batavia. An agreement between Japanese oil importing companies and the Netherlands East Indies producing companies for additional export to Japan, which was initiated on November 12, 1940, was extended in May, 1941. Early in November Kobayashi returned to Japan without having achieved the objectives. His successor, former Foreign Minister Yoshizawa, arrived at the end of the year and presented the first memorandum in mid-January of the following year. For nearly six months the Japanese envoy continued the negotiations but left on June 27 without securing for Japan the economic advantages that were greatly desired by the military.

Anticipating the need of securing friendly cooperation, the Japanese government took the initiative in mediating the boundary dispute between Thailand (Siam) and French Indo-China in 1941, thereby ingratiating itself with the former and succeeding in entrenching itself securely economically and politically. On February 7, a mediation conference opened in Tōkyō with representatives of Thailand and French Indo-China in attendance. An agreement was reached in March granting Siam a portion of Laos and Cambodia. As a reward for the service, Japan secured commercial privileges and access to Siam's rice surplus, as well as to raw materials such as tin and rubber, which the Japanese needed badly for their war industries. On May 9, peace was restored between Siam and French Indo-China and on July 5 an exchange of ratifications for the arbitration treaty took place. The good will of Siam, which the Japanese secured, proved helpful to the military in the early stages of the Pacific War, which was then less than six months away.

Chapter 35. The War in the Pacific

Gathering War Clouds. Ambivalence characterized German-Japanese relations in the political marriage of convenience consummated between Hitler's Nazi Germany and army-dominated Japan. However, the conclusion of the Tripartite Pact on September 26, 1940, resulting in the creation of the Rome-Berlin-Tōkyō Axis, had committed Japan, though perhaps not irrevocably, to common action with the Nazis and Fascists, and placed her in the camp opposing the democratic coalition of powers. Barring unforeseen and almost miraculous developments that could bring the military element under control, any attempt to change the course seemed doomed to failure. Foreign Minister Matsuoka had declared after his return from Germany in an address at a public meeting in Tōkyō that if need be Japan was prepared to commit double suicide with Germany.[1] The year 1941 opened with ominous shadows over the Far East and the Pacific.

In addressing the Congress on January 6, 1941, President Roosevelt declared that never had American security been so seriously threatened from without, and that direct assaults on the democratic way of life were being made persistently both by arms and by deadly propaganda. At a hearing of the Foreign Affairs Committee of the House of Representatives on the Lend Lease bill, Secretary of State Hull underscored the disturbing fact that Japan's leaders had openly declared their intention to achieve and maintain a dominant position in the entire region of the Western Pacific by force of arms and to make themselves masters of an area containing almost half of the entire population of the world. From Tōkyō, Ambassador Grew warned, before the month of January was over, that there were reports that Japanese military forces were planning a surprise attack on Pearl Harbor in the event of hostilities with the United States.[2]

Foreign Minister Matsuoka asserted on January 21 in his address to the Diet[3] that the Netherlands East Indies lay within the Greater East Asia co-prosperity sphere, a concept that his predecessor Arita had stated on June 5 of the preceding year. He emphasized too that there was no other course open to Japan but to secure "economic self-sufficiency" within the region of Greater East

[1] Baba Tsunego, *Konoe Naikaku Shiron*, p. 14.

[2] Telegram from Ambassador Grew to the Secretary of State, Tōkyō, January 27, 1941. *Foreign Relations of the United States, Japan*, Vol. II, p. 133.

[3] Shepard Jones and Denys P. Myers, *Documents on American Foreign Relations*, Vol. III, pp. 260–267.

Asia. Speaking before the Budget Committee of the Diet a month later, he declared that "ultimately diplomacy is force and it goes without saying that diplomacy not backed by strength can accomplish nothing." [4] The implications were clear. The Foreign Minister was reflecting the views of the army as well as his own.

On March 11 President Roosevelt signed the Lend Lease Act and four days later declared that the compromise with tyranny and the forces of oppression had come to an end. Congress responded with speed to the President's request for 7 billion dollars to implement the law designed to stop the march of aggression.

In Japan, the eight months immediately preceding the outbreak of hostilities in the Pacific were a trying period for the leaders of the peace faction, who fought against odds, hoping to break the stalemate in American-Japanese conversations, which were being hampered by the machinations and jockeying of the military and its rightist imperialist supporters. It was a race for time in which the fate of the nation hung in a precarious balance by a slender thread of hope, as the issue of peace or war was fought secretly behind the scenes unknown to the public and witnessed by only a few of the participants.

AMERICAN-JAPANESE CONVERSATIONS

A faint ray of hope appeared on April 9 when a proposal [5] was presented to the Department of State through private American and Japanese individuals who were desirous of readjusting the unsatisfactory relationship between the two countries through the resumption of friendly relations. The draft proposal included as areas of adjustment such broad categories as the concepts of international relations, attitudes toward the European war, peaceful settlement between China and Japan, commerce, and economic activity in the Pacific area, and suggested a meeting between President Roosevelt and Premier Konoe in Honolulu in May. This was the crystallization, during the absence of Foreign Minister Matsuoka in Europe, of the private conversations that had been started between American and Japanese individuals during the later part of 1940.[6]

President Roosevelt and Secretary Hull both realized the probability that Japan had gone so far in a policy of conquest that it would be impossible to use effectively moral suasion or any other form of persuasion to stop or change her course. Nevertheless, the American goverment felt impelled by even a slender hope that a peaceful solution might somehow be worked out to partici-

[4] London *Times*, February 19, 1941.

[5] For the text, see *Foreign Relations of the United States, Japan,* Vol. II, pp. 398–402.

[6] Those who participated in the conversations included Colonel Iwakuro Hideo, assistant military attaché, Japanese Embassy in Washington, Ikawa Tadao, Father Walsh, and Postmaster-General Walker. Baba, *op. cit.,* pp. 6–7.

pate in exploratory conversations to ascertain whether there existed any basis for negotiations.

On April 16 Secretary Hull assured Ambassador Nomura in Washington that the latter was at the fullest liberty to submit the document in question to the Japanese government. Accordingly, the draft proposal was transmitted to Tōkyō on April 18. America Bureau Director Terasaki of the Foreign Office, War Ministry's Military Affairs Bureau Director Mutō, and the Navy Ministry's Naval Affairs Bureau Director Oka studied the proposal carefully and reported it favorably to Premier Konoe. That very evening a liaison conference between the supreme military command and the government was hurriedly called to deliberate on the American proposal. The decision was reached by the conference to open negotiations with the United States, but the sending of a reply was to await the return of Foreign Minister Matsuoka from Europe.

Matsuoka's Visit to Axis Partners. Viewed in retrospect, there seems to be little doubt that Matsuoka's visit [7] to the Axis partners and Soviet Russia in the spring of 1941 was a decisive factor in Japan's following the course that led inevitably to war. In Berlin Matsuoka was given by both Foreign Minister von Ribbentrop and the Führer himself a grossly exaggerated picture of Germany's military might,[8] and was told in no uncertain terms that not only were the Nazis complete masters of the situation on the entire continent of Europe, but also that the conquest of Britain was merely a question of time. Ribbentrop brazenly declared that the war had already been definitely won for the Axis and could no longer be lost.[9] He emphasized at the same time, however, that the Führer thought it would be very desirable if Japan would decide as soon as possible to take an active part in the war against England and that a quick attack upon Singapore would be a very decisive factor in the defeat of England.

Hitler urged on Matsuoka on March 27 that "now was the most favorable time" for Japan to act since "such a moment would never return." Matsuoka replied that it was "only a question of time when Japan would attack" and that in connection with his efforts to bring about the Tripartite Pact he had oftentimes intentionally given the impression of having a pro-American or pro-British attitude in order to deceive his opponents.[10] Ribbentrop urged again on March 28 that "When an opportunity was offered Japan under such circum-

[7] Matsuoka left Tōkyō on March 12 and returned on April 22.

[8] Ribbentrop told Matsuoka that the Führer had at his command perhaps the strongest military power that the world had ever seen, and that the *Luftwaffe* was not only a match for England and America, but was definitely superior to them. He later told Matsuoka that Admiral Raeder thought American submarines were so poor that Japan need not concern herself about them at all.

[9] Memorandum of conversation between Ribbentrop and Matsuoka. U.S. Department of State, *Nazi-Soviet Relations, 1939–1941*, pp. 281–288.

[10] Memorandum of Hitler-Matsuoka interview, *ibid.*, pp. 289–298.

stances, she ought to weigh matters carefully and not let the opportunity slip out of her hand." [11]

On the eve of his departure Matsuoka had another interview with Hitler, who assured him that "if Japan got into conflict with the United States, Germany on her part would take the necessary steps at once, since it made no difference with whom the United States first came into conflict, Germany or Japan." Matsuoka in response stated that he had always declared that if Japan continued in the same fashion as at present, a war with the United States sooner or later would be unavoidable. In his view this conflict might better occur sooner than later; therefore, "why should not Japan decide to act with determination at the proper moment and take the risk of a war against America?" [12]

En route back home, Matsuoka stopped in Moscow and in quick order concluded a neutrality pact that Ribbentrop had only a few days earlier recommended should not be discussed in Moscow, since it "probably would not altogether fit into the framework of the present situation." [13] The treaty was a compromise, since Matsuoka's original demands were for a nonaggression pact and the purchase of North Sakhalin by Japan. Molotov on his part had to abandon his demand that Japan give up her concessions for oil and coal in North Sakhalin for a consideration, because of Matsuoka's rejection.

The Soviet-Japanese Neutrality Pact,[14] which was signed in Moscow on April 13, 1941, had for its purpose the maintenance of friendly relations and mutual respect for the territorial integrity and inviolability of the other contracting party. It was agreed that in the event one of the parties became involved in hostilities with one or more third powers, the other party would remain neutral. In addition, the two powers solemnly pledged, in an appended Joint Frontier Declaration, to respect reciprocally the territorial integrity and inviolability of Manchukuo and of the Mongolian People's Republic.

Matsuoka's departure from Moscow was an occasion of unexpected demonstration of Soviet-Japanese cordiality, which surprised foreign diplomatic circles. Stalin and Molotov appeared at the station completely unexpectedly both to the Japanese and the Russians, exchanged friendly greetings, and wished Matsuoka and his party a pleasant journey home.[15] Foreign Minister Matsuoka was gratified that the Pact would make a powerful impression on Chiang Kai-shek, and appreciably ease Japanese negotiations with him. He thought it would also

[11] Ribbentrop-Matsuoka conversations, *ibid.,* p. 300.

[12] Hitler-Matsuoka interview on April 4, 1941, *ibid.,* p. 314. In Moscow, U.S. Ambassador Steinhardt tried to find out from Matsuoka whether a Japanese attack on the United States had been decided upon in Berlin. Matsuoka denied any such decision. *Ibid.,* p. 321.

[13] Ribbentrop-Matsuoka conversations, *ibid.,* p. 302. Ribbentrop had no objection to the conclusion of purely commercial agreements.

[14] Jones and Myers, *op. cit.,* pp. 291–293.

[15] Telegram from German Ambassador Schulenburg to the German Foreign Office, April 13, 1941. *Nazi-Soviet Relations,* pp. 323–324.

strengthen the Japanese position towards the United States and Great Britain.

Resumption of American-Japanese Conversations. Foreign Minister Matsuoka's return on the afternoon of April 21 was followed that very evening by an emergency meeting held between the government and the military supreme command. A draft counterproposal that had been prepared by the three Bureau Directors was shown Matsuoka, but he did not approve of it at all. He argued that if the United States were to enter the European war, Japan would be obligated by the Tripartite Pact to join the hostilities, in which case there was no point in effecting an American-Japanese *rapprochement*. Contending that it would be disadvantageous to act rashly, he asked for about two weeks' time in which to think matters over, and shortly after eleven o'clock that night he excused himself and left the meeting that was still going on.

Matsuoka was resorting to dilatory tactics. Moreover, he insisted on notifying the Axis partners of the American proposal. In spite of Premier Konoe's disapproval, he went ahead and consulted Germany and Italy.[16] Consequently it was not until May 12, after German and Italian reactions had been received, that Ambassador Nomura was instructed to hand the Japanese draft proposal to Secretary Hull.[17] Prior to this, on May 7, Ambassador Nomura, in apologizing to Secretary Hull on the undue delay in hearing from his government, had made some reference to politicians and Matsuoka, with the inference that they were causing the delays and complications.[18]

On May 12, Secretary Hull reiterated and underscored the remark that Nomura had made only a few days earlier to the effect that it would be an incalculable loss to the two countries as well as to civilization should the United States and Japan become engaged in war. He emphasized to the Japanese Ambassador that it "will require all of the united efforts of civilized nations like Japan, the United States, and Great Britain to shape the course of the world in a different direction," if world civilization were to avoid the great risk of being destroyed by Hitler's movement.[19] This was clearly an American bid for Japan's cooperation.

President Roosevelt, on May 27, proclaimed the existence of an "unlimited national emergency" and America's determination to resist wherever necessary Hitler's attempts to extend his domination to the Western Hemisphere, to gain control of the seas, and to give every possible assistance to Great Britain and all countries resisting with force of arms Hitlerism or its equivalent. The President left little doubt of the course which the United States had resolved to follow.

On May 31 an unofficial, exploratory, noncommittal American draft proposal was handed to Ambassador Nomura, who transmitted it to his government.

[16] Baba, *op. cit.,* p. 11.
[17] *Foreign Relations of the United States, Japan: 1931–1941,* Vol. II, pp. 420–425.
[18] Memorandum of the Secretary of State, *ibid.,* pp. 411–415.
[19] *Ibid.,* p. 418.

Matsuoka insisted that the oral explanation for suggested amendments to the Japanese draft that was appended contained an inference that someone within the Japanese government was not desirous of success in American-Japanese conversations. He took umbrage, regarding it as a gratuitous attempt on the part of the United States to meddle in Japan's internal politics. That this was a perversion on the part of the Foreign Minister was quite clear.

On June 21, Secretary Hull gave the Japanese Ambassador a comprehensive oral statement [20] of the American attitude together with a draft proposal including the following points: (1) affirmation by both governments that their national policies were directed toward the establishment of lasting peace and the inauguration of an era of reciprocal confidence and cooperation between the two nations; (2) affirmation by the Japanese government that the Tripartite Pact was defensive and designed to prevent an extension of the European war, and assurance by the American government that its attitude toward the European war was and would continue to be determined solely by considerations of protection and self-defense; (3) American suggestion to China for Sino-Japanese negotiations; (4) resumption of normal American-Japanese trade relations; (5) American-Japanese cooperation toward obtaining through peaceful means non-discriminatory access to supplies of natural resources needed by each; (6) mutual affirmation of peace throughout the Pacific area as the basic national policy and a mutual disclaimer of territorial designs in the area; and (7) Japanese declaration of her willingness to negotiate with the United States with a view to concluding a treaty for the neutralization of the Philippines, when her independence was achieved.

On June 22, the day on which Hitler reneged on the Soviet-German Non-aggression Pact and invaded Russia, Foreign Minister Matsuoka expressed his view in an audience with the Emperor that Japan was obligated, under the Tripartite Pact, to take up arms against the Soviet Union, and, should Great Britain and the United States ally themselves with Russia, Japan would be forced to fight them too.[21] It was soon after this that reports reached the United States from various sources to the effect that the Japanese government was seriously considering going to war with the Soviet Union.

The Japanese government was reminded on July 6 by the United States that, should Japan enter upon a course of military aggression and conquest, it would destroy the cherished hope of the American government that the peace in the Pacific area might be strengthened.[22] This message, which was sent to Premier Konoe by Secretary Hull at the specific request of the President, brought a reply two days later stating that the Japanese government had "not so far considered the possibility of joining the hostilities against the Soviet Union." Interestingly

[20] *Ibid.*, pp. 485–486.
[21] Baba, *op. cit.*, p. 12.
[22] *Foreign Relations of the United States, Japan*, Vol. II, pp. 502–503.

enough, the Japanese reply also contained an inquiry as to whether or not the United States President or government entertained any thought of intervening in the European war. Only a few days earlier, on July 2, in an oral statement to the Soviet Ambassador, Matsuoka confessed that Japan found herself in the most awkward position, but gave assurances that his government felt no compulsion to modify its policy towards the Soviet Union.[23] Matsuoka assured him that he would do his best, but left considerable latitude for action when he asserted "that future developments will largely decide if the Japanese Government can consistently abide by this policy."

Meanwhile, the United States implemented her resolute stand against the Nazi threat on July 7. President Roosevelt announced to the Congress that in accordance with an understanding reached with Iceland, American forces had been sent there to supplement and eventually to replace the British forces for the purpose of ensuring adequate defense of the country.

So perverted and inflamed was Foreign Minister Matsuoka that, in complete disregard of the decision reached at the liaison conference between the government and the supreme military command, he cabled Ambassador Nomura on July 14 instructions demanding the retraction of Secretary Hull's Oral Explanation for Suggested Amendments to the Japanese Draft.[24] This unwarranted action precipitated the cabinet crisis that led to the resignation two days later of the second Konoe Cabinet. As a means of restoring cabinet unity, the Emperor had suggested the dropping of Matsuoka, but Premier Konoe decided to assume the responsibility for having appointed Matsuoka himself and resigned.

Japan Moves into French Indo-China. Only a few days after the emergence of the third Konoe Cabinet, on July 21, the French government at Vichy yielded to the pressure applied by the Axis and signed a joint defense agreement, granting Japan the right to maintain troops and establish air and naval bases in southern Indo-China. The Japanese government explained the action as necessary for ensuring an uninterrupted source of supply of rice and other foodstuffs as well as raw materials, the flow of which might be obstructed by Chinese forces and De Gaullist activities in southern Indo-China. It was claimed further that the step was taken as a safeguard against the encirclement of Japan by the ABCD powers (American, British, Chinese, and Dutch governments).

On July 24 President Roosevelt stated emphatically to Admiral Nomura that the new Japanese move in French Indo-China created an exceedingly serious problem for the United States and proposed that, if the Japanese government would refrain from occupying Indo-China with its military and naval forces, he would do everything in his power to obtain a binding declaration from the

[23] *Ibid.,* p. 504.

[24] *Ibid.,* pp. 506–509. Memorandum of conversations between Ambassador Nomura, Maxwell Hamilton, and Joseph W. Ballantine on July 15.

ABCD governments to regard Indo-China as a neutralized area, provided Japan made a similar commitment.[25] In spite of the bitter criticism against the administration, President Roosevelt had permitted oil to be shipped from the United States to Japan, lest she attempt to seize the oil supplies in the Netherlands East Indies. His policy had been to take every precaution to prevent war from breaking out in the Pacific.

By the end of July Japanese troops had moved into southern Indo-China and virtually completed the encirclement of the Philippines, placing vital trade routes within easy striking distance. The situation had become extremely critical, and the risk of war was so great that the United States and other countries concerned were no longer engrossed in trying to avoid risk; they began to take steps to prevent the breakdown of their security. It was deemed by the American government that the discontinuance of trade had become not only an appropriate and warranted but a necessary step, a warning to Japan as well as a measure of self-defense. Accordingly, President Roosevelt issued an executive order on July 26, 1941, freezing Japanese assets in the United States, which resulted in the virtual cessation of American-Japanese trade.

THE ATLANTIC CHARTER

In the memorable meeting held at sea between President Roosevelt and Prime Minister Winston Churchill in the summer of 1941, when the German threat was mounting, the whole problem of supplying munitions of war as provided in the Lend Lease Act of March 11, 1941, was discussed. But perhaps the most significant outcome of this meeting was the joint declaration of August 14, the Atlantic Charter, which constituted a statement of common principles in the national policies on which the two nations based their hopes for a better future for the world. In it they declared that their countries sought no aggrandizement, desired to see no territorial changes not in accord with the freely expressed wishes of the peoples concerned, respected the right of all peoples to choose the form of government under which they would live, would endeavor to further the enjoyment by all nations of equal access to trade and raw materials needed for their economic prosperity, desired to bring about the fullest world economic cooperation with a view to securing improved labor standards, economic advancement, and social security, hoped after the final destruction of Nazi tyranny for world peace, which would guarantee freedom from fear and want as well as the freedom of the seas, and believed that all nations must abandon the use of force.

Shortly after the meeting that produced the Atlantic Charter, on August 18,

[25] U.S. Department of State, *Peace and War: United States Foreign Policy, 1931–1941,* p. 120.

Foreign Minister Admiral Toyoda suggested to Ambassador Grew the desirability of a meeting in Honolulu between President Roosevelt and Premier Konoe, who was determined to find some sort of *modus vivendi* in spite of the strong objection of the extremists. Grew strongly urged the Secretary of State to give the proposal "prayerful consideration," as not only was it "unprecedented in Japanese history, but it is an indication that Japanese intransigence is not crystallized completely, owing to the fact that the proposal has the approval of the Emperor and the highest authorities in the land." [26]

Ten days later Premier Konoe sent a message to President Roosevelt requesting a meeting as soon as possible. The President expressed his preference for Juneau, Alaska, over Honolulu, which had been suggested by the Japanese. However, as a result of the publicity given to the proposal, the extremist and pro-Axis elements were given a chance to add fuel to the fire and inflamed public opinion at home, especially as it came on the heels of the President's executive order freezing Japanese assets, the announcement that American tankers bearing oil to the Soviet Union had left California ports, and the decision to send a military mission to Chiang Kai-shek.[27] Roosevelt's reply to Konoe suggested, that, in view of the existence of concepts in some Japanese quarters that appeared capable of raising obstacles to successful collaboration, it was desirable to take precaution to ensure that the proposed meeting would prove to be a success by entering immediately upon preliminary discussion of the fundamental and essential questions on which agreement was to be sought.

Meanwhile, on September 5, 1941, on the day before the Imperial Conference was to be held, the Emperor summoned the Chief of General Staff Sugiyama and Chief of the Naval General Staff Nagano and inquired as to the length of time required to terminate the war, should this come to pass. Sugiyama replied that the army expected to finish it in about three months so far as the South Seas region was concerned. The Emperor refreshed Sugiyama's memory by pointing out that as War Minister at the time of the outbreak of the China War in 1937 he had predicted victory in a month, whereas even after four years the end was not yet in sight. Sugiyama apologetically pointed out that operations had been difficult to execute as planned because of the vastness of China. The Emperor rejoined in a reprimanding tone, emphasizing that the expanse of the Pacific was even greater. When pressed by the Emperor on how he was able to arrive at the figure of three months, Sugiyama was unable to give any reply and withdrew after admitting the wisdom of adjusting American-Japanese relations by negotiation.

On September 6 an Imperial Conference was held and a deadline was set for

[26] Ambassador Grew to the Secretary of State, *Foreign Relations of the United States, Japan: 1931–1941,* Vol. II, p. 565.

[27] White House Press Release of August 26, 1941. U.S. Department of State, *Bulletin,* Vol. V, No. 114, p. 166, August 30, 1941.

the early part of October for the satisfactory conclusion of American-Japanese relations.[28] The deadline having arrived on October 12, and a solution being still a long way off, Premier Konoe called together the War, Navy, and Foreign Ministers to discuss the next step in American-Japanese negotiations. The navy had indicated its willingness the day before to leave the matter entirely to the decision of the Premier. War Minister Tōjō, however, adamantly maintained that there was absolutely no hope of agreement. The Four Ministers' Conference was resumed the next day, but General Tōjō refused to agree on the withdrawal of troops from China, which Navy Minister Toyoda emphasized as a necessary prerequisite to a reconciliation or *rapprochement* with the United States. At the Cabinet meeting held a week later, War Minister Tōjō virtually monopolized the floor in an exposition of his views and urged the necessity of deciding on war. Four times Konoe talked to Tōjō in the hope of changing his mind, but after the fourth meeting, Tōjō refused to see the Premier, assuming the attitude that it was futile to talk any further with him.

The War Minister was as unbending as he was irrational in the stand he took. When Konoe pointed out the superiority of the manpower and material resources of the United States, he countered by mentioning the large number of Americans of German extraction and the possibility of labor troubles, and criticized the Premier for emphasizing only America's assets and ignoring completely her liabilities. Moreover, he pointed out that neither the Sino-Japanese War of 1894–95 nor the Russo-Japanese War of 1904–05 was started with absolute certainty of victory.

Having reached an impasse in the negotiations with the United States through the obstructionist tactics of the extremists and pro-Axis elements as well as the stubborn attitude of War Minister Tōjō, the third Konoe Cabinet had no alternative but to resign. Two days later, on October 18, the government of General Tōjō emerged. Privy Seal Marquis Kido, the chief supporter of the bellicose War Minister, was mainly responsible for recommending him for the premiership.

The palace advisers, of which Marquis Kido was the official leader, selected General Tōjō in the belief that he could avert war with the United States by controlling the war faction within the army. They were led to believe that there was no other army leader capable of effectively controlling the dissident elements in the army. An abysmal ignorance as well as an incredible blindness of the palace advisers regarding the real character and motives of General Tōjō and the role of the army were responsible for the fatal decision. Tōjō had already indicated his warlike attitude as early as August, 1939, when as War Minister he had blusteringly stated in his address to the Imperial Reservists' Association that

---

[28] It was brought out in the course of the war crimes trial in Tōkyō that Director of Military Affairs Bureau General Mutō told Major F. D. Merrill of the Office of the U.S. Military Attaché on October 8 that hostilities would start within six weeks if negotiations were not successful.

Japan should be ready to carry on a two-front war, taking on simultaneously Soviet Russia as well as Great Britain and the United States, if necessary for the termination of the China War.

General Tōjō surrounded himself with flunkeys to do his bidding. Moreover, he had developed an effective technique over the years, especially since 1935, when he became commandant of the gendarmerie of the Kwantung Army, in which position he systematically and meticulously collected evidence of scandalous connections between army personnel in Manchuria and profit-seeking interests. The dossier he built up and the technique he perfected in the effective use of the gendarmerie were used with devastating effect later during the war when he took over the helm of state. He made use of the gendarmerie not only in the control of military personnel but in intimidating and suppressing civilians as well. When he became War Minister in 1940, he banished to distant posts those officers whom he disliked or who disagreed with him. He retired his strongest rivals, Generals Ishihara and Tada, and placed General Nishio on the reserve list. Even his onetime superior and mentor, War Minister Itagaki, came dangerously close to being relieved from active service. Key posts in the army were given only to those who demonstrated unquestioning obedience. Under his regime the Director of the Military Affairs Bureau and virtually all the army officers assigned to the various ministries, offices, and boards meddled in political and economic matters with his tacit approval and blessing.

Throughout his entire tenure as Premier, he was concurrently War Minister. In the beginning he held the Home Affairs portfolio until he was satisfied that the early stages of the military offensive were successful, for he wanted to be sure that the home front was kept under strict control. At different times he was concurrently Chief of General Staff, Munitions Minister, Foreign Minister, and Education Minister, showing not even the slightest hesitation in holding any portfolio. His behavior at times reflected megalomaniacal tendencies and his decisions were frequently distaff controlled, intuitive, irrational, and ill-considered.

INCREASING NAZI PRESSURE

As October wore on, it became increasingly apparent that Nazi pressure was being brought to bear on the Japanese military leaders with telling effect. German representatives and agents in large numbers had been active in advising the government in various capacities not only in technical matters but in political matters as well, exerting a great deal of influence in the various ministries and carrying on effective propaganda. On October 10 Foreign Minister Admiral Toyoda expressed to Ambassador Grew his concern lest the government be unable to control extremist groups, if no tangible results were achieved in the American-Japanese conversations. The Nazis were pressing the Japanese government for an official statement confirming the interpretation given the Tripartite Pact by

Matsuoka in June to the effect that Japan would declare war on the United States in the event of hostilities between Germany and the United States.[29] Since it was not to the interests of the Nazis for Japan to arrive at any sort of agreement with the United States, Hitler's agents threw every obstacle in the way. Toyoda made known to Grew a plan to send an experienced diplomat with the rank of Ambassador to Washington to assist Admiral Nomura, and inquired if the United States government would be prepared to make reservations available for the official in question on the airplane from Manila to San Francisco.[30] This was arranged, and on November 15 Ambassador Kurusu arrived in Washington to assist Nomura in minimizing the possibility of committing any blunder.

On November 12 Secretary Hull, in amplifying his suggestion regarding mutual exchanges of pledges between China and Japan for the establishment of real friendship and collaboration between the two countries, made a strong appeal to the Japanese government on the basis of the unique opportunity that such an agreement afforded in enhancing Japan's moral prestige on a basis of moral force in a way that military might could never accomplish. He emphasized that what was envisaged was an implementation of the kind of constructive, liberal, and peaceful world program that had been discussed in the exploratory conversations, contemplating "practical application of basic principles directed toward the preservation of order under law, peace with justice, and the social and economic welfare of mankind." Such a program envisaged "peaceful collaboration among nations, mutual respect for the rights of all, no aggrandizement, and the adopting of broad gauge economic policies that would provide liberalization of trade, afford fair access to and development of natural resources, and raise living standards to the betterment of all peoples." [31] Even as Secretary Hull was exerting himself for peace, Ambassador Grew, in his telegram of November 17 to the State Department, emphasized once again the need to guard against sudden Japanese naval or military actions that would exploit every possible tactical advantage such as surprise and initiative.[32]

On November 26 the Secretary of State handed Ambassador Nomura a tentative outline of the proposed basis for agreement, which proved to be the last, since it was perverted by the Japanese government as tantamount to an ultimatum.[33] When handed copies of the outline and oral statement, Kurusu's reaction was that the American response to the Japanese proposal could be interpreted as an act terminating the conversations.[34] The document was designed,

[29] Memorandum by Ambassador Grew. *Foreign Relations of the United States, Japan: 1931–1941,* Vol. II, p. 686.
[30] *Ibid.,* pp. 677–679.
[31] *Ibid.,* pp. 726–727.
[32] *Ibid.,* p. 743.
[33] *Ibid.,* pp. 768–770.
[34] *Ibid.,* pp. 764–766.

however, as a mutual declaration of policy by the two governments to the effect that their national policies were directed toward lasting and extensive peace throughout the Pacific area. It was an affirmation that, in their national policies, they would actively support and give practical application to the fundamental principles of inviolability of territorial integrity and sovereignty of nations, non-interference in the internal affairs of other countries, equality that included equality of commercial opportunity and treatment, and reliance upon international cooperation and conciliation for the prevention and pacific settlement of disputes and for the improvement of international conditions by peaceful methods and processes.

To these ends, efforts were to be made by the two governments to achieve the following: (1) conclusion of a multilateral nonaggression pact among the British Empire, Japan, the Netherlands, the Soviet Union, and the United States; (2) agreement among the American, British, Chinese, Dutch, Japanese and Thai governments, pledging to respect the territorial integrity of French Indo-China; (3) withdrawal of all Japanese military, naval, air, and police forces from China and from Indo-China; (4) nonsupport militarily, politically, or economically of any government or regime in China other than the Nationalist government at Chungking; (5) abandonment of all extraterritorial rights in China including the international settlements, concessions, and rights under the Boxer Protocol of 1901; (6) negotiations for the conclusion of an American-Japanese trade agreement based upon reciprocal most-favored-nation treatment and reduction of trade barriers; (7) mutual removal of freezing restrictions between the two countries; (8) agreement on a plan for the stabilization of the dollar-yen rate; (9) agreement that no treaty that either had entered into with any third power or powers should be interpreted in such a way as to conflict with the fundamental purpose of the establishment and preservation of peace throughout the Pacific area, and (10) the securing of adherence of other governments and giving practical application to the basic economic principles set forth in this agreement.

Premier Tōjō construed the American draft proposal as a virtual ultimatum and decided that there was no point in endeavoring further to reach any sort of agreement. This was brought out clearly in the government's announcement to the nation through the Foreign Office after the blow had been struck at Pearl Harbor. There was not even a faint suggestion that the American document was only a tentative draft outline of the proposed basis of agreement, which could not by the greatest stretch of imagination be interpreted as an ultimatum. By deliberately misinterpreting it, the government had found a pretext by which the nation was plunged into war.

PEARL HARBOR

On early Sunday morning of December 7, while most of Honolulu and the Islands continued in tranquil slumber, more than 100 Japanese bomber, fighter, and torpedo planes unleashed a savage attack on the great American naval base at Pearl Harbor, as the warships of the Pacific Fleet rode at anchor. When the two-hour dawn raid ended, eight battleships, three light cruisers and four other vessels had been either sunk or damaged. Approximately 90 per cent of the naval and air strength of the United States in the Hawaiian Islands was immobilized, permitting the Japanese to strike crippling blows at other points without interference from the United States Fleet.

Simultaneous raids were carried out on the same day against Wake, Guam, Midway, the Philippine Islands, and Hong Kong. The attack on the British crown colony garrisoned by 12,000 British and Canadian troops began with dive bombing, followed by the landing of troops. Subsequently, the Kowloon defense lines were pierced and water supply facilities were destroyed by aerial and artillery bombardment, reducing Hong Kong to a helpless state and forcing it to surrender on Christmas day.

The next day, Japanese troops landed on the east coast of Malaya with the airfields at Kota Baru, Singora, and Patani as their immediate objectives. Pushing their troops across the Kra Isthmus, they severed land communications between Malaya and Burma. In a two-pronged drive simultaneously down the east and west coasts of the peninsula they pushed rapidly through the treacherous jungles executing a swift flanking movement and meeting with only weak and sporadic resistance from the hard-pressed British defenders, who had not expected or prepared for an overland invasion by the Japanese. The British suffered severe naval loss in the first few days of the war, when Japanese planes sank the *Prince of Wales* and the *Repulse,* which had been sent northward from Singapore without any air cover.

On January 11 Japanese forces captured Kuala Lumpur and pushed ahead, forcing the British to withdraw on January 31 to Singapore Island. The Japanese quickly repaired the blasted causeway connecting Singapore with the mainland and pushed toward the city. On February 15 the great British naval bastion of Singapore, a symbol of British power in eastern Asia, fell into Japanese hands without having fired a single shot from its huge rifles, which were fixedly pointed seaward. General Percival and his 75,000 beleaguered defenders surrendered to the overwhelming Japanese military power commanded by General Yamashita, "the tiger of Malaya."

Eight hours after the surprise attack on Pearl Harbor, Japanese planes struck at American airfields in the Philippines, destroying most of the planes on the ground. The naval base at Cavite was destroyed on December 10, and on the same day Japanese troops began landing on northern Luzon. Assaults by the Japanese began in earnest on December 21, and the siege of Bataan commenced on January 1, 1942. The following day Manila fell. On March 11, General Douglas MacArthur left Bataan for Australia by air under presidential orders to assume command of the Southwest Pacific Area. The heroes of Bataan held out against insuperable odds until long after Hong Kong, Singapore, Rangoon, and Batavia had fallen. They fought to the last in the hope of getting reenforcements, which never came. On May 6 the intrepid but exhausted defenders of Corregidor, after withstanding a terrific pounding from the air, capitulated to the overwhelmingly superior Japanese force.

Almost simultaneously with the fall of Singapore Japanese forces captured Moulmein and pushed on further into Burma, securing Rangoon on March 10. Faced by superior enemy forces, the British troops under General Sir Harold Alexander and the Chinese Fifth and Sixth Armies under American General Joseph Stilwell were forced to retreat up the Irrawaddy after the fall of Rangoon. Fighting rear guard actions, Stilwell led his troops in a heartbreaking retreat over the Naga hills and into India. On the last day of April the Japanese forces occupied Lashio, key to the celebrated Burma Road, and held it until they were dislodged later as the Allied offensive started to roll.

Amphibious operations were launched against the Netherlands East Indies, and on December 22 Japanese troops effected a landing on the northern coast of Borneo in British Sarawak. From their airfields at Davao they started bombing raids in January. On December 11 the oil depot of Tarakan and strategic bases in Borneo and Menado in the Celebes were captured. Amphibious forces from their base at Truk in the Caroline Islands landed at Rabaul, New Britain, and Kavieng, New Ireland, on January 23, followed by Bougainville a week later. In spite of severe damages inflicted upon the Japanese invasion fleet in the Battle of Macassar Strait on January 23 and 24, the Japanese advance was not checked effectively.

Dutch forces resorted to delaying action in the hope of giving the British and American forces time to come to their relief, but were unsuccessful. Japanese paratroopers were landed on southern Sumatra in mid-February followed by seaborne troops and, after forcing the Dutch to withdraw to Java, they overran the oil fields of Palambang. Organized naval resistance by the Allies in the Netherlands East Indies came to an end by March 1, after a superior Japanese force defeated the Allied fleet off Surabaya and Sunda Strait in the closing days of February. On March 5 Batavia fell, Surabaya two days later, and the Dutch capitulated on the ninth.

Rapid overrunning of a vast area in a short space of less than six months exceeded even the most sanguine expectations of the militarists, and produced an attitude of overconfidence. This overoptimism was reflected in the propaganda broadcasts emanating from Tōkyō, which blandly and blatantly predicted that the successful termination of the war was already in sight. Military leaders deluded themselves into thinking that it was merely a question of time before the Allies sued for peace.

The Doolittle raid on Tōkyō on April 18, 1942, by sixteen carrier-based B-25 medium bombers launched from the U.S.S. *Hornet* within 800 miles of the Japanese coast served as a warning of what was to come. It was a foretaste of American striking power, which dispelled once and for all the Japanese militarists' boast that her zone of inner defense could never be successfully penetrated by air power. Admittedly, the Doolittle raid had little strategic value, but its morale effect to the Allies was tremendous, coming as it did in the dark days of the Pacific War.

In a few short months Japanese forces had spread out rapidly over most of the Southwest Pacific without encountering any serious resistance. On May 3 the Japanese began to occupy Florida Island in the southern Solomons. The next objective appeared to be Port Moresby, the Allied base on the southeast coast of New Guinea, which would have provided an ideal jumping off point for a thrust at the northeast corner of Australia.

HOME FRONT DEVELOPMENTS

The initial successes of the war caused the Tōjō Government to rest more or less on its laurels for most of the year 1942, during which it devoted its major energies at home to mobilizing the nation to the fullest extent. On January 16 it organized the Imperial Rule Assistance Youth Corps (Dai Nihon Yokusan Sōnen Dan) designed as shock troops of the Imperial Rule Assistance Association to spark the total mobilization effort.[35] This nationwide movement, not unlike Hitler's youth movement in conception, was headed by a retired General Tatekawa, onetime Ambassador to Moscow, while the Director of its Central Headquarters was Colonel Hashimoto, whose artillery regiment was implicated in the Panay Incident.

In January the Technical Board (Gijutsuin) was also organized for the purpose of achieving full mobilization in science and technology. Although it was charged with the stimulation of research and production, it was unable to get many results because of the distrust of the military. In May the Japan Aviation Technological Society (Dai Nihon Kōkū Gijutsu Kyōkai) was organized to promote aeronautical research and production. The Army Aircraft Industry Association (Rikugun Kōkū Kōgyōkai) was created in November to bring together aircraft manufacturers in an organization designed to function as a control society.

---

[35] Inspiration for the organization had come from an advisory group comprising the Vice Ministers, and directors of the Military Affairs Bureau and the Naval Affairs Bureau.

Amalgamation of all feminine activities under one roof in keeping with the government's totalitarian policy was achieved on February 2, when the Japan Women's Association was launched under the joint auspices of the IRAA and the Welfare Ministry. Merged into the new organization were the Patriotic Women's Association, National Defense Women's Association, Federated Women's Association, and others. All women twenty years of age and over were mobilized in the movement to place home life on an emergency basis, protect family health, promote family education, participate in civilian defense training, render mutual aid in neighborhood groups, and give assistance in other matters.

The Imperial Rule Assistance Association deprived national politics of what little substance it had, for the election of April 30, 1942, was seized upon by the Tōjō Government as an opportunity for the strengthening of national spiritual mobilization as well as its grip on the nation. The second Konoe Cabinet had extended the term of the Diet members through a legislative act until the spring of 1942. Premier Tōjō was determined to utilize this national election to bolster the morale and unity of the nation, which had fallen short of his expectations. In the cabinet meeting of February 18 he therefore decided to carry out an election that would truly be an assistance to imperial rule.[36] To achieve this he set up an *ad hoc* body headed by General Abe Nobuyuki, which served virtually as the government's nominating committee. It endorsed 381 successful candidates for the 466 seats in the House of Representatives.

Those who were endorsed by the government received 5,000 yen toward their campaign expenditure, which was later discovered as having come out of the army's emergency funds. Voicing opposition against government policies and even the expression of constructive criticisms were regarded as treasonable by the government, and those who dared to commit such acts were turned over to the gendarmerie or the special higher police. Significant was the fact that only 85 out of the 614 candidates who ran without the blessings of the Tōjō Government were successful. As a result of interference, the government secured better than 80 per cent of the entire lower house membership.

In order to ensure the election of government-endorsed candidates, the Youth Corps went into action. Governors of prefectures, as heads of the prefectural branches of the IRAA, participated in the recommending of candidates. The same procedure was followed right down the line in municipal, town, and village elections in order to ensure the election of candidates who had been duly endorsed by the government.

However, all was not well on the propaganda front at home. Spiritual mobilization needed a shot in the arm. On May 15, at the halfway point between the government-tampered election and the disastrous defeat at Midway, the Tōjō Cabinet decided on the functional overhauling of the IRAA. This was followed

[36] Tōkyō *Asahi*, February 19, 1942.

on June 9 by the appointment of General Andō Kisaburō, Vice President of the IRAA, to the post of Minister without Portfolio in a move to tighten the government's propaganda grip on the people. Further structural changes were carried out in November and December in an attempt to bring together more closely the loose ends of the spiritual mobilization movement. Finally in mid-January, 1943, a propaganda headquarters was set up in the IRAA for the explicit purpose of molding and guiding public opinion.

UNITED STATES ASSUMES THE OFFENSIVE

Early in May, Admiral Fletcher, in command of the aircraft carrier *Yorktown*, unleashed a successful attack on Japanese forces on Guadalcanal and combat ships in Tulagi harbor. Joined by a task force of Admiral Kinkaid and a group in command of Admiral Grace, Admiral Fletcher's fleet, suspecting enemy activity, seized the initiative and inflicted severe damages on the Japanese. In the ensuing Battle of the Coral Sea, a major naval engagement in which not a single shot was exchanged between surface ships, the Americans definitely stopped Japanese advance at the cost of the carrier *Lexington*.

In diversionary tactics designed to induce the Americans to rush reserves to Alaska and to distract their attention from the Central Pacific in preparation for a major thrust at Midway, Japanese forces launched an attack on the North American continent with an aerial bombardment of Dutch Harbor on June 3. A few days later they followed it up with landings on Attu, Kiska, and Agattu in the Aleutians. American naval and air power, however, remained concentrated at Midway in anticipation of the enemy thrust. American forces were in possession of intelligence pointing to Midway as the enemy's next main objective.

On June 5 and 6 the expected Japanese attack on Midway materialized and American forces were ready to meet it. Reconnaissance had spotted the Japanese naval forces long before they came within American striking distance. Land- and carrier-based army, navy, and marine corps planes were sent out to meet the invading carrier force, which was taken by surprise. An offensive action by American forces had not been included in the calculations of the Japanese. Four of the newest Japanese carriers were sent to the bottom and the engagement which, like the Battle of the Coral Sea, was fought entirely by aircraft without any exchange of shots between surface vessels ended in a disastrous rout for the Japanese naval force. This brought the period of Japanese offensive on the seas to an end.

In spite of the fact that the sensational initial successes of the Japanese forces had been achieved through effective use of air power, the Japanese admirals clung to the traditional fondness and reliance on heavy battleships and did not fully develop the striking power of a highly mobile task force based upon air power. Moreover, the Japanese high command had underestimated the tremendous industrial potential of the United States, which was speedily mobilized, enabling it not only to offset in less than six months the damages suffered at Pearl Harbor, but also to build up naval and air power more than adequate to cope with Japan's military power.

The winning streak for Japan came to an end as American forces began to assume the offensive in the summer of 1942, when the decision was made to invade the Solomons. In July, Japan began the construction of an airfield on Guadalcanal, from where land-based planes could menace the Allied bases in the New Hebrides, New Caledonia, and Port Moresby. To forestall this, the First United States Marine Division under General Vandegrift was called into action and suprise landings were made on Guadalcanal and Florida Island on August 7. Within thirty-six hours the airfield on Guadalcanal and Tulagi harbor were taken by the Americans. In the Battle of the Savo Sea, on the night of August 9, resulting from a Japanese naval force trying to retake the islands lost to the Allies, the Japanese suffered another serious setback. In mid-October American reenforcements started to arrive, and later in the month the Japanese made a desperate but unsuccessful attempt to dislodge American troops. Stubborn Japanese resistance continued for the next few months but in January, 1943, their troops began to evacuate. By February 10 Guadalcanal had fallen securely into American hands as organized Japanese resistance came to an end.

In the latter part of July, Japanese forces attempted to advance to Port Moresby in an overland drive from the northeast coast of New Guinea across the rugged Stanley Owen Mountains. Although by September 14 they were within thirty miles of their objective, the difficulties of jungle terrain and the problem of logistics coupled with the stiffened resistance of the seasoned Australian jungle fighters backed by reenforcements completely foiled the Japanese attempt, and troops were forced to fall back. By mid-November, they were penned up in small pockets of resistance and on January 2, 1943, they were eliminated.

BOLSTERING THE HOME FRONT

After the Battle of Midway news dispatches from the front began to show an increasingly pessimistic tone. Knowing that Premier Tōjō disliked unfavorable reports, General Mutō, Director of the Military Affairs Bureau, deleted portions that were distressingly unpalatable. The Premier in turn submitted to the Emperor battle reports that had been carefully edited. Suppression of the freedom of speech and press was carried out vigorously and systematically by the Tōjō Government. In the 84th ordinary session of the Diet, which opened in December, 1943, altogether eighty-four different items were stricken off the shorthand records, while for twenty-seven items shorthand notes were dispensed with completely. Interpellations and addresses on the floor of the Diet were censored in advance as they had to be submitted to the Premier's private secretary, Colonel Akamatsu.

The tremendous casualties suffered in the disastrous defeat at Midway were carefully concealed from the public. All the wounded were brought back to the Yokosuka Naval Hospital, where they were packed in like sardines and held incommunicado. In the War Ministry, aside from Tōjō, there were only two or three others who knew the full extent of the disastrous defeat. Then the newspaper *Mainichi* came out the day after the American task force attacked Truk with a banner headline "Wars Cannot Be Won by Bamboo Spears" and derided the idea that wars could be won by spiritual superiority, as had been drummed into the ears of the people by Tōjō. The *Mainichi* was merely reflecting the clamor that had developed in the Navy Ministry after Midway for more airplanes and scientific warfare, without which it was insisting there could be only defeat. Tōjō berated the officials for their failure to prevent the publication and sale of the paper and instructed Army Press Bureau Director Colonel Yahagi and Information Board Vice President Miyoshi to discharge the political editor responsible for the offending item.[37]

Intent on securing complete control of continental policy, both in planning and execution, the army had been carrying on a vigorous campaign and finally, nearly a year after Pearl Harbor, it succeeded. The Greater East Asia Ministry which opened on November 1, 1942, took over all the diplomatic functions pertaining to East Asia, absorbing the East Asia and South Seas Bureaus of the Foreign Office, the Manchurian Affairs Bureau, the Asia Development Board (China Affairs Board), and the entire Overseas Ministry. This effected the separation of foreign relations with East Asia from those of the rest of the world and placed them under the army's control. Dual diplomacy, which had existed *de facto* up to this time, was now given legal recognition.

The power of appointment and dismissal of diplomatic and consular officials in the region of "Greater East Asia" was taken away from the Foreign Minister and vested firmly in the army. Diplomatic personnel was chosen from the various ministries as well as the army. Needless to say, the new setup created an anomalous situation, enabling the military to carry on its East Asia policies without reference or regard to the rest of the world.

As the war entered its second year it became increasingly apparent that the cumbersome administrative machinery needed overhauling to step up war production, which was lagging behind. In March, 1943, simplification in administration and administrative procedure was effected through the cutting of red tape. At the same time the system of administrative inspection was instituted to stimulate administrative efficiency, discipline, and the thorough dissemination of national policies among the industrialists. Administrative inspectors

[37] Mori, *Sempū Nijūnen*, p. 124.

were appointed from among the Ministers without Portfolio and cabinet advisers to inspect and report on the conditions of war production and administration throughout the nation.

Of particular significance in this connection was the strengthening of the powers of the Premier under the Special Wartime Administrative Powers Law.[38] This legislation empowered the Premier to issue necessary directives to the ministries in order to increase production in the five designated essential categories: iron and steel, coal, light metals, ships, and aircraft. When necessary, he could take over the functions exercised by the various ministries in the procurement of labor, materials, power, and capital and even assign officials temporarily to offices and ministries other than those to which they belonged. This was an unprecedented strengthening of the powers of the Premier under wartime necessity.

In line with the policy of strengthening the central government, important changes were effected simultaneously in local administration.[39] Mayors of cities were made appointive by the Home Minister, while mayors of towns and villages who were elected by the respective assemblies required the approval of the prefectural governor, who was given the power of removal for cause. Functions and powers of mayors were limited to those enumerated, but at the same time they were given power to issue directives to public bodies and organizations for over-all planning and execution of policies. An advisory system under the mayoralty was instituted on the different levels.

Even more important in the coordination of the national war effort was the setting up of regional administrative councils on July 1, 1943.[40] Japan proper was divided into eight administrative regions for the purpose of integrating and coordinating a multitude of activities, financial, economic, and industrial, ranging all the way from tax and customs administration to mining and labor administration. The regional administration was headed by the governor of the key prefecture of the region, who was empowered to issue directives to all those within his jurisdiction.

The administrative setup of Tōkyō was changed by a law enacted by the Diet on January 10, 1943, at the instance of Home Minister General Andō.[41] This brought to an end the more than half a century of municipal rule in the nation's capital, placing it directly under the control of the Home Ministry. Citizens of Tōkyō lost the right of self-government as it had existed, for they were made part of the prefecture under the governor appointed by the central government.

[38] Promulgated as Law No. 75 on March 18, 1943, and taking effect the same day. For text, see 1944 *Asahi Nenkan,* p. 118.

[39] Promulgated as Laws Nos. 79, 80, and 81 and taking effect June 1, 1943. See 1944 *Asahi Nenkan,* p. 109.

[40] The organization was set up by Imperial Ordinance No. 548, *Chihō Gyōsei Kaigi Rei.* See Tōkyō *Asahi,* June 29, 1943.

[41] Promulgated on June 19 as Law No. 89.

Ward assemblies were retained but limited to the management of ward property and buildings without any policy-making or administrative functions, not even tax collecting. The reasons for the change were alleged to be the need for direct control by the central government for air defense purposes and the need for an efficient prefectural government, which would serve as the model for the rest of the country.

The last session of the Tōkyō Municipal Assembly was held on June 21 and that of the old prefectural assembly on June 24. The ceremony marking the end of prefectural and municipal governments was observed on June 30, and Governor Ōdachi took over the new metropolitan government on July 1. The election of the one hundred members of the new Tōkyō Metropolitan Assembly followed on September 13. Modeled after the central government, it was claimed to represent a simplification of administration.[42]

ALLIED OFFENSIVE INTENSIFIED

The decisions reached by the United States and British chiefs at the Casablanca Conference in January, 1943, to increase the flow of supplies to China and draw up strategic plans for operations in the South and Southwest Pacific were translated into action soon thereafter. In March American commanders and staff officers of the Central, South, and Southwest Pacific areas were summoned to Washington to coordinate their theater plans with the over-all strategic plans of the Allies.

Only a few months later the Japanese suffered one of the severest blows of the war. Admiral Yamamoto, Commander in Chief of the Combined Fleet, who was at Rabaul directing in person the operations against the Allies, was on his way back to his headquarters at Buin on April 18, 1943, when his plane and two others carrying his staff officers were attacked by American planes and shot down near Bougainville. The Admiral's death deeply affected the morale of the officers and men in his command in the Southwest Pacific and cast a dark shadow over the future of Japanese operations in that region.

American offensive rapidly gained momentum as "island hopping" started in the South Pacific. Japanese forces were dislodged from their positions as Allied forces advanced from Rendova, Colombangara, Munda, Salamaua, Lae, and on November 1, 1943, American marines landed on Bougainville. Earlier in May Attu had been wrested from the Japanese, in August, Kiska was retaken, and the Aleutians were once more safely in American hands.

Far-reaching strategic decisions were made at the Quebec Conference of August, 1943. Greater attention was paid to the Pacific War than at any previous meeting. American and British ground forces were unified and brought under

[42] Tōkyō *Asahi*, June 30, 1943.

the Southeast Asia Command under Admiral Louis Mountbatten with General Stilwell as deputy commander. The air forces of the two countries were combined into the Eastern Air Command under American Major General Stratemeyer. Strategic plans for the Pacific offensive against Japan were developed by the Allied Powers as follows: General MacArthur's operations along the New Guinea coast were to continue, the timetable calling for his return to the Philippines in the fall of 1944. The South Pacific forces, army and navy, under Admiral Halsey were to continue to enjoy operational autonomy, but under the strategic control of General MacArthur. Admiral Nimitz, Pacific Ocean Area Commander, was to strike across the Central Pacific through the Gilbert, Marshall and Marianas Islands to secure a foothold on Ryūkyū in the spring of 1945. Plans of General Arnold, Chief of the U.S. Army Air Forces, to soften Japan by extensive B-29 Superfortress bombing raids from bases in China and the Marianas were to be executed by the Twentieth Air Force, operating as a strategic air unit under the direction of the United States Joint Chiefs of Staff.

Operations for the Central Pacific offensive were launched by Admiral Nimitz in the fall of 1943 in accordance with the directive evolved at the Quebec Conference in August. On November 21 United States forces made simultaneous landings on the Marshall and Makin Islands. The landing on Makin was opposed by a relatively weak and ineffective Japanese garrison. At Tarawa, a tiny coral atoll, the Second Marine Division fought one of the bloodiest battles of the Pacific War and secured it on March 24 after a seventy-four-hour battle in which heavy casualties were suffered.

Severe Strains on Japan's Internal Structure. The administrative structure of the national government underwent almost periodic changes as increasing demands were made upon it by the urgency of war production. On November 1, 1943, the Munitions Ministry was created to take over all matters pertaining to war production previously handled by the Planning Board, Commerce and Industry Ministries, and other ministries. The new ministry, staffed by a large number of active army and navy officers as well as civilian bureaucrats, devoted itself to the coordination of efforts and increase of production of war materials and particularly aircraft. Simultaneously, the newly organized Agriculture and Commerce Ministry assumed jurisdiction of all civilian production, distribution, and price administration in the fields of agriculture, forestry, fishery, mining, commerce and manufacturing. The Transportation and Communications Ministry, also a new department, was entrusted with the task of keeping the transportation and communications facilities at the highest possible level of efficiency for the prosecution of the war.

In the emergency session of the Diet, held immediately following Pearl Harbor, the Tōjō Government submitted emergency legislation to suppress freedom of speech, press, association, and meeting. Its object was to prevent the development of opposition against the government and to permit only a single controlled political party. When it was known that the bill was to be submitted, the Tōhō-kai, led by Nakano Seigō, was outraged, and its Diet member Mitamura Takeo registered the party's opposition with the Justice and Home Ministries.

Nakano was determined to force the downfall of the Tōjō Cabinet. On the night of February 17, 1942, while the nation was still drunk with the capture of Singapore, he discussed the Pacific War with Admiral Nakamura Ryōzō. The two men agreed that steps should be taken to terminate the war right then. Immediately after the fall of Singapore conditions were quite favorable for an overture to terminate the war, but Tōjō refused to listen. Instead he went ahead with his plans to extend the war to India and Australia.[43]

In the general election of April, 1942, the forty-seven Tōhōkai candidates who refused the government's endorsement were suppressed by Tōjō, and only six of them, including Nakano, were elected. On November 11, the government organized the Imperial Rule Assistance Political Society based on the totalitarian system, which had met the test in Manchukuo under the Concordia Society setup. As part of this totalitarianization, the Tōhōkai was forcibly dissolved. From this time Nakano and his followers publicly opposed the Tōjō Cabinet.

Convinced that something must be done, especially after the reverses at Guadalcanal and Midway, Nakano lectured at a public meeting at Waseda University in mid-November and at Hibiya Hall on November 20 with the hope of inducing the reflection of the government. However, Tōjō retaliated by revising the Special Wartime Criminal Law (Senji Keiji Tokubetsuhō) and ordering that Nakano and members of the defunct Tōhōkai never be allowed to appear at public meetings under any circumstances. It would have been a relatively simple thing to liquidate Tōjō by employing terroristic methods, since there were members of the Gen'yōsha in the Tōhōkai and support had been pledged by various groups. However, Nakano decided upon a different course, namely, an appeal to the ex-Premiers and palace advisers, only to find that they too together with Princes Higashikuni and Kaya had been thinking of forcing out the Tōjō Cabinet.

By July, 1943, the fall of the Tōjō Cabinet appeared more probable, though it did not actually come for another year. Plans had been made to force Tōjō to relinquish the premiership at the conference of palace advisers on August 30. This was to be followed by the thorough house cleaning within the army by getting rid of those army men turned politicians, and dropping military personnel that had become entrenched in government offices and munitions companies, as well as the retirement of active officers, including Tōjō, who formed the core of the military clique. The expulsion of military-dominated bureaucrats from their posts was also planned. Contrary to expectations, Tōjō refused to relinquish his post. He had brazenly reported to the Emperor that 99 per cent of the nation supported him and that the Diet was giving him unanimous sup-

---

[43] Mori, *op. cit.,* p. 126.

port, leaving only a small proportion of undesirables opposing the government.

Premier Tōjō arrested 170 former members of the Tōhōkai, and when the extraordinary session of the Diet was called in October, 1943, he arrested all the Diet members formerly affiliated with the Tōhōkai in complete disregard of their constitutional guarantee. Investigations were started by the gendarmerie, but no crimes could be proved against Nakano, who was released and placed under surveillance with gendarmerie guard. On the early morning of October 27 Nakano committed suicide in the traditional manner apparently because of his strong reluctance to divulge the names of the imperial princes implicated in the plot to overthrow the Tōjō Government.

MOUNTING ALLIED OFFENSIVE

Preceded by a two-day softening aerial and naval bombardment a composite army and naval landing force struck at Kwajelein atoll in the Marshalls on January 31, 1944, and secured it on February 9, when all resistance ended. With the securing of the Eniwetok atoll on February 22 by amphibious marine and army forces, operations for the Marshalls came to a successful conclusion. Truk offered only weak resistance. On February 20, a little over 200 planes that had been scraped together by the Japanese air force were blasted out of the skies, and some twenty ships, including three light cruisers, were sent to the bottom in the harbor of Truk. To the navy's desperate pleas for more planes, Premier Tōjō turned deaf ears and diverted all the planes to the army. While the naval forces fought desperately on the islands, they were unable to withstand the terrific assaults of American forces.

Late in February a Japanese carrier force came out to the Marianas to meet American attacks with some thousand aircraft, land-based fighters, and bombers, as well as carrier-based bombers. But more than 100 planes were destroyed on the ground immediately upon their arrival, and on March 3 Admiral Koga, Commander in Chief of the Combined Fleet, successor to the luckless Admiral Yamamoto, was also killed in action. On June 15 an amphibious American force landed on Saipan. On July 7 came the desperate *banzai* charge. Two days later the American forces secured it after twenty-five days of hard fighting. On July 24 Tinian, located three miles to the south of Saipan, was secured.

The Battle of the Philippine Sea, which was fought on June 19 and 20, resulted in the loss of three Japanese carriers and 400 planes. Surviving the battle were only 40 planes and 100 pilots. Thus, Japan's carrier-based air power had been all but destroyed by Admiral Spruance's Fifth Fleet. Meanwhile, on June 21, American forces landed on Guam and reconquered the island on August 10. From Saipan, the base of the Twentieth Air Force, systematic bombing of Japanese cities was started later in the year.

On September 15 simultaneous landings on Peleliu of the Palau group and on

Morotai in the Moluccas were executed. With the landing on Peleliu the Central Pacific forces under Admiral Nimitz were brought to the western Caroline Islands within 500 miles east of Mindanao. The Morotai landing placed General MacArthur's Southwest Pacific forces at a point 300 miles southwest of Mindanao. The Philippine Islands thus lay ahead as the next great American objective on the road to Tōkyō.

Starting in October American bombers ranged far and wide over the Philippines, Formosa, and Okinawa. The final stages of the Pacific War had been entered by the fall of 1944, beginning with the return of the American troops to the Philippines. American landings on the east coast of Leyte on October 20 by General MacArthur's forces took the Japanese by surprise. After two long years of fighting, General MacArthur's parting words to the brave defenders of Bataan in the dark days of 1942 had been realized with his return. A preliminary warning to the Japanese had been given on September 14 when planes from Admiral Halsey's Third Fleet had struck at the central Philippines.

Following the Leyte landings by three days came the Battle for Leyte Gulf,[44] which was the greatest naval engagement of the Second World War and which represented the supreme naval test for the Japanese, who threw in practically their entire remaining naval strength. The three Japanese fleets included nine battleships, two of which were the new 64,000-ton superdreadnaughts, carrying nine 18-inch guns and designed as the most powerful warships afloat,[45] two hybrid carrier-battleships, *Ise* and *Hyūga,* which had their flight decks aft, an innovation in naval history, and four carriers.[46]

The American forces, Admiral Halsey's Third Fleet and Admiral Kinkaid's Seventh Fleet, which met the Japanese attempt to dislodge the American troops from the newly established beachhead on Leyte, included thirty-two carriers, compared with only three in the Battle of Midway, and as against Japan's six, and twelve battleships as against Japan's nine. It was primarily a battle between air power and battleship strength of the American forces and the heavy ordinance and armor of Japanese battleships, in which the former demonstrated conclusive superiority. The Japanese by this time possessed only negligible air power. Suicidal aerial attacks by Kamikaze pilots were introduced for the first time and demonstrated considerable destructive power, but their effects were not decisive.[47] The engagement ended in a disastrous defeat for the Japanese navy, which was all but annihilated as an effective striking force. It was also the end of Japanese air power.

In November, shortly after the naval defeat at Leyte Gulf, the Japanese high

[44] The official story of this naval battle is given in the U.S. Navy Department Communiqué No. 554.

[45] James A. Field, *The Japanese at Leyte,* p. 167.

[46] The remainder was made up of 13 heavy cruisers, 8 light cruisers, and 41 destroyers.

[47] C. V. Woodward, *The Battle for Leyte Gulf,* p. 2.

command appointed General Yamashita as commander in chief of Japanese forces in the Philippines in a desperate but futile effort to check the American advance. By December 21 American forces had brought all organized resistance on Leyte to an end. On January 3 to 4, 1945, carrier-based planes struck at Formosa and Okinawa in a diversionary move, and on the ninth the Sixth Army landed at Lingayen Bay to begin the assault on Luzon. In less than a month, on February 5, American forces reentered Manila.

On February 19, while the Philippine campaign was in progress, American marines landed on the east coast of Iwōjima. After what was perhaps the bloodiest battle of the Pacific War, lasting almost a month, the well fortified volcanic isle was taken. On April 1, after a devastating naval and aerial bombardment to soften the island, American army and marine forces landed on Okinawa. After the costly two-month fighting the Okinawa campaign came to an end on June 21. The defeat was a major disaster for the Japanese, as the home islands were now vulnerable to attack. The invasion of Japan proper seemed imminent to the people, who had been stunned by the news of the loss of Okinawa. On July 14, a month before surrender, the American fleet sailed boldly into Japanese waters and shelled northern Honshū and Hokkaidō. The Japanese were no longer in possession of an effective striking force, either on the sea or in the air, to fight back. The American air force had swept the skies clear of Japanese planes, and the once proud and powerful navy had been sent to a watery grave. Out of the twelve battleships, including the two leviathans, which were thought to be unsinkable, only four were left, none of which were even seaworthy or able to proceed under their own steam, as they were beached, water-logged, and lying helpless in Japanese waters as a result of terrific blasting from the air.[48]

Air Attack on Japan Intensified. In the fourth year of the war Allied air power was concentrated heavily on Japan's war economy. Among the earlier industrial targets of American long-range bombers were the Yawata Steel Works in northern Kyūshū and the Showa Steel Works in Anshan, Manchuria. In July and August naval dockyards at Sasebo and the city of Nagasaki were bombed. Until late 1944 the weight of air operations had been predominantly tactical, being directed against enemy air and surface forces. The bombing offensive against industrial objectives in the Japanese home islands, which was initiated late in November, was predicated upon military plans looking to the ground force invasion of the islands. In the targets selected, top priority was given to aircraft factories, arsenals, electronic plants, and finished military goods, the destruction of which could weaken the strength of Japanese forces opposing

[48] Early in October, 1946, well over a year after surrender, the Japanese government released complete figures on the naval losses suffered during the Pacific War. See *Yomiuri Shimbun,* October 4, 1946.

American landing parties on the beachheads of southern Kyūshū in the projected Operation Olympic, set for November, 1945.

However, in April, 1945, active consideration was given to putting pressure through bombing on the whole economic and social order by attacking the distribution of raw materials, energy, finished, and semi-finished goods. In June, urban area incendiary attacks were resumed by Marianas-based B-29's in order to achieve the heaviest possible morale and shock effect by widespread attack upon the Japanese civilian population.[49] According to the Home Ministry figures released shortly after the end of hostilities, air-raid casualties were 241,000 killed, 313,000 wounded, 2,333,000 homes completely destroyed, and 111,000 homes partially destroyed. Those who were affected in one way or another numbered in excess of 8,000,000. Damages inflicted by air raids were extensive. Only nine out of the forty-six prefectures escaped with only minor damages. Over eighty cities suffered heavily, and more than 30 per cent of the urban dwelling units were destroyed.

In the war of attrition Japan's shipping suffered irreparable losses as the result of terrific air and submarine attacks. In May, 1945, her shipping had been whittled down to one-fourth of the tonnage she had at the time of the outbreak of hostilities. Lack of fuel as well as the acute shortage of bottoms plus mounting Allied air offensive disrupted shipping activities and made the task of maintaining a supply line to the Asiatic continent and the southern regions impossible. Even on land the deterioration of rolling stocks and the constant air raids reduced efficiency of domestic rail transportation to one half that of the preceding year, 1944. The securing of basic industrial needs, such as coal and raw materials, was interrupted and the destruction of production facilities in the homeland wrought havoc on war industries. Steel output, for instance, dropped from 4,200,000 tons in 1941 to 270,000 tons in 1945. Aluminum fell from a peak of 140,000 tons in 1943 to a mere 9,000 tons. The chemical industry was near paralysis. Food shortage had become acute, and by April, 1945, there was a rice deficit of 410,000,000 bushels.

PRELUDE TO SURRENDER

The fall of Saipan and the loss of the Marianas in July, 1944, was a turning point in the war as far as the Japanese leaders were concerned, for they began to feel that the war was lost. A major political repercussion resulting from the loss of confidence in victory was the ousting of the Tōjō Cabinet, which came finally in late July. However, all of one year had to elapse before the peace faction was able to maneuver itself into a position to terminate the war, which had already

[49] U.S. Strategic Bombing Survey, *The Effects of Strategic Bombing on Japan's War Economy*, p. 38.

been lost militarily. The time lag between military defeat and the political recognition of the fact of defeat had unfortunate consequences on Japan, but it was inevitable under the power structure that obtained in the country. The fall of Okinawa brought a change in government. The appearance on April 9 of the government of Admiral Suzuki, comprising palace advisers, was a clear indication of the desire to terminate the war. Its chief task was to prepare the way for a "negotiated peace," if possible.

Intensive aerial pounding of Tōkyō by B-29's, beginning in March, 1945, not only intensified the fears of the residents but convinced the leaders that the nation could not withstand such a terrific pounding very long. The peace faction was becoming bolder in its attempts to bring the war to an end. On April 15 the new War Minister, General Anami, ordered the arrest of former Ambassador Yoshida Shigeru, the leader of the peace faction, after the gendarmerie had seized the letter he had written Konoe expressing his desire to present his views regarding peace to the Emperor. Under orders of the War Minister, the gendarmerie rounded up some 400 persons who were regarded as leading figures of the peace faction and threatened them with a court martial. Included among them were officials, journalists, commentators, and others.[50] Although the army insisted on court martialling them, the palace advisers were able to circumvent the army's last arbitrary act.

After the surrender of Germany on May 8, the Supreme Council for the Direction of War began to discuss openly ways and means of ending the war. Attempts were made to secure the good offices of the Vatican, Switzerland, and Sweden, but it was decided that the Soviet Union should be asked to mediate in terminating the war. Beginning in late May the Foreign Minister and ex-Premier Hirota conferred frequently and in secrecy in Tōkyō, as Hirota served as a liaison between the Foreign Office and the Soviet Ambassador. In Moscow, Ambassador Satō approached Foreign Commissar Molotov as well as Stalin for Soviet good offices. Although the Japanese government sent on June 29 a secret telegram to Stalin expressing its willingness to send Prince Konoe as special envoy, the response was less than lukewarm. A second telegram was sent to Moscow on July 13, just as the Soviet chief was preparing to attend the Potsdam meeting. Stalin showed his willingness to mediate and asked the Japanese government to wire back by code the conditions under which Japan would capitulate. Stalin delayed his departure for Berlin a whole day to wait for the Japanese reply, which did not reach the Kremlin in time.

On July 26 the United States, Great Britain, and China advised the "unconditional surrender of all Japanese armed forces" to Japan in the Potsdam Declara-

---

[50] Among those rounded up by the gendarmerie were commentators Baba Tsunego and Iwabuchi Tatsuo, Governor Kimishima Seikichi of Niigata, and a number of Foreign Office officials.

tion. The conditions of peace offered were (1) the elimination of the authority and influence of those who had deceived and misled the people of Japan into embarking on world conquest; (2) the occupation of designated points in Japanese territory to secure the achievement of basic objectives; (3) the limitation of Japanese sovereignty to the islands of Honshū, Hokkaidō, Kyūshū, Shikoku, and such minor islands as should be determined; (4) the return of Japanese military forces, after their complete disarming, to their homes with the opportunity to lead peaceful and productive lives; (5) no enslavement or destruction of the Japanese as a nation, but stern justice to all war criminals; the removal of all obstacles to the revival and strengthening of democratic tendencies among the Japanese people and the establishment of freedom of speech and religion and of thought as well as respect for the fundamental human rights; (6) retention of such industries as would sustain her economy and permit the payment of just reparations in kind, but not those industries which would enable her to rearm for war; access to raw materials and eventual participation in world trade relations; and (7) withdrawal of allied occupation forces as soon as the objectives had been accomplished and a peacefully inclined and responsible government established in accordance with the freely expressed will of the Japanese people.

Hoping against hope for some sort of negotiated peace that would save it from humiliation the Japanese government was waiting expectantly for a Soviet response, which never came much to the disappointment of the leaders. Premier Suzuki decided against the acceptance of the Potsdam Declaration in view of the opposition of the service ministers, who insisted on holding out. On August 6, as the government was still hoping for Soviet response, the first atomic bomb in history was dropped on Hiroshima. The terrific blast took a toll of over 78,000 lives and practically pulverized four square miles of the city. Japanese scientists knew immediately that it was the atomic bomb, for they too had been working on it for years.[51]

On August 8 Ambassador Satō was notified by the Soviet government that in view of Japan's rejection on July 27 of the Potsdam Declaration, the basis for Japan's request for mediation had been nullified and that as a result of adherence to the Potsdam Declaration, the Soviet government was declaring the existence of a state of war with Japan as of August 9. On the day that the second atom bomb was dropped on Nagasaki, Russia declared war on Japan.

The atomization of Hiroshima and Nagasaki and the declaration of war by the Soviet Union were impelling reasons that moved the leaders to hasten their efforts to terminate the war. As a matter of fact, the leaders had already made up their minds regarding the termination of war, but not on the terms or method of capitulation. On August 9 a meeting of the Supreme Council for the Direction

[51] Professor Yukawa of Kyōto University was one of the scientists who had been working on atomic research and had predicted it back in 1935. Dr. Ōdan was killed in an explosion in his laboratory as he was carrying on experiments in Tōkyō towards the end of the war.

of War [52] was held in the morning, followed by an emergency meeting in the afternoon. That very evening, in an unprecedented move, the Emperor called an imperial conference on his own initiative, since the government leaders seemed unable to reach a final decision. This meeting, which was attended by the Premier, the President of the Privy Council, the War Minister, Navy Minister, Chief of General Staff, and Chief of Naval General Staff, discussed surrender and decided on the acceptance of the Potsdam Declaration "with the understanding that the said declaration does not comprise any demand which prejudices the prerogatives of His Majesty as a sovereign ruler." War Minister Anami insisted that the war should be fought to the bitter end, but the Emperor called for a vote and it was decided to accept the Allied terms.

On the following day the palace advisers met to discuss the method of announcing surrender. On August 11 notice of tentative acceptance of the Potsdam Declaration was transmitted to the Allied Powers through the Swiss government. This was followed the next day by Board of Information President Shimomura's public announcement to the effect that Japan was now facing its most serious crisis in history. Newspapers in Tōkyō stated in unison that Japan had reached the last stand in the war, exhorting the people to uphold the honor of the Japanese race and preserve the pride and calmness befitting a great nation. The Tōkyō *Asahi* in its editorial warned the nation that it faced the gravest crisis in its history, far beyond that of the Mongol invasions of 1274 and 1281. It admonished the people not to despair, falter, or be faint-hearted, but to resign themselves to weather the crisis to preserve the national polity. The *Mainichi* editorial included the reminder that nations had their ups and downs and stressed the fact that a great nation does not flinch in the face of the greatest crisis. It was obvious the nation was being prepared for the worst news.

On August 14 the last imperial conference of the war was held [53] to deliberate on the reply to be given to the Allied response to Japan's conditional acceptance of the Potsdam Declaration. The Allied reply had clearly stated that the authority of the Emperor and the Japanese government to rule the state would be subject to the Supreme Commander for the Allied Powers, who was empowered to take such steps as would be necessary to effectuate the terms of surrender. The Emperor stated that he did not care what happened to him, but that he could not bear to see the people suffer any longer. The Emperor's firm decision to end the war stood as he accepted the conditions of surrender. Moreover, he decided

[52] The Supreme Council for the Direction of War consisted of Premier Suzuki, Foreign Minister Tōgō, War Minister Anami, Navy Minister Yonai, Chief of General Staff Umezu and Chief of Naval General Staff Toyoda.

[53] Present were Hiranuma, Umezu, Toyoda, Premier Suzuki, and all the cabinet ministers, four cabinet bureau and board directors, Military Affairs Bureau Director Yoshizumi, and Naval Affairs Bureau Director Hoshina.

to take the unprecedented step of announcing the news personally to the nation by radio.

A half hour before midnight of the same day the Emperor made recordings of the imperial rescript announcing surrender, which was to be broadcast at noon of the following day. Field grade officers at the War Ministry and the General Staff Office who learned of the decision to surrender immediately went into action in an attempt to seize the recordings to prevent the broadcast and to force the reversal of the surrender decision. They had concluded that the decision was not the Emperor's own but had been forced upon him against his will by those who were close to him. Shortly after midnight they forced themselves into the headquarters of the Imperial Guard Division and shot its commanding officer Lt. Gen. Mori when he refused to cooperate with them. After locking up the Division's Chief of Staff, they issued a spurious order posting various companies at various points around the Imperial Palace and with some 600 troops they occupied the grounds. After locking up the Grand Chamberlain General Hasunuma, they searched in vain for Privy Seal Kido and Imperial Household Minister Ishiwata. Notified by the Imperial Guard Division Chief of Staff of the occurrence, the Commander in Chief of the Eastern Army Command, General Tanaka, hastened to the Imperial Palace and lectured to the insurgents for three hours. Four of the leaders who were responsible for the outrageous plot committed suicide on the spot, bringing to an end the abortive August 15 Incident. Just before dawn on the same day another group led by a Captain Sasaki sprayed machine gun bullets and set fire to the private homes of Premier Suzuki and Privy Council President Hiranuma, which were burned to the ground. Aside from these two incidents acts of violence were practically unknown.

The imperial rescript announcing surrender came as a bolt out of the blue in spite of the press forewarnings. The news was received by the nation in stupor. Thousands of subjects gathered at the plaza in front of the Imperial Palace and kneeled down to ask forgiveness for their insufficient efforts. Among the prominent leaders who committed suicide were War Minister Anami, Field Marshal Sugiyama and his wife, onetime Education Minister Hashida, and several others. In addition mass suicides took place.[54] For days the people could not even comprehend the magnitude or the historical import of the event. They had seen their cities devastated, but the propaganda by the military urging the nation to fight to the bitter end even with their bare hands had concealed the real plight of the nation, the horrible deterioration and depletion of national strength, so effectively that the people could not believe that the nation was so

---

[54] Twenty-one executive officers at the Yokosuka Naval Base committed suicide. Ten members of patriotic societies took their lives on August 22, twelve members of another society, Meirōkai, committed suicide in front of the Imperial Palace on the next day, and thirteen students of Daitō School committed suicide at the Yoyogi Parade Grounds on the day after that.

close to the brink of disaster, and the war would come to an end so abruptly.

Early on the evening of August 14 President Truman announced from the White House to the American people that the war was over. Spontaneous rejoicing broke out throughout the length and breadth of the nation. In the words of *The New York Times,* "Not since the ending of the war of 1861–65 has this nation been through such a moving experience."[55] General of the Army Douglas MacArthur was designated Supreme Commander for the Allied Powers to accept Japan's surrender and to carry out the occupation of the country in accordance with the Potsdam Declaration.

On August 16 the Emperor issued the cease fire order to the troops scattered over the vast area. Three days later a group of high-ranking officials and military men headed by Lt. Gen. Kawabe Torashirō arrived in Manila to receive from General MacArthur the military conditions for surrender, disarmament, and occupation of the islands. They received all the necessary instructions and furnished information regarding the location and strength of Japanese military forces and within twenty-four hours of their arrival they were on their way back. Upon their return, the emissaries expressed appreciation of the fact that the Americans did not impose "any more indignities than necessary to a defeated nation." They were impressed especially by American efficiency as well as their understanding of the position of the Emperor.[56]

During the last days of August small advance units of the Eleventh Airborne Division landed at Atsugi Airport without any untoward incident. Instead of encountering opposition of any sort, they were given a courteous reception by Japanese officials. General MacArthur himself arrived on August 30, two days after the first units had landed. On September 1 the main forces of the United States Eighth Army began landing, and American control was rapidly extended throughout the Tōkyō Bay area with the cooperation of the Japanese government.

Formal surrender ceremonies took place on September 2 aboard the U.S.S. *Missouri,* flagship of Admiral Halsey's Third Fleet, anchored in Tōkyō Bay, which had been the scene ninety-two years earlier of another great historical event, the arrival of Commodore Perry. Representatives of the Japanese government and armed forces were received by General MacArthur and the representatives of the United Nations and affixed their signatures on the Instrument of Surrender.[57] Almost simultaneously, the Emperor issued an imperial rescript announcing the formal surrender. The Imperial General Headquarters issued an order instructing all the Japanese armed forces to cease hostilities at once, to lay

[55] *The New York Times,* Editorial, "Eighteen Fateful Days," August 19, 1945.
[56] Dōmei broadcast in *kana* to Greater East Asia, August 21, 1945.
[57] For text, see U.S. Department of State, *Occupation of Japan, Policy and Progress,* pp. 62–63.

down their arms, to remain in their present locations, and to surrender unconditionally.

Although an official explanation of the defeat by Premier Higashikuni was not offered the nation until two days after the signing of the formal surrender document, various reasons were given by the press and individuals shortly after the acceptance of the Potsdam Declaration. Dr. Yagi, former President of the Board of Technology, attributed the defeat among other things to jealousy and feudalistic sectionalism, as well as the absence of the freedom of the press, speech, and association. Professor Takasaka of Kyōto Imperial University emphasized the national characteristics of irrationalism or the lack of scientific attitude and objectivity, inferiority in science and technology, and the lack of public spirit and cooperation. Hatoyama Ichirō, member of the Diet, attributed the defeat to the monopolization of government and economic affairs by a few and the decadence, arbitrary and self-righteous attitude, and dereliction of duty on the part of the bureaucracy. The newspaper *Asahi* came out strongly in condemnation of the bureaucracy, charging it with avarice, corruption, and selfishness, and the want of courage, competence, and conviction.

The basic premises on which the military leaders based their decision to go to war were unsound and were predicated upon irrational, unscientific, and emotional calculations, as well as wishful thinking and self-delusion. The belief in German victory was based on clever German propaganda, to which even Matsuoka seemed to have fallen a victim. The belief that the United States was too soft to carry on a long war and that by delivering swift crushing blows in the early stages of the war Japan would force the United States to sue for peace, reflected her lack of understanding of American psychology and industrial potential. The military's desperate decision that by fighting on another front or several other fronts, the China War might be settled was either masterful self-deception or a piece of utter irrationalism.

No small part of the defeat could be attributed to the long standing, deep-rooted, and smouldering army-navy cleavage that broke out in the open during the war. The consuming antagonisms flared up incessantly and took various forms, such as clashes over military strategy and tactical operations, resulting in noncooperation, as in the case of a number of island battles where the naval forces got little help from the army, while at Kiska the army received little help from the navy. In some cases, noncooperation was carried to extremes as the army was forced to perform naval functions, while the navy had to concern itself with matters normally assigned to the army. The interservice scramble for munitions and particularly for airplanes was unbelievably intense. Disagreement in regard to domestic policies was the rule, while friction in military government in occupied areas was interminable.

The Koiso-Yonai Cabinet, which succeeded the Tōjō Government after the fall of the Marianas in July, 1944, under a system of virtual army-navy co-premiership was an unsuccessful attempt to close the breach that later developed into an unbridgeable chasm as the tide of war turned rapidly against Japan.

The technological inferiority of the Japanese was amply demonstrated in the absence of superior electronic equipment, notably radar, which became standard equipment for the American forces. Even in radio equipment only one out of three Japanese planes was equipped. Although production capacity was partly responsible for technical inferiority, the military leaders underestimated the power of science. In the development of the death ray, some 160 Japanese scientists spent a million yen and five and a half years to develop a lethal instrument with the very limited power of killing a rat 30 yards away. However, when scientists asked for a meager research grant of 50,000 yen to carry on atomic research, the army laughed it off as a pipe dream of the scientists. Only when Dr. Ōdan and two buildings, including his laboratory, exploded before their very eyes did the military take notice, but by that time the atomic bomb was a reality in the United States. The traditional emphasis of the Japanese military on mind over matter, spiritual over material power, helped to make them take science lightly. Their inability to grasp the full meaning of total war while emphasizing it and the myth of invincibility that they had created and nourished proved to be their undoing.

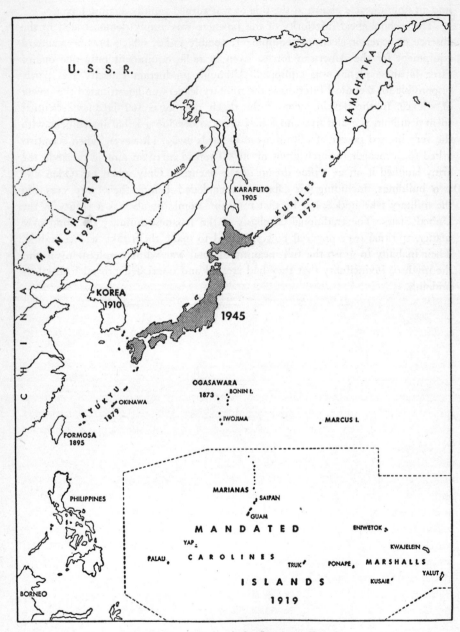

The Rise and Fall of the Japanese Empire

Chapter 36. Occupation and Reconstruction

When the people recovered from the shock of the crushing defeat administered by Allied might, they began to realize how completely they had been deceived and misled. Their natural reaction was to doubt and distrust the authorities. Little by little they learned the truth and soon saw that Japan had suffered a general collapse, political, economic, and moral no less than military. Against such a background the leaders clearly foresaw the tremendous difficulties that lay ahead in the immediate post-surrender period. With the acceptance of the Potsdam Declaration in mid-August the Suzuki Cabinet had fulfilled its *raison d'être* and resigned. On August 17 Prince Higashikuni, a member of the Imperial family, assumed the premiership.

The appointment of a member of the Imperial family as Premier was of great significance, not only because it was without precedent, but also because it was a tacit recognition of the fact that reconciling the nation to defeat was an extremely difficult task, to which an individual who lacked weight and prestige might find himself unequal. The 88th Diet, which was specially convened in September, was called for the sole purpose of explaining to the nation the events that led inevitably to surrender, and the only business taken up was the Premier's "policy address."

Premier Higashikuni's address constituted the first official explanation of the causes and conditions that contributed to the inevitable defeat, emphasized the seriousness of the situation, and admonished the people to carry out faithfully the terms of the Potsdam Declaration in order to regain the confidence and trust of the world and to reestablish friendly relations with the powers. He exhorted the nation to return to the spirit of the Charter Oath of Five Articles and, without surrendering to defeatism in the face of the tragedy or brooding over the past or despairing of the future, to abandon all bitterness, to strive to regain the friendship of nations, to pursue lofty ideals that would contribute to world progress by forging ahead in the establishment of a new Japan, based on peaceful, cultural attainments. He appealed to the nation to bear the unbearable in the difficult years ahead.

The Occupation Begins. The substance of the initial post-surrender policy of the United States for Japan, formulated jointly by the State, War, and Navy Departments, was transmitted to General MacArthur by radio on August 29.[1]

---

[1] This document was approved by President Truman on September 6, on which date it was sent to General MacArthur by messenger. The White House released it on September 22. *The New York Times,* September 23, 1945.

This document set forth the ultimate objectives of the United States. These consisted of ensuring that Japan would not again become a menace to the United States or to the peace and security of the world, and the eventual establishment of a peaceful and responsible government that would respect the rights of other states and would support the objectives of the United States as reflected in the ideals and principles of the Charter of the United Nations. It was the express desire of the United States that the new government should conform "as closely as may be to principles of democratic self-government."

Achievement of the objectives was to be attained through the (1) restriction of Japanese sovereignty to the four main islands and such minor outlying islands as might be determined in accordance with the Cairo Declaration and other agreements; (2) complete disarmament and demilitarization of the nation, which would totally eliminate the authority of militarists and the influence of militarism from her economic, political, and social life; (3) encouragement of the Japanese in the development of a desire for individual liberties and respect for fundamental human rights, particularly freedoms of religion, assembly, speech and the press, and (4) opportunity to develop for themselves an economy that would enable them to meet the peacetime requirements of the population.

Immediately after his arrival General MacArthur set out to achieve the twofold objective of occupation: the destruction of Japan's ability to wage war and her reconstruction as an independent democratic nation capable of standing on her own economic feet. The Japanese people responded without any apparent bitterness to the orders of the occupation authorities, while the officials cooperated willingly. On September 13 the Imperial General Headquarters was disbanded and the demilitarization of the nation began. The War and Navy Ministries were converted into demobilization ministries to disarm and return to civilian life the 2,576,000 soldiers and 1,300,000 sailors. The task of destroying the Japanese war machine and war potential was achieved within four months. Six and a half million Japanese overseas who were scattered from Manchuria and China to Southeast Asia and the islands of the Pacific had to be repatriated. By March, 1947, nearly 6 million Japanese had been returned to their homeland.

The Far Eastern Commission and the Allied Council for Japan. On August 21 the government of the United States proposed to Great Britain, China, and the Soviet Union the creation of an international body to help formulate future policy in Japan and to aid in the planning of an organization to make certain that the Japanese government fulfilled its obligations. Because of the unwillingness of the Soviet Union to participate in a body that was only advisory no progress was made until a compromise could be worked out. Finally, on December 27, the Moscow Conference of Foreign Ministers reached the decision to set up a Far Eastern Commission and an Allied Council for Japan and Soviet participation was assured. From Washington the representatives of eleven powers on the Far Eastern Commission began in February, 1946, "to formulate the policies, principles, and standards in conformity with which the fulfillment by Japan of its obligations under the terms of surrender may be accomplished." The Allied Council, composed of representatives of the United States, the British Commonwealth, the Soviet Union, and China, began functioning in Tōkyō by consulting with and advising the Supreme Commander for the Allied Powers.

The execution and implementation of the policy decisions of the Far Eastern Commission were placed in the hands of the Supreme Commander for the Allied Powers. The control of Japan was to be exercised through the Japanese government, whose authority was made subordinate to SCAP. In the translation of occupation policies into action and performance an organization staffed by specially trained and qualified personnel was set up within the General Headquarters of SCAP. It is through these channels that policies are transmitted to the Japanese government, which in turn carries them out.

REAPPEARANCE OF POLITICAL PARTIES

Efforts to revive political parties started as soon as the formal surrender was effectuated. On September 6 a dozen members of the Diet met to form a party that would devote itself to the cause of social democracy. This group emerged shortly thereafter as the Social Democratic Party. On the following day those Diet members who belonged to the Japan Political Association organized the Society for the Construction of a New Japan (Shin Nihon Kensetsu Chōsakai) to study national policies with a view to building a new Japan. It was not until after the directive liberating political prisoners was issued early in October that the political parties showed vigorous activity.

Toward the middle of October veteran Communists, who had been released from prison in consequence of the directive of October 4, formed the Communist Party under the leadership and direction of Tokuda Kyūichi, Shiga Yoshio, and Nozaka Sanzō, a Moscow trained Communist, who spent the war years at Yenan under the name of Okano Susumu. For the first time in Japan's history the Communist Party was able to enjoy legal existence.

By the end of 1946 more than sixty political parties had emerged. These included, interestingly enough, the Japan Women's Party, which looked to the establishment of permanent peace, elimination of social evils, and extension of the scope of feminine activities, which had been greatly circumscribed. In the sudden mushrooming of political parties between October, 1945, and April, 1946, was reflected the eagerness and activity of the politically enfranchised and ambitious, but there were few ideas that reflected any originality or freshness of thought or principles. The Liberal Party and the Progressive Party were no more than the revival of the old major parties, the Seiyūkai and Minseitō, both in leadership and policies. The former advocated laissez-faire economy and intensive industrialization, while the latter stood for a moderate amount of government control. The Social Democratic Party, which stood for the nationalization of industries, was made up largely of former proletarian and labor leaders and ran the whole gamut of ideology from the extreme left to the extreme right.

STEPS TOWARD POLITICAL DEMOCRACY

In what was tantamount to a Japanese "bill of rights" to establish political, civil, and religious liberties, SCAP issued on October 4 a directive ordering the abrogation and suspension of all laws, decrees, orders, ordinances, and regulations that restricted the freedom of thought, of religion, of assembly, of speech, and of the collection and dissemination of information, and those laws that discriminated in favor of or against any person by reason of race, nationality, creed, or political opinion. The directive also ordered release within a week of all persons detained, imprisoned, or under "protection and surveillance" by reason of their thought, speech, religion, political beliefs, or assembly.

Simultaneously all organizations or agencies that had been created to enforce restrictive regulations were abolished. These included the secret police, the special higher police, the Police Bureau, and other departments of the Home Ministry charged with supervision of publications, public meetings, and organizations, censorship of motion pictures, those entrusted with the control of thought, speech, religion, or assembly, and the Justice Ministry organs in charge of the surveillance and rehabilitation of thought offenders. Officials and employees of these liquidated organizations and agencies were barred from employment in the Ministries of Home Affairs and Justice or any police organ. The civil police force was newly established with an authorized strength of 93,935. The Civil Defense Police (Keibitai), however, was not abolished until January, 1946.

The dissemination of news and information was encouraged by SCAP from the very beginning to offset the effects of the news blackout enforced by the wartime government in Japan. The SCAP directive of September 10 was intended to facilitate the free flow of news. On September 24, SCAP ordered the elimination of government subsidies, which had the effect of divesting the government of all direct and indirect control of the newspapers and news agencies. This was followed on the twenty-ninth by the abolishing of wartime and peacetime curbs on the freedom of the press and of communication. The government of Prince Higashikuni decided to abolish the Newspaper Enterprise Law, by which the government had imposed censorship on the press. No longer could the government take punitive action against any newspaper for whatever policy or opinion it might express except for the publication of false news or reports deemed by SCAP disturbing to public tranquillity. Nor could it exercise the power of revoking permission to publish, to arrest, to impose fines on publications, or to curtail paper supplies as punishment for editorial comment.

Newspapers and periodicals were urged, if not ordered, to print stories that had formerly been suppressed or distorted, such as the stories of the army's atrocities and the mistreatment of prisoners, both military and civilian. This was a means of informing the public regarding the mechanics of democratic government. On the positive side, selected American films were distributed through regular channels and shown to the public in order to give the Japanese people some idea of life in a country under democratic government.

Disestablishment of State Shintō. In accordance with the directive of December 15, the Japanese government withdrew all state support from Shintō, abolished the teaching of Shintō in educational institutions, and freed all Japanese from any compulsion to believe in or profess to believe in Shintō. It also terminated the propagation of militaristic and ultranationalist ideology, including the doctrine that the Emperor of Japan is superior to heads of other states because of ancestry, descent, or special origin. Such doctrines as the superiority of the Japanese people, the Japanese islands, and other Shintō theory and beliefs that might be perverted to delude the people into embarking upon wars of aggression or to glorify the use of force as an instrument for the settlement of disputes with other peoples were banned.

Shintō was stripped of its official sponsorship and placed on a par with other religions such as Buddhism and Christianity. The sponsorship, support, perpetuation, control, and dissemination of Shintō by the government on any level or by any public official were prohibited as well as the custom of reporting to any shrine by a government official his assumption of office, or the participation of a representative of the government in any Shintō ceremony. Shintō was divested of the political theory that had been built around it.

Not long after the arrival of General MacArthur the Emperor called upon the Supreme Commander for the Allied Powers at his headquarters in the United States Embassy. This was the first step in the conscious and deliberate effort to "humanize" the Japanese ruler, who had been kept in "dignified" seclusion and inaccessible to the public, and to bring him into close contact with the people. Tours were planned in which the Emperor appeared at the factories, the mines, on the streets, on the farms, in the schools, in short at every conceivable place, to speak to and be spoken to by the people. The respect for the Emperor, however, did not diminish in the least. On the contrary, the prestige of the Emperor was enhanced as the people began to feel a closer bond than heretofore.

In his memorable New Year's Day rescript to the nation on January 1, 1946, the Emperor repudiated his divinity, which he attributed to a false conception, and stated that the Japanese people are neither superior to other races nor destined to rule the world. He called upon the people to rally to the principles embodied in the Charter Oath of Five Articles, which, he emphasized, should serve as the basis for a regenerated and peaceful Japan, and he invited the people to contribute substantially to the welfare and advancement of mankind.

In the rescript, which was couched in simple, understandable language for the first time, the Emperor bade the nation rise to the occasion and put the country back on its feet through unremitting efforts. In a traditional fashion, the Emperor resorted to exhortation and moral suasion to point the way for the nation to follow.

Removal of Undesirable Personnel. A purge of undesirable personnel from public office was ordered on January 4, 1946, in conformity with the provision of the Potsdam Declaration, which stipulated a peaceful Japan. The Imperial Ordinance of February 28 and a cabinet ordinance of the same date set forth those to be purged, such as government officials, personnel of special corporations, banks, control societies, and key personnel of corporations in which investments had been made by the government, national policy companies, special banks, and others. Also removed from public office and excluded from government service were active exponents of militaristic nationalism and aggression, influential members of ultranationalistic, terroristic, or secret patriotic societies, its agencies or affiliates, or those influential in the activities of the Imperial Rule Assistance Association, the Imperial Rule Political Society, or the Japan Political Association. This covered practically all the experienced public servants of any consequence who had served the government between July 7, 1937, the beginning of the China War and September 2, 1945, the date of the formal surrender.

The Public Office Eligibility Committee (Kōshoku Tekihi Shinsa Iinkai) was created on June 29, 1946, with Dr. Minobe Tatsukichi as chairman to screen incumbents as well as candidates for public office. By August, the government had screened 5,520 office holders, 3,384 Diet candidates, all elected members of the Diet and nominees for the House of Peers, 814 ranking government officials, 9 new Diet members, and 6,202 under the civil liberties directive. In all, 186,000 persons had been excluded from office. The purge necessitated the reorganization of the Cabinet and disqualified 90 per cent of the Diet membership for reelection. The Progressive Party lost 200 members for reelection to the House of Representatives. In not a few instances political enemies were purged. Foreign Minister Ashida barely escaped being a victim of a purge at the hands of political enemies.

It was inevitable that the purge should adversely affect, if not cause a serious setback of, economic rehabilitation and industrial recovery, inasmuch as a large number of experienced executives were removed from the leading corporations and banks, leaving their management to clerks, former cashiers, and assistant vice presidents.

The purge was applied to local government personnel on November 8 and to those in political, economic, and cultural activities on November 21. This brought corporations, banks, newspapers, publishing houses, amusement companies, and radio broadcasting companies within the purview of the purge directives.

The government carried out at the same time the abolition and prohibition of any political party, association, society, or other organization and activity that resisted or opposed the occupation authorities, supported or justified aggressive military action abroad, arrogated for Japan leadership of other Asiatic, Indonesian or Malayan peoples, excluded foreigners in Japan from trade, commerce, or the professions, opposed a free cultural or intellectual exchange, provided military or quasi-military training, or stood for alteration of policy by assassination or other terroristic programs.

First Postwar Election. On January 12, 1946, the Japanese government was authorized to hold a general election of members of the House of Representatives not earlier than March 15 under the new electoral law that enfranchised women and lowered the age qualification for voters from 25 years to 20 years and office holders from 30 years to 25 years. The question was raised by the Far Eastern Commission as to the wisdom of holding the election so soon in view of the fact that there had not been sufficient time for the parties of a more liberal tendency to circulate their views and organize support. Some members of the Commission were apprehensive lest it might give a decisive advantage to the reactionary parties. SCAP, on the contrary, felt that any postponement of the election would result in greater advantage to the more experienced and better organized reactionary groups that had been crippled by the purge, inasmuch as it could give the time and opportunity needed to regroup and strengthen themselves.

In spite of the misgivings of some of the members of the Far Eastern Commission, the first postwar election was held on April 10 as scheduled by the Supreme Commander for the Allied Powers. Not only was the election free from interference and corruption, but such a wide choice was given the electorate that it proved rather bewildering to a great many of the voters. More than 27 million persons went to the polls, a remarkable turnout, representing 72 per cent of all the eligible voters. Sixty-six per cent of all eligible women voters cast their ballots in their first election in history. There was a marked tendency to vote for individuals rather than for parties or their platforms. But this was to be expected, for the Japanese have traditionally emphasized the government of men rather than the government of laws.

The electorate favored neither the extreme right nor left, but sought a middle course. In spite of the sensational and highly vocal campaign it carried out, the Communist Party won only five seats, a showing that was not at all commensurate with the publicity it received or the efforts it expended. The Liberal and Progressive parties captured 139 and 93 seats respectively, the Social Democrats 92, and the Cooperatives 14. One of the unexpected outcomes of the election was the large number of women elected, owing partly to the misunderstanding on the part of many that they were supposed to support candidates of their own sex. As it turned out, the first election under universal suffrage was an initiation more into the mechanics of democracy than into its spirit. The path toward democracy was still a long and hard one for the average Japanese, who had little if any understanding of the real meaning of democracy. There was little in his nation's past to which he could turn for any lesson in the democratic way of life.

Premier Shidehara remained in office until April 22, when his cabinet resigned. Attempts at forming a Liberal-Socialist coalition on the heels of cabinet resignation collapsed because of the inability of the two parties to reach an understanding. Retiring Premier Shidehara recommended on May 3 a Liberal Party government, but its president, Hatoyama, was disqualified in a last minute purge. Yoshida Shigeru therefore succeeded to the presidency on May 10, and a Liberal-Progressive coalition cabinet emerged twelve days later with Yoshida as Premier.

The New Role of Labor. A broad outline of the program of democratization was furnished in the directive of September 22, 1945, which enjoined the Japanese government to encourage democratic organizations in labor, industry, and agriculture, along with a wide distribution of income and property. The occupation policy envisaged and took steps to strengthen three classes, the small businessmen, the workingmen, and the small landowning farmers, who were to furnish the backbone of a new democratic Japan.

Labor policy was predicated upon the assumption that the working class constituted potentially the strongest base for a democratic government, inasmuch as the middle class was regarded as economically and spiritually weak and therefore not the group to be bolstered. Consequently, efforts were made to develop among the working classes the desire and the ability to support democratic ideas and institutions. On September 30, as a preliminary step, the Patriotic Industrial Association (Sangyō Hōkokukai), the government's wartime agency for the physical and spiritual regimentation of labor, was disbanded and the way was paved for the unhampered activity of the working class.

On October 11, a week after restrictions on political, civil, and religious liberties were removed, Premier Shidehara was directed to undertake the encouragement of the unionization of labor. In December, the Diet enacted the Trade Union Law, which was closely patterned after the United States National Labor Relations Act of 1935. Shortly thereafter, Labor Relations Committees were set up in Tōkyō and in the prefectures with representation given equally to labor, management, and the public to apply and enforce the law.

Efforts were continued in the building up of a strong democratic labor movement and in February, 1946, a Trade Union Ordinance was promulgated. Activity of the labor unions increased at a rapid rate. May Day was observed in 1946 for the first time in a decade, and over a million persons participated in parades and demonstrations throughout the country. "Workers' control of production," a technique used by labor in pushing their demands against management became frequent. Labor's tactics included occupying the plants when employers failed to grant almost anything that was demanded. In order to cope with these tactics, the government decided in late May to create a Ministry of Labor, which would take over those functions relating to labor from the Ministries of Commerce, Transportation and Welfare.

Labor development had become the concern, not only of the Japanese government, but also of the United States as well. At the meeting of the Allied Council in Tōkyō on May 16, George Atcheson, Jr., American representative and Chairman of the Allied Council, asserted emphatically that the United States did not favor communism in Japan or at home. In Washington, the following day, Acting Secretary of State Dean Acheson [2] stated at the press conference that the Department of State concurred in the assertion of Atcheson. This was the upshot of heated discussions regarding Communist tactics that was occasioned by the submission of a manifesto by a Japanese leftist group to the Allied Council following the monster May Day demonstration in Tōkyō.

In August, 1946, two major federations came into being, the Japanese Federation of Labor, which was linked closely to the Social Democratic Party and the Congress of Industrial Unions, which reflected considerable Communist influence. In the following month, the Labor Relations Adjustment Law (Rōdō Kankei Chōseihō) [3] was enacted, providing for a logical and comprehensive system for the adjustment of labor disputes through conciliation, mediation or arbitration. The prohibition of strikes for a specified period pending mediation in certain industries affecting the public welfare was strongly opposed by most of the unions, which regarded it as a weapon that could be used by the government to weaken labor. Compulsory arbitration in utilities' strikes was objected to strenuously by the Congress of Industrial Unions.

On August 29, in the strongest measure taken until this time to curb labor unrest, SCAP informed the Japanese government that "strikes, walkouts, or other work stoppages inimical to the objectives of the military occupation are prohibited." These were the harshest words addressed up to that time by SCAP to the Japanese labor movement, whose right to organize and bargain collectively had been established less than a year earlier by an Allied order. On half a dozen occasions the unions had threatened to tie up the shaky economic reconstruction program and military objectives of the Allied forces by stopping the operation of vital public utilities. Railways employees had voted to stop the railroads if the government failed to meet their demands for a seven hour day and the hiring of 30,000 additional workers. This dispute, however, ended in a compromise agreement. The seamen's strike at Sasebo was stopped by the intervention of SCAP, and the ships engaged in repatriation work were not tied up.

[2] Department of State, *Press Release* No. 338, May 17, 1946. See also *The New York Times*, May 16, 1946.

[3] This was enacted on September 27, 1946, as Law No. 25.

The All Japan Newspaper and Radio Workers' Union had voted for a general strike for October 4, but only a few hours before the deadline, the employees of the nation's largest newspaper, *Asahi,* voted to remain on their jobs, and the government took over the radio facilities, thereby preventing the strike threat from materializing. Waves of strikes inspired and called by the Communist-infiltrated Congress of Industrial Unions to force the resignation of the conservative Yoshida Government became a serious political problem, not only for the Japanese government, but also for the occupation authorities.[4]

That widespread inflation and runaway prices as well as the fear of large scale unemployment contributed to labor unrest was quite evident. However, at the same time union leadership with the support of leftist groups began to use strikes as a political weapon. The government countered by charging that the strikes were Communist instigated and employed the police to suppress the demonstrations. Education Minister Tanaka refused to entertain typical Communist "struggle" tactics from the All Japan Teachers' Union, which called a strike for November 20, inasmuch as the political nature of the strike was unmistakably clear. One of the demands they presented was the raising of income tax exemption to 1,500 yen and the other was the abolition of the 500-yen limit placed on cash payment of salaries. Obviously neither of these demands was within the power of the Education Minister to grant. Toward the end of November, Welfare Minister Kawai asserted that strikes would be dealt with more severely in the future.[5] The extreme leftist program was to halt all industrial production, thereby forcing the downfall of the conservative government. A mass meeting was held jointly by the Congress of Industrial Unions, the Japanese Federation of Labor, and industry-wide unions on December 17 with the avowed purpose of unseating the Yoshida Government. This was an extension of labor's October offensive, looking to the improving of economic conditions of the working classes and it continued until early the following year.

The Far Eastern Commission statement of December 18 sanctioning the labor organizations to engage in political activities was given wide publicity. Both the *Asahi* and *Mainichi* carried it on December 21. Labor leaders interpreted it to mean that they could actively engage in politics. Some union leaders actually tried to turn their unions into outright political organizations. As a result, in his New Year's Day message, Premier Yoshida condemned the use of the walkout as a political weapon.

The creation of the Wage Examination Commission on January 21, 1947, by Premier Yoshida, who himself became its head, was part of an effort to check the recurring strike threat. Its function was to survey the economic situa-

---

[4] *The New York Times,* October 13, 1946.

[5] *Ibid.,* November 30, 1946.

tion and eventually to establish a minimum wage level for the workers. This body, comprising the representatives of the government, industry, labor, and the public, was empowered to call expert witnesses and make decisions by a majority vote.

Government workers, including railway and communications workers, tax collectors, and school teachers voted for a general strike for February 1, 1947, which if carried out would have paralyzed transportation of food and coal, shut off electric power and water, suspended postal and telegraph service, and plunged the country into chaos. In a dramatic appeal backed by his supreme authority, General MacArthur prevented the general strike a few hours before the deadline, thus averting the most serious situation since the beginning of occupation. The General ordered the union leaders to desist from the use of the "deadly social weapon" in the face of the "impoverished and emaciated condition" of the country and emphasized that he was acting to forestall "dreadful consequences in every Japanese home" and possibly actual starvation. Although the general strike was averted, the Yoshida Government was forced to make sweeping concessions to the workers.

Inability of labor and management to compose their differences and assume responsibility for economic recovery forced a noticeable change in SCAP labor policy. It was made clear that the Supreme Commander for the Allied Powers would not countenance the trade-unions and radical parties advancing their own cause by public disorder, paralysis of essential public services, or threats to bring the nation to its knees by extraparliamentary methods. However, he was in favor of any plan to induce orderly changes for the better through parliamentary action. On February 7, a week after the general strike was averted, General MacArthur decided on a new election that would serve as a safety valve, since important changes had taken place since the election of April, 1946, and a new expression of national opinion was deemed to be in order.[6] Both the management and the government began to show apprehension that organized labor was gaining too much power and getting out of hand. Public opinion, which had generally been against the Yoshida Cabinet, had rallied to the government's support in the threatened strike of government workers.

In March, 1947, the entire membership of 6,000 of the *Mainichi* local broke away from the left wing dominated All Japan Newspaper and Radio Workers' Union. This started a movement representing a swing back of the newspaper workers to a more moderate attitude and away from radicalism, which had been reflected in such militant strategy as the seizure of the newspapers. Labor, which

---

[6] The *Asahi* in its editorial of January 10, 1947, was highly critical of the Yoshida Government, which it characterized as neither a party nor a bureaucratic government, and it asserted emphatically that the reconstruction of the nation could not be achieved by such a conservative government.

had veered toward communism and direct action in the first year and a half, began to show evidence of moderation and sober attitude after the strike ban of February 1. The unions began to reexamine their leadership as the occupation authorities made it clear that they disapproved of the use of force and terrorism to achieve union objectives. The Communists had utilized their Youth Action Corps, which were manned by former service men, many of whom were officers in the Special Attack Corps or the Kamikaze Corps.

Forthright condemnation of improper political activities designed to bypass or short-circuit normal parliamentary processes by both George Atcheson, Jr., American Chairman of the Allied Council, and Willard S. Townsend, President of the United Transport Service Employes of America and delegate of the World Federation of Trade Unions, served to induce reflection among the labor leaders. Extremist leaders were forced out and moderate leaders gained prestige. Professional agitators and self-seeking individuals with little if any interest in the welfare of the workingmen, who had joined the labor movement for the purpose of advancing their own personal and political fortunes, were not completely eliminated, but their influence was greatly lessened.

The anticommunist drive started by the All Japan Railway Workers' Union in October, 1947, and the "democratization" campaign launched by the Federation of Labor in January, 1948, was bolstered by a drive opened against Communist factions within the Congress of Industrial Unions in February. However, labor is resorting to methods short of paralyzing stoppages in key industries in order to avoid running afoul of the SCAP ban on general strikes. Communications workers went on strike on March 12, and Tōkyō was cut off from the rest of the country for twenty-four hours, as long distance telephone and telegraph were tied up. Successive one day strikes were planned and carried out in installments.

Although labor unrest continued to be one of the major headaches of the government, Premier Ashida expressed gratification at the rapid growth of the labor movement and promised full support for the acceleration of its sound growth and development as well as the faithful observance of the requirements of the Potsdam Declaration for the establishment of a democratic government. Collective bargaining has made a start and is making progress, though rather slowly, because the rank and file of Japanese labor is not accustomed to thinking, and even if they do think, it is not organized or orderly, but uncrystallized and even chaotic. Added to this difficulty is the fact that the leadership is motivated or influenced too often by considerations of personal interests, advantages, or glory and is not accustomed to or familiar with democratic processes. The growth of labor unions has been almost phenomenal. Since the passage of the Trade Union Law, membership in labor unions increased rapidly and by

April of 1948 there were more than 6 million or about 48 per cent of the entire working class of 13 million.[7]

The Dissolution of Combines. The dissolution of the combines [8] was an integral part of the broad program to encourage wide distribution of income, ownership, and forms of activity and organization that were considered likely to strengthen the peaceful disposition of the Japanese people and to make it difficult to marshal economic activities in support of military ends. There was no intention of effecting a reform of the existing social system. The purpose was to bring about a psychological and institutional demobilization, since the *zaibatsu* had served as an instrument of the government in international politics.

A plan of dissolution was proposed in October, 1945, by the top holding company of the Yasuda combine in behalf of the four great combines, including itself. The Yasuda plan was approved by SCAP on November 6. The government, however, was directed to submit additional plans for the dissolution of combines, abrogation of legislative and administrative measures that fostered private monopoly, the elimination of private monopolies and restraints of trade, undesirable interlocking directorates and corporate security ownership, the segregation of banking from commerce, industry and agriculture, and the ensuring of equal competitive opportunity in economic activities.[9]

As proposed in the Yasuda plan, the Holding Company Liquidation Commission was created on April 20, 1946, by imperial ordinance. Early in June, twenty-nine *zaibatsu* holding companies and their subsidiaries were placed on the restricted list and required to furnish comprehensive reports on their assets and liabilities, corporate connections, and holders of their securities. Their bank accounts as well as those of certain individuals who exercised control over them were frozen and members of *zaibatsu* families were forbidden to make new investments. Three months later, on September 30, the Holding Company Liquidation Commission took over the operating and subsidiary shares held by the five largest *zaibatsu* holding companies for eventual sale to the public.[10] October 18 saw the enactment of the Enterprise Reconstruction and Reorganization Law. As part of the broad program to dissolve monopolistic combines, assets of the ten wealthiest families were frozen on November 27.

---

[7] Dr. Ayusawa Iwao, executive director of Japan's Central Labor Relations Board, predicted that in eight years total labor union membership would reach 10 million. *The New York Times,* April 20, 1948.

[8] Corwin D. Edwards, "The Dissolution of Japanese Combines," *Pacific Affairs,* September, 1946, is an excellent account.

[9] In order to secure expert advice and recommendations on the Yasuda plan, an American economic mission was sent by the State and War Departments, headed by Dr. Corwin D. Edwards, resulting in the *Report of the Mission on Japanese Combines* (Department of State Publications No. 2628, Far Eastern Series 14.)

[10] These were Mitsui, Mitsubishi, Sumitomo, Yasuda, and Fuji Industrial.

On December 9, 1947, the House of Councilors in the dying moments of the session approved the Economic Deconcentration Law, providing for the breaking up of Japanese corporations into small units to make possible greater competition than heretofore possible. Coming under this law was any company controlling 5 per cent of any critical commodity, or any company whose operations or absence from the market could seriously influence prices or money rates, or any company formed by a merger since 1941, unless it could be shown that such fragmentation would adversely affect production. It provided for the elimination of brands and company names with monopolistic advantages and prohibition of control of production, distribution, or services that were unrelated in productive process or in use.

Rural Land Reform. The Japanese government was directed on December 9, 1945, to map out a program of land reform that would liquidate "those pernicious ills which have long blighted the agrarian structure" of the country where more than three-fourths of the farmers were partially or totally tenants and paying rentals amounting to half or more of their annual crops. Little over four months later, on March 15, 1946, the government submitted a program. After considerable changes suggested by the Allied Council, which went much farther than the Japanese government was willing to go at first, the program was enacted into the Land Reform Law of October, 1946. The election of local and prefectural land commissions, in whose hands the administration of the law was vested, took place in February, 1947. By the last quarter of the year, the tenants were able to begin buying land from the government.

This process of creating landowners out of tenant farmers proved to be tortuously slow because of several factors that stand in the way of the modernization of Japanese agriculture. The increase in surplus agricultural population, resulting from the return of repatriates, the effects of black marketing on the farmers, who found themselves in an unbelievably prosperous condition, the scarcity of modern agricultural implements, coupled with the chronic shortage of electric power, the rice-centric nature of Japanese agriculture, resistance of the landowner class to land reform, and the feudalistic ideologies of the agrarian populace, who have been conservative for centuries, all stand in the way of the land reform program. Meanwhile, nothing has been attempted to change the centuries-old exiguous scale farming that is a serious obstacle to modernization of agricultural techniques. Thus, it appears that a thoroughgoing reform in the land system involves more than just an economic change.

THE REBUILDING OF JAPAN

As early as April 6, 1946, in his Army Day address, President Truman succinctly stated United States policy toward the Far East. Asserting that the roots of democracy "will not draw much nourishment in any nation from a soil of poverty and economic distress," he stated: "It is a part of our strategy of peace, therefore, to assist in the rehabilitation and development of the Far Eastern countries. We seek to encourage a quick revival of economic activity and international trade in the Far East."

Shortly before the second post-surrender general election, General MacArthur stated at a luncheon given him by correspondents in Tōkyō in March, 1947, that Japan should be allowed to resume trade and be given economic encouragement. Then in May came Undersecretary of State Dean Acheson's speech at Cleveland, Mississippi, in which he set forth the American policy of rebuilding Japan. He stated that Japan should be made the workshop of the Far East upon which to ultimately base the reconstruction and recovery of the whole of Asia. This was clearly an integral part of the United States policy of rebuilding the world and containing communism.

In spite of the eagerness of the United States to rebuild Japan, the reparations tangle proved to be a serious obstacle and deterrent to the execution of the program. For many months, the Far Eastern Commission argued and disagreed on the amount of reparations to be taken from Japan. This kept Japanese industry in suspense and production practically at a standstill. The United States favored the paring down of reparations as far as possible to speed up the rebuilding of Japan, but the other members of the Far Eastern Commission generally assumed a punitive attitude. China and Russia made tremendously large reparations claims.

The British Government protested to the United States against a decision of General MacArthur to authorize a second Japanese whaling expedition to the Antarctic. The complaint was based on the failure of the State Department to consult other interested countries, Great Britain, Australia, and Norway. Foreign Minister Herbert V. Evatt of Australia strongly opposed the reestablishment of the Japanese whaling industry in the Antarctic, which he looked upon as a restoration of the Japanese naval potential.[11] However, on June 25, Secretary of State Marshall replied that the United States would proceed with plans for a Japanese-manned whaling expedition despite protests from Great Britain, Australia, New Zealand, and Norway, inasmuch as the expedition's prospective catch would preclude a direct cost to the United States in occupation expenses of 10 million dollars and also a loss of approximately 6 million dollars in foreign exchange from the sale of whale oil.[12] On June 30, R. G. Menzies, the opposition leader, criticized MacArthur's decision to permit a second whaling expedition to the Antarctic and to allow the Japanese to work phosphate deposits on Angaur Island.

The Supreme Commander for the Allied Powers meanwhile busied himself

[11] *The New York Times,* June 24, 1947.
[12] *Ibid.,* June 25, 1947.

in an effort to secure foreign exchange for Japan's economic recovery. He was in favor of a proposal to exempt Japanese assets in neutral countries from reparations claims as well as to the securing of trade loans abroad. Moreover, he favored raising dollars in Japan through Allied residents by charging fares for train and trolley rides, hotel services, and a possible arrangement to allow dollar credits for goods sold in the army's post exchanges.[13] In July, at a ceremony commemorating the arrival of Commodore Perry, the Japanese were assured by Ambassador George Atcheson, Jr., that Americans wanted Japan to become self-supporting as soon as possible, and that they had "neither the intention nor desire to take from Japan what she required for peacetime economy which will enable her to develop democratically and assume her future responsibilities in a world order under law." [14]

United States Ambassador Walter Bedell Smith approached Foreign Commissar Molotov on July 11, 1947, regarding a preliminary peace conference for Japan. In rejecting summarily on July 22 the American proposal for an eleven-nation preliminary Japanese peace talk, Moscow accused the United States of acting unilaterally in trying to call the conference without consulting the Soviet Union, Great Britain, or China.[15] The Soviet government, however, made a counterproposal that the Big Four, constituting a Council of Foreign Ministers, fix the date of the conference. The State Department was determined to proceed with a peace treaty for Japan through the agency of the several Pacific powers rather than through the Council of Foreign Ministers.

By late July, Washington had decided to speed up the reconstruction of Japan through necessary financing. Industrial activity nearly twelve months after surrender was barely a third of the prewar level because of the lack of essential raw materials and low worker efficiency because of damaged or obsolete industrial equipment. Meanwhile, inflation in living costs continued to advance, and labor unrest mounted as food, clothing, and other necessities became scarce.

Exactly two years after surrender, on the second anniversary of the acceptance of the Potsdam Declaration, Japan was reopened to private foreign trade. This came only four months after General MacArthur had asked that trade be resumed. This reinstatement of the nation in world intercourse was an integral part of the process of rehabilitating Japan economically and a prelude to her readmission into the comity of nations.

Indications were given by the State Department on August 21 that talks to draft a peace treaty for Japan would be delayed until late fall or early the following year.[16] Originally, in the immediate post-surrender period, the State Department was all for going the limit in reducing Japan's industrial potential.

[13] *Ibid.*, June 25, 1947.
[14] *Ibid.*, July 7, 1947.
[15] *Ibid.*, July 24, 1947.
[16] *Ibid.*, August 22, 1947.

However, subsequent developments on the international scene caused grave concern among American policy makers over the possible effect of such drastic measures on Japan's wobbly economy. A change in policy came about after Undersecretary of War Draper warned that the application of the FEC-230 would make Japan a permanent ward of the United States.

The controversial document, FEC-230, which set forth American economic objectives in Japan, was first submitted to the Far Eastern Commission on May 12, 1947, and communicated to SCAP subsequently. It stipulated the breakup of the *zaibatsu,* the great family monopolies that controlled most of the nation's economic life, and was based on the thesis that "the dissolution of excessive private concentrations of economic power is essential to the democratization of Japanese economic and political life." Undersecretary of Army Draper had found during his visit to Japan in September, 1947, that it also provided for the virtual destruction of Japanese business and the sale of its assets at nominal prices to selected purchasers including the Communist-dominated labor unions. Because of the storm of controversy it stirred up, the document was subsequently withdrawn.

The American policy of rebuilding Japan was not without repercussions. Premier Chang Chun, in an address to the fourth plenary session of the Kuomintang Central Executive Committee early in September, declared that China was opposed to the American policy of "fostering Japanese strength" and that she would insist on what amounted to virtually a veto power in the drafting of the Japanese peace treaty.[17] It was obvious that China was apprehensive of the political and economic effects of the "revival of the Japanese Empire." Premier Chang's revealing statement that geographical proximity had made it necessary to sign the Sino-Soviet treaty of 1945 and his hope that the Soviet government would fulfill its treaty obligations in Manchuria seemed to explain indirectly China's cautious reluctance to side with the United States in opposition to Russia's stand on the question of the Japanese peace treaty.

By late September, prospects for a Japanese peace conference seemed brighter, as a clearer picture of the issues to be brought before it began to develop largely as the result of Anglo-American understanding. The final draft of the American peace proposals was being circulated among government officials. In late October, Undersecretary of State Robert A. Lovett revealed that the Department of State was proceeding in the hope that the negotiation for a peace treaty for Japan would be undertaken by the end of the year.[18] The United States was advocating the negotiation of the treaty by the eleven nations on the Far Eastern Commission through a procedure by which decisions would be taken on a two-thirds vote.

The Soviet Union objected and insisted on negotiations by the Big Four,

[17] *Ibid.,* September 10, 1947.
[18] *Ibid.,* October 23, 1947.

namely, the United States, Great Britain, the Soviet Union, and China. A compromise was suggested by China under which decisions would be reached by a majority vote with the Big Four concurring. This was felt in diplomatic circles as tantamount to giving China a veto power. The State Department appeared hopeful that differences with China could be ironed out without much difficulty. Washington diplomatic circles were of the belief that the United States was prepared to proceed with the negotiations without the Soviet Union in the event Russia proved adamant in her stand.

By the end of October, however, American hope for holding an immediate Japanese peace conference regardless of Soviet participation faded, although Australia, which had been critical of some American occupation policies, announced support of the American position after the visit of the Australian Minister of External Affairs Herbert V. Evatt to Japan. The Chinese government, which was expected to agree, informed the United States that it would not participate in the peace conference on terms which were unacceptable to the Soviets and offered to open direct negotiations with the Russian government with a view to finding a possible basis of compromise. These developments resulted in the indefinite postponement of a peace conference.

In the face of the prospect of a long and bitter struggle between the West and the Soviet Union, the United States and Great Britain were impelled to modify their ideas on the future of their ex-enemies. The importance of a comparatively strong Germany and Japan to the Western powers became increasingly apparent and began to weigh heavily in the consideration of future policies. At the time of the surrender the prevailing concept was that Japan should be stripped of her conquests and industrial potential and made incapable of regaining any substantial degree of military, political, or economic power. However, developments soon forced a revision of the initial policy.

The persistent and concentrated effort on the part of the United States to develop a strong, united, and democratic China to supersede Japan as the dominant power in the Far East encountered practically insurmountable obstacles and the prospect of success in the foreseeable future all but vanished. General Marshall's efforts to bring an end to the devastating civil strife in China failed. The United States government realized that it could not afford to sit back and wait for China to become strong, unified, and democratic. The inevitable alternative was that for a long time the United States would have to look to Japan to provide in the Far East the necessary elements of stability and security regarded as vital to the Western powers.

Even more important perhaps was the fact that since the end of the war Soviet policy in the Far East as elsewhere has been in serious conflict with American and British policies. There was apprehension that the Soviet Union might replace prewar Germany and Japan as the major threat to world security and peace. Thus, the problem of peace settlements was no longer merely to assure a weak Germany and Japan. It became a problem of strategy to be considered in relation to a possible future clash between the Soviet and Western powers. Japan could serve as a bulwark against Soviet power in the Far East.

Japan's prospects of becoming a potential aggressor in the foreseeable future, on the other hand, was deemed by American officials to be even more remote than Germany's, and the revival of the industrial power of Japan, therefore, could not in itself be a real threat of aggression. To the high policy makers it also appeared that the political and economic unrest resulting from the suppression of a virile nation such as Japan would not only impose serious responsibilities, economically and politically, on the United States, but would also offer the Soviet Union favorable conditions for ideological and political infiltration, which could conceivably sabotage and wreck the work of occupation and the democratization of Japan. Thus, by late October, 1947, slightly more than two years after the end of the Pacific War, American policy had undergone a considerable change.

Deconcentration of Economic Power. The process of breaking up the *zaibatsu* domination of Japan's economic life had been set into motion, as their shares and securities from the majority of their holding companies were confiscated, and members of their families were forbidden to engage in business, while the Holding Company Liquidation Commission was charged with the redistribution of securities of the companies it dissolved or reorganized. In the purchase of securities preference was given to employees, labor unions, cooperatives, and other small investors. An Antitrust Law was enacted to prevent the development of new monopolies. The policy of breaking up economic power was soon found to be affecting adversely the policy of rebuilding Japan.

On December 19, only ten days after the Economic Deconcentration Law was enacted by the Diet specially to implement the FEC-230, Senator William F. Knowland of California told the Senate that the Far Eastern Commission document included "shocking" economic policies that were "unbelievable" coming from the United States. He also charged that the provisions for purging owners and managers of large Japanese companies were contrary to American "decency and fairness," criticized the Department of State for keeping it secret, and urged a full scale investigation.[19]

United States government officials privately intimated in Washington in the latter part of January, 1948, that an eventual Marshall plan for the Far East might be evolved around an industrially revived Japan, inasmuch as any recovery program for the Far East would be difficult to carry out without the help of Japanese industry. This was one reason for the newly expressed American determination to speed the time when Japan becomes self-supporting and can make her proper contribution to the economic rehabilitation of world economy and can take her place in the community of nations.

[19] On January 6, 1948, Army Secretary Kenneth C. Royall called for the revision of FEC-230 and other economic policies for Japan. *Newsweek,* March 1, 1948.

A policy decision of the United States government along these lines was laid before the Far Eastern Commission on January 21 by Major General Frank R. McCoy, its chairman, who stated that the $350 million a year burden on American taxpayers for sustaining Japan's civilian economy must be lifted. It was revealed that the United States government would shortly ask Congress for funds to supply not only bare necessities for the Japanese people, but also for the procurement of industrial raw materials, spare parts, and other items to assist Japan to expand the output of her peaceful industries. This announcement to put Japan on her economic feet was met immediately with favorable reactions in Japanese political, economic, and industrial circles.

Spurred by the encouraging news, in a policy speech before a boisterous and unruly session of the Diet, Premier Katayama set the nation's goal at an immediate 40 per cent increase in production of essential key industries and a 10 per cent boost in food production. The Premier called on the nation for intensification of efforts to prepare for the peace conference.

Increasing concern on the part of the United States Congress over the problem of Japanese recovery was reflected in the approval of the $240 million deficiency appropriation requested by the Army Department to defray the expenses of Japanese occupation for the rest of the fiscal year 1947 ending June 30, 1948. When SCAP made the request for $250 million it had not expected to receive more than 50 per cent of the amount. Consequently, the occupation authorities were surprised when Congress voted to give 96 per cent of the amount requested.[20]

By far the most definite recommendation for the rebuilding of Japan was contained in the Strike Report, made for the Army Department by the Overseas Consultants, Inc., and comprising thirty prominent American engineers under the direction of Clifford S. Strike in March, 1948. The report, which called for the selection of Japan instead of China as the dominant force in the East and rebuilding her into a strong nation to play the main role in Asia, stressed that the full recovery of Japan would take at least five years if not longer. It also advised against the removal of productive facilities that could be used effectively in Japan. It emphasized that the "removal of productive facilities beyond primary war facilities would hurt world production, would reduce the likelihood of her becoming self-supporting, and in any case, increase the time required to reach this objective; would be expensive to the American taxpayer and, in our opinion, would not be to the best interests of claimant nations." Considerable reductions in the heavy reparations bill, as outlined in the Pauley Report of 1946, were recommended by the Strike Report. Needless to say, Japanese business and industrial circles received the report enthusiastically as they did also the press

[20] *United States News and World Report,* January 6, 1948, p. 40.

conference given by Army Undersecretary Draper in Washington after his return from his visit to Japan.[21]

On March 20, Undersecretary of the Army William H. Draper, who arrived in Japan with an economic mission, stated that the policy of the Army Department was to make Japan self-supporting by 1952 or 1953.[22] The four-man committee of business experts who made an economic survey of Japan emphasized in their report, which they submitted to the Army Department upon their return, that Japanese recovery constituted an essential part of the rebuilding of the economy of the Far East [23] and recommended that Congress grant the Army Department's request for $140 million to start a Japanese economic recovery program.

President Truman requested Congress on May 19 for an appropriation of $150 million to help the economic recovery of Japan, Korea, and the Ryūkyū Islands during the twelve-month period beginning July 1, 1948. Japanese industry at the time of the presidential request was operating at less than 45 per cent of the 1930–1934 level, owing largely to the lack of raw materials and ruined transport and production facilities, and was badly in need of substantial aid.

Meanwhile, in Nanking President Chiang Kai-shek, in his inaugural address, made a surprising reversal of China's previous stand when he stated: "Within the limits set by the Allied Powers, Japan should be allowed to rebuild its economy so its common people may be assured of a means of livelihood." But the Chinese students continued their anti-American demonstrations in Peiping as well as in Shanghai, accusing the United States of imperialistic policies and denouncing her policy of bolstering Japan. In England, at the British Labor Party Conference in Scarborough, Foreign Secretary Ernest Bevin, who had previously shown indifference to Japan, called for an immediate Japanese peace conference.[24] Thus, the industrial recovery of Japan on a peaceful basis, which the United States has been advocating as a primary objective of the occupation, suddenly gained the unexpected support of both the British Labor Government and the Chinese Nationalist government of Generalissimo Chiang.

Repercussions in the Philippines to the report of the Johnston Committee [25] recommending aid from other Asiatic countries in assisting Japan to rebuild her industry took the form of violent opposition in the press. The subject had become an issue for public debate, as fear was aroused that an economically re-

[21] *The New York Times,* April 11, 1948.

[22] *Ibid.,* March 27, 1948.

[23] *Ibid.,* May 20, 1948.

[24] *Newsweek,* May 31, 1948.

[25] The Committee consisted of Percy H. Johnston, Chairman of the Chemical Bank and Trust Company, Paul G. Hoffman, subsequently Economic Cooperation Administrator, Robert F. Loree, Chairman of the National Trade Council, and Sidney H. Scheuer, senior partner of Scheuer & Co.

vived Japan would reestablish the old pattern of industrial and trade supremacy at the expense of neighboring raw-material countries.[26] But the program of economic recovery for Japan was pushed ahead. Early in June, General MacArthur approved a $60 million revolving loan to Japan to enable her to purchase raw cotton wherever available. The credit, which has been made available by the United States Export Import Bank, the Bank of America, the Chase National Bank, the National City Bank of New York, and the J. Henry Schroeder Banking Corporation enabled private cotton traders and spinners to import raw cotton from sterling as well as dollar areas and hastened Japan's industrial recovery particularly in the cotton and textile fields.[27]

GOVERNMENT AND POLITICS UNDER OCCUPATION

The last session of the war Diet met for less than a month during November and December, 1945, to enact several important pieces of legislation, including the new Electoral Law, Trade Union Law, and the Agricultural Land Law, designed to break up large feudalistic land holdings and to eliminate sharecropping.[28] A new postwar House of Representatives came into being as a result of the election of April 10, 1946. Little change was noticeable in the character of the new lawmakers for the first plenary session of the new Diet on June 21, which broke up in confusion after fist fights broke out and general disorder developed out of uncontrolled heckling on the floor.

Called to implement the new Constitution by enacting necessary enabling legislation, the 91st extraordinary session of the Diet met during November and December, 1946. It enacted the new Imperial House Law, which safeguarded the regal status of the existing imperial line, and gave the Diet almost complete control of the purse strings through the Imperial House Economic Law, which took effect simultaneously with the new Constitution on May 3, 1947. The properties of the Imperial House were transferred to the state, making it necessary for the Diet to vote its annual income. The law abolishing the House of Peers was enacted and in its place the House of Councilors with a total membership of 250 was created. One hundred of them were to represent the nation at large while 150 members were to be the representatives of the forty-six prefectures. The new upper house was designed as a brake on a possible runaway lower chamber, which is constitutionally empowered to override the action of the former.

The last session of the Diet under the old Constitution ended its deliberations and dissolved itself on March 31, 1947, bringing to a close the old parliamentary system that began in 1890. It was the last session for the House of Peers. A total

[26] *The New York Times,* June 9, 1948.
[27] *Ibid.,* June 8, 1948.
[28] *Ibid.,* December 18, 1945.

of eighty laws were enacted during the session. Among the more important of these were the new Election Law, the Labor Standards Law, which provided for a forty-eight-hour work week, equality of employment for men and women, and a mechanism for settling national minimum wages and forbidding exploitation through labor contracts.[29] The basic Education Law (Kyōiku Kihonhō), extending compulsory education from six years to nine years and removing all administrative barriers to coeducation, the Anti-monopoly Law (Dokusen Kinshihō), the Government Corporation Law, establishing state monopolies in the distribution of coal and oil and in foreign trade, the Diet Law, and Judicial Courts Law were also passed.

Simultaneously with the close of the last Diet under the old Constitution the new Democratic Party (Minshūtō) came into existence with Shidehara Kijūrō as supreme adviser, Professor Tanaka Kōtarō as adviser, and Ashida Hitoshi, Saitō Takao, and Inukai Ken as party doyens. This party had for its nucleus the faction, led by Shidehara, that had bolted the Liberal Party. On May 15 Ashida was made president of the party, which was to be given less than a year later the opportunity to form a government in coalition with the Socialists. Preceding it by three weeks was the National Cooperative Party (Kokumin Kyōdōtō), which was formed around those who were active in the various cooperative organizations.

As a necessary preliminary to the taking effect of the Constitution on May 3, 1947, a series of elections were planned. In October, 1946, the Home Ministry announced the elections that were to be held from December 7 until March 10, 1947. This original schedule had to be changed as a result of delays, and it was not until late spring that elections were actually held. On April 5, the nation went to the polls to elect for the first time by a democratic process governors in forty-six prefectures. Mayors of the five largest cities were also chosen on the same day. When the votes were counted, it was found that no sweeping changes had been made, for the vast majority of the independents who were elected were conservatives and were endorsed by or close to the moderate Liberal and Democratic parties. The largest number of those elected were incumbents. Socialists captured four governorships, including that of Hokkaidō. The Communist Party failed to elect a single governor. What resulted from the election could be characterized as a conservative middle-of-the-road type of political representation.

The House of Councilors election, which took place on April 20, attracted a far larger number of nationally known figures, giving evidence that the national legislature holds a much stronger appeal for the Japanese than the governorship. For the 250 seats there were 583 candidates. The largest number of candi-

---

[29] The new labor law actually imposed upon impoverished Japan the same high standards enjoyed by American labor.

dates, 251 in all, ran without any party label. Socialists ran 102 candidates, Liberals 75, Democrats 53, Communists 42, and Cooperatives 25. Thirteen women were among the candidates. The Socialists became the largest single group in the upper house as the result of the election.[30]

On April 25 came the most important of elections, that of the members of the House of Representatives. At the close of official registration on April 18, a week before the date of election, 1,604 men and women had announced their candidacy for the 466 seats. Most significant was the fact that 1,251, or approximately 78 per cent, of the candidates were newcomers in the political field, having played no part in national politics previously. Unlike the House of Councilors candidates, independents did not comprise the largest single group. Instead, the leading parties presented the majority of candidates.[31] The Socialist Party won the largest number of seats—143 which was 45 more than in the preceding Diet—to become the leading party with the right to name a premier from its ranks.[32] Liberals captured 133 seats and the Democrats 126. The Communist Party won only 4 seats, representing a 50 per cent loss of their House strength.

In his official statement two days after the election, General MacArthur expressed satisfaction at the results. In regard to the Communist setback he stated: "Since the inception of the occupation, when thousands of its adherents were freed from the stern suppression of prison cells, this philosophy and its leaders had been given the fullest liberty and freedom of political action in open and fair competition with democratic forces and beliefs. It thus had its full chance, and on the merits has failed." He pronounced that the "Japanese people have firmly and decisively rejected its leadership and overwhelmingly have chosen a moderate course sufficiently centered from either extreme to ensure the preservation of freedom and the enhancement of individual dignity." [33]

THE NEW CONSTITUTION TAKES EFFECT

On March 6, a whole month before the national election took place, the Emperor issued a rescript indicating his desire to realize the provision of the Potsdam Declaration, stipulating that "the ultimate form of Japanese government is to be determined by the freely expressed will of the Japanese people." He em-

[30] Several well-known names from the old House of Peers were seen among the membership of the new upper house, such as Tokugawa Yorisada, ex-President of the House of Peers, Matsudaira Tsuneo, former Imperial Household Minister, and Saionji Kinkazu, son of the last Elder Statesman.

[31] Democrats ran 338 candidates, Liberals 328, Socialists 289, Cooperatives 112, Communists 121, minor parties 152, and independents 264.

[32] Actually the Democrats and Liberals polled larger votes than the Socialists with 6.8 million and 6.7 million, respectively, as against 6.6 million.

[33] *The New York Times,* April 28, 1947.

phasized the need for a drastic revision of the Constitution, the national aspirations to live peacefully and promote cultural enlightenment, and the firm resolve to renounce war and to foster friendship with all nations of the world. On the same day, the first draft of the new Constitution was made public.[34] A revised draft was submitted to the Supreme Commander for the Allied Powers on April 22.[35] After further revisions were made, it was formally promulgated by the Emperor on November 3 and became effective six months later on May 3, 1947.

That the new Constitution was American inspired, if not American drafted, was quite apparent not only from the concepts embodied in the document but from the preamble, which was couched in a language highly suggestive of the preamble to the Constitution of the United States, the Declaration of Independence, and the Atlantic Charter. By far the most unique feature of the new organic law was the renunciation of war as an instrument of national policy and the abandoning of the right to maintain armed forces. Highly significant was the recognition of the theory of legislative supremacy by virtue of which the Diet became the highest organ of state. Sovereignty was now legally recognized to reside with the people, and the Emperor became a mere "symbol of the state and of the unity of the people." The acts of the Emperor were made subject to the advice and approval of the Cabinet. The subordination of the executive to the legislative branch was effectuated by the provision making the Cabinet responsible collectively to the Diet. Furthermore, it was required that the majority of the members of the Cabinet, including the Premier, be members of the House of Representatives. The military, past and future, was shut out completely from the government by the requirement that cabinet ministers should be civilians. Not only was a Bill of Rights provided without the restrictions of former times, but an equality provision giving equal rights to women was also made a part of the basic law of the land. The right and obligation to work were clearly stipulated, as was *habeas corpus*. Strong emphasis was given to the principle of local autonomy, on which the hope of democratization was pinned. The introduction of the doctrine of judicial review through a new Supreme Court, empowered to rule on the constitutionality of legislation, constituted an innovation of peculiarly American nature. Peerage and the Privy Council were abolished to facilitate the process of democratization.[36]

First Diet Session under the New Constitution. The first session of the Diet under the new Constitution opened on May 20, preceded on its eve by a grand display of fireworks. For more than four hours rockets flared from the Imperial Palace grounds and thrilled the crowd gathered in the plaza outside. On May 23,

[34] *Ibid.*, March 9, 1946.

[35] U.S. Department of State, *Occupation of Japan*, pp. 117–132.

[36] For a discussion of the background of the Constitution, see David N. Rowe, "The New Japanese Constitution," *Far Eastern Survey*, January 29 and February 12, 1947.

the House of Representatives gave Katayama Tetsu, president of the Socialist Party, a 420 to 2 vote for the premiership. Thus, the 59-year-old Christian labor lawyer, who had been a prominent Socialist since the 1920's, became the first Premier under the new democratic Constitution. To him also went the distinction of becoming the first Christian Premier in history. The Cabinet, which emerged on June 1, represented a coalition of the Socialist, Democratic, and National Cooperative parties.

Because of the many "firsts" this first session of the Diet was an impressive and memorable one. Unable to finish its business on time, it found itself forced to extend the session four times. It was a protracted session, the longest in the parliamentary history of Japan, lasting 204 days from May 20 to December 9, 1947. To the average citizen, it left the impression of unprecedented disorderliness and ineffectiveness.[37] Its inefficiency was due to several factors, among which was the delay caused in the submission of bills by the government's negligence. Proceedings were held up because of the utter lack of a feeling of urgency and conscientiousness on the part of the lawmakers, reflected in the high rate of absenteeism. Standing committees functioned poorly as a result of faulty organization and inept management. This was to some extent inevitable in view of the paucity of legislative experience and know-how of a predominantly inexperienced gathering of newcomers.[38] Another complicating factor was the inability of the coalition to function smoothly. Consequently, the sessions were characterized by dilatory tactics and wrangling. For several days virtual pandemonium reigned in the legislative chambers, where the public had expected dignified and enlightened deliberation. Frequent and noisy heckling, which developed into fisticuffs, bore out the impression that many members regarded the Diet as a place for partisan demonstrations. On the whole, the unfavorable publicity, both at home and abroad, given to the disorderliness left many a Japanese wondering whether Japan was really capable of working democratic political institutions successfully.

Although the Diet passed a record number of bills, which totalled 157, the overwhelmingly large proportion of them was not initiated by the lawmakers themselves but by the government.[39] On the last day, December 9, thirty-nine bills were rammed through the House of Councilors under government pressure, practically in the last moments of the session, to enact necessary legislation. Among the more important laws enacted were those designed to implement the process of democratization, which had been set into motion at the very outset of the oc-

[37] *Nippon Times,* editorial, December 11, 1947.

[38] A round table discussion of the Diet session, held with five members of the Diet, was highly critical of the inefficiency of the legislative body. *Tōkyō Mimpō,* December 11, 1947.

[39] The government introduced 161 bills out of which 150 were enacted; the House of Representatives introduced 20 bills of which only 7 became law while the 2 private bills introduced by members of the House of Councilors failed to pass.

cupation, such as the Economic Deconcentration Law, Coal Nationalization Law, Government Corporation Law, Unemployment Allowance Law, Unemployment Insurance Law, Agricultural Cooperative Law, revisions of the Criminal Code and the Civil Code, the creation of the Ministry of Labor, the Office of the Attorney General, National Public Service Law, and Police Decentralization Law.

No sooner was the first Diet session officially closed than the second session was convoked on the following day. After the various committees were organized, the Diet went into the customary year-end recess. The reopening of the session following the recess was marked by a significant event. The Emperor appeared in civilian morning clothes instead of the customary formal court uniform as in the past and, in reading his usual rescript opening the Diet, he asserted that "We the people of Japan" have an important mission to fulfill: to weather the economic crisis and to build a peaceful democratic state that would win the confidence of the world. This, in effect, was the implementation of his New Year's Day Rescript of January 1, 1946, in which he repudiated his "divinity." He officially referred to the Diet as "the highest organ of state power."

Fall of the Katayama Cabinet. In spite of the difficulties of keeping the coalition from falling apart, the Katayama Government, the first under the new Constitution, lasted more than eight months. The left wing faction of the Social Democratic Party was responsible for precipitating the resignation of the Cabinet on February 10 by a revolt against the party's compromise with the other two parties making up the coalition. Although harried constantly by problems inherent in a coalition government, the Socialist cabinet of Premier Katayama could claim for itself an imposing list of legislative and administrative achievements. Beginning with the appointment of the fifteen justices of the Supreme Court in August, it launched the Ministry of Labor on September 1, started the enforcement of the Labor Standards Law the following month, enacted the Economic Decentralization Law early in December, and abolished the Home Ministry, the citadel of bureaucracy, on December 27. In addition, it had also sponsored the enactment of the National Public Service Law and the Police Decentralization Law and abolished the Cabinet Bureau of Legislation and the Central Liaison Office of the Foreign Office.

Although the Liberal Party claimed the next premiership by reason of its position as the leading opposition party, it failed to garner sufficient votes in the House of Representatives for its president, Yoshida Shigeru. After a long period of political maneuvering, the Democratic Party succeeded in winning the support of most of the Social Democratic Party and Dr. Ashida Hitoshi was elected Premier by the House of Representatives on February 21.[40] Although the balloting in the House of Councilors gave Yoshida two more votes than Ashida, con-

[40] Ashida got 216 votes, Yoshida 180, Katayama 8, Tokuda 3, and 14 votes were invalidated.

stitutional provisions made the lower house choice the official choice of the Diet.[41]

The task of completing the Cabinet was a long and arduous one for Ashida for it was not until March 10, more than half a month after he was elected, that his government was formally installed. In a public statement Premier Ashida asserted that true democratization of the nation constituted the most important prerequisite for the spiritual and economic reconstruction of a new Japan dedicated to peace and working to regain the trust and confidence of the world. He made clear his intention to pursue a firm middle-of-the-road policy and not to tolerate either extreme, since radical ideologies were inimical to the healthy growth of democracy. At the same time, he pledged to take positive steps to curb the activities of those who were aiding and abetting labor strife, social unrest, and disruption of industry, which would hamper the reconstruction of war-torn economy. Ashida's position was no less difficult than that of Katayama, since his coalition of Democratic, Socialist, and Cooperative parties was shaky from the very outset. The major problems confronting the Ashida Cabinet, like those of the preceding cabinets, were primarily economic. Stabilization of national livelihood was given first priority and was to be achieved through a fight against inflation. Production was to be increased by a system of priority to key industries and particularly in the development of hydroelectric power, the encouragement of small and medium enterprises, and the stimulation of export and tourist trades.

In his address to the reconvened Diet on March 20, 1948, Premier Ashida reiterated his policy as expressed in the earlier statement. He expressed perturbation at the persistent political instability that plagued the neighboring nations of the Far East, which stood in the way of the recovery of Japan as well as the Far East. His utterances indirectly reflected the wistful wish of the nation to become a member of the United Nations. Of significance was his assertion that the occupation is "one of fairness and tolerance unparalleled in history." [42]

Formation of the Democratic Liberal Party. The fluidity of the political situation was reflected constantly in the appearance and disappearance of parties as well as in their splits and mergers. On March 15 more than 200 members of the Diet formally inaugurated the conservative Democratic Liberal Party, whose platform called for the restoration of free economy and an end to socialist controls. Headed by Yoshida Shigeru, the new party immediately claimed 169 seats in the lower house, the largest single bloc, and topping the Socialists by 40 seats. The government coalition of Democratic, Socialist, and Cooperative parties together controlled only 200 votes or less than a majority. The new party was built closely around Yoshida's old Liberal Party supported by former Democratic Party

[41] Yoshida received 104 votes to Ashida's 102 in the House of Councilors.

[42] Supreme Commander for the Allied Powers, *Summation of Non-Military Activities in Japan,* March, 1948, pp. 46–52.

members headed by Shidehara, who bolted the party over the issue of state control of coal mines in late 1947. Although it was opposed to a planned economy, to which the Ashida Government was committed, the *Nippon Times* found it difficult to see in it anything other than "the old Liberal Party and its friends under a new and inappropriate label." [43]

Political Apathy and Official Corruption. The public at large seemed to the newspaper *Mainichi* and to others to have lost interest in politics and was apathetic to current events.[44] Most people did not even know whether or not the Diet was in session. In the recent by-election held in Hiroshima only 5 or 6 per cent of the registered voters cast their votes. Diet attendance hovered about the halfway mark as many of the members were visiting constituencies for electioneering purposes. The public showed evidence of interest in such matters as rumored scandals, black-market dealings in political funds, and dishonest political maneuvers to secure power. Thus, in spite of the position of supremacy accorded it by the new Constitution, the Diet was losing the respect as well as the interest of the public.

That the introduction of a new constitution in itself could not bring about changes overnight in the complexion and nature of bureaucracy was made evident before long. The bureaucracy, which thrived under military domination of Japanese affairs in the latter part of the 1930's, had not only firmly entrenched itself in power but had become nearly unbearable to the general public. Particularly offensive was the almost ingrained "holier-than-thou" attitude of government officials, which was reflected in their patronizing and condescending, if not haughty and discourteous, attitude toward the people.[45] Their self-righteous and knowing attitude, bolstered by the self-delusion that they were virtually infallible, their disregard of public opinion, and their ignorance of existing conditions all contributed to the low efficiency of government officials even during the war years. In March, 1947, Communications Minister Hitotsumatsu revealed that a million yen had disappeared from his department, and that the officials had become brazenly corrupt. In one instance a subordinate had advised him to resign for having started an investigation of official corruption.[46]

Almost simultaneously with the taking effect of the new Constitution, the nation's leading dailies, *Asahi, Mainichi,* and *Yomiuri,* launched a campaign for the reform of the bureaucracy, which, because of the practically absolute security it enjoyed, continued to function almost as a government within a government, independent of the popular will and ignoring parliamentary orders.[47] The *Mainichi* emphasized that the bureaucrats should be deprived of their power and be made

[43] *The New York Times,* March 15, 1948.
[44] *Ibid.,* April 11, 1948.
[45] Tōkyō *Asahi,* January 6, 1940.
[46] *Ibid.,* March 15, 1947.
[47] *The New York Times,* May 30, 1947.

administrative technicians if the political parties were to carry out their policies. As a step toward discouraging the bureaucratic and feudalistic element as well as eliminating undue respect for officials, inordinate contempt for the masses, and an attitude of self-righteousness, Premier Katayama directed that the use of honorifics in the terms of address for cabinet officers and even for the Premier be discontinued.

In the summer of 1947, scandals were exposed in connection with the illegal disposal of huge stockpiles of accumulated war supplies as a result of disclosures in the Diet by a Liberal Party member who had been a special investigator for the Economic Stabilization Board.[48] It was disclosed that corrupt bureaucrats in collusion with others were enriching themselves by allowing illegally hoarded supplies to be diverted into the black market and industrial channels. The scandals, which involved party politicians as well as the bureaucrats, caused the public to lose confidence in both the bureaucracy and the political parties.

A systematic search for hoarded goods became one of the major activities of the government. In a three-month drive from November, 1947, through January, 1948, procurators throughout the country uncovered 10 billion yen worth of illegally hidden or hoarded goods, which were brought out into legal rationing channels.[48a] The Katayama Cabinet set up the Illegal Transactions Investigations Committee late in January to uncover hoarded goods and eliminate bureaucratic profiteers and racketeers. The great bulk of army supplies illegally appropriated by professional army personnel, bureaucrats, capitalists, and party bosses and subsequently channeled into the black market contributed materially to inflation.[49] The tremendous scale on which these illegal transactions were carried out became a source of embarrassment to the authorities.

Official corruption continued to be exposed, and local government officials were found to be deeply involved. Misappropriations of funds by prefectural officials were disclosed with distressing frequency. Practices that were thought nation-wide consisted of listing "ghosts" on the payrolls, politicians paying themselves large bonuses of all sorts and giving themselves special allowances for such items as "clothing," "year-end gifts," "hotel expenses," and even "hush money." [50]

EDUCATIONAL REFORMS

It was early recognized that if the democratization of the nation was to be aided materially, the reform of the educational system was imperative. In order that the Japanese might benefit from the experiences and knowledge of American

[48] *Ibid.,* July 28, 1947.

[48a] Among those involved were Yokosuka and Maizuru Naval Bases, Kure Naval Arsenal, Nakajima Aircraft Company and Tōyō Brewery of Shizuoka.

[49] *Tōkyō Mimpō,* editorial, March 18, 1948.

[50] *Nippon Times,* March 6. 1948.

educational leaders, SCAP invited a group of twenty-one prominent leaders of American education to visit Japan. The United States Education Mission, which was headed by Dr. George D. Stoddard[51] and which included among its membership women educators, labor leaders, educational administrators, and a Negro university president,[52] spent the month of March, 1946, visiting schools, colleges, universities, and other institutions, and conferring with SCAP officials, Japanese educators, and individuals from all walks of life. After studying the educational needs of a nation committed to a program of democratization, the Committee submitted a report[53] that furnished a broad basis for the educational reforms that were instituted soon thereafter.

In keeping with the general objective of the Potsdam Declaration, the Education Mission sought to discover and liquidate "those restricting and strangling forces" that prevented a cultural Renaissance in Japan. Consequently, decentralization was made the key to the revamping of the educational system, which had suffered from the domination of an entrenched bureaucracy and had been subjected to ultranationalistic and militaristic propaganda as well as to regimentation. The revamping of the Japanese educational system was started with the enactment of the Basic Education Law and the creation of the Education Renovation Commission (Kyōiku Sasshin Iinkai).

History teaching, which had been banned along with geography and morals for a whole year since surrender, was resumed in the fall of 1946 as new history textbooks were completed.[54] Discarding the mythological treatment of the divine origin of the nation, the textbook begins a chapter on the dawn of Japanese history with a discussion of shell heaps, burial mounds, and private life in a scientific, matter-of-fact manner. Stripped of martial spirit and ultranationalistic Shintō ideology, the new texts emphasize peaceful concepts and the world viewpoint rather than nationalism. The life of the people is made the center of the historical narrative of the development of Japan. Cultural, social, and economic emphasis serves to offset the predominantly political emphasis of the old textbook. In place of the military exploits of old and modern Japan are found the achievements of scientists and men of letters.

Moral concepts that promoted submissiveness and that were regarded as a separate compartment have been revamped to interpenetrate all phases of everyday life and thus made an integral part of the activities of free individuals. Thus, the course on morals was vitalized and modified into a course on civics. Closer

[51] At the time, Dr. Stoddard was New York State Commissioner of Education but subsequently he became President of the University of Illinois.

[52] Dr. Charles S. Johnson was then Professor of Sociology but subsequently he became President of Fisk University.

[53] *Report of the United States Education Mission to Japan*, Department of State Publications 2579, Far Eastern Series 11, 1946.

[54] Tōkyō *Asahi*, October 20, 1946.

relationship and integration with society are the goals set through the encouragement of student activities and self-government. The basic aims of education as envisaged by the new system consist of training individuals to respect the dignity of the individual and the establishment of a general creative culture. Reorganization on the elementary and secondary levels of education was achieved through the adoption of the American 6-3-3 plan, which represents a definite improvement over the Japanese system.[55]

Language reform is being carried out gradually through the introduction of romanization in the schools and the life of the community and the nation through such media as newspapers, periodicals, and books, as well as the adoption of a more democratic or classless form of the spoken language. Considerable reduction has been achieved already in the number of characters used in the textbooks and in general reading material. Teaching methods and materials emphasizing rote memory, conformity, and a vertical, nonreciprocal system of duties and loyalties are being modified to encourage and emphasize independent thinking, personality development, and the rights as well as the responsibilities of democratic citizenship.

Steps are being taken to foster adult and continuation education to the greatest possible extent in order that individual responsibility may be developed in an enlightened citizenry. The role of the library in the entire educational program is being given a very prominent place. In this connection, the National Diet Library Law, which was passed unanimously by both houses of the Diet on February 4, 1948, deserves special mention.[56] This legislation provides for the establishment of an institution comparable in size and scope to the American Library of Congress, the French Bibliothèque Nationale, and the British Museum. In addition to facilities for an extensive legislative reference service for the Diet, it sets up a national bibliographical reference and research service for the benefit of local governments, industry, agriculture, labor unions, and other groups. The great importance attached to this national library is seen by the fact that the Chief Librarian [57] is given a rank equivalent to that of a cabinet member and his deputy that of a vice minister.

Higher education has been charged with the function of setting a standard of free thought, bold inquiry and action. In other words, it is charged with the function of bringing about a cultural renaissance in the arts, letters, and religion, as well as to furnish the leadership in the reeducation of the people to their new responsibilities. Consequently, higher education should not continue to be a

[55] The plan was adopted in 1947 to become partially effective during the fiscal year 1947.

[56] This legislation was based on the recommendation made by the United States Library Mission, which visited Japan in 1947 at the invitation of the Diet.

[57] The first appointee to this post is Dr. Kanamori Tokujirō, former Minister of State, who had the responsibility of seeing the new Constitution through the Diet and was prominently mentioned as a candidate for Chief Justice of the Supreme Court.

privilege of the economically fortunate few, but should become an opportunity for the many through a system of financial help to talented men and women unable to continue into higher institutions of learning on their own resources. Freedom of access to higher learning on the basis of merit has been established.

All the higher schools (*kōtō gakkō*) are being raised to university status with a four-year curriculum. Some 645 institutions were at one time seeking university status. In order to increase the opportunities for liberal education at higher levels, curriculums in the higher schools and specialized colleges (*semmon gakkō*) are being liberalized, and four-year liberal arts colleges are being planned.

To offset the too early and too narrow specialization and too great a professional emphasis in the curriculums of Japanese institutions of higher learning, greater opportunity for general education has been provided to cultivate a broader humanistic attitude as a necessary background for free thought and inquiry.

Improvement of the quality of higher education is to be achieved through the stimulation and improvement of research, cooperation in the use of library facilities, and interchange of faculty members among the institutions of learning. In the field of social sciences Japan has to make up for much that has been lost during the period since 1931, when studies were deflected according to the political demands of the government and partly suppressed or neglected. Studies, therefore, are being revived rapidly in a spirit of free inquiry and thought for the reexamination and reappraisal of the past, while new inquiries are being started on world problems as well as domestic political, social, and economic questions. Plans are under way for the interchange of both students and professors between Japanese institutions and those of other countries as an integral part of the educational program of the internationally oriented and vitalized Japan.

Faculty autonomy in academic affairs and the freedom to pursue and experiment with ideas in the search for truth and knowledge, free from intellectual surveillance or suppression, are now materializing. Freedom from financial as well as political pressure, due recognition of the position of the professor in society through adequate salaries, pension, or retirement benefits, and abolition of civil service ratings for government university faculties have been assured.

Participation of Japan in the United Nations now appears to be a question of time. Preparations are being made in anticipation of that eventuality. On December 17, 1947, the United Nations Association was launched with the backing of some 300 notables. Interest in the United Nations Educational, Scientific, and Cultural Organization is running high. There have been formed in various parts of the country UNESCO Cooperation Societies, which are brought together under the National Federation of UNESCO Cooperation Societies. At the same time, the government is laying the groundwork for effective participation in the activities of the UNESCO through groups in the Diet, the Education Ministry and the Educational Reform Committee, all of which are devoting a great deal of attention to the problem of cultural cooperation. Thus, Japan has charted a course for peace and international cooperation, intent on regaining her position and prestige in the family of nations.

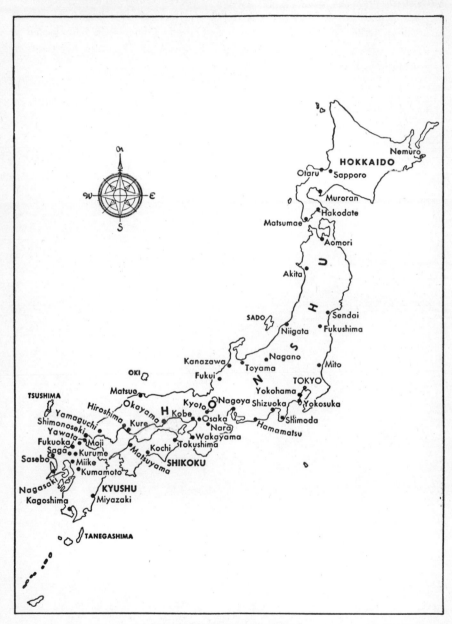

Principal Cities of Japan

Bibliography

WORKS IN WESTERN LANGUAGES

Alcock, Sir Rutherford: *The Capital of the Tycoon,* London, 1863.

Allen, George C.: *Japan, the Hungry Guest,* New York, 1938.

――――: *Japanese Industry: Its Recent Development and Present Condition,* New York, 1940.

――――: *Modern Japan and Its Problems,* New York, 1928.

――――: *A Short Economic History of Japan, 1867–1937,* London, 1946.

Ariga, Nagao: *La Guerre russo-japonaise au point de vue continental et le droit international d'après les documents officiels du Grand État-major japonais,* Paris, 1908.

――――: *La Guerre sino-japonaise au point de vue du droit international,* Paris, 1896.

Asada, Keiichi: *Expenditures of the Sino-Japanese War,* New York, 1922.

Asakawa, Kan'ichi: *The Russo-Japanese Conflict, Its Causes and Issues,* Boston, 1904.

Aston, William G.: *A History of Japanese Literature,* London, 1933.

Bailey, Thomas A.: *A Diplomatic History of the American People,* New York, 1940.

――――: *Theodore Roosevelt and the Japanese-American Crises,* Stanford, 1934.

Baker, Ray Stannard: *Woodrow Wilson and World Settlement,* 3 vols., Garden City, 1922.

Balfour, A. J.: *Retrospect: an Unfinished Autobiography,* Boston, 1930.

Ball, W. Macmahon: *Japan Enemy or Ally?* New York, 1949.

Ballard, George A.: *The Influence of the Sea on the Political History of Japan,* New York, 1921.

Beard, Charles A.: *The Administration and Politics of Tokyo,* New York, 1923.

――――: *President Roosevelt and the Coming of the War, 1941,* New Haven, 1948.

Belden, Jack: *Retreat with Stilwell,* New York, 1943.

Bemis, Samuel F.: *A Diplomatic History of the United States,* New York, 1936.

Benedict, Ruth: *The Chrysanthemum and the Sword,* Boston, 1946.

Beresford, Lord Charles W.: *The Break Up of China,* New York, 1899.

Birdsall, Paul: *Versailles Twenty Years After,* New York, 1941.

Bishop, Joseph B.: *Theodore Roosevelt and His Time,* 2 vols., New York, 1921.

Bisson, Thomas A.: *Japan in China,* New York, 1938.

Blakeslee, George H.: *Conflicts af Policy in the Far East,* Boston, 1934.

――――: *Japan and Japanese-American Relations,* New York, 1912.

Bonsal, Stephen: *Suitors and Suppliants,* New York, 1946.

――――: *Unfinished Business,* New York, 1944.

Borg, Dorothy: *American Policy and the Chinese Revolution, 1925–28,* New York, 1947.

Borton, Hugh: *Japan Since 1931, Its Social and Political Development*, New York, 1940.

Broughton, William R.: *Voyage of Discovery to the North Pacific Ocean, 1795–1798*, London, 1804.

Bryn-Jones, David: *Frank B. Kellogg*, New York, 1937.

Buell, Raymond L.: *Japanese Immigration*, Boston, 1924.

———: *The Washington Conference*, New York, 1922.

Byas, Hugh: *Government by Assassination*, New York, 1942.

Byrnes, James F.: *Speaking Frankly*, New York, 1947.

Bywater, Hector C.: *Sea Power in the Pacific; a Study of the American-Japanese Naval Problem*, New York, 1921.

Cameron, Meribeth E.: *The Reform Movement in China, 1898–1912*, Stanford, 1931.

Cary, Otis: *A History of Christianity in Japan*, 2 vols., New York, 1909.

Causton, E. E. N.: *Militarism and Foreign Policy in Japan*, London, 1936.

Chamberlin, William H.: *Japan over Asia*, Boston, 1937.

Clark, Grover: *Economic Rivalries in China*, New Haven, 1932.

———: *The Great Wall Crumbles*, New York, 1935.

Cleland, Robert G.: *California in Our Time, 1900–1940*, New York, 1947.

Clement, Ernest W.: *Constitutional Imperialism in Japan*, New York, 1916.

Clements, Paul H.: *The Boxer Rebellion*, New York, 1915.

Clyde, Paul H.: *The Far East, a History of the Impact of the West on Eastern Asia*, New York, 1948.

———: *A History of the Modern and Contemporary Far East*, New York, 1937.

———: *International Rivalries in Manchuria, 1689–1922*, Columbus, 1926.

———: *United States Policy toward China; Diplomatic and Public Documents, 1839–1939*, Durham, 1940.

Cole, Allan B., ed.: *Yankee Surveyors in the Shogun's Seas*, Princeton, 1947.

Colegrove, Kenneth: *Militarism in Japan*, Boston, 1936.

Crocker, William R.: *The Japanese Population Problem, the Coming Crisis*, New York, 1931.

Curzon, Lord George N.: *Problems of the Far East*, New York, 1896.

Dennett, Tyler: *Americans in Eastern Asia*, New York, 1922.

———: *Roosevelt and the Russo-Japanese War*, Garden City, 1925.

Dennis, Alfred L. P.: *Adventures in American Diplomacy, 1896–1906*, New York, 1928.

———: *The Anglo-Japanese Alliance*, Berkeley, 1923.

Dewey, John: *China, Japan and the United States*, New York, 1921.

Dillon, E. J.: *The Eclipse of Russia*, London, 1918.

Douglas, Sir R. K.: *Europe and the Far East, 1506–1912*, London, 1913.

Dugdale, Blanche E. C.: *Arthur James Balfour*, 2 vols., New York, 1936.

Dugdale, E. T. C.: *German Diplomatic Documents, 1871–1914*, 4 vols., London, 1928–1931.

Dulles, Foster Rea: *Forty Years of American-Japanese Relations*, New York, 1937.

Eckardstein, Baron von: *Ten Years at the Court of St. James*, New York, 1922.

Eckel, Paul E.: *The Far East since 1500*, New York, 1947.

Eckstein, Gustave: *Noguchi*, New York, 1931.

Embree, John F.: *The Japanese Nation, a Social Survey*, New York, 1945.

————: *Suye Mura, a Japanese Village*, Chicago, 1939.

Etherton, P. T.: *Japan: Mistress of the Pacific?* London, 1933.

Fahs, Charles B.: *Government in Japan, Recent Trends in Scope and Operation*, New York, 1940.

Falk, Edwin A.: *From Perry to Pearl Harbor: the Struggle for Supremacy in the Pacific*, Garden City, 1943.

————: *Togo and the Rise of Japanese Sea Power*, New York, 1936.

Far Eastern Commission: *Activities of the Far Eastern Commission: Report of the Secretary-General*, Washington, 1947.

Fay, Sidney B.: *The Origins of the World War*, 2 vols., New York, 1928.

Field, Frederick V.: *American Participation in the China Consortiums*, Chicago, 1931.

Field, James A.: *The Japanese at Leyte Gulf*, Princeton, 1947.

Fischer, Louis: *The Soviets in World Affairs*, 2 vols., London, 1930.

Fisher, Galen M.: *Creative Forces in Japan*, New York, 1922.

Florinsky, Michael T.: *World Revolution and the U.S.S.R.*, New York, 1933.

Foster, John W.: *American Diplomacy in the Orient*, Boston, 1903.

————: *Diplomatic Memoirs*, 2 vols., Boston, 1909.

Francis, David R.: *Russia from the American Embassy*, New York, 1921.

Fujisawa Rikitaro: *The Recent Aims and Political Development of Japan*, New Haven, 1923.

Fukuzawa, Yukichi: *Autobiography*, Tōkyō, 1934.

Garvin, James L.: *The Life of Joseph Chamberlain*, 3 vols., New York, 1932–1934.

Gerard, Auguste: *Ma Mission au Japon*, 1907–1914, Paris, 1919.

Golovnin, V. P.: *Narrative of My Captivity in Japan, 1811–1813*, London, 1818.

Gooch, G. P.: *British Documents on the Origins of the War, 1898–1914*, 11 vols., London, 1926–1938.

Goodwin, Cardinal: *The Transmississippi West, 1803–1853*, New York, 1922.

Graves, William S.: *America's Siberian Venture, 1918–1920*, New York, 1931.

Grew, Joseph C.: *Ten Years in Japan*, New York, 1944.

Griffis, William E.: *Japanese Nation in Evolution*, New York, 1907.

————: *Matthew Calbraith Perry*, Boston, 1887.

————: *The Mikado's Empire*, New York, 1913.

————: *Townsend Harris, First American Envoy in Japan*, Boston, 1895.

————: *Verbeck of Japan*, New York, 1900.

Griswold, A. Whitney: *The Far Eastern Policy of the United States*, New York, 1938.

Gubbins, J. H.: *The Making of Modern Japan*, London, 1922.

————: *The Progress of Japan, 1853–1917*, Oxford, 1911.

Hanazono, Kanesada: *The Development of Japanese Journalism*, Osaka, 1934.

Harada, Shuichi: *Labor Conditions in Japan*, New York, 1928.

Haring, Douglas, ed.: *Japan's Prospects*, Cambridge, 1946.

Harris, Townsend: *The Complete Journal of Townsend Harris*, New York, 1930.

Hawks, Francis L.: *Narrative of the Expedition of an American Squadron to the China Seas and Japan, 1852, 1853, and 1854*, New York, 1856.

Heco, Joseph: *The Narrative of a Japanese*, 2 vols., Yokohama, 1892.

Henderson, Daniel: *From the Volga to the Yukon*, New York, 1944.

Hersey, John R.: *Hiroshima*, New York, 1946.

Hershey, Amos S.: *The International Law and Diplomacy of the Russo-Japanese War*, New York, 1906.

Hicks, Charles R.: *Japan's Entry into the War, 1914*, Reno, 1944.

Hishida, Seiji G.: *The International Position of Japan as a Great Power*, New York, 1905.

Hokkaido Imperial University: *The Semi-Centennial of the Hokkaido Imperial University, Japan, 1876–1926*, Sapporo, 1927.

Holcombe, Arthur N.: *The Chinese Revolution*, New York, 1930.

Holland, William L., ed.: *Commodity Control in the Pacific Area*, Stanford, 1935.

Holtom, Daniel C.: *Modern Japan and Shintō Nationalism*, Chicago, 1943.

————: *National Faith of Japan: A Study in Modern Shintō*, London, 1938.

Honjo, Eijiro: *The Social and Economic History of Japan*, Kyōto, 1935.

Hornbeck, Stanley K.: *Contemporary Politics in the Far East*, New York, 1916.

Hubbard, G. E.: *Eastern Industrialization and Its Effects on the West with Special Reference to Great Britain and Japan*, London, 1936.

Hudson, Manley O.: *The Permanent Court of International Justice, 1930–1942*, New York, 1943.

Hull, Cordell: *Memoirs of Cordell Hull*, 2 vols., New York, 1948.

Hunt, Frazier: *MacArthur and the War against Japan*, New York, 1944.

Ichihashi, Yamato: *Japanese in the United States*, Stanford, 1932.

————: *The Washington Conference and After*, Stanford, 1928.

Idditti, S.: *The Life of Marquis Shigenobu Okuma, A Maker of Modern Japan*, Tōkyō, 1941.

Ishii, Kikujiro: *Diplomatic Commentaries*, Baltimore, 1936.

Ishii, Ryoichi: *Population Pressure and Economic Life in Japan*, London, 1937.

Iswolsky, Alexander: *Memoirs, Recollections of a Foreign Minister*, New York, 1921.

Ito, Hirobumi: *Commentaries on the Constitution of the Empire of Japan*, Tōkyō, 1889.

Iwasaki, Uichi: *The Working Forces in Japanese Politics, 1867–1920*, New York, 1921.

Jensen, Oliver: *Carrier War: Task Force 58 and the Pacific Sea Battles*, New York, 1945.

Johnston, Lt. James D.: *China and Japan; Being a Narrative of the Cruise of the Steam Frigate Powhatan*, Philadelphia, 1861.

Johnstone, William C.: *The Future of Japan*, New York, 1944.

————: *The United States and Japan's New Order*, New York, 1941.

Jones, Francis C.: *Extraterritoriality in Japan and the Diplomatic Relations Resulting in Its Abolition, 1853–1899*, New Haven, 1931.

Karig, Walter: *Battle Report I, Pearl Harbor to the Coral Sea*, New York, 1944.

————: *Battle Report III, Pacific War, Middle Phase*, New York, 1947.

————: *Battle Report IV, the End of an Empire*, New York, 1948.

Kawabe, Kisaburo: *The Press and Politics in Japan*, Chicago, 1921.

Keenleyside, Hugh L.: *History of Japanese Education and Present Educational System*, Tōkyō, 1937.

Keimeikai: *Present Day Japan: Actual Conditions of Its Industry, Trade, Communications, Transportation, Education, Art, Literature and Social Work*, Tōkyō, 1938.

Kennan, George: *E. H. Harriman's Far Eastern Plans*, New York, 1917.

Kennedy, Malcolm D.: *The Changing Fabric of Japan,* London, 1930.

————: *The Military Side of Japanese Life,* London, 1924.

La Fargue, Thomas E.: *China and the World War,* Stanford, 1937.

Langer, William H.: *The Diplomacy of Imperialism, 1890–1902,* 2 vols., New York, 1935.

Latourette, Kenneth S.: *The History of Japan,* New York, 1947.

————: *A Short History of the Far East,* New York, 1946.

Lattimore, Owen: *Manchuria, Cradle of Conflict,* New York, 1935.

Linebarger, Paul M. A.: *China of Chiang Kai-shek,* Boston, 1941.

————: *The Political Doctrines of Sun Yat-sen,* Baltimore, 1937.

Lloyd George, David: *Memoirs of the Peace Conference,* 2 vols., New Haven, 1941.

————: *War Memoirs, 1914–1917,* 3 vols., Boston, 1933–1934.

Lory, Hillis: *Japan's Military Masters, the Army, in Japanese Life,* New York, 1943.

McCordock, R. S.: *British Far Eastern Policy, 1894–1900,* New York, 1931.

McGovern, William M.: *Modern Japan, Its Political, Military and Industrial Organization,* London, 1920.

McLaren, Walter W.: *A Political History of Japan during the Meiji Era, 1867–1912,* London, 1916.

Mahan, Alfred T.: *From Sail to Steam, Recollections of Naval Life,* New York, 1907.

————: *The Influence of Sea Power upon History,* Boston, 1898.

————: *The Problem of Asia,* Boston, 1900.

Maki, John M.: *Japanese Militarism, Its Causes and Cure,* New York, 1945.

Matsukata, Masayoshi: *Report on the Adoption of the Gold Standard in Japan,* Tōkyō, 1899.

————: *Report on the Post-Bellum Financial Administration in Japan, 1896–1900,* Tōkyō, 1900.

Mears, Eliot G.: *Resident Orientals on the Pacific Coast,* Chicago, 1928.

Mears, Helen: *Mirror for Americans—Japan,* New York, 1948.

————: *Year of the Wild Boar,* New York, 1942.

Miller, David Hunter: *The Drafting of the Covenant,* 2 vols., New York, 1928.

————: *The Peace Pact of Paris,* New York, 1928.

————: *Treaties and Other International Acts of the United States of America,* Vol. VII, Washington, 1942.

Millis, H. A.: *The Japanese Problem in the United States,* New York, 1915.

Mitchell, Kate: *Japan's Industrial Strength,* New York, 1942.

Mitsubishi Economic Research Bureau: *Japanese Trade and Industry, Present and Future,* New York, 1936.

Miyake, Masataro: *An Outline of the Japanese Judiciary,* Tōkyō, 1935.

Mogi, Sobei, and Vere Redman: *The Problem of the Far East,* London, 1935.

Mook, Hubertus J. van: *The Netherlands Indies and Japan: Battle on Paper, 1940–41,* New York, 1944.

Moore, Harriet L.: *Soviet Far Eastern Policy,* Princeton, 1944.

Morgenstern, George E.: *Pearl Harbor: the Story of the Secret War,* New York, 1947.

Morley, Felix: *The Society of Nations,* Washington, 1932.

Morse, H. B., and Harley F. MacNair: *Far Eastern International Relations,* Boston, 1931.

Moulton, Harold G.: *Japan, an Economic and Financial Appraisal*, Washington, 1931.

Murdoch, James, and I. Yamagata: *A History of Japan*, 3 vols., London, 1925–1926.

Myers, W. S.: *The Foreign Policies of Herbert Hoover, 1929–1933*, New York, 1940.

Myers, W. S., ed.: *The State Papers and Other Public Writings of Hoover*, 2 vols., New York, 1934.

Nasu, Shiroshi: *Land Utilization in Japan*, Tōkyō, 1929.

————: *Aspects of Japanese Agriculture, a Preliminary Survey*, New York, 1941.

Nitobe, Inazo: *Intercourse between the United States and Japan*, Baltimore, 1891.

————: *Japan: Some Phases of Her Problems and Development*, New York, 1931.

————: *Lectures on Japan*, Chicago, 1938.

————: *Western Influences in Modern Japan*, Chicago, 1931.

Norman, E. Herbert: *Japan's Emergence as a Modern State, Political and Economic Problems of the Meiji Period*, New York, 1940.

Norton, Henry K.: *The Far Eastern Republic of Siberia*, London, 1923.

Odate, Gyoju: *Japan's Financial Relations with the United States*, New York, 1922.

Ogata, Kiyoshi: *The Cooperative Movement in Japan*, London, 1923.

Ogawa, Gotaro: *Conscription System in Japan*, New York, 1921.

————: *Expenditures of the Russo-Japanese War*, New York, 1923.

Okakura, Lakuzo: *The Awakening of Japan*, New York, 1904.

Okuma, Count Shigenobu: *Fifty Years of New Japan*, 2 vols., London, 1910.

Oliphant, Laurence: *Narrative of the Earl of Elgin's Mission to China and Japan*, 2 vols., New York, 1860.

Ono, Giichi: *War and Armament Expenditures of Japan*, New York, 1922.

Orchard, John B.: *Japan's Economic Position, the Progress of Industrialization*, New York, 1930.

Overlach, Theodore W.: *Foreign Financial Control in China*, New York, 1919.

Paul, Rodman W.: *The Abrogation of the Gentlemen's Agreement*, Cambridge, 1936.

Paullin, C. O.: *Diplomatic Negotiations of American Naval Officers*, Baltimore, 1912.

Peffer, Nathaniel: *Basis for Peace in the Far East*, New York, 1942.

Penrose, Ernest F.: *Food Supply and Raw Materials in Japan*, Chicago, 1930.

————: *Population Theories and Their Application with Special Reference to Japan*, Stanford, 1934.

Pollard, Robert T.: *China's Foreign Relations, 1917–1931*, New York, 1933.

Pooley, A. M.: *Japan's Foreign Policies*, New York, 1920.

————, ed.: *The Secret Memoirs of Count Tadasu Hayashi*, New York, 1915.

Porter, Robert P.: *Japan, the Rise of a Modern Power*, Oxford, 1918.

Pratt, Fletcher: *The Marines' War*, New York, 1948.

————: *Fleet against Japan*, New York, 1946.

Pratt, Julius W.: *Expansionists of 1898*, Baltimore, 1936.

Price, Ernest B.: *The Russo-Japanese Treaties of 1907–1916 Concerning Manchuria and Mongolia*, Baltimore, 1933.

Quigley, Harold S.: *Chinese Politics and Foreign Powers*, New York, 1927.

————: *Far Eastern War, 1937–1941*, Boston, 1942.

————: *Japanese Government and Politics*, New York, 1933.

Redman, H. Vere: *Japan in Crisis*, Harrisburg, 1936.

Reid, John Gilbert: *The Manchu Abdication and the Powers*, Berkeley, 1935.

Reinsch, Paul S.: *American Diplomat in China, 1913–1919*, Garden City, 1922.

Reischauer, Edwin O.: *Japan Past and Present*, New York, 1946.

Reischauer, Robert K.: *Japan Government Politics*, New York, 1939.

Remer, C. F.: *Foreign Investments in China*, New York, 1933.

———: *A Study of Chinese Boycotts*, Baltimore, 1933.

Report on the Economic Position and Prospects of Japan and Korea and the Measures Required to Improve Them, Washington, 1948 (Johnston Report).

Report on Industrial Reparations Survey of Japan to the United States of America, by the Overseas Consultants, New York, 1948 (Strike Report).

Report on Japanese Reparations to the President of the United States, Washington, 1946 (Pauley Report).

Riegel, Roy F.: *America Moves West*, New York, 1947.

Roberts, S. H.: *Population Problems of the Pacific*, London, 1927.

Roosevelt, Nicholas: *The Restless Pacific*, New York, 1928.

Roosevelt, Theodore: *Autobiography*, New York, 1913.

Rosen, Baron: *Forty Years of Diplomacy*, 2 vols., New York, 1920.

Rosinger, Lawrence K.: *China's Wartime Politics, 1937–1944*, Princeton, 1945.

Rowe, David N.: *China among the Powers*, New York, 1945.

Russell, Oland D.: *The House of Mitsui*, Boston, 1939.

Sansom, George B.: *Japan, a Short Cultural History*, New York, 1931.

Satow, Sir Ernest M.: *A Diplomat in Japan*, London, 1921.

Schumpeter, Elizabeth B.: *The Industrialization of Japan and Manchukuo, 1930–1940, Population, Raw Materials and Industry*, New York, 1940.

Scidmore, G. H.: *Outline Lectures on the History, Organization, Jurisdiction and Practice of the Ministerial and Consular Courts of the U.S.A. in Japan*, Tōkyō, 1887.

Semyonov, Yuri: *The Conquest of Siberia*, London, 1944.

Seward, William H.: *Travels around the World*, New York, 1873.

Seymour, Charles: *American Diplomacy during the World War*, Baltimore, 1934.

———: *Intimate Papers of Colonel House*, 4 vols., Boston, 1928.

Sherwood, Robert E.: *Roosevelt and Hopkins*, New York, 1948.

Shotwell, James T.: *War as an Instrument of National Policy*, New York, 1929.

Steed, H. Wickham: *Through Thirty Years, 1892–1922*, 2 vols., 1924.

Steiger, G. Nye: *China and the Occident: the Origin and Development of the Boxer Movement*, New Haven, 1927.

Stimson, Henry L.: *The Far Eastern Crisis: Recollections and Observations*, New York, 1936.

———: *On Active Service in Peace and War*, New York, 1948.

Sullivan, Mark: *The Great Adventure at Washington: the Story of the Conference*, New York, 1922.

Supreme Commander for Allied Powers: *Summation of Non-military Activities in Japan*, Tōkyō, 1945–.

Suyematsu, Kencho: *The Risen Sun*, London, 1905.

Takagi, Yasaka: *Foreign Policy of Japan, 1914–1939*, Tōkyō, 1940.

Takahashi, Sakue: *Cases on International Law during the Chino-Japanese War*, Cambridge, 1899.

Takahashi Seizaburo: *Japan and World Resources*, Tōkyō, 1937.

Takekoshi, Yosaburo: *Economic Aspects of the History of Civilization of Japan*, 3 vols., New York, 1930.

Takeuchi, Tatsuji: *War and Diplomacy in the Japanese Empire*, New York, 1935.

T'ang Leang-li: *The Inner History of the Chinese Revolution*, London, 1930.

Taylor, George E.: *The Struggle for North China*, New York, 1940.

Temperley, H. W. V., ed.: *A History of the Peace Conference of Paris*, 6 vols., London, 1920–1924.

Thompson, Warren S.: *Danger Spots in World Population*, New York, 1930.

———: *Population and Peace in the Pacific*, Chicago, 1946.

Tolischus, Otto D.: *Tokyo Record*, New York, 1943.

Toynbee, Arnold J.: *Survey of International Affairs, 1920–1938*, London, 1925–1941.

Treat, Payson J.: *Diplomatic Relations between the United States and Japan, 1853–1895*, 2 vols., Stanford, 1932.

———: *Diplomatic Relations between the United States and Japan, 1895–1905*, Stanford, 1938.

Tregaskis, Richard: *Guadalcanal Diary*, New York, 1943.

Tsuchida, Kyoson: *Contemporary Thought of Japan and China*, London, 1927.

Tsurumi, Yusuke: *Present Day Japan*, New York, 1926.

Tupper, Eleanor, and George E. McReynolds: *Japan in American Public Opinion*, New York, 1937.

Ueda, Teijiro: *Future of the Japanese Population*, Tōkyō, 1933.

———: *The Recent Development of Japanese Foreign Trade*, Tōkyō, 1936.

———: *The Small Industries of Japan: their Growth and Development*, New York, 1938.

U.S. Adjutant General's Office: *Reports on Military Operations in South Africa and China*, Washington, 1901.

U.S. Department of State: *Papers Relating to the Foreign Relations of the United States. Japan: 1931–1941*, 2 vols., Washington, 1943.

———: *Occupation of Japan, Policy and Progress*, Washington, 1946.

———: *Report of the Mission on Japanese Combines*, Washington, 1946.

———: *Report of the U.S. Education Mission to Japan*, Washington, 1946.

———: *The Textile Mission to Japan*, Washington, 1946.

U.S. Marine Corps: *The Battle for Tarawa*, Washington, 1947.

U.S. Strategic Bombing Survey: *Summary Report (Pacific War)*, Washington, 1946.

———: *Japan's Struggle to End the War*, Washington, 1946.

———: *Effects of Atomic Bombs on Hiroshima and Nagasaki*, Washington, 1946.

———: *Effects of Strategic Bombing on the Japanese Economy*, Washington, 1946.

Uyehara, George Etsujiro: *The Political Development of Japan, 1867–1909*, London, 1910.

Uyehara, Shigeru: *The Industry and Trade of Japan*, London, 1936.

Vinacke, Harold M.: *History of the Far East in Modern Times*, New York, 1942.

———: *Modern Constitutional Development in China*, Princeton, 1920.

Vogel, William: *Yankee Schoolmaster in Japan*, New York, 1948.

Wada, Teijun: *American Foreign Policy towards Japan During the Nineteenth Century*, Tōkyō, 1928.

Ward, Sir A. W., and G. P. Gooch: *Cambridge History of British Foreign Policy, 1783–1919,* 3 vols., New York, 1922–1923.

Watarai, Toshiharu: *Nationalization of Railways in Japan,* New York, 1915.

Welles, Sumner: *Where Are We Heading?* New York, 1946.

Wilbur, Ray Lyman, and Arthur M. Hyde: *The Hoover Policies,* New York, 1937.

Wildes, Harry Emerson: *Social Currents in Japan with Special Reference to the Press,* Chicago, 1927.

Willoughby, Westel W.: *China at the Conference, a Report,* Baltimore, 1922.

———: *Foreign Rights and Interests in China,* 2 vols., Baltimore, 1927.

———: *Japan's Case Examined,* Baltimore, 1940.

———: *The Sino-Japanese Controversy and the League of Nations,* Baltimore, 1935.

Witte, Count Sergius: *Memoirs,* New York, 1921.

Wolfert, Ira: *Battle for the Solomons,* Boston, 1943.

Woodward, C. Vann: *The Battle for Leyte Gulf,* New York, 1947.

Yamasaki, Kakujiro, and Ogawa, Gotaro: *The Effect of World War Upon the Commerce and Industry of Japan,* New Haven, 1929.

Young, A. Morgan: *Japan in Recent Times,* New York, 1929.

Young, C. Walter: *The International Legal Status of the Kwantung Leased Territory,* Baltimore, 1931.

———: *The International Relations of Manchuria,* Chicago, 1929.

———: *Japan's Special Position in Manchuria,* Baltimore, 1931.

———: *Japanese Jurisdiction in the South Manchuria Railway Areas,* Baltimore, 1931.

Young, E. J.: *Powerful America,* New York, 1936.

Young, John Russell: *Around the World with General Grant,* 2 vols., New York, 1879.

———: *Men and Memoirs,* 2 vols., New York, 1901.

Zabriskie, Edward H.: *American Russian Rivalry in the Far East, a Study in Diplomatic and Power Politics, 1895–1914,* Philadelphia, 1946.

Zetland, Lawrence J. L. D. (Earl of Ronaldshay): *Life of Lord Curzon,* 3 vols., London, 1928.

WORKS IN THE JAPANESE LANGUAGE

Akamatsu Katsumaro: *Nihon Rōdō Undō Hattatsu Shi* (History of the Japanese Labor Movement), Tōkyō, 1925.

Akashi Teruo: *Meiji Ginkō Shi* (History of Meiji Banking), Tōkyō, 1935.

Akiyama Kenzō: *Nisshi Kōshō Shiwa* (Essays on Sino-Japanese Relations), Tōkyō, 1935.

———: *Nisshi Kōshōshi Kenkyū* (A Study of Sino-Japanese Relations), Tōkyō, 1939.

Amako Todomu: *Heimin Saisō Wakatsuki Reijirō* (Wakatsuki Reijirō, Commoner Premier), Tōkyō, 1926.

Amakusa Rintarō: *Nihon Kyōsantō Daikenkyo Shi* (History of Wholesale Arrests of the Japan Communist Party), Tōkyō, 1929.

Amano Masaharu: *Kokushi Jiken Ronshū* (Essays on Japanese Historical Events), Tōkyō, 1932.

Aoki Keiichirō: *Nihon Nōmin Kumiai Undō Shi* (History of the Japan Farmers' Union Movement), Tōkyō, 1931.

Aoyagi Ikutarō: *Burajiru ni Okeru Nihonjin Hatten Shi* (History of the Japanese in Brazil), Tōkyō, 1941.

Arakawa Hidetoshi: *Nihon Kishōgakushi* (History of Japanese Meteorology), Tōkyō, 1943.

Ariga Nagao: *Dai Nihon Rekishi* (History of Japan), 2 vols., Tōkyō, 1907.

———: *Saikin Sanjūnen Gaikō Shi* (Diplomatic History of the Last Thirty Years), 2 vols., Tōkyō, 1914.

Asada Mitsuteru, and Nakamura Shūichirō: *Nihon Shihon Shugi Shakai Seiritsu Shi* (History of the Japanese Capitalist Society), Tōkyō, 1948.

Asaga Tetsujirō: *Nihon Kyōiku no Kaiko to Sono Shōrai* (Japanese Education, Past and Future), Tōkyō, 1936.

Asahi Shimbun: *Meiji Taishō Shi* (History of the Meiji and Taisho Eras), 6 vols., Tōkyō, 1930–1932.

———: *Nihon Gaikō Hiroku* (Inside Stories of Japanese Diplomacy), Tōkyō, 1934.

———: *Shōwa Zaikai Shi* (History of the Fnancial World in the Shōwa Era), Ōsaka, 1936.

———: *Sōdōin-hō no Zembō* (An Over-all View of the National General Mobilization Law), Tōkyō, 1935.

Asai Kiyoshi: *Meiji Rikken Shisō Shi ni Okeru Eikoku Gikai Seido no Eikyō* (The Influence of British Parliametary System on Meiji Constitutional Thought), Tōkyō, 1939.

———: *Shin Kempō to Naikaku* (The New Constitution and the Cabinet), Tōkyō, 1947.

Ashida Hitoshi: *Saikin Sekai Gaikō Shi* (Recent History of World Diplomacy), 3 vols., Tōkyō, 1934.

Asō Yoshiteru: *Kinsei Nihon Tetsugaku Shi* (History of Recent Japanese Philosophy), Tōkyō, 1942.

Ayusawa Toshio: *Dai Nihon Seisantō Jūnen Shi* (Ten Years of the Japan Production Party), Tōkyō, 1941.

Azuma Tōsaku: *Meiji Shakai Seisaku Shi* (History of Meiji Social Policy), Tōkyō, 1940.

———: *Meiji Zenki Nōsei Shi no Shomondai* (Problems of Early Meiji Agricultural Administration), Tōkyō, 1936.

Baba Tsunego: *Konoe Naikaku Shiron* (History of the Konoe Cabinet), Tōkyō, 1946.

Chūgai Shōgyō: *Chūken Zaibatsu no Shin Kenkyū: Kantō Hen* (New Study of Major Combines: Kantō Region), Tōkyō, 1937.

———: *Zaibatsu Yasuda no Kenkyū* (Study of the Yasuda Combine), Tōkyō, 1937.

Dai Ichi Ginkō: *Dai Ichi Ginkō Gojūnen Shōshi* (A Short History of the Fifty Years of the Dai Ichi Bank), Tōkyō, 1926.

Dai Nihon Bummei Kyōkai: *Ōbeijin no Nihon Kan* (European and American Concepts of Japan), 3 vols., Tōkyō, 1908.

Dai Nihon Teikoku Gikaishi Kankōkai: *Dai Nihon Teikoku Gikai Shi* (History of the Japanese Diet), 17 vols., Tōkyō, 1926– . History of the Japanese Diet based on the shorthand records of both houses from the beginning to the 54th session.

Dai Saigō Zenshū Kankōkai: *Dai Saigō Zenshū* (Complete Collection on Saigō), 3 vols., Tōkyō, 1926–1927.

Dajōkan: *Fukko Ki* (Chronicles of the Meiji Restoration), 15 vols., Tōkyō, 1929–1931.

Danshaku Yamakawa Sensei Kinenkai: *Danshaku Yamakawa Sensei Den* (Life of Baron Dr. Yamakawa), Tōkyō, 1940.

Dōshisha University: *Dōshisha Gojūnen Shi* (Fifty Years of Dōshisha), Kyōto, 1930.

Ebihara Hachirō: *Nihon Ōji Shimbun Zasshi Shi* (History of European Language Newspapers and Periodicals in Japan), Tōkyō, 1934.

Fujii Jintarō: *Meiji Ishin Shi Kōwa* (Lectures on the Meiji Restoration), Tōkyō, 1929.

————: *Nihon Kempō Seitei Shi* (History of the Establishment of the Meiji Constitution), Tōkyō, 1929.

Fujii Shin'ichi: *Teikoku Kempō to Kaneko Haku* (The Japanese Constitution and Count Kaneko), Tōkyō, 1944.

Fujikawa, Yū: *Nihon Igaku Shi* (History of Japanese Medicine), Tōkyō, 1941.

Fujimura Tsukuru: *Meiji Bungaku Josetsu* (Introduction to Meiji Literature), Tōkyō, 1932.

Fujita Gorō: *Nihon Kindai Sangyō no Seisei* (The Emergence of Present Day Japanese Industries), Tōkyō, 1948.

Fujiwara Kiyozō: *Meiji Kyōiku Shisō Shi* (History of Meiji Educational Thought), Tōkyō, 1909.

Fukagai Hiroharu: *Kashizoku Chitsuroku Shobun no Kenkyū* (Study of the Disposition of the Money Pensions of Nobility and the Samurai Class), Tōkyō, 1941.

Fukai Eigo: *Kaiko Shichijūnen* (Recollections of Seventy Years), Tōkyō, 1941.

Fukuchi Gen'ichirō: *Bakufu Suibō Ron* (The Decline and Fall of the Shogunate), Tōkyō, 1936.

————: *Bakumatsu Seijika* (Statesmen of the Closing Years of the Shogunate), Tōkyō, 1906.

Fukuda Hisamichi: *Meiji Bungaku Kenkyū* (Study of Meiji Literature), Tōkyō, 1933.

Fukuda Masatoshi: *Seiji Undō Gojūnen no Kaiko* (Reminiscences of Fifty Years of Political Movements), Tōkyō, 1941.

Fukuzawa Yukichi: *Fukuō Jiden* (Autobiography of Fukuzawa), Tōkyō, 1898.

Furushima Toshio: *Kinsei Nihon Nōgyō no Kōzō* (Structure of Modern Japanese Agriculture), Tōkyō, 1943.

Furuta Tokujirō: *Senji Nihon no Seiji no Saihensei* (Reorganization of Japan's Wartime Politics), Tōkyō, 1941.

Gaimushō: *Jōyaku Isan* (Collection of Treaties), 9 vols., Tōkyō, 1926–1929.

————: *Gaikō Shikō* (Diplomatic History), 2 vols., Tōkyō, 1884.

Gakushūin: *Gakushūin Shi* (History of the Peers' School), Tōkyō, 1928.

Godai Ryūsaku: *Godai Tomoatsu Den* (Life of Godai Tomoatsu), Tōkyō, 1933.

Gotō Keiji: *Nihon Gekijō Shi* (History of the Japanese Theater), Tōkyō, 1925.

Gyōsei Saibanjo: *Gyōsei Saibanjo Gojūnen Shi* (Fifty Years of the Court of Administrative Litigation), Tōkyō, 1941.

Hagino Yoshiyuki: *Nihon Shi Kōwa* (Lectures on Japanese History), Tōkyō, 1934.

————: *Ōsei Fukko no Rekishi* (History of the Restoration), Tōkyō, 1934.

Hamaguchi Yūkō: *Zuikan Roku* (Recollections), Tōkyō, 1931.

Hani Gorō: *Satō Nobuhiro ni Kansuru Kisoteki Kenkyū* (A Basic Study on Satō Shin'en), Tōkyō, 1929.

Hara Takashi Zenshū Kankōkai: *Hara Takashi Zenshu* (Complete Collection on Hara Takashi), 2 vols., Tōkyō, 1929.

Hasegawa Mitsutarō: *Zaikai Seisui Ki* (Fluctuations in the Finanical World), Tōkyō, 1929.

Hasegawa Nyozekan: *Nihon Fasshizumu Hihan* (An Appraisal of Japanese Fascism), Tōkyō, 1932.

Hasegawa Yoshio: *Nōmin Undō no Shiteki Kōsatsu* (A History of Agrarian Movements), Tōkyō, 1924.

Hashimoto Hiroshi: *Ishin Nisshi* (Diaries of the Restoration Period), 7 vols., Tōkyō, 1932–1934.

Hata Kiyoshi: *Ishin no Ura wo Tsuku* (Behind the Scene Account of the Meiji Restoration), Tōkyō, 1943.

Hatano Kanae: *Tōsei Keizai Kōwa* (Lectures on Controlled Economy), Tōkyō, 1940.

Hattori Bunshirō: *Senji Keizai to Keizai Shidō* (War Economy and Economic Guidance), Tōkyō, 1941.

Hayakawa Junsaburō, ed.: *Kiheitai Nikki* (Journal of the Kiheitai), 4 vols., Tōkyō, 1918.

Hayashi Gonsuke: *Waga Shichijūnen wo Kataru* (Reminiscences of My Seventy Years), Tōkyō, 1939.

Hayashi Tadasu: *Nochi wa Mukashi no Ki* (Recollections), Tōkyō, 1910.

Hayashida Kametarō: *Nihon Seitō Shi* (History of Japanese Political Parties), 2 vols., Tōkyō, 1927.

Higashikuni Naruhiko: *Watakushi no Kiroku* (My Record), Tōkyō, 1947.

Higashiura Shōji: *Nihon Sangyō Kumiai Shi* (History of Japanese Industrial Cooperatives), Tōkyō, 1935.

Higuchi Hiroshi: *Keikaku Keizai to Nihon Zaibatsu* (Planned Economy and the Japanese Zaibatsu), Tōkyō, 1941.

————: *Nihon no Taishi Tōshi* (Japanese Investments in China), Tōkyō, 1940.

————: *Nihon Zaibatsu Ron* (The Japanese Combines), 2 vols., Tōkyō, 1940.

Hijikata Shigeyoshi: *Nihon Keizai Kenkyū* (Studies on Japanese Economy), 3 vols., Tōkyō, 1928.

————: *Nihon Keizai Seisaku* (Japanese Economic Policies), Tōkyō, 1937.

————: *Nihon Zaisei no Hatten* (Development of Japanese Finance), Tōkyō, 1943.

————: *Nihon Zaisei to Kokubō* (Japanese Finance and National Defense), Tōkyō, 1941.

————: *Waga Kokumin Keizai to Zaisei* (Japanese National Economy and Public Finance), Tōkyō, 1926.

Hijikata Teiichi: *Kindai Nihon Yōga Shi* (History of Western Painting in Japan in Recent Times), Tōkyō, 1941.

Hirabayashi Hatsunosuke: *Nihon Jiyū Shugi no Hattatsu Shi* (History of the Development of Liberalism in Japan), Tōkyō, 1924.

Hiraga Yoshinori: *Tōkyō Kabushiki Torihikijo Gojūnen Shi* (History of Fifty Years of the Tōkyō Stock Exchange), Tōkyō, 1928.

Hirano Yoshitarō: *Nihon Shihon Shugi Shakai no Kikō* (Structure of Japanese Capitalist Society), Tōkyō, 1934.

Hirao Michio: *Shishaku Tani Tateki Den* (Life of Viscount Tani Tateki), Tōkyō, 1935.

Hiratsuka Atsushi: *Itō Hirobumi Hiroku* (Confidential Papers of Itō Hirobumi), Tōkyō, 1929.

Hiratsuka Atsushi: *Zoku Itō Hirobumi Hiroku* (Confidential Papers of Itō Hirobumi, *Continued*), Tōkyō, 1930.

Hiratsuka Masunori: *Nihon Kirisutokyō Shugi Kyōiku Bunka Shi* (History of Christian Eduation in Japan), Tōkyō, 1937.

Hirose Hikota: *Enomoto Takeaki Shiberia Nikki* (Enomoto Takeaki's Siberian Diary), Tōkyō, 1943.

Hirota Naoe: *Naikaku Kōtetsu Gojūnen Shi* (History of Fifty Years of Cabinet Changes), Tōkyō, 1930.

Hiyane Antei: *Nihon Kinsei Kirisutokyō Jimbutsu Shi* (History of Christian Personages in Modern Japan), Tōkyō, 1935.

————: *Nihon Shūkyō Shi* (Religious History of Japan), Tōkyō, 1928.

Homma Hisao: *Meiji Bungaku Shi* (History of Meiji Literature), 2 vols., Tōkyō, 1935.

Honda Kumatarō: *Tamashii no Gaikō* (Marquis Komura during the Russo-Japanese War), Tōkyō, 1941.

Hon'iden Yoshio: *Kyōdō Kumiai Kenkyū* (A Study of Cooperatives), Tōkyō, 1937.

Honjō Eijirō: *Bakumatsu no Shinsaku* (New Policies of the Closing Years of the Shogunate), Tōkyō, 1935.

————: *Kinsei Hōken Shakai no Kenkyū* (Study of Feudal Society in the Modern Period), Tōkyō, 1933.

————: *Nihon Keizaishi Gaisetsu* (Outline of Japanese Economic History), Tōkyō, 1936.

————: *Nihon Keizai Shisō Shi Gaisetsu* (Outline History of Japanese Economic Thought), Tōkyō, 1940.

————: *Shiteki Kenkyū Nihon no Keizai to Shisō* (Historical Study of Japanese Economy and Thought), Kyōto, 1943.

————, ed.: *Meiji Ishin Keizai Shi Kenkyū* (Economic History of the Meiji Restoration), Tōkyō, 1930.

————, ed.: *Nihon Keizai Shi Jiten* (Encyclopedia of Japanese Economic History), 2 vols., Tōkyō, 1940.

Hori Tsuneo: *Meiji Keizaigaku Shi* (History of Economics in the Meiji Era), Tōkyō, 1935.

Horie Yasuzō: *Nihon Shihon Shugi no Seiritsu* (The Establishment of Japanese Capitalism), Tōkyō, 1938.

————: *Nihon Keizai Bunka Shi* (History of Japanese Economic Culture), Tōkyō, 1941.

Horiguchi Hitoyoshi: *Shakai Kōkyō Jigyō Shi* (History of Public Utilities), Tōkyō, 1941.

Horikawa Takeo: *Nihon Gaikō Hyakunen Shi* (One Hundred Years of Japanese Foreign Relations), 2 vols., Tōkyō, 1941.

Horikawa Toyonaga: *Kindai Nihon Kagakusha* (Modern Japanese Men of Science), Tōkyō, 1941.

Horiuchi Ken'ichi: *Nihon no Hansei* (Japan's Reflection), Tōkyō, 1946.

Hoshino Tōru: *Meiji Mimpō Hensan Shi Kenkyū* (History of the Compilation of the Meiji Civil Code), Tōkyō, 1943.

Hosoi Hajime: *Batsuzoku Zaiaku Shi* (History of the Clan Evils), Tōkyō, 1919.

Hozumi Nobushige: *Inkyo Ron* (A Treatise on Retirement from Active Life), Tōkyō, 1915.

Ibara Toshirō: *Meiji Engeki Shi* (History of Meiji Drama), Tōkyō, 1920.

Ichikawa Shōichi: *Nihon Kyōsantō Sosō Shi* (History of the Struggles of the Japan Communist Party), Tōkyō, 1948.

Ijiri Tsunekichi: *Rekidai Kenkan Roku* (Roster of Successive Cabinet Officials), Tōkyō, 1925.

Ikeda Ken: *Shōwa Seiji Keizai Shi* (Political and Social History of the Shōwa Era), Tōkyō, 1947.

Ikeda Yoshinaga: *Nōson Shakaigaku Kenkyū* (Study of Rural Sociology), Tōkyō, 1938.

Imai Gosuke: *Nihon Sangyō Hattatsu Shi* (History of Japanese Sericulture), Tōkyō, 1927.

Imamura, Yabe, and others: *Dai Nihon Yōshu Kanzume Enkaku Shi* (History of Beer Brewing and Canning Industries in Japan), Tōkyō, 1915.

Imanaka Tsugimaro: *Nihon Seiji Shi Taikō* (Outline of Japanese Political History), Tōkyō, 1936.

Inagaki Suesaburō: *Tōkyō Kaijō Kasai Hoken Kabushiki Kaisha Rokujūnen Shi* (Sixty Years of the Tōkyō Marine Fire Insurance Company), Tōkyō, 1941.

Inatomi Eijirō: *Meiji Shoki Kyōiku Shisō no Kenkyū* (A Study of Educational Thought of the Early Meiji Period), Tōkyō, 1944.

Inobe Shigeo: *Bakumatsu Shi Gaisetsu* (Outline History of the Closing Years of the Tokugawa Shogunate), Tōkyō, 1930.

————: *Bakumatsu Shi no Kenkyū* (A Study of the Closing Years of the Tokugawa Shogunate), Tōkyō, 1927.

————: *Ishin Shikō* (Historical Studies on the Restoration), Tōkyō, 1933.

————: *Ishin Shi Taikan* (Outline History of the Meiji Restoration), Tōkyō, 1943.

————: *Meiji Ishin Shi* (History of the Meiji Restoration), Tōkyō, 1929.

Inoue Junnosuke: *Sengo ni Okeru Waga Kuni no Keizai oyobi Kin'yū* (Japan's Post War Economy and Finance), Tōkyō, 1935.

Inoue Kaoru Kō Denki Hensankai: *Segai Inoue Kō Den* (Life of Marquis Inoue Kaoru), 5 vols., Tōkyō, 1933–1934.

Inoue Kazuo: *Hanhō, Bakufuhō to Ishinhō* (Laws and Legislation of the Feudatories, the Shogunate and the Restoration), Tōkyō, 1940.

Inoue Masaaki: *Hakushaku Kiyoura Keigo Den* (Life of Count Kiyoura Keigo), Tōkyō, 1935.

Irizawa Sōju: *Nihon Kyōiku no Dentō to Kensetsu* (Japanese Education, Its Traditions and Establishment), Tōkyō, 1937.

Ishii Kendō: *Meiji Jibutsu Kigen* (Origins of Things in the Meiji Period), Tōkyō, 1936.

Ishii Kikujirō: *Gaikō Kaisō Dampen* (Fragments of Diplomatic Reminiscences), Tōkyō, 1939.

————: *Gaikō Yoroku* (Diplomatic Commentaries), Tōkyō, 1933.

Ishii Mitsuru: *Nitobe Inazō Den* (Life of Nitobe Inazō), Tōkyō, 1934.

Ishii Takashi: *Bakumatsu Bōeki Shi no Kenkyū* (Study of the Foreign Trade of the Closing Years of the Shogunate), Tōkyō, 1944.

Ishikawa Jun: *Teikoku Gikai Tsūkan* (History of the Japanese Diet), 2 vols., Tōkyō, 1908.

Ishikawa Kammei: *Fukuzawa Yukichi Den* (Life of Fukuzawa Yukichi), 4 vols., Tōkyō, 1932–1933.

Ishikawa Ken: *Nihon Shomin Kyōiku Shi* (History of Common Education in Japan), Tōkyō, 1938.

Ishikawa Ryōichi: *Minken Jiyūtō Shi* (History of the Liberal Party), Tōkyō, 1929.

Ishikawa Sanshirō: *Shakai Shugi Undō Shi* (History of the Socialist Movement), Tōkyō, 1929.

Ishikawa Tsunetarō: *Nihon Rōnin Shi* (History of Japanese Free Lances), Tōkyō, 1931.

Ishin Shiryō Hensankai: *Gaikan Ishin Shi* (Outline History of the Meiji Restoration), Tōkyō, 1940.

————: *Dai Nihon Ishin Shiryō* (Historical Materials of the Meiji Restoration), Tōkyō, 1938–. Begun in 1938, this represents the most ambitious undertaking in the collection and compilation of materials on the history of the Restoration. It is expected to total some 200 volumes.

————: *Ishin Shi* (History of the Meiji Restoration), 6 vols., Tōkyō, 1939–1942.

Ishizawa Kyūgorō: *Hompō Ginkō Hattatsu Shi* (History of Japanese Banking), Tōkyō, 1920.

Itani Zen'ichi: *Meiji Ishin Keizai Shi* (Economic History of the Meiji Restoration), Tōkyō, 1928.

————: *Nihon Shihon Shugi* (Japanese Capitalism), Tōkyō, 1927.

Itō Hirobumi: *Kempō Shiryō* (Materials on the Constitution), 3 vols., Tōkyō, 1935.

————: *Hisho Ruisan Hōsei Kankei Shiryō* (Materials on Legislation), 2 vols., Tōkyō, 1935.

————: *Hisho Ruisan Gaikō Hen* (Materials on Foreign Relations), 2 vols., Tōkyō, 1935.

Itō Kinjirō: *Kan'ryō Washi ga Kuni Sa* (Bureaucracy Rampant), Tōkyō, 1940.

Itō Masanori: *Katō Takaaki* (Life of Katō Takaaki), 2 vols., Tōkyō, 1929.

————: *Shimbun Gojūnen Shi* (History of Fifty Years of Journalism), Tōkyō, 1943.

Itō Takeru: *Konoe Kō Seidan* (Views and Opinions of Prince Konoe), Tōkyō, 1937.

Iwabuchi Tatsuo: *Gendai Nihon Seiji Ron* (Recent Japanese Politics), Tōkyō, 1941.

————: *Jūshin Ron* (The Palace Advisers), Tōkyō, 1941.

————: *Seikai Gojūnen Shi* (Fifty Years of Japanese Politics), Tōkyō, 1948.

Iwai Ryōtarō: *Sensō to Zaibatsu* (The War and the Zaibatsu), Tōkyō, 1938.

Iwaki Juntarō: *Meiji Bungaku Shi* (History of Meiji Literature), Tōkyō, 1927.

————: *Meiji Taishō no Kokubungaku* (Literature of the Meiji and Taishō Eras), Tōkyō, 1925.

Iwakura Kō Kyūseki Hozonkai: *Iwakura Kō Jikki* (Authentic Records of Prince Iwakura), 3 vols., Tōkyō, 1927.

Iwanami Kōza: *Nihon Bungaku* (Japanese Literature), 20 vols., Tōkyō, 1931–1933.

————: *Nihon Rekishi* (Japanese History), Tōkyō, 1933–1934.

Iwata Arata: *Nihon Mimpō Shi* (History of Japanese Civil Law), Tōkyō, 1928.

Jiji Shimpōsha: *Fukuzawa Zenshū* (Complete Works of Fukuzawa), 10 vols., Tōkyō, 1925–1926.

Jimbunkaku: *Kindai Nihon no Kagakusha* (Modern Japanese Men of Science), 4 vols., Tōkyō.

Kada Tetsuji: *Meiji Shoki Shakai Keizai Shisō Shi* (History of Social Economic Thought of the Early Meiji Period), Tōkyō, 1937.

————: *Meiji Shoki Shakai Shisō no Kenkyū* (Study of the Social Thought of the Early Meiji Period), Tōkyō, 1933.

————: *Nihon Kokka Shugi no Hatten* (The Development of Japanese Nationalism), Tōkyō, 1938.

————: *Kindai Nihon Shakai Seiritsu Shi* (History of Present Day Japanese Social Structure), Tōkyō, 1948.

Kaigo Tokiomi: *Nihon Kyōiku Shi* (History of Japanese Education), Tōkyō, 1938.

Kakuyūkai: *Ōkura Kakugen-Ō* (Life of Baron Ōkura Kihachirō), Tōkyō, 1924.

Kambe Isaburō: *Nihon Rika Kyōiku Hatten Shi* (History of Science Education in Japan), Tōkyō, 1938.

Kanakura Masami: *Meiji Ishin Zaisei Keizai Shikō* (Studies on the Economic and Financial History of the Meiji Restoration), Tōkyō, 1943.

————: *Meiji Sangyō Hassei Shi* (History of the Beginnings of Meiji Industries), Tōkyō, 1942.

Kanamori Tokujirō: *Nihon Kempō Minshūka no Shōten* (The Focus of Democratization of the Japanese Constitution), Tōkyō, 1946.

Kaneko Kentarō: *Nihon ni Kaeru* (Return to Japan), Tōkyō, 1941.

————: *Kempō Seitei to Ōbeijin no Hyōron* (European and American Comments on the Establishment of the Constitution), Tōkyō, 1937.

Kanno Watarō: *Nihon Kaisha Kigyō Hassei Shi no Kenkyū* (Origins of Corporate Enterprises in Japan), Tōkyō, 1940.

Kantō Kyoku: *Kantō Kyoku Shisei Sanjūnen Shi* (Thirty Years of Kwantung Bureau Administration), Tōkyō, 1936.

Kashima Morinosuke: *Gendai no Gaikō* (Contemporary Foreign Relations), Tōkyō, 1937.

————: *Saikin Nihon no Kokusaiteki Chii* (Recent International Position of Japan), Tōkyō, 1938.

————: *Teikoku Gaikō no Kihon Seisaku* (Basic Policies of Japan's Foreign Relations), Tōkyō, 1940.

Kataoka Ryōichi: *Kindai Nihon no Sakka to Sakuhin* (Recent Japanese Authors and Their Works), Tōkyō, 1939.

Katō Nihei: *Nihon Kinsei Kyōiku Shisō Shi* (History of Modern Japanese Educational Thought), Tōkyō, 1937.

Katō Takaaki Den Kankōkai: *Katō Takaaki Den* (Life of Katō Takaaki), Tōkyō, 1928.

Katsu Awa: *Kaikoku Kigen* (The Opening of the Country), 3 vols., Tōkyō, 1893.

Kawada Shirō: *Nihon Shakai Seisaku* (Japanese Social Policies), Tōkyō, 1937.

Kawahara Yasaburo: *Seiyū Hontō Shi* (History of the Seiyū Hontō Party), Tōkyō, 1927.

Kawai Eijirō: *Meiji Shisō Shi no Ichi Dampen* (An Aspect of the History of Meiji Thought), Tōkyō, 1941.

Kawai Hiromichi: *Nihon Shakaigaku Genri* (Principles of Japanese Sociology), Tōkyō, 1941.

Kawanishi Shōgo: *Nihon Nōmin Shi* (History of the Japanese Peasantry), Tōkyō, 1930.

Kawase Sohoku: *Nihon Shōnin Gohyakunen Shi* (History of Five Centuries of Japanese Merchants), Tōkyō, 1924.

Kawata Mizuho: *Kataoka Kenkichi Sensei Den* (Life of Kataoka Kenkichi), Kyōto, 1940.

Kawatake Shigetoshi: *Tsubouchi Shōyō*, Tōkyō, 1939.

Kazahaya Yasoji: *Nihon Shakai Seisaku Shi* (History of Japanese Social Policies), Tōkyō, 1937.

Keimeikai: *Nihon Bunka no Hattatsu* (The Development of Japanese Culture), Tōkyō, 1941.

———: *Nihon Bunka Saikin Nijūnen Shi* (Japanese Cultural Development of the Last Twenty Years), Tōkyō, 1937.

Keiō Gijuku: *Keiō Gijuku Shichijūgonen Shi* (Seventy-five Years of Keiō University), Tōkyō, 1932.

———: *Zoku Fukuzawa Zenshū* (Complete Works of Fukuzawa, *Continued*), 7 vols., Tōkyō, 1933–1934.

Keishichō: *Shoki no Keisatsu Seido* (The Police System in Its Early Stages), 2 vols., Tōkyō, 1937.

Kenseikaishi Hensanjo: *Kenseikai Shi* (History of the Kenseikai Party), Tōkyō, 1926.

Kido Kō Denki Hensanjo: *Shōkiku Kido Kō Den* (Life of Marquis Kido), 2 vols., Tōkyō, 1927.

Kido Kōin: *Kido Kōin Nikki* (Diaries of Kido Kōin), 3 vols., Tōkyō, 1932–1933.

Kikuchi San'ya: *Eta Zoku ni Kansuru Kenkyū* (A Study of the Eta Class), Tōkyō, 1923.

Kikukawa Tadao: *Gakusei Shakai Undō Shi* (History of the Student Socialist Movement), Tōkyō, 1931.

Kimiya Yasuhiko: *Nisshi Kōtsū Shi* (History of Sino-Japanese Relations), 2 vols., Tōkyō, 1926–1927.

———: *Nihon Minzoku to Kaiyō Shisō* (The Japanese and Their Oceanic Concepts), Tōkyō, 1942.

Kimura Takeshi: *Meiji Bungaku Tembō* (A Survey of Meiji Literature), Tōkyō, 1928.

———: *Saionji Kimmochi* (Life of Prince Saionji), Tōkyō, 1937.

———: *Meiji Bungaku wo Kataru* (On Meiji Literature), Tōkyō, 1934.

Kimura Yasuji: *Nihon Nōmin Sōdō Shi* (History of Japanese Peasant Disturbances), Tōkyō, 1925.

———: *Nihon Nōmin Sōtō Shi* (History of the Struggles of the Japanese Peasantry), Tōkyō, 1930.

Kinoshita Hanji: *Nihon Kokka Shugi Undō Shi* (History of Japanese Nationalist Movements), Tōkyō, 1941.

Kin'yū Kenkyūkai: *Waga Kuni ni Okeru Ginkō Gōdō no Taisei* (The General Trend of Bank Mergers in Japan), 2 vols., Tōkyō, 1934.

Kitabayashi Sōkichi: *Asano Sōichirō Den* (Life of Asano Sōichirō), Tōkyō, 1930.

Kiyohara Sadao: *Meiji Jidai Shisō Shi* (History of Thought of the Meiji Period), Tōkyō, 1921.

━━━━: *Meiji Shoki Bunka Shi* (Cultural History of the Early Meiji Period), Tōkyō, 1935.

Kiyomi Rikurō: *Okakura Tenshin Den* (Life of Okakura Kakuzō), Tōkyō, 1934.

Kiyoura Keigo: *Meiji Hōsei Shi* (History of Meiji Legislation), Tōkyō, 1899.

Kizokuin Jimukyoku: *Kizokuin Giji Sokki Roku* (Stenographic Record of the Proceedings of the House of Peers), Tōkyō, 1890–1945.

Kobayakawa Kingo: *Meiji Hōsei Shiron* (History of Meiji Legislation), 2 vols., Tōkyō, 1940.

Kobayashi Ushijirō: *Meiji Taishō Zaisei Shi* (History of Meiji Taishō Finance), Tōkyō, 1927.

Kobayashi Yūgo: *Rikken Seiyūkai Shi* (History of the Seiyūkai Party), 4 vols., Tōkyō, 1924–1926.

Kōda Shigetomo: *Nichi-Ō Kōtsū Shi* (History of Intercourse between Japan and Europe), Tōkyō, 1942.

Kōda Rohan: *Shibusawa Eiichi Den* (Life of Shibusawa Eiichi), Tōkyō, 1939.

Koike Motoyuki: *Nihon Nōgyō Kōzō Ron* (Structure of Japanese Agriculture), Tōkyō, 1944.

Kokka Gakkai: *Meiji Kensei Keizai Shiron* (Essays on the Constitutional and Economic History of the Meiji Period), Tōkyō, 1919.

Kokumin Seishin Bunka Kenkyūjo: *Nihon Kyōiku Shi Shiryōsho* (Materials on the History of Japanese Education), 5 vols., Tōkyō, 1937.

Kokura Ichirō: *Nichiei Kōshōshi Gaisetsu* (Introduction to Anglo-Japanese Relations), Tōkyō, 1943.

Kokuryūkai: *Nikkan Gappei Hishi* (The Inner History of the Annexation of Korea), 2 vols., Tōkyō, 1930–1931.

━━━━: *Nisshi Kōshō Gaishi* (Unofficial History of the Relations between China and Japan), 2 vols., Tōkyō, 1938–1939.

━━━━: *Tōa Senkaku Shishi Den* (Exponents of East Asiatic Expansion), 3 vols., Tōkyō, 1940.

Komatsu Midori, ed.: *Itō Kō Zenshū* (Compete Works of Prince Itō), 3 vols., Tōkyō, 1928.

━━━━: *Meiji Shijitsu Gaikō Hiwa* (Inner History of Meiji Diplomacy), Tōkyō, 1927.

Kōno Mitsu: *Nihon Musan Seitō Shi* (History of Japanese Proletarian Parties), Tōkyō, 1931.

Kudō Takeshige: *Kaitei Meiji Kensei Shi* (Revised Constitutional History of the Meiji Era), Tōkyō, 1934.

━━━━: *Taishō Kensei Shi* (Constitutional History of the Taishō Era), 2 vols., Tōkyō, 1930.

━━━━: *Teikoku Gikai Shi* (History of the Japanese Diet), 3 vols., Tōkyō, 1901–1906.

Kume Kunitake: *Tokumei Zenken Taishi Ōbei Kairan Jikki* (Record of the Embassy to America and Europe), 5 vols., Tōkyō, 1878.

Kurihara Hyakuju: *Nihon Nōgyō no Kiso Kōzō* (The Basic Structure of Japanese Agriculture), Tōkyō, 1943.

Kurihara Shin'ichi: *Meiji Kaika Shiron* (History of Meiji Civilization), Tōkyō, 1944.

Kurita Motoji: *Kaisetsu Nihon Bunka Shi* (Cultural History of Japan), Tōkyō, 1935.
————: *Sōgō Nihon Shi Gaisetsu* (General History of Japan), 2 vols., Tōkyō, 1926–1928.
Kuroda Kōshirō: *Gensui Terauchi Hakushaku Den* (Life of Marshal Count Terauchi), Tōkyō, 1920.
Kuroita Katsumi: *Kōtei Kokushi no Kenkyū* (A Study of Japanese History), 3 vols., Tōkyō, 1933–1936.
Kuroki Yūkichi: *Komura Jutarō*, Tōkyō, 1941.
Kuzuu Yoshihisa: *Tōa Senkaku Shishi Kiden* (Biographies of Pioneer Exponents of East Asiatic Expansion), 2 vols., Tōkyō, 1933–1935.
Kyōchōkai: *Saikin no Shakai Undō* (Recent Social Movements), Tōkyō, 1929.
Machida Norifumi: *Meiji Kokumin Kyōiku Shi* (History of National Education in the Meiji Period), Tōkyō, 1928
Maki Kenji: *Nihon Hōsei Shi Gairon* (Outline History of Japanese Legislation), Kyōto, 1935.
Makino Eiichi: *Nihon Chūshō Shōgyō no Kōzō* (The Structure of Middle and Small Scale Business in Japan), Tōkyō, 1939.
Makino Nobuaki: *Shōtō Kandan* (Reminiscences), Tōkyō, 1940.
Mantetsu: *Mantetsu Sanjūnen Shi* (Thirty Years of the South Manchuria Railway Company), Dairen, 1937.
Maruyama Kunio: *Gendai Nihon Gaikō Shi* (History of Contemporary Japanese Diplomacy), Tōkyō, 1941.
————: *Nihon Hoppō Hatten Shi* (History of Japan's Northward Expansion), Tōkyō, 1942.
————: *Nihon Kindai Gaikō Shi* (Recent History of Japanese Diplomacy), Tōkyō, 1941.
Masuda Harukichi: *Senji Keizai wo Suishin suru Hitobito* (Those Who Propel Wartime Economy), Tōkyō, 1941.
Matsui Haruo: *Nihon Shigen Seisaku* (Japanese Policy on Resources), Tōkyō, 1938.
Matsumoto Jun'ichirō: *Nihon Shakaigaku* (Japanese Sociology), Tōkyō, 1937.
Matsuoka Minoru: *Nihon Rōdō Kumiai Undō Hattatsu Shi* (History of the Japanese Trade Union Movement), Tōkyō, 1931.
Matsushita Yoshio: *Meiji Gunsei Shi Ronshū* (Essays on the History of Meiji Military Administration), Tōkyō, 1938.
————: *Chōheirei Seitei Shi* (History of the Establishment of Military Conscription), Tōkyō, 1943.
————: *Kindai Nihon Gunji Shi* (Recent Military History of Japan), Tōkyō, 1941.
Meiji Zaiseishi Hensankai: *Meiji Zaisei Shi* (History of Public Finance of the Meiji Era), 15 vols., Tōkyō, 1926–1928.
Mihei Kōshi: *Nihon Mengyō Hattatsu Shi* (History of the Japanese Cotton Industry), Tōkyō, 1941.
Mikami Sanji: *Edo Jidai Shi* (History of the Edo Period), Tōkyō, 1943.
Mikasa Shobō: *Nihon Gendai Shi Zensho* (Modern Japanese Historical Series), 16 vols., Tōkyō, 1941–1945.
Minobe Tatsukichi: *Shin Kempō no Kihon Genri* (The Basic Principles of the New Constitution), Tōkyō, 1947.

Minokuchi Tokijirō: *Jinkō Mondai* (Population Problem), Tōkyō, 1941.

————: *Jinteki Shigen Ron* (A Treatise on Manpower Resources), Tōkyō, 1941.

Mishima Sukeharu: *Gumbu no Mokuhyō* (The Goal of the Military), Tōkyō, 1941.

————: *Kessen Taiseika no Shisō Taisaku* (Wartime Measures Pertaining to Thought Control), Tōkyō, 1941.

Mitsui Ginkō: *Mitsui Ginkō Gojūnen Shi* (Fifty Years of the Mitsui Bank), Tōkyō, 1926.

Mitsuyuki Hisashi: *Shin Taiseika no Shimbun Kōsō* (Newspapers under the New Political Structure), Tōkyō, 1940.

Miyajima Shinzaburō: *Ikō Meiji Bungaku Gairon* (Outline of Meiji Literature), Tōkyō, 1934.

————: *Meiji Bungaku Jūnikō* (Twelve Lectures on Meiji Literature), Tōkyō, 1925.

————: *Taishō Bungaku Jūshikō* (Fourteen Lectures on Taishō Literature), Tōkyō, 1926.

Miyake Setsurei: *Meiji Shisō Shōshi* (Brief History of Meiji Thought), Tōkyō, 1913.

Miyamoto Chū: *Sakuma Shōzan,* Tōkyō, 1932.

Miyamoto Gennosuke: *Meiji Un'yu Shi* (History of Meiji Transportation), Tōkyō, 1913.

Miyatake Tokotsu: *Meiji Mittei Shi* (History of Political Espionage in the Meiji Period), Tōkyō, 1929.

Mizuno Takeo: *Senji Nihon no Shokuryō* (Japan's Wartime Food Problem), Tōkyō, 1941.

Mizuno Yōshū: *Meiji Bungaku no Chōryū* (Currents of Meiji Literature), Tōkyō, 1944.

Mizuta Nobutoshi: *Bakumatsu ni Okeru Waga Kaigun to Oranda* (The Japanese Navy and Holland in the Closing Years of the Shogunate), Tōkyō, 1929.

Mochizuki Shigeru: *Shin Nihon Minken Shi* (History of Popular Rights in New Japan), Tōkyō, 1947.

Mombushō: *Gakusei Shichijūnen Shi* (Seventy Years of Japanese Educational System), Tōkyō, 1942.

————: *Jitsugyō Kyōiku Gojūnen Shi* (Fifty Years of Vocational Education), Tōkyō, 1934.

————: *Sōtei Shisō Chōsa* (A Study of the Ideas of Conscripts)', Tōkyō, 1931.

Mori Goroku: *Kensei to Gunjin* (Parliamentary Government and the Military), Tōkyō, 1936.

Mori Junsaburō: *Ōgai Mori Rintarō* (Life of Mori Ōgai), Tōkyō, 1934.

Mori Kōjirō: *Senji Shakai Seisaku* (Wartime Social Policy), Tōkyō, 1941.

Mori Shōzō: *Sempū Nijūnen Shi* (History of Twenty Turbulent Years), 2 vols., Tōkyō, 1945.

Morita Yoshio: *Waga Kuni no Shihonka Dantai* (Japanese Capitalist Organizations), Tōkyō, 1926.

Moriya Hidesuke: *Kaikoku Yori Ishin E* (From the Opening of the Country to the Meiji Restoration), Tōkyō, 1942.

Murakami Sensei and Tsuji Zennosuke: *Meiji Ishin Shimbutsu Bunri Shiryō* (Materials on the Disestablishment of Buddhism in the Restoration Period), 3 vols., Tōkyō, 1926–1927.

Murakawa Kengo: *Nihon Gaikō Shi* (History of Japanese Diplomacy), Tōkyō, 1940.

Murata Minejirō: *Shinagawa Shishaku Den* (Life of Viscount Shinagawa), Tōkyō, 1910.

Murata Tsutomu: *Ebara Soroku Sensei Den* (Life of Ebara Soroku), Tōkyō, 1935.

Murayama Shigetada: *Nihon Rōdō Sōgi Shi* (History of Labor Struggle in Japan), Tōkyō, 1946.

Mutsu Hirokichi: *Hakushaku Mutsu Munemitsu Ikō* (Posthumous Works of Count Mutsu Munemitsu), Tōkyō, 1929.

Mutsu Munemitsu: *Ken-ken Roku* (Diplomatic Memoirs of the Sino-Japanese War Period), Tōkyō, 1938.

Nagai Tōru: *Nihon Jinkō Ron* (Japanese Population Problem), Tōkyō, 1929.

Naganuma Kenkai: *Nihon Bunka Shi no Kenkyū* (A Study of Japanese Cultural History), Tōkyō, 1937.

Nagaoka R.: *Kanryō Nijūgonen* (Twenty-five Years a Bureaucrat), Tōkyō, 1939.

Nagoya Shi: *Nagoya Shikai Shi* (History of the Nagoya Municipal Assembly), Nagoya, 1941.

Naigai Shoseki: *Nihon Shin Bunka Shi* (New Cultural History of Japan), 12 vols., Tōkyō, 1941–1942.

——: *Sōgō Nihon Shi Taikei* (A Comprehensive History of Japan), 12 vols., Tōkyō, 1926–1936.

Naikaku Kiroku Kyoku: *Meiji Shokukan Enkaku Hyō* (Table of Government Organizational Changes during the Meiji Period), 19 vols., Tōkyō, 1886–1893.

Naimushō: *Chō-Fu-Ken Keisatsu Enkaku Shi* (History of the Prefectural Police), 4 vols., Tōkyō, 1927.

Naitō Norisuke: *Itō-Kō Enzetsu Zenshū* (Complete Collection of Addresses of Prince Itō), Tōkyō, 1910.

Nakaizumi Tetsutoshi: *Nihon Kinsei Kyōiku Kikan no Kenkyū* (Study of Modern Japanese Educational Institutions), Tōkyō, 1937.

Nakajima Kurō: *Satō Nobuhiro*, Tōkyō, 1941.

Nakamura Katsumaro: *Ii Tairō to Kaikō* (Ii Naosuke and the Opening of the Ports), Tōkyō, 1909.

Nakamura Kichiji: *Nihon Shakai Shi Gaisetsu* (Introduction to Japanese Social History), Tōkyō, 1947.

Nakamura Mutsuo: *Kōryū Nihon no Zaikai-jin* (Financial Figures of Rising Japan), 2 vols., Tōkyō, 1941.

Nakamura Naokatsu: *Nara Shi Shi* (History of the City of Nara), Nara, 1937.

Nakamura Shōgo: *Nagata-chō Ichibanchi* (Number One Nagata-chō), Tōkyō, 1947.

Nakano Seigō: *Meiji Minken Shi* (History of Popular Rights in the Meiji Period), Tōkyō, 1913.

Nakata Sembō: *Nihon Gaikō Hiwa* (Inside Stories of Japanese Diplomacy), Tōkyō, 1940.

Nasu Shiroshi: *Jinkō Shokuryō Mondai* (Population and Food Problems), Tōkyō, 1927.

Negishi Kitsusaburō: *Bakumatsu Kaikoku Shinkan* (New Views on the Opening of the Country), Tōkyō, 1937.

Nichibei Kyōkai: *Man'en Gannen Dai Ikkai Kembei Shisetsu Nikki* (Diaries of the First Japanese Embassy to the United States in 1860), Tōkyō, 1919.

Nihon Ginkō: *Nihon Ginkō Enkaku Shi* (History of the Bank of Japan), 11 vols., Tōkyō, 1913–1915.

Nihon Hyōron Sha: *Nihon Keizai Shi Jiten* (Encyclopedia of Japanese Economic History), 3 vols., Tōkyō, 1937.

————: *Nihon Rekishigaku Taikei* (Outline of Japanese History), 20 vols., Tōkyō, 1944–1946.

Nihon Kangyō Ginkō: *Nihon Kangyō Ginkō Sanjūnen Shi* (Thirty Years of the Japan Hypothec Bank), Tōkyō, 1927.

Nihon Kōgakukai: *Meiji Kōgyō Shi* (Industrial History of the Meiji Period), 10 vols., Tōkyō, 1928–1931.

Nihon Rekishi Chiri Gakkai: *Nihon Nōmin Shi* (History of the Japanese Peasantry), Tōkyō, 1939.

Nihon Shiseki Kyōkai: *Kengai Shisetsu Nikki Sanshū* (Collection of Diaries of Embassies Sent Abroad), 3 vols., Tōkyō, 1928–1930.

Nishimura Kenkichi: *Shōwa Nōgyō Hattatsu Shi* (History of Agriculture in the Shōwa Period), Ōsaka, 1939.

Nishimura Shinji: *Nihon Kaigai Hatten Shi* (History of Japanese Overseas Migration), Tōkyō, 1942.

————: *Ono Azusa Den* (Life of Ono Azusa), Tōkyō, 1935.

————: *Ono Azusa Zenshū* (Complete Works of Ono Azusa), 2 vols., Tōkyō, 1936.

Noda Ritsuta: *Hyōgikai Tōsō Shi* (History of the Struggle of the Japan Labor Union Council), Tōkyō, 1931.

Noda Yoshio: *Meiji Kyōiku Shi* (History of Meiji Education), Tōkyō, 1907.

Noma Kaizō: *Nihon no Jinkō to Keizai* (Japan's Population and Economy), Tōkyō, 1941.

Nomura Junnosuke: *Nihon Kin'yū Shihon Hattatsu Shi* (Growth of Japan's Finance Capital), Tōkyō, 1931.

Noro Eitarō: *Nihon Shihon Shugi Hattatsu Shi* (History of the Development of Japanese Capitalism), Tōkyō, 1930.

Nōshōmushō: *Dai Nihon Nōshi* (History of Japanese Agriculture), 3 vols., Tōkyō, 1903.

Oguri Mataichi, ed.: *Ryūkei Yano Fumio Den* (Life of Yano Fumio), Tōkyō, 1930.

Oka Yōnosuke: *Nihon Shakai Undō Shi* (History of Japanese Social Movements), Tōkyō, 1927.

Okabe Tomio: *Dai Nihon Kyōiku Shi* (History of Japanese Education), Tōkyō, 1937.

Okada Sumio: *Shibusawa-Ō wa Kataru* (Viscount Shibusawa Speaks), Tōkyō, 1932.

Okano Takeo: *Shomotsu kara Mita Meiji no Bungei* (Meiji Literary Art as Seen through Writings), Tōkyō, 1942.

Ōkubo Toshikazu: *Ōkubo Toshimichi Monjo* (Papers of Ōkubo Toshimichi), 10 vols., Tōkyō, 1927–1931.

Ōkubo Toshimichi: *Ōkubo Toshimichi Nikki* (Diaries of Ōkubo Toshimichi), 2 vols., Tōkyō, 1927.

Okudaira Masahiro: *Nihon Bengoshi Shi* (History of the Legal Profession in Japan), Tōkyō, 1914.

Ōkuma Shigenobu, ed.: *Kaikoku Gojūnen Shi* (History of the Fifty Years Since the Opening of the Country), 2 vols., Tōkyō, 1907–1908.

Ōkuma Shigenobu: *Kaikoku Taisei Shi* (History of the Opening of the Country), Tōkyō, 1913.

Ōkuma-Kō Hachijūgonen Shi Hensankai: *Ōkuma-Kō Hachijūgonen Shi* (Eighty-five Years of Marquis Ōkuma), 3 vols., Tōkyō, 1926.

Okumura Kiwao: *Henkakuki Nihon no Seiji Keizai* (Politics and Economy of Japan in Transition), Tōkyō, 1941.

Ōkura Mitsuo: *Nichi-Ran Kōshō Sambyaku Nen Shi* (Three Hundred Years of Dutch-Japanese Relations), Tōkyō, 1943.

Ōkurashō: *Meiji Taishō Zaisei Shi* (Financial History of the Meiji and Taishō Eras), 20 vols., Tōkyō, 1936–1940.

————: *Nihon Zaisei Keizai Shiryō* (Materials on Japan Finance and Economy), 11 vols., Tōkyō, 1922–1925.

Ōmori Kingorō: *Dai Nihon Zenshi* (Complete History of Japan), 3 vols., Tōkyō, 1921–1922.

————: *Gendai Nihon Shi* (History of Contemporary Japan), Tōkyō, 1935.

Ono Hideo: *Nihon Shimbun Hattatsu Shi* (History of the Development of Japanese Newspapers), Tōkyō, 1924.

Ono Hisato: *Meiji Ishin Zengo ni Okeru Seiji Shisō no Tenkai* (Political Thought of the Meiji Restoration Period), Tōkyō, 1944.

Ono Takeo: *Ishin Nōson Shakai Shiron* (History of Agrarian Society of the Restoration Period), Tōkyō, 1932.

————: *Nihon Sonraku Shi Gaisetsu* (Outline History of the Japanese Village), Tōkyō, 1936.

————: *Nōson Kikō no Bunretsu Katei* (Disintegration of Agrarian Structure), Tōkyō, 1928.

Osadake Takeki: *Bakumatsu Ishin no Jimbutsu* (Personalities of the Bakumatsu and Restoration Periods), Tōkyō, 1935.

————: *Ishin Shi Sōsetsu* (Studies of Restoration History), Tōkyō, 1935.

————: *Iteki no Kuni E* (To the Land of the Barbarians), Tōkyō, 1929.

————: *Ishin Zengo ni Okeru Rikken Shisō* (Constitutional Ideas in the Restoration Period), 2 vols., Tōkyō, 1929.

————: *Kinsei Nihon no Kokusai Kannen no Hattatsu* (Development of International Concepts in Japan in Recent Times), Tōkyō, 1932.

————: *Kokusaishō yori Mitaru Bakumatsu Gaikō Monogatari* (Diplomatic Episodes of the Closing Years of the Shogunate in the Light of International Law), Tōkyō, 1926.

————: *Meiji Bunka to shite no Nihon Baishin Shi* (History of the Japanese Jury System as Part of Meiji Culture), Tōkyō, 1926.

————: *Meiji Hishi Gigoku Monogatari* (Scandals of the Meiji Period), Tōkyō, 1929.

————: *Meiji Ishin* (The Meiji Restoration), 3 vols., Tōkyō, 1948.

————: *Meiji Seiji Shi Tembyō* (Highlights of Meiji Political History), Tōkyō, 1938.

————: *Meiji Taishō Seijishi Kōwa* (Lectures on Meiji Taishō Political History), Tōkyō, 1943.

————: *Nihon Kempō Seitei Shiyō* (History of the Establishment of the Constitution), Tōkyō, 1938.

————: *Nihon Kensei Shi* (Constitutional History of Japan), Tōkyō, 1930.

Osadake Takeki: *Nihon Kensei Shi Taikō* (Outline of Japanese Constitutional History), 2 vols., Tōkyō, 1938–1939.

———: *Shimbun Zasshi no Sōshisha Yanagawa Shunzō* (Yanagawa Shunzō, Originator of Newspaper and Magazine in Japan), Tōkyō, 1920.

Ōta Hisayoshi: *Yokohama Enkaku Shi* (History of Yokohama), Tōkyō, 1892.

Ōta Tamesaburō: *Nichiro Karafuto Gaikō* (Russo-Japanese Diplomacy over Sakhalin), Tōkyō, 1941.

Ōtaki Kurama: *Jitsugyōkai Dai Hishi Mitsubishi Ōkoku* (The Mitsubishi Empire: Inner Story of the Business World), Tōkyō, 1926.

Ōtani Takeo: *Shin Taisei Nihon no Seiji Keizai Bunka* (Japanese Politics and Economy under the New Structure), Tōkyō, 1940.

Ōtani Yoshitaka: *Shin Seiji Taisei no Genri* (Principles of the New Political Structure), Tōkyō, 1941.

Ototake Iwazō: *Nihon Kyōiku Shi no Kenkyū* (A History of Japanese Education), Tōkyō, 1935.

———: *Nihon Shomin Kyōiku Shi* (History of Common Education in Japan), 3 vols., Tōkyō, 1929.

Ōtsu Jun'ichirō: *Dai Nihon Kensei Shi* (Constitutional History of Japan), 10 vols., Tōkyō, 1927–1928.

Ōtsuka Minao: *Meiji Ishin to Doitsu Shisō* (Meiji Restoration and German Thought), Tōkyō, 1943.

Ōtsuka Takematsu, ed.: *Iwakura Tomomi Kankei Monjo* (Papers Relating to Iwakura Tomomi), 8 vols., Tōkyō, 1927–1935.

———: *Kawaji Toshiakira Monjo* (Papers Relating to Kawaji Toshiakira), 8 vols., Tōkyō, 1932–1934.

———: *Meiji Boshin Kyokugai Chūritsu Temmatsu* (An Account of the Declaration of Neutrality by the Powers in 1868), Tōkyō, 1932.

Ōtsuki Fumihiko: *Mitsukuri Rinshō Kun* (Life of Mitsukuri Rinshō), Tōkyō, 1907.

Ozaki Yukio: *Haisen no Hansei* (Reflection on Defeat), Tōkyō, 1946.

———: *Seisen Rokujūnen* (Sixty Years of Political Life), Tōkyō, 1935.

Rōyama Masamichi: *Musan Seitō Ron* (Proletarian Political Parties), Tōkyō, 1930.

———: *Sekai no Henkyoku to Nihon no Sekai Seisaku* (The Shifting World Situation and Japanese Policies), Tōkyō, 1938.

Ryūgin Sha: *Meiji Ikō Kyōiku Seido Hattatsu Shi* (History of the Educational System Since the Beginning of the Meiji Period), 12 vols., Tōkyō, 1941.

Saitō Eisaburō: *Senji Nihon Keizai Shi* (History of Japan's Wartime Economy), Tōkyō, 1941.

Saitō Morihiko: *Meiji Fūzokushi* (History of Meiji Customs and Manners), Tōkyō, 1941.

Saitō Ryūzō: *Kinsei Sesō Shi Gaikan* (General View of Recent Social Conditions), Tōkyō, 1940.

———: *Shinkō Dai Nihon Shi* (A New History of Japan), 3 vols., Tōkyō, 1941.

Sakuragi Akira: *Sokumenkan Bakumatsu Shi* (A Sideview of the History of the Closing Years of the Shogunate), Tōkyō, 1905.

Sakurai Tadashi: *Meiji Shūkyō Undō Shi* (History of Meiji Religious Movements), Tōkyō, 1932.

Sanetō Keishū: *Meiji Nisshi Bunka Kōshō* (Sino-Japanese Cultural Relations of the Meiji Period), Tōkyō, 1943.

Sangyō Kumiai Chūōkai: *Nihon Sangyō Kumiai Shi* (History of Japanese Industrial Cooperatives), Tōkyō, 1926.

Sasahara Masashi: *Teikoku Gikai Kaisan Shi* (History of the Dissolutions of the Imperial Diet), Tōkyō, 1932.

Sasaki Nobutsuna: *Meiji Bungaku no Hen'ei* (Glimpses of Meiji Literature), Tōkyō, 1934.

Sashihara Yasuzō: *Meiji Seishi* (Political History of the Meiji Period), 2 vols., Tōkyō, 1929.

Satō Kōseki: *Kōa no Senkakusha Arao Sei* (Arao Sei, Pioneer Exponent of Asiatic Expansion), Tōkyō, 1941.

Satō Shunzō: *Shina Kinsei Seitō Shi* (History of Recent Chinese Political Parties), Tōkyō, 1940.

Sawada Akira: *Meiji Zaisei no Kisoteki Kenkyū* (A Basic Study of Meiji Finance), Tōkyō, 1934.

————: *Segai Inoue-Kō Jireki Ishin Zaiseidan* (An Account of Inoue Kaoru's Restoration Financial Policies), 3 vols., Tōkyō, 1921.

Seibundō Shinkō Sha: *Nihon Bunka Shi Taikei* (Outline History of Japanese Civilization), 12 vols., Tōkyō, 1937–1940.

Sembai Kyoku: *Sembai Shi* (History of Government Monopolies), 8 vols., Tōkyō, 1937.

————: *Tabako Sembai Shi* (History of the Government Tobacco Monopoly), Tōkyō, 1915.

Setoguchi Torao: *Nihon Hatsumei Kagakusha Den* (Biographies of Japanese Inventors), Tōkyō, 1942.

Shakai Kagaku: *Nihon Shakai Shugi Undō Shi* (History of the Socialist Movement in Japan), Tōkyō, 1928.

Shakai Keizai Rōdō Kenkyūjo: *Kindai Nihon Rōdōsha Undō Shi* (History of Recent Japanese Labor Movements), Tōkyō, 1948.

Shibata Ken'ichi: *Nihon Minzoku Kaigai Hatten Shi* (History of Japanese Overseas Migration), Tōkyō, 1941.

Shibata Shunzō: *Nichi-Ei Gaikō Rimen Shi* (Inside Account of Anglo-Japanese Diplomacy), Tōkyō, 1941.

Shibusawa Eiichi: *Meiji Shōkō Shi* (History of Commerce and Industry in the Meiji Period), Tōkyō, 1911.

————: *Seien Kaiko Roku* (Recollections), 2 vols., Tōkyō, 1927.

————: *Tokugawa Keiki-Kō Den* (Life of Tokugawa Keiki), 8 vols., Tōkyō, 1918.

Shigaku Kai: *Meiji Ishin Shi Kenkyū* (Studies on the Meiji Restoration Period), Tōkyō, 1929.

Shiina Etsusaburō: *Senji Keizai to Busshi Chōsei* (Wartime Economy and Commodities Adjustment), Tōkyō, 1941.

Shima Yasuhiko: *Tōyō Shakai to Seiō Shisō* (Oriental Society and Western European Thought), Tōkyō, 1941.

Shimada Saburō: *Kaikoku Shimatsu, Ii Kamon no Kami Naosuke Den* (The Opening of the Country: the Life of Ii Naosuke), Tōkyō, 1888.

Shimizu Kaneo: *Nihon Keizai Tōseihō* (Japanese Economic Control Law), Tōkyō, 1940.

Shimojō Yasumaro: *Nihon Shakai Seisakuteki Shisetsu Shi* (History of Japanese Social Policy Institutions), Tōkyō, 1941.

Shimozono Sakichi: *Makino Nobuaki Haku* (Count Makino Nobuaki), Tōkyō, 1940.

Shinano Kyōiku Kai: *Shōzan Zenshū* (Complete Works of Sakuma Shōzan), 2 vols., Tōkyō, 1913.

Shinobu Jumpei: *Taishō Gaikō Jūgonen Shi* (Diplomatic History of the Fifteen Years of the Taishō Era), Tōkyō, 1929.

Shinobu Seizaburō: *Gotō Shimpei,* Tōkyō, 1941.

———: *Mutsu Munemitsu,* Tōkyō, 1939.

———: *Nisshin Sensō* (The Sino-Japanese War), Tōkyō, 1935.

Shiohara Matasaku: *Takamine Hakushi* (Dr. Takamine Jōkichi), Tōkyō, 1926.

Shiojima Jinkichi: *Teiken Taguchi Sensei Den* (Life of Dr. Taguchi Ukichi), Tōkyō, 1912.

Shiomi Saburō: *Nihon Zaisei Seisaku* (Japanese Financial Policy), Tōkyō, 1938.

Shiraishi Kitarō: *Shibusawa Eiichi-Ō* (Life of Viscount Shibusawa), Tōkyō, 1933.

Shirayanagi Shūko: *Gendai Zaibatsu Zaiaku Shi* (History of the Recent Transgressions of the Zaibatsu), Tōkyō, 1932.

———: *Iwasaki Yatarō Den* (Life of Iwasaki Yatarō), Tōkyō, 1932.

———: *Meiji Taishō Kokumin Shi* (History of the Meiji Taishō Eras), 5 vols., Tōkyō, 1940.

———: *Nakamigawa Hikojirō Den* (Life of Nakamigawa Hikojirō), Tōkyō, 1940.

———: *Nihon Fugō Hasseigaku* (A Study of the Emergence of Japan's Millionaires), Tōkyō, 1931.

Shiryō Hensanjo: *Meiji Shiyō* (History of the Meiji Period), 2 vols., Tōkyō, 1933.

Shishido Shinzan: *Meiji Taishō Shōwa Taikan Roku* (A Record of High Government Officials of Meiji, Taishō and Shōwa Eras), Tōkyō, 1931.

Shōda Magoya: *Kōtō Itsuwa* (Anecdotes of Ōkubo Toshimichi), Tōkyō, 1928.

———: *Ōkubo Toshimichi Den* (Life of Ōkubo Toshimichi), 3 vols., Tōkyō, 1921.

———: *Saigō Takamori Den* (Life of Saigō Takamori), 5 vols., Tōkyō, 1894–1895.

Shōda Teiji: *Nihon Keizai no Gōrika* (The Rationalization of Japanese Economy), Tōkyō, 1930.

———: *Nihon Zentai Shugi Keizai no Seikaku* (Nature of Japan's Totalitarian Economy), Tōkyō, 1941.

———: *Nihon Keizai no Kiso Kōsei* (Basic Structure of Japanese Economy), Tōkyō, 1927.

Shūgiin Jimu Kyoku: *Shūgiin Giji Tekiyō* (Summary of the Proceedings of the House of Representatives), Tōkyō, 1911–.

Shumpo-Kō Tsuishō Kai: *Itō Hirobumi Den* (Life of Itō Hirobumi), 3 vols., Tōkyō, 1940.

Shunjū Sha: *Nihon Kontsuerun Zensho* (Complete Work on Japanese Combines), 18 vols., Tōkyō, 1936–1938.

Shūshi Kyoku: *Hyakkan Rireki* (Curriculum Vitae of Officials), 2 vols., Tōkyō, 1927–1928.

Sōma Moto: *Tō-Nichi Shichijūnen Shi* (Seventy Years of the Newspaper *Tōkyō Nichi Nichi*), Tōkyō, 1941.

Suematsu Kenchō: *Bōchō Kaiten Shi* (History of the Yamaguchi Prefecture), 12 vols., Tōkyō, 1921.

———: *Itō Inoue Ni-Genrō Jikiwa Ishin Fūun Roku* (Restoration Upheaval: First-hand Accounts by Elder Statesmen Itō and Inoue), Tōkyō, 1900.

Sugimoto Masayuki: *Zenkoku Nōkō Ginkō Hattatsu Shi* (History of Agricultural and Industrial Banks in Japan), Tōkyō, 1924.

Sugimura Shun: *Meiji Nijūshichihachinen Zaikan Kushin Roku* (An Account of Trying Experiences in Korea during the Sino-Japanese War), Tōkyō, 1932.

Sugiyama Heisuke: *Nihon Bunka to Shakai* (Japanese Culture and Society), Tōkyō, 1941.

Sumitomo Ginkō: *Sumitomo Ginkō Sanjunen Shi* (Thirty Years of Sumitomo Bank), Tōkyō, 1926.

Suzuki Eitarō: *Nihon Nōson Shakaigaku Genri* (Principles of Japanese Rural Sociology), Tōkyō, 1941.

Suzuki Kaichi: *Tonarigumi to Jōkai* (Neighborhood Associations and Their Meetings), Tōkyō, 1941.

Suzuki Norihisa: *Saikin Nihon Zaisei Shi* (Recent History of Japanese Finance), Tōkyō, 1929.

Suzuki Toshiichi: *Dai Ichi Seimei Hoken Sōgo Kaisha Nijūgonen Shi* (Twenty-five Years of Dai Ichi Mutual Life Insurance Company), Tōkyō, 1929.

Suzuki Yasuzō: *Kanri Seido no Kenkyū* (Studies on the Bureacratic System), Tōkyō, 1948.

———: *Kempō no Rekishiteki Kenkyū* (Historical Study of the Constitution), Tōkyō, 1934.

———: *Kindai Nihon no Seitō to Gikai* (History of Japanese Political Parties and the Diet in Recent Times), Tōkyō, 1947.

———: *Nihon Kempō Shi Gaisetsu* (An Outline History of the Japanese Constitution), Tōkyō, 1941.

———: *Nihon Kempō Shi Kenkyū* (A Study of the History of the Japanese Constitution), Tōkyō, 1935.

———: *Nihon Kensei Seiritsu Shi* (History of the Establishment of the Japanese Constitutional System), Tōkyō, 1933.

———: *Meiji Kempō to Shin Kempō* (The Meiji Constitution and the New Constitution), Tōkyō, 1947.

———: *Nihon no Kempō* (The Japanese Constitution), Tōkyō, 1947.

———: *Nihon Seiji no Kijun* (The Basis of Japanese Politics), Tōkyō, 1941.

Tabohashi Kiyoshi: *Kindai Nihon Gaikoku Kankei Shi* (History of Recent Japanese Foreign Relations), Tōkyō, 1930.

———: *Kindai Nisshisen Kankei no Kenkyū* (A Study of Recent Sino-Korean-Japanese Relations), Keijo, 1930.

Taguchi Ukichi: *Nihon Kaika Shōshi* (A Short History of Japanese Civilization), Tōkyō, 1930.

Taishōkaku: *Nihon Bunka Shi* (A Cultural History of Japan), 12 vols., Tōkyō, 1922.

Takahashi Kamekichi: *Makki no Nihon Shihon Shugi Keizai to Sono Tenkan* (Japanese Capitalistic Economy: Its Last Phase and Turning Point), Tōkyō, 1925.

———: *Meiji Taishō Sangyō Hattatsu Shi* (History of Meiji Taishō Industrial Development), Tōkyō, 1929.

———: *Nihon Keizai no Yukitsumari to Musan Kaikyū no Taisaku* (The Impasse of Japan's National Economy and the Counter-measures of the Propertyless Class), Tōkyō, 1926.

———: *Nihon Sangyō Rōdō Ron* (On Japanese Industrial Labor), Tōkyō, 1937.

———: *Nihon Shihon Shugi Keizai no Kenkyū* (A Study of Japan's Capitalist Economy), Tōkyō, 1924.

———: *Nihon Zaibatsu no Kaibō* (The Anatomy of Japanese Combines), Tōkyō, 1930.

———: *Saikin no Keizai Shi* (Recent Japanese Economic History), Tōkyō, 1934.

Takahashi Korekiyo: *Korekiyo-Ō Ichidai Ki* (Autobiography of Takahashi Korekiyo), 2 vols., Tōkyō, 1929–1930.

Takahashi Masao: *Tenkeiki no Seiji to Keizai* (Japanese Politics and Economy in Transition), Tōkyō, 1947.

Takahashi Sadaki: *Tokushu Buraku Shi* (History of Eta Communities), Tōkyō, 1924.

Takahashi Shunjō: *Nihon Kyōiku Shi* (History of Japanese Education), Tōkyō, 1929.

———: *Nihon Kyōiku Bunka Shi* (History of Japanese Education and Culture), Tōkyō, 1933.

Takahashi Yūsai: *Keisatsu Seido Gairon* (Outline of the Police System), Tōkyō, 1948.

Takano Iwasaburō: *Hompō Jinkō no Genzai to Shōrai* (Japan's Population, Present and Future), Tōkyō, 1923.

Takasu Yoshijirō: *Meiji Bungaku Shiron* (History of Meiji Literature), Tōkyō, 1934.

Takebayashi Kumahiko: *Kinsei Nihon Bunko Shi* (History of Japanese Libraries in Recent Times), Tōkyō, 1943.

Takebayashi Shōtarō: *Nihon Chūshōshō no Kōzō* (The Structure of Middle and Small Scale Business in Japan), Tōkyō, 1941.

Takeuchi Masatora: *Nihon Kōkū Hattatsu Shi* (History of Japanese Aviation), Tōkyō, 1940.

Takikawa Masajirō: *Nihon Shakai Shi* (A Social History of Japan), Tōkyō, 1929.

Takimoto Seiichi: *Nihon Keizai Taiten* (Source Materials on Japanese Political Economy), 55 vols., Tōkyō, 1928.

Takita Teiji: *Futsugaku Shiso Murakami Hidetoshi* (Murakami Hidetoshi: Pioneer in French Studies), 3 vols., Tōkyō, 1935.

Tamura Eitarō: *Nihon no Gijutsusha* (Japanese Technologists), Tōkyō, 1943.

———: *Nihon no Sangyō Shidōsha* (Leaders of Japanese Industry), Tōkyō, 1944.

Tamura Tokuji: *Shin Taisei no Mokuhyō* (The Goal of the New Political Structure), Tōkyō, 1941.

Tanabe Taichi: *Bakumatsu Gaikō Dan* (Diplomatic Tales of the Last Days of the Shogunate), Tōkyō, 1898.

Tanaka Kan'ichi: *Nihon no Jinteki Shigen* (Japan's Manpower Resources), Tōkyō, 1941.

Tanaka Kōtarō: *Jichi Gojūnen Shi* (Fifty Years of Self-government), Tōkyō, 1941.

Tanaka Sōgorō: *Iwasaki Yatarō*, Tōkyō, 1940.

Tanaka Sōgorō: *Kido Takayoshi*, Tōkyō, 1941.

———: *Kindai Nihon Kanryō Shi* (History of Recent Japanese Bureaucracy), Tōkyō, 1941.

———: *Meiji Ishin Undō no Tenkai* (The Unfolding of the Meiji Restoration Movement), Tōkyō, 1943.

———: *Nihon Kan'ryō Seiji Shi* (History of Japanese Bureaucratic Government), Tōkyō, 1947.

———: *Sōgō Meiji Ishin Shi* (General History of the Meiji Restoration), Tōkyō, 1945.

———: *Nihon no Jiyū Minken* (Japan's Liberty and Popular Rights), Tōkyō, 1947.

Tanaka Yukichi: *Meiji Taishō Nihon Igaku Shi* (History of Japanese Medicine in the Meiji Taishō Eras), Tōkyō, 1927.

Tanimoto Tomi: *Meiji Kyōka no Kigen* (The Origin of Meiji Educational Indoctrination), Tōkyō, 1908–1910.

Teikoku Keiba Kyōkai: *Nihon Basei Shi* (History of Japanese Horse Administration), 5 vols., Tōkyō, 1928.

Teikoku Tsūshin Sha: *Nihon Sangyō Shi* (History of Japanese Industries), 2 vols., Tōkyō, 1928.

Teishinshō: *Teishin Jigyō Shi* (History of Postal and Communications Services), Tōkyō, 1941.

Terao Kōji: *Meiji Shoki Kyōto Keizai Shi* (Economic History of Kyōto in the Early Meiji Period), Kyōto, 1943.

Tetsudōin: *Hompō Tetsudō no Shakai oyobi Keizai ni Oyoboseru Eikyō* (Social and Economic Effects of the Railroad in Japan), 3 vols., Tōkyō, 1916.

Tetsudōshō: *Nihon Tetsudō Shi* (History of Japanese Railways), 3 vols., Tōkyō, 1921.

Tōa Dōbunkai: *Taishi Kaiko Roku* (Recollections of Sino-Japanese Affairs), 2 vols., Tōkyō, 1937.

Tōbata Seiichi: *Nihon Nōgyō no Kadai* (The Task of Japanese Agriculture), Tōkyō, 1941.

Toda Shintarō: *Nihon Shihon Shugi to Nihon Nōgyō no Hattatsu* (Japanese Capitalism and the Development of Japanese Agriculture), Tōkyō, 1947.

Togawa Sadao: *Hashimoto Kingorō*, Tōkyō, 1941.

Tokushige Asakichi: *Ishin Seishin Shi Kenkyū* (Spiritual History of the Meiji Restoration), Tōkyō, 1928.

Tokutomi Iichirō: *Ishin Kaiten Shi no Ichimen* (An Aspect of the History of the Restoration), Tōkyō, 1928.

———: *Kōshaku Katsura Tarō Den* (Life of Prince Katsura Tarō), 2 vols., Tōkyō, 1917.

———: *Kōshaku Matsukata Masayoshi Den* (Life of Marquis Matsukata Masayoshi), 2 vols., Tōkyō, 1935.

———: *Ōkubo Kōtō Sensei* (Ōkubo Toshimichi), Tōkyō, 1927.

———: *Kōshaku Yamagata Aritomo Den* (Life of Prince Yamagata), 3 vols., Tōkyō, 1933.

———: *Seijika to Shite no Katsura Kō* (Prince Katsura as a Statesman), Tōkyō, 1913.

Tōkyō Kabushiki Torihikijo: *Tōkyō Kabushiki Torihiki Gojūnen Shi* (Fifty Years of the Tōkyō Stock Exchange), Tōkyō, 1928.

Tōkyō Teikoku Daigaku: *Tōkyō Teikoku Daigaku Gojūnen Shi* (Fifty Years of the Tōkyō Imperial University), 2 vols., Tōkyō, 1932.

Tominari Kimahei: *Gendai Nihon Kagaku Shi* (History of Modern Japanese Science), Tōkyō, 1941.

Toyama Usaburō: *Nippo Bōeki Shōshi* (Short History of Trade between Japan and Portugal), Tōkyō, 1942.

Tōyō Bunka Kyōkai: *Bakumatsu Meiji Taishō Kaiko Hachijūnen Shi* (History of the Eighty Years from the Closing Days of the Tokugawa Shogunate through the Meiji and Taishō Eras), 10 vols., Tōkyō, 1933.

Tōyō Keizai Shimpō Sha: *Chūbu Nihon no Jigyō to Kaisha* (Enterprises and Corporations of Central Japan), Tōkyō, 1941.

――――: *Gendai Nihon Bummei Shi* (History of Contemporary Japanese Civilization), 11 vols., Tōkyō, 1940–1944.

――――: *Meiji Taishō Nōson Keizai no Hensen* (Evolution of Agrarian Economy during the Meiji and Taishō Eras), Tōkyō, 1926.

――――: *Meiji Zaisei Shikō* (Outline History of Meiji Finance), Tōkyō, 1911.

Toyosaki Minoru: *Nihon Kikai Kōgyō no Kiso Kōzō* (Basic Structure of Japanese Machine Industry), Tōkyō, 1941.

Tsuchiya Takao: *Nihon Keizai Shi Gaiyō* (Outline Economic History of Japan), Tōkyō, 1935.

――――: *Nihon Shakai Keizai Shi no Shomondai* (Problems in Japanese Social and Economic History), Tōkyō, 1935.

――――: *Nihon Shihon Shugi Hattatsu Shi Gaisetsu* (Outline History of Japanese Capitalism), Tōkyō, 1937.

――――: *Nihon Shihon Shugijō no Shidōsha* (Leaders of Japanese Capitalism), Tōkyō, 1939.

――――: *Nihon Shihon Shugi Ronshū* (Essays on Japanese Capitalism), Tōkyō, 1937.

――――: *Zoku Nihon Keizai Shi Gaiyō* (Outline of Japanese Economic History, Continued), Tōkyō, 1939.

Tsuchiya Takao and Ono Michio: *Meiji Shonen Nōmin Sōjō Roku* (Peasant Disturbances of the Early Meiji Period), Tōkyō, 1931.

Tsuchiya Takao and Ōuchi Hyōe: *Meiji Zenki Zaisei Keizai Shiryō Shūsei* (Source Materials on Early Meiji Finance and Economy), 20 vols., Tōkyō, 1931–1937.

Tsuji Makoto: *Nihon Sangyō Kumiai Shikō* (History of Japanese Industrial Cooperatives), Tōkyō, 1937.

Tsuji Zennosuke: *Kaigai Kōtsū Shiwa* (Essays on the History of Foreign Relations), Tōkyō, 1930.

Tsumaki Chūta: *Shōkiku Kido Kō Den* (Life of Marquis Kido), 2 vols., Tōkyō, 1927.

――――: *Kido Kōin Bunsho* (Papers of Kido Kōin), 8 vols., Tōkyō, 1929–1931.

Uchida Ginzō: *Kinsei no Nihon* (Japan in the Modern Period), Tōkyō, 1939.

Uchida Shigetaka: *Nihon Seiji Shakai Shisō Shi* (History of Japanese Political and Social Thought), Tōkyō, 1931.

Uda Tomoi: *Rikken Jiyūtō Shi* (History of the Liberal Party), 2 vols., Tōkyō, 1910.

Ueda Teijirō: *Nihon Jinkō Mondai Kenkyū* (A Study of the Japanese Population Problem), 3 vols., Tōkyō, 1939.

Uehara Etsujirō: *Demokurashii to Nihon no Kaizō* (Democracy and the Reconstruction of Japan), Tōkyō, 1920.

————: *Nihon Minken Hattatsu Shi* (History of the Development of Popular Rights in Japan), Tōkyō, 1916.

Uzaki Rojō: *Inukai Tsuyoshi Den* (Life of Inukai Tsuyoshi), Tōkyō, 1932.

Wada Hidekichi: *Ni-ni-roku Igo* (Since the February 26 Incident), Tōkyō, 1937.

Wakabayashi Hiroshi: *Dai Nihon Seitō Shi* (History of Japanese Political Parties), Tōkyō, 1913.

Waseda Daigaku: *Dai Nihon Jidai Shi* (History of Japan by Periods), 10 vols., Tōkyō, 1915–1916.

Washio Yoshinao: *Inukai Mokudō Den* (Life of Inukai Tsuyoshi), 3 vols., Tōkyō, 1939.

Watanabe Ikujirō: *Bunsho yori Mitaru Ōkuma Shigenobu Kō* (Marquis Ōkuma as Seen through Documents), Tōkyō, 1932.

————: *Kyōiku Chokugo Kampatsu no Yurai* (Reasons for the Promulgation of the Imperial Rescript on Education), Tōkyō, 1935.

————: *Meiji Shi Kōwa* (Lectures on the History of the Meiji Period), Tōkyō, 1936.

————: *Meiji Tennō to Meiji no Kensetsu* (Emperor Meiji and the Building of Japan), Tōkyō, 1939.

————: *Mutsu Munemitsu Den* (Life of Mutsu Munemitsu), Tōkyō, 1934.

————: *Nihon Kinsei Gaikō Shi* (Recent Japanese Diplomatic History), Tōkyō, 1938.

————: *Nihon Senji Gaikō Shiwa* (Topics on the History of Japanese Wartime Diplomacy), Tōkyō, 1937.

————: *Nihon Shakai Undō Shikan* (Views on the History of Japanese Social Movements), Tōkyō, 1925.

————: *Ōkuma Shigenobu*, Tōkyō, 1943.

————: *Ōkuma Shigenobu Kankei Bunsho* (Papers Relating to Ōkuma Shigenobu), 3 vols., 1932–1933.

Watanabe Michitarō: *Waga Kuni Rōdō Kumiai no Kenkyū* (A Study of Japanese Labor Unions), Tōkyō, 1930.

Watanabe Shūjirō: *Abe Masahiro Jiseki* (Abe Masahiro's Role in the Opening of Japan), 2 vols., Tōkyō, 1910.

Yabe Teiji: *Saikin Nihon Gaikō Shi* (History of Recent Japanese Diplomacy), Tōkyō, 1940.

Yamada Moritarō: *Nihon Shihon Shugi Bunseki* (Analysis of Japanese Capitalism), Tōkyō, 1934.

Yamaguchi Kazuo: *Bakumatsu Bōeki Shi* (History of Foreign Trade in the Closing Years of the Shogunate), Tōkyō, 1943.

Yamaguchi-Ken Kyōiku Kai: *Yoshida Shōin Zenshū* (Complete Works of Yoshida Shōin), 8 vols., Tōkyō, 1935.

Yamamoto Fumio: *Nihon Shimbun Shi* (History of Japanese Newspapers), Tōkyō, 1948.

Yamamoto Kazuo: *Nihon Keisatsu Shi* (History of the Japanese Police), Tōkyō, 1935.

Yamashita Sōen: *Nihon Hawaii Kōryūshi* (History of Hawaiian-Japanese Relations), Tōkyō, 1943.

Yamaura Kan'ichi: *Konoe Jidai no Jimbutsu* (Contemporaries of Prince Konoe), Tōkyō, 1940.

————: *Mori Kaku wa Ikite-iru* (Mori Kaku Is Alive), Tōkyō, 1941.

————: *Tōa Shin Taisei no Senkaku Mori Kaku* (Mori Kaku, the Pioneer Exponent of the New Order in East Asia), Tōkyō, 1940.

Yamazaki Benji: *Nihon Shōhi Kumiai Undō Shi* (History of Japanese Consumer Cooperative Movement), Tōkyō, 1932.

Yamazaki Kazuo: *Dai Nihon Seisen Kiroku Shi* (History of National Election Contests), Tōkyō, 1930.

Yamazaki Saiji: *Nihon Kyōiku Gyōseihō* (Japanese Educational Administration Laws), Tōkyō, 1937.

Yamazaki Yasuzumi: *Tenkanki Nihon no Seiji Keizai* (Japanese Politics and Economy in Transition), Tōkyō, 1938.

Yanagida Izumi: *Meiji Shoki no Hon'yaku Bungaku* (Literature in Translation of the Early Meiji Period), Tōkyō, 1935.

Yanagida Kunio: *Nihon Nōmin Shi* (History of the Japanese Peasantry), Tōkyō, 1940.

Yanase Haruo: *Nihon Minzoku Kaigai Yakushin Shi* (History of Japanese Overseas Migration), Tōkyō, 1943.

Yano Fumio: *Yasuda Zenjirō Den* (Life of Yasuda Zenjirō), Tōkyō, 1925.

Yano Jin'ichi: *Nisshin Ekigo Shina Gaikō Shi* (History of Chinese Diplomacy after the Sino-Japanese War of 1894–1895), Kyōto, 1937.

Yaoita Masao: *Shōwa Kin'yū Seisaku Shi* (History of Shōwa Financial Policy), Tōkyō, 1943.

Yashidai: *Ishin Shiryō* (Historical Materials on the Restoration), 182 vols., Tōkyō, 1888.

Yashiro Yukio: *Nihon Bijutsu no Tokushitsu* (Special Characteristics of Japanese Art), Tōkyō, 1944.

Yasui Shōtarō: *Tōkyō Denki Kabushiki Kaisha Gojūnen Shi* (Fifty Years of the Tōkyō Electric Light Company), Tōkyō, 1941.

Yokoi Tokifuyu: *Nihon Kōgyō Shi* (History of Japanese Manufacturing), Tōkyō, 1929.

————: *Nihon Shōgyō Shi* (History of Japanese Commerce), Tōkyō, 1929.

Yokoi Tokio: *Shōnan Ikō* (Posthumous Work of Yokoi Shōnan), Tōkyō, 1888.

Yokose Yau: *Meiji Shonen no Sesō* (Social Conditions of the Early Meiji Period), Tōkyō, 1927.

Yokoyama Katsutarō: *Kenseikai Shi* (History of the Kenseikai Party), Tōkyō, 1926.

Yoshida Kumaji: *Hompō Kyōiku Shi Gaisetsu* (Outline History of Japanese Education), Tōkyō, 1922.

Yoshida Seiichi: *Kindai Nihon Rōmanshugi Kenkyū* (Study of Recent Japanese Romanticism), Tōkyō, 1943.

Yoshida Tōgo: *Ishin Shi Hakkō* (Eight Lectures on the Meiji Restoration), Tōkyō, 1910.

————: *Tōjo Nihon Shi* (Japanese History in Reverse Order), 11 vols., Tōkyō, 1913.

Yoshikawa Hidezō: *Meiji Ishin Shakai Keizai Shi Kenkyū* (Social and Economic History of the Meiji Restoration), Tōkyō, 1943.

Yoshino Sakuzō: *Gendai Kensei no Un'yō* (Workings of Present Day Parliamentary Government), Tōkyō, 1930.

————: *Nihon Musan Seitō Ron* (Japanese Proletarian Parties), Tōkyō, 1929.

————: *Nijū Seifu to Iaku Jōsō* (Dual Government and Direct Access to the Throne), Tōkyō, 1922.

————, ed.: *Meiji Bunka Zenshū* (Collected Materials on Meiji Civilization), 24 vols., Tōkyō, 1929–1930.

Yoshioka Usaburo: *Rikken Minseitō Shi* (History of the Minseitō Party), Tōkyō, 1935.

Zaisei Keizai Gakkai: *Nihon Zaisei Keizai Shiryō* (Materials on Japanese Finance and Economy), 10 vols., Tōkyō, 1915.

Zenkoku Keizai Chōsa Kikan Rengōkai: *Saikin Nihon Keizai no Jūnen* (The Last Ten Years of Japan's Economy), 2 vols., Tōkyō, 1930.

Zōsen Kyōkai: *Nihon Kinsei Zōsen Shi* (History of Recent Japanese Shipbuilding), Tōkyō, 1911.

Index

695

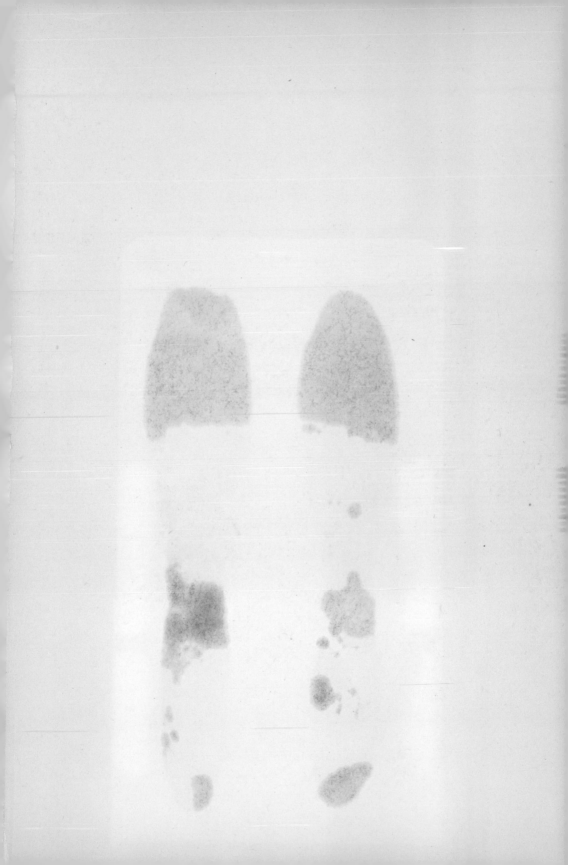

PRINCIPLES OF
ALGEBRAIC GEOMETRY

PRINCIPLES OF ALGEBRAIC GEOMETRY

PHILLIP GRIFFITHS and JOSEPH HARRIS
Harvard University

A WILEY-INTERSCIENCE PUBLICATION

JOHN WILEY & SONS, New York • Chichester • Brisbane • Toronto

Library of Congress Cataloging in Publication Data

Griffiths, Phillip, 1938–
    Principles of algebraic geometry.

    (Pure and applied mathematics)
    "A Wiley-Interscience publication."
    Includes bibliographical references.
    1. Geometry, Algebraic. I. Harris, Joseph,
1951–   joint author. II. Title.
QA564.G64   516'.35   78-6993
ISBN 0-471-32792-1

PREFACE

Algebraic geometry is among the oldest and most highly developed subjects in mathematics. It is intimately connected with projective geometry, complex analysis, topology, number theory, and many other areas of current mathematical activity. Moreover, in recent years algebraic geometry has undergone vast changes in style and language. For these reasons there has arisen about the subject a reputation of inaccessibility. This book gives a presentation of some of the main general results of the theory accompanied by—and indeed with special emphasis on –the applications to the study of interesting examples and the development of computational tools.

A number of principles guided the preparation of the book. One was to develop only that general machinery necessary to study the concrete geometric questions and special classes of algebraic varieties around which the presentation was centered.

A second was that there should be an alternation between the general theory and study of examples, as illustrated by the table of contents. The subject of algebraic geometry is especially notable for the balance provided on the one hand by the intricacy of its examples and on the other by the symmetry of its general patterns; we have tried to reflect this relationship in our choice of topics and order of presentation.

A third general principle was that this volume should be self-contained. In particular any "hard" result that would be utilized should be fully proved. A difficulty a student often faces in a subject as diverse as algebraic geometry is the profusion of cross-references, and this is one reason for attempting to be self-contained. Similarly, we have attempted to avoid allusions to, or statements without proofs of, related results. This book is in no way meant to be a survey of algebraic geometry, but rather is designed to develop a working facility with specific geometric questions. Our approach to the subject is initially analytic: Chapters 0 and 1 treat the basic techniques and results of complex manifold theory, with some emphasis on results applicable to projective varieties. Beginning in Chapter 2 with the theory of Riemann surfaces and algebraic curves, and continuing in Chapters 4 and 6 on algebraic surfaces and the quadric line

v

complex, our treatment becomes increasingly geometric along classical lines. Chapters 3 and 5 continue the analytic approach, progressing to more special topics in complex manifolds.

Several important topics have been entirely omitted. The most glaring are the arithmetic theory of algebraic varieties, moduli questions, and singularities. In these cases the necessary techniques are not fully developed here. Other topics, such as uniformization and automorphic forms or monodromy and mixed Hodge structures have been omitted, although the necessary techniques are for the most part available.

We would like to thank Giuseppe Canuto, S. S. Chern, Maurizio Cornalba, Ran Donagi, Robin Hartshorne, Bill Hoffman, David Morrison, David Mumford, Arthur Ogus, Ted Shifrin, and Loring Tu for many fruitful discussions; Ruth Suzuki for her wonderful typing; and the staff of John Wiley, especially Beatrice Shube, for enormous patience and skill in converting a very rough manuscript into book form.

PHILLIP GRIFFITHS
JOSEPH HARRIS

May 1978
Cambridge, Massachusetts

CONTENTS

PRINCIPLES OF
ALGEBRAIC GEOMETRY

0
FOUNDATIONAL
MATERIAL

In this chapter we sketch the foundational material from several complex variables, complex manifold theory, topology, and differential geometry that will be used in our study of algebraic geometry. While our treatment is for the most part self-contained, it is tacitly assumed that the reader has some familiarity with the basic objects discussed. The primary purpose of this chapter is to establish our viewpoint and to present those results needed in the form in which they will be used later on. There are, broadly speaking, four main points:

1. *The Weierstrass theorems and corollaries*, discussed in Sections 1 and 2. These give us our basic picture of the local character of analytic varieties. The theorems themselves will not be quoted directly later, but the picture—for example, the local representation of an analytic variety as a branched covering of a polydisc—is fundamental. The foundations of local analytic geometry are further discussed in Chapter 5.

2. *Sheaf theory*, discussed in Section 3, is an important tool for relating the analytic, topological, and geometric aspects of an algebraic variety. A good example is the *exponential sheaf sequence*, whose individual terms $\mathbb{Z}$, $\mathcal{O}$, and $\mathcal{O}^*$ reflect the topological, analytic, and geometric structures of the underlying variety, respectively.

3. *Intersection theory*, discussed in Section 4, is a cornerstone of classical algebraic geometry. It allows us to treat the incidence properties of algebraic varieties, a priori a geometric question, in topological terms.

4. *Hodge theory*, discussed in Sections 6 and 7. By far the most sophisticated technique introduced in this chapter, Hodge theory has, in the present context, two principal applications: first, it gives us the *Hodge decomposition* of the cohomology of a Kähler manifold; then, together with the formalism introduced in Section 5, it gives the vanishing theorems of the next chapter.

1

1. RUDIMENTS OF SEVERAL COMPLEX VARIABLES

Cauchy's Formula and Applications

NOTATION. We will write $z = (z_1, \ldots, z_n)$ for a point in $\mathbb{C}^n$, with

$$z_i = x_i + \sqrt{-1}\, y_i;$$
$$\|z\|^2 = (z, z) = \sum_{i=1}^{n} |z_i|^2.$$

For U an open set in $\mathbb{C}^n$, write $C^\infty(U)$ for the set of C^∞ functions defined on U; $C^\infty(\overline{U})$ for the set of C^∞ functions defined in some neighborhood of the closure $\overline{U}$ of U.

The cotangent space to a point in $\mathbb{C}^n \cong \mathbb{R}^{2n}$ is spanned by $\{dx_i, dy_i\}$; it will often be more convenient, however, to work with the complex basis

$$dz_i = dx_i + \sqrt{-1}\, dy_i, \qquad d\bar{z}_i = dx_i - \sqrt{-1}\, dy_i$$

and the dual basis in the tangent space

$$\frac{\partial}{\partial z_i} = \frac{1}{2}\left(\frac{\partial}{\partial x_i} - \sqrt{-1} \frac{\partial}{\partial y_i} \right), \qquad \frac{\partial}{\partial \bar{z}_i} = \frac{1}{2}\left(\frac{\partial}{\partial x_i} + \sqrt{-1} \frac{\partial}{\partial y_i} \right).$$

With this notation, the formula for the total differential is

$$df = \sum_i \frac{\partial f}{\partial z_i}\, dz_i + \sum_j \frac{\partial f}{\partial \bar{z}_j}\, d\bar{z}_j.$$

In one variable, we say a C^∞ function f on an open set $U \subset \mathbb{C}$ is *holomorphic* if f satisfies the Cauchy-Riemann equations $\partial f/\partial \bar{z} = 0$. Writing $f(z) = u(z) + \sqrt{-1}\, v(z)$, this amounts to

$$\mathrm{Re}\left(\frac{\partial f}{\partial \bar{z}} \right) = \frac{\partial u}{\partial x} - \frac{\partial v}{\partial y} = 0,$$
$$\mathrm{Im}\left(\frac{\partial f}{\partial \bar{z}} \right) = \frac{\partial u}{\partial y} + \frac{\partial v}{\partial x} = 0.$$

We say f is *analytic* if, for all $z_0 \in U$, f has a local series expansion in $z - z_0$, i.e.,

$$f(z) = \sum_{n=0}^{\infty} a_n (z - z_0)^n$$

in some disc $\Delta(z_0, \varepsilon) = \{z : |z - z_0| < \varepsilon\}$, where the sum converges absolutely and uniformly. The first result is that f is analytic if and only if it is holomorphic; to show this, we use the

Cauchy Integral Formula. *For Δ a disc in $\mathbb{C}$, $f \in C^\infty(\overline{\Delta})$, $z \in \Delta$,*

$$f(z) = \frac{1}{2\pi\sqrt{-1}} \int_{\partial\Delta} \frac{f(w)\, dw}{w - z} + \frac{1}{2\pi\sqrt{-1}} \int_\Delta \frac{\partial f(w)}{\partial \bar{w}} \frac{dw \wedge d\bar{w}}{w - z},$$

where the line integrals are taken in the counterclockwise direction (the fact that the last integral is defined will come out in the proof).

Proof. The proof is based on Stokes' formula for a differential form with singularities, a method which will be formalized in Chapter 3. Consider the differential form

$$\eta = \frac{1}{2\pi\sqrt{-1}} \frac{f(w)\,dw}{w-z};$$

we have for $z \neq w$

$$\frac{\partial}{\partial\overline{w}}\left(\frac{1}{w-z}\right) = 0$$

and so

$$d\eta = -\frac{1}{2\pi\sqrt{-1}} \frac{\partial f(w)}{\partial\overline{w}} \frac{dw \wedge d\overline{w}}{w-z}.$$

Let $\Delta_\varepsilon = \Delta(z,\varepsilon)$ be the disc of radius ε around z. The form η is C^∞ in $\Delta - \Delta_\varepsilon$, and applying Stokes' theorem we obtain

$$\frac{1}{2\pi\sqrt{-1}} \int_{\partial\Delta_\varepsilon} \frac{f(w)\,dw}{w-z} = \frac{1}{2\pi\sqrt{-1}} \int_{\partial\Delta} \frac{f(w)\,dw}{w-z}$$

$$+ \frac{1}{2\pi\sqrt{-1}} \int_{\Delta-\Delta_\varepsilon} \frac{\partial f}{\partial\overline{w}} \frac{dw \wedge d\overline{w}}{w-z}.$$

Setting $w - z = re^{i\theta}$,

$$\frac{1}{2\pi\sqrt{-1}} \int_{\partial\Delta_\varepsilon} \frac{f(w)\,dw}{w-z} = \frac{1}{2\pi} \int_0^{2\pi} f(z + \varepsilon e^{i\theta})\,d\theta,$$

which tends to $f(z)$ as $\varepsilon \to 0$; moreover,

$$dw \wedge d\overline{w} = -2\sqrt{-1}\,dx \wedge dy = -2\sqrt{-1}\,r\,dr \wedge d\theta$$

so

$$\left| \frac{\partial f(w)}{\partial\overline{w}} \frac{dw \wedge d\overline{w}}{w-z} \right| = 2\left| \frac{\partial f}{\partial\overline{w}}\,dr \wedge d\theta \right| \leq c\,|dr \wedge d\theta|.$$

Thus $(\partial f/\partial\overline{w})(dw \wedge d\overline{w})/(w-z)$ is absolutely integrable over Δ, and

$$\int_{\Delta_\varepsilon} \frac{\partial f}{\partial\overline{w}} \frac{dw \wedge d\overline{w}}{w-z} \to 0$$

as $\varepsilon \to 0$; the result follows. Q.E.D.

Now we can prove the

Proposition. *For* U *an open set in* $\mathbb{C}$ *and* $f \in C^\infty(U)$, f *is holomorphic if and only if* f *is analytic.*

Proof. Suppose first that $\partial f/\partial \bar{z}=0$. Then for $z_0 \in U$, ε sufficiently small, and z in the disc $\Delta = \Delta(z_0, \varepsilon)$ of radius ε around z_0,

$$
\begin{aligned}
f(z) &= \frac{1}{2\pi\sqrt{-1}} \int_{\partial\Delta} \frac{f(w)\,dw}{w-z} \\
&= \frac{1}{2\pi\sqrt{-1}} \int_{\partial\Delta} \frac{f(w)\,dw}{(w-z_0)-(z-z_0)} \\
&= \frac{1}{2\pi\sqrt{-1}} \int_{\partial\Delta} \frac{f(w)\,dw}{(w-z_0)\left(1-\dfrac{z-z_0}{w-z_0}\right)} \\
&= \sum_{n=0}^{\infty} \left(\frac{1}{2\pi\sqrt{-1}} \int_{\partial\Delta} \frac{f(w)\,dw}{(w-z_0)^{n+1}} \right)(z-z_0)^n;
\end{aligned}
$$

so, setting

$$
a_n = \frac{1}{2\pi\sqrt{-1}} \int_{\partial\Delta} \frac{f(w)\,dw}{(w-z_0)^{n+1}},
$$

we have

$$
f(z) = \sum_{n=0}^{\infty} a_n (z-z_0)^n
$$

for $z \in \Delta$, where the sum converges absolutely and uniformly in any smaller disc.

Suppose conversely that $f(z)$ has a power series expansion

$$
f(z) = \sum_{n=0}^{\infty} a_n (z-z_0)^n
$$

for $z \in \Delta = \Delta(z_0, \varepsilon)$. Since $(\partial/\partial\bar{z})(z-z_0)^n = 0$, the partial sums of the expansion satisfy Cauchy's formula without the area integral, and by the uniform convergence of the sum in a neighborhood of z_0 the same is true of f, i.e.,

$$
f(z) = \frac{1}{2\pi\sqrt{-1}} \int_{\partial\Delta} \frac{f(w)\,dw}{w-z}.
$$

We can then differentiate under the integral sign to obtain

$$
\frac{\partial}{\partial\bar{z}} f(z) = \frac{1}{2\pi\sqrt{-1}} \int_{\partial\Delta} \frac{\partial}{\partial\bar{z}}\left(\frac{f(w)}{w-z} \right) dw = 0,
$$

since for $z \neq w$

$$
\frac{\partial}{\partial\bar{z}}\left(\frac{1}{w-z} \right) = 0. \qquad\qquad\qquad \text{Q.E.D.}
$$

We prove a final result in one variable, that given a C^∞ function g on a disc Δ the equation

$$\frac{\partial f}{\partial \bar{z}} = g$$

can always be solved on a slightly smaller disc; this is the

$\bar{\partial}$-Poincaré Lemma in One Variable. *Given* $g(z) \in C^\infty(\bar{\Delta})$, *the function*

$$f(z) = \frac{1}{2\pi\sqrt{-1}} \int_\Delta \frac{g(w)}{w-z}\, dw \wedge d\bar{w}$$

is defined and C^∞ *in* Δ *and satisfies*

$$\frac{\partial f}{\partial \bar{z}} = g.$$

Proof. For $z_0 \in \Delta$ choose ε such that the disc $\Delta(z_0, 2\varepsilon) \subset \Delta$ and write

$$g(z) = g_1(z) + g_2(z),$$

where $g_1(z)$ vanishes outside $\Delta(z_0, 2\varepsilon)$ and $g_2(z)$ vanishes inside $\Delta(z_0, \varepsilon)$. The integral

$$f_2(z) = \frac{1}{2\pi\sqrt{-1}} \int_\Delta g_2(w) \frac{dw \wedge d\bar{w}}{w-z}$$

is well-defined and C^∞ for $z \in \Delta(z_0, \varepsilon)$; there we have

$$\frac{\partial}{\partial \bar{z}} f_2(z) = \frac{1}{2\pi\sqrt{-1}} \int_\Delta \frac{\partial}{\partial \bar{z}} \left(\frac{g_2(w)}{w-z} \right) dw \wedge d\bar{w} = 0.$$

Since $g_1(z)$ has compact support, we can write

$$\frac{1}{2\pi\sqrt{-1}} \int_\Delta g_1(w) \frac{dw \wedge d\bar{w}}{w-z} = \frac{1}{2\pi\sqrt{-1}} \int_C g_1(w) \frac{dw \wedge d\bar{w}}{w-z}$$

$$= \frac{1}{2\pi\sqrt{-1}} \int_C g_1(u+z) \frac{du \wedge d\bar{u}}{u},$$

where $u = w - z$. Changing to polar coordinates $u = re^{i\theta}$ this integral becomes

$$f_1(z) = -\frac{1}{\pi} \int_C g_1(z + re^{i\theta}) e^{-i\theta}\, dr \wedge d\theta,$$

which is clearly defined and C^∞ in z. Then

$$\frac{\partial f_1(z)}{\partial \bar{z}} = -\frac{1}{\pi} \int_C \frac{\partial g_1}{\partial \bar{z}} (z + re^{i\theta}) e^{-i\theta}\, dr \wedge d\theta$$

$$= \frac{1}{2\pi\sqrt{-1}} \int_\Delta \frac{\partial g_1}{\partial \bar{w}} (w) \frac{dw \wedge d\bar{w}}{w-z};$$

but g_1 vanishes on $\partial\Delta$, and so by the Cauchy formula

$$\frac{\partial}{\partial\bar{z}}f(z) = \frac{\partial}{\partial\bar{z}}f_1(z) = g_1(z) = g(z).$$ Q.E.D.

Several Variables

In the formula

$$df = \sum_{i=1}^{n} \frac{\partial f}{\partial z_i} dz_i + \sum_{i=1}^{n} \frac{\partial f}{\partial\bar{z}_i} d\bar{z}_i$$

for the total differential of a function f on $\mathbb{C}^n$, we denote the first term ∂f and the second term $\bar{\partial}f$; ∂ and $\bar{\partial}$ are differential operators invariant under a complex linear change of coordinates. A C^∞ function f on an open set $U \subset \mathbb{C}^n$ is called *holomorphic* if $\bar{\partial}f = 0$; this is equivalent to $f(z_1,\ldots,z_n)$ being holomorphic in each variable z_i separately.

As in the one-variable case, a function f is holomorphic if and only if it has local power series expansions in the variables z_i. This is clear in one direction: by the same argument as before, a convergent power series defines a holomorphic function. We check the converse in the case $n=2$; the computation for general n is only notationally more difficult. For f holomorphic in the open set $U \subset \mathbb{C}^2$, $z_0 \in U$, we can fix Δ the disc of radius r around $z_0 \in U$ and apply the one-variable Cauchy formula twice to obtain, for $(z_1, z_2) \in \Delta$,

$$f(z_1, z_2) = \frac{1}{2\pi\sqrt{-1}} \int_{|w_2 - z_{0_2}| = r} \frac{f(z_1, w_2)\, dw_2}{w_2 - z_2}$$

$$= \frac{1}{2\pi\sqrt{-1}} \int_{|w_2 - z_{0_2}| = r} \left[\frac{1}{2\pi\sqrt{-1}} \int_{|w_1 - z_{0_1}| = r} \frac{f(w_1, w_2)\, dw_1}{w_1 - z_1} \right] \frac{dw_2}{w_2 - z_2}$$

$$= \left(\frac{1}{2\pi\sqrt{-1}} \right)^2 \int\int_{|w_i - z_{0_i}| = r} \frac{f(w_1, w_2)\, dw_1\, dw_2}{(w_1 - z_1)(w_2 - z_2)}.$$

Using the series expansion

$$\frac{1}{(w_1 - z_1)(w_2 - z_2)} = \sum_{m,n=0}^{\infty} \frac{(z_1 - z_{0_1})^m (z_2 - z_{0_2})^n}{(w_1 - z_{0_1})^{m+1}(w_2 - z_{0_2})^{n+1}},$$

we find that f has a local series expansion

$$f(z_1, z_2) = \sum_{m,n=0}^{\infty} a_{m,n}(z_1 - z_{0_1})^m (z_2 - z_{0_2})^n.$$ Q.E.D.

Many results in several variables carry directly over from the one-variable theory, such as the identity theorem: *If* f *and* g *are holomorphic on a connected open set* U *and* f $=$ g *on a nonempty open subset of* U, *then* f $=$ g, and the maximum principle: *the absolute value of a holomorphic function* f *on an open set* U *has no maximum in* U. There are, however, some striking differences between the one- and many-variable cases. For example, let U be the polydisc $\Delta(r) = \{(z_1, z_2) : |z_1|, |z_2| < r\}$, and let $V \subset U$ be the smaller polydisc $\Delta(r')$ for any $r' < r$. Then we have

Hartogs' Theorem. *Any holomorphic function* f *in a neighborhood of* $U - V$ *extends to a holomorphic function on* U.

Proof. In each vertical slice $z_1 = $ constant, the region $U - V$ looks either like the annulus $r' < |z_2| < r$ or like the disc $|z_2| < r$. We try to extend f in each slice by Cauchy's formula, setting

$$F(z_1, z_2) = \frac{1}{2\pi\sqrt{-1}} \int_{|w_2| = r} \frac{f(z_1, w_2)\, dw_2}{w_2 - z_2}.$$

F is defined throughout U; it is clearly holomorphic in z_2, and since $(\partial/\partial\bar{z}_1)f = 0$, it is holomorphic in z_1 as well. Moreover, in the open subset $|z_1| > r'$ of $U - V$, $F(z_1, z_2) = f(z_1, z_2)$ by Cauchy's formula; thus $F|_{U-V} = f$.
$$\text{Q.E.D.}$$

Hartogs' theorem applies to many pairs of sets $V \subset U \subset\subset \mathbb{C}^n$; it is commonly applied in the form

A holomorphic function on the complement of a point in an open set $U \subset \mathbb{C}^n$ $(n > 1)$ *extends to a holomorphic function in all of* U.

Weierstrass Theorems and Corollaries

In one variable, every analytic function has a unique local representation

$$f(z) = (z - z_0)^n u(z), \qquad u(z_0) \neq 0,$$

from which we see in particular that the zero locus of f is discrete. Similarly, the Weierstrass theorems give local representations of holomorphic functions in several variables, from which we get a picture of the local geometry of their zero sets.

Suppose we are given a function $f(z_1, \ldots, z_{n-1}, w)$ holomorphic in some neighborhood of the origin in $\mathbb{C}^n$, with $f(0, \ldots, 0) = 0$. Assume that f does not vanish identically on the w-axis, i.e., the power series expansion for f around the origin contains a term $a \cdot w^d$ with $a \neq 0$ and $d \geq 1$; clearly this will be the case for most choices of coordinate system.

For suitable r, δ, and $\varepsilon > 0$, then, $|f(0,w)| \geqslant \delta > 0$ for $|w| = r$, and consequently $|f(z,w)| \geqslant \delta/2$ for $|w| = r$, $\|z\| \leqslant \varepsilon$. Now if $w = b_1, \ldots, b_d$ are the roots of $f(z,w) = 0$ for $|w| < r$, by the residue theorem

$$b_1^q + b_2^q + \cdots + b_d^q = \frac{1}{2\pi\sqrt{-1}} \int_{|w|=r} \frac{w^q(\partial f/\partial w)(z,w)}{f(z,w)} \, dw;$$

so the power sums $\Sigma b_i(z)^q$ are analytic functions of z for $\|z\| < \varepsilon$. Let $\sigma_1(z), \ldots, \sigma_d(z)$ be the elementary symmetric polynomials in $b_1, \ldots, b_d$; $\sigma_1, \ldots, \sigma_d$ can be expressed as polynomials in the power sums $\Sigma b_i(z)^q$. Thus the function

$$g(z,w) = w^d - \sigma_1(z)w^{d-1} + \cdots + (-1)^d \sigma_d(z)$$

is holomorphic in $\|z\| < \varepsilon$, $|w| < r$, and vanishes on exactly the same set as f. The quotient

$$h(z,w) = \frac{f(z,w)}{g(z,w)}$$

is defined and holomorphic in $\|z\| < \varepsilon$, $|w| < r$, at least outside the zero set of f and g. Moreover, for fixed z, $h(z,w)$ has only removable singularities in the disc $|w| < r$, so h can be extended to a function in all of $\|z\| < \varepsilon$, $|w| < r$ and analytic in w for each fixed z, as well as in the complement of the zero locus. Writing

$$h(z,w) = \frac{1}{2\pi\sqrt{-1}} \int_{|u|=r} \frac{h(z,u)\,du}{u-w},$$

we see that h is holomorphic in z as well.

DEFINITION.   A *Weierstrass polynomial* in w is a polynomial of the form

$$w^d + a_1(z)w^{d-1} + \cdots + a_d(z), \qquad a_i(0) = 0.$$

We have proved the existence part of the

Weierstrass Preparation Theorem.   *If* f *is holomorphic around the origin in* $\mathbb{C}^n$ *and is not identically zero on the* w-*axis, then in some neighborhood of the origin* f *can be written uniquely as*

$$f = g \cdot h,$$

where g *is a Weierstrass polynomial of degree* d *in* w *and* h$(0) \neq 0$.

The uniqueness is clear, since the coefficients of any Weierstrass polynomial g vanishing exactly where f does are given as polynomials in the integrals

$$\int_{|w|=r} \frac{w^q(\partial f/\partial w)(z,w)\,dw}{f(z,w)}.$$

We see from the Weierstrass theorem that the zero locus of a function f, holomorphic in a neighborhood of the origin in $\mathbb{C}^n$, is for most choices of coordinate system $z_1, \ldots, z_{n-1}, w$ the zero locus of a Weierstrass polynomial

$$g(z, w) = w^d + a_1(z) w^{d-1} + \cdots + a_d(z).$$

Now, the roots $b_i(z)$ of the polynomial $g(z, \cdot)$ are, away from those values of z for which $g(z, \cdot)$ has a multiple root, locally single-valued holomorphic functions of z. Since the discriminant of $g(z, \cdot)$ is an analytic function of z,

The zero locus of an analytic function $f(z_1, \ldots, z_{n-1}, w)$, *not vanishing identically on the* w-*axis, projects locally onto the hyperplane* $(w=0)$ *as a finite-sheeted cover branched over the zero locus of an analytic function.*

As a corollary of the preparation theorem, we have the

Riemann Extension Theorem. *Suppose* $f(z, w)$ *is holomorphic in a disc* $\Delta \subset \mathbb{C}^n$ *and* $g(z, w)$ *is holomorphic in* $\overline{\Delta} - \{f = 0\}$ *and bounded. Then* g *extends to a holomorphic function on* Δ.

Proof (in a neighborhood of 0). Assume that the line $z = 0$ is not contained in $\{f = 0\}$. As before, we can find r, ε, and $\delta > 0$ such that $|f(0, w)| \geqslant \delta > 0$ for $|w| = r$ and ε such that $|f(z, w)| > \delta/2$ for $\|z\| < \varepsilon$, $|w| = r$; f then has zeros only in the interior of the discs $z = z_0$, $|w| \leqslant r$. By the one-variable Riemann extension theorem, we can extend g to a function $\tilde{g}$ in $|z| < \varepsilon$, $|w| < r$, holomorphic away from $\{f = 0\}$ and holomorphic in w everywhere. As before, we write

$$\tilde{g}(z, w) = \frac{1}{2\pi\sqrt{-1}} \int_{|u|=r} \frac{\tilde{g}(z, u)\,du}{u - w}$$

to see that $\tilde{g}$ is holomorphic in z as well.   Q.E.D.

We recall some facts and definitions from elementary algebra:

Let R be an *integral domain*, i.e., a ring such that for $u, v \in R$, $u \cdot v = 0 \Rightarrow u = 0$ or $v = 0$. An element $u \in R$ is a *unit* if there exists $v \in R$ such that $u \cdot v = 1$; u is *irreducible* if for $v, w \in R$, $u = v \cdot w$ implies v is a unit or w is a unit. R is a *unique factorization domain* (*UFD*) if every $u \in R$ can be written as a product of irreducible elements $u_1, \ldots, u_l$, the u_i's unique up to multiplication by units. The main facts we shall use are

1. R is a UFD $\Rightarrow R[t]$ is a UFD (Gauss' lemma).
2. If R is a UFD and $u, v \in R[t]$ are relatively prime, then there exist relatively prime elements $\alpha, \beta \in R[t]$, $\gamma \neq 0 \in R$, such that

$$\alpha u + \beta v = \gamma.$$

γ is called the *resultant* of u and v.

Let $\mathcal{O}_{n,z}$ denote the ring of holomorphic functions defined in some neighborhood of $z \in \mathbb{C}^n$; write $\mathcal{O}_n$ for $\mathcal{O}_{n,0}$. $\mathcal{O}_n$ is an integral domain by the identity theorem, and moreover is a *local ring* whose *maximal ideal m* is $\{f: f(0)=0\}$. $f \in \mathcal{O}_n$ is a unit if and only if $f(0) \neq 0$. The first result is

Proposition. $\mathcal{O}_n$ *is a UFD.*

Proof. We proceed by induction. Assume $\mathcal{O}_{n-1}$ is a UFD and let $f \in \mathcal{O}_n$. We may assume f is regular with respect to $w = z_n$; i.e., $f(0,\ldots,0,w) \not\equiv 0$. Write

$$f = g \cdot u,$$

where u is a unit in $\mathcal{O}_n$ and $g \in \mathcal{O}_{n-1}[w]$ is a Weierstrass polynomial. $\mathcal{O}_{n-1}[w]$ is a UFD by Gauss' lemma, and so we can write g as a product of irreducible elements $g_1,\ldots,g_m \in \mathcal{O}_{n-1}[w]$

$$(*) \qquad f = g_1 \cdots g_m \cdot u,$$

where the factors g_i are uniquely determined up to multiplication by units. Now suppose we write f as a product of irreducible elements $f_1,\ldots,f_k \in \mathcal{O}_n$. Each f_i must be regular with respect to w, and we can write

$$f_i = g_i' \cdot u_i$$

with u_i a unit, g_i' a Weierstrass polynomial, necessarily irreducible in $\mathcal{O}_{n-1}[w]$. We have

$$f = g \cdot u = \prod g_i' \cdot \prod u_i',$$

with g and $\prod g_i'$ both Weierstrass polynomials; by the Weierstrass preparation theorem

$$g = \prod g_i',$$

and since $\mathcal{O}_{n-1}[w]$ is a UFD, it follows that the g_i' are the same, up to units, as the g_i. Thus the expression $(*)$ represents a unique factorization of f in $\mathcal{O}_n$. Q.E.D.

Proposition. *If* f *and* g *are relatively prime in* $\mathcal{O}_{n,0}$, *then for* $\|z\| < \varepsilon$, f *and* g *are relatively prime in* $\mathcal{O}_{n,z}$.

Proof. We may assume that f and g are regular with respect to z_n and are both Weierstrass polynomials; for each fixed $z' \in \mathbb{C}^{n-1}$ sufficiently small we have $f(z',z_n) \not\equiv 0$ in z_n. Now we can write

$$\alpha f + \beta g = \gamma$$

with $\alpha, \beta \in \mathcal{O}_{n-1}[w]$, $\gamma \in \mathcal{O}_{n-1}$; the equation holds in some neighborhood of $0 \in \mathbb{C}^n$.

If for some small $z_0 \in \mathbb{C}^n$, $f(z_0) = g(z_0) = 0$ and f and g have a common factor $h(z',z_n)$ in $\mathcal{O}_{n,z_0}$ with $h(z_0) = 0$, then

$$h | f, h | g \Rightarrow h | \gamma$$
$$\Rightarrow h \in \mathcal{O}_{n-1}.$$

But then $h(z_0, \ldots, z_{0_{n-1}}, z_n)$ vanishes identically in z_n, contradicting our assumption that $f(z_0, \ldots, z_{0_{n-1}}, z_n) \not\equiv 0$. Q.E.D.

We now prove the

Weierstrass Division Theorem. *Let* $g(z, w) \in \mathcal{O}_{n-1}[w]$ *be a Weierstrass polynomial of degree* k *in* w. *Then for any* $f \in \mathcal{O}_n$, *we can write*

$$f = g \cdot h + r$$

with $r(z, w)$ *a polynomial of degree* $< k$ *in* w.

Proof. For $\varepsilon, \delta > 0$ sufficiently small, define for $\|z\| < \varepsilon$, $|w| < \delta$,

$$h(z, w) = \frac{1}{2\pi\sqrt{-1}} \int_{|u|=\delta} \frac{f(z, u)}{g(z, u)} \frac{du}{u - w}.$$

h is clearly holomorphic, and hence so is $r = f - gh$. We have

$$r(z, w) = f(z, w) - g(z, w) \cdot h(z, w)$$

$$= \frac{1}{2\pi\sqrt{-1}} \int_{|u|=\delta} \left[f(z, u) - g(z, w) \frac{f(z, u)}{g(z, u)} \right] \frac{du}{u - w}$$

$$= \frac{1}{2\pi\sqrt{-1}} \int_{|u|=\delta} \frac{f(z, u)}{g(z, u)} \frac{g(z, u) - g(z, w)}{u - w} du.$$

But $(u - w)$ divides $[g(z, u) - g(z, w)]$ as polynomials in w; thus

$$p(z, u, w) = \frac{g(z, u) - g(z, w)}{u - w}$$

is a polynomial in w *of degree* $< k$. Since the factor w appears only in p in the expression for $r(z, w)$, we see that $r(z, w)$ is a polynomial of degree $< k$ in w. Explicitly, if

$$p(z, u, w) = p_1(z, u) \cdot w^{k-1} + \cdots + p_k(z, u),$$

then

$$r(z, w) = a_1(z) \cdot w^{k-1} + \cdots + a_k(z),$$

where

$$a_i(z) = \frac{1}{2\pi\sqrt{-1}} \int_{|u|=\delta} \frac{f(z, u)}{g(z, u)} p_i(z, u) \, du. \qquad \text{Q.E.D.}$$

Corollary (Weak Nullstellensatz). *If* $f(z, w) \in \mathcal{O}_n$ *is irreducible and* $h \in \mathcal{O}_n$ *vanishes on the set* $f(z, w) = 0$, *then* f *divides* h *in* $\mathcal{O}_n$.

Proof. First, we may assume f is a Weierstrass polynomial of degree k in w. Since f is irreducible, f and $\partial f / \partial w$ are relatively prime in $\mathcal{O}_{n-1}[w]$ ($\deg_w f > \deg_w \partial f / \partial w$); thus we can write

$$\alpha \cdot f + \beta \cdot \frac{\partial f}{\partial w} = \gamma, \qquad \gamma \in \mathcal{O}_{n-1}, \quad \gamma \not\equiv 0.$$

If, for a given z_0, $f(z_0, w) \in \mathbb{C}[w]$ has a multiple root u, we have

$$f(z_0, u) = \frac{\partial f}{\partial w}(z_0, u) = 0$$
$$\Rightarrow \gamma(z_0) = 0;$$

thus: f(z, w) *has* k *distinct roots in* w *for* $\gamma(z) \neq 0$.

Now by the division theorem, we can write

$$h = f \cdot g + r, \qquad r \in \mathcal{O}_{n-1}[w], \quad \deg r < k.$$

But for any z_0 outside the locus $(\gamma = 0)$, $f(z_0, w)$ and hence $h(z_0, w)$ have at least k distinct roots in w. Since degree $r < k$, this implies $r(z_0, w) = 0 \in \mathbb{C}[w]$; it follows that $r \equiv 0$ and $h = f \cdot g$.   Q.E.D.

Analytic Varieties

The main purpose of the results given above is to describe the basic local properties of analytic varieties in $\mathbb{C}^n$. We say a subset V of an open set $U \subset \mathbb{C}^n$ is an *analytic variety* in U if, for any $p \in U$, there exists a neighborhood U' of p in U such that $V \cap U'$ is the common zero locus of a finite collection of holomorphic functions $f_1, \ldots, f_k$ on U'. In particular, V is called an *analytic hypersurface* if V is locally the zero locus of a single nonzero holomorphic function f.

An analytic variety $V \subset U \subset \mathbb{C}^n$ is said to be *irreducible* if V cannot be written as the union of two analytic varieties $V_1, V_2 \subset U$ with $V_1, V_2 \neq V$; it is said to be *irreducible at* $p \in V$ if $V \cap U'$ is irreducible for small neighborhoods U' of p in U. Note first that if $f \in \mathcal{O}_n$ is irreducible in the ring $\mathcal{O}_n$, then the analytic hypersurface $V = \{f(z) = 0\}$ given by f in a neighborhood of 0 is irreducible at 0: if $V = V_1 \cup V_2$, with V_1, V_2 analytic varieties $\neq V$, then there exist $f_1, f_2 \in \mathcal{O}_n$ with f_1 (respectively f_2) vanishing identically on V_1 (respectively V_2) but not on V_2 (respectively V_1). By the Nullstellensatz, f must divide the product $f_1 \cdot f_2$; since f is irreducible, it follows that f must divide either f_1 or f_2, i.e., either $V_1 \supset V$ or $V_2 \supset V$, a contradiction. In addition to the basic picture of an analytic hypersurface (p. 9) we see that

1. Suppose $V \subset U \subset \mathbb{C}^n$ is an analytic hypersurface, given by $V = \{f(z) = 0\}$ in a neighborhood of $0 \in V$. Since $\mathcal{O}_n$ is a UFD, we can write

$$f = f_1 \cdots f_n$$

with f_i irreducible in $\mathcal{O}_n$; if we set $V_i = \{f_i(z) = 0\}$ then we have

$$V = V_1 \cup \cdots \cup V_k$$

with V_i irreducible at 0. Thus if p is any point on any analytic hypersurface $V \subset U \subset \mathbb{C}^n$, V *can be expressed uniquely in some neighborhood* U' *of* p *as the union of a finite number of analytic hypersurfaces irreducible at* p.

2. Let $W \subset U \subset \mathbb{C}^n$ be an analytic variety given in a neighborhood Δ of $0 \in W$ as the zero locus of two functions $f, g \in \mathcal{O}_n$. If W contains no analytic hypersurface through 0, then f and g are necessarily relatively prime in $\mathcal{O}_n$; if W does not contain the line $\{z'=0\}$, then by taking linear combinations we may assume that neither $\{f(z)=0\}$ or $\{g(z)=0\}$ contains $\{z'=0\}$, and hence that f and g are Weierstrass polynomials in z_n. Let

$$\gamma = \alpha f + \beta g \neq 0 \in \mathcal{O}_{n-1}$$

be the resultant of f and g. We claim that the image of W under the projection map $\pi: \mathbb{C}^n \to \mathbb{C}^{n-1}$ is just the locus of γ. To see this, write

$$\alpha = hg + r$$

with the degree of r strictly less than the degree of g. Then

$$\gamma = rf + (\beta + hf)g.$$

Now, if for some z in $\mathbb{C}^{n-1}$, γ vanishes at z but f and g have no common zeros along the line $\pi^{-1}(z)$, it follows that r vanishes at all the zeros of g in $\pi^{-1}(z)$; since $\deg(r) < \deg(g)$, this implies that r, and hence $\beta + hf$, vanish identically on $\pi^{-1}(z)$. Thus r and $\beta + hf$ both are zero on the inverse image of any component of the zero locus of γ other than $\pi(W)$; but r and $\beta + hf$ are relatively prime and so have no common components. We see then that $\pi(W)$ *is an analytic hypersurface in a neighborhood of the origin in* $\mathbb{C}^{n-1}$, and, reiterating our basic description of analytic hypersurfaces, that *projection of* W *onto a suitably chosen* $(n-2)$-*plane* $\mathbb{C}^{n-2} \subset \mathbb{C}^n$ *expresses* W *locally as a finite-sheeted branched cover of a neighborhood of the origin in* $\mathbb{C}^{n-2}$.

3. Last, let $V \subset U \subset \mathbb{C}^n$ be an analytic variety irreducible at $0 \in V$ such that for arbitrarily small neighborhoods Δ of 0 in $\mathbb{C}^n$, $\pi(V \cap \Delta)$ contains a neighborhood of 0 in $\mathbb{C}^{n-1}$. Write

$$V = \{f_1(z) = \cdots = f_k(z) = 0\}$$

near 0. Then the functions $f_i \in \mathcal{O}_n$ must all have a common factor in $\mathcal{O}_n$, since otherwise V would be contained in the common locus of two relatively prime functions, and by assertion 2, $\pi(V \cap \Delta)$ would be a proper analytic subvariety of $\mathbb{C}^{n-1}$. If we let $g(z)$ be the greatest common divisor of the f_i's, then we can write

$$V = \{g(z)=0\} \cup \left\{\frac{f_1(z)}{g(z)} = \cdots = \frac{f_k(z)}{g(z)} = 0\right\}.$$

Since V is irreducible at 0 and since the locus $\{f_i(z)/g(z)=0,$ all $i\}$ cannot contain $\{g(z)=0\}$, we must have

$$V = \{g(z)=0\},$$

i.e., V is an analytic hypersurface near 0.

The results 1, 2, and 3 above, together with our basic picture of an analytic hypersurface, give us a picture of the local behavior of those analytic varieties cut out locally by one or two holomorphic functions. In fact, the same picture is in almost all respects valid for general analytic varieties, but to prove this requires some relatively sophisticated techniques from the theory of several complex variables. Since the primary focus of the material in this book is on the codimension 1 case, we will for the time being simply state here without proof the analogous results for general analytic varieties:

1. If $V \subset U \subset \mathbb{C}^n$ is any analytic variety and $p \in V$, then in some neighborhood of p, V can be uniquely written as the union of analytic varieties V_i irreducible at p with $V_i \not\subset V_j$.
2. Any analytic variety can be expressed locally by a projection map as a finite-sheeted cover of a polydisc Δ branched over an analytic hypersurface of Δ.
3. If $V \subset \mathbb{C}^n$ does not contain the line $z_1 = \cdots = z_{n-1} = 0$, then the image of a neighborhood of 0 in V under the projection map $\pi : (z_1, \ldots, z_n) \to (z_1, \ldots, z_{n-1})$ is an analytic subvariety in a neighborhood of $0 \in \mathbb{C}^{n-1}$.

The difficulties in proving these results are more technical than conceptual. For example, to prove assertion 3, note that if V is given near $0 \in \mathbb{C}^n$ by functions $f_1, \ldots, f_k$, then $\pi(V)$ is defined in a neighborhood of $0 \in \mathbb{C}^{n-1}$ by the resultants of all pairs of relatively prime linear combinations of the f_i. The problem then is to show that the zero locus of an arbitrary collection of holomorphic functions in a polydisc is in fact given by a finite number of holomorphic functions in a slightly smaller polydisc. Granted assertions 3 and 1, 2 is not hard to prove by a sequence of projections.

All of these facts will follow from the proper mapping theorem, which we shall state in the next section and prove in Chapter 3.

Finally, several more foundational results in several complex variables will be proved by the method of residues in Chapter 5.

2. COMPLEX MANIFOLDS

Complex Manifolds

DEFINITION. A *complex manifold* M is a differentiable manifold admitting an open cover $\{U_\alpha\}$ and coordinate maps $\varphi_\alpha : U_\alpha \to \mathbb{C}^n$ such that $\varphi_\alpha \circ \varphi_\beta^{-1}$ is holomorphic on $\varphi_\beta(U_\alpha \cap U_\beta) \subset \mathbb{C}^n$ for all α, β.

A function on an open set $U \subset M$ is *holomorphic* if, for all α, $f \cdot \varphi_\alpha^{-1}$ is holomorphic on $\varphi_\alpha(U \cap U_\alpha) \subset \mathbb{C}^n$. Likewise, a collection $z = (z_1, \ldots, z_n)$ of functions on $U \subset M$ is said to be a *holomorphic coordinate system* if $\varphi_\alpha \circ z^{-1}$ and $z \circ \varphi_\alpha^{-1}$ are holomorphic on $z(U \cap U_\alpha)$ and $\varphi_\alpha(U \cap U_\alpha)$, respectively, for each α; a map $f : M \to N$ of complex manifolds is *holomorphic* if it is given in terms of local holomorphic coordinates on N by holomorphic functions.

Examples

1. A one-dimensional complex manifold is called a *Riemann surface*.

2. Let $\mathbb{P}^n$ denote the set of lines through the origin in $\mathbb{C}^{n+1}$. A line $l \subset \mathbb{C}^{n+1}$ is determined by any $Z \neq 0 \in l$, so we can write

$$\mathbb{P}^n = \frac{\{[Z] \neq 0 \in \mathbb{C}^{n+1}\}}{[Z] \sim [\lambda Z]}.$$

On the subset $U_i = \{[Z] : Z_i \neq 0\} \subset \mathbb{P}^n$ of lines not contained in the hyperplane $(Z_i = 0)$, there is a bijective map φ_i to $\mathbb{C}^n$ given by

$$\varphi_i([Z_0, \ldots, Z_n]) = \left(\frac{Z_0}{Z_i}, \ldots, \frac{\hat{Z}_i}{Z_i}, \ldots, \frac{Z_n}{Z_i} \right).$$

On $(z_j \neq 0) = \varphi_i(U_j \cap U_i) \subset \mathbb{C}^n$,

$$\varphi_j \circ \varphi_i^{-1}(z_1, \ldots, z_n) = \left(\frac{z_1}{z_j}, \ldots, \frac{\hat{z}_j}{z_j}, \ldots, \frac{1}{z_j}, \ldots, \frac{z_n}{z_j} \right)$$

is clearly holomorphic; thus $\mathbb{P}^n$ has the structure of a complex manifold, called *complex projective space*. The "coordinates" $Z = [Z_0, \ldots, Z_n]$ are called *homogeneous coordinates* on $\mathbb{P}^n$; the coordinates given by the maps φ_i are called *Euclidean coordinates*. $\mathbb{P}^n$ is compact, since we have a continuous surjective map from the unit sphere in $\mathbb{C}^{n+1}$ to $\mathbb{P}^n$. Note that $\mathbb{P}^1$ is just the Riemann sphere $\mathbb{C} \cup \{\infty\}$.

Any inclusion $\mathbb{C}^{k+1} \to \mathbb{C}^{n+1}$ induces an inclusion $\mathbb{P}^k \to \mathbb{P}^n$; the image of such a map is called a *linear subspace* of $\mathbb{P}^n$. The image of a hyperplane in $\mathbb{C}^{n+1}$ is again called a *hyperplane*, the image of a 2-plane $\mathbb{C}^2 \subset \mathbb{C}^{n+1}$ is a line, and in general the image of a $\mathbb{C}^{k+1} \subset \mathbb{C}^{n+1}$ is called a *k-plane*. We may speak of linear relations among points in $\mathbb{P}^n$ in these terms: for example, the *span* of a collection $\{p_i\}$ of points in $\mathbb{P}^n$ is taken to be the image in $\mathbb{P}^n$ of the subspace in $\mathbb{C}^{n+1}$ spanned by the lines $\pi^{-1}(p_i)$; k points are said to be *linearly independent* if their corresponding lines in $\mathbb{C}^{n+1}$ are, that is, if their span in $\mathbb{P}^n$ is a $(k-1)$-plane.

Note that the set of hyperplanes in $\mathbb{P}^n$ corresponds to the set $\mathbb{C}^{n+1*} - \{0\}$ of nonzero linear functionals on $\mathbb{C}^{n+1}$ modulo scalar multiplication; it is thus itself a projective space, called the *dual projective* space and denoted $\mathbb{P}^{n*}$.

It is sometimes convenient to picture $\mathbb{P}^n$ as the compactification of $\mathbb{C}^n$ obtained by adding on the hyperplane H at infinity. In coordinates the inclusion $\mathbb{C}^n \to \mathbb{P}^n$ is $(z_1, \ldots, z_n) \to [1, z_1, \ldots, z_n]$; H has equation $(Z_0 = 0)$, and the identification $H \cong \mathbb{P}^{n-1}$ comes by considering the hyperplane at infinity as the directions in which we can go to infinity in $\mathbb{C}^n$.

3.   Let $\Lambda = \mathbb{Z}^k \subset \mathbb{C}^n$ be a discrete lattice. Then the quotient group $\mathbb{C}^n/\Lambda$ has the structure of a complex manifold induced by the projection map $\pi : \mathbb{C}^n \to \mathbb{C}^n/\Lambda$. It is compact if and only if $k = 2n$; in this case $\mathbb{C}^n/\Lambda$ is called a *complex torus*.

In general, if $\pi : M \to N$ is a topological covering space and N is a complex manifold, then π gives M the structure of a complex manifold as well; if M is a complex manifold and the deck transformations of M are holomorphic, then N inherits the structure of a complex manifold from M.

Another example of this construction is the *Hopf surface*, defined to be the quotient of $\mathbb{C}^2 - \{0\}$ by the group of automorphisms generated by $z \mapsto 2z$. The Hopf surface is the simplest example of a compact complex manifold that cannot be imbedded in projective space of any dimension.

Let M be a complex manifold, $p \in M$ any point, and $z = (z_1, \ldots, z_n)$ a holomorphic coordinate system around p. There are three different notions of a tangent space to M at p, which we now describe:

1. $T_{\mathbb{R},p}(M)$ is the usual *real tangent space* to M at p, where we consider M as a real manifold of dimension $2n$. $T_{\mathbb{R},p}(M)$ can be realized as the space of $\mathbb{R}$-linear derivations on the ring of real-valued C^∞ functions in a neighborhood of p; if we write $z_i = x_i + iy_i$,

$$T_{\mathbb{R},p}(M) = \mathbb{R}\left\{ \frac{\partial}{\partial x_i}, \frac{\partial}{\partial y_i} \right\}.$$

2. $T_{\mathbb{C},p}(M) = T_{\mathbb{R},p}(M) \otimes_{\mathbb{R}} \mathbb{C}$ is called the *complexified tangent space* to M at p. It can be realized as the space of $\mathbb{C}$-linear derivations in the ring of complex-valued C^∞ functions on M around p. We can write

$$T_{\mathbb{C},p}(M) = \mathbb{C}\left\{ \frac{\partial}{\partial x_i}, \frac{\partial}{\partial y_i} \right\}$$

$$= \mathbb{C}\left\{ \frac{\partial}{\partial z_i}, \frac{\partial}{\partial \bar{z}_i} \right\}$$

where, as before,

$$\frac{\partial}{\partial z_i} = \frac{1}{2}\left(\frac{\partial}{\partial x_i} - \sqrt{-1}\, \frac{\partial}{\partial y_i} \right), \qquad \frac{\partial}{\partial \bar{z}_i} = \frac{1}{2}\left(\frac{\partial}{\partial x_i} + \sqrt{-1}\, \frac{\partial}{\partial y_i} \right).$$

3. $T'_p(M) = \mathbb{C}\{\partial/\partial z_i\} \subset T_{\mathbb{C},p}(M)$ is called the *holomorphic tangent space* to M at p. It can be realized as the subspace of $T_{\mathbb{C},p}(M)$ consisting of derivations that vanish on antiholomorphic functions (i.e., f such that $\bar{f}$ is holomorphic), and so is independent of the holomorphic coordinate system

$(z_1,\ldots,z_n)$ chosen. The subspace $T_p''(M)=\mathbb{C}\{\partial/\partial\bar{z}_i\}$ is called the *antiholomorphic tangent space* to M at p; clearly

$$T_{\mathbb{C},p}(M) = T_p'(M) \oplus T_p''(M).$$

Observe that for M,N complex manifolds any C^∞ map $f: M \to N$ induces a linear map

$$f_*: T_{\mathbb{R},p}(M) \to T_{\mathbb{R},f(p)}(N)$$

and hence a map

$$f_*: T_{\mathbb{C},p}(M) \to T_{\mathbb{C},f(p)}(N),$$

but does not in general induce a map from $T_p'(M)$ to $T_{f(p)}'(N)$. In fact, *a map* $f: M \to N$ *is holomorphic if and only if*

$$f_*(T_p'(M)) \subset T_{f(p)}'(N)$$

for all $p \in M$.

Note also that since $T_{\mathbb{C},p}(M)$ is given naturally as the real vector space $T_{\mathbb{R},p}(M)$ tensored with $\mathbb{C}$, the operation of conjugation sending $\partial/\partial z_i$ to $\partial/\partial\bar{z}_i$ is well-defined and

$$T_p''(M) = \overline{T_p'(M)}.$$

It follows that the projection

$$T_{\mathbb{R},p}(M) \to T_{\mathbb{C},p}(M) \to T_p'(M)$$

is an $\mathbb{R}$-linear isomorphism. This last feature allows us to "do geometry" purely in the holomorphic tangent space. For example, let $z(t)$ $(0 \leqslant t \leqslant 1)$ be a smooth arc in the complex z-plane. Then $z(t) = x(t) + \sqrt{-1}\, y(t)$, and the tangent to the arc may be taken either as

$$x'(t)\frac{\partial}{\partial x} + y'(t)\frac{\partial}{\partial y} \qquad \text{in } T_{\mathbb{R}}(\mathbb{C})$$

or

$$z'(t)\frac{\partial}{\partial z} \qquad \text{in } T'(\mathbb{C}),$$

and these two correspond under the projection $T_{\mathbb{R}}(\mathbb{C}) \to T'(\mathbb{C})$.

Now let M,N be complex manifolds, $z = (z_1,\ldots,z_n)$ be holomorphic coordinates centered at $p \in M$, $w = (w_1,\ldots,w_m)$ holomorphic coordinates centered at $q \in N$ and $f: M \to N$ a holomorphic map with $f(p) = q$. Corresponding to the various tangent spaces to M and N at p and q, we have different notions of the *Jacobian* of f, as follows:

1. If we write $z_i = x_i + \sqrt{-1}\, y_i$ and $w_\alpha = u_\alpha + \sqrt{-1}\, v_\alpha$, then in terms of the bases $\{\partial/\partial x_i, \partial/\partial y_i\}$ and $\{\partial/\partial u_\alpha, \partial/\partial v_\alpha\}$ for $T_{\mathbb{R},p}(M)$ and $T_{\mathbb{R},q}(N)$, the

linear map f_* is given by the $2m \times 2n$ matrix

$$\mathcal{J}_{\mathbb{R}}(f) = \begin{vmatrix} \dfrac{\partial u_\alpha}{\partial x_j} & \dfrac{\partial u_\alpha}{\partial y_j} \\ \dfrac{\partial v_\alpha}{\partial x_j} & \dfrac{\partial v_\alpha}{\partial y_j} \end{vmatrix}.$$

In terms of the bases $\{\partial/\partial z_i, \partial/\partial \bar{z}_i\}$ and $\{\partial/\partial w_\alpha, \partial/\partial \bar{w}_\alpha\}$ for $T_{\mathbb{C},p}(M)$ and $T_{\mathbb{C},q}(N)$, f_* is given by

$$\mathcal{J}_{\mathbb{C}}(f) = \begin{pmatrix} \mathcal{J}(f) & 0 \\ 0 & \overline{\mathcal{J}(f)} \end{pmatrix}$$

where

$$\mathcal{J}(f) = \begin{pmatrix} \dfrac{\partial w_\alpha}{\partial z_j} \end{pmatrix}.$$

Note in particular that rank $\mathcal{J}_{\mathbb{R}}(f) = 2 \cdot$ rank $\mathcal{J}(f)$ and that if $m = n$, then

$$\det \mathcal{J}_{\mathbb{R}}(f) = \det \mathcal{J}(f) \cdot \det \overline{\mathcal{J}(f)}$$
$$= |\det \mathcal{J}(f)|^2 \geq 0,$$

i.e., *holomorphic maps are orientation preserving*. We take the *natural orientation* on $\mathbb{C}^n$ to be given by the $2n$-form

$$\left(\frac{\sqrt{-1}}{2} \right)^n (dz_1 \wedge d\bar{z}_1) \wedge (dz_2 \wedge d\bar{z}_2) \wedge \cdots \wedge (dz_n \wedge d\bar{z}_n)$$
$$= dx_1 \wedge dy_1 \wedge \cdots \wedge dx_n \wedge dy_n;$$

it is clear that if $\varphi_\alpha : U_\alpha \to \mathbb{C}^n$, $\varphi_\beta : U_\beta \to \mathbb{C}^n$ are holomorphic coordinate maps on the complex manifold M, the pullbacks via φ_α and φ_β of the natural orientation on $\mathbb{C}^n$ agree on $U_\alpha \cap U_\beta$. Thus *any complex manifold has a natural orientation* which is preserved under holomorphic maps.

Submanifolds and Subvarieties

Now that we have established the relations among the various Jacobians of a holomorphic map, it is not hard to prove the

Inverse Function Theorem. *Let* U, V *be open sets in* $\mathbb{C}^n$ *with* $0 \in U$ *and* $f : U \to V$ *a holomorphic map with* $\mathcal{J}(f) = (\partial f_i/\partial z_j)$ *nonsingular at* 0. *Then* f *is one-to-one in a neighborhood of* 0, *and* f^{-1} *is holomorphic at* $f(0)$.

Proof. First, since $\det |\mathcal{J}_{\mathbb{R}}(f)| = |\det(\mathcal{J}(f))|^2 \neq 0$ at 0, by the ordinary inverse function theorem f has a C^∞ inverse f^{-1} near 0. Now we have

$$f^{-1}(f(z)) = z$$

so

$$0 = \frac{\partial}{\partial \bar{z}_i} \left(f^{-1}(f(z)) \right)$$

$$= \sum_k \frac{\partial f_j^{-1}}{\partial z_k} \cdot \frac{\partial f_k}{\partial \bar{z}_i} + \sum_k \frac{\partial f_j^{-1}}{\partial \bar{z}_k} \cdot \frac{\partial \bar{f}_k}{\partial \bar{z}_i}$$

$$= \sum_k \frac{\partial f_j^{-1}}{\partial \bar{z}_k} \cdot \left(\frac{\overline{\partial f_k}}{\partial z_i} \right) \qquad \text{for all } i,j.$$

Since $(\partial f_k / \partial z_i)$ is nonsingular, this implies $\partial f_j^{-1} / \partial \bar{z}_k = 0$ for all j,k, so f^{-1} is holomorphic.   Q.E.D.

Similarly, we have the

Implicit Function Theorem.   *Given* $f_1, \ldots, f_k \in \mathcal{O}_n$ *with*

$$\det \left(\frac{\partial f_i}{\partial z_j}(0) \right)_{1 \leqslant i,j \leqslant k} \neq 0,$$

there exist functions $w_1, \ldots, w_k \in \mathcal{O}_{n-k}$ *such that in a neighborhood of 0 in* $\mathbb{C}^n$,

$$f_1(z) = \cdots = f_k(z) = 0 \Leftrightarrow z_i = w_i(z_{k+1}, \ldots, z_n), \qquad 1 \leqslant i \leqslant k.$$

Proof.   Again, by the C^∞ implicit function theorem we can find C^∞ functions $w_1, \ldots, w_k$ with the required property; to see that they are holomorphic we write, for $z = (z_{k+1}, \ldots, z_n)$, $k+1 \leqslant \alpha \leqslant n$,

$$0 = \frac{\partial}{\partial \bar{z}_\alpha} \left(f_j(w(z), z) \right)$$

$$= \frac{\partial f_j}{\partial \bar{z}_\alpha}(w(z), z) + \sum \frac{\partial w_l}{\partial \bar{z}_\alpha} \cdot \frac{\partial f_j}{\partial w_l}(w(z), z) + \sum \frac{\partial \bar{w}_l}{\partial \bar{z}_\alpha} \cdot \frac{\partial f_j}{\partial \bar{w}_l}(w(z), z)$$

$$= \sum \frac{\partial w_l}{\partial \bar{z}_\alpha} \cdot \frac{\partial f_j}{\partial w_l}(w(z), z)$$

$$\Rightarrow \frac{\partial w_l}{\partial \bar{z}_\alpha} = 0 \qquad \text{for all } \alpha, l.   \text{Q.E.D.}$$

One special feature of the holomorphic case is the following:

Proposition.   *If* $f: U \to V$ *is a one-to-one holomorphic map of open sets in* $\mathbb{C}^n$ *then* $|\mathcal{J}(f)| \neq 0$, *i.e.,* f^{-1} *is holomorphic.*

Proof.   We prove this by induction on n; the case $n=1$ is clear. Let $z = (z_1, \ldots, z_n)$ and $w = (w_1, \ldots, w_n)$ be coordinates on U and V, respectively, and suppose $\mathcal{J}(f)$ has rank k at $0 \in U$; we may assume then that the matrix

$((\partial f_i / \partial z_j)(0))_{0 \leqslant i,j \leqslant k}$ is nonsingular. Set

$$z_i' = f_i(z), \qquad 1 \leqslant i \leqslant k,$$
$$z_\alpha' = z_\alpha, \qquad k+1 \leqslant \alpha \leqslant n;$$

by the inverse function theorem, $z' = (z_1', \ldots, z_n')$ is a holomorphic coordinate system for U near 0. But now f maps the locus $(z_1' = \cdots = z_k' = 0)$ one-to-one onto the locus $(w_1 = \cdots = w_k = 0)$ and the Jacobian $(\partial f_\alpha / \partial z_\beta')$ of $f|_{(z_1' = \cdots = z_k' = 0)}$ is singular at 0; by the induction hypothesis, either $k = 0$ or $k = n$. We see then that the Jacobian matrix of f vanishes identically wherever its determinant is zero, i.e., that f maps every connected component of the locus $|\mathcal{J}(f)| = 0$ to a single point in V. Since f is one-to-one and the zero locus of the holomorphic function $|\mathcal{J}(f)|$ is positive-dimensional if nonempty, it follows that $|\mathcal{J}(f)| \neq 0$.   Q.E.D.

Note that this proposition is in contrast to the real case, where the map $t \mapsto t^3$ on $\mathbb{R}$ is one-to-one but does not have a C^∞ inverse.

Now we can make the

DEFINITION. A *complex submanifold* S of a complex manifold M is a subset $S \subset M$ given locally either as the zeros of a collection $f_1, \ldots, f_k$ of holomorphic functions with rank $\mathcal{J}(f) = k$, or as the image of an open set U in $\mathbb{C}^{n-k}$ under a map $f: U \to M$ with rank $\mathcal{J}(f) = n - k$.

The implicit function theorem assures us that the two alternate conditions of the definition are in fact equivalent, and that the submanifold S has naturally the structure of a complex manifold of dimension $n - k$.

DEFINITION. An *analytic subvariety* V of a complex manifold M is a subset given locally as the zeros of a finite collection of holomorphic functions. A point $p \in V$ is called a *smooth point* of V if V is a submanifold of M near p, that is, if V is given in some neighborhood of p by holomorphic functions $f_1, \ldots, f_k$ with rank $\mathcal{J}(f) = k$; the locus of smooth points of V is denoted V^*. A point $p \in V - V^*$ is called a *singular point* of V; the *singular locus* $V - V^*$ of V is denoted V_s. V is called *smooth* or *nonsingular* if $V = V^*$, i.e., if V is a submanifold of M.

In particular, if p is a point of an analytic hypersurface $V \subset M$ given in terms of local coordinates z by the function f, we define the *multiplicity* $\operatorname{mult}_p(V)$ to be the order of vanishing of f at p, that is, the greatest integer m such that all partial derivatives

$$\frac{\partial^k f}{\partial z_{i_1} \cdots \partial z_{i_k}}(p) = 0, \qquad k \leqslant m - 1.$$

We should mention here a piece of terminology that is pervasive in algebraic geometry: the word *generic*. When we are dealing with a family of objects parametrized locally by a complex manifold or an analytic subvariety of a complex manifold, the statement that "a (or the) generic member of the family has a certain property" means exactly that "the set of objects in the family that do not have that property is contained in a subvariety of strictly smaller dimension".

In general, it will be clear how the objects in our family are to be parametrized. One exception will be a reference to "the generic k-plane in $\mathbb{P}^n$": until the section on Grassmannians, we have—at least officially—no way of parametrizing linear subspaces of projective space. The fastidious reader may substitute "the linear span of the generic $(k+1)$-tuple of points in $\mathbb{P}^n$."

A basic fact about analytic subvarieties is the

Proposition. V_s *is contained in an analytic subvariety of* M *not equal to* V.

Proof. For $p \in V$ let k be the largest integer such that there exist k functions $f_1, \ldots, f_k$ in a neighborhood U of p vanishing on V and such that $\mathcal{J}(f)$ has a $k \times k$ minor not everywhere singular on V; we may assume that $|(\partial f_i/\partial z_j)_{1 \leqslant i,j \leqslant k}| \not\equiv 0$ on V. Let $U' \subset U$ be the locus of $|(\partial f_i/\partial z_j)_{1 \leqslant i,j \leqslant k}| \neq 0$ and V' the locus $f_1 = \cdots = f_k = 0$. Then $V' = V \cap U'$ is a complex submanifold of U', and for any holomorphic function f vanishing on V the differential $df \equiv 0$ on V', i.e., f is constant on V'. It follows that for $q \in V'$ near p, $V = V'$ is a manifold in a neighborhood of q and so $V_s \subset (|(\partial f_i/\partial z_j)_{1 \leqslant i,j \leqslant k}| = 0)$. Q.E.D.

It is in fact the case that V_s is an analytic subvariety of M—if we choose local defining functions $f_1, \ldots, f_l$ for V carefully, V_s will be the common zero locus of the determinants of the $k \times k$ minors of $\mathcal{J}(f)$. For our purposes, however, we simply need to know that the singular locus of an analytic variety is comparatively small, and so we will not prove this stronger assertion.

We state one more result on analytic varieties:

Proposition. *An analytic variety* V *is irreducible if and only if* V* *is connected.*

Proof. One direction is clear: if $V = V_1 \cup V_2$ with $V_1, V_2 \subsetneq V$ analytic varieties, then $(V_1 \cap V_2) \subset V_s$, so V^* is disconnected.

The converse is harder to prove in general; since we will use it only for analytic hypersurfaces, we will prove it in this case. Suppose V^* is disconnected, and let $\{V_i\}$ denote the connected components of V^*; we want to show that $\overline{V}_i$ is an analytic variety. Let $p \in \overline{V}_i$ be any point, f a defining function for V near p, and $z = (z_1, \ldots, z_n)$ local coordinates around p; we may assume that f is a Weierstrass polynomial of degree k in z_n.

Write

$$g = \alpha \cdot f + \beta \cdot \frac{\partial f}{\partial z_n}, \qquad g \neq 0 \in \mathcal{O}_{n-1};$$

then for Δ some polydisc around p and Δ' a polydisc in $\mathbb{C}^{n-1}$, the projection map $\pi \colon (z_1, \ldots, z_n) \mapsto (z_1, \ldots, z_{n-1})$ expresses $V_i \cap (\Delta - (g=0))$ as a covering space of $\Delta' - (g=0)$. Let $\{w_\nu(z')\}$ denote the z_n-coordinates of the points in $\pi^{-1}(z')$ for $z' = (z_1, \ldots, z_{n-1}) \in \Delta' - (g=0)$ and let $\sigma_1(z'), \ldots, \sigma_k(z')$ denote the elementary symmetric functions of the w_ν. The functions σ_i are well-defined and bounded on $\Delta' - (g=0)$, and so extend to Δ'; the function

$$f_i(z) = z_n^k + \sigma_1(z') z_n^{k-1} + \cdots + \sigma_k(z')$$

is thus holomorphic in a neighborhood of p and vanishes exactly on $\overline{V}_i$.

Q.E.D.

We take the *dimension* of an irreducible analytic variety V to be the dimension of the complex manifold V^*; we say that a general analytic variety is of dimension k if all of its irreducible components are.

A note: if $V \subset M$ is an analytic subvariety of a complex manifold M, then we may define the *tangent cone* $T_p(V) \subset T_p'(M)$ to V at any point $p \in V$ as follows: if $V = (f=0)$ is an analytic hypersurface, and in terms of holomorphic coordinates $z_1, \ldots, z_n$ on M centered around p we write

$$f(z_1, \ldots, z_n) = f_m(z_1, \ldots, z_n) + f_{m+1}(z_1, \ldots, z_n) + \cdots$$

with $f_k(z_1, \ldots, z_n)$ a homogeneous polynomial of degree k in $z_1, \ldots, z_n$, then the tangent cone to V at p is taken to be the subvariety of $T_p'(M) = \mathbb{C}\{\partial/\partial z_i\}$ defined by

$$\left\{ \sum \alpha_i \frac{\partial}{\partial z_i} : f_m(\alpha_1, \ldots, \alpha_n) = 0 \right\}.$$

In general, then, the tangent cone to an analytic variety $V \subset M$ at $p \in V$ is taken to be the intersection of the tangent cones at p to all local analytic hypersurfaces in M containing V. In case V is smooth at p, of course, this is just the tangent space to V at p.

More geometrically, the tangent cone $T_p(V) \subset T_p'(M)$ may be realized as the union of the tangent lines at p to all analytic arcs $\gamma \colon \Delta \to V \subset M$.

The *multiplicity* of a subvariety V of dimension k in M at a point p, denoted $\mathrm{mult}_p(V)$, is taken to be the number of sheets in the projection, in a small coordinate polydisc on M around p, of V onto a generic k-dimensional polydisc; note that p is a smooth point of V if and only if $\mathrm{mult}_p(V) = 1$. In general, if $W \subset M$ is an irreducible subvariety, we define the *multiplicity* $\mathrm{mult}_W(V)$ *of* V *along* W to be simply the multiplicity of V at a generic point of W.

De Rham and Dolbeault Cohomology

Let M be a differentiable manifold. Let $A^p(M, \mathbb{R})$ denote the space of differential forms of degree p on M, and $Z^p(M, \mathbb{R})$ the subspace of closed p-forms. Since $d^2 = 0$, $d(A^{p-1}(M, \mathbb{R})) \subset Z^p(M, \mathbb{R})$; the quotient groups

$$H^p_{DR}(M, \mathbb{R}) = \frac{Z^p(M, \mathbb{R})}{dA^{p-1}(M, \mathbb{R})}$$

of closed forms modulo exact forms are called the *de Rham cohomology groups of* M.

In the same way, we can let $A^p(M)$ and $Z^p(M)$ denote the spaces of complex-valued p-forms and closed complex-valued p-forms on M, respectively, and let

$$H^p_{DR}(M) = \frac{Z^p(M)}{dA^{p-1}(M)}$$

be the corresponding quotient; clearly

$$H^p_{DR}(M) = H^p_{DR}(M, \mathbb{R}) \otimes \mathbb{C}.$$

Now let M be a complex manifold. By linear algebra, the decomposition

$$T^*_{\mathbb{C}, z}(M) = T^{*'}_z(M) \oplus T^{*''}_z(M)$$

of the cotangent space to M at each point $z \in M$ gives a decomposition

$$\wedge^n T^*_{\mathbb{C}, z}(M) = \bigoplus_{p+q=n} (\wedge^p T^{*'}_z(M) \otimes \wedge^q T^{*''}_z(M)).$$

Correspondingly, we can write

$$A^n(M) = \bigoplus_{p+q=n} A^{p,q}(M),$$

where

$$A^{p,q}(M) = \{\varphi \in A^n(M): \varphi(z) \in \wedge^p T^{*'}_z(M) \otimes \wedge^q T^{*''}_z(M) \text{ for all } z \in M \}.$$

A form $\varphi \in A^{p,q}(M)$ is said to be of *type* (p, q). By way of notation, we denote by $\pi^{(p,q)}$ the projection maps

$$A^*(M) \to A^{p,q}(M),$$

so that for $\varphi \in A^*(M)$,

$$\varphi = \sum \pi^{(p,q)} \varphi;$$

we usually write $\varphi^{(p,q)}$ for $\pi^{(p,q)} \varphi$.

If $\varphi \in A^{p,q}(M)$, then for each $z \in M$,

$$d\varphi(z) \in (\wedge^p T^{*'}(M) \otimes \wedge^q T^{*''}_z(M)) \wedge T^*_{\mathbb{C}, z}(M),$$

i.e.,

$$d\varphi \in A^{p+1,q}(M) \oplus A^{p,q+1}(M).$$

We define the operators

$$\bar{\partial}: A^{p,q}(M) \to A^{p,q+1}(M)$$
$$\partial: A^{p,q}(M) \to A^{p+1,q}(M)$$

by

$$\bar{\partial} = \pi^{(p,q+1)} \circ d, \qquad \partial = \pi^{(p+1,q)} \circ d;$$

accordingly, we have

$$d = \partial + \bar{\partial}.$$

In terms of local coordinates $z = (z_1, \ldots, z_m)$, a form $\varphi \in A^n(M)$ is of type (p,q) if we can write

$$\varphi(z) = \sum_{\substack{\#I=p \\ \#J=q}} \varphi_{IJ}(z)\, dz_I \wedge d\bar{z}_J,$$

where for each multiindex $I = \{i_1, \ldots, i_p\}$,

$$dz_I = dz_{i_1} \wedge \cdots \wedge dz_{i_p}.$$

The operators ∂ and $\bar{\partial}$ are then given by

$$\bar{\partial}\varphi(z) = \sum_{I,J,j} \frac{\partial}{\partial \bar{z}_j} \varphi_{IJ}(z)\, d\bar{z}_j \wedge dz_I \wedge d\bar{z}_J,$$

$$\partial\varphi(z) = \sum_{I,J,i} \frac{\partial}{\partial z_i} \varphi_{IJ}(z)\, dz_i \wedge dz_I \wedge d\bar{z}_J.$$

In particular, we say that a form φ of type $(q,0)$ is *holomorphic* if $\bar{\partial}\varphi = 0$; clearly this is the case if and only if

$$\varphi(z) = \sum_{\#I=q} \varphi_I(z)\, dz_I$$

with $\varphi_I(z)$ holomorphic.

Note that since the decomposition $T^*_{\mathbb{C},z} = T^{*'}_z \oplus T^{*''}_z$ is preserved under holomorphic maps, so is the decomposition $A^* = \oplus A^{p,q}$. For $f: M \to N$ a holomorphic map of complex manifolds,

$$f^*(A^{p,q}(N)) \subset A^{p,q}(M)$$

and

$$\bar{\partial} \circ f^* = f^* \circ \bar{\partial} \qquad \text{on } A^{p,q}(N).$$

Let $Z^{p,q}_{\bar{\partial}}(M)$ denote the space of $\bar{\partial}$-closed forms of type (p,q). Since $\partial^2/\partial\bar{z}_i\partial\bar{z}_j = \partial^2/\partial\bar{z}_j\partial\bar{z}_i$

$$\bar{\partial}^2 = 0$$

on $A^{p,q}(M)$, and we have

$$\bar{\partial}(A^{p,q}(M)) \subset Z^{p,q+1}_{\bar{\partial}}(M);$$

accordingly, we define the *Dolbeault cohomology groups* to be

$$H_{\bar{\partial}}^{p,q}(M) = \frac{Z_{\bar{\partial}}^{p,q}(M)}{\bar{\partial}(A^{p,q-1}(M))}.$$

Note in particular that if $f: M \to N$ is a holomorphic map of complex manifolds, f induces a map

$$f^*: H_{\bar{\partial}}^{p,q}(N) \to H_{\bar{\partial}}^{p,q}(M).$$

The ordinary Poincaré lemma that every closed form on $\mathbb{R}^n$ is exact assures us that the de Rham groups are locally trivial. Analogously, a fundamental fact about the Dolbeault groups is the

$\bar{\partial}$-**Poincaré Lemma.**   *For* $\Delta = \Delta(r)$ *a polycylinder in* $\mathbb{C}^n$,

$$H_{\bar{\partial}}^{p,q}(\Delta) = 0, \qquad q \geq 1.$$

Proof.   First note that if

$$\varphi = \sum_{\substack{\#I=p \\ \#J=q}} \psi_{IJ} \cdot dz_I \wedge d\bar{z}_J$$

is a $\bar{\partial}$-closed form, then the forms

$$\varphi_I = \sum_{\#J=q} \varphi_{IJ} \cdot d\bar{z}_J \in A^{0,q}(\Delta)$$

are again closed, and that if

$$\varphi_I = \bar{\partial}\eta_I$$

then

$$\varphi = \pm\bar{\partial}\left(\sum_I dz_I \wedge \eta_I \right);$$

thus it is sufficient to prove that the groups $H_{\bar{\partial}}^{0,q}(\Delta)$ vanish.

We first show that if φ is a $\bar{\partial}$-closed $(0,q)$-form on $\Delta = \Delta(r)$, then for any $s < r$, we can find $\psi \in A^{0,q-1}(\Delta(s))$ with $\bar{\partial}\psi = \varphi$ in $\Delta(s)$. To see this, write

$$\varphi = \sum \varphi_I d\bar{z}_I;$$

we claim that if $\varphi \equiv 0$ modulo $(d\bar{z}_1, \ldots, d\bar{z}_k)$—that is, if $\varphi_I \equiv 0$ for $I \not\subset \{1, \ldots, k\}$—then we can find $\eta \in A^{0,q-1}(\Delta(s))$ such that

$$\varphi - \bar{\partial}\eta \equiv 0 \text{ modulo } (d\bar{z}_1, \ldots, d\bar{z}_{k-1});$$

this will clearly be sufficient. So assume $\varphi \equiv 0$ modulo $(d\bar{z}_1, \ldots, d\bar{z}_k)$ and set

$$\varphi_1 = \sum_{I: \, k \in I} \varphi_I \cdot d\bar{z}_{I-\{k\}},$$

$$\varphi_2 = \sum_{I: \, k \notin I} \varphi_I \cdot d\bar{z}_I,$$

so that $\varphi = \varphi_1 \wedge d\bar{z}_k + \varphi_2$, with $\varphi_2 \equiv 0$ modulo $(d\bar{z}_1, \ldots, d\bar{z}_{k-1})$. If $l > k$, $\bar{\partial}\varphi_2$ contains no terms with a factor $d\bar{z}_k \wedge d\bar{z}_l$; since $\bar{\partial}\varphi = \bar{\partial}\varphi_1 + \bar{\partial}\varphi_2 = 0$, it follows that

$$\frac{\partial}{\partial \bar{z}_l} \varphi_I = 0$$

for $l > k$ and I such that $k \in I$.

Now set

$$\eta = \sum_{I:\, k \in I} \eta_I \, d\bar{z}_{I - \{k\}}$$

where

$$\eta_I(z) = \frac{1}{2\pi \sqrt{-1}} \int_{|w_k| \leqslant s_k} \varphi_I(z_1, \ldots, w_k, \ldots, z_n) \frac{dw_k \wedge d\bar{w}_k}{w_k - z_k}.$$

By the proposition on p. 5, we have

$$\frac{\partial}{\partial \bar{z}_k} \eta_I(z) = \varphi_I(z),$$

and for $l > k$,

$$\frac{\partial}{\partial \bar{z}_l} \eta_I(z) = \frac{1}{2\pi \sqrt{-1}} \int_{|w_k| \leqslant s_k} \frac{\partial}{\partial \bar{z}_l} \varphi_I(z_1, \ldots, w_k, \ldots, z_n) \frac{dw_k \wedge d\bar{w}_k}{w_k - z_k}$$
$$= 0$$

Thus

$$\varphi - \bar{\partial}\eta \equiv 0 \text{ modulo } (d\bar{z}_1, \ldots, d\bar{z}_{k-1})$$

in $\Delta(s)$ as was desired.

To prove the full $\bar{\partial}$-Poincaré lemma let $\{r_i\}$ be a monotone increasing sequence tending to r. By the first step, we can find $\psi_k \in A^{0,q-1}(\Delta)$ such that $\bar{\partial}\psi_k = \varphi$ in $\Delta(r_k)$—take $\psi_k' \in A^{0,q-1}(\Delta(r_{k+1}))$ with $\bar{\partial}\psi_k' = \varphi$, ρ_k a C^∞ bump function $\equiv 1$ on $\Delta(r_k)$ and having compact support in $\Delta(r_{k+1})$, and set $\psi_k = \rho_k \cdot \psi_k'$—the problem is to show that we can choose $\{\psi_k\}$ so that they converge suitably on compact sets. We do this by induction on q. Suppose we have ψ_k as above. Take $\alpha \in A^{0,q-1}(\Delta)$ with $\bar{\partial}\alpha = \varphi$ in $\Delta(r_{k+1})$; then

$$\bar{\partial}(\psi_k - \alpha) = 0 \qquad \text{in } \Delta(r_k),$$

and, if $q \geqslant 2$, then by the induction hypothesis we can find $\beta \in A^{0,q-2}(\Delta)$ with

$$\bar{\partial}\beta = \psi_k - \alpha \qquad \text{in } \Delta(r_{k-1}).$$

Set

$$\psi_{k+1} = \alpha + \bar{\partial}\beta;$$

then $\bar{\partial}\psi_{k+1} = \bar{\partial}\alpha = \varphi$ in $\Delta(r_{k+1})$ and

$$\psi_{k+1} = \psi_k \qquad \text{in } \Delta(r_{k-1}).$$

Thus the sequence $\{\psi_k\}$ chosen in this way converges uniformly on compact sets.

It remains to consider the case $q = 1$. Again, say $\psi_k \in C^\infty(\Delta)$ with $\bar{\partial}\psi_k = \varphi$ in $\Delta(r_k)$, $\alpha \in C^\infty(\Delta)$ with $\bar{\partial}\alpha = \varphi$ in $\Delta(r_{k+1})$; then $\psi_k - \alpha$ is a holomorphic function in $\Delta(r_k)$ and hence has a power series expansion around the origin in $\mathbb{C}^n$. Truncate this series expansion to obtain a polynomial β with

$$\sup_{\Delta(r_{k-1})} |(\psi_k - \alpha) - \beta| < \frac{1}{2^k},$$

and set

$$\psi_{k+1} = \alpha + \beta.$$

Then $\bar{\partial}\psi_{k+1} = \bar{\partial}\alpha = \varphi$ in $\Delta(r_{k+1})$, $\psi_{k+1} - \psi_k$ is holomorphic in $\Delta(r_k)$, and

$$\sup_{\Delta(r_{k-1})} |\psi_{k+1} - \psi_k| < \frac{1}{2^k},$$

so $\psi = \lim \psi_k$ exists, and $\bar{\partial}\psi = \varphi$. $\qquad\qquad$ Q.E.D.

Note that the proof works for $r = \infty$.

We leave it as an exercise for the reader to prove, using a similar argument with annuli and Laurent expansions, that

$$H_{\bar{\partial}}^{p,q}(\Delta^{*k} \times \Delta^l) = 0 \qquad \text{for } q \geqslant 1,$$

where Δ^* is the punctured disc $\Delta - \{0\}$.

Calculus on Complex Manifolds

Let M be a complex manifold of dimension n. A *hermitian metric* on M is given by a positive definite hermitian inner product

$$(\ , \ )_z : T_z'(M) \otimes \overline{T_z'(M)} \to \mathbb{C}$$

on the holomorphic tangent space at z for each $z \in M$, depending smoothly on z—that is, such that for local coordinates z on M the functions

$$h_{ij}(z) = \left(\frac{\partial}{\partial z_i}, \frac{\partial}{\partial z_j} \right)_z$$

are C^∞. Writing $(\ , \ )_z$ in terms of the basis $\{dz_i \otimes d\bar{z}_j\}$ for

$$(T_z'(M) \otimes \overline{T_z'(M)})^* = T_z^*(M) \otimes T_z^{*''}(M),$$

the hermitian metric is given by

$$ds^2 = \sum_{i,j} h_{ij}(z) dz_i \otimes d\bar{z}_j.$$

A *coframe* for the hermitian metric is an n-tuple of forms $(\varphi_1,\ldots,\varphi_n)$ of type $(1,0)$ such that

$$ds^2 = \sum_i \varphi_i \otimes \bar{\varphi}_i,$$

i.e., such that, in terms of the inner product induced on $T_z^*(M)$ by $(\ ,\ )_z$ on $T_z'(M)$, $(\varphi_1(z),\ldots,\varphi_n(z))$ is an orthonormal basis for $T_z^{*'}(M)$. From this description it is clear that coframes always exist locally: we can construct one by applying the Gram-Schmidt process to the basis $(dz_1,\ldots,dz_n)$ for $T_z^{*'}(M)$ at each z.

The real and imaginary parts of a hermitian inner product on a complex vector space give an ordinary inner product and an alternating quadratic form, respectively, on the underlying real vector space. Since we have a natural $\mathbb{R}$-linear isomorphism

$$T_{\mathbb{R},z}(M) \longrightarrow T_z'(M),$$

we see that for a hermitian metric ds^2 on M,

$$\mathrm{Re}\, ds^2:\ T_{\mathbb{R},z}(M) \otimes T_{\mathbb{R},z}(M) \to \mathbb{R}$$

is a *Riemannian metric* on M, called the induced Riemannian metric of the hermitian metric. When we speak of distance, area, or volume on a complex manifold with hermitian metric, we always refer to the induced Riemannian metric.

We also see that since the quadratic form

$$\mathrm{Im}\, ds^2:\ T_{\mathbb{R},p}(M) \otimes T_{\mathbb{R},p}(M) \to \mathbb{R}$$

is alternating, it represents a real differential form of degree 2; $\omega = -\frac{1}{2}\mathrm{Im}\, ds^2$ is called the *associated (1,1)-form* of the metric.

Explicitly, if $(\varphi_1,\ldots,\varphi_n)$ is a coframe for ds^2, we write

$$\varphi_i = \alpha_i + \sqrt{-1}\,\beta_i,$$

where α_i, β_i are real differential forms; then

$$ds^2 = \left(\sum(\alpha_i + \sqrt{-1}\,\beta_i)\right) \otimes \left(\sum(\alpha_i - \sqrt{-1}\,\beta_i)\right)$$
$$= \sum_i (\alpha_i \otimes \alpha_i + \beta_i \otimes \beta_i) + \sqrt{-1}\sum_i(-\alpha_i \otimes \beta_i + \beta_i \otimes \alpha_i).$$

The induced Riemannian metric is given by

$$\mathrm{Re}\, ds^2 = \sum(\alpha_i \otimes \alpha_i + \beta_i \otimes \beta_i),$$

and the associated (1,1)-form of the metric is given by

$$\omega = -\tfrac{1}{2}\mathrm{Im}\, ds^2$$
$$= \sum \alpha_i \wedge \beta_i$$
$$= \frac{\sqrt{-1}}{2}\sum \varphi_i \wedge \bar{\varphi}_i.$$

It follows from this last representation that the metric $ds^2 = \sum \varphi_i \otimes \bar{\varphi}_i$ may be directly recovered from its associated $(1,1)$-form $\omega = \frac{1}{2}\sqrt{-1} \sum \varphi_i \wedge \bar{\varphi}_i$. Indeed, any real differential form ω of type $(1,1)$ on M gives a hermitian form $H(\ ,\ )$ on each tangent space $T_z'(M)$. The form H will be positive definite—i.e., will induce a hermitian metric on M—if and only if for every $z \in M$ and holomorphic tangent vector $v \in T_z'(M)$,

$$\sqrt{-1} \cdot \langle \omega(z), v \wedge \bar{v} \rangle > 0.$$

Such a differential form ω is called a *positive $(1,1)$-form*; in terms of local holomorphic coordinates $z = (z_1, \ldots, z_n)$ on M, a form ω is positive if

$$\omega(z) = \frac{\sqrt{-1}}{2} \sum_{i,j} h_{ij}(z)\, dz_i \wedge d\bar{z}_j$$

with $H(z) = (h_{ij}(z))$ a positive definite hermitian matrix for each z.

If $S \subset M$ is a complex submanifold, then for $z \in S$ we have a natural inclusion

$$T_z'(S) \subset T_z'(M);$$

consequently a hermitian metric on M induces the same on S by restriction. More generally, if $f : N \to M$ is any holomorphic map such that

$$f_* : T_z'(N) \to T_{f(z)}'(M)$$

is injective for all $z \in N$, a metric on M induces a metric on N by setting

$$\left(\frac{\partial}{\partial w_\alpha}, \frac{\partial}{\partial w_\beta} \right)_z = \left(f_* \frac{\partial}{\partial w_\alpha}, f_* \frac{\partial}{\partial w_\beta} \right)_{f(z)}.$$

Note that in this case we can always find, for $U \subset N$ small, a coframe $(\varphi_1, \ldots, \varphi_n)$ on $f(U) \subset M$ with $\varphi_{k+1}, \ldots, \varphi_n \in \operatorname{Ker} f^* : T_{f(z)}^{*\prime}(M) \to T_z^{*\prime}(N)$; then $f^*\varphi_1, \ldots, f^*\varphi_k$ form a coframe on U for the induced metric on N. The associated $(1,1)$-form ω_N on N is thus given by

$$\omega_N = \frac{\sqrt{-1}}{2} \sum_{i=1}^{k} f^*\varphi_i \wedge f^* \bar{\varphi}_i$$

$$= f^* \left(\frac{\sqrt{-1}}{2} \sum_{i=1}^{k} \varphi_i \wedge \bar{\varphi}_i \right)$$

$$= f^* \left(\frac{\sqrt{-1}}{2} \sum_{i=1}^{n} \varphi_i \wedge \bar{\varphi}_i \right)$$

$$= f^* \omega_M,$$

i.e., *the associated $(1,1)$-form of the induced metric on* N *is the pullback of the associated $(1,1)$-form of the metric on* M.

Examples

1.   The hermitian metric on $\mathbb{C}^n$ given by

$$ds^2 = \sum_{i=1}^{n} dz_i \otimes d\bar{z}_i$$

is called the *Euclidean* or *standard* metric; the induced Riemannian metric is, of course, the standard metric on $\mathbb{C}^n = \mathbb{R}^{2n}$.

2.   If $\Lambda \subset \mathbb{C}^n$ is a full lattice, then the metric given on the complex torus $\mathbb{C}^n/\Lambda$ by

$$ds^2 = \sum dz_i \otimes d\bar{z}_i$$

is again called the *Euclidean metric* on $\mathbb{C}^n/\Lambda$.

3.   Let $Z_0, \ldots, Z_n$ be coordinates on $\mathbb{C}^{n+1}$ and denote by $\pi: \mathbb{C}^{n+1} - \{0\} \to \mathbb{P}^n$ the standard projection map. Let $U \subset \mathbb{P}^n$ be an open set and $Z: U \to \mathbb{C}^{n+1} - \{0\}$ a lifting of U, i.e., a holomorphic map with $\pi \circ Z = id$; consider the differential form

$$\omega = \frac{\sqrt{-1}}{2\pi} \partial\bar{\partial} \log \|Z\|^2.$$

If $Z': U \to \mathbb{C}^{n+1} - \{0\}$ is another lifting, then

$$Z' = f \cdot Z$$

with f a nonzero holomorphic function, so that

$$\frac{\sqrt{-1}}{2\pi} \partial\bar{\partial} \log \|Z'\|^2 = \frac{\sqrt{-1}}{2\pi} \partial\bar{\partial}\left(\log \|Z\|^2 + \log f + \log \bar{f}\right)$$

$$= \omega + \frac{\sqrt{-1}}{2\pi}\left(\partial\bar{\partial} \log f - \bar{\partial}\partial \log \bar{f}\right)$$

$$= \omega.$$

Therefore ω is independent of the lifting chosen; since liftings always exist locally, ω is a globally defined differential form in $\mathbb{P}^n$. Clearly ω is of type $(1,1)$. To see that ω is positive, first note that the unitary group $U(n+1)$ acts transitively on $\mathbb{P}^n$ and leaves the form ω invariant, so that ω is positive everywhere if it is positive at one point. Now let $\{w_i = Z_i/Z_0\}$ be coordinates on the open set $U_0 = (Z_0 \neq 0)$ in $\mathbb{P}^n$ and use the lifting $Z = (1, w_1, \ldots, w_n)$ on U_0; we have

$$\omega = \frac{\sqrt{-1}}{2\pi} \partial\bar{\partial} \log\left(1 + \sum w_i \bar{w}_i\right)$$

$$= \frac{\sqrt{-1}}{2\pi} \partial\left[\frac{\sum w_i d\bar{w}_i}{1 + \sum w_i \bar{w}_i}\right]$$

$$= \frac{\sqrt{-1}}{2\pi}\left[\frac{\sum dw_i \wedge d\bar{w}_i}{1 + \sum w_i \bar{w}_i} - \frac{\left(\sum \bar{w}_i dw_i\right) \wedge \left(\sum w_i d\bar{w}_i\right)}{\left(1 + \sum w_i \bar{w}_i\right)^2}\right].$$

At the point $[1, 0, \ldots, 0]$,

$$\omega = \frac{\sqrt{-1}}{2\pi} \sum dw_i \wedge d\bar{w}_i > 0.$$

Thus ω defines a hermitian metric on $\mathbb{P}^n$, called the *Fubini-Study metric*.

The Wirtinger Theorem. The interplay between the real and imaginary parts of a hermitian metric now gives us the Wirtinger theorem, which expresses another fundamental difference between Riemannian and hermitian differential geometry. Let M be a complex manifold, $z = (z_1, \ldots, z_n)$ local coordinates on M, and

$$ds^2 = \sum \varphi_i \otimes \bar{\varphi}_i$$

a hermitian metric on M with associated $(1, 1)$-form ω. Write $\varphi_i = \alpha_i + \sqrt{-1}\,\beta_i$; then the associated Riemannian metric on M is

$$\mathrm{Re}(ds^2) = \sum_{i,j} \alpha_i \otimes \alpha_i + \beta_i \otimes \beta_i,$$

and the volume element associated to $\mathrm{Re}(ds^2)$ is given by

$$d\mu = \alpha_1 \wedge \beta_1 \wedge \cdots \wedge \alpha_n \wedge \beta_n.$$

On the other hand, we have

$$\omega = \sum \alpha_i \wedge \beta_i,$$

so that the nth exterior power

$$\begin{aligned} \omega^n &= n! \cdot \alpha_1 \wedge \beta_1 \wedge \cdots \wedge \alpha_n \wedge \beta_n \\ &= n! \cdot d\mu. \end{aligned}$$

Now let $S \subset M$ be a complex submanifold of dimension d. As we have observed, the $(1, 1)$-form associated to the metric induced on S by ds^2 is just $\omega|_S$, and applying the above to the induced metric on S, we have the

Wirtinger Theorem

$$\mathrm{vol}(S) = \frac{1}{d!} \int_S \omega^d.$$

The fact that the volume of a complex submanifold S of the complex manifold M is expressed as the integral over S of a globally defined differential form on M is quite different from the real case. For a C^∞ arc

$$t \mapsto (x(t), y(t))$$

in $\mathbb{R}^2$, for example, the element of arc length is given by

$$\left(x'(t)^2 + y'(t)^2\right)^{1/2} dt,$$

which is not, in general, the pullback of any differential form in $\mathbb{R}^2$.

To close this section, we discuss integration over analytic subvarieties of a complex manifold M. To begin with, we define the integral of a differential form φ on M over a possibly singular subvariety V to be the integral of φ over the smooth locus V^* of V. The first thing to prove is the

Proposition. V^* *has finite volume in bounded regions.*

Proof.   Since the question is local and the volume increases by increasing the metric, it is sufficient to prove it for $V \subset \mathbb{C}^n$ with the Euclidean metric. Suppose V is of dimension k and choose coordinates on $\mathbb{C}^n$ so that, in a neighborhood of 0, V meets each of the coordinate $(n-k)$-planes $(z_{i_1} = z_{i_2} = \cdots = z_{i_k} = 0)$ only in discrete points. The $(1,1)$-form associated to the Euclidean metric on $\mathbb{C}^n$ is

$$\omega = \frac{\sqrt{-1}}{2} \sum dz_i \wedge d\bar{z}_i,$$

and so for $c = (\sqrt{-1}/2)^k (-1)^{k(k-1)/2} \cdot k!$

$$\omega^k = c \cdot \sum_{\#I = k} dz_I \wedge d\bar{z}_I.$$

Thus it will suffice to prove that

$$c \int_{V^* \cap \Delta} dz_I \wedge d\bar{z}_I < \infty$$

for $I = \{1, \ldots, k\}$, Δ a small polydisc around the origin. But the projection map

$$\pi: V^* \to \mathbb{C}^k$$

$$: (z_1, \ldots, z_n) \mapsto (z_1, \ldots, z_k)$$

expresses V^* as a d-sheeted branched cover of $\Delta' = \pi(\Delta)$ and consequently

$$c \int_{V^* \cap \Delta} dz_I \wedge d\bar{z}_I \leqslant d \cdot c \int_{\Delta'} dz_I \wedge d\bar{z}_I < \infty. \qquad \text{Q.E.D.}$$

Note again the contrast to the C^∞ case, where the set of manifold points of the zero locus of a smooth function—e.g., $f(y) = (e^{-y^{-2}} - 1) \sin(1/y)$—need not have locally finite area.

As a corollary of the proof, we see that for any region $U \subset M$ with $\bar{U}$ compact and $\varphi \in A^*(\bar{U})$,

$$\int_{V^* \cap U} \varphi < \infty.$$

An obvious but fundamental observation is that if V^* has dimension k, $A^{p,q}(V^*) = 0$ for p or $q > k$; consequently for any form φ,

$$\int_V \varphi = \int_V \varphi^{(k,k)}.$$

We can now prove

Stokes' Theorem for Analytic Varieties.   *For* M *a complex manifold,* $V \subset M$
an analytic subvariety of dimension k, *and* φ *a differential form of degree*
$2k - 1$ *with compact support in* M,

$$\int_V d\varphi = 0.$$

Proof.   The question is local, i.e., it will be sufficient to show that for
every $p \in V$, there exists a neighborhood U of p such that for any
$\varphi \in A_c^{2k-1}(U)$

$$\int_V d\varphi = 0.$$

For any $p \in V$, we can find a coordinate system $z = (z_1, \ldots, z_n)$ and a
polycylinder Δ around p such that the projection map $\pi: (z_1, \ldots, z_n) \rightarrow$
$(z_1, \ldots, z_k)$ expresses $V \cap \Delta$ as a branched cover of $\Delta' = \pi(\Delta)$, branched over
an analytic hypersurface $D \subset \Delta'$. Let T_ε be the ε-neighborhood of D in Δ'
and

$$V_\varepsilon = (V \cap \Delta) - \pi^{-1}(T_\varepsilon).$$

For $\varphi \in A_c^{2k-1}(\Delta)$,

$$\int_V d\varphi = \lim_{\varepsilon \to 0} \int_{V_\varepsilon} d\varphi$$

$$= \lim_{\varepsilon \to 0} \int_{\partial V_\varepsilon} \varphi$$

$$= \lim_{\varepsilon \to 0} \int_{\partial \pi^{-1}(T_\varepsilon)} \varphi.$$

Thus to prove the result, we simply have to prove that the volume of
$\partial \pi^{-1}(T_\varepsilon) \to 0$ as $\varepsilon \to 0$. But $\partial \pi^{-1}(T_\varepsilon)$ is a finite cover of ∂T_ε; so we need
prove only that $\mathrm{vol}(\partial T_\varepsilon) \to 0$ as $\varepsilon \to 0$. To see this, let D_1 be the singular
locus of D, D_2 the singular locus of D_1, and so on; let T_ε^i be the
ε-neighborhood of $D_i^* = D_i - D_{i+1}$ in $\Delta - D_{i+1}$. Then D_i^* is a submanifold
of real dimension $\leqslant 2k - 2$ having finite volume in $\Delta - D_{i+1}$, and so the
volume of ∂T_ε^i goes to 0 as $\varepsilon \to 0$. But $\partial T_\varepsilon \subset \cup (\partial T_\varepsilon^i)$, and so $\mathrm{vol}(\partial T_\varepsilon) \to 0$ as
$\varepsilon \to 0$.   Q.E.D.

This result has to do with the fact that singularities of complex-analytic
subvarieties occur only in real codimension 2. It assures us that integration
over analytic varieties is much the same as integration over submanifolds;
perhaps most importantly, it allows us to show (p. 61) that an analytic
subvariety of a compact complex manifold always defines a homology
class in $H_*(M, \mathbb{R})$.

Finally, we can state the

Proper Mapping Theorem. *If* M, N *are complex manifolds,* $f: M \rightarrow N$ *a holomorphic map, and* $V \subset M$ *an analytic variety such that* $f|_V$ *is proper, then* $f(V)$ *is an analytic subvariety of* N.

The proof will be given in Section 2 of Chapter 3.

3. SHEAVES AND COHOMOLOGY

Origins: The Mittag-Leffler Problem

Let S be a Riemann surface, not necessarily compact, p a point of S with local coordinate z centered at p. A *principal part* at p is the polar part $\sum_{k=1}^{n} a_k z^{-k}$ of a Laurent series. If $\mathcal{O}_p$ is the local ring of holomorphic functions around p, $\mathfrak{M}_p$ the field of meromorphic functions around p, a principal part is just an element of the quotient group $\mathfrak{M}_p / \mathcal{O}_p$. The *Mittag-Leffler* question is, given a discrete set $\{p_n\}$ of points in S and a principal part at p_n for each n, does there exist a meromorphic function f on S, holomorphic outside $\{p_n\}$, whose principal part at each p_n is the one specified? The question is clearly trivial locally, and so the problem is one of passage from local to global data. Here are two approaches, both of which lead to cohomology theories.

Čech. Take a covering $\underline{U} = \{U_\alpha\}$ of S by open sets such that each U_α contains at most one point p_n, and let f_α be a meromorphic function on U_α solving the problem in U_α. Set

$$f_{\alpha\beta} = f_\alpha - f_\beta \in \mathcal{O}(U_\alpha \cap U_\beta).$$

In $U_\alpha \cap U_\beta \cap U_\gamma$, we have

$$f_{\alpha\beta} + f_{\beta\gamma} + f_{\gamma\alpha} = 0.$$

Solving the problem globally is equivalent to finding $\{g_\alpha \in \mathcal{O}(U_\alpha)\}$ such that

$$f_{\alpha\beta} = g_\beta - g_\alpha \quad \text{in} \quad U_\alpha \cap U_\beta:$$

given such g_α, $f = f_\alpha + g_\alpha$ is a globally defined function satisfying the conditions, and conversely. In the Čech theory,

$$\{\{f_{\alpha\beta}\} : f_{\alpha\beta} + f_{\beta\gamma} + f_{\gamma\alpha} = 0\} = Z^1(\underline{U}, \mathcal{O})$$

$$\{\{f_{\alpha\beta}\} : f_{\alpha\beta} = g_\beta - g_\alpha, \quad \text{some } \{g_\alpha\}\} = \delta C^0(\underline{U}, \mathcal{O})$$

and the *first Čech cohomology group*

$$H^1(\underline{U}, \mathcal{O}) = \frac{Z^1(\underline{U}, \mathcal{O})}{B^1(\underline{U}, \mathcal{O})}$$

is the obstruction to solving the problem in general.

Dolbeault. As before, take f_α to be a local solution in U_α and let ρ_α be a bump function, 1 in a neighborhood of $p_n \in U_\alpha$ and having compact support contained in U_α. Then

$$\varphi = \sum_\alpha \bar{\partial}(\rho_\alpha f_\alpha)$$

is a $\bar{\partial}$-closed C^∞ $(0,1)$-form on S ($\varphi \equiv 0$ in a neighborhood of p_n). If $\varphi = \bar{\partial}\eta$ for $\eta \in C^\infty(S)$, then the function

$$f = \sum_\alpha \rho_\alpha f_\alpha - \eta$$

satisfies the conditions of the problem; thus the obstruction to solving the problem is in $H_{\bar{\partial}}^{0,1}(S)$.

Sheaves

Given X a topological space, a *sheaf* $\mathcal{F}$ on X associates to each open set $U \subset X$ a group $\mathcal{F}(U)$, called the sections of $\mathcal{F}$ over U, and to each pair $U \subset V$ of open sets a map $r_{V,U} : \mathcal{F}(V) \to \mathcal{F}(U)$, called the restriction map, satisfying

1. For any triple $U \subset V \subset W$ of open sets,
$$r_{W,U} = r_{V,U} \cdot r_{W,V}.$$
By virtue of this relation, we may write $\sigma|_U$ for $r_{V,U}(\sigma)$ without loss of information.

2. For any pair of open sets $U, V \subset M$ and sections $\sigma \in \mathcal{F}(U), \tau \in \mathcal{F}(V)$ such that

$$\sigma|_{U \cap V} = \tau|_{U \cap V}$$

there exists a section $\rho \in \mathcal{F}(U \cup V)$ with

$$\rho|_U = \sigma, \qquad \rho|_V = \tau.$$

3. If $\sigma \in \mathcal{F}(U \cup V)$ and

$$\sigma|_U = \sigma|_V = 0$$

then $\sigma = 0$.

Notation. The following are the sheaves we will be dealing with most often. In every case the restriction maps are the obvious ones, and the groups are additive unless otherwise stated.

1. On any C^∞ manifold M, we define sheaves C^∞, C^*, $\mathcal{C}^p$, $\mathcal{Z}^p$, $\mathbb{Z}$, $\mathbb{Q}$, $\mathbb{R}$, and $\mathbb{C}$ by

$C^\infty(U) = C^\infty$ functions on U
$C^*(U) =$ multiplicative group of nonzero C^∞ functions on U,
$\mathcal{C}^p(U) = C^\infty$ p-forms on U,
$\mathcal{Z}^p(U) =$ closed C^∞ p-forms on U,
$\mathbb{Z}(U)$, $\mathbb{Q}(U)$, $\mathbb{R}(U)$, $\mathbb{C}(U) =$ locally constant $\mathbb{Z}$-, $\mathbb{Q}$-, $\mathbb{R}$-, or $\mathbb{C}$-valued functions on U.

2. If M is a complex manifold, $V \subset M$ an analytic subvariety of M, and $E \to M$ a holomorphic vector bundle (defined below), we define the sheaves $\mathcal{O}$, $\mathcal{O}^*$, Ω^p, $\mathcal{C}^{p,q}$, $\mathcal{Z}_{\bar\partial}^{p,q}$, $\mathcal{I}_V$, $\mathcal{O}(E)$, and $\mathcal{C}^{p,q}(E)$ by

$\mathcal{O}(U) =$ holomorphic functions on U,
$\mathcal{O}^*(U) =$ multiplicative group of nonzero holomorphic functions on U,
$\Omega^p(U) =$ holomorphic p-forms on U,
$\mathcal{C}^{p,q}(U) = C^\infty$ forms of type (p,q) on U,
$\mathcal{Z}_{\bar\partial}^{p,q}(U) = \bar\partial$-closed C^∞ forms of type (p,q) on U,
$\mathcal{I}_V(U) =$ holomorphic functions on U vanishing on $V \cap U$,
$\mathcal{O}(E)(U) =$ holomorphic sections of E over U,
$\mathcal{C}^{p,q}(E)(U) = C^\infty$ E-valued (p,q)-forms over U.

3. If M is again a complex manifold, a *meromorphic function f* on an open set $U \subset M$ is given locally as the quotient of two holomorphic functions—i.e., for some covering $\{U_i\}$ of U, $f|_{U_i} = g_i/h_i$, where g_i, h_i are relatively prime in $\mathcal{O}(U_i)$ and $g_i h_j = g_j h_i$ in $\mathcal{O}(U_i \cap U_j)$. This definition makes implicit use of the proposition on p. 10. A meromorphic function f is not, strictly speaking, a function even if we consider ∞ a value: at points where $g_i = h_i = 0$, it is not defined. The sheaf of meromorphic functions on M is denoted $\mathfrak{M}$; the multiplicative sheaf of meromorphic functions not identically zero is denoted $\mathfrak{M}^*$.

A *map of sheaves* $\mathcal{F} \xrightarrow{\alpha} \mathcal{G}$ on M is given by a collection of homomorphisms $\{\alpha_U \colon \mathcal{F}(U) \to \mathcal{G}(U)\}_{U \subset M}$ such that for $U \subset V \subset M$, α_U and α_V commute with the restriction maps. The *kernel* of the map $\alpha \colon \mathcal{F} \to \mathcal{G}$ is just the sheaf $\mathrm{Ker}(\alpha)$ given by $\mathrm{Ker}(\alpha)(U) = \mathrm{Ker}(\alpha_U \colon \mathcal{F}(U) \to \mathcal{G}(U))$; it is easy to check that this assignment does in fact define a sheaf. The *cokernel* of α is harder to define: if we set $\mathrm{Coker}(\alpha)(U) = \mathcal{G}(U)/\alpha_U \mathcal{F}(U)$, Coker may not satisfy the conditions on p. 35. [The basic example of this is the sheaf map

$$\exp \colon \ \mathcal{O} \to \mathcal{O}^*$$

on $\mathbb{C} - \{0\}$ given by sending $f \in \mathcal{O}(U)$ to $e^{2\pi \sqrt{-1} f} \in \mathcal{O}^*(U)$. The section $z \in \mathcal{O}^*(\mathbb{C} - \{0\})$ is not in the image of $\mathcal{O}(\mathbb{C} - \{0\})$ under exp, but its restriction to any contractible open set $U \subset \mathbb{C} - \{0\}$ is in the image of $\mathcal{O}(U)$.] Instead, we take a section of the cokernel sheaf $\mathrm{Coker}(\alpha)$ over U to be given by an open cover $\{U_\alpha\}$ of U together with sections $\sigma_\alpha \in \mathcal{G}(U_\alpha)$ such that for all α, β,

$$\sigma_\alpha|_{U_\alpha \cap U_\beta} - \sigma_\beta|_{U_\alpha \cap U_\beta} \in \alpha_{U_\alpha \cap U_\beta}(\mathcal{F}(U_\alpha \cap U_\beta));$$

we identify two such collections $\{(U_\alpha, \sigma_\alpha)\}$ and $\{(U'_\alpha, \sigma'_\alpha)\}$ if for all $p \in U$ and $U_\alpha, U'_\beta \ni p$, there exists V with $p \in V \subset (U_\alpha \cap U'_\beta)$ such that $\sigma'_\alpha|_V - \sigma'_\beta|_V \in \alpha_V(\mathcal{F}(V))$.

We say that a sequence of sheaf maps

$$0 \to \mathcal{E} \overset{\alpha}{\to} \mathcal{F} \overset{\beta}{\to} \mathcal{G} \to 0$$

is *exact* if $\mathcal{E} = \mathrm{Ker}(\beta)$ and $\mathcal{G} = \mathrm{Coker}(\alpha)$; in this case we also say that $\mathcal{E}$ is a *subsheaf* of $\mathcal{F}$ and $\mathcal{G}$ the *quotient sheaf* of $\mathcal{F}$ by $\mathcal{E}$, written $\mathcal{F}/\mathcal{E}$. More generally, we say a sequence

$$\cdots \to \mathcal{F}_n \overset{\alpha_n}{\longrightarrow} \mathcal{F}_{n+1} \overset{\alpha_{n+1}}{\longrightarrow} \mathcal{F}_{n+2} \to \cdots$$

is exact if $\alpha_{n+1} \circ \alpha_n = 0$ and

$$0 \to \mathrm{Ker}(\alpha_n) \to \mathcal{F}_n \to \mathrm{Ker}(\alpha_{n+1}) \to 0$$

is exact for each n. Note that by our definition of Coker, this does not imply that

$$0 \longrightarrow \mathcal{E}(U) \overset{\alpha_U}{\longrightarrow} \mathcal{F}(U) \overset{\beta_U}{\longrightarrow} \mathcal{G}(U) \longrightarrow 0$$

is exact for all U; it does imply that this sequence is exact at the first two stages for all U, and that for any section $\sigma \in \mathcal{G}(U)$ and any point $p \in U$ there exists a neighborhood V of p in U such that $\sigma|_V$ is in the image of β_V.

A note: if $M \subset N$ is a subspace, $\mathcal{F}$ a sheaf on M, we can "*extend $\mathcal{F}$ by zero*" to obtain a sheaf $\tilde{\mathcal{F}}$ on N, setting

$$\tilde{\mathcal{F}}(U) = \mathcal{F}(U \cap M)$$

and letting the restriction maps be the obvious ones. Thus we may consider $\mathcal{F}$ as a sheaf on either M or N.

Examples

1. On any complex manifold, the sequence

$$0 \to \mathbb{Z} \overset{i}{\to} \mathcal{O} \overset{\exp}{\to} \mathcal{O}^* \to 0$$

is exact, where i is the obvious inclusion and exp the exponential map $\exp(f) = e^{2\pi\sqrt{-1} f}$. This fundamental sequence is called the *exponential sheaf sequence*.

2. If M is a complex manifold, $V \subset M$ a complex submanifold, the sheaf $\mathcal{O}_V$ may, by extension by zero, be considered a sheaf on M. The sequence

$$0 \to \mathcal{I}_V \xrightarrow{i} \mathcal{O}_M \xrightarrow{r} \mathcal{O}_V \to 0,$$

where i is inclusion and r restriction, is then exact.

3. By the ordinary Poincaré lemma, the sequence

$$0 \to \mathbb{R} \to \mathcal{C}^\infty \xrightarrow{d} \mathcal{Q}^1 \xrightarrow{d} \mathcal{Q}^2 \to \cdots$$

is exact on any real manifold.

4. By the $\bar{\partial}$-Poincaré lemma, the sequence

$$0 \to \Omega^p \to \mathcal{Q}^{p,0} \xrightarrow{\bar{\partial}} \mathcal{Q}^{p,1} \xrightarrow{\bar{\partial}} \mathcal{Q}^{p,2} \to \cdots$$

is exact on any complex manifold.

5. If M is a Riemann surface and we let $\mathcal{PP}$ be the quotient sheaf of the sheaf $\mathcal{M}$ by the subsheaf $\mathcal{O} \xrightarrow{i} \mathcal{M}$, then for $U \subset M$ open,

$$\mathcal{PP}(U) = \{(p_n, f_n)\} : \quad \begin{cases} \{p_n\} \subset U & \text{discrete,} \\ f_n \in \mathcal{M}_{p_n}/\mathcal{O}_{p_n}; \end{cases}$$

i.e., giving a section of $\mathcal{PP}$ over U is the same as specifying the data of a Mittag-Leffler problem for U.

Cohomology of Sheaves

Let $\mathcal{F}$ be a sheaf on M, and $\underline{U} = \{U_\alpha\}$ a locally finite open cover. We define

$$C^0(\underline{U}, \mathcal{F}) = \prod_\alpha \mathcal{F}(U_\alpha),$$

$$C^1(\underline{U}, \mathcal{F}) = \prod_{\alpha \neq \beta} \mathcal{F}(U_\alpha \cap U_\beta),$$

$$\vdots$$

$$C^p(\underline{U}, \mathcal{F}) = \prod_{\alpha_0 \neq \alpha_1 \neq \cdots \neq \alpha_p} \mathcal{F}(U_{\alpha_0} \cap \cdots \cap U_{\alpha_p}).$$

An element $\sigma = \{\sigma_I \in \mathcal{F}(\cap U_{i_k})\}_{\#I = p+1}$ of $C^p(\underline{U}, \mathcal{F})$ is called a p-*cochain* of $\mathcal{F}$. We define a *coboundary operator*

$$\delta : C^p(\underline{U}, \mathcal{F}) \to C^{p+1}(\underline{U}, \mathcal{F})$$

by the formula

$$(\delta\sigma)_{i_0, \ldots, i_{p+1}} = \sum_{j=0}^{p+1} (-1)^j \sigma_{i_0, \ldots, i_j, \ldots, i_{p+1}} \Big|_{U_{i_0} \cap \cdots \cap U_{i_p}}$$

In particular, if $\sigma = \{\sigma_U\} \in C^0(\underline{U}, \mathcal{F})$,

$$(\delta\sigma)_{U,V} = -\sigma_U + \sigma_V;$$

and if $\sigma = \{\sigma_{U,V}\} \in C^1(\underline{U}, \mathcal{F})$,

$$(\delta\sigma)_{U,V,W} = \sigma_{UV} + \sigma_{VW} - \sigma_{UW}$$

(omitting the restriction).

A p-cochain $\sigma \in C^p(\underline{U}, \mathcal{F})$ is called a *cocycle* if $\delta\sigma = 0$. Note that any cocycle σ must satisfy the skew-symmetry condition

$$\sigma_{i_0,\dots,i_p} = -\sigma_{i_0,\dots,i_{q-1},i_{q+1},i_q,i_{q+2},\dots,i_p}.$$

σ is called a *coboundary* if $\sigma = \delta\tau$ for some $\tau \in C^{p-1}(\underline{U}, \mathcal{F})$. It is easy to see that $\delta^2 = 0$—i.e., a coboundary is a cocycle—and we set

$$Z^p(\underline{U}, \mathcal{F}) = \mathrm{Ker}\,\delta \subset C^p(\underline{U}, \mathcal{F})$$

and

$$H^p(\underline{U}, \mathcal{F}) = \frac{Z^p(\underline{U}, \mathcal{F})}{\delta C^{p-1}(\underline{U}, \mathcal{F})}.$$

Now, given two coverings $\underline{U} = \{U_\alpha\}_{\alpha \in I}$ and $\underline{U}' = \{U'_\beta\}_{\beta \in I'}$ of M, we say that $\underline{U}'$ is a *refinement* of $\underline{U}$ if for every $\beta \in I'$ there exists $\alpha \in I$ such that $U'_\beta \subset U_\alpha$; we write $\underline{U}' < \underline{U}$. If $\underline{U}' < \underline{U}$, we can choose a map $\varphi : I' \to I$ such that $U'_\beta \subset U_{\varphi\beta}$ for all β; then we have a map

$$\rho_\varphi : C^p(\underline{U}, \mathcal{F}) \to C^p(\underline{U}', \mathcal{F})$$

given by

$$(\rho_\varphi\sigma)_{\beta_0\cdots\beta_p} = \sigma_{\varphi\beta_0\cdots\varphi\beta_p}\big|_{U_{\beta_0} \cap \cdots \cap U_{\beta_p}}.$$

Evidently $\delta \circ \rho_\varphi = \rho_\varphi \circ \delta$, and so ρ_φ induces a homomorphism

$$\rho : H^p(\underline{U}, \mathcal{F}) \to H^p(\underline{U}', \mathcal{F}),$$

which is independent of the choice of φ. (The reader may wish to check that the chain maps ρ_φ and ρ_ψ associated to two inclusion associations φ and ψ are *chain homotopic* and thus induce the same map on cohomology.) We define the pth *Čech cohomology group* of $\mathcal{F}$ on M to be the direct limit of the $H^p(\underline{U}, \mathcal{F})$'s as $\underline{U}$ becomes finer and finer:

$$H^p(M, \mathcal{F}) = \varinjlim_{\underline{U}} H^p(\underline{U}, \mathcal{F}).$$

Where there is a possibility of confusion, we will denote Čech cohomology groups by $\check{H}$. Clearly, for any covering $\underline{U}$

$$H^0(M, \mathcal{F}) = H^0(\underline{U}, \mathcal{F}) = \mathcal{F}(M).$$

Note that if $M \subset N$ is a closed subspace, $\mathcal{F}$ any sheaf on M, then extending $\mathcal{F}$ by zero to a sheaf on N, we have

$$H^*(M, \mathcal{F}) = H^*(N, \mathcal{F}).$$

The definition of $H^*(M, \mathcal{F})$ as a direct limit is, in practice, more or less impossible to work with. What is needed is a simple sufficient condition on a cover $\underline{U}$ for

$$H^*(\underline{U}, \mathcal{F}) = H^*(M, \mathcal{F}),$$

and this is provided by the

Leray Theorem. *If the covering $\underline{U}$ is acyclic for the sheaf $\mathcal{F}$ in the sense that*

$$H^q\big(U_{i_1} \cap \cdots \cap U_{i_p}, \mathcal{F}\big) = 0, \qquad q > 0, \quad any \; i_1 \cdots i_p,$$

then $H^*(\underline{U}, \mathcal{F}) \cong H^*(M, \mathcal{F})$.

We will prove the Leray theorem in those cases where it will be used.

The most basic property of sheaf cohomology is: Given an exact sequence

$$0 \to \mathcal{E} \xrightarrow{\alpha} \mathcal{F} \xrightarrow{\beta} \mathcal{G} \to 0$$

of sheaves on M, we have maps

$$C^p(\underline{U}, \mathcal{E}) \xrightarrow{\alpha} C^p(\underline{U}, \mathcal{F}), \qquad C^p(\underline{U}, \mathcal{F}) \xrightarrow{\beta} C^p(\underline{U}, \mathcal{G})$$

that commute with δ and hence induce maps

$$H^p(M, \mathcal{E}) \xrightarrow{\alpha^*} H^p(M, \mathcal{F}), \qquad H^p(M, \mathcal{F}) \xrightarrow{\beta^*} H^p(M, \mathcal{G}).$$

We next define the coboundary map $\delta^* : H^p(M, \mathcal{G}) \to H^{p+1}(M, \mathcal{E})$: given $\sigma \in C^p(\underline{U}, \mathcal{G})$ with $\delta\sigma = 0$, we can always pass to a refinement $\underline{U}'$ of $\underline{U}$ and find $\tau \in C^p(\underline{U}', \mathcal{F})$ such that $\beta(\tau) = \rho\sigma$. Then $\beta\delta\tau = \delta\beta\tau = \delta\rho\sigma = 0$, so by passing to a further refinement $\underline{U}''$ we can find $\mu \in C^{p+1}(\underline{U}'', \mathcal{E})$ such that $\alpha\mu = \delta\tau$; $\alpha\delta\mu = \delta\alpha\mu = \delta^2\tau = 0$ and since α is injective this means $\delta\mu = 0$. Thus $\mu \in Z^{p+1}(\underline{U}'', \mathcal{E})$ and we take $\delta^*\sigma = M \in H^{p+1}(M, \mathcal{E})$.

Basic Fact. *The sequence*

$$0 \to H^0(M, \mathcal{E}) \to H^0(M, \mathcal{F}) \to H^0(M, \mathcal{G})$$
$$\to H^1(M, \mathcal{E}) \to H^1(M, \mathcal{F}) \to H^1(M, \mathcal{G}) \to \cdots$$
$$\vdots$$
$$\to H^p(M, \mathcal{E}) \to H^p(M, \mathcal{F}) \to H^p(M, \mathcal{G}) \to \cdots$$

is exact.

For most exact sequences $0 \to \mathcal{E} \to \mathcal{F} \to \mathcal{G} \to 0$ that actually arise naturally —and certainly for all sheaves with which we shall deal in this book—it is the case that there exist arbitrarily fine coverings $\underline{U}$ such that for every open set $U = U_{i_0} \cap \ldots \cap U_{i_p}$ the sequence

$$0 \to \mathcal{E}(U) \to \mathcal{F}(U) \to \mathcal{G}(U) \to 0$$

is exact. Thus, we can find arbitrarily fine coverings $\underline{U}$ of M for which the cochain groups form an exact sequence

$$0 \to C^p(\underline{U}, \mathcal{E}) \to C^p(\underline{U}, \mathcal{F}) \to C^p(\underline{U}, \mathcal{G}) \to 0.$$

In this case, our basic fact is easy to verify: for example, to see that

$$H^p(\underline{U}, \mathcal{F}) \xrightarrow{\beta^*} H^p(\underline{U}, \mathcal{G}) \xrightarrow{\delta^*} H^{p+1}(\underline{U}, \mathcal{E})$$

is exact, let $\sigma \in C^p(\underline{U}, \mathcal{G})$ with $\delta\sigma = 0$ and $\delta^*\sigma = 0$ in $H^{p+1}(\underline{U}, \mathcal{E})$. Then there exists $\tau \in C^p(\underline{U}, \mathcal{F})$ such that $\beta\tau = \sigma$ and $\mu \in C^{p+1}(\underline{U}, \mathcal{F})$ such that $\alpha\mu = \delta\tau$; by definition $\mu = \delta^*\sigma$ in $H^{p+1}(\underline{U}, \mathcal{E})$, so $\mu = \delta\nu$ for some $\nu \in C^p(\underline{U}, \mathcal{E})$. Then $\tau - \alpha\nu$ is a cocycle in $C^p(\underline{U}, \mathcal{F})$ with $\beta(\tau - \alpha\nu) = \beta\tau = \sigma$, showing $\sigma \in \beta^*(H^p(\underline{U}, \mathcal{F}))$. Conversely, it is clear that $\delta^*\beta^* = 0$. The remaining stages are similar but easier.

The most common application of the *exact cohomology sequence* associated to a sheaf sequence

$$0 \to \mathcal{E} \xrightarrow{\alpha} \mathcal{F} \xrightarrow{\beta} \mathcal{G} \to 0$$

is to answer the question: given a global section σ of $\mathcal{G}$, when is σ the image under β of a global section of $\mathcal{F}$? The answer, according to the exact cohomology sequence, is that this is the case exactly when $\delta^*\sigma = 0$ in $H^1(M, \mathcal{E})$.

For example, we consider again the exact sequence

$$0 \to \mathcal{O} \xrightarrow{\alpha} \mathfrak{M} \xrightarrow{\beta} \mathcal{P}\mathcal{P} \to 0$$

on a Riemann surface M. The data of the Mittag-Leffler problem consist of a global section $g \in \mathcal{P}\mathcal{P}(M) = H^0(M, \mathcal{P}\mathcal{P})$; the question is whether $g = \beta^* f$ for some global meromorphic function f. If $\{f_U\}$ are the local solutions of the problem, we have seen that

$$(\delta^* g)_{U,V} = f_V - f_U$$

and that $g = \alpha^* f$ if and only if $\delta^* g = 0$ in $H^1(M, \mathcal{O})$.

There are, roughly speaking, three kinds of sheaves we will encounter:

1. *Holomorphic sheaves*—such as $\mathcal{O}$, $\mathcal{G}_V$, $\mathcal{O}(E)$, and Ω^p—whose sections are given locally by n-tuples of holomorphic functions. These contain for us the most information and are the principal objects of interest.

2. C^∞ *sheaves*, such as $\mathcal{C}^{p,q}$, whose local sections can be expressed as n-tuples of C^∞ functions. These are generally used in an auxiliary manner.

3. *Constant sheaves*, such as $\mathbb{Z}, \mathbb{R}, \mathbb{C}$. These, as we will see, contain topological information about the underlying manifold.

There are a couple of observations to be made about the latter two classes of sheaves:

1. $H^p(M, \mathcal{C}^{r,s}) = 0$ for $p > 0$.

Proof.   Given any locally finite cover $\underline{U} = \{U_\alpha\}_{\alpha \in I}$ of M, we can find a *partition of unity subordinate* to $\underline{U}$, i.e., C^∞ functions ρ_α on M such that $\Sigma \rho_\alpha \equiv 1$ and support$(\rho_\alpha) \subset U_\alpha$. Now given $\sigma \in Z^p(\underline{U}, \mathcal{C}^{r,s})$, we define $\tau \in C^{p-1}(\underline{U}, \mathcal{C}^{r,s})$ by setting

$$\tau_{\alpha_0 \cdots \alpha_{p-1}} = \sum_{\beta \in I} \rho_\beta \sigma_{\beta, \alpha_0, \ldots, \alpha_{p-1}},$$

where the section $\rho_\beta \cdot \sigma_{\beta, \alpha_0, \ldots, \alpha_{p-1}}$ extends to $U_{\alpha_0} \cap \cdots \cap U_{\alpha_{p-1}}$ by zero; one verifies that $\delta \tau = \sigma$. In the case $p = 1$, explicitly:

$$\sigma = \{\sigma_{UV} \in \mathcal{C}^{r,s}(U \cap V)\};$$
$$\sigma_{UV} + \sigma_{VW} + \sigma_{WU} = 0 \qquad \text{in} \quad U \cap V \cap W.$$

Set $\tau_U = \Sigma_V \rho_V \sigma_{VU}$; then

$$
\begin{aligned}
(\delta \tau)_{UV} &= -\tau_U + \tau_V \\
&= -\sum_W \rho_W \sigma_{WU} + \sum_W \rho_W \sigma_{WV} \\
&= \sum_W \rho_W \sigma_{UV} = \sigma_{UV}.
\end{aligned}
$$

In general, sheaves that admit partitions of unity [more precisely, for any $U = \cup U_\alpha$, maps $\eta_\alpha : \mathcal{F}(U_\alpha) \to \mathcal{F}(U)$ such that the support of $(\eta_\alpha \sigma)$ is contained in U_α and $\Sigma \eta_\alpha(\sigma|_{U_\alpha}) = \sigma$ for $\sigma \in \mathcal{F}(U)$] are called *fine*, and the same argument shows that their higher cohomology groups vanish.

2. For K a simplicial complex with underlying topological space M,

$$H^*(K, \mathbb{Z}) \cong \check{H}^*(M, \mathbb{Z}),$$

that is, *the Čech cohomology of the constant sheaf $\mathbb{Z}$ on M is isomorphic to the simplicial cohomology of the complex* K. To see this, we associate to every vertex ν_α in K the open set St(ν_α), called the *star* of ν_α, which is the interior of the union of all simplices in K having ν_α as a vertex. $\underline{U} = \{U_\alpha = \text{St}(\nu_\alpha)\}$ is an open covering of M. $\cap_{i=0}^p \text{St}(\nu_{\alpha_i})$ is nonempty and connected if $\nu_{\alpha_0} \cdots \nu_{\alpha_p}$ are the vertices of a p-simplex in our decomposition; otherwise it is empty. Thus a p-cochain σ of the sheaf $\mathbb{Z}$ associates to every $(\alpha_0 \cdots \alpha_p)$ an element

$$\sigma_{\alpha_0 \cdots \alpha_p} \in \mathbb{Z}\big(\cap \text{St}(\nu_{\alpha_i})\big) = \begin{cases} \mathbb{Z} & \text{if } \nu_{\alpha_i} \text{ span a } p\text{-simplex}, \\ 0 & \text{otherwise.} \end{cases}$$

Given $\sigma \in C^p(\underline{U}, \mathbb{Z})$, we are led to define a simplicial p-cochain σ' by setting, for $\Delta = \langle \nu_{\alpha_0} \cdots \nu_{\alpha_p} \rangle$ a p-simplex with vertices $\nu_{\alpha_0} \cdots \nu_{\alpha_p}$,

$$\sigma'(\Delta) = \sigma_{\alpha_0 \cdots \alpha_p}.$$

$\sigma \mapsto \sigma'$ gives an isomorphism of Abelian groups

$$C^p(\underline{U}, \mathbb{Z}) \longrightarrow C^p(K, \mathbb{Z}),$$

and

$$\delta\sigma'(\langle \alpha_0 \cdots \alpha_{p+1} \rangle) = \sum_i (-1)^{i+1} \sigma'(\langle \alpha_0 \cdots \hat{\alpha}_i \cdots \alpha_{p+1} \rangle)$$
$$= (\delta\sigma)',$$

so that we have an isomorphism of chain complexes $C^*(\underline{U}, \mathbb{Z}) \to C^*(K, \mathbb{Z})$, hence an isomorphism $H^*(\underline{U}, \mathbb{Z}) \to H^*(K, \mathbb{Z})$. Since we can subdivide the complex K to make the cover $\underline{U}$ of M arbitrarily fine without changing $H^*(K, \mathbb{Z})$, we finally obtain

$$\check{H}^*(M, \mathbb{Z}) \cong H^*(\underline{U}, \mathbb{Z}) \cong H^*(K, \mathbb{Z}).$$

The de Rham Theorem

Let M be a real C^∞ manifold. We say that a singular p-chain σ on M, given as a formal linear combination $\sum a_i f_i$ of maps $\Delta \xrightarrow{f_i} M$ of the standard p-simplex $\Delta \subset \mathbb{R}^p$ to M, is *piecewise smooth* if the maps f_i extend to C^∞ maps of a neighborhood of Δ to M. Let $C_p^{ps}(M, \mathbb{Z})$ denote the space of piecewise smooth integral p-chains. Clearly the boundary of a piecewise smooth chain is again piecewise smooth, so $C_*^{ps}(M, \mathbb{Z})$ forms a subcomplex of $C_*(M, \mathbb{Z})$ and we can set

$$Z_p^{ps}(M, \mathbb{Z}) = \text{Ker} \, \partial : C_p^{ps}(M, \mathbb{Z}) \to C_{p-1}^{ps}(M, \mathbb{Z})$$
$$H_p^{ps}(M, \mathbb{Z}) = \frac{Z_p^{ps}(M, \mathbb{Z})}{\partial C_{p+1}^{ps}(M, \mathbb{Z})}.$$

By a foundational result from differential topology, the inclusion map $C_*^{ps}(M, \mathbb{Z}) \to C_*(M, \mathbb{Z})$ induces an isomorphism

$$H_p^{ps}(M, \mathbb{Z}) \cong H_p(M, \mathbb{Z});$$

in other words, every homology class in $H_p(M, \mathbb{Z})$ can be represented by a piecewise smooth p-cycle, and if a piecewise smooth p-cycle σ is homologous to 0 in the usual sense, there exists a piecewise smooth $(p+1)$-chain τ with $\partial\tau = \sigma$.

Now let $\varphi \in A^p(M)$ be a C^∞ p-form and $\sigma = \sum a_i f_i$ a piecewise smooth p-chain; we set

$$\langle \varphi, \sigma \rangle = \int_\sigma \varphi$$
$$= \sum_i a_i \int_\Delta f_i^* \varphi.$$

If φ is a closed form, then for σ the boundary of a $(p+1)$-chain τ, by Stokes' theorem

$$\int_\sigma \varphi = \int_\tau d\varphi = 0,$$

so that φ defines a real-valued singular p-cocycle. Again by Stokes' theorem, we have for σ a cycle

$$\int_\sigma \varphi = \int_\sigma \varphi + d\eta$$

for any $\eta \in A^{p-1}(M)$; thus there is a map

$$H^*_{DR}(M) \to H^*_{sing}(M, \mathbb{R}).$$

The *de Rham theorem* says that this map is in fact an isomorphism.

De Rham's theorem was originally proved essentially by defining relative de Rham groups and showing that the resulting homology theory satisfied the axioms of Eilenberg and Steenrod. We will give here the shorter sheaf-theoretic argument that, while not so geometric, can be merely rephrased to give a proof of the Dolbeault theorem later.

First, since any differentiable manifold M can be realized as the underlying topological space of a simplicial complex K, we have

$$H^*_{sing}(M, \mathbb{R}) \cong H^*(K, \mathbb{R}) \cong \check{H}^*(M, \mathbb{R}).$$

Next by the ordinary Poincaré lemma, the sequence of sheaves

$$0 \to \mathbb{R} \to \mathcal{C}^0 \xrightarrow{d} \mathcal{C}^1 \xrightarrow{d} \mathcal{C}^2 \to \cdots$$

on M is exact; in other words, the sequences

$$0 \to \mathbb{R} \to \mathcal{C}^0 \xrightarrow{d} \mathcal{Z}^1 \to 0$$

$$\vdots$$

$$0 \to \mathcal{Z}^p_d \to \mathcal{C}^p \xrightarrow{d} \mathcal{Z}^{p+1} \to 0$$

are all exact. Now we have seen that

$$H^q(M, \mathcal{C}^p) = 0$$

for $q > 0$ and all p; by the exact cohomology sequences associated to the short exact sheaf sequences above,

$$\check{H}^p(M, \mathbb{R}) \cong H^{p-1}(M, \mathcal{Z}^1)$$

$$\cong H^{p-2}(M, \mathcal{Z}^2)$$

$$\vdots$$

$$\cong H^1(M, \mathcal{Z}^{p-1})$$

$$\cong \frac{H^0(M, \mathcal{Z}^p)}{\delta H^0(M, \mathcal{C}^{p-1})}$$

$$= \frac{Z^p(M)}{dA^{p-1}(M)}$$

$$= H^p_{DR}(M). \qquad\qquad \text{Q.E.D.}$$

Note that the de Rham isomorphism is functorial: if $f: M \to N$ is a differentiable map of C^∞ manifolds, φ a closed p-form on N representing $[\varphi] \in H^p_{\text{sing}}(N, \mathbb{R})$ under the de Rham map and $\sigma = \Sigma a_i f_i$ a piecewise smooth p-cycle on M,

$$\langle f^*\varphi, \sigma \rangle = \sum_i a_i \int_\Delta f_i^* f^* \varphi$$

$$= \langle \varphi, f_* \sigma \rangle$$

i.e., $f^*[\varphi] = [f^*\varphi]$.

The Dolbeault Theorem

We saw in the beginning of this section that the obstruction to solving the Mittag-Leffler problem on a Riemann surface S can be taken to lie in either $H^1(S, \mathcal{O})$ or $H^{0,1}_{\bar\partial}(S)$. In fact, this represents a special case of the

Dolbeault Theorem.   *For* M *a complex manifold,*

$$H^q(M, \Omega^p) \cong H^{p,q}_{\bar\partial}(M).$$

Proof.   By the $\bar\partial$-Poincaré lemma the sequences

$$0 \to \Omega^p \to \mathcal{A}^{p,0} \xrightarrow{\bar\partial} \mathcal{Z}^{p,1}_{\bar\partial} \to 0$$

$$\vdots$$

$$0 \to \mathcal{Z}^{p,q}_{\bar\partial} \to \mathcal{A}^{p,q} \xrightarrow{\bar\partial} \mathcal{Z}^{p,q+1}_{\bar\partial} \to 0$$

are exact for all p, q. Since

$$H^r(M, \mathcal{A}^{p,q}) = 0$$

for $r > 0$, all p, q, the long exact cohomology sequences associated to these sheaf sequences give us

$$H^q(M, \Omega^p) \cong H^{q-1}(M, \mathcal{Z}^{p,1}_{\bar\partial})$$

$$\cong H^{q-2}(M, \mathcal{Z}^{p,2}_{\bar\partial})$$

$$\vdots$$

$$\cong H^1(M, \mathcal{Z}^{p,q-1}_{\bar\partial})$$

$$\cong \frac{H^0(M, \mathcal{Z}^{p,q}_{\bar\partial})}{\bar\partial H^0(M, \mathcal{A}^{p,q-1})}$$

$$= H^{p,q}_{\bar\partial}(M). \qquad \qquad \text{Q.E.D.}$$

As an application we will prove a special case of Leray's theorem: for a locally finite cover $\underline{U} = \{U_\alpha\}$ of M that is *acyclic* for the structure sheaf $\mathcal{O}$, i.e., has the property

$$H^p(U_{\alpha_1} \cap \cdots \cap U_{\alpha_q}, \mathcal{O}) = 0 \qquad \text{for} \quad p > 0,$$

we have

$$H^*(\underline{U}, \mathcal{O}) \cong H^*(M, \mathcal{O}).$$

Proof. We have, by hypothesis,

$$\mathcal{Z}_{\bar{\partial}}^{0,r}\left(U_{\alpha_0} \cap \cdots \cap U_{\alpha_p}\right) = \bar{\partial}\mathcal{C}^{0,r-1}\left(U_{\alpha_0} \cap \cdots \cap U_{\alpha_p}\right);$$

i.e., we have exact sequences of cochain groups

$$0 \to C^p\left(\underline{U}, \mathcal{Z}_{\bar{\partial}}^{0,r-1}\right) \to C^p(\underline{U}, \mathcal{C}^{0,r-1}) \to C^p\left(\underline{U}, \mathcal{Z}_{\bar{\partial}}^{0,r}\right) \to 0,$$

which by the usual algebraic reasoning gives exact sequences

$$\cdots \to H^p(\underline{U}, \mathcal{C}^{0,r-1}) \to H^p\left(\underline{U}, \mathcal{Z}_{\bar{\partial}}^{0,r}\right) \to H^{p+1}\left(\underline{U}, \mathcal{Z}_{\bar{\partial}}^{0,r-1}\right)$$

$$\to H^{p+1}(\underline{U}, \mathcal{C}^{0,r-1}) \to \cdots .$$

Since $H^p(\underline{U}, \mathcal{C}^{0,r}) = 0$ for $p > 0$ by the partition of unity argument, we find

$$H^q(\underline{U}, \mathcal{O}) \cong H^{q-1}(\underline{U}, \mathcal{Z}_{\bar{\partial}}^{0,1})$$

$$\cong H^{q-2}(\underline{U}, \mathcal{Z}_{\bar{\partial}}^{0,2})$$

$$\vdots$$

$$\cong H^1(\underline{U}, \mathcal{Z}_{\bar{\partial}}^{0,q-1})$$

$$\cong \frac{H^0\left(\underline{U}, \mathcal{Z}_{\bar{\partial}}^{0,q}\right)}{\bar{\partial}H^0(\underline{U}, \mathcal{C}^{0,q-1})}$$

$$= H_{\bar{\partial}}^{0,q}(M) \cong H^q(M, \mathcal{O}). \qquad\qquad \text{Q.E.D.}$$

The same argument works as well for the sheaves Ω^p.

Computations

   1. The first observation is that if M is an n-dimensional complex manifold, then

$$H^q(M, \mathcal{O}) \cong H_{\bar{\partial}}^{0,q}(M) = 0 \qquad \text{for } q > n.$$

   2. By the $\bar{\partial}$-Poincaré lemma,

$$H^q(\mathbb{C}^n, \mathcal{O}) = 0 \qquad \text{for } q > 0$$

and more generally

$$H^q((\mathbb{C})^k \times (\mathbb{C}^*)^l, \mathcal{O}) = 0 \qquad \text{for } q > 0.$$

Since $\mathbb{C}^n$ is contractible, moreover, we see that

$$H^q(\mathbb{C}^n, \mathbb{Z}) = 0 \qquad \text{for } q > 0.$$

Now, from the long exact cohomology sequence associated to the exponential sheaf sequence on $\mathbb{C}^n$,

$$H^q(\mathbb{C}^n, \mathcal{O}) \to H^q(\mathbb{C}^n, \mathcal{O}^*) \to H^{q+1}(\mathbb{C}^n, \mathbb{Z})$$

is exact, and it follows that

$$H^q(\mathbb{C}^n, \mathcal{O}^*) = 0 \qquad \text{for } q > 0.$$

As an immediate consequence, we have the answer to the *Cousin problem*:

Any analytic hypersurface in $\mathbb{C}^n$ is the zero locus of an entire function.

Proof. We have seen that in a neighborhood of any point p in $\mathbb{C}^n$ an analytic hypersurface $V \subset \mathbb{C}^n$ may be given as the zero locus of a holomorphic function $f \in \mathcal{O}_p$, and if we choose f not divisible by the square of any nonunit in $\mathcal{O}_p$ then f is unique up to multiplication by a unit. We can thus find a cover $\underline{U} = \{U_\alpha\}$ of $\mathbb{C}^n$ and functions $f_\alpha \in \mathcal{O}(U_\alpha)$ such that the locus $(f_\alpha = 0) = V \cap U_\alpha$, and such that for any α, β,

$$g_{\alpha\beta} = \frac{f_\alpha}{f_\beta} \in \mathcal{O}^*(U_\alpha \cap U_\beta).$$

But since $H^1(\mathbb{C}^n, \mathcal{O}^*) = 0$, the cocycle

$$\{g_{\alpha\beta}\} \in C^1(\underline{U}, \mathcal{O}^*)$$

is a coboundary, i.e., after refinement of the covering if necessary there exists a cochain

$$\{h_\alpha\} \in C^0(\underline{U}, \mathcal{O}^*)$$

such that

$$\frac{f_\alpha}{f_\beta} = g_{\alpha\beta} = \frac{h_\beta}{h_\alpha}.$$

The entire function

$$f = f_\alpha h_\alpha = f_\beta h_\beta$$

then has zero locus exactly V.   Q.E.D.

Another application of the vanishing $H^q((\mathbb{C})^k \times (\mathbb{C}^*)^l, \mathcal{O}) = 0$ is that a covering of a complex manifold by products of planes and punctured planes is acyclic, a fact we will use in the following two computations.

3. To compute the cohomology groups $H^q(\mathbb{P}^1, \mathcal{O})$, take u and $v = 1/u$ Euclidean coordinates on $\mathbb{P}^1$, and set $U = (v \neq 0)$, $V = (u \neq 0)$. U and V are biholomorphic to $\mathbb{C}$ via the coordinates u and v, respectively, while $U \cap V = \mathbb{C}^*$; thus the cover $\{U, V\}$ of $\mathbb{P}^1$ is acyclic. Now

$$C^0(\{U, V\}, \mathcal{O}) = \{(f, g): f \in \mathcal{O}(U), g \in \mathcal{O}(V)\}$$

and

$$C^1(\{U, V\}, \mathcal{O}) = \{h \in \mathcal{O}(U \cap V)\}.$$

Given $(f,g) \in C^0(\{U,V\}, \mathcal{O})$ we can write

$$f = \sum_{n=0}^{\infty} a_n u^n, \qquad g = \sum_{n=0}^{\infty} b_n v^n = \sum_{n=0}^{\infty} b_n u^{-n}.$$

Thus $\delta((f,g)) = -f + g \in \mathcal{O}(U \cap V)$ is zero if and only if $a_n = b_n = 0$ for n positive and $a_0 = b_0$, i.e.,

$$H^0(\mathbb{P}^1, \mathcal{O}) \cong \mathbb{C},$$

or in other words the only global holomorphic functions on $\mathbb{P}^1$ are constants.

In general it is clear from the maximum principle that $H^0(M, \mathcal{O}) \cong \mathbb{C}$ for any compact, connected complex manifold.

On the other hand, given any

$$h = \sum_{n=-\infty}^{\infty} a_n u^n = \sum_{n=-\infty}^{\infty} a_n v^{-n} \in C^1(\{U,V\}, \mathcal{O})$$

we can write

$$h = \delta((f,g)),$$

where

$$f = -\sum_{n=0}^{\infty} a_n u^n, \qquad g = \sum_{n=1}^{\infty} a_{-n} v^n,$$

and it follows that

$$H^1(\mathbb{P}^1, \mathcal{O}) = 0.$$

Similarly, any element (ω, η) of

$$C^0(\{U,V\}, \Omega^1) = \{(\omega, \eta): \omega \in \Omega^1(U), \eta \in \Omega^1(V)\}$$

may be written as

$$\omega = \left(\sum_{n=0}^{\infty} a_n u^n\right) du; \qquad \eta = \left(\sum_{n=0}^{\infty} b_n v^n\right) dv = \left(-\sum_{n=0}^{\infty} b_n u^{-n-2}\right) du,$$

since $dv = d(u^{-1}) = -u^{-2} du$. We see from this that $\delta((\omega, \eta)) = 0$ if and only if $\omega = \eta = 0$, that is,

$$H^0(\mathbb{P}^1, \Omega^1) = 0.$$

By the same token, an element

$$\nu = \left(\sum_{n=-\infty}^{\infty} a_n u^n\right) du \in C^1(\{U,V\}, \Omega^1) = \Omega^1(U \cap V)$$

is expressible as $\delta((\omega, \eta)) = -\omega + \eta$ if and only if $a_{-1} = 0$; thus

$$H^1(\mathbb{P}^1, \Omega^1) \cong \mathbb{C}.$$

The reader may, in the same manner, verify that in general

$$H^p(\mathbb{P}^n, \Omega^q) = \begin{cases} \mathbb{C} & \text{if } p = q \leqslant n, \\ 0 & \text{otherwise,} \end{cases}$$

a fact which we will prove later by means of Hodge theory.

   4.   Let $M = \mathbb{C}^2 - \{0\}$. By Hartogs' theorem we have $\mathcal{O}(\mathbb{C}^2 - \{0\}) = \mathcal{O}(\mathbb{C}^2)$. Take the covering $U_1 = \{z_1 \neq 0\}, U_2 = \{z_2 \neq 0\}$; this is again an acyclic cover $(U_1 \cong U_2 \cong \mathbb{C} \times \mathbb{C}^*; U_1 \cap U_2 \cong \mathbb{C}^* \times \mathbb{C}^*)$. Now $C^1(\{U_1, U_2\}, \mathcal{O}) = \mathcal{O}(U_1 \cap U_2)$ consists of Laurent series

$$f(z_1, z_2) = \sum_{m,n=-\infty}^{\infty} a_{mn} z_1^m z_2^n;$$

$\mathcal{O}(U_1)$ consists of series

$$f(z_1, z_2) = \sum_{m \geqslant 0} b_{mn} z_1^m z_2^n$$

and $\mathcal{O}(U_2)$ of series

$$f(z_1, z_2) = \sum_{n \geqslant 0} c_{mn} z_1^m z_2^n.$$

Thus $\delta C^0(\{U_1, U_2\}, \mathcal{O}) = \mathcal{O}(U_1) + \mathcal{O}(U_2)$ contains no Laurent series with terms $z_1^m z_2^n$, $m, n < 0$; we see that $\dim H^1(\mathbb{C}^2 - \{0\}, \mathcal{O}) = \infty$.

4.   TOPOLOGY OF MANIFOLDS

Intersection of Cycles

Consider the standard torus T and the two 1-cycles A and B drawn in Figure 1. It is intuitively reasonable that any 1-cycle homologous to B must intersect any 1-cycle homologous to A, while a cycle holomologous to A—for example, A'—may well be disjoint from A. This is an invariant of the classes $\alpha = (A)$ and $\beta = (B)$ in $H_1(T, \mathbb{Z})$, which we would like to formalize. The problem is that the number of points of intersection of cycles representing α and β is indeterminate: we can have, for example, either of the situations shown in Figure 2. What is needed is a way of counting up the points of intersection of two cycles on T such that "extraneous" intersections cancel each other out. We may do this as follows: first choose an orientation on T. Then if two cycles A and B on T intersect transversely at a point p, we define the *intersection index* $\iota_p(A \cdot B)$ of A and B at p to be $+1$ if the tangent vectors to A and B in turn form an oriented basis for $T_p(M)$, -1 if not; we define the *intersection number* $^\#(A \cdot B)$ of cycles A and B meeting transversely in smooth points to be the

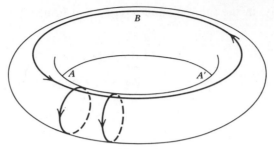

Figure 1

sum

$$^{\#}(A\cdot B) = \sum_{p\in A\cap B} \iota_p(A\cdot B).$$

It is easy to see that $^{\#}(A\cdot B)$ depends only on the homology classes of A and B: if A is homologous to zero—that is, if A is the boundary of regions $C_i \subset T$ with the tangent vector to A and the inward normal vector to ∂C_i always forming an oriented basis for $T(M)$—then the path B will intersect A positively every time it enters a region C_i and negatively every time it leaves; thus

$$^{\#}(A\cdot B) = 0$$

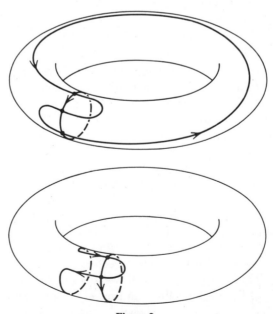

Figure 2

and, in general, since the intersection number is linear in either factor, if $A \sim A'$ then

$$^\#(A' \cdot B) = {}^\#(A \cdot B).$$

Finally, since for any two homology classes $\alpha, \beta \in H_1(T, \mathbb{Z})$ we can find cycles A and B on T representing α and β and intersecting transversely, we have defined a bilinear pairing

$$H_1(T, \mathbb{Z}) \times H_1(T, \mathbb{Z}) \longrightarrow \mathbb{Z}.$$

The definition of intersection of cycles on a general oriented manifold differs from this special case only in the difficulty of verifying the transversality statements made. Suppose M is an oriented n-manifold, A and B two piecewise smooth cycles on M of dimensions k and $n - k$, respectively, and $p \in A \cap B$ a point of transverse intersection of A and B. Let $v_1, \ldots, v_k \in T_p(A) \subset T_p(M)$ be an oriented basis for $T_p(A)$, $w_1, \ldots, w_{n-k}$ an oriented basis for $T_p(B) \subset T_p(M)$; we define the *intersection index* $\iota_p(A \cdot B)$ of A with B at p to be $+1$ if $v_1, \ldots, v_k, w_1, \ldots, w_{n-k}$ is an oriented basis for $T_p(M) = T_p(A) \oplus T_p(B)$, and -1 if not. If A and B intersect transversely everywhere, we define the *intersection number* $^\#(A \cdot B)$ to be

$$^\#(A \cdot B) = \sum_{p \in A \cap B} \iota_p(A \cdot B).$$

Note that this sum is finite, since A and B are compactly supported and by hypothesis $A \cap B$ is discrete.

We now have to show that the intersection number $^\#(A \cdot B)$ depends only on the homology class of A and B; i.e., that

$$A \sim 0 \Rightarrow {}^\#(A \cdot B) = 0.$$

In this case we may take $A = \partial C$ to be the sum of boundaries of piecewise smooth $(k+1)$-manifolds C_i, so that at each smooth point $p \in A$ an oriented basis $v_1, \ldots, v_k$ for $T_p(A)$ together with an inward normal vector to C_i gives the orientation on C_i. By a standard transversality argument, we may take the chain C to meet B transversely almost everywhere, so that the intersection $C \cap B$ will consist of a collection $\{\gamma_\alpha\}$ of piecewise smooth arcs. The endpoints of these arcs will, of course, constitute the points of intersection of A with B; we claim that for each γ, the two endpoints $\gamma(0), \gamma(1) \in A \cap B$ will have opposite intersection index for A and B. (See Figure 3.) This is not hard to see: we can find C^∞ vector fields $\{v_i(t) \in T_{\gamma(t)}(C)\}_{i=1,\ldots,k}$ to C along γ and $\{v_i(t) \in T_{\gamma(t)}(B)\}_{i=k+2,\ldots,n}$ to B along γ, such that for all t

1. $v_1(t), \ldots, v_k(t), \gamma'(t)$ is an oriented basis for $T_{\gamma(t)}(C)$,
2. $\gamma'(t), v_{k+2}(t), \ldots, v_n(t)$ is an oriented basis for $T_{\gamma(t)}(B)$,
3. $v_1(t), \ldots, v_k(t), \gamma'(t), v_{k+2}(t), \ldots, v_n(t)$ is an oriented basis for $T_{\gamma(t)}(M)$,

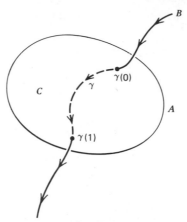

Figure 3

and such that $v_1(0),\ldots,v_k(0)$ is an oriented basis for $T_{\gamma(0)}(A)$, $v_1(1),\ldots,v_k(1)$ a basis for $T_{\gamma(1)}(A)$. (Satisfying all these conditions may require reversing the assigned direction of γ.) Then since $\gamma'(1)$ is outward normal to C and $v_1(1),\ldots,v_k(1),\gamma'(1)$ is positively oriented for C, the basis $v_1(1),\ldots,v_1(1)$ for $T_{\gamma(1)}(A)$ must be negatively oriented. Thus

$$\iota_{\gamma(0)}(A\cdot B) = +1 \quad \text{and} \quad \iota_{\gamma(1)}(A\cdot B) = -1,$$

and we are done.

Now if $\alpha \in H_k(M,\mathbb{Z})$ and $\beta \in H_{n-k}(M,\mathbb{Z})$ are any two homology classes, we may find C^∞ piecewise smooth cycles A and B on M representing α and β and intersecting transversely. The intersection number $^\#(A\cdot B)$ is determined by the classes α,β, and so we have defined a bilinear pairing

$$H_k(M,\mathbb{Z}) \times H_{n-k}(M,\mathbb{Z}) \longrightarrow \mathbb{Z},$$

called the *intersection pairing*, and denoted by $^\#(\alpha\cdot\beta)$. Note that from the definition of the intersection index,

$$^\#(\beta\cdot\alpha) = (-1)^{k(n-k)\#}(\alpha\cdot\beta).$$

We can also define a product

$$H_{n-k_1}(M,\mathbb{Z}) \times H_{n-k_2}(M,\mathbb{Z}) \longrightarrow H_{n-k_1-k_2}(M,\mathbb{Z})$$

on the homology of M in arbitrary dimensions: if $\alpha \in H_{n-k_1}(M)$ and $\beta \in H_{n-k_2}(M)$ are classes, we can find cycles A and B representing them and intersecting transversely almost everywhere. The intersection C is given the orientation such that if $v_1,\ldots,v_{n-k_1-k_2}$ is an oriented basis for $T_p(C)$ at a smooth point of C and we complete it to bases

$$w_1,\ldots,w_{k_2},v_1,\ldots,v_{n-k_1-k_2}$$

and

$$v_1, \ldots, v_{n-k_1-k_2}, u_1, \ldots, u_{k_1}$$

for $T_p(A)$ and $T_p(B)$, respectively, the full basis

$$w_1, \ldots, w_{k_2}, v_1, \ldots, v_{n-k_1-k_2}, u_1, \ldots, u_{k_1}$$

is positively oriented for $T_p(M)$. C, with this orientation, is called the *intersection cycle $A \cdot B$* of A and B. Again, to show that intersection is well-defined on homology—that is, that the cycle $A \cdot B$ is homologous to zero if A is—we have to show first that we can find a chain C with

$$\partial C = A$$

intersecting B transversely almost everywhere, and then that the set-theoretic relation

$$A \cdot B = \partial(C \cdot B)$$

holds as well on the level of oriented cycles. The techniques used to prove these assertions are similar but more complicated than those used in the case of complementary dimension.

A point of terminology: when we speak of the intersection number or "topological intersection" of two cycles A and B on a manifold M, we shall always refer to the intersection number of the classes $\alpha, \beta \in H_*(M, \mathbb{Z})$ they represent. Thus the expression ${}^{\#}(A \cdot B)$ willl have meaning even when A and B fail to meet transversely.

Poincaré Duality

The fundamental result on intersection of cycles is the

Theorem (Poincaré Duality). *If* M *is a compact, oriented* n*-manifold, the intersection pairing*

$$H_k(M, \mathbb{Z}) \times H_{n-k}(M, \mathbb{Z}) \longrightarrow \mathbb{Z}$$

is unimodular; i.e., any linear functional $H_{n-k}(M, \mathbb{Z}) \longrightarrow \mathbb{Z}$ *is expressible as intersection with some class* $\alpha \in H_k(M, \mathbb{Z})$, *and any class* $\alpha \in H_k(M, \mathbb{Z})$ *having intersection number* 0 *with all classes in* $H_{n-k}(M, \mathbb{Z})$ *is a torsion class.*

Proof. As in the previous section, we may assume that M is the underlying manifold of a simplicial complex $K = \{\sigma_\alpha^k, \partial\}_{\alpha, k}$. The essential step in the proof is the construction of the *dual cell decomposition* of M, as follows. (See Figure 4.) First let $\{\tau_\alpha^k, \partial\}$ be the first barycentric subdivision of the complex K. For each vertex σ_α^0 in the original triangulation, let

$$*\sigma_\alpha^0 = \bigcup_{\tau_\beta^n \ni \sigma_\alpha^0} \tau_\beta^n$$

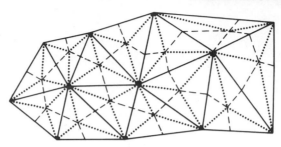

Figure 4

be the n-cell given as the union of the n-simplices τ_β^n in the subdivision having σ_α^0 as a vertex. Then for each k-simplex σ_α^k in the original decomposition, let

$$*\sigma_\alpha^k = \bigcap_{\sigma_\beta^0 \in \sigma_\alpha^k} *\sigma_\beta^0$$

be the intersection of the n-cells $*\sigma_\beta^0$ associated to the $k+1$ vertices of σ_α^k. The cells $\{\Delta_\alpha^{n-k} = *\sigma_\alpha^k\}$ then give a decomposition of M, called the dual cell decomposition to $\{\sigma_\alpha\}$.

Note that since the only point of a k-complex σ_α^k of our original complex held in common by $k+1$ cells of the dual decomposition is its barycenter, *the dual cell $\Delta_\alpha^{n-k} = *\sigma_\alpha^k$ of σ_α is the only $(n-k)$-cell of the dual decomposition meeting σ_α^k*; Δ_α^{n-k} will intersect σ_α^k transversely. Given an orientation on σ_α^k, we may take the dual orientation on Δ_α^{n-k} to be the one such that at $p = \sigma_\alpha^* \cap \sigma_\alpha$,

$$\iota_p(\sigma_\alpha, \Delta_\alpha) = +1.$$

Hereafter, if σ_α is considered an oriented simplex, $*\sigma_\alpha$ will denote the oriented cell Δ_α with the dual orientation; we will also write $*\Delta_\alpha$ to denote the original oriented simplex σ_α.

We now relate the boundary operator ∂ on the complex $\{\sigma_\alpha^k\}$ to the coboundary operator δ on $\{\Delta_\alpha^{n-k}\}$. Note first that if σ_α^k has vertices $\sigma_0^0, \ldots, \sigma_k^0$, then the dual cell $\Delta_\alpha^{n-k} = *\sigma_\alpha^k$ is given as the $(k+1)$-fold intersection $\cap_i \Delta_i^n = \cap_i *\sigma_i^0$ of the dual n-cells, and so the cells appearing in the coboundary $\delta\Delta_\alpha^{n-k}$ of Δ_α^{n-k} will be just the k-fold intersections $\Delta_j^{n-k+1} = \cap_{i \neq j}\Delta_i^n$ of the cells Δ_i^n, that is, the dual cells of the faces σ_j^{k-1} of σ^k. We claim now that the basic relation

$$\delta(\Delta_\alpha^{n-k}) = (-1)^{n-k+1} *(\partial\sigma_\alpha^k)$$

holds on the level of oriented cells, i.e., that if σ_j and Δ_j are oriented as the boundary and coboundary of σ_α and Δ_α, respectively, then at $p' = \sigma_j \cap \Delta_j$,

$$\iota_{p'}(\sigma_j \cdot \Delta_j) = (-1)^{n-k+1}.$$

(See Figure 5.) This is the same sort of argument as made in the verification of homology-invariance of intersection number. The simplex σ_α^k intersects the cell Δ_j^{n-k+1} in an arc γ running from the barycenter $p = \gamma(0)$ of σ_α to the barycenter $p' = \gamma(1)$ of the face σ_j of σ_α. Let $v_1,\ldots,v_{k-1}$ then be vector fields to σ_α along γ and $v_{k+1},\ldots,v_n$ vector fields to Δ_j along γ such that $v_1(0),\ldots,v_{k-1}(0)$, $\gamma'(0)$ is an oriented basis for $T_{\gamma(0)}(\sigma_\alpha)$ and $v_{k+1}(0),\ldots,v_n(0)$ an oriented basis for $T_{\gamma(0)}(\Delta_\alpha)$, and such that $v_1(1),\ldots,v_{k-1}(1) \in T_{\gamma(1)}(\sigma_\alpha)$, $v_{k+1}(1),\ldots,v_n(1) \in T_{\gamma(1)}(\Delta_j)$. By the hypothesis

$$\iota_{\gamma(0)}(\Delta_\alpha \cdot \sigma_\alpha) = +1,$$

the basis $v_1(0),\ldots,v_{k-1}(0),\gamma'(0),v_{k+1}(0),\ldots,v_n(0)$ is positive for the given orientation on M. Moreover, since $\gamma'(0)$ is inward normal to Δ_j at $\gamma(0)$, and since $v_{k+1}(0),\ldots,v_n(0)$ is positively oriented for $T_{\gamma(0)}(\Delta_\alpha)$, the basis

$$\gamma'(0),v_{k+1}(0),\ldots,v_n(0)$$

will have sign $(-1)^{n-k}$ with respect to the orientation on Δ_j. By continuity, these last two assertions will hold as well as $\gamma(1)$. There, since $\gamma'(0)$ is outward normal to Δ_α at $\gamma(1)$ and since $v_1(1),\ldots,v_{k-1}(1)$, $\gamma'(1)$ is positively oriented for $T_{\gamma(1)}(\sigma_\alpha)$, the basis $v_1(1),\ldots,v_{k-1}(1)$ will be negatively oriented for σ_j. Thus

$$\iota_{\gamma(1)}(\sigma_j \cdot \Delta_j) = (-1)^{n-k+1}$$

as desired.

We see from this that the map

$$\sigma_\alpha^p \longrightarrow \tilde{\Delta}_\alpha^{n-p}$$

induces an isomorphism between the complex (C_*,∂) of chains in the original simplicial decomposition of M and the complex $(\tilde{C}^*,\delta)$ of cochains in the dual cell decomposition. The resulting isomorphisms

$$D : H_k(M,\mathbb{Z}) \to H^{n-k}(M,\mathbb{Z})$$

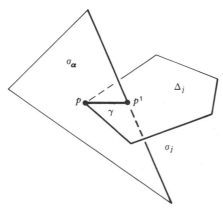

Figure 5

have the property that

$$^{\#}(\gamma \cdot \lambda) = D\gamma(\lambda)$$

for any $\gamma \in H_k(M, \mathbb{Z})$ and $\lambda \in H_{n-k}(M, \mathbb{Z})$; and the theorem follows.

Q.E.D.

A somewhat weaker version of Poincaré duality is the statement that the map

$$H_k(M, \mathbb{Q}) \overset{P}{\longrightarrow} H_{n-k}(M, \mathbb{Q})^* \cong H^{n-k}(M, \mathbb{Q})$$

given by

$$P(A)(B) = {}^{\#}(A \cdot B)$$

is an isomorphism, omitting the fact that the intersection pairing is unimodular. Via the de Rham isomorphism

$$H_{DR}^{n-k}(M) \longrightarrow H^{n-k}(M, \mathbb{C})$$

this is equivalent to the assertion that for any k-cycle A on M there exists a closed $(n-k)$-form φ such that for any $(n-k)$ cycle B on M,

$$\int_B \varphi = {}^{\#}(A \cdot B).$$

Suppose φ and ψ are two closed forms on the oriented manifold M. Then the wedge product $\varphi \wedge \psi$ is closed, and by virtue of the relation

$$\varphi \wedge (\psi + d\eta) = \varphi \wedge \psi + (-1)^{\deg \varphi} d(\varphi \wedge \eta)$$

we see that the de Rham class of $\varphi \wedge \psi$ depends only on the de Rham classes of φ and ψ. Thus we have bilinear maps

$$H_{DR}^k(M) \otimes H_{DR}^{k'} \longrightarrow H_{DR}^{k+k'}(M)$$

and in particular a pairing

$$H_{DR}^k(M) \otimes H_{DR}^{n-k}(M) \longrightarrow H_{DR}^n(M) \cong \mathbb{C}.$$

We will now relate this pairing in de Rham cohomology to the intersection of cycles via Poincaré duality; to do this we must first establish the Künneth formula.

Suppose $M = \{\sigma_\alpha^k\}_{\alpha, k}$ and $N = \{\sigma_\alpha'^k\}_{\alpha, k}$ are two simplicial complexes. The products $\sigma_\alpha^k \times \sigma_\beta'^l$ give a cell decomposition of the product space $M \times N$, with boundary operator

$$\partial(\sigma_\alpha^k \times \sigma_\beta'^l) = \partial\sigma_\alpha^k \times \sigma_\beta'^l + (-1)^k \sigma_\alpha^k \times \partial\sigma_\beta'^l.$$

The product

$$A \times B = \sum a_\alpha b_\beta \sigma_\alpha^k \times \sigma_\beta'^l$$

of two cycles

$$A = \sum a_\alpha \sigma_\alpha^k \quad \text{and} \quad B = \sum b_\beta \sigma_\beta''$$

in M and N is a cycle, and the homology class of $A \times B$ depends only on the homology classes of A and B, since

$$(A + \partial C) \times B = A \times B + \partial(C \times B).$$

We have thus a map

$$H_*(M, \mathbb{Z}) \otimes H_*(N, \mathbb{Z}) \longrightarrow H_*(M \times N, \mathbb{Z});$$

we claim that it is, modulo torsion, an isomorphism. This is readily seen once we express the chains of the complexes M and N in terms of canonical bases, that is, ones in terms of which the boundary operators are diagonal. We may construct such a basis for the chains in M as follows. Suppose M has dimension m; let $\{\tau_\alpha^m\}$ be a rational basis for the m-cycles in M. Complete $\{\tau_\alpha^m\}$ to a rational basis for the m-chains of M; call the additional basis elements $\{\mu_\alpha^m\}$. Set

$$\sigma_\alpha^{m-1} = \partial \mu_\alpha^m;$$

so that $\{\sigma_\alpha^{m-1}\}$ is a basis for the boundaries of M in dimension $m-1$; complete $\{\sigma_\alpha^{m-1}\}$ to a rational basis $\{\sigma_\alpha^{m-1}, \tau_\beta^{m-1}\}$ for the $(m-1)$-cycles of M and complete $\{\sigma_\alpha^{m-1}, \tau_\beta^{m-1}\}$ to a rational basis $\{\sigma_\alpha^{m-1}, \tau_\beta^{m-1}, \mu_\gamma^{m-1}\}$ for all $(m-1)$-chains on M. Set $\sigma_\alpha^{m-2} = \partial \mu_\alpha^{m-1}$; continuing in this way, we obtain a rational basis $\{\sigma_\alpha^k, \tau_\alpha^k, \mu_\alpha^k\}$ for the chains of M, with $\{\sigma_\alpha^k\}$ a basis for the boundaries, $\{\sigma_\alpha^k, \tau_\alpha^k\}$ a basis for the cycles, and $\partial \mu_\alpha^k = \sigma_\alpha^{k-1}$.

Now let $\{\sigma_\alpha'^k, \tau_\alpha'^k, \mu_\alpha'^k\}$ be a similarly constructed basis for the chains of N, and let A be a cycle in $M \times N$, expressed as a linear combination of the products of the basis elements in M and N. Since the products $\sigma_\alpha^k \times \sigma_\beta''$, $\sigma_\alpha^k \times \tau_\beta''$, and $\tau_\alpha^k \times \sigma_\beta''$ are the boundaries of $\mu_\alpha^{k+1} \times \sigma_\beta''$, $\mu_\alpha^{k+1} \times \tau_\beta''$, and $(-1)^k \tau_\alpha^k \times \mu_\beta''^{+1}$, respectively, we may, after replacing A with a homologous cycle, assume that no such terms appear in the expression for A. Also, if a term

$$\sigma_\alpha^k \times \mu_\beta''$$

appears in A, we may remove it by subtracting from A the boundary

$$\partial(\mu_\alpha^{k+1} \times \mu_\beta'') = \sigma^k \times \mu_\beta'' + (-1)^{k+1} \mu_\alpha^{k+1} \times \sigma_\beta''^{-1}.$$

Thus we can write

$$A = \sum a_{\alpha\beta kl} \tau_\alpha^k \times \tau_\beta'' + \sum b_{\alpha\beta kl} \tau_\alpha^k \times \mu_\beta''$$

$$+ \sum c_{\alpha\beta kl} \mu_\alpha^k \times \tau_\beta'' + \sum d_{\alpha\beta kl} \mu_\alpha^k \times \mu_\beta''$$

$$+ \sum e_{\alpha\beta kl} \mu_\alpha^k \times \sigma_\beta''.$$

Taking the boundary, we have

$$0 = \partial A = \sum b_{\alpha\beta kl} (-1)^k \tau_\alpha^k \times \sigma_\beta''^{-1}$$
$$+ \sum c_{\alpha\beta kl} \sigma_\alpha^{k-1} \times \tau_\beta'' + \sum d_{\alpha\beta kl} \sigma_\alpha^{k-1} \times \mu_\beta''$$
$$+ \sum (-1)^k d_{\alpha\beta kl} \mu_\alpha^k \times \sigma_\beta''^{-1}$$
$$+ \sum e_{\alpha\beta kl} \sigma_\alpha^{k-1} \times \sigma_\beta''.$$

But now all the terms in the sum are linearly independent, and so each must be zero; thus $b_{\alpha\beta kl} = c_{\alpha\beta kl} = d_{\alpha\beta kl} = e_{\alpha\beta kl} = 0$ for each α, β, k, l and

$$A = \sum a_{\alpha\beta kl} \tau_\alpha^k \times \tau_\beta''$$

is a linear combination of products of cycles of M and N. Similarly, we see that A is homologous to 0 in $M \times N$ only if $a_{\alpha\beta kl} = 0$ for each α, β, k, l, and so we have established the *Künneth formula*:

$$H_*(M \times N, \mathbb{Q}) \cong H_*(M, \mathbb{Q}) \otimes H_*(N, \mathbb{Q}).$$

We now relate intersections of cycles to wedge products of forms on a compact oriented n-manifold M. Suppose σ is a k-cycle on M and τ an $(n-k)$-cycle and let $\varphi \in A^{n-k}(M), \psi \in A^k(M)$ be closed forms on M representing the cohomology classes Poincaré dual to the classes of σ and τ, i.e., such that for any $(n-k)$-cycle μ,

$$\int_\mu \varphi = {}^\#(\sigma \cdot \mu)$$

and for any k-cycle ν

$$\int_\nu \psi = {}^\#(\tau \cdot \nu).$$

On the product $M \times M$, with projection maps π_1, π_2, we have

$$\int_{\mu \times \nu} \pi_1^* \varphi \wedge \pi_2^* \psi = \int_\mu \varphi \cdot \int_\nu \psi$$
$$= {}^\#(\sigma \cdot \mu) \cdot {}^\#(\tau \cdot \nu).$$

On the other hand, if (p_1, p_2) is a point of intersection of $\sigma \times \tau$ with $\mu \times \nu$, then writing out the orientations we see that

$$\iota_{(p_1, p_2)}(\sigma \times \tau, \mu \times \nu) = (-1)^{n-k} \iota_{p_1}(\sigma \cdot \mu) \cdot \iota_{p_2}(\tau \cdot \nu).$$

Thus

$${}^\#(\sigma \times \tau, \mu \times \nu) = (-1)^{n-k} {}^\#(\sigma \cdot \mu) \cdot {}^\#(\tau \cdot \nu)$$
$$= (-1)^{n-k} \int_{\mu \times \nu} \pi_1^* \varphi \wedge \pi_2^* \psi;$$

note that this formula holds for any $(n-k')$-cycle μ and k-cycle ν: if $k \neq k'$, both sides are zero. By Künneth such products of cycles generate

$H_n(M \times M, \mathbb{Q})$, and so it follows that the form $\pi_1^* \varphi \wedge \pi_2^* \psi$ is Poincaré dual to the cycle $(-1)^{n-k} \sigma \times \tau$, i.e., for any n-cycle η in $M \times M$,

$$(-1)^{n-k} \int_\eta \pi_1^* \varphi \wedge \pi_2^* \psi = {}^\#(\sigma \times \tau \cdot \eta).$$

We apply this in particular to the diagonal $\Delta \subset M \times M$. On the one hand,

$$\int_\Delta \pi_1^* \varphi \wedge \pi_2^* \psi = \int_M \varphi \wedge \psi.$$

On the other hand, a point (p,p) of intersection of $\sigma \times \tau$ with Δ corresponds to a point p of intersection of σ with τ, and examining the orientations we find that for such a point p,

$$\iota_{(p,p)}(\sigma \times \tau \cdot \Delta) = (-1)^{n-k} \iota_p(\sigma \cdot \tau).$$

Thus

$$^\#(\sigma \cdot \tau) = (-1)^{n-k} {}^\#(\sigma \times \tau \cdot \Delta) = \int_M \varphi \wedge \psi,$$

i.e., *intersection of cycles in homology is Poincaré dual to wedge product in cohomology*.

Note that we can identify the Poincaré dual of the pullback map on cohomology. Explicitly, if $f: M \to N$ is a C^∞ map of manifolds nonsingular over the cycle $A \subset N$, then with the proper orientation *the cycle* $f^{-1}(A)$ *is Poincaré dual to the pullback via* f *of the Poincaré dual of* A. This is not hard to see: if $B \subset M$ is any cycle on M meeting $f^{-1}(A)$ transversely, then $f(B)$ will meet A transversely at $f(B \cap f^{-1}(A))$. If φ is a closed form on N Poincaré dual to A, then,

$$\int_B f^* \varphi = \int_{f(B)} \varphi = {}^\#(f(B) \cdot A) = {}^\#(B \cdot f^{-1}(A)),$$

so $f^{-1}(A)$ is Poincaré dual to $f^* \varphi$.

In this context, the weaker form of duality may be restated once again as the assertion that the pairing

$$H_{DR}^k(M) \otimes H_{DR}^{n-k}(M) \longrightarrow \mathbb{R}$$

given by

$$([\varphi], [\psi]) \longrightarrow \int_M \varphi \wedge \psi$$

is nondegenerate, or that for any closed k-form φ on M there exists an $(n-k)$-cycle A, unique up to homology, such that for any closed $(n-k)$-form ψ,

$$\int_M \varphi \wedge \psi = \int_A \psi.$$

A note: The ordinary cup product $\alpha \cup \beta$ of two cohomology classes $\alpha \in H^k(M, \mathbb{Q})$ and $\beta \in H^{k'}(M, \mathbb{Q})$ may be defined as the pullback

$$\alpha \cup \beta = \Delta^*(\alpha \otimes \beta)$$

via the diagonal map $\Delta: M \to M \times M$ of the class $\alpha \otimes \beta$ on $M \times M$ defined by

$$\alpha \otimes \beta(\sigma \times \tau) = \alpha(\sigma) \cdot \beta(\tau)$$

for all cycles σ, τ on M. With this definition, it is clear that if φ and ψ are closed forms on M representing α and β, the form $\pi_1^*\varphi \wedge \pi_2^*\psi$ on $M \times M$ represents $\alpha \otimes \beta$, and hence that $\varphi \wedge \psi$ represents the class $\alpha \cup \beta$. Thus wedge product of forms corresponds, via the de Rham isomorphism, to cup product of cocycles.

As an example, let us compute the homology algebra of $\mathbb{P}^n$. To do this denote by $X = (X_0, \ldots, X_n)$ Euclidean coordinates on $\mathbb{C}^{n+1}$ and $0 = V_0 \subset V_1 \subset \cdots \subset V_n = \mathbb{C}^n$ the *flag* in $\mathbb{C}^{n+1}$ given by

$$V_i = (X_n = \cdots = X_{i+1} = 0);$$

let $\mathbb{P}^k \subset \mathbb{P}^n$ be the image of V^{k+1}. As we have seen, the complement $\mathbb{P}^n - \mathbb{P}^{n-1}$ of the hyperplane $\mathbb{P}^{n-1}$ in $\mathbb{P}^n$ is $\mathbb{C}^n$ with Euclidean coordinates $X_0/X_n, \ldots, X_{n-1}/X_n$; similarly, the complement of $\mathbb{P}^{k-1}$ in $\mathbb{P}^k$ is $\mathbb{C}^k$ with coordinates $X_0/X_k, \ldots, X_{k-1}/X_k$. We have therefore a cell-decomposition of $\mathbb{P}^n$,

$$\mathbb{P}^n = (\mathbb{P}^n - \mathbb{P}^{n-1}) \cup (\mathbb{P}^{n-1} - \mathbb{P}^{n-2}) \cup \cdots \cup (\mathbb{P}^1 - \mathbb{P}^0) \cup \mathbb{P}^0,$$

as a union of $2k$-cells $\mathbb{P}^k - \mathbb{P}^{k-1} \cong \mathbb{C}^k$, one for each $k = 0, \ldots, n$, generalizing the familiar picture of the Riemann sphere. Since there are cells only in even dimension, all boundary maps are zero, and so the homology of $\mathbb{P}^n$ is freely generated by the classes of the closures $\mathbb{P}^k$ of the cells, i.e., by the homology classes of its linear subspaces given the natural orientation.

Inasmuch as a k-plane $\mathbb{P}^k$ and an $(n-k)$-plane $\mathbb{P}^{n-k}$ in $\mathbb{P}^n$ will generically intersect transversely in one point, Poincaré duality is clear in this case. Indeed, since an $(n-k_1)$-plane will generically intersect an $(n-k_2)$-plane transversely in an $(n-k_1-k_2)$-plane,

$$((\mathbb{P}^{n-k_1}) \cdot (\mathbb{P}^{n-k_2})) = \pm (\mathbb{P}^{n-k_1-k_2}).$$

Intersection of Analytic Cycles

Suppose now that M is a compact complex manifold of dimension n, $V \subset M$ a possibly singular analytic subvariety of dimension k. As we have seen, Stokes' theorem

$$\int_V d\psi = 0$$

holds for any $(2k-1)$-form φ on M. We may thus define a linear functional on $H_{\mathrm{DR}}^{2k}(M)$ by

$$[\varphi] \longrightarrow \int_V \varphi,$$

where V is given the natural orientation. By Poincaré duality this linear functional determines a cohomology class $\eta_V \in H_{\mathrm{DR}}^{2n-2k}(M)$, called the *fundamental class* of V.

We may also define the fundamental class of V by means of the intersection pairing. For any homology class $\alpha \in H_{2n-2k}(M,\mathbb{Z})$ we may find a cycle A representing α and intersecting V transversely in smooth points. In fact, the intersection number

$$^{\#}(V{\cdot}A) = \sum_{p \in A \cap V} \iota_p(V,A)$$

—where V again is given the natural orientation—depends only on the homology class α: if $A' \sim A$, then *since the singular locus of* V *has real codimension* $\geqslant 2$ we can find a $(2n-2k+1)$-chain C on M avoiding the singular set of V, meeting V transversely almost everywhere and such that

$$\partial C = A - A'.$$

The proof that $^{\#}(A{\cdot}V) = {}^{\#}(A'{\cdot}V)$ then proceeds exactly as at the beginning of this section. Consequently V defines a linear functional

$$H_{2n-2k}(M,\mathbb{Z}) \longrightarrow \mathbb{Z};$$

the corresponding cohomology class $\eta_V \in H^{2n-2k}(M)$ is the fundamental class of V.

Note: When we speak of the fundamental class of a variety $V \subset M$ we may also refer to its Poincaré dual—that is, the element of homology given by the linear functional

$$H_{\mathrm{DR}}^{2n-2k}(M) \longrightarrow \mathbb{C}$$

$$[\varphi] \longmapsto \int_V \varphi$$

Usually it will either be clear from the context or unimportant which of these we are referring to.

We now make a very simple observation. Suppose V and W are analytic varieties of dimension k and $n-k$ intersecting transversely at a point p on the complex manifold M. We may take holomorphic coordinates $z = (z_1, \ldots, z_n)$ on M near p such that V and W are given by

$$V = (z_{k+1} = \cdots = z_{n-k} = 0)$$

and

$$W = (z_1 = \cdots = z_k = 0).$$

Writing $z_i = x_i + \sqrt{-1}\, y_i$, the natural orientation on M is given by the basis

$$\left(\frac{\partial}{\partial x_1}, \frac{\partial}{\partial y_1}, \ldots, \frac{\partial}{\partial x_n}, \frac{\partial}{\partial y_n} \right)$$

for $T_p(V)$, while the natural orientations for V and W are given by

$$\left(\frac{\partial}{\partial x_1}, \frac{\partial}{\partial y_1}, \ldots, \frac{\partial}{\partial x_k}, \frac{\partial}{\partial y_k} \right)$$

and

$$\left(\frac{\partial}{\partial x_{k+1}}, \frac{\partial}{\partial y_{k+1}}, \ldots, \frac{\partial}{\partial x_n}, \frac{\partial}{\partial y_n} \right).$$

We see, then, that if V, W, and M are all given the natural orientations,

$$\iota_p(V \cdot W) = +1.$$

This trivial observation, that *the intersection index of two analytic subvarieties meeting transversely is always positive*, is in fact one of the cornerstones of algebraic geometry. It relates the set-theoretic intersection of two varieties—a priori a geometric invariant—to the intersection number—a topological invariant—and so provides a basic link. Before we can fully utilize this bond, however, we have to extend it to varieties that may not intersect transversely. This goes as follows (alternate discussion of intersections of analytic varieties will be given in Section 2 of Chapter 3 and in Section 2 of Chapter 5).

Let V and W be two analytic varieties of dimension k and $n-k$ in the polycylinder Δ of radius 1 in $\mathbb{C}^n$ having the origin as their only point of intersection. Consider in the product $\Delta' \times \Delta'$ of the polycylinder of radius $\frac{1}{2}$ with itself the two varieties

$$\tilde{V} = \pi_1^{-1}(V) = \{(z,w): z \in V\}$$

and

$$\tilde{W} = \{(z,w): z - w \in W\}.$$

For each ε, of course, the varieties $\tilde{V}$ and $\tilde{W}$ meet the fiber $\pi_2^{-1}(\varepsilon) = \Delta' \times \{\varepsilon\} \cong \Delta'$ in the analytic variety V and the analytic variety $W + \varepsilon$—that is, W translated by ε—respectively; moreover, $\pi_2^{-1}(\varepsilon)$ will meet the intersection $\tilde{V} \cap \tilde{W}$ transversely at a point (p, ε) exactly when V and $W + \varepsilon$ meet transversely at p. The intersection $\tilde{V} \cap \tilde{W} \subset \Delta' \times \Delta'$ is an analytic variety of dimension n, and so the projection $\pi_2 \colon \tilde{V} \cap \tilde{W} \longrightarrow \Delta'$ expresses $\tilde{V} \cap \tilde{W}$ as a branched μ-sheeted cover of Δ'; accordingly, we see that *for $\varepsilon \in \Delta'$ lying outside an analytic subvariety of Δ', the varieties V and W + ε will meet transversely in μ points in Δ'*. The number μ is called the *intersection multiplicity* of V and W at 0 and is written

$$\mu = m_0(V \cdot W).$$

By the construction the intersection multiplicity is always positive, and by the implicit function theorem will be 1 if and only if $\tilde{V} \cap \tilde{W}$ meets the fiber $\pi_2^{-1}(0)$ transversely—that is, if and only if V and W meet transversely at the origin. Note that the definition does not depend on the choice of coordinates z, so that it applies as well to two analytic subvarieties of a complex manifold. We now check that if V and W are analytic subvarieties of complementary dimension on a compact complex manifold M, then

$$^{\#}(V \cdot W) = \sum_{p \in V \cap W} m_p(V \cdot W).$$

To do this let z, w be local coordinates around a point $p \in V \cap W$, with $p = (0,0)$ the only point of intersection of V with W in the ball Δ of radius 1. Let $\rho(r)$ be a C^∞ bump function, identically 1 on the ball Δ'' of radius $\frac{1}{4}$ and identically zero outside the ball Δ' of radius $\frac{1}{2}$. Then for ε generic and sufficiently small, the locus

$$W_\varepsilon = \{(z): z - \rho(\|z\|) \cdot \varepsilon \in W\} \subset \Delta$$

will

1. agree with W outside Δ',
2. be disjoint from V in $\Delta' - \Delta''$,
3. be an analytic variety in Δ'', meeting V transversely in $\mu = m_p(V \cdot W)$

points.

Now let $\{p_i\} = V \cap W$. Choose coordinate balls Δ_i around p_i and values ε_i as above; set

$$W' = (W - \cup \Delta_i) \cup (\cup W_{\varepsilon_i}).$$

W' is then smooth manifold outside a locus of codimension 2 or more, and so by our general method represents a cohomology class $\eta_{W'}$ in M; indeed, $\eta_{W'} = \eta_W$, since in each Δ_i

$$W - W' = \partial(\{(z: z - t \cdot \varepsilon_i \in W, 0 \leq t \leq \rho(\|z\|)\}).$$

Finally, since W' meets V transversely in $m_{p_i}(V \cdot W)$ points in Δ_i''—where W' and V are both analytic varieties with the natural orientation—and nowhere else,

$$^{\#}(W \cdot V) = {}^{\#}(W' \cdot V) = \sum m_{p_i}(V \cdot W)$$

as desired.

Summarizing,

The topological intersection number $^{\#}(V \cdot W)$ of two analytic subvarieties of complementary dimension meeting in a finite set of points on a compact complex manifold is given by

$$^{\#}(V \cdot W) = \sum_{p \in V \cap W} m_p(V \cdot W).$$

The intersection multiplicity $m_p(V \cdot W)$ *satisfies*

$$m_p(V \cdot W) \geqslant 1$$

with equality holding if and only if V *and* W *meet transversely at* p.

One important corollary of this is that if V and W meet in isolated points, their topological intersection number $^\#(V \cdot W)$ is greater than or equal to their set-theoretic intersection $^\#\{V \cap W\}$. Thus, for instance, if the intersection $V \cap W$ of two analytic varieties in M contains more than $^\#(V \cdot W)$ points, it follows that $V \cap W$ must contain a curve.

As a simple consequence of this assertion, note that

If M *is any complex submanifold of projective space* $\mathbb{P}^n$, V $\subset$ M *an analytic subvariety, then the fundamental class of* V *is nonzero in the homology of* M.

This is easy: if M has dimension m and V dimension k, we can find a linear subspace $\mathbb{P}^{n-k}$ of $\mathbb{P}^n$ meeting V in isolated points, and setting $W = M \cap \mathbb{P}^{n-k}$,

$$^\#(W \cdot V) > 0,$$

which implies $\eta_V \neq 0 \in H^{2n-2k}(M)$.

As a corollary, we see that

The even Betti numbers of M *are positive,*

since by the above the intersection V of M with a linear subspace $\mathbb{P}^{n-m+k}$ in $\mathbb{P}^n$ is an analytic subvariety of dimension k in M, and so represents a nonzero element of $H_{2k}(M)$.

Similarly,

Any analytic subvariety of $\mathbb{P}^n$ *homologous to a hyperplane is a hyperplane.*

To see this, we note that if V is homologous to a hyperplane it has intersection number 1 with a line. Then if p_1, p_2 are any two points of V, the line $L = \overline{p_1 p_2}$, having two points in common with V, must have a curve in common with V; that is, L must be contained in V. V thus contains the line joining any two of its points, and so is a linear subspace of $\mathbb{P}^n$.

From this it follows that

Any holomorphic automorphism of $\mathbb{P}^n$ *is induced by a linear transformation of* $\mathbb{C}^{n+1}$.

Let $X_0, \ldots, X_n$ be homogeneous coordinates on $\mathbb{P}^n$, $x_i = X_i / X_0$ the corresponding Euclidean coordinates on the complement of the hyperplane $H = (X_0 = 0)$. Since the fundamental class of a hyperplane in $\mathbb{P}^n$ generates $H^2(\mathbb{P}^n, \mathbb{Z}) \cong \mathbb{Z}$, any holomorphic automorphism φ of $\mathbb{P}^n$ must take a hyperplane into a complex submanifold of $\mathbb{P}^n$ homologous to a hyperplane, hence to a hyperplane. Consequently, after composing φ with a linear transformation of $\mathbb{P}^n$, we may assume that $\varphi(H) = H$. Similarly, φ must carry the coordinate hyperplanes $H_i = (x_i = 0)$ into hyperplanes other than H, and so we can write

$$\varphi(H_i) = (a_{1,i} x_1 + \cdots + a_{n,i} x_n + a_{0,i} = 0).$$

The pullback $\varphi^*(x_i)$ of the Euclidean coordinate x_i is then a meromorphic function on $\mathbb{P}^n$ with a simple pole along H and a zero along $\varphi(H_i)$; it follows that the function

$$\frac{\varphi^*(x_i)}{a_0 + a_1 x_1 + \cdots + a_n x_n}$$

is holomorphic on all of $\mathbb{P}^n$, hence constant. Thus

$$\varphi^*(x_i) = a'_{0,i} + a'_{1,i} x_1 + \cdots + a'_{n,i} x_n,$$

and so φ is linear.

Note that the group of automorphisms of $\mathbb{P}^n$ is thus the quotient PGL_{n+1} of the general linear group GL_{n+1} by the one-dimensional subgroup of scalar matrices $\{\lambda I\}$.

A final remark: when two analytic subvarieties V and W of a complex manifold M—not necessarily of complementary dimension—intersect transversely, they likewise intersect positively in the sense that the variety $V \cap W$ is counted with the natural orientation in the topological intersection of V and W. More generally, if we define the *intersection multiplicity* $m_Z(V \cdot W)$ of V and W along an irreducible variety $Z \subset V \cap W$ to be the multiplicity

$$\text{mult}_p((V \cap H) \cdot (W \cap H))_H,$$

where p is a generic smooth point of Z and H a submanifold in a neighborhood of p intersecting Z transversely at p, then the topological intersection of V and W is given by

$$(V \cdot W) = \sum_{Z_{\text{irr}} \subset V \cap W} \text{mult}_{Z_i}(V \cdot W) \cdot Z_i.$$

5. VECTOR BUNDLES, CONNECTIONS, AND CURVATURE

Complex and Holomorphic Vector Bundles

Let M be a differentiable manifold. A C^∞ *complex vector bundle* on M consists of a family $\{E_x\}_{x \in M}$ of complex vector spaces parametrized by M, together with a C^∞ manifold structure on $E = \cup_{x \in M} E_x$ such that

1. The projection map $\pi : E \to M$ taking E_x to x is C^∞, and
2. For every $x_0 \in M$, there exists an open set U in M containing x_0 and a diffeomorphism

$$\varphi_U : \pi^{-1}(U) \longrightarrow U \times \mathbb{C}^k$$

taking the vector space E_x isomorphically onto $\{x\} \times \mathbb{C}^k$ for each $x \in U$; φ_U is called a *trivialization* of E over U.

The dimension of the *fibers* E_x of E is called the *rank* of E; in particular, a vector bundle of rank 1 is called a *line bundle*.

Note that for any pair of trivializations φ_U and φ_V the map

$$g_{UV} : U \cap V \to \mathrm{GL}_k$$

given by

$$g_{UV}(x) = \left(\varphi_U \circ \varphi_V^{-1}\right)\big|_{\{x\} \times \mathbb{C}^k}$$

is C^∞; the maps g_{UV} are called *transition functions* for E relative to the trivializations φ_U, φ_V. The transition functions of E necessarily satisfy the identities

$$g_{UV}(x) \cdot g_{VU}(x) = I \qquad \text{for all } x \in U \cap V$$

$$g_{UV}(x) \cdot g_{VW}(x) \cdot g_{WU}(x) = I \qquad \text{for all } x \in U \cap V \cap W.$$

Conversely, given an open cover $\underline{U} = \{U_\alpha\}$ of M and C^∞ maps $g_{\alpha\beta} : U_\alpha \cap U_\beta \to \mathrm{GL}_k$ satisfying these identities, there is a unique complex vector bundle $E \to M$ with transition functions $\{g_{\alpha\beta}\}$: it is not hard to check that E as a point set must be the union

$$\bigcup_\alpha U_\alpha \times \mathbb{C}^k$$

with points $(x, \lambda) \in U_\beta \times \mathbb{C}^k$ and $(x, g_{\alpha\beta}(x) \cdot \lambda) \in U_\alpha \times \mathbb{C}^k$ identified and with the manifold structure induced by the inclusions $U_\alpha \times \mathbb{C}^k \hookrightarrow E$.

As a general rule, operations on vector spaces induce operations on vector bundles. For example, if $E \to M$ is a complex vector bundle, we take the *dual bundle* $E^* \to M$ to be the complex vector bundle with fiber $E_x^* = (E_x)^*$; trivializations

$$\varphi_U : E_U \to U \times \mathbb{C}^k$$

(where $E_U = \pi^{-1}(U)$) then induce maps

$$\varphi_U^*: E_U^* \to U \times \mathbb{C}^{k^*} \cong U \times \mathbb{C}^k,$$

which give $E^* = \cup E_x^*$ the structure of a manifold. The construction is most easily expressed in terms of transition functions: if $E \to M$ has transition functions $\{g_{\alpha\beta}\}$, then $E^* \to M$ is just the complex vector bundle given by transition functions

$$j_{\alpha\beta}(x) = {}^t g_{\alpha\beta}(x)^{-1}.$$

Similarly, if $E \to M$, $F \to M$ are complex vector bundles of rank k and l with transition functions $\{g_{\alpha\beta}\}$ and $\{h_{\alpha\beta}\}$, respectively, then one can define bundles

1. $E \oplus F$, given by transition functions

$$j_{\alpha\beta}(x) = \begin{pmatrix} g_{\alpha\beta}(x) & 0 \\ 0 & h_{\alpha\beta}(x) \end{pmatrix} \in \mathrm{GL}(\mathbb{C}^k \oplus \mathbb{C}^l),$$

2. $E \otimes F$, given by transition functions

$$j_{\alpha\beta}(x) = g_{\alpha\beta}(x) \otimes h_{\alpha\beta}(x) \in \mathrm{GL}(\mathbb{C}^k \otimes \mathbb{C}^l),$$

3. $\bigwedge^r E$, given by transition functions

$$j_{\alpha\beta}(x) = \bigwedge^r g_{\alpha\beta}(x) \in \mathrm{GL}(\bigwedge^r \mathbb{C}^k).$$

In particular, $\bigwedge^k E$ is a line bundle given by

$$j_{\alpha\beta}(x) = \det g_{\alpha\beta}(x) \in \mathrm{GL}(1, \mathbb{C}) = \mathbb{C}^*,$$

called the *determinant* bundle of E.

A *subbundle* $F \subset E$ of a bundle E is a collection $\{F_x \subset E_x\}_{x \in M}$ of subspaces of the fibers E_x of E such that $F = \cup F_x \subset E$ is a submanifold of E; F is clearly a vector bundle itself. The condition that $F \subset E$ is a submanifold is equivalent to saying that for every $x \in M$, there exists a neighborhood U of x in M and a trivialization

$$\varphi_U: E_U \xrightarrow{\ \ } U \times \mathbb{C}^k$$

such that

$$\varphi_U|_{F_U}: F_U \xrightarrow{\ \ } U \times \mathbb{C}^l \subset U \times \mathbb{C}^k.$$

The transition functions g_{UV} of E relative to these trivializations will then look like

$$g_{UV}(x) = \left(\begin{array}{c|c} h_{UV}(x) & k_{UV}(x) \\ \hline 0 & j_{UV}(x) \end{array}\right).$$

The bundle F will have transition functions h_{UV}, and the maps j_{UV} are transition functions for the *quotient bundle* E/F given by $(E/F)_x = E_x/F_x$.

Given a C^∞ map $f: M \to N$ of differentiable manifolds M and N and a complex vector bundle $E \to N$, we can define the *pullback bundle* f^*E by setting

$$(f^*E)_x = E_{f(x)}.$$

If

$$\varphi: E_U \to U \times \mathbb{C}^n$$

is a trivialization of E in a neighborhood of $f(x)$, then the map

$$f^*\varphi: f^*E_{f^{-1}U} \to f^*U \times \mathbb{C}^n$$

gives f^*E its manifold structure over the open set $f^{-1}U$. Transition functions for the pullback f^*E will, of course, be the pullback of the transition functions for E.

A map between vector bundles E and F on M is given by a C^∞ map $f: E \to F$ such that $f(E_x) \subset F_x$ and $f_x = f|_{E_x}: E_x \to F_x$ is linear. Note that

$$Ker(f) = \cup \, Ker f_x \subset E$$

and

$$Im(f) = \cup \, Im f_x \subset F$$

are subbundles of E and F, respectively if and only if the maps f_x all have the same rank. Two bundles E and F on M are *isomorphic* if there exists a map $f: E \to F$ with $f_x: E_x \to F_x$ an isomorphism for all $x \in M$; a vector bundle on M is called *trivial* if it is isomorphic to the product bundle $M \times \mathbb{C}^k$.

Finally, a *section* σ of the vector bundle $E \xrightarrow{\pi} M$ over $U \subset M$ is a C^∞ map

$$\sigma: U \to E$$

such that $\sigma(x) \in E_x$ for all $x \in U$. A *frame* for E over $U \subset M$ is a collection $\sigma_1, \ldots, \sigma_k$ of sections of M over U such that $\{\sigma_1(x), \ldots, \sigma_k(x)\}$ is a basis for E_x for all $x \in U$. A frame for E over U is essentially the same thing as a trivialization of E over U: given

$$\varphi_U: E_U \to U \times \mathbb{C}^k$$

a trivialization, the sections

$$\sigma_i(x) = \varphi_U^{-1}(x, e_i)$$

form a frame, and conversely given $\sigma_1, \ldots, \sigma_k$ a frame, we can define a trivialization φ_U by

$$\varphi_U(\lambda) = (x, (\lambda_1, \ldots, \lambda_k))$$

for $\lambda = \sum \lambda_i \sigma_i(x)$ in E_x.

Note that given a trivialization φ_U of E over U, we can represent every section σ of E over U uniquely as a C^∞ vector-valued function $f = (f_1, \ldots, f_k)$ by writing

$$\sigma(x) = \sum f_i(x) \cdot \varphi_U^{-1}(x, e_i);$$

if φ_V is a trivialization of E over V and $f' = (f_1', \ldots, f_k')$ the corresponding representation of $\sigma|_{V \cap U}$, then

$$\sum f_i(x) \cdot \varphi_U^{-1}(x, e_i) = \sum f_i'(x) \cdot \varphi_V^{-1}(x, e_i)$$

so

$$\sum f_i(x) \cdot e_i = \sum f_i'(x) \cdot \varphi_U \varphi_V^{-1}(x, e_i)$$

i.e.

$$f = g_{UV} f'.$$

Thus, in terms of trivializations $\{\varphi_\alpha : E_{U_\alpha} \to U_\alpha \times \mathbb{C}^k\}$, sections of E over $\cup U_\alpha$ correspond exactly to collections $\{f_\alpha = (f_{\alpha_1}, \ldots, f_{\alpha_k})\}_\alpha$ of vector-valued C^∞ functions such that

$$f_\alpha = g_{\alpha\beta} \cdot f_\beta$$

for all α, β, where the $g_{\alpha\beta}$ are transition functions of E relative to $\{\varphi_\alpha\}$.

Now, let M be a complex manifold. A *holomorphic vector bundle* $E \xrightarrow{\pi} M$ is a complex vector bundle together with the structure of a complex manifold on E, such that for any $x \in M$ there exists $U \ni x$ in M and a trivialization

$$\varphi_U : E_U \to U \times \mathbb{C}^k$$

that is a biholomorphic map of complex manifolds. Such a trivialization is called a *holomorphic trivialization*. Note that if $\{\varphi_\alpha : E_{U_\alpha} \to U_\alpha \times \mathbb{C}^k\}$ are holomorphic trivializations, then the transition functions for E relative to $\{\varphi_\alpha\}$ are holomorphic maps, and that, conversely, given holomorphic maps $g_{\alpha\beta} : U_\alpha \cap U_\beta \to \mathrm{GL}_k$ satisfying the identities on p. 66, we can construct a holomorphic vector bundle $E \to M$ with transition functions $g_{\alpha\beta}$.

All the vector-bundle phenomena discussed so far carry over directly to the category of holomorphic vector bundles. We can define the dual bundle and direct, tensor, and alternating product bundles of holomorphic vector bundles to be holomorphic; likewise we observe that the pullback f^*E of a holomorphic vector bundle E under a holomorphic map $f : M \to N$ of complex manifolds has a natural holomorphic structure. A holomorphic map of holomorphic vector bundles E, F on M is a holomorphic map

$f: E \to F$ with $f: E_x \to F_x$ linear; a holomorphic subbundle of a holomorphic bundle E is a subbundle $F \subset E$ with F a complex submanifold of E, and the quotient bundle is again holomorphic. A section σ of the holomorphic bundle E over $U \subset M$ is said to be holomorphic if $\sigma: U \to E$ is a holomorphic map, a frame $\sigma = (\sigma_1, \dots, \sigma_k)$ is called holomorphic if each σ_i is; and in terms of a holomorphic frame $\{\sigma_i\}$ any section

$$\sigma(x) = \sum f_i(x) \cdot \sigma_i(x)$$

is holomorphic if and only if the functions f_i are.

One important difference between C^∞ and holomorphic vector bundles is this: while there is no naturally defined exterior derivative d on the space of sections of a vector bundle, on a holomorphic vector bundle E the $\bar{\partial}$-operator

$$\bar{\partial}: A^{p,q}(E) \to A^{p,q+1}(E)$$

from E-valued (p,q)-forms to E-valued $(p, q+1)$-forms is well-defined: we take $\{e_1, \dots, e_k\}$ any local holomorphic frame for E over U, write $\sigma \in A^{p,q}(E)$ as

$$\sigma = \sum \omega_i \otimes e_i, \qquad \omega \in A^{p,q}(U),$$

and set

$$\bar{\partial}\sigma = \sum \bar{\partial}\omega_i \otimes e_i.$$

If $\{e_1', \dots, e_k'\}$ is any other holomorphic frame for E over U, with

$$e_i = \sum g_{ij} e_j'.$$

then

$$\sigma = \sum g_{ij}\omega_i \otimes e_j'$$

and

$$\bar{\partial}\sigma = \sum \bar{\partial}(g_{ij}\omega_i) \otimes e_j' = \sum g_{ij} \cdot \bar{\partial}\omega_i \otimes e_j' = \sum \bar{\partial}\omega_i \otimes e_i,$$

so $\bar{\partial}\sigma$ does not depend on the frame.

Examples

Let M be a complex manifold, and let $T_x(M)$ be the complex tangent space to M at x (p. 16). For $x \in U \subset M$ and $\varphi_U: U \to \mathbb{C}^n$ a coordinate chart, we have maps

$$\varphi_{U_*}: T_x(M) \to T_{\varphi(x)}(U) \cong \mathbb{C}\left\{ \frac{\partial}{\partial x_i}, \frac{\partial}{\partial y_i} \right\} \cong \mathbb{C}^{2n}$$

for each $x \in U$, hence a map

$$\varphi_{U_*}: \bigcup_{x \in U} T_x(M) \to U \times \mathbb{C}^{2n}$$

giving $T(M) = \bigcup_{x \in M} T_x(M)$ the structure of a complex vector bundle, called the *complex tangent bundle*. Transition functions for $T(M)$ are given by

$$j_{U,V} = \mathcal{J}_{\mathbb{R}}(\varphi_U \varphi_V^{-1}).$$

Now for each $x \in M$

$$T_x(M) = T_x'(M) \oplus T_x''(M),$$

where $T_x'(M)$ and $T_x''(M)$ are as on p. 17. The subspaces $\{T_x'(M) \subset T_x(M)\}$ form a subbundle $T'(M) \subset T(M)$, called the *holomorphic tangent bundle*. Transition functions for $T'(M)$ are given by

$$j_{U,V} = \mathcal{J}_{\mathbb{C}}(\varphi_U \varphi_V^{-1}),$$

and so we see that $T'(M)$ has naturally the structure of a holomorphic vector bundle.

Similarly, we define:

$T^*(M) = T(M)^*$: the complex cotangent bundle,
$T^{*'}(M), T^{*''}(M)$: the holomorphic and antiholomorphic cotangent bundles,
$$T^{*(p,q)}(M) = \wedge^p T^{*'}(M) \otimes \wedge^q T^{*''}(M).$$

The tensor, symmetric, and exterior products of the holomorphic and complexified tangent and cotangent bundles are called *tensor bundles*.

If $V \subset M$ is a complex submanifold, we define the *normal bundle* $N_{V/M}$ to V in M to be the quotient of the tangent bundle to M, restricted to V, by the subbundle

$$T'(V) \hookrightarrow T'(M)|_V.$$

The *conormal* bundle $N_{V/M}^*$ to V in M is the dual of the normal bundle.

Metrics, Connections, and Curvature

Let $E \to M$ be a complex vector bundle. A *hermitian metric* on E is a hermitian inner product on each fiber E_x of E, varying smoothly with $x \in M$—i.e., such that if $\zeta = \{\zeta_1, \ldots, \zeta_k\}$ is a frame for E, then the functions

$$h_{ij}(x) = (\zeta_i(x), \zeta_j(x))$$

are C^∞. A frame ζ for E is called *unitary* if $\zeta_1(x), \ldots, \zeta_k(x)$ is an orthonormal basis for E_x for each x; unitary frames always exist locally, since we can take any frame and apply the Gram-Schmidt process.

If E is a bundle with hermitian metric, $F \subset E$ a subbundle, then the subspaces $\{F_x^\perp \subset E_x\}$ form a subbundle of E, C^∞ isomorphic to the quotient bundle E/F.

A holomorphic vector bundle with a hermitian metric is called a *hermitian vector bundle.*

DEFINITION.   A *connection D* on a complex vector bundle $E \to M$ is a map

$$D: \; \mathcal{Q}^0(E) \to \mathcal{Q}^1(E)$$

satisfying Leibnitz' rule

$$D(f \cdot \zeta) = df \otimes \zeta + f \cdot D(\zeta)$$

for all sections $\zeta \in \mathcal{Q}^0(E)(U), f \in C^\infty(U)$.

A connection is essentially a way of differentiating sections: for $\xi \in \mathcal{Q}^0(E)(U)$ the contraction of $D\xi$ with a tangent vector $v \in T_x(M)$ may be thought of as the derivative of ξ in the direction v. It is, however, only a first-order approximation of differentiation, inasmuch as mixed partials will in general not be equal.

Let $e = e_1, \ldots, e_n$ be a frame for E over U. Given a connection D on E, we can decompose De_i into its components, writing

$$De_i = \sum \theta_{ij} e_j.$$

The matrix $\theta = (\theta_{ij})$ of 1-forms is called the *connection matrix* of D with respect to e. The data e and θ determine D: for a general section $\sigma \in \mathcal{Q}^0(E)(U)$, writing

$$\sigma = \sum \sigma_i e_i,$$

we have

$$Do = \sum d\sigma_i \cdot e_i + \sum \sigma_i \cdot De_i$$
$$= \sum_j \left(d\sigma_j + \sum_i \sigma_i \theta_{ij} \right) e_j.$$

The connection matrix θ at a point $z_0 \in U$ depends on the choice of frame in a neighborhood of z_0: if $e' = e'_1, \ldots, e'_n$ is another frame with

$$e'_i(z) = \sum g_{ij}(z) e_j(z),$$

then

$$De'_i = \sum dg_{ij} \cdot e_j + \sum g_{ik} \theta_{kj} \cdot e_j,$$

so that

$$\theta_{e'} = dg \cdot g^{-1} + g \cdot \theta_e \cdot g^{-1} \qquad (g = (g_{ij})).$$

There is in general no "natural" connection on a vector bundle E. If M is complex and E hermitian, however, we can make two requirements that dictate a canonical choice of connection.

1.   Using the decomposition $T^* = T^{*\prime} \oplus T^{*\prime\prime}$, we can write $D = D' + D''$, with $D': \mathcal{C}^0(E) \to \mathcal{C}^{1,0}(E)$ and $D'': \mathcal{C}^0(E) \to \mathcal{C}^{0,1}(E)$. Now we say that a connection D on E is *compatible with the complex structure* if $D'' = \bar{\partial}$.

2.   If E is hermitian, D is said to be *compatible with the metric* if

$$d(\xi, \eta) = (D\xi, \eta) + (\xi, D\eta).$$

Lemma.   *If* E *is a hermitian vector bundle, there is a unique connection* D *on* E *compatible with both the metric and the complex structure.*

Proof.   Let $e = e_1, \ldots, e_n$ be a *holomorphic* frame for E, and let $h_{ij} = (e_i, e_j)$. If such a D exists, its matrix θ with respect to e must have type $(1,0)$, and consequently

$$dh_{ij} = d(e_i, e_j)$$

$$= \sum_k \theta_{ik} h_{kj} + \sum_k \bar{\theta}_{jk} h_{ik}$$

$$= \text{type } (1,0) + \text{type } (0,1).$$

Comparing types, we have

$$\partial h_{ij} = \sum \theta_{ik} h_{kj}, \qquad \text{i.e.,} \quad \partial h = \theta h,$$

$$\bar{\partial} h_{ij} = \sum \bar{\theta}_{jk} h_{ik}, \qquad \text{i.e.,} \quad \bar{\partial} h = h^t \bar{\theta},$$

and we see that $\theta = \partial h \cdot h^{-1}$ is the unique solution to both equations. Since θ is determined by the conditions of compatibility, θ is well-defined globally.

Q.E.D.

The unique connection compatible with the complex and metric structures on E is called the associated, or *metric*, connection. As mentioned in the proof, its matrix with respect to a holomorphic frame is of type $(1,0)$; on the other hand if $e_1, \ldots, e_n$ is a unitary frame,

$$0 = d(e_i, e_j) = \theta_{ij} + \bar{\theta}_{ji},$$

so its matrix with respect to a unitary frame is skew-hermitian.

The metric connections of hermitian vector bundles behave well with respect to bundle operations, as we see in the next two lemmas.

Lemma.   *Let* E $\to$ M *be a hermitian vector bundle and* F $\subset$ E *a holomorphic subbundle. Then* F *is itself a hermitian bundle with metric connection* D_F. *On the other hand, the metric connection* D_E *in* E *and direct-sum decomposition* E $=$ F $\oplus$ F$^\perp$ *induced by the metric give a connection* $\pi_F D_E$ *in* F, *and*

$$D_F = \pi_F \circ D_E,$$

where π_F *is the projection onto* F.

Proof. If ζ is a section of F, then $(\pi_F \circ D_E)''(\zeta) = \pi_F(D_E''\zeta) = \pi_F(\bar{\partial}\zeta) = \bar{\partial}\zeta$, so that $\pi_F \circ D_E$ is compatible with the complex structure. If ζ, ζ' are sections of F, then

$$
\begin{aligned}
d(\zeta, \zeta') &= (D_E\zeta, \zeta') + (\zeta, D_E\zeta') \\
&= (\pi_F \circ D_E\zeta, \zeta') + (\zeta, \pi_F \circ D_E\zeta'),
\end{aligned}
$$

so that $\pi_F \circ D_E$ is compatible with the metric.   Q.E.D.

Similarly, if E, E' are hermitian vector bundles, there is a natural metric on $E \otimes E'$ given by

$$
(\lambda \otimes \lambda', \delta \otimes \delta') = (\lambda, \delta) \cdot (\lambda', \delta')
$$

for $\lambda, \delta \in E_x$, $\lambda', \delta' \in E'_x$. Let $D_E, D_{E'}, D_{E \otimes E'}$ denote the metric connections on E, E', and $E \otimes E'$, respectively, and let $D_E \otimes 1$ be the connection on $E \otimes E'$ given by

$$
(D_E \otimes 1)(\zeta \otimes \xi) = D\zeta \otimes \xi;
$$

define $1 \otimes D_{E'}$ analogously. Then we have

Lemma. $D_{E \otimes E'} = D_E \otimes 1 + 1 \otimes D_{E'}$.

Proof. Clearly $(D_E \otimes 1 + 1 \otimes D_{E'})'' = \bar{\partial}$; thus we just have to check compatibility with the metric. Let ζ, ξ be sections of E, ζ', ξ' sections of E'. Then

$$
\begin{aligned}
d(\zeta \otimes \zeta', \xi \otimes \xi') &= (\zeta', \xi')((D_E\zeta, \xi) + (\zeta, D_E\xi)) + (\zeta, \xi)((D_{E'}\zeta', \xi') + (\zeta', D_{E'}\xi')) \\
&= ((D_E \otimes 1 + 1 \otimes D_{E'})(\zeta \otimes \zeta', \xi \otimes \xi') \\
&\quad + (\zeta \otimes \zeta', (D_E \otimes 1 + 1 \otimes D_{E'})(\xi \otimes \xi')).
\end{aligned}
$$
         Q.E.D.

Finally, note that a hermitian metric on the holomorphic bundle E induces a metric on E^*—if e is a unitary frame for E, e^* the dual frame for E^*, set

$$
(e_i^*, e_j^*) = \delta_{ij}
$$

—and the metric connection D^* on E^* can be defined by the requirement

$$
d\langle \sigma, \tau \rangle = \langle D\sigma, \tau \rangle + \langle \sigma, D^*\tau \rangle
$$

for $\sigma \in \mathscr{C}^0(E)(U)$, $\tau \in \mathscr{C}^0(E^*)(U)$.

Now, returning to the general discussion, given a connection D on a complex vector bundle $E \to M$ we can define operators

$$
D: \mathscr{C}^p(E) \to \mathscr{C}^{p+1}(E)
$$

by forcing Leibnitz' rule

$$
D(\psi \wedge \xi) = d\psi \otimes \xi + (-1)^p \psi \wedge D\xi
$$

for $\psi \in \mathscr{C}^p(U)$, $\xi \in \mathscr{C}^0(E)(U)$. In particular we can discuss the operator

$$
D^2: \mathscr{C}^0(E) \to \mathscr{C}^2(E).
$$

The first fact about D^2 is that it is linear over $\mathcal{C}^0$, i.e., for σ a section of E and f a C^∞ function,

$$
\begin{aligned}
D^2(f\cdot\sigma) &= D(df\otimes\sigma + f\cdot D\sigma) \\
&= -df\wedge D\sigma + df\wedge D\sigma + f\cdot D^2\sigma \\
&= f\cdot D^2\sigma.
\end{aligned}
$$

Consequently the map $D^2\colon \mathcal{C}^0(E)\to\mathcal{C}^2(E)$ is induced by a bundle map $E\to\wedge^2 T^*\otimes E$, or in other words, D^2 corresponds to a global section Θ of the bundle

$$
\wedge^2 T^*\otimes \operatorname{Hom}(E,E) = \wedge^2 T^*\otimes(E^*\otimes E).
$$

If e is a frame for E, then in terms of the frame $\{e_i^*\otimes e_j\}$ for $E^*\otimes E$, we can represent $\Theta\in A^2(E^*\otimes E)$ by a matrix Θ_e of 2-forms—i.e., we can write

$$
D^2 e_i = \sum \Theta_{ij}\otimes e_j;
$$

Θ_e is called the *curvature matrix* of D in terms of the frame e. If $\{e_i' = \sum g_{ij}e_j\}$ is another frame, then

$$
\begin{aligned}
D^2 e_i' &= D^2\Big(\sum g_{ij}e_j\Big) \\
&= \sum g_{ij}\Theta_{jk}e_k \\
&= \sum g_{ij}\Theta_{jk}g_{kl}^{-1}e_l',
\end{aligned}
$$

that is,

$$
\Theta_{e'} = g\cdot\Theta_e\cdot g^{-1}.
$$

The curvature matrix is readily expressed in terms of the connection matrix: by definition

$$
\begin{aligned}
D^2 e_i &= D\Big(\sum \theta_{ij}\otimes e_j\Big) \\
&= \sum\Big(d\theta_{ij}-\sum\theta_{ik}\wedge\theta_{kj}\Big)\otimes e_j.
\end{aligned}
$$

In matrix notation, therefore,

$$
\Theta_e = d\theta_e - \theta_e\wedge\theta_e.
$$

This is called the *Cartan structure equation*.

We can say more about Θ in the holomorphic case. If $E\to M$ is hermitian and the connection D on E is compatible with the complex structure, then $D''=\bar\partial$ implies $D''^2=0$ and hence $\Theta^{0,2}=0$. If, moreover, D is compatible with the metric, then in terms of a unitary frame e, the connection matrix θ_e is skew-hermitian and hence so is $\Theta = d\theta - \theta\wedge\theta$; thus $\Theta^{2,0} = -{}^t\overline{\Theta}^{0,2}=0$. Since the type of Θ is clearly invariant under change of frame, we see that *the curvature matrix of the metric connection on a hermitian bundle is a hermitian matrix of $(1,1)$-forms.*

To close this section, we give computations of the metric connection and curvature matrices of hermitian bundles in two special cases.

First, recall that for E a hermitian bundle with metric connection D, the metric connection D^* on E^* satisfies

$$d\langle \sigma, \tau \rangle = \langle D\sigma, \tau \rangle + \langle \sigma, D^*\tau \rangle$$

for all $\sigma \in \mathcal{C}^0(E)(U)$, $\tau \in \mathcal{C}^0(E^*)(U)$. In particular, if e is a frame for E and e^* the dual frame in E^*, θ and θ^* the corresponding connection matrices, we have

$$0 = d\langle e_i, e_j^* \rangle = \theta_{ij} + \theta_{ji}^*,$$

so that $\theta = -\,{}^t\theta^*$.

In view of this, a special situation holds when we consider the metric connection on the holomorphic tangent bundle of a hermitian manifold: we can compare the dual connection D^* on the holomorphic cotangent bundle with the ordinary exterior derivative. Thus

$$D^*: A^{1,0} \to A^{1,0} \otimes A^1 = (A^{1,0} \otimes A^{1,0}) \oplus (A^{1,0} \otimes A^{0,1})$$
$$d: A^{1,0} \to A^{2,0} \oplus (A^{1,0} \otimes A^{0,1}).$$

Since D^* is compatible with the complex structure, we have $D^{*''} = \bar{\partial}$; i.e., the two operators agree in the factor $A^{1,0} \otimes A^{0,1}$. As will now be seen, this gives us an effective means of computing the connection matrix of D. Let $ds^2 = \sum h_{ij}\, dz_i \otimes d\bar{z}_j = \sum \varphi_i \otimes \bar{\varphi}_i$ be a hermitian metric on M.

Lemma. *There exists a unique matrix ψ_{ij} of 1-forms such that $\psi + {}^t\bar{\psi} = 0$ and*

$$(*) \qquad\qquad d\varphi_i = \sum_j \psi_{ij} \wedge \varphi_j + \tau_i,$$

where τ_i is of type $(2,0)$.

Proof. Write $\psi = \psi' + \psi''$ for the type decomposition of ψ. Then

$$\bar{\partial}\varphi_i = \sum \psi_{ij}'' \wedge \varphi_j$$

determines ψ'', and $\psi + {}^t\bar{\psi} = 0 \Rightarrow \psi' = -{}^t\bar{\psi}''$. (Explicitly: if we write $\varphi_i = \sum a_{ij}\, dz_j$, where $a\,{}^t\bar{a} = h$, we have

$$\bar{\partial}\varphi_i = \sum_k \bar{\partial} a_{ik} \wedge dz_k$$
$$= \sum_{j,k} \bar{\partial} a_{ik} \wedge a_{kj}^{-1} \cdot \varphi_j,$$

so $\psi'' = \bar{\partial} a a^{-1}$.)   Q.E.D.

Let $v = v_1, \ldots, v_n$ be the frame for the tangent bundle $T'(M)$ dual to the frame $\varphi_1, \ldots, \varphi_n$; let θ be the connection matrix of D with respect to the frame v and θ^* the matrix for D^* in the frame $\varphi_1, \ldots, \varphi_n$. Then

$$D^{*\prime\prime} = \bar{\partial} \Rightarrow \theta^{*\prime\prime} = \psi^{\prime\prime}$$
$$\Rightarrow \theta^* = \psi$$

since $\theta^* + {}^t\bar{\theta}^* = 0$ and $\psi + {}^t\bar{\psi} = 0$. Thus we have

$$\theta = -{}^t\theta^* = -{}^t\psi.$$

In summary, using the basic *structure equation* (∗) we may determine the connection matrix $\theta = -{}^t\psi$ in the holomorphic tangent bundle $T'(M)$ by knowing the exterior derivatives $d\varphi_i$ of a unitary coframe. The vector $\tau = (\tau_1, \ldots, \tau_n)$ is called the *torsion*; a metric is called *Kähler* if its torsion vanishes. Later on we shall give alternate definitions of the Kähler condition.

Examples

Let M be a Riemann surface with local coordinate z; a metric on M is given by

$$ds^2 = h^2 \, dz \otimes d\bar{z} = \varphi \otimes \bar{\varphi},$$

where $\varphi = h \, dz$. Then

$$d\varphi = \bar{\partial} h \wedge dz = \frac{\bar{\partial} h}{h} \wedge \varphi,$$

so $\psi^{\prime\prime} = \bar{\partial} \log h$ and $\psi = (\bar{\partial} - \partial) \log h$; by the structure equation the matrix for the metric connection on the tangent bundle is given by

$$\theta = -\psi = (\partial - \bar{\partial}) \log h$$
$$= \frac{\partial}{\partial z} \log h \cdot dz - \frac{\partial}{\partial \bar{z}} \log h \cdot d\bar{z}.$$

Now $\theta \wedge \theta = 0$, so by the Cartan structure equation

$$\Theta = d\theta = -2\left(\frac{\partial^2}{\partial z \, \partial \bar{z}} \log h \right) dz \wedge d\bar{z}$$

$$= -\frac{1}{2}\left(\frac{\partial^2}{\partial x^2} + \frac{\partial^2}{\partial y^2} \right) \log h \cdot dz \wedge d\bar{z}$$

$$= -\tfrac{1}{2} \Delta \log h \cdot dz \wedge d\bar{z}.$$

Comparing the curvature "matrix" Θ with the associated $(1,1)$-form $\Phi = (\sqrt{-1}/2)\varphi \wedge \bar{\varphi} = (\sqrt{-1}/2)h^2 \, dz \wedge d\bar{z}$, we obtain

$$\sqrt{-1}\,\Theta = K \cdot \Phi,$$

where $K = (-\Delta \log h)/h^2$ is the usual *Gaussian curvature*.

Our second computation involves the curvature operator of sub- and quotient bundles of a hermitian bundle. While we cannot make a complete computation, we will run across a fundamental distinction between the C^∞ and holomorphic cases: the presence of a sign in the curvature of a hermitian bundle.

Let $E \to M$ be a hermitian bundle, $S \subset E$ a holomorphic subbundle, and $Q = E/S$ the quotient bundle. As mentioned earlier, Q is isomorphic, as a C^∞ vector bundle, to the orthogonal complement $S^\perp$ of S in E, and so both S and Q inherit hermitian structures from E; let D_E, D_S, and D_Q denote the corresponding metric connections. By the lemma on p. 73, D_S is equal to the composition of the operator

$$D_E|_{\mathcal{C}^0(S)} : \mathcal{C}^0(S) \to \mathcal{C}^1(E)$$

with the projection $\mathcal{C}^1(E) \to \mathcal{C}^1(S)$; thus the operator

$$A = D_E|_{\mathcal{C}^0(S)} - D_S$$

maps $\mathcal{C}^0(S)$ to $\mathcal{C}^1(Q)$. A is called the *second fundamental form* of S in E; clearly, it is of type $(1,0)$ and linear over C^∞ functions, i.e.,

$$A \in \mathcal{C}^{1,0}(\mathrm{Hom}(S,Q)).$$

To compute curvatures, we choose a unitary frame $e_1, \ldots, e_r$ for E such that $e_1, \ldots, e_s$ is a frame for S. Using this frame and our lemma, the connection matrix for E is

$$\theta_E = \begin{pmatrix} \theta_S & {}^t\overline{A} \\ A & \theta_Q \end{pmatrix},$$

where θ_S, θ_Q are the respective connection matrices for S and Q. Then

$$\Theta_E = d\theta_E - \theta_E \wedge \theta_E$$

$$= \begin{bmatrix} d\theta_S - \theta_S \wedge \theta_S - {}^t\overline{A} \wedge A & * \\ * & d\theta_Q - \theta_Q \wedge \theta_Q - A \wedge {}^t\overline{A} \end{bmatrix},$$

which implies that

$$\Theta_S = \Theta_E|_S + {}^t\overline{A} \wedge A,$$

$$\Theta_Q = \Theta_E|_Q + A \wedge {}^t\overline{A}.$$

Now, we say that a curvature operator

$$\Theta \in A^2(\mathrm{Hom}(E,E))$$

is *positive* at $x \in M$ if for $\lambda \neq 0 \in E_x$, the multivector

$$(\lambda, \Theta\lambda) \in \Lambda^2 T_x^*(M)$$

is positive of type $(1,1)$, or equivalently if for any holomorphic tangent vector $v \in T_x'(M)$, the hermitian matrix

$$-\sqrt{-1}\,\langle\Theta(x);v,\bar{v}\rangle \in \mathrm{Hom}(E_x,E_x)$$

is positive definite. We write $\Theta > 0$ if Θ is positive everywhere, $\Theta \geq 0$ if Θ is positive semidefinite, and $\Theta > \Theta'$ if $\Theta - \Theta' > 0$.

Let A be the second fundamental form of the subbundle $S \subset E$ above, and write

$$A = \sum_{\substack{1 \leq j \leq s \\ s < \lambda \leq r}} a_{\lambda j}^{\alpha}\, dz_{\alpha} \otimes e_{\lambda} \otimes e_j^*,$$

so

$${}^t\overline{A} = \sum \bar{a}_{\lambda j}^{\alpha}\, d\bar{z}_{\alpha} \otimes e_{\lambda}^* \otimes e_j$$

and

$$A \wedge {}^t\overline{A} = \sum a_{ik}^{\alpha} \bar{a}_{\mu k}^{\beta}\, dz_{\alpha} \wedge d\bar{z}_{\beta} \otimes e_i \otimes e_j^*.$$

Thus, if we let $A^{\alpha} = (a_{ij}^{\alpha})$,

$$\left\langle A \wedge {}^t\overline{A};\, \frac{\partial}{\partial z_{\alpha}},\, \frac{\partial}{\partial \bar{z}_{\alpha}} \right\rangle = \sum a_{ik}^{\alpha} \bar{a}_{jk}^{\alpha} e_i \otimes e_j^* = A^{\alpha \, t}\overline{A}^{\alpha} \geq 0,$$

which implies that

$$\Theta_S \leq \Theta_E|_S,$$

$$\Theta_Q \geq \Theta_E|_Q,$$

with equality holding if and only if $A \equiv 0$. The principle that *curvature decreases in holomorphic subbundles and increases in holomorphic quotient bundles* is in marked contrast to the real case.

For example, if $M \subset \mathbb{C}^n$ is a complex submanifold with the metric induced from the Euclidian metric an $\mathbb{C}^n$, we see that

$$T'(M) \subset T'(\mathbb{C}^n)|_M \Rightarrow \Theta_M \leq \Theta_{\mathbb{C}^n}|_M = 0.$$

If M is a Riemann surface, then by the calculations on p. 77, this just means that its Gaussian curvature $K \leq 0$.

Another basic fact that comes out of this calculation is the following: suppose $E \to M$ is a holomorphic bundle and that there exist global holomorphic sections $\sigma_1, \ldots, \sigma_n \in \Gamma(M, E)$ such that, for all $x \in M$, $\{\sigma_1(x), \ldots, \sigma_n(x)\}$ generate E_x. Then we have a surjective holomorphic bundle map

$$M \times \mathbb{C}^n \to E \to 0$$

given by

$$(x, \lambda) \to \sum \lambda_i \sigma_i(x) \in E_x$$

for $x \in M$, $\lambda \in \mathbb{C}^n$. It follows that, if we give E the metric induced from the Euclidean metric on $M \times \mathbb{C}^n$,

$$\Theta_E \geqslant 0;$$

i.e., *any holomorphic bundle with a finite number of global sections that generate each fiber has a metric with nonnegative curvature.*

The connection between the sign of the curvature of a vector bundle and the existence of global sections is fundamental in the theory of complex manifolds.

6. HARMONIC THEORY ON COMPACT COMPLEX MANIFOLDS

The Hodge Theorem

This section is devoted to the statement and proof of the Hodge theorem for the $\bar{\partial}$-operator together with some of its immediate corollaries.

M will be a connected, compact complex manifold of complex dimension n. We choose a hermitian metric ds^2 with associated $(1,1)$-form

$$\omega = \frac{\sqrt{-1}}{2} \sum_j \varphi_j \wedge \bar{\varphi}_j$$

in terms of a unitary coframe $\{\varphi_1, \ldots, \varphi_n\}$. The metric ds^2 induces a hermitian metric on all tensor bundles $T^{*(p,q)}(M)$; the inner product in $T_z^{*(p,q)}(M)$ is given by taking the basis $\{\varphi_I(z) \wedge \bar{\varphi}_J(z)\}_{\#I=p, \#J=q}$ to be orthogonal and of length $\|\varphi_I \wedge \bar{\varphi}_J\|^2 = 2^{p+q}$ (recall that $\|dz_i\|^2 = 2$ on $\mathbb{C}^n$). Let $C_n = (-1)^{n(n-1)/2}(\sqrt{-1}/2)^n$ and

$$\Phi = \frac{\omega^n}{n!} = C_n \varphi_1 \wedge \cdots \wedge \varphi_n \wedge \bar{\varphi}_1 \wedge \cdots \wedge \bar{\varphi}_n$$

be the volume form on M associated to the metric. The global inner product

$$(\psi, \eta) = \int_M (\psi(z), \eta(z)) \Phi(z)$$

makes the space $A^{p,q}(M)$ into a pre-Hilbert space. We pose the question: *Given a $\bar{\partial}$-closed form $\psi \in Z_{\bar{\partial}}^{p,q}(M)$, among all the forms $\{\psi + \bar{\partial}\eta\}$ representing the Dolbeault cohomology class $[\psi] \in H_{\bar{\partial}}^{p,q}(M)$ of φ, can we find one of smallest norm?* To answer this we pretend for a moment that $A^{p,q}(M)$ is complete and $\bar{\partial}$ is bounded, and define the adjoint operator

$$\bar{\partial}^* : A^{p,q}(M) \to A^{p,q-1}(M)$$

by requiring that

$$(\bar{\partial}^*\psi, \eta) = (\psi, \bar{\partial}\eta)$$

for all $\eta \in A^{p,q-1}(M)$. This will be justified in a moment, but first we show

Lemma. *A $\bar{\partial}$-closed form $\psi \in Z^{p,q}_{\bar{\partial}}(M)$ is of minimal norm in $\psi +$ $\bar{\partial}A^{p,q-1}(M)$ if and only if $\bar{\partial}^*\psi = 0$.*

Proof. If $\bar{\partial}^*\psi = 0$, then for any $\eta \in A^{p,q-1}(M)$ with $\bar{\partial}\eta = 0$

$$
\begin{aligned}
\|\psi + \bar{\partial}\eta\|^2 &= (\psi + \bar{\partial}\eta, \psi + \bar{\partial}\eta) \\
&= \|\psi\|^2 + \|\bar{\partial}\eta\|^2 + 2\operatorname{Re}(\psi, \bar{\partial}\eta) \\
&= \|\psi\|^2 + \|\bar{\partial}\eta\|^2 + 2\operatorname{Re}(\bar{\partial}^*\psi, \eta) \\
&= \|\psi\|^2 + \|\bar{\partial}\eta\|^2 \\
&> \|\psi\|^2,
\end{aligned}
$$

so ψ has minimal norm. Conversely, if ψ is of smallest norm, then for any $\eta \in A^{p,q-1}(M)$

$$
\frac{\partial}{\partial t}\|\psi + t\bar{\partial}\eta\|^2(0) = 0.
$$

But at $t = 0$

$$
\frac{\partial}{\partial t}(\psi + t\bar{\partial}\eta, \psi + t\bar{\partial}\eta) = 2\operatorname{Re}(\psi, \bar{\partial}\eta)
$$

and

$$
\frac{\partial}{\partial t}(\psi + t\bar{\partial}(i\eta), \psi + t\bar{\partial}(i\eta)) = 2\operatorname{Im}(\psi, \bar{\partial}\eta).
$$

So

$$
(\bar{\partial}^*\psi, \eta) = (\psi, \bar{\partial}\eta) = 0
$$

for all $\eta \in A^{p,q-1}(M)$, and hence $\bar{\partial}^*\psi = 0$.   Q.E.D.

So, at least formally, the Dolbeault cohomology group $H^{p,q}_{\bar{\partial}}(M) = Z^{p,q}_{\bar{\partial}}(M)/\bar{\partial}A^{p,q-1}(M)$ is represented exactly by the solutions of the two first-order equations

$$
\bar{\partial}\psi = 0, \qquad \bar{\partial}^*\psi = 0.
$$

These two may be replaced by the single second-order equation

$$
\Delta_{\bar{\partial}}\psi = (\bar{\partial}\bar{\partial}^* + \bar{\partial}^*\bar{\partial})\psi = 0:
$$

clearly $\bar{\partial}\psi = 0 = \bar{\partial}^*\psi \Rightarrow \Delta\psi = 0$, and conversely

$$
\begin{aligned}
(\Delta_{\bar{\partial}}\psi, \psi) &= (\bar{\partial}\bar{\partial}^*\psi, \psi) + (\bar{\partial}^*\bar{\partial}\psi, \psi) \\
&= \|\bar{\partial}^*\psi\|^2 + \|\bar{\partial}\psi\|^2,
\end{aligned}
$$

so $\Delta_{\partial}\psi = 0 \Rightarrow \bar{\partial}\psi = \bar{\partial}^*\psi = 0$. The operator

$$
\Delta_{\bar{\partial}} : A^{p,q}(M) \longrightarrow A^{p,q}(M)
$$

is called the $\bar{\partial}$-*Laplacian*, or simply the *Laplacian* (written Δ) if no ambiguity is likely. Differential forms satisfying the *Laplace equation*

$$\Delta\psi = 0$$

are called *harmonic forms*; the space of harmonic forms of type (p,q) is denoted $\mathcal{H}^{p,q}(M)$ and called the *harmonic space*. What the above formal argument suggests is the isomorphism

(*) $$\mathcal{H}^{p,q}(M) \cong H_{\bar{\partial}}^{p,q}(M);$$

if this can be proved, then we will have a unique representative for each cohomology class, which should certainly be an advantage. The isomorphism (*) is part of the Hodge theorem, whose proof together with the corollaries of (*) will occupy this section.

We begin by giving an explicit formula for the adjoint $\bar{\partial}^*$, thereby proving its existence. First we define the *star*, or *duality operator*,

$$*: A^{p,q}(M) \to A^{n-p,n-q}(M)$$

by requiring

$$(\psi(z),\eta(z))\Phi(z) = \psi(z) \wedge *\eta(z)$$

for all $\psi \in A^{p,q}(M)$. This is an algebraic operator, which is given locally as follows: if we write

$$\eta = \sum_{I,J} \eta_{I\bar{J}}\varphi_I \wedge \bar{\varphi}_J$$

then

$$*\eta = 2^{p+q-n}\sum_{I,J} \varepsilon_{IJ}\bar{\eta}_{I\bar{J}}\varphi_{I^0} \wedge \bar{\varphi}_{J^0},$$

where $I^0 = \{1,\ldots,n\} - I$ and we write $\varepsilon_{I,J}$ for the sign of the permutation

$$(1,\ldots,n,1',\ldots,n') \to \left(i_1,\ldots,i_p,j_1,\ldots,j_q,i_1^0,\ldots,i_{n-p}^0,j_1^0,\ldots,j_{n-q}^0\right).$$

The signs work out so that

$$**\eta = (-1)^{p+q}\eta.$$

In terms of star, the adjoint operator is

$$\bar{\partial}^* = -*\bar{\partial}*.$$

Indeed, we have, for $\psi \in A^{p,q-1}(M)$ and $\eta \in A^{p,q}(M)$

$$(\bar{\partial}\psi,\eta) = \int_M \bar{\partial}\psi \wedge *\eta$$
$$= (-1)^{p+q}\int_M \psi \wedge \bar{\partial}*\eta + \int_M \bar{\partial}(\psi \wedge *\eta).$$

Since $\bar{\partial} = d$ on forms of type $(n, n-1)$, the second term on the right is

$$\int_M d(\psi \wedge *\eta) = 0$$

by Stokes' theorem. Thus, for all ψ,

$$(\bar{\partial}\psi, \eta) = -\int_M \psi \wedge *(*\bar{\partial}*\eta)$$

so that $\bar{\partial}^*$ is defined by the above formula. Note that $\bar{\partial}^2 = 0 \Rightarrow \bar{\partial}^{*2} = 0$.

We now digress for a moment to explain the origins of the terminology Laplacian and harmonic. Provided we work with compactly supported forms, the above definitions are valid for any complex manifold. It is reasonable to expect the case of $\mathbb{C}^n$ with the Euclidean metric to provide a good local approximation to what is going on. Suppose we take $p = q = 0$ and write $dz = dz_1 \wedge \cdots \wedge dz_n$. Then, for $f \in C_c^\infty(\mathbb{C}^n)$,

$$\Delta(f) = \bar{\partial}^* \bar{\partial} f$$

$$= \bar{\partial}^* \left(\sum_j \frac{\partial f}{\partial \bar{z}_j} d\bar{z}_j \right)$$

$$= *\bar{\partial} \left(2^{1-n} \sum \pm \frac{\overline{\partial f}}{\partial \bar{z}_j} dz \wedge d\bar{z}_j{}^\circ \right)$$

$$= * \left(2^{1-n} \sum_j -\frac{\partial}{\partial \bar{z}_j} \left(\frac{\overline{\partial f}}{\partial \bar{z}_j} \right) \right) dz \wedge d\bar{z}$$

$$= v * \left(2^{1-n} \sum_j -\frac{\partial^2 f}{\partial z_j \partial \bar{z}_j} \right) dz \wedge d\bar{z}$$

$$= \left(2 \sum_j -\frac{\partial^2 f}{\partial z_j \partial \bar{z}_j} \right).$$

Since

$$2\frac{\partial^2}{\partial z_j \partial \bar{z}_j} = \frac{1}{2} \left(\frac{\partial^2}{\partial x_j^2} + \frac{\partial^2}{\partial y_j^2} \right),$$

we find that, up to a constant, $\Delta(f)$ is the usual Laplacian on functions in $\mathbb{C}^n \cong \mathbb{R}^{2n}$. Later on, in the discussion of Kähler manifolds, this computation will be extended to show that

$$\Delta(f\,dz_I \wedge d\bar{z}_J) = \left(-2 \sum_j \frac{\partial^2 f}{\partial z_j \partial \bar{z}_j} \right) dz_I \wedge d\bar{z}_J,$$

which explains the terminology for compactly supported forms in $\mathbb{C}^n$.

Returning to our compact, complex manifold M, we are aiming for the famous

Hodge Theorem

1. dim $\mathcal{H}^{p,q}(M) < \infty$; *and*
2. *because of this, the orthogonal projection*

$$\mathcal{H}: A^{p,q}(M) \to \mathcal{H}^{p,q}(M)$$

is well-defined, and there exists a unique operator, the Green's operator,

$$G: A^{p,q}(M) \longrightarrow A^{p,q}(M),$$

with $G(\mathcal{H}^{p,q}(M)) = 0$, $\bar{\partial}G = G\bar{\partial}$, $\bar{\partial}^*G = G\bar{\partial}^*$ *and*

$$(**) \qquad\qquad I = \mathcal{H} + \Delta G$$

on $A^{p,q}(M)$.

The equation $(**)$ in the form

$$\psi = \mathcal{H}(\psi) + \bar{\partial}(\bar{\partial}^* G\psi) + \bar{\partial}^*(\bar{\partial}G\psi)$$

is called the *Hodge decomposition on forms*, since it directly implies the orthogonal direct-sum decomposition

$$A^{p,q}(M) = \mathcal{H}^{p,q}(M) \oplus \bar{\partial}A^{p,q-1}(M) \oplus \bar{\partial}^*A^{p,q+1}(M).$$

The content of $(**)$ is sometimes expressed by saying that, given η, the equation

$$\Delta\psi = \eta$$

has a solution ψ if and only if $\mathcal{H}(\eta) = 0$, and then

$$\psi = G(\eta)$$

is the unique solution satisfying $\mathcal{H}(\psi) = 0$. So, in effect what we shall be doing is trying to solve the Laplace equation on a compact manifold. The idea is to first solve this equation in the *weak sense*—i.e., in the Hilbert-space completion $\mathcal{L}^{p,q}(M)$ of $A^{p,q}(M)$ to find a ψ such that

$$(\psi, \Delta\varphi) = (\eta, \varphi)$$

for all $\varphi \in A^{p,q}(M)$—and then to prove that this ψ is in fact C^∞. The first step is pretty much formal Hilbert-space theory, and the second—usually called the *regularity theorem*—is at least a local problem, since φ may be written as a sum of forms with compact support in coordinate patches.

Proof of the Hodge Theorem I: Local Theory

The proof of the Hodge theorem given here uses elementary Hilbert-space techniques. We are looking for the element of smallest norm in the affine subspace $\psi + \bar{\partial} A^{p,q-1}(M) \subset A^{p,q}(M)$. Clearly such an element can be found in the closure of $\psi + \bar{\partial} A^{p,q-1}(M)$ in the completion $\mathcal{L}^{p,q}(M)$ of the pre-Hilbert space $A^{p,q}(M)$, simply by orthogonal projection. The problem then is to show that the element found in this way in fact lies in $A^{p,q}(M)$. We start by discussing functions on the torus. This will provide a model for the formalism underlying the basic estimates; also, by rendering transparent the behavior of the Euclidean Laplacian on the torus, we will gain some idea of what to expect in general.

Let T be the real torus $(\mathbb{R}/(2\pi\mathbb{Z}))^n$ with coordinates $x = (x_1, \ldots, x_n)$. Denote by $\mathcal{F}$ the space of formal Fourier series

$$u = \sum_{\xi \in \mathbf{Z}^n} u_\xi e^{i\langle \xi, x \rangle}.$$

The *Sobolev s-norm is given by*

$$\|u\|_s^2 = \sum_\xi (1 + \|\xi\|^2)^s |u_\xi|^2,$$

and we define the *Sobolev spaces* H_s by

$$H_s = \{u \in \mathcal{F} : \|u\|_s < \infty\}.$$

These are Hilbert spaces; we have clearly a sequence of inclusions

$$\supset H_{-n} \supset H_{-n+1} \supset \cdots \supset H_{-1} \supset H_0 \supset H_1 \supset \cdots \supset H_n \supset \cdots,$$

and we let

$$H_\infty = \cap H_s, \qquad H_{-\infty} = \cup H_s.$$

Now let $C^s(T)$ be the functions of class s on T. A function $\varphi \in C^0(T)$ has a Fourier expansion $\sum \varphi_\xi e^{i\langle \xi, x \rangle}$, where

$$\varphi_\xi = \int_T \varphi(x) e^{-i\langle \xi, x \rangle} dx \qquad \left(dx = \frac{dx_1 \wedge \cdots \wedge dx_n}{(2\pi)^n} \right).$$

We have *Parseval's identity*

$$\begin{aligned}
\int_T |\varphi|^2 &= \int_T \left(\sum \varphi_\xi e^{i\langle \xi, e \rangle} \right) \left(\sum \bar{\varphi}_{\xi'} e^{-i\langle \xi', x \rangle} \right) \\
&= \int_T \varphi_\xi \bar{\varphi}_{\xi'} e^{i\langle \xi - \xi', x \rangle} dx \\
&= \int_T \sum_\xi |\varphi_\xi|^2 dx \\
&= \sum_\xi |\varphi_\xi|^2,
\end{aligned}$$

so that $C^0(T)$ maps into H_0 injectively with $\| \quad \|_0$ as L^2-norm on $C^0(T)$. The justification of this interchange of limits is done by using partial sums and the Cauchy-Schwarz inequality.

We set $D_j = (1/\sqrt{-1})(\partial/\partial x_j)$ and use the standard multiindex notations

$$D^\alpha = D_1^{\alpha_1} \cdots D_n^{\alpha_n}, \quad \alpha = (\alpha_1, \ldots, \alpha_n),$$
$$[\alpha] = \alpha_1 + \cdots + \alpha_n,$$
$$\xi^\alpha = \xi_1^{\alpha_1} \cdots \xi_n^{\alpha_n}.$$

By integration by parts

$$\int_T D^\alpha \varphi \cdot \bar\psi = \int_T \varphi \, \overline{D^\alpha \psi}, \quad \varphi, \psi \in C^\infty(T),$$

and so for $\varphi \in C^s(T)$ and $[\alpha] \leqslant s$

$$(D^\alpha \varphi)_\xi = \int_T D^\alpha \varphi \, e^{-i\langle \xi, x \rangle} dx$$
$$= \int_T \varphi \xi^\alpha e^{-i\langle \xi, x \rangle} dx$$
$$= \xi^\alpha \varphi_\xi,$$

i.e.,

$$\|D^\alpha \varphi\|_0^2 = \sum_\xi |\xi^\alpha|^2 |\varphi_\xi|^2.$$

Thus there is an inclusion

$$C^s(T) \subset H_s,$$

and from

$$\sum_{[\alpha] \leqslant s} |\xi^{2\alpha}| \leqslant (1 + \|\xi\|^2)^s \leqslant C_s \sum_{[\alpha] \leqslant s} |\xi^{2\alpha}|$$

we see that on $C^s(T) \subset H_s$ the Sobolev norm $\|\ \|_s$ is equivalent to

$$\sum_{[\alpha] \leqslant s} \|D^\alpha \varphi\|_0^2,$$

which we may describe as *the L^2-norm of the function φ together with its derivatives up to order* s. Indeed, H_s is the completion of $C^\infty(T)$ in this norm.

There is a partial converse to this, the important

Sobolev Lemma. $H_{s+[n/2]+1} \subset C^s(T)$; *that is, every* $u \in H_{s+[n/2]+1}$ *is the Fourier series of a function* $\varphi \in C^s(T)$, *and this series converges uniformly to* φ.

Proof. First, consider the case $s = 0$; let

$$u = \sum_\xi u_\xi e^{i\langle \xi, x \rangle}$$

with

$$\sum_\xi (1 + \|\xi\|^2)^{[n/2]+1} |u_\xi|^2 < \infty.$$

The partial sums

$$S_R = \sum_{\|\xi\| \leqslant R} u_\xi e^{i\langle \xi, x \rangle}$$

are continuous, and for $R \leqslant R'$,

$$|S_R(x) - S_{R'}(x)| \leqslant \sum_{\|\xi\| > R} |u_\xi|$$

$$= \sum_{\|\xi\| > R} \frac{\left((1 + \|\xi\|^2)^{[n/2]+1} |u_\xi|^2 \right)^{1/2}}{\left((1 + \|\xi\|^2)^{[n/2]+1} \right)^{1/2}}$$

$$\leqslant \|u\|_{[n/2]+1} \left[\sum_{\|\xi\| > R} \left(\frac{1}{(1 + \|\xi\|^2)^{[n/2]+1}} \right) \right]^{1/2}.$$

Now apply the integral test in $\mathbb{R}^n$ to conclude that

$$\sum_\xi \left(\frac{1}{(1 + \|\xi\|^2)^{[n/2]+1}} \right)^{1/2} \leqslant \sum_{\xi \neq 0} \frac{1}{\|\xi\|^{n+1}}$$

converges, from which it follows that $S_R(x)$ converges uniformly to $\varphi \in C^0(T)$ with $\varphi_\xi = u_\xi$.

Now we proceed by induction on s. Since the proof for general n involves only inessential formalism beyond what we have just done together with the one-variable case, we shall complete the argument only when $n = 1$.

So, we suppose $H_{s+1} \subset C^s(T)$ and

$$u = \sum_{\xi \in \mathbb{Z}} u_\xi e^{i\xi x}$$

satisfies $u \in H_{s+2}$, i.e.,

$$\sum_\xi |\xi|^{2s+4} |u_\xi|^2 < \infty.$$

Set

$$v = \sum_{\xi \neq 0} i\xi u_\xi e^{i\xi x}.$$

Then $v \in H_{s+1}$, and therefore is a function in $C^s(T)$ by induction hypothesis. The convergence being uniform, we may integrate term-by-term:

$$\int_0^x v(t)\, dt = \sum_\xi u_\xi e^{i\xi x}\, dx = u(x) - u_0,$$

so $u'(x) = v(x)$ and $u \in C^{s+1}(T)$.   Q.E.D.

Summarizing, we have shown that the Fourier series mapping $C^0(T) \to \mathcal{F}$ leads to inclusions

$$C^s(T) \subset H_s,$$
$$H_{s+[n/2]+1} \subset C^s(T),$$
$$C^\infty(T) = H_\infty.$$

A useful remark is that the proof of the Sobolev lemma gives an estimate

$$\sup_{x \in T} |D^\alpha \varphi(x)| \leqslant C_\alpha \|\varphi\|_{[n/2]+1+[\alpha]}.$$

Rellich Lemma.   *For* $s > r$ *the inclusion*

$$H_s \subset H_r$$

is compact.

Proof.   Given a bounded sequence $\{u_k\}$ in H_s, we want to find a convergent subsequence in H_r. Since, for all k we have

$$\sum (1+\|\xi\|^2)^r |u_{k,\xi}|^2 \leqslant \sum_\xi (1+\|\xi\|^2)^s |u_{k,\xi}|^2 < C,$$

for fixed ξ the sequence $\left\{ (1+\|\xi\|^2)^{r/2} u_{k,\xi} \right\}_k$ is bounded and hence has a Cauchy subsequence. By the standard diagonalization, then, we can find a subsequence $\{u_k\}$ such that $\left\{ (1+\|\xi\|^2)^{r/2} u_{k,\xi} \right\}_k$ is Cauchy for every ξ.

Now we separate the terms with small ξ, of which there are only a finite number, from those with large ξ where the factor $(1+\|\xi\|^2)^r$ will help: given $\varepsilon > 0$, choose R and m such that

$$\frac{4C}{(1+\|\xi\|^2)^{s-r}} < \frac{\varepsilon}{2} \quad \text{for} \quad \|\xi\| > R,$$

$$\sum_{\|\xi\| \leqslant R} (1+\|\xi\|^2)^r |u_{k,\xi} - u_{l,\xi}|^2 < \frac{\varepsilon}{2}$$

for $k,l \geqslant m$. Then

$$\|u_k - u_l\|_r^2 = \sum_{\|\xi\| \leqslant R} (1+\|\xi\|^2)^r |u_{k,\xi} - u_{l,\xi}|^2$$

$$+ \sum_{\|\xi\| > R} \frac{(1+\|\xi\|^2)^s}{(1+\|\xi\|^2)^{s-r}} |u_{k,\xi} - u_{l,\xi}|^2$$

$$< \frac{\varepsilon}{2} + \frac{\varepsilon}{2} = \varepsilon. \qquad \qquad \text{Q.E.D.}$$

We now wish to examine the Laplace equation on the torus T. Essentially we are going to prove in this case the Hodge theorem for 0-forms, or functions, with the standard Euclidean metric and relative to the exterior derivative d.

Although it is probably unnecessary, we remark that on a compact Riemannian manifold M we may define the adjoint d^* of d, form the Laplacian $\Delta_d = dd^* + d^*d$, and arrive at the exact same formalism as for $\bar{\partial}$ on complex manifolds. The Hodge theorem is, of course, also true, and the proof is the same as the one we shall give in the complex case.

For $\varphi \in C^\infty(T)$ the Laplacian is

$$\Delta_d \varphi = \sum_i D_i^2 \varphi$$

$$= -\sum_i \frac{\partial^2 \varphi}{\partial x_i^2}$$

$$= -\sum_\xi \varphi_\xi \|\xi\|^2 e^{i\langle \xi, x\rangle}.$$

We will discuss the equation

(∗) $$\Delta_d \varphi = \psi$$

in a manner such that the conclusions carry over to a general compact manifold. A function $\varphi \in L^2(T) = H_0$ is said to be a *weak solution* to (∗) if

$$(\Delta_d \eta, \varphi) = (\eta, \psi)$$

for all $\eta \in C^\infty(T)$. In case the weak solution φ is also a C^∞ function, the Laplacian is self-adjoint, meaning that

$$(\eta, \Delta_d \varphi) = (\eta, \psi)$$

for all $\eta \in C^\infty(T)$, and so $\Delta_d \varphi = \psi$ in the usual sense. Weak solutions are easy to find by Hilbert-space methods, and the point is to prove regularity.

We first note that the weak solutions of the homogeneous equation

$$\Delta_d \varphi = 0$$

satisfy

$$(\|\xi\|^2 e^{i\langle \xi, x\rangle}, \varphi) = 0$$

for all ξ. Thus the weak harmonic space consists of the constant functions, defined by $\varphi_\xi = 0$ for $\xi \neq 0$.

Next, we observe that (∗) makes sense when $\psi \in L^2(T) = H_0$. A necessary condition for it to have a weak solution is that $\psi_0 = 0$, i.e., ψ should be orthogonal to the harmonic space.

Now, assuming this to be the case,

$$\varphi = -\sum_{\xi \neq 0} \frac{1}{\|\xi\|^2} \psi_\xi e^{i\langle \xi, x\rangle}$$

gives a formal Fourier series solution to (∗). Since clearly $\psi \in L^2(T) \Rightarrow \varphi \in L^2(T)$, it is a weak solution. In fact we can say more:

For $\psi \in L^2(T)$, if we define the Green's operator by

$$G(\psi) = -\sum_{\xi \neq 0} \frac{1}{\|\xi\|^2} \psi_\xi e^{i\langle \xi, x \rangle},$$

then

$$G: H_s \longrightarrow H_{s+2}$$

is a bounded linear operator. In case ψ is perpendicular to the harmonic space,

$$\varphi = G(\psi)$$

gives a weak solution to (*). By the Sobolev lemma, if $\psi \in C^\infty(T)$ then $\varphi \in C^\infty(T)$ and φ is a solution of (*) in the usual sense. Finally, by the Rellich lemma

$$G: L^2(T) \to L^2(T)$$

is a compact, self-adjoint operator. The spectral decomposition for G on $L^2(T)$ is just Fourier series.

At this juncture the observations of the preceding paragraph more than establish the Hodge theorem for zero-forms on a torus. The essential point is this: The operator

$$I + \Delta_d: H_s \longrightarrow H_{s-2}$$

is trivially bounded, since Δ is second order. More importantly, the identity

$$\|(I + \Delta_d)\varphi\|_{s-2}^2 = \|\varphi\|_s^2$$

allows us to invert $I + \Delta_d$ on $L^2(T)$ using the closed graph theorem. This inverse is a compact smoothing operator and contains the information of the Green's operator. If, on a general compact manifold M, we carry over the Sobolev-space formalism and can prove the *basic estimate*

$$\|(I + \Delta_d)\varphi\|_{s-2}^2 \geq C_s \|\varphi\|_s^2$$

by calculus, then we can hope to obtain the same sort of picture as on the torus.

We conclude the Fourier series discussion with some remarks concerning *distributions*, defined as the linear functions

$$\lambda: C^\infty(T) \longrightarrow \mathbb{C},$$

which are continuous in the sense that

$$|\lambda(\varphi)| \leq C_\lambda \sup_{\substack{[\alpha] \leq k \\ x \in T}} |D^\alpha \varphi(x)|$$

for some k. Each distribution generates a formal Fourier series $\sum \lambda_\xi e^{i\langle \xi, x \rangle}$ where

$$\lambda_\xi = \lambda(e^{-i\langle \xi, x \rangle}).$$

It follows from the definition of continuity of λ and the above estimate on $\sup_{x \in T} |D^\alpha \varphi(x)|$ that each distribution λ is a continuous linear function on H_s for some s. The pairing

$$(u, v) = \sum_\xi u_\xi v_\xi$$

identifies H_{-s} with the dual of H_s, so that $\lambda \in H_{-s}$ with its formal Fourier series given above. If we denote by $\mathcal{D}(T)$ the space of distributions, then we conclude that

$$\mathcal{D}(T) = H_{-\infty}.$$

The derivatives of a distribution are defined by

$$D^\alpha \lambda(\varphi) = \lambda(D^\alpha \varphi).$$

The Fourier coefficients of $D^\alpha \lambda$ are $(D^\alpha \lambda)_\xi = \xi^\alpha \lambda_\xi$. With this definition, a distribution is obtained by taking a finite number of derivatives of a continuous function.

A final piece of useful terminology is this: A distribution λ is said *to be in* L^2 in case $\lambda \in H_0 \subset H_{-\infty}$. Then we may describe the Sobolev spaces by

H_s *consists of all distributions* λ *such that the distributional derivatives* $D^\alpha \lambda$ *are in* L^2 *for* $[\alpha] \leqslant s$.

An example of an interesting distribution is the *delta function* defined by

$$\delta(\varphi) = \varphi(0).$$

It has formal Fourier series

$$\delta = \sum_\xi e^{i\langle \xi, x \rangle}.$$

We shall not use distributions in proving the Hodge theorem, but they will be rather extensively discussed in Section 1 of Chapter 3. Note in passing that the equation

$$\Delta_d \varphi = \psi,$$

where ψ is a distribution, may be solved provided that $\psi(\eta) = 0$ for any harmonic η. If $\psi \in H_s$ for any s, positive or negative, then $\varphi \in H_{s+2}$. In particular, regularity holds for distribution solutions as well as weak Hilbert-space solutions. We shall work in this latter setting in order to take advantage of the standard theory of compact, self-adjoint operators on Hilbert spaces.

Proof of the Hodge Theorem II: Global Theory

On a torus the Sobolev s-norm is given equivalently by a weighted Fourier series norm or by the L^2-norm

$$\sum_{[\alpha] \leqslant s} \int_T |D^\alpha \varphi|^2 \, dx.$$

This latter may be extended to vector bundles over manifolds so that the Sobolev lemma and Rellich lemma both remain valid. We now explain how this is done.

To begin with, suppose that $U \subset V \subset \mathbb{R}^n$ are open sets in $\mathbb{R}^n$ with each relatively compact in the next. Functions with compact support in U may be considered as functions on a torus T. Suppose that $v_1(x), \ldots, v_n(x)$ are C^∞ vector fields in V that are everywhere linearly independent, and that $\rho(x)$ is a positive function on V. For $\varphi \in C_c^\infty(U)$ the Sobolev 0- and 1-norms are equivalent to

$$\int_V \rho(x) |\varphi(x)|^2 \, dx, \qquad \int_V \rho(x) \left\{ |\varphi(x)|^2 + \sum_i |v_i(x) \cdot \varphi(x)|^2 \right\} dx,$$

respectively. More generally, note that the commutator

$$[v_i, v_j] \varphi = v_i(v_j \varphi) - v_j(v_i \varphi)$$

is an operator of order 1, where an operator of *order* s is one involving at most s-derivatives and denoted by a generic symbol $A^s \varphi$. An expression

$$v^\alpha \varphi = v_1^{\alpha_1}(v_2^{\alpha_2} \cdots (v_n^{\alpha_n} \varphi) \cdots)$$

is independent of the ordering modulo operators of order $< [\alpha]$. It follows that the Sobolev s-norm of $\varphi \in C_c^\infty(U)$ is equivalent to

$$\sum_{[\alpha] \leqslant s} \int |v^\alpha \varphi(x)|^2 \, dx.$$

Suppose now that $E \to M$ is a vector bundle over a compact manifold M. Assume that we have connection ∇ in E and in the tangent bundle $T(M)$ of M. (It is more convenient to denote the connection operator by ∇, rather than D as in Section 5 of Chapter 0.) If $\{e_\alpha\}$ is a local frame for E and $\{v_i\}$ a local frame for $T(M)$ with dual coframe $\{\varphi_i\}$, then the covariant derivatives $\nabla_i f_\alpha = f_{\alpha,i}$ of a section $f = \sum_\alpha f_\alpha e_\alpha$ of $E \to M$ are defined by

$$\nabla f = \sum_{\alpha, i} f_{\alpha, i} e_\alpha \otimes \varphi_i.$$

We have

$$f_{\alpha, i} = v_i f_\alpha + A^0(f),$$

where A^0 is an operator of order zero involving the connection matrix.

Applying these considerations to $E \otimes T^*(M)$, we may define $f_{\alpha,i,j} = \nabla_j(\nabla_i f_\alpha)$, and so forth. The commutation rule

$$[\nabla_i, \nabla_j] f_\alpha = A^1(f)$$

follows from the above expression for $f_{\alpha,i}$.

Suppose now that E and $T(M)$ have metrics and that $\{e_\alpha\}, \{v_i\}$ are orthonormal frames. The global *Sobolev s-norm* of sections $f \in C^\infty(M, E)$ is defined by

$$\|f\|_s^2 = \sum_{k \leqslant s} \int_M \| \nabla^k f \|_0^2 dx,$$

where

$$\nabla^k f = \nabla(\nabla(\cdots(\nabla f)\cdots)).$$
$$k \text{ times}$$

Denote by $\mathcal{H}_s(M, E)$ the completion of $C^\infty(M, E)$ in this norm. Since, by our remarks at the beginning of this section, the global Sobolev norm induces a norm equivalent to the usual Sobolev norm on sections compactly supported in a neighborhood of a point, by using a partition of unity we may conclude the

Global Sobolev Lemma. $\mathcal{H}_{[n/2]+1+s}(M, E) \subset C^s(M, E)$, *the sections of differentiability class* s *on* M, *and*

$$\bigcap_s \mathcal{H}_s(M, E) = C^\infty(M, E).$$

Global Rellich Lemma. *For* s $>$ r *the inclusion*

$$\mathcal{H}_s(M, E) \to \mathcal{H}_r(M, E)$$

is a compact operator.

Now let M be a compact hermitian manifold with hermitian connection in the tangent bundle. Denote by $\mathcal{H}_s^{p,q}(M)$ the completion of $A^{p,q}(M)$ in the Sobolev s-norm, $\| \ \| = \| \ \|_0$, and define the *Dirichlet inner product* and *Dirichlet norm*, respectively, by

$$\mathcal{D}(\varphi, \psi) = (\varphi, \psi) + (\bar{\partial}\varphi, \bar{\partial}\psi) + (\bar{\partial}^*\varphi, \bar{\partial}^*\psi)$$
$$= (\varphi, (I + \Delta)\psi)$$
$$\mathcal{D}(\varphi) = \mathcal{D}(\varphi, \varphi) = \|\varphi\|^2 + \|\bar{\partial}\varphi\|^2 + \|\bar{\partial}^*\varphi\|^2.$$

The basic estimate in the theory is provided by

Gårding's Inequality. *For* $\varphi \in A^{p,q}(M)$

$$\|\varphi\|_1^2 \leqslant C\mathcal{D}(\varphi) \qquad (C > 0).$$

We remark that the operator $I + \Delta$, rather than just the Laplacian Δ, is being used, since $\Delta \geqslant 0$ implies that $I + \Delta$ has no kernel and therefore we have a better chance of inverting it.

One use of the Gårding inequality will be to prove the

Regularity Lemma I.   *Suppose that* $\varphi \in \mathcal{H}_s^{p,q}(M)$, *and that* $\psi \in \mathcal{H}_0^{p,q}(M)$ *is a weak solution of the equation*

$$\Delta \psi = \varphi$$

in the sense that

$$(\psi, \Delta \eta) = (\varphi, \eta)$$

for all $\eta \in A^{p,q}(M)$. *Then* $\psi \in \mathcal{H}_{s+2}^{p,q}(M)$.

For example, suppose that $\varphi \in \mathcal{H}_0^{p,q}(M)$ is an *eigenfunction* for the Laplacian, meaning that, for a constant λ, the equation

$$\Delta \varphi = \lambda \varphi$$

holds in the weak sense. Then by the regularity lemma, $\varphi \in \mathcal{H}_s^{p,q}(M)$ for all s, and by the global Sobolev lemma we conclude that any eigenfunction for Δ is smooth.

We note that any eigenvalue $\lambda \geqslant 0$, and $\lambda = 0 \Leftrightarrow \varphi$ is harmonic in the weak sense. By the regularity and Sobolev lemmas any such weakly harmonic form is C^∞ and harmonic in the usual sense.

We shall assume the Gårding inequality and regularity lemma and go ahead and complete the proof of the Hodge theorem. After this is done we shall prove the Gårding inequality. The regularity lemma will be proved when we discuss smoothing of distributions in general. The reader who wishes to have the complete argument at hand may find the proof at the end of the subsection entitled "Smoothing and Regularity" in Section 1 of Chapter 3.

The basic Hilbert-space tool is the spectral theorem for compact self-adjoint operators, together with the principle of representing bounded linear functions by taking the inner product with a fixed vector, in the form of the following

Lemma.   *Given* $\varphi \in \mathcal{H}_0^{p,q}(M)$, *there exists a unique* $\psi \in \mathcal{H}_1^{p,q}(M)$ *such that*

$$(\varphi, \eta) = \mathcal{D}(\psi, \eta) = (\psi, (I + \Delta)\eta)$$

for all $\eta \in A^{p,q}(M)$. *The mapping*

$$\psi = T(\varphi)$$

from $\mathcal{H}_0^{p,q}(M)$ *to* $\mathcal{H}_1^{p,q}(M)$ *is bounded, and therefore the mapping*

$$T: \mathcal{H}_0^{p,q}(M) \to \mathcal{H}_0^{p,q}(M)$$

is compact and self-adjoint.

Proof. The Gårding inequality says that the Dirichlet norm is equivalent to the Sobolev 1-norm on $\mathcal{H}_1^{p,q}(M)$. The linear functional

$$\eta \to (\varphi, \eta) \qquad (\eta \in A^{p,q}(M))$$

extends to a bounded linear form on $\mathcal{H}_1^{p,q}(M)$ with the Dirichlet norm, by virtue of

$$|(\varphi, \eta)| \leqslant \|\varphi\|_0 \|\eta\|_0 \leqslant \|\varphi\|_0 \mathcal{D}(\eta).$$

Thus the equation

$$(\varphi, \eta) = \mathcal{D}(\psi, \eta)$$

has a unique solution $\psi = T(\varphi)$ characterized by

$$(\varphi, \eta) = (T\varphi, (I + \Delta)\eta) \qquad (\eta \in A^{p,q}(M)).$$

T is self-adjoint, since this is true of I and Δ. From

$$2\alpha\beta \leqslant \varepsilon\alpha^2 + \frac{1}{\varepsilon}\beta^2$$

and

$$\begin{aligned}
\|T\varphi\|_1^2 &\leqslant C \mathcal{D}(T\varphi, T\varphi) \\
&= C(\varphi, T\varphi) \\
&\leqslant C \|\varphi\|_0 \|T\varphi\|_0 \\
&\leqslant 2\varepsilon C \|T\varphi\|_0^2 + \frac{2C}{\varepsilon} \|\varphi\|_0^2
\end{aligned}$$

we deduce that

$$\|T\varphi\|_1^2 \leqslant C' \|\varphi\|_0^2.$$

This says that T is bounded as a map from $\mathcal{H}_0^{p,q}(M)$ to $\mathcal{H}_1^{p,q}(M)$, and by the global Rellich lemma it is compact as an operator on $\mathcal{H}_0^{p,q}(M)$. Q.E.D.

According to the spectral theorem for compact, self-adjoint operators there is a Hilbert-space decomposition

$$\mathcal{H}_0^{p,q}(M) = \bigoplus_m E(\rho_m),$$

where ρ_m are the eigenvalues of T and $E(\rho_m)$ are the *finite-dimensional* eigenspaces. Since T is one-to-one, all $\rho_m \neq 0$; moreover, the equation

$$T\varphi = \rho_m \varphi$$

is the same as

$$(\varphi, \eta) = (\rho_m \varphi, (I + \Delta)\eta) \qquad (\eta \in A^{p,q}(M)),$$

which implies that

$$\Delta\varphi = \left(\frac{1 - \rho_m}{\rho_m}\right)\varphi$$

in the weak sense. It follows that the eigenspaces for T and Δ are the same and are finite-dimensional vector spaces consisting of C^∞ forms. The eigenvalues λ_m for Δ and ρ_m for T are related by

$$\lambda_m = \frac{1-\rho_m}{\rho_m}$$

$$\rho_m = \frac{1}{1+\lambda_m}.$$

We may assume that

$$0 = \lambda_0 < \lambda_1 < \cdots,$$

where $\lambda_m \uparrow \infty$, $\rho_m \downarrow 0$ as $m \to \infty$. The harmonic space $\mathcal{H}^{p,q}(M)$ corresponds to $\lambda_0 = 0$. For $\varphi \in \mathcal{H}^{p,q}(M)^\perp$

$$\|\Delta\varphi\|_0 \geqslant \lambda_1 \|\varphi\|_0 \qquad (\lambda_1 > 0),$$

and if we define the *Green's operator* by

$$\begin{cases} G = 0 & \text{on } \mathcal{H}^{p,q}(M), \\ G\varphi = \dfrac{1}{\lambda_m}\varphi, & \varphi \in E\left(\dfrac{1}{1+\lambda_m}\right), \end{cases}$$

then G is a compact, self-adjoint operator with spectral decomposition

$$\mathcal{H}_0^{p,q}(M) = \mathcal{H}^{p,q}(M) \oplus \left(\bigoplus_m E(\rho_m)\right),$$

where

$$G\varphi = \left(\frac{\rho_m}{1-\rho_m}\right)\varphi, \qquad \varphi \in E(\rho_m).$$

At this point, we have proved the Hodge theorem. The essential idea is to produce the Green's operator by a Hilbert-space trick, and then to use the basic estimate to show that it is a compact smoothing operator. Actually, G is an integral operator of the form

$$(G\varphi)(x) = \int_M G(x,y)\varphi(y),$$

where $G(x,y)$ is a beautiful kernel on $M \times M$ with certain singularities along the diagonal Δ. The Hilbert-space method has the disadvantage of not giving us the Green's operator in this form. If we were working with distributions rather than just L^2-forms, then we could produce $G(x,y)$ by solving a distributional equation of the type

$$\Delta_x G(x,y) = \delta_y + S_y,$$

where δ_y is a delta function at y and S_y is an operator of order $-\infty$. Such equations will be discussed in Section 1 of Chapter 3.

Proof of the Gårding Inequality. We suppose that $\varphi_1, \ldots, \varphi_n$ is a local unitary coframe for the hermitian metric, so that

$$ds^2 = \sum_i \varphi_i \bar{\varphi}_i.$$

A form of type (p, q) is written locally as

$$\psi = \frac{1}{p!\,q!} \sum_{I,J} \psi_{I,\bar{J}} \varphi_I \wedge \bar{\varphi}_J,$$

where $\psi_{I,\bar{J}}$ is skew-symmetric in the indices i_α and $\bar{j}_\beta$. There is a famous formula for the Laplacian, the *Weitzenböck identity*, which we shall use in the crude form

(W) $$\qquad (\Delta\psi)_{I\bar{J}} = \left(-\sum_{k=1}^{n} \nabla_k \nabla_{\bar{k}} \psi_{I,\bar{J}} \right) + A^1(\psi).$$

In other words, modulo lower-order terms the global Laplacian on forms looks like the Euclidean Laplacian $-\sum_k \partial^2/(\partial z_k \partial\bar{z}_k)$ on vector-valued functions.

The precise Weitzenböck formula identifies the lower-order terms. For a general hermitian metric, $A^1(\psi)$ is a messy operator involving the torsion in its terms of first order. However, when the metric is Kähler, these drop out and $A^1(\psi)$ is the algebraic operator

$$A^1(\psi)_{I\bar{J}} = \sum_{k,\,j_\alpha \in J} R_{j_\alpha k} \psi_{I\bar{j}_1 \cdots \bar{k} \cdots \bar{j}_q} \qquad (k \text{ in } \alpha\text{th spot}),$$

where

$$R_{j\bar{k}} = \sum_i R^i_{ij\bar{k}}$$

is the *Ricci curvature*.

To prove the Weitzenböck formula we shall let $v_1, \ldots, v_n$ be the vector field frame dual to $\varphi_1, \ldots, \varphi_n$, and $v_{\bar{i}} = \bar{v}_i$. For a function f

$$\bar{\partial}f = \sum_i (v_{\bar{i}} \cdot f) \bar{\varphi}_i,$$

and for a tensor $\tau = \{\tau_I\}$ the components of the $\bar{z}$-covariant differential $\bar{\nabla}\tau$ are given by

$$(\bar{\nabla}\tau)_I = \bar{\partial}\tau_I + A^0(\tau).$$

It is convenient to use the symbol "$\equiv$" to denote "modulo lower-order terms," so that, e.g.,

$$(\bar{\nabla}\tau)_I \equiv \bar{\partial}\tau_I.$$

We set $\Phi' = \varphi_1 \wedge \cdots \wedge \varphi_n$.

It will suffice to prove (W) when $\psi = f\varphi_I \wedge \bar{\varphi}_J$ (no summation). Since the dz's act as, so to speak, vector bundle indices, we will assume $p=0$. Finally, by the symmetry in the formula we may take $J=(1,\ldots,q)$, so that

$$\psi = f\bar{\varphi}_1 \wedge \cdots \wedge \bar{\varphi}_q.$$

Now we compute:

$$\bar{\partial}\psi \equiv (-1)^q \sum_{k>q} f_{\bar{k}} \bar{\varphi}_1 \wedge \cdots \wedge \bar{\varphi}_q \wedge \bar{\varphi}_k$$

$$*\bar{\partial}\psi \equiv (-1)^q 2^{q+1-n} \sum_{k>q} (-1)^{k-q-1} \bar{f}_{\bar{k}} \bar{\varphi}_{q+1} \wedge \cdots \wedge \hat{\bar{\varphi}}_k \wedge \cdots \wedge \bar{\varphi}_n \wedge \Phi'$$

$$\bar{\partial}*\bar{\partial}\psi \equiv \left(2^{q+1-n} \sum_{k>q} \bar{f}_{\bar{k},k} \right) \bar{\varphi}_{q+1} \wedge \cdots \wedge \bar{\varphi}_n \wedge \Phi'$$

$$+ \sum_{\substack{k>q \\ l\leqslant q}} 2^{q+1-n} (-1)^{k-1} \bar{f}_{\bar{k},l} \bar{\varphi}_l \wedge \bar{\varphi}_{q+1} \wedge \cdots \wedge \hat{\bar{\varphi}}_k \wedge \cdots \wedge \bar{\varphi}_n \wedge \Phi'$$

$$*\bar{\partial}*\bar{\partial}\psi \equiv \left(2 \sum_{k>q} f_{\bar{k},k} \right) \bar{\varphi}_1 \wedge \cdots \wedge \bar{\varphi}_q$$

$$+ 2 \sum_{\substack{k>q \\ l\leqslant q}} (-1)^{l-1+q} f_{\bar{k},l} \bar{\varphi}_1 \wedge \cdots \wedge \hat{\bar{\varphi}}_l \wedge \cdots \wedge \bar{\varphi}_q \wedge \bar{\varphi}_k.$$

This gives $*\bar{\partial}*\bar{\partial}\psi$, and the other term $\bar{\partial}*\bar{\partial}*\psi$ is similar but shorter:

$$*\psi = 2^{q-n} \bar{f} \bar{\varphi}_{q+1} \wedge \cdots \wedge \bar{\varphi}_n \wedge \Phi'$$

$$\bar{\partial}*\psi \equiv 2^{q-n} \sum_{l\leqslant q} \bar{f}_l \bar{\varphi}_l \wedge \bar{\varphi}_{q+1} \wedge \cdots \wedge \bar{\varphi}_n \wedge \Phi'$$

$$*\bar{\partial}*\psi \equiv 2 \sum_{l\leqslant q} (-1)^{l-1} f_l \bar{\varphi}_1 \wedge \cdots \wedge \hat{\bar{\varphi}}_l \wedge \cdots \wedge \bar{\varphi}_q$$

$$\bar{\partial}*\bar{\partial}*\psi \equiv \left(2 \sum_{l\leqslant q} f_{l,\bar{l}} \right) \bar{\varphi}_1 \wedge \cdots \wedge \bar{\varphi}_q$$

$$+ \left(2 \sum_{\substack{l\leqslant q \\ k>q}} (-1)^{q+l} f_{l,\bar{k}} \bar{\varphi}_1 \wedge \cdots \wedge \hat{\bar{\varphi}}_l \wedge \cdots \wedge \bar{\varphi}_q \wedge \bar{\varphi}_k \right).$$

Now $v_i(v_{\bar{j}}f) - v_{\bar{j}}(v_i f) \equiv A^1(f)$, so that modulo first-order terms

$$\Delta\psi = \left(-2 \sum_k f_{\bar{k},k} \right) \bar{\varphi}_1 \wedge \cdots \wedge \bar{\varphi}_q$$

$$+ \left(2 \sum_{\substack{l\leqslant q \\ k>q}} (-1)^{l-1+q} f_{\bar{k}} \bar{\varphi}_1 \wedge \cdots \wedge \hat{\bar{\varphi}}_l \wedge \cdots \wedge \bar{\varphi}_n \wedge \bar{\varphi}_k \right.$$

$$+ 2 \sum_{\substack{l\leqslant q \\ k>q}} (-1)^{l+q} f_{\bar{k},l} \bar{\varphi}_1 \wedge \cdots \wedge \hat{\bar{\varphi}}_l \wedge \cdots \wedge \bar{\varphi}_n \wedge \bar{\varphi}_k \left. \right).$$

The last two terms cancel to give

$$\Delta\psi \equiv \left(-2\sum_k f_{\bar{k},k}\right)\bar{\varphi}_1 \wedge \cdots \wedge \bar{\varphi}_q.$$

This proves the Weitzenböck formula.

We now come to the proof of the Gårding inequality, where we assume the Weitzenböck in the form

$$(\Delta\psi)_{I\bar{J}} = \left(-2\sum_k \psi_{I\bar{J},\bar{k},k}\right) + A^1(\psi).$$

Inequalities of the type

$$(*) \qquad\qquad 2\alpha\beta \leqslant \varepsilon\alpha^2 + \frac{1}{\varepsilon}\beta^2$$

will be used repeatedly, and $\Phi = C_n\Phi' \wedge \overline{\Phi'}$ denotes the volume form. Set

$$\eta = C_n\left(-\sum_{I,J,k}(-1)^{k-1}\psi_{I\bar{J},\bar{k}}\,\overline{\psi_{I\bar{J}}}\,\varphi_1 \wedge \cdots \wedge \hat{\varphi}_k \wedge \cdots \wedge \varphi_n\right) \wedge \Phi'$$

$$= C_n'\left((\overline{\nabla}\psi,\psi) \wedge \omega^{n-1}\right).$$

The second expression shows that η is globally defined, and since it has type $(n-1,n)$, $d\eta = \partial\eta$. By Stokes' theorem

$$\int_M \partial\eta = 0.$$

On the other hand

$$\partial\eta = \left(-2\sum_{I,J,k}\psi_{I\bar{J},\bar{k},k}\bar{\psi}_{I\bar{J}}\right)\Phi - \left(2\sum_{I,J,k}\psi_{I\bar{J},\bar{k}}\,\overline{\psi_{I\bar{J},\bar{k}}}\right)\Phi + (A^1\psi,\psi)\Phi.$$

Thus, by the Weitzenböck formula

$$(\Delta\psi,\psi) = \|\overline{\nabla}\psi\|^2 + (A^1\psi,\psi),$$

where

$$\|\overline{\nabla}\psi\|^2 = \int_M (\overline{\nabla}\psi,\overline{\nabla}\psi)\,\Phi$$

is the L^2-norm of the $\bar{z}$-covariant differential of the tensor ψ, and $A^1(\psi)$ is a first-order operator involving $\bar{z}$-derivatives of ψ. Using $(*)$, we obtain

$$2|(A^1\psi,\psi)| \leqslant \varepsilon\|\overline{\nabla}\psi\|^2 + \frac{1}{\varepsilon}\|\psi\|^2,$$

which implies that

$$\|\overline{\nabla}\psi\|^2 \leqslant C'\{(\Delta\psi,\psi) + \|\psi\|^2\}, \qquad C' > 0.$$

We now repeat the argument applied this time to

$$\gamma = C_n\left(-\sum_{I,J,k}(-1)^{k-1}\psi_{I\bar{J},k}\,\overline{\psi_{I\bar{J}}}\,\bar{\varphi}_1 \wedge \cdots \wedge \hat{\bar{\varphi}}_k \wedge \cdots \wedge \bar{\varphi}_n\right) \wedge \Phi'$$

and use $f_{k,\bar{k}}=f_{\bar{k},k}+A^1(f)$ to estimate the L^2-norm $\|\nabla\psi\|^2$ of the z-derivatives from below by the Dirichlet norm. Putting these together,

$$\|\nabla\psi\|^2+\|\bar{\nabla}\psi\|^2+\|\psi\|^2\geqslant C''((\Delta\psi,\psi)+\|\psi\|^2)=C''\mathcal{D}(\psi),$$

which is the Gårding inequality.

Remark. In the Kähler case one may use the precise Weitzenböck formula and the above integration by parts calculation to prove the *Kodaira identity*

$$(\Delta\psi,\psi)=\|\bar{\nabla}\psi\|^2+(R\psi,\psi),$$

where, for $\psi\in A^{0,q}(M)$ and summing repeated indices,

$$(R\psi,\psi)=q\int_M\left(R_{i\bar{j}}\psi_{\bar{i}_1\cdots\bar{i}_{q-1}i}\bar{\psi}_{\bar{i}_1\cdots\bar{i}_{q-1}\bar{j}}\right)\Phi.$$

If ψ is harmonic and the hermitian form

$$R_{i\bar{j}}\xi^i\bar{\xi}^j$$

is positive definite, then we deduce that $\psi\equiv0$. By the Hodge theorem

$$0=\mathcal{H}^{0,q}(M)\cong H_{\bar{\partial}}^{0,q}(M),\qquad q>0.$$

This is a special case of the famous Kodaira vanishing theorem, for which the general argument will be given in Section 3 of Chapter 1.

Applications of the Hodge Theorem

We begin by noting the isomorphism

$$\mathcal{H}^{p,q}(M)\longrightarrow H_{\bar{\partial}}^{p,q}(M)$$

between the harmonic space and Dolbeault cohomology groups. In fact, by the Hodge decomposition every $\bar{\partial}$-closed form $\psi\in Z_{\bar{\partial}}^{p,q}(M)$ is

$$\psi=\mathcal{H}(\psi)+\bar{\partial}(\bar{\partial}^*G\psi),$$

since $\bar{\partial}G\psi=G\bar{\partial}\psi=0$. Combining this isomorphism with the Dolbeault isomorphism, we find

$$\mathcal{H}^{p,q}(M)\xrightarrow{\sim}H^q(M,\Omega^p).$$

By the first statement in the Hodge theorem, this implies

Finite Dimensionality

$$\dim H^q(M,\Omega^p)<\infty.$$

It is instructive to give a direct proof of finite dimensionality in the case $q=0$. Let $\{U_i\}$ be a finite coordinate covering of M with holomorphic coordinates $z_{i,1}, \ldots, z_{i,n}$ in U_i. We may find relatively compact open subsets $V_i \subset U_i$ that still constitute a covering of M. A global section

$$\varphi \in H^0(M, \Omega^q) = H^0(\{U_i\}, \Omega^q)$$
$$= H^0(\{V_i\}, \Omega^q)$$

is given in U_i by

$$\varphi = \sum_J \varphi_{iJ}(z) \, dz_{i,J},$$

where $\phi_{iJ}(z) \in \mathcal{O}(U_i)$. We define the norm

$$\|\varphi\| = \sum_{i,J} \sup_{z \in V_i} |\varphi_{i,J}(z)|.$$

This norm is finite, and since (1) $H^0(\{V_i\}, \Omega^q) \cong H^0(\{U_i\}, \Omega^q)$ and (2) any sequence of analytic functions $\psi_\nu \in \mathcal{O}(U_i)$ satisfying $\sup_{z \in V_i} |\psi_\nu(z) - \psi_\mu(z)| \to 0$ has a subsequence converging uniformly to a holomorphic function $\psi \in \mathcal{O}(V_i)$, we deduce that with this norm $H^0(M, \Omega^q)$ is a complete Banach space. By the Montel theorem, given a sequence $\varphi_\nu \in H^0(M, \Omega^q)$ with $\|\varphi_\nu\| \leqslant 1$ we may extract a subsequence whose coefficient functions $\varphi_{\nu,i,J}(z) \in \mathcal{O}(U_i)$ converge uniformly to some $\varphi_{i,J}(z) \in \mathcal{O}(V_i)$. Thus the unit ball in this Banach space is compact, and by a result in Banach-space theory this implies that it is finite dimensional.

Actually, it is obvious that a Hilbert space whose unit ball is compact is finite dimensional, and we may make $H^0(M, \Omega^q)$ into a Hilbert space by defining

$$(\varphi, \psi) = \sum_{i,J} \int_{V_i} \varphi_{i,J}(z) \overline{\psi_{i,J}(z)} \, \Phi(z_i),$$

where $\Phi(z_i)$ is the Euclidean volume form in the coordinates z_i. Since (1) a sequence $\psi_\nu \in \mathcal{O}(U_i)$ that is Cauchy in $L^2(V_i)$ has a subsequence converging uniformly on compact subsets of V_i to $\psi \in \mathcal{O}(V_i)$, and (2) a sequence $\psi_\nu \in \mathcal{O}(U_i)$ that is bounded in $L^2(V_i)$ has a similarly convergent subsequence, we may adopt the previous argument to this Hilbert-space setting.

This argument may be modified to prove the finite dimensionality of all $H^q(M, \Omega^p)$, and indeed the finite dimensionality of $H^q(M, \mathcal{F})$ for any coherent analytic sheaf $\mathcal{F}$—these matters will be discussed further in Section 3 of Chapter 5, where it will emerge that the finite dimensionality is the central fact in the global theory of coherent sheaf cohomology on a compact manifold.

A second application of the Hodge theorem is to Kodaira-Serre duality. From the formula $\bar{\partial}^* = - *\bar{\partial}*$ we see that

$$*\Delta = \Delta *.$$

This implies that the star operator induces an isomorphism

$$*: \mathcal{H}^{p,q}(M) \longrightarrow \mathcal{H}^{n-p,n-q}(M).$$

In particular

$$\mathcal{H}^{n,n}(M) \cong \mathbb{C} \cdot \Phi,$$

where $\Phi = *1$ is the volume form of the metric.

To put this isomorphism in intrinsic form not depending on the choice of a metric, we remark in a general fashion that, given sheaves $\mathcal{F}$, $\mathcal{G}$, and $\mathcal{H}$ over a space X and a sheaf mapping

$$\mathcal{F} \otimes \mathcal{G} \longrightarrow \mathcal{H},$$

there is an induced cup product

$$H^*(X, \mathcal{F}) \otimes H^*(X, \mathcal{G}) \longrightarrow H^*(X, \mathcal{H})$$

given by the cochain formula at the end of the discussion of de Rham's theorem. In particular, the pairings

$$\Omega^p \otimes \Omega^q \longrightarrow \Omega^{p+q}$$

induced by the exterior product of holomorphic differential forms induce

$$(*) \qquad\qquad H^*(M, \Omega^p) \otimes H^*(M, \Omega^q) \longrightarrow H^*(M, \Omega^{p+q}).$$

On the other hand, the pairing

$$\{\ ,\ \}: A^{p,r}(M) \otimes A^{q,s}(M) \longrightarrow A^{p+q,r++s}(M)$$

given by

$$\{\psi, \eta\} = \psi \wedge \eta$$

satisfies

$$\bar{\partial}\{\psi,\eta\} = \{\bar{\partial}\psi, \eta\}(-1)^{\deg\psi}\{\psi, \bar{\partial}\eta\}$$

and so induces

$$(**) \qquad\qquad H^{p,*}_{\bar{\partial}}(M) \otimes H^{q,*}_{\bar{\partial}}(M) \longrightarrow H^{p+q,*}_{\bar{\partial}}(M).$$

The pairings $(*)$ and $(**)$ correspond under the Dolbeault isomorphism, at least modulo signs, for the same reason as in the discussion at the end of de Rham's theorem. With this understood we have the

Kodaira-Serre Duality Theorem

1. $H^n(M, \Omega^n) \xrightarrow{\sim} \mathbb{C}$, *and*
2. *the pairing*

$$H^q(M, \Omega^p) \otimes H^{n-q}(M, \Omega^{n-p}) \longrightarrow H^n(M, \Omega^n)$$

is nondegenerate.

Proof. The mapping in 1. is given by composing

$$H^n(M,\Omega^n) \cong H^{n,n}_{\bar{\partial}}(M)$$

with the linear function

$$H^{n,n}_{\bar{\partial}}(M) \longrightarrow \mathbb{C}$$

defined by

$$\psi \longrightarrow \int_M \psi,$$

which is well-defined on account of Stokes' theorem and $d=\bar{\partial}$ on $A^{n,n-1}(M)$. The fact that 1. is an isomorphism results from

$$H^{n,n}_{\bar{\partial}}(M) \cong \mathcal{H}^{n,n}(M) \cong \mathbb{C} \cdot \Phi,$$

since

$$\int_M \Phi = \mathrm{vol}(M) > 0.$$

The pairing 2. is given by composing

$$H^q(M,\Omega^p) \cong H^{p,q}_{\bar{\partial}}(M)$$

with the pairing

$$H^{p,q}_{\bar{\partial}}(M) \otimes H^{n-p,n-q}_{\bar{\partial}}(M) \longrightarrow \mathbb{C}$$

defined by

$$\psi \otimes \eta \longrightarrow \int_M \psi \wedge \eta.$$

It is nondegenerate, since

$$H^{p,q}_{\bar{\partial}}(M) \cong \mathcal{H}^{p,q}(M),$$

and for a harmonic form $\psi \not\equiv 0$

$$\psi \otimes *\psi \longrightarrow \int_M \psi \wedge *\psi = \|\psi\|^2 > 0. \qquad\qquad \text{Q.E.D.}$$

We now come to the Künneth formula. Given compact, complex manifolds M and N, we consider the product $M \times N$. The projections onto the two factors induce maps

$$H^*(M,\Omega^p_M) \longrightarrow H^*(M \times N, \Omega^p_{M \times N}),$$
$$H^*(N,\Omega^p_N) \longrightarrow H^*(M \times N, \Omega^p_{M \times N}).$$

We will prove in a minute that these are injective, and will identify these groups with their images. This being understood, the cup product gives

$$(*) \qquad H^*(M,\Omega^*_M) \otimes H^*(M,\Omega^*_N) \longrightarrow H^*(M \times N, \Omega^*_{M \times N}).$$

The *Künneth formula* asserts that this is an isomorphism.

We will prove this using harmonic forms. Hermitian metrics on M and N induce the product metric on $M \times N$, and we will show that, with this choice of metrics,

$$(**) \qquad \mathcal{H}^{u,v}(M \times N) \cong \bigoplus_{\substack{p+r=u \\ q+s=v}} (\mathcal{H}^{p,q}(M) \otimes \mathcal{H}^{r,s}(N)).$$

This will establish the Künneth theorem.

To carry this out, we denote by z, w generic local coordinates on M and N. Given forms ψ, η on M, N, respectively, we will denote by $\psi \otimes \eta$ the induced form on $M \times N$ given by

$$(\psi \otimes \eta)(z, w) = \psi(z) \wedge \eta(w).$$

These forms will be said to be *decomposable*.

Lemma. *The decomposable forms are* L^2-*dense in all the forms on* $M \times N$.

Proof. We will do this in the case of functions; the modifications necessary to treat general forms will be clear.

It must be proved that a function $\varphi(z, w)$ that satisfies

$$\int_{M \times N} \varphi(z, w)(\overline{\psi(z)\eta(w)}) = 0$$

for all ψ and η is zero. Suppose $\operatorname{Re}\varphi(z_0, w_0) > 0$, choose $\psi(z), \eta(w)$ to have compact support near z_0, w_0, respectively, and satisfy

$$\operatorname{Re}(\varphi(\psi\eta)) \geq 0, \qquad \operatorname{Re}(\varphi(z_0, w_0)\overline{\psi(z_0)\eta(w_0)}) > 0.$$

This is easy to accomplish using a real nonnegative bump function. Then the above integral is nonzero.   Q.E.D.

Forms on $M \times N$ are locally written

$$\varphi(z, w) = \sum \varphi_{II'JJ'} \, dz_I \wedge dw_{I'} \wedge d\bar{z}_J \wedge d\bar{w}_{J'},$$

and then

$$\bar{\partial}_{M \times N} = \bar{\partial}_M \pm \bar{\partial}_N$$

where $\bar{\partial}_M$ is exterior derivative with respect to the $\bar{z}_j$'s and similarly for $\bar{\partial}_N$. Since the metric is a product, we may choose an orthonormal coframe for $M \times N$ of the form

$$\{\varphi_1(z), \ldots, \varphi_m(z); \psi_1(w), \ldots, \psi_n(w)\},$$

where the $\varphi_i(z)$ are an orthonormal coframe for M and the $\psi_\alpha(w)$ are the same for N. Using the formula

$$\bar{\partial}^* = - *\bar{\partial}*,$$

we find that

$$\begin{cases} \bar{\partial}^*_{M \times N} = \bar{\partial}^*_M \pm \bar{\partial}^*_N, \\ \bar{\partial}_M \bar{\partial}^*_N + \bar{\partial}^*_V \bar{\partial}_M = 0 = \bar{\partial}^*_M \bar{\partial}_N + \bar{\partial}_N \bar{\partial}^*_M \end{cases}.$$

These relations imply that

$$\Delta_{M \times N} = \Delta_M + \Delta_N.$$

More precisely, on decomposable forms

$$\Delta_{M \times N}(\psi \otimes \eta) = (\Delta_M \psi) \otimes \eta + \psi \otimes (\Delta_N \eta),$$

and by the lemma this determines $\Delta_{M \times N}$ on all forms.

Now we come to the main point. If $\psi_1, \psi_2, \ldots$ are a complete set of eigenforms for Δ_M and $\eta_1, \eta_2, \ldots$ a complete set of eigenforms for Δ_N, then the forms

$$\psi_i \otimes \eta_\alpha$$

are eigenforms for $\Delta_{M \times N}$. By the lemma they form a complete set. If

$$\Delta_M \psi_i = \lambda_i \psi_i, \qquad \lambda_i \geq 0,$$
$$\Delta_N \eta_\alpha = \mu_\alpha \eta_\alpha, \qquad \mu_\alpha \geq 0,$$

then

$$\Delta_{M \times N}(\psi_i \otimes \eta_\alpha) = (\lambda_i + \mu_\alpha)(\psi_i \otimes \eta_\alpha).$$

Since $\lambda_i + \mu_\alpha = 0 \Leftrightarrow \lambda_i = \mu_\alpha = 0$, the assertion (**) about the harmonic forms follows.   Q.E.D. for Künneth.

If we define the *Hodge numbers*

$$h^{p,q}(M) = \dim H^q(M, \Omega^p),$$

then we have proved that

$$h^{p,q}(M) < \infty,$$
$$\begin{cases} h^{n,n}(M) = 1 \quad \text{and} \\ h^{p,q}(M) = h^{n-p, n-q}(M), \end{cases}$$
$$h^{u,v}(M \times N) = \sum_{\substack{p+r=u \\ q+s=v}} h^{p,q}(M) h^{r,s}(N).$$

In case M is Kähler, there will be additional deeper-lying relations among the Hodge numbers, such as

$$h^{p,q}(M) = h^{q,p}(M),$$
$$b_r(M) = \sum_{p+q=r} h^{p,q}(M),$$
$$h^{p,p}(M) \geq 1,$$

where $b_r(M) = \dim H^r(M, \mathbb{C})$ is the rth Betti number. These, and much more, will be derived in the next section.

One final comment. In general the exterior product of harmonic forms is not harmonic. Similarly, the restriction of a harmonic form to a submanifold is generally not harmonic for the induced metric. Otherwise the cohomology ring would have only those relations imposed by exterior algebra. Moreover, the two Laplacians on a hermitian manifold,

$$\Delta_{\bar{\partial}} = \bar{\partial}\bar{\partial}^* + \bar{\partial}^*\bar{\partial},$$

$$\Delta_d = dd^* + d^*d,$$

are generally unrelated. It is a miraculous fact that, when the metric is Kähler, both these general principles are violated and the theory of harmonic forms has an extraordinary amount of symmetry. More on this in the next section.

7. KÄHLER MANIFOLDS

The Kähler Condition

Let M be a compact complex manifold with Hermitian metric ds^2, and suppose that in some open set $U \subset M$, ds^2 is Euclidean; that is, there exist local holomorphic coordinates $z = (z_1, \ldots, z_n)$ such that

$$ds^2 = \sum dz_i \otimes d\bar{z}_i.$$

Write $z_i = x_i + \sqrt{-1}\, y_i$; one may directly verify that for a differential form

$$\varphi = \sum \varphi_{I\bar{J}} dz_I \wedge d\bar{z}_J$$

compactly supported in U,

$$\Delta_{\bar{\partial}}(\varphi) = -2 \sum_{I,J,i} \frac{\partial^2}{\partial z_i \partial \bar{z}_i} \varphi_{I\bar{J}} \cdot dz_I \wedge d\bar{z}_J$$

$$= -\frac{1}{2} \sum_{I,J,i} \left(\frac{\partial^2}{\partial x_i^2} + \frac{\partial^2}{\partial y_i^2} \right) \varphi_{I\bar{J}} \cdot dz_I \wedge d\bar{z}_J$$

$$= \frac{1}{2} \cdot \Delta_d(\varphi),$$

i.e., the $\bar{\partial}$-Laplacian is equal to the ordinary d-Laplacian in U, up to a constant (cf. Section 6 above). Of course, very few compact complex manifolds have everywhere Euclidean metrics, but as it turns out in order to insure the identity

$$\Delta_{\bar{\partial}} = \frac{1}{2} \cdot \Delta_d$$

on a complex manifold, it is sufficient that the metric approximate the Euclidean metric to order 2 at each point. This is the *Kähler condition*, and we will spend the greater part of this section discussing the condition and its consequences.

We start by giving three alternate forms of the Kähler condition. Again, let

$$ds^2 = \sum h_{ij} \, dz_i \otimes d\bar{z}_j = \sum \varphi_i \otimes \bar{\varphi}_i$$

be a Hermitian metric on the complex manifold M. We say that ds^2 is *Kähler* if its associated $(1,1)$-form

$$\omega = \frac{\sqrt{-1}}{2} \sum \varphi_i \wedge \bar{\varphi}_i$$

is d-closed. In Section 5 above we showed that there was a unique matrix ψ of 1-forms satisfying

$$\psi_{ij} + \bar{\psi}_{ji} = 0, \qquad d\varphi_i = \sum \psi_{ij} \wedge \varphi_j + \tau_i$$

where τ_i is of type $(2,0)$; there we said that the metric was Kähler if the torsion $\tau = 0$. We now show that these conditions are equivalent. Write

$$\frac{2}{\sqrt{-1}} \, d\omega = \sum d\varphi_i \wedge \bar{\varphi}_i - \sum \varphi_i \wedge d\bar{\varphi}_i$$

$$= \sum \psi_{ij} \wedge \varphi_j \wedge \bar{\varphi}_i - \sum \varphi_i \wedge \bar{\psi}_{ij} \wedge \bar{\varphi}_j + \sum \tau_i \wedge \bar{\varphi}_i - \sum \varphi_i \wedge \bar{\tau}_i.$$

We have

$$\sum \psi_{ij} \wedge \varphi_j \wedge \bar{\varphi}_i - \sum \varphi_i \wedge \bar{\psi}_{ij} \wedge \bar{\varphi}_j = \sum \psi_{ij} \wedge \varphi_j \wedge \bar{\varphi}_i + \sum \varphi_i \wedge \psi_{ji} \wedge \bar{\varphi}_j = 0$$

and so $(2/\sqrt{-1}\,)d\omega = \sum \tau_i \wedge \bar{\varphi}_i - \sum \varphi_i \wedge \bar{\tau}_i$. But τ_i is of type $(2,0)$ and the $\bar{\varphi}_i$ are pointwise linearly independent $(0,1)$-forms, which implies that $d\omega = 0$ if and only if $\tau = 0$.

Another interpretation of the Kähler condition that gives some geometric insight is this: We say a metric ds^2 on M *osculates to order* k to the Euclidean metric on $\mathbb{C}^n$ if for every point $z_0 \in M$ we can find a holomorphic coordinate system (z) in a neighborhood of z_0 for which

$$ds^2 = \sum (\delta_{ij} + g_{ij}) dz_i \otimes d\bar{z}_j,$$

where g_{ij} vanishes up to order k at z_0; we usually write

$$ds^2 = \sum (\delta_{ij} + [k]) dz_i \otimes d\bar{z}_j.$$

Lemma. *ds^2 is Kähler if and only if it osculates to order 2 to the Euclidean metric everywhere.*

Proof. One direction is clear: if

$$\omega = \frac{\sqrt{-1}}{2} \sum \left(\delta_{ij} + [2] \right) dz_i \wedge d\bar{z}_j$$

in some coordinate system around z_0, then $d\omega(z_0) = 0$.

Conversely, we can always find coordinates (z) for which $h_{ij}(z_0) = \delta_{ij}$; i.e.,

$$\omega = \frac{\sqrt{-1}}{2} \sum_{i,j,k} \left(\delta_{ij} + a_{ijk} z_k + a_{ij\bar{k}} \bar{z}_k + [2] \right) dz_i \wedge d\bar{z}_j;$$

note that

$$h_{ij} = \overline{h_{ji}} \Rightarrow a_{ji\bar{k}} = \overline{a_{ijk}}$$

and

$$d\omega = 0 \Rightarrow a_{ijk} = a_{kji}.$$

We want to find a change of coordinates

$$z_k = w_k + \frac{1}{2} \sum b_{klm} w_l w_m$$

such that

(∗) $$\omega = \frac{\sqrt{-1}}{2} \sum \left(\delta_{ij} + [2] \right) dw_i \wedge d\bar{w}_j;$$

we normalize by requiring

$$b_{klm} = b_{kml}.$$

Then

$$dz_k = dw_k + \sum b_{klm} w_l dw_m,$$

so that

$$\frac{2}{\sqrt{-1}} \omega = \sum \left(dw_i + \sum b_{ilm} w_l dw_m \right) \wedge \sum \left(d\bar{w}_i + \sum \overline{b_{ipq}} \, \bar{w}_p \, d\bar{w}_q \right)$$

$$+ \sum \left(a_{ijk} w_k + a_{ij\bar{k}} \bar{w}_k \right) dw_i \wedge d\bar{w}_j + [2]$$

$$= \sum \left(\delta_{ij} + \sum_k \left(a_{ijk} w_k + a_{ij\bar{k}} \bar{w}_k + b_{jki} w_k + \overline{b_{ikj}} \, \bar{w}_k \right) \right) dw_i \wedge d\bar{w}_j + [2].$$

If we set

$$b_{jki} = -a_{ijk};$$

then

$$b_{jki} = -a_{ijk} = -a_{kji} = b_{jik}$$

and

$$\overline{b_{ikj}} = -\overline{a_{jik}} = -a_{ij\bar{k}},$$

so that the coordinate change does in fact satisfy the condition (∗). Q.E.D.

Another way of expressing this condition that is useful in computation is to say that for each point $z_0 \in M$ we can find a unitary coframe $\varphi_1, \ldots, \varphi_n$ for the metric in some neighborhood of z_0 such that $d\varphi_i(z_0) = 0$.

A manifold is called *Kähler* if it admits a Kähler metric; we now give some examples of Kähler manifolds.

Examples

Any metric on a compact Riemann surface is Kähler, since $d\omega$ is a 3-form, and hence zero.

If Λ is a lattice in $\mathbb{C}^n$, the complex torus $T = \mathbb{C}^n / \Lambda$ is Kähler with the Euclidean metric $ds^2 = \sum dz_i \otimes d\bar{z}_i$.

If M and N are Kähler then $M \times N$ is Kähler, with the product metric.

If $S \subset M$ is a submanifold, ω the associated $(1,1)$-form of a Kähler metric on M, we have already noted in Section 2 above that the associated $(1,1)$-form of the induced metric on S is just the pullback to S of ω; thus if M is Kähler then S is Kähler.

Recall that the Fubini-Study metric on $\mathbb{P}^n$ is given by its associated $(1,1)$ form

$$\omega = \frac{\sqrt{-1}}{2\pi} \partial\bar{\partial} \log \|Z\|^2$$

where Z is a local lifting of $U \subset \mathbb{P}^n$ to $\mathbb{C}^{n+1} - \{0\}$. Since $\partial\bar{\partial} = -\bar{\partial}\partial$,

$$\omega = \frac{\sqrt{-1}}{4\pi} (\partial + \bar{\partial})(\bar{\partial} - \partial) \log \|Z\|^2$$

$$= \frac{\sqrt{-1}}{4\pi} d\big((\bar{\partial} - \partial) \log \|Z\|^2\big),$$

so we see that ω is closed, and the Fubini-Study metric is Kähler.

(*Note*: It is convenient to define an operator d^c by

$$d^c = \frac{\sqrt{-1}}{4\pi} (\bar{\partial} - \partial).$$

d and d^c are both real differential operators, and

$$dd^c = -d^c d = \frac{\sqrt{-1}}{2\pi} \partial\bar{\partial}.$$

We can consequently write

$$\omega = dd^c \log \|Z\|^2.)$$

Note by the above that *any compact complex manifold that can be embedded in projective space $\mathbb{P}^n$ is Kähler*.

We give some immediate topological consequences of the Kähler condition: For M a compact Kähler manifold,

1.   *The even Betti numbers* $b_{2q}(M)$ *are positive;*

2.   *The holomorphic q-forms* $H^0(M, \Omega^q)$ *inject into the cohomology* $H^q_{DR}(M)$, *i.e., every such* η *is closed, and is never exact; and*

3.   *The fundamental class* η_V *of any analytic subvariety* $V \subset M$ *is nonzero.*

Proofs. 2.   Let η be a holomorphic $(q,0)$-form; we want to show $d\eta = 0$, and that $\eta = d\psi$ only if $\eta \equiv 0$. Let $\varphi_1, \ldots, \varphi_n$ be a local unitary coframe; if

$$\eta = \sum_I \eta_I \varphi_I,$$

then

$$\eta \wedge \bar{\eta} = \sum_{I,J} \eta_I \bar{\eta}_J \varphi_I \wedge \bar{\varphi}_J.$$

Now

$$\omega = \frac{\sqrt{-1}}{2} \sum \varphi_i \wedge \bar{\varphi}_i,$$

so

$$\omega^{n-q} = C_q(n-q)! \sum_{\#K = n-q} \varphi_K \wedge \bar{\varphi}_K;$$

thus, for suitable $C_q \neq 0$,

$$\eta \wedge \bar{\eta} \wedge \omega^{n-q} = C_q \sum_I |\eta_I|^2 \cdot \Phi$$

where Φ is the volume form. Consequently,

$$\int_M \eta \wedge \bar{\eta} \wedge \omega^{n-q} \neq 0 \qquad \text{if } \eta \neq 0. \quad \cdot$$

Now suppose $\eta = d\psi$. Then $d\eta = d\bar{\eta} = 0$, and since $d\omega = 0$ we have

$$\int_M \eta \wedge \bar{\eta} \wedge \omega^{n-q} = \int_M d(\psi \wedge \bar{\eta} \wedge \omega^{n-q}) = 0.$$

Thus $\eta = d\psi$ implies that $\eta \equiv 0$. Finally, since $d\eta = \partial\eta$ is a holomorphic $(q+1)$-form and is exact, it follows that $d\eta = 0$.

1.   To show $b_{2q}(M) > 0$, we exhibit ω^q as a closed $2q$-form that is not exact: if $\omega^q = d\psi$, then we have

$$\int_M \omega^n = \int_M d(\psi \wedge \omega^{n-q}) = 0.$$

But $\omega^n / n!$ is the volume form on M, and so this cannot happen.

3.   The proof of 3 is clear: for V of complex dimension d, by the Wirtinger theorem from Section 2 above

$$\text{vol}(V) = \frac{1}{d!} \int_V \omega^d \neq 0;$$

so $(\eta_V) \neq 0$ in $H_{2d}(M)$.   Q.E.D.

Note that 1 and 3 are extensions of the propositions proved on p. 64 for submanifolds of projective space.

The Hodge Identities and the Hodge Decomposition

Let M be a compact complex manifold with hermitian metric ds^2 and associated $(1,1)$-form ω. We have defined a number of operators on the space $A^*(M)$ of differential forms on M, such as ∂, $\bar{\partial}$, d, d^c, their respective adjoints and associated Laplacians, and the decompositions

$$\Pi^{p,q}: A^*(M) \to A^{p,q}(M)$$

$$\Pi^r = \bigoplus_{p+q=r} \Pi^{p,q}: A^*(M) \to A^r(M)$$

by type and degree. We define an additional operator

$$L: A^{p,q}(M) \to A^{p+1,q+1}(M)$$

by

$$L(\eta) = \eta \wedge \omega$$

and let

$$\Lambda = L^*: A^{p,q}(M) \to A^{p-1,q-1}(M)$$

be its adjoint. Now, for general M there are no nonobvious relationships among these various operators. If we assume that the metric on M is Kähler, however, we get a host of identities relating them, called the *Hodge identities*. Indeed, the Kähler condition is exactly that which insures a strong interplay between the real potential theory associated to the Riemannian metric and the underlying complex structure. The basic identity, from which all the others will easily follow, is

$(*)$ $$[\Lambda, d] = -4\pi d^{c*},$$

where $[A, B]$ denotes the commutator $AB - BA$; or equivalently,

$$[L, d^*] = 4\pi d^c.$$

Proof. By decomposition into type, this identity is equivalent to

$$[\Lambda, \bar{\partial}] = -\sqrt{-1}\, \partial^* \quad \text{and} \quad [\Lambda, \partial] = \sqrt{-1}\, \bar{\partial}^*.$$

Since Λ, d, and d^c are real operators, either of these implies the other; we will prove $[\Lambda, \partial] = \sqrt{-1}\, \bar{\partial}^*$. We make the computation first on $\mathbb{C}^n$ with the Euclidean metric. Here it is messy but straightforward and will be facilitated by our breaking it up into component steps. To do this, we introduce some new operators on forms in $\mathbb{C}^n$: for each $k = 1, \ldots, n$, let $e_k: A_c^{p,q}(\mathbb{C}^n) \to A_c^{p+1,q}(\mathbb{C}^n)$ be the operator on compactly supported forms defined by

$$e_k(\varphi) = dz_k \wedge \varphi;$$

let $\bar{e}_k : A_c^{p,q}(\mathbb{C}^n) \to A_c^{p,q+1}(\mathbb{C}^n)$ similarly be given by

$$\bar{e}_k(\varphi) = d\bar{z}_k \wedge \varphi.$$

Let i_k and $\bar{i}_k$ be the adjoints of e_k and $\bar{e}_k$, respectively. Note that e_k, $\bar{e}_k$, i_k, and $\bar{i}_k$ are all linear over $C^\infty(\mathbb{C}^n)$. Now

$$i_k(dz_J \wedge d\bar{z}_K) = 0, \qquad \text{if } k \notin J,$$

and, recalling that the length $\|dz_k\| = 2$,

$$i_k(dz_k \wedge dz_J \wedge d\bar{z}_K) = 2\, dz_J \wedge d\bar{z}_K;$$

since in the former case, we have for any multiindexes L and M

$$\big(i_k(dz_J \wedge d\bar{z}_K), dz_L \wedge d\bar{z}_M\big) = (dz_J \wedge d\bar{z}_K, dz_k \wedge dz_L \wedge d\bar{z}_M)$$
$$= 0,$$

so $i_k(dz_J \wedge d\bar{z}_K) = 0$, while in the latter case

$$\big(i_k(dz_k \wedge dz_J \wedge d\bar{z}_K), dz_L \wedge d\bar{z}_M\big) = (dz_k \wedge dz_J \wedge d\bar{z}_K, dz_k \wedge dz_L \wedge d\bar{z}_M)$$
$$= 2(dz_J \wedge d\bar{z}_K, dz_L \wedge d\bar{z}_M).$$

Similarly, we see that

$$\bar{i}_k(dz_J \wedge d\bar{z}_K) = 0, \qquad \text{if } k \notin K,$$

and

$$\bar{i}_k(d\bar{z}_k \wedge dz_J \wedge d\bar{z}_K) = 2\, dz_J \wedge d\bar{z}_K.$$

Note also that for any monomial $dz_J \wedge d\bar{z}_K$,

$$i_k \cdot e_k(dz_J \wedge d\bar{z}_K) = \begin{cases} 0, & \text{if } k \in J, \\ 2\, dz_J \wedge d\bar{z}_K, & \text{if } k \notin J \end{cases}$$

while

$$e_k \cdot i_k(dz_J \wedge d\bar{z}_K) = \begin{cases} 2\, dz_J \wedge d\bar{z}_K, & \text{if } k \in J, \\ 0, & \text{if } k \notin J. \end{cases}$$

Thus

$$i_k e_k + e_k i_k = 2$$

and likewise $\bar{i}_k \bar{e}_k + \bar{e}_k \bar{i}_k = 2$. On the other hand, we have for $k \neq l$,

$$i_k \cdot e_l(dz_k \wedge dz_J \wedge d\bar{z}_K) = i_k(dz_l \wedge dz_k \wedge dz_J \wedge d\bar{z}_K)$$
$$= i_k(-dz_k \wedge dz_l \wedge dz_J \wedge d\bar{z}_K)$$
$$= -2(dz_l \wedge dz_J \wedge d\bar{z}_K)$$
$$= -2e_l(dz_J \wedge d\bar{z}_K)$$
$$= -e_l \cdot i_k(dz_k \wedge dz_J \wedge d\bar{z}_K),$$

while

$$i_k \cdot e_l(dz_J \wedge dz_K) = e_l \cdot i_k(dz_J \wedge d\bar{z}_K) = 0$$

in case $k \notin J$, so we have

$$e_k i_l + i_l e_k = 0.$$

We also define operators ∂_k and $\bar{\partial}_k$ on $A_c^{p,q}(\mathbb{C}^n)$ by

$$\partial_k \left(\sum \varphi_{I\bar{J}} dz_I \wedge d\bar{z}_J \right) = \sum \frac{\partial \varphi_{I\bar{J}}}{\partial z_k} dz_I \wedge d\bar{z}_J$$

and

$$\bar{\partial}_k \left(\sum \varphi_{I\bar{J}} dz_I \wedge d\bar{z}_J \right) = \sum \frac{\partial \varphi_{I\bar{J}}}{\partial \bar{z}_k} dz_I \wedge d\bar{z}_J.$$

Note that ∂_k and $\bar{\partial}_k$ commute with e_l, $\bar{e}_l$, i_l, and $\bar{i}_l$ and with each other. Finally, we see that the adjoint of ∂_k is $-\bar{\partial}_k$: we have for $\varphi = \sum \varphi_{I\bar{J}} dz_I \wedge d\bar{z}_K$ any compactly supported form, L and M any multiindices and ψ any C^∞ function,

$$
\begin{aligned}
\left(-\bar{\partial}_k \varphi, \psi \, dz_L \wedge dz_M \right) &= \left(-\frac{\partial}{\partial \bar{z}_k} (\varphi_{L\bar{M}}) \, dz_L \wedge d\bar{z}_M, \psi \, dz_L \wedge d\bar{z}_M \right) \\
&= 2^{\#L + \#M} \int_{\mathbb{C}^n} -\frac{\partial}{\partial \bar{z}_k} (\varphi_{L\bar{M}}) \cdot \bar{\psi} \\
&= 2^{\#L + \#M} \int_{\mathbb{C}^n} \varphi_{L\bar{M}} \cdot \frac{\partial}{\partial \bar{z}_k} (\bar{\psi}) \quad \text{(by integration by parts)} \\
&= 2^{\#L + \#M} \int_{\mathbb{C}^n} \varphi_{L\bar{M}} \cdot \overline{\frac{\partial}{\partial z_k} (\psi)} \\
&= \left(\varphi_{L\bar{M}} dz_L \wedge d\bar{z}_M, \partial_k (\psi \cdot dz_L \wedge d\bar{z}_M) \right) \\
&= \left(\varphi, \partial_k (\psi \, dz_L \wedge d\bar{z}_M) \right).
\end{aligned}
$$

Likewise, the adjoint of $\bar{\partial}_k$ is $-\partial_k$.

We can express all of our operators on $A_c^{**}(\mathbb{C}^n)$ in terms of these elementary operators: clearly

$$\partial = \sum_k \partial_k e_k = \sum_k e_k \partial_k,$$

$$\bar{\partial} = \sum \bar{\partial}_k \bar{e}_k = \sum \bar{e}_k \bar{\partial}_k,$$

and, taking adjoints,

$$\partial^* = -\sum \partial_k \bar{i}_k,$$

$$\bar{\partial}^* = -\sum \bar{\partial}_k i_k.$$

L is defined as exterior product with the standard Kähler form defined on $\mathbb{C}^n$, so

$$L = \frac{\sqrt{-1}}{2} \sum e_k \bar{e}_k$$

and, taking the adjoint,

$$\Lambda = -\frac{\sqrt{-1}}{2} \sum \bar{\imath}_k i_k.$$

so

$$\Lambda \partial = -\frac{\sqrt{-1}}{2} \sum_{k,l} \bar{\imath}_k i_k \partial_l e_l$$

$$= -\frac{\sqrt{-1}}{2} \sum_{k,l} \partial_l \bar{\imath}_k i_k e_l$$

$$= -\frac{\sqrt{-1}}{2} \left(\sum_k \partial_k \bar{\imath}_k i_k e_k + \sum_{k \neq l} \partial_l \bar{\imath}_k i_k e_l \right).$$

To evaluate the first term, write

$$-\frac{\sqrt{-1}}{2} \sum_k \partial_k \bar{\imath}_k i_k e_k = \frac{\sqrt{-1}}{2} \sum \partial_k \bar{\imath}_k e_k i_k - \frac{2\sqrt{-1}}{2} \sum \partial_k \bar{\imath}_k$$

$$= -\frac{\sqrt{-1}}{2} \sum \partial_k e_k \bar{\imath}_k i_k - \sqrt{-1} \sum \partial_k \bar{\imath}_k.$$

For the second term

$$-\frac{\sqrt{-1}}{2} \sum_{k \neq l} \partial_l \bar{\imath}_k i_k e_l = \frac{\sqrt{-1}}{2} \sum_{l \neq k} \partial_l \bar{\imath}_k e_l i_k$$

$$= -\frac{\sqrt{-1}}{2} \sum \partial_l e_l \bar{\imath}_k i_k.$$

Thus

$$\Lambda \partial = -\frac{\sqrt{-1}}{2} \sum_{k,l} \partial_l e_l \bar{\imath}_k i_k + \sqrt{-1} \sum \partial_k \bar{\imath}_k$$

$$= \partial \Lambda + \sqrt{-1} \, \bar{\partial}^*,$$

so the identity is proved on $\mathbb{C}^n$.

To prove the result on a Kähler manifold M we use the condition of osculation to show that the identity holds at any point: for $z_0 \in M$, we can choose a coframe $\varphi_1, \ldots, \varphi_n$ for the metric such that $d\varphi_i(z_0) = 0$. The expression for Λ holds with dz_l replaced by φ_l; we can make essentially the same computation for $[\Lambda, \bar{\partial}]\eta$ as on $\mathbb{C}^n$ except that we will get terms involving $\bar{\partial}\varphi_i$. Since $[\Lambda, \bar{\partial}]$ involves only first derivatives, however, all the additional terms will have a factor $\bar{\partial}\varphi_i$ and hence will vanish at z_0. Likewise, we have computed $\partial^*\eta = C_n *\partial *\eta$ on $\mathbb{C}^n$ where it agrees with $\sqrt{-1} \, [\Lambda, \bar{\partial}]\eta$; the computation on M in terms of the φ_i will again be the same except for additional terms involving $\bar{\partial}\varphi_i$, which vanish at z_0. Thus we see that the identity holds at z_0, hence everywhere.

This argument is just one instance of a general principle: *any intrinsically defined identity that involves the metric together with its first derivatives and which is valid on $\mathbb{C}^n$ with the Euclidean metric, is also valid on a Kähler manifold.*

Now, some consequences: if $\Delta_d = dd^* + d^*d$ is the d-Laplacian, we have

$$[L, \Delta_d] = 0$$

or, equivalently,

$$[\Lambda, \Delta_d] = 0.$$

Proof. First note that since ω is closed,

$$d(\omega \wedge \eta) = \omega \wedge d\eta,$$

i.e.,

$$[L, d] = 0$$

and so by taking adjoints

$$[\Lambda, d^*] = 0.$$

Now

$$
\begin{aligned}
\Lambda(dd^* + d^*d) &= (d\Lambda d^* - 4\pi d^{c*}d^*) + d^*\Lambda d \\
&= d\Lambda d^* + (4\pi d^*d^{c*} + d^*\Lambda d) \\
&= (dd^* + d^*d)\Lambda. \qquad\qquad \text{Q.E.D.}
\end{aligned}
$$

We also have, as mentioned earlier,

$$\Delta_d = 2\Delta_{\bar\partial} = 2\Delta_\partial.$$

Proof. First we show that $\partial\bar\partial^* + \bar\partial^*\partial = 0$: since $\Lambda\partial - \partial\Lambda = \sqrt{-1}\,\bar\partial^*$, we have

$$
\begin{aligned}
\sqrt{-1}\,(\partial\bar\partial^* + \bar\partial^*\partial) &= \partial(\Lambda\partial - \partial\Lambda) + (\Lambda\partial - \partial\Lambda)\partial \\
&= \partial\Lambda\partial - \partial\Lambda\partial = 0.
\end{aligned}
$$

Now,

$$
\begin{aligned}
\Delta_d &= (\partial + \bar\partial)(\partial^* + \bar\partial^*) + (\partial^* + \bar\partial^*)(\partial + \bar\partial) \\
&= (\partial\partial^* + \partial^*\partial) + (\bar\partial\bar\partial^* + \bar\partial^*\bar\partial) + (\partial\bar\partial^* + \bar\partial\partial^* + \partial^*\bar\partial + \bar\partial^*\partial) \\
&= (\partial\partial^* + \partial^*\partial) + (\bar\partial\bar\partial^* + \bar\partial^*\bar\partial) \\
&= \Delta_\partial + \Delta_{\bar\partial},
\end{aligned}
$$

so we have to show

$$\Delta_\partial = \Delta_{\bar\partial}.$$

For this

$$
\begin{aligned}
-\sqrt{-1}\,\Delta_\partial &= \partial(\Lambda\bar\partial - \bar\partial\Lambda) + (\Lambda\bar\partial - \bar\partial\Lambda)\partial \\
&= \partial\Lambda\bar\partial - \partial\bar\partial\Lambda + \Lambda\bar\partial\partial - \bar\partial\Lambda\partial
\end{aligned}
$$

and consequently

$$\sqrt{-1}\,\Delta_{\bar{\partial}} = \left(\bar{\partial}(\Lambda\partial - \partial\Lambda) + (\Lambda\partial - \partial\Lambda)\bar{\partial}\right)$$
$$= \bar{\partial}\Lambda\partial - \bar{\partial}\partial\Lambda + \Lambda\partial\bar{\partial} - \partial\Lambda\bar{\partial}$$
$$= \sqrt{-1}\,\Delta_{\partial},$$

since $\bar{\partial}\partial = -\partial\bar{\partial}$.   Q.E.D.

As an immediate corollary we see that Δ_d preserves bidegree; i.e.,

$$[\Delta_d, \Pi^{pq}] = 0.$$

There are two main applications of these identities, the *Hodge decomposition* and the *Lefschetz decomposition* and theorem. We do Hodge first:
Set

$$H^{p,q}(M) = \frac{Z_d^{p,q}(M)}{dA^*(M) \cap Z_d^{p,q}(M)},$$
$$\mathcal{H}_d^{p,q}(M) = \{\eta \in A^{p,q}(M): \Delta_d\eta = 0\},$$
$$\mathcal{H}_d(M) = \{\eta \in A^r(M): \Delta_d\eta = 0\}.$$

Note that the first group is intrinsically defined by the complex structure, while the latter two depend on the particular metric. By the commutativity of Δ_d and $\Pi^{p,q}$ and the fact that Δ_d is real, the harmonic forms satisfy

$$(*) \qquad \begin{cases} \mathcal{H}^r(M) = \displaystyle\bigoplus_{p+q=r} \mathcal{H}^{p,q}(M), \\ \mathcal{H}^{p,q}(M) = \overline{\mathcal{H}^{q,p}(M)}. \end{cases}$$

On the other hand, for η a closed form of pure type (p,q),

$$\eta = \mathcal{H}(\eta) + dd^*G(\eta),$$

where the harmonic part $\mathcal{H}(\eta)$ also has pure type (p,q). Thus

$$H^{p,q}(M) \cong \mathcal{H}^{p,q}(M).$$

Combining this with $(*)$ and the Hodge theorem

$$H^*_{DR}(M) \cong \mathcal{H}^*(M)$$

for the Laplacian Δ_d, we obtain the famous

Hodge Decomposition. *For a compact Kähler manifold* M, *the complex cohomology satisfies*

$$\begin{cases} H^r(M, \mathbb{C}) \cong \displaystyle\bigoplus_{p+q=r} H^{p,q}(M), \\ H^{p,q}(M) = \overline{H^{q,p}(M)}. \end{cases}$$

Since $\Delta_d = 2\Delta_{\bar{\partial}}$, we have $\mathcal{H}_d^{p,q}(M) = \mathcal{H}_{\bar{\partial}}^{p,q}(M)$ and consequently

$$H^{p,q}(M) \cong H_{\bar{\partial}}^{p,q}(M) \cong H^q(M, \Omega^p).$$

In particular, taking $q=0$,

$$H^{p,0}(M) = H^0(M, \Omega^p)$$

is the space of holomorphic p-forms. *The holomorphic forms are therefore harmonic for any Kähler metric on a compact manifold.*

We note also that

The Betti numbers $b_{2q+1}(M)$ of odd degree are even.

Proof. If we define the *Hodge numbers* by

$$h^{p,q}(M) = \dim H^{p,q}(M),$$

then the Hodge decomposition gives

$$b_r(M) = \sum_{p+q=r} h^{p,q}(M),$$

$$h^{p,q}(M) = h^{q,p}(M).$$

Taking $r=2q+1$, we find

$$b_{2q+1}(M) = 2\left[\sum_{p=0}^{q} h^{p,2q+1-p}(M) \right].$$

We can put the cohomology groups of a compact Kähler manifold diagrammatically in the *Hodge diamond* (Figure 6), so that the kth cohomology group of M can be read off as the sum of the groups in the kth horizontal row. The star operator gives a symmetry about the center of the diamond; conjugation gives a symmetry about the center vertical line.

As an immediate application of the Hodge decomposition, we have the

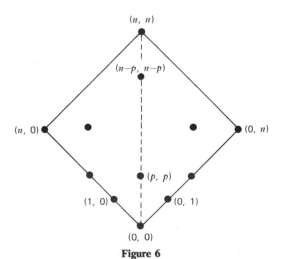

Figure 6

Corollary.

$$H^q(\mathbb{P}^n, \Omega^p) = H^{p,q}_{\bar{\partial}}(\mathbb{P}^n) = \begin{cases} 0, & \text{if } p \neq q, \\ \mathbb{C}, & \text{if } p = q. \end{cases}$$

Proof. This is clear: since $H^{2k+1}(\mathbb{P}^n, \mathbb{Z}) = 0$, we have $H^{p,q}_{\bar{\partial}}(\mathbb{P}^n) = 0$ for $p + q$ odd; since $H^{2k}(\mathbb{P}^n, \mathbb{Z}) = \mathbb{Z}$, we have for $p \neq k$,

$$1 = b_{2k}(\mathbb{P}^n) \geqslant h^{p,2k-p}(\mathbb{P}^n) + h^{2k-p,\,p}(\mathbb{P}^n)$$
$$= 2 \cdot h^{p,2k-p}$$
$$\Rightarrow h^{p,2k-p}(\mathbb{P}^n) = 0$$

and hence

$$H^{p,p}_{\bar{\partial}}(\mathbb{P}^n) \cong H^{2p}_{DR}r(\mathbb{P}^n) \cong \mathbb{C}. \qquad \text{Q.E.D.}$$

Note in particular that

There are no nonzero global holomorphic forms on $\mathbb{P}^n$.

The Lefschetz Decomposition

Another important application of the Hodge identities is the Lefschetz decomposition of the cohomology of a compact Kähler manifold. To put this in proper perspective, we must first digress for a moment and discuss representations of sl_2.

Representations of sl_2. sl_2 is the Lie algebra of the group SL_2; it is realized as the vector space of 2×2 complex matrices with trace 0, and with the bracket

$$[A, B] = AB - BA.$$

We take as standard generators

$$X = \begin{pmatrix} 0 & 1 \\ 0 & 0 \end{pmatrix}, \qquad H = \begin{pmatrix} 1 & 0 \\ 0 & -1 \end{pmatrix}, \qquad Y = \begin{pmatrix} 0 & 0 \\ 1 & 0 \end{pmatrix},$$

with the relations

$$[X, Y] = H, \qquad [H, X] = 2X, \qquad [H, Y] = -2Y.$$

Now, let V be a finite-dimensional complex vector space, $gl(V)$ its algebra of endomorphisms. We want to study Lie algebra maps

$$\rho: sl_2 \to gl(V),$$

i.e., linear maps ρ such that

$$\rho([A, B]) = \rho(A)\rho(B) - \rho(B)\rho(A).$$

Such a map is called a *representation of* sl_2 *in* V; V is called an sl_2-*module*.

A subspace of V fixed under $\rho(sl_2)$ is called a submodule; V (or ρ) is called *irreducible* if V has no nontrivial submodules. By a fundamental result, which we won't prove here, every submodule W of an sl_2-module V has a complementary submodule $W^\perp$; thus every sl_2-module is the direct sum of irreducible sl_2-modules, and to study representations of sl_2 we need only look at irreducible ones.

Suppose then that V is an irreducible sl_2-module. The key to analyzing the structure of V is to look at the eigenspaces for $\rho(H)$ (from now on, we will omit the ρ's). These are called *weight spaces*. First of all, note that if $v \in V$ is an eigenvector of H with eigenvalue λ, then Xv and Yv are also eigenvectors of H, with eigenvalues $\lambda+2$ and $\lambda-2$, respectively: this follows from

$$H(Xv) = XHv + [H,X]v$$
$$= X\lambda v + 2Xv$$
$$= (\lambda+2)Xv,$$

and similarly for Yv. Since H can have only a finite number of eigenvalues, we see from this that X and Y are nilpotent. We say that $v \in V$ is *primitive* if v is an eigenvector for H and $Xv = 0$; clearly primitive elements exist.

Proposition. *If* $v \in V$ *is primitive, then* V *is generated as a vector space by*

$$v, Yv, Y^2v,\ldots.$$

Proof. Since V is irreducible, we need only show that the linear span V' of $\{Y^iv\}$ is fixed under sl_2. Clearly $HV' \subset V'$ and $YV' \subset V'$. We show $XV' \subset V'$ by an induction: $Xv = 0$ trivially lies in V', and in general

$$XY^nv = YXY^{n-1}v + HY^{n-1}v;$$

so

$$XY^{n-1}v \in V' \Rightarrow XY^nv \in V'. \qquad \text{Q.E.D.}$$

Note that the elements $\{Y^nv\}_n$ that are nonzero are linearly independent, since they are all eigenvectors for H with different eigenvalues. Thus we have the picture of V: $V = \oplus V_\lambda$, where each V_λ is one-dimensional,

$$H(V_\lambda) = V_\lambda, \qquad X(V_\lambda) = V_{\lambda+2}, \qquad Y(V_\lambda) = V_{\lambda-2}.$$

Proposition. *All eigenvalues for* H *are integers, and we can write*

$$V = V_n \oplus V_{n-2} \oplus \cdots \oplus V_{-n+2} \oplus V_{-n}.$$

Proof. Let v be primitive, and suppose

$$Y^nv \neq 0, \qquad Y^{n+1}v = 0,$$

and $Hv = \lambda v$. Then

$$Xv = 0,$$
$$XYv = YXv + Hv = \lambda v,$$
$$XY^2v = YXYv + HYv$$
$$= Y\lambda v + (\lambda - 2)Yv = (\lambda + (\lambda - 2))Yv,$$

and in general $XY^mv = YXY^{m-1}v + HY^{m-1}v$, so we have

$$XY^mv = (\lambda + (\lambda - 2) + (\lambda - 4) + \cdots + (\lambda - 2(m-1)))Y^{m-1}v$$
$$= (m\lambda - m^2 + m)Y^{m-1}v,$$

and since $Y^nv \neq 0$, $Y^{n+1}v = 0$,

$$(n+1)\lambda - (n+1)^2 + n + 1 = 0 \Rightarrow \lambda = n. \qquad \text{Q.E.D.}$$

In summary, *the irreducible* sl_2 *modules are indexed by nonnegative integers* n; *for each such* n *the corresponding* sl_2-*module* V(n) *has dimension* n+1. *Explicitly,*

$$V(n) \cong \mathrm{Sym}^n(\mathbb{C}^2)$$

is the n*th symmetric power of the vector space* $\mathbb{C}^2$. *The eigenvalues of* H *acting on* V(n) *are* $-n, -n+2, \ldots, n-2, n$, *each appearing with multiplicity* 1.

For any sl_2-module V, not necessarily irreducible, we define the *Lefschetz decomposition of* V as follows: let $PV = \mathrm{Ker}\,\rho(X)$; then

$$V = PV \oplus YPV \oplus Y^2PV \oplus \cdots,$$

and this decomposition is compatible with the decomposition of V into eigenspaces V_m for H. We also see that the maps

$$V_m \underset{X^m}{\overset{Y^m}{\rightleftarrows}} V_{-m}$$

are isomorphisms. Finally, in general,

$$(\mathrm{Ker}\,X) \cap V_k = \mathrm{Ker}(Y^{k+1}: V_k \to V_{-k-2}).$$

We return now to our compact complex manifold M with Kähler metric $ds^2 = \Sigma \varphi_i \otimes \bar{\varphi}_i$. First, we want to compute the commutator $[L, \Lambda]$ of the operators L and Λ; this may be done on $\mathbb{C}^n$ using the operators e_k, $\bar{e}_k$, i_k, and $\bar{i}_k$ defined earlier. Recall that

$$L = \frac{\sqrt{-1}}{2} \sum e_k \bar{e}_k \quad \text{and} \quad \Lambda = -\frac{\sqrt{-1}}{2} \sum \bar{i}_k i_k;$$

we have then

$$[L, \Lambda] = \frac{1}{4}\left(\sum_{k,l} e_k \bar{e}_k \bar{i}_l i_l - \sum_{k,l} \bar{i}_l i_l e_k \bar{e}_k\right)$$
$$= \frac{1}{4} \sum_{k \neq l} \left(e_k \bar{e}_k \bar{i}_l i_l - \bar{i}_l i_l e_k \bar{e}_k\right)$$
$$+ \frac{1}{4} \sum_k \left(e_k \bar{e}_k \bar{i}_k i_k - \bar{i}_k i_k e_k \bar{e}_k\right).$$

By our commutation relations, every term in the first sum is zero; for the second, we have

$$e_k \bar{e}_k \bar{i}_k i_k = 2e_k i_k - e_k \bar{i}_k \bar{e}_k i_k,$$
$$\bar{i}_k i_k e_k \bar{e}_k = 2\bar{i}_k \bar{e}_k - \bar{i}_k e_k i_k \bar{e}_k,$$

and, since $e_k \bar{i}_k \bar{e}_k i_k = \bar{i}_k e_k i_k \bar{e}_k$, this yields

$$[L, \Lambda] = \frac{1}{2} \sum_k \left(e_k i_k - \bar{i}_k \bar{e}_k \right)$$

$$= \frac{1}{2} \sum_k \left(2 - i_k e_k - \bar{i}_k \bar{e}_k \right)$$

$$= n - \frac{1}{2} \sum_k \left(i_k e_k + \bar{i}_k \bar{e}_k \right).$$

To evaluate this, note that $i_k e_k (dz_J \wedge d\bar{z}_K)$ is zero if $k \in J$, and $2 dz_J \wedge d\bar{z}_K$ otherwise; $\bar{i}_k \bar{e}_k (dz_J \wedge d\bar{z}_K)$ is zero if $k \in K$ and $2 dz_J \wedge d\bar{z}_K$ if not. Thus

$$\sum_k \left(i_k e_k + \bar{i}_k \bar{e}_k \right)(dz_J \wedge dz_K) = 2 \sum_{k \notin J} dz_J \wedge d\bar{z}_K + 2 \sum_{k \notin K} dz_J \wedge d\bar{z}_K$$

$$= (2(n - {}^\# J) + 2(n - {}^\# K))(dz_J \wedge d\bar{z}_K).$$

and so on $A_c^{p,q}(\mathbb{C}^n)$

$$[L, \Lambda] = p + q - n.$$

Since L and Λ are both algebraic operators, this identity will hold on any Kähler manifold.

Now set

$$h = \sum_{p=0}^{2n} (n - p) \Pi^p;$$

since $L : A^p(M) \to A^{p+2}(M)$ and $\Lambda : A^p(M) \to A^{p-2}(M)$, we obtain

$$[\Lambda, L] = h,$$
(*) $$[h, L] = -2L,$$
$$[h, \Lambda] = 2\Lambda.$$

The operators L, Λ, and h all commute with Δ_d, and so act on the harmonic space $\mathcal{H}_d^*(M) \cong H^*(M)$ with relations (*). We may therefore give a representation of sl_2 on $H^*(M)$ by sending

$$X = \begin{pmatrix} 0 & 1 \\ 0 & 0 \end{pmatrix} \to \Lambda,$$

$$Y = \begin{pmatrix} 0 & 0 \\ 1 & 0 \end{pmatrix} \to L,$$

$$H = \begin{pmatrix} 1 & 0 \\ 0 & -1 \end{pmatrix} \to h;$$

the eigenspace for h with eigenvalue $(n-p)$ will be $H^p(M)$. Applying our results on finite-dimensional representations of sl_2 to this representation yields the

Hard Lefschetz Theorem. *The map*

$$L^k: \ H^{n-k}(M) \longrightarrow H^{n+k}(M),$$

is an isomorphism; and if we define the primitive *cohomology*

$$P^{n-k}(M) = \operatorname{Ker} L^{k+1}: \ H^{n-k}(M) \to H^{n+k+2}(M)$$
$$= (\operatorname{Ker} \Lambda) \cap H^{n-k}(M),$$

then we have

$$H^m(M) = \bigoplus_k L^k P^{m-2k}(M),$$

called the Lefschetz decomposition.

Note that the Lefschetz decomposition is compatible with the Hodge decomposition; i.e., if we set

$$P^{p,q}(M) = (\operatorname{Ker} \Lambda) \cap H^{p,q}(M),$$

then

$$P^l(M) = \bigoplus_{p+q=l} P^{p,q}(M).$$

We can give the following geometric interpretation of the Lefschetz theory in case the manifold M is embedded in projective space $\mathbb{P}^N$ with the induced metric. We have seen that the form

$$\omega = \frac{\sqrt{-1}}{2\pi} \partial\bar{\partial} \log \|Z\|^2$$

is closed and not exact in $\mathbb{P}^N$. Since $H^2(\mathbb{P}^N)$ is one-dimensional, it follows that $[\omega] \in H^2_{DR}(\mathbb{P}^N)$ is Poincaré dual to some nonzero multiple of the homology class of a hyperplane $H \subset \mathbb{P}^N$. In fact, $[\omega]$ is Poincaré dual to (H), as the reader may verify by integrating ω over a line $l \cong \mathbb{P}^1$ to obtain

$$\int_l \omega = 1 = {}^\#(H \cdot l).$$

We see from this that for $M \subset \mathbb{P}^N$ a submanifold, the associated $(1,1)$ form $\omega|_M$ of the induced metric is Poincaré dual to the homology class (V) of the analytic subvariety $V = M \cap H \subset M$. The Poincaré-dualized version of the hard Lefschetz theorem says that the operation of intersection with an $(N-k)$-plane $\mathbb{P}^{N-k} \subset \mathbb{P}^N$ gives an isomorphism

$$H_{n+k}(M) \overset{\cap \, \mathbb{P}^{N-k}}{\longrightarrow} H_{n-k}(M).$$

Note that in this interpretation, the primitive cohomology $P^{n-k}(M)$ of

M corresponds via the isomorphisms

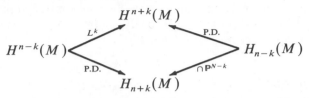

to the subgroup of $(n-k)$-cycles that do not intersect a hyperplane, i.e., the image of the map

$$H_{n-k}(M-V) \to H_{n-k}(M).$$

Such cycles are called *finite cycles* since $M-V$ is the "finite part" $M \cap \mathbb{C}^N$ of M; their importance will be more apparent when we prove the Lefschetz theorem on hyperplane sections.

As another application of the Hodge and Lefschetz decompositions, we will now describe the Hodge-Riemann bilinear relations. We define a bilinear form

$$Q: H^{n-k}(M) \otimes H^{n-k}(M) \to \mathbb{C}$$

by setting

$$Q(\xi, \eta) = \int_M \xi \wedge \eta \wedge \omega^k.$$

Note that since ω is real, Q defines a real bilinear form on $H^{n-k}(M, \mathbb{R})$. By consideration of type, we see that

$$Q(H^{p,q}, H^{p',q'}) = 0 \qquad \text{unless } p = q', q = p'.$$

The *Hodge-Riemann bilinear relations* assert that for $\xi \in P^{p,q}(M)$ a primitive class and $k = p + q$,

$$\sqrt{-1}^{\,p-q}(-1)^{(n-k)(n-k-1)/2} Q(\xi, \bar{\xi}) > 0.$$

In the case $p+q$ even, this is the same as saying that on the real vector space

$$(P^{p,q} \oplus P^{q,p}) \cap H^{p+q}(M, \mathbb{R}) = \{\xi + \bar{\xi}, \xi \in P^{p+q}(M)\} \subset H^{p+q}(M),$$

the quadratic form $(\sqrt{-1})^{p-q}(-1)^{(n-k)(n-k-1)/2} Q$ is positive definite; in the case $p+q$ odd, the bilinear relations tell us at least that Q is a nondegenerate skew-symmetric form on $P^{p+q}(M)$. In either case, since we have the Lefschetz decomposition

$$H^m = \oplus L^k P^{m-2k}$$

and $Q(L^k\xi, L^k\eta) = Q(\xi, \eta)$; the bilinear relations tell us that Q is nondegenerate on $H^{n-k}(M)$.

We will not prove the bilinear relations in full generality, but will verify them in some cases including all those to be used in our applications to geometry. (The general proof may be based on the following observations: In the full exterior algebra

$$V = \Lambda^* \mathbb{C}^n \otimes \Lambda^* \overline{\mathbb{C}^n}$$

corresponding to the differential forms at a point $x \in M$, there is an sl_2-action given by $\{L, \Lambda, h\}$ as above. Decomposing V into primitive spaces $P^k V$ is the same as decomposing V under the action of the unitary group U_n, and thus by Schur's lemma any U_n-invariant quadratic form on $P^k V$ is necessarily definite. The primitive harmonic forms on M are those which lie in $P^k V$ (fixed k) for each $x \in M$, and this yields a proof. The result that decomposing V under sl_2 together with $\pi^{(p,q)}$ yields the same irreducible factors as under the action of U_n is proved in Herman Weyl's book *The Classical Groups*—it implies that, in general, there are no further Hodge identities.)

First, let M be a compact Riemann surface. By the Hodge decomposition,

$$H^1(M, \mathbb{C}) = H^{1,0}(M) \oplus H^{0,1}(M)$$
$$\cong H^0(M, \Omega^1) \oplus \overline{H^0(M, \Omega^1)}.$$

The number of independent holomorphic 1-forms on M (classically called *differentials of the first kind*) is thus equal to $b_1(M)/2$; this in fact was one of the first links established between the topology of a complex manifold and its analytic structure. To verify the bilinear relations for M let $\xi = h(z) dz \in H^{1,0}(M)$; we have $(\sqrt{-1})^{p-q}(-1)^{(n-k)(n-k-1)/2} = \sqrt{-1}$, and

$$Q(\xi, \bar{\xi}) = \sqrt{-1} \int_M |h(z)|^2 dz \wedge d\bar{z}$$
$$> 0.$$

In general, for M of any dimension, $H^{p,0}(M)$ and $H^{0,p}(M)$ are primitive by consideration of type, and the same calculation works to verify the bilinear relations for them. In fact, it was in effect by deducing the Hodge-Riemann bilinear relations for holomorphic q-forms that we first proved that the holomorphic forms inject into the cohomology of a compact Kähler manifold.

Now let $\dim M = 2$; it remains only to verify the bilinear relations for $P^{1,1}$. Let ξ be a real, primitive harmonic $(1,1)$-form; in terms of a local unitary coframe φ_1, φ_2 we write

$$\xi = \sum \xi_{ij} \varphi_i \wedge \bar{\varphi}_j.$$

Since ξ is real, $\xi_{ij} = -\bar{\xi}_{ji}$; writing

$$\omega = \frac{\sqrt{-1}}{2}(\varphi_1 \wedge \bar{\varphi}_1 + \varphi_2 \wedge \bar{\varphi}_2),$$

$$\xi \wedge \omega = \frac{\sqrt{-1}}{2}(\xi_{11} + \xi_{22})\varphi_1 \wedge \bar{\varphi}_1 \wedge \varphi_2 \wedge \bar{\varphi}_2,$$

we see that ξ primitive implies $\xi_{11} + \xi_{22} = 0$. For the bilinear relation

$$(\sqrt{-1})^{p-q}(-1)^{(n-k)(n-k-1)/2}Q(\xi,\bar{\xi}) = -\int_M \xi \wedge \bar{\xi}$$

$$= -\int_M (-\xi_{11}\bar{\xi}_{22} + 2|\xi_{12}|^2 - \xi_{22}\bar{\xi}_{11})$$

$$\times \varphi_1 \wedge \bar{\varphi}_1 \wedge \varphi_2 \wedge \bar{\varphi}_2$$

$$= -\left(\frac{2}{\sqrt{-1}}\right)^2 \int_M (2|\xi_{11}|^2 + 2|\xi_{12}|^2)\Phi$$

$$> 0.$$

Recall that on a general oriented compact real manifold X of dimension $2k$, we have a bilinear form on $H^k(X, \mathbb{R}) = H^k_{DR}(X)$ defined by

$$\underline{Q}(\eta, \xi) = \int_M \eta \wedge \xi;$$

by Poincaré duality Q is nondegenerate. If k is even, Q is symmetric, and we can associate to X as a topological invariant the *signature* of Q, defined as the number of positive eigenvalues minus the number of negative eigenvalues in a matrix representation of Q. The signature of Q is called the *index* $I(X)$ of the manifold X. Of course, if M is a compact Kähler manifold of dimension $2n$, then $Q = \bar{Q}$ on $H^{2n}(M, \mathbb{R})$ and we may use the bilinear relations to compute the index of M:

$$H^{2n}(M) = \oplus L^k P^{2(n-k)}(M)$$

$$= \bigoplus_{\substack{p+q\equiv 0(2) \\ \leqslant 2n}} L^{n-(p+q)/2} P^{p,q}(M).$$

We know that for $p+q \equiv 0(2)$, $(\sqrt{-1})^{p-q}(-1)^{(p+q)(p+q-1)/2}Q > 0$ on the real space $(P^{p,q} \oplus P^{q,p}) \cap H^{p+q}(M, \mathbb{R})$; since $Q(L\eta, L\xi) = Q(\eta, \xi)$, we have

$$I(M) = \sum_{\substack{p+q\equiv 0(2) \\ \leqslant 2n}} (\sqrt{-1})^{p-q}(-1)^{(p+q)(p+q-1)/2} \dim P^{p,q}(M)$$

$$= \sum_{\substack{p+q\equiv 0(2) \\ \leqslant 2n}} (-1)^p \dim P^{p,q}(M).$$

Now we have by the Lefschetz decomposition

$$h^{p,p+j} = \sum_{i=0}^{p} \dim P^{i,i+j};$$

thus, along a vertical line in the Hodge diamond,

$$\sum_{i=0}^{p-1} (-1)^i \dim P^{i,i+j} = (-1)^p h^{p,p+j} + 2 \sum (-1)^i h^{i,i+j}$$

and we can write, finally,

$$I(M) = \sum_{p+q=2n} (-1)^p h^{p,q} + 2 \sum_{\substack{p+q\equiv 0(2) \\ <2n}} (-1)^p h^{p,q},$$

or

$$I(M) = \sum_{p+q\equiv 0(2)} (-1)^p h^{p,q},$$

the last equality holding by virtue of the duality $h^{p,q} = h^{n-p,n-q}$. Note in particular that on a Kähler surface M the cup product Q on $H^{1,1}(M)$ has exactly one positive eigenvalue; this fact is frequently called the *index theorem* for surfaces.

Note, finally, one distinction between the Hodge and Lefschetz theorems of this section: the Lefschetz theorems are essentially topological, while the Hodge decomposition reflects the analytic structure of the particular manifold M. For instance, if we take a real manifold and give it two different Kähler complex structures, the Hodge decomposition of H^* may vary—the rank of the groups $(H^{p,q}(M) \oplus H^{q,p}(M)) \cap H^{p+q}(M, \mathbb{Z})$ may even jump—but the Lefschetz isomorphism and decomposition remain the same.

REFERENCES

We give here a few references that should be helpful to the reader in supplementing the material in this chapter. This list is not meant to be a bibliography but is a small sampling of sources having a notation and point of view similar to that taken here. Moreover, many of these references have extensive bibliographies and so may be used as a guide to the literature.

General References

R. Gunning and H. Rossi, *Analytic Functions of Several Complex Variables*, Prentice-Hall, Englewood Cliffs, N.J., 1965.

S. S. Chern, *Complex Manifolds without Potential Theory*, Van Nostrand Reinhold Company, New York, 1967.

REFERENCES

Specific References

Section 1

L. Hormander, *An Introduction to Complex Analysis in Several Variables*, Van Nostrand Reinhold Company, New York, 1966.

R. Narasimhan, *Introduction to the Theory of Analytic Spaces*, Springer-Verlag, Berlin-Heidelberg-New York, 1966.

Section 2

K. Kodaira and J. Morrow, *Complex Manifolds*, Holt, Rinehart, and Winston, New York, 1971.

G. Stolzenberg, *Volumes, Limits and Extensions of Analytic Varieties*, Springer-Verlag, Berlin-Heidelberg-New York, 1966.

R. O. Wells, *Differential Analysis on Complex Manifolds*, Prentice-Hall, Englewood Cliffs, N. J., 1973.

Section 3

R. Godement, *Theorie des Faisceaux*, Hermann, Paris, 1958.

F. Hirzebruch, *Topological Methods in Algebraic Geometry*, Springer-Verlag, Berlin-Heidelberg-New York, 1966.

Section 4

There are many contemporary books on algebraic topology. A classic whose treatment of homology and intersection theory has largely been adopted here is

S. Lefschetz, *Topology*, American Math. Society Colloquium Publications, Vol. 12 (1930).

Section 6

G. de Rham, *Varietes différentiables*, Hermann, Paris, 1954.

F. Warner, *Introduction to Manifolds*, Scott-Foresman, New York, 1971.

Note: Our proof of the Hodge theorem is a variant of one given by Joe Kohn in a course at Princeton University in 1961–62.

1

COMPLEX ALGEBRAIC VARIETIES

An *algebraic variety* is defined to be the set of complex zeros of homogeneous polynomials in projective space and may be viewed a priori as an analytic subvariety of $\mathbb{P}^n$. In case the variety is smooth, we may consider the associated abstract compact complex manifold, whose properties will be intrinsic to—i.e., not depending on the particular embedding of—the variety. Broadly speaking, we will approach algebraic geometry as the study of the interplay between the intrinsic and extrinsic or projective properties of algebraic varieties.

In Section 1 we introduce the notion of divisors and line bundles; the material here is central for all that follows. Since a compact complex manifold admits no global holomorphic functions, we might rather expect its structure to be reflected in the global meromorphic functions and related linear systems of divisors on the manifold; this notion is a basic one in classical algebraic geometry. Associated to a divisor is a holomorphic line bundle, to a meromorphic function a line bundle together with a holomorphic section, and to a line bundle its Chern class. The subsequent formalism, developed by Kodaira and Spencer and others in the early 1950s, gives an extremely useful technique for dealing with codimension-one subvarieties (points on a curve, curves on a surface, etc.) on an algebraic variety.

The basic question of constructing meromorphic functions with prescribed properties—e.g., the principal parts on a Riemann surface—is a problem admitting local solutions where the obstruction to patching these together globally may be measured by a sheaf cohomology group. The *Kodaira vanishing theorem* provides the most useful condition under which these higher groups are zero. It is a remarkable result, one which is proved by potential theory and differential geometry, but which in the end turns out to be equivalent to the Lefschetz theorem concerning the topological position of a hyperplane section of a complex algebraic variety. Explaining these matters occupies Section 2.

In Section 3 we began the transition

$$\left\{ \begin{array}{c} \text{abstract compact} \\ \text{complex manifold} \end{array} \right\} \longrightarrow \left\{ \begin{array}{c} \text{algebraic variety} \\ \text{in projective space} \end{array} \right\}$$

The intermediate step is an analytic variety in projective space; the *Chow theorem* asserts that this must be an algebraic variety. The essential philosophical point here is illustrated by the identity of the two objects "global meromorphic function on the Riemann sphere" and "rational function of one complex variable." The practical consequence is that we may work either locally complex analytically or globally algebraically with the same end result. Our approach at this stage is analytic, as this ties in more readily with the topological and metric properties of an algebraic variety, but the understanding that in the end we are talking about solutions of polynomial equations is fundamental.

In Section 4 we state and prove Kodaria's characterization of those compact complex manifolds which are derived from algebraic varieties, thus providing the essential link between the intrinsic and extrinsic properties of a variety. This embedding theorem and Chow's theorem are existence theorems—they do not by themselves provide a constructive method for finding the equations defining the image of a variety under a projective embedding—but together they form the philosophical cornerstone for our analytic treatment of algebraic geometry.

In the final section of this chapter we explain in some detail the Grassmannian, a variety whose points parametrize the linear subspaces of some fixed dimension in projective space and whose internal structure reflects the nongeneric intersections of a variable linear space with a fixed one. One reason for placing this discussion here is that the Grassmannian illustrates quite nicely the general structure theorems of this chapter. Another is that extensive use will be made in the following chapters of the Schubert calculus, a quantitative expression of the nongeneric incidence relations among linear spaces that is inherent in the structure of the Grassmannian.

1. DIVISORS AND LINE BUNDLES

Divisors

Let M be a complex manifold of dimension n, not necessarily compact. We recall from Section 1 of Chapter 0 some facts about analytic hypersurfaces in M:

Any analytic subvariety $V \subset M$ of dimension $n-1$ is an analytic hypersurface, i.e., for any point $p \in V \subset M$, V can be given in a neighborhood of p as the zeros of a single holomorphic function f. Moreover, any holomorphic function g defined at p and vanishing on V is divisible by f in a neighborhood of p. f is called a *local defining function* for V near p, and is unique up to multiplication by a function nonzero at p.

If V_1^* is a connected component of $V^* = V - V_s$, then $\overline{V_1^*}$ is an analytic subvariety in M. Thus V can be expressed uniquely as the union of irreducible analytic hypersurfaces

$$V = V_1 \cup \cdots \cup V_m,$$

where the V_i's are the closures of the connected components of V^*. In particular, V is irreducible if and only if V^* is connected.

Now we define:

DEFINITION. A *divisor* D on M is a locally finite formal linear combination

$$D = \sum a_i \cdot V_i$$

of irreducible analytic hypersurfaces of M.

"Locally finite" here means that for any $p \in M$, there exists a neighborhood of p meeting only a finite number of the V_i's appearing in D; of course, if M is compact, this just means the sum is finite. The set of divisors in M is naturally an additive group, denoted $\mathrm{Div}(M)$.

A divisor $D = \sum a_i V_i$ is called *effective* if $a_i \geqslant 0$ for all i; we write $D \geqslant 0$ for D effective. An analytic hypersurface V will usually be identified with the divisor $\sum V_i$ where the V_i's are the irreducible components of V.

Let $V \subset M$ be an irreducible analytic hypersurface, $p \in V$ any point, and f a local defining function for V near p. For any holomorphic function g defined near p, we define the *order* $\mathrm{ord}_{V,p}(g)$ *of* g *along* V *at* p to be the largest integer a such that in the local ring $\mathcal{O}_{M,p}$,

$$g = f^a \cdot h.$$

By the result from p. 10 that relatively prime elements of $\mathcal{O}_{M,p}$ stay relatively prime in nearby local rings, we see that for g a holomorphic function on M, $\mathrm{ord}_{V,p}(g)$ *is independent of* p. Thus we can define the *order* $\mathrm{ord}_V(g)$ *of* g *along* V to be simply the order of g along V at any point $p \in V$. Note that for g, h any holomorphic functions, V any irreducible hypersurface,

$$\mathrm{ord}_V(gh) = \mathrm{ord}_V(g) + \mathrm{ord}_V(h).$$

Now let f be a meromorphic function on M, written locally as

$$f = \frac{g}{h}$$

with g, h holomorphic and relatively prime. For V an irreducible hyper-surface, we define

$$\operatorname{ord}_V(f) = \operatorname{ord}_V(g) - \operatorname{ord}_V(h).$$

We usually say that f *has a zero of order* a *along* V if $\operatorname{ord}_V(f) = a > 0$, and that f has a *pole of order* a *along* V if $\operatorname{ord}_V(f) = -a < 0$.

We define the *divisor* (f) *of the meromorphic function* f by

$$(f) = \sum_V \operatorname{ord}_V(f) \cdot V.$$

If f is written locally as g/h, we take the *divisor of zeros* $(f)_0$ of f to be

$$(f)_0 = \sum_V \operatorname{ord}_V(g) \cdot V$$

and the *divisor of poles* $(f)_\infty$ to be

$$(f)_\infty = \sum_V \operatorname{ord}_V(h) \cdot V.$$

Clearly these are well-defined as long as we require g and h to be relatively prime, and

$$(f) = (f)_0 - (f)_\infty.$$

Divisors can also be described in sheaf-theoretic terms, as follows: Let $\mathcal{M}^*$ denote the multiplicative sheaf of meromorphic functions on M not identically 0, and $\mathcal{O}^*$ the subsheaf of nonzero holomorphic functions. Then *a divisor* D *on* M *is simply a global section of the quotient sheaf* $\mathcal{M}^*/\mathcal{O}^*$. On the one hand, a global section $\{f\}$ of $\mathcal{M}^*/\mathcal{O}^*$ is given by an open cover $\{U_\alpha\}$ of M and meromorphic functions $f_\alpha \not\equiv 0$ in U_α with

$$\frac{f_\alpha}{f_\beta} \in \mathcal{O}^*(U_\alpha \cap U_\beta);$$

for any $V \subset M$, then,

$$\operatorname{ord}_V(f_\alpha) = \operatorname{ord}_V(f_\beta),$$

and we can associate to $\{f\}$ the divisor

$$D = \sum_V \operatorname{ord}_V(f_\alpha) \cdot V,$$

where for each V we choose α such that $V \cap U_\alpha \neq \varnothing$. On the other hand, given

$$D = \sum_{V_i} a_i V_i,$$

we can find an open cover $\{U_\alpha\}$ of M such that in each U_α, every V_i appearing in D has a local defining function $g_{i\alpha} \in \mathcal{O}(U_\alpha)$. We can then set

$$f_\alpha = \prod_i g_{i\alpha}^{a_i} \in \mathcal{M}^*(U_\alpha)$$

to obtain a global section of $\mathfrak{M}^*/\mathcal{O}^*$. The f_α's are called *local defining functions* for D. It follows immediately from the definitions that the identification

$$H^0(M, \mathfrak{M}^*/\mathcal{O}^*) = \mathrm{Div}(M)$$

is in fact a homomorphism.

Given a holomorphic map $\pi: M \to N$ of complex manifolds, we define a map

$$\pi^*: \mathrm{Div}(N) \to \mathrm{Div}(M)$$

by associating to every divisor $D = (\{U_\alpha\}, \{f_\alpha\})$ on N the *pullback divisor* $\pi^*D = (\{\pi^{-1}U_\alpha\}, \{\pi^*f_\alpha\})$ on M; this is well-defined as long as $\pi(M) \not\subset D$. Note that for a divisor on N given by an analytic hypersurface $V \subset N$, the pullback divisor π^*V on M lies over V but need not coincide with the analytic hypersurface $\pi^{-1}(V) \subset M$—multiplicities may occur.

We want to make one more remark before going on to consider line bundles. On a Riemann surface M, any point is an irreducible analytic hypersurface, and so clearly $\mathrm{Div}(M)$ is always large. This is, in a sense, misleading: *a complex manifold* M *of dimension greater than one need not have any nonzero divisors on it at all*. If, however M is embedded in projective space $\mathbb{P}^N$, the intersections of M with hyperplanes in $\mathbb{P}^N$ generate a large number of divisors. In fact, among all compact complex manifolds those which are embeddable in projective space can be characterized by having "sufficiently many" divisors, in a sense that we shall make precise in later sections.

Line Bundles

All line bundles discussed in this section are taken to be holomorphic. Recall that for any holomorphic line bundle $L \overset{\pi}{\to} M$ on the complex manifold M, we can find an open cover $\{U_\alpha\}$ of M and trivializations

$$\varphi_\alpha: L_{U_\alpha} \overset{\sim}{\longrightarrow} U_\alpha \times \mathbb{C}$$

of $L_{U_\alpha} = \pi^{-1}(U_\alpha)$. We define the transition functions $g_{\alpha\beta}: U_\alpha \cap U_\beta \to \mathbb{C}^*$ for L relative to the trivializations $\{\varphi_\alpha\}$ by

$$g_{\alpha\beta}(z) = \left(\varphi_\alpha \circ \varphi_\beta^{-1}\right)\big|_{L_z} \in \mathbb{C}^*.$$

The functions $g_{\alpha\beta}$ are clearly holomorphic, nonvanishing, and satisfy

$$(*) \qquad \begin{cases} g_{\alpha\beta} \cdot g_{\beta\alpha} = 1, \\ g_{\alpha\beta} \cdot g_{\beta\gamma} \cdot g_{\gamma\alpha} = 1; \end{cases}$$

conversely, given a collection of functions $\{g_{\alpha\beta} \in \mathcal{O}^*(U_\alpha \cap U_\beta)\}$ satisfying these identities, we can construct a line bundle L with transition functions

$\{g_{\alpha\beta}\}$ by taking the union of $U_\alpha \times \mathbb{C}$ over all α and identifying $\{z\} \times \mathbb{C}$ in $U_\alpha \times \mathbb{C}$ and $U_\beta \times \mathbb{C}$ via multiplication by $g_{\alpha\beta}(z)$.

Now, given L as above, for any collection of nonzero holomorphic functions $f_\alpha \in \mathcal{O}^*(U_\alpha)$ we can define alternate trivializations of L over $\{U_\alpha\}$ by

$$\varphi_\alpha' = f_\alpha \cdot \varphi_\alpha;$$

transition functions $g_{\alpha\beta}'$ for L relative to $\{\varphi_\alpha'\}$ will then be given by

$$(**) \qquad\qquad g_{\alpha\beta}' = \frac{f_\alpha}{f_\beta} \cdot g_{\alpha\beta}.$$

On the other hand, any other trivialization of L over $\{U_\alpha\}$ can be obtained in this way, and so we see that collections $\{g_{\alpha\beta}\}$ and $\{g_{\alpha\beta}'\}$ of transition functions define the same line bundle if and only if there exist functions $f_\alpha \in \mathcal{O}^*(U_\alpha)$ satisfying $(**)$.

The description of line bundles by transition functions lends itself well to a sheaf-theoretic interpretation. First, the transition functions $\{g_{\alpha\beta} \in \mathcal{O}^*(U_\alpha \cap U_\beta)\}$ for a line bundle $L \to M$ represent a Čech 1-cochain on M with coefficients in $\mathcal{O}^*$; the relation $(*)$ simply asserts that $\delta(\{g_{\alpha\beta}\}) = 0$, i.e., $\{g_{\alpha\beta}\}$ is a Čech cocycle. Moreover, by the last paragraph, two cocycles $\{g_{\alpha\beta}\}$ and $\{g_{\alpha\beta}'\}$ define the same line bundle if and only if their difference $\{g_{\alpha\beta} \cdot g_{\alpha\beta}'^{-1}\}$ is a Čech coboundary; consequently *the set of line bundles on* M *is just* $H^1(M, \mathcal{O}^*)$.

We can give the set of line bundles on M the structure of a group, multiplication being given by tensor product and inverses by dual bundles. If L is given by data $\{g_{\alpha\beta}\}$, L' by $\{g_{\alpha\beta}'\}$, we have seen that

$$L \otimes L' \sim \{g_{\alpha\beta} g_{\alpha\beta}'\}, \qquad L^* \sim \{g_{\alpha\beta}^{-1}\},$$

and so the group structure on the set of line bundles is the same as the group structure on $H^1(M, \mathcal{O}^*)$. The group $H^1(M, \mathcal{O}^*)$ is called the *Picard group* of M, denoted Pic(M).

We now describe the basic correspondence between divisors and line bundles. Let D be a divisor on M, with local defining functions $f_\alpha \in \mathcal{M}^*(U_\alpha)$ over some open cover $\{U_\alpha\}$ of M. Then the functions

$$g_{\alpha\beta} = \frac{f_\alpha}{f_\beta}$$

are holomorphic and nonzero in $U_\alpha \cap U_\beta$, and in $U_\alpha \cap U_\beta \cap U_\gamma$ we have

$$g_{\alpha\beta} \cdot g_{\beta\gamma} \cdot g_{\gamma\alpha} = \frac{f_\alpha}{f_\beta} \cdot \frac{f_\beta}{f_\gamma} \cdot \frac{f_\gamma}{f_\alpha} = 1.$$

The line bundle given by the transition functions $\{g_{\alpha\beta}=f_\alpha/f_\beta\}$ is called the *associated line bundle* of D, and written $[D]$. We check that it is well-defined: if $\{f'_\alpha\}$ are alternate local data for D, then $h_\alpha=f_\alpha/f'_\alpha\in\mathcal{O}^*(U_\alpha)$, and

$$g'_{\alpha\beta} = \frac{f'_\alpha}{f'_\beta} = g_{\alpha\beta}\cdot\frac{h_\beta}{h_\alpha}$$

for each α,β.

The correspondence [ ] has these immediate properties: First, if D and D' are two divisors given by local data $\{f_\alpha\}$ and $\{f'_\alpha\}$, respectively, then $D+D'$ is given by $\{f_\alpha\cdot f'_\alpha\}$; it follows that

$$[D+D'] = [D]\otimes[D']$$

so the map

$$[\ \ ]:\ \mathrm{Div}(M)\to\mathrm{Pic}(M)$$

is a homomorphism. Second, if $D=(f)$ for some meromorphic function f on M, we may take as local data for D over any cover $\{U_\alpha\}$ the functions $f_\alpha=f|_{U_\alpha}$; then $f_\alpha/f_\beta=1$ and so $[D]$ is trivial. Conversely, if D is given by local data $\{f_\alpha\}$ and the line bundle $[D]$ is trivial, then there exist functions $h_\alpha\in\mathcal{O}^*(U_\alpha)$ such that

$$\frac{f_\alpha}{f_\beta} = g_{\alpha\beta} = \frac{h_\alpha}{h_\beta};$$

$f=f_\alpha\cdot h_\alpha^{-1}=f_\beta\cdot h_\beta^{-1}$ is then a global meromorphic function on M with divisor D. Thus *the line bundle* [D] *associated to a divisor* D *on* M *is trivial if and only if* D *is the divisor of a meromorphic function.* We say that two divisors D,D' on M are *linearly equivalent* and write $D\sim D'$ if $D=D'+(f)$ for some $f\in\mathfrak{M}^*(M)$, or equivalently if $[D]=[D']$.

Also, note that [ ] is functorial: that is, if $f:M\to N$ is a holomorphic map of complex manifolds, it is easy to check that for any $D\in\mathrm{Div}(N)$,

$$\pi^*([D]) = [\pi^*(D)].$$

All these assertions are implicit in the following cohomological interpretation of the correspondence [ ]. The exact sheaf sequence

$$0\to\mathcal{O}^*\xrightarrow{i}\mathfrak{M}^*\xrightarrow{j}\mathfrak{M}^*/\mathcal{O}^*\to 0$$

on M gives us, in part, the exact sequence

$$H^0(M,\mathfrak{M}^*)\xrightarrow{j_*}H^0(M,\mathfrak{M}^*/\mathcal{O}^*)\xrightarrow{\delta}H^1(M,\mathcal{O}^*)$$

of cohomology groups. The reader may easily verify that under the natural identifications

$$\mathrm{Div}(M) = H^0(M,\mathfrak{M}^*/\mathcal{O}^*)\quad\text{and}\quad\mathrm{Pic}(M) = H^1(M,\mathcal{O}^*)$$

for any meromorphic function f on M,

$$j_* f = (f),$$

and for any divisor D on M,

$$\delta D = [D].$$

Indeed, we will generally violate the previous multiplicative notation and write $L + L'$ for the tensor product of two line bundles or mL for the mth tensor power $L^{\otimes m}$ of L.

We now wish to discuss holomorphic and meromorphic sections of line bundles. Let $L \to M$ be a holomorphic line bundle, with trivializations $\varphi_\alpha : L_{U_\alpha} \to U_\alpha \times \mathbb{C}$ over an open cover $\{U_\alpha\}$ of M and transition functions $\{g_{\alpha\beta}\}$ relative to $\{\varphi_\alpha\}$. As we have seen, the trivializations φ_α induce isomorphisms

$$\varphi_\alpha^* : \mathcal{O}(L)(U_\alpha) \longrightarrow \mathcal{O}(U_\alpha);$$

we see via the correspondence

$$s \in \mathcal{O}(L)(U) \to \{s_\alpha = \varphi_\alpha^*(s) \in \mathcal{O}(U \cap U_\alpha)\}$$

that a section of L over $U \subset M$ is given exactly by a collection of functions $s_\alpha \in \mathcal{O}(U \cap U_\alpha)$ satisfying

$$s_\alpha = g_{\alpha\beta} \cdot s_\beta$$

in $U \cap U_\alpha \cap U_\beta$.

In the same way, a *meromorphic* section s of L over U—defined to be a section of the sheaf $\mathcal{O}(L) \otimes_{\mathcal{O}} \mathcal{M}$—is given by a collection of meromorphic functions $s_\alpha \in \mathcal{M}(U \cap U_\alpha)$ satisfying $s_\alpha = g_{\alpha\beta} \cdot s_\beta$ in $U \cap U_\alpha \cap U_\beta$. Note that the quotient of two meromorphic sections $s, s' \not\equiv 0$ of L is a well-defined meromorphic function.

If s is a global meromorphic section of L, $s_\alpha / s_\beta \in \mathcal{O}^*(U_\alpha \cap U_\beta)$, and so for any irreducible hypersurface $V \subset M$,

$$\mathrm{ord}_V(s_\alpha) = \mathrm{ord}_V(s_\beta).$$

Thus we can define the *order* of s along V by

$$\mathrm{ord}_V(s) = \mathrm{ord}_V(s_\alpha)$$

for any α such that $U_\alpha \cap V \neq \varnothing$; we take the *divisor* (s) *of the meromorphic section* s to be given by

$$(s) = \sum_V \mathrm{ord}_V(s) \cdot V.$$

With this convention s is holomorphic if and only if (s) is effective.

Now if $D \in \mathrm{Div}(M)$ is given by local data $f_\alpha \in \mathcal{M}(U_\alpha)$, then the functions f_α clearly give a meromorphic section s_f of $[D]$ with $(s_f) = D$.

Conversely, if L is given by trivializations φ_α with transition functions $g_{\alpha\beta}$ and s is any global meromorphic section of L, we see that

$$\frac{s_\alpha}{s_\beta} = g_{\alpha\beta},$$

i.e., $L=[(s)]$. Thus if D *is any divisor such that* $[D]=L$, *there exists a meromorphic section* s *of* L *with* $(s)=D$, *and for any meromorphic section* s *of* L, $L=[(s)]$. In particular, we see that L is the line bundle associated to some divisor D on M if and only if it has a global meromorphic section not identically zero; it is the line bundle of an effective divisor if and only if it has a nontrivial global holomorphic section.

We can also view this correspondence as follows: Given a divisor

$$D = \sum a_i V_i$$

on M, let $\mathcal{L}(D)$ denote the space of meromorphic functions f on M such that

$$D + (f) \geqslant 0,$$

i.e., that are holomorphic on $M - \cup V_i$ with

$$\mathrm{ord}_{V_i}(f) \geqslant -a_i.$$

We denote by $|D| \subset \mathrm{Div}(M)$ the set of all effective divisors linearly equivalent to D; if $L=[D]$, we write $|L|$ for $|D|$. Let s_0 be a global meromorphic section of $[D]$ with $(s_0)=D$. Then for any global holomorphic section s of $[D]$, the quotient

$$f_s = \frac{s}{s_0}$$

is a meromorphic function on M with

$$(f_s) = (s) - (s_0) \geqslant -D,$$

i.e.,

$$f_s \in \mathcal{L}(D)$$

and

$$(s) = D + (f_s) \in |D|.$$

On the other hand, for any $f \in \mathcal{L}(D)$ the section $s = f \cdot s_0$ of $[D]$ is holomorphic. Thus *multiplication by* s_0 *gives an identification*

$$\mathcal{L}(D) \overset{\otimes s_0}{\longrightarrow} H^0(M, \mathcal{O}([D])).$$

Now suppose M is compact. For every $D' \in |D|$, there exists $f \in \mathcal{L}(D)$ such that

$$D' = D + (f),$$

and conversely any two such functions f, f' differ by a nonzero constant. Thus we have the additional correspondence

$$|D| \cong \mathbb{P}(\mathcal{L}(D)) \cong \mathbb{P}(H^0(M, \mathcal{O}([D]))).$$

In general, the family of effective divisors on M corresponding to a linear subspace of $\mathbb{P}(H^0(M, \mathcal{O}(L)))$ for some $L \to M$ is called a *linear system* of divisors; a linear system is called *complete* if it is of the form $|D|$, i.e., if it contains every effective divisor linearly equivalent to any of its members. When we speak of the *dimension* of a linear system, we will refer to the dimension of the projective space parametrizing it; thus, when we write $\dim |D|$ for the dimension of the complete linear system associated to a divisor D, we have

$$\dim |D| = h^0(M, \mathcal{O}(D)) - 1.$$

A linear system of dimension 1 is called a *pencil*, of dimension 2 a *net*, and of dimension 3 a *web*.

We will mention here two special properties of linear systems. The first is elementary: if $E = \{D_\lambda\}_{\lambda \in \mathbb{P}^n}$ is a linear system, then for any $\lambda_0, \ldots, \lambda_n$ linearly independent in $\mathbb{P}^n$,

$$D_{\lambda_0} \cap \cdots \cap D_{\lambda_n} = \bigcap_{\lambda \in \mathbb{P}^n} D_\lambda.$$

The common intersection of the divisors in a linear system is called the *base locus* of the system; in particular, a divisor F in the base locus—that is, such that $D_\lambda - F \geqslant 0$ for all λ—is called a *fixed component* of E.

The second property is more remarkable; like the first, it is peculiar to linear systems and is not the case for general families of divisors, even general families of linearly equivalent divisors. This is

Bertini's Theorem. *The generic element of a linear system is smooth away from the base locus of the system.*

Proof. If the generic element of a linear system is singular away from the base locus of the system, then the same will be true for a generic pencil contained in the system; thus it suffices to prove Bertini for a pencil.

Suppose $\{D_\lambda\}_{\lambda \in \mathbb{P}^1}$ is a pencil, given in a polydisc Δ contained in M by

$$D_\lambda = (f(z_1, \ldots, z_n) + \lambda \cdot g(z_1, \ldots, z_n) = 0)$$

and suppose P_λ is a singular point of the divisor $D_\lambda (\lambda \neq 0, \infty)$ but not in the base locus B of the pencil. We have then

$$f(P_\lambda) + \lambda g(P_\lambda) = 0$$

and

$$\frac{\partial f}{\partial z_i}(P_\lambda) + \lambda \frac{\partial g}{\partial z_i}(P_\lambda) = 0, \qquad i = 1, \ldots, n.$$

Since P_λ is not a base point of $\{D_\lambda\}$, f and g cannot both vanish at P_λ and so neither one can; thus

$$\lambda = -\frac{f(P_\lambda)}{g(P_\lambda)}$$

and

$$\frac{\partial f}{\partial z_i}(P_\lambda) - \frac{f(P_\lambda)}{g(P_\lambda)} \cdot \frac{\partial g}{\partial z_i}(P_\lambda) = 0.$$

Then

$$\frac{\partial}{\partial z_i}\left(\frac{f}{g}\right)(P_\lambda) = \frac{(\partial f/\partial z_i)(P_\lambda) - [f(P_\lambda)/g(P_\lambda)] \cdot (\partial g/\partial z_i)(P_\lambda)}{g(P_\lambda)} = 0.$$

Now the locus V of singular points of the divisors D_λ, being locally the image in Δ of the variety $S \subset \Delta \times \mathbb{P}^1_\lambda$ cut out by the equations $\{f + \lambda g = 0, \partial f/\partial z_i + \lambda \partial g/\partial z_i = 0\}$, is an analytic subvariety of Δ. But by the calculation above *the ratio f/g is constant on every connected component of* $V - B$ and so V can meet only finitely many divisors D_λ away from the base locus of $\{D_\lambda\}$. Q.E.D.

The essential point here is that a pencil $\{D_\lambda\}_{\lambda \in \mathbb{P}^1}$ with base locus B gives a holomorphic mapping

$$M - B \to \mathbb{P}^1$$

since by linearity every $p \in M - B$ is on a *unique* D_λ. The Bertini theorem is a refinement of Sard's theorem for this mapping.

We make one final remark about sections of line bundles, which will be used repeatedly throughout the book. Recall that if $D = \Sigma a_i V_i$ is any effective divisor on the complex manifold M, $s_0 \in H^0(M, \mathcal{O}([D]))$ a section of $[D]$ with divisor D, then tensoring with s_0 gives an identification between the meromorphic functions on M with poles of order $\leq a_i$ on V_i and holomorphic sections of $[D]$. More generally, if E is any holomorphic vector bundle on M, $\mathcal{E}$ its sheaf of holomorphic sections, we write $\mathcal{E}(D)$ for the sheaf of meromorphic sections of E with poles of order $\leq a_i$ on V_i, $\mathcal{E}(-D)$ for the sheaf of sections of E vanishing to order $\geq a_i$ along V_i. Again, *tensoring with* s_0 *or* s_0^{-1} *gives identifications*

$$\mathcal{E}(D) \xrightarrow{\otimes s_0} \mathcal{O}(E \otimes [D]),$$

(*)

$$\mathcal{E}(-D) \xrightarrow{\otimes s_0^{-1}} \mathcal{O}(E \otimes [-D]).$$

Thus in particular if D is a smooth analytic hypersurface, the sequence of sheaves

$$0 \to \mathcal{O}_M(E \otimes [-D]) \xrightarrow{\otimes s_0} \mathcal{O}_M(E) \xrightarrow{r} \mathcal{O}_D(E|_D) \to 0,$$

where r is the restriction map, is exact. Henceforth, *we shall make the identification* (∗) *implicitly and write* $\mathcal{O}(D)$ *for* $\mathcal{O}([D])$.

Chern Classes of Line Bundles

Let M now be a compact complex manifold of dimension n. The exact sequence of sheaves

$$0 \to \mathbb{Z} \to \mathcal{O} \xrightarrow{\exp} \mathcal{O}^* \to 0$$

gives a boundary map in cohomology

$$H^1(M, \mathcal{O}^*) \xrightarrow{\delta} H^2(M, \mathbb{Z}).$$

For a line bundle $L \in \text{Pic}(M) = H^1(M, \mathcal{O}^*)$, we define the *first Chern class* $c_1(L)$ of L (or simply *Chern class*) to be $\delta(L) \in H^2(M, \mathbb{Z})$; for D a divisor on M, we define the Chern class of D to be $c_1([D])$. By a slight abuse of language, we will sometimes write $c_1(L) \in H^2_{\text{DR}}(M)$ for the image of $c_1(L)$ under the natural map $H^2(M, \mathbb{Z}) \to H^2_{\text{DR}}(M)$.

As an immediate consequence of the definition, note that

$$c_1(L \otimes L') = c_1(L) + c_1(L')$$

and

$$c_1(L^*) = -c_1(L).$$

Also, if $f: M \to N$ is a holomorphic map of complex manifolds, the diagram

$$\begin{array}{ccc} H^1(M, \mathcal{O}^*) & \longrightarrow & H^2(M, \mathbb{Z}) \\ \uparrow{\scriptstyle f^*} & & \uparrow{\scriptstyle f^*} \\ H^1(N, \mathcal{O}^*) & \longrightarrow & H^2(N, \mathbb{Z}) \end{array}$$

commutes, so that for $L \to N$ any line bundle,

$$c_1(f^*L) = f^*c_1(L).$$

We will be concerned in this subsection with giving two alternate interpretations of the Chern class; first, however, we want to make one observation:

Let $\mathcal{E}$ and $\mathcal{E}^*$ denote the sheaves of C^∞ functions and nonzero C^∞ functions, respectively. The transition functions of a C^∞ complex line bundle L then give a Čech cocycle

$$\{g_{\alpha\beta}\} \in C^1(M, \mathcal{C}^*),$$

and by the same argument as for holomorphic bundles, the bundle L is determined, up to C^∞ isomorphism, by the cohomology class $[\{g_{\alpha\beta}\}] \in H^1(M, \mathcal{C}^*)$. Now we have an exact sheaf sequence

$$0 \to \mathbb{Z} \to \mathcal{C} \xrightarrow{\text{exp}} \mathcal{C}^* \to 0$$

and since the long exact sequence in Čech cohomology is functorial, the inclusion maps $\mathcal{O} \to \mathcal{C}$ and $\mathcal{O}^* \to \mathcal{C}^*$ give a commutative diagram

$$\begin{array}{ccccc}
H^1(M, \mathcal{C}) & \longrightarrow & H^1(M, \mathcal{C}^*) & \xrightarrow{\delta'} & H^2(M, \mathbb{Z}) \\
\Big\uparrow & & \Big\uparrow & & \| \\
H^1(M, \mathcal{O}) & \longrightarrow & H^1(M, \mathcal{O}^*) & \xrightarrow{\delta} & H^2(M, \mathbb{Z})
\end{array}$$

with both rows exact. Thus we can define the Chern class $c_1(L)$ of a C^∞ line bundle to be $\delta'(L)$, and this definition agrees with the one above for holomorphic bundles. But in the upper row we have $H^1(M, \mathcal{C}) = 0$, since the sheaf $\mathcal{C}$ is fine; the conclusion is that *a complex line bundle is determined up to C^∞ isomorphism by its Chern class*.

Recall now that for any vector bundle $E \to M$ of rank k and any connection D on E, the curvature operator D^2 is represented, in terms of a trivialization φ_α of E over U_α, by a $k \times k$ matrix Θ_α of 2-forms; if φ_β is another trivialization, we have

$$\Theta_\alpha = g_{\alpha\beta} \cdot \Theta_\beta \cdot g_{\alpha\beta}^{-1},$$

where $g_{\alpha\beta} : U_\alpha \cap U_\beta \to GL_k$ is the transition function relative to φ_α and φ_β. In particular, if E is a line bundle, since $GL_1 = \mathbb{C}^*$ is commutative $\Theta = \Theta_\alpha = \Theta_\beta$ is a closed, globally defined differential form of degree 2, called the *curvature form* of E.

Recall also that for any analytic subvariety $V \subset M$ of dimension k, we have defined the *fundamental class* $(V) \in H_{2k}(M, \mathbb{R})$ to be given by the linear functional

$$\varphi \mapsto \int_V \varphi$$

on $H_{\text{DR}}^{2k}(M)$; we denote its Poincaré dual by η_V. In particular, we take the fundamental class of a divisor $D = \sum a_i V_i$ on M to be $\sum a_i(V_i)$; we denote its Poincaré dual by

$$\eta_D = \sum a_i \cdot \eta_{V_i}.$$

This subsection will be devoted to proving the

Proposition. 1. *For any line bundle* L *with curvature form* Θ,

$$c_1(L) = \left[\frac{\sqrt{-1}}{2\pi} \Theta \right] \in H^2_{DR}(M).$$

2. *If* L=[D] *for some* D∈Div(M),

$$c_1(L) = \eta_D \in H^2_{DR}(M).$$

Proof.   First, we unwind the definition of $c_1(L)$ for $L \to M$ a line bundle with trivializations φ_α and transition functions $g_{\alpha\beta}$ relative to a cover $\underline{U} = \{U_\alpha\}$ of M. We may assume the open sets U_α are simply connected and set

$$h_{\alpha\beta} = \frac{1}{2\pi\sqrt{-1}} \log g_{\alpha\beta}.$$

By the definition of δ, if we set

$$\begin{aligned} z_{\alpha\beta\gamma} &= h_{\alpha\beta} + h_{\beta\gamma} - h_{\alpha\gamma} \\ &= \frac{1}{2\pi\sqrt{-1}} (\log g_{\alpha\beta} + \log g_{\beta\gamma} - \log g_{\alpha\gamma}), \end{aligned}$$

then $\{z_{\alpha\beta\gamma}\} \in Z^2(\underline{U}, \mathbb{Z})$ is a cocycle representing $c_1(L)$.

Now choose any connection D on L. In terms of the frame $e_\alpha(z) = \varphi_\alpha^{-1}(z,1)$ on U_α, D is given by its connection matrix, which in this case is a 1-form θ_α. As was worked out in Section 5 of Chapter 0, in $U_\alpha \cap U_\beta$

$$\theta_\alpha = g_{\alpha\beta}\theta_\beta g_{\alpha\beta}^{-1} + dg_{\alpha\beta} \cdot g_{\alpha\beta}^{-1},$$

i.e.,

$$\theta_\beta - \theta_\alpha = -g_{\alpha\beta}^{-1} dg_{\alpha\beta} = -d(\log g_{\alpha\beta}),$$

and the curvature matrix is the global 2-form

$$\Theta = d\theta_\alpha - \theta_\alpha \wedge \theta_\alpha = d\theta_\alpha = d\theta_\beta.$$

Since Θ is given as a closed 2-form and $c_1(L)$ is given as a Čech cocycle, we must now look at the explicit form of the de Rham isomorphism. From the proof of de Rham's theorem, we have exact sequences of sheaves

$$0 \to \mathbb{R} \to \mathcal{C}^0 \to \mathcal{Z}^1_d \to 0, \qquad 0 \to \mathcal{Z}^1_d \to \mathcal{C}^1 \to \mathcal{Z}^2_d \to 0,$$

giving us boundary isomorphisms

$$\frac{H^0(\mathcal{Z}^2_d)}{dH^0(\mathcal{C}^1)} \xrightarrow{\delta_1} H^1(\mathcal{Z}^1_d), \qquad H^1(\mathcal{Z}^1_d) \xrightarrow{\delta_2} H^2(\mathbb{R}).$$

To calculate $\delta_1(\Theta)$, we write Θ locally as $d\theta_\alpha$; we see from the definition of δ_1 that

$$\delta_1(\Theta) = \{\theta_\beta - \theta_\alpha\} \in Z^1(\mathcal{Z}^1_d).$$

Now $\theta_\beta - \theta_\alpha = -d\log g_{\alpha\beta}$, so

$$\begin{aligned}
\delta_2\delta_1(\Theta) &= \delta_2(\{\theta_\beta - \theta_\alpha\}) \\
&= \{-(\log g_{\alpha\beta} + \log g_{\beta\gamma} - \log g_{\alpha\gamma})\} \\
&= -2\pi\sqrt{-1} \cdot c_1(L).
\end{aligned}$$

To prove assertion 2 we have to show that, for Θ a curvature matrix for the bundle $[D]$, the cohomology class $[(\sqrt{-1}/2\pi)\Theta]$ is the Poincaré dual of $(D) = \Sigma a_i(V_i)$—i.e., that for every real, closed form $\psi \in A^{2n-2}(M)$,

$$\frac{\sqrt{-1}}{2\pi} \int_M \Theta \wedge \psi = \sum a_i \int_{V_i} \psi.$$

Since both $D \mapsto c_1([D])$ and $D \mapsto \eta_D$ are homomorphisms from $\mathrm{Div}(M)$ to $H^2_{\mathrm{DR}}(M)$, we may take $D = V$ an irreducible subvariety.

First, we compute the curvature form of a metric connection on $[D]$. To do this, let e be a local nonzero holomorphic section of $[V]$ and write

$$|e(z)|^2 = h(z).$$

Then for any section $s = \lambda \cdot e$, the connection matrix θ for the metric connection D in terms of the frame e must satisfy

$$\theta = \theta^{1,0}$$

and

$$\begin{aligned}
d(|s|^2) &= (Ds,s) + (s,Ds) \\
&= ((d\lambda + \theta\lambda)e, \lambda e) + (\lambda e, (d\lambda + \theta\lambda)e) \\
&= h \cdot \bar\lambda \cdot d\lambda + h \cdot \lambda \cdot d\bar\lambda + h \cdot |\lambda|^2(\theta + \bar\theta).
\end{aligned}$$

Now

$$\begin{aligned}
d(|s|^2) &= d(\lambda \cdot \bar\lambda \cdot h) \\
&= h \cdot \bar\lambda \cdot d\lambda + h \cdot \lambda \cdot d\bar\lambda + |\lambda|^2 \cdot dh.
\end{aligned}$$

So we have

$$\theta + \bar\theta = \frac{dh}{h},$$

i.e., $\theta = \partial \log h = \partial \log|e|^2$, and

$$\begin{aligned}
\Theta &= d\theta - \theta \wedge \theta = d\theta \\
&= \bar\partial\partial \log|e|^2 \\
&= 2\pi\sqrt{-1} \, dd^c \log|e|^2.
\end{aligned}$$

Note that this holds for any nonzero holomorphic section e.

Now let $D = V$ be given by local data f_α and let s be a global section $\{f_\alpha\}$ of $[D]$ vanishing exactly on V. Set

$$D(\varepsilon) = (|s(z)| < \varepsilon) \subset M.$$

For small ε, $D(\varepsilon)$ is just a tubular neighborhood around V in M, and

$$\int_M \Theta \wedge \psi = \lim_{\varepsilon \to 0} 2\pi \sqrt{-1} \int_{M-D(\varepsilon)} dd^c \log|s|^2 \wedge \psi$$

$$= \lim_{\varepsilon \to 0} \left(\frac{2\pi}{\sqrt{-1}} \right) \int_{\partial D(\varepsilon)} d^c \log|s|^2 \wedge \psi$$

by Stokes' theorem. In $U_\alpha \cap D(\varepsilon)$, write

$$|s|^2 = |f_\alpha|^2 \cdot h_\alpha = f_\alpha \cdot \bar{f}_\alpha \cdot h_\alpha$$

with $h_\alpha > 0$; we have

$$d^c \log|s|^2 = d^c \log(f_\alpha \cdot \bar{f}_\alpha \cdot h_\alpha)$$

$$= \frac{\sqrt{-1}}{4\pi} (\bar{\partial} \log \bar{f}_\alpha - \partial \log f_\alpha + (\bar{\partial} - \partial)\log h_\alpha).$$

Since $d^c \log h_\alpha$ is bounded and, as we have seen in the proof of Stokes' theorem for analytic varieties, $\mathrm{vol}(\partial D(\varepsilon)) \to 0$ as $\varepsilon \to 0$, we deduce that

$$\lim_{\varepsilon \to 0} \int_{\partial D(\varepsilon)} d^c \log h_\alpha \wedge \psi = 0.$$

Moreover, $\bar{\partial} \log \bar{f}_\alpha = \overline{\partial \log f_\alpha}$ and, since ψ is real, this implies

$$\int_{\partial D(\varepsilon)} \bar{\partial} \log \bar{f}_\alpha \wedge \psi = \overline{\int_{\partial D(\varepsilon)} \partial \log f_\alpha \wedge \psi} \,.$$

Thus in U_α,

$$\lim_{\varepsilon \to 0} \frac{2\pi}{\sqrt{-1}} \int_{\partial D(\varepsilon)} d^c \log|s|^2 = \lim_{\varepsilon \to 0} -\sqrt{-1} \cdot \mathrm{Im} \int_{\partial D(\varepsilon)} \partial \log f_\alpha \wedge \psi.$$

Now in the neighborhood of any smooth point $z_0 \in V \cap U_\alpha$, we can find a holomorphic coordinate system $w = (w_1, \dots, w_n)$ with $w_1 = f_\alpha$. Write $\psi = \psi(w) dw' \wedge d\bar{w}' + \varphi$, where $w' = (w_2, \dots, w_n)$ and all terms of φ contain either dw_1 or $d\bar{w}_1$; then in any polydisc Δ around z_0,

$$\lim_{\varepsilon \to 0} \int_{\partial D(\varepsilon) \cap \Delta} \partial \log f_\alpha \wedge \psi = \lim_{\varepsilon \to 0} \int_{|w_1| = \varepsilon} \frac{dw_1}{w_1} \cdot \psi(w) \cdot dw' \wedge d\bar{w}'$$

$$= 2\pi\sqrt{-1} \int_{w'} \psi(0, w') \cdot dw' \wedge d\bar{w}'$$

$$= 2\pi\sqrt{-1} \int_{V \cap \Delta} \psi$$

and so

$$\int_M \Theta \wedge \psi = -\sqrt{-1} \cdot \mathrm{Im} \left(2\pi\sqrt{-1} \int_V \psi \right)$$

$$= \frac{2\pi}{\sqrt{-1}} \int_V \psi. \qquad \text{Q.E.D.}$$

The conclusion that *the Chern class* $c_1([D])$ *represents, on the one hand, the Poincaré dual of the fundamental homology cycle carried by a divisor* D, *and on the other hand is given in de Rham cohomology by* $(\sqrt{-1}/2\pi)$ *times the curvature of any connection in the line bundle* [D], is of fundamental importance for what follows. The method of proof of this proposition, i.e., applying Stokes' theorem to a differential form with singularities—is likewise ubiquitous, and will be systematized in Chapter 3.

The simplest consequence of this proposition is the fact that the divisor (f) of a meromorphic function is homologous to zero. This is intuitively clear: drawing an arc γ from $\lambda_0 = \infty$ to $\lambda_1 = \infty$ on the Riemann sphere P^1_λ, the divisors

$$\{(\lambda_0 f + \lambda_1)\}_{[\lambda_0, \lambda_1] \in \gamma}$$

trace out a chain with boundary $(f)_0 - (f)_\infty$.

Examples

1. In case M is a compact connected Riemann surface, a divisor D on M is just a finite sum

$$D = \sum n_i p_i$$

of points $p_i \in M$ with multiplicities n_i. The *degree* of D is defined to be its fundamental class $(D) \in H_0(M, \mathbb{Z}) \cong \mathbb{Z}$; clearly

$$\deg D = \sum n_i.$$

By the above proposition, if Θ is the curvature form of a connection in the line bundle $[D]$,

$$\frac{\sqrt{-1}}{2\pi} \int_M \Theta = \langle c_1([D]), [M] \rangle = \deg D.$$

In general, we define the *degree* of a line bundle on M by

$$\deg(L) = \langle c_1(L), [M] \rangle,$$

or in other words $\deg(L) = c_1(L)$ under the isomorphism $H^2(M, \mathbb{Z}) \cong \mathbb{Z}$ given by the natural orientation on M.

Note that by the relation proved on page 77 between the curvature form Θ of a metric connection on the tangent bundle of a Riemann surface and the ordinary Gaussian curvature K_M the classical Gauss-Bonnet theorem gives

$$\deg T'(M) = \frac{1}{4\pi} \int_M K_M \cdot \Phi = \chi(M).$$

2. By the exact cohomology sequence

$$H^1(\mathbb{P}^n, \mathcal{O}) \to H^1(\mathbb{P}^n, \mathcal{O}^*) \xrightarrow{c_1} H^2(\mathbb{P}^n, \mathbb{Z})$$

arising from the exponential sheaf sequence on $\mathbb{P}^n$ and by the vanishing of $H^1(\mathbb{P}^n, \mathcal{O})$ (Section 7 of Chapter 1), we see that *every line bundle on $\mathbb{P}^n$ is determined by its Chern class*, i.e.,

$$\text{Pic}(\mathbb{P}^n) \cong H^2(\mathbb{P}^n, \mathbb{Z}) \cong \mathbb{Z}.$$

In other words, *every divisor on $\mathbb{P}^n$ is linearly equivalent to a multiple of the hyperplane divisor* $H = \mathbb{P}^{n-1} \subset \mathbb{P}^n$. The bundle $[H]$ associated to a hyperplane in $\mathbb{P}^n$ is called *the hyperplane bundle*; its inverse, $J = [H]^* = [-H]$, is called *the universal bundle* on $\mathbb{P}^n$.

We can give a direct geometric construction of the universal bundle J on $\mathbb{P}^n$ as follows. Let $\mathbb{P}^n \times \mathbb{C}^{n+1}$ be the trivial bundle of rank $n+1$ on $\mathbb{P}^n$, with all fibers identified to $\mathbb{C}^{n+1}$. Then the universal bundle is just the subbundle J of $\mathbb{P}^n \times \mathbb{C}^{n+1}$ whose fiber at each point $Z \in \mathbb{P}^n$ is the line in $\mathbb{C}^{n+1}$ represented by Z, i.e.,

$$J_Z = \{\lambda(Z_0, \ldots, Z_n), \lambda \in \mathbb{C}\}.$$

To see that in fact $J = [-H]$, consider the section e_0 of J over $U_0 = (Z_0 \neq 0) \subset \mathbb{P}^n$ given by

$$e_0(Z) = \left(1, \frac{Z_1}{Z_0}, \ldots, \frac{Z_n}{Z_0}\right).$$

e_0 is clearly holomorphic and nonzero in U_0 and extends to a global meromorphic section of J with a pole of order 1 along the hyperplane $(Z_0 = 0) \subset \mathbb{P}^n$. Thus $J = [(e_0)] = [-H]$.

If $M \subset \mathbb{P}^n$ is a submanifold of projective space, we usually call the restriction of $[H] \to \mathbb{P}^n$ to M simply the *hyperplane bundle on M*; by functoriality, it is the line bundle associated to a generic hyperplane section $\mathbb{P}^{n-1} \cap M$ of M.

3. Let M be a compact complex manifold, $V \subset M$ a smooth analytic hypersurface. Recall that we defined the *normal bundle* N_V on V to be the quotient line bundle

$$N_V = \frac{T'_M|_V}{T'_V}.$$

We defined the *conormal bundle* N_V^* to be the dual of N_V; it is the subbundle of $T_M^{*\prime}|_V$ consisting of cotangent vectors to M that are zero on $T'_V \subset T'_M|_V$.

There is an easy formula for the conormal bundle of a smooth hypersurface V, which we now derive: Suppose V is given locally by functions $f_\alpha \in \mathcal{O}(U_\alpha)$; the line bundle $[V]$ on M is then given by transition functions $\{g_{\alpha\beta} = f_\alpha / f_\beta\}$. Now since $f_\alpha \equiv 0$ on $V \cap U_\alpha$, the differential df_α is a section of the conormal bundle N_V^* of V; since V is smooth, df_α is everywhere nonzero. On $U_\alpha \cap U_\beta \cap V$, moreover, we have

$$
\begin{aligned}
df_\alpha &= d(g_{\alpha\beta} f_\beta) \\
&= dg_{\alpha\beta} \cdot f_\beta + g_{\alpha\beta} \cdot df_\beta \\
&= g_{\alpha\beta} \cdot df_\beta,
\end{aligned}
$$

i.e., *the sections* $df_\alpha \in \Gamma(U_\alpha, \mathcal{O}(N_V^*))$ *together give a nonzero global section of* $N_V^* \otimes [V]$. Thus $N_V^* \otimes [V]$ is the trivial line bundle; this is the

Adjunction Formula I

$$
N_V^* = [-V]|_V.
$$

4. One of the most important line bundles in general is the highest exterior power of the holomorphic cotangent bundle

$$
K_M = \wedge^n T_M^{*\prime},
$$

called the *canonical bundle* of the n-dimensional complex manifold M. Holomorphic sections of K_M are holomorphic n-forms, i.e., $\mathcal{O}(K_M) = \Omega_M^n$.

We will compute the canonical bundle $K_{\mathbb{P}^n}$ of projective space: Let $Z_0, \ldots, Z_n$ be homogeneous coordinates on $\mathbb{P}^n$, $w_i = Z_i / Z_0$ Euclidean coordinates on $U_0 = (Z_0 \neq 0)$, and consider the meromorphic n-form

$$
\omega = \frac{dw_1}{w_1} \wedge \frac{dw_2}{w_2} \wedge \cdots \wedge \frac{dw_n}{w_n}.
$$

ω is clearly nonzero in U_0 with a single pole along each hyperplane $(Z_i = 0)$, $i = 1, \ldots, n$. Now if $w_i' = Z_i / Z_j$, $i = 0, \ldots, \hat{j}, \ldots, n$ are Euclidean coordinates on $U_j = (Z_j \neq 0)$, then

$$
w_i = \frac{w_i'}{w_0'}, \quad i \neq j; \qquad w_j = \frac{1}{w_0'},
$$

which gives

$$
\frac{dw_i}{w_i} = \frac{dw_i'}{w_i'} - \frac{dw_0'}{w_0'}, \quad i \neq j; \qquad \frac{dw_j}{w_j} = \frac{-dw_0'}{w_0'},
$$

and so in terms of $\{w_i'\}$,

$$
\omega = (-1)^j \cdot \frac{dw_0'}{w_0'} \wedge \cdots \wedge \widehat{\frac{dw_j'}{w_j'}} \wedge \cdots \wedge \frac{dw_n'}{w_n'}.
$$

Thus we see that ω has likewise a single pole along the hyperplane $(Z_0 = 0)$, and consequently

$$
K_{\mathbb{P}^n} = [(\omega)] = [-(n+1)H].
$$

In general, we can compute the canonical bundle K_V of a smooth analytic hypersurface V in a manifold M in terms of K_M as follows. We have an exact sequence of vector bundles on V

$$0 \to N_V^* \to T_M^{*\prime}|_V \to T_V^{*\prime} \to 0.$$

By simple linear algebra,

$$(\wedge^n T_M^{*\prime})|_V \cong \wedge^{n-1} T_V^{*\prime} \otimes N_V^*,$$

i.e.,

$$K_V = K_M|_V \otimes N_V.$$

Combining this with the adjunction formula I above, we have the

Adjunction Formula II

$(*)$
$$K_V = (K_M \otimes [V])|_V.$$

We can give the corresponding map on sections

$$\Omega_M^n(V) \xrightarrow{\text{P.R.}} \Omega_V^{n-1}$$

as follows: Considering a section ω of $\Omega_M^n(V)$ as a meromorphic n-form with a single pole along V and holomorphic elsewhere, we write

$$\omega = \frac{g(z) \, dz_1 \wedge \cdots \wedge dz_n}{f(z)},$$

where $z = (z_1, \ldots, z_n)$ are local coordinates on M and V is given locally by $f(z)$. Under the isomorphism $(*)$, then, ω corresponds to the form ω' such that

$$\omega = \frac{df}{f} \wedge \omega'.$$

Explicitly,

$$df = \sum \frac{\partial f}{\partial z_i} \cdot dz_i,$$

and so we can take

$$\omega' = (-1)^{i-1} \frac{g(z) \, dz_1 \wedge \cdots \wedge \widehat{dz_i} \wedge \cdots \wedge dz_n}{\partial f / \partial z_i}$$

for any i such that $\partial f / \partial z_i \neq 0$. The map

$$\frac{g(z) \, dz_1 \wedge \cdots \wedge dz_n}{f(z)} \to (-1)^{i-1} \frac{g(z) \, dz_1 \wedge \cdots \wedge \widehat{dz_i} \wedge \cdots \wedge dz_n}{\partial f / \partial z_i} \Bigg|_{f=0}$$

is called the *Poincaré residue map*, denoted P.R.

Note that the kernel of the Poincaré residue map consists simply of the holomorphic n-forms on M. The exact sheaf sequence

$$0 \to \Omega_M^n \to \Omega_M^n(V) \xrightarrow{\text{P.R.}} \Omega_V^{n-1} \to 0$$

then gives us, in part, the exact sequence

$$H^0(M,\Omega_M^n(V)) \xrightarrow{\text{P.R.}} H^0(V,\Omega_V^{n-1}) \xrightarrow{\delta} H^1(M,\Omega_M^n),$$

i.e., the Poincaré residue map is surjective on global sections if $H^1(M,\Omega_M^n)$ $= H^{n,1}(M)=0$. For example, since $H^{n,1}(\mathbb{P}^n)=0$ for $n>1$, *every holomorphic form of top degree on a hypersurface* V *in* $\mathbb{P}^n$ *is the Poincaré residue of a meromorphic form on* $\mathbb{P}^n$. We will see later that the meromorphic n-forms on $\mathbb{P}^n$ are easy to describe, so that we can readily write down the holomorphic $(n-1)$-forms on V.

2. SOME VANISHING THEOREMS AND COROLLARIES

The Kodaira Vanishing Theorem

Let M be a compact Kähler manifold.

DEFINITION. A line bundle $L \to M$ is *positive* if there exists a metric on L with curvature form Θ such that $(\sqrt{-1}/2\pi)\Theta$ is a positive $(1,1)$-form; L is *negative* if L^* is positive. A divisor D on M is positive if the line bundle $[D]$ is.

The positivity of a line bundle is a topological property, as we see from the

Proposition. *If ω is any real, closed $(1,1)$-form with*

$$[\omega] = c_1(L) \in H_{DR}^2(M),$$

then there exists a metric connection on L *with curvature form* $\Theta = (\sqrt{-1}/2\pi)\omega$. *Thus* L *is positive if and only if its Chern class may be represented by a positive form in* $H_{DR}^2(M)$.

Proof. Let $|s|^2$ be a metric on L with curvature form Θ. If $\varphi: L_U \to U \times \mathbb{C}$ is a trivialization of L over an open set U, s a section of L over U and s_U the corresponding holomorphic function, then

$$|s|^2 = h(z) \cdot |s_U|^2$$

for some positive function $h(z)$. The curvature form and Chern class are given by

$$\Theta = -\partial\bar\partial \log h(z),$$
$$c_1(L) = \left[\frac{\sqrt{-1}}{2\pi}\Theta\right] \in H_{DR}^2(M).$$

Now let $|s|'^2$ be another metric on L with curvature form Θ'. Then $|s|'^2/|s|^2 = e^\rho$ for some real C^∞ function ρ on M, and from the local formula

$$h'(z) = e^{\rho(z)} h(z)$$

it follows that

$$\Theta = \partial \bar{\partial} \rho + \Theta'.$$

In particular,

$$\left[\frac{\sqrt{-1}}{2\pi} \Theta \right] = \left[\frac{\sqrt{-1}}{2\pi} \Theta' \right].$$

Working in the other direction, suppose that $(\sqrt{-1}/2\pi)\varphi$ is a real, closed $(1,1)$-form representing $c_1(L)$ in $H^2_{DR}(M)$. If we can solve the equation

$$\Theta = \partial \bar{\partial} \rho + \varphi$$

for a real C^∞ function ρ, then the metric $e^\rho |s|^2$ on L will have curvature form φ. Our proposition therefore follows from the

Lemma. *If η is any (p,q)-form on a compact Kähler manifold, and η is d-, ∂-, or $\bar{\partial}$-exact, then*

$$\eta = \partial \bar{\partial} \gamma$$

for some $(p-1, q-1)$-form γ. If $p = q$ and η is real, then we may take $\sqrt{-1}\,\gamma$ also to be real.

Proof. Let G_d denote the Green's operator associated to the Laplacian Δ_d, and similarly for G_∂ and $G_{\bar{\partial}}$. From the basic identity of page 115

$$\frac{1}{2} \Delta_d = \Delta_\partial = \Delta_{\bar{\partial}}$$

it follows first that

$$2G_d = G_\partial = G_{\bar{\partial}},$$

and then that all the operators d, ∂, $\bar{\partial}$, d^*, ∂^*, and $\bar{\partial}^*$ commute with the Green's operators.

Now, since η is d-, ∂-, or $\bar{\partial}$-exact, its harmonic projection under any of the above Laplacians is zero. By the Hodge decomposition for $\bar{\partial}$,

$$\eta = \bar{\partial} \bar{\partial}^* G_{\bar{\partial}} \eta.$$

But $\bar{\partial}^* G_{\bar{\partial}} \eta$ has pure type $(p, q-1)$ and so

$$\partial(\bar{\partial}^* G_{\bar{\partial}} \eta) = \pm \bar{\partial}^* G_{\bar{\partial}} (\partial \eta) = 0.$$

Since the harmonic space for ∂ is the same as the harmonic space for $\bar{\partial}$ and hence is orthogonal to the range of $\bar{\partial}^*$, we deduce by the Hodge decomposition for ∂ that

$$\bar{\partial}^* G_{\bar{\partial}} \eta = \partial \partial^* G_\partial (\bar{\partial}^* G_{\bar{\partial}} \eta).$$

By commuting the various operators,

$$\eta = \pm\bar\partial\partial\big(\partial^*\bar\partial^* G_{\bar\partial}^2\,\eta\big),$$

which implies the lemma.   Q.E.D.

The basic example of a positive line bundle is the hyperplane bundle $[H]$ on $\mathbb{P}^n$. Recall that the dual of the hyperplane bundle is the bundle J whose fiber at $Z \in \mathbb{P}^n$ is the line $\{\lambda Z\} \subset \mathbb{C}^{n+1}$; we can put a metric on J by setting $|(Z_0,\ldots,Z_n)|^2 = \Sigma |Z_i|^2$. If Z is any nonzero section of J—i.e., a local lifting $U \subset \mathbb{P}^n \to \mathbb{C}^{n+1} - \{0\}$—then the curvature form in J is given by

$$\Theta^* = \bar\partial\partial\log\|Z\|^2 = 2\pi\sqrt{-1}\ dd^c\log\|Z\|^2.$$

The curvature form Θ for the dual metric in $[H]$ is then $-\Theta^*$, and consequently

$$\frac{\sqrt{-1}}{2\pi}\Theta = dd^c\log\|Z\|^2,$$

i.e., $(\sqrt{-1}/2\pi)\Theta$ is just the associated $(1,1)$-form ω of the Fubini-Study metric on $\mathbb{P}^n$, which we have seen is positive. As a corollary, we see again that the Poincaré dual of $[\omega] \in H_{\mathrm{DR}}^2(\mathbb{P}^n)$ is the fundamental class (H) of a hyperplane.

Note that since the restriction to a submanifold $V \subset M$ of a positive form is again positive, $L|_V \to V$ will be positive if $L \to M$ is. In particular, the hyperplane bundle on any complex submanifold of $\mathbb{P}^n$ is positive.

Our aim in this section is to prove that certain Čech cohomology groups $H^q(M, \Omega^p(L))$ associated to a positive line bundle $L \to M$ are zero. To begin with, we transpose the problem into one involving $\bar\partial$-cohomology and harmonic forms by a technique that will be familiar from the previous discussion.

Recall that for any holomorphic vector bundle $E \to M$, the $\bar\partial$-operator

$$\bar\partial:\ A^{p,q}(E) \to A^{p,q+1}(E)$$

is defined for global C^∞ E-valued differential forms, and satisifes $\bar\partial^2 = 0$. We let $Z_{\bar\partial}^{p,q}(E)$ denote the space of $\bar\partial$-closed E-valued differential forms of type (p,q), and we define the *Dolbeault cohomology groups* $H_{\bar\partial}^{p,q}(E)$ *of E* to be

$$H_{\bar\partial}^{p,q}(E) = \frac{Z_{\bar\partial}^{p,q}(E)}{\bar\partial A^{p,q-1}(E)}.$$

Let $\mathcal{Z}_{\bar\partial}^{p,q}(E)$ denote the sheaf of $\bar\partial$-closed E-valued (p,q)-forms. The exact sheaf sequences

$$0 \to \mathcal{Z}_{\bar\partial}^{p,q}(E) \to \mathcal{C}^{p,q}(E) \overset{\bar\partial}{\to} \mathcal{Z}_{\bar\partial}^{p,q+1}(E) \to 0$$

give us isomorphisms

$$H^i\left(M, \mathcal{Z}_{\bar{\partial}}^{p,q+1}(E)\right) \xrightarrow{\delta} H^{i+1}\left(M, \mathcal{Z}_{\bar{\partial}}^{p,q}(E)\right),$$

since the sheaves $\mathcal{C}^{p,q}(E)$ admit partitions of unity and hence have no Čech cohomology. Thus, repeating the reasoning from the proof of de Rham's theorem,

$$H^q(M, \Omega^p(E)) \cong H_{\bar{\partial}}^{p,q}(E).$$

Next we want to discuss harmonic theory in holomorphic vector bundles. Suppose we have metrics given on M and E; we have then induced metrics on all tangential tensor bundles of M tensored with E or E^*. In particular, if $\{\varphi_i\}$ is a local coframe for the metric on $T_M^{*\prime}$ and $\{e_\alpha\}$ a unitary frame for E, any section η of $A^{p,q}(E)$ can be written locally as

$$\eta(z) = \frac{1}{p!q!} \sum_{I,J,\alpha} \eta_{I,J,\alpha}(z) \varphi_I \wedge \bar{\varphi}_J \otimes e_\alpha;$$

for $\eta, \psi \in A^{p,q}(E)$,

$$(\eta(z), \psi(z)) = \frac{2^{p+q-n}}{p!q!} \sum_{I,J,\alpha} \eta_{I,J,\alpha}(z) \cdot \overline{\psi_{I,J,\alpha}(z)}.$$

Again, we define an inner product on $A^{p,q}(E)$ by setting

$$(\eta, \psi) = \int_M (\eta(z), \psi(z)) \Phi,$$

where Φ is the volume form on M.

We have a "wedge product"

$$\wedge : A^{p,q}(E) \otimes A^{p',q'}(E^*) \mapsto A^{p+p',q+q'}(M)$$

defined by

$$(\eta \otimes s) \wedge (\eta' \otimes s') = \langle s, s' \rangle \cdot \eta \wedge \eta';$$

we define an operator

$$*_E : A^{p,q}(E) \to A^{n-p,n-q}(E^*)$$

by requiring, for $\eta, \psi \in A^{p,q}(E)$,

$$(\eta, \psi) = \int_M \eta \wedge *_E \psi.$$

Explicitly, if $\{e_\alpha\}$ and $\{e_\alpha^*\}$ are dual unitary frames for E and E^*, then for $\eta \in A^{p,q}(E)$ written as

$$\eta = \sum \eta_\alpha \otimes e_\alpha, \qquad \eta_\alpha \in A^{p,q}(M),$$
$$*_E \eta = \sum *\eta_\alpha \otimes e_\alpha^*,$$

where $*$ is the usual star operator on $A^{p,q}(M)$.

We take

$$\bar{\partial}^*: A^{p,q}(E) \to A^{p,q-1}(E)$$

to be given by

$$\bar{\partial}^* = -*_E \cdot \bar{\partial} \cdot *_E;$$

as before, $\bar{\partial}^*$ is the adjoint of $\bar{\partial}$, i.e., for all $\varphi \in A^{p,q-1}(E)$ and $\psi \in A^{p,q}(E)$,

$$(\bar{\partial}\varphi, \psi) = (\varphi, \bar{\partial}^*\psi).$$

Finally, the $\bar{\partial}$-Laplacian on E is defined by

$$\Delta = \bar{\partial}\bar{\partial}^* + \bar{\partial}^*\bar{\partial}: A^{p,q}(E) \to A^{p,q}(E).$$

An E-valued form φ is called *harmonic* if $\Delta\varphi = 0$. (Again, harmonic forms φ are exactly the forms of smallest norm in their Dolbeault cohomology class $\varphi + \bar{\partial}A^{p,q-1}(E)$.) We let

$$\mathcal{H}^{p,q}(E) = \text{Ker } \Delta$$

be the *harmonic space*.

Now, the analytic part of the proof of the Hodge theorem for the $\bar{\partial}$-Laplacian on ordinary differential forms on M is essentially local: we can always find appropriate solutions of $\Delta\varphi = 0$ in the completion of $A^{p,q}(M)$ in the L_2-norm; the problem is to show that these solutions are in fact C^∞. Writing out E-valued forms in terms of a frame for E, all the local estimates used in the proof of the Hodge theorem for $A^*(M)$ go over to $A^{p,q}(E)$—the only difference is that in each estimate we will get lower-order terms involving the coefficient functions for the metric on E as well as the metric on T_M^*, and these can be estimated out as before. Thus the Hodge theorem holds for the $\bar{\partial}$-Laplacian on E, that is:

1. $\mathcal{H}^{p,q}(E)$ is finite dimensional, and
2.   If $\mathcal{H}$ denotes the orthogonal projection $A^{p,q}(E) \to \mathcal{H}^{p,q}(E)$, there exists an operator

$$G: A^{p,q}(E) \to A^{p,q}(E)$$

such that

$$G(\mathcal{H}^{p,q}(E)) = 0,$$
$$[G, \bar{\partial}] = [G, \bar{\partial}^*] = 0,$$

and

$$I = \mathcal{H} + \Delta G.$$

3.   Consequently, there is an isomorphism

$$\mathcal{H}^{p,q}(E) \xrightarrow{\quad} H^{p,q}_{\bar{\partial}}(E),$$

and

4. The *-operator gives an isomorphism

$$H^q(M, \Omega^p(E)) \cong H^{n-q}(M, \Omega^{n-p}(E^*)).*$$

For $p = 0$, this last result reads

$$H^q(M, \mathcal{O}(E)) \cong H^{n-q}(M, \mathcal{O}(E^* \otimes K_M)).*$$

This isomorphism is called *Kodaira-Serre duality*.

Now if M is Kähler with associated $(1, 1)$-form ω, we define the operator

$$L: A^{p,q}(E) \to A^{p+1,q+1}(E)$$

by setting, for $\eta \in A^{p,q}(M)$ and $s \in A^0(E)$,

$$L(\eta \otimes s) = \omega \wedge \eta \otimes s;$$

let $\Lambda = L^*$ be the adjoint of L. If $D = D' + D''$ $(D'' = \bar{\partial})$ is the metric connection on E, then we have the *basic identity*

$$[\Lambda, \bar{\partial}] = -\frac{\sqrt{-1}}{2} D'^*.$$

This identity follows from the analogous identity $[\Lambda, \bar{\partial}] = -(\sqrt{-1}/2)\partial^*$ on scalar forms $A^{p,q}(M)$, which we have already proved. To see this, pick a local frame $\{e_\alpha\}$ for E; if $\theta = \theta' + \theta''$ is the connection matrix for D in terms of $\{e_\alpha\}$, we can write, for $\eta \in A^{p,q}(E)$,

$$\eta = \sum_\alpha \eta_\alpha \otimes e_\alpha, \qquad \eta_\alpha \in A^{p,q}(M),$$

$$\bar{\partial}\eta = \sum_\alpha \bar{\partial}\eta_\alpha \otimes e_\alpha + \sum_{\alpha,\beta} (\eta_\alpha \wedge \theta''_{\alpha\beta}) \otimes e_\beta,$$

$$\Lambda\eta = \sum_\alpha \Lambda(\eta_\alpha) \otimes e_\alpha,$$

so

$$[\Lambda, \bar{\partial}]\eta = \sum [\Lambda, \bar{\partial}]\eta_\alpha \otimes e_\alpha + [\Lambda, \theta'']\eta$$

$$= \sum -\frac{\sqrt{-1}}{2} \partial^* \eta_\alpha \otimes e_\alpha + [\Lambda, \theta'']\eta.$$

Similarly,

$$D'\eta = \sum_\alpha \partial\eta_\alpha \otimes e_\alpha + \sum_{\alpha,\beta} (\eta_\alpha \wedge \theta'_{\alpha\beta}) \otimes e_\beta,$$

i.e.

$$D'^*\eta = \sum_i \partial^* \eta_\alpha \otimes e_\alpha + \theta'^*\eta.$$

The difference

$$[\Lambda, \bar{\partial}] + \frac{\sqrt{-1}}{2} D'^* = [\Lambda, \theta''] + \frac{\sqrt{-1}}{2} \theta'^*$$

is consequently an *intrinsically defined algebraic operator*; since we can choose at each $z_0 \in M$ a frame for E in a neighborhood of z_0 for which $\theta(z_0)$ vanishes, we see that $[\Lambda, \bar{\partial}] + (\sqrt{-1}\,/2)D'^* = 0$.

We will use the representation of Čech cohomology by harmonic forms to prove our first main result on the cohomology of vector bundles, the

Kodaira-Nakano Vanishing Theorem. *If* $L \to M$ *is a positive line bundle, then*

$$H^q(M, \Omega^p(L)) = 0 \quad \text{for } p + q > n.$$

*Proof.** By hypothesis we can find a metric in L whose curvature form Θ is $2\pi/\sqrt{-1}$ times the associated $(1,1)$-form of a Kähler metric; let the metric on M be the one given by $\omega = (\sqrt{-1}/2\pi)\Theta$. Now by harmonic theory

$$H^q(M, \Omega^p(L)) \cong \mathcal{H}^{p,q}(L).$$

To prove the result, we will show that there are no nonzero harmonic L-valued forms of degree larger than n. We do this by interpreting the curvature operator $\Theta\eta = \Theta \wedge \eta$ alternately as $(2\pi/\sqrt{-1}\,)L(\eta)$, and as $D^2\eta$, where D is the metric connection on L, and using the basic identity above.

Let $\eta \in \mathcal{H}^{p,q}(L)$ be a harmonic form. Then

$$\Theta = D^2 = \bar{\partial}D' + D'\bar{\partial},$$

so from $\bar{\partial}\eta = 0$

$$\Theta\eta = \bar{\partial}D'\eta,$$

and

$$2\sqrt{-1}\,(\Lambda\Theta\eta, \eta) = 2\sqrt{-1}\,(\Lambda\bar{\partial}D'\eta, \eta)$$

$$= 2\sqrt{-1}\,\left(\left(\bar{\partial}\Lambda - \frac{\sqrt{-1}}{2}D'^*\right)D'\eta, \eta\right)$$

$$= (D'^*D'\eta, \eta) = (D'\eta, D'\eta) \geqslant 0,$$

since $(\bar{\partial}\Lambda D'\eta, \eta) = (\Lambda D'\eta, \bar{\partial}^*\eta) = 0$. Similarly,

$$2\sqrt{-1}\,(\Theta\Lambda\eta, \eta) = 2\sqrt{-1}\,(D'\bar{\partial}\Lambda\eta, \eta)$$

$$= 2\sqrt{-1}\,\left(D'\left(\Lambda\bar{\partial} + \frac{\sqrt{-1}}{2}D'^*\right)\eta, \eta\right)$$

$$= -(D'D'^*\eta, \eta) = -(D'^*\eta, D'^*\eta) \leqslant 0.$$

*This proof is due to Y. Akizuki and S. Nakano, Note on Kodaira-Spencer's proof of Lefschetz's theorems, *Proc. Japan Acad.*, Vol. 30 (1954).

Combining,

$$2\sqrt{-1}\,([\Lambda,\Theta]\eta,\eta) \geqslant 0.$$

But $\Theta = (2\pi/\sqrt{-1}\,)L$, and so

$$2\sqrt{-1}\,([\Lambda,\Theta]\eta,\eta) = 4\pi([\Lambda,L]\eta,\eta)$$
$$= 4\pi(n-p-q)\|\eta\|^2 \geqslant 0.$$

Thus $p+q>n \Rightarrow \eta=0$.   Q.E.D.

As was suggested when we first introduced cohomology, the groups $H^q(M,\Omega^p(E))$ $(q \geqslant 1)$ most frequently arise as obstructions to globally solving analytic problems—this is especially true for $q=1$ as in the Mittag-Leffler problem, but once one admits H^1's, then all the rest become involved. The Kodaira vanishing theorem—together with its variants to be discussed later—is the best general method for eliminating cohomology.

Dualizing the Kodaira vanishing theorem, we obtain:

$H^q(M,\Omega^p(L)) = 0$ for p + q < n in case L $\rightarrow$ M is a negative line bundle.

The special case when $p=q=0$ can be proved by elementary methods as follows: What we have to show is that

$$(*) \qquad\qquad H^0(M,\mathcal{O}(L)) = 0$$

in case $L \rightarrow M$ has a metric with curvature form equal to $2/\sqrt{-1}$ times a negative $(1,1)$-form. Suppose $s \neq 0 \in H^0(M,\mathcal{O}(L))$, and let $x_0 \in M$ be a point where $|s|^2$ attains a maximum. By hypothesis, if we write $z_i = x_i + \sqrt{-1}\,y_i$ the coefficient matrix for the curvature form

$$\left(\frac{\partial}{\partial z_i}\frac{\partial}{\partial \bar{z}_j}\log\left(\frac{1}{|s|^2}\right)\right) = \frac{1}{4}\left(\left(\frac{\partial^2}{\partial x_i \partial x_j}+\frac{\partial^2}{\partial y_i \partial y_j}\right)\right.$$
$$\left.+\sqrt{-1}\left(\frac{\partial^2}{\partial x_j \partial y_i}-\frac{\partial^2}{\partial y_j \partial x_i}\right)\right)\left(\log\frac{1}{|s|^2}\right)$$

is negative definite hermitian, and in particular the real symmetric matrix

$$\left(\frac{\partial^2}{\partial x_i \partial x_j}+\frac{\partial^2}{\partial y_i \partial y_j}\right)\log\frac{1}{|s|^2}$$

is negative definite. But $\log(1/|s|^2)$ attains a minimum at x_0, and by the maximum principle, the matrices

$$\left(\frac{\partial^2}{\partial x_i \partial x_j}\right)\log\frac{1}{|s|^2} \quad\text{and}\quad \left(\frac{\partial^2}{\partial y_i \partial y_j}\right)\log\frac{1}{|s|^2}$$

must both be positive semidefinite—a contradiction.

In case M is a Riemann surface, the special case $(*)$ is the general case, since $p + q < 1 \Rightarrow p = q = 0$. The theorem then is even more elementary: if Θ is a curvature form for L with $(\sqrt{-1}/2\pi)\Theta$ negative, we have

$$c_1(L) = \int_M \frac{\sqrt{-1}}{2\pi} \Theta < 0.$$

But if $s \neq 0 \in H^0(M, \mathcal{O}(L))$, then L is the line bundle associated to the effective divisor $D = (s)$, and we have

$$c_1(L) = \deg D \geqslant 0,$$

a contradiction.

As an immediate consequence of the vanishing theorem, we see that

$$H^q(\mathbb{P}^n, \mathcal{O}_{\mathbb{P}^n}(kH)) = 0 \qquad \text{for } 1 \leqslant q \leqslant n-1, \quad \text{all } k.$$

This follows directly from the dualized version of the vanishing theorem in case k is negative; if k is nonnegative,

$$H^q(\mathbb{P}^n, \mathcal{O}_{\mathbb{P}^n}(kH)) = H^q(\mathbb{P}^n, \Omega^n_{\mathbb{P}^n}(kH - K_{\mathbb{P}^n}))$$

$$= H^q(\mathbb{P}^n, \Omega^n_{\mathbb{P}^n}((k+n+1)H))$$

$$= 0$$

by the original version of the theorem.

The Lefschetz Theorem on Hyperplane Sections

Using the Kodaira vanishing theorem, we can give a proof of the famous Lefschetz theorem relating the homology of a projective variety to that of its hyperplane sections.

Let M be an n-dimensional compact, complex manifold and $V \subset M$ a smooth hypersurface with $L = [V]$ positive—e.g., $M \subset \mathbb{P}^N$ a submanifold of projective space and $V = M \cap H$ a hyperplane section of M. Then we have the

Lefschetz Hyperplane Theorem.   *The map*

$$H^q(M, \mathbb{Q}) \to H^q(V, \mathbb{Q})$$

induced by the inclusion $i: V \hookrightarrow M$ *is an isomorphism for* $q \leqslant n-2$ *and injective for* $q = n-1$.

Proof.   It will suffice to prove the result over $\mathbb{C}$. By the Hodge decomposition

$$H^r(M, \mathbb{C}) = \bigoplus_{p+q=r} H^{p,q}(M),$$

and by Dolbeault

$$H^{p,q}(M) \cong H^{p,q}_{\bar{\partial}}(M) \cong H^q(M, \Omega^p_M).$$

The same holding for V, it is sufficient to prove that the map

$$H^p(M, \Omega_M^q) \to H^p(V, \Omega_V^q)$$

is an isomorphism for $p + q \leqslant n - 2$, and injective for $p + q = n - 1$.

To see this, we factor the restriction map $\Omega_M^p \to \Omega_V^p$ by

$$\Omega_M^p \overset{r}{\to} \Omega_M^p|_V \overset{i}{\to} \Omega_V^p,$$

where $\Omega_M^p|_V$ is the sheaf of sections of $(\wedge^p T_M^{*\prime})|_V$—considered either as a sheaf on V or, by extension, as a sheaf on M—r is the restriction map, and i is the pullback map induced by the natural projection $(\wedge^p T_M^{*\prime})|_V \to \wedge^p T_V^{*\prime}$.

The kernel of the restriction map r is clearly just the sheaf of holomorphic p-forms on M vanishing along V, so we have an exact sequence of sheaves on M

$$(*) \qquad 0 \to \Omega_M^p(-V) \to \Omega_M^p \overset{r}{\to} \Omega_M^p|_V \to 0.$$

We can likewise fit the map i into an exact sequence: for $p \in V$, the sequence

$$0 \to N_{V,p}^* \to T_p^{*\prime}(M) \to T_p^{*\prime}(V) \to 0,$$

yields, by linear algebra,

$$0 \to N_{V,p}^* \otimes \wedge^{p-1} T_p^{*\prime}(V) \to \wedge^p T_p^{*\prime}(M) \to \wedge^p T_p^{*\prime}(V) \to 0,$$

and consequently an exact sequence of sheaves on V

$$0 \to \Omega_V^{p-1}(N_V^*) \to \Omega_M^p|_V \overset{i}{\to} \Omega_V^p \to 0.$$

But by the adjunction formula I, $N_V^* = [-V]|_V$; we can thus rewrite this last sequence as

$$(**) \qquad 0 \to \Omega_V^{p-1}(-V) \to \Omega_M^p|_V \to \Omega_V^p \to 0.$$

Now $[-V]$ is negative on M, and likewise $[-V]|_V$ is negative on V. The Kodaira vanishing theorem accordingly gives

$$H^q(M, \Omega_M^p(-V)) = 0, \qquad p + q < n,$$
$$H^q(V, \Omega_V^{p-1}(-V)) = 0, \qquad p + q < n.$$

By the exact cohomology sequences associated to the sheaf sequences $(*)$ and $(**)$, recalling that $H^*(M, \Omega_M^p|_V) = H^*(V, \Omega_M^p|_V)$,

$$H^q(M, \Omega_M^p) \overset{r^*}{\cong} H^q(M, \Omega_M^p|_V) \overset{i^*}{\cong} H^q(V, \Omega_V^p)$$

for $p + q \leqslant n - 2$, and with both maps injective for $p + q = n - 1$.   Q.E.D.

The Lefschetz theorem on hyperplane sections is, of course, purely topological. There is another proof using a little Morse theory; we will give here a sketch of the argument:[*]

---

[*]Due to R. Bott, On a theorem of Lefschetz, *Mich. Math. J.*, Vol. 6 (1959), pp. 211–216.

To begin with, suppose that A is a compact manifold, $B \subset A$ a smooth submanifold, and $\varphi: A \to \mathbb{R}^+$ a C^∞ function such that $\varphi^{-1}(0) = B$. A *critical point* $x_\nu \in A$ of φ is a point such that $d\varphi(x_\nu) = 0$; $\varphi(x_\nu)$ is called a *critical value* of φ. At each critical point the *Hessian* $\partial^2\varphi/(\partial u_i \partial u_j) = H(\varphi)$ is a well-defined quadratic form in the tangent space $T_{x_\nu}(A)$; the critical point is *nondegenerate* in case $H(\varphi)$ is nonsingular. The function φ is called a *Morse function* if all critical points of φ are nondegenerate; according to a standard approximation theorem, such functions are dense in the C^2-topology. By the main lemma of Morse theory, if φ is a Morse function and the Hessian $H(\varphi)$ is nonsingular in the normal bundle to B in A, then the homotopy type of

$$A_t = \{x \in A : \varphi(x) \leqslant t\},$$

remains the same as long as t does not cross a critical value (this is obvious; we just retract along the gradient vector field of φ), and changes by attaching a cell of dimension k when we cross a critical value whose Hessian has exactly k negative eigenvalues. (This requires a local analysis of the Morse function ψ around the critical point x_ν, and is the main step.)

Now let M be a compact, complex manifold, $L \to M$ a positive holomorphic line bundle, and $s \in H^0(M, \mathcal{O}(L))$ a holomorphic section whose zero divisor $V = (s)$ is a smooth hypersurface. Choose a metric for $L \to M$ such that $(\sqrt{-1}/2\pi)\Theta = (\sqrt{-1}/2\pi)\partial\bar{\partial}\log|s|^{-2}$ is positive and set

$$\varphi(x) = \log|s|^2.$$

φ—or a function near φ in the C^2 topology—may be used as a Morse function (the fact that $\varphi: M \to [-\infty, \infty)$ with $\varphi^{-1}(-\infty) = V$ causes no essential difficulty; what is important is that $d(|s|) \neq 0$ along V). Now for any critical point $x \in M$ of φ, the matrix

$$\left(\frac{\partial}{\partial z_i}\frac{\partial}{\partial \bar{z}_j}\right)\log\frac{1}{|s|^2} = \left(\frac{1}{4}\left(\frac{\partial^2}{\partial x_i \partial x_j} + \frac{\partial^2}{\partial y_i \partial y_j}\right) + \frac{\sqrt{-1}}{4}\left(\frac{\partial^2}{\partial y_i \partial x_j} - \frac{\partial^2}{\partial x_j \partial y_i}\right)\right)\log|s|^2$$

is negative definite hermitian, and consequently the Hessian

$$H(\varphi) = \begin{vmatrix} \dfrac{\partial^2}{\partial x_i \partial x_j} & \dfrac{\partial^2}{\partial x_i \partial y_j} \\[2ex] \dfrac{\partial^2}{\partial x_j \partial y_i} & \dfrac{\partial^2}{\partial y_i \partial y_j} \end{vmatrix} \log|s|^2$$

of φ has at least n negative eigenvalues. Clearly, this will also be true for functions ψ sufficiently close to φ in the C^2-topology. Thus, by Morse theory, as far as homotopy type is concerned M is obtained from V by attaching cells of dimension at least n, and this gives the Lefschetz theorem on the homotopy level and for homology with $\mathbb{Z}$-coefficients.   Q.E.D.

When $n=1$, the theorem doesn't say anything. However, when $n=2$—i.e., M is a (connected and compact) complex surface—and $V \subset M$ is a Riemann surface embedded as a positive divisor, then the Lefschetz theorem gives

$$H_0(V, \mathbb{Z}) \cong H_0(M, \mathbb{Z}) = \mathbb{Z},$$
$$H_1(V, \mathbb{Z}) \to H_1(M, \mathbb{Z}) \to 0,$$

i.e., all of the first homology of the 4-manifold M lies on the irreducible embedded Riemann surface V.

We may also apply it to hypersurfaces of projective space: since any effective nonzero divisor on $\mathbb{P}^n$ is positive, the theorem tells us that if V is any smooth hypersurface in $\mathbb{P}^n$, then $H^{2k-1}(V)=0$ for $k \neq n/2$, while $H^{2k}(V)$ is generated by the class of a k-plane section of V for $k < n/2$. In particular any smooth hypersurface of dimension 2 or more is connected and simply connected. The same results apply, for an appropriate range of k, to any submanifold of projective space given as the transverse intersection of hypersurfaces.

A final remark on the Lefschetz theorem: Lefschetz's method was insofar as possible to study the topology of an algebraic variety M inductively, reducing questions about the homology of M to questions about the homology of a smaller-dimensional variety. His original proof of the last theorem asserted that for a hyperplane section V of M, the map $H_q(V, \mathbb{Z}) \to H_q(M, \mathbb{Z})$ is an isomorphism for $q < n-1$ and surjective in dimension $n-1$. By the hard Lefschetz theorem, the homology of M in dimension above n is mirrored in dimensions less than n, and by the Lefschetz decomposition, any nonprimitive cycle in dimension n can be obtained by intersecting a cycle in dimension greater than n with hyperplanes. Thus, the Lefschetz theorems together assert that the only "new" rational homology in varieties in each dimension is the primitive homology of the middle dimension.

Theorem B

Our second vanishing theorem for the cohomology of holomorphic vector bundles is less precise but broader in scope than the Kodaira Vanishing Theorem:

Theorem B. *Let* M *be a compact, complex manifold and* L→M *a positive line bundle. Then for any holomorphic vector bundle* E, *there exists* μ *such that*

$$H^q(M, \mathcal{O}(L^\mu \otimes E)) = 0 \qquad for\ q > 0, \mu \geqslant \mu_0.$$

Proof. Before we prove this, note that in case E is a line bundle the result is already implied by the Kodaira theorem: just take μ_0 such that $L^\mu \otimes E \otimes$

K_M^* is positive for $\mu \geqslant \mu_0$; then since $c_1(L^\mu \otimes E) = \mu c_1(L) + c_1(E)$

$$H^q(M, \mathcal{O}(L^\mu \otimes E)) = H^q(M, \Omega^n(L^\mu \otimes E \otimes K_M^*)) = 0$$

for $q > 0$, $\mu \geqslant \mu_0$. Indeed, the proof of Theorem B is essentially the same as that of Kodaira's theorem, the only difference being that now we must associate a definite sign to the curvature operator on a general vector bundle.

First, by Kodaira-Serre duality,

$$H^q(M, \mathcal{O}(L^\mu \otimes E)) \cong H^{n-q}(M, \mathcal{O}(L^{-\mu} \otimes E^* \otimes K_M)),$$

so it will be sufficient to prove that for any E, there exists μ_0 such that

$$H_{\bar{\partial}}^{0,p}(M, L^{-\mu} \otimes E) \cong H^p(M, \mathcal{O}(L^{-\mu} \otimes E)) = 0$$

for $\mu \geqslant \mu_0$, $p < n$.

Choose a metric in L such that $\omega = (\sqrt{-1}/2\pi)\Theta_L$ is positive, where Θ_L is the curvature form associated to the metric; let the metric on M be the one given by ω. Now we have seen that if E, E' are two hermitian vector bundles and if we give $E \otimes E'$ the induced metric, then

$$D_{E \otimes E'} = D_E \otimes 1 + 1 \otimes D_{E'}$$

and so

$$\Theta_{E \otimes E'} = \Theta_E \otimes 1 + 1 \otimes \Theta_{E'}$$

where D, Θ always refer to the metric connection and curvature. In particular, for L and E as above with any metric on E,

$$\Theta_{L^\mu \otimes E} = \frac{2\pi\mu}{\sqrt{-1}} \omega \otimes 1_E + \Theta_E.$$

Let $\eta \in \mathcal{K}^{0,p}(L^{-\mu} \otimes E)$ be harmonic. Writing Θ for $\Theta_{L^{-\mu} \otimes E}$, D for $D_{L^{-\mu} \otimes E}$, we have

$$\Theta = D^2 = D'\bar{\partial} + \bar{\partial}D',$$

so

$$\Theta\eta = \bar{\partial}D'\eta,$$

and by the Kähler identity

$$[\Lambda, \bar{\partial}] = -\frac{\sqrt{-1}}{2}D'^*$$

we see that

$$2\sqrt{-1}\,(\Lambda\Theta\eta, \eta) = 2\sqrt{-1}\,(\Lambda\bar{\partial}D'\eta, \eta)$$
$$= 2\sqrt{-1}\left(\left(\bar{\partial}\Lambda + \frac{1}{2\sqrt{-1}}D'^*\right)D'\eta, \eta\right)$$
$$= (D'^*D'\eta, \eta) = (D'\eta, D'\eta) \geqslant 0,$$

since $(\bar{\partial}\Lambda D'\eta, \eta) = (\Lambda D'\eta, \bar{\partial}^*\eta) = 0$. On the other hand,

$$2\sqrt{-1}\,(\Theta\Lambda\eta, \eta) = 2\sqrt{-1}\,(D'\bar{\partial}\Lambda\eta, \eta)$$
$$= 2\sqrt{-1}\left(\left(\Lambda\bar{\partial} - \frac{1}{2\sqrt{-1}}D'^*\right)\eta, D'^*\eta\right)$$
$$= -(D'^*\eta, D'^*\eta) \leqslant 0.$$

Thus we have

$$2\sqrt{-1}\,([\Lambda, \Theta]\eta, \eta) \geqslant 0.$$

But now

$$\Theta = \Theta_{L^{-\mu}\otimes E} = \Theta_E - \frac{2\pi}{\sqrt{-1}}\mu\omega,$$

and so

$$2\sqrt{-1}\,([\Lambda, \Theta]\eta, \eta) = 2\sqrt{-1}\,([\Lambda, \Theta_E]\eta, \eta) - 4\pi\mu([\Lambda, L]\eta, \eta)$$
$$= 2\sqrt{-1}\,([\Lambda, \Theta_E]\eta, \eta) - 4\pi\mu(n-p)\|\eta\|^2.$$

Now $[\Lambda, \Theta_E]$ is bounded on $A^{0,*}(L^{-\mu}\otimes E)$, so we can write

$$|([\Lambda, \Theta_E]\eta, \eta)| \leqslant C\|\eta\|^2,$$

and consequently for $p < n$,

$$\mu > \frac{C}{2\pi} \Rightarrow \eta = 0$$

i.e.,

$$\mathcal{H}^{0,p}(L^{-\mu}\otimes E) = 0 \quad \text{for } \mu > \frac{C}{2\pi}, \quad p < n. \qquad \text{Q.E.D.}$$

The Lefschetz Theorem on (1,1)-classes

As an application of Theorem B, we will complete our picture of the correspondences among divisors, line bundles, and Chern classes on a complex submanifold of projective space. First, we have the

Proposition. *Let* $M \subset \mathbb{P}^N$ *be a submanifold. Then every line bundle on* M *is of the form* L=[D] *for some divisor* D; *i.e.,*

$$\text{Pic}(M) \cong \frac{\text{Div}(M)}{\textit{linear equivalence}}.$$

Proof. To prove this, we have to show that every line bundle on M has a global meromorphic section. To find such a section, let H denote the restriction to M of the hyperplane bundle on $\mathbb{P}^N$. We will show that for $\mu \gg 0$, $L + \mu H$ has a nontrivial global holomorphic section s; then if t is any global holomorphic section of $[H]$ over M, s/t^μ will be a global meromorphic section of L as desired.

We proceed by induction on $n = \dim M$: assume that for every submanifold $V \subset \mathbb{P}^N$ of dimension less than n and every line bundle $L \to V$, $H^0(V, \mathcal{O}(L + \mu H)) \neq 0$ for $\mu \gg 0$. By Bertini's theorem we can find a hyperplane $\mathbb{P}^{N-1} \subset \mathbb{P}^N$ with $V = \mathbb{P}^{N-1} \cap M$ smooth; we consider the exact sheaf sequence

$$0 \to \mathcal{O}_M(L + (\mu - 1)H) \xrightarrow{\otimes s} \mathcal{O}_M(L + \mu H) \xrightarrow{r} \mathcal{O}_V(L + \mu H) \to 0,$$

where s is the section of H vanishing exactly on H and r is the restriction map. For $\mu \gg 0$ we have both

$$H^0(V, \mathcal{O}(L + \mu H)) \neq 0$$

by induction and

$$H^0(M, \mathcal{O}(L + \mu H)) \to H^0(V, \mathcal{O}(L + \mu H)) \to 0,$$

since

$$H^1(M, \mathcal{O}(L + (\mu - 1)H)) = 0$$

by Theorem B. Thus $H^0(M, \mathcal{O}(L + \mu H)) \neq 0$, and the result is proved.
Q.E.D.

We now consider for a moment the general problem of analytic cycles. On a compact Kähler manifold M, the Hodge decomposition

$$H^n(M, \mathbb{C}) = \bigoplus_{p+q=n} H^{p,q}(M)$$

on complex cohomology gives a slightly coarser decomposition of real cohomology

$$H^n(M, \mathbb{R}) = \bigoplus_{\substack{p+q=n \\ p \leqslant q}} (H^{p,q}(M) \oplus H^{q,p}(M)) \cap H^n(M, \mathbb{R}).$$

A natural question to ask is whether we can characterize geometrically the classes in homology that are Poincaré dual to classes in one of these factors. For example, we say a homology class $\gamma \in H_{2p}(M, \mathbb{Z})$ is *analytic* if it is a rational linear combination of fundamental classes of analytic subvarieties of M; dually, we say a cohomology class is *analytic* if its Poincaré dual is. Now, we have seen for purely local reasons that if $V \subset M$ is an analytic subvariety of dimension p and ψ any differential form on M,

$$\int_V \psi = \int_V \psi^{n-p,n-p}.$$

Thus if η is the harmonic form on M representing the cohomology class η_V

and ψ any harmonic form,

$$\int_M \psi \wedge \eta = \int_V \psi = \int_V \psi^{n-p,n-p} = \int_M \psi \wedge \eta^{p,p}$$

i.e., $\eta = \eta^{p,p}$, and so we see that *any analytic cohomology class of degree* 2p *is of pure type* (p,p). The famous *Hodge Conjecture* asserts that the converse is also true: On $M \subset \mathbb{P}^N$ a submanifold of projective space every rational cohomology class of type (p,p) is analytic. Whether the Hodge conjecture is true or false is at present unknown; it is a very beautiful and very difficult problem. The only case which has been proved in general is the case $p = 1$; this is the

Lefschetz Theorem on (1,1)-Classes. *For* $M \subset \mathbb{P}^N$ *a submanifold, every cohomology class*

$$\gamma \in H^{1,1}(M) \cap H^2(M, \mathbb{Z})$$

is analytic; in fact

$$\gamma = \eta_D$$

for some divisor D *on* M.

Here, of course, we are writing $H^2(M, \mathbb{Z})$ for its image under the natural inclusion in $H^2(M, \mathbb{R})$.

Proof.   Consider again the exact sequence

$$0 \to \mathbb{Z} \to \mathcal{O} \to \mathcal{O}^* \to 0$$

and the associated cohomology sequence

$$H^1(M, \mathcal{O}^*) \overset{c_1}{\longrightarrow} H^2(M, \mathbb{Z}) \overset{i_*}{\longrightarrow} H^2(M, \mathcal{O}) \cong H^{0,2}(M).$$

We claim that the map i_* is given by first mapping $H^2(M, \mathbb{Z}) \to H^2(M, \mathbb{C})$ and then projecting onto the $(0,2)$-factor of $H^2(M, \mathbb{C})$ in the Hodge decomposition; i.e., that the diagram

$$
\begin{array}{ccc}
H^2(M, \mathbb{Z}) & \overset{i_*}{\longrightarrow} & H^2(M, \mathcal{O}) \\
\downarrow & & \\
H^2(M, \mathbb{C}) & & \wr\ \text{Dolbeault} \\
{\scriptstyle \text{de Rham}} \downarrow \wr & & \\
H^2_{DR}(M, \mathbb{C}) & \overset{\pi^{0,2}}{\longrightarrow} & H^{0,2}_{\bar{\partial}}(M)
\end{array}
$$

commutes. (The map $\pi^{0,2}$ is defined on the form level, since for $\omega = \omega^{2,0} + \omega^{1,1} + \omega^{0,2} \in Z^2_d(M)$, $\bar{\partial}\omega^{0,2} = (d\omega)^{0,3} = 0$). To see this, let $z = (z_{\alpha\beta\gamma}) \in Z^2(M, \mathbb{Z})$; to find the image of z under the de Rham isomorphism, we take

$f_{\alpha\beta} \in A^0(U_\alpha \cap U_\beta)$ such that

$$z_{\alpha\beta\gamma} = f_{\alpha\beta} + f_{\beta\gamma} - f_{\alpha\gamma} \qquad \text{in } U_\alpha \cap U_\beta \cap U_\gamma;$$

since $z_{\alpha\beta\gamma}$ is constant, $df_{\alpha\beta} + df_{\beta\gamma} - df_{\alpha\gamma} = 0$, so $(df_{\alpha\beta}) \in Z^1(M, \mathcal{Z}_k^1)$ and we can find $\omega_\alpha \in A^1(U_\alpha)$ such that

$$df_{\alpha\beta} = \omega_\beta - \omega_\alpha \qquad \text{in } U_\alpha \cap U_\beta.$$

The global 2-form $d\omega_\alpha = d\omega_\beta$ then represents the image of z in $H^2_{DR}(M, \mathbb{C})$. On the other hand, take the image of $i_* z$ under the Dolbeault isomorphism: we write

$$z_{\alpha\beta\gamma} = f_{\alpha\beta} + f_{\beta\gamma} - f_{\alpha\gamma},$$
$$\bar{\partial} f_{\alpha\beta} = \omega_\beta^{0,1} - \omega_\alpha^{0,1},$$

and we see that $\bar{\partial}\omega_\alpha^{0,1} = (d\omega_\alpha)^{0,2}$ represents z in $H^{0,2}_{\bar{\partial}}(M)$.

Now we are just about done: given $\gamma \in H^{1,1}(M) \cap H^*(M, \mathbb{Z})$, we have $i_*(\gamma) = 0$, and hence $\gamma = c_1(L)$ is the Chern class of some line bundle $L \in H^1(M, \mathcal{O}^*)$. Writing $L = [D]$ for some divisor $D = \Sigma n_i V_i$,

$$\gamma = c_1([D]) = \eta_D. \qquad\qquad \text{Q.E.D.}$$

Note that since the isomorphism

$$L^{n-1} : H^{1,1}(M, \mathbb{Q}) \longrightarrow H^{n-1,n-1}(M, \mathbb{Q})$$

of the hard Lefschetz theorem is given by intersection with $n-1$ hyperplanes, it takes analytic classes to analytic classes; thus the Lefschetz $(1,1)$ theorem also implies the Hodge conjecture for $H^{2n-2}(M, \mathbb{Q}) \cap H^{n-1,n-1}(M)$. In particular, we see that *the intersection pairing between divisors and curves on a submanifold of projective space is nondegenerate.*

3. ALGEBRAIC VARIETIES

Analytic and Algebraic Varieties

Let $X_0, \ldots, X_n$ denote Euclidean coordinates on $\mathbb{C}^{n+1}$ and also the corresponding homogeneous coordinates on $\mathbb{P}^n$. Recall that the *universal bundle* $J \to \mathbb{P}^n$ is the subbundle of the trivial bundle $\mathbb{C}^{n+1} \times \mathbb{P}^n \to \mathbb{P}^n$ whose fiber over a point $X \in \mathbb{P}^n$ is simply the line $\{\lambda X\}_\lambda \subset \mathbb{C}^{n+1}$ corresponding to X. The *hyperplane bundle* $H \to \mathbb{P}^n$ is the dual of J, i.e., it is the bundle whose fiber over $X \in \mathbb{P}^n$ corresponds to the space of linear functionals on the line $\{\lambda X\}$. As we saw in Section 1 of this chapter, the Chern class of H is the fundamental class ω of a hyperplane in $\mathbb{P}^n$—that is, a generator of $H^2(\mathbb{P}^n, \mathbb{Z})$—and it follows from $H^1(\mathbb{P}^n, \mathcal{O}) = 0$ that every line bundle on $\mathbb{P}^n$ is a multiple H^d of H.

Consider now the global sections of the bundle H. First, we note that any linear functional L on $\mathbb{C}^{n+1}$ induces a section σ_L of H by restriction, i.e., by setting

$$\sigma_L(X) = L|_{\{\lambda X\}}.$$

Clearly σ_L is identically zero only if L is, so we have an injection

$$\mathbb{C}^{n+1*} \longrightarrow H^0(\mathbb{P}^n, \mathcal{O}(H)).$$

In fact, all of $H^0(\mathbb{P}^n, \mathcal{O}(H))$ is obtained in this way: if σ is any section of H, $D = (\sigma)$ its zero divisor, then the fundamental class η_D is given by

$$\eta_D = c_1(H) = \omega$$

and by the argument of Section 4, Chapter 0, it follows that D is a hyperplane in $\mathbb{P}^n$. If we let $L \in \mathbb{C}^{n+1*}$ be any linear functional vanishing on the hyperplane $\pi^{-1}D \subset \mathbb{C}^{n+1}$, then, the meromorphic function σ/σ_L will be holomorphic on all of $\mathbb{P}^n$, hence constant.

In general, the fiber of a power H^d of H over a point X corresponds to the space of d-linear forms on the line $\{\lambda X\} \subset \mathbb{C}^{n+1}$, and so as before any d-linear form F on $\mathbb{C}^{n+1}$ induces by restriction a global section

$$\sigma_F(X) = F|_{\{\lambda X\}}$$

of H^d. Since we are restricting F to one line at a time, we see that $\sigma_F = 0$ if F is alternating in any two factors, and so we have a map

$$\text{Sym}^d(\mathbb{C}^{n+1*}) \longrightarrow H^0(\mathbb{P}^n, \mathcal{O}(H^d))$$

from the space of symmetric d-linear forms on $\mathbb{C}^{n+1}$—that is, homogeneous polynomials $F(X_0, \ldots, X_n)$ of degree d in $X_0, \ldots, X_n$—to the space of global sections of H^d. Again, the map is injective, and the zero divisor of the section σ_F is just the image in $\mathbb{P}^n$ of the zero locus of $F(X_0, \ldots, X_n)$ in $\mathbb{C}^{n+1}$.

We claim now that *these are all the global sections* of H^d. To show this, let σ be any global section of H^d, and denote by σ_F be the section of H^d corresponding to an arbitrary homogeneous polynomial $F(X_0, \ldots, X_n)$. The quotient σ/σ_F is then a meromorphic function on $\mathbb{P}^n$; let

$$G' = \pi^*\left(\frac{\sigma}{\sigma_F}\right)$$

be its pullback to $\mathbb{C}^{n+1} - \{0\}$. G' has a simple pole along the divisor $F = 0$ in $\mathbb{C}^{n+1} - \{0\}$ and is holomorphic elsewhere, so the function

$$G = G' \cdot F$$

is holomorphic everywhere in $\mathbb{C}^{n+1} - \{0\}$ *and hence by Hartogs' theorem extends to an entire holomorphic function on $\mathbb{C}^{n+1}$*. Now since $G'(\lambda X) = G'(X)$ for all $X \in \mathbb{C}^{n+1}$ and $\lambda \in \mathbb{C}$, and $F(\lambda X) = \lambda^d F(X)$,

$$G(\lambda X) = \lambda^d G(X),$$

i.e., G is homogeneous of degree d. Thus if $\iota: t \to (\mu_0 t, \ldots, \mu_n t)$ is any line through the origin in $\mathbb{C}^{n+1}$, the pullback $\iota^* G$ either is identically zero or has a zero of order d at $t=0$ and a pole of order d at $t=\infty$, i.e.,

$$\iota^* G = \mu \cdot t^d$$

for some μ. It follows that the power series expansion

$$G(X_0,\ldots,X_n) = \sum a_{i_0,\ldots,i_n} X_0^{i_0} \cdots X_n^{i_n}$$

for G around the origin in $\mathbb{C}^{n+1}$ contains no terms of degree other than d, i.e., that G *is a homogeneous polynomial of degree* d *in* $X_0,\ldots,X_n$. Thus $\sigma = \sigma_G$ is of the desired form, and we have shown that every global section of H^d is given by a homogeneous polynomial in $X_0,\ldots,X_n$.

We note in passing that there is a useful formula for the dimension $h^0(\mathbb{P}^n, \mathcal{O}(H^d))$. of the space of global sections of H^d, that is, the number of monomials $X_0^{i_0},\ldots,X_n^{i_n}$ of degree d in $(n+1)$ variables. We associate to any sequence $i_0,\ldots,i_n$ of integers with $\Sigma i_k = d$ the set of n integers

$$\{i_0+1, i_0+i_1+2, \ldots, i_0+\cdots+i_{n-1}+n\} \subset \{1,\ldots,d+n\}.$$

This subset of $\{1,\ldots,d+n\}$ determines the sequence i_k, and conversely any subset of n distinct numbers between 1 and $d+n$ corresponds to such a sequence. Thus the number of monomials of degree d in $X_0,\ldots,X_n$ is just the number $\binom{d+n}{n}$ of subsets of order n in a set of order $d+n$, and so

$$h^0(\mathbb{P}^n, \mathcal{O}(H^d)) = \binom{d+n}{n}.$$

Note that the locus of a homogeneous polynomial $F(X_0,\ldots,X_n)$ of degree d in the homogeneous coordinates X_i may also be given in terms of Euclidean coordinates $x_i = X_i/X_0$, $i=1,\ldots,n$ in $(X_0 \neq 0)$ by the inhomogeneous polynomial of degree $\leqslant d$

$$f(x_1,\ldots,x_n) = F(1,x_1,\ldots,x_n) = \frac{1}{X_0^d} F(X_0,\ldots,X_n),$$

and conversely any such polynomial

$$f(x_1,\ldots,x_n) = \sum a_{i_1\ldots i_n} x_1^{i_1} \cdots x_n^{i_n}$$

corresponds to a homogeneous polynomial

$$F(X_0,\ldots,X_n) = \sum a_{i_1,\ldots,i_n} X_0^{d-\Sigma i_k} \cdot X_1^{i_1} \cdots X_n^{i_n}.$$

f is called the *affine*, or *inhomogeneous* form of F.

We now make the

DEFINITION.   An *algebraic variety* $V \subset \mathbb{P}^n$ is the locus in $\mathbb{P}^n$ of a collection of homogeneous polynomials $\{F_\alpha(X_0,\ldots,X_n)\}$.

An algebraic variety is clearly an analytic subvariety of $\mathbb{P}^n$ and will be considered primarily as such (i.e., an algebraic variety $V \subset \mathbb{P}^n$ is called smooth, irreducible, connected, etc. if it has these properties as an analytic subvariety of $\mathbb{P}^n$). Conversely, we will show that any analytic subvariety of projective space is expressible as the locus of homogeneous polynomials. We have already done this in essence for hypersurfaces: if $V \subset \mathbb{P}^n$ is any divisor, the line bundle $[V]$ is of the form H^d for some d, and V is the zero locus of some section σ of $[V]$. But all sections σ of H^d are of the form σ_F, and so

$$V = (\sigma_F) = (F(X_0,\dots,X_n)=0)$$

is algebraic. In general, suppose $V \subset \mathbb{P}^n$ is a k-dimensional variety, $p \in \mathbb{P}^n$ any point not lying on V. We can find an $(n-k-1)$-plane $\mathbb{P}^{n-k-1}$ in $\mathbb{P}^n$ through p and missing V; let $\mathbb{P}^{n-k-2}$ be an $(n-k-2)$-plane in $\mathbb{P}^{n-k-1}$ disjoint from p. Let π denote the projection from $\mathbb{P}^{n-k-2}$ onto a complementary $(k+1)$-plane $\mathbb{P}^{k+1}$; choose coordinates $X_0,\dots,X_n$ on $\mathbb{P}^n$ so that

$$\mathbb{P}^{k+1} = (X_{k+2}=\cdots=X_n=0)$$
$$\mathbb{P}^{n-k-2} = (X_0=\cdots=X_{k+1}=0)$$

and

$$\pi([X_0,\dots,X_n]) = [X_0,\dots,X_{k+1}].$$

By the proper mapping theorem the image $\pi(V)$ of V in $\mathbb{P}^{k+1}$ is an analytic hypersurface in $\mathbb{P}^{k+1}$, and by the hypothesis that $\mathbb{P}^{n-k-1} = \overline{\mathbb{P}^{n-k-2},p}$ misses V, $\pi(p)$ will lie outside $\pi(V)$. By what we have seen, we can find a homogeneous polynomial $F(X_0,\dots,X_{k+1})$ vanishing along $\pi(V)$ but not at $\pi(p)$; correspondingly, the polynomial

$$\tilde{F}(X_0,\dots,X_n) = F(X_0,\dots,X_{k+1})$$

vanishes on V but not at p. We can thus find, for any point $p \in V$, a polynomial vanishing identically on V but not at p, and so we have

Chow's Theorem. *Any analytic subvariety of projective space is algebraic.*

If $F(X_0,\dots,X_n)$ and $G(X_0,\dots,X_n) \neq 0$ are two homogeneous polynomials of the same degree d in the homogeneous coordinates X on $\mathbb{P}^n$, the quotient

$$\varphi(X) = \frac{F(X)}{G(X)}$$

is a well-defined meromorphic function on $\mathbb{P}^n$; such a mermorphic function is called a *rational function*. Note that after dividing top and bottom by powers of X_0, we may write the function φ as

$$\varphi(x_1,\dots,x_n) = \frac{f(x_1,\dots,x_n)}{g(x_1,\dots,x_n)},$$

where f and g are polynomials (not necessarily both of degree d) in the Euclidean coordinates x_i. Thus the field $K(\mathbb{P}^n)$ of rational functions on $\mathbb{P}^n$ is isomorphic to $\mathbb{C}(x_1,\dots,x_n)$.

It is not hard to see that any meromorphic function on $\mathbb{P}^n$ is rational. By Chow's theorem, both the zero-divisor $(\varphi)_0$ and the polar divisor $(\varphi)_\infty$ of φ are expressible as the loci of homogeneous polynomials $F(X)$ and $G(X)$. Since moreover the divisor (φ) is homologous to zero, F and G have the same degree, so F/G is a well-defined rational function on $\mathbb{P}^n$; then from

$$(F/G) = (\varphi)$$

it follows that

$$\varphi = \lambda F/G$$

for some $\lambda \in \mathbb{C}$.

Now if $V \subset \mathbb{P}^n$ is any smooth variety, a meromorphic function on V is called rational if it is the restriction to V of a rational function on $\mathbb{P}^n$. The rational functions of V a priori form a subfield of the field $\mathfrak{M}(V)$ of meromorphic functions; in fact,

Every meromorphic function on an algebraic variety $V \subset \mathbb{P}^n$ *is rational.*

The proof of this assertion is in two stages: first, we express V as a branched cover of a linear subspace $\mathbb{P}^k \subset \mathbb{P}^n$ by projection, and deduce from this representation that the pullback $\pi^* K(\mathbb{P}^k)$ to V of the field of rational functions on $\mathbb{P}^k$ has index at most $d = \deg(V)$ in the field $\mathfrak{M}(V)$; we then show that the field $K(V)$ is an extension of degree at least d over $\pi^* K(\mathbb{P}^k)$.

For the first part, choose a generic $(n-k-1)$-plane $\mathbb{P}^{n-k-1}$ in $\mathbb{P}^n$; at this stage we require only that $\mathbb{P}^{n-k-1}$ be disjoint from V. Let $\mathbb{P}^k$ be a complementary k-plane, and $\pi : V \to \mathbb{P}^k$ the projection from $\mathbb{P}^{n-k-1}$. For each point p of $\mathbb{P}^k$, the inverse image $\pi^{-1}(p)$ is just the intersection of V with the $(n-k)$-plane $\overline{\mathbb{P}^{n-k-1}, p}$; since $\overline{\mathbb{P}^{n-k-1}, p}$ will generically intersect V in $d = \deg(V)$ points, π expresses V as a d-sheeted branched cover of $\mathbb{P}^k$ almost everywhere. In fact, π must be everywhere finite: if for any point p in $\mathbb{P}^k$ the $(n-k)$-plane $\overline{\mathbb{P}^{n-k-1}, p}$ intersected V in a curve, that curve would necessarily meet the hyperplane $\mathbb{P}^{n-k-1} \subset \overline{\mathbb{P}^{n-k-1}, p}$, contrary to the hypothesis that $\mathbb{P}^{n-k-1}$ is disjoint from V.

Note that if we choose homogeneous coordinates $X = [X_0, \ldots, X_n]$ on $\mathbb{P}^n$ such that $\mathbb{P}^{n-k-1}$ is given as $(X_0 = \cdots = X_k = 0)$ and $\mathbb{P}^k$ as $(X_{k+1} = \cdots = X_n = 0)$, the map π is given by

$$\pi([X_0, \ldots, X_n]) = [X_0, \ldots, X_k].$$

In particular, the pullback $\pi^* f$ to V of any rational function f on $\mathbb{P}^k$ is clearly rational, so that on V we have inclusions

$$\pi^* K(\mathbb{P}^k) \subset K(V) \subset \mathfrak{M}(V).$$

Now, to see that $\pi^* K(\mathbb{P}^k)$ has index at most d in $M(V)$, let φ be any meromorphic function on V and let $D = (\varphi)_\infty$. Let $B \subset \mathbb{P}^k$ be the branch locus of π; on $\mathbb{P}^k - B$ we can define functions ψ_i by

$$\psi_1(p) = \sum_{q \in \pi^{-1}(p)} \varphi(q),$$

$$\psi_2(p) = \sum_{q \neq q' \in \pi^{-1}(p)} \varphi(q) \cdot \varphi(q'),$$

$$\vdots$$

$$\psi_d(p) = \prod_{q \in \pi^{-1}(p)} \varphi(q),$$

i.e., we let $\psi_i(p)$ be the ith symmetric polynomial in the values of φ at the d points of $\pi^{-1}(p)$ in V. ψ_i is then a holomorphic function on $\mathbb{P}^k - B - \pi(D)$, and being bounded away from $\pi(D)$ it extends by the Riemann extension theorem to a holomorphic function on $\mathbb{P}^k - \pi(D)$. We claim that ψ_i extends to a meromorphic function on all of $\mathbb{P}^k$. If $p \in \pi(D)$ is any point and $f(X)$ a local defining function for $\pi(D)$ in a neighborhood Δ of p, then for m sufficiently large, the function

$$\varphi' = \varphi \cdot \pi^* f^m$$

will be holomorphic in $\pi^{-1}(\Delta)$. For $q \in \Delta - B$, then, let

$$\psi_i'(q) = \sum_{\alpha_1, \ldots, \alpha_i} \left(\prod \varphi'(p_{\alpha_1}) \cdots \varphi'(p_{\alpha_i}) \right)$$

be the ith symmetric function of the values of φ' at the points of $\pi^{-1}(q)$; being bounded in any compact subset of Δ, ψ_i' likewise extends to a holomorphic function on Δ. Writing

$$\psi_i = \frac{\psi_i'}{f^{i-m}},$$

we see that ψ_i extends to a meromorphic function in Δ, and hence in all of $\mathbb{P}^k$. Thus the functions ψ_i are rational functions. But now on V we have

$$\varphi^d - \pi^* \psi_1 \cdot \varphi^{d-1} + \pi^* \psi_2 \cdot \varphi^{d-2} - \cdots + (-1)^d \pi^* \psi \equiv 0,$$

i.e., every meromorphic function $\varphi \in \mathfrak{M}(V)$ satisfies a polynomial relation of degree d over $\pi^* K(\mathbb{P}^k)$. By the primitive element theorem, then, the field extension $\mathfrak{M}(V) \supset \pi^* K(\mathbb{P}^k)$ is finite of degree at most d.

To complete the proof of our assertion, we want to exhibit a rational function on V which satisfies no polynomial relation of degree less than d over the field $\pi^* K(\mathbb{P}^k)$. To do this, we factor the projection map π: choose generic planes $\mathbb{P}^{n-k-2} \subset \mathbb{P}^{n-k-1}$ and $\mathbb{P}^{k+1} \subset \mathbb{P}^k$, and let $\pi' : V \to \mathbb{P}^{k+1}$ be projection from $\mathbb{P}^{n-k-2}$. We may take homogeneous coordinates $X = [X_0, \ldots, X_n]$ on $\mathbb{P}^n$ such that

$$\mathbb{P}^{n-k-1} = (X_0 = \cdots = X_k = 0), \qquad \mathbb{P}^k = (X_{k+1} = \cdots = X_n = 0),$$

$$\mathbb{P}^{n-k-2} = (X_0 = \cdots = X_{k+1} = 0), \qquad \mathbb{P}^{k+1} = (X_{k+2} = \cdots = X_n = 0);$$

in terms of these coordinates, π is given as before and

$$\pi'([X_0,\dots,X_n]) = [X_0,\dots,X_{k+1}]$$

so that π is just the composition of π' with projection from the point $(X_0 = \dots = X_k = X_{k+2} = \dots = X_n = 0)$ in $\mathbb{P}^{k+1}$ onto $\mathbb{P}^k$. Note that, $\mathbb{P}^{n-k-2}$ having been chosen generically, the map π' will be one-to-one over an open set in its image: this will be the case as long as for some point p in V the $(n-k-1)$-plane $\overline{\mathbb{P}^{n-k-2}, p}$ meets V only at p—but for any p in V, the generic $(n-k-1)$-plane through p meets V only at p.

Now, consider the rational function

$$x_{k+1} = \frac{X_{k+1}}{X_0}$$

on V. Suppose that x_{k+1} satisfied an equation of the form

$$x_{k+1}^{d'} + \psi_1(x_1,\dots,x_k)\cdot x_{k+1}^{d'-1} + \dots + \psi_{d'}(x_1,\dots,x_k) \equiv 0, \, d' < d.$$

Then for a generic point $p = [\alpha_0,\dots,\alpha_k]$ in $\mathbb{P}^k$, the inverse image of p in $\pi'(V) \subset \mathbb{P}^{k+1}$ would consist of at most of the d' points $\{[\alpha_0,\dots,\alpha_k,\beta]\}$, where

$$\beta^{d'} + \psi_1\left(\frac{\alpha_1}{\alpha_0},\dots,\frac{\alpha_k}{\alpha_0}\right)\beta^{d'-1} + \dots + \psi_{d'}\left(\frac{\alpha_1}{\alpha_0},\dots,\frac{\alpha_k}{\alpha_0}\right) = 0.$$

But since the projection $\pi' : V \to \mathbb{P}^{k+1}$ is generically one-to-one onto its image and the fibers of π generically consist of $d > d'$ points, this is impossible.   Q.E.D.

Note, as a consequence, that the field of rational functions on an algebraic variety V is independent of the embedding. Thus, the *sheaf of germs of polynomial functions on* V, which associates to every open set U on V the ring of rational functions on V finite in U, is intrinsically associated to V. This sheaf, the basic structure sheaf in algebraic treatments of the subject, is also denoted by $\mathcal{O}_V$.

It is not hard to see by the same sort of argument that

1.   Any meromorphic differential form on a smooth variety is algebraic, that is, expressible in terms of rational functions and their differentials.
2.   Any holomorphic map between smooth varieties may be given by rational functions.
3.   Any holomorphic vector bundle on a smooth variety is algebraic, that is, may be given by rational transition functions.

The first assertion we can prove now: clearly the differentials $d\varphi$ of the rational functions on V span the cotangent space to V at every point, and so a finite number of them do; any meromorphic form on V is then a linear combination of wedge products of these forms with meromorphic, hence rational, coefficient functions. The second assertion will follow once we see in the following section that the product $V \times W$ of two algebraic varieties is again a variety; by Chow's theorem the graph $\Gamma \subset V \times W \subset \mathbb{P}^n$ is then cut out by polynomials. The third assertion will be clear once we have discussed the Grassmannian manifold and proved an embedding theorem for vector bundles on algebraic varieties in Sections 5 and 6 of this chapter.

All these results are special instances of the general *G.A.G.A. principle** that *any global analytic object on an algebraic variety is algebraic*. The importance of Chow's theorem and the G.A.G.A. principle is, in this treatment, primarily philosophical rather than practical. While we shall not use them as tools in our study—most of our techniques apply uniformly to all analytic phenomena on a variety, so it will not be useful for us to know, for instance, that a given meromorphic function or map is rational—they assure us that, in treating varieties as analytic rather than algebraic entities, we are still dealing with the same class of objects.

Degree of a Variety

The fundamental projective invariant of an algebraic variety $V \subset \mathbb{P}^n$ is its degree, defined as follows: Taking the class of a k-plane $\mathbb{P}^k \subset \mathbb{P}^n$ as generator, we have an isomorphism

$$H_{2k}(\mathbb{P}^n, \mathbb{Z}) \cong \mathbb{Z}.$$

The *degree* of a k-dimensional variety $V \subset \mathbb{P}^n$ is its fundamental class in $H_{2k}(\mathbb{P}^n, \mathbb{Z})$ via this identification.

Alternative definitions abound. First, by Bertini applied to the smooth locus of V the generic $(n-k)$-plane $\mathbb{P}^{n-k} \subset \mathbb{P}^n$ will intersect V transversely, and so will meet V in exactly

$$^{\#}(\mathbb{P}^{n-k} \cdot V) = \text{degree}(V)$$

points; thus we may define the degree of a variety to be the number of points of intersections of V with a generic linear subspace of complementary dimension. On the other hand, if ω is the standard Kähler form on $\mathbb{P}^n$,

$$\int_V \omega^k = \text{degree}(V) \cdot \int_{\mathbb{P}^k} \omega^k = \text{degree}(V),$$

so we may define the degree of V to be simply its volume divided by $k!$. (This is sometimes called the Wirtinger theorem.) In case $V \subset \mathbb{P}^n$ is a hypersurface, we have seen that it may be given in terms of homogeneous

---

*So named after J. P. Serre's paper, Geometrie Algebrique et Geometrie Analytique, *Annals of the Institute Fourier*, Vol. 6.

coordinates $X_0, \ldots, X_n$ on $\mathbb{P}^n$ as the locus

$$V = (F(X_0, \ldots, X_n) = 0)$$

of a homogeneous polynomial F. If F has degree d, then the fundamental class of $V = (\sigma_F)$ is $\eta_V = c_1(H^d)$—that is, d times the class of a hyperplane —so V has degree d. Alternatively, if

$$[Y_0, Y_1] \xrightarrow{\mu} [a_0 Y_0 + b_0 Y_1, \ldots, a_n Y_0 + b_n Y_1]$$

is a generic line in $\mathbb{P}^n$, the pullback $\mu^* F$ of F to $\mathbb{P}^1$ will be homogeneous of degree d in Y_0 and Y_1, and so by the fundamental theorem of algebra will have exactly d roots. The degree of V is thus the degree d of the polynomial F.

A basic fact about degree is that it is multiplicative with respect to intersections. Since a $\mathbb{P}^{n-k_1}$ and a $\mathbb{P}^{n-k_2}$ intersect transversely in a $\mathbb{P}^{n-k_1-k_2}$, the degree of the intersection of two varieties meeting transversely almost everywhere is the product of their degrees. More generally, if V and W are varieties of degrees d_1 and d_2 in $\mathbb{P}^n$ intersecting in a variety of the appropriate dimension, $\{Z_i\}$ the irreducible components of $V \cap W$, then

$$d_1 \cdot d_2 = \sum_i \text{mult}_{Z_i}(V \cdot W) \cdot \text{degree}(Z_i)$$

with $\text{mult}_{Z_i}(V \cdot W)$ defined as in Section 4 of Chapter 0. This is of particular interest in the case of complementary dimension. For example, if C and D are two curves in $\mathbb{P}^2$ of degree d_1 and d_2 and having no component in common—that is, intersecting only in points—we see that they can have at most $d_1 d_2$ points of intersection. This is a weak form of

Bezout's Theorem. *Two relatively prime polynomials* $f(x, y)$, $g(x, y) \in \mathbb{C}[x, y]$ *of degrees* d_1 *and* d_2 *can have at most* $d_1 d_2$ *simultaneous solutions.*

The degree also behaves well with respect to the geometric operations of projection and coning. Clearly, if $V \subset \mathbb{P}^n$ is any variety, $p \in \mathbb{P}^n$ any point not on V, and $\pi_p : V \to \mathbb{P}^{n-1}$ the projection onto a hyperplane, then

$$\deg(V) = \deg(\pi_p(V)):$$

the number of points of intersection of $\pi(V)$ with a generic $(n-k-1)$-plane $\mathbb{P}^{n-k-1}$ in $\mathbb{P}^{n-1}$ is just the number of points of intersection of V with the $(n-k)$-plane $\mathbb{P}^{n-k} = \overline{\mathbb{P}^{n-k-1}, p}$ in $\mathbb{P}^n$; since by Bertini the generic $\mathbb{P}^{n-k}$ through p meets V transversely, this is just the degree of V.

Coning is an operation we have not previously encountered. If $V \subset \mathbb{P}^n$ is any variety, $p \in \mathbb{P}^n$ at any point lying off V, we take the *cone* $\overline{p, V}$ *through* p *over* V to be the union of the lines through p meeting V. That $\overline{p, V}$ is a variety is easy to see: it is the image under projection on the first factor of the incidence correspondence $I \subset \mathbb{P}^n \times \mathbb{P}^n$ defined by

$$I = \{(q,r): r \in V, p \wedge q \wedge r = 0\},$$

itself an analytic subvariety of $\mathbb{P}^n \times \mathbb{P}^n$. (Alternatively, if in homogeneous coordinates $p = [0, \ldots, 0, 1]$, let $\mathbb{P}^{n-1}$ be the hyperplane $X_n = 0$; if the image $\pi_p(V) \subset \mathbb{P}^{n-1}$ of V under projection from p is cut out in $\mathbb{P}^{n-1}$ by polynomials $\{F_\alpha(X_0, \ldots, X_{n-1})\}$, then the cone $\overline{p,V}$ is cut out by the polynomials $\{\tilde{F}_\alpha(X_0, \ldots, X_n) = F_\alpha(X_0, \ldots, X_{n-1})\}$.) Now if $H \subset \mathbb{P}^n$ is a generic hyperplane, not containing p, then the intersection of H with the cone $\overline{p,V}$ will be simply the projection $\pi_p(V)$ of V from p into H; so

$$\deg(\overline{p,V}) = \deg(H \cap \overline{p,V})$$

$$= \deg(\pi_p(V)) = \deg(V).$$

Another variety we may associate with a variety $V \subset \mathbb{P}^n$ is its *chordal variety* $C(V)$, defined to be the union of all lines meeting V twice or, in the limiting case, tangent to V. $C(V)$ is the image under projection on the third factor of the closure of the incidence correspondence $I \subset \mathbb{P}^n \times \mathbb{P}^n \times \mathbb{P}^n$ defined by

$$I = \{(p,q,r): p \neq q \in V, p \wedge q \wedge r = 0\}.$$

$\bar{I}$ is an analytic subvariety of $\mathbb{P}^n \times \mathbb{P}^n \times \mathbb{P}^n$, and so $C(V)$ is an analytic variety in $\mathbb{P}^n$. Note that since projection on the first factor maps I onto V with $(\dim V + 1)$-dimensional fibers, I has dimension $2 \cdot \dim V + 1$. $C(V)$ will thus have dimension at most $2 \cdot \dim V + 1$; generally, this will be exact. In particular, since the projection π_p of a smooth variety into a hyperplane will be an embedding if and only if $p \notin C(V)$, we see that if $n > 2 \cdot \dim V + 1$, then V may be smoothly projected into a hyperplane. Thus

Any smooth algebraic variety of dimension k *may be embedded in* $\mathbb{P}^{2k+1}$.

As we shall see, the degree of the chordal variety $C(V)$ of a variety does not depend on the degree of V alone.

A variety $V \subset \mathbb{P}^n$ is called *nondegenerate* if it does not lie in a hyperplane. We have the following condition on the degree of a nondegenerate variety:

If $V \subset \mathbb{P}^n$ *is an irreducible, nondegenerate,* k-*dimensional variety, then*

$$\deg(V) \geqslant n - k + 1.$$

We prove this first for V a curve in $\mathbb{P}^n$. Any n points of V lie in a hyperplane H, and if the degree of V were less than n, then H, having n

points in common with V, would have a curve in common with V; being irreducible, V would then lie in H.

Turning to the general case, we have to show that the generic hyperplane section $H \cap V$ of an irreducible nondegenerate variety V of dimension $\geqslant 2$ is again irreducible and nondegenerate in H. The latter part is clear: the condition that $H \cap V$ be degenerate is a closed one on $H \in \mathbb{P}^{n*}$, and since V itself is nondegenerate, we can find n points of V spanning a hyperplane, so not every hyperplane section of V can be degenerate.

The former half of our assertion—that the generic hyperplane section of an irreducible variety is irreducible—is somewhat harder. We note first that in case V is smooth, this follows easily from the Bertini theorem and the Lefschetz theorem on hyperplane sections: by Bertini, the generic hyperplane section $H \cap V$ is smooth, and so by Lefschetz,

$$H_0(H \cap V, \mathbb{C}) \cong H_0(V, \mathbb{C}) \cong \mathbb{C};$$

i.e., $H \cap V$ is connected. Thus, if $H \cap V$ were reducible, the components of $H \cap V$ would have to meet each other; but their points of intersection would be singular points of $H \cap V$, and so this cannot happen.

To prove the assertion in the general case requires a different approach. We argue as follows: let $p \in V$ be any smooth point, and let $\mathbb{P}^{n-2} \subset \mathbb{P}^n$ be an $(n-2)$-plane meeting V transversely at p; let Z be the irreducible component of $V \cap \mathbb{P}^{n-2}$ containing p. Now consider the pencil $\{H_\lambda\}$ of hyperplanes in $\mathbb{P}^n$ containing $\mathbb{P}^{n-2}$. Each hyperplane section $H_\lambda \cap V$ of V contains Z, but since each H_λ intersects V transversely at p, p—being a smooth point of $H_\lambda \cap V$—can lie on at most one of the irreducible components of $H_\lambda \cap V$ for each λ. Let V' be the union of the irreducible components of the sections $H_\lambda \cap V$ that contain Z. Then V' is an open k-dimensional analytic variety contained in V, and hence its closure $\overline{V'}$ must be all of V; thus $H_\lambda \cap V = H_\lambda \cap V'$ is irreducible for generic λ.

Now the original lemma follows readily from the curve case: if $V \subset \mathbb{P}^n$ is any irreducible nondegenerate k-dimensional variety of degree d, then the generic intersection of V with $k-1$ hyperplanes is an irreducible, nondegenerate curve of degree d in $\mathbb{P}^{n-k+1}$, and so

$$d \geqslant n - k + 1.$$

We can restate the lemma as follows: any irreducible k-dimensional variety $V \subset \mathbb{P}^n$ of degree d must lie in a linear space of dimension $d + k - 1$; as a corollary, then, we see again that any variety of degree one in $\mathbb{P}^n$ is a linear subspace.

We shall see that varieties that realize this lower bound on the degree——e.g., curves of degree n in $\mathbb{P}^n$, surfaces of degree $n-1$ in $\mathbb{P}^n$, etc.—are of a special character.

Tangent Spaces to Algebraic Varieties

To a variety $V \subset \mathbb{P}^n$ and a smooth point $p \in V$ is associated a linear subspace of $\mathbb{P}^n$, the *tangent space to V at p*. This may be defined in several ways; we mention two here.

1.   The complement of a hyperplane $H \subset \mathbb{P}^n$ is isomorphic to $\mathbb{C}^n$ via Euclidean coordinates; we may take the tangent space to $V \subset \mathbb{P}^n$ at p to be the closure in $\mathbb{P}^n$ of the usual tangent subspace $T_p(V) \subset T_p(\mathbb{C}^n)$. Explicitly, if $x_1, \ldots, x_n$ are Euclidean coordinates on $\mathbb{P}^n$ in a neighborhood of $p = (\alpha_1, \ldots, \alpha_n)$ and V is cut out by functions $\{f_\alpha(x_1, \ldots, x_n)\}$, this is just the linear subspace of $\mathbb{P}^n$ defined by

$$\sum_{i=1}^{n} \frac{\partial f_\alpha}{\partial x_i}(p) \cdot (x_i - \alpha_i) = 0.$$

2.   Alternatively, if V is given in terms of homogeneous coordinates $X_0, \ldots, X_n$ as the locus of polynomials $\{F_\alpha(X_1, \ldots, X_n)\}$, this is the linear subspace

$$\sum_{i=0}^{n} \frac{\partial F_\alpha}{\partial X_i}(p) \cdot X_i = 0,$$

where the differentiation is formal: if f_α is the inhomogeneous form of F_α, then $\partial f_\alpha / \partial x_i$ is the inhomogeneous form of $\partial F_\alpha / \partial X_i$, and by virtue of the relation

$$\frac{1}{d} \cdot \sum_{i=0}^{n} \frac{\partial F}{\partial X_i} = F,$$

where $d = \deg(F)$, we can write

$$\sum_{i=0}^{n} \frac{\partial F_\alpha}{\partial X_i}(p) \cdot X_i = X_0 \sum_{i=0}^{n} \frac{\partial F_\alpha}{\partial X_i}(p) \cdot x_i$$

$$= X_0 \sum_{i=0}^{n} \frac{\partial F_\alpha}{\partial X_i}(p) \cdot (x_i - \alpha_i)$$

$$= X_0 \cdot \sum_{i=1}^{n} \frac{\partial f_\alpha}{\partial x_i}(p) \cdot (x_i - \alpha_i),$$

so the homogeneous form describes the same subspace.

In a similar way we may define the *tangent cone* to a variety $V \subset \mathbb{P}^n$ at a (possibly singular) point $p \in V$. First, if V is a hypersurface cut out by the homogeneous polynomial F, and p a point of multiplicity k on V—so that all the partial derivatives of F of order $\leqslant k-1$ vanish—we take the tangent cone to V at p to be the locus

$$T_p(V) = \left(\sum \frac{\partial^k F}{\partial^{i_0} X_0 \cdots \partial^{i_n} X_n}(p) \cdot X_0^{i_0} \cdots X_n^{i_n} = 0 \right).$$

In general, we will take the tangent cone to a variety $V \subset \mathbb{P}^n$ at a point p to be the intersection of the tangent cones at p to all the hypersurfaces containing V near p.

This may be realized alternately as the union of the tangent lines at p to all curves lying on V and passing through p; or as the limiting position of chords $\lim_{\lambda \to 0} \overline{p, q(\lambda)}$ where $q(\lambda)$ is an arc in V with $q(0) = p$.

4.   THE KODAIRA EMBEDDING THEOREM

Line Bundles and Maps to Projective Space

We will be concerned in this section with determining exactly when a compact complex manifold is an algebraic variety, i.e., when it can be embedded in projective space. We first establish a basic formalism for maps to $\mathbb{P}^N$.

Let M be a compact complex manifold, $L \to M$ a holomorphic line bundle. Recall that to any subspace E of the vector space $H^0(M, \mathcal{O}(L))$ is associated the linear system

$$|E| = \{(s)\}_{s \in E} \subset \mathrm{Div}(M)$$

of divisors on M. Since M is compact, $(s) = (s')$ only if $s = \lambda s'$ for some nonzero constant $\lambda \in \mathbb{C}$; thus $|E|$ is parametrized by the projective space $\mathbb{P}(E)$.

Suppose in addition that the linear system $|E|$ has no base points, i.e., that not all $s \in E$ vanish at any point $p \in M$. Then for each $p \in M$ the set of sections $s \in E$ vanishing at p forms a hyperplane $\tilde{H}_p \subset E$—or, equivalently, the set of divisors $D \in |E|$ containing p forms a hyperplane H_p in $\mathbb{P}(E)$—and so we can define a map

$$\iota_E : M \to \mathbb{P}(E)^*,$$

by sending $p \in M$ to $H_p \in \mathbb{P}(E)^*$.

We can describe the map ι_E more explicitly as follows. Choose a basis $s_0, \ldots, s_N$ for E. If we let $s_{i,\alpha} = \varphi_\alpha^*(s_i) \in \mathcal{O}(U)$ for any trivialization φ_α of L over an open set $U \in M$, it is clear that the point $[s_{0,\alpha}(p), \ldots, s_{N,\alpha}(p)] \in \mathbb{P}^N$ is independent of the trivialization φ_α chosen; we denote this point by $[s_0(p), \ldots, s_N(p)]$. In terms of the identifications $\mathbb{P}(E)^* \cong \mathbb{P}^N$ corresponding to the choice of basis $s_0, \ldots, s_N$, then, the map ι_E is given by

$$\iota_E(p) = [s_0(p), \ldots, s_N(p)].$$

We see from this representation that ι_E is holomorphic.

Now let H be the hyperplane bundle on $\mathbb{P}^N$. The pullback bundle $\iota_E^*(H)$ on M is given by the divisor (s_i) —that is,

$$L = \iota_E^*(H).$$

Moreover, any section $s = \Sigma a_i s_i \in E$ is the pullback of the section $\Sigma a_i Z_i$ of H on $\mathbb{P}^N$; i.e.,

$$E = \iota_E^*\big(H^0(\mathbb{P}^N, \mathcal{O}(H))\big) \subset H^0(M, \mathcal{O}(L)).$$

Thus $\iota_E : M \to \mathbb{P}^N$ determines both the line bundle L and the subspace $E \subset H^0(M, \mathcal{O}(L))$, and we have a basic dictionary

$$\left\{ \begin{array}{l} \text{nondegenerate maps} \\ f \colon M \to \mathbb{P}^N, \text{ modulo} \\ \text{projective} \\ \text{transformations} \end{array} \right\} \rightleftarrows \left\{ \begin{array}{l} \text{line bundles } L \to M \\ \text{with } E \subset H^0(M, \mathcal{O}(L)) \\ \text{such that } |E| \text{ has no base points} \end{array} \right\}$$

where the choice of homogeneous coordinates on $\mathbb{P}^N$ corresponds to the choice of basis $s_0, \ldots, s_N$ for E.

We will often write ι_L for $\iota_{H^0(M, \mathcal{O}(L))}$ and ι_D for $\iota_{[D]}$.

Note that the degree of the image of M under ι_E—that is, the intersection of M with n general hyperplanes in $\mathbb{P}^n$—is just the n-fold self-intersection of a representative divisor $D \in |E|$, that is,

$$\deg(\iota_E M) = c_1(L)^n.$$

A variety $V \subset \mathbb{P}^n$ is called *normal* if the linear system on V giving the embedding $\iota : V \hookrightarrow \mathbb{P}^n$ is complete, that is, if the restriction map

$$H^0(\mathbb{P}^n, \mathcal{O}(H)) \to H^0(V, \mathcal{O}(H))$$

is surjective. Note that *any hypersurface* $V \subset \mathbb{P}^n$ *is normal*: from the exact sheaf sequence

$$0 \to \mathcal{O}_{\mathbb{P}^n}(H - V) \to \mathcal{O}_{\mathbb{P}^n}(H) \xrightarrow{r} \mathcal{O}_V(H) \to 0$$

we have an exact sequence of cohomology groups

$$H^0(\mathbb{P}^n, \mathcal{O}_{\mathbb{P}^n}(H)) \xrightarrow{r} H^0(V, \mathcal{O}_V(H)) \to H^1(\mathbb{P}^n, \mathcal{O}_{\mathbb{P}^n}(H - V)),$$

But

$$H^1(\mathbb{P}^n, \mathcal{O}_{\mathbb{P}^n}(H - V)) = H^1(\mathbb{P}^n, \mathcal{O}_{\mathbb{P}^n}((1 - d)H)) = 0$$

so r must be surjective. Note that two normal varieties $V, V' \subset \mathbb{P}^n$ will be *projectively isomorphic*—that is, V may be carried into V' by an automorphism of $\mathbb{P}^n$—if V is biholomorphic to V' via a mapping carrying $H_{V'}$ to H_V. In particular, if V and V' are smooth hypersurfaces of dimension $\geqslant 3$

and degree $d \neq n+1$ in $\mathbb{P}^n$, then by the adjunction formula

$$K_V = (K_{\mathbb{P}^n} \otimes [V])|_V = [(d-n-1)H]$$

and likewise for V'. But by the Lefschetz theorem on hyperplane sections

$$H^1(V, \mathcal{O}) \cong H^1(\mathbb{P}^n, \mathcal{O}) = 0, \qquad H^2(V, \mathcal{O}) \cong H^2(\mathbb{P}^n, \mathcal{O}) = 0$$

so from the long exact cohomology sequence associated to the exponential sheaf sequence and the Lefschetz theorem again

$$\text{Pic}(V) = H^1(V, \mathcal{O}^*) \cong H^2(V, \mathbb{Z}) \cong H^2(\mathbb{P}^n, \mathbb{Z}) = \mathbb{Z}$$

and likewise for V'. Thus if $\varphi : V \to V'$ is biholomorphic,

$$\varphi^* K_{V'} = K_V \Rightarrow \varphi^*(H|_{V'}) = H|_V,$$

so V and V' are projectively isomorphic. In conclusion

> *Two smooth hypersurfaces of dimension $\geqslant 3$ and degree* $d \neq n+1$ *in* $\mathbb{P}^n$ *are isomorphic if and only if they are projectively isomorphic; or, equivalently,*
>
> *Any automorphism of a smooth hypersurface of dimension $\geqslant 3$ and degree* $d \neq n+1$ *in* $\mathbb{P}^n$ *is induced by an automorphism of* $\mathbb{P}^n$.

This result in fact holds for surfaces V of degree $d \neq 4$ in $\mathbb{P}^3$ as well: to apply the previous argument, we need to know only that $H^2(V, \mathbb{Z})$ contains no torsion; this follows from the fact that V is simply connected (Lefschetz theorem once more), and the statement of Poincaré duality for the torsion part $H_{*, \text{tor}}$ of homology:

$$H_{i, \text{tor}}(M, \mathbb{Z}) \cong H_{\text{tor}}^{n-i-1}(M, \mathbb{Z}).$$

We may illustrate the correspondence between maps to projective space and base-point-free linear systems with a classical example: the *Veronese map* associated to the line bundle dH on $\mathbb{P}^n$. We have seen that the global sections of dH correspond to homogeneous polynomials of degree d in $Z = [Z_0, \ldots, Z_n]$, so that if $\{Z^\alpha = Z_0^{\alpha_0} \cdots Z_n^{\alpha_n}\}$ denotes the set of monomials of degree d in Z, then the Veronese map is given by

$$[Z_0, \ldots, Z_n] \mapsto [\ldots, Z^\alpha, \ldots].$$

It is easily verified that the Veronese map is a smooth embedding, with the property that every hypersurface of degree d in $\mathbb{P}^n$ becomes a hyperplane section of $\iota_{dH}(\mathbb{P}^n) \subset \mathbb{P}^N$. Here are a few cases:

1. The Veronese map

$$\iota_{nH} : \mathbb{P}^1 \to \mathbb{P}^n$$

is given, in terms of the Euclidean coordinate $t = Z_1 / Z_0$ on $\mathbb{P}^1$, by

$$t \mapsto [1, t, t^2, \ldots, t^n].$$

Its image is a nondegenerate curve of degree n, called the *rational normal curve*.

Conversely, if $C \subset \mathbb{P}^n$ is an irreducible, nondegenerate curve of degree n, let $p_1,\ldots,p_{n-1}$ be any $n-1$ independent points of C, $V = \overline{p_1,\ldots,p_{n-1}} \cong \mathbb{P}^{n-2}$ their linear span, and $\{H_\lambda\}_{\lambda \in \mathbb{P}^1}$ the pencil of hyperplanes in $\mathbb{P}^n$ containing V. Each hyperplane H_λ will then intersect C in n points: $p_1,\ldots,p_{n-1}$, and an additional point we will call $q(\lambda)$. (In case H_λ is the hyperplane containing V and tangent to C at p_i, the point $q(\lambda) = p_i$.) Every point of C will lie on a unique hyperplane H_λ, and so the map $q: \mathbb{P}^1 \to C$ is an isomorphism. Since moreover nH is the unique line bundle of degree n on $\mathbb{P}^1$, it follows that *every irreducible nondegenerate curve of degree n in $\mathbb{P}^n$ is projectively isomorphic to the rational normal curve.*

2. In terms of Euclidean coordinates $s = Z_1/Z_0$, $t = Z_2/Z_0$ on $\mathbb{P}^2$, the Veronese map $f = \iota_{2H}: \mathbb{P}^2 \to \mathbb{P}^5$ is given by

$$(s,t) \mapsto [1, s, t, s^2, st, t^2].$$

The image $S = f(\mathbb{P}^2)$ is a nondegenerate surface of degree $c_1(f^*H_{\mathbb{P}^5})^2 = c_1(2H_{\mathbb{P}^2})^2 = 4$; note that this degree is minimal in the sense of the last section.

We digress for a moment to discuss a curious feature of the Veronese surface $S \subset \mathbb{P}^5$: *it is the unique nondegenerate surface in $\mathbb{P}^5$ whose variety of chords* $C(S) = \cup_{p,q \in S} \overline{pq}$ *is a proper subvariety of $\mathbb{P}^5$.* To see this, note that for any point $p \in \mathbb{P}^5$ lying on the chord $\overline{f(u), f(u')}$ of S, the line $L = \overline{uu'} \subset \mathbb{P}^2$ is mapped into a curve of degree

$$^\#(H_{\mathbb{P}^5} \cdot f(L)) = {}^\#(2H_{\mathbb{P}^2} \cdot L) = 2$$

$\mathbb{P}^5$, hence by the result of p. 173 is a conic lying in a 2-plane $V_2 \subset \mathbb{P}^5$. Now $p \in \overline{f(u), f(u')} \subset V_2$, and any line through p in V_2 must intersect $f(L)$ twice, so that *any point of $\mathbb{P}^5$ lying on a chord of S lies on infinitely many chords of S.* In particular, if we let L_0 be the line $(s=0)$ in $\mathbb{P}^2$, and let $u_0 = L_0 \cap L$, then the line $\overline{f(u_0), p} \subset \mathbb{P}^5$ is a chord of S. Thus

$$C(S) = \bigcup_{\substack{p \in L_0 \\ q \in \mathbb{P}^2}} \overline{f(p), f(q)},$$

from which we see that $C(S)$ is of dimension at most four. Explicitly, we describe $C(S)$ as the locus

$$\{\alpha \cdot f(s,t) + (1-\alpha) \cdot f(0,t')\} = \{[1, \alpha s, \alpha t + (1-\alpha)t', \alpha s^2, \alpha st, \alpha t^2 + (1-\alpha)t'^2]\}.$$

Now we solve for α, s, t, and t': given $X = [X_0,\ldots,X_5] \in C(S)$, X must be the point $\alpha \cdot f(s,t) + (1-\alpha) \cdot f(0,t')$ for the values

$$s = X_3/X_1, \quad t = X_4/X_1, \quad \alpha = X_1^2/X_0X_3,$$
$$t' = (X_2X_3 - X_1X_4)/(X_0X_3 - X_1^2).$$

Consequently the coordinates of $X \in C(S)$ must satisfy

$$X_5/X_0 = \alpha t^2 + (1-\alpha)t'^2$$
$$= X_4^2/X_0X_3 + (X_2X_3 - X_1X_4)^2/(X_0X_3(X_0X_3 - X_1^2)),$$

i.e.,

$$(X_0X_3 - X_1^2)X_5 = X_0X_4^2 + X_2^2X_3 - 2X_1X_2X_4,$$

and we see that the variety of chords of the Veronese surface in $\mathbb{P}^5$ is a cubic hypersurface.

We may state the original question of this section as: Given $L \to M$ a holomorphic line bundle, when is $\iota_L : M \to \mathbb{P}^N$ an embedding? First, in order for ι_L to be well-defined the linear system $|L|$ cannot have any base points, i.e., for each $x \in M$ the restriction map

$$H^0(M, \mathcal{O}(L)) \overset{r_x}{\longrightarrow} L_x$$

must be surjective. Granted this, ι_L will be an embedding if

1. ι_L *is one-to-one.* Clearly this is the case if and only if for all x and y in M, there exists a section $s \in H^0(M, \mathcal{O}(L))$ vanishing at x but not at y, i.e., if and only if the restriction map

$$(*) \qquad\qquad H^0(M, \mathcal{O}(L)) \overset{r_{x,y}}{\longrightarrow} L_x \otimes L_y$$

is surjective for all $x \neq y \in M$. Note that if L satisfies this condition, then $|L|$ must be base-point-free.

2. ι_L *has nonzero differential everywhere.* If φ_α is a trivialization of L near x, then this is the case if and only if for all $v^* \in T_x^*(M)$, there exists $s \in H^0(M, \mathcal{O}(L))$ with $s_\alpha(x)=0$ and $ds_\alpha(x)=v^*$ where $s_\alpha = \varphi_\alpha^* s$. We can express this requirement more intrinsically as follows: let $\mathcal{I}_x \subset \mathcal{O}$ denote the sheaf of holomorphic functions on M vanishing at x, and let $\mathcal{I}_x(L)$ be the sheaf of sections of L vanishing at x. If s is any section of $\mathcal{I}_x(L)$ defined near x, and $\varphi_\alpha, \varphi_\beta$ are trivializations of L in a neighborhood U of x, then writing $s_\alpha = \varphi_\alpha^* s$, $s_\beta = \varphi_\beta^* s$, $s_\alpha = g_{\alpha\beta}s_\beta$, we have

$$d(s_\alpha) = d(s_\beta) \cdot g_{\alpha\beta} + dg_{\alpha\beta} \cdot s_\beta$$
$$= d(s_\beta) \cdot g_{\alpha\beta} \qquad \text{at } x.$$

Thus we have a well-defined sheaf map

$$d_x : \mathcal{I}_x(L) \to T_x^{*\prime} \otimes L_x$$

and condition 2 can be stated as requiring that the map

$$(**) \qquad\qquad H^0(M, \mathcal{I}_x(L)) \overset{d_x}{\longrightarrow} T_x^{*\prime} \otimes L_x$$

be surjective for all $x \in M$. Note that $(**)$ is the limiting case of $(*)$ when $y \to x$.

The result we are aiming for is the

Kodaira Embedding Theorem. *Let* M *be a compact complex manifold and* L→M *a positive line bundle. Then there exists* k_0 *such that for* $k \geqslant k_0$, *the map*

$$\iota_{L^k}: M \to \mathbb{P}^N$$

is well-defined and is an embedding of M.

Let us consider how one might go about proving this. The first thing to do is to fit the maps (∗) and (∗∗) into exact sequences and try to use our vanishing theorems directly. To this end, let $\mathcal{I}_{x,y}(L)$ denote the sheaf of sections of L vanishing at x and y, and $\mathcal{I}_x^2(L)$ the sheaf of sections of L vanishing to order 2 at x, i.e., sections s of $\mathcal{I}_x(L)$ such that $d_x(s)=0$. We have exact sheaf sequences

$$0 \to \mathcal{I}_{x,y}(L) \to \mathcal{O}(L) \xrightarrow{r_{x,y}} L_x \oplus L_y \to 0$$

and

$$0 \to \mathcal{I}_x^2(L) \to \mathcal{I}_x(L) \xrightarrow{d_x} T_x^{*\prime} \otimes L_x \to 0;$$

so that to show that the maps (∗) and (∗∗) are surjective, it would suffice to prove that

$$H^1(M, \mathcal{I}_x^2(L)) = H^1(M, \mathcal{I}_{x,y}(L)) = 0;$$

indeed, replacing L by L^k and using $H^1(M, \mathcal{O}(L^k))=0$ for $k \geqslant k_1$, the reader may check that our theorem is equivalent to this vanishing theorem for high powers of L. The problem is that unless M is of dimension 1 neither of the sheaves $\mathcal{I}_{x,y}(L)$ and $\mathcal{I}_x^2(L)$ is the sheaf of sections of a holomorphic vector bundle—for $E \to M$ a holomorphic vector bundle and $V \subset M$ a subvariety, the kernel of the restriction map $\mathcal{O}_M(E) \to \mathcal{O}_V(E)$ is the sheaf of sections of a vector bundle if and only if V is of codimension 1 in M—and so we cannot get a direct grip on them using our technique of harmonic theory. $\mathcal{I}_x^2$ and $\mathcal{I}_{x,y}$ are examples of *coherent sheaves*, a class of sheaves broader than, but closely related to, sheaves of sections of holomorphic vector bundles. The theory of coherent sheaves will be discussed in Chapter 5.

Another approach to the problem might be to emulate the proof of the proposition on p. 161 and do an induction on the dimension of M—for example, if we could find a smooth hypersurface $V \subset M$ containing x and y, then to show the map (∗) surjective, we would only have to prove it for $L|_V$ on V and show that the restriction map

$$H^0(M, \mathcal{O}_M(L)) \to H^0(V, \mathcal{O}_V(L))$$

was surjective, i.e., that

$$H^1(M, \mathcal{O}_M(L - V)) = 0.$$

But this is very nearly presupposing the result to be proved: a priori, M need not have any divisors on it at all.

It is clear by now that our difficulty lies in the simple fact that, unless M is a Riemann surface, a point on M is not a divisor. We can overcome this problem by means of a beautiful classical construction called *blowing up*, which transforms points on a complex manifold into divisors.

Blowing Up

We will first describe the blow-up of the origin in a disc Δ in $\mathbb{C}^n$. Let $z = (z_1, \ldots, z_n)$ be Euclidean coordinates in Δ and $l = [l_1, \ldots, l_n]$ corresponding homogeneous coordinates on $\mathbb{P}^{n-1}$. Let $\tilde{\Delta} \subset \Delta \times \mathbb{P}^{n-1}$ be the submanifold of $\Delta \times \mathbb{P}^{n-1}$ given by the quadratic relations

$$\tilde{\Delta} = \{(z, l) : z_i l_j = z_j l_i \qquad \text{for all } i, j\}.$$

If we consider points $l \in \mathbb{P}^{n-1}$ as lines in $\mathbb{C}^n$, then writing these equations as $z \wedge l = 0$ we see that this is just the *incidence correspondence* defined as $\{(z, l) : z \in l\}$.

Now $\tilde{\Delta}$ maps onto Δ via projection on the first factor $\pi : (z, l) \mapsto z$; from the geometric interpretation it follows that the map is an isomorphism away from the origin in Δ, and $\pi^{-1}(0)$ is just the projective space of lines in Δ. In effect, $\tilde{\Delta}$ *consists of all the lines through the origin in Δ made disjoint*. $\tilde{\Delta}$, together with its projection map π to Δ, is called the *blow-up* of Δ at 0. The real points of the blow-up of $\Delta \subset \mathbb{C}^2$ are pictured in Figure 1.

Note that we have encountered the manifold $\tilde{\Delta}$ before: together with the projection $\pi' : \tilde{\Delta} \to \mathbb{P}^{n-1}$ on the second factor it is the universal bundle J on $\mathbb{P}^{n-1}$.

Now let M be a complex manifold of dimension n, $x \in M$ any point, and $z : U \to \Delta$ a coordinate polydisc centered around $x \in M$. The restriction of the projection map

$$\pi : \tilde{\Delta} - E \longrightarrow U - \{x\} \subset M$$

gives an isomorphism between a neighborhood of $E = \pi^{-1}x$ in $\tilde{\Delta}$ and a neighborhood of x in M; we define the *blow-up* $\tilde{M}_x$ *of M at* x to be the complex manifold

$$\tilde{M}_x = M - \{x\} \cup_\pi \tilde{\Delta}$$

obtained by replacing $\Delta \subset M$ with $\tilde{\Delta}$, together with the natural projection map $\pi : \tilde{M}_x \to M$. Again, the projection $\pi : \tilde{M}_x - \{\pi^{-1}(x)\} \to M - \{x\}$ is an isomorphism; the inverse image $\pi^{-1}(x)$ in $\tilde{M}_x$ is called the *exceptional divisor* of the blow-up, and is usually denoted E or E_x.

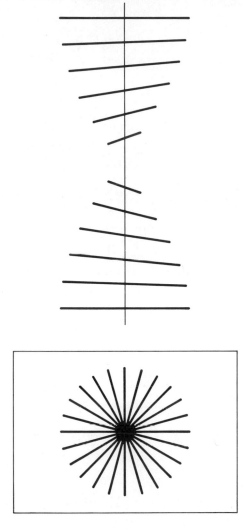

Figure 1

Note that the blow-up $\tilde{M} \to M$ is independent of the coordinates used in the disc Δ: if $\{z_i' = f_i(z)\}$ are other coordinates in Δ with $f_i(0) = 0$, $\tilde{\Delta}'$ the blow up of Δ in terms of these coordinates, then the isomorphism

$$f: \tilde{\Delta} - E \to \tilde{\Delta}' - E'$$

may be extended over E by setting $f(0, l) = (0, l')$, where

$$l_j' = \sum \frac{\partial f_j}{\partial z_i}(0) \cdot l_i.$$

Indeed, we see from this that the identification

$$E \longrightarrow \mathbb{P}(T_x(M))$$

given by

$$(0,l) \mapsto \left[\sum l_i \cdot \frac{\partial}{\partial z_i} \right]$$

is likewise independent of the coordinate system chosen.

Now we will describe the geometry of $\tilde{M}_x$ near E in more detail. First, we give local coordinates near E on $\tilde{M}_x$: let $z = (z_1, \ldots, z_n)$ be local coordinates on $U \ni x$ with center x. Then

$$\tilde{U} = \pi^{-1}(U) = \{(z,l) \in U \times \mathbb{P}^{n-1}: z_i l_j = z_j l_i\};$$

and we set

$$\tilde{U}_i = (l_i \neq 0) \subset \tilde{U}.$$

In this way we obtain an open cover of the neighborhood $\tilde{U}$ of E, and in each open set $\tilde{U}_i$ we have local coordinates $z(i)_j$:

$$z(i)_j = \frac{l_j}{l_i} = \frac{z_j}{z_i}, \quad j \neq i,$$

and

$$z(i)_i = z_i.$$

The map $\pi: \tilde{M}_x \to M$ is given in $\tilde{U}_i$ by

$$(z(i)_1, \ldots, z(i)_i, \ldots, z(i)_n)) \mapsto / (z((i)_i \cdot z(i)_1, \ldots, z(i)_i, \ldots, z(i)_i \cdot z(i)_n)$$

and the divisor E is given by

$$E = (\tilde{z}(i)_i = 0)$$

in $\tilde{U}_i$. In $\tilde{U}_i \cap \tilde{U}_j$,

$$z(i)_k = z(j)_i^{-1} \cdot z(j)_k,$$
$$z(i)_j = z(j)_j^{-1},$$
$$z_i = z(j)_i \cdot z_j.$$

Now, since $E = (z_i)$ in $\tilde{U}_i$, the line bundle $[E]$ is given in $\tilde{U}$ by transition functions

$$g_{ij} = z(j)_i = \frac{z_i}{z_j} = \frac{l_i}{l_j}, \text{ in } U_i \cap U_j$$

and so we can realize $[E]|_{\tilde{U}}$ by identifying the fiber

$$(*) \qquad\qquad [E]_{(z,l)} = \{\lambda(l_1, \ldots, l_n), \lambda \in \mathbb{C}\}.$$

In particular, we see that *the line bundle* $[E]|_E$ *is just the universal bundle* $J = -H$ *on* $E \cong \mathbb{P}^{n-1}$.

Dually, the line bundle $[-E] = [E]^*$ has as fiber over any point $(z, l) \in \tilde{U}$ the space of linear functionals on the line $l \subset \mathbb{C}^n$; $[-E]|_E$ is the hyperplane bundle on E.

Now we have seen that E is naturally identified with $\mathbb{P}(T_x'(M))$, so that the global sections of $[-E]$ over E correspond exactly to the linear functionals on the tangent space, i.e.,

$$(**) \qquad H^0(E, \mathcal{O}_E(-E)) = T_x^{*\prime}(M).$$

On the other hand, given a function f on U vanishing at x, the function $\pi^* f \in \mathcal{O}(\tilde{U})$ vanishes along E and so can be considered as a section of $[-E]$ over $\tilde{U}$. By explicit computation we check that for any $f \in \mathcal{I}_x(U)$ *the restriction to* E *of the section* $\pi^* f \in \mathcal{O}(-E)(\tilde{U})$ *corresponds, via the identification* $(**)$, *to the differential* $df(x)$ *of* f *at* x, i.e., the diagram

$$
\begin{array}{ccc}
H^0(\tilde{U}, \mathcal{O}(-E)) & \xrightarrow{\ r_E\ } & H^0(E, \mathcal{O}(-E)) \\
\uparrow & & \| \\
H^0(U, \mathcal{I}_x) & \xrightarrow{\ d_x\ } & T_x^{*\prime}(U)
\end{array}
$$

commutes.

This correspondence reflects a basic aspect of the local analytic character of blow-ups: the infinitesimal behavior of functions, maps, or differential forms at the point x of M is transformed into global phenomena on $\tilde{M}$. Indeed, in classical terminology, a point in the exceptional divisor of the blow-up of M at x was called an "infinitely near point" of x; the exceptional divisor itself was called an "infinitesimal neighborhood" of x.

The next thing to do is to compute the curvature of the line bundles $[E]$ and $[-E]$ on $\tilde{M}$. We construct a metric on $[E]$ as follows: let h_1 be the metric on $[E]|_{\tilde{U}}$ given, in terms of the representation $(*)$ of E, by

$$|(l_1, \ldots, l_n)|^2 = \|l\|^2.$$

Let $\sigma \in H^0(\tilde{M}, \mathcal{O}([E]))$ be the above global section of $[E]$ on $\tilde{M}$ with $(\sigma) = E$, so that σ is nonzero on $\tilde{M} - E$; let h_2 be the metric on $[E]|_{\tilde{M}-E}$ given by

$$|\sigma(z)| \equiv 1.$$

For $\varepsilon > 0$, denote by U_ε the ball $(\|z\| < \varepsilon)$ around x in U and set $\tilde{U}_\varepsilon = \pi^{-1}(U_\varepsilon)$; let ρ_1, ρ_2 be a partition of unity for the cover $\{\tilde{U}_{2\varepsilon}, \tilde{M} - \tilde{U}_\varepsilon\}$ of $\tilde{M}$, and let h be the global metric given by

$$h = \rho_1 \cdot h_1 + \rho_2 \cdot h_2.$$

We will compute the curvature of $[E]$ with this metric. For notational convenience, let $\Omega_{[E]}$ denote $\sqrt{-1}/2$ times the curvature $\Theta_{[E]}$ of $[E]$. It is necessary to consider three cases:

1.　On $\tilde{M} - \tilde{U}_{2\varepsilon}$, $\rho_2 \equiv 1$ so $|\sigma|^2 \equiv 1$; consequently

$$\Omega_{[E]} = dd^c \log \frac{1}{|\sigma|^2} \equiv 0.$$

2.　On $\tilde{U}_\varepsilon - E \cong U_\varepsilon - \{x\}$, let σ be given in terms of the representation (∗) by

$$\sigma(z,l) = z;$$

then

$$\Omega_{[E]} = dd^c \log \frac{1}{\|z\|^2} = -dd^c \log \|z\|^2,$$

i.e., $-\Omega_{[E]}$ is just the pullback $\pi'^*\omega$ of the associated $(1,1)$-form ω of the Fubini-Study metric on $\mathbb{P}^{n-1}$ under the map $\pi': \tilde{U}_\varepsilon \to \mathbb{P}^{n-1}$ given by $(z,l) \mapsto l$. Thus

$$-\Omega_{[E]} \geq 0 \qquad \text{on } \tilde{U}_\varepsilon - E.$$

3.　We have seen that $-\Omega_{[E]} = \pi'^*\omega$ on $\tilde{U}_\varepsilon - E$; by continuity it follows that $-\Omega_{[E]} = \pi'^*\omega$ throughout $\tilde{U}_\varepsilon$, and in particular

$$-\Omega_{[E]}|_E = \omega > 0$$

on E.

Summing up, if we let $\Omega_{[-E]}$ be $\sqrt{-1}/2$ times the curvature form of the dual metric in $[E]^* = [-E]$, we have

$$\Omega_{[-E]} = -\Omega_{[E]} = \begin{cases} 0 & \text{on } \tilde{M} - \tilde{U}_{2\varepsilon}, \\ \geq 0 & \text{on } \tilde{U}_\varepsilon, \\ > 0 & \text{on } T'_x(E) \subset T'_x(\tilde{M}) \quad \text{for all } x \in E. \end{cases}$$

The point of this computation is the following: let $L \to M$ be a positive line bundle with a metric h_L whose curvature form Θ_L is $2/\sqrt{-1}$ times a positive form Ω_L. Then if Ω_{π^*L} is $\sqrt{-1}/2$ times the curvature form of the induced metric on the bundle $\pi^*L \to \tilde{M}$,

$$\Omega_{\pi^*L} = \pi^*\Omega_L,$$

hence $\Omega_{\pi^*L} > 0$ on $\tilde{M} - E$. Moreover, for any $x \in E$ and tangent vector $v \in T_x(\tilde{M})$,

$$\langle \Omega_{\pi^*L}; v, \bar{v} \rangle = \langle \Omega_L; \pi_*v, \overline{\pi_*v} \rangle \geq 0$$

with equality holding if and only if $\pi_*(v) = 0$, i.e., if and only if v is tangent to E. Thus

$$\Omega_{\pi^*L} = \begin{cases} \geqslant 0 & \text{everywhere,} \\ > 0 & \text{on } \tilde{M} - E, \\ > 0 & \text{on } T'_x(\tilde{M})/T'_x(E) \quad \text{for all } x \in E, \end{cases}$$

and the form

$$\Omega_{\pi^*L^k \otimes [-E]} = \Omega_{\pi^*L^k} + \Omega_{[-E]}$$
$$= k\Omega_{\pi^*L} + \Omega_{[-E]}$$

is positive everywhere in $\tilde{U}_\varepsilon$ and $\tilde{M} - \tilde{U}_{2\varepsilon}$. Moreover, since the form $\Omega_{[-E]}$ is bounded below in $\tilde{U}_{2\varepsilon} - \tilde{U}_\varepsilon$ and Ω_{π^*L} is strictly positive there, we see that $\Omega_{\pi^*L^k \otimes [-E]}$ is everywhere positive for k sufficiently large; i.e., *there exists k_0 such that $\pi^*L^k - E$ is a positive line bundle on $\tilde{M}$ for* $k \geqslant k_0$.

Note that by the same argument, for any positive integer n the bundle $\pi^*L^k - nE$ will be positive for $k \gg 0$.

We need to establish one more relation between $\tilde{M}_x$ and M:

Lemma. $K_{\tilde{M}} = \pi^*K_M + (n-1)E.$

Proof.   This is easy in case M has a nontrivial meromorphic n-form ω. In terms of local coordinates $z_1, \ldots, z_n$ in a neighborhood U of x, write

$$\omega(z) = \frac{f(z)}{g(z)} \cdot dz_1 \wedge \cdots \wedge dz_n.$$

Now let $z(i)_j$ be local coordinates in as before. The map π is given in $\tilde{U}_i$ by

$$(z(i)_1, \ldots, z(i)_n) \to (z(i)_1 z_i, \ldots, z_i, \ldots, z(i)_n z_i),$$

and so

$$\pi^*\omega = \pi^*(f/g) \cdot d(z(i)_1 z_i) \wedge \cdots \wedge dz_i \wedge \cdots \wedge d(z(i)_n z_i)$$
$$= \pi^*(f/g) \cdot z_i^{(n-1)} dz(i)_1 \wedge \cdots \wedge dz(i)_n.$$

Thus we see that in a neighborhood of $E = \pi^{-1}(x_0)$, the divisor $(\pi^*\omega)$ is given by $\pi^*(\omega) + (n-1)E$. Since clearly $(\pi^*\omega) = \pi^*(\omega)$ away from E,

$$K_{\tilde{M}} = [(\pi^*\omega)] = \pi^*K_M + (n-1)E$$

as desired. Thus the formula is proved under the assumption that M has a meromorphic n-form; this is the easiest way to see the result.

To prove the lemma in general, we let $\underline{U} = \{U_0, U_\alpha\}_\alpha$ be an open coordinate cover of M with $x \in U_0$, $x \notin U_\alpha$ and all sets U_α having non-empty intersection with U_0 lying in one coordinate patch with coordinates $z_1, \ldots, z_n$. Let

$$\underline{\tilde{U}} = \left\{ \tilde{U}_\alpha = \pi^{-1}U_\alpha, \ \tilde{U}_i = \pi^{-1}U_0 \cap (l_i \neq 0) \right\}$$

be a corresponding cover for $\tilde{M}$; we compute the transition functions $\{g_{ij}, g_{i\alpha}, g_{\alpha\beta}\}$ for $K_{\tilde{M}}$ in terms of the coordinates $z(i)_j$ on $\tilde{U}_i$ and $w_{i,\alpha} = \pi^* w_{i,\alpha}$ on $\tilde{U}_\alpha$, where $\{w_{i,\alpha}\}_i$ are coordinates on U_α in M. First we have in $\tilde{U}_1 \cap \tilde{U}_2$

$$z(2)_1 = z(1)_2^{-1},$$
$$z_2 = z(1)_2 \cdot z_1,$$
$$z(2)_i = z(1)_i \cdot z(1)_2^{-1}, \qquad i \neq 1, 2,$$

and so the Jacobian matrix for the change of coordinates is

$$J_{12} = \begin{bmatrix} 0 & -z(1)_2^{-2} & 0 & \cdots & & 0 \\ z(1)_2 & z_1 & 0 & \cdots & & 0 \\ 0 & & & & & \\ \vdots & & & & & \\ 0 & -z(1)_j \cdot z(1)_2^{-2} & 0 & \cdots & 0 \; z(1)_2^{-1} \; 0 & \cdots & 0 \\ \vdots & & & & & \end{bmatrix};$$

in general

$$g_{ij} = \det J_{ij} = z(1)_j^{-n+1}.$$

Similarly, in $\tilde{U}_\alpha \cap \tilde{U}_1$

$$w_{1,\alpha} = z_1, \qquad w_{i,\alpha} = z_1 \cdot z(1)_i,$$

$$J_{1\alpha} = \begin{bmatrix} 1 & 0 & \cdots & 0 & \cdots & 0 \\ \vdots & & & & & \\ z(1)_i & 0 & \cdots & z_1 & \cdots & 0 \\ \vdots & & & & & \end{bmatrix},$$

and in general

$$g_{i\alpha} = z_i^{(n-1)}.$$

Also

$$g_{\alpha\beta} = \pi^* g'_{\alpha\beta},$$

where $g'_{\alpha\beta}$ are the transition functions for K_M with respect to coordinates $w_{i,\alpha}$ in U_α, $w_{i,\beta}$ in U_β.

Now E is given in $\tilde{U}_i$ by (z_i), in $\tilde{U}_\alpha$ by (1); so the transition functions for $[E]$ over $\tilde{U}$ are

$$h_{ij} = \frac{z_i}{z_j} = z(i)_j^{-1},$$
$$h_{i\alpha} = z_i,$$
$$h_{\alpha\beta} = 1.$$

Thus the transition functions for the bundle $K_{\tilde{M}} \otimes [E]^{-n+1}$ are

$$f_{ij} = z(i)_j^{-n+1} \cdot z(i)_j^{n-1} = 1,$$
$$f_{i\alpha} = {}_i z_i^{n-1} \cdot {}_i z_i^{-n+1} = 1,$$
$$f_{\alpha\beta} = \pi^* g_{\alpha\beta},$$

and we see that $K_{\tilde{M}} - (n-1)E$ is just the pullback via π of the bundle on M given by transition functions

$$e_{0\alpha} = 1, \qquad e_{\alpha\beta} = g_{\alpha\beta};$$

i.e., $K_{\tilde{M}} - (n-1)E = \pi^* K_M$. Q.E.D.

We will develop a much more complete picture of the geometry of blow-ups later on in the chapter on surfaces; for the time being, we have enough information to proceed to the proof of the embedding theorem.

Proof of the Kodaira Theorem

Again, let $L \to M$ be a positive line bundle on the compact complex manifold M. We want to prove that there exists k_0 such that

1. The restriction map

$$H^0(M, \mathcal{O}(L^k)) \overset{r_{x,y}}{\to} L_x^k \oplus L_y^k$$

is surjective for all $x \neq y \in M$, $k \geqslant k_0$; and
2. The differential map

$$H^0(M, \mathcal{I}_x(L^k)) \overset{d_x}{\to} T_x^{*\prime} \otimes L_x^k$$

is surjective for all $x \in M$, $k \geqslant k_0$.

To prove assertion 1, let $\tilde{M} \overset{\pi}{\to} M$ denote the blow-up of M at both x and y, $E_x = \pi^{-1}(x)$ and $E_y = \pi^{-1}(y)$ the exceptional divisors of the blow-up; for notational convenience, let E denote the divisor $E_x + E_y$ and $\tilde{L} = \pi^* L$. (Here we are tacitly assuming that $n = \dim(M) \geqslant 2$; in case M is a Riemann surface, all the arguments that follow will be valid for $\tilde{M} = M$, $\pi = id$.)

Consider the pullback map on sections

$$\pi^*: H^0(M, \mathcal{O}_M(L^k)) \to H^0(\tilde{M}, \mathcal{O}_{\tilde{M}}(\tilde{L}^k)).$$

For any global section $\tilde{\sigma}$ of $\tilde{L}^k$, the section of L^k given by σ over $M - \{x,y\}$ extends by Hartogs' theorem to a global section $\sigma \in H^0(M, \mathcal{O}(L^k))$, and so we see that π^* is an isomorphism. Furthermore, by definition $\tilde{L}^k$ is trivial along E_x and E_y, i.e.,

$$(\tilde{L}^k)|_{E_x} = E_x \times L_x^k, \quad (\tilde{L}^k)|_{E_y} = E_y \times L_y^k,$$

so that

$$H^0(E, \mathcal{O}_E(\tilde{L}^k)) \cong L_x^k \oplus L_y^k,$$

and if r_E denotes the restriction map to E, the diagram

$$H^0(\tilde{M}, \mathcal{O}_{\tilde{M}}(\tilde{L}^k)) \xrightarrow{r_E} H^0(E, \mathcal{O}_E(\tilde{L}^k))$$
$$\uparrow \qquad\qquad \|$$
$$H^0(M, \mathcal{O}(L^k)) \xrightarrow{r_{x,y}} L_x^k \oplus L_y^k$$

commutes. Thus to prove assertion 1 for x and y, we have to show the map r_E is surjective.

Now, on $\tilde{M}$ we have the exact sheaf sequence

$$0 \to \mathcal{O}_{\tilde{M}}(\tilde{L}^k - E) \to \mathcal{O}_{\tilde{M}}(\tilde{L}^k) \xrightarrow{r_E} \mathcal{O}_E(\tilde{L}^k) \to 0.$$

Choose k_1 such that $L^{k_1} + K_M^*$ is positive on M. By virtue of the computation on p. 186, we can choose k_2 such that $\tilde{L}^k - nE$ is positive on $\tilde{M}$ for $k \geqslant k_2$. By the previous lemma

$$K_{\tilde{M}} = \tilde{K}_M + (n-1)E,$$

where $\tilde{K}_M = \pi^* K_M$; and so for $k \geqslant k_0 = k_1 + k_2$,

$$\mathcal{O}_{\tilde{M}}(\tilde{L}^k - E) = \Omega_{\tilde{M}}^n(\tilde{L}^k - E + K_{\tilde{M}}^*)$$
$$= \Omega_{\tilde{M}}^n((\tilde{L}^{k_1} + \tilde{K}_M^*) \otimes (\tilde{L}^{k'} - nE))$$

with $k' \geqslant k_2$. Now by hypothesis, $\tilde{L}^{k'} - nE$ has a positive definite curvature form on $\tilde{M}$; $L^{k_1} + K_M^*$ has a positive curvature form on M, and so $(\tilde{L}^{k_1} + \tilde{K}_M^*)$ has a positive semidefinite one on $\tilde{M}$. Thus the line bundle $(\tilde{L}^{k_1} + \tilde{K}_M^*) + \tilde{L}^{k'} - nE$ is positive on $\tilde{M}$, and by the Kodaira vanishing theorem,

$$H^1(\tilde{M}, \mathcal{O}_{\tilde{M}}(\tilde{L}^k - E)) = H^1(\tilde{M}, \Omega_{\tilde{M}}^n((\tilde{L}^{k_1} + \tilde{K}_M^*) + (\tilde{L}^{k'} - nE)))$$
$$= 0 \qquad \text{for } k \geqslant k_0.$$

Hence the map

$$r_E: H^0(\tilde{M}, \mathcal{O}_{\tilde{M}}(\tilde{L}^k)) \to H^0(E, \mathcal{O}_E(\pi^* L^k))$$

is surjective for $k \geqslant k_0$, and so assertion 1 is proved for x and y.

Assertion 2 is proved similarly. Let $\tilde{M} \xrightarrow{\pi} M$ now denote the blow-up of M at x, $E = \pi^{-1}(x)$ the exceptional divisor. Again, the pullback map

$$\pi^*: H^0(M, \mathcal{O}_M(L^k)) \to H^0(\tilde{M}, \mathcal{O}_{\tilde{M}}(\tilde{L}^k))$$

is an isomorphism. Further, if $\sigma \in H^0(M, \mathcal{O}_M(L^k))$, then $\sigma(x) = 0$ if and only if $\tilde{\sigma} = \pi^* \sigma$ vanishes on E; thus π^* restricts to give an isomorphism

$$\pi^*: H^0(M, \mathcal{I}_x(L^k)) \to H^0(\tilde{M}, \mathcal{O}_{\tilde{M}}(\tilde{L}^k - E)).$$

As before, we can identify

$$H^0(E, \mathcal{O}_E(\tilde{L}^k - E)) = L_x^k \otimes H^0(E, \mathcal{O}_E(-E)) \cong L_x^k \otimes T_x^{*\prime},$$

and the diagram

$$H^0(\tilde{M}, \mathcal{O}_{\tilde{M}}(\tilde{L}^k - E)) \xrightarrow{r_E} H^0(E, \mathcal{O}_E(\tilde{L}^k - E))$$

$$\Vert \uparrow_{\pi^*} \qquad \qquad \Vert$$

$$H^0(M, \mathcal{I}_x(L^k)) \xrightarrow{d_x} T_x^{*\prime} \otimes L_x^k$$

commutes. Thus we must prove that r_E is surjective for $k \gg 0$.

On $\tilde{M}$, there is an exact sequence

$$O \rightarrow \mathcal{O}_{\tilde{M}}(\tilde{L}^k - 2E) \rightarrow \mathcal{O}_{\tilde{M}}(\tilde{L}^k - E) \xrightarrow{r_E} \mathcal{O}_E(\tilde{L}^k - E) \rightarrow 0.$$

Again, choose k_1 such that $L^{k_1} + K_M^*$ is positive on M and k_2 such that $\tilde{L}^{k'} - (n+1)E$ is positive on $\tilde{M}$ for $k' \geq k_2$. For $k \geq k_0 = k_1 + k_2$

$$\mathcal{O}_{\tilde{M}}(\tilde{L}^k - 2E) = \Omega_{\tilde{M}}^n((\tilde{L}^{k_1} + \tilde{K}_M^*) \otimes (\tilde{L}^{k'} - (n+1)E))$$

with $k' \geq k_2$. It follows by the Kodaira vanishing theorem that

$$H^1(\tilde{M}, \mathcal{O}_{\tilde{M}}(\tilde{L}^k - 2E)) = 0$$

for $k \geq k_0$; hence r_E is surjective on global sections and assertion 2 is proved for arbitrary fixed x.

All that remains now to be proved is that we can find one value of k_0 such that assertions 1 and 2 hold for all choices of x and y and all $k \geq k_0$. But clearly if ι_{L^k} is defined at x and y and $\iota_{L^k}(x) \neq \iota_{L^k}(y)$, the same will be true for x' near x and y' near y, and likewise if ι_{L^k} is smooth at x it will be smooth at x' near x and separate points $x' \neq x''$ near x. Since M is compact, then, the result follows. Q.E.D.

Before proceeding to some examples and corollaries, we give a somewhat more intrinsic restatement of the theorem:

Kodaira Embedding Theorem. *A compact complex manifold M is an algebraic variety—i.e., is embeddable in projective space—if and only if it has a closed, positive $(1, 1)$-form ω whose cohomology class $[\omega]$ is rational.*

Proof. If $[\omega] \in H^2(M, \mathbb{Q})$, then for some k, $[k\omega] \in H^2(M, \mathbb{Z})$; in the exact sequence

$$H^1(M, \mathcal{O}^*) \rightarrow H^2(M, \mathbb{Z}) \xrightarrow{\iota_*} H^2(M, \mathcal{O})$$

$\iota_*([k\omega]) = 0$, and so there exists a holomorphic line bundle $L \rightarrow M$ with $c_1(L) = [k\omega]$. The line bundle L will then be positive. Q.E.D.

A metric whose $(1, 1)$-form is rational is called a *Hodge metric*.

Corollary. *If M, M' are algebraic varieties, then M × M' is.*

Proof. If ω, ω' are closed, integral, positive $(1,1)$-forms on M, M', respectively, and $\pi : M \times M' \to M$, $\pi' : M \times M' \to M'$ are the projection maps, then $\pi^*\omega + \pi'^*\omega'$ is again closed, integral, and positive of type $(1,1)$.   Q.E.D.

A classical example of this is the *Segré map* $\mathbb{P}^n \times \mathbb{P}^m \to \mathbb{P}^N$ given by the complete linear system of the line bundle $\pi_1^* H \otimes \pi_2^* H$ on $\mathbb{P}^n \times \mathbb{P}^m$. For example, the Segré map $\mathbb{P}^1 \times \mathbb{P}^1 \to \mathbb{P}^3$ is given, in terms of homogeneous coordinates $[z_0, z_1]$ and $[w_0, w_1]$ on $\mathbb{P}^1$, by

$$([z_0, z_1], [w_0, w_1]) \to [z_0 w_0, z_0 w_1, z_1 w_0, z_1 w_1].$$

The image is just the quadric hypersurface $(X_0 X_3 = X_1 X_2)$ in $\mathbb{P}^3$.

Corollary. *If M is an algebraic variety, $\tilde{M} \overset{\pi}{\to} M$ the blow-up of M at a point x, then $\tilde{M}$ is algebraic.*

Proof. We have seen in the course of the proof of the embedding theorem that if $L \to M$ is positive and $E = \pi^{-1}(x)$, then $\pi^* L^k - E$ is positive for $k \gg 0$.

Corollary. *If $\tilde{M} \overset{\pi}{\to} M$ is a finite unbranched covering of compact complex manifolds, then M is algebraic if and only if $\tilde{M}$ is.*

Proof. Clearly, if $L \to M$ is positive, then $c_1(\pi^* L) = \pi^* c_1(L)$ implies that $\pi^* L$ is positive. Conversely, say ω is an integral, positive $(1,1)$-form on $\tilde{M}$. For any $p \in M$, we have isomorphisms of a neighborhood U of p in M with neighborhoods U_i of the points $q_i \in \pi^{-1}(p)$; we can define a $(1,1)$-form ω' on M by

$$\omega'(p) = \sum_{q \in \pi^{-1}(p)} \omega(q).$$

Then ω' is closed and of type $(1,1)$, and if $\eta \in H_{DR}^{2n-2}(M)$ is any integral cohomology class, then

$$\int_M \omega' \wedge \eta = \frac{1}{m} \int_{\tilde{M}} \omega \wedge \pi^* \eta \in \mathbb{Q},$$

where m is the number of sheets of the cover. Thus $[\omega']$ is rational.

DEFINITION. We say that a line bundle $L \to M$ over an algebraic variety is *very ample* if $H^0(M, \mathcal{O}(L))$ gives an embedding $M \to \mathbb{P}^N$, i.e., if there exists an embedding $f : M \hookrightarrow \mathbb{P}^N$ such that $L = f^* H$.

Now from the proof of the Kodaira embedding theorem, we see

Corollary. *If $E \to M$ is any line bundle and $L \to M$ a positive line bundle, then for $k \gg 0$, the bundle $L^k + E$ is very ample.*

5. GRASSMANNIANS

Definitions; The Cell Decomposition and Schubert Cycles

In this section, we will construct and describe the Grassmannians, a fundamental family of compact complex manifolds. Grassmannians may be thought of as a generalization of projective space; the analogy will be apparent throughout.

Let V be a complex vector space of dimension n. The *Grassmannian* $G(k, V)$ is defined to be the set of k-dimensional linear subspaces of V; we write $G(k, n)$ for $G(k, \mathbb{C}^n)$. Given a k-plane Λ in $\mathbb{C}^n$, we may represent Λ by a set of k row vectors in $\mathbb{C}^n$ spanning Λ, i.e., by a $k \times n$ matrix

$$\begin{bmatrix} v_{11} & \cdots & v_{1n} \\ \vdots & & \vdots \\ v_{k1} & \cdots & v_{kn} \end{bmatrix}$$

of rank k. Clearly any such matrix represents an element of $G(k, n)$ and any two such matrices A, A' represent the same element of $G(k, n)$ if and only if $\Lambda = g\Lambda'$ for some $g \in GL_k$.

For every multiindex $I = \{i_1, \ldots, i_k\} \subset \{1, \ldots, n\}$ of cardinality k, let $V_{I^\circ} \subset \mathbb{C}^n$ be the $(n-k)$-plane in $\mathbb{C}^n$ spanned by the vectors $\{e_j : j \notin I\}$, and let

$$U_I = \{\Lambda \in G(k, n) : \Lambda \cap V_{I^\circ} = \{0\}\};$$

U_I is just the set of $\Lambda \in G(k, n)$ such that the Ith $k \times k$ minor of one, and hence for any, matrix representation for Λ is nonsingular. Any $\Lambda \in U_I$ has a unique matrix representation Λ^I whose Ith $k \times k$ minor is the identity matrix, e.g., any $\Lambda \in U_{\{1, \ldots, k\}}$ can be represented uniquely by a matrix of the form

$$\begin{bmatrix} 1 & 0 & 0 & \cdots & 0 & * & \cdots & * \\ 0 & 1 & & & \vdots & * & & \\ \vdots & & \ddots & & 0 & \vdots & \ddots & \vdots \\ 0 & & & \cdots & 1 & * & \cdots & * \end{bmatrix}.$$

(Note that the row vectors of such a matrix representative for $\Lambda \in U_I$ are just the points of intersection of Λ with the affine $(n-k)$-planes $\{V_{I^\circ} + e_j : j \in I\}$.) Conversely, any $k \times n$ matrix of the form above represents a k-plane $\Lambda \in U_I$; thus the $k(n-k)$ entries of the I°th $k \times (n-k)$ minor $\Lambda_{I^\circ}^I$ of Λ^I give a bijection of sets

$$\varphi_I : U_I \to \mathbb{C}^{k(n-k)}$$

for each I. Note that $\varphi_I(U_I \cap U_{I'})$ is open in $\mathbb{C}^{k(n-k)}$ for all I, I'; we claim that in fact the map $\varphi_I \circ \varphi_{I'}^{-1}$ is holomorphic on this open set and hence that the maps φ_I give $G(k,n)$ the structure of a complex manifold. But this is clear: if, for $\Lambda \in U_I \cap U_{I'}$, we let $\Lambda_{I'}^I$ be the I'th $k \times k$ minor of Λ^I, then

$$\Lambda^{I'} = (\Lambda_{I'}^I)^{-1} \cdot \Lambda^I,$$

and since the entries of $(\Lambda_{I'}^I)^{-1}$ vary holomorphically with the entries of Λ^I, $\varphi_I \circ \varphi_{I'}^{-1}$ is holomorphic.

With this topology $G(k,n)$ is compact and connected, since the unitary group U_n maps surjectively and continuously onto $G(k,n)$ by the map

$$g \mapsto g(V_k),$$

where $V_k = \{e_1, \ldots, e_k\} \subset \mathbb{C}^n$. The full linear group GL_n likewise acts transitively on $G(k,n)$.

Note in particular that $G(1,n)$ is biholomorphic to $\mathbb{P}^{n-1}$ as a complex manifold: the "matrix representative" $(v_1, \ldots, v_n)$ for a line $\Lambda \in G(1,n)$ corresponds, via the natural set-theoretic identification of $G(1,n)$ with $\mathbb{P}^{n-1}$, to the homogeneous coordinates of $\Lambda \in \mathbb{P}^{n-1}$, and

$$\Lambda^{\{i\}} = \left(\frac{v_1}{v_i}, \ldots, 1, \ldots, \frac{v_n}{v_i} \right),$$

so

$$\varphi_{\{i\}} = \Lambda \mapsto \left(\frac{v_1}{v_i}, \ldots, \frac{v_n}{v_i} \right),$$

i.e., the coordinates on $G(1,n)$ given by $\varphi_{\{i\}}$ are just the Euclidean coordinates on $\mathbb{P}^{n-1}$. Dually, we have $G(n-1,n) \cong \mathbb{P}^{n-1*}$, the projective space of hyperplanes in $\mathbb{P}^{n-1}$.

Finally, we note that $G(k,n)$ can be considered either as the set of linear k-planes Λ in $\mathbb{C}^n$, or equivalently as the set of $(k-1)$-planes $\overline{\Lambda}$ in $\mathbb{P}^{n-1}$. Our viewpoint in this section will for the most part be the former, as it is easier to keep track of dimension and codimension of cycles, but when Grassmannians arise in geometric questions we will generally want to think of them in the latter way.

The Cell Decomposition

Recall that the cell decomposition

$$\mathbb{P}^n = \mathbb{C}^n \cup \mathbb{C}^{n-1} \cup \cdots \cup \mathbb{C}^1 \cup \mathbb{C}^0$$

of $\mathbb{P}^n = G(1, n+1)$ is obtained by choosing a *flag*

$$V = \left(V_1 \subsetneq \cdots \subsetneq V_{n-1} \subsetneq V_n \subsetneq \mathbb{C}^{n+1} \right)$$

of linear subspaces of $\mathbb{C}^{n+1}$ and taking $W_i \cong \mathbb{C}^{i-1} = \{l \subset \mathbb{C}^{n+1} : l \subset V_i, l \not\subset V_{i-1}\}$. The same technique works to give a cell decomposition of the Grassmannian: if we set $V_i = \{e_1, \ldots, e_i\} \subset \mathbb{C}^n$, then the set of $\Lambda \in G(k,n)$ whose intersection with each V_i is of a specified dimension turns out, as we shall see, to be a simple cell. The set-up is as follows: for every $\Lambda \in G(k,n)$ consider the increasing sequence of subspaces

$$(*) \qquad 0 \subset \Lambda \cap V_1 \subset \Lambda \cap V_2 \subset \cdots \subset \Lambda \cap V_{n-1} \subset \Lambda \cap V_n = \Lambda.$$

For generic Λ, $\Lambda \cap V_i$ will be zero for $i \leqslant n-k$, and $(i+k-n)$-dimensional thereafter—indeed, we have seen that the set of such Λ is just the open set $U_{I^\circ} \cong \mathbb{C}^{k(n-k)} \subset G(k,n)$. Now, for any sequence of integers $a_1, \ldots, a_k$, set

$$W_{a_1, \ldots, a_k} = \{\Lambda \in G(k,n) : \dim(\Lambda \cap V_{n-k+i-a_i}) = i\}.$$

We observe that $\dim(\Lambda + V_{n-k+i-a_i}) = n - a_i$, and consequently $W_{a_1, \ldots, a_k}$ will be empty unless $a_1, \ldots, a_k$ is a nonincreasing sequence of integers $\leqslant n-k$. Since $\dim(\Lambda \cap V_{n-k+i-a_i}) = i$ if and only if the rank of the *last* $k \times (k + a_i - i)$ minor of a matrix representative for Λ is exactly $k-i$ it follows that the closure

$$\overline{W}_{a_1, \ldots, a_k} = \{\Lambda : \dim(\Lambda \cap V_{n-k+i-a_i}) \geqslant i\}$$

is an analytic subvariety of $G(k,n)$.

We can choose a special basis for a k-plane $\Lambda \in W_{a_1, \ldots, a_k}$ as follows: let v_1 be a generator for the line $\Lambda \cap V_{n-k+1-a_1}$, normalized so that $\langle v_1, e_{n-k+1-a_1} \rangle = 1$; i.e.,

$$v_1 = (*, *, \ldots, *, 1, 0, \ldots, 0).$$

Now take v_2 so that v_1 and v_2 together span $\Lambda \cap V_{n-k+2-a_2}$, normalized so that

$$\langle v_2, e_{n-k+1-a_1} \rangle = 0, \qquad \langle v_2, e_{n-k+2-a_2} \rangle = 1.$$

Continue in this way, choosing v_i so that $v_1, \ldots, v_i$ span $\Lambda \cap V_{n-k+i-a_i}$ and such that

$$\langle v_i, e_{n-k+j-a_j} \rangle = \begin{cases} 0, & j < i, \\ 1, & j = i. \end{cases}$$

Clearly, the choice of v_i at each stage is completely specified by these conditions; thus the k-plane Λ has a unique matrix representative of the form

$$\begin{bmatrix} v_1 \\ \vdots \\ v_k \end{bmatrix} =$$

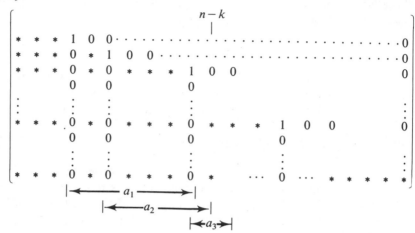

Conversely, any matrix of this form describes a k-plane $\Lambda \in W_{a_1,\dots,a_k}$. Since $(k^2 + \Sigma a_i)$ entries are specified in the diagram and the rest are completely free to vary, we have homeomorphisms

$$W_{a_1,\dots,a_k} \cong \mathbb{C}^{k(n-k) - \Sigma a_i};$$

consequently, the sets $W_{a_1,\dots,a_k}$ give a cell decomposition of $G(k,n)$. Since we have cells only in even dimensions, all boundary maps are zero, and we deduce the

Proposition. *The integral homology of the Grassmannian* $G(k,n)$ *has no torsion and is freely generated by the cycles* $\sigma_{a_1,\dots,a_k} = \overline{[W_{a_1,\dots,a_k}]}$ *in real codimension* $2\Sigma a_i$, *where* $\{(a_1,\dots,a_k)\}$ *ranges over all nonincreasing sequences of integers between* 0 *and* $n-k$. *In particular, all cohomology in* $G(k,n)$ *is analytic.*

In general, for any flag $V = (V_1 \subset V_2 \subset \cdots \subset V_{n-1} \subset V_n)$ in $\mathbb{C}^n$ we let

$$\sigma_a(V) = \{\Lambda : \dim(\Lambda \cap V_{n-k+i-a_i}) \geq i\}.$$

Clearly the homology class of the subvariety $\sigma_a(V)$ is independent of the flag chosen, since we can find a continuous family of linear automorphisms of $\mathbb{C}^n$ taking any flag into any other. The subvarieties $\sigma_a(V)$ are called the *Schubert cycles* of the Grassmannian.

The simplest example of a Grassmannian different from projective space is the $G(2,4)$ of 2-planes in $\mathbb{C}^4$. The Schubert cycles on $G(2,4)$ are

$$\text{codim } 1: \quad \sigma_{1,0}(V_2) = \{\Lambda: \dim(\Lambda \cap V_2) \geqslant 1\},$$
$$\text{codim } 2: \quad \sigma_{1,1}(V_3) = \{\Lambda: \Lambda \subset V_3\},$$
$$\sigma_{2,0}(V_1) = \{\Lambda: \Lambda \supset V_1\},$$
$$\text{codim } 3: \quad \sigma_{2,1}(V_1, V_3) = \{\Lambda: V_1 \subset \Lambda \subset V_3\}.$$

Alternatively, if we think of $G(2,4)$ as the set of lines l in $\mathbb{P}^3$ and fix the projective flag $p \in l_0 \subset h$ consisting of a point, line, and hyperplane in $\mathbb{P}^3$, then

$$\sigma_{1,0}(l_0) = \{l: l \cap l_0 \neq \emptyset\},$$
$$\sigma_{2,0}(p) = \{l: p \in l\},$$
$$\sigma_{1,1}(h) = \{l: l \in h\},$$
$$\sigma_{2,1}(p,h) = \{l: p \in l \subset h\}.$$

The Schubert Calculus

Now that we have determined the additive cohomology of $G(k,n)$, we would like to describe its multiplicative structure—that is, to express the intersection of general Schubert cycles σ_a, σ_b as a linear combination of other Schubert cycles in homology.

The first task is to write down the intersection pairing in complementary dimensions. To do this, let

$$\sigma_a(V) = \left\{\Lambda: \dim(\Lambda \cap V_{n-k+i-a_i}) \geqslant i\right\}$$

and

$$\sigma_b(V') = \left\{\Lambda: \dim(\Lambda \cap V'_{n-k+i-b_i}) \geqslant i\right\}$$

be general Schubert cycles. Then for each i and any $\Lambda \in \sigma_a(V) \cap \sigma_b(V')$,

$$\dim(\Lambda \cap V_{n-k+i-a_i}) \geqslant i,$$
$$\dim(\Lambda \cap V'_{n-k+(k-i+1)-b_{k-i+1}}) \geqslant k-i+1$$
$$\Rightarrow \Lambda \cap V_{n-k+i-a_i} \cap V'_{n-i+1-b_{k-i+1}} \neq (0).$$

But now if $a_i + b_{k-i+1} > n - k$, we have

$$(n-k+1-a_i) + (n-i+1-b_{k-i+1}) = 2n - k + 1 - (a_i + b_{k-i+1})$$
$$\leqslant n,$$

and so we can choose our flags V and V' such that $V_{n-k+i-a_i}$ and $V'_{n-i+1-b_{k-i+1}}$ intersect only at the origin. Consequently the cycles $\sigma_a(V)$

and $\sigma_b(V')$ can be made disjoint, i.e.,

$$^{\#}(\sigma_a \cdot \sigma_b) = 0 \qquad \text{unless } a_i + b_{k-i+1} \leqslant n - k, \quad \text{for all } i.$$

Now suppose σ_a and σ_b are cycles of complementary dimension, so that

$$\sum a_i + \sum b_i = k(n-k);$$

then

$$a_i + b_{k-i+1} \leqslant n - k \text{ for all } i \Rightarrow b_{k-i+1} = n - k - a_i,$$

i.e., the cycle σ_a has intersection number zero with all Schubert cycles in complementary dimension except $\sigma_{n-k-a_n,\ldots,n-k-a_1}$. Since the Schubert cycles form an integral basis for $H_*(G(k,n),\mathbb{Z})$, it follows either by Poincaré duality and the fact that analytic cycles intersect positively or by direct examination that

$$^{\#}(\sigma_a, \sigma_{n-k-a_n,\ldots,n-k-a_1}) = 1.$$

Summing up, then, we have the formula

$$^{\#}(\sigma_a \cdot \sigma_b) = \delta_{(a_1,\ldots,a_k)}^{(n-k-b_k,\ldots,n-k-b_1)}.$$

This enables us to express an arbitrary cycle γ on $G(k,n)$ as a linear combination of Schubert cycles, by computing intersections, i.e.,

$$\gamma = \sum {}^{\#}(\gamma \cdot \sigma_{n-k-a_k,\ldots,n-k-a_1}) \cdot \sigma_a,$$

and in particular reduces the problem of computing the intersection of pairs of Schubert cycles in arbitrary dimension to the problem of computing triple intersections in complementary dimension:

$$(\sigma_a \cdot \sigma_b) = \sum {}^{\#}(\sigma_a \cdot \sigma_b \cdot \sigma_{n-k-c_k,\ldots,n-k-c_1}) \cdot \sigma_c.$$

As an example, for any hypersurface $W \subset \mathbb{P}^n$ of degree 2, let $\tau(W) \subset G(2,n+1)$ denote the set of lines in $\mathbb{P}^n$ lying on W. $\tau(W)$ is clearly an analytic cycle in $G(2,n+1)$, and since a line $l \subset \mathbb{P}^n$ lies on W if and only if three points of l lie on W, $\tau(W)$ has complex codimension 3. $G(2,n+1)$ has only two Schubert cycles of codimension 3—$\sigma_{3,0}$ and $\sigma_{2,1}$—and so we can write

$$\tau(W) = {}^{\#}(\tau(W) \cdot \sigma_{n-1,n-4}) \cdot \sigma_{3,0} + {}^{\#}(\tau(W) \cdot \sigma_{n-2,n-3}) \cdot \sigma_{2,1}.$$

Now, $\sigma_{n-1,n-4}$ is the set of lines in $\mathbb{P}^n$ containing a point p and contained in a 4-plane $V_4 \subset \mathbb{P}^n$; if we choose our point p to lie off W, clearly $\tau(W)$ will be disjoint from $\sigma_{n-1,n-4}$. On the other hand, $\sigma_{n-2,n-3}$ is the cycle of lines meeting a line $l_0 \subset \mathbb{P}^n$ and contained in a 3-plane $S \subset \mathbb{P}^n$ containing l_0. Generically, $W' = W \cap S$ will be a smooth quadric surface in $S \cong \mathbb{P}^3$, with l_0 meeting it at two points p_1 and p_2; clearly any line $l \subset \tau(W) \cap \sigma_{n-2,n-3}$

will pass through either p_1 or p_2. But any line on W' through p_i must lie in the tangent plane $T_{p_i}(W')$; and $T_{p_i}(W') \cap W$ is a singular curve of degree 2, hence consists of two lines. Thus $\tau(W)$ meets $\sigma_{n-2,n-3}$ in four points generically, and so

$$\tau(W) \sim 4 \cdot \sigma_{2,1}.$$

In particular, if W and W' are two generic quadric hypersurfaces in $\mathbf{P}^4$, meeting transversally in a smooth surface S, then by the above S will have

$${}^{\#}(\tau(W) \cdot \tau(W'))_{G(2,5)} = {}^{\#}(4\sigma_{2,1} \cdot 4\sigma_{2,1})_{G(2,5)} = 16$$

lines in $\mathbf{P}^4$ lying on it. We will verify this in Section 4 of Chapter 4.

Similarly, we will be able to compute the homology class of $\tau(W) \subset G(2, n+1)$ for other hypersurfaces of low degree, once we know a few more things about special cases.

Before we go on to consider general intersections, we want to offer two general observations.

First, we will alter our formalism slightly, as follows: for *any* sequence $a = a_1, a_2, \ldots$ of nonnegative integers, we let $\sigma_a(V)$ denote the cycle

$$\sigma_a(V) = \left\{ \Lambda : \dim(\Lambda \cap V_{n-k+i-a_i}) \geqslant i \right\} \subset G(k,n)$$

so that the symbol σ_a can be used to refer to a Schubert cycle in any Grassmannian. Of course, σ_a will be null in $G(k,n)$ unless $a_i \leqslant n-k$ for all i, $a_i = 0$ for all $i > k$, and a is nonincreasing.

Now, the inclusion $\mathbb{C}^n \to \mathbb{C}^{n+1}$ induces inclusions

$$\iota_1 : G(k,n) \to G(k, n+1)$$

and

$$\iota_2 : G(k,n) \to G(k+1, n+1)$$

obtained by sending $\Lambda \subset \mathbb{C}^n$ to $\Lambda \subset \mathbb{C}^{n+1}$ and $\Lambda \oplus \{e_{n+1}\} \subset \mathbb{C}^{n+1}$, respectively. Under these inclusions, it is not hard to see that for appropriate choices of flags V in $\mathbb{C}^n$ and V' in $\mathbb{C}^{n+1}$,

$$\sigma_a(V) = \iota_1^{-1}(\sigma_a(V')) = \iota_2^{-1}(\sigma_a(V')),$$

i.e., if we denote the Poincaré dual of σ_a by $\tilde{\sigma}_a$,

$$\iota_1^* \tilde{\sigma}_a = \iota_2^* \tilde{\sigma}_a = \tilde{\sigma}_a.$$

Thus any formula

$$(\sigma_a \cdot \sigma_b) = \sum n_c \cdot \sigma_c$$

for the intersection of Schubert cycles in $G(k, n+1)$ or $G(k+1, n+1)$ holds as well in $G(k,n)$, and we can define the *universal Schubert coefficients*

$\delta(a,b;c)$ to be such that the formula

$$(\sigma_a \cdot \sigma_b) = \sum \delta(a,b;c) \cdot \sigma_c$$

holds in all $G(k,n)$.

Note that by our first computation, we have

$$\delta(a,b;c) = {}^{\#}\left(\sigma_a \cdot \sigma_b \cdot \sigma_{n-k-c_k,\ldots,n-k-c_1}\right)_{G(k,n)}$$

for any k,n such that σ_c is nonnull in $G(k,n)$, i.e., such that $c_i \leqslant n-k$ for all i and $c_i = 0$ for all $i > k$. In particular, if we let $l(c)$ denote the length of the sequence c, that is, the number of nonzero entries, we may take $k = l(c)$, $n - k = c_1$ in the above to obtain

$$(*) \qquad \delta(a,b;c) = {}^{\#}\left(\sigma_a \cdot \sigma_b \cdot \sigma_{c_1 - c_k, \ldots, c_1 - c_2}\right) \qquad \text{in } G(l(c), l(c) + c_1).$$

As an immediate consequence, we see that $\delta(a,b;c) = 0$ if σ_a or σ_b is null in $G(l(c), l(c) + c_1)$, i.e., $\delta(a,b;c) = 0$ if either

1. $c_1 < a_1$ or $c_1 < b_1$, or
2. $l(c) < l(a)$ or $l(c) < l(b)$.

Next, note that for any vector space W of dimension n, we have a natural isomorphism

$$*: G(k, W) \longrightarrow G(n-k, W^*)$$

defined by

$$*\Lambda = \mathrm{Ann}(\Lambda) = \{l \in V^*: l(\Lambda) = 0\}.$$

Let $V = \{V_1 \subset V_2 \subset \cdots \subset V_n = W\}$ be a flag in W, and let $V^* = \{V_1^* \subset V_2^* \subset \cdots \subset V_n^* = W^*\}$ be the dual flag in W^* given by

$$V_i^* = \mathrm{Ann}(V_{n-i}).$$

By linear algebra, for Λ any k-plane in W,

$$\dim(\Lambda \cap V_{n-k+i-a_i}) \geqslant i \Longleftrightarrow \dim(*\Lambda \cap V_{k-i+a_i}^*) \geqslant a_i,$$

Thus, *for any* a, *the image* $*\sigma_a \subset G(n-k, n)$ *of the Schubert cycle* $\sigma_a \subset G(k,n)$ *is the Schubert cycle* a*, *where* a* *is defined to be the smallest nonincreasing sequence such that*

$$a_{a_i}^* \geqslant i \qquad \text{for all } i.$$

For example,

$$*(\sigma_2) = \sigma_{1,1}, \qquad *(\sigma_{2,1,1}) = \sigma_{3,1}.$$

In general, we will have

$$\delta(a,b;c) = \delta(a^*, b^*; c^*),$$

and so we may expect that any formula for the intersection of Schubert cycles σ_a, σ_b gives a dual formula, when applied to $\sigma_{a^*}, \sigma_{b^*}$.

Note that

$$l(a^*) = a_1 \quad \text{and} \quad a_1^* = l(a)$$

so that the formulas 1 and 2 above are, as expected, equivalent under the $*$ map.

We turn now to the original problem of computing $\delta(a, b; c)$ for general a, b, and c. We will first give a reduction that allows us to compute effectively in many cases.

Our basic technique is simply a linear algebra reduction to smaller Grassmannians. For example, consider a triple of indices α, β, γ such that $\alpha + \beta + \gamma = 2k + 1$. Then for any k-plane $\Lambda \in \sigma_a(V) \cap \sigma_b(V') \cap \sigma_c(V'')$,

$$\dim\left(\Lambda \cap V_{n-k+\alpha-a_\alpha}\right) \geqslant \alpha,$$

$$\dim\left(\Lambda \cap V'_{n-k+\beta-b_\beta}\right) \geqslant \beta,$$

$$\dim\left(\Lambda \cap V''_{n-k+\gamma-c_\gamma}\right) \geqslant \gamma$$

$$\Rightarrow \dim\left(\Lambda \cap V_{n-k+\alpha-a_\alpha} \cap V'_{n-k+\beta-b_\beta} \cap V''_{n-k+\gamma-c_\gamma}\right) \geqslant 1.$$

Thus $^{\#}(\sigma_a \cdot \sigma_b \cdot \sigma_c) = 0$ in $G(k, n)$ if

$$(k - \alpha + a_\alpha) + (k - \beta + b_\beta) + (k - \gamma + c_\gamma) > n - 1,$$

i.e., if

$$a_\alpha + b_\beta + c_\gamma > n - k.$$

Suppose on the other hand that $a_\alpha + b_\beta + c_\gamma = n - k$, i.e., that generically chosen subspaces $V_{n-k+\alpha-a_\alpha}$, $V'_{n-k+\beta-b_\beta}$, and $V''_{n-k+\gamma-c_\gamma}$ will intersect in a line $L \subset \mathbb{C}^n$. Then any $\Lambda \in \sigma_a(V) \cap \sigma_b(V') \cap \sigma_c(V'')$ must contain L. Let L^0 denote a subspace complementary to L in $\mathbb{C}^n$ and let π denote the projection of $\mathbb{C}^n$ onto L^0 with kernel L. Let

$$\overline{V}_1 = \pi(V_1),$$

$$\vdots$$

$$\overline{V}_{n-k+\alpha-a_\alpha-1} = \pi(V_{n-k+\alpha-a_\alpha-1}) = \pi(V_{n-k+\alpha-a_\alpha}),$$

$$\vdots$$

$$\overline{V}_{n-2} = \pi(V_{n-1}),$$

$$\overline{V}_{n-1} = \pi(V_n) = L^0,$$

and define $\overline{V}'_i$ and $\overline{V}''_i$ similarly. Then $\overline{V} = \{\overline{V}_i\}$, $\overline{V}' = \{\overline{V}'_i\}$, and $\overline{V}'' = \{\overline{V}''_i\}$

are transverse flags in L^0, and for any $(k-1)$-plane $\overline{\Lambda} \subset L^0$, we see that

$$\Lambda = \overline{L,\Lambda} \in \sigma_a(V) \cap \sigma_b(V') \cap \sigma_c(V'')$$
$$\Leftrightarrow \overline{\Lambda} \in \sigma_{a_1,\ldots,\hat{a}_\alpha,\ldots,a_k}(\overline{V}) \cap \sigma_{b_1,\ldots,\hat{b}_\beta,\ldots,b_k}(\overline{V'}) \cap \sigma_{c_1,\ldots,\hat{c}_\gamma,\ldots,c_k}(\overline{V'}).$$

Thus we have the

Reduction Formula I. *For any three indices* $0 \leqslant \alpha,\beta,\gamma \leqslant k$ *with* $\alpha+\beta+\gamma = 2k+1$,

$${}^{\#}(\sigma_a{\cdot}\sigma_b{\cdot}\sigma_c)_{G(k,n)} = \begin{cases} 0 & \text{if } a_\alpha + b_\beta + c_\gamma > n-k, \\ {}^{\#}(\sigma_{a-a_\alpha}{\cdot}\sigma_{b-b_\beta}{\cdot}\sigma_{c-c_\gamma})_{G(k-1,n-1)} & \text{if } a_\alpha + b_\beta + c_\gamma = n-k. \end{cases}$$

Note that in case we take $\beta = \gamma = k$, this reduction applies if $a_1 = n-k$; in case we take $\gamma = k$, it applies if $a_i + b_{k+1-i} = n-k$ for any i.

As suggested, we can apply this first reduction to the intersection of cycles ${}^{\#}(\sigma_{a*}{\cdot}\sigma_{b*}{\cdot}\sigma_{c*})$ in $G(n-k,n)$; we obtain

Reduction Formula II. *For any three coefficients* $a_\alpha, b_\beta, c_\gamma$ *with* $a_\alpha + b_\beta + c_\gamma \geqslant 2(n-k)+1$,

$$\begin{aligned} &{}^{\#}(\sigma_a{\cdot}\sigma_b{\cdot}\sigma_c)_{G(k,n)} \\ &= \begin{cases} 0 & \text{if } \alpha+\beta+\gamma > k \\ {}^{\#}(\sigma_{a_1-1,\ldots,a_\alpha-1,a_{\alpha+1},\ldots,a_k}{\cdot}\sigma_{b_1-1,\ldots,b_\beta-1,b_{\beta+1},\ldots,b_k}{\cdot}\sigma_{c_1-1,\ldots,c_\gamma-1,c_{\gamma+1},\ldots,c_k})_{G(k,n-1)} \\ \quad \text{if } \alpha+\beta+\gamma = k. \end{cases} \end{aligned}$$

For the purposes of this formula, we may set $a_0 = b_0 = c_0 = n-k$ formally; thus in case we take $\gamma = \beta = 0$, this reduction applies if $a_k \neq 0$, and if we take $\gamma = 0$, it applies in case $a_i + b_{k-i} \geqslant n-k+1$ for some i.

Note also that if the sequence $b_1 - 1, \ldots, b_{\beta-1}, b_{\beta+1}, \ldots$ appearing in the formula is no longer nonincreasing—i.e., if $b_\beta = b_{\beta+1}$—then the intersection number is zero: just apply the formula to $\alpha, \beta+1, \gamma$. Thus we may use the formula in all circumstances, if we adopt the convention that σ_b is null for b not a nonincreasing sequence.

As a sample calculation, we compute the coefficient $\delta(311,21;521)$ of σ_{521} in the expression for $(\sigma_{311}{\cdot}\sigma_{21})$ as a linear combination of Schubert cycles. By $(*)$ and the reductions we have

$$\begin{aligned} \delta(311,21;521) = {}^{\#}(\sigma_{311}{\cdot}\sigma_{21}{\cdot}\sigma_{43}) & \quad \text{in } G(3,8) \\ = {}^{\#}(\sigma_2{\cdot}\sigma_{21}{\cdot}\sigma_{43}) & \quad \text{in } G(3,7) \\ = {}^{\#}(\sigma_2{\cdot}\sigma_{21}{\cdot}\sigma_3) & \quad \text{in } G(2,6) \\ = {}^{\#}(\sigma_2{\cdot}\sigma_1{\cdot}\sigma_3) & \quad \text{in } G(2,5) \\ = {}^{\#}(\sigma_2{\cdot}\sigma_1) & \quad \text{in } G(1,4) = \mathbb{P}^3 \\ = 1. \end{aligned}$$

The two formulas given here will not apply every time, but in low codimension will yield the answer more often than not. They work especially well in case one of the factors σ_a is a *special Schubert cycle*, defined to be one of the form $\sigma_{a,0,0,\ldots}$. In this case, we can use the reductions to obtain the general

Pieri's Formula. *If* $a = a,0,0,\ldots$, *then for any* b,

$$(\sigma_a \cdot \sigma_b) = \sum_{\substack{b_i \leqslant c_i \leqslant b_{i-1} \\ \Sigma c_i = a + \Sigma b_i}} \sigma_c.$$

Proof. We want to show that, for σ_c of appropriate codimension,

$$\delta(a,b;c) = \begin{cases} 1, & \text{if } b_i \leqslant c_i \leqslant b_{i-1}, \\ 0, & \text{otherwise.} \end{cases}$$

We have, setting $k = l(c)$,

$$\delta(a,b;c) = {}^{\#}(\sigma_a \cdot \sigma_b \cdot \sigma_{c_1 - c_k, \ldots, c_1 - c_2, 0}) \qquad \text{in } G(k, k + c_1).$$

To start, suppose that $c_i < b_{i-1}$ for some i. Then we have

$$c_1 + b_{i-1} + (c_1 - c_i) \geqslant 2c_1 + 1,$$

and applying the second reduction formula with $\sigma = 0$, $\beta = i - 1$, and $\gamma = k - i + 1$, we obtain

$$\delta(a,b;c) = {}^{\#}(\sigma_a \cdot \sigma_{b_1 - 1, \ldots, b_{i-1} - 1, b_i, \ldots} \cdot \sigma_{c_1 - c_k - 1, \ldots, c_1 - c_i - 1, c_1 - c_{i-1}, \ldots})$$

$$\text{in } G(k, k + c_1 - 1)$$

$$= \delta(a, b'; c')$$

where

$$b' = b_1 - 1, \ldots, b_{i-1} - 1, b_i, \ldots$$

and

$$c' = c_1 - 1, \ldots, c_{i-1} - 1, c_i, \ldots.$$

Now

$$(b_i \leqslant c_i \leqslant b_{i-1} \text{ for all } i) \Leftrightarrow (b_i' \leqslant c_i' \leqslant b_{i-1}' \text{ for all } i)$$

and of course

$$b_{i-1}' - c_i' = b_{i-1} - c_i - 1 \geqslant 0.$$

Thus we may assume from the start that $c_i \geqslant b_{i-1}$ *for all i.* Since $\Sigma c_i = a + \Sigma b_i$, it follows that $a \geqslant c_1$; and so there are three cases:

1. If $c_i > b_{i-1}$ for some i, then $a > c_1$ and so $\delta(a,b;c) = 0$.
2. If $c_i < b_i$ for any i, then $c_i \geqslant b_{i-1}$ implies that $b_i > b_{i-1}$, i.e., the sequence b is not nonincreasing and σ_b is taken to be null; so $\delta(a,b;c) = 0$.
3. If $b_i \leqslant c_i \leqslant b_{i-1}$ for all i, it follows that $c_i = b_{i-1}$ for all i, hence $a = c_1, b_k = 0$, and applying the first reduction formula with $\alpha = 1$ and

$\beta = \gamma = k$ we have

$$\delta(a,b;c) = {}^{\#}(\sigma_a \cdot \sigma_b \cdot \sigma_{c_1-c_k,\ldots,c_1-c_2,0}) \qquad \text{in } G(k,k+c_1)$$

$$= {}^{\#}(\sigma_b \cdot \sigma_{c_1-c_k,\ldots,c_1-c_2}) \qquad \text{in } G(k-1,k+c_1-1)$$

$$= {}^{\#}(\sigma_b \cdot \sigma_{c_1-b_{k-1},\ldots,c_1-b_1})$$

$$= 1. \qquad\qquad\qquad\qquad\qquad\qquad\qquad\qquad \text{Q.E.D.}$$

Our final result on Schubert cycles is a formula that expresses the general Schubert cycle as a polynomial in the special Schubert cycles $\sigma_{b,0,\ldots}$.

We proceed as follows: for $\sigma_{a_1,\ldots,a_d}$ any Schubert cycle, we consider the cycle

$$(*) \qquad\qquad \tilde{\sigma}_a = \sum_{j=1}^{d} (-1)^j \sigma_{a_1,\ldots,a_{j-1},a_{j+1}-1,\ldots,a_d-1} \cdot \sigma_{a_j+d-j}.$$

Note that $\tilde{\sigma}_a$ has the same dimension as σ_a. Now, we can by Pieri's formula write out each of the intersections in the sum $(*)$ as a sum of Schubert cycles. Let $\sigma_{c_1,\ldots,c_d}$ be any Schubert cycle; if σ_c appears in this expression, consider the sequence of integers

$$c_1 - 1, c_2 - 2, \ldots, c_d - d.$$

By Pieri, at most one of these numbers will lie in each of the $(d+1)$ closed intervals

$$[a_1 - 1, n - k],$$

$$[a_2 - 2, a_1 - 2],$$

$$\vdots$$

$$[a_d - d, a_{d-1} - d],$$

$$[-d-1, a_d - d - 1],$$

and so exactly one of these intervals will fail to contain an integer $c_i - i$. By cases, then:

1. If no integer $c_i - i$ lies in the interval $[-d-1, a_d-d-1]$, then

$$c_i - i \in [a_i - i, a_{i-1} - i],$$

and σ_c can appear only in the last term of the sum $(*)$. But since

$$c_i \geqslant a_i \quad \text{and} \quad \sum c_i = \sum a_i,$$

it follows that $c = a$. The Schubert cycle $\sigma_{a_1,\ldots,a_d}$ thus appears once in $(*)$, with coefficient $(-1)^d$.

2. If no integer $c_i - i$ appears in the interval $[a_k - k, a_{k-1} - k]$, then we have

$$c_1 - 1 \quad \in [a_1 - 1, n - k],$$

$$\vdots$$

$$c_{k-1} - k + 1 \in [a_{k-1} - k + 1, a_k - k + 1],$$
$$c_k - k \quad \in [a_{k+1} - k - 1, a_k - k - 1],$$

$$\vdots$$

$$c_d - d \quad \in [-d - 1, a_d - d - 1],$$

i.e.,

$$a_i \leqslant c_i \leqslant a_{i-1}, \quad i = 1, \ldots, k - 1,$$

and

$$a_{i+1} - 1 \leqslant c_i \leqslant a_i - 1, \quad i = k, \ldots, d.$$

In this case, the Schubert cycle σ_c will appear twice in the expression for (∗): once in the kth term, and once in the $(k-1)$st term. Since these two have opposite sign, σ_c will not appear in the final expression for $\tilde{\sigma}_a$.

3. If the interval $[a_1 - 1, n - k]$ is unoccupied, we have

$$c_i - i \in [a_{i+1} - i - 1, a_i - i - 1]$$

for each i—but then $c_i \leqslant a_i - 1$, and hence $\Sigma c_i < \Sigma a_i$, so σ_c cannot appear in (∗).

We have, then, the formula

$$(\ast\ast) \quad (-1)^d \sigma_{a_1, \ldots, a_d} = \sum_{j=1}^{d} (-1)^j \sigma_{a_1, \ldots, a_{j-1}, a_{j+1} - 1, \ldots, a_d - 1} \cdot \sigma_{a_j + d - j}.$$

Note that since each factor on the right has length $< d$, this already implies that σ_a is expressible as a polynomial in the special Schubert cycles $\sigma_{b,0,\ldots}$, i.e., that

The cohomology ring of the Grassmannian $G(k, n)$ *is generated by the classes of the special Schubert cycles.*

Now, we will use the relation (∗∗) to prove *Giambelli's formula*

$$\sigma_{a_1, \ldots, a_d} = \begin{vmatrix} \sigma_{a_1} & \sigma_{a_1 + 1} & \sigma_{a_1 + 2} & \cdots & \sigma_{a_1 + d - 1} \\ \sigma_{a_2 - 1} & \sigma_{a_2} & \sigma_{a_2 + 1} & \cdots & \sigma_{a_2 + d - 2} \\ \sigma_{a_3 - 2} & \sigma_{a_3 - 1} & \sigma_{a_3} & & \\ \vdots & & & & \vdots \\ \sigma_{a_d - d + 1} & & \cdots & & \sigma_{a_d} \end{vmatrix}.$$

We will prove this by induction; clearly it is true for $d=1$. Assume that it holds for $d-1$; expanding by cofactors along the left-hand row, the determinant is given by

$$\sum (-1)^j \sigma_{a_j+d-j} \cdot \begin{vmatrix} \sigma_{a_1} & \cdots & \sigma_{a_1+d-2} \\ \vdots & & \vdots \\ \sigma_{a_{j-1}-j} & \cdots & \sigma_{a_{j-1}+d-j} \\ \sigma_{a_{j+1}-j-2} & \cdots & \sigma_{a_{j+1}+d-j-2} \\ \vdots & & \vdots \\ \sigma_{a_d-d+1} & \cdots & \sigma_{a_d-1} \end{vmatrix}$$

$$= \sum (-1)^j \sigma_{a_j+d-j} \cdot \sigma_{a_1,\ldots,a_{j-1},a_{j+1}-1,\ldots,a_d-1}$$
$$= \sigma_{a_1,\ldots,a_d},$$

and the formula is proved.   Q.E.D.

Note that Pieri's formula together with the formula (∗∗) give an algorithm for evaluating an arbitrary intersection of Schubert cycles.

The Schubert calculus will appear frequently in the remainder of the book, in a variety of contexts; for the time being we give some applications of our formulas to elementary problems in enumerative geometry. Perhaps the simplest nontrivial such problem is the question: given four lines L_1, L_2, L_3, L_4 in $\mathbb{P}^3$ in general position, how many lines meet all four? The answer is easily obtained: since the set of lines meeting L_i is just the Schubert cycle $\sigma_1(L_i)$, the answer is just the fourfold self-intersection number of σ_1 in $G(2,4)$; this is

$$\sigma_1^4 = \sigma_1^2 \cdot (\sigma_{1,1} + \sigma_2)$$
$$= \sigma_1 \cdot (2\sigma_{2,1})$$
$$= 2.$$

In general, the number of lines meeting four $(n+1)$-planes in general position in $\mathbb{P}^{2n+1}$ is given by the fourfold self-intersection of σ_n in $G(2, 2n+2)$; this is

$$(\sigma_n)^4 = (\sigma_n^2)^2$$
$$= \left(\sum_{i=0}^{n} \sigma_{2n-i,i} \right)^2$$
$$= n+1.$$

In a similar vein, the number of lines in $\mathbb{P}^4$ meeting six 2-planes in general position is given by σ_1^6 in $G(2,5)$; we have

$$\sigma_1^3 = \sigma_1(\sigma_{1,1} + \sigma_2) = 2\sigma_{2,1} + \sigma_3,$$

so

$$\sigma_1^6 = (2\sigma_{2,1} + \sigma_3)^2 = 4 + 1 = 5.$$

Universal Bundles

Let $\mathbb{C}^n \times G(k,n)$ denote the trivial vector bundle of rank n over $G(k,n)$. We define the *universal subbundle* $S \to G(k,n)$ to be the subbundle of $\mathbb{C}^n \times G(k,n)$ whose fiber at each point $\Lambda \in G(k,n)$ is just the subspace $\Lambda \subset \mathbb{C}^n$. S is clearly a holomorphic subbundle of $\mathbb{C}^n \times G(k,n)$—explicitly, in each open $U_I \subset G(k,n)$ the row vectors of the normalized matrix representatives for $\Lambda \in U_I$ give a frame for S over U_I; transition functions relative to these frames are given in $U_I \cap U_{I'}$ by $g_{U_I U_{I'}} = \Lambda_{I'} \cdot \Lambda_{I'}^{-1}$. The quotient bundle $Q = \mathbb{C}^n / S$ is called the *universal quotient bundle* on $G(k,n)$. Note that under the identification $* : G(k,n) \to G(n-k,n)$, the universal subbundle on $G(n-k,n)$ corresponds to the *dual* of the universal quotient bundle in $G(k,n)$, and likewise $Q \to G(n-k,n)$ pulls back to the dual $S^* \to G(k,n)$. Note in particular that the universal subbundle $S \to G(1,n) \cong \mathbb{P}^{n-1}$ is just the universal line bundle mentioned earlier.

Now let $E \to M$ be any holomorphic vector bundle of rank k on a complex manifold M, $V \subset H^0(M, \mathcal{O}(E))$ an n-dimensional vector space of global holomorphic sections, and suppose that the values $\{\sigma(x)\}_{\sigma \in V}$ of the sections σ in V span E_x for all $x \in M$. Then for each $x \in M$, the subspace $\Lambda_x \subset V$ of sections $\sigma \in V$ vanishing at x is an $(n-k)$-dimensional subspace; accordingly, we obtain a map

$$\iota_V : M \to G(n-k, V) = G(k, V^*)$$

with

$$E = \iota_V^* S^* \quad \text{and} \quad V = \iota_V^* \left(H^0(G(k,n), \mathcal{O}(S^*)) \right)$$

just as for line bundles. Explicitly, if we choose a basis $\sigma_1, \dots, \sigma_n$ for V and a frame $e_1, \dots, e_k$ for E locally and write

$$\sigma_i = \sum a_{i\alpha} e_\alpha,$$

then in terms of the corresponding identification $G(n-k, V) \cong G(k, V^*)$ the map ι_V is given by

$$x \mapsto \begin{bmatrix} a_{11} & \cdots & a_{1n} \\ \vdots & & \vdots \\ a_{k1} & \cdots & a_{kn} \end{bmatrix},$$

so that ι_V is clearly holomorphic.

As in the case of line bundles, we have an embedding theorem:

Theorem. *For* M *any compact complex manifold,* L $\to$ M *a positive line bundle and* E $\to$ M *any holomorphic vector bundle, then for* m *sufficiently large, the map* $\iota_{E \otimes L^m}$ *is an embedding.*

Proof. Most of the work has been done for us already by the Kodaira embedding theorem: since M has a positive line bundle, we may take

$M \subset \mathbb{P}^N$ an algebraic variety and $L \to M$ the hyperplane bundle.

Now $\iota_{E \otimes L^m}$ will be 1-1 if for all $x, y \in M$, the restriction map

$$(*) \qquad H^0(M, \mathcal{O}(E \otimes L^m)) \to (E \otimes L^m)_x \oplus (E \otimes L^m)_y$$

is surjective. Similarly, we have a differential map

$$(**) \qquad H^0(M, \mathcal{I}_x(E \otimes L^m)) \to T_x^{*\prime} \otimes (E \otimes L^m)_x$$

defined as for line bundles; $\iota_{E \otimes L^m}$ will be smooth at x if this map is surjective. The compactness argument used in the proof of the Kodaira embedding theorem again assures us that to prove the result, it is sufficient to show that for any particular choice of x and y, the above two maps are surjective for m sufficiently large.

We proceed by induction on the dimension of M. For any $x, y \in M$, consider the linear system of hyperplane sections of $M \subset \mathbb{P}^N$ containing x and y: by Bertini's theorem, the generic element of this system is smooth outside the base locus $\{x, y\}$ of the system, and it is easy to see that, unless M is a curve with $T_x(M) = T_y(M) \subset \mathbb{P}^N$ (which circumstance we can always avoid by embedding M differently), the generic element of the system will be smooth at x and y as well. Thus we can find a smooth hyperplane section $V = H \cap M$ of M containing x and y. Consider the sequence

$$0 \to \mathcal{O}_M(E \otimes L^{m-1}) \to \mathcal{O}_M(E \otimes L^m) \to \mathcal{O}_V(E \otimes L^m) \to 0.$$

By Theorem B, there exists m_1 such that for $m > m_1$, $H^1(M, \mathcal{O}(E \otimes L^{m-1})) = 0$, so that the restriction map

$$H^0(M, \mathcal{O}(E \otimes L^m)) \to H^0(V, \mathcal{O}(E \otimes L^m))$$

will be surjective. On the other hand, by induction there exists m_2 such that for $m > m_2$,

$$H^0(V, \mathcal{O}_V(E \otimes L^m)) \to (E \otimes L^m)_x \oplus (E \otimes L^m)_y$$

is surjective. For $m > m_0 = \max(m_1, m_2)$, then, the map $(*)$ will be surjective.

Similarly, for each of a generating set of cotangent vectors $\{\omega_\alpha\}$ for $T_x^{*\prime}$ we can find a smooth hyperplane section V_α of M through x, such that ω_α is not in the kernel of the natural projection map $T_x^*(M) \to T_x^*(V_\alpha)$. Then by induction we can find m_α such that for $m > m_\alpha$, the differential map

$$H^0(V_\alpha, \mathcal{I}_x(E \otimes L^m)) \to T_x^*(V_\alpha) \otimes (E \otimes L^m)_x$$

is surjective. Likewise, from the sequence

$$0 \to \mathcal{O}_M(E \otimes L^{m-1}) \to \mathcal{I}_{x,M}(E \otimes L^m) \to \mathcal{I}_{x,V_\alpha}(E \otimes L^m) \to 0$$

we see that for $m > m_1$ as before,

$$H^0(M, \mathcal{I}_x(E \otimes L^m)) \to H^0(V_\alpha, \mathcal{I}_x(E \otimes L^m))$$

is surjective. Thus for $m > m'_0 = \max(m_1, m_\alpha)$, we have

$$
\begin{array}{ccc}
H^0(M, \mathcal{I}_x(E \otimes L^m)) & \xrightarrow{d_x} & T_x^{*'}(M) \otimes (E \otimes L^m)_x \\
\downarrow & & \downarrow \\
H^0(V_\alpha, \mathcal{I}_x(E \otimes L^m)) & \xrightarrow{d_x} & T_x^*(V_\alpha) \otimes (E \otimes L^m)_x
\end{array}
$$

for all α, i.e., the map (∗∗) is surjective.   Q.E.D.

The Plücker Embedding

We close this section by describing the classical Plücker embedding of the Grassmannian $G(k, n)$ in projective space; this will illustrate both the Kodaira embedding theorem and Chow's theorem. The embedding line bundle over $G(k, n)$ will be $L = \det S^* = \det Q$. L may be seen to be positive by introducing a suitable metric with a positive curvature form in a similar manner to the Fubini-Study metric on projective space; rather than do this, however, we shall give the Plücker embedding directly. The *Plücker map*

$$
p: \ G(k, n) \to \mathbb{P}(\wedge^k \mathbb{C}^n) = \mathbb{P}^{\binom{n}{k} - 1}
$$

simply sends a k-plane $\Lambda = \mathbb{C}\{v_1, \ldots, v_k\} \subset \mathbb{C}^n$ to the multivector $v_1 \wedge \cdots \wedge v_k$. Explicitly, in terms of the basis $\{e_I = e_{i_1} \wedge \cdots \wedge e_{i_k}\}_{\#I = k}$ for $\wedge^k \mathbb{C}^n$, this map is given by

$$
\Lambda \mapsto [\ldots, |\Lambda_I|, \ldots],
$$

i.e., the homogeneous coordinates of the map are just the determinants $|\Lambda_I|$ of all the $k \times k$ minors Λ_I of a matrix representative of Λ. It follows that (1) p is holomorphic, (2) p takes every Schubert cycle of the form

$$
\sigma_1(V) = \{\Lambda \in G(k, n): \ \dim(\Lambda \cap V_{n-k}) \geq 1\}
$$

into a hyperplane section of $p(G(k, n)) \subset \mathbb{P}^{\binom{n}{k} - 1}$. We can always find, for $\Lambda \neq \Lambda' \in G(k, n)$, an $(n - k)$-plane V_{n-k} such that $\Lambda \cap V_{n-k} \neq (0)$, $\Lambda' \cap V_{n-k} = (0)$, so p is 1-1; and since, in each open set $U_I = \{\Lambda: |\Lambda_I| \neq 0\}$ the Euclidean coordinates on $G(k, n)$ described above appear as

$$
a_{jk} = \frac{|\Lambda_{I-j+k}|}{|\Lambda_I|},
$$

the map p has nonzero differential. Thus the Plücker mapping is an embedding.

Now we shall determine equations which define the Plücker image of $G(k, V)$ in $\mathbb{P}(\wedge^k V)$. What we are asking for are the conditions that a multivector $\Lambda \in \bigwedge^k V$ be *decomposable*, i.e., of the form

$$\Lambda = v_1 \wedge \cdots \wedge v_k.$$

For this we pose the more general problem of determining the minimal linear subspace $W \subset V$ such that Λ is in the image of

$$\bigwedge^k W \to \bigwedge^k V.$$

If dim $W = l$, then $l \geq k$ with equality holding if and only if Λ is decomposable.

Recall the contraction operator

$$i(v^*) : \bigwedge^k V \to \bigwedge^{k-1} V$$

defined for $v^* \in V^*$ by

$$\langle i(v^*)\Lambda, \Xi \rangle = \langle \Lambda, v^* \wedge \Xi \rangle$$

for all $\Xi \in (\bigwedge^{k-1} V)^* \cong \bigwedge^{k-1} V^*$. We associate to Λ the linear spaces

$$\Lambda^\perp = \{ v^* \in V^* : i(v^*)\Lambda = 0 \} \subset V^*$$

and

$$W = \operatorname{Ann}(\Lambda^\perp) \subset V.$$

Lemma. W *is the minimal subspace of* V *such that* Λ *is in the image of* $\bigwedge^k W \to \bigwedge^k V$.

Proof. Let $w_1, \ldots, w_l$ be a basis for W, and complete it by $u_{l+1}, \ldots, u_n$ to a basis for V. Denote the dual basis of V^* by $\{ w_i^*, u_\alpha^* \}$. Setting $U = \mathbb{C}\{ u_{l+1}, \ldots, u_n \}$, the direct sum decomposition $V = W \oplus U$ induces

$$\bigwedge^k V \cong \bigwedge^k W \oplus (\bigwedge^{k-1} W \otimes U) \oplus (\bigwedge^{k-2} W \otimes \bigwedge^2 U) \oplus \cdots.$$

We want to show that Λ lies in the first factor. Write the component of Λ in the second factor as $\sum_{\alpha=l+1}^n \Lambda_\alpha \otimes u_\alpha$, where $\Lambda_\alpha \in \bigwedge^{k-1} W$. Since

$$i(u_\alpha^*) : \bigwedge^{k-m} W \otimes \bigwedge^m U \to \bigwedge^{k-m} W \otimes \bigwedge^{m-1} U$$

and $i(u_\alpha^*)\Lambda = 0$, we deduce that all $\Lambda_\alpha = 0$. Similarly, the other factors of Λ in $\bigwedge^{k-m} W \otimes \bigwedge^m U$ ($m \geq 2$) are zero, and consequently $\Lambda \in \bigwedge^k W$. It is easy to see that W is the minimal such subspace.   Q.E.D.

We now define

$$W' = \{ w \in W : w \wedge \Lambda = 0 \}.$$

If Λ is decomposable, then clearly $W' = W$. Conversely, if Λ is not decomposable so that dim $W = l > k$, then since the pairing $\bigwedge^k W \otimes \bigwedge^{l-k} W \to \bigwedge^l W$ is nondegenerate we deduce that $W' \neq W$. So Λ is decomposable if and only if $W' = W$.

We now express this condition by duality, in two ways. For the first we use the operator

$$i(\Xi) : \bigwedge^k V \to V^*$$

defined for $\Xi \in \bigwedge^{k+1} V^*$ by

$$\langle i(\Xi)\Lambda, v \rangle = \langle \Xi, \Lambda \wedge v \rangle$$

for all $v \in V$. We observe that, by the definition of $\Lambda^{\perp}$, for $v \in W$ the left-hand side depends only on the image of Ξ under the natural projection

$$\bigwedge^{k+1} V^* \to \bigwedge^{k+1}\left(\frac{V^*}{\Lambda^{\perp}}\right) \cong \bigwedge^{k+1} W^*.$$

Consequently, the condition $\Lambda \wedge w = 0$ for all $w \in W$ is equivalent to $i(\Xi)\Lambda \in \Lambda^{\perp}$ for all Ξ, which is in turn equivalent to

$$(*) \qquad\qquad i(i(\Xi)\Lambda)\Lambda = 0 \qquad \text{for all } \Xi \in \bigwedge^{k+1} V^*.$$

The left-hand side of $(*)$ gives $\binom{n}{k+1}$ quadratic forms in the homogeneous coordinates Λ_I of $p(G(k,V))$; setting them equal to zero gives the classical *Plücker relations*. In sum,

> *the image of the Grassmannian under the Plücker embedding* $p : G(k, V) \to \mathbb{P}(\bigwedge^k V)$ *is cut out by the linear system of quadrics given by* $(*)$.

Alternatively, we may characterize W as being the image of

$$\bigwedge^{k-1} V^* \to V$$

under the map

$$\Xi \to i(\Xi)\Lambda, \qquad \Xi \in \bigwedge^{k-1} V^*.$$

Then the condition $W' = W$ is equivalent to

$$(**) \qquad\qquad (i(\Xi)\Lambda) \wedge \Lambda = 0 \qquad \text{for all } \Xi \in \bigwedge^{k-1} V^*.$$

For example, suppose that

$$\Lambda = \tfrac{1}{2}\sum_{i,j} \lambda_{ij} e_i \wedge e_j, \qquad \lambda_{ij} + \lambda_{ji} = 0,$$

is a bivector. Since for $v^* \in V^*$

$$(i(v^*)\Lambda) \wedge \Lambda = \tfrac{1}{2} i(v^*)(\Lambda \wedge \Lambda),$$

we may rewrite the conditions $(**)$ as

$$\Lambda \wedge \Lambda = 0.$$

When $n = 4$ we find the single equation

$$\lambda_{12}\lambda_{34} - \lambda_{13}\lambda_{24} + \lambda_{14}\lambda_{23} = 0$$

expressing the condition that $\Lambda \in \mathbb{P}(\bigwedge^2 \mathbb{C}^4) \cong \mathbb{P}^5$ be decomposable. In other words, $G(2,4)$ is *naturally realized as a nonsingular quadric hypersurface in* $\mathbb{P}^5$. We will see more of this in the final chapter.

2

RIEMANN SURFACES AND ALGEBRAIC CURVES

The dominant theme of this chapter is the interplay between the extrinsic projective geometry of algebraic curves and the intrinsic structure of Riemann surfaces. The subject, initially studied in extrinsic terms, underwent a basic shift in viewpoint with the introduction of the notion of abstract Riemann surface; nonetheless, the central aspects of the theory of algebraic curves as presented here are the same in either approach. Most of the results of this chapter were stated, if not proved, before the turn of the century.

We begin in Section 1 by refining the Kodaira embedding theorem in the case of dimension one. We then describe the local structure of maps between Riemann surfaces, and we use this to prove the Riemann-Hurwitz and genus formulas.We suggest the reader start with Section 2 and refer back to Section 1 as needed.

In Section 2 we introduce the theory of Abelian integrals and prove Abel's theorem and its converse. This theorem is perhaps most accessible in the case of elliptic curves—where indeed it was originally found—and we conclude with a discussion of this case.

We turn in Section 3 to the study of linear systems on curves. The fundamental result here is, of course, the Riemann-Roch formula. Next, we introduce the canonical curve, an intrinsically defined projective model of any nonhyperelliptic Riemann surface. The importance of the canonical curve is suggested by the geometric version of the Riemann-Roch; its full significance will continue to emerge through the remainder of the chapter. We initiate our study of special linear systems with Castelnuovo's bound on the genus of a curve of given degree in projective space; following a discussion of hyperelliptic curves and Riemann's count—which establishes our notion of the dependence of a Riemann surface on parameters—we start out on the road toward the solution of the complementary problem of Brill and Noether.

212

Sections 4 and 5 represent a shift of focus toward the extrinsic aspect of curves. In section 4 we prove the general Plücker formulas and the Plücker formulas for plane curves. There is a basic distinction between these results: the general Plücker formulas apply to curves in projective space of arbitrary dimension but deal only with the local character of the curve, while the formulas for plane curves describe such global phenomena as bitangents and double points, but apply only to curves in $\mathbb{P}^2$. The apparent gap is partially filled in the following section, where we introduce the powerful computational technique of correspondences and as an application derive formulas for the geometry of space curves. In both sections, the application of projective-geometric formulas to the canonical curve yields results about the intrinsic structure of Riemann surfaces: in Section 4 we obtain the count of Weierstrass points, and in Section 5 we solve some special cases of the Brill-Noether problem.

In the final two sections of the chapter we return to the study of the Jacobian variety associated to a compact Riemann surface. To begin with we give in Section 6 the rudiments of the theory of Abelian varieties; the dominant theme here is the working out of the Kodaira embedding theorem in the case of complex tori. In Section 7 we specialize to the case of the Jacobian of a curve. We see, by two lovely theorems of Riemann, how the geometry of the Jacobian is intimately connected to the special linear systems on the curve; following this we are finally able to prove some results on the Brill-Noether problem. The chapter concludes with Torelli's theorem, following Andreotti.

1. PRELIMINARIES

Embedding Riemann Surfaces

Let S be a compact Riemann surface. Throughout this chapter we assume that S is connected. If ds^2 is any metric on S with associated $(1,1)$-form ω, then $d\omega$ has degree 3 and so is trivially 0; thus any metric on S is Kähler. Indeed, since the $\bar{\partial}$-Laplacian of any metric commutes with the decomposition into type, we see that a form φ, written in terms of a local coordinate $z = x + \sqrt{-1}\,y$ as

$$\varphi = p\,dx + q\,dy = \alpha\,dz + \beta\,d\bar{z},$$

is harmonic if and only if $\varphi^{1,0} = \alpha\,dz$ is holomorphic and $\varphi^{0,1} = \beta\,dz$ is antiholomorphic. This will be the case if and only if

$$\partial\varphi = \bar{\partial}\varphi = 0,$$

or equivalently, if and only if

$$d\varphi = d^c\varphi = 0.$$

If $d\varphi = 0$, then locally $\varphi = df$ for some C^∞ function f; we have

$$d^c\varphi = d^c\,df = -\frac{1}{\pi}\left(\frac{\partial^2 f}{\partial x^2} + \frac{\partial^2 f}{\partial y^2}\right)dx \wedge dy,$$

i.e., φ is harmonic if and only if f is harmonic in the usual sense of one complex variable. In particular, we see that the harmonic space $\mathcal{H}^1(S)$ does not depend on the choice of metric.

Now let ds^2 be a metric with $(1,1)$-form ω, multiplied by a constant so that

$$\int_S \omega = 1.$$

$[\omega] \in H^2_{\mathrm{DR}}(S)$ is an integral cohomology class, and by the Kodaira embedding theorem S can be embedded in projective space $\mathbb{P}^N$. In fact, as suggested in the discussion of the embedding theorem, a sharper statement and a simpler proof of the theorem are possible for Riemann surfaces, and we give these here.

Let $L \to S$ be a holomorphic line bundle. Recall that the *degree* of L is defined to be its first Chern class $c_1(L) \in H^2(S, \mathbb{Z})$ under the identification $H^2(S, \mathbb{Z}) = \mathbb{Z}$ given by the natural orientation of S. If $L = [D]$ for

$$D = \sum a_i p_i \in \mathrm{Div}(S),$$

then

$$\deg L = \sum a_i.$$

As we have seen, L has a nontrivial global holomorphic section only if $c_1(L) \geq 0$, i.e.,

$$\deg L < 0 \Rightarrow H^0(S, \mathcal{O}(L)) = 0.$$

On the other hand, since the generator of $H^2(S, \mathbb{Z}) \cong \mathbb{Z}$ corresponding to $+1$ is represented by a positive form,

$$L \text{ positive} \Leftrightarrow \deg L > 0.$$

Thus, if $\deg L > \deg K_S$, then $L \otimes K_S^*$ is positive, and by Kodaira vanishing

$$H^1(S, \mathcal{O}(L)) = H^1(S, \Omega^1(L + K_S^*)) = 0.$$

Alternatively, this fact follows from Kodaira-Serre duality:

$$\deg L > \deg K_S \Rightarrow \deg(K_S \otimes L^*) < 0$$
$$\Rightarrow H^1(S, \mathcal{O}(L)) \cong H^0(S, \mathcal{O}(K_S \otimes L^*)) = 0.$$

Now for any $p \in S$, consider the exact sequence

$$0 \longrightarrow \mathcal{O}(L-p) \longrightarrow \mathcal{O}(L) \overset{r_p}{\longrightarrow} L_p \longrightarrow 0.$$

If $\deg(L-p)=\deg L \ -1 > \deg K_S$, then $H^1(S,\mathcal{O}(L)-p))=0$ and it follows that

$$H^0(S,\mathcal{O}(L)) \to L_p \to 0,$$

that is, the complete linear system of a line bundle of degree greater than $\deg K_S + 1$ has no base points. Moreover, if $\deg L > \deg K_S + 2$, then from the exact sequences

$$0 \longrightarrow \mathcal{O}(L-p-q) \longrightarrow \mathcal{O}(L) \overset{r_{p,q}}{\longrightarrow} L_p \oplus L_q \longrightarrow 0,$$

$$0 \longrightarrow \mathcal{O}(L-2p) \longrightarrow \mathcal{O}(L) \overset{d_p}{\longrightarrow} T_p'^* \otimes L_p \longrightarrow 0,$$

and the vanishing

$$H^1(S,\mathcal{O}(L-p-q)) = H^1(S,\mathcal{O}(L-2p)) = 0,$$

it follows that the complete linear system of L gives an embedding $\iota_L : S \to \mathbb{P}^N$.

Summarizing, we have:

1. $\deg L < 0 \Rightarrow H^0(S,\mathcal{O}(L))=0$.
2. $\deg L > \deg K_S \Rightarrow H^1(S,\mathcal{O}(L))=0$.
3. $\deg L > \deg K_S + 2 \Rightarrow \iota_L : S \to \mathbb{P}^N$ is well-defined and an embedding.

The phrases *compact Riemann surface* and *smooth algebraic curve* or just *curve* will be used pretty much interchangeably from now on. This is somewhat imprecise, as a smooth algebraic curve may be thought of as carrying the additional structure of an embedding—i.e., as a Riemann surface S together with a line bundle $L \to S$ and subspace $E \subset H^0(S,\mathcal{O}(L))$ —but hopefully no confusion should arise. What is important is the ability to think alternately of the abstract analytic object—the compact Riemann surface—and the algebraic object—the zeros of polynomials in $\mathbb{P}^N$; this is implicit in the use of the two terminologies.

As we saw in Section 4 of Chapter 1, the variety $C(S)$ of chords of an algebraic curve $S \subset \mathbb{P}^N$ is a closed subvariety of dimension $\leqslant 3$ in $\mathbb{P}^N$. Projecting from a point $p \notin C(S)$ to any hyperplane $H \subset \mathbb{P}^N$ gives an embedding of S in $H \cong \mathbb{P}^{N-1}$; thus any curve can be smoothly embedded in 3-space $\mathbb{P}^3$. We cannot, in general, embed a curve in $\mathbb{P}^2$. Given a smooth curve $S \subset \mathbb{P}^3$, however, we can find a point $p \in \mathbb{P}^3$ that does not lie on any tangent line to S in $\mathbb{P}^3$, or on any line meeting S in more than two points, or on any line meeting S in two points with intersecting tangent lines. The projection map $\pi_p|_S : S \to \mathbb{P}^2$ will then have everywhere nonzero differential and will be at most 2-1 at isolated points; the image $\pi_p(S) \subset \mathbb{P}^2$ will be a plane algebraic curve whose only singularities are *ordinary double points*, or *nodes*—i.e., near a singular point, $\pi_p(S)$ will look like the union of two smooth analytic arcs meeting at a point with distinct tangents. (This discussion will be sharpened considerably in Section 4 of this chapter.)

Note also that for a curve $S \subset \mathbb{P}^N$ and smooth point $p \in S$, the projection map $\pi_p : S - \{p\} \rightarrow \mathbb{P}^{N-1} \subset \mathbb{P}^N$ to a hyperplane can be extended continuously, hence holomorphically, over all of S by sending p to the point of intersection of its tangent line with $\mathbb{P}^{N-1}$. The intersection of a general hyperplane $H \subset \mathbb{P}^{N-1}$ with the image $\pi_p(S)$ will be just the intersection of the hyperplane $\overline{H,p} \subset \mathbb{P}^N$ with $S - \{p\}$, so that

$$\deg \pi_p(S) = \deg S - 1$$

for $p \in S$. The simplest case here is the stereographic projection of a plane conic C from a point of C onto a line. (See Figure 1.)

The Riemann-Hurwitz Formula

We know from elementary topology that a compact Riemann surface S has only one topological invariant, which we may take to the be the *genus*

$$g(S) = \frac{b_1(S)}{2} = \frac{-\chi(S)+2}{2},$$

or, commonly, the "number of handles."

We saw in Section 2 of Chapter 1 that the curvature form of a metric on the holomorphic tangent bundle $T'(S) = K_S^*$ is just the Gaussian curvature of the metric times the volume form divided by $\sqrt{-1}$. By the classical Gauss-Bonnet theorem, then,

$$\deg K_S = -\chi(S) = 2g - 2.$$

This is a form of the *Riemann-Hurwitz formula* and can be proved directly as follows: Let $f : S \rightarrow S'$ be a holomorphic map between compact Riemann

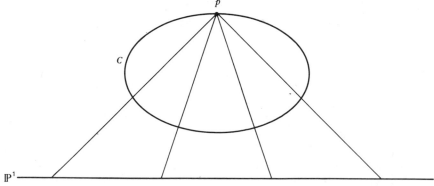

Figure 1

surfaces S and S'. For the induced map $f_* : H_2(S, \mathbb{Z}) \to H_2(S', \mathbb{Z})$, in homology

$$f_*([S]) = n \cdot [S'];$$

the integer n is called the *sheet number*, or *degree*, of the map. For any point $p \in S'$, let Θ be a curvature form for the line bundle $[(p)]$ associated to the divisor (p). Then $f^*\Theta$ is a curvature form for the line bundle $f^*[(p)] = [f^*(p)]$ on S, and we see from the proposition in Section 2 of Chapter 1 that

$$\deg f^*(p) = \int_S f^* \left(\frac{\sqrt{-1}}{2\pi} \Theta \right) = n \int_{S'} \left(\frac{\sqrt{-1}}{2\pi} \Theta \right) = n,$$

so the map f assumes all values $p \in S'$ exactly n times, counting multiplicity in the sense of divisors.

For any $p \in S$, we can find local coordinates z around p in S and w near $f(p)$ in S' such that the map f is given locally by

$$w = z^v.$$

The number v is called the *ramification index* of the map f at p; p is called a *branch point* if $v(p) > 1$. The *branch locus* of the map f is taken to be either the divisor

$$B = \sum_{p \in S} (v(p) - 1) \cdot p$$

on S or its image

$$B' = \sum_{p \in S} (v(p) - 1) \cdot f(p)$$

on S'. For any point $p \in S'$, we can write

$$f^*(p) = \sum_{q \in f^{-1}(p)} v(q) \cdot q,$$

$$\deg f^*(p) = n = \sum_{q \in f^{-1}(p)} v(q),$$

where the summation is over distinct points. This then gives us a picture of the map f: away from the branch locus of f in S', f is a covering map; at a branch point $p \in S$ of ramification index k, k sheets of the covering come together.

We can, in terms of the sheet number and ramification of f, relate the genus of S to the genus of S'. Take a triangulation of S' in which every point of the branch locus appears as a vertex. Because f is a covering map away from B, we can take a triangulation of S whose open cells are just the connected components of the inverse images of the open cells in our triangulation of S'. Then if c_0, c_1, c_2 denote the number of 0-, 1-, and 2-cells in S', respectively, we will have $n \cdot c_1$ 1-cells and $n \cdot c_2$ 2-cells in S. Since for any $p \in S'$,

$$\sum_{q \in f^{-1}(p)} v(q) = n,$$

we see also that the number of distinct points

$$^{\#}(f^{-1}(p)) = n - \sum_{q \in f^{-1}(p)} (v(q) - 1).$$

Consequently the number of vertices in our triangulation of S is

$$n \cdot c_0 - \sum_{q \in S} (v(q) - 1),$$

and the Euler characteristic

$$\chi(S) = n \cdot c_2 - n \cdot c_1 + n \cdot c_0 - \sum_{q \in S} (v(q) - 1)$$

$$= n \cdot \chi(S') - \sum_{q \in S} (v(q) - 1),$$

so

$$g(S) = n \cdot (g(S') - 1) + 1 + \frac{1}{2} \sum_{q \in S} (v(q) - 1).$$

We can also relate the canonical bundle of S to that of S'. Let ω be a global meromorphic 1-form on S', written locally as

$$\omega = \frac{g(w)}{h(w)} dw.$$

For any point $p \in S$ of ramification index v we can find a coordinate z on S centered around p, with f given by

$$w = z^v.$$

Then

$$f^*\omega = \frac{g(z^v)}{h(z^v)} dz^v$$

$$= v \cdot z^{v-1} \cdot \frac{g(z^v)}{h(z^v)} \cdot dz,$$

so

$$\mathrm{ord}_p(f^*\omega) = v \cdot \mathrm{ord}_{f(p)}(\omega) + (v - 1).$$

This implies the equation of divisors on S

$$(f^*\omega) = f^*(\omega) + \sum_{p \in S} (v(p) - 1) \cdot p$$

i.e.,

$$K_S = f^* K_{S'} + B,$$

$$\deg K_S = n \cdot \deg K_{S'} + \sum_{p \in S} (v(p) - 1).$$

Now any compact Riemann surface S admits a holomorphic map to $\mathbb{P}^1$: if $f \in \mathfrak{M}(S)$ is any global meromorphic function written locally as g/h with g, h relatively prime, then f gives a map of S to $\mathbb{P}^1$ by $p \mapsto [g(p), h(p)]$. Let $f : S \to \mathbb{P}^1$ be such a map; on $\mathbb{P}^1$ we have

$$\chi(\mathbb{P}^1) = 2 = -\deg K_{\mathbb{P}^1},$$

and so

$$\chi(S) = n \cdot \chi(\mathbb{P}^1) - \sum_{p \in S} (v(p) - 1)$$

$$= -n \cdot \deg K_{\mathbb{P}^1} - \sum_{p \in S} (v(p) - 1)$$

$$= -\deg K_S.$$

Thus for any S,

$$\deg K_S = -\chi(S) = 2g - 2,$$

and the Riemann-Hurwitz formula is established.

We will sometimes refer to the Riemann-Hurwitz formula as being any of the following:

$$\deg K_S = 2g - 2,$$

$$\chi(S) = n\chi(S') - \sum_{q \in S} (v(q) - 1),$$

$$K_S = f^* K_{S'} + B.$$

Note two things about maps $f : S \to S'$ between compact Riemann surfaces: first, that the number of branch points of f, counting multiplicity, is always even; and second, that unless f is constant, $g(S) \geqslant g(S')$. The latter follows also from the fact that a Riemann surface of genus g has exactly g linearly independent holomorphic 1-forms on it; if $f : S \to S'$ is nonconstant, it is easy to see that $f^* : H^0(S', \Omega^1_{S'}) \to H^0(S, \Omega^1_S)$ is injective, and hence $g(S) \geqslant g(S')$.

The Genus Formula

We will give here three proofs of the *genus formula*, which gives the genus of a smooth plane curve in terms of its degree.

First, the topological argument. Suppose $S \subset \mathbb{P}^2$ is a smooth curve of degree d, given in $\mathbb{P}^2$ as the locus of zeros of a homogeneous polynomial $F(Z_0, Z_1, Z_2)$ of degree d. In terms of Euclidean coordinates $z_1 = Z_1/Z_0$, $z_2 = Z_2/Z_0$ on $C^2 \subset \mathbb{P}^2$, the equation is

$$f(z_1, z_2) = F(1, z_1, z_2).$$

Choose a point $p \in \mathbb{P}^2$ not on S and a line H not containing p; after a linear change of coordinates we may take

$$p = [0,0,1], \qquad H = (Z_2 = 0);$$

we may also assume the line L at infinity $(Z_0 = 0)$ is not tangent to S.

Now consider the map $\pi_p : S \to \mathbb{P}^1$ given by projecting from p to H. Near a point $q \in S$ with $(\partial f / \partial z_2)(q) \neq 0$, z_1 will serve as local coordinate on S, so the map is unramified; if $(\partial f / \partial z_2)(q) = 0$, then $(\partial f / \partial z_1)(q) \neq 0$ and—taking z_2 as local coordinate on S near q, $z_1 = z_1(z_2)$ as a function of z_2—we can write

$$f(z_1(z_2), z_2) \equiv 0$$

so by the chain rule

$$\frac{\partial f}{\partial z_2} + \frac{\partial f}{\partial z_1} \cdot \frac{\partial z_1}{\partial z_2} \equiv 0 \text{ on } S.$$

Consequently the order of vanishing of $\partial z_1 / \partial z_2$ at q—that is, the ramification index $v(q)$ of the map π_p at q minus one—is equal to the order of zero of $\partial f / \partial z_2$ at $q \in S$—that is, the multiplicity of intersection of S with the curve $(\partial f / \partial z_2 = 0)$ at q. $(\partial f / \partial z_2 = 0)$ is a curve of degree $d - 1$ in $\mathbb{P}^2$, and so its intersection number with S is $d(d-1)$; since all points of $S \cap (\partial f / \partial z_2 = 0)$ lie in the finite plane $(Z_0 \neq 0)$,

$$\sum (v(q) - 1) = d(d-1).$$

Now $[S] = d \cdot [H]$ in $H_2(\mathbb{P}^2, \mathbb{Z})$, so the sheet number of the projection map π_p is d; by the Riemann-Hurwitz formula,

$$\chi(S) = d \cdot \chi(\mathbb{P}^1) - \sum_{q \in S} (v(q) - 1)$$

$$= 2d - d(d-1)$$

and so

$$g(S) = \frac{2 - \chi(S)}{2}$$

$$= \frac{(d-1)(d-2)}{2}.$$

A second way to arrive at this formula is by the *adjunction formula* from Section 2 of Chapter 1. It gives

$$K_S = K_{\mathbb{P}^2}|_S \otimes N_S$$

$$= (K_{\mathbb{P}^2} + S)|_S.$$

Now from that section $K_{\mathbb{P}^2} = -3H$ and $S = dH$, so $K_{\mathbb{P}^2} + S = (d-3)H$ on

$\mathbb{P}^2$. Thus

$$\chi(S) = -\deg K_S$$
$$= -{}^{\#}(S \cdot (d-3)H) = -d(d-3)$$

and

$$g(S) = \frac{2-\chi(S)}{2} = \frac{(d-1)(d-2)}{2}.$$

The third way to compute $g(S)$ is by the Poincaré residue map. Recall (p. 147) that for a meromorphic 2-form ω on $\mathbb{P}^2$ holomorphic on $\mathbb{P}^2 - S$ and with a single pole along S, and written locally as

$$\omega = g(z_1, z_2) \frac{dz_1 \wedge dz_2}{f(z_1, z_2)},$$

the Poincaré residue $R(\omega)$ is given by

$$R(\omega) = -g(z_1, z_2) \frac{dz_1}{(\partial f / \partial z_2)(z_1, z_2)}$$
$$= g(z_1, z_2) \frac{dz_2}{(\partial f / \partial z_1)(z_1, z_2)}.$$

Recall also that the Poincaré residue map gives in this case an isomorphism

$$H^0(\mathbb{P}^2, \Omega^2(S)) \longrightarrow H^0(S, \Omega_S^1).$$

Now consider $\omega \in H^0(\mathbb{P}^2, \Omega^2(S))$, written as above. The form $dz_1 \wedge dz_2$ extends to a meromorphic 2-form on $\mathbb{P}^2$; since $K_{\mathbb{P}^2} = -3H$ and $dz_1 \wedge dz_2$ is nonzero holomorphic on $\mathbb{P}^2 - L$, it follows that $dz_1 \wedge dz_2$ must have a pole of order 3 along the line L. Similarly, f extends to a meromorphic function on $\mathbb{P}^2$, and since f is a polynomial with a single zero along a curve of degree d in $\mathbb{P}^2 - L$, it must have a pole of order d along L. It follows that g must extend to a meromorphic function with a pole of order $\leqslant d-3$ along L, i.e., g must be a polynomial of degree $\leqslant d-3$ in z_1, z_2. Thus *the holomorphic 1-forms in S are exactly the differentials*

$$\omega = g(z_1, z_2) \frac{dz_1}{(\partial f / \partial z_2)(z_1, z_2)}$$

for g a polynomial of degree $\leqslant d-3$. We have seen that the number of monomials of degree $\leqslant d$ in n variables is $\binom{n+d}{d}$, and so

$$g(S) = h^0(S, \Omega^1)$$
$$= \binom{d-1}{2} = \frac{(d-1)(d-2)}{2}.$$

Later on we will see how to extend this formula to certain singular curves.

Cases $g = 0, 1$

First, let S be any compact Riemann surface of genus 0. Then

$$h^1(S, \mathcal{O}) = h^0(S, \Omega^1) = 0$$

and so, for $L = [p]$ the line bundle associated to any point $p \in S$ we see from the long exact cohomology sequence associated to the sequence

$$0 \to \mathcal{O}_S \to \mathcal{O}_S(L) \to L_p \to 0$$

that L has a global section nonzero at p, i.e., there exists a nonconstant meromorphic function f on S, holomorphic away from p and having only a simple pole at p. But such a function assumes the value ∞, and hence every value λ, exactly once, and so gives an isomorphism $f: S \to \mathbb{P}^1$. Thus,

any compact Riemann surface of genus 0 is the Riemann sphere $\mathbb{P}^1$

Next, we consider curves of genus 1. The full story on these curves will not be available to us until the next section; for the time being we will start by proving that *any compact Riemann surface S of genus 1 can be realized as a nonsingular cubic curve in $\mathbb{P}^2$*.

The proposition is easy to prove: we know that $\deg K_S = 0$, and so, by the embedding theorem, for any $p \in S$ the complete linear system of the line bundle $L = [3p]$ gives an embedding of S as a cubic curve in $\mathbb{P}^N$ where $N = h^0(S, \mathcal{O}(L)) - 1 \geqslant 2$. But $H^0(S, \mathcal{O}(L))$ corresponds to meromorphic functions on S holomorphic on $S - \{p\}$ and of order $\geqslant -3$ at p; since any such function is uniquely determined by its principal part

$$\frac{a_{-3}}{z^3} + \frac{a_{-2}}{z^2} + \frac{a_{-1}}{z} + a_0 + \cdots.$$

at p, and since there cannot exist a meromorphic function with only a single pole at p—as noted before, such a function would give a 1-1 map of S to $\mathbb{P}^1$—we see that $h^0(S, \mathcal{O}(L)) \leqslant 3$, hence $h^0(S, \mathcal{O}(L)) = 3$ and we are done.

It is worthwhile, however, to go through the process explicitly in this case. First we shall establish a basic general fact:

Lemma (Residue Theorem). *For φ a meromorphic one-form on a compact Riemann surface S with polar divisor $a_1 + \cdots + a_d$,*

$$\sum_i \text{Res}_{a_i}(\varphi) = 0.$$

Proof. Letting $B_\varepsilon(a_i)$ be an ε-disc around a_i, we have by Stokes' theorem

$$0 = -\int_{S-\cup_i B_\varepsilon(a_i)} d\varphi = \int_{\partial(\cup_i B_\varepsilon(a_i))} \varphi = \sum_i \text{Res}_{a_i}(\varphi). \qquad \text{Q.E.D.}$$

Applying this to $\varphi = df/f$ shows again that meromorphic function f on S has the same number of zeroes as poles.

We return to our Riemann surface S of genus 1. As noted before, there are no nonconstant meromorphic functions on S with only a single pole at p. On the other hand, by the vanishing theorem

$$H^1(S, \mathcal{O}(p)) = 0,$$

and so the exact sequence

$$0 \to \mathcal{O}(p) \to \mathcal{O}(2p) \to \mathbb{C}_p \to 0$$

tells us that there does indeed exist a meromorphic function F on S with a double pole at p, holomorphic elsewhere. Next,

$$h^0(S, \Omega^1) = g(S) = 1,$$

so S has a nonzero holomorphic 1-form ω; since $\deg K_S = \deg(\omega) = 0$, ω must be everywhere nonzero. Consider the meromorphic form $F \cdot \omega$; it is holomorphic on $S - \{p\}$, and by the residue theorem

$$\text{Res}_p(F \cdot \omega) = 0.$$

Consequently if z is any local coordinate around p, after multiplying by a constant and adding a constant we can write the series expansion of F as

$$F(z) = \frac{1}{z^2} + [1].$$

Now consider the meromorphic function dF/ω on S. Since ω is nonzero everywhere, dF/ω is holomorphic on $S - \{p\}$ and has a triple pole at p; setting

$$F' = \lambda \frac{dF}{\omega} + \lambda'F + \lambda''$$

for suitable constants $\lambda, \lambda', \lambda''$, we can write

$$F'(z) = \frac{1}{z^3} + [1]$$

near p.

The map $\iota_L : S \to \mathbb{P}^2$ associated to the line bundle $L = [3p]$ can thus be given by

$$q \mapsto [1, F(q), F'(q)].$$

Writing out expansions around p, we have

$$F'(z)^2 = \frac{1}{z^6} + \frac{c}{z^2} + [-1]$$

and

$$F(z)^3 = \frac{1}{z^6} + \frac{c'}{z^3} + \frac{c''}{z^2} + [-1],$$

so that the meromorphic function

$$F'(z)^2 + c'F'(z) - F(z)^3 + (c''-c)F(z)$$

is holomorphic away from p, with at most a single pole at p, hence equal to a constant. The image of S under the embedding ι_L is accordingly the locus of the polynomial

$$y^2 + c'y = x^3 + ax + b,$$

where $x = Z_1/Z_0$, $y = Z_2/Z_0$ are Euclidean coordinates on $\mathbb{P}^2$. After a linear change of the coordinate y, we may take this polynomial of the form

$$(*) \qquad\qquad y^2 = x^3 + ax + b,$$

and finally, after a linear change in the x-coordinate, taking two of the roots of the polynomial $x^3 + ax + b$ to 0 and 1, we see that *any curve of genus 1 is the zero locus in $\mathbb{P}^2$ of a cubic polynomial*

$$y^2 = x \cdot (x-1) \cdot (x-\lambda)$$

for some $\lambda \in \mathbb{C}$.

Note that by the above a Riemann surface of genus 1 is determined by the one parameter λ in the polynomial $(*)$ above; since the quotient $\mathbb{C}/\Lambda$ of $\mathbb{C}$ by any rank 2 lattice $\Lambda \subset \mathbb{C}$ is a Riemann surface of genus 1, and since one complex parameter is required to specify a lattice $\Lambda \subset \mathbb{C}$ of rank 2 up to an automorphism of $\mathbb{C}$, we might expect that in fact all curves of genus 1 may be realized as $\mathbb{C}/\Lambda$. This is in fact the case, as we shall see in the next section.

In closing we note that meromorphic functions on $S = \mathbb{C}/\Lambda$ are the same as entire meromorphic functions on $\mathbb{C}$, which are periodic for the lattice Λ.

2. ABEL'S THEOREM

Abel's Theorem—First Version

The indefinite integrals of the form

$$(*) \qquad\qquad \int \frac{dx}{\sqrt{x^2 + ax + b}}$$

are readily solved in closed form; more generally, any integral

$$\int R(x, \sqrt{x^2 + ax + b}\,)\,dx,$$

for R a rational function, has a closed-form solution involving only elementary functions. The solutions to integrals of this type have been known since the early days of calculus. For a long time, however, mathematicians were unable to do much with the integrals

$(**)$
$$\int \frac{dx}{\sqrt{x^3 + ax^2 + bx + c}}$$

or, more generally, the *Abelian integrals*

$$\int R(x,y)\,dx,$$

where R is a rational function, and x and y are related by a polynomial equation $f(x,y) = 0$ of degree > 2.

In view of the genus formula of the last section, one reason for the difficulty is easy to spot: the first integral $(*)$ can be thought of as the line integral

$$\int \frac{dx}{y}$$

of the meromorphic form dx/y on the curve C given in terms of Euclidean coordinates x,y in $\mathbb{P}^2$ by $y^2 = x^2 + ax + b$. Now C is a conic curve, hence isomorphic to $\mathbb{P}^1$ via a polynomial map; if $t = t(x,y)$ is a Euclidean coordinate on $\mathbb{P}^1$, the meromorphic form dx/y on C must be of the form $R(t)\,dt$ on $\mathbb{P}^1$ with R a rational function. Thus for $(x_0,y_0), (x,y) \in C$,

$$\int_{(x_0,y_0)}^{(x,y)} \frac{dx}{y} = \int_{t(x_0,y_0)}^{t(x,y)} R(t)\,dt,$$

and the latter integral is easy to solve. Note moreover that since $\mathbb{P}^1$ is simply connected and dx/y is closed, the only dependence of the integral on the choice of path arises from the residues of dx/y, which are readily calculated.

The integral $(**)$, on the other hand, is the integral of the form dx/y on the cubic curve $C = (y^2 = x^3 + ax^2 + bx + c)$. Now, if C is smooth then by the genus formula it has genus 1, and hence cannot be parametrized by a single meromorphic function; thus no such simple expression as the one given above for $(*)$ is possible for $(**)$. Moreover, C is topologically a torus and therefore not simply connected; so the integral

$$\int_p^q \frac{dx}{y}$$

is well-defined only modulo the *periods* of dx/y, that is, the integrals of dx/y over closed loops $\gamma \in H_1(C, \mathbb{Z})$. More precisely, note that from the preceding section the form $\omega = dx/y$ is everywhere holomorphic on C and so is a generator of $H^0(C, \Omega^1)$. Let γ_1, γ_2 be closed loops on C generating $H_1(C, \mathbb{Z}) \cong \mathbb{Z} \oplus \mathbb{Z}$, and denote by

$$a_1 = \int_{\gamma_1} \omega, \qquad a_2 = \int_{\gamma_2} \omega$$

the corresponding periods of ω. The general periods of ω on C will then be of the form $n \cdot a_1 + m \cdot a_2$, $n, m \in \mathbb{Z}$. If a_1 and a_2 were linearly dependent over $\mathbb{R}$, we could write

$$k_1 \int_{\gamma_1} \omega + k_2 \int_{\gamma_2} \omega = 0$$

for $k_1, k_2 \in \mathbb{R}$; we would then have

$$k_1 \int_{\gamma_1} \bar{\omega} + k_2 \int_{\gamma_2} \bar{\omega} = 0,$$

and since ω and $\bar{\omega}$ generate $H^{1,0}(C) \oplus H^{0,1}(C) = H^1_{DR}(C)$, this would imply that

$$k_1[\gamma_1] + k_2[\gamma_2] = 0 \in H_1(C, \mathbb{R}),$$

which is impossible. Thus a_1 and a_2 are independent over $\mathbb{R}$, and so *the periods* $\Lambda = \{n \cdot a_1 + m \cdot a_2\}_{n, m \in \mathbb{Z}} \subset \mathbb{C}$ *of* ω *in* $\mathbb{C}$ *form a lattice in* $\mathbb{C}$. Correspondingly, the value of the integral

$$\int_{p_0}^{p} \omega,$$

while not a well-defined number, is well-defined as a point of the complex torus $\mathbb{C}/\Lambda$.

The first major step toward understanding integrals of this type was made by Abel in 1826. Abel noted that, while the single integral above is a highly intractable function of the point $p = (x, y)$ on C, the qualitative behavior of the more general *Abelian sums*

$$\sum \int_{p_0}^{p_i} \omega$$

was in fact subject to easily expressed relations. A special case of what Abel proved is the following: for C and ω as above, and for any line $L \subset \mathbb{P}^2$, let $p_1(L)$, $p_2(L)$, and $p_3(L)$ denote the three points of intersection of L with C (the ordering of these points, of course, is not well-defined). Let $\psi(L)$ denote the Abelian sum

$$\psi(L) = \sum_{i=1}^{3} \int_{p_0}^{p_i} \omega;$$

as before, $\psi(L)$ is well-defined modulo the periods Λ of ω. Then we have

Abel's Theorem (First Version)

$$\psi(L) = \text{constant} \ (\text{mod} \, \Lambda)$$

Proof. A modern version of the proof is deceptively easy. We consider ψ as a map

$$\psi : \ \mathbb{P}^{2*} \to \mathbb{C}/\Lambda$$

from the space $\mathbb{P}^{2*}$ of lines in $\mathbb{P}^2$ to the complex torus $\mathbb{C}/\Lambda$; clearly it is holomorphic. Let z be a Euclidean coordinate on $\mathbb{C}/\Lambda$ and dz the corresponding global 1-form; then, since $H^{1,0}(\mathbb{P}^2) = H^0(\mathbb{P}^2, \Omega^1) = 0$,

$$\psi^* \, dz \equiv 0,$$

and hence ψ is constant.   Q.E.D.

In a similar way, we prove a slight generalization: again let C be a curve of genus 1, $\omega \in H^0(C, \Omega^1)$ a holomorphic differential, $\Lambda \subset \mathbb{C}$ the period lattice of ω. Then, if $D = (g) = \sum p_i - \sum q_i$ is the divisor of a meromorphic function f on C, we have

$$\sum_i \int_{q_i}^{p_i} \omega \equiv 0 \ (\text{modulo} \ \Lambda),$$

i.e., *there exists a collection of paths* α_i *from* q_i *to* p_i *such that*

$$\sum_i \int_{\alpha_i} \omega = 0.$$

Proof. Write $D_\lambda = (\lambda_0 f - \lambda_1) = \sum p_i(\lambda) - \sum q_i(\lambda)$ for $\lambda = [\lambda_0, \lambda_1] \in \mathbb{P}^1$; set

$$\psi(\lambda) = \sum_i \int_{q_i(\lambda)}^{p_i(\lambda)} \omega \quad (\text{modulo} \ \Lambda).$$

ψ is thus a holomorphic map $\mathbb{P}^1 \to \mathbb{C}/\Lambda$; by the same argument as before we see

$$\psi^* \, dz \in H^0(\mathbb{P}^1, \Omega^1_{\mathbb{P}^1}) = 0$$

$\Rightarrow \psi$ constant and since, as $\lambda_0 \to 0$, $\{p_i(\lambda)\} \to \{q_i(\lambda)\}$, we have $\psi \equiv 0$ (modulo Λ).   Q.E.D.

Following some preliminaries concerning the reciprocity formulas, we will give the converse to this version of Abel's theorem for Riemann surfaces of arbitrary genus. Together with the Riemann-Roch formula, these constitute the fundamental tools in the study of algebraic curves.

Let S now be a compact Riemann surface of genus g, and let $\delta_1, \ldots, \delta_{2g}$ be 1-cycles in S forming a basis for $H_1(X, \mathbb{Z})$. We may take $\delta_1, \ldots, \delta_{2g}$ to be a *canonical basis*, i.e., such that δ_i intersects δ_{i+g} once positively, and does not intersect any other δ_j. In such a canonical basis, the cycles $\delta_1, \ldots, \delta_g$ are called the *A-cycles*, $\delta_{g+1}, \ldots, \delta_{2g}$ the *B-cycles*.

Now let $\omega_1, \ldots, \omega_g \in H^0(S, \Omega^1)$ be a basis for the space of holomorphic 1-forms on S. The *period matrix* of S is the $g \times 2g$ matrix

$$
\Omega = \begin{bmatrix} \int_{\delta_1} \omega_1 & \cdots & \int_{\delta_{2g}} \omega_1 \\ \vdots & & \vdots \\ \int_{\delta_1} \omega_g & \cdots & \int_{\delta_{2g}} \omega_g \end{bmatrix}.
$$

The (transposed) column vectors $\Pi_i = (\int_{\delta_i} \omega_1, \ldots, \int_{\delta_i} \omega_g) \in \mathbb{C}^q$ of the period matrix are called the *periods*; we first check that they are linearly independent over $\mathbb{R}$: If we have $\sum k_i \Pi_i = 0$, $k_i \in \mathbb{R}$, then

$$
\sum k_i \int_{\delta_i} \omega_j = 0 \text{ for all } j \Rightarrow \sum k_i \int_{\delta_i} \bar{\omega}_j = 0 \text{ for all } j,
$$

$$
\Rightarrow \sum k_i [\delta_i] = 0 \in H_1(S, \mathbb{R}),
$$

since $\{\omega_j, \bar{\omega}_j\}$ span $H_{\mathrm{DR}}^1(S)$; this is impossible, since $\{\delta_i\}$ is a basis for $H_1(S, \mathbb{Z})$.

The $2g$ periods $\Pi_i \in \mathbb{C}^g$ thus generate a lattice

$$
\Lambda = \{m_1 \Pi_1 + \cdots + m_{2g} \Delta_{2g}, m_i \in \mathbb{Z}\}
$$

in $\mathbb{C}^g$; we define the *Jacobian variety* $\mathcal{J}(S)$ of S to be the complex torus $\mathbb{C}^g / \Lambda$. The Jacobian is a natural range for Abelian integrals: whereas the integral $\int_p^q \omega$ of a single holomorphic differential ω is defined only modulo the $2g$ periods of ω, which are usually dense in $\mathbb{C}$, the vector

$$
\left(\int_p^q \omega_1, \ldots, \int_p^q \omega_g \right),
$$

is well-defined as a vector in $\mathbb{C}^g$ modulo the discrete lattice $\Lambda \subset \mathbb{C}^g$. Picking a base point $p_0 \in S$, accordingly, we have a natural map

$$
\mu: S \to \mathcal{J}(S)
$$

given by

$$
\mu(p) = \left(\int_{p_0}^p \omega_1, \ldots, \int_{p_0}^p \omega_g \right) \in \mathcal{J}(S).
$$

More generally, if $\mathrm{Div}^0(S)$ denotes the group of divisors of degree 0 on S, we define $\mu: \mathrm{Div}^0(S) \to \mathcal{J}(S)$ by

$$
\mu\left(\sum p_\lambda - \sum q_\lambda \right) = \left(\sum \int_{q_\lambda}^{p_\lambda} \omega_1, \ldots, \sum \int_{q_\lambda}^{p_\lambda} \omega_g \right).
$$

To study this map, we need to learn something about the relations among the periods of the ω_i. These are expressed in the reciprocity laws, one of which we now derive.

The First Reciprocity Law and Corollaries

To begin with, we may assume that all of the cycles δ_i on the Riemann surface S issue from a common point $s_0 \in S$. The complement of the δ_i's is then a simply connected region Δ on S; the boundary $\partial \Delta$ contains each δ_i twice with opposite orientation, and may be pictured as in Figure 2. What we are doing is making the familiar topological representation of a surface of genus g as a polygon with $4g$ sides, which are identified in pairs.

Now let ω be a holomorphic differential on S, η a meromorphic form whose only singularities are simple poles at points $s_\lambda \in S$. Assuming that η has no poles on the paths δ_i, let Π^i and N^i denote the periods of ω and η, respectively, along the path δ_i. Since the region Δ is simply connected and ω is holomorphic, we can set

$$\pi(s) = \int_{s_0}^{s} \omega$$

to obtain a holomorphic function π in $\overline{\Delta}$ with $\omega = d\pi$. (See Figure 3.) Note that for any pair of points $p \in \delta_i$, $p' \in \delta_i^{-1}$ on $\partial \Delta$ that are identified on S

$$\pi(p') - \pi(p) = \int_p^{p'} \omega$$

$$= \int_p^{\delta_i(1)} \omega + \int_{\delta_{g+i}} \omega + \int_{\delta_i(1)}^{p'} \omega$$

$$= \int_{\delta_{g+i}} \omega$$

$$= \Pi^{g+i}$$

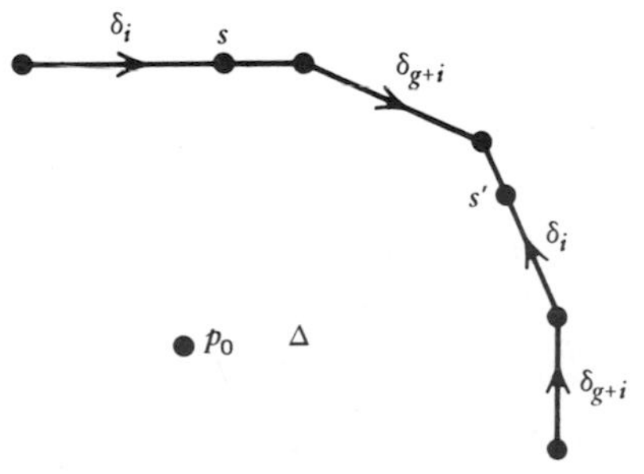

Figure 2

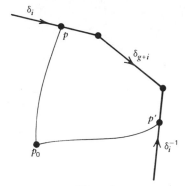

Figure 3

and similarly for $p \in \delta_{g+i}, p' \in \delta_{g+i}^{-1}$ identified on S,

$$\pi(p') - \pi(p) = -\Pi^i.$$

Consider the meromorphic 1-form $\pi \cdot \eta$ in $\bar{\Delta}$. By the residue theorem, since η has only first order poles,

$$\int_{\partial \Delta} \pi \cdot \eta = 2\pi \sqrt{-1} \sum_\lambda \operatorname{Res}_{s_\lambda}(\pi \cdot \eta)$$

$$= 2\pi \sqrt{-1} \sum_\lambda \operatorname{Res}_{s_\lambda}(\eta) \cdot \int_{s_0}^{s_\lambda} \omega.$$

On the other hand, we can compute the integral of $\pi \cdot \eta$ around $\partial \Delta$ explicitly by considering together the contributions of the pair of sides of $\partial \Delta$ corresponding to δ_i and δ_i^{-1}: since, for points $p \in \delta_i$ and $p' \in \delta_i^{-1}$ identified on S, the difference $\Pi(p') - \Pi(p)$ is a constant Π^{g+i}, we see that

$$\int_{\delta_i + \delta_i^{-1}} \pi \cdot \eta = -\Pi^{g+i} \cdot \int_{\delta_i} \eta = -\Pi^{g+i} \cdot N^i.$$

Similarly

$$\int_{\delta_{g+i} + \delta_{g+i}^{-1}} \pi \cdot \eta = \Pi^i \cdot N^{g+i}.$$

Comparing the two expressions for $\int_{\partial \Delta} \pi \cdot \eta$, we find the

Reciprocity Law I

$$\sum_{i=1}^{g} (\Pi^i N^{g+i} - \Pi^{g+i} N^i) = 2\pi \sqrt{-1} \sum_\lambda \operatorname{Res}_{s_\lambda}(\eta) \cdot \int_{s_0}^{s_\lambda} \omega,$$

where the integrals on the right are taken in the interior of Δ.

This is classically known as the *reciprocity law for differentials of the first and third kinds*. In classical terminology, a *differential of the first kind* on a

Riemann surface S is a holomorphic 1-form; a *differential of the second kind* is a meromorphic 1-form with no residues, and a *differential of the third kind* is a meromorphic form with only single poles. Clearly a differential is of the first kind if and only if it is both of the second kind and of the third kind; we shall see shortly that any meromorphic 1-form is the sum of differentials of the second and third kinds. Later on we will prove a reciprocity law for differentials of the first and second kinds.

Before we can apply the reciprocity law, we need to prove a similar result, which will enable us to normalize our basis for $H^0(S, \Omega^1)$. Let ω, ω' be two holomorphic 1-forms on S, Π^i and Π'^i their respective periods around δ_i. Let Δ and π be as above, and consider the integral around $\partial \Delta$ of the form $\pi \cdot \overline{\omega}'$. The exterior derivative $d(\pi \cdot \overline{\omega}') = d\pi \wedge \overline{\omega}' = \omega \wedge \overline{\omega}'$, and so by Stokes' theorem

$$\int_{\partial \Delta} \pi \cdot \overline{\omega}' = \int_S \omega \wedge \overline{\omega}',$$

and, evaluating the line integral just as in the proof of the reciprocity law, we obtain

$$\int_S \omega \wedge \overline{\omega}' = \sum \left(\Pi^i \cdot \overline{\Pi'^{i+g}} - \Pi^{i+g} \overline{\Pi'^i} \right).$$

In particular if we take $\omega' = \omega$, then since $\omega \wedge \overline{\omega}$ is positive we find that

$$(**) \qquad 0 < \sqrt{-1} \int_S \omega \wedge \overline{\omega} = \sqrt{-1} \sum_{i=1}^g \left(\Pi^i \overline{\Pi^{g+i}} - \Pi^{g+i} \overline{\Pi^i} \right)$$

for $\omega \not\equiv 0$. It follows from this that *any holomorphic 1-form ω whose A-periods all vanish must be identically zero*, i.e., the first $g \times g$ minor of the period matrix Ω is nonsingular. Once we know this, we can take our basis $\omega_1, \ldots, \omega_g$ for $H^0(S, \Omega^1)$ so that

$$\int_{\delta_i} \omega_j = \delta_{ij} \qquad \text{for} \qquad 1 \leqslant i, j \leqslant g,$$

i.e., so that the period matrix has the form

$$(I_g, Z).$$

Such a basis for $H^0(S, \Omega^1)$ is called *normalized*.

We now return to the reciprocity law and deduce some consequences. First, consider the case where $\eta = \omega'$ is a holomorphic 1-form; write Π'^i for the periods of ω'. Since ω' has no residues, the formula reads

$$\sum_{i=1}^g \left(\Pi^i \Pi'^{g+i} - \Pi^{g+i} \Pi'^i \right) = 0.$$

This is the *first Riemann bilinear relation* in the periods. In particular, if

$\omega = \omega_i, \omega' = \omega_j$ are elements of our normalized basis, all but two terms in the expression on the right vanish, and we have

$$\int_{\delta_{g+i}} \omega_j - \int_{\delta_{g+j}} \omega_i = 0,$$

i.e., the right-hand block Z in the period matrix above is symmetric. Note that since the quadratic form on $H^0(S, \Omega^1)$ given by

$$(\omega_i, \omega_j) = \sqrt{-1} \int_S \omega_i \wedge \bar{\omega}_j = \sqrt{-1} \overline{\int_{\delta_{g+i}} \omega_j} - \sqrt{-1} \int_{\delta_{g+j}} \omega_i = 2 \cdot \text{Im} \int_{\delta_{g+i}} \omega_j$$

is positive definite, the imaginary part $\text{Im}(Z)$ of Z is positive definite; this is the *second Riemann bilinear relation*. In sum, the two Riemann bilinear relations imply that for a normalized basis of $H^0(S, \Omega^1)$, the period matrix Ω of S has the form

$$\Omega = (I, Z) \quad \text{with} \quad Z = {}^tZ, \quad \text{Im} Z > 0.$$

Abel's Theorem—Second Version

Let S as before be a Riemann surface of genus g, $D = \Sigma(p_\lambda - q_\lambda)$ a divisor of degree 0 on S, and consider the Abelian sum

$$\mu(D) = \left(\Sigma \int_{q_\lambda}^{p_\lambda} \omega_1, \dots, \Sigma \int_{q_\lambda}^{p_\lambda} \omega_g \right) \in \mathcal{J}(S).$$

Abel's theorem in the case $g = 1$ tells us that if D is the divisor (f) of a meromorphic function f on S, then $\mu(D) = 0$. It is not hard to extend this statement to the case of genus g: If $D = (f)$, then the map

$$\psi: [\lambda_0, \lambda_1] \to \mu((\lambda_0 f - \lambda_1))$$

from $\mathbb{P}^1$ to $\mathcal{J}(S)$ is holomorphic, and since the holomorphic 1-forms dz_i on the complex torus $\mathcal{J}(S)$ span the cotangent space at each point,

$$\psi^*(dz_i) \equiv 0 \Rightarrow \psi \quad \text{is constant}$$
$$\Rightarrow \mu(D) = \psi(0) = \psi(\infty) = 0.$$

Conversely, we will now show that *if* $D = \Sigma(p_\lambda - q_\lambda)$ *is any divisor on S of degree 0 and* $\mu(D) = 0$, *then D is the divisor of a meromorphic function.*

The problem, which may at first seem difficult, becomes straightforward once we transpose it from a question about the existence of a meromorphic function to one about the existence of a certain meromorphic form. Note that if f is a meromorphic function with $(f) = \Sigma(p_\lambda - q_\lambda)$, then the differential

$$\eta = \frac{1}{2\pi\sqrt{-1}} d\log f = \frac{1}{2\pi\sqrt{-1}} \frac{df}{f}$$

is a meromorphic form with polar divisor

$$(\eta)_\infty = -\left(\sum_\lambda (p_\lambda + q_\lambda)\right) \qquad 1)$$

$$\text{Res}_{p_\lambda}(\eta) = \frac{a_\lambda}{2\pi\sqrt{-1}}, \qquad \text{Res}_{q_\lambda}(\eta) = \frac{b_\lambda}{2\pi\sqrt{-1}}, \qquad 2)$$

where we are now writing

$$D = \sum a_i p_i + \sum b_i q_i$$

with the p_λ, q_λ distinct; and moreover

$$\int_\gamma \eta \in \mathbb{Z} \qquad 3)$$

for any closed loop γ on $S - \{p_i, q_i\}$. Conversely, if η is any meromorphic form with these three properties, we can set

$$f(p) = e^{2\pi i \int_{p_0}^p \eta}$$

to obtain a well-defined meromorphic function f with $(f) = D$. Thus, to prove the converse to Abel's theorem, we have to show that for $D = \Sigma(p_\lambda - q_\lambda)$ with $\mu(D) = 0$, there exists a differential of the third kind η, holomorphic on $S - \{p_\lambda, q_\lambda\}$ with residues a_λ at p_λ, b_λ at q_λ, and having all integral periods. First, we check that we can at least find a meromorphic differential with the requisite singularities:

Lemma. *Given a finite set of points $\{p_\lambda\}$ on S and complex numbers a_λ such that $\Sigma a_\lambda = 0$, there exists a differential of the third kind on S, holomorphic on $S - \{p_\lambda\}$ and having residue a_λ at p_λ.*

Proof. Consider the exact sheaf sequence on S

$$0 \longrightarrow \Omega^1 \longrightarrow \Omega^1(\Sigma p_\lambda) \overset{\text{res.}}{\longrightarrow} \oplus \mathbb{C}_{p_\lambda} \longrightarrow 0.$$

By Kodaira-Serre duality

$$H^1(S, \Omega^1) \cong H^0(S, \mathcal{O}) \cong \mathbb{C},$$

so that the image of $H^0(S, \Omega^1([\Sigma p_\lambda]))$ in $\oplus \mathbb{C}_{p_\lambda}$ has codimension at most 1. But we have seen that the sum of the residues of any meromorphic 1-form on S is zero; so the image of $H^0(S, \Omega^1([\Sigma p_\lambda]))$ is contained in, hence equal to, the hyperplane $(\Sigma a_\lambda = 0) \subset \oplus \mathbb{C}_{p_\lambda}$. Q.E.D.

Now choose cycles $\delta_1, \ldots, \delta_{2g}$ representing a canonical basis for $H_1(S, \mathbb{Z})$ as on p. 227 such that no point p_λ, q_λ lies on one of the paths δ_j, and let $\omega_1, \ldots, \omega_g$ be a normalized basis for $H^0(S, \Omega^1)$ with respect to $\{\delta_1, \ldots, \delta_{2g}\}$. By the lemma, there exists a differential of the third kind with residues $a_\lambda/(2\pi\sqrt{-1})$ at p_λ, $b_\lambda/(2\pi\sqrt{-1})$ at q_λ; any two such forms differ by a holomorphic form on S, and hence there exists a unique such form η such that the A-periods

$$N^i = \int_{\delta_i} \eta = 0, \qquad i = 1,\ldots,g.$$

The problem now is to alter η so as to make all its B-periods integral; clearly we can do this without disturbing the singularities of η or the integrality of its A-periods only by adding on an integral linear combination of the forms ω_i. To see if this is possible, we read off the B-periods of η by the reciprocity law: since $N^i = 0$ for $i = 1,\ldots,g$, we have for each i,

$$N^{g+i} = \sum_\lambda a_\lambda \int_{p_0}^{p_\lambda} \omega_i + \sum_\lambda b_\lambda \int_{p_0}^{q_\lambda} \omega_i$$

$$= \sum_\lambda \int_{q_\lambda}^{p_\lambda} \omega_i$$

for some choice of paths α_λ from q_λ to p_λ. Now we are essentially done. By hypothesis,

$$\mu(D) = \left(\sum_\lambda \int_{\alpha_\lambda} \omega_1, \ldots, \sum_\lambda \int_{\alpha_\lambda} \omega_g \right) \in \Lambda,$$

i.e., there exists a cycle

$$\gamma \sim \sum_{k=1}^{2g} m_k \cdot \delta_k, \qquad m_k \in \mathbb{Z}$$

such that for each i,

$$\sum_\lambda \int_{\alpha_\lambda} \omega_i = \int_\gamma \omega_i,$$

and so

$$N^{g+i} = \int_\gamma \omega_i \qquad \text{for all } i.$$

Set

$$\eta' = \eta - \sum_{k=1}^{g} m_{g+k} \omega_k.$$

The periods N'^i of η' are then given by

$$N'^i = -m_{g+i}, \qquad i = 1,\ldots,g,$$

$$N'^{g+i} = N^{g+i} - \sum_{k=1}^{g} m_{g+k} \int_{\delta_{g+i}} \omega_k$$

$$= \sum_{k=1}^{2g} m_k \int_{\delta_k} \omega_i - \sum_{k=1}^{g} m_{g+k} \int_{\delta_{g+i}} \omega_k$$

$$= m_i + \sum_{k=1}^{g} m_{g+k} \left(\int_{\delta_{g+k}} \omega_i - \int_{\delta_{g+i}} \omega_k \right)$$

$$= m_i,$$

by the first bilinear relation of Riemann. Thus η' has all integral periods, and $D=(f)$ for $f(p)=\exp(2\pi\sqrt{-1}\int_{p_0}^{p}\eta')$.

Summarizing, we have proved

Abel's Theorem (Second Version). *Given* $D=\Sigma(p_\lambda-q_\lambda)\in\mathrm{Div}(S)$ *and* $\omega_1,\dots,\omega_g$ *a basis for the space of holomorphic 1-forms on* S, *then* $D=(f)$ *for some meromorphic function* f *on* S *if and only if*

$$\varphi(D)=\left(\sum_\lambda\int_{q_\lambda}^{p_\lambda}\omega_1,\dots,\sum_\lambda\int_{q_\lambda}^{p_\lambda}\omega_g\right)\equiv 0(\Lambda).$$

In fancier language: recalling that $\mathrm{Pic}^0(S)$ is the group of divisors of degree zero on S modulo linear equivalence, the map

$$\mu:\mathrm{Div}^0(S)\to\mathcal{J}(S)$$

factors

$$\mathrm{Div}^0(S)\overset{\mu}{\to}\mathcal{J}(S)$$
$$\searrow\qquad\nearrow\;\bar\mu$$
$$\mathrm{Pic}^0(S)$$

to give an injection $\bar\mu:\mathrm{Pic}^0(S)\to\mathcal{J}(S)$.

Jacobi Inversion

The second statement of Abel's theorem above suggests our next question: Is the map $\mu:\mathrm{Div}^0(S)\to\mathcal{J}(S)$ given by Abelian sums surjective, or, in other words, is the induced map $\bar\mu:\mathrm{Pic}^0(S)\to\mathcal{J}(S)$ an isomorphism? The Jacobi inversion theorem asserts that the answer to this question is yes, and in fact tells us that we obtain what is suggested by counting dimensions.

Theorem (Jacobi Inversion). *Given* S *a curve of genus* g, $p_0\in S$ *and* $\omega_1,\dots,\omega_g$ *a basis for* $H^0(S,\Omega^1)$, *for any* $\lambda\in\mathcal{J}(S)$ *we can find* g *points* $p_1,\dots,p_g\in S$ *such that*

$$(*)\qquad\qquad \mu\left(\sum_i(p_i-p_0)\right)=\lambda,$$

i.e., for any vector $\lambda\in\mathbb{C}^g$, *we can find* $p_1,\dots,p_g\in S$ *and paths* α_i *from* p_0 *to* p_i *such that*

$$\sum_i\int_{\alpha_i}\omega_j=\lambda_j\qquad\text{for all } j.$$

Moreover, for generic $\lambda\in\mathbb{C}^g$, *the divisor* Σp_i *is unique.*

Proof. For now, we will just prove the result; in Section 7 of this chapter, after introducing Riemann's theta function, we will see how to solve the equation $(*)$ explicitly.

First let $S^{(d)}$ denote the set of effective divisors of degree d on S, i.e., the set of *unordered* d-tuples of points $\{p_1, \ldots, p_d\}$ on S, not necessarily distinct. $S^{(d)}$ is the quotient of the d-fold product $S^d = S \times S \times \cdots \times S$ of S with itself d times by the action of the symmetric group Σ_d on d letters; as such it inherits from S^d the structure of a topological space. In fact, the projection map $\pi : S^d \to S^{(d)}$ gives $S^{(d)}$ the structure of a complex manifold: for a point $D = \Sigma p_i \in S^{(d)}$, let z_i be a local coordinate in a neighborhood U_i of p_i in S, where we take $U_i \cap U_j = \emptyset$ for $p_i \neq p_j$ and $z_i = z_j$ in $U_i = U_j$ for $p_i = p_j$. Then if we let $\sigma_1, \ldots, \sigma_d$ denote the elementary symmetric functions, by the fundamental theorem of algebra the map

$$\Sigma\, q_i \mapsto (\sigma_1\{z_i(q_i)\}, \ldots, \sigma_d\{z_i(q_i)\})$$

gives a coordinate chart on $\pi(U_1 \times \cdots \times U_d) \subset S^{(d)}$. Note that away from the branch locus the map π is a covering map and we can take coordinates $(z_1(p_1), \ldots, z_d(p_d))$ on $S^{(d)}$. At the other extreme, around a point $d \cdot p$ local coordinates are

$$(z_1 + \cdots + z_d, \ \ldots, \ z_1 \cdots z_d)$$

The compact complex manifold $S^{(d)}$ is called the dth *symmetric product* of S. (It is interesting to verify that $\mathbb{P}^{1(d)} = \mathbb{P}^d$.) Fixing a base point $p_0 \in S$, there are inclusions

$$\iota : \ S^{(d)} \to \mathrm{Div}^0(S)$$

given by

$$\Sigma\, p_\lambda \mapsto \Sigma\, (p_\lambda - p_0)$$

and, correspondingly, holomorphic maps

$$\mu^{(d)} : \ S^{(d)} \to \mathcal{J}(S)$$

$$: \ \Sigma\, p_\lambda \mapsto \left(\sum_\lambda \int_{p_0}^{p_\lambda} \omega_1, \ldots, \sum_i \int_{p_0}^{p_\lambda} \omega_g \right).$$

In this context, the Jacobi inversion theorem asserts that for S of genus g, the map $\mu^{(g)}$ is surjective and generically one-to-one.

Now let $D = \Sigma p_i$ be a point of $S^{(g)}$ with all p_i distinct, z_i a local coordinate on S centered at p_i, and $(z_1, \ldots, z_g)$ corresponding coordinates on $S^{(g)}$ near D. For $D' = \Sigma z_i$ near D, by calculus

$$\frac{\partial}{\partial z_i}(\mu^{(g)}(D')) = \frac{\partial}{\partial z_i}\left(\int_{p_0}^{z_i} \omega_j \right)$$

$$= \omega_j / dz_i,$$

where we write ω / dz for the function $h(z)$ such that $\omega = h(z)\,dz$. Thus, and this is a fundamental observation, the Jacobian matrix of the map $\mu^{(d)}$ is given near D by

$$\mathcal{J}(\mu^{(d)}) = \begin{bmatrix} \omega_1/dz_1 & \cdots & \omega_1/dz_g \\ \vdots & & \vdots \\ \omega_g/dz_1 & \cdots & \omega_g/dz_g \end{bmatrix}.$$

We note that changing the local coordinate z_i multiplies the ith column by a nonzero factor but does not affect the rank of $\mathcal{J}(\mu^{(d)})$.

We may choose p_1 so that $\omega_1(p_1) \neq 0$, and then, subtracting a multiple of ω_1 from $\omega_2, \ldots, \omega_g$, we may arrange that $\omega_2(p_1) = \cdots = \omega_g(p_1) = 0$. Next, we may choose p_2 so that $\omega_2(p_2) \neq 0$, and then arrange as before that $\omega_3(p_2) = \cdots = \omega_g(p_2) = 0$. Continuing in this way, the Jacobian matrix at D will be triangular with zeros below the diagonal and nonzero on the diagonal, and so has maximal rank at D.

Thus the map $\mu^{(g)}$ is not everywhere singular, and the Jacobi inversion theorem follows from the fact that any holomorphic map $f: M \to N$ between compact connected equidimensional complex manifolds is surjective if $|\mathcal{J}(f)| \not\equiv 0$. This follows immediately from the proper mapping theorem: $f(M) \subset N$ is an analytic subvariety and contains an open set, hence $f(M) = N$. For a more elementary argument, let ψ_N be a volume form on N. Since f is orientation preserving and $|\mathcal{J}(f)| \not\equiv 0$,

$$\int_M f^* \psi_N > 0.$$

On the other hand, for any $q \in N$ we have

$$H^{2n}(N - \{q\}, \mathbb{R}) = 0,$$

hence in $N - \{q\}$

$$\psi_N = d\varphi$$

for some $\varphi \in A^{2n-1}(N - \{q\})$. Then if $q \not\in f(M)$,

$$\int_M f^* \psi_N = \int_{\partial M} df^* \varphi = 0,$$

a contradiction.

The only thing that remains to be proved is that $\mu^{(g)}$ is generically one-to-one. But this is clear: by Abel's theorem the fiber of $\mu^{(g)}$ over any point $\lambda \in \mathcal{J}(S)$ consists of the set $|D|$ of effective divisors linearly equivalent to any divisor $D \in \mu^{(g)^{-1}}(\lambda)$, which is a projective space. On the other hand, by dimension considerations the generic fiber of $\mu^{(g)}$ is 0-dimensional; it follows that the generic fiber of $\mu^{(g)}$ is one point. (The map $\mu^{(g)}$ is an example of a *birational map*; we shall discuss these in detail in Chapter 4.) Q.E.D.

Note that as a corollary to Jacobi inversion, we see that *every divisor of degree* $\geqslant$ g *on a Riemann surface of genus* g *is linearly equivalent to an effective divisor.*

Consider in particular the case of a Riemann surface S of genus 1. Then $\mathcal{J}(S) = \mathbb{C}/\Lambda$ and the map $\mu^{(1)}$ is given simply by

$$\mu: p \mapsto \int_{p_0}^{p} \omega,$$

where ω is a generator of $H^0(S, \Omega^1)$. By Abel's theorem, $\mu(p) = \mu(p')$ only if there exists a meromorphic function f on S with $(f) = (p - p_0) - (p' - p_0) = p - p'$; since we have seen that there are no meromorphic functions on S with only a single pole, it follows that the map $\mu^{(1)}$ is injective. By the Jacobi inversion theorem, the map is surjective as well, and so we have an isomorphism

$$\mu: S \longrightarrow \mathcal{J}(S),$$

i.e., *every Riemann surface of genus 1 is of the form* $\mathbb{C}/\Lambda$ *for some lattice* $\Lambda \subset \mathbb{C}$.

We have thus established the fundamental fact that the nonsingular cubic curves in $\mathbb{P}^2$ are the same as the compact Riemann surfaces $\mathbb{C}/\Lambda$ for a suitable lattice Λ in the complex plane. It follows that every such curve C has a group structure; we want to briefly discuss this.

First, recall that at the end of the previous section we constructed meromorphic functions F and F' on a Riemann surface C of genus 1, having a double and triple pole, respectively, at a base point $p_0 \in C$ and holomorphic elsewhere. We chose F and F' so that in terms of a local coordinate w around p_0,

$$F(w) = \frac{1}{w^2} + [1]$$

and

$$F'(w) = \frac{1}{w^3} + [1]$$

and

$$dF = F' \cdot \omega,$$

where ω is a global nonzero holomorphic 1-form on C. Now, we may express C as the complex torus $\mathbb{C}/\Lambda$; let z be the Euclidean coordinate on C with $\omega = dz$. The function F is then the *Weierstrass* $\mathcal{P}$-function; its derivative $(\partial/\partial z)\mathcal{P} = -2F'$ is denoted $\mathcal{P}'$. Note that the Laurent expansion for $\mathcal{P}$ around p_0 can contain no terms of odd degree, since otherwise

$\mathcal{P}(z) - \mathcal{P}(-z)$ would be a nonconstant holomorphic function on C. Thus

$$\mathcal{P}(z) = \frac{1}{z^2} + az^2 + bz^4 + [6],$$

$$\mathcal{P}'(z) = -\frac{2}{z^3} + 2az + 4bz^3 + [5],$$

$$\mathcal{P}(z)^3 = \frac{1}{z^6} + \frac{3a}{z^2} + 3b + [2],$$

$$\mathcal{P}'(z)^2 = \frac{4}{z^6} - \frac{8a}{z^2} - 16b + [1],$$

from which we deduce that $\mathcal{P}$ and $\mathcal{P}'$ satisfy the relation

$$\mathcal{P}'^2 = 4 \cdot \mathcal{P}^3 - 20a \cdot \mathcal{P} - 28b;$$

it is conventional to write g_2 for $20a$ and g_3 for $28b$.

Now the holomorphic map

$$\psi: \mathbb{C}/\Lambda \to \mathbb{P}^2$$

given by

$$z \mapsto [1, \mathcal{P}(z), \mathcal{P}'(z)]$$

embeds $\mathbb{C}/\Lambda$ as the locus of the polynomial $f(x,y) = y^2 - 4x^3 + g_2 \cdot x + g_3$. The differential $\omega = dz$ on $C = \mathbb{C}/\Lambda$ is the Poincaré residue

$$\omega = R\left(\frac{dx \wedge dy}{f(x,y)}\right) = \frac{dx}{\partial f/\partial y} = \frac{dx}{y},$$

and the inverse of ψ is the Abelian integral

$$\psi^{-1}(p) = \int_{p_0}^p \frac{dx}{y} \qquad \text{(mod periods)}$$

where we take in this case $p_0 = \psi(0) = [0, 0, 1] \in \mathbb{P}^2$. If $p_1, p_2, p_3 \in C$ and $z_1, z_2, z_3 \in \mathbb{C}$ are the corresponding points in $\mathbb{C}/\Lambda$, then Abel's theorem is equivalent to the assertion

$$z_1 + z_2 + z_3 \equiv 0(\lambda) \Leftrightarrow (3p_0 - p_1 - p_2 - p_3) \sim 0,$$

i.e., there exists a meromorphic function $f(z)$ on C with a triple pole at p_0 and zeros at p_1, p_2, p_3. To see this, let $A(x,y) = ax + by + c$ be the equation of the line L joining p_1 and p_2 in $\mathbb{P}^2$ and denote by p' the third point of intersection of L with C (Figure 4). Then since the line at infinity intersects C in the divisor $3p_0$ $A(\mathcal{P}(z), \mathcal{P}'(z))$ is a meromorphic function on $C = \mathbb{C}/\Lambda$ with divisor $p_1 + p_2 + p' - 3p_0$. Thus $p' \sim p_3$ and so $p' = p_3$. In summary:

$(*)$ $\qquad z_1 + z_2 + z_3 \equiv 0(\lambda) \Leftrightarrow p_1, p_2, p_3 \quad$ are collinear.

Setting $p_i = [1, \mathscr{P}(z_i), \mathscr{P}'(z_i)]$, we may rewrite $(*)$ in the form

$$(**) \qquad \begin{vmatrix} 1 & \mathscr{P}(z_1) & \mathscr{P}'(z_1) \\ 1 & \mathscr{P}(z_2) & \mathscr{P}'(z_2) \\ 1 & \mathscr{P}(z_3) & \mathscr{P}'(z_3) \end{vmatrix} = 0 \Leftrightarrow z_1 + z_2 + z_3 \equiv 0(\Lambda).$$

This beautiful relation may be interpreted in several—eventually equivalent—ways. One is as the famous *addition theorem* for elliptic functions expressing $\mathscr{P}(-z_1 - z_2) = \mathscr{P}(z_1 + z_2)$ and $\mathscr{P}'(-z_1 - z_2) = -\mathscr{P}'(z_1 + z_2)$ rationally in terms of $\mathscr{P}(z_1)$, $\mathscr{P}(z_2)$, $\mathscr{P}'(z_1)$, and $\mathscr{P}'(z_2)$. Alternately, we may give the group structure on the cubic curve C geometrically by making the construction with lines dictated by $(**)$. In any case, the inversion of the elliptic integral via Abel's theorem and corresponding theory of cubic curves in the plane occupies a singular position of harmony and depth in the subject of algebraic geometry.

3. LINEAR SYSTEMS ON CURVES

Reciprocity Law II

Let S be a compact Riemann surface of genus g, ω a global holomorphic 1-form on S, and η a differential of the second kind, i.e., a global meromorphic 1-form with no residues. We want, as in the first reciprocity law, to relate the periods of ω and η to the singularities of η. Since these singularities are not described by the intrinsically defined residue, we choose a local coordinate z around each singular point p of η, and write

$$\eta(z) = (a^p_{-n} z^{-n} + \cdots + a^p_0 + a^p_1 z + \cdots) dz,$$
$$\omega(z) = (b^p_0 + b^p_1 z + \cdots) dz.$$

Note that $a^p_{-1} = \operatorname{Res}_p(\eta) = 0$, and that $b^p_0(p) = (\omega/dz)(p)$ as defined earlier.

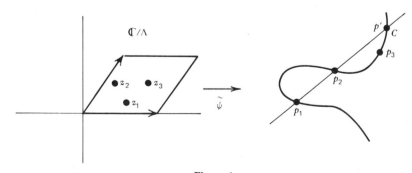

Figure 4

Now let $\delta_1, \ldots, \delta_{2g}$ be cycles on S representing a canonical basis for $H_1(S, \mathbb{Z})$, disjoint except for a common base point $s_0 \in S$ and not containing any singular points of η; let Π^i and N^i denote the periods of ω and η along δ_i. As before, $\Delta = S - \cup \delta_i$ is simply connected and we can set

$$\pi(s) = \int_{s_0}^{s} \omega$$

to obtain a holomorphic function π in Δ with $d\pi = \omega$. Consider the meromorphic differential $\pi \cdot \eta$ on Δ; since η is smooth on the arcs δ_i, the integral of $\pi \cdot \eta$ along the boundary of Δ is well-defined, and by the same argument as used in the first reciprocity law

$$\int_{\partial \Delta} \pi \cdot \eta = \sum_{i=1}^{g} (\Pi^i N^{g+i} - \Pi^{g+i} N^i).$$

On the other hand, near a singular point p of η with local coordinate z as above,

$$\pi(z) = \int_{s_0}^{p} \omega + b_0^p z + \tfrac{1}{2} b_1^p z^2 + \tfrac{1}{3} b_2^p z^3 + \cdots,$$

so that

$$\int_{\partial \Delta} \pi \cdot \eta = 2\pi \sqrt{-1} \sum_{p} \operatorname{Res}_p (\pi \cdot \eta) = 2\pi \sqrt{-1} \sum_{p} \left[\sum_{j=2}^{n} \frac{a_{-j}^p \cdot b_{j-2}^p}{j-1} \right].$$

Thus we have the *reciprocity law for differentials of the first and second kind*:

$$\sum_{i=1}^{g} (\Pi^i N^{g+i} - \Pi^{g+i} N^i) = 2\pi \sqrt{-1} \sum_{p,j} \frac{a_{-j}^p b_{j-2}^p}{j-1}.$$

The two reciprocity laws stated are the only ones we shall use in our discussion of curves. It should be pointed out, however, that more general laws can be obtained in the same way with little additional effort. For example, in either of the two formulas given, we may take ω to be a differential of the second kind: the function

$$\pi(s) = \int_{s_0}^{s} \omega$$

will then be meromorphic but still well-defined, and again we will have

$$\sum (\Pi^i N^{g+i} - \Pi^{g+i} N^i) = 2\pi \sqrt{-1} \sum_{p} \operatorname{Res}_p (\pi \cdot \eta).$$

Similarly, a reciprocity law for a pair of differentials of the third kind can be proved if we excise some additional arcs from our region Δ. We will not derive all these formulas—the general formalism should by now be evident —but we will mention one rather pretty result that is similarly obtained:

Theorem (Weil). *Let* f,g *be meromorphic functions on the compact Riemann surface* S, *with* (f) *disjoint from* (g). *Then*

$$\prod_{p \in S} f(p)^{\mathrm{ord}_p(g)} = \prod_{p \in S} g(p)^{\mathrm{ord}_p(f)}.$$

Proof. Let $\delta_1, \ldots, \delta_{2g}$ and Δ be as above. Let $\{p_i\}$ denote the support of (f), $\{q_i\}$ the support of (g), and draw smooth arcs α_i from s_0 to p_i disjoint except for their common base point s_0 and not containing any of the points $\{q_i\}$. Let Δ' be the complement of the arcs α_i in Δ; Δ' can again be considered as a polygon with sides $\ldots, \delta_i, \delta_{g+i}, \delta_i^{-1}, \delta_{g+i}^{-1}, \ldots, \alpha_i, \alpha_i^{-1}, \ldots$ as drawn in Figure 5. Since Δ' is simply connected and f is nonzero holomorphic in Δ', we can choose a single branch of the function $\log f$ in Δ'; we consider the meromorphic differential

$$\varphi = \log f \cdot d \log g = \log f \cdot \frac{dg}{g}$$

in Δ'. First, since dg/g has a single pole with residue $\mathrm{ord}_{q_i}(g)$ at each q_i, we have by the residue theorem

$$\int_{\partial \Delta'} \varphi = 2\pi \sqrt{-1} \sum_{q_i} \mathrm{Res}_{q_i}(\varphi)$$

$$= 2\pi \sqrt{-1} \sum_{q_i} \mathrm{ord}_{q_i}(g) \cdot \log f(q_i).$$

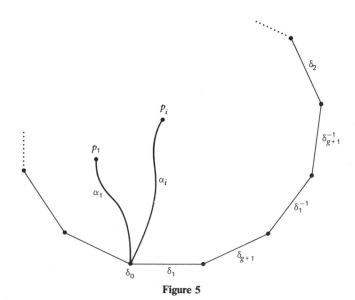

Figure 5

Now, for points $p \in \delta_i$, $p' \in \delta_i^{-1}$ on $\partial \Delta'$ identified on S,

$$\log f(p') = \log f(p) + \int_{\delta_{g+i}} d \log f,$$

and so

$$\int_{\delta_i + \delta_i^{-1}} \varphi = \left(\int_{\delta_i} d \log g \right)\left(-\int_{\delta_{g+i}} d \log f \right)$$

and similarly

$$\int_{\delta_{g+i} + \delta_{g+i}^{-1}} \varphi = \left(\int_{\delta_{g+i}} d \log g \right)\left(\int_{\delta_i} d \log f \right).$$

We also see that for points $p \in \alpha_i$, $p' \in \alpha_i^{-1}$ on $\partial \Delta'$ identified on S,

$$\log f(p') - \log f(p) = -2\pi \sqrt{-1} \cdot \mathrm{ord}_{p_i} (f),$$

and hence

$$\int_{\alpha_i + \alpha_i^{-1}} \varphi = 2\pi \sqrt{-1} \ \mathrm{ord}_{p_i} (f) \int_{s_0}^{p_i} d \log g.$$

Thus,

$$\sum_i \int_{\alpha_i + \alpha_i^{-1}} \varphi = 2\pi \sqrt{-1} \left(\sum \mathrm{ord}_{p_i} (f) \cdot (\log g(p_i) - \log g(s_0)) \right)$$

$$= 2\pi \sqrt{-1} \sum \mathrm{ord}_{p_i} (f) \cdot \log g(p_i),$$

since $\sum_{p_i} \mathrm{ord}_{p_i} (f) = 0$. In sum, we have

$$2\pi \sqrt{-1} \left(\sum \mathrm{ord}_{q_i} (g) \cdot \log f(q_i) - \sum \mathrm{ord}_{p_i} (f) \cdot \log g(p_i) \right)$$

$$= \sum_{i=1}^{g} \left(\left(\int_{\delta_i} d \log f \right)\left(\int_{\delta_{g+i}} d \log g \right) - \left(\int_{\delta_i} d \log g \right)\left(\int_{\delta_{g+i}} d \log f \right) \right)$$

But $\int_{\delta_i} d \log f$ is always an integral multiple of $2\pi \sqrt{-1}$; thus the right-hand term above is an integral multiple of $(2\pi \sqrt{-1})^2$ and we see that

$$\sum \mathrm{ord}_{q_i} (g) \cdot \log f(q_i) - \sum \mathrm{ord}_{p_i} (f) \cdot \log g(p_i) \in 2\pi \sqrt{-1} \ \mathbb{Z}.$$

Exponentiating, we obtain

$$\prod_i f(q_i)^{\mathrm{ord}_{q_i}(g)} = \prod_i g(p_i)^{\mathrm{ord}_{p_i}(f)}$$

as desired. Q.E.D.

The Riemann-Roch Formula

The starting point for our discussion of linear systems is the natural question: given a divisor D on a Riemann surface S of genus g, determine the dimension of $H^0(S, \mathcal{O}(D))$, i.e., the number of meromorphic functions f on S with

$$(f) + D \geqslant 0.$$

We will try to answer the question first for an effective divisor $D = \Sigma p_\lambda$ of degree d on S. We will assume moreover that the points p_λ are distinct —the only difference in the following computation if D has multiple points is a much more cumbersome notation.

As with Abel's theorem, the problem becomes tractable when expressed in terms of differentials. Now if $f \in \mathfrak{M}(S)$ with $(f) + D \geqslant 0$, then df is a meromorphic 1-form on S holomorphic on $S - \{p_\lambda\}$, with no periods, no residues, and a pole of order $\leqslant 2$ at each p_λ. Conversely, given any such differential η, the meromorphic function

$$f(p) = \int_{p_0}^{p} \eta$$

is well-defined and satisfies $(f) + D \geqslant 0$. Since $df = df' \Leftrightarrow f = f' + \lambda$, $\lambda \in \mathbb{C}$, we see that the dimension of $H^0(S, \mathcal{O}(D))$ is one more than the dimension of the vector space V of differentials of the second kind holomorphic on $S - \{p_\lambda\}$ with no periods and poles of order $\leqslant 2$ at p_λ.

By the Kodaira vanishing theorem, for any $p \in S$

$$H^1(S, \Omega^1(p)) = 0,$$

and so from the exact sequence

$$0 \to \Omega^1(p) \to \Omega^1(2p) \to \mathbb{C}_p \to 0$$

we see that there exists a meromorphic form on S, holomorphic on $S - \{p\}$ and having a double pole at p; clearly this form cannot have any residues. It follows that if we let z_λ be a local coordinate around the point p_λ, for any sequence $a_1, \ldots, a_d$ of complex numbers *there exists a meromorphic 1-form η_a on S, holomorphic on S $- \{p_\lambda\}$ and having principal part*

$$\eta_a(z) = \left(a_\lambda \cdot z_\lambda^{-2} + [0] \right) dz_\lambda$$

at p_λ. Since any two such forms differ by a holomorphic 1-form on S, we see moreover that *there exists a unique such differential φ_a with all A-periods zero.* Let $W \cong \mathbb{C}^d$ denote the vector space of such forms, and consider the linear map

$$\psi: W \to \mathbb{C}^g$$

obtained by integration over the B-cycles of S:

$$\psi: \varphi_a \mapsto \left(\int_{\delta_{g+1}} \varphi_a, \ldots, \int_{\delta_{2g}} \varphi_a \right).$$

Clearly, the vector space V above is just the kernel of the map ψ.

To describe ψ explicitly, let $\omega_1,\ldots,\omega_g$ be a normalized basis for $H^0(S,\Omega^1)$. By the reciprocity law for differentials of the first and second kinds,

$$\int_{\delta_{g+j}} \varphi_a = 2\pi\sqrt{-1}\sum_{\lambda} a_\lambda \cdot (\omega_j/dz_\lambda)(p_\lambda),$$

i.e., the map ψ is given by the matrix

$$\begin{bmatrix} (\omega_1/dz_1)(p_1) & \cdots & (\omega_1/dz_d)(p_d) \\ \vdots & & \vdots \\ (\omega_g/dz_1)(p_1) & \cdots & (\omega_g/dz_d)(p_d) \end{bmatrix}.$$

Now the number of independent relations among the row vectors of this matrix is just the number of linearly independent holomorphic differentials vanishing at p_λ for all λ, that is, the dimension of $H^0(S,\Omega^1(-D))$. Thus

$$\begin{aligned} h^0(D) &= \dim(\ker\psi)+1 \\ &= d - \mathrm{rank}\,\psi + 1 \\ &= d - g + h^0(K-D) + 1. \end{aligned}$$

This is the classical *Riemann-Roch formula*.

We have proved the Riemann-Roch for effective divisors, and hence for all divisors of degree $\geq g$. For a general D of degree $\leq g-2$, we apply the formula to $K-D$ to obtain

$$h^0(K-D) = (2g-2-d) - g + 1 + h^0(D)$$

$$\Rightarrow h^0(D) = d - g + 1 + h^0(K-D).$$

Finally, if $\deg D = g-1$ and neither D nor $K-D$ is linearly equivalent to an effective divisor, then $h^0(D) = h^0(K-D) = 0$, and the formula again holds.

The Riemann-Roch formula gives us immediately a picture of the behavior of generic linear systems: for generic effective divisors $D = \sum_{\lambda=1}^d p_\lambda$ of degree d the matrix $((\omega_i/dz_\lambda)(p_\lambda))$ has maximal rank, and so

$$h^0(D) = \begin{cases} 1, & d \leq g, \\ d-g+1, & d > g, \end{cases}$$

for D outside an analytic subvariety in $S^{(d)}$.

An effective divisor D such that $h^0(K-D) \neq 0$ is called *special*; a special divisor whose associated linear system is larger than that of the generic divisor of its degree—i.e., such that $h^0(K-D) > g-d$—is called *irregular*. A linear system is called special or irregular if its individual divisors are.

It should be mentioned at this point that the Riemann-Roch formula can be given a sheaf-theoretic proof. In general, if $E \to M$ is a holomorphic vector bundle on a compact complex manifold M, we define the *holomorphic Euler characteristic* of E to be

$$\chi(E) = \sum (-1)^p h^p(M, \mathcal{O}(E));$$

we usually write $\chi(\mathcal{O}_M)$ for the holomorphic Euler characteristic of the trivial line bundle, i.e.,

$$\chi(\mathcal{O}_M) = \sum (-1)^p h^{0,p}(M).$$

Now for a line bundle L on a Riemann surface S, by Kodaira-Serre duality we have

$$\begin{aligned} \chi(L) &= h^0(S, \mathcal{O}(L)) - h^1(S, \mathcal{O}(L)) \\ &= h^0(L) - h^0(K - L) \\ \chi(\mathcal{O}_S) &= h^{0,0}(S) - h^{0,1}(S) \\ &= 1 - g, \end{aligned}$$

and so the Riemann-Roch formula reads simply

$$\chi(L) = \chi(\mathcal{O}_S) + c_1(L).$$

To prove the Riemann-Roch in this form, we note that it is clear for the trivial bundle, and show that it holds for any $L = [D]$, if and only if it holds as well for $L' = [D + p]$ and $L'' = [D - p]$, $p \in S$ any point. This is easy: the exact sheaf sequence

$$0 \to \mathcal{O}(D) \to \mathcal{O}(D + p) \to \mathbb{C}_p \to 0$$

gives us the exact cohomology sequence

$$0 \to H^0(S, \mathcal{O}(D)) \to H^0(S, \mathcal{O}(D + p))$$
$$\to \mathbb{C}_p \to H^1(S, \mathcal{O}(D)) \to H^1(S, \mathcal{O}(D + p)) \to 0,$$

and since the alternating sum of the dimensions of the vector spaces in an exact sequence is zero, this implies that

$$\chi([D + p]) = \chi([D]) + 1. \qquad\qquad \text{Q.E.D.}$$

This version of the Riemann-Roch formula, while not as explicit as the first, points the way toward generalizations in higher dimensions. The principal fact that holds in general is this: the holomorphic Euler characteristic of a vector bundle $E \to M$ on a compact complex manifold is a topological invariant of E and M. In these terms, the essential point of the classical Riemann-Roch formula is the duality $h^1(D) = h^0(K - D)$.

Canonical Curves

Let S be a compact Riemann surface of genus $g \geqslant 2$, K the canonical bundle on S. We note immediately that the complete linear system $|K|$ has no base points: if $p \in S$ were in the base locus of $|K|$, we would have

$$h^0(K-p) = h^0(K) = g,$$

and hence by Riemann-Roch

$$h^0(p) = \deg(p) - g + 1 + h^0(K-p) = 1 - g + 1 + g = 2,$$

i.e., there would exist a nonconstant meromorphic function on S holomorphic on $S - \{p\}$ and having only a single pole at p, so S would be biholomorphic to $\mathbb{P}^1$. It follows that the line bundle K gives a map

$$\iota_K \colon S \to \mathbb{P}^{g-1}$$
$$: p \mapsto [\omega_1(p), \ldots, \omega_g(p)],$$

where $\omega_1, \ldots, \omega_g$ are a basis for $H^0(S, \Omega^1)$. ι_K is called the *canonical mapping* of S, $\iota_K(S) \subset \mathbb{P}^{g-1}$ the *canonical curve* of S.

Now, the map ι_K is 1-1 if for any points $p, q \in S$, we can find a $\omega \in H^0(S, \Omega^1)$ with $\omega(p) = 0$, $\omega(q) \neq 0$; it is an immersion if for any $p \in S$ there exists ω vanishing exactly to order 1 at p. Thus, ι_K is an imbedding if and only if for any points p, q, not necessarily distinct,

$$h^0(K-p-q) < h^0(K-p) = g - 1.$$

By Riemann-Roch,

$$h^0(K-p-q) = g - 3 + h^0(p+q),$$

and so

$$h^0(K-p-q) < h^0(K-p) \Leftrightarrow h^0(p+q) = 1.$$

Thus ι_K *fails to be an embedding if and only if there exists a meromorphic function on S having only two poles, i.e., if S can be expressed as a two-sheeted branched covering of* $\mathbb{P}^1$. Such a Riemann surface is called *hyperelliptic*. Hyperelliptic Riemann surfaces form an important subset of the set of all curves of genus g, with properties that often differ markedly from those of a general Riemann surface. We will discuss them in detail later on in this section; for the time being, we merely assure the reader that the "general" Riemann surface of genus $g \geqslant 3$ is indeed nonhyperelliptic.

Note that if $L \to S$ is any line bundle of degree $2g - 2$, then

$$h^0(K-D) = \begin{cases} 0 & \text{if } D \neq K, \\ 1 & \text{if } D = K; \end{cases}$$

by Riemann-Roch, if $D \neq K$ we find $h^0(D) = g - 1$. This implies that: *if* $S \subset \mathbb{P}^{g-1}$ *is any nondegenerate curve of genus g and degree* $2g - 2$, *then S is a canonical curve.*

The canonical curve of a Riemann surface S derives much of its importance from the fact that it is intrinsically defined by S, and so as a general rule, *any projective invariant of the canonical curve reflects the intrinsic structure of* S. We will see this principle applied when we discuss Weierstrass points, and again in discussing the Torelli theorem.

We can rephrase the Riemann-Roch formula in terms of the geometry of the canonical curve: for any divisor $D = \Sigma p_i$ on the Riemann surface S, $h^0(K - D)$ is just the number of hyperplanes in $\mathbb{P}^{g-1}$ containing the points $\iota_K(p_i)$, and so $h^0(D)$ is equal to the degree of D minus the dimension of the linear space $\overline{D}$ spanned by the points p_i on the canonical curve. Here, of course, we take the "linear span" of a point p_i with multiplicity a_i in D to be the span of p_i together with the first $a_i - 1$ derivatives of the canonical map. Finally, since the dimension of the linear span of d points on C is just $d-1$ less the number of independent linear relations on the points, we have the *geometric version of the Riemann-Roch*:

The dimension r *of the complete linear system containing a divisor* $D = \Sigma p_i$ *is equal to the number of independent linear relations on the points* p_i *on the canonical curve,*

i.e.,

The points of D *span exactly a* (d − r − 1)-*plane.*

Indeed, the Riemann-Roch formula may be quite easily proved in this geometric form. To start, we prove the inequality

(∗) $\dim \overline{D} \leqslant (d-1) - \dim |D|.$

Proof. Suppose that $D = \sum p_i$ moves in an r − dimensional linear system; that is, there exist $r + 1$ independent meromorphic functions $f_0, \ldots, f_r$ on S with

$$(f_\nu) + D \geqslant 0.$$

We may take $f_0 = 1$; then no nontrivial linear combination of the functions $f_1, \ldots, f_r$ will be holomorphic. Equivalently, if z_i is a local coordinate on S centered around p_i and if we write

$$f_\nu(z_i) = a_{\nu,i} z_i^{-1} + \cdots$$

then the matrix

$$\begin{bmatrix} a_{1,1} & \cdots & a_{1,d} \\ \vdots & & \vdots \\ a_{r,1} & \cdots & a_{r,d} \end{bmatrix}$$

has maximal rank r. Now, if ω is any holomorphic 1-form on S, then by the residue theorem, for each ν,

$$0 = \sum_i \operatorname{Res}_{p_i} (f_\nu \omega)$$

$$= \sum_i a_{\nu,i} \cdot \left(\frac{\omega(p_i)}{dz_i} \right).$$

This gives r independent relations on the points p_i on the canonical curve, establishing the inequality (∗).

We may now prove the opposite inequality by applying (∗) to the residual series $K - D$ of D. Suppose that on the canonical curve

$$\dim \overline{D} = d - s - 1.$$

The hyperplanes in $\mathbb{P}^{g-1}$ containing D then cut out a linear subseries of $|K - D|$ of dimension

$$(g-1) - (d-s-1) - 1 = g - d + s - 1.$$

Applying (∗) to a divisor $E \in |K - D|$, then, we see that

$$\dim \overline{E} \leqslant \deg E - 1 - (g - d + s - 1)$$
$$= (2g - 2 - d) - 1 - (g - d + s - 1)$$
$$= g - s - 2.$$

But now the hyperplanes in $\mathbb{P}^{g-1}$ containing E will cut out on S a linear subseries of $|D|$ having dimension at least

$$(g-1) - (g - s - 2) - 1 = s,$$

that is,

$$\dim |D| \geqslant s = d - 1 - \dim \overline{D}$$

and so the Riemann-Roch formula is proved. Q.E.D.

Special Linear Systems I

The Riemann-Roch formula describes exactly the behavior of the "generic" linear system on a Riemann surface, but it does not tell us much about irregular linear systems. We will now try to fill in the gap with some classical theorems relating the dimension, degree, and genus of special linear systems. Our basic lemma is

Lemma. *For $C \subset \mathbb{P}^n$ a nondegenerate curve, the points of a generic hyperplane section of C are in general position, i.e., no* n *of them are linearly dependent.*

Proof. Suppose C has degree d, and let $H_0 \subset \mathbb{P}^n$ be a hyperplane meeting C in d distinct points $p_1, \ldots, p_d$. Then for H in a sufficiently small neighborhood U of H_0 in $\mathbb{P}^{n*}$, the points $\{p_i(H)\}$ of intersection of H with C will vary holomorphically with $H \in \mathbb{P}^{n*}$. Accordingly, for every multiindex $I = \{i_1, \ldots, i_n\} \subset \{1, \ldots, d\}$, we get a map

$$\pi_I : U \to C^n = C \times C \times \cdots \times C,$$
$$: H \mapsto (p_{i_1}(H), \ldots, p_{i_n}(H));$$

moreover, since for any point $(q_1, \ldots, q_n) \in C^n$ sufficiently near $\pi_I(H_0)$, there is a hyperplane $H \in U$ containing $q_1, \ldots, q_n$, *the image of* U *under* π_I *contains an open set in* C^n.

Now let $D \subset C^n$ be the locus of points $(q_1, \ldots, q_n)$ such that $q_1, \ldots, q_n$ are linearly dependent. Since C is nondegenerate, D is a proper analytic subvariety of C^n, and so $\pi_I^{-1}(D)$ is likewise a proper subvariety of U. Thus, for $H \in U - \cup_I \pi_I^{-1}(D)$, the points of $H \cap C$ are in general position. Q.E.D.

Now, we can characterize the dimension of a linear system $|D|$ as follows: $\dim |D| \geqslant t$ *if and only if for every* t *points* $p_1, \ldots, p_t \in S$ *there exists a divisor* $E \in |D|$ *containing* $p_1, \ldots, p_t$. Thus, if D and D' are two effective divisors on S, we can find a divisor, $E \sim D + D'$ containing any $h^0(D) - 1 + h^0(D') - 1$ points of S, and so we have

$$h^0(D + D') \geqslant h^0(D) + h^0(D') - 1$$

In particular, suppose D is special, so that $h^0(K - D) \neq 0$ and we can take $D' = K - D$. Then $h^0(D + D') = h^0(K) = g$, and we have

$$h^0(D) + h^0(K - D) \leqslant g + 1$$
$$\underline{h^0(D) - h^0(K - D) = d - g + 1}$$
$$2h^0(D) \qquad \leqslant d + 2$$

Note as well that equality holds in the last line if and only if every divisor in the canonical series $|D + D'| = |K|$ is the sum of a divisor in the linear system $|D|$ and a divisor from $|D'|$, and if $j(D) + j(D') = g - 3$. Now if ι_K was one-to-one and $D, D' \neq 0$,

$$\deg D + \deg D' = 2g - 2$$

and

$$j(D) + j(D') = g - 3$$

together imply the points of either $\iota_K(D)$ or $\iota_K(D')$ are not in general position. But by our lemma the points of a generic hyperplane section of $\iota_K(S)$ are in general position, and so $2h^0(D)$ can equal $d + 2$ only if $D = 0$, $D = K$, or ι_K is not one-to-one. Summing up, then, we have

Clifford's Theorem.　*For any two effective divisors on the compact Riemann surface S,*

$$\dim|D| + \dim|D'| \leqslant \dim|D + D'|$$

and for D *special*

$$\dim|D| \leqslant \frac{d}{2}$$

with equality holding only if D=0, D=K, *or* S *is hyperelliptic.*

Corollary.　*If* $C \subset \mathbb{P}^n$ *is any curve of degree* d<2n *and genus* g,

$$g \leqslant d - n$$

with equality if and only if C *is normal.*

Proof.　Let D be the hyperplane section of C. Then

$$\dim|D| = h^0(D) - 1 = n > \frac{d}{2},$$

and so by Clifford's theorem D is nonspecial. Thus $h^0(K-D)=0$, and by Riemann-Roch

$$g = d - h^0(D) + 1$$
$$\leqslant d - n. \qquad\qquad\qquad \text{Q.E.D.}$$

Of course, this bound can be realized by any Riemann surface of genus $g = d - n$, and any linear system of degree d.

It remains now to find the maximal genus of a curve of degree d in $\mathbb{P}^n$ for $d > 2n$, or equivalently to find a sharper bound on the dimension of a linear system than that provided by Clifford's theorem when $d \ll g$. We offer here an argument originally given by Castelnuovo in 1889.

Let $C \subset \mathbb{P}^n$ be a curve of degree d and genus g, with hyperplane section D. Consider the linear systems $|kD|$ for $k = 1, 2, \ldots$. By our basic lemma, we can take the points of D to be in general position in a hyperplane in $\mathbb{P}^n$.

Let $m = [(d-1)/(n-1)]$ be the greatest integer less than or equal to $(d-1)/(n-1)$, and for each integer $k \leqslant m$ choose a set Γ of $k(n-1)+1$ points of D. We claim that the hyperplanes in $H^0(C, \mathcal{O}(kD))$ corresponding to the points of Γ are all independent; to prove it we will exhibit, for any point $q \in \Gamma$, a hypersurface of degree k in $\mathbb{P}^n$ containing $\Gamma - \{q\}$ but not q. This is easy: if we partition the remaining points of Γ into k sets

$$\left\{ p_1^1, p_2^1, \ldots, p_{n-1}^1 \right\}, \left\{ p_1^2, \ldots, p_{n-1}^2 \right\}, \ldots, \left\{ p_1^k, \ldots, p_{n-1}^k \right\}$$

of $(n-1)$ points each, then each set $\{p_\alpha^i\}_\alpha$ will be linearly independent, and its linear span will not contain q. We can thus find hyperplanes

$H_1, \ldots, H_k$ in $\mathbb{P}^n$ containing the points $\{p_\alpha^i\}_\alpha$ but not q; the sum $H_1 + \cdots + H_k$ is the desired hypersurface of degree k.

We see from this that the vector space of sections of $[kD]$ vanishing on all the points of D has codimension at least $k(n-1)+1$ in $H^0(C, \mathcal{O}(kD))$, i.e.,

$$h^0(kD) - h^0((k-1)D) \geqslant k(n-1)+1, \qquad \text{for } k \leqslant m.$$

The same argument likewise shows that for $k > m$ we can find k hyperplanes in $\mathbb{P}^n$ containing all but any one of the points of D, so that

$$h^0(kD) - h^0((k-1)D) = d \qquad \text{for } k > m.$$

Thus we have

$$h^0(D) \geqslant n+1,$$

$$h^0(2D) \geqslant n+1 + 2(n-1) + 1$$
$$= 3(n-1) + 3,$$

$$h^0(3D) \geqslant 6(n-1) + 4,$$

$$\vdots$$

$$h^0(mD) \geqslant \frac{m(m+1)}{2}(n-1) + m + 1,$$

$$\vdots$$

$$h^0((l+m)D) \geqslant \frac{m(m+1)}{2}(n-1) + m + 1 + ld.$$

But now for m sufficiently large, the divisor $(l+m)D$ will be nonspecial. By Riemann-Roch, then,

$$h^0((l+m)D) = (l+m)d - g + 1,$$

so that

(*)
$$g \leqslant (l+m)d \frac{m(m+1)}{2}(n-1) - m - 1 - ld + 1$$
$$= \frac{m(m-1)}{2}(n-1) + m(d - m(n-1) - 1)$$

Thus *the genus of a nondegenerate curve of degree* d *in* $\mathbb{P}^n$ *is at most*

$$\frac{m(m-1)}{2}(n-1) + m\varepsilon, \qquad \text{where } m = \left[\frac{d-1}{n-1}\right], d-1 = m(n-1) + \varepsilon.$$

We will see in the section on ruled surfaces that in fact this bound is realized for each d and n, and give an explicit description of these curves of maximal genus. For the time being, let us summarize what we know in general about nondegenerate curves in $\mathbb{P}^n$: if C has degree d, then

$d < n \Rightarrow C$ is degenerate,

$d = n \Rightarrow C$ is the rational normal curve,

$n < d < 2n \Rightarrow g \leqslant d - n$, with equality if C is normal,

$d = 2n \Rightarrow g \leqslant n + 1$ with equality if and only if
C is a canonical curve,

$d \geqslant 2n \Rightarrow g \leqslant \dfrac{m(m-1)}{2}(n-1) + m\varepsilon,$

$$\text{where } m = \left[\frac{d-1}{n-1}\right], d - 1 = m(n-1) + \varepsilon.$$

Note that if C achieves this bound, then equality must hold in the basic inequality $(*)$ above, and it follows that the complete linear system $|kD|$ on C is cut out by hypersurfaces of degree k; or, in other words, the map

$$H^0(\mathbb{P}^n, \mathcal{O}(kH)) = \text{Sym}^k H^0(\mathbb{P}^n, \mathcal{O}(H)) \to H^0(C, \mathcal{O}(kH))$$

must be surjective. Applying this in particular to the canonical curve, we have

Noether's Theorem. *For any curve nonhyperelliptic* C, *the map*

$$\text{Sym}^l H^0(C, \mathcal{O}(K)) \to H^0(C, \mathcal{O}(lK))$$

is surjective for all l.

Castelnuovo's inequality can be inverted in two ways to give an upper bound on n in terms of d and g and a lower bound on d in terms of n and g. Without going through the manipulation, we have

$$n \leqslant \frac{2(l(d-1)-g)}{l(l+1)}, \qquad l = \left[\frac{2(g-1)}{d} + 1\right],$$

$$d \geqslant \frac{(j+1)}{2}(n-1) + \frac{g}{j} + 1, \qquad j(j-1) < \frac{2g}{n-1} \leqslant j(j+1).$$

Hyperelliptic Curves and Riemann's Count

Recall that a compact Riemann surface S of genus $g \geqslant 2$ is called hyperelliptic if there exists a meromorphic function f on S with only two poles, i.e., if S admits a 2-1 map $f: S \to \mathbb{P}^1$ to the Riemann sphere. By the Riemann-Hurwitz formula the number of branch points of such a map f is given by

$$b = 2g - 2 + 2\chi(\mathbb{P}^1)$$
$$= 2g + 2;$$

of course, since f has only two sheets, it cannot have a multiple branch point. Let $z_1, \ldots, z_{2g+2}$ be the branch points, assumed finite, of f in $\mathbb{P}^1$, and consider the curve $S' = (w^2 = \prod_{i=1}^{2g+2}(z - z_i)) \subset \mathbb{C}^2$, together with the projection map π on the z-plane. Since the points z_i are distinct S' is smooth, and for $R > \max(|z_i|)$ we see that $\pi^{-1}(|z| > R)$ consists simply of two disjoint punctured discs; we can complete S' to a compact Riemann surface $\tilde{S}$ by replacing these punctured discs with full discs. The map $\pi: S' \to \mathbb{C}$ can be extended continuously, hence holomorphically, to a map $\tilde{\pi}: \tilde{S} \to \mathbb{P}^1$ by mapping the two added points to $z = \infty$. Thus $\tilde{S}$ will again be a double cover of $\mathbb{P}^1$ branched at the points $\{z_i\}$.

Now in general if two Riemann surfaces M, M' have maps $f: M \to \mathbb{P}^1$, $f': M' \to \mathbb{P}^1$ with the same branch locus $B \subset \mathbb{P}^1$, and if $f^{-1}(\mathbb{P}^1 - B)$ is isomorphic to $f'^{-1}(\mathbb{P}^1 - B)$ as topological covering spaces of $\mathbb{P}^1 - B$, then M and M' will be isomorphic: the isomorphism between $f^{-1}(\mathbb{P}^1 - B)$ and $f'^{-1}(\mathbb{P}^1 - B)$ will extend continuously, hence holomorphically, over the branch loci of f and f'. In the case at hand, it follows that the Riemann surfaces S and $\tilde{S}$ are isomorphic, i.e., that *any hyperelliptic Riemann surface of genus g can be realized as the smooth completion of the locus*

$$w^2 = g(z)$$

in $\mathbb{C}^2$, for g(z) a polynomial of degree 2g+2.

If S is a hyperelliptic Riemann surface given as the completion of $(w^2 = \prod_{i=1}^{2g+2}(z - z_i)) \subset \mathbb{C}^2$, we can compute explicitly a basis for $H^0(S, \Omega^1)$. First, note that we have an automorphism $j: S \to S$ of order 2 given by $j: (w, z) \mapsto (-w, z)$; j is called the *hyperelliptic involution* on S. The induced linear transformation

$$j^*: \ H^0(S, \Omega^1) \to H^0(S, \Omega^1)$$

is likewise of order 2, and so a priori we obtain a decomposition of $H^0(S, \Omega^1)$ into eigenspaces with eigenvalues $+1$ and -1. In fact, the $+1$ eigenspace is trivial, since a holomorphic 1-form ω on S with $j^*\omega = \omega$ would descend to give a holomorphic 1-form on $\mathbb{P}^1$, and none such exists. Thus we have $j^*\omega = -\omega$ for all $\omega \in H^0(S, \Omega^1)$.

Now consider the 1-form

$$\omega_0 = \frac{dz}{w}$$

on S. ω_0 is holomorphic and nonzero away from the points at ∞, since the points where w vanishes are exactly the zeros of dz. Since the total degree of ω_0 is $2g - 2$ and ω_0 has the same order of zero or pole at the points of S lying over $z = \infty$, ω_0 must have a zero of order $g - 1$ at each of these two points. If ω is any other holomorphic 1-form on S,

$$\omega = h \cdot \omega_0,$$

where h is a meromorphic function on S, holomorphic away from ∞. But we have $j^*\omega = -\omega$, $j^*\omega_0 = -\omega_0$, and so $j^*h = h$, i.e., h is a function of z alone, and so necessarily a polynomial in z. If h is of degree d, then h has $2d$ zeros on the finite part of S and hence a pole of order d at each of the points at ∞; since ω_0 has zeros of order $g-1$ at ∞ and $h\cdot\omega_0$ is holomorphic, we have $\deg h \leqslant g-1$. Thus we can write out a basis for $H^0(S, \Omega^1)$:

$$\left\{ \frac{dz}{w}, z\frac{dz}{w}, \ldots, z^{g-1}\frac{dz}{w} \right\}.$$

The canonical map ι_K of S is then given by

$$\iota_K(z, w) = [1, z, \ldots, z^{g-1}] \in \mathbb{P}^{g-1};$$

the image of S under ι_K is thus the rational normal curve in $\mathbb{P}^{g-1}$. Note, moreover that the canonical map factors through the projection f; since ι_K is intrinsically defined, it follows that *the map* f *is unique up to an automorphism of* $\mathbb{P}^1$.

To show that not all Riemann surfaces are hyperelliptic, we count the number of parameters needed to specify both a hyperelliptic curve and a general curve of genus g. First, we have seen that given any collection of $2g+2$ distinct points $z_i \in \mathbb{P}^1$ there is a unique hyperelliptic curve S with a 2-fold map $f: S \to \mathbb{P}^1$ having branch locus $B = \{z_i\}$. We can send any three points $z_1, z_2, z_3 \in B$ to 0, 1, and ∞ respectively by an automorphism of $\mathbb{P}^1$, and so we see that the general hyperelliptic Riemann surface of genus g can be described by specifying $(2g+2) - 3 = 2g-1$ points on $\mathbb{P}^1$. Conversely, since f is unique up to an automorphism of $\mathbb{P}^1$, any hyperelliptic curve S corresponds to only finitely many such collections of $2g-1$ points; thus the family of such curves has $2g-1$ parameters locally.

We will now count the number of parameters needed to describe a general Riemann surface of genus g, following an argument of Riemann. Choose any integer n greater than $2g$. Any Riemann surface of genus g can be expressed as an n-sheeted branched cover of $\mathbb{P}^1$; the number of branch points of such a map is given by

$$b = 2g - 2 + n\cdot\chi(\mathbb{P}^1)$$

$$= 2n + 2g - 2.$$

Conversely we claim that given any divisor B on $\mathbb{P}^1$ of degree $2n+2g-2$ and taking no point with multiplicity $> n-1$, there exist a finite number of Riemann surfaces S of genus g expressible as n-sheeted covers of $\mathbb{P}^1$ with branch locus B. We will construct these Riemann surfaces in case $B = \Sigma z_i$ consists of $2n+2g-2$ distinct points; the general case is more complicated but conceptually no more difficult.

Draw disjoint arcs γ_i in $\mathbb{P}^1$ from z_i to z_{i+1}; let $T_1,\ldots,T_n$ be n disjoint copies of $\mathbb{P}^1 - \cup \gamma_i$. (See Figure 6.) Choose a sequence of permutations $\sigma_0,\ldots,\sigma_{2n+2g-2} \in S_n$ with $\sigma_0 = \sigma_{2n+2g-2} = e$ and $\sigma_j \cdot \sigma_{j+1}^{-1}$ a nontrivial simple transposition for each j, such that $\{\sigma_j\}$ is transitive on $\{1,\ldots,n\}$; we can always find a finite number of such sequences. For each i, $1 \leqslant i \leqslant 2n+2g -3$, adjoin to $\cup_j T_j$ n copies $\{\gamma_i^j\}_j$ of the arc γ_i, identifying γ_i^j with the boundary of T_j along the upper edge of the cut γ_i and also with the boundary of $T_{\sigma_i(j)}$ along the lower edge of the cut γ_i. Let S be the resulting topological space, $f: S \to \mathbb{P}^1$ the obvious projection map. $f^{-1}(\mathbb{P}^1 - B) \subset S$ is a covering space of $\mathbb{P}^1 - B$, and so inherits uniquely a complex structure; this structure extends over all of S, taking as local coordinate at a point $p \in f^{-1}(z_i)$ either $(z - z_i)$ or $\sqrt{z - z_i}$ according to whether the map f is 1-1 or 2-1 in a neighborhood of p. Thus S is a compact Riemann surface that maps to $\mathbb{P}^1$ with branch locus B, and by the remark made earlier S is determined completely by the choices of permutations σ_i made in the construction.

We have seen that any divisor B of degree $2n+2g-2$ as above corresponds to a finite number of Riemann surfaces of genus g together with n-fold maps f to $\mathbb{P}^1$. It remains to see how many such divisors correspond to a single such Riemann surface S. Now the map f on S can be specified by giving first its polar divisor $D = (f)_\infty \in S^{(n)}$ and then the element of the linear system $H^0(S, \mathcal{O}([D]))$ corresponding to f. Clearly the choice of D depends on n parameters; since $n > 2g$, $h^0(K - D) = 0$, and by Riemann-Roch,

$$h^0(D) = n - g + 1,$$

so the choice of $f \in H^0(S, \mathcal{O}([D]))$ depends on $n - g + 1$ parameters. Thus the family of n-fold maps $f: S \to \mathbb{P}^1$ is

$$n + (n - g + 1) = 2n - g + 1$$

-dimensional. Since the family of divisors B as above is $(2n+2g-2)$-dimensional, it follows that the general Riemann surface of genus g depends locally on

$$2n + 2g - 2 - (2n - g + 1) = 3g - 3$$

parameters. In particular we note that for $g \geqslant 3$, the "generic" Riemann surface of genus g is nonhyperelliptic.

It is amusing to verify Riemann's count explicitly in cases $g = 3$, 4, and 5. First, as we have seen, the canonical curve of any Riemann surface of genus 3 is a quartic curve in $\mathbb{P}^2$, determined up to an automorphism of $\mathbb{P}^2$, and conversely if $C \subset \mathbb{P}^2$ is a smooth quartic curve, by the adjunction

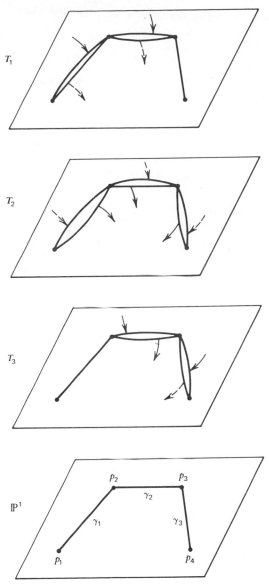

Figure 6. An example: $\sigma_1 = (1,2)$, $\sigma_2 = (1,3,2)$, $\sigma_3 = (2,3)$.

formula

$$K_C = (K_{\mathbb{P}^2} + C)|_C$$
$$= (-3H + 4H)|_C$$
$$= H|_C,$$

so C is a canonical curve. Now the space of quartic curves in $\mathbb{P}^2$ has dimension

$$\binom{6}{2} - 1 = \frac{6 \cdot 5}{2} - 1 = 14,$$

and $\dim \mathrm{PGL}_3 = 9 - 1 = 8$; thus a curve of genus 3 depends on $14 - 8 = 6$ parameters, as predicted.

Next, let $C \subset \mathbb{P}^3$ be a canonical curve of genus 4. By Riemann-Roch, since $2K_C$ is nonspecial,

$$h^0(C, 2K_C) = 12 - 4 + 1 = 9.$$

But $h^0(\mathbb{P}^3, \mathcal{O}(2H)) = 10$, and so the restriction map

$$H^0(\mathbb{P}^3, \mathcal{O}(2H)) \to H^0(C, \mathcal{O}(2H_C))$$
$$= H^0(C, 2K_C)$$

has a kernel, i.e., C lies on a quadric surface Q; since a reducible quadric consists of two planes and so cannot contain C, Q is irreducible. Also, since

$$h^0(C, 3K_C) = 18 - 4 + 1 = 15$$

and

$$h^0(\mathbb{P}^3, \mathcal{O}(3H)) = 20,$$

C lies on a four-dimensional linear system of cubics in $\mathbb{P}^3$. The system of cubics containing Q is only $h^0(\mathbb{P}^3, \mathcal{O}(3H - Q)) - 1 = h^0(\mathbb{P}^3, \mathcal{O}(H)) - 1 = 3$-dimensional, and it follows that C also lies on a cubic Q' not containing Q. Since Q is irreducible, Q and Q' must then intersect in a curve of degree 6; but $C \subset Q \cap Q'$ and $\deg C = 6$, so

$$C = Q \cap Q'.$$

Conversely, by the adjunction formula, for any cubic Q' and quadric Q meeting in a smooth curve C, we have

$$K_Q = (K_{\mathbb{P}^3} + Q')|_{Q'}$$
$$= (-4H + 3H)|_{Q'} = -H_{Q'}$$

and

$$K_C = (K_{Q'} + Q)|_C$$
$$= (-H + 2H)|_C = H|_C,$$

so C is a canonical curve of genus 4.

Now the quadric Q depends, as we said before, on 9 parameters. Two cubic polynomials will cut out the same curve on Q if their difference vanishes identically on Q; the vector space of cubics vanishing on Q has dimension

$$H^0(\mathbb{P}^3, \mathcal{O}(3H - 2H)) = 4,$$

and so, Q having been chosen, the choice of Q' depends on

$$19 - 4 = 15$$

parameters. Bertini's theorem, moreover, assures us that the generic pair (Q, Q') do indeed meet transversely. Finally, PGL_4 has dimension 15, and so the number of parameters needed to describe a curve of genus 4 locally is

$$9 + 15 - 15 = 9,$$

as expected.

The case $g = 5$ is somewhat easier. For $C \subset \mathbb{P}^4$ a canonical curve of genus 5, we have

$$H^0(C, 2K_C) = 16 - 5 + 1 = 12.$$

But

$$H^0(\mathbb{P}^4, \mathcal{O}(2H)) = \binom{6}{4} = 15,$$

so the curve C must lie on three independent quadric surfaces Q, Q', and Q''; by the Enriques theorem of Section 3, Chapter 4, it is generically the intersection of these quadrics. Conversely, if Q, Q', and Q'' are any three quadrics in $\mathbb{P}^4$ meeting transversely, the adjunction formula applied three times tells us that C is a canonical curve of genus 5.

Now C is determined by specifying a three-dimensional subvector space of the vector space of polynomials of degree 2 on $\mathbb{P}^4$, i.e., by specifying a point in the Grassmannian $G = G(3, H^0(\mathbb{P}^4, \mathcal{O}(3H))$. G has dimension $3(15 - 3) = 36$, and by Bertini's theorem applied three times we see that the linear system of quadrics corresponding to a generic point of G do in fact meet in a smooth curve. PGL_5 is 24-dimensional, and so we see that a curve of genus 5 depends locally on

$$36 - 24 = 12$$

parameters.

Special Linear Systems II

Earlier in this section we asked, what is the greatest possible genus of a nondegenerate curve of degree d in $\mathbb{P}^n$? Inverted, this is equivalent to the problem, what is the largest possible dimension of a linear system of degree d (or, the smallest possible degree of a linear system of dimension n) on a Riemann surface S of genus g, not counting those that factor through a quotient of S? We gave an answer to this question (which we shall later see is the correct one), but as we can now see, in case $d > 2n$ or $n > g - 1$ this bound cannot be realized by every Riemann surface of genus g. For example, we have seen that the greatest possible genus of a plane curve of degree d is $(d-1)(d-2)/2$; and of course this bound is sharp, being achieved by any smooth plane curve. The smallest degree of a two-dimensional linear system on a curve S of genus g which does not factor through a quotient of S is thus M, where

$$\frac{(M-1)(M-2)}{2} \geqslant g > \frac{(M-2)(M-3)}{2}.$$

We can see, however, that not every Riemann surface of genus g possesses such a linear system: if $g = (d-1)(d-2)/2$, then the family of Riemann surfaces of genus g with such a linear system—that is, plane curves of degree d—has dimension at most

$$h^0(\mathbb{P}^2, \mathcal{O}(dH)) - 1 - \dim \mathrm{PGL}_3 = \frac{(d+1)(d+2)}{2} - 9$$

while the family of all Riemann surfaces of genus g has dimension

$$3g - 3 = \frac{3(d-1)(d-2)}{2} - 3.$$

For $d \geqslant 5$, then, the curves S of genus $g = (d-1)(d-2)/2$ having a net degree d are exceptional.

This example suggests another question, complementary to Castelnuovo's: what special linear systems exist on the *generic* Riemann surface of genus g? This is the *Brill-Noether problem*, which we will discuss further later in this chapter.

The presumed answer to—if not a proof of—the Brill-Noether problem is given by a simple-minded dimension count. Consider a canonical curve C of genus g in $\mathbb{P}^{g-1}$. By the geometric form of Riemann-Roch, an effective divisor $D = \Sigma p_i$ of degree d with $\dim|D| = r$ consists of d points on C spanning a $(d-1-r)$-plane in $\mathbb{P}^{g-1}$, that is, a d-secant $(d-1-r)$-plane to C. C will thus have a linear system of degree d and dimension r if and only if it has at least an r-dimensional family of d-secant $(d-r-1)$-planes.

Now the Grassmannian $G = G(d-r, g)$ of $(d-r-1)$-planes in $\mathbb{P}^{g-1}$ has dimension $(d-r)(g-d+r)$. The subvariety $\sigma_{g-d+r}(p)$ of $(d-r-1)$-planes passing through a point p has codimension $g - d + r$ in G, so the subvariety of $(d-r-1)$-planes meeting the curve C has codimension $g - d + r - 1$. We may expect, then, that the subvariety of $(d-r-1)$-planes meeting C d times has codimension $d(g-d+r-1)$ in G, so that there will be an

r-dimensional family of such planes if

$$(d-r)(g-d+r) - d(g-d+r-1) \geqslant r.$$

Solving, we see that this will be the case when

$$(d-r)(r+1) - rg \geqslant 0.$$

Our count thus suggests that

> *The generic Riemann surface of genus* g *will possess a linear system of degree* d *and dimension* r *if and only if*
>
> $$d \geqslant \frac{rg}{r+1} + r$$
>
> *and there will in general be a* [(d−r)(r+1)−rg]-*dimensional family of such linear systems.*

Clearly, our argument as it stands falls far short of a proof; a proof of one direction will be given in the final section of this chapter. Two cases we can check now are $r=1$ and 2. Since a linear system of degree d and dimension 1 without base points on a Riemann surface S gives a d-sheeted map $S \to \mathbb{P}^1$, the statement for $r=1$ amounts to

> *The generic Riemann surface of genus* g *is expressible as a branched cover of* $\mathbb{P}^1$ *with*
>
> $$d = \left[\frac{g+1}{2}\right] + 1$$
>
> *sheets, but no fewer; in case* g *is even it is so expressible in a finite number of ways (up to automorphisms of* $\mathbb{P}^1$*), while if* g *is odd there is a one-dimensional family of such representations.*

We can verify this in one direction by a count of parameters. A d-sheeted map of a curve of genus g to $\mathbb{P}^1$ has by Riemann-Hurwitz

$$b = 2g - 2 + 2d$$

branch points. By our general argument, then, the family of Riemann surfaces expressible as d-sheeted covers of $\mathbb{P}^1$ has dimension at most

$$b - 3 = 2g + 2d - 5.$$

If the generic Riemann surface of genus g is so expressible, then, we have by Riemann's count

$$2g + 2d - 5 \geqslant 3g - 3$$

i.e.,

$$d \geqslant \frac{g}{2} + 1.$$

In case $r=2$, our result may be stated as

The generic Riemann surface may be represented as a plane curve of degree

$$d = \left[\frac{2g+2}{3} \right] + 2$$

and no smaller.

Again we can check this in one direction. In the linear system of all plane curves of degree d, those that have a double point or worse form a subvariety of codimension 1, and the generic such curve has just one ordinary double point. Similarly if $\delta \leqslant (d-1)(d-2)/2$, the variety of curves of degree d having δ double points or worse has codimension δ, and the generic such curve has just δ ordinary double points. Now, as we shall see in the next section, the genus of a plane curve of degree d with δ ordinary double points is

$$g = \frac{(d-1)(d-2)}{2} - \delta;$$

there is, accordingly, an

$$h^0(\mathbb{P}^2, \mathcal{O}(dH)) - 1 - \delta = \frac{(d+1)(d+2)}{2} - 1 + g - \frac{(d-1)(d-2)}{2}$$
$$= 3d + g - 1$$

-dimensional family of plane curves of degree d and genus g. Since the group PGL_3 acts on the family of such curves, the number of Riemann surfaces so expressible has dimension

$$3d + g - 1 - 8 = 3d + g - 9.$$

Thus the generic Riemann surface of genus g may be represented in this way only if

$$3d + g - 9 \geqslant 3g - 3,$$

i.e., if

$$d \geqslant \tfrac{2}{3}g + 2,$$

as predicted.

Some amusing enumerative problems arise from this discussion. For example, we have seen that the generic Riemann surface of genus $g=2k$ has a finite number of pencils of degree $k+1$; we may ask how many. This question will be answered in the cases $g=2, 4, 6,$ and 8 in the discussion of correspondences in the next section, and in general in the final section.

4. PLÜCKER FORMULAS

Associated Curves

In this section we will concern ourselves with the *extrinsic geometry* of curves, i.e., the study of properties of curves $C \subset \mathbb{P}^n$ having to do with the embedding. To a certain extent, our study of associated curves is the complex analogue of the Frenet formalism in classical Euclidean differential geometry. Because of the complex analytic structure, however, the subject is much richer; we will obtain quantitative and qualitative results that could not be hoped for in the C^∞ case.

We make one remark before procceding. Clearly, if $f: S \to \mathbb{P}^n$ is any map of a Riemann surface into projective space, then we can lift f locally to $\mathbb{C}^{n+1}$—that is, in a neighborhood of any point $p \in S$ we can find a holomorphic vector-valued function v to $\mathbb{C}^{n+1}$ such that $f(z) = [v_0(z), \ldots, v_n(z)]$. Conversely, for $v: S \to \mathbb{C}^{n+1}$ any vector-valued function, *the map* $f(z) = [v_0(z), \ldots, v_n(z)]$ *is well-defined even if* $v = 0$ *at isolated points.* To see this, simply let z be a local coordinate centered around a zero p of v; then if $k = \min(\mathrm{ord}_p v_i)$, the map

$$\tilde{f}(z) = \left[z^{-k} v_0(z), \ldots, z^{-k} v_n(z) \right]$$

is well-defined and extends f.

Now suppose S is a compact Riemann surface, and $f: S \to \mathbb{P}^n$ a nondegenerate map to $\mathbb{P}^n$. Let f be given locally by the vector function $v(z) = [v_0(z), \ldots, v_n(z)]$. We define the kth *associated curve* of f:

$$f_k: \ S \to G(k+1, n+1) \subset \mathbb{P}(\Lambda^{k+1} \mathbb{C}^{n+1})$$

by

$$f_k(z) = \left[v(z) \wedge v'(z) \wedge \cdots \wedge v^{(k)}(z) \right].$$

We emphasize that the curve is the abstract Riemann surface together with the map.

In order to assure ourselves that f_k is well-defined, we have to check three things: that $v(z) \wedge \cdots \wedge v^{(k)}(z)$ cannot be identically zero, and that it is independent, up to multiplication by a scalar, of the choice of lifting v and local coordinate z. To show the first, suppose that for some $k \leqslant n$, $v(z) \wedge \cdots \wedge v^{(k)}(z) \equiv 0$ but $v(z) \wedge \cdots \wedge v^{(k-1)}(z) \not\equiv 0$. Then evidently

$$v^{(k)}(z) \equiv 0 \bmod (v(z), \ldots, v^{(k-1)}(z)),$$

i.e.,

$$\begin{aligned} (v(z) \wedge \cdots \wedge v^{(k-1)}(z))' &= v(z) \wedge \cdots \wedge v^{(k-2)}(z) \wedge v^{(k)}(z) \\ &= \lambda(z) \cdot v(z) \wedge \cdots \wedge v^{(k-1)}(z), \end{aligned}$$

so that $f_{k-1}(z)$ must be constant and $f(S)$ lies in a $(k-1)$-plane in $\mathbb{P}^n$, contradicting our assumption of nondegeneracy.

Now let $\tilde{v}(z) = \rho(z) \cdot v(z)$ be another lifting of f. Then

$$\tilde{v}' = \rho' \cdot v + \rho \cdot v'$$

so

$$\tilde{v}' \wedge \tilde{v} = \rho^2 \cdot (v \wedge v')$$

and in general

$$\tilde{v} \wedge \cdots \wedge \tilde{v}^{(k)} = \rho^{k+1} \cdot v \wedge \cdots \wedge v^{(k)}.$$

Similarly, let w be another local coordinate on S. Then

$$\frac{\partial v}{\partial w} = \frac{\partial z}{\partial w} \cdot \frac{\partial v}{\partial z},$$

and so

$$v \wedge \frac{\partial v}{\partial w} = \frac{\partial z}{\partial w} \left(v \wedge \frac{\partial v}{\partial z} \right).$$

In general, we will have

$$v \wedge \cdots \wedge \frac{\partial^k v}{\partial w^k} = \left(\frac{\partial z}{\partial w} \right)^{k(k+1)/2} v \wedge \cdots \wedge \frac{\partial^k v}{\partial z^k},$$

and so f_k is well-defined.

Geometrically, for a point $z \in S$ with $v(z) \wedge \cdots \wedge v^{(k)}(z) \neq 0$, the k-plane $f_k(z) \subset \mathbb{P}^n$ is the unique k-plane having contact of order at least $k+1$ with $f(S)$ at z, called the *osculating k-plane*. In the case of a plane curve $f: S \to \mathbb{P}^2$, the map $f_1: S \to \mathbb{P}^{2*}$ is just the Gauss map sending $z \in S$ to the tangent line to $f(S)$ at $f(z)$; the curve $f_1(S)$, often written f^*, is called the *dual curve* of f. Note that even at a singular point z_0 of $f(S)$ the tangent line is well-defined by the remark at the beginning of this section. In practice, $f_1(z_0)$ corresponds to what would ordinarily be called the tangent line at z_0: the limiting position of the tangent lines at nearby points. (See Figure 7.)

Ramification

Let $f: S \to \mathbb{P}^n$ be any curve, given in terms of Euclidean coordinates in a neighborhood of $f(z_0)$ by $f_1(z), \ldots, f_n(z)$. We define the *ramification index* $\beta(z_0)$ of f at z_0 to be the order of vanishing of the Jacobian $(\partial f_1/\partial z, \ldots, \partial f_n/\partial z)$, i.e.,

$$\beta(z_0) = \min \left(\operatorname{ord}_{z_0} \left(\frac{\partial f_i}{\partial z} \right) \right).$$

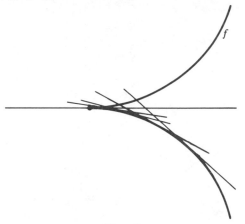

Figure 7

Clearly $\beta(z_0)=0$ if and only if the map f is smooth at z_0; in general, $\beta(z_0)$ is a measure of the singularity of f at z_0.

Another way to define the ramification index is as follows. Let ω be the associated $(1,1)$-form of the Fubini-Study metric on $\mathbb{P}^n$. Then $\beta(z_0)$ is the unique integer such that

$$f^*\omega = \frac{\sqrt{-1}}{2}|z-z_0|^{2\beta(z_0)} \cdot h(z) \cdot dz \wedge d\bar{z}$$

with $h(z)$ C^∞ and nonzero at z_0. To see that these two definitions are indeed equivalent, let $v(z)$ be any lifting of f near z_0. Then we have

$$f^*\omega = \frac{\sqrt{-1}}{2}\,\partial\bar{\partial}\log\|v(z)\|^2$$

$$= \frac{\sqrt{-1}}{2}\,\partial\left(\frac{(v,v')}{(v,v)}d\bar{z}\right)$$

$$= \frac{\sqrt{-1}}{2}\,,\,\frac{(v,v)(v',v')-(v,v')(v',v)}{(v,v)^2}\,dz\wedge d\bar{z}$$

$$= \frac{\sqrt{-1}}{2}\cdot\frac{1}{\|v\|^4}\cdot\sum_{i\neq j}|v_i v_j' - v_j v_i'|^2 \cdot dz\wedge d\bar{z}.$$

In particular we may take the lifting

$$v(z) = [1, f_1(z), \dots, f_n(z)];$$

then

$$f^*\omega = \frac{\sqrt{-1} \cdot dz \wedge d\bar{z}}{2\|v\|^4} \left(\sum_{i=1}^{n} |f_i'|^2 + \sum_{i \neq j} |f_i f_j' - f_i' f_j|^2 \right)$$

and so clearly

$$f^*\omega = \frac{\sqrt{-1}}{2} |z - z_0|^{2\beta(z_0)} \cdot h(z) \cdot dz \wedge d\bar{z}$$

with $\beta(z_0) = \min(\mathrm{ord}_{z_0}(f_i'))$ as originally claimed.

Now we will be concerned not only with the ramification indices $\beta(z)$ of a curve $f: S \to \mathbb{P}^n$, but also with the ramification indices $\beta_k(z)$ of its associated curves. In order to make the numbers $\beta_k(z_0)$ computable for a given point $z_0 \in S$, we may put the curve in *normal form* at z_0 as follows:

Write $f(z) = [v(z)] = [v_0(z), \ldots, v_n(z)]$ with $v(z_0) \neq 0$. Making a linear change of coordinates in $\mathbb{C}^{n+1}$, we may take

$$v(z_0) = (1, 0, \ldots, 0).$$

We have $v_1(z_0) = \cdots = v_n(z_0) = 0$; write

$$(v_1(z), \ldots, v_n(z)) = (z - z_0)^{\alpha_1 + 1} (v_1^1(z), \ldots, v_n^1(z))$$

with $(v_1^1(z_0), \ldots, v_n^1(z_0)) \neq 0$. Now make a linear change of the last n coordinates in $\mathbb{C}^{n+1}$ so that $(v_1^1(z_0), \ldots, v_n^1(z_0)) = (1, 0, \ldots, 0)$; we write

$$(v_2^1(z), \ldots, v_n^1(z)) = (z - z_0)^{\alpha_2 + 1} (v_2^2(z), \ldots, v_n^2(z))$$

with $(v_2^2(z_0), \ldots, v_n^2(z_0)) \neq 0$. We change the last $n - 1$ coordinates on $\mathbb{C}^{n+1}$ so that $(v_2^2(z_0), \ldots, v_n^2(z_0)) = (1, 0, \ldots, 0)$, and continuing in this way we end up with a system of coordinates for $\mathbb{C}^{n+1}$ in terms of which

$$v(z) = \left(1 + \cdots, (z - z_0)^{\alpha_1 + 1} + \cdots, (z - z_0)^{2 + \alpha_1 + \alpha_2} + \cdots, \right.$$
$$\left. \ldots, (z - z_0)^{n + \alpha_1 + \cdots + \alpha_n} + \cdots \right).$$

This is called the *normal form* of the curve f near z_0; from it we see that $f_k(z_0)$ is the $\mathbb{P}^k$ spanned by the first $k + 1$ linearly independent vectors from the sequence $v(z_0), v'(z_0), v''(z_0), \ldots$. Putting a curve in normal form amounts to choosing a basis $e_0, \ldots, e_n$ for $\mathbb{C}^{n+1}$ such that $f_k(z_0)$ is spanned by $\{e_0, \ldots, e_k\}$.

Now we compute the ramification index $\beta_k(z_0)$ of the kth associated curve of f at z_0 in terms of the exponents $\alpha_1, \ldots, \alpha_n$ appearing in the normal form: assume $z_0 = 0$, normalize the homogeneous vector by making the first entry $v_0(z) \equiv 1$, and then write

$$v(z) = (1, z^{1 + \alpha_1} + \cdots, z^{2 + \alpha_1 + \alpha_2} + \cdots, \ldots, z^{n + \alpha_1 + \cdots + \alpha_n} + \cdots).$$

The homogeneous coordinates of $f_k(z)$ are then the determinants of the

$(k+1) \times (k+1)$ minors of the matrix

$$
\begin{bmatrix}
v(z) \\
v'(z) \\
\vdots \\
v^{(k)}(z)
\end{bmatrix}
$$

$$
= \begin{bmatrix}
1 + \cdots & z^{1+\alpha_1} + \cdots & z^{2+\alpha_1+\alpha_2} + \cdots & \cdots & z^{n+\alpha_1+\cdots+\alpha_n} + \cdots \\
0 & (1+\alpha_1)z^{\alpha_1} + \cdots & & & \\
0 & & & \vdots & \\
\vdots & \vdots & & & \\
0 & & & &
\end{bmatrix}
$$

The minor whose determinant vanishes to least order at 0 is clearly the left-hand minor Λ_{I_0}, $I_0 = \{1,\ldots,k+1\}$, and so we may take as Euclidean coordinates on $f_k(S)$ near z_0 the quotients $\{|\Lambda_I|/|\Lambda_{I_0}|\}_I$; the minor other than Λ_{I_0} whose determinant vanishes to smallest order at 0 is Λ_J, for $J = \{1,\ldots,k,k+2\}$, and so the index of ramification of f_k at z_0 is the order of vanishing of

$$
\frac{\partial}{\partial z}\left(\frac{|\Lambda_J(z)|}{|\Lambda_{I_0}(z)|} \right).
$$

Now we have

$$
|\Lambda_{I_0}(z)| = z^{k\alpha_1 + \cdots + \alpha_k} \cdot
\begin{vmatrix}
\alpha_1 + 1 & \cdots & k + \alpha_1 + \cdots + \alpha_{k-1} \\
\alpha_1(\alpha_1 + 1) & & \vdots \\
\vdots & & \\
& \cdots &
\end{vmatrix} + \cdots
$$

and

$$
|\Lambda_J(z)| = z^{k\alpha_1 + \cdots + \alpha_k + \alpha_{k+1} + 1} \cdot
\begin{vmatrix}
\alpha_1 + 1 & \cdots & k + 1 + \alpha_1 + \cdots + \alpha_k \\
\alpha_1(\alpha_1 + 1) & & \vdots \\
\vdots & & \\
& \cdots &
\end{vmatrix} + \cdots
$$

and, since neither of the determinants appearing on the right is zero,

$$
\text{ord}_{z_0}\left(\frac{|\Lambda_J(z)|}{|\Lambda_{I_0}(z)|} \right) = \alpha_{k+1} + 1,
$$

hence

$$\beta_k(z_0) = \alpha_{k+1}.$$

The General Plücker Formulas I

Our aim now is to relate two invariants of the associated curves f_k of a curve $f: S \to \mathbb{P}^n$: the *degree* d_k of $f_k: S \to \mathbb{P}(\Lambda^{k+1}\mathbb{C}^{n+1})$ (or, if one prefers to think of f_k as a map to $G(k+1, n+1)$, the intersection number of $f_k(S)$ with the Schubert cycle σ_1, i.e., the number of osculating k-planes to $S \subset \mathbb{P}^n$ meeting a generic $(n-k-1)$-plane in $\mathbb{P}^n$) and the *total ramification* β_k of f_k, defined as the sum of $\beta_k(z)$ over all $z \in S$. We do this by considering the pullback $f_k^*(ds^2)$ to S of the standard metric on $\mathbb{P}(\Lambda^{k+1}\mathbb{C}^{n+1})$. On the one hand, $f_k^*(ds^2)$ is a metric on S away from the singular points of f_k, and so by a Gauss-Bonnet-type argument we can express the integral of its curvature form over S as a function of the genus of S and β_k; on the other hand, we can compute this curvature form directly and relate it to the degrees d_k of the various associated curves.

First, we say that a positive semidefinite inner product φ on the tangent bundle of a Riemann surface is a *pseudo-metric* if it is given locally as

$$\varphi = h(z) \cdot dz \otimes d\bar{z},$$

where

$$h(z) = |z|^{2\nu} \cdot h_0(z)$$

with

$$h_0(z) > 0.$$

We say that φ has a zero of order ν at $z = 0$ and write $\operatorname{ord}_p(\varphi) = \nu$; the divisor

$$D_\varphi = \sum_{p \in S} \operatorname{ord}_p(\varphi) \cdot p$$

is called the *singular divisor* of the pseudo-metric φ. In fact, φ defines an honest metric on the line bundle $T' \otimes [D_\varphi]$: if we identify sections of $T' \otimes [D_\varphi]$ with meromorphic vector fields $\theta = f(z) \cdot (\partial/\partial z)$ having poles of order at most $\operatorname{ord}_p(\varphi)$ at p, then the inner product

$$(\theta, \theta) = |f(z)|^2 \cdot h(z)$$

will be a well-defined metric. Now the curvature form Θ of φ, considered as a metric on $T' \otimes [D_\varphi]$, will be given by

$$\Theta = -\partial\bar{\partial} \log h(z),$$

and so we have from the proposition on page 141

$$\frac{\sqrt{-1}}{2\pi} \int_S \Theta = \deg(T' + D_\varphi)$$
$$= 2 - 2g + \deg(D_\varphi).$$

In particular, if we take $\varphi = f_k^*(ds^2)$ to be the pullback via f_k of the standard metric on $\mathbb{P}(\Lambda^{k+1}\mathbb{C}^{n+1})$,

$$D_\varphi = \sum_{p \in S} \beta_k(p) \cdot p,$$

and so if Θ is the curvature form of φ,

$$\frac{\sqrt{-1}}{2\pi} \int_S \Theta = 2 - 2g + \beta_k.$$

The problem now is to evaluate directly the curvature form of the pseudo-metric $f_k^*(ds^2)$. Let ω be the $(1,1)$-form associated to the Fubini-Study metric on $\mathbb{P}^n$; let $v(z)$ be as before a lifting of f, and set $\Lambda_k(z) = v(z) \wedge \cdots \wedge v^{(k)}(z) \in \Lambda^{k+1}\mathbb{C}^{n+1}$. Then we have the

Infinitesimal Plücker Formula

$$f_k^*(\omega) = \frac{\|\Lambda_{k-1}\|^2 \cdot \|\Lambda_{k+1}\|^2}{\|\Lambda_k\|^4} \cdot \frac{\sqrt{-1}}{2} dz \wedge d\bar{z}.$$

Proof. First, note that the expression on the right is independent of the choice of lifting, as indeed it must be. Now if $\tilde{v}(z) = \rho(z) \cdot v(z)$ is another lifting, we have

$$\tilde{v}' = \rho' \cdot v + \rho \cdot v',$$
$$\tilde{v}'' = \rho'' \cdot v + 2 \cdot \rho' \cdot v' + \rho \cdot v'',$$
$$\vdots$$
$$\tilde{v}^{(k+1)} = \rho^{(k+1)} \cdot v + \binom{k+1}{1} \rho^{(k)} v' + \cdots + \binom{k+1}{k} \rho' v^{(k)} + \rho \cdot v^{(k+1)}.$$

In particular, we see that we can find a function ρ with $\rho(z_0) \neq 0$ such that $\tilde{v}^{(k+1)}(z_0)$ is orthogonal to $v(z_0), v'(z_0), \ldots, v^{(k)}(z_0)$, and hence to $\tilde{v}(z_0), \tilde{v}'(z_0), \ldots, \tilde{v}^{(k)}(z_0)$; i.e., *at any point z_0 such that $\Lambda_{k+1}(z_0) \neq 0$, we can choose a lifting v of f with $v^{(k+1)}(z_0)$ orthogonal to $v(z_0), \ldots, v^{(k)}(z_0)$.*
Now write

$$f_k^*(\omega) = \frac{\sqrt{-1}}{2} \partial\bar{\partial} \log \|\Lambda_k\|^2$$

$$= \frac{\sqrt{-1}}{2} \partial\left(\frac{(\Lambda_k, \Lambda_k')}{(\Lambda_k, \Lambda_k)} d\bar{z} \right)$$

$$= \left(\frac{(\Lambda_k, \Lambda_k)(\Lambda_k', \Lambda_k') - (\Lambda_k, \Lambda_k')(\Lambda_k', \Lambda_k)}{(\Lambda_k, \Lambda_k)^2} \right) \cdot \frac{\sqrt{-1}}{2} dz \wedge d\bar{z}$$

with

$$\Lambda_k' = v \wedge v' \wedge \cdots \wedge v^{(k-1)} \wedge v^{(k+1)}.$$

Let $V_0 \subset \mathbb{C}^{n+1}$ be the linear span of $v(z_0), \ldots, v^{(k)}(z_0)$; let $V_0^\perp$ denote the orthogonal complement of V_0 in $\mathbb{C}^{n+1}$. Then the decomposition $\mathbb{C}^{n+1} = V_0 \oplus V_0^\perp$ gives a decomposition

$$\Lambda^{k+1}\mathbb{C}^{n+1} = \bigoplus_{p+q=k+1} (\Lambda^p V_0 \otimes \Lambda^q V_0^\perp)$$

of $\Lambda^{k+1}\mathbb{C}^{n+1}$ *as an inner product space*, with the induced metric on each factor $\Lambda^p V_0 \otimes \Lambda^q (V_0^\perp)$. If we assume that $v^{(k+1)}(z_0) \in V_0^\perp$, we have

$$\Lambda_k(z_0) \in \Lambda^{k+1} V_0, \qquad \Lambda_k'(z_0) \in \Lambda^k V_0 \otimes \Lambda^1 V_0^\perp;$$

hence

$$(\Lambda_k(z_0), \Lambda_k'(z_0)) = 0,$$
$$(\Lambda_k'(z_0), \Lambda_k'(z_0)) = \|\Lambda_{k-1}(z_0)\|^2 \cdot \|v^{(k+1)}(z_0)\|^2,$$

and

$$(\Lambda_k(z_0), \Lambda_k(z_0)) \cdot (\Lambda_k'(z_0), \Lambda_k'(z_0)) = \|\Lambda_{k-1}(z_0)\|^2 \cdot \|v^{(k+1)}(z_0)\|^2 \cdot \|\Lambda_k(z_0)\|^2$$
$$= \|\Lambda_{k-1}(z_0)\|^2 \cdot \|\Lambda_{k+1}(z_0)\|^2,$$

proving the lemma.

The curvature form of pseudo-metric $f_k^*(ds^2)$ is then given by

$$\frac{\sqrt{-1}}{2} \Theta = \frac{-\sqrt{-1}}{2} \partial\bar{\partial} \log\left(\frac{\|\Lambda_{k+1}\|^2 \cdot \|\Lambda_{k-1}\|^2}{\|\Lambda_k\|^4} \right)$$
$$= -f_{k-1}^*(\omega) + 2f_k^*(\omega) - f_{k+1}^*(\omega)$$

and so by the Wirtinger theorem,

$$\frac{\sqrt{-1}}{2\pi} \int_S \Theta = -d_{k-1} + 2d_k - d_{k+1}.$$

Comparing this with our first evaluation of $\int_S \Theta$, we have the

Global Plücker Formula

$$d_{k-1} - 2d_k + d_{k+1} = 2g - 2 - \beta_k.$$

As an immediate application of the Plücker formula, we show that we can characterize the rational normal curve by the absence of inflectionary behavior.

Proposition. *The only totally unramified curve* $f: S \to \mathbb{P}^n$ *is the rational normal curve.*

Proof. We can take a linear combination of the various Plücker formulas to eliminate d_k for $k > 0$:

$$\sum_{k=0}^{n-1} (n-k)(d_{k-1} - 2d_k + d_{k+1}) = \sum_{k=0}^{n-1} (n-k)(2g - 2 - \beta_k),$$

obtaining

$$\sum (n-k)\beta_k = (n+1)d + n(n+1)(g-1).$$

In particular, if $\beta_i = 0$ for all i

$$n(n+1)(g-1) < 0 \Rightarrow g = 0,$$

and so this formula reads

$$-(n+1)d = -n(n+1),$$

i.e., $d = n$ and the curve S is the rational normal curve. Q.E.D.

The General Plücker Formulas II

We now wish to give a second proof of the general Plücker formulas which, while it does not admit a local analogue, is of a more geometric character.

Let $f: C \to \mathbb{P}^n$ be a nondegenerate curve, $v(z)$ a local lifting of f to $\mathbb{C}^{n+1}$, and denote the cast of characters

$$\Lambda_k(z) = v(z) \wedge \cdots \wedge v^{(k)}(z) \in \wedge^{k+1}\mathbb{C}^{n+1},$$

$$f_k: C \to G(k+1, n+1) \subset \mathbb{P}(\wedge^{k+1}\mathbb{C}^{n+1}),$$

$$d_k = \deg f_k(C) \subset \mathbb{P}(\wedge^{k+1}\mathbb{C}^{n+1})$$

$$= {}^{\#}(f_k(C) \cdot \sigma_1)_{G(k+1, n+1)}$$

$$\beta_k = \sum_{z \in C} \beta_k(z)$$

as before; for convenience, set

$$m = \dim \mathbb{P}(\wedge^{k+1}\mathbb{C}^{n+1}) = \binom{n+1}{k+1} - 1.$$

Let V_{m-2} be a generic $(m-2)$-plane in $\mathbb{P}(\wedge^{k+1}\mathbb{C}^{n+1})$, disjoint from C and consider the map

$$\pi_V: C \to \mathbb{P}^1$$

obtained by projecting $f_k(C)$ from V_{m-2} onto a line. The sheet number of π_V is clearly just the degree d_k of $f_k(C)$; by Riemann-Hurwitz, then,

$$2g - 2 = -2d_k + \tau_k,$$

where τ_k is the number of branch points of π_V.

To evaluate τ_k, put the map f_k in normal form at $z_0 \in C$:

$$f_k(z) = \left[1 + \cdots, (z - z_0)^{\gamma_1 + 1} + \cdots, (z - z_0)^{\gamma_1 + \gamma_2 + 2} + \cdots, \ldots\right].$$

(Here the exponent γ_i is the ramification index of the $(i-1)$st associated curve of f_k at z_0; thus $\gamma_1 = \beta_k(z_0)$, while the remaining integers $\gamma_2, \ldots$ have no bearing on the proceedings.) From this normal form we see that z_0 will be a branch point of order $(\gamma_{l+1} + \cdots + \gamma_1 + l - 1)$ of π_V exactly when the hyperplane $\overline{V_{m-2}, f_k(z_0)} \subset \mathbb{P}^m$ contains the osculating l-plane to $f_k(C)$ at z_0, but not the osculating $(l+1)$-plane. In particular, if we choose a sufficiently generic V_{m-2}—i.e., such that V_{m-2} does not meet the tangent line to $f_k(C)$ at any stationary point f_k, and does not meet the osculating 2-plane to any point of $f_k(C)$ in a line—then a singular point z_0 of $f_k(C)$ will be a branch point of order $\beta_k(z_0)$ of the map π_V, while a smooth point z_0 of $f_k(C)$ will be a simple branch point of π_V if the tangent line $T_{z_0}(f_k(C))$ to $f_k(C)$ at z_0 meets V_{m-2}, not a branch point otherwise. The number of branch points of π_V will thus be the total ramification index β_k of f_k, plus the number of times a tangent line to $f_k(C)$ meets a generic $(m-2)$-plane in $\mathbb{P}^m$—that is, the degree of the *tangential ruled surface*

$$T(f_k(C)) = \bigcup_{z \in C} T_z(f_k(C)) \subset \mathbb{P}^m$$

of $f_k(C)$.

Our computation of $\deg T(f_k(C))$ is based on one observation. The tangent line to $f_k(C)$ at a smooth point z is spanned by the vectors

$$\Lambda_k(z) = v(z) \wedge v'(z) \wedge \cdots \wedge v^{(k)}(z)$$

and

$$\Lambda'_k(z) = v(z) \wedge v'(z) \wedge \cdots \wedge v^{(k-1)}(z) \wedge v^{(k+1)}(z)$$

Thus the tangent line

$$T_z(f_k(C)) = \left\{ [v(z) \wedge \cdots \wedge v^{(k-1)}(z) \wedge (\lambda_0 v^{(k)}(z) + \lambda_1 v^{(k+1)}(z))] \right\}_{[\lambda_0, \lambda_1] \in \mathbb{P}^1}$$

lies entirely in the Grassmannian $G(k+1, n+1) \subset \mathbb{P}^m$—in fact, *it is simply the Schubert cycle of k-planes in $\mathbb{P}^n$ containing the osculating $(k-1)$-plane $\Lambda_{k-1}(z)$ to f at z and contained in the osculating $(k+1)$-plane $\Lambda_{k+1}(z)$ to f at z.* Since the hyperplane section of $G(k+1, n+1) \subset \mathbb{P}^m$ is the Schubert cycle σ_1, we can then write

$$\deg T(f_k(C)) = {}^\#(T(f_k(C)) \cdot V_{m-2})_{\mathbb{P}^m}$$
$$= {}^\#(T(f_k(C)) \cdot \sigma_1^2)_{G(k+1, n+1)}.$$

Now by the Schubert calculus from Section 6 of Chapter 1, σ_1^2 is homologous to the Schubert cycle $\sigma_{1,1}(\Gamma_{n-k})$ of k-planes in $\mathbb{P}^n$ meeting an $(n-k)$-plane Γ_{n-k} in a line, plus the Schubert cycle $\sigma_2(\Gamma_{n-k-2})$ of k-planes meeting an $(n-k-2)$-plane Γ_{n-k-2}. We see, moreover, that the cycle $T_z(f_k(C)) \subset G(k+1, n+1)$ of k-planes in $\mathbb{P}^n$ containing $\Lambda_{k-1}(z)$ and contained in $\Lambda_{k+1}(z)$ will meet the Schubert cycle $\sigma_2(\Gamma_{n-k-2})$ if and only if Γ_{n-k-2} has a point in common with $\Lambda_{k+1}(z)$, so that the intersection number of $T(f_k(C))$ with σ_2 in $G(k+1, n+1)$ is just the number of points

$z \in C$ whose $(k+1)$st osculating plane meets a generic $(n-k-2)$-plane $\Gamma_{n-k-2} \subset \mathbb{P}^n$, that is, *the degree* d_{k+1} *of the* $(k+1)$*st associated curve* $f_{k+1}(C)$. Similarly, $T_z(f_k(C))$ will meet the cycle $\sigma_{1,1}(\Gamma_{n-k})$ exactly when $\Lambda_{k-1}(z)$ has a point in common with Γ_{n-k}, so the intersection number of $T(f_k(C))$ with $\sigma_{1,1}$ is the number of points $z \in C$ whose $(k-1)$st osculating plane meets a generic $(n-k)$-plane $\Gamma_{n-k} \subset \mathbb{P}^n$, i.e., the degree d_{k-1} of the $(k-1)$st associated curve. We have thus

$$\deg T(f_k(C)) \subset \mathbb{P}^m = {}^{\#}(T(f_k(C)) \cdot (\sigma_{1,1} + \sigma_2))_{G(k+1,n+1)}$$
$$= d_{k-1} + d_{k+1},$$

and so the number of branch points of π_V is given by

$$\tau_k = \beta_k + d_{k-1} + d_{k+1}.$$

From Riemann-Hurwitz, then, we obtain the general Plücker formulas

$$2g - 2 = -2d_k + \tau_k$$
$$= -2d_k + \beta_k + d_{k-1} + d_{k+1}.$$

Weierstrass Points

In general, the Plücker formulas deal with extrinsic invariants of curves. Following the general principle that projective invariants of a canonical curve S correspond to intrinsic properties of S, however, we apply the Plücker formulas to the canonical curves and obtain a count of the number of Weierstrass points on a Riemann surface, as follows.

Let S be a Riemann surface of genus g, $p \in S$ any point, and consider the linear systems associated to the divisors $k \cdot p$, $k = 1, 2, \ldots$. We know by Riemann-Roch that $h^0(kp) = k - g + 1$ for $k \geq 2g - 1$, and, in general,

$$h^0(kp) = \begin{cases} h^0((k-1)p) + 1, & \text{if there exists } f \in \mathfrak{M}(S) \text{ such that } (f)_\infty = kp, \\ h^0((k-1)p), & \text{if there does not exist } f \in \mathfrak{M}(S) \text{ such that } (f)_\infty = kp. \end{cases}$$

It follows that *there exist exactly* g *positive integers* $a_1, \ldots, a_g$ *such that there does not exist a meromorphic function* f *on* S *with* $(f)_\infty = a_i p$. These integers $a_1 < a_2 < \cdots < a_g$ are called the *gap values* of the point $p \in S$.

Now we might expect that for a generic $p \in S$, all the divisors kp will be regular, i.e.,

$$h^0(kp) = \begin{cases} 1, & k \leq g, \\ k - g + 1, & k \geq g, \end{cases}$$

so that

$$a_i = i, \quad i = 1, \ldots, g.$$

We say a point p is a *Weierstrass point* of S if any of the divisors kp is irregular, or in other words if there exists a meromorphic function f on S holomorphic on $S - \{p\}$ and with a pole of order $\leq g$ at p. We take the *weight* of the Weierstrass point p to be

$$W(p) = \sum (a_i - i),$$

where the a_i are the gap values of $p \in S$. For example, if S is hyperelliptic with $h^0(2p) = 2$, then the gap values of p are

$$a_i = 2i - 1$$

and p is called a *hyperelliptic Weierstrass point*; at the other end of the scale, a point p with weight 1 has gap values

$$1, 2, 3, \ldots, g - 1, g + 1$$

—i.e., has minimal deviation from the expected pattern—and is called a *normal Weierstrass point* of S.

We can characterize Weierstrass points on a nonhyperelliptic Riemann surface S in another way. Let $C \subset \mathbb{P}^{g-1}$ be the canonical curve of S. Then by our geometric version of Riemann-Roch, for any $p \in C$, $h^0(gp) > 1$ if and only if the point $p \in C$ and its first $g - 1$ derivatives fail to span all of $\mathbb{P}^{g-1}$, i.e., p is a *Weierstrass point of* S *if and only if it is a singular point of one of the associated curves of* C. Precisely, if the canonical map ι_K is given, in terms of a local coordinate z centered around p, by

$$\iota_K(z) = \left[1, z^{1 + \alpha_1} + \cdots, z^{2 + \alpha_1 + \alpha_2} + \cdots, \ldots, z^{g - 1 + \alpha_1 + \cdots + \alpha_{g-1}} + \cdots \right],$$

then the gap values of $p \in S$ are

$$a_1 = 1,$$
$$a_2 = 2 + \alpha_1,$$
$$a_3 = 3 + \alpha_1 + \alpha_2,$$
$$\vdots$$
$$a_g = g + \alpha_1 + \alpha_2 + \cdots + \alpha_{g-1},$$

and the weight of p is

$$W(p) = \sum_{k=1}^{g-1} (g - k)\alpha_k$$
$$= \sum_{k=0}^{g-2} (g - k - 1)\beta_k(p).$$

Now we can count the number of Weierstrass points on S by applying the Plücker formulas obtained in the argument for the rational normal curve: setting $d = 2g - 2$ and $n = g - 1$, we have

$$\sum (g - k - 1)\beta_k = g(2g - 2) + (g - 1)g(g - 1) = (g - 1)g(g + 1)$$

i.e., *the total weight of the Weierstrass points on a Riemann surface of genus* g *is exactly* $(g-1) \cdot g \cdot (g+1)$.

Weierstrass points are of interest because they are "marked" points on a Riemann surface, i.e., points intrinsically defined. For example, we can apply our last result to show:

Theorem. *Any Riemann surface* S *of genus* >1 *has only finitely many automorphisms.*

Proof. Any automorphism of S must permute its Weierstrass points; since there are only a finite number of these points, it will suffice to consider automorphisms of S fixing each of the Weierstrass points of S. Suppose now that S is nonhyperelliptic. First, note that by Clifford's theorem for any point $p \in S$ we have

$$h^0(kp) < \frac{k}{2} + 1$$

so

$$a_i \leqslant 2i - 2, \qquad i = 2, \dots, g,$$

and

$$\begin{aligned} W(p) &= \sum_{i=1}^{g} a_i - i \\ &\leqslant \sum_{i=2}^{g} i - 2 \\ &\leqslant \frac{(g-1)(g-2)}{2}, \end{aligned}$$

and so the number of distinct Weierstrass points on S is at least

$$\frac{(g-1)g(g+1)}{\frac{1}{2}(g-1)(g-2)} = \frac{2g(g+1)}{g-2} \geqslant 2g + 6.$$

Now suppose that S is nonhyperelliptic and let C be the canonical curve of S. Any automorphism of S is then induced by an automorphism of $\mathbb{P}^{g-1}$ fixing C; let $\tau : \mathbb{P}^{g-1} \to \mathbb{P}^{g-1}$ be such an automorphism fixing each of the Weierstrass points of S. It follows then that τ preserves all of the osculating planes at each Weierstrass point p_i; in particular, if we let V_i be the osculating $(g-3)$-plane to C at p_i, then τ preserves V_i and the pencil of hyperplanes $\{H_\lambda^i\}_{\lambda \in \mathbb{P}^1}$ containing V_i. Suppose V_i contains k points of C other than p_i. Then any hyperplane containing V_i has $k + g - 2$ points of intersection with C lying inside V_i, *and hence contains at most* $g - k$ Weierstrass points outside V_i. But there are at least

$$2g + 2 - (k+1) = 2g - k + 1$$

Weierstrass points of C lying off V_i. Thus at least three of the hyperplanes $\{H_\lambda^i\}_{\lambda \in \mathbb{P}^1}$ contain a Weierstrass point outside V_i, and so are fixed by τ; it follows that τ fixes each of the hyperplanes H_λ^i, and hence, since the hyperplane sections of C are finite, that τ has finite order.

Suppose now that τ has order d and consider the quotient curve S' of S by the group $\{\tau^i\}$ of automorphisms. The projection map π expresses S as a d-sheeted cover of S', with each Weierstrass point a $(d-1)$-fold branch point; then we have

$$2g - 2 \geqslant d(2g(S')-2) + (d-1)(2g+2)$$
$$\geqslant (d-1)(2g-2) + 2d \cdot g(S') + 2(d-2),$$

so $d \geqslant 2 \Rightarrow g(S')=0$ and $d=2$, i.e., S is hyperelliptic. Thus *if S is nonhyperelliptic, any automorphism fixing the Weierstrass points of S is the identity*, and so the theorem is proved in this case.

In case S is hyperelliptic, any automorphism of S is given, modulo the hyperelliptic involution, by an automorphism of $C \subset \mathbb{P}^{g-1}$; but C is rational, and so any automorphism of C fixing the $2g+2>3$ Weierstrass points of C is the identity.   Q.E.D.

Now, let S be a Riemann surface of genus $g \geqslant 3$. By our last result, if S has any automorphisms at all, it has an automorphism φ of prime order p. Let S' be the quotient of S by the group of automorphisms $\{\varphi^i\}$, and g' the genus of S'. Since a fixed point of any power φ^i of φ is a fixed point of φ, the branch locus of the quotient map $\pi : S \rightarrow S'$ consists simply of a certain number k of $(p-1)$-fold branch points; and to specify the surface S up to a finite number of choices we simply have to specify the surface S', together with k points on S'. This is a total of $3g'+3+k$ parameters; but now by Riemann-Hurwitz,

$$2g - 2 = p(2g'-2) + k(p-1),$$

i.e.,

$$k = \frac{2g-2-p(2g'-2)}{p-1} = \frac{2g-2pg'}{p-1} + 2.$$

Thus we have at most

$$3g' + \frac{2g-2pg'}{p-1} - 1$$

parameters for S; and since we must have $g' \geqslant (1/p)(g-1)+1 \geqslant \frac{1}{2}(g+1)$ this number is less than $3g-3$. We conclude, then, that

The generic Riemann surface of genus g $\geqslant$ 3 has no automorphisms.

The reader may check, by essentially the same techniques, that no Riemann surface of genus $g \geqslant 2$ can have more than $84(g-1)$ automorphisms.

A final note on Weierstrass points: we can see by a count of parameters that the generic Riemann surface of genus $g \geqslant 3$ has no Weierstrass points with gap value $a_i > i$ for $i < g$. To see this, suppose the contrary—i.e., that the generic Riemann surface S contains points p with $\dim|(g-1)p| \geqslant 1$. S is then expressible as a $(g-1)$-sheeted cover of $\mathbb{P}^1$, with p appearing as a branch point of order $g-2$; the branch locus B of this map consists of $(g-2)p$ plus

$$2g - 2 + 2(g-1) - (g-2) = 3g - 2$$

other points, and so depends on $3g-1$ parameters. S thus depends on at most $3g-1-3=3g-4$ parameters, a contradiction. Likewise, the reader may verify that a generic Riemann surface of genus $g \geqslant 3$ contains no points p with $\dim |(g+1)p|) \geqslant 3$, by counting (as on p. 262) the number of parameters for plane curves of genus g and degree $g+1$ possessing a $(g+1)$-fold tangent line. Together, these two assertions imply that *the generic Riemann surface of genus* $g \geqslant 3$ *has only normal Weierstrass points.*

Plücker Formulas for Plane Curves

We want to consider now the projective invariants of plane curves. This calls for somewhat different techniques from those used previously: the Plücker formulas we have derived thus far deal only with singularities of a curve $f: S \to \mathbb{P}^n$ arising from the local character of the map f. We have seen, however, that plane curves $f: S \to \mathbb{P}^2$ are subject to singularities arising from the global behavior of f—e.g., nodes—that are not reflected thus far in our general formulas. To obtain a reasonably broad range of applicability, we will consider curves in $\mathbb{P}^2$ with *traditional singularities*, which we now define.

DEFINITION. We say that a curve $f: S \to \mathbb{P}^2$ has *traditional singularities* if every point $p \in S$ is one of the following:

1. A *regular point*, which is a smooth point of both f and the dual curve f^*. At such a point $\beta_0(p) = \beta_1(p) = 0$, and f has the local normal form

$$f(z) = [1, z + \cdots, z^2 + \cdots].$$

2. An *ordinary flex* of f; i e., a smooth point of f where the tangent line has contact of order three. In normal form

$$f(z) = [1, z + \cdots, z^3 + \cdots],$$
$$f^*(z) = [1, z^2 + \cdots, z^3 + \cdots].$$

3. A *cusp* of f, i.e., a singular point of f that has normal form

$$f(z) = [1, z^2 + \cdots, z^3 + \cdots].$$

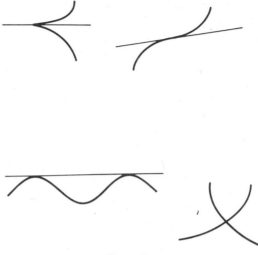

Figure 8

Thus, *p is a flex of* f⟺*p is a cusp of* f*.

4.   A *bitangent* of f, i.e., a point p, not a flex, where the tangent line is also simply tangent at some other point $q \neq p$.

5.   An *ordinary double point* of f, i.e., a point where two nonsingular branches of $f(S)$ cross transversely. Clearly p *is bitangent for* f ⟺ p *is an ordinary double point of* f*.

Note one important point: if $f: S \to \mathbb{P}^2$ is any plane curve, $f^*: S \to \mathbb{P}^{2*}$ its dual, then for a point $z_0 \in S$ the tangent line $f^*(z_0) \in \mathbb{P}^{2*}$ is the limiting position of the secant lines $\overline{f(z_0)f(z)}$ as $z \to z_0$. (See Figure 9.) Similarly, $(f^*)^*(z_0)$—that is, the point in $\mathbb{P}^2$ corresponding to the tangent line to $f^*(S) \subset \mathbb{P}^{2*}$ at $f^*(z_0)$—is the limiting position of the intersection of the tangent lines to $f(S)$ at z and z_0, as $z \to z_0$, which is of course z_0. We see then that *the dual of the dual is the original curve*.

Now suppose $f: S \to \mathbb{P}^2$ has traditional singularities and let $C = f(S)$, $C^* = f^*(S)$. With the notations

g = genus of S,
$d = \deg C$, $d^* = \deg C^*$,
b = number of bitangent lines of C, b^* = number of bitangent lines of C^*,
f = number of flexes of C, f^* = number of flexes of C^*,
κ = number of cusps of C, κ^* = number of cusps of C^*,
δ = number of double points of C, δ^* = number of double points of C^*,

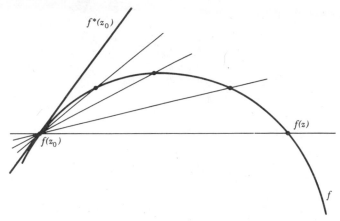

Figure 9

we have the relations

$$b = \delta^*, \qquad b^* = \delta,$$
$$f = \delta^*, \qquad f^* = \kappa.$$

The degree of the dual of C—usually called the *class* of C—is by definition the number of points of intersection of C^* with a generic line in $\mathbb{P}^{2*}$, that is, the number of tangent lines to C containing a generic point $p \in \mathbb{P}^2$. Let p be such a point, and assume moreover that p does not lie on any of the tangent lines to C at any of the singular points of C. Choose coordinates $[X_0, X_1, X_2]$ on $\mathbb{P}^2$ with $p = [0, 0, 1]$; if C is given in these coordinates as the locus of the polynomial $g(X_0, X_1, X_2) = 0$, then the tangent lines to C through p correspond exactly to the smooth points of C such that $(\partial g/\partial X_2)(q) = 0$. Now the curve $C' = (\partial g/\partial X_2 = 0)$ has degree $d - 1$, and passes through each double point and cusp of C with intersection multiplicity 2 and 3, respectively. Thus the number of points of intersection of C' with the smooth points of C is $(C \cdot C') - 2\delta - 3\kappa$; i.e.,

$$(*) \qquad\qquad d^* = d(d-1) - 2\delta - 3\kappa.$$

Similarly, consider the projection map π of C from p onto a line. π expresses C as a d-sheeted cover of $\mathbb{P}^1$, and so we have

$$\chi(S) = 2 - 2g = 2d - b,$$

where b is the number of branch points of the map $\pi \circ f : S \to \mathbb{P}^1$. Now, as in the argument for the original genus formula, a smooth point q of C is a branch point of $\pi \circ f$ if and only if $(\partial g/\partial X_2)(q) = 0$; thus we have $d(d-1) - 2\delta - 3\kappa$ branch points of $\pi \circ f$ among the smooth points of C. In addition we see that, while neither of the points of S corresponding to an ordinary double point of C is a branch point of $\pi \circ f$, every cusp of C is a branch point of order 1 on S. Thus

$$b = d(d-1) - 2\delta - 3\kappa + \kappa$$
$$= d(d-1) - 2\delta - 2\kappa,$$

and so

$$2 - 2g = 2d - d(d-1) + 2\delta + 2\kappa$$

$(**)$
$$g = \frac{(d-1)(d-2)}{2} - \delta - \kappa.$$

Applying the relations $(*)$ and $(**)$ to the dual curve C^* as well, we obtain the *classical Plücker formulas*

$$d^* = d(d-1) - 2\delta - 3\kappa \qquad g = \frac{(d-1)(d-2)}{2} - \delta - \kappa$$

$$d = d^*(d^* - 1) - 2b - 3f \qquad g = \frac{(d^* - 1)(d^* - 2)}{2} - b - f.$$

It will be useful to us later on to have a formula for the canonical bundle of a Riemann surface S expressed as a curve C of degree d in the plane with traditional singularities. To find this, let $f : S \rightarrow \mathbb{P}^2$ and $\pi : C \rightarrow \mathbb{P}^1$ be as above, and consider the pullback ω to S of the meromorphic 1-form $d(X_1/X_0)$. First, ω will have double poles over the points of intersection of C with the line $X_0 = 0$; thus

$$(\omega)_\infty = f^*(2H).$$

Now consider the section $\sigma \in H^0(\mathbb{P}^2, \mathcal{O}((d-1)H))$ given by the homogeneous polynomial $\partial g / \partial X_2$, g as above. Away from the singular locus of C, we have

$$(\omega)_0 = (f^*\sigma);$$

at an ordinary double point $p = f(q) = f(q')$ of C, on the other hand, ω will be nonzero while $f^*\sigma$ will vanish at both q and q'; at a cusp $p = f(q)$ of C, ω will have a simple zero while $f^*\sigma$ will vanish to order 3. If $D \subset S$ is the inverse image of the singular points of C (counting the inverse image of a cusp twice), then

$$(\omega)_0 = (f^*\sigma) - D,$$

and so finally

$$K_S = (\omega)_0 - (\omega)_\infty = f^*((d-3)H) - D.$$

We turn now to some special cases:

Plane Cubics. Let C be a nonsingular plane cubic. Then $d = 3$, $g = 1$, $K = \delta = 0$. Moreover, the number b of bitangents is zero, since no line can have four intersections with C. Similarly, any general flex with normal form

$$z \rightarrow [1, z + \cdots, z^{3+l} + \cdots] \qquad (l \geqslant 0)$$

must be an ordinary flex (i.e., $l=0$). The singularities are thus traditional, and the classical Plücker formulas give

$$d^* = 6, \qquad f = 9.$$

The nine flexes are distinct and can be found as follows: If $0 \in C$ is one flex, then according to the discussion of the inversion of the elliptic integral in Section 2 of this chapter we may describe C parametrically by

$$f: \mathbb{C} \to \mathbb{P}^2,$$

where

$$f(z) = [1, \mathcal{P}(z), \mathcal{P}'(z)],$$

$$z = \int_0^{f(z)} \omega$$

with $\omega \in H^0(C, \Omega^1)$ a generator. By the addition theorem the condition that points A, B, C be the points of intersection of a line is exactly

$$\int_0^A \omega + \int_0^B \omega + \int_0^C \omega \equiv 0(\Lambda),$$

where $\Lambda = f^{-1}(0)$ is the lattice in $\mathbb{C}$. The flexes are those lines for which $A = B = C$; i.e., they are just the nine points

$$[1, \mathcal{P}(z), \mathcal{P}'(z)], \qquad \text{where } 3z \in \Lambda.$$

From this we deduce the statement from classical geometry: *If a line* L *passes through two flexes of a nonsingular plane cubic, then it also passes through a third flex.*

Note that if C has an ordinary double point, then the number of flexes of C drops to three, while if C has a cusp, it has only one flex point.

Plane Quartics. In case C is a smooth plane quartic with ordinary singularities, the degree of C^* is

$$d^* = d(d-1) = 12.$$

We have, then,

$$2b + 3f = 12 \cdot 11 - 4 = 128.$$

On the other hand, C has genus 3, and so

$$3 = \frac{11 \cdot 10}{2} - b - f,$$

i.e., $b+f=52$. Solving, we find

$$f = (2b+3f) - (2b+2f)$$
$$= 128 - 2 \cdot 52$$
$$= 24$$

and

$$b = (3b+3f) - (2b+3f)$$
$$= 3 \cdot 52 - 128$$
$$= 28,$$

i.e., C has 24 flexes and 28 bitangents. We will see the 28 bitangents to a smooth plane quartic reappear in Section 4 of Chapter 4, in another context.

In general, if C is a *smooth* plane curve of degree d having traditional singularities,

$$d^* = d(d-1)$$

and

$$g = \frac{(d-1)(d-2)}{2},$$

so

$$2b + 3f = d(d-1) \cdot (d(d-1)-1) - d$$

and

$$b + f = \frac{(d(d-1)-1)(d(d-1)-2)}{2} - \frac{(d-1)(d-2)}{2}.$$

Thus

$$f = (2b+3f) - (2b+2f)$$
$$= 3d(d-2)$$

and

$$b = (3b+3f) - (2b+3f)$$
$$= \tfrac{1}{2}d(d+1)(d-1)(d-2) - 4d(d-2).$$

5. CORRESPONDENCES

Definitions and Formulas

A *correspondence* $T: C \rightarrow C'$ of degree d between two curves C and C' associates to every point $p \in C$ a divisor $T(p)$ of degree d on C', varying holomorphically with p. It may be given either as a holomorphic map

$$C \rightarrow C'^{(d)}$$

from C to the dth symmetric product of C', or equivalently—and more usefully to us—by its *curve of correspondence* (intuitively, its graph)

$$D = \{(p,q): q \in T(p)\} \subset C \times C';$$

conversely, given any curve $D \subset C \times C'$, we can define an associated correspondence by

$$T(p) = i_p^*(D) \in \mathrm{Div}(C'),$$

where $i_p : C' \to C \times C'$ sends q to (p,q). A correspondence will be called *irreducible* if its curve of correspondence is.

The *inverse* of a correspondence $T : C \to C'$ with curve of correspondence $D \subset C \times C^1$ is defined to be the correspondence given by the curve

$$D' = \{(q,p) : (p,q) \in D\} \subset C' \times C,$$

i.e., by

$$T^{-1}(q) = \sum_{q \in T(p)} p.$$

Some basic correspondences are:

1. If $\{D_\lambda\}$ is a pencil on the curve C without base points, or equivalently a branched covering map $C \xrightarrow{\pi} \mathbb{P}^1$, then for each $p \in C$ there is a unique divisor $D(p) \in \{D_\lambda\}$ containing p; we may define a correspondence T by

$$T(p) = D(p) - p,$$

i.e., T is given by the curve

$$D = \{(p,q) : D_\lambda - p - q \geq 0 \text{ for some } \lambda\} \subset C \times C.$$

Note that T is symmetric, that is, $T = T^{-1}$.

2. If $C \subset \mathbb{P}^2$ is a smooth plane curve, we define a correspondence $T : C \to C$ by

$$T(p) = T_p(C) \cdot C - 2p,$$

i.e., T is given by the closure D in $C \times C$ of the locus

$$\{(p,q) : p \neq q, q \in T_p(C)\}.$$

Note that $p \in T(p)$ only if $T_p(C)$ meets C with multiplicity 3 or more at p, i.e., if p is a flex of C. T is called the *tangential* correspondence on C.

The phenomena associated to correspondences with which we will be concerned are these:

1. A *coincident point* of a correspondence $T : C \to C'$ is a pair $(p,q) \in C \times C'$ such that q appears in $T(p)$ with multiplicity 2 or more; we say that (p,q) is a coincident point of multiplicity m for T if q appears with multiplicity $(m+1)$ in $T(p)$. In example 1 above, a pair (p,q) will be a coincident point of T if q is a branch point of the map $C \xrightarrow{\pi} \mathbb{P}^1$ given by the pencil $\{D_\lambda\}$ and $p \neq q \in \pi^{-1}(\pi(q))$; in example 2 a coincident point corresponds to a bitangent line to C.

In general, if $T: C \to C'$ is a correspondence given by the curve $D \subset C \times C'$, a coincident point is either a branch point of the projection

$$\pi_1: D \to C$$

of D on the first factor, or a singular point of D.

2. A *united point* of a correspondence $T: C \to C$ from a curve to itself is a point $p \in C$ such that $p \in T(p)$; we say that p is a united point of multiplicity m for T if p appears with multiplicity m in $T(p)$. In example 1 above, the united points p of T are the branch points of the map $C \to \mathbb{P}^1$ given by $\{D_\lambda\}$; in example 2 they are the flexes of C. In general, if $T: C \to C$ is given by the curve $D \subset C \times C$, a united point is a point of intersection of D with the diagonal $\Delta \subset C \times C$.

3. A *common point* of two correspondences $T, S: C \to C'$ is, as the name suggests, a pair $(p, q) \in C \times C'$ such that q is in both $T(p)$ and $S(p)$. If T and S are given by curves D and F in $C \times C'$, a common point is just a point of intersection of D and F.

4. A correspondence $T: C \to C$ from a curve of genus $g \geq 1$ to itself is said to have *valence* k if the linear equivalence class of the divisor

$$T(p) + k \cdot p$$

is independent of p. The correspondence of examples 1 and 2 above have valence 1 and 2, respectively. A correspondence need not, in general, have any valence; if it does have a valence though, the valence is unique: if for $k > k'$ the linear equivalence classes of $T(p) + k \cdot p$ and $T(p) + k' \cdot p$ were both constant, it would follow that the divisors $(k - k') \cdot p$ all belonged to some linear system E, of dimension r. Since the generic point of the curve $\iota_E(C) \subset \mathbb{P}^r$ meets any hyperplane with multiplicity at most r, it follows that $r = k - k'$—but then $\iota_E(C)$ is the rational normal curve, contrary to the hypothesis that $g(C) \geq 1$.

In practice, the information about a correspondence $T: C \to C$ that will be most readily available to us is the *degree* of T—that is, the intersection number $^{\#}(D \cdot E)$ of the curve of correspondence $D \subset C \times C$ with the vertical fibers $E_p = \pi_1^{-1}(p) \subset C \times C$; the *degree of* T^{-1}—the intersection number of D with the horizontal fibers $F_p = \pi_2^{-1}(p) \subset C \times C$; and the valence of T if it has one. On the other hand, as we shall see, to compute the number of coincident, or united, points of T, we will want to know the *homology class* of the curve $D \subset C \times C$. This is, in general, impossible: the group

$$H^{1,1}(C \times C) \cap H^2(C \times C, \mathbb{Z})$$

of divisors on $C \times C$ modulo homology has highly unpredictable rank. What makes it possible to compute effectively with some correspondences is the fundamental

Lemma. *Let* $T:C \to C$ *be a correspondence,* $D \subset C \times C$ *its curve of correspondence. Then* T *has valence* k *if and only if* D *is homologous to a linear combination*

$$D \sim aE + bF - k\Delta$$

of the two fibers E, F *of* $C \times C$ *and the diagonal* $\Delta \subset C \times C$.

Proof. First, assume that $D \sim aE + bF - k\Delta$. We claim to begin with that D is then *linearly equivalent* to a sum

$$G = \sum a_i E_{p_i} + \sum b_i F_{q_i} - k\Delta,$$

where $E_p = \pi_1^{-1}(p)$, $F_q = \pi_2^{-1}(q)$. This follows from the Künneth formulas: since the first two vertical maps of the diagram

$$H^1(C \times C, \mathbb{Z}) \longrightarrow H^1(C \times C, \mathcal{O}) \longrightarrow \mathrm{Pic}^0(C \times C) \to 0$$

$$\uparrow{\pi_1^* \times \pi_2^*} \qquad\qquad \uparrow{\pi_1^* \times \pi_2^*} \qquad\qquad \uparrow{\pi_1^* \times \pi_2^*}$$

$$H^1(C, \mathbb{Z}) \oplus H^1(C, \mathbb{Z}) \to H^1(C, \mathcal{O}) \oplus H^1(C, \mathcal{O}) \to \mathrm{Pic}^0(C) \times \mathrm{Pic}^0(C) \to 0$$

are isomorphisms, the last one is also. Now if $D \subset C \times C$ is linearly equivalent to the divisor G written above, then for generic $p \in C$, the divisor $T(p) = i_p^*(D)$ is linearly equivalent to the divisor $i_p^*(G) = \sum b_i q_i - k \cdot p$; clearly, then, the linear equivalence class of $T(p) + k(p)$ is independent of p. Conversely, suppose that the correspondence T has valence k. Write

$$T(p) + k \cdot p = \sum b_i q_i;$$

and

$$T^{-1}(q_0) + k \cdot q_0 = \sum a_i p_i,$$

and let L be the line bundle

$$L = D - \sum a_i E_{p_i} - \sum b_i F_{q_i} + k\Delta.$$

Then by hypothesis the restriction of L to *any* fiber E_p of π_1, and to the fiber F_{q_0} of π_2 as well, is trivial. We claim now that under these circumstances L must be trivial; this will certainly suffice to prove the lemma. To see this, let s_0 be a global nonzero holomorphic section of the restriction of L to F_{q_0}. For each $p \in C$, then, there will be a unique global section $t(p)$ of $L|_{E_p}$ such that $t(p)(p,q) = s_0(p, q_0)$; set

$$t(p, q) = t(p)(q).$$

t is then a global nonzero holomorphic section of L, and consequently L is trivial.   Q.E.D.

Note: It may seem, at first glance, that the notion of valence is an unlikely one, and that correspondences with valency will be relatively rare.

In fact, just the opposite is true: *on a generic Riemann surface there are no correspondences without valency*. (Here "generic" has a meaning slightly different from usual, as will be seen.) We will not prove this, but the reader may see why it should be true: by the Künneth formula,

$$H^{1,1}(C \times C) = (H^{1,1}(C) \otimes H^{0,0}(C)) \oplus (H^{1,0}(C) \otimes H^{0,1}(C))$$
$$\oplus (H^{0,1}(C) \otimes H^{1,0}(C)) \oplus (H^{0,0}(C) \otimes H^{1,1}(C)).$$

The first and last terms in this expression are one-dimensional and are generated by the classes of the fibers E and $F \subset C \times C$, respectively. Writing out a basis for $(H^{1,0}(C) \otimes H^{0,1}(C)) \oplus (H^{0,1}(C) \otimes H^{1,0}(C))$, and integrating over a basis for $H_2(C \times C, \mathbb{Z}) = H_1(C, \mathbb{Z}) \otimes H_1(C, \mathbb{Z})$, the reader will see that the requirement that there exist an integral class in the middle factor other than that of the diagonal $\Delta \subset C \times C$ is that the period matrix of C satisfy certain rationality conditions (cf. Section 4 in Chapter 3 for similar computations); the set of curves of genus g possessing correspondence without valence is thus expected to be a countable union of proper subvarieties of the family of all curves of genus g.

For example, the reader may check that a curve of genus one has correspondences without valence if and only if it has *complex multiplication*, that is, writing

$$C = \frac{\mathbb{C}}{\Lambda},$$

where Λ is the lattice generated by 1 and τ, if and only if τ satisfies a quadratic polynomial over $\mathbb{Q}$.

Now, with our basic lemma, we can derive the three basic formulas for correspondences. The first thing to do is to determine the intersection pairing on the subspace of $H_2(C \times C, \mathbb{Z})$ spanned by the classes of E, F, and Δ. We have, clearly,

$$^\#(E \cdot F) = 1,$$
$$^\#(E \cdot E) = {}^\#(F \cdot F) = 0,$$

and

$$^\#(\Delta \cdot E) = {}^\#(\Delta \cdot F) = 1;$$

it remains only to determine $\Delta \cdot \Delta$. To do this, let $\{D_\lambda\}$ be a pencil of degree d on C and let T be the correspondence defined by $\{D_\lambda\}$ as in example 1 above; let $D \subset C \times C$ be its curve of correspondence. Since T has valence 1, we can write

$$D \sim aE + bF - \Delta.$$

Since T and T^{-1} both have degree $d - 1$, moreover, we have

$$d - 1 = {}^\#(D \cdot E) = b - 1$$

and

$$d - 1 = {}^\#(D{\cdot}F) = a - 1,$$

i.e.,

$$D \sim dE + dF - \Delta.$$

Now, the number ${}^\#(D{\cdot}\Delta)$ of united points of T is just the number b of branch points of the map $C{\to}\mathbb{P}^1$ given by $\{D_\lambda\}$; this being a d-sheeted cover, we have by Riemann-Hurwitz

$$2g - 2 = -2d + b,$$

i.e.,

$$b = 2g - 2 + 2d.$$

Thus

$$2g - 2 + 2d = {}^\#(D{\cdot}\Delta)$$
$$= d{}^\#(E{\cdot}\Delta) + d{}^\#(F{\cdot}\Delta) - {}^\#(\Delta{\cdot}\Delta),$$
$$= 2d - {}^\#(\Delta{\cdot}\Delta)$$

and so we have

$$\Delta \cdot \Delta = 2 - 2g.$$

The intersection pairing is therefore

#	E	F	Δ
E	0	1	1
F	1	0	1
Δ	1	1	$2-2g$

Now suppose T is any correspondence with $\deg(T)=d$, $\deg(T^{-1})=d'$, and valence k. If D is the curve of correspondence of T, we write

$$D \sim aE + bF - k\Delta.$$

Then, since

$$d = \deg T = {}^\#(D{\cdot}E) = b - k$$

and

$$d' = \deg T^{-1} = {}^\#(D{\cdot}F) = a - k,$$

we obtain

$$D \sim (d'+k)E + (d+k)F - k\Delta.$$

Consequently

$$D \cdot \Delta = d' + k + d + k - k(2-2g)$$
$$= d + d' + 2kg,$$

i.e.,

(∗) T *has* d + d' + 2kg *united points*,

this is known as the *Cayley-Brill* formula.

Similarly, if S is another correspondence with $\deg(S) = e$, $\deg(S^{-1}) = e'$, and valence l, given by the curve $G \subset C \times C$,

$$G \sim (e' + l)E + (e + l)F - \Delta.$$

By an obvious computation using the intersection table,

$$^\#(D \cdot G) = ed' + e'd - 2gkl,$$

i.e.,

(**) *The correspondences* T *and* S *have* ed' + e'd − 2gkl *common points.*

The computation for the number of coincident points of a correspondence $T: C \to C$ is slightly more difficult. With T and D as above,

$$D \sim (d' + k)E + (d + k)F - k \cdot \Delta.$$

In case D is smooth and irreducible, we may apply the *adjunction formula*

$$K_D = (K_{C \times C} + D)|_D$$

for the canonical bundle of D to obtain

$$\deg K_D = {}^\#(K_{C \times C} \cdot D) + {}^\#(D \cdot D).$$

Once we have evaluated these intersection numbers, we will be done; by the Hurwitz formula, the number b of branch points of the projection $\pi_1 : D \to C$ on the first factor is given by

$$\deg K_D = d \cdot \deg K_C + b,$$

i.e.,

$$b = \deg K_D - d \cdot \deg K_C$$
$$= {}^\#(K_{C \times C} \cdot D) + {}^\#(D \cdot D) - d(2g - 2).$$

Now if ω, ω' are holomorphic 1-forms on C, then the divisor of the 2-form $\pi_1^* \omega \wedge \pi_2^* \omega'$ on $C \times C$ is

$$(\pi_1^* \omega \wedge \pi_2^* \omega') = \pi_1^*(\omega) + \pi_2^*(\omega').$$

Thus the homology class of $K_{C \times C}$ is

$$K_{C \times C} \sim \pi_1^* K_C + \pi_2^* K_C$$
$$= (2g - 2)E + (2g - 2)F.$$

We then obtain

$$^\#(D \cdot K_{C \times C}) = (2g - 2)(d + k) - k(2g - 2) + (2g - 2)(d' + k) - k(2g - 2)$$
$$= (2g - 2)(d + d')$$

and by another straightforward manipulation

$$^\#(D \cdot D) = 2dd' - 2gk^2.$$

Putting everything together,

$$b = {}^{\#}(K_{C\times C}\cdot D) + {}^{\#}(D\cdot D) - d(2g-2)$$
$$= (d+d')(2g-2) + 2dd' - 2gk^2 - d(2g-2)$$
$$= 2dd' + (2g-2)d' - 2gk^2$$

i.e.,

(***) *The correspondence* T *has* $2dd' + (2g-2)d' - 2gk^2$ *coincident points.*

This computation may be readily extended to the case where the correspondence T is given by a sum of smooth irreducible curves $D_i \subset C \times C$—the coincident points of T will then consist of coincident points for the correspondence T_i defined by the curves D_i, plus common points of the correspondences D_i and D_j for $i \neq j$ (to be counted, as we shall see, with multiplicity 2), and it is easily checked that the formula holds. A more serious objection is that the formula as stated holds only for correspondences given by smooth curves D. Since this will not always be the case, we will borrow a couple of results from Section 2 of Chapter 4 to see how to handle at least the case where D has ordinary double points.

Suppose that $D \subset C \times C$ has δ ordinary double points (p_i, q_i) and is otherwise smooth. Assuming that neither branch of D at such a double point (p, q) is tangent to the fiber $E_p = \pi_1^{-1}(p)$, (p, q) will appear as a simple coincident point of T. From Section 2 of Chapter 4 we see that D is the image of a smooth curve $\tilde{D}$ via a map $\tilde{\pi} : \tilde{D} \to D \subset C \times C$ that is one-to-one and smooth away from the double points of D—we simply separate the two branches of D around the double points. The Riemann surface $\tilde{D}$, moreover, will have genus (cf. page 280)

$$g(\tilde{D}) = \frac{{}^{\#}(K_{C\times C}\cdot D) + {}^{\#}(D\cdot D)}{2} + 1 - \delta,$$

i.e.,

$$\deg K_{\tilde{D}} = {}^{\#}(K_{C\times C}\cdot D) + {}^{\#}(D\cdot D) - 2\delta.$$

The composite map $\pi_1 \cdot \tilde{\pi} : \tilde{D} \to C$ will thus have

$$b = \deg K_{\tilde{D}} - d \cdot \deg K_C$$
$$= 2dd' + (2g-2)d' - 2gk^2 - 2\delta$$

branch points; i.e., the correspondence T will have

$$2dd' + (2g-2)d' - 2gk^2 - 2\delta$$

coincident points apart from the double points (p_i, q_i) of D. We see, then, that *the formula given above for the number of coincident points of* T *holds if we count with multiplicity* 2 *a coincident point arising from an ordinary double point of* D.

In practice, it will be easy to distinguish an ordinary coincident point of T from one corresponding to a double point of D: a smooth point $(p,q) \in D$ can be a branch point of only one of the projections $\pi_1 : D \to C$ and $\pi_2 : D \to C$, while a double point $(p,q) \in D$ will appear as a coincident point for both T and T^{-1}.

We apply our formulas to the correspondence of example 2 on a smooth plane curve C of degree d. As we saw, T has degree $d-2$ and valence 2; the degree of T^{-1} is the number of tangent lines to C other than $T_q(C)$ passing through a point $q \in C$, i.e., the number b of branch points of the projection π_q of C from q onto a line. The projection is $(d-1)$-sheeted, and so by Riemann-Hurwitz,

$$
\begin{aligned}
\deg T^{-1} = b &= 2g - 2 + 2(d-1) \\
&= (d-1)(d-2) - 2 + 2(d-1) \\
&= (d+1)(d-2).
\end{aligned}
$$

By the formula (∗), the number of united points of T—that is, the number of flexes of C—is

$$
\begin{aligned}
f &= (d-2) + (d+1)(d-2) + 2kg \\
&= (d-2) + (d+1)(d-2) + 2(d-1)(d-2) \\
&= 3d(d-2),
\end{aligned}
$$

which agrees with our computation in the last subsection of Plücker formulas. To compute the number of bitangent lines to C we have to be careful: if q and p are distinct points of C with $T_p(C) = T_q(C)$, then both (p,q) and (q,p) are coincident points of T. The number b of bitangent lines to C is thus half the number of coincident points of T; by (∗∗∗) this is

$$
\begin{aligned}
b &= \tfrac{1}{2}\big[2(d-2)(d-2)(d+1) + (2g-2)(d-2)(d+1) - 2gk^2 \big] \\
&= \tfrac{1}{2}d(d+1)(d-1)(d-2) - 4d(d-2),
\end{aligned}
$$

as we found earlier.

Geometry of Space Curves

We will now illustrate the technique of correspondences by an application to the geometry of *space curves*, i.e., curves in $\mathbb{P}^3$. Our primary goal will be to find the number of quadrisecants to a space curve C of degree d and genus g; along the way we will come across several other invariants.

Before we begin, we want to make one observation. The family of lines in $\mathbb{P}^3$ meeting a curve C has codimension 1 in the four-dimensional Grassmannian $G(2,4)$. By a naive dimension count, then, we may expect that C will have finitely many quadrisecants but no lines meeting C five times. Similarly, we expect that there will be a finite number of points of C whose tangent lines meet a given tangent line to C, hence a finite number of trisecants $\overline{p,q,r}$ such that $T_p(C)$ and $T_q(C)$ meet, but no such quadrise-cants. In general, we say that a curve has *nondegenerate behavior* if no such phenomena occur that are not predicted by a dimension count. We will be assuming, in the following discussion, that this is the case; in particular we will assume that

1. C has no quintisecant lines.
2. The tangent lines to the four points of intersection of each quadrise-cant to C are disjoint.
3. No line has contact of order 3 with C, i.e., the first associated curve of C is smooth.
4. No osculating 2-plane to C contains another tangent line to C.

Now, the central object of our discussion will be the *trisecant correspon-dence* T on C, defined by the curve

$$D = \{(p,q): \overline{pq} \text{ is a trisecant of } C \}.$$

We first compute degree of T: if p is a generic point of C, then the image of C under projection of C from p will be a plane curve of degree $d-1$ having only ordinary double points, and the double points of this curve will correspond to the trisecants to C passing through p. By the Plücker formulas, the number of trisecants through p is

$$\delta = \frac{(d-2)(d-3)}{2} - g,$$

and since $T(p)$ will contain two points for each trisecant of C through p,

$$\deg T = (d-2)(d-3) - 2g.$$

(Note that by our bound on the genus of space curves (p. 252), this number will be positive unless $d=3$, $g=0$ or $d=4$, $g=1$.) Since T is symmetric, this is also the degree of T^{-1}.

Now T has valence, as we see from the following: if $\pi_p : C \rightarrow \mathbb{P}^2$ is the projection of C from a generic point $p \in C$ as above, then as we proved in the preceding section, since $\deg \pi_p C = d-1$

$$K_C = \pi_p^*((d-4)H_{\mathbb{P}^2}) - D,$$

where D is the inverse image in C of the double points of $\pi_p(C)$. But now on C we have

$$\pi_p^*(H_{\mathbb{P}^2}) = H_{\mathbb{P}^3} - p,$$

and of course

$$D = T(p),$$

so

$$K_C = (d-4)H_{\mathbb{P}^3} - (d-4)p - T(p),$$

i.e.,

$$T(p) + (d-4)p = (d-4)H_{\mathbb{P}^3} - K_C$$

is constant as a linear equivalence class, and so T has valence $k = (d-4)$.

Consider now the coincident points of the correspondence T. For $p \in C$, $T(p)$ will contain a multiple point if it fails to contain $(d-2)(d-3) - 2g$ distinct points. This will be the case exactly when the projected curve has singularities other than ordinary double points; this may happen in the following three ways:

1. If a line through p is simply tangent to C at another point q, then the image of q in $\pi_p(C) \subset \mathbb{P}^2$ will be a cusp of $T_p(C)$. (See Figure 10.) By the Plücker formulas, in the absence of other special behavior $\pi_p(C)$ will have $\delta = (d-2)(d-3)/2 - g - 1$ double points apart from $\pi_p(q)$, and so $T(p)$ will contain $(d-2)(d-3) - 2g - 2$ points besides q; q is thus taken in $T(p)$ with multiplicity 2.

Note that (p,q) is not a coincident point of T^{-1}, so (p,q) is a simple point of the curve of correspondence D.

A line tangent to C and meeting C again elsewhere is called a *tangential trisecant* of C. We see that there will be one coincident point of T for every tangential trisecant to C.

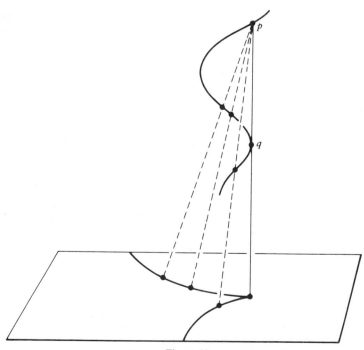

Figure 10

2. If a line through p meets C in two other points q and q', and the tangent lines to C at q and q' meet, then the image point $\pi_p(q) = \pi_p(q') \in \pi_p(C)$ will be a double point of $\pi_p(C)$, but not an ordinary one: the tangent lines to the two branches of $\pi_p(C)$ at $\pi_p(q)$ will coincide. (See Figure 11.) Such a double point is called a *tacnode*. Now, as we will see in Section 2 of Chapter 4, a tacnode drops the genus of a curve by 2, so if $\pi_p(C)$ has a tacnode, it will have only $(d-2)(d-3)/2 - g - 2$ other double points. $T(p)$ thus contains $(d-2)(d-3) - 2g - 4$ points other than q and q', and so each of the pairs (p,q) and (p,q') will be a coincident point of T. Again, since neither (p,q) nor (p,q') is a coincident point of T^{-1}, they will both be smooth points of $\overline{D}$.

A trisecant $\overline{p,q,q'}$ such that $T_q(C)$ and $T_{q'}(C)$ meet is called a *stationary trisecant* of C; by the above, there will be two coincident points of T for every stationary trisecant to C.

3. If a line through p meets C in three other points q_1, q_2, and q_3, then the image point $\pi_p(q_1) = \pi_p(q_2) = \pi_p(q_3)$ will be an ordinary triple point of $\pi_p(C)$. (See Figure 12.) Looking ahead again to Section 2 of Chapter 4, we see that a triple point drops the genus of a curve by 3, so that $T(p)$ will have only $(d-2)(d-3) - 2g - 6$ coincident points other than q_1, q_2, and q_3;

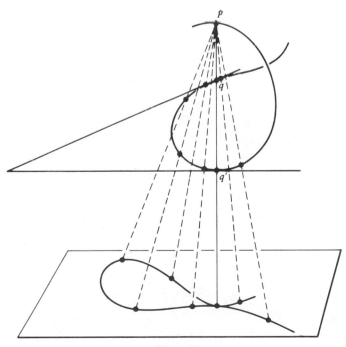

Figure 11

each of the pairs (p,q_1), (p,q_2), and (p,q_3) will thus be a coincident point of T. Moreover, (p,q_i) will by the same argument be a coincident point of T^{-1}, so (p,q_i) is in fact a double point of D. Thus, if $L=\overline{p_1 p_2 p_3 p_4}$ is a quadrisecant of C, each of the 12 pairs (p_i,p_j) will be a double point of D, and so there are 24 coincident points of T for every quadrisecant to C.

Now, knowing the degree and valence of T, we can compute the total number of coincident points of T, so to find the number Q of quadrisecants to C we have to find the number of tangential and stationary trisecants. The number t of tangential trisecants is easy, since clearly the trisecants $\overline{p,q}$ with $q \in T_p(C)$ correspond exactly to the united points (p,p) of T. By the formula $(*)$,

$$t = (d-2)(d-3) - 2g + (d-2)(d-3) - 2g + 2(d-4)g$$
$$= 2(d-2)(d-3) + 2(d-6)g.$$

The number s of stationary trisecants is somewhat more difficult to calculate. To find it, we introduce the *bitangential correspondence* S on C,

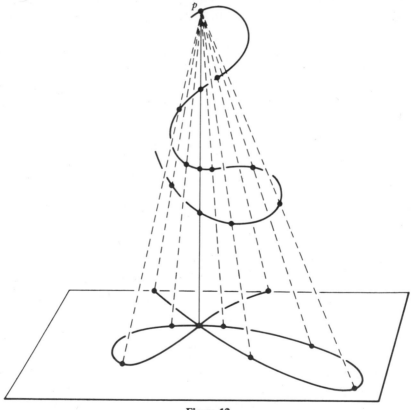

Figure 12

defined by the curve

$$G = \overline{\{(p,q): p \neq q, T_p(C) \cap T_q(C) \neq \emptyset\}} \subset C \times C.$$

For each $p \in C$, the divisor $S(p)$ is the branch locus of the projection map π_L of C from the tangent line $L = T_p(C)$ to C at p onto a line; since π_L has degree $d-2$, by the Riemann-Hurwitz formula

$$\deg S = 2g - 2 + 2(d-2)$$
$$= 2g + 2d - 6.$$

Since S is symmetric, this is also the degree of S^{-1}. We have, moreover,

$$K_C = \pi_L^*(-2H_{\mathbb{P}^1}) + S(p),$$

and because $\pi_L^*(H_{\mathbb{P}^1}) = H_{\mathbb{P}^3} - 2p$, this yields

$$S(p) + 4p = K_C + 2H_{\mathbb{P}^3},$$
$$S(p) + 4p = K_C + 2H_{\mathbb{P}^3},$$

i.e., S has valence $l = 4$.

Consider now the common points of the two correspondences T and S. (See Figure 13.) These can occur in two ways: if $\overline{p,q,q'}$ is a stationary trisecant of C with $T_q(C) \cap T_{q'}(C) \neq \emptyset$, then each of the pairs (q,q') and (q',q) will be a common point of S and T. Alternately, if $\overline{p,q}$ is a tangential trisecant with $q \in T_p(C)$, then (p,q) and (q,p) are both common points of S and T. The number of common points of S and T is therefore $2s + 2t$; we have by the formula $(**)$,

$$2s + 2t = 2((d-2)(d-3) - 2g)(2g+2d-6) - 2g(d-4) \cdot 4,$$

i.e.,

$$\begin{aligned} s &= ((d-2)(d-3) - 2g)(2g+2d-6) - 4g(d-4) \\ &\quad - 2(d-2)(d-3) - 2(d-6)g \\ &= 2d(d-2)(d-3) - 2(d-2)(d-3) - 6(d-2)(d-3) \\ &\quad + 2g((d-2)(d-3) - 2g - 2d + 6 - 2(d-4) - (d-6)) \\ &= 2(d-2)(d-3)(d-4) + 2g(d^2 - 10d + 26 - 2g). \end{aligned}$$

We now have enough to calculate the number Q of quadrisecants to C. As we have seen, the total number of coincident points of the correspondence T is $t + 2s + 24Q$; by our formula $(***)$,

$$\begin{aligned} t + 2s + 24Q &= 2((d-2)(d-3) - 2g)^2 \\ &\quad + 2g - 2((d-2)(d-3) - 2g) - 2g(d-4)^2, \end{aligned}$$

i.e.,

$$\begin{aligned} Q &= \tfrac{1}{12}((d-2)(d-3) - 2g)^2 + (g-1)((d-2)(d-3) \\ &\quad - 2g - g(d-4)^2 - (d-2)(d-3) - (d-6)g \\ &\quad - 2(d-2)(d-3)(d-4) - 2g(d^2 - 10d + 26 - 2g) \end{aligned}$$

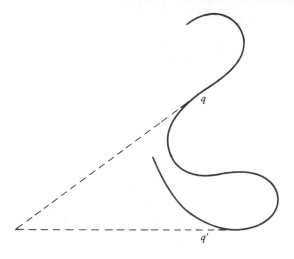

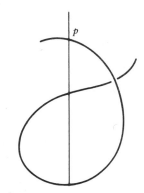

Figure 13

Omitting the explicit reduction, this gives

$$Q = \tfrac{1}{12}(d-2)(d-3)^2(d-4) - \tfrac{1}{2}g(d^2-7d+13-g).$$

One point: while the formulas derived in this discussion apply a priori to curves that do not exhibit degenerate behavior, it should be clear from the derivation how to account for such behavior. For example, if $L = \overline{p_1,\ldots,p_5}$ is a quintisecant to C, we can verify that each of the 20 pairs (p_i,p_j) is a triple point of the curve D and so drops the genus of D by 3; going back to the derivation of (∗∗∗), we see that each pair (p_i,p_j) counts as six coincident points. L thus contributes 120 coincident points to T, i.e., in terms of the last formula a quintisecant line to C is equivalent to $120/24 = 5$ quadrisecants.

Finally we take the opportunity here of remarking that some enumerative problems having to do with the extrinsic properties of more than one curve in $\mathbb{P}^3$ may also be solved by means of the Schubert calculus. For example, if C and C' are space curves, we may ask for the number of common chords of C and C'. To answer this, let $V(C) \subset G(2,4)$ be the algebraic surface of chords to C, in the Grassmannian of lines in $\mathbb{P}^3$. The fourth homology group of $G(2,4)$ is generated by the cycles

$$\sigma_2(p) = \{ l \subset \mathbb{P}^3 : p \in l \}$$

and

$$\sigma_{1,1}(H) = \{ l \subset \mathbb{P}^3 : l \subset H \};$$

we have clearly

$$^{\#}(\sigma_2 \cdot \sigma_2) = {}^{\#}(\sigma_{1,1} \cdot \sigma_{1,1}) = 1; \qquad {}^{\#}(\sigma_2 \cdot \sigma_{1,1}) = 0.$$

If we write

$$V(C) \sim a \cdot \sigma_{1,1} + b \cdot \sigma_2,$$

then

$$a = {}^{\#}(V(C) \cdot \sigma_{1,1}), \qquad b = {}^{\#}(V(C) \cdot \sigma_2).$$

These numbers are readily calculable. A generic hyperplane H will meet C in d distinct points $\{p_i\}$ and so contain exactly the $d(d-1)/2$ chords $\overline{\{p_i p_j\}}_{i \neq j}$; consequently

$$a = \frac{d(d-1)}{2}.$$

On the other hand, for p a generic point of $\mathbb{P}^3$, the number of chords to C passing through p will be just the number of double points of the image of C under projection from p into a hyperplane; by the Plücker formulas, this is

$$b = \frac{(d-1)(d-2)}{2} - g.$$

Combining,

$$V(C) \sim \frac{d(d-1)}{2} \cdot \sigma_{1,1} + \left(\frac{(d-1)(d-2)}{2} - g \right) \sigma_2.$$

If C' has degree d' and genus g', and if C and C' are in general position with respect to one another so that $V(C)$ and $V(C')$ meet transversely, then C and C' will have

$$^{\#}(V(C) \cdot V(C')) = \frac{d(d-1) \cdot d'(d-1)}{4} + \frac{(d-1)(d-2)(d'-1)(d'-2)}{4}$$
$$- (d-1)(d-2)g' - (d'-1)(d'-2)g + gg'$$

common chords.

Special Linear Systems III

As promised earlier, we will use the results on correspondences to answer some of the enumerative questions arising from the Brill-Noether problem. We have seen that the generic Riemann surface of genus $g = 2k$ has a finite number of pencils of degree $k + 1$; the question is, how many? We will answer this in cases $g = 4$, 6, and 8. (Note that in case $g = 2$ the answer 1 has already been obtained.)

$g = 4$.   If S is a Riemann surface of genus 4, its canonical curve is a curve of degree 6 in $\mathbb{P}^3$. Now if $D = \Sigma p_i$ is a divisor of degree 3 on S, then by the geometric version of the Riemann-Roch, $l(D)$ will be 1 exactly when the points p_i are collinear; for each pencil of degree 3 there will be one such divisor through a generic point $p \in S$. The number of such pencils is thus the number of trisecants to S through a generic point $p \in S$—and this we have seen is

$$n = \tfrac{1}{2}(d-2)(d-3) - g$$
$$= \tfrac{1}{2}(4 \cdot 3) - 4 = 2,$$

i.e., there are two pencils of degree 3 on S. Thus, *the generic Riemann surface of genus 4 is expressible as a 3-sheeted cover of $\mathbb{P}^1$ in two ways.*

   It is interesting to actually locate these two pencils. We saw in the last section that the canonical curve of S is the smooth intersection of a quadric Q and cubic Q' in $\mathbb{P}^3$; generically the quadric will be smooth. Now a smooth quadric surface in $\mathbb{P}^3$ (discussed on pages 478–480 below) contains two families of lines $\{L_t\}, \{L_t'\}$, each parametrized by $t \in \mathbb{P}^1$; since S is cut out on Q by the cubic Q', each line L_t or L_t' will meet S in three points; the divisors

$$D_t = L \cap S \quad \text{and} \quad D_t' = L_t' \cap S$$

then form two pencils of degree 3 on S. Conversely, if $D = \Sigma_{i=1}^3 p_i$ is any divisor consisting of three collinear points, then the line $L = \overline{p_1 p_2 p_3}$, meeting Q in three points, must lie in Q; L is thus an L_t or an L_t' and D a D_t or a D_t'.

   Note that in case Q is singular, S will contain only one pencil of degree 3; the projection of S from any point of S into a hyperplane will have not two ordinary double points but one tacnode.

$g = 6$.   If $D = \Sigma_{i=1}^4 p_i$ is a divisor of degree 4 and $\dim|D| = 1$ on a curve S of genus 6, then the divisor $K - D$ will have degree $2g - 2 - 4 = 6$, and by Riemann-Roch

$$h^0(K - D) = \deg(K - D) - g + 1 + h^0(D)$$
$$= 6 - 6 + 1 + 2$$
$$= 3,$$

i.e., the complete linear system $|K-D|$ will have dimension 2. Consequently the number of pencils of degree 4 on S is the number of nets of degree 6; it is this number that we shall compute.

Now by the geometric Riemann-Roch formula a divisor D of degree 6 with $\dim|D|=2$ on S consists of six points on the canonical curve of S spanning a 3-plane in $\mathbb{P}^5$; and if $p,q \in S$ are generic points for every net of degree 6 on S, there will be one such divisor containing p and q. If $D=p+q+r_1+\cdots+r_4$ is such a divisor, moreover, then the images of the points r_i under the projection

$$\pi_L : S \to \mathbb{P}^3$$

of S from the line $L=\overline{pq}$ onto a 3-plane will be collinear, and conversely, if any four points $\pi_L(r_i)$ of $\pi_L(S)$ are collinear, then the points $p,q,r_1,\ldots,r_4$ all lie in the 3-plane spanned by L and $\{\pi_L(r_i)\}$. *The number of nets of degree* 6 *on* S *will thus be the number of quadrisecants to* $\pi_L(S)$ *in* $\mathbb{P}^3$. Since $\pi_L(S)$ has degree $d=\deg(S)-2=8$ and genus $g=6$, by our previous formula this number is

$$n = \tfrac{1}{12}\cdot 6\cdot 5\cdot 5\cdot 4 - \tfrac{1}{2}6(64-56+13-6)$$

$$= 50 - 3\cdot 15 = 5.$$

We see that *the generic Riemann surface of genus* 6 *is expressible as a* 4-*sheeted cover of* $\mathbb{P}^1$ *in five ways.*

$g=8$.   If D is a divisor of degree 5 with $\dim|D|=1$ on a Riemann surface S of genus 8, then the divisor $K-D$ has degree $14-5=9$ and

$$h^0(K-D) = \deg(K-D) - g + 1 + h^0(D)$$

$$= 9 - 8 + 1 + 2$$

$$= 4,$$

i.e., $\dim|K-D|=3$. By the Riemann-Roch, then, D will be represented by five points spanning a 3-plane on the canonical curve of S, while $K-D$ will be represented by nine points of S spanning a 5-plane.

To compute the number of pencils of degree 5 on S, we first prove the

Lemma.   *If* D,D' *are two divisors of degree* 5 *on* S, $\dim|D|=\dim|D'|=1$, *then there will be a divisor* $E \in |K-D'|$ *containing* D *if and only if* D *and* D' *are not linearly equivalent; if* E *exists, it is unique.*

Proof.   We want to show that

$$h^0(K-D-D') = \begin{cases} 1, & \text{if } D \not\sim D', \\ 0, & \text{if } D \sim D'. \end{cases}$$

(Note that since C is generic, it has no pencil of degree 4; thus

$$h^0(K-D-D') \leqslant 1.)$$

By Riemann-Roch,

$$h^0(K-D-D') = \deg(K-D-D') - g + 1 + h^0(D+D')$$
$$= 4 - 8 + 1 + h^0(D+D'),$$

i.e., we have to show that

$$h^0(D+D') = \begin{cases} 3, & \text{if } D \sim D', \\ 4, & \text{if } D \not\sim D'. \end{cases}$$

But now if $h^0(D+D')$ were 3—i.e., if $|D+D'|$ were parametrized by $\mathbb{P}^2$—then for any $D_0 \in |D|, D_0' \in |D'|$ the two lines $D_0 + |D'|$ and $D_0' + |D| \subset |D+D'|$ would meet; we would then have $D_0 \in |D'|$ and $D \sim D'$.

On the other hand, any divisor $G \in |K-D|$ consists of nine points spanning a 5-plane and so lies on a pencil $\{H_t\}$ of hyperplanes in $\mathbb{P}^7$; the divisors

$$D_t = (H_t \cdot C) - G$$

comprise the linear system $\{D_t\}$. Clearly, then, for $t \neq t'$, D_t and $D_{t'}$ will lie in no hyperplane in $\mathbb{P}^7$, i.e., $K - D_t - D_{t'} \sim K - 2D$ is not effective.   Q.E.D.

Now suppose $D = \sum_{i=1}^5 p_i$ is any divisor on S of degree 5 and $\dim |D| = 1$. Then by our lemma the pencils of degree 5 in S *other than* D correspond exactly to 9-secant 5-planes to the canonical curve $S \subset \mathbb{P}^7$ containing D. If $\overline{p_1, \ldots, p_5, q_1, \ldots, q_4}$ is any such 9-secant 5-plane, then the images of the points q_i under the projection

$$\pi_V: S \to \mathbb{P}^3$$

of S from the 3-plane $V = \overline{p_1, \ldots, p_5}$ will be collinear, and conversely. Thus the number of pencils of degree 5 on S other than $|D|$ is just the number of quadrisecants to $\pi_V(S) \subset \mathbb{P}^3$. $\pi_V(S)$ has degree $d = \deg(S) - 5 = 9$, and so this number is

$$\tfrac{1}{12} 7 \cdot 6 \cdot 6 \cdot 5 - \tfrac{1}{2} 8 \cdot (81 - 63 + 13 - 8) = 105 - 4 \cdot 23 = 13.$$

Summarizing, we see that *the generic Riemann surface of genus 8 may be expressed as a 5-sheeted cover of $\mathbb{P}^1$ in 14 ways*.

6.   COMPLEX TORI AND ABELIAN VARIETIES

The Riemann Conditions

En route to our analysis of the relationship between a compact Riemann surface and its Jacobian, we given here an introduction to the general theory of complex tori.

First, we make a definition: for V a complex vector space of dimension n, $\Lambda \subset V$ a discrete lattice of maximal rank $2n$, the complex torus $M = V/\Lambda$ is called an *Abelian variety* if it is a projective algebraic variety, i.e., if it admits an embedding in projective space.

Our first task will be to determine when a complex torus $M = V/\Lambda$ is an Abelian variety. Since the cohomology of M is easily expressed in terms of V and Λ, Kodaira's embedding theorem will give us necessary and sufficient conditions; later on, we will verify the sufficiency of these conditions by direct computation. To begin with, we make some general remarks about the cohomology of complex tori.

Let $M = V/\Lambda$ as above. Since Λ is a subgroup of V, M likewise has the structure of a group: for any $\mu \in M$, and any $x \in V$ over μ, the map

$$\tau_\mu : V \to V$$
$$: v \mapsto v + x$$

induces a map $\tau_\mu : M \to M$, called *translation by μ*.

Now we have a natural identificaton

$$T''_\mu(M) \cong V$$

for each $\mu \in M$; accordingly, any hermitian inner product on the vector space V gives a Kähler metric on M, invariant under the automorphisms $\{\tau_\mu\}$. We claim first that with respect to such a metric, the harmonic forms are exactly the forms invariant under $\{\tau_\mu\}$. To see this, note first that since τ_μ preserves the metric, $\tau_\mu^* : A^*(M) \to A^*(M)$ sends harmonic forms to harmonic forms. Then, since τ_μ is homotopic to the identity map and by the Hodge theorem $\mathcal{H}^*(M)$ maps isomorphically to $H^*(M, \mathbb{C})$,

$$\tau_\mu^* : \mathcal{H}^*(M) \to \mathcal{H}^*(M)$$

is just the identity, i.e., *harmonic forms are invariant*. But now an invariant form on M is determined by its values on the tangent space $T_{p,\mathbb{C}}(M) = T'_p(M) \oplus T''_p(M)$ to M at a point p, and this tangent space is naturally identified with the vector space $V \oplus \overline{V}$. Letting $\mathcal{I}^*(M)$ denote the space of invariant forms on M, then,

$$\mathcal{I}^*(M) = \wedge^*(T_{p,\mathbb{C}}(M)^*) \cong \wedge^* V^* \otimes \wedge^* \overline{V}^*.$$

But we know that topologically $M \cong (S^1)^{2n}$, so the dimension of the space of harmonic forms of degree k is $\binom{2n}{k}$; since $\mathcal{H}^*(M) \subset \mathcal{I}^*(M)$, we count dimensions to obtain

$$H^*(M, \mathbb{C}) \cong \mathcal{H}^*(M) = \wedge^* V \otimes \wedge^* \overline{V}^*.$$

Thus if $z = (z_1, \ldots, z_n)$ are Euclidean coordinates on V, $\{dz_1, \ldots, dz_n\}$ and

$\{d\bar{z}_1, \ldots, d\bar{z}_n\}$ the corresponding global 1-forms on M,

$$\mathcal{H}^*(M) = \mathbb{C}\{dz_I \wedge d\bar{z}_J\}_{I,J}$$

with

$$\mathcal{H}^{p,q}(M) = \mathbb{C}\{dz_I \wedge d\bar{z}_J\}_{\#I=p, \#J=q}.$$

On the other hand, note that any loop $\gamma \in H_1(M, \mathbb{Z})$ with base point $[0] \in M$ lifts to a path $\tilde{\gamma}$ in V starting at 0 and ending at a point $\lambda \in \Lambda \subset V$; since V is the universal covering space of M, we can make the identification

$$H_1(M, \mathbb{Z}) = \Lambda.$$

Let $\lambda_1, \ldots, \lambda_{2n} \in \Lambda$ be lattice vectors forming an integral basis for Λ; $\lambda_1, \ldots, \lambda_{2n}$ will also be a basis for the real vector space V. Let $x_1, \ldots, x_{2n}$ be the dual real coordinates on V and $dx_1, \ldots, dx_{2n}$ the corresponding 1-forms on M. Then

$$\int_{\lambda_i} dx_j = \delta_{ij},$$

i.e.,

$$H^1(M, \mathbb{Z}) = \mathbb{Z}\{dx_1, \ldots, dx_{2n}\}$$

and in general

$$H^k(M, \mathbb{Z}) = \mathbb{Z}\{dx_I\}_{\#I=k}.$$

Thus we have two alternate bases for the cohomology of M: the first, $\{dz_\alpha, d\bar{z}_\alpha\}$ reflecting the complex structure on $H^*(M)$ and the second, $\{dx_i\}$, reflecting the rational structure. Now the Kodaira embedding theorem says that M is algebraic if and only if there exists a *Hodge form* on M, i.e., a closed, positive form of type $(1, 1)$ representing a rational cohomology class. Moreover, if $\tilde{\omega}$ is any such form, written

$$\tilde{\omega} = \frac{\sqrt{-1}}{2} \sum \tilde{h}_{\alpha\beta}(z) dz_\alpha \wedge d\bar{z}_\beta,$$

and $d\mu$ is the invariant Euclidean measure on M with $\mu(M) = 1$, we can set

$$h_{\alpha\beta} = \int_M \tilde{h}_{\alpha\beta}(z) d\mu$$

and

$$\omega = \frac{\sqrt{-1}}{2} \sum h_{\alpha\beta} dz_\alpha \wedge d\bar{z}_\beta$$

to obtain an *invariant* form that is again closed, positive of type $(1, 1)$, and integral. Thus M has a Hodge form if and only if it has an invariant Hodge form. Accordingly, to determine whether such a form exists, we have to relate our two bases for $H^*(M)$.

Let $\Pi = (\pi_{i\alpha})$ be the $2n \times n$ matrix such that

$$dx_i = \sum_\alpha \pi_{i\alpha} \, dz_\alpha + \sum_\alpha \overline{\pi}_{i\alpha} \, d\bar{z}_\alpha,$$

i.e., such that the $2n \times 2n$ matrix $\tilde{\Pi} = (\Pi, \overline{\Pi})$ gives the change of basis from $\{dz_\alpha, d\bar{z}_\alpha\}$ to $\{dx_i\}$. Then, if ω is an invariant, integral 2-form, we can write

$$\omega = \tfrac{1}{2} \sum q_{ij} \, dx_i \wedge dx_j$$

with $Q = (q_{ij})$ an integral skew-symmetric $2n \times 2n$ matrix. In terms of the $dz_\alpha, d\bar{z}_\alpha$, we have

$$\omega = \tfrac{1}{2} \sum q_{ij} (\pi_{i\alpha} \, dz_\alpha + \overline{\pi}_{i\alpha} \, d\bar{z}_\alpha) \wedge (\pi_{j\beta} \, dz_\beta + \overline{\pi}_{j\beta} \, d\bar{z}_\beta)$$

$$= \tfrac{1}{2} \sum q_{ij} \pi_{i\alpha} \pi_{j\beta} \, dz_\alpha \wedge dz_\beta + \tfrac{1}{2} \sum q_{ij} \overline{\pi}_{i\alpha} \overline{\pi}_{j\beta} \, d\bar{z}_\alpha \wedge d\bar{z}_\beta$$

$$+ \tfrac{1}{2} \sum q_{ij} (\pi_{i\alpha} \overline{\pi}_{j\beta} - \overline{\pi}_{i\beta} \pi_{j\alpha}) \, dz_\alpha \wedge d\bar{z}_\beta.$$

From this we see that ω is of type $(1, 1)$ if and only if the coefficient matrix

$$\tfrac{1}{2} \left(\sum_{i,j} q_{ij} \pi_{i\alpha} \pi_{j\beta} \right) = {}^t\Pi \cdot Q \cdot \Pi$$

is zero, and that if this is the case, then ω is positive if and only if

$$\frac{1}{2\sqrt{-1}} \left(\sum_{i,j} q_{ij} (\pi_{i\alpha} \overline{\pi}_{j\beta} - \overline{\pi}_{i\beta} \pi_{j\alpha}) \right)_{\alpha\beta}$$

$$= \frac{1}{2\sqrt{-1}} ({}^t\Pi Q \overline{\Pi} - {}^t\Pi' Q \overline{\Pi}) = \frac{1}{\sqrt{-1}} {}^t\Pi Q \overline{\Pi}$$

is hermitian positive definite. Thus we have the

Riemann Conditions I. M *is an Abelian variety if and only if there exists an integral, skew-symmetric matrix* Q *such that*

$${}^t\Pi \cdot Q \cdot \Pi = 0$$

and

$$-\sqrt{-1} \, {}^t\Pi Q \overline{\Pi} > 0.$$

We can also express these conditions in terms of the square matrix $\tilde{\Pi} = (\Pi, \overline{\Pi})$:

$${}^t\tilde{\Pi} \cdot Q \cdot \overline{\tilde{\Pi}} = \begin{pmatrix} {}^t\Pi \\ {}^t\overline{\Pi} \end{pmatrix} \cdot Q \cdot (\overline{\Pi}, \Pi) = \begin{pmatrix} {}^t\Pi \cdot Q \cdot \overline{\Pi} & {}^t\Pi \cdot Q \cdot \Pi \\ {}^t\overline{\Pi} \cdot Q \cdot \overline{\Pi} & {}^t\overline{\Pi} \cdot Q \cdot \Pi \end{pmatrix}$$

and ${}^t\overline{\Pi} Q \Pi = {}^t({}^t\Pi' Q \overline{\Pi}) = -{}^t({}^t\Pi \cdot Q \cdot \overline{\Pi})$, so M is an Abelian variety if and only if there exists an integral, skew-symmetric matrix Q with

$$-\sqrt{-1} \, {}^t\tilde{\Pi} \cdot Q \cdot \overline{\tilde{\Pi}} = \begin{pmatrix} H & 0 \\ 0 & -{}^tH \end{pmatrix}$$

with $H > 0$.

The usual form of the Riemann conditions is in terms of the dual change-of-basis matrix. For $\lambda_1,\ldots,\lambda_{2n}$ an integral basis for Λ and $e_1,\ldots,e_n$ a complex basis for V, we take the *period matrix* of $\Lambda \subset V$ to be the $n \times 2n$ matrix $\Omega = (\omega_{\alpha i})$ such that

$$\lambda_i = \sum_\alpha \omega_{\alpha i} e_\alpha.$$

Then we have

$$dz_\alpha = \sum_i \omega_{\alpha i}\, dx_i,$$

$$d\bar{z}_\alpha = \sum_i \bar{\omega}_{\alpha i}\, dx_i,$$

so that the matrix $\tilde{\Omega} = \begin{pmatrix} \Omega \\ \bar{\Omega} \end{pmatrix}$ gives the change of basis from $\{dx_i\}$ to $\{dz_\alpha, d\bar{z}_\alpha\}$. Thus

$$\tilde{\Omega} \cdot \tilde{\Pi} = I_{2n} \quad \text{or} \quad \Omega\Pi = I_n, \quad \Omega\overline{\Pi} = 0.$$

Now

$$-\sqrt{-1}\ {}^t\tilde{\Pi} \cdot Q \cdot \overline{\tilde{\Pi}} = -\sqrt{-1}\ {}^t\tilde{\Omega}^{-1} \cdot Q \cdot \overline{\tilde{\Omega}}^{-1},$$

and so in terms of Ω we can write the Riemann conditions as

$$\sqrt{-1} \cdot \overline{\tilde{\Omega}} \cdot Q^{-1} \cdot {}^t\tilde{\Omega} = \begin{pmatrix} H^{-1} & 0 \\ 0 & -{}^t H^{-1} \end{pmatrix},$$

where $H > 0$. But $H > 0 \Leftrightarrow H^{-1} > 0$; thus

Riemann Conditions II.   M *is an Abelian variety if and only if there exists an integral, skew-symmetric matrix* Q *satisfying*

$$\Omega \cdot Q^{-1} \cdot {}^t\Omega = 0, \quad -\sqrt{-1}\ \Omega \cdot Q^{-1} \cdot {}^t\bar{\Omega} > 0.$$

It will be noticed that the period matrix Ω of $\Lambda \subset V$ depends on the choice of basis for both Λ and V. By normalizing our choice of both with respect to a given form, we can simplify the Riemann conditions somewhat. First, we prove the

Lemma.   *If* Q(,) *is an integral, skew-symmetric quadratic form on* $\Lambda = \mathbb{Z}^{2n}$, *then there exists a basis* $\lambda_1,\ldots,\lambda_{2n}$ *for* Λ *in terms of which* Q *is given by the matrix*

$$Q = \begin{pmatrix} 0 & \Delta_\delta \\ -\Delta_\delta & 0 \end{pmatrix}, \quad \Delta_\delta = \begin{bmatrix} \delta_1 & & 0 \\ & \ddots & \\ 0 & & \delta_n \end{bmatrix}, \quad \delta_i \in \mathbb{Z}.$$

Proof.   For each $\lambda \in \Lambda$ the set of values $\{Q(\lambda,\lambda'), \lambda' \in \Lambda\}$ forms a principal ideal $d_\lambda \mathbb{Z}$ in $\mathbb{Z}$, $d_\lambda \geq 0$. Let $\delta_1 = \min(d_\lambda : \lambda \in \Lambda, d_\lambda \neq 0)$, and take λ_1 and λ_{n+1}

such that $Q(\lambda_1,\lambda_{n+1})=\delta_1$. Then for every $\lambda\in\Lambda$, δ_1 divides $Q(\lambda,\lambda_1)$ and $Q(\lambda,\lambda_{n+1})$, and we can write

$$\lambda + \frac{Q(\lambda,\lambda_1)}{\delta_1}\cdot\lambda_{n+1} - \frac{Q(\lambda,\lambda_{n+1})}{\delta_1}\cdot\lambda_1 \in \mathbb{Z}\{\lambda_1,\lambda_{n+1}\}^{\perp},$$

i.e.,

$$\Lambda = \mathbb{Z}\{\lambda_1,\lambda_{n+1}\} \oplus \mathbb{Z}\{\lambda_1,\lambda_{n+1}\}^{\perp}.$$

Set $\Lambda'=\mathbb{Z}\{\lambda_1,\lambda_{n+1}\}^{\perp}$; we can repeat this process to obtain two elements $\lambda_2,\lambda_{n+2}\in\Lambda'$ with

$$\Lambda' = \mathbb{Z}\{\lambda_2,\lambda_{n+2}\} \oplus \mathbb{Z}\{\lambda_2,\lambda_{n+2}\}^{\perp}.$$

Continuing in this way, we obtain a basis $(\lambda_1,\ldots,\lambda_{2n})$ for Λ having the desired properties.

Note that the integers $\{\delta_i\}$ obtained satisfy $\delta_1|\delta_2$, $\delta_2|\delta_3$, and so on: if, for example, $\delta_1 \nmid \delta_2$, then for some k we would have

$$0 < Q(k\lambda_1+\lambda_2,\lambda_{n+1}+\lambda_{n+2}) < \delta_1.$$

We observe that with the additional condition $\delta_i|\delta_{i+1}$ the integers δ_i are invariants of the quadratic form Q.   Q.E.D.

We see from the lemma that if ω is any integral, invariant 2-form on $M=V/\Lambda$, we can find a basis $\lambda_1,\ldots,\lambda_{2n}$ for Λ such that in terms of the dual coordinates $x_1,\ldots,x_{2n}$ on V,

$$\omega = \sum_{i=1}^{n} \delta_i\, dx_i \wedge dx_{n+i}, \qquad \delta_i \in \mathbb{Z}.$$

Now if ω is nondegenerate—that is, if $\omega^n\neq0$, as will be the case if ω is positive—then $\delta_\alpha\neq0$ for all α, and we can take as our basis for the complex vector space V the vectors

$$e_\alpha = \delta_\alpha^{-1}\lambda_\alpha, \qquad \alpha = 1,\ldots,n.$$

The period matrix of $\Lambda\subset V$ will then be of the form

$$\Omega = (\Delta_\delta, Z);$$

such a period matrix is called *normalized*. As before, ω will be of type $(1,1)$ if

$$\Omega\cdot Q_\delta^{-1}\cdot{}^t\Omega = 0,$$

i.e., if

$$(\Delta_\delta, Z)\begin{pmatrix} 0 & -\Delta_{\delta^{-1}} \\ \Delta_{\delta^{-1}} & 0 \end{pmatrix}\begin{pmatrix} \Delta_\delta \\ {}^tZ \end{pmatrix} = (\Delta_\delta, Z)\begin{pmatrix} -\Delta_\delta^{-1}\cdot{}^tZ \\ I \end{pmatrix}$$

$$= Z - {}^tZ = 0,$$

i.e., if Z is symmetric; and ω will be positive as well if

$$-\sqrt{-1}\cdot\Omega\cdot Q_\delta^{-1}\cdot{}^t\overline{\Omega} > 0,$$

i.e., if

$$-\sqrt{-1}\,(\Delta_\delta,Z)\begin{pmatrix}0 & -\Delta_{\delta^{-1}} \\ \Delta_{\delta^{-1}} & 0\end{pmatrix}\begin{pmatrix}\Delta_\delta \\ {}^t\overline{Z}\end{pmatrix} = -\sqrt{-1}\,(Z-{}^t\overline{Z}) = 2\cdot\operatorname{Im}Z > 0.$$

Thus we have

Riemann Conditions III. $\mathrm{M}=V/\Lambda$ *is an Abelian variety if and only if there exists an integral basis* $\lambda_1,\ldots,\lambda_{2n}$ *for* Λ *and complex basis* $e_1,\ldots,e_n$ *for* V *such that*

$$\Omega = (\Delta_\delta, Z)$$

with Z *symmetric and* $\operatorname{Im}Z$ *positive definite.*

Note that the matrix Π above likewise takes a relatively simple form in terms of the bases $\{\lambda_1,\ldots,\lambda_{2n}\}$ and $\{e_1,\ldots,e_n\}$: solving

$$(\Pi,\overline{\Pi})\cdot\begin{pmatrix}\Omega \\ \overline{\Omega}\end{pmatrix} = I_{2n},$$

we see that

$$\Pi = \begin{pmatrix}\Pi_1 \\ \Pi_2\end{pmatrix}$$

with

$$\Pi_2 = \frac{1}{2\sqrt{-1}}(\operatorname{Im}Z)^{-1},$$

$$\Pi_1 = \frac{\sqrt{-1}}{2}\Delta_\delta^{-1}\overline{Z}(\operatorname{Im}Z)^{-1}.$$

The cohomology class $[\omega]$ of a Hodge form ω on an Abelian variety $M=V/\Lambda$ is called a *polarization* of M. The integers δ_α appearing in the expression

$$\omega = \sum \delta_\alpha\, dx_\alpha \wedge dx_{n+\alpha}, \qquad \delta_\alpha | \delta_{\alpha+1}$$

for ω in terms of coordinates $\{x_i\}$ dual to an integral basis for Λ are invariants of the class $[\omega]$, and are called the *elementary divisors* of the polarization; $[\omega]$ is called a *principal polarization* if $\delta_\alpha = 1$ for all α.

Now if S is a compact Riemann surface of genus g with bases $\delta_1,\ldots,\delta_{2g}$ for $H_1(S,\mathbb{Z})$ and $\omega_1,\ldots,\omega_g$ for $H^0(S,\Omega^1)$, the Jacobian variety

$$\mathcal{J}(S) = \frac{\mathbb{C}^g}{\mathbb{Z}\{\lambda_1,\ldots,\lambda_{2g}\}},$$

where the λ_i are the column vectors.

$$\lambda_i = {}^t\left(\int_{\delta_i} \omega_1, \ldots, \int_{\delta_i} \omega_g\right)$$

of the period matrix Ω of S. We have seen in Section 2 of this chapter that if $\delta_1, \ldots, \delta_{2g}$ is a normalized basis for $H_1(S, \mathbb{Z})$, we can choose a basis $\omega_1, \ldots, \omega_g$ for $H^0(S, \Omega^1)$ such that

$$\int_{\delta_i} \omega_\alpha = \delta_{i\alpha}, \qquad 1 \leqslant i, \alpha \leqslant g;$$

the period matrix will then be of the form

$$\Omega = (I, Z),$$

and by the two Riemann bilinear relations also proved in Section 2, $Z = X + \sqrt{-1}\, Y$ is symmetric with $Y > 0$. Thus $\mathcal{J}(S)$ is an Abelian variety, and moreover has a principal polarization given in terms of the basis $\{dx_i\}$ for $H^1(\mathcal{J}(S), \mathbb{Z})$ dual to $\{\lambda_i\} \in H_1(\mathcal{J}(S), \mathbb{Z})$ by

$$\omega = \sum dx_\alpha \wedge dx_{n+\alpha}.$$

In intrinsic terms, the Jacobian variety $\mathcal{J}(S) = V(S)/\Lambda(S)$, where $V(S) = H^0(S, \Omega^1)^*$ and the lattice $\Lambda(S) \cong H_1(S, \mathbb{Z})$ is embedded in $V(S)$ by integration. The polarizing form $\omega \in H^2(\mathcal{J}(S), \mathbb{Z}) \cong \mathrm{Hom}_\mathbb{Z}(\wedge^2 H_1(S, \mathbb{Z}), \mathbb{Z})$ is the skew-symmetric bilinear form

$$Q: H_1(S, \mathbb{Z}) \otimes_\mathbb{Z} H_1(S, \mathbb{Z}) \to \mathbb{Z}$$

given by intersection of cycles; the fact that the polarization is principal is a reflection of Poincaré duality. Note that the polarizing class $[\omega]$ does not depend on the choice of basis $\delta_1, \ldots, \delta_{2g}$ for $H_1(S, \mathbb{Z})$.

A note: Up to now, we have indexed our complex basis $\{e_\alpha\}$ and dual complex coordinates $\{z_\alpha\}$ for V by $\alpha = 1, \ldots, n$; the integral basis $\{\lambda_i\}$ and dual real coordinates $\{x_i\}$ by $i = 1, \ldots, 2n$. Once we have normalized our basis, however, we can no longer maintain the notational distinction; we will instead denote the integral basis by

$$\{\lambda_\alpha, \lambda_{n+\alpha}\}_{\alpha=1,\ldots,n} \quad \text{and} \quad \{x_\alpha, x_{n+\alpha}\}_{\alpha=1,\ldots,n}.$$

Line Bundles on Complex Tori

We will now give explicit descriptions of positive line bundles on a complex torus $M = V/\Lambda$. The fundamental observation, proved on p. 46, is simply that, since $H^1(\mathbb{C}^n, \mathcal{O}) = H^2(\mathbb{C}^n, \mathbb{Z}) = 0$, *any line bundle on* $V \cong \mathbb{C}^n$ *is trivial.* Thus if $L \to M$ is any line bundle, the pullback $\pi^* L$ of L to V is trivial, and we can find a global trivialization

$$\varphi: \pi^* L \longrightarrow V \times \mathbb{C}.$$

Now for $z \in V$, $\lambda \in \Lambda$, the fibers of π^*L at z and $z + \lambda$ are by definition both identified with the fiber of L at $\pi(z)$, and comparing the trivialization φ at z and $z + \lambda$ yields a linear automorphism of $\mathbb{C}$:

$$\mathbb{C} \xleftarrow{\varphi_z} (\pi^*L)_z = L_{\pi(z)} = (\pi^*L)_{z+\lambda} \xrightarrow{\varphi_{z+\lambda}} \mathbb{C}.$$

Such an automorphism is given as multiplication by a nonzero complex number; if we denote this number by $e_\lambda(z)$, we obtain a collection of functions

$$\{e_\lambda \in \mathcal{O}^*(V)\}_{\lambda \in \Lambda}$$

called a set of *multipliers* for L. The functions e_λ necessarily satisfy the compatibility relation

$$e_{\lambda'}(z+\lambda)e_\lambda(z) = e_\lambda(z+\lambda')e_{\lambda'}(z) = e_{\lambda+\lambda'}(z)$$

for all $\lambda, \lambda' \in \Lambda$.

Conversely, given any collection of entire nonzero holomorphic functions $\{e_\lambda\}_{\lambda \in \Lambda}$ satisfying these relations, we can construct a line bundle $L \to M$ having multipliers $\{e_\lambda\}$: we take L to be the quotient space of $V \times \mathbb{C}$ under the identifications

$$(z, \xi) \sim (z+\lambda, e_\lambda(z) \cdot \xi).$$

Note that by the compatibility relations, we can give such a collection $\{e_\lambda\}$ by specifying e_{λ_α} for some basis $\{\lambda_\alpha\}$ for Λ so long as the functions $\{e_{\lambda_\alpha}\}$ satisfy

$$(*) \qquad e_{\lambda_\alpha}(z+\lambda_\beta)e_{\lambda_\beta}(z) = e_{\lambda_\beta}(z+\lambda_\alpha)e_{\lambda_\alpha}(z).$$

Our aim now is to show that any line bundle $L \to M$ can be given by multipliers $\{e_\lambda(z)\}$ of a very simple character. We will do this in two stages: first, we will construct line bundles having arbitrary positive Chern class, using elementary functions e_λ; then we will show that any positive line bundle $L \to M$ is determined, up to translation in M, by its Chern class.

One simplification is immediate: If $\{\lambda_1, \ldots, \lambda_{2n}\}$ is any basis for Λ over $\mathbb{Z}$ with $\lambda_1, \ldots, \lambda_n$ linearly independent over $\mathbb{C}$, then we have

$$\frac{V}{\mathbb{Z}\{\lambda_1, \ldots, \lambda_n\}} \cong (\mathbb{C}^*)^n,$$

and we can factor our projection map $\pi: V \to M$ by

$$V \to \frac{V}{\mathbb{Z}\{\lambda_1, \ldots, \lambda_n\}} \xrightarrow{\pi_1} M.$$

Now we have also seen on p. 27 that

$$H^1((\mathbb{C}^*)^n, \mathcal{O}) = H^2((\mathbb{C}^*)^n, \mathcal{O}) = 0,$$

and hence

$$H^1((\mathbb{C}^*)^n, \mathcal{O}^*) \xrightarrow[\sim]{c_1} H^2((\mathbb{C}^*)^n, \mathbb{Z}),$$

i.e., any line bundle on $(\mathbb{C}^*)^n$ is determined by its Chern class. For any L we can choose our basis $\lambda_1, \ldots, \lambda_{2n}$ for Λ such that in terms of the dual coordinates $x_1, \ldots, x_{2n}$ on V,

$$c_1(L) = \sum_{\alpha=1}^{n} \delta_\alpha \, dx_\alpha \wedge dx_{n+\alpha}.$$

But $x_{n+\alpha}$ is a well-defined function on $V/\mathbb{Z}\{\lambda_1, \ldots, \lambda_n\}$, so $[dx_{n+\alpha}] = 0 \in H^1_{DR}(V/\mathbb{Z}\{\lambda_1, \ldots, \lambda_n\})$. Thus

$$c_1(\pi_1^* L) = \pi_1^*(c_1(L)) = 0,$$

and consequently $\pi_1^* L$ is trivial. If we then take a trivialization $\tilde{\varphi} : \pi_1^* L \to (\mathbb{C}^*)^n \times \mathbb{C}$ and choose our trivialization φ of $\pi^* L$ to extend $\tilde{\varphi}$, we have

$$e_{\lambda_\alpha}(z) \equiv 1, \qquad \alpha = 1, \ldots, n.$$

Now suppose ω is any invariant integral form, positive of type $(1,1)$. Choose a basis $\lambda_1, \ldots, \lambda_{2n}$ for Λ over $\mathbb{Z}$ such that in terms of dual coordinates $x_1, \ldots, x_{2n}$ on V

$$\omega = \sum_{\alpha=1}^{n} \delta_\alpha \, dx_\alpha \wedge dx_{n+\alpha}, \qquad \delta_\alpha \in \mathbb{Z}.$$

Since ω is nondegenerate, $\delta_\alpha \neq 0$ for all α, and we can set

$$e_\alpha = \delta_\alpha^{-1} \lambda_\alpha, \qquad \alpha = 1, \ldots, n;$$

let $z_1, \ldots, z_n$ be linear coordinates on V dual to the basis $e_1, \ldots, e_n$. Then as before we can write

$$(\lambda_1, \ldots, \lambda_{2n}) = \begin{bmatrix} e_1 \\ \vdots \\ e_n \end{bmatrix} \Omega,$$

i.e.,

$$\begin{bmatrix} dz_1 \\ \vdots \\ dz_n \end{bmatrix} = {}^t\Omega(dx_1, \ldots, dx_{2n})$$

with

$$\Omega = (\Delta_\delta, Z);$$

and again, by the Riemann Conditions III, ω positive of type $(1,1)$ implies that $Z = {}^tZ$, $\operatorname{Im} Z > 0$. Our fundamental calculation is the

Lemma.   *The line bundle* L→M *given by multipliers*

$$e_{\lambda_\alpha} \equiv 1, \qquad e_{\lambda_{n+\alpha}}(z) = e^{-2\pi i z_\alpha}, \qquad \alpha = 1,\dots,n,$$

has Chern class $c_1(L) = [\omega]$.

Proof.   We first check that the multipliers given do indeed satisfy the relations (*) above. Clearly (*) is satisfied for α or $\beta \leqslant n$; and writing $Z = (Z_{\alpha\beta})$, we have

$$e_{\lambda_{n+\beta}}(z + \lambda_{n+\alpha}) \cdot e_{\lambda_{n+\alpha}}(z) = e^{-2\pi i(z_\beta + Z_{\beta\alpha} + z_\alpha)}$$

$$= e^{-2\pi i(z_\alpha + Z_{\alpha\beta} + z_\beta)}$$

$$= e_{\lambda_{n+\alpha}}(z + \lambda_{n+\beta}) \cdot e_{\lambda_{n+\beta}}(z)$$

as required.

Now let $\varphi: \pi^*L \to V \times \mathbb{C}$ be a trivialization of π^*L inducing the multipliers given. Then for any section $\tilde{\theta}$ of L over $U \subset M$, $\theta = \varphi^*(\pi^*\tilde{\theta})$ is an analytic function on $\pi^{-1}(U)$ satisfying

$$\theta(z + \lambda_\alpha) = \theta(z),$$

$$\theta(z + \lambda_{n+\alpha}) = e^{-2\pi i z_\alpha}\theta(z),$$

and conversely any such function defines a section of L. Now if $\|\ \|$ is any metric on L, we can write

$$\|\tilde{\theta}(z)\|^2 = h(z) \cdot |\theta(z)|^2$$

for any section $\tilde{\theta}$ of L; evidently h will be a positive C^∞ function of z satisfying

$$h(z)|\theta(z)|^2 = \|\tilde{\theta}(z)\|^2 = h(z+\lambda)|\theta(z+\lambda)|^2$$

for any $\lambda \in \Lambda$; thus

$$h(z + \lambda_\alpha) = h(z),$$
$$h(z + \lambda_{n+\alpha}) = |e^{2\pi i z_\alpha}|^2 h(z).$$

Conversely, any such function h defines a metric on L. Now write $Z = X + \sqrt{-1}\,Y$ as before; since $Y > 0$, we can set $W = (W_{\alpha\beta}) = Y^{-1}$. Then we claim that the function

$$h(z) = e^{(\pi/2)\sum W_{\alpha\beta}(z_\alpha - \bar{z}_\alpha)(z_\beta - \bar{z}_\beta - 2iY_{\beta\beta})}$$

satisfies the functional equations above. Clearly $h(z + \lambda_\alpha) = h(z)$; for the others, write

$$\log h(z+\lambda_{n+\gamma}) = \frac{\pi}{2} \sum_{\alpha,\beta} W_{\alpha\beta}(z_\alpha - \bar{z}_\alpha + 2iY_{\alpha\gamma})(z_\beta - \bar{z}_\beta + 2i(Y_{\beta\gamma} - Y_{\beta\beta}))$$

$$= \frac{\pi}{2} \sum_{\alpha,\beta} W_{\alpha\beta}(z_\alpha - \bar{z}_\alpha)(z_\beta - \bar{z}_\beta - 2iY_{\beta\beta}) + \frac{\pi}{2} \sum_{\alpha,\beta} W_{\alpha\beta}(z_\alpha - \bar{z}_\alpha) \cdot 2iY_{\beta\gamma}$$

$$+ \frac{\pi}{2} \sum_{\alpha,\beta} W_{\alpha\beta} \cdot 2iY_{\alpha\gamma}(z_\beta - \bar{z}_\beta + 2i(Y_{\beta\gamma} - Y_{\beta\beta}))$$

$$= \log h(z) + \frac{\pi}{2} \sum_\alpha \delta_{\alpha\gamma} \cdot 2i(z_\alpha - \bar{z}_\alpha) + \frac{\pi}{2} \sum_\beta \delta_{\beta\gamma} \cdot 2i(z_\beta - \bar{z}_\beta + 2i(Y_{\beta\gamma} - Y_{\beta\beta}))$$

(since $Y \cdot W = I$ and $W = {}^tW$)

$$= \log h(z) + \pi i(z_\gamma - \bar{z}_\gamma) + \pi i(z_\gamma - \bar{z}_\gamma)$$
$$= \log h(z) - 4\pi \operatorname{Im}(z_\gamma);$$

hence

$$h(z+\lambda_{n+\gamma}) = |e^{2\pi i z_\gamma}|^2 h(z).$$

Now we can compute the curvature form Θ_L associated to the metric in L given by h:

$$\Theta_L = \partial\bar{\partial} \log \frac{1}{h}$$

$$= -\frac{\pi}{2} \partial\bar{\partial}\left(\sum_{\alpha,\beta} W_{\alpha\beta}(z_\alpha - \bar{z}_\alpha)(z_\beta - \bar{z}_\beta - 2iY_{\beta\beta}) \right)$$

$$= \frac{\pi}{2} \partial \sum_{\alpha,\beta} W_{\alpha\beta}\big((z_\alpha - \bar{z}_\alpha)d\bar{z}_\beta + (z_\beta - \bar{z}_\beta - 2iY_{\beta\beta})d\bar{z}_\alpha\big)$$

$$= \pi \sum_{\alpha,\beta} W_{\alpha\beta}\, dz_\alpha \wedge d\bar{z}_\beta.$$

We want to express this in terms of the basis $\{dx_\alpha, dx_{n+\alpha}\}$; we have

$$dz_\alpha = \delta_\alpha dx_\alpha + \sum_\beta z_{\alpha\beta}\, dx_{n+\beta},$$

$$d\bar{z}_\alpha = \delta_\alpha dx_\alpha + \sum_\beta \overline{z_{\alpha\beta}}\, dx_{n+\beta},$$

so

$$\Theta_L = \pi \sum W_{\alpha\beta}\, dz_\alpha \wedge d\bar{z}_\beta$$

$$= \pi \sum_{\alpha,\beta} W_{\alpha\beta}\delta_\alpha\delta_\beta\, dx_\alpha \wedge dx_\beta$$

$$+ \pi \sum_{\alpha,\beta,\gamma} W_{\alpha\beta}\delta_\alpha(\bar{Z}_{\beta\gamma} - Z_{\beta\gamma})\, dx_\alpha \wedge dx_{n+\gamma}$$

$$+ \pi \sum_{\alpha,\beta,\gamma,\varepsilon} W_{\alpha\beta} Z_{\alpha\gamma}\bar{Z}_{\beta\varepsilon}\, dx_{n+\gamma} \wedge dx_{n+\varepsilon}.$$

Since $W = {}^tW$ and $Z = {}^tZ$, the first and last of these three terms are zero, and hence

$$\Theta = \pi \sum_{\alpha,\beta,\gamma} \delta_\alpha W_{\alpha\beta} \left(\overline{Z}_{\beta\gamma} - Z_{\beta\gamma} \right) dx_\alpha \wedge dx_{n+\gamma}$$

$$= -2\pi\sqrt{-1} \sum_{\alpha,\beta,\gamma} \delta_\alpha W_{\alpha\beta} Y_{\beta\gamma} \, dx_\alpha \wedge dx_{n+\gamma}$$

$$= -2\pi\sqrt{-1} \sum_\alpha \delta_\alpha \, dx_\alpha \wedge dx_{n+\alpha},$$

and so finally

$$c_1(L) = \left[\frac{\sqrt{-1}}{2\pi} \Theta \right] = [\omega]. \qquad\qquad \text{Q.E.D.}$$

To continue our description of line bundles on M we want to consider the set of line bundles $L \to M$ having a given positive Chern class. We note that for any $\mu \in M$ the translation $\tau_\mu : M \to M$ is homotopic to the identity and hence for any line bundle $L \to M$,

$$c_1(\tau_\mu^* L) = c_1(L).$$

Note, moreover, that if L is given by multipliers

$$e_{\lambda_\alpha} \equiv 1, \qquad e_{\lambda_{n+\alpha}}(z) = e^{-2\pi i z_\alpha},$$

then $\tau_\mu^* L$ can be given by multipliers

$$e'_{\lambda_\alpha}(z) = e_{\lambda_\alpha}(z+\mu) \equiv 1$$
$$e'_{\lambda_{n+\alpha}}(z) = e_{\lambda_{n+\alpha}}(z+\mu)$$
$$= e^{-2\pi i(z_\alpha + \mu_\alpha)},$$

i.e., e'_λ will differ from e_λ by multiplication by a constant $e^{-2\pi i \mu_\alpha}$. Conversely, if L' is any line bundle with multipliers $e'_{\lambda_\alpha} \equiv 1$ and $e'_{\lambda_{n+\alpha}} \equiv c_\alpha \cdot e_{\lambda_{n+\alpha}}$, $c_\alpha \in \mathbb{C}^*$, then, setting

$$\mu = \sum \frac{\sqrt{-1}}{2\pi} \log c_\alpha \cdot e_\alpha \in V,$$

we have

$$L' = \tau_\mu^* L.$$

Thus, to prove that any line bundle having the same Chern class as L must be a translate of L, it will suffice to show that any line bundle with Chern class 0 can be realized by constant multipliers. To this end we first note that the inclusion of exact sheaf sequences

$$
\begin{array}{ccccccccc}
0 & \longrightarrow & \mathbb{Z} & \longrightarrow & \mathcal{O} & \overset{\exp}{\longrightarrow} & \mathcal{O}^* & \longrightarrow & 0 \\
& & \| & & \uparrow & & \uparrow & & \\
0 & \longrightarrow & \mathbb{Z} & \longrightarrow & \mathbb{C} & \longrightarrow & \mathbb{C}^* & \longrightarrow & 0
\end{array}
$$

on any compact Kähler manifold X induces a commutative diagram

$$H^1(X,\mathcal{O}) \longrightarrow H^1(X,\mathcal{O}^*) \overset{c_1}{\longrightarrow} H^2(X,\mathbb{Z})$$

$$\uparrow_{\iota_1^*} \qquad\qquad \uparrow_{\iota_2^*} \qquad\qquad \|$$

$$H^1(X,\mathbb{C}) \longrightarrow H^1(X,\mathbb{C}^*) \longrightarrow H^2(X,\mathbb{Z}).$$

The map ι_1^* represents projection of $H^1(X,\mathbb{C}) = H^{1,0}(X) \oplus H^{0,1}(X)$ on the second factor, and so is surjective. It follows that any cocycle $\gamma \in H^1(X,\mathcal{O}^*)$ in the kernel of c_1 is in the image of ι_2^*, i.e., is cohomologous to a cocycle with constant coefficients; thus *any line bundle on X with Chern class 0 can be given by constant transition functions.*

Now if $L \to M = V/\Lambda$ is any line bundle with trivial Chern class, we can find an open cover $\underline{U} = \{U_\alpha\}$ of M such that for each $\alpha, \pi^{-1}(U_\alpha) = \{U_{\alpha j}\}_j$ is a disjoint collection of open sets isomorphic via π to U_α, and a collection of trivializations $\varphi_\alpha : L_{U_\alpha} \to U_\alpha \times \mathbb{C}$ *having constant transition functions* $\{g_{\alpha j}\}$. *We can then define constants* $\{h_{\alpha j}\}_{\alpha,j}$ *by taking* $h_{\alpha_0 j_0} \equiv 1$ *for some* α_0, j_0 *and setting*

$$h_{\alpha j} = h_{\alpha' j'} \cdot g_{\alpha \alpha'} \qquad \text{for } \alpha, j, \alpha', j' \text{ such that } U_{\alpha j} \cap U_{\alpha' j'} \neq \varnothing.$$

It is not hard to see that by the cocycle rule on $\{g_{\alpha\alpha'}\}$ this is well-defined, and the trivializations

$$\varphi_{\alpha j}: \pi^* L_{U_{\alpha i}} \to U_{\alpha j} \times \mathbb{C}$$

defined by

$$\varphi_{\alpha j} = h_{\alpha j} \cdot \pi^* \varphi_\alpha$$

patch together to give a trivialization of $\pi^* L$ having constant multipliers.

To shed some light on this argument, we will describe in more detail the geometry of the group of line bundles on M. Recall that by the exponential sheaf sequence

$$H^1(M,\mathbb{Z}) \to H^1(M,\mathcal{O}) \to H^1(M,\mathcal{O}^*) \overset{c_1}{\longrightarrow} H^2(M,\mathbb{Z})$$

the group $\mathrm{Pic}^0(M)$ of holomorphic line bundles on M with Chern class zero is given by

$$\mathrm{Pic}^0(M) = \frac{H^1(M,\mathcal{O})}{H^1(M,\mathbb{Z})}. \qquad *$$

Now, $H^1(M,\mathcal{O}) = \mathcal{H}^{0,1}(M)$ is the space of invariant forms of type $(0,1)$ on M, i.e., the space $\overline{V}^* = \mathrm{Hom}_{\mathbb{C}}(\overline{V},\mathbb{C})$ of conjugate linear functionals on V. $H^1(M,\mathbb{Z})$, on the other hand, is the space of real invariant 1-forms ω on M having integral periods, that is, the space of real linear functionals on V taking integral values on $\Lambda \subset V$. The map

$$H^1(M,\mathbb{Z}) \to H^1(M,\mathcal{O})$$

is given simply by

$$\omega \mapsto \omega^{0,1};$$

since for ω real

$$\int_\lambda \omega = \int_\lambda \omega^{1,0} + \int_\lambda \omega^{0,1}$$

$$= \left(\int_\lambda \omega^{0,1}\right) + \overline{\left(\int_\lambda \omega^{0,1}\right)}$$

is integral for all $\lambda \in \Lambda$ if and only if

$$2\,\mathrm{Re} \int_\lambda \omega^{0,1} \in \mathbb{Z}$$

for all $\lambda \in \Lambda$, we see that *the image* $\overline{\Lambda}^*$ *of* $H^1(M, \mathbb{Z})$ *in* $H^1(M, \mathcal{O}) = \overline{V}^*$ *consists exactly of conjugate linear functionals on* V *whose real part is half-integral on* $\Lambda \subset V$. Thus $\mathrm{Pic}^0(M)$ is again a complex torus, often called the *dual Abelian varitey* of M and denoted $\hat{M}$.

Explicitly, if $x_1,\ldots,x_{2n}$ are, as above, real coordinates on V dual to the basis $\lambda_1,\ldots,\lambda_{2n}$, and we let x_i^* denote the conjugate linear part of the real functional x_i, then the x_i^* form a basis for Λ^*. Writing

$$x_i = \sum \pi_{i\alpha} z_\alpha + \sum \overline{\pi}_{i\alpha} \overline{z}_\alpha,$$

we have

$$x_i^* = \sum \overline{\pi}_{i\alpha} \overline{z}_\alpha,$$

where, as we found above

$$\Pi = \begin{bmatrix} \dfrac{\sqrt{-1}}{2} \Delta_\delta^{-1} \overline{Z} Y^{-1} \\[2mm] \dfrac{1}{2\sqrt{-1}} Y^{-1} \end{bmatrix}.$$

Reordering our basis $\{x^*\}$ for Λ^* by setting

$$y_\alpha^* = -x_{n+\alpha}^*, \qquad y_{n+\alpha}^* = x_\alpha^*,$$

we see that

$$(y_{n+1}^*,\ldots,y_{2n}^*) = -\frac{\sqrt{-1}}{2} \Delta_\delta^{-1} ZY^{-1}(\overline{z}_1,\ldots,\overline{z}_n)$$

$$= \Delta_\delta^{-1} Z(y_1^*,\ldots,y_n^*).$$

Consequently, if we order the elementary divisors δ_α so that $\delta_1|\delta_2|\cdots|\delta_n$, we may set

$$e_\alpha^* = \frac{\delta_\alpha}{\delta_n} y_\alpha^*;$$

we then have

$$(y_1^*,\ldots,y_n^*) = \delta_n\Delta_\delta^{-1}(e_1^*,\ldots,e_n^*)$$

and

$$(y_{n+1}^*,\ldots,y_{2n}^*) = \delta_n\Delta_\delta^{-1}Z\Delta_\delta^{-1}(e_1^*,\ldots,e_n^*).$$

The period matrix of $\hat{M}$ in terms of the bases (y_α^*) for Λ^* and (e_α^*) for $\bar{V}^*$ is then

$$\Omega^* = \left(\delta_n\Delta_\delta^{-1}, \delta_n\Delta_\delta^{-1}Z\Delta_\delta^{-1}\right).$$

Since $\delta_\alpha|\delta_n$ for all α, $\delta_n\Delta_\delta^{-1}$ is again diagonal and integral; and since

$$
\begin{aligned}
{}^t\left(\delta_n\Delta_\delta^{-1}Z\Delta_\delta^{-1}\right) &= \delta_n^t\Delta_\delta^{-1}{}^tZ\,{}^t\Delta_\delta^{-1} \\
&= \delta_n\Delta_\delta^{-1}Z\Delta_\delta^{-1}
\end{aligned}
$$

and

$$\mathrm{Im}\left(\delta_n\Delta_\delta^{-1}Z\Delta_\delta^{-1}\right) = \delta_n\Delta_\delta^{-1}Y\Delta_\delta^{-1}$$

is again positive definite, we see that $\hat{M}$ is an Abelian variety; indeed, the original polarization on M induces a polarization on $\hat{M}$ with "dual" elementary divisors $\{\delta_n/\delta_\alpha\}$.

Now let L be a positive line bundle on M. We can define a map

$$\varphi_L\colon M \to \mathrm{Pic}^0(M)$$

by

$$\varphi_L(\mu) = L^{-1}\otimes\tau_\mu^*L.$$

We want to describe φ_L explicitly in terms of the bases $\{\lambda_\alpha\}$ for Λ and $\{e_\alpha\}$ for V normalized with respect to L, and the dual bases $\{y_\alpha^*\}$ for Λ^* and $\{e_\alpha^*\}$ for $\bar{V}^*$.

First, we trace out the map

$$H_{\bar\partial}^{0,1}(M) \overset{\delta}{\to} H^1(M,\mathcal{O}) \to \mathrm{Pic}^0(M),$$

where δ is the Dolbeault isomorphism. If

$$\sigma = \sum \sigma_\alpha\, d\bar{z}_\alpha, \qquad \sigma_\alpha \in \mathbb{C},$$

is a constant $(0,1)$-form on M, then in each open set U_i of a sufficiently fine open cover we may write

$$\sigma = \bar\partial f_i(z),$$

where

$$f_i(z) = \sum \sigma_\alpha\bar{z}_\alpha$$

for a suitable choice of branch of z_α. The line bundle associated to σ thus has transition functions

$$g_{ij}(z) = e^{2\pi i(f_i(z)-f_j(z))}$$

and, correspondingly, in terms of a suitable trivialization, multipliers

$$e_{\lambda_\alpha}(z) = e^{-2\pi i \delta_\alpha \sigma_\alpha}, \qquad e_{\lambda_{n+\alpha}} = e^{-2\pi i \sum \sigma_\beta \bar{Z}_{\alpha\beta}}.$$

Multiplying the trivializations by the function

$$f(z) = e^{2\pi i \sum \sigma_\alpha z_\alpha},$$

yields the normalized multipliers

$$e_{\lambda_\alpha}(z) = 1,$$

$$e_{\lambda_{n+\alpha}}(z) = e^{-2\pi i \sum \sigma_\beta (\bar{Z}_{\alpha\beta} - Z_{\alpha\beta})}$$

$$= e^{-4\pi \sum \sigma_\beta Y_{\alpha\beta}},$$

where $Y = \operatorname{Im} Z$ as above. In terms of the coordinates x_α^* on V, we see that the line bundle associated to

$$\sum_{\alpha=1}^{n} c_\alpha x_\alpha^* = \frac{\sqrt{-1}}{2} \sum \delta_\alpha^{-1} c_\alpha Z_{\alpha\beta} Y_{\beta\gamma}^{-1} dz_\gamma$$

has multipliers

$$e_{\lambda_\alpha} \equiv 1, \qquad e_{\lambda_{n+\beta}}(z) = e^{-2\pi i \sum \delta_\alpha^{-1} c_\alpha Z_{\alpha\beta}}$$

and, likewise, the bundle corresponding to

$$\sum c_\alpha x_{n+\alpha}^* = \frac{1}{2\sqrt{-1}} \sum c_\alpha Y_{\alpha\beta}^{-1} d\bar{z}_\beta$$

has multipliers

$$e_{\lambda_\alpha} \equiv 1, \qquad e_{\lambda_{n+\beta}}(z) = e^{2\pi i c_\alpha}.$$

On the other hand, since the line bundle L is given by

$$e_{\lambda_\alpha} \equiv 1, \qquad e_{\lambda_{n+\alpha}} = e^{-2\pi i z_\alpha},$$

for any $\mu = \sum \mu_\alpha e_\alpha \in V$, $\tau_\mu^* L$ is given by $e_{\lambda_\alpha} \equiv 1$ and

$$e_{\lambda_{n+\alpha}} = e^{-2\pi i (z_\alpha + \mu_\alpha)};$$

thus $\varphi(L) = L^{-1} \otimes \tau_\mu^* L$ has multipliers

$$e_{\lambda_\alpha} \equiv 1 \quad \text{and} \quad e_{\lambda_{n+\alpha}} = e^{-2\pi i \mu_\alpha}.$$

In particular, if $\mu = \sum c_\alpha \lambda_\alpha = \sum c_\alpha \delta_\alpha e_\alpha$, we see that $\varphi_L(\sum c_\alpha \lambda_\alpha)$ has multipliers

$$e_{\lambda_\alpha} \equiv 1 \quad \text{and} \quad e_{\lambda_{n+\beta}} = e^{-2\pi i \delta_\alpha c_\alpha},$$

i.e.,

$$\varphi_L\left(\sum c_\alpha \lambda_\alpha\right) = -\sum c_\alpha \delta_\alpha x_{n+\alpha}^* = \sum c_\alpha \delta_\alpha y_\alpha^*,$$

and if $v = \sum c_\alpha \lambda_{n+\alpha} = \sum c_\alpha Z_{\alpha\beta} e_\beta$, then $\varphi_L(\sum c_\alpha \lambda_{n+\alpha})$ has multipliers

$$e_{\lambda_\alpha} \equiv 1 \quad \text{and} \quad e_{\lambda_{n+\beta}} = e^{-2\pi i Z_{\alpha\beta}},$$

i.e.,

$$\varphi_L\left(\sum c_\alpha \lambda_{n+\alpha}\right) = \sum \delta_\alpha c_\alpha x_\alpha^* = \sum c_\alpha \delta_\alpha y_{n+\alpha}^*.$$

(These last two assertions are equivalent, since φ_L is complex linear and so

$$\begin{aligned}
\varphi_L\left(\sum c_\alpha \lambda_{n+\alpha}\right) &= \varphi_L\left(\sum c_\alpha Z_{\alpha\beta} \delta_\beta^{-1} \lambda_\beta\right) \\
&= \sum c_\alpha Z_{\alpha\beta} y_\beta^* \\
&= \sum c_\alpha Z_{\alpha\beta} (\delta_n/\delta_\beta) e_\beta^* \\
&= \sum c_\alpha \delta_\alpha \delta_n \left(\delta_\alpha^{-1} Z_{\alpha\beta} \delta_\beta^{-1} e_\beta^*\right) \\
&= \sum c_\alpha \delta_\alpha y_{n+\alpha}^*).
\end{aligned}$$

In any event, we see clearly from this that the kernel of φ_L is exactly the subgroup of M generated by $\{\delta_\alpha^{-1}\lambda_\alpha, \delta_\alpha^{-1}\lambda_{n+\alpha}\}$; i.e., that *the line bundle* L *is fixed under exactly the* $\Pi\delta_\alpha^2$ *translations*

$$\left\{\tau_v : v \in \mathbb{Z}\left\{\delta_\alpha^{-1}\lambda_\alpha, \delta_\alpha^{-1}\lambda_{n+\alpha}\right\}\right\}.$$

Theta-Functions

Having described a positive line bundle $L \to M$ on an Abelian variety $M = V/\Lambda$ as a quotient of the trivial bundle $V \times \mathbb{C}$, we can accordingly realize global holomorphic sections of L as entire holomorphic functions on $V \cong \mathbb{C}^n$ satisfying certain functional equations. These functions are called *theta-functions*, and by examining them we shall prove the

Theorem. *Let* L$\to$M *be any positive line bundle, and let* $\delta_1, \ldots, \delta_n$ *be the elementary divisors of the polarization* $c_1(L)$ *of* M. *Then*

   1. $\dim H^0(M, \mathcal{O}(L)) = \prod_\alpha \delta_\alpha.$
   2. $H^0(M, \mathcal{O}(L^k))$ *has no base points for* $k \geq 2$ *and gives an embedding of* M *for* $k \geq 3$.

Before proving this theorem, we make a few remarks. First, since $K_M = 0$, we have by the Kodaira vanishing theorem

$$h^p(M, \mathcal{O}(L)) = h^p(M, \Omega^n(L)) = 0, \qquad p > 0,$$

and hence

$$h^0(M, \mathcal{O}(L)) = \chi(L).$$

On the other hand, we can find an integral basis $\{dx_1, \ldots, dx_{2n}\}$ for $H^1(M, \mathbb{Z})$ such that

$$c_1(L) = \sum \delta_\alpha \, dx_\alpha \wedge dx_{n+\alpha}$$

and so

$$c_1(L)^n = n! \prod \delta_\alpha \in H^{2n}(M, \mathbb{Z}) \cong \mathbb{Z}.$$

Thus assertion 1 may be thought of as a special case of the general Riemann-Roch formula, expressing the holomorphic Euler characteristic of a line bundle in terms of its topological invariants.

Assertion 2, due to Lefschetz, is of a deeper character, and will emerge later.

To prove the first statement, choose $\{\lambda_1,\ldots,\lambda_{2n}\}$ an integral basis for Λ such that in terms of dual coordinates $x_1,\ldots,x_{2n}$,

$$c_1(L) = \sum \delta_\alpha \, dx_\alpha \wedge dx_{n+\alpha}.$$

As before, set

$$e_\alpha = \delta_\alpha^{-1} \lambda_\alpha$$

and let $z_1,\ldots,z_n$ be the corresponding complex coordinates on V, so that the period matrix Ω of $\Lambda \subset V$ is of the form

$$\Omega = (\Delta_\delta, Z)$$

with $Z = X + \sqrt{-1}\, Y$ symmetric and $Y > 0$.

Now we have seen that the line bundle L is a translate of the bundle L_0 given by multipliers

$$e_{\lambda_\alpha} \equiv 1, \qquad e_{\lambda_{n+\alpha}}(z) = e^{-2\pi i z_\alpha}.$$

Since $h^0(L)$ is clearly invariant under translation, we will prove assertion 1 for $L = \tau_\mu^* L_0$, where

$$\mu = \tfrac{1}{2} \sum Z_{\alpha\alpha} \cdot e_\alpha$$

Multipliers for L are thus

$$e_{\lambda_\alpha} \equiv 1, \qquad e_{\lambda_{n+\alpha}} = e^{-2\pi i z_\alpha - \pi i Z_{\alpha\alpha}},$$

and so global sections $\tilde{\theta}$ of L are given by entire holomorphic functions θ on V satisfying

$$\theta(z + \lambda_\alpha) = \theta(z), \qquad \theta(z + \lambda_{n+\alpha}) = e^{-2\pi i z_\alpha - \pi i Z_{\alpha\alpha}} \cdot \theta(z).$$

By the first condition, such a function θ must have a power series expansion in the variables $z_\alpha^* = e^{2\pi i \delta_\alpha^{-1} z_\alpha}$; we can write

$$\theta(z) = \sum_{l \in \mathbb{Z}^n} a_l \cdot z_1^{*l_1} \cdots z_n^{*l_n}$$

$$(*) \qquad \qquad = \sum_{l \in \mathbb{Z}^n} a_l \cdot e^{2\pi i \sum_\alpha l_\alpha \delta_\alpha^{-1} z_\alpha}$$

$$= \sum_{l \in \mathbb{Z}^n} a_l \cdot e^{2\pi i \langle l, \Delta_\delta^{-1} z \rangle}.$$

Now the second set of conditions gives us recursive relations among the coefficients a_l of θ; to begin with

$$\theta(z+\lambda_{n+\alpha}) = \sum_{l\in\mathbb{Z}^n} a_l \cdot e^{2\pi i\langle l, \Delta_\delta^{-1}(z+\lambda_{n+\alpha})\rangle}$$

$$= \sum_{l\in\mathbb{Z}^n} a_l \cdot e^{2\pi i\langle l, \Delta_\delta^{-1}\lambda_{n+\alpha}\rangle} \cdot e^{2\pi i\langle l, \Delta_\delta^{-1}z\rangle}.$$

But the second condition above asserts that

$$\theta(z+\lambda_{n+\alpha}) = e^{-2\pi i z_\alpha - \pi i Z_{\alpha\alpha}} \cdot \theta(z)$$

$$= e^{-2\pi i z_\alpha - \pi i Z_{\alpha\alpha}} \sum_{l\in\mathbb{Z}^n} a_l e^{2\pi i\langle l, \Delta_\delta^{-1}z\rangle}$$

$$= \sum_{l\in\mathbb{Z}^n} a_{l+\Delta_\delta e_\alpha} \cdot e^{-\pi i Z_{\alpha\alpha}} \cdot e^{2\pi i\langle l, \Delta_\delta^{-1}z\rangle}.$$

Comparing these two Fourier expansions for $\theta(z+\lambda_{n+\alpha})$, we obtain

$$a_{l+\delta_\alpha e_\alpha} = e^{2\pi i\langle l, \Delta_\delta^{-1}\lambda_{n+\alpha}\rangle + \pi i Z_{\alpha\alpha}} \cdot a_l.$$

Thus θ is completely determined by the choice of coefficients

$$\{a_l\}_{l:\ 0\leqslant l_\alpha < \delta_\alpha},$$

and accordingly we have

$$h^0(M, \mathcal{O}(L)) \leqslant \Pi\delta_\alpha.$$

To prove equality, we have to show that the series (∗) determined by an arbitrary choice of coefficients $\{a_l\}_{l:0\leqslant l_\alpha < \delta_\alpha}$ does in fact converge. Now we can write

$$\theta(z) = \sum_{0\leqslant l_{0_\alpha} < \delta_\alpha} \left(\sum_{l\in\mathbb{Z}^n} a_{l_0+\Delta_\delta l} \cdot e^{2\pi i\langle l_0+\Delta_\delta l, \Delta_\delta^{-1}z\rangle} \right)$$

$$= \sum_{0\leqslant l_{0_\alpha} < \delta_\alpha} e^{2\pi i\langle l_0, \Delta_\delta^{-1}z\rangle} \cdot \left(\sum_{l\in\mathbb{Z}^n} a_{l_0+\Delta_\delta l} \cdot e^{2\pi i\langle l, z\rangle} \right).$$

Let

(∗∗) $$\theta_{l_0}(z) = e^{2\pi i\langle l_0, \Delta_\delta^{-1}z\rangle} \sum_{l\in\mathbb{Z}^n} a_{l_0+\Delta_\delta l} \cdot e^{2\pi i\langle l, z\rangle}$$

be the series determined by the choice $a_{l_0}=1$ and the recursion relations above; by the linearity of these relations we see that the general theta-function is of the form

$$\theta(z) = \sum_{0\leqslant l_{0_\alpha} < \delta_\alpha} a_{l_0}\theta_{l_0}(z),$$

and so it will suffice to prove the series (∗∗) converges.

For convenience, set $b_l = a_{l_0 + \Delta_\delta l}$; the recursion relations then read

$$
\begin{aligned}
b_{l+e_\alpha} &= a_{l_0 + \Delta_\delta l + \Delta_\delta e_\alpha} \\
&= e^{2\pi i \langle (l_0 + \Delta_\delta l), \Delta_\delta^{-1} \lambda_{n+\alpha} \rangle + \pi i Z_{\alpha\alpha}} \cdot a_{l_0 + \Delta_\delta l} \\
&= e^{2\pi i \langle l, \lambda_{n+\alpha} \rangle + 2\pi i \langle l_0, \Delta_\delta^{-1} \lambda_{n+\alpha} \rangle + \pi i Z_{\alpha\alpha}}.
\end{aligned}
$$

We can solve these relations by setting

$$
b_l = e^{\pi i \langle l, Zl \rangle + 2\pi i \langle \Delta_\delta^{-1} l_0, Zl \rangle};
$$

to verify this, we have

$$
\begin{aligned}
b_{l+e_\alpha} &= e^{\pi i \langle (l+e_\alpha), Z(l+e_\alpha) \rangle + 2\pi i \langle \Delta_\delta^{-1} l_0, Z(l+e_\alpha) \rangle} \\
&= e^{\pi i \langle l, Zl \rangle + 2\pi i \langle l, Ze_\alpha \rangle + \pi i \langle e_\alpha, Ze_\alpha \rangle + 2\pi i \langle \Delta_\delta^{-1} l_0, Zl \rangle + 2\pi i \langle \Delta_\delta^{-1} l_0, Ze_\lambda \rangle} \\
&= e^{2\pi i \langle l, \lambda_{n+\alpha} \rangle + \pi i Z_{\alpha\alpha} + 2\pi i \langle \Delta_\delta^{-1} l_0, \lambda_{n+\alpha} \rangle} b_l,
\end{aligned}
$$

since $Z = {}^t Z$, and $Ze_\alpha = \lambda_{n+\alpha}$. Thus the b_l given are indeed the solutions to the recursion relations.

Now

$$
|b_l| = e^{-\pi \langle l, Yl \rangle - 2\pi \langle \Delta_\delta^{-1} l_0, Yl \rangle},
$$

where $Y = \operatorname{Im} Z$ as above. But Y is positive definite, and so

$$
\langle l, Yl \rangle > c' \cdot \|l\|^2
$$

for some constant $c' > 0$. Also, clearly

$$
|\langle \Delta_\delta^{-1} l_0, Yl \rangle| < c'' \cdot \|l\|
$$

for some constant c'', and so for some constant $c > 0$ we have

$$
|b_l| < e^{-c\|l\|^2}
$$

for l sufficiently large. Thus the series $(**)$ converges uniformly on compact sets in $\mathbb{C}^n$, and we are done.

Note that in particular if $c_1(L)$ is a principal polarization of M, $H^0(M, \mathcal{O}(L))$ is one-dimensional and is generated by the section $\tilde{\theta}$ corresponding to the function

$$
\theta(z) = \sum_{l \in \mathbb{Z}^n} e^{\pi i \langle l, Zl \rangle} \cdot e^{2\pi i \langle l, z \rangle},
$$

which satisfies the functional equations

$$
\begin{aligned}
\theta(z + e_\alpha) &= \theta(z), \\
\theta(z + \lambda_{n+\alpha}) &= e^{-2\pi i (z_\alpha + Z_{\alpha\alpha}/2)} \cdot \theta(z),
\end{aligned}
$$

and

$$
\theta(z) = \theta(-z).
$$

This beautiful entire function is called the *Riemann θ-function* of the principally polarized Abelian variety $(M, [\omega])$.

Note also that since $h^0(M, \mathcal{O}(L)) = 1$, the divisor $\Theta = [\tilde{\theta}]$ is uniquely determined by L and hence determined up to translation by the cohomology class $[\omega]$; Θ is called the *Riemann theta-divisor* of the polarized Abelian variety $(M, [\omega])$.

It may help in understanding the last result to consider the following configuration: let Λ, λ, x, e, z, δ, and Z be as above. Let $\Lambda' \subset V$ be the lattice generated by the vectors

$$\lambda'_\alpha = \delta_\alpha^{-1} \lambda_\alpha, \qquad \lambda'_{n+\alpha} = \lambda_{n+\alpha};$$

set $M' = V/\Lambda'$. Since Λ is a sublattice of index $\Delta = \prod \delta_\alpha$ in Λ', the projection map

$$\pi' : M \to M'$$

expresses M as a Δ-sheeted covering of M', the deck transformations being just the translations $\{\tau_\mu\}_{\mu \in \Lambda'/\Lambda}$.

But now the period matrix for $\Lambda' \subset V$ in terms of the bases $\{\lambda'_i\}$ and $\{e_\alpha\}$ is just

$$\Omega' = (I, Z).$$

Consequently if $x'_1, \ldots, x'_{2n}$ are real coordinates dual to $\{\lambda'_i\}$, the class

$$[\omega] = \left[\sum dx'_\alpha \wedge dx'_{n+\alpha} \right] = \left[\sum \delta_\alpha \, dx_\alpha \wedge dx_{n+\alpha} \right]$$

is a principal polarization of M. Since L is determined up to translation by its Chern class $c_1(L) = [\omega]$, it follows that we can find a line bundle $L' \to M'$ such that $\pi'^* L' = L$. Summarizing, *if* $L \to M = V/\Lambda$ *is any positive line bundle on an Abelian variety, we can find an Abelian variety* M' *with principally polarizing line bundle* $L' \to M'$ *and a finite map* $\pi' : M \to M'$ *such that* $\pi'^* L' = L$.

It is fairly clear that the Δ sections $\tilde{\theta}_{l_0}$ corresponding to the theta-functions θ_{l_0} defined in the proof of assertion 1 are, up to multiplication, all translates of one another by the deck transformations of $\pi' : M \to M'$, and that the generator $\tilde{\theta}$ of $H^0(M', \mathcal{O}(L'))$ is given by

$$\pi'^* \tilde{\theta} = \sum_{\lambda \in \Lambda'/\Lambda} \tau_\lambda^* \tilde{\theta}$$

We now prove assertion 2 for a line bundle L with $c_1(L)$ a principal polarization; the idea is to use the group law on the torus. Let $L \to M$ be principally polarized and normalize everything as in the last paragraph. We have

$$H^0(M, \mathcal{O}(L^k))$$
$$= \left\{ \theta \in \mathcal{O}(V) : \theta(z + e_\alpha) = \theta(z), \ \theta(z + \lambda_{n+\alpha}) = e^{-2k\pi i (z_\alpha + Z_{\alpha\alpha}/2)} \theta(z) \right\}.$$

In particular, if θ is the Riemann theta-function for (M, L), then for any

$\mu \in M$

$$\Theta_\mu(z) = \theta(z+\mu)\theta(z-\mu) \in H^0(M, \mathcal{O}(L^2)).$$

Now if $z^* \in M$, we can find $\mu \in M$ such that $\theta(z^*+\mu) \neq 0$ and $\theta(z^*-\mu) \neq 0$; i.e., $\Theta_\mu(z^*) \neq 0$. Thus the linear system $|L^2|$ has no base points, and hence it gives a map $\iota_{L^2} : M \to \mathbb{P}^N$.

To see that the map $\iota_{L^3} : M \to \mathbb{P}^N$ given by the line bundle L^3 is an embedding, let $\theta_0, \ldots, \theta_N$ be a basis for $H^0(M, \mathcal{O}(L^3))$, and set

$$\mathcal{J}(z) = \begin{vmatrix} \theta_0(z) & \cdots & \theta_N(z) \\ \dfrac{\partial\theta_0}{\partial z_1}(z) & \cdots & \dfrac{\partial\theta_N}{\partial z_1}(z) \\ \vdots & & \vdots \\ \dfrac{\partial\theta_0}{\partial z_n}(z) & \cdots & \dfrac{\partial\theta_N}{\partial z_n}(z) \end{vmatrix}.$$

We will show first that the rank of $\mathcal{J}(z)$ is $n+1$, and hence that ι_{L^3} is an immersion. Let $\theta(z)$ be the Riemann θ-function and set

$$\Theta(z, \mu, \nu) = \theta(z+\mu)\theta(z+\nu)\theta(z-\mu-\nu).$$

Θ is a holomorphic function of the three variables z, μ, and ν; for fixed μ and ν, $\Theta_{\mu,\nu}(z) = \Theta(z, \mu, \nu)$ is a global section of L^3. Thus we can write

$$\Theta(z, \mu, \nu) = c_0(\mu, \nu) \cdot \theta_0(z) + \cdots + c_N(\mu, \nu) \cdot \theta_N(z)$$

with c_i well-defined and holomorphic in μ, ν.

Now assume that $\mathcal{J}(z^*)$ has rank $< n+1$ for some $z^* \in M$, i.e., that

$$a_0\theta_i(z^*) = a_1\frac{\partial\theta_i}{\partial z_1}(z^*) + \cdots + a_n\frac{\partial\theta_i}{\partial z_n}(z^*)$$

for $0 \le i \le N$. Then

$$a_0\Theta(z^*, \mu, \nu) = a_1\frac{\partial\Theta}{\partial z_1}(z^*, \mu, \nu) + \cdots + a_n\frac{\partial\Theta}{\partial z_n}(z^*, \mu, \nu)$$

for all μ, ν. If we define the entire meromorphic function

$$\varphi(z) = a_1\frac{\partial\log\theta}{\partial z_1}(z) + \cdots + a_n\frac{\partial\log\theta}{\partial z_n}(z),$$

then

$$\varphi(z^*+\mu) + \varphi(z^*+\nu) + \varphi(z^*-\mu-\nu) = \sum a_i\frac{\partial\log\Theta}{\partial z_i}(z^*, \mu, \nu)$$

$$= \frac{1}{\Theta(z^*, \mu, \nu)}\sum a_i\frac{\partial\Theta}{\partial z_i}(z^*, \mu, \nu) = a_0$$

for all μ, ν. Now for any μ, we can find a ν such that $\varphi(z^* + \nu) \neq \infty$ and $\varphi(z^* - \mu - \nu) \neq \infty$, i.e., such that both $z^* + \nu$ and $z^* - \mu - \nu$ are outside the polar divisor of φ; since $\varphi(z^* + \mu) + \varphi(z^* + \nu) + \varphi(z^* - \mu - \nu) = a_0$, it follows that $\varphi(z^* + \mu)$ is an entire *holomorphic* function of μ. Now clearly $\varphi(z + e_\alpha) = \varphi(z)$; and since

$$\theta(z + \lambda_{n+\alpha}) = e^{-2\pi i (z_\alpha + Z_{\alpha\alpha}/2)} \theta(z),$$

$$\log \theta(z + \lambda_{n+\alpha}) = -2\pi i \left(z_\alpha + \frac{Z_{\alpha\alpha}}{2} \right) + \log \theta(z),$$

i.e.,

$$\varphi(z + \lambda_{n+\alpha}) = \varphi(z) - 2\pi i \cdot a_\alpha.$$

Thus each partial derivative $\partial \varphi / \partial z_i$ is periodic for the lattice Λ, hence bounded in $V \cong \mathbb{C}^n$ and therefore constant. Consequently φ must be linear; write

$$\varphi(z) = \sum_\alpha b_\alpha \cdot z_\alpha + c.$$

But $\varphi(z + e_\alpha) = \varphi(z) \Rightarrow b_\alpha = 0$ for all α; hence $\varphi(z + \lambda_{n+\alpha}) = \varphi(z) = c$. Then

$$\varphi(z + \lambda_{n+\alpha}) - \varphi(z) = 2\pi i \cdot a_\alpha \Rightarrow a_\alpha = 0 \qquad \text{for all } \alpha.$$

We deduce that the presumed linear relation

$$a_0 \theta_j(z^*) = \sum a_i \frac{\partial \theta_j}{\partial z_i} (z^*) \qquad \text{for all } j$$

is trivial, and ι_{L^3} is an immersion.

It remains to show by a similar argument that ι_{L^3} is one-to-one. Suppose there exist $z_1, z_2 \in \mathbb{C}^n$ with

$$\theta_i(z_1) = \rho \cdot \theta_i(z_2) \qquad \text{for all } i;$$

we will prove that z_1 and z_2 represent the same point on M. From the general relation

$$\Theta(z, \mu, \nu) = \sum_{i=0}^N c_i(\mu, \nu) \cdot \theta_i(z)$$

it follows that

$$\frac{\Theta(z_1, \mu, \nu)}{\Theta(z_2, \mu, \nu)} = \frac{\theta(z_1 + \mu) \theta(z_1 + \nu) \theta(z_1 - \mu - \nu)}{\theta(z_2 + \mu) \theta(z_2 + \nu) \theta(z_1 - \mu - \nu)} = \rho$$

identically in μ and ν. For any $\mu \in \mathbb{C}^n$, we can find ν such that

$$\theta(z_1 + \nu), \theta(z_1 - \mu - \nu), \theta(z_2 + \nu), \theta(z_2 - \mu - \nu)$$

are all nonzero; consequently $\theta(z_1 + \mu) / \theta(z_2 + \mu)$ is a nonzero entire function of μ. Then we can set

$$\psi(z) = \log \frac{\theta(z_1 + z)}{\theta(z_2 + z)}$$

and obtain an entire holomorphic function. By the functional equations of the θ-function,

$$\psi(z + e_\alpha) = \psi(z) + 2\pi i b_\alpha, \qquad\qquad b_\alpha \in \mathbb{Z},$$

$$\psi(z + \lambda_{n+\alpha}) = \psi(z) - 2\pi i (z_1 - z_2)_\alpha + 2\pi i c_\alpha, \qquad c_\alpha \in \mathbb{Z}.$$

As before this implies that $\partial\psi/\partial z_i$ is constant for all i, so we can write

$$\psi(z) = 2\pi i \sum a_\beta \cdot z + d.$$

Then $\psi(z + e_\alpha) = \psi(z) + 2\pi i b_\alpha \Rightarrow a_\beta = b_\beta \in \mathbb{Z}$; this in turn implies that

$$\psi(z + \lambda_{n+\alpha}) - \psi(z) = 2\pi i \sum a_\beta Z_{\alpha\beta}$$

$$\Rightarrow \qquad 2\pi i (z_1 - z_2)_\alpha = -2\pi i c_\alpha + 2\pi i \sum a_\beta Z_{\alpha\beta}$$

$$\Rightarrow \qquad z_1 - z_2 = -\sum c_\alpha \cdot e_\alpha + \sum a_\beta \lambda_{n+\beta},$$

i.e., $z_1 - z_2 \in \Lambda$.

Finally, note that for $L \to M$ an arbitrary positive line bundle, we can construct as before an Abelian variety M' with principally polarizing line bundle $L' \to M'$ and finite map

$$\pi' : M \to M'$$

such that

$$\pi'^*(L') = L.$$

Since the map π' is nowhere singular, the argument above applied to L' shows that ι_{L^3} is likewise an immersion, and that for p and q with $\pi'(p) \neq \pi'(q)$, $\iota_{L^3}(p) \neq \iota_{L^3}(q)$. That ι_{L^3} separates points in $\pi^{-1}(p)$ can be seen directly from the explicit form of the θ-functions given on p. 319.
Q.E.D.

The first case beyond curves is the embedding

$$\iota_{L^3} : M \hookrightarrow \mathbb{P}^8$$

of a principally polarized Abelian surface. As a special case, if $M = E_1 \times E_2$ is the product of two elliptic curves, $L_1 \to E_1$ and $L_2 \to E_2$ line bundles of degree 1, and $\iota_{L^3} : E_i \to \mathbb{P}^2$ the corresponding embeddings, then $L = \pi_1^* L_1 \otimes \pi_2^* L_2$ is principally polarizing, and ι_{L^3} is just the Segré map $\mathbb{P}^2 \times \mathbb{P}^2 \to \mathbb{P}^8$ applied to $M = E_1 \times E_2 \hookrightarrow \mathbb{P}^2 \times \mathbb{P}^2$.

The Group Structure on an Abelian Variety

To close our discussion of complex tori, we want to make a few general remarks about the group structure on an Abelian variety.

Any complex torus $M = \mathbb{C}^n / \Lambda$ is a *complex Lie group*—that is, a complex manifold having a group structure in which the group operations are holomorphic. Conversely, we have

Proposition. *Any connected compact complex Lie group* M *is a complex torus.*

Proof. We first show that M must be commutative. For every $g \in M$, let $\mathrm{Ad}(g)$ denote the automorphism of M given by

$$\mathrm{Ad}(g): h \mapsto ghg^{-1}.$$

Clearly the identity e is a fixed point of $\mathrm{Ad}(g)$ for all $g \in M$.

Now let $z_1, \ldots, z_n$ be holomorphic coordinates around $e \in M$, and for each $g \in M$, write out the power series expansion of $\mathrm{Ad}(g)^* z_i$ as

$$\mathrm{Ad}(g)^*(z_i) = \sum a_{i_1,\ldots,i_n}(g) z_1^{i_1} \cdots z_n^{i_n}.$$

For each index $(i_1, \ldots, i_n)$ the function $a_{i_1,\ldots,i_n}(g)$ is clearly a holomorphic function of g; since M is compact and connected, it follows that $a_{i_1,\ldots,i_n}(g)$ is constant. Thus

$$\mathrm{Ad}(g)^*(z_i) = \mathrm{Ad}(e)^*(z_i) = z_i,$$

and so

$$\mathrm{Ad}(g)^* \equiv I,$$

i.e., M is commutative.

Next, for any tangent vector $v \in T'_e(M)$ to M at e, let let $\tilde{v}$ be the vector field on M defined by

$$\tilde{v}(g) = (t_g)_*(v),$$

where $t_g : M \to M$ is multiplication by g; clearly $\tilde{v}$ is holomorphic. Let $\varphi_{t,v} : M \to M$ be the endomorphism of M obtained by integrating the vector field $\tilde{v}$ to time t, and let

$$\pi : T'_e(M) \to M$$

be the *exponential map*, defined by

$$\pi(v) = \varphi_{1,v}(e).$$

Since M is commutative, π is in fact a group homomorphism. Thus M is the quotient of $T'_e(M) \cong \mathbb{C}^n$ by a discrete subgroup, which must be a lattice Λ; since M is compact, Λ must have maximal rank $2n$, and hence $M = \mathbb{C}^n / \Lambda$ is a complex torus. Q.E.D.

Note that if $M = \mathbb{C}^n / \Lambda$, $M' = \mathbb{C}^m / \Lambda'$ are two complex tori and $f: M \to M'$ any holomorphic map, then f lifts to a map

$$\tilde{f}: \mathbb{C}^n \to \mathbb{C}^m.$$

We see then that in terms of Euclidean coordinates $z = (z_1, \ldots, z_n)$ and $w = (w_1, \ldots, w_m)$ on $\mathbb{C}^n$ and $\mathbb{C}^m$ respectively, *the Jacobian matrix*

$$\mathcal{J}_f = \left(\frac{\partial w_i}{\partial z_j} \right)$$

is a well-defined global holomorphic function on M, *hence constant.* It follows that $\tilde{f}$ is an affine linear transformation, and we have

Proposition. *Any holomorphic map between complex tori is a group homomorphism followed by a translation.*

An Abelian variety is a *homogeneous algebraic variety*—that is, it admits a transitive group of biholomorphic automorphisms. Other homogeneous varieties are Grassmannians, quadrics, etc. There is an important difference between these two types. In the latter examples the automorphisms may be taken to be projective transformations—i.e., for a suitable embedding $M \subset \mathbb{P}^N$, the automorphism group $\text{Aut}(M)$ is just the group of linear automorphisms of $\mathbb{P}^N$ leaving M fixed. On the other hand:

Theorem. *If* $M \subset \mathbb{P}^N$ *is an Abelian variety, the group of automorphisms of* M *induced by linear transformations on* $\mathbb{P}^N$ *is finite.*

Proof. Let $L \to M$ be the hyperplane bundle on M. Then if $\varphi: M \to M$ is any automorphism induced by a linear transformation of $\mathbb{P}^N$, clearly $\varphi^* L = L$. But L is positive, and so it is preserved by only a finite group of translations of M. Thus it will suffice to prove that the group of automorphisms φ of M fixing L and fixing the point $p = \pi(0)$ in M is finite. Now any such automorphism lifts to a linear transformation $\tilde{\varphi}: \mathbb{C}^n \to \mathbb{C}^n$ fixing the lattice $\Lambda \subset \mathbb{C}^n$; *since φ takes* L *to itself, moreover,* $\tilde{\varphi}$ *must be unitary with respect to the hermitian inner product given by* $c_1(L) \in H^{1,1}(M) = V \otimes \overline{V}$. In particular, $\tilde{\varphi}$ must take each lattice vector λ_i in a basis to a lattice vector of the same length. But there can be only a finite number of such lattice vectors for each i, and so the result is proved.

Intrinsic Formulations

It is frequently convenient to have the results on Abelian varieties expressed in a coordinate free manner, and we shall now give this together with a few applications.

Suppose that $V_{\mathbb{R}}$ is a real even-dimensional vector space containing a full lattice Λ, and with a decomposition of the complexification $V_{\mathbb{C}} = V_{\mathbb{R}} \otimes \mathbb{R}$

$$(*) \qquad\qquad\qquad V_{\mathbb{C}} = V \oplus \overline{V},$$

into conjugate subspaces being given. Then the image of Λ in $V_{\mathbb{C}}$ projects onto a full lattice in V which we still denote by Λ; and

$$M = V/\Lambda$$

is a complex torus. We will see in the next paragraph that every complex torus arises in this way with $V_{\mathbb{R}} = \Lambda \otimes_{\mathbb{Z}} \mathbb{R}$.

The natural isomorphisms

$$\Lambda \cong H_1(M,\mathbb{Z}), \qquad V^* \cong H^0(M,\Omega^1)$$

have already been noted. If $\dim_{\mathbb{C}} V = n$, then by Kodaira-Serre and Poincaré dualities

$$V \cong H^{n-1,n}(M), \qquad \Lambda \cong H^{2n-1}(M,\mathbb{Z}).$$

It follows that $V_{\mathbb{R}} = \Lambda \otimes_{\mathbb{Z}} \mathbb{R}$ is canonically isomorphic to $H^{2n-1}(M,\mathbb{R})$ with (*) being the Hodge decomposition

$$H^{2n-1}(M,\mathbb{C}) = H^{n-1,n}(M) \oplus \overline{H^{n-1,n}(M)}.$$

According to the proposition in the preceding section, an arbitrary holomorphic mapping

$$\varphi: \frac{V}{\Lambda} \to \frac{V'}{\Lambda'}$$

is given by an affine linear mapping $V \to V'$. To see explicitly what this mapping is, we compose φ with a translation so that $\varphi(e) = e'$ and let

$$\Phi: \Lambda \to \Lambda'$$

denote the induced map on homology. Since φ^* preserves the Hodge decomposition, we see that

$$\Phi: V \to V',$$

and this is the linear mapping inducing φ.

The Riemann conditions for the existence of a polarization may be formulated as follows: A class in $H^2(M,\mathbb{Z})$ is given by a bilinear form

$$Q: \Lambda \otimes_{\mathbb{Z}} \Lambda \to \mathbb{Z}, \qquad Q(\lambda,\lambda') = -Q(\lambda',\lambda).$$

Identifying $\Lambda \otimes_{\mathbb{Z}} \mathbb{C}$ with $V \oplus \overline{V}$, the bilinear relations are

$$Q(v,v') = 0, \qquad v,v' \in V,$$

$$-\sqrt{-1}\, Q(v,\bar{v}) > 0, \qquad 0 \neq v \in V.$$

For example, if S is a compact Riemann surface with Jacobian variety

$$\mathcal{J}(S) = \frac{H^{0,1}(S)}{H^1(S,\mathbb{Z})},$$

the principal polarization given by the divisor Θ is that given by the cup product

$$H^1(S, \mathbb{Z}) \otimes H^1(S, \mathbb{Z}) \to \mathbb{Z},$$

which is unimodular by Poincaré duality. In general, if Q has elementary divisors $\delta_1, \ldots, \delta_n$, then $\Delta = \delta_1 \cdot \ldots \cdot \delta_n$ is called the *Pfaffian* of Q and

$$\det Q = \Delta^2.$$

We shall use this intrinsic formulation to construct the *Poincaré line bundle*

$$P \to M \times \hat{M},$$

where $\hat{M} = \mathrm{Pic}^0(M)$ is the complex torus dual to M. Recall that $\mathrm{Pic}^0(M)$ is defined to be the group of holomorphic line bundles with first Chern class zero. Via the cohomology sequence of the exponential sheaf sequence we make the natural identifications

$$\mathrm{Pic}^0(M) \cong \frac{H^1(M, \mathcal{O})}{H^1(M, \mathbb{Z})}$$

$$\cong \frac{\bar{V}^*}{\Lambda^*}, \qquad \Lambda^* = \mathrm{Hom}(\Lambda, \mathbb{Z})$$

and denote by $P_\xi \to M$ the line bundle corresponding to $\xi \in \mathrm{Pic}^0(M)$.

Lemma.   *There is a unique holomorphic line bundle*

$$P \to M \times \hat{M},$$

called the Poincaré *line bundle, which is trivial on* $e \times \hat{M}$ *and which satisfies*

$$P|_{M \times \{\xi\}} \cong P_\xi.$$

Proof.   Using $\hat{M} = H^{0,1}(M)/H^1(M, \mathbb{Z})$, the cohomology sequence of the exponential sheaf sequence and Künneth formula give

$$H^1(M \times \hat{M}, \mathcal{O}) \to H^1(M \times \hat{M}, \mathcal{O}^*) \to H^2(M \times \hat{M}, \mathbb{Z}) \to H^2(M \times \hat{M}, \mathcal{O}).$$

$$\uparrow \qquad\qquad\qquad\qquad\qquad\qquad \uparrow$$

$$H^1(M, \mathcal{O}) \oplus H^1(\hat{M}, \mathcal{O}) \qquad\qquad H^1(M, \mathbb{Z}) \otimes H^1(\hat{M}, \mathbb{Z})$$

$$\| \uparrow$$

$$\mathrm{Hom}(H^1(M, \mathbb{Z}), H^1(M, \mathbb{Z}))$$

Now the identity $I \in \mathrm{Hom}(H^1(M, \mathbb{Z}), H^1(M, \mathbb{Z}))$ has Hodge type $(1,1)$ since it preserves the Hodge decomposition on $H^1(M, \mathbb{C})$. By the Lefschetz theorem on $(1,1)$ classes, then, we obtain a holomorphic line bundle $P \to M \times \hat{M}$ with $c_1(P) = I$. The restriction $P|_{M \times \{\xi\}}$ has zero Chern class, and hence is $P_{\varphi(\xi)}$ for some holomorphic mapping

$$\varphi: \hat{M} \to \mathrm{Pic}^0(M).$$

Normalizing so that $\varphi(e) = \hat{e}$, which is achieved by multiplying P by $\pi_1^* P_{-\xi_0}$ where $\xi_0 = \varphi(e)$, the induced homology mapping is, by construction, just the identity. Thus φ is also the identity, and this proves the existence of the Poincaré bundle.

If P, P' are two such line bundles, then $Q = P^* \otimes P'$ has the properties

$$Q|M \times \{\xi\} \cong M \times \mathbb{C}; \qquad Q|\{e\} \times \hat{M} \cong \hat{M} \times \mathbb{C}.$$

Denote the second trivialization by ψ and let $\sigma(\lambda, \xi) \in Q_{(\lambda, \xi)}$ be the unique section of $Q|_{M \times \{\xi\}}$ which has the value $\psi^{-1}(1)$ at (e, ξ). Then σ is a nonvanishing holomorphic section of Q, which must then be the trivial line bundle.   Q.E.D.

For $L \to M$ a positive line bundle we set $L \otimes P = \pi_1^* L \otimes P$ on $M \times \hat{M}$; then

$$L \otimes P|_{M \times \{\xi\}} \cong L \otimes P_{\xi}$$
$$= L_{\xi}$$

where the last step is a definition. For use in Section 5 of Chapter 3 on differentials of the second kind, we will prove the

Proposition.   *There exist Δ sections $\theta_j(\lambda, \xi) \in H^0(M \times \hat{M}, \mathcal{O}(L \otimes P))$ inducing a basis of $H^0(M, \mathcal{O}(L_{\xi}))$ for each $\xi \in \hat{M}$.*

The proof will follow some preliminary observations on the map

$$\varphi_L: M \to \hat{M}$$

defined by

$$\varphi_L(\lambda) = \tau_{\lambda}^* L \otimes L^*$$

which was discussed in the preceding section. Since $\varphi_L(e) = \hat{e}$, according to our general remarks φ_L is uniquely specified by the induced homology map

$$\Phi_L: \Lambda \to \Lambda^*$$
$$: H^{2n-1}(M, \mathbb{Z}) \to \mathrm{Hom}(H^{2n-1}(M, \mathbb{Z}), \mathbb{Z}).$$

We will compute Φ_L, thereby giving another proof of the fact that φ_L is an *isogeny*—i.e., a finitely sheeted covering mapping—of degree Δ^2.

For this we consider the group law

$$m: M \times M \to M$$

given by

$$m(\lambda', \lambda) = \lambda' + \lambda.$$

By construction

$$(*) \qquad\qquad \varphi_L(\lambda) = \pi_1^* L^* \otimes m^* L|_{M \times \{\lambda\}}.$$

If $x_1, \ldots, x_{2n}$ are real coordinates on $V_{\mathbb{R}}$ such that the Chern class of $L \to M$ is

$$\omega = \sum_{\alpha} \delta_{\alpha} \, dx_{\alpha} \wedge dx_{n+\alpha},$$

then using (u_{α}, v_{β}) as corresponding coordinates on $M \times M$

$$m^*\omega = \sum_{\alpha} \delta_{\alpha} (du_{\alpha} + dv_{\alpha}) \wedge (du_{n+\alpha} + dv_{n+\alpha}).$$

If $\eta \in H^{2n-1}(M, \mathbb{Z})$, we let $\eta_1 \in H^{2n-1}(M \times M, \mathbb{Z})$ be the class $\pi_1^*\eta$, and similarly for η_2. From $(*)$ we easily deduce that Φ_L is given by the bilinear form on $H^{2n-1}(M, \mathbb{Z})$ defined by

$$\Phi_L(\eta, \eta') = \int_{M \times M} m^*\omega \wedge \eta_1 \wedge \eta_2'.$$

For the explicit computation we write

$$\eta = \sum (-1)^{i-1} \eta_i \, dx_1 \wedge \cdots \wedge \widehat{dx_i} \wedge \cdots \wedge dx_{2n},$$
$$\eta' = \sum (-1)^{j-1} \eta_j \, dx_1 \wedge \cdots \wedge \widehat{dx_j} \wedge \cdots \wedge dx_{2n},$$

and then by the formulas for $m^*\omega$ and Φ_L

$$\Phi_L(\eta, \eta') = \sum_{\alpha} \delta_{\alpha} (\eta_{\alpha} \eta'_{n+\alpha} - \eta_{n+\alpha} \eta'_{\alpha}).$$

This implies the previous assertion that

$\varphi_L : M \to \hat{M}$ *is an isogeny of degree* Δ^2, *or, equivalently, the line bundle* $L \to M$ *is fixed exactly under the group of translations*

$$\mathbb{Z}\{\delta_{\alpha}^{-1} x_{\alpha}, \delta_{\alpha}^{-1} x_{n+\alpha}\}$$

Returning to the proof of the proposition, the equation

$$\xi = \varphi_L(\lambda)$$

has Δ^2 solutions $\lambda_{\alpha}(\xi)$. If $\theta(z) \in \mathcal{O}(V)$ is a θ-function giving a section of $L \to M$, then $\theta_{\lambda}(z) = \theta(z + \lambda)$ gives a section of $\tau_{\lambda}^* L = L \otimes L_{\varphi_L(\lambda)}$. Now if $\rho : M \times M \to M \times \hat{M}$ is the isogeny defined by $\rho(\lambda', \lambda) = (\lambda', \varphi_L(\lambda))$, then $\theta(z, \lambda) = \theta(z + \lambda)$ gives a section of

$$\pi_1^* L \otimes \rho^* P = \rho^*(L \otimes P) \to M \times \hat{M}.$$

Since $\theta(z + \lambda_a(\xi)) = \theta(z + \lambda_b(\xi))$, this section is induced from a section $\theta(z, \xi) \in H^0(M \times \hat{M}, \mathcal{O}(L \otimes P))$. In this way we may construct the sections required by the proposition.   Q.E.D.

We conclude by discussing some complex tori which are intrinsically associated to an arbitrary compact Kähler manifold M. Recalling the Hodge decomposition

$$H^{2q-1}(V, \mathbb{C}) = \bigoplus_{r+s=2q-1} H^{r,s}(M)$$

from Section 1 of Chapter 2, we set

$$V_q = H^{q-1,q}(M) \oplus \cdots \oplus H^{0,2q-1}(M)$$

for $1 \leqslant q \leqslant n = \dim M$. Then

$$H^{2q+1}(M, \mathbb{C}) = V_q \oplus \overline{V}_q,$$

and, if we let Λ_q denote the image of $H^{2q+1}(M, \mathbb{Z}) \to V_q$, then the qth *intermediate Jacobian* is defined to be the complex torus

$$\mathcal{J}_q(M) = \frac{V_q}{\Lambda_q}.$$

We shall discuss briefly the extreme cases $q = 1$ and $q = n$.

When $q = 1$, we find the Picard variety

$$\mathcal{J}_1(M) = \frac{H^{0,1}(M)}{H^1(M, \mathbb{Z})}$$

$$= \mathrm{Pic}^0(M).$$

For $q = n$ we obtain the *Albanese variety*

$$\mathcal{J}_n(M) = \frac{H^{n-1,n}(M)}{H^{2n-1}(M, \mathbb{Z})}$$

$$\cong \frac{H^0(M, \Omega^1)^*}{H_1(M, \mathbb{Z})}$$

$$= \mathrm{Alb}(M),$$

where the last step is a definition. Now, for the same reasons as in our discussion of Abel's theorem, choosing a base point $p_0 \in M$ and basis $\omega_1, \ldots, \omega_q \in H^0(M, \Omega^1)$ the map

$$\mu: M \to \mathrm{Alb}(M)$$

given by

$$\mu(p) = \left(\int_{p_0}^p \omega_1, \ldots, \int_{p_0}^p \omega_q \right)$$

is well-defined and holomorphic. The induced mappings

$$\mu_*: \frac{H_1(M, \mathbb{Z})}{\text{torsion}} \to H_1(\mathrm{Alb}(M), \mathbb{Z}),$$

$$\mu^*: H^0(\mathrm{Alb}(M), \Omega^1) \to H^0(M, \Omega^1)$$

are, by construction, isomorphisms. Using our intrinsic formulations, we have

$$\text{Pic}^0(\text{Alb}(M)) = \frac{H^{0,1}(M)}{H^1(M,\mathbb{Z})}$$

$$= \text{Pic}^0(M),$$

$$\text{Alb}(\text{Pic}^0(M)) = \frac{H^{n-1,n}(M)}{H^{2n-1}(M,\mathbb{Z})}$$

$$= \text{Alb}(M).$$

In particular, $\text{Alb}(M)$ and $\text{Pic}^0(M)$ are, in a natural way, dual complex tori.

Suppose now that $\omega \in H^{1,1}(M) \cap H^2(M,\mathbb{Z})$ is the Chern class of a positive line bundle. Then, by the Hodge-Riemann bilinear relations, the bilinear form

$$Q: \Lambda_1 \otimes \Lambda_1 \to \mathbb{Z}$$

given by

$$Q(\eta,\eta') = \int_M \omega^{n-1} \wedge \eta \wedge \eta'$$

induces a polarization on $\text{Pic}^0(M)$, which by the previous discussion induces a polarization on the dual torus $\text{Alb}(M)$. For $L \to \text{Alb}(M)$ a positive line bundle and $P \to \text{Alb}(M) \times \text{Pic}^0(\text{Alb}(M))$ the Poincaré bundle we set $L_\xi = L \otimes P|_{\text{Alb}(M) \times \{\xi\}}$, where $\xi \in \text{Pic}^0(\text{Alb}(M))$. Then for each section $\theta \in H^0(\text{Alb}(M),L)$ we have constructed $\theta_\xi \in H^0(\text{Alb}(M),L_\xi)$. Pulling this back under the canonical mapping

$$\mu: M \to \text{Alb}(M)$$

and making the previous identification $\text{Pic}^0(\text{Alb}(M)) \cong \text{Pic}^0(M)$, we deduce that:

There are holomorphic line bundles $L_\xi \to M$ parametrized by $\xi \in \text{Pic}^0(M)$ with $L_\xi \otimes L_e^* = \xi$, and holomorphic sections $\theta_\xi \in H^0(M, \mathcal{O}(L_\xi))$ depending holomorphically on ξ.

If $q = \frac{1}{2}b_1(M)$, then setting $D_\xi = (\theta_\xi)$ this last assertion was classically stated as saying that on M there is a family D_ξ of ∞^q linearly *inequivalent* divisors.

7. CURVES AND THEIR JACOBIANS

Preliminaries

Let S now be a compact Riemann surface of genus g. Choose a canonical basis $\{a_1,\ldots,a_g,b_1,\ldots,b_g\}$ for $H_1(S,\mathbb{Z})$, so that

$$^{\#}(a_\alpha \cdot a_\beta) = {}^{\#}(b_\alpha \cdot b_\beta) = 0, \qquad {}^{\#}(a_\alpha \cdot b_\beta) = \delta_{\alpha\beta};$$

let $\omega_1,\ldots,\omega_g$ in turn be a basis for $H^0(S,\Omega^1)$ normalized with respect to $\{a_\alpha, b_\alpha\}$, i.e., such that

$$\int_{a_\alpha} \omega_\beta = \delta_{\alpha\beta}.$$

Recall that the Jacobian $\mathcal{J}(S)$ of S is given by $\mathcal{J}(S) = \mathbb{C}^g / \Lambda$, where Λ is the lattice generated by the vectors

$$e_\alpha = \lambda_\alpha = \left(\int_{a_\alpha} \omega_1, \ldots, \int_{a_\alpha} \omega_g \right)$$

$$\lambda_{g+\alpha} = \left(\int_{b_\alpha} \omega_1, \ldots, \int_{b_\alpha} \omega_g \right).$$

By the Riemann bilinear relations, the period matrix Ω of $\Lambda \subset \mathbb{C}^g$ is of the form

$$\Omega = (I, Z)$$

with $Z = {}^tZ$ and $Y = \operatorname{Im} Z > 0$; thus if we let $x_1,\ldots,x_{2g}$ be real coordinates on $\mathbb{C}^g$ dual to the real basis $\{\lambda_i\}$, the differential form

$$\omega = \sum_\alpha dx_\alpha \wedge dx_{n+\alpha}$$

represents a principal polarization of $\mathcal{J}(S) = \mathbb{C}^g / \Lambda$. In terms of standard complex coordinates $z = (z_1,\ldots,z_g)$ on $\mathbb{C}^g$, we can also write

$$\omega = \frac{\sqrt{-1}}{2} \sum Y_{\alpha\beta}^{-1} dz_\alpha \wedge d\bar{z}_\beta$$

with $Y = \operatorname{Im} Z$ as above.

(*Note*: Inasmuch as the Jacobian of a Riemann surface is always principally polarized, we will, after normalizing as above, write e_α for λ_α, and

$$Z_\alpha = (Z_{\alpha 1},\ldots,Z_{\alpha g}) = \left(\int_{b_\alpha} \omega_1, \ldots, \int_{b_\alpha} \omega_g \right)$$

for $\lambda_{n+\alpha}$.)

Let L be the line bundle on $\mathcal{J}(S)$ with Chern class $[\omega]$, translated so that a global section $\tilde{\theta}$ of L is represented by the Riemann theta function $\theta \in \mathcal{O}(\mathbb{C}^n)$ satisfying

$$\theta(z+e_\alpha) = \theta(z), \qquad \theta(z+Z_\alpha) = e^{-2\pi i(Z_\alpha + Z_{\alpha\alpha}/2)}\theta(z);$$

let $\Theta \subset \mathcal{J}(S)$ be the divisor of the section $\tilde{\theta}$.

Now, choose once and for all a base point $z_0 \in S$, and let $\mu: S \to \mathcal{J}(S)$ be the map given by

$$\mu(z) = \left(\int_{z_0}^z \omega_1, \ldots, \int_{z_0}^z \omega_g \right).$$

We compute first of all the intersection number of the curve $\mu(S) \subset \mathcal{J}(S)$ with the divisor Θ; to do this we simply count the zeros of the section $\mu^*\tilde{\theta}$ of μ^*L on S. Assume the cycles a_α, b_α are disjoint except for a common base point and, as in Section 2 of this chapter, represent S as a polygon Δ in the plane whose sides correspond in order to the cycles $a_1, b_1, a_1^{-1}, b_1^{-1}$, etc. (See Figure 14.) Then if $\tilde{\mu}: \Delta \to \mathbb{C}^g$ is the obvious lifting of μ given by integrating from z_0 to z in Δ and $\theta \in \mathcal{O}(\mathbb{C}^n)$ is the Riemann θ-function above, we see that

$$\text{number of zeros of } \tilde{\mu}^*\theta = \frac{1}{2\pi\sqrt{-1}} \int_{\partial\Delta} d\log\theta(\mu(z)).$$

To evaluate this integral, we consider together the contributions of the sides a_β and a_β^{-1}, b_β and b_β^{-1} in $\partial\Delta$. If z, z^* are corresponding points on a_β

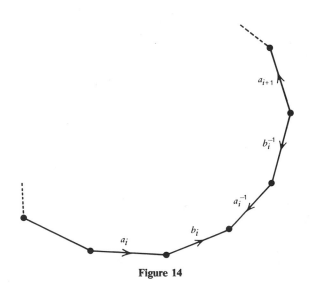

Figure 14

and a_β^{-1}, respectively, we have

$$\tilde{\mu}_\alpha(z^*) - \tilde{\mu}_\alpha(z) = \int_z^{z^*} \omega_\alpha = \int_z^{P_0} \omega_\alpha + \int_{b_\beta} \omega_\alpha + \int_{P_0}^{z^*} \omega_\alpha = \int_{b_\beta} \omega_\alpha = Z_{\beta\alpha},$$

i.e.,

$$\tilde{\mu}(z^*) = \tilde{\mu}(z) + Z_\beta.$$

Thus

$$\theta(\tilde{\mu}(z^*)) = e^{-2\pi i(\tilde{\mu}_\beta(z) + Z_{\beta\beta}/2)}\theta(\tilde{\mu}(z)),$$

so

$$\frac{1}{2\pi\sqrt{-1}}\int_{a_\beta} d\log\theta(\tilde{\mu}(z)) + \frac{1}{2\pi\sqrt{-1}}\int_{a_\beta^{-1}} d\log\theta(\tilde{\mu}(z))$$

$$= \frac{1}{2\pi\sqrt{-1}}\int_{a_\beta^{-1}} d\log e^{-2\pi i(\tilde{\mu}(z)_\beta + Z_{\beta\beta}/2)}$$

$$= \int_{a_\beta} d\tilde{\mu}(z)_\beta$$

$$= \int_{a_\beta} \omega_\beta = 1.$$

Similarly, we see that for z, z^* corresponding points on b_β, b_β^{-1},

$$\tilde{\mu}(z^*) = \tilde{\mu}(z) - e_\beta,$$

hence $\theta(\tilde{\mu}(z^*)) = \theta(\tilde{\mu}(z))$ and

$$(*) \qquad \frac{1}{2\pi i}\int_{b_\beta} d\log\theta(\tilde{\mu}(z)) + \frac{1}{2\pi i}\int_{b_\beta^{-1}} d\log\theta(\tilde{\mu}(z)) = 0.$$

Adding up the contributions from all the sides of Δ, we find

$$\deg\mu^* L = \frac{1}{2\pi\sqrt{-1}}\int_{\partial\Delta} d\log\theta(\tilde{\mu}(z)) = g.$$

Note that we assume in the course of this computation that $\tilde{\mu}^*\theta \not\equiv 0$ on S; if this is not the case, we may take instead of L the translate $L_\lambda = \tau_\lambda^* L$ and corresponding section $\theta_\lambda(z) = \theta(z - \lambda) \in H^0(\mathcal{J}(S), \mathcal{O}(L_\lambda))$ for a suitable $\lambda \in \mathbb{C}^n$.

Another way to compute $\deg\mu^* L$ is topological:

$$\deg\mu^* L = \int_S c_1(\mu^* L) = \int_S \mu^* c_1(L) = \int_S \mu^*\left(\sum_\alpha dx_\alpha \wedge dx_{n+\alpha}\right).$$

Now $\mu_*(a_\alpha) = \lambda_\alpha, \mu_*(b_\alpha) = \lambda_{g+\alpha}$, and so

$$\int_{a_\beta} \mu^* dx_\alpha = \int_{\mu(a_\beta)} dx_\alpha = \delta_{\alpha\beta};$$

$$\int_{b_\beta} \mu^* dx_\alpha = \int_{\mu(b_\beta)} dx_\alpha = 0.$$

From this we see that $[\mu^* dx_\alpha]$ is Poincaré dual to the cycle $-b_\alpha$, and $[\mu^* dx_{n+\alpha}]$ is dual to $+a_\alpha$. Thus

$$\int_S \mu^*(dx_\alpha \wedge dx_{n+\alpha}) = {}^\#(-b_\alpha \cdot a_\alpha) = 1,$$

hence

$$\deg \mu^*(L) = \int_S \mu^*\left(\sum dx_\alpha \wedge dx_{n+\alpha}\right) = g.$$

Now let $\Theta = (\theta)$ denote the divisor of the line bundle L and $\Theta_\lambda = \Theta + \lambda = (\theta_\lambda)$, where $\theta_\lambda(z) = \theta(z - \lambda)$, denote the divisor of the translated bundle $L_\lambda = \tau_\lambda^* L$. Since $c_1(L_\lambda) = c_1(L)$, we have shown by the last computation that for any $\lambda \in \mathcal{J}(S)$, either

1. $\mu(S) \subset \Theta_\lambda$; or
2. $\mu(S)$ intersects Θ_λ in exactly g points, counting multiplicity.

For $\lambda \in \mathcal{J}(S)$ such that $\mu(S) \not\subset \Theta_\lambda$, write the divisor

$$(\mu^* \theta_\lambda) = z_1(\lambda) + \cdots + z_g(\lambda).$$

Now by the Abel and Jacobi theorems, the point $\lambda \in \mathcal{J}(S)$ represents a linear equivalence class of divisors of degree 0 on S. In fact, it turns out that up to a constant κ, λ is just the class of the divisor $\sum z_i(\lambda) - g \cdot z_0$. We express this as the

Lemma. *For a suitable constant* $\kappa \in \mathcal{J}(S)$,

$$\sum_{i=1}^{g} \mu(z_i(\lambda)) + \kappa = \lambda$$

for all $\lambda \in \mathcal{J}(S)$ *such that* $\mu(S) \not\subset \Theta_\lambda$.

Note that this lemma gives our promised explicit solution to the Jacobi inversion problem, at least for a general $\lambda \in \mathcal{J}(S)$ such that the curve $\mu(S)$ does not lie in Θ_λ.

Proof. Represent S again as a polygon Δ in the plane, with $\tilde{\mu} : \Delta \to \mathbb{C}^g$ the corresponding lifting of μ. $\tilde{\mu}^* \theta_\lambda$ vanishes exactly on the points $z_i(\lambda)$, and so by residues

$$\sum_i \tilde{\mu}_\alpha(z_i(\lambda)) = \frac{1}{2\pi\sqrt{-1}} \int_{\partial \Delta} \tilde{\mu}_\alpha(z) \cdot d\log \theta_\lambda(\tilde{\mu}(z)).$$

We evaluate this integral as before by considering corresponding points z, z^* on sides a_β, a_β^{-1} of $\partial \Delta$. Since

$$\tilde{\mu}_\alpha(z^*) = \tilde{\mu}_\alpha(z) + Z_{\alpha\beta},$$

the functional equation for the θ-function gives

$$\theta_\lambda(\tilde{\mu}(z^*)) = e^{-2\pi i(\tilde{\mu}_\beta(z) + Z_{\beta\beta}/2 - \lambda_\beta)} \theta_\lambda(\tilde{\mu}(z))$$

hence

$$d\log\theta_\lambda(\tilde{\mu}(z^*)) = d\log\theta_\lambda(\tilde{\mu}(z)) - 2\pi\sqrt{-1} \cdot \omega_\beta(z).$$

Consequently

$$\frac{1}{2\pi\sqrt{-1}}\left(\int_{a_\beta}\tilde{\mu}_\alpha(z)\,d\log\theta_\lambda(\tilde{\mu}(z)) + \int_{a_\beta^{-1}}\tilde{\mu}_\alpha(z)\,d\log\theta_\lambda(\tilde{\mu}(z))\right)$$

$$= -\frac{Z_{\alpha\beta}}{2\pi\sqrt{-1}}\int_{a_\beta}d\log\theta_\lambda(\tilde{\mu}(z)) + Z_{\alpha\beta}\int_{a_\beta}\omega_\beta(z) + \int_{a_\beta}\tilde{\mu}_\alpha(z)\omega_\beta(z).$$

The last two terms of this expression are independent of λ and hence may be absorbed in the constant κ_α. As for the first term, if z_1 and z_2 are the endpoints of the arc a_β, then $\tilde{\mu}(z_2) = \tilde{\mu}(z_1) \pm e_\beta$; hence $\theta_\lambda(\tilde{\mu}(z_1)) = \theta_\lambda(\tilde{\mu}(z_2))$ and

$$\frac{1}{2\pi\sqrt{-1}}\int_{a_\beta}d\log\theta_\lambda(\tilde{\mu}(z)) \in \mathbb{Z}.$$

Thus the first term must likewise be constant and can be absorbed in κ_α. Now if z and z^* are corresponding points of b_β and b_β^{-1}, we have

$$\tilde{\mu}(z^*) = \tilde{\mu}(z) - e_\beta, \qquad \theta_\lambda(\tilde{\mu}(z^*)) = \theta_\lambda(\tilde{\mu}(z));$$

so

$$\frac{1}{2\pi\sqrt{-1}}\left(\int_{b_\beta}\tilde{\mu}_\alpha(z)\,d\log\theta_\lambda(\tilde{\mu}(z)) + \int_{b_\beta^{-1}}\tilde{\mu}_\alpha(z)\,d\log\theta_\lambda(\tilde{\mu}(z))\right)$$

$$= \frac{\delta_{\alpha\beta}}{2\pi\sqrt{-1}}\int_{b_\beta}d\log\theta_\lambda(\tilde{\mu}(z)).$$

Again, if z_1 and z_2 are the endpoints of b_β, we have $\tilde{\mu}(z_2) = \tilde{\mu}(z_1) + Z_\beta$; hence

$$\theta_\lambda(\tilde{\mu}(z_2)) = e^{-2\pi i\left(\tilde{\mu}_\beta(z) - \lambda_\beta + Z_{\beta\beta}/2\right)}\theta_\lambda(\tilde{\mu}(z_1)),$$

$$\frac{1}{2\pi\sqrt{-1}}\int_{b_\beta}d\log\theta_\lambda(\tilde{\mu}(z)) - \lambda_\beta \equiv \tilde{\mu}_\beta(z) + \frac{Z_{\beta\beta}}{2} \qquad (\text{mod } \mathbb{Z}).$$

The expression on the right does not depend on λ; thus the expression on the left must be constant and can be absorbed into κ_α. Adding up the contributions from all the sides, we finally obtain

$$\sum_i\tilde{\mu}_\alpha(z_i(\lambda)) = \frac{1}{2\pi\sqrt{-1}}\int_{\partial\Delta}\tilde{\mu}_\alpha(z)\,d\log\theta_\lambda(\tilde{\mu}(z)) = \lambda_\alpha + \kappa_\alpha. \quad \text{Q.E.D.}$$

Following our discussion of Riemann's theorem, we will be able to identify the constant κ and determine exactly when $\mu(S) \subset \Theta_\lambda$.

Riemann's Theorem

We can use our last result to obtain a geometric description of the divisor Θ of θ. It will be convenient to change our notation slightly, and denote by

$$D = p_1 + \cdots + p_d \in S^{(d)}$$

an effective divisor of degree d, and by z_i a local coordinate around p_i. Once we have chosen z_i, we may define functions Ω_α around p_i by

$$\omega_\alpha(p) = \Omega_\alpha(p) \cdot dz_i;$$

Ω_α is the function we have previously written as $\omega_\alpha(p)/dz_i$.

As before, we define

$$\mu: S^{(d)} \to \mathcal{J}(S)$$

by

$$\mu(p_1 + \cdots + p_d) = \mu(p_1) + \cdots + \mu(p_d)$$

$$= \left(\sum_i \int_{p_0}^{p_i} \omega, \ldots, \sum_i \int_{p_0}^{p_i} \omega \right)$$

At a point $D = p_1 + \cdots + p_d$ with the points p_i distinct the Jacobian matrix of the map μ is given, in terms of the coordinates $z_1, \ldots, z_d$ on $S^{(d)}$, by

$$\mathcal{J}(\mu) = \begin{bmatrix} \Omega_1(p_1) & \cdots & \Omega_g(p_1) \\ \vdots & & \vdots \\ \Omega_1(p_d) & \cdots & \Omega_g(p_d) \end{bmatrix}$$

This matrix has maximal rank exactly when the points p_i are linearly independent on the canonical curve of S; since this is generically the case as long as $d \leqslant g$, it follows that *for* $d \leqslant g$ *the image*

$$W_d = \mu(S^{(d)})$$

is an analytic subvariety of dimension d, and since the fibers of μ are linear spaces, that the *map* μ *is generically one-to-one*. The geometry of this mapping—especially its relation to the special linear systems on S—will be examined in the following two subsections.

We have intrinsically associated to the Jacobian $\mathcal{J}(S)$ of S two divisors, unique up to translation: the divisor Θ of the line bundle $L \to \mathcal{J}(S)$ with Chern class given by the intersection form on $H_1(S, \mathbb{Z}) \cong H_1(\mathcal{J}(S), \mathbb{Z})$, and the image W_{g-1} of $S^{(g-1)}$ under μ. The first of these divisors is defined purely in terms of the linear algebra of $\mathcal{J}(S)$ and $[\omega]$, while the second involves directly the geometry of S and μ. Of fundamental importance, accordingly, is

Riemann's Theorem

$$\Theta = W_{g-1} + \kappa,$$

where κ is the constant appearing the last lemma.

Proof. We first show that $W_{g-1} \subset \Theta_{-\kappa}$. To see this, let $D = p_1 + \cdots + p_g \in S^{(g)}$ be a generic divisor, so that the points p_i are all distinct, $\mu : S^{(g)} \to \mathcal{J}(S)$ is one-to-one at D, and $\mu(S) \not\subset \Theta_{\kappa+\mu(D)}$. Set

$$\lambda = \mu(D) + \kappa,$$

so that by the preceding lemma,

$$\Theta_\lambda \cap \mu(S) = \mu(p_1) + \cdots + \mu(p_g).$$

Now—and this is the crucial step—we have seen that $\theta(\mu) = \theta(-\mu)$; therefore, using $\theta_\lambda(\mu(p_i)) = 0$ for $i = g$,

$$\theta(\mu(p_1) + \cdots + \mu(p_{g-1}) + \kappa) = \theta(\lambda - \mu(p_g)) = \theta_\lambda(\mu(p_g)) = 0,$$

i.e.,

$$\theta_{-\kappa}(\mu(p_1) + \cdots + \mu(p_{g-1})) = 0.$$

Thus $\mu^* \theta_{-\kappa}$ vanishes in an open set in $S^{(g-1)}$, hence in all of $S^{(g-1)}$, and we see that $W_{g-1} \subset \Theta_{-\kappa}$.

Now from Section 1 of Chapter 1 we can write

$$\Theta_{-\kappa} = a \cdot W_{g-1} + \Theta'$$

with $a > 0 \in \mathbb{Z}$ and Θ' an effective divisor on $\mathcal{J}(S)$. We want to show first that $a = 1$, and then that $\Theta' = 0$; the first step will be to show that $^{\#}(\mu(S) \cdot W_{g-1}) \geq g$. To prove this, note that the involution $\mu \mapsto -\mu$ acts as the identity on $H_2(\mathcal{J}(S)) = H_1(\mathcal{J}(S)) \wedge H_1(\mathcal{J}(S))$, and so the cycle $-\mu(S)$ is homologous to $\mu(S)$. Now take $\lambda = \mu(p_1) + \cdots + \mu(p_g)$ a generic point of $\mathcal{J}(S)$ so that $-\mu(S) \not\subset W_{g-1} - \lambda$; then $-\mu(S)$ and $W_{g-1} - \lambda$ meet in isolated points, and for each $i = 1, \ldots, g$ we have

$$-\mu(p_i) = \mu\left(\sum_{j \neq i} p_j\right) - \lambda \in W_{g-1} - \lambda.$$

Thus $^{\#}(\mu(S), W_{g-1}) \geq g$.

Now we have proved that the intersection number of Θ with $\mu(S)$ is g, and consequently

$$a \cdot {}^{\#}(\mu(S) \cdot W_{g-1}) + {}^{\#}(\mu(S) \cdot \Theta') = g.$$

But we can always find $\lambda \in \mathcal{J}(S)$ such that $\mu(S) \not\subset \Theta' + \lambda$; thus $^{\#}(\mu(S), \Theta') \geq 0$, and it follows that $a = 1$, $^{\#}(\mu(S) \cdot W_{g-1}) = g$, and $^{\#}(\mu(S) \cdot \Theta') = 0$.

It remains to show that $\Theta' = 0$. We use the following argument: since $^{\#}(\mu(S) \cdot \Theta') = 0$,

$$\mu(S) \cap \Theta'_\lambda \neq \varnothing \Rightarrow \mu(S) \subset \Theta'_\lambda \qquad \text{for any } \lambda \in \mathcal{J}(S);$$

it follows from this that

$$\Theta'_\lambda \cap W_2 \neq \varnothing \Rightarrow W_2 \subset \Theta'_\lambda \qquad \text{for any } \lambda \in \mathcal{J}(S),$$

since

$$\Theta'_\lambda \ni \mu(p_1) + \mu(p_2)$$

$$\Rightarrow \Theta'_{\lambda + \mu(p_1)} \ni \mu(p_2)$$

$$\Rightarrow \Theta'_{\lambda + \mu(p_1)} \ni \mu(p_2^*) \qquad \text{for all } p_2^* \in S$$

$$\Rightarrow \Theta'_\lambda \ni \mu(z_1) + \mu(p_2^*) \qquad \text{for all } p_2^* \in S$$

$$\Rightarrow \Theta'_\lambda \ni \mu(z_1^*) + \mu(p_2^*) \qquad \text{for all } p_1^*, p_2^* \in S$$

i.e., $W_2 \subset \Theta'_\lambda$. Repeating the argument gives

$$\Theta'_\lambda \cap W_n \neq \varnothing \Rightarrow \Theta'_\lambda \supset W_n$$

for any n. But by Jacobi's theorem $W_g = \mathcal{J}(S)$, and hence $\Theta'_\lambda \cap W_g = \varnothing$; thus $\Theta'_\lambda = 0$.   Q.E.D.

Note that by Riemann-Roch, if D is any effective divisor of degree $g-1$, then $K - D$ is also; it follows that

$$W_{g-1} = \mu(K) - W_{g-1}.$$

It is now possible to identify the constant κ appearing in Riemann's theorem: we have

$$W_{g-1} + \kappa = \Theta$$

$$= -\Theta$$

$$= -W_{g-1} - \kappa$$

$$= W_{g-1} - \kappa - \mu(K).$$

Since W_{g-1} is the theta-divisor of a principal polarization, by the result of p. 317 it cannot be fixed by any nonzero translation, and we find that

$$2\kappa = -\mu(K).$$

Similarly, we can determine exactly when $\mu(S) \subset \Theta_\lambda$: clearly, $\lambda - \mu(p) \in W_{g-1}$ if and only if $\lambda = \mu(D)$ for some $D \in S^{(g)}$ containing the point $p \in S$. Thus $\lambda - \mu(S) \subset W_{g-1}$ if and only if $\lambda = \mu(D)$ for D such that $h^0(D) > 1$. Now for any $\lambda = \mu(D)$, we have

$$\lambda - \mu(S) \subset W_{g-1} \Leftrightarrow \lambda - \mu(S) + \kappa \subset \Theta$$

$$\Leftrightarrow \mu(S) - \lambda - \kappa \subset \Theta$$

$$\Leftrightarrow \mu(S) \subset \Theta + \kappa + \lambda,$$

i.e., $\mu(S) \subset \Theta_\kappa + \lambda$ *if and only if* $\lambda = \mu(D)$ *for* $D \in S^{(g)}$ *such that* $h^0(D) > 0$. We can express this more intrinsically by noting that *the lemma above* (p. 336) *fails to give an explicit answer to the Jacobi inversion problem—finding* $D \in S^{(g)}$ *such that* $\mu(D) = \lambda$ *for a given* $\lambda \in \mathcal{J}(S)$—*exactly when that answer is not unique, i.e., when such a D varies in a nontrivial linear system.*

Riemann's Singularity Theorem

We turn our attention now to the subvariety $W_d = \mu(S^{(d)}) \subset \mathcal{J}(S)$ parametrizing linear equivalence classes of effective divisors of degree d on S. Our goal will be to prove a theorem, of which a special case was suggested by Riemann, relating the local geometry of the varieties W_d—specifically their tangent cones at various points $\mu(D)$—to the geometry of the corresponding linear systems $|D|$ on the canonical curve of S in $\mathbb{P}^{g-1}$.

To start, note that we have a natural identification

$$\mathbb{P}(T_\mu'(\mathcal{J}(S))) \cong \mathbb{P}(H^0(S, \Omega_S^1)^*)$$

between the projective space associated to the tangent space to the Jacobian $\mathcal{J}(S)$, and the ambient space of the canonical map

$$\iota_K : S \longrightarrow \mathbb{P}(H^0(S, \Omega_S^1)^*) \cong \mathbb{P}^{g-1}.$$

Hereafter, when we refer to $\mathbb{P}^{g-1}$ we will always mean specifically $\mathbb{P}(H^0(S, \Omega_S^1)^*)$. In particular, the projective tangent cones

$$P(T_\mu''(X)) \subset \mathbb{P}(T_\mu''(\mathcal{J}(S))) = \mathbb{P}^{g-1}$$

to any subvariety $X \subset \mathcal{J}(S)$ at any point $\mu \in X$ will be considered as subvarieties of the ambient space $\mathbb{P}^{g-1}$ of the canonical curve; we will denote this variety by $T_\mu(X)$.

To recall our notation, let $\omega_1, \ldots, \omega_g$ be a basis for the holomorphic 1-forms on S, so that the map

$$\mu : S \longrightarrow \mathcal{J}(S)$$

is given by

$$\mu(p) = \left(\int_{p_0}^p \omega_1, \ldots, \int_{p_0}^p \omega_g \right)$$

and the map $\mu : S^{(d)} \to \mathcal{J}(S)$ by

$$\mu(p_1 + \cdots + p_d) = \mu(p_1) + \cdots + \mu(p_d).$$

Whenever we have a local coordinate z on S we will define functions Ω_α by

$$\omega_\alpha(p) = \Omega_\alpha(p)\, dz$$

so that the vector

$$\Omega(p) = (\Omega_1(p), \ldots, \Omega_g(p))$$

represents the point p on the canonical curve in $\mathbb{P}^{g-1}$.

Our first object is to describe geometrically the tangent cone to the variety W_d at a point $\mu(D)$. Suppose first that the divisor D is regular, i.e., that $\dim|D| = 0$. By the geometric version of the Reimann-Roch, the linear span $\overline{D}$ of the points of D on the canonical curve is a $(d-1)$-plane, and we claim that

W_d *is smooth at* $\mu(D)$, *with tangent space* $T_{\mu(D)}(W_d) = \overline{D}$.

Proof. Suppose first that $D = p_1 + \cdots + p_d$ with the points p_i distinct, so that local coordinates z_i on S near p_i furnish local coordinates on $S^{(d)}$ near D. The map $\mu : S^{(d)} \to \mathcal{J}(S)$ is given by

$$\mu(p_1 + \cdots + p_d) = \left(\sum_i \int_{p_0}^{p_i} \omega_1, \ldots, \sum_i \int_{p_0}^{p_i} \omega_g \right).$$

Differentiating, we find that the Jacobian $\mathcal{J}(\mu)$ of the map μ is

$$\mathcal{J}(\mu) = \begin{bmatrix} \Omega_1(p_1), \ldots, \Omega_g(p_1) \\ \vdots \\ \Omega_1(p_d), \ldots, \Omega_g(p_d) \end{bmatrix}.$$

By hypothesis, the row vectors $\Omega(p_i) = (\Omega_1(p_i), \ldots, \Omega_g(p_i))$, representing the point p_i on the canonical curve, are all independent. Thus $\mathcal{J}(\mu)$ has maximal rank d at D, so $W_d = \mu(S^{(d)})$ is smooth at $\mu(D)$, with tangent plane spanned by the points p_i.

We will illustrate what happens at the diagonals of $S^{(d)}$ by assuming that $D = 2p_1 + p_2 + \cdots + p_{d-1}$ where the p_i are distinct; the general situation is only notationally more complicated. Let z be a coordinate of p varying in a neighborhood of p_1, and for $\Omega(p) = (\Omega_1(z), \ldots, \Omega_g(z))$ as above we define

$$\Omega'(p) = \left(\frac{d\Omega_1}{dz}, \ldots, \frac{d\Omega_g}{dz} \right).$$

The line $\overline{\Omega(p)\Omega'(p)}$ in $\mathbb{P}^{g-1}$ determined by $\Omega(p)$ and $\Omega'(p)$ is the tangent line to the canonical curve at p. For

$$w_1 = \frac{z_1 + z_2}{2}, \qquad w_2 = z_1 z_2$$

we set

$$F_\alpha(w_1, w_2) = \int_{p_0}^{z_1} \omega_\alpha + \int_{p_0}^{z_2} \omega_\alpha.$$

From

$$\frac{\partial F_\alpha}{\partial w_1} d\left(\frac{z_1 + z_2}{2} \right) + \frac{\partial F_\alpha}{\partial w_2} d(z_1 z_2) = \omega_\alpha(z_1) + \omega_\alpha(z_2)$$

we deduce that

$$\frac{\partial F_\alpha}{\partial w_1} = \frac{1}{2}(\Omega_\alpha(z_1) + \Omega_\alpha(z_2)); \qquad \frac{\partial F_\alpha}{\partial w_2} = \frac{\Omega(z_1) - \Omega(z_2)}{z_2 - z_1}.$$

Letting z_2 go to z_1 it follows that the Jacobian matrix evaluated at $D = 2p_1 + p_2 + \cdots + p_{d-1}$ is

$$
\begin{bmatrix}
\Omega(p_1) \\
-\Omega'(p_1) \\
\Omega(p_2) \\
\vdots \\
\Omega(p_{d-1})
\end{bmatrix}
$$

and the argument proceeds as before when the points were distinct. Q.E.D.

Suppose now that D moves in an r-dimensional linear system, and denote the divisors in $|D|$ by

$$
D_\lambda = p_1(\lambda) + \cdots + p_d(\lambda), \qquad \lambda \in \mathbb{P}^r.
$$

According to Riemann-Roch, the points $p_i(\lambda)$ of each D_λ will span a $(d-r-1)$-plane $\overline{D}_\lambda$ in $\mathbb{P}^{g-1}$; we claim that in this case

The projective tangent cone to W_d *at the point* $\mu(D)$ *is the union*

$$
T_{\mu(D)}(W_d) = \bigcup_{\lambda \in \mathbb{P}^r} \overline{D}_\lambda
$$

of the planes spanned by the divisors of the linear system $|D|$.

Proof. Recall that the tangent cone to W_d at $\mu(D)$ is the locus of all tangent lines at $\mu(D)$ to analytic arcs in W_d. Now, let

$$
D(t) = q_1(t) + \cdots + q_d(t)
$$

be any path in the symmetric product $S^{(d)}$ with

$$
D(0) = D_\lambda = p_1(\lambda) + \cdots + p_d(\lambda)
$$

for some $D_\lambda \in |D|$. The image arc

$$
w(t) = \mu(D(t))
$$

then lies in W_d with $w(0) = \mu(D)$; and conversely any arc in W_d may be given in this fashion. For simplicity of notation we assume that $p_i(\lambda)$ are distinct and let z_i be a local coordinate around $p_i(\lambda)$. Then if $q_i(t)$ has coordinate $z_i(t)$,

$$
w(t) = \mu(q_1(t)) + \cdots + \mu(q_d(t))
$$

$$
= \left(\ldots, \sum_{i=1}^{d} \int_{p_0}^{z_i(t)} \Omega_\alpha(z_i)\, dz_i, \ldots \right)
$$

where $\omega_\alpha = \Omega_\alpha(z_i)\,dz_i$ near $p_i(\lambda)$ as before. Differentiating,

$$\frac{dw}{dt} = \left(\ldots, \sum_i \Omega_\alpha(z_i(t))z_i'(t), \ldots\right),$$

and, setting $t = 0$, the tangent line to $w(t)$ at $\mu(D)$ is

$$\sum_{i=1}^d z_i'(0)\Omega(p_i(\lambda)).$$

Now the numbers $z_i'(0)$ and point $\lambda \in \mathbb{P}^r$ may be prescribed arbitrarily, which implies that as a set

$$T_{\mu(D)}(W_d) = \bigcup_\lambda \overline{p_1(\lambda), \ldots, p_d(\lambda)}$$

as desired.   Q.E.D.

Note in particular that if $r > 0$, then $T_{\mu(D)}(W_d)$ contains the r-secant variety of the canonical curve; since this does not lie in any linear subspace of $\mathbb{P}^{g-1}$, we conclude that

$\mu(D)$ *is a singular point of* W_d *if and only if* $\dim |D| > 0$.

We may interpret intrinsically the preceding computation as follows: With the identification $|D| = \mathbb{P}^r$, the linear system $|D| \subset S^{(d)}$ is a complex submanifold with normal bundle $N \to \mathbb{P}^r$. We denote by $\mathbb{P}(N)$ the associated projective bundle whose fibers are given by

$$\mathbb{P}(N)_\lambda = \mathbb{P}(N_\lambda).$$

Since $\mu: S^{(d)} \to \mathcal{J}(S)$ maps $\mathbb{P}^r$ to the point $\mu(D)$, the differential μ_* is zero on tangent vectors to $\mathbb{P}^r$ and hence $\mu_*(\xi) \in T'_{\mu(D)}(\mathcal{J}(S))$ is well-defined for any $\xi \in N_\lambda$. This induces a holomorphic mapping

$$\mu_*: \mathbb{P}(N) \longrightarrow \mathbb{P}^{g-1},$$

whose image is the tangent cone $T_{\mu(D)}(W_d)$. For each λ the fiber $\mathbb{P}(N)_\lambda$ is parametrized by arcs in $S^{(d)}$ passing through D_λ, and what the above computation shows is that μ_* maps $\mathbb{P}(N)_\lambda$ isomorphically to the subspace $\overline{D}_\lambda \subset \mathbb{P}^{g-1}$.

One aspect of the behavior of the planes $\overline{D}$ in a linear system which will be useful is the following:

Lemma. *If a point* $q \in \mathbb{P}^{g-1}$ *lies on two secant planes* $\overline{D}_\lambda, \overline{D}_{\lambda'}$, *it lies on* $\overline{D}_\mu$ *for every* D_μ *in the pencil spanned by* D_λ *and* $D_{\lambda'}$; *or, in other words, the fibers of the map* $\mu_*: \mathbb{P}(N) \to T_{\mu(D)}(W_d)$ *are linear spaces.*

Proof. Suppose that the dimension of the complete linear system $|D|$ is r. By Riemann-Roch, the points of any divisor $F \in |K - D|$ span a

$(g-r-2)$-plane $\bar{F}$. *The linear system of hyperplanes in* $\mathbb{P}^{g-1}$ *containing* F *thus cuts out on the canonical curve the complete linear system* $|D|$; *in particular, any pencil* $\{D_\mu\}\subset|D|$ *is cut out by a pencil of hyperplanes through* F. Thus, if q lies on two secant planes $\bar{D}_\lambda$ and $\bar{D}_{\lambda'}$ of the pencil $\{D_\mu\}$, it lies in the hyperplane spanned by any plane $\bar{D}_\mu$ and any divisor $F\in|K-D|$. But of course the residual intersection of the canonical curve with any hyperplane containing D_μ is a divisor of the system $|K-D|$, so this implies q lies on any hyperplane containing D_μ, i.e., q lies on $\bar{D}_\mu$.

Q.E.D.

Next, we set $\mathbb{T}=T_{\mu(D)}(W_d)$ and will prove the

Proposition. *For* $D\in S^{(d)}$ *with* $\dim|D|=r$, *the degree of the projective tangent cone* $\mathbb{T}\subset\mathbb{P}^{g-1}$ *is* $\begin{pmatrix}g-d+r\\r\end{pmatrix}$.

Proof. Let $q_1,\ldots,q_{g-d+r}$ be generic points of S, in particular such that

$(*)$ $\qquad\qquad \dim|D+q_1+\cdots+q_{g-d+r}| = \dim|D| = r$

and for any subset $q_1,\ldots,q_\alpha$ with $\alpha\leqslant r$,

$(**)$ $\qquad\qquad \dim|D-q_1\cdots-q_\alpha| = \dim|D|-\alpha = r-\alpha.$

Note that by $(*)$ the points $q_1,\ldots,q_{g-d+r}$ are all independent on the canonical curve; denote by $\bar{E}$ the linear space $\mathbb{P}^{g-d+r-1}\subset\mathbb{P}^{g-1}$ they span.

To prove the proposition we will show that E intersects $\mathbb{T}$ transversely in a variety of degree $\begin{pmatrix}g-d+r\\r\end{pmatrix}$; specifically, we will prove that

1. The intersection $\mathbb{T}\cap\bar{E}$ is the union

$$\bigcup_{\substack{I\subset\{1,\ldots,g-d+r\}\\ \#I=r}} \overline{q_{i_1},\ldots,q_{i_r}}$$

of the $\begin{pmatrix}g-d+r\\r\end{pmatrix}$ coordinate $(r-1)$-planes in $\mathbb{P}^{d-g+r-1}$; and
2. This intersection is transverse.

To prove the first statement, we note that for any multiindex $I=\{i_1,\ldots,i_r\}\subset\{1,\ldots,g-d+r\}$, we can find a divisor $D_\lambda\in|D|$ containing the points $q_{i_1},\ldots,q_{i_r}$; we then have

$$\overline{q_{i_1},\ldots,q_{i_r}} \subset \bar{D}_\lambda$$

and hence in general

$$\bigcup_I \overline{q_{i_1},\ldots,q_{i_r}} \subset \mathbb{T}\cap\bar{E}.$$

Conversely, suppose that D_λ is any divisor in $|D|$, and that D_λ contains exactly α of the points q_i, which we may take to be $q_1,\ldots,q_\alpha$ (by $(*)$, of course, $\alpha \leqslant r$). Then since by $(**)$

$$\dim|D + q_{\alpha+1} + \cdots + q_{g-d+r}| = \dim|D| = r$$

we have by the Riemann-Roch formula that

$$\dim(\overline{D_\lambda \cup E}) = \dim \overline{D_\lambda, q_{\alpha+1}, \ldots, q_{g-d+r}} = g - 1 - \alpha.$$

It follows from linear algebra that

$$\dim(\overline{D}_\lambda \cap \overline{E}) = \dim \overline{D}_\lambda + \dim \overline{E} - \dim \overline{D_\lambda \cup E}$$
$$= \alpha - 1$$

i.e., that $\overline{D}_\lambda$ meets $\overline{E}$ *only* in the span $\overline{q_1, \ldots, q_\alpha}$. Thus

$$\overline{E} \cap \mathbb{T} \subset \bigcup_I \overline{q_{i_1}, \ldots, q_{i_r}}$$

and the first part of the lemma is proved.

Note that by this argument, for $q_1, \ldots, q_r$ generic points on S and q any point in $\overline{q_1, \ldots, q_r}$ not in the span of a proper subset of $q_1, \ldots, q_r$, there will be a unique plane $\overline{D}_\lambda$ containing q. Thus,

the map μ_* is generically one-to-one, i.e., the planes $\overline{D}_\lambda$ sweep out the variety $\mathbb{T}$ only once.

In particular, this assures us that $\mathbb{T}$ does indeed have dimension $d-1$.

The first—and principal—step in the proof of part 2 is to show that

$(*)$ *For $q_1, \ldots, q_r \in S$ generic, the variety $\mathbb{T}$ is smooth in the complement*

$$\overline{q_1, \ldots, q_r} - \bigcup_{i=1}^r \overline{q_1, \ldots, q_{i-1}, q_{i+1}, \ldots, q_r}$$

of the coordinate hyperplanes in $\overline{q_1, \ldots, q_r}$.

We have already seen that μ_* is one-to-one over such a point q; in order to prove this, we have to show that the map $\mu_* : \mathbb{P}(N) \to \mathbb{T}$ has nonzero differential at q. For this we work in a neighborhood $U \subset \mathbb{P}^r$ with coordinates $\lambda = (\lambda_1, \ldots, \lambda_r)$ in which the $p_i(\lambda)$ are single-valued functions of λ; we choose a local coordinate z_i around $p_i(0)$ and consider $z_i(\lambda) = z_i(p_i(\lambda))$ as a function of λ. At any given point it is possible to choose the λ_a $(1 \leqslant a \leqslant r)$ such that $\partial z_a(\lambda)/\partial \lambda_b = \delta_b^a$.

We may assume that $p_1(\lambda), \ldots, p_{d-r}(\lambda)$ span $\overline{D}_\lambda$; then for $t = [t_1, \ldots, t_{d-r}]$ the corresponding homogeneous coordinates in the fibers of $\mathbb{P}(N)|_U$ the mapping μ_* has a lifting

$$\tilde{\mu}_* : U \times \mathbb{C}^{d-r} \longrightarrow \mathbb{C}^g$$

defined by

$$\tilde{\mu}_*(\lambda, t) = t_1 \Omega(p_1(\lambda)) + \cdots + t_{d-r} \Omega(p_{d-r}(\lambda)).$$

Noting that $\tilde{\mu}_*$ is linear on each fiber of $\mathbb{P}^n$, it is straightforward to check that the Jacobian matrix of μ_* has rank one less than that of $\tilde{\mu}_*$, and we shall compute the latter. Using the index range $1 \leqslant \sigma \leqslant d-r$, the Jacobian of $\tilde{\mu}_*$ is

$$
\begin{bmatrix}
\partial\tilde{\mu}_*/\partial t_1 \\
\vdots \\
\partial\tilde{\mu}_*/\partial t_{d-r} \\
\partial\tilde{\mu}_*/\partial\lambda_1 \\
\vdots \\
\partial\tilde{\mu}_*/\partial\lambda_r
\end{bmatrix}
=
\begin{bmatrix}
\Omega(p_1(\lambda)) \\
\vdots \\
\Omega(p_{d-r}(\lambda)) \\
\sum_\sigma t_\sigma(\partial z_\alpha/\partial\lambda_1)\Omega'(p_\sigma(\lambda)) \\
\vdots \\
\sum_\sigma t_\sigma(\partial z_\alpha/\partial\lambda_r)\Omega'(p_\sigma(\lambda))
\end{bmatrix} .
$$

At a point where $\partial z_a(\lambda)/\partial\lambda_b = \delta_b^a$ this is

$$
\begin{bmatrix}
\Omega(p_1(\lambda)) \\
\vdots \\
\Omega(p_{d-r}(\lambda)) \\
t_1\Omega'(p_1(\lambda)) + \sum_{\sigma \geqslant r+1} t_\sigma(\partial z_\sigma/\partial\lambda_1)\Omega'(p_\sigma(\lambda)) \\
\vdots \\
t_r\Omega'(p_r(\lambda)) + \sum_{\sigma \geqslant r+1} t_\sigma(z_\sigma/\partial\lambda_r)\Omega'(p_\sigma(\lambda))
\end{bmatrix} ;
$$

at a point $p \in \overline{p_1,\ldots,p_r}$ in the span of the first r points p_i—so that $t_{r+1} = \cdots = t_{d-r} = 0$—but not in the span of any proper subset of them—so that $t_\alpha \neq 0$ for $\alpha \leqslant r$—the rank of this matrix is just the rank of

$$
\begin{bmatrix}
\Omega(p_1) \\
\vdots \\
\Omega(p_{d-r}) \\
\Omega'(p_1) \\
\vdots \\
\Omega'(p_r)
\end{bmatrix}
$$

But now if $p_1,\ldots,p_r$ are generic, then

$$
\dim|D + p_1 + \cdots + p_r| = \dim|D| = r
$$

and so by Riemann-Roch the span

$$
\overline{D_\lambda + p_1 + \cdots + p_r} = \overline{2p_1 + \cdots + 2p_r + p_{r+1} + \cdots + p_d}
$$
$$
= \overline{\Omega(p_1),\ldots,\Omega(p_{d-r}),\Omega'(p_1),\ldots,\Omega'(p_r)}
$$

has dimension $d-1$. Thus the Jacobian has maximal rank at a generic point of $p_1, \ldots, p_r$, and the first assertion is proved.

The remaining two steps in the proof of part 2 are much easier. The second step is to show that

> *For some* $q_1, \ldots, q_{g-d+r}$, *the intersection* $\overline{E} \cap \mathbb{T}$ *is transverse at a generic point of* $\overline{q_1, \ldots, q_r}$.

This is immediate: choose $q_1, \ldots, q_r$ generically, take any $q \in \overline{q_1, \ldots, q_r}$ lying away from the hyperplanes $\overline{q_1, \ldots, q_{i-1}, q_{i+1}, \ldots, q_r}$, and then choose $q_{r+1}, \ldots, q_{g-d+r}$ independent modulo the subspace $T_q(\mathbb{T})$.

Finally, we claim that for generic $q_1, \ldots, q_{g-d+r}$ on S,

> (∗)   *the intersection* $\overline{E} \cap \mathbb{T}$ *is transverse at a generic point of each* $(\mathrm{r}-1)$-*plane* $\overline{q_{i_1}, \ldots, q_{i_r}}$.

To see this, consider the map

$$\pi: \; S^{(r)} \times S^{(g-d)} \longrightarrow S^{(g-d+r)}$$

sending $(q_1 + \cdots + q_r, q_{r+1} + \cdots + q_{g-d+r})$ to $(q_1 + \cdots + q_{g-d+r})$, and let $B \subset S^{(g-d+r)}$ be the locus of $q_1, \ldots, q_{g-d+r}$ for which (∗) fails to hold. By the second step, $\pi^{-1}(B) \neq S^{(r)} \times S^{(g-d)}$, and since $S^{(r)} \times S^{(g-d)}$ is irreducible, it follows that the dimension of B is strictly less than $g-d+r$; thus the proposition is proved.   Q.E.D.

In sum, we have proved the

Riemann-Kempf Singularity Theorem*.   *For* $|D|$ *a linear system of degree* d *and dimension* r, *the tangent cone*

$$T_{\mu(D)}(W_d) = \bigcup_{D_\lambda \in |D|} \overline{D}_\lambda$$

is the union of the planes $\overline{D}_\lambda = \mathbb{P}^{d-r-1}$ *spanned by the points of the divisors* $D_\lambda \in |D|$. *It has degree* $\binom{g-d+r}{r}$, *and is swept out once by the planes* $\overline{D}_\lambda$.

In case $d = g-1$, we have seen that W_d is the translate $\Theta_{-\kappa}$ of the theta-divisor Θ on $\mathcal{J}(S)$, and this gives us the result originally stated by Riemann:

$$\mathrm{mult}_{\mu(D)}(\Theta_{-\kappa}) = h^0(D);$$

in particular, the singular locus of the theta-divisor corresponds to those divisors of degree $g-1$ which move in a linear system. Using this, we see

---

*Cf. G. Kempf, On the geometry of a theorem of Riemann, *Annals of Math.*, Vol. 98 (1973), 178–185.

readily that

The singular locus of Θ has dimension at least $g-4$.

Proof. Assume, on the contrary, that the singular locus of $\Theta_{-\kappa}$ has dimension $\leqslant g-5$. A generic set of points $p_1,\ldots,p_{g-3}$ on the canonical curves spans a $\mathbb{P}^{g-4}$. Let $\varphi: S \to \mathbb{P}^2$ be the projection of S from this $\mathbb{P}^{g-4}$. For points $p \neq q$ on S,

$$\varphi(p) = \varphi(q)$$

if, and only if,

$$\overline{p,p_1,\ldots,p_{g-3}} = \overline{q,p_1,\ldots,p_{g-3}}$$

which is equivalent to

$$\dim \overline{p,q,p_1,\ldots,p_{g-3}} = q-3,$$

i.e.,

$$\dim |p + q + p_1 + \cdots + p_{g-3}| = 1.$$

Counting dimensions, we deduce that if $\dim(\Theta_{-\kappa})_s$ were strictly less than $g-4$, there would be ∞^{g-4} divisors $D \in S^{(g-1)}$ with $\dim \overline{D} \leqslant g-3$, and hence for generic choice of $p_1,\ldots,p_{g-3}$ the mapping φ would be one-to-one. But then the image curve would be a smooth plane curve of degree $(2g-2)-(g-3)=g+1$ and genus $g(g-1)/2$. Since $g < (g)(g-1)/2$ for $g \geqslant 4$, we have a contradiction. Q.E.D.

The reader may enjoy working out the Riemann singularity theorem in the special case of a linear system of degree 5 and dimension 2 on a Riemann surface S of genus 6. After checking that such a linear system $|D|$ always embeds S as a smooth plane quintic—so that $2D = K$—it is not hard to see that the tangent cone to W_5 at the point $\mu(D)$ is the chordal variety of the Veronese surface $\iota_{2H}(\mathbb{P}^2) \subset \mathbb{P}^5$, and that the singular locus of $\mathbb{T}$ is just the Veronese surface itself.

Special Linear Systems IV

We now have at our disposal the techniques necessary to answer in part the question of the existence of special linear systems on curves. For each pair of integers d and r with $1 \leqslant d \leqslant g-1$ we denote by W_d^r the image of the linear systems of degree d and dimension $\geqslant r$ under the map

$$\mu: S^{(d)} \longrightarrow \mathcal{J}(S).$$

By the proper mapping theorem, W_d^r is an analytic subvariety, and we will show that it has at least the dimension predicted by the naïve dimension count of Section 3 in this chapter.

We begin by computing the homology class of the subvariety $W_d = \mu(S^{(d)})$; the answer is *Poincaré's formula*

$$W_d \sim \frac{1}{(g-d)!} \Theta^{g-d}.$$

Proof. In terms of the real coordinates $x_1, \ldots, x_{2g}$ on $\mathcal{J}(S)$ corresponding to a choice of canonical basis $\delta_1, \ldots, \delta_{2g}$ for $H_1(S, \mathbb{Z})$, we have proved that the Poincaré dual of Θ is

$$\omega = \sum_{\alpha=1}^{g} dx_\alpha \wedge dx_{\alpha+g}.$$

Letting $A = (\alpha_1, \ldots, \alpha_k)$ run over index sets with $1 \leqslant \alpha_1 < \cdots < \alpha_k \leqslant g$ and setting $dx_A = dx_{\alpha_1} \wedge \cdots \wedge dx_{\alpha_k}$, $A + g = (\alpha_1 + g, \ldots, \alpha_k + g)$,

$$\omega^{g-d} = (g-d)!(-1)^{g-d} \sum_{\#A = g-d} dx_A \wedge dx_{A+g}.$$

If $J = (j_1, \ldots, j_k)$ runs over index subsets from $(1, \ldots, 2g)$, then since the dx_J give a basis for $H^k(\mathcal{J}(S))$ it will suffice to establish that

$$\int_{W_d} dx_J = \frac{1}{(g-d)!} \int_{\mathcal{J}(S)} \omega^{g-d} \wedge dx_J.$$

Using the formula for ω^{g-d}, the right-hand side is

$$\frac{1}{(g-d)!} \int_{\mathcal{J}(S)} \omega^{g-d} \wedge dx_J = \begin{cases} 1 & \text{if } J = (A, A+g) \text{ for} \\ & \text{some } A = (\alpha_1, \ldots, \alpha_d), \\ 0 & \text{otherwise.} \end{cases}$$

On the other hand, since the map $\mu^{(d)} : S^{(d)} \to W_d$ has degree one and $\pi : S^d \to S^{(d)}$ has degree $d!$,

$$\int_{W_d} dx_J = \frac{1}{d!} \int_{S^d} (\mu^d)^* dx_J$$

where $\mu^d = \mu^{(d)} \circ \pi : S^d \to W_d$ is the composition. Now

$$(\mu^d)^* dx_j = \sum_{k=1}^{d} \pi_k^* \mu^* dx_j, \qquad 1 \leqslant j \leqslant 2g,$$

where $\pi_k : S^d \to S$ is projection on the kth factor and $\mu = \mu^1$; since the $\mu^* dx_j \in H_{DR}^1(S)$ are Poincaré dual to cycles δ_j,

(*) $$\int_S \mu^* dx_\alpha \wedge \mu^* dx_{\alpha+g} = 1$$

and all other integrals of $\mu^* dx_i \wedge \mu^* dx_j$ for $i < j$ are zero. Thus, by iteration,

$$\int_{S^d} (\mu^d)^* \, dx_J = \int_{S^d} \bigwedge_{j \in J} \left(\sum_{k=1}^{d} \pi_k^* \mu^* \, dx_j \right)$$

is zero unless $J = (B, B+g)$ for some $B = (\beta_1, \ldots, \beta_d)$, and in this case by (∗)

$$\int_{S^d} (\mu^d)^* \, dx_{B, B+g} = d!. \qquad\qquad \text{Q.E.D.}$$

We now introduce a construction developed by Kempf and Kleiman-Laksov.* Recall from pp. 328–332 that the principal polarization on the Jacobian leads to an identification

$$\text{Pic}^0(\mathcal{J}(S)) \cong \mathcal{J}(S),$$

and also to the Poincaré bundle

$$P \longrightarrow \mathcal{J}(S) \times \mathcal{J}(S)$$

with the properties:

1. under the above identification,

$$P|_{\mathcal{J}(S) \times \lambda} = P(\lambda)$$

is the line bundle corresponding to $\lambda \in \text{Pic}^0(\mathcal{J}(S))$; and
2. if $p_0 \in S$ is a base point, then for any p

$$P(\lambda)_p \cong P(\lambda + \mu(p))_{p_0}.$$

Now we fix a divisor D_0 of degree $n > 2g-2$ on S and set

$$L(\lambda) = P(\lambda) + D_0$$

As λ varies over $\mathcal{J}(S)$ the $L(\lambda)$ vary over all line bundles of degree n on S. Choose $m > n$ generic points $p_1, \ldots, p_m$ on S. By property 2 there is a natural identification

$$L(\lambda)_{p_i} \cong P(\lambda + \mu(p_i))_{p_0} \otimes L_{p_i}.$$

Since, when restricted to $p_0 \times \mathcal{J}(S)$, the Poincaré bundle is topologically trivial, there is an isomorphism

$$L(\lambda)_{p_i} \longrightarrow L_{p_i}$$

which depends C^∞—but *not* holomorphically—on $\lambda \in \mathcal{J}(S)$.

By Riemann-Roch $h^0(\mathcal{O}(L(\lambda))) = n - g + 1$. Since no section of $L(\lambda)$ can vanish at m points, then, there is an injection

$$H^0(\mathcal{O}(L(\lambda))) \longrightarrow \bigoplus_{i=1}^{m} L(\lambda)_{p_i}$$

*S. Kleiman and D. Laksov, On the existence of special divisors, *Amer. J. Math.*, Vol. 93 (1972), 431–436.

whose image S_λ is an $(n-g+1)$-dimensional subspace S_λ varying holomorphically with λ. More precisely, there is a rank m holomorphic vector bundle $E \to \mathcal{J}(S)$ with fibers

$$E_\lambda = \bigoplus_{i=1}^{m} L(\lambda)_{p_i};$$

if $G(n-g+1,E)$ is the associated Grassmannian bundle with fibers

$$G(n-g+1,E)_\lambda = G(n-g+1,E_\lambda),$$

then the subspaces $\{S_\lambda \subset E_\lambda\}$ give a holomorphic section of

$$G(n-g+1,E).$$

The point of the construction is this: for each d we consider the holomorphic subbundle $V_{m-n+d} \subset E$ with fibers

$$V_{m-n+d,\lambda} = \bigoplus_{i=1}^{m-n+d} L(\lambda)_{p_i}.$$

and set

$$E_d(\lambda) = L(\lambda) - p_{m-n+d+1} - \cdots - p_m$$
$$= P(\lambda) + D_0 - p_{m-n+d+1} - \cdots - p_m.$$

We have, then, that

$$h^0(E_d(\lambda)) = \dim S_\lambda \cap V_{m-n+d}.$$

This may be rephrased as follows: combining the C^∞ identifications $L(\lambda)_{p_i} \cong L_{p_i}$ with isomorphisms $L_{p_i} \cong \mathbb{C}$ gives a C^∞ trivialization

$$\varphi: E \longrightarrow \mathcal{J}(S) \times \mathbb{C}^m$$

taking the direct sum decomposition $E = \bigoplus_{i=1}^{m} L(\lambda)_{p_i}$ into the coordinate axes of $\mathbb{C}^m$. We have thus a C^∞ map

$$\alpha: \mathcal{J}(S) \to G(n-g+1,m)$$

given by $\alpha(\lambda) = \varphi(S_\lambda)$. If $e_1,\ldots,e_m$ is the standard basis of $\mathbb{C}^m$ and $V_{m-n+d} = \{e_1,\ldots,e_{m-n+d}\}$, then

The translate by $\mu(-D_0 + p_{m-n+d+1} + \cdots + p_m)$ of the variety W_d^r is set-theoretically the inverse image under α of the Schubert cycle

$$\sigma_{g+r-d,\ldots,g+r-d}(V_{m-n+d})$$
$$= \{\Lambda \in G(n-g+1,m): \dim(\Lambda \cap V_{m-n+d}) \geq r+1\}.$$

We note that, even though the mapping α is not holomorphic, the inverse image under α of any Schubert cycle corresponding to a flag whose subspaces are coordinate $\mathbb{C}^k$'s in $\mathbb{C}^m$ is a complex analytic subvariety of $\mathcal{J}(S)$. Alternatively, the Schubert conditions for these cycles makes sense in the fibers of the Grassmannian bundle.

The result we are aiming for is the lower bound on $\dim W_r^d$ given on p. 358 below. The crucial step in the proof is the

Lemma. $\alpha(\mathcal{J}(S))$ *meets the special Schubert cycles* $\sigma_{g-d}(V_{m-n+d})$ *transversely away from* $\sigma_{g-d,\,g-d}(V_{m-n+d})$.

Recall that set-theoretically $\alpha^{-1}(\sigma_{g-d}(V_{m-n+d}))$ is a translate of W_d; since W_d is irreducible, the lemma essentially amounts to showing that $\alpha(\mathcal{J}(S))$ is not everywhere tangent to $\sigma_{g-d}(V_{d+1})$ along the intersection.

Assuming for a moment the lemma, the idea behind the remainder of the proof is this: First, by the lemma the fundamental class of W_d is $\alpha^*(\sigma_{g-d})$. Then, by the Poincaré formula

$$\alpha^*(\sigma_{g-d}) \sim \frac{1}{(g-d)!}\,\Theta^{g-d}.$$

Finally, as proved in Section 6 of Chapter I, every Schubert cycle—in particular $\sigma_{g-d+r,\ldots,g-d+r}$—can be expressed as a polynomial in the basic Schubert cycles σ_k; carrying this out explicitly will give

$$\alpha^*(\sigma_{g-d+r,\ldots,g-d+r}) = c\Theta^{(r+1)(g+r-d)}, \qquad c \neq 0,$$

and this implies the bound $\dim W_d^r \geqslant g - (r+1)(g+r-d)$.

Proof of the Lemma. Take $\lambda_0 \in \alpha^{-1}\sigma_{g-d}(V_{m-n+d})$. Choose points $q_1, \ldots, q_g$ independent on the canonical curve of S, and set

$$E_0 = q_1 + \cdots + q_g - P(\lambda_0).$$

Since $\mu: S^{(g)} \to \mathcal{J}(S)$ is one-to-one around $q_1 + \cdots + q_g$, then, there will be for all λ near λ_0 uniquely determined points $q_1(\lambda), \ldots, q_g(\lambda)$ such that

$$P(\lambda) = [q_1(\lambda) + \cdots + q_g(\lambda) - E_0]; \quad q_i(\lambda_0) = q_i.$$

Set

$$\begin{aligned}
\mathcal{L}(\lambda) &= \mathcal{L}\left(\sum_{i=1}^{g} q_i(\lambda) - E_0 + D_0\right) \\
&= \left\{ f \in \mathcal{M}(S): (f) + \sum q_\alpha(\lambda) - \sum r_k + D_0 \geqslant 0 \right\} \\
&\cong H^0(\mathcal{O}(L(\lambda))),
\end{aligned}$$

and consider the map

$$\mathcal{L}\left(\sum q_i(\lambda) - E_0 + D_0\right) \overset{R}{\to} \overset{m}{\underset{i=1}{\oplus}} \mathbb{C}_{p_i}$$

given by

$$R(f) = (f(p_i), \ldots, f(p_m)).$$

This defines, for λ in a neighborhood U of λ_0, a map

$$\tilde{\alpha}: H^0(\mathcal{O}(L(\lambda))) \longrightarrow \mathbb{C}^m,$$

which is just the map α in a suitable local trivialization of E.

Now let

$$\beta: U \to G(m-n+g-1,m)$$

be the composition of $\tilde{\alpha}$ with the natural isomorphism

$$*: G(n-g+1,\mathbb{C}^m) \to G(m-n+g-1,\mathbb{C}^{m*}),$$

so that $\beta(\lambda)$ is just the $m-n+g-1$-dimensional vector space of relations on the values $R(f)$ for $f \in \mathcal{L}(\lambda)$ at the points $p_1,\ldots,p_m$. We want to show that $\beta(U)$ meets the dual Schubert cycle

$$*(\sigma_{g-d}) = \{\Lambda^*: \dim(\Lambda^* \cap \operatorname{Ann} V_{m-n+d}) \geq g-d\}$$

transversely at $\beta(\lambda_0)$.

Now, if λ_0 corresponds to a divisor $D \in W_d$ not in W_d^1, that is, if

$$h^0(P(\lambda_0)+D_0-p_{m-n+d+1}-\cdots-p_m) = 1,$$

then for some choice of i between 1 and $m-n+d$, and $j_1,\ldots,j_{g-d}$ between $m-n+d+1$ and m, we will have

$$h^0(P(\lambda_0)+D_0-p_{m-n+d+1}-\cdots-p_m-p_i+p_{j_1}+\cdots+p_{j_{g-d}}) = 0.$$

For notational convenience we may take $i=1$, $j_1,\ldots,j_{g-d}=m-n+d+1,\ldots,m-n+g$. This means then that the subspace $\alpha(\lambda_0)$ in $\mathbb{C}^m$ is complementary to the subspace

$$\mathbb{C}_{p_2} \oplus \cdots \oplus \mathbb{C}_{p_{m-n+g}}.$$

As we saw in Section 5 of Chapter 2, then, any Λ in a neighborhood of $\beta(\lambda_0)$ is uniquely represented by a matrix of the form

$$\begin{bmatrix} a_{1,1} & & 1 & 0 & \cdots & 0 & 0 & a_{1,m-n+g+1} & & \cdots & a_{1,m} \\ & & 0 & 1 & \cdots & 0 & 0 & \cdot & & & \\ \vdots & & \vdots & \vdots & & \vdots & \vdots & \vdots & & & \vdots \\ & & 0 & 0 & \cdots & 1 & 0 & \cdot & & & \\ a_{m-n+g-1,1} & & 0 & 0 & \cdots & 0 & 1 & a_{m-n+g-1,m-n+g+1} & & \cdots & a_{m-n+g-1,m} \end{bmatrix}$$

The unspecified entries a_{ij} in this matrix are Plücker coordinates on $G(m-n+g-1,m)$ near $\beta(\lambda_0)$; and the Schubert cycle $*\sigma_{g-d}(\operatorname{Ann} V_{m-n+d})$ is given, in these coordinates, by

$$a_{m-n+d,1} = \cdots = a_{m-n+g-1,1} = 0.$$

To give the map β around λ_0 in terms of these coordinates we first find the linear relations on the subspace $R(\mathcal{L}(\lambda))$ as follows: by Riemann-Roch,

$$h^0\left(S,\Omega^1\left(E_0-\sum q_i(\lambda)+\sum p_i-D_0\right)\right) = m-n+g-1.$$

Let $\eta_1,\ldots,\eta_{m-n+g-1}$ be a basis of this space of meromorphic differentials. For any function $f \in \mathcal{L}(\lambda)$ the meromorphic forms $f \cdot \eta_\alpha$ will have poles only at the points p_i, and adding up the residues we have

$$\sum_i \text{Res}_{p_i}(f \cdot \eta_\alpha) = \sum_i f(p_i) \cdot \text{Res}_{p_i}(\eta_\alpha) = 0$$

for each $\alpha = 1, \ldots, m - n + g - 1$. These are our desired relations, and the matrix $(\text{Res}_{p_i}(\eta_\alpha))$ represents the space $\beta(\lambda) \subset C^{m^*}$. (Note that we do get all the relations on $\mathcal{L}(\lambda)$ this way: since $h^0(S, \Omega^1(E_0 - \sum q_i - D_0)) = 0$, the matrix $(\text{Res}_{p_i}(\eta_\alpha))$ has maximal rank $m - n + g - 1$.)

We can realize the coordinates of the map β geometrically: again by Riemann-Roch,

$$h^0\left(S, \Omega^1\left(E_0 + \sum p_i - D_0\right)\right) = m - n + 2g - 1;$$

consider the corresponding embedding of S in $\mathbb{P}^{m-n+2g-2}$. By hypothesis the points $p_2, \ldots, p_{m-n+g}$ and $q_1(\lambda), \ldots, q_g(\lambda)$ are linearly independent; let V be the $(m - n + g - 2)$-plane spanned by the points $p_2, \ldots, p_{m-n+g}$ and $W(\lambda)$ the $(g - 1)$-plane spanned by the points $q_i(\lambda)$. (See Figure 15.) Then, since

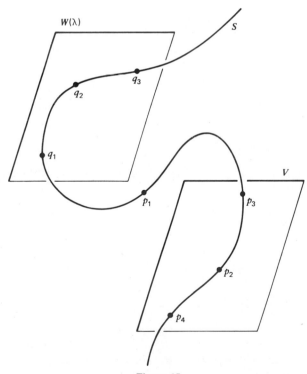

Figure 15

the forms

$$\eta_\alpha \in H^0\left(S, \Omega^1\left(E_0 - \sum q_i(\lambda) + \sum p_i - D_0\right)\right)$$

correspond to the hyperplanes in $\mathbb{P}^{m-n+2g-2}$ containing the points $q_i(\lambda)$, we see that

> *The Plucker coordinates* $a_{1,k}, \ldots, a_{m-n+g-1,k}$ *of* $\beta(\lambda)$ *are the homogeneous coordinates of the image* $\pi_{W(\lambda)}(p_k)$ *of the point* p_k *under projection from* $W(\lambda)$ *to* V, *in a coordinate system on* V *in which the points* $p_2, \ldots, p_{m-n+g}$ *represent the coordinate axes.*

Thus, to prove the transversality of β at λ_0 we have to show that the map

$$\pi : U \to V \cong \mathbb{P}^{m-n+g-1}$$

given by

$$\pi(\lambda) = \pi_{W(\lambda)}(p_1)$$

is transverse to the subspace of V spanned by the points $p_2, \ldots, p_{m-n+d}$. To see this, let the point $q_i(\lambda)$ vary. Since $\pi(\lambda)$ is the intersection of V with the subspace $\overline{q_1(\lambda), \ldots, q_g(\lambda), p_1}$, the tangent line to the arc formed by $\pi(\lambda)$ as $q_i(\lambda)$ varies is just the intersection of V with the space spanned by $q_1(\lambda), \ldots, q_{i-1}(\lambda), q_{i+1}(\lambda), \ldots, q_g(\lambda), p_1$ and the tangent line to S at $q_i(\lambda)$. Thus π can fail to be transverse to $p_2, \ldots, p_{m-n+d}$ only if the tangent lines $\{T_{q_i(\lambda)}(S)\}_{i=1,\ldots,g}$, together with the points $p_1, \ldots, p_{m-n+d}$, fail to span $\mathbb{P}^{m-n+2g-2}$. But this is equivalent to the statement

$$h^0\left(S, \Omega^1\left(E_0 + \sum p_i - D_0 - 2 \cdot \sum q_i(\lambda_0) - p_1 - \cdots - p_{m-n+d}\right)\right)$$
$$= h^0\left(S, \Omega^1\left(-P(\lambda_0) - D_0 + p_{m-n+d} + \cdots + p_m - q_i(\lambda_0)\right)\right)$$
$$= h^0\left(S, \Omega^1\left(-E_d(\lambda_0) - \sum q_i(\lambda_0)\right)\right) \neq 0;$$

and since the points $q_i(\lambda)$ are independent on the canonical curve of S, this is not the case.

It follows from the lemma that

> *The fundamental class of the variety* W_d *on* $\mathcal{J}(S)$ *is the pullback via* α *of the cohomology class of the Schubert cycle* σ_{g-d} *on* $G(n-g+1,m)$.

By the Poincaré formula

$$\alpha^* \sigma_{g-d} \sim \frac{1}{(g-d)!} \Theta^{g-d}.$$

Now, by Giambelli's formula the class of the cycle $\sigma_{g+r-d,\ldots,g+r-d}$ is given by the determinant

$$\sigma_{g+r-d,\ldots,g+r-d} = \begin{vmatrix} \sigma_{g+r-d} & \sigma_{g+r-d+1} & \cdots & \sigma_{g+2r-d} \\ \sigma_{g+r-d-1} & \sigma_{g+r-d} & & \\ \vdots & & & \vdots \\ \sigma_{g-d} & & & \sigma_{g+r-d} \end{vmatrix}$$

and so we can write

$$\alpha^* \sigma_{g+r-d,\ldots,g+r-d} \sim \Theta^{(r+1)(g+r-d)}$$

$$\cdot \begin{vmatrix} \dfrac{1}{(g+r-d)!} & \dfrac{1}{(g+r-d+1)!} & \cdots & \dfrac{1}{(g+2r-d)!} \\ \dfrac{1}{(g+r-d-1)!} & & & \\ \vdots & & & \vdots \\ \dfrac{1}{(g+d)!} & & \cdots & \dfrac{1}{(g+r-d)!} \end{vmatrix}$$

To evaluate in general the determinant $D(x,y)$ of the $(y+1)$-by-$(y+1)$ matrix

$$\left(a_{ij} = \frac{1}{(x-i+j)!} \right),$$

for each $k=2,\ldots,y+1$ in turn multiply the kth column by $(x+k-1)$ and subtract that quantity from the $(k-1)$st column. The new matrix A' will then be

$$a'_{ij} = \frac{1}{(x-i+j)!} - \frac{(x+j)}{(x-i+j+1)!}$$
$$= \frac{x-i+j+1}{(x-i+j+1)!} - \frac{x+j}{(x-i+j+1)!}$$
$$= \frac{1-i}{(x-i+k+1)!}, \qquad j \neq y+1,$$

$$a'_{i,y+1} = a_{i,y+1} = \frac{1}{(x-i+y+1)!}.$$

In particular, all the entries of the top row will be zero, except $a'_{1,y+1} = 1/(x+y)!$; and its cofactor will be $y! \cdot D(x,y-1)$; thus

$$D(x,y) = \frac{y!}{(x+y)!} D(x,y-1),$$

and, since $D(x,1) = 1/x$, this gives

$$D(x,y) = \frac{y!(y-1)!\cdots 0!}{(x+y)!\cdots x!}.$$

Applying this to the cycles $\alpha^*\sigma_{g-d+r,\ldots,g-d+r}$, we have

$$\alpha^*\sigma_{g-d+r,\ldots,g-d+r}\frac{r!(r-1)!\cdots 0!}{(g+2r-d)!\cdots(g+r-d)!}\cdot\Theta^{(r+1)(g+r-d)}.$$

Suppose now that the variety had dimension less than $g-(r+1)(g-d+r)$. Then we could find a cycle V on $\mathcal{J}(S)$ of dimension $(r+1)(g-d+r)$ missing W_d^r. We would then have

$$\alpha^*\sigma_{g-d+r,\ldots,g-d+r}(V) = {}^\#\left(\alpha(V)\cdot\sigma_{g-d+r,\ldots,g-d+r}\right)$$
$$= 0.$$

But on the other hand

$$\alpha^*\sigma_{g-d+r,\ldots,g-d+r}(V) = \frac{r!(r-1)!\cdots 0!}{(g+2r-d)!\cdots(g+r-d)!}\cdot{}^\#\left(V\cdot\Theta^{(r+1)(g+r-d)}\right)$$
$$> 0,$$

since Θ is positive. Thus we have, finally, the

Theorem. *The variety* $W_d^r \subset \mathcal{J}(S)$ *of linear systems of degree* d *and dimension* r *on* S *has dimension at least* $g-(r+1)(g+r-d)$. *In particular, if* $g \geqslant (r+1)(g+r-d)$, *then every Riemann surface of genus* g *has such a linear system.*

Note that it will not always be the case that $\alpha(\mathcal{J}(S))$ will meet the Schubert cycles $\sigma_{g+d+r,\ldots,g-d+r}$ transversely—we have seen many cases where the variety $W_d^r = \alpha^{-1}\sigma_{g-d+r,\ldots,g-d+r}$ has dimension greater than that expected. Thus we cannot say with certainty what the class of W_d^r will be. It is worth stating, however, the obvious fact that

In case $\alpha(\mathcal{J}(S))$ *is transverse to* $\sigma_{g-d+r,\ldots,g-d+r}$, *the class of* W_d^r *is*

$$W_d^r \sim \frac{r!(r-1)!\cdots 0!}{(g+2r-d)!\cdots(g+r-d)!}\Theta^{(r+1)(g+r-d)}.$$

This gives us an "expected" answer to the enumerative questions raised in earlier discussions of special linear systems. For example, we have seen that a generic Riemann surface of genus $g=2k$ will have finitely many pencils of degree $k+1$, and asked how many; in case $\alpha(\mathcal{J}(S))$ is transverse to the Schubert cycle $\sigma_{k,k}$, this number will be

$$W_{k+1}^1 = \frac{1}{(k+1)!k!} \cdot \Theta^g$$

$$= \frac{(2k)!}{(k+1)!k!}$$

since $\Theta^g = g!$. Note that in cases $g = 2, 4, 6,$ and 8 this gives 1, 2, 5, and 14, which agrees with our previous computations.

Torelli's Theorem

Recall that a *polarized Abelian variety* is a pair $(M,[\omega])$, where M is an Abelian variety and $[\omega] \in H^2(M, \mathbb{Z})$ is a polarizing class on M. A mapping between polarized Abelian varieties $(M,[\omega])$ and $(M',[\omega'])$ is given by a holomorphic mapping $f: M \to M'$ with $f^*([\omega']) = [\omega]$. We have seen that a compact Riemann surface S of genus $g \geq 1$ gives a principally polarized Abelian variety $(\mathcal{J}(S),[\omega_S])$ where, in intrinsic terms, $\mathcal{J}(S)$ is the quotient of $(H^0(S,\Omega^1))^*$ by the lattice $\Lambda(S) \cong H_1(S,\mathbb{Z})$ of functionals on $H^0(S,\Omega^1)$ obtained by integration over the 1-cycles of S, and the class

$$[\omega_S]: H_2(\mathcal{J}(S),\mathbb{Z}) \to \mathbb{Z}$$

is given, in terms of the natural identification

$$H_2(\mathcal{J}(S),\mathbb{Z}) = \Lambda^2(H_1(S,\mathbb{Z})),$$

by

$$[\omega_S](\alpha \wedge \beta) = {}^\#(\alpha \cdot \beta).$$

We will now prove that in fact the curve S can be reconstructed from the data $[\mathcal{J}(S),[\omega]]$: this is

Torelli's Theorem. *If* S *and* S' *are compact Riemann surfaces such that*

$$(\mathcal{J}(S),[\omega_S]) \cong (\mathcal{J}(S'),[\omega_{S'}])$$

as polarized Abelian varieties, then $S \cong S'$.

*Proof.** We remark first that the essential transcendental step in the proof of Torelli's theorem—as stated above—consists of Riemann's theorem, which relates the divisor Θ as defined up to translation by $[\omega_S]$ to the divisor W_{g-1}; what follows now is a reconstruction of S from W_{g-1}.

We will prove Torelli's theorem first in the case S and S' are nonhyperelliptic. Recall that if $M = \mathbb{C}^g/\Lambda$ is any complex torus, then the tangent

---

*This proof is due to A. Andreotti, On Torelli's theorem, *Am. J. Math.*, Vol. 80 (1958), pp. 801–821.

spaces $\{T'_\lambda(M)\}_{\lambda \in M}$ are all naturally identified with $\mathbb{C}^g$. Thus if $X \subset M$ is any analytic subvariety of dimension k, $X^* = X - X_{\text{sing}}$ the smooth locus of X, we can define the *Gauss map*

$$\mathcal{G}_X: \ X^* \rightarrow G(k,g)$$

on X^* by

$$\mathcal{G}_X(\lambda) = T'_\lambda(X) \subset T'_\lambda(M) = \mathbb{C}^g.$$

We see immediately that $\mathcal{G}_X$ is intrinsically defined and that it does not vary if X is translated in M.

For example, consider the standard mapping $\mu: S \rightarrow \mathcal{J}(S)$ given by

$$\mu(z) = \left(\int_{z_0}^{z} \omega_1, \ldots, \int_{z_0}^{z} \omega_g \right).$$

The Gauss map

$$\mathcal{G}_\mu: \ S \rightarrow G(1,g) = \mathbb{P}^{g-1}$$

is then given by

$$\mathcal{G}_\mu(z) = \left[\frac{\partial}{\partial z} \mu_1(z), \ldots, \frac{\partial}{\partial z} \mu_g(z) \right]$$
$$= \left[\omega_1(z)/dz, \ldots, \omega_g(z)/dz \right].$$

i.e., *The Gauss map of $\mu(S)$ is simply the canonical mapping $\iota_K: S \rightarrow \mathbb{P}^{g-1}$.*

Now consider the Gauss map

$$\mathcal{G}: \ \Theta^*_{-\kappa} = W^*_{g-1} \rightarrow G(g-1,g) = (\mathbb{P}^{g-1})^*$$

associated to the theta-divisor $\Theta_{-\kappa} \subset \mathcal{J}(S)$. We have seen that a point $\mu(D) \in \Theta_{-\kappa}$ is smooth if and only if the divisor $D = \sum p_i$ is regular, and that, if this is the case, the tangent plane to $\Theta_{-\kappa}$ at $\mu(D)$ is the hyperplane spanned by the points p_i on the canonical curve C of S. Since every hyperplane section of C contains only a finite number of points, it follows that the map $\mathcal{G}: \Theta^*_{-\kappa} \rightarrow \mathbb{P}^{g-1*}$ is everywhere finite; since the generic hyperplane section consists of $2g-2$ points in general position, we see that generically $\mathcal{G}$ has

$$\binom{2g-2}{g-1} = \frac{g \cdot (g+1) \cdots (2g-2)}{(g-1)!}$$

sheets.

Now let $B \subset (\mathbb{P}^{g-1})^*$ denote the branch locus of $\mathcal{G}$, that is, the image in $(\mathbb{P}^{g-1})^*$ of the set of points in $\Theta^*_{-\kappa}$ where the map $\mathcal{G}$ is singular. At a point $\mu(D) \in \Theta^*_{-\kappa}$, $D = \sum p_i \in S^{(g-1)}$, we may take as coordinates on $\Theta_{-\kappa}$ the local coordinates $z_1, \ldots, z_{g-1}$ around the points $p_1, \ldots, p_{g-1}$ on S. It is clear, then, that if the tangent line to any of the points p_i on C lies in the plane spanned by $p_1, \ldots, p_{g-1}$,

$$\frac{\partial}{\partial z_i} \mathcal{G}(\mu(D)) = 0,$$

i.e. $\mu(D)$ is a singular point of $\mathcal{G}$. Thus if we let $V \subset (\mathbb{P}^{g-1})^*$ denote the proper subvariety of hyperplanes in $\mathbb{P}^{g-1}$ whose intersections with C are not in general position, we see that *any tangent hyperplane* H *to* C *lying outside* V *is in the branch locus* B *of* $\mathcal{G}$.

Conversely, if H is not a tangent hyperplane to C, then H meets C in $2g-2$ distinct points $z_1(H), \ldots, z_{2g-2}(H)$ that vary analytically with H. For H' near H, the $\binom{2g-2}{g-1}$ branches of $\mathcal{G}$ are given by

$$\left\{ D_I(H') = z_{i_1}(H') + \cdots + z_{i_{g-1}}(H') \right\}_{\#I = g-1},$$

and since no two of these branches come together at H, H cannot be a branch point. Denoting by $C^* \subset (\mathbb{P}^{g-1})^*$ the set of tangent hyperplanes to C, we have shown that

$$B \subset C^* \qquad \text{everywhere,}$$
$$B = C^* \qquad \text{in } (\mathbb{P}^{g-1})^* - V.$$

But now we see that C^* is irreducible: it is the image of the incidence correspondence $I = \{p, H\} : H \supset T_p(C)\} \subset C \times \mathbb{P}^{g-1*}$, which is itself fibered over C with irreducible fibers, and hence irreducible.

It follows, then, that in $(\mathbb{P}^{g-1})^*$,

$$\overline{B} = C^*,$$

i.e., *the set of tangent hyperplanes to the canonical curve of* S *is the closure in* $(\mathbb{P}^{g-1})^*$ *of the branch locus of the Gauss map* $\mathcal{G}$ *on the theta-divisor* $\Theta \subset \mathcal{J}(S)$.

Now we are just about finished with the proof: since the data $(\mathcal{J}(S), [\omega])$ determine Θ and $\mathcal{G}$, and hence C^* up to an automorphism of $(\mathbb{P}^{g-1})^*$, all that remains is to show that if C and $C' \subset \mathbb{P}^{g-1}$ are two canonical curves with $C^* = C'^*$, then $C \cong C'$. This is not hard: just note that for every point $p \in C$, the $(g-3)$-plane

$$T_p(C)^* = \left\{ H \in (\mathbb{P}^{g-1})^* : H \supset T_p(C) \right\}$$

is contained in $C^* = C'^*$. But by Bertini's theorem, the generic element of the linear system

$$\{ H \cdot C' \}_{H \in T_p(C)^*}$$

is smooth outside the base locus $T_p(C) \cap C'$ of the system; since $T_p(C) \subset C'^*$, it follows that $T_p(C)$ *must be a tangent line to* C'. We see, moreover, that if $g > 3$, no line can be tangent to C' at two points $q, q' \in C'$: if it were, by the geometric version of Riemann-Roch we would have $h^0(2q+2q')=3$, and by Clifford's theorem the curve C' would have to be hyperelliptic. Thus we can write $T_p(C)=T_{p'}(C')$ for a unique point $p' \in C'$, and the map $p \mapsto p'$ gives an isomorphism of C with C'. In case $g=3$, we have seen that there are only a finite number of bitangents to the quartic curves C and C' in $\mathbb{P}^2$; the map $p \mapsto p'$ will extend over these points to give an isomorphism $C \cong C'$.

Essentially the same proof will go over to the hyperelliptic case: again, the branch locus of $\mathcal{G}_\Theta$ in $(\mathbb{P}^{g-1})^*$ will consist of those hyperplanes H such that $\iota_\kappa^{-1}(H \cap C)$ contains multiple points. In the hyperelliptic case, however, this can occur in two ways: if H is tangent to C, or if H passes through any of the points in the branch locus of ι_κ. Thus $\bar{B}$ will consist of C^*, together with the hyperplane $p^*=\{H : H \in p\} \subset (\mathbb{P}^{g-1})^*$ for each p in the branch locus of ι_κ. In effect, then, $\bar{B}$ determines C and also determines $2g+2$ points $\{p_i\}$ on C such that S is expressible as a double cover of $C \cong \mathbb{P}^1$ branched exactly at $\{p_i\}$; as we saw in our discussion of hyperelliptic curves, these data determine S.   Q.E.D.

The Torelli theorem assures us that theoretically all the behavior of a Riemann surface S is reflected in its polarized Jacobian $(\mathcal{J}(S), [\omega])$. In closing, we would like to make the remark that this is the case in practice as well as in theory—the reader may note that every result we have proved in this chapter can be readily expressed in terms of the geometry of the maps

$$\mu: S^{(d)} \to \mathcal{J}(S).$$

Indeed, as we have seen, some of the deeper properties of curves become tractable when expressed in terms of the essentially linear Jacobians. The relationship between curves and their Jacobians is, accordingly, an extraordinarily rich one. Unfortunately, no analogous technique for studying higher-dimensional varieties has been found, though analogous constructions may be made via the Hodge decomposition.

REFERENCES

The literature on Riemann surfaces and algebraic curves is incredibly vast. We do not attempt any sort of complete bibliography but simply list a few sources that best supplement the material in this chapter.

F. Enriques and O. Chisini, *Teoria geometrica delle equazioni e delle funzioni algebriche*, Zanichelli, Bologna, 1934.

C. L. Siegel, *Topics in Complex Function Theory*, 3 vols., Wiley-Interscience, New York, 1969–1973.

H. Weyl, *Die Idee der Riemannschen Fläche*, 3rd ed., Teubner, Stuttgart, 1955.

J. L. Coolidge, *A Treatise on Algebraic Plane Curves*, Oxford, 1931.

D. Mumford, *Curves and Their Jacobians*, University of Michigan Press, Ann Arbor, 1975. This reference gives a valuable up-to-date overview together with a guide to further literature, especially the history and sources for the generalized Riemann singularity theorem.

3
FURTHER TECHNIQUES

We return now to the subject of general analytic varieties in order to develop some further techniques especially intended for higher-dimensional considerations. The motif of this chapter is *differential forms*; the theme is their wide variety of applications, cohomological and otherwise, to complex analytic geometry.

We begin in Sections 1 and 2 with the theory of currents, or differential forms with distribution coefficients. This theory, initiated by de Rham to include both the C^∞ forms and piecewise smooth chains in the same framework, is especially fruitful in the complex analytic case. A pattern for the entire chapter is established, in that first the real or C^∞ situation is discussed and then the theory in the richer complex-analytic case developed. The topics in Section 1 are pretty much standard and well described by the table of contents. Coming to Section 2, there has recently been a flurry of research into the remarkable properties of currents associated to complex-analytic varieties. We have taken advantage of this to illustrate how the theory of currents is useful in establishing many of the foundational results required in an analytic treatment of algebraic geometry. For example, there is now an elegant method for recognizing when a current is one defined by an analytic variety, and this affords a direct method for proving such results as Remmert's proper mapping theorem which, although intuitively plausible, were traditionally rather difficult to establish rigorously.

Next we turn to the theory of Chern classes. The definition by differential forms that are polynomials in the curvature matrix provides a quick and easy derivation of the functoriality properties, especially Whitney duality, of the Chern classes as well as exhibiting directly the type and positivity properties in the complex analytic case. This is carried out in the beginning of Section 3; and in the second part we prove that the Chern classes are Poincaré dual to the basic Schubert cycles in the Grassmannian. This identifies the differential-form Chern classes with the usual topological ones, at least modulo torsion, and establishes the basic link between the Chern classes and enumerative questions in algebraic geometry, a recurrent theme in the remainder of the book.

In Section 4 the currents and Chern classes are combined to establish two global formulas, the holomorphic Lefschetz fixed-point formula and Bott's residue formula. Although the external circumstances are different, in both cases we use the intersection-and-smoothing theory of currents to reduce the proof to an application of Stokes' theorem where the integrand is a singular differential form. This technique of Stokes' theorem with singularities is ubiquitous throughout the general theory presented in the book—e.g., it appears in Section 1 of Chapter 1, throughout Chapter 2, and again in the general residue theorem given in Section 1 of Chapter 5—and we have to some extent formalized it in Section 1 of this chapter. The "principal part" of the singular differential forms inevitably turns out to be the Bochner-Martinelli kernel—a glance at the index will attest to its presence. Here we wish to point out that what is important is not so much its specific formula but rather its role as a fundamental solution for the $\bar{\partial}$-equation on $\mathbb{C}^n$. This is brought out in Section 1 of Chapter 5, the upshot of which is that *any* such fundamental solution would do—what is essential is the implicit duality. On the other hand, the Bochner-Martinelli kernel is characterized among all fundamental solutions by unitary invariance, and this particular symmetry is manifest in the aforementioned two global formulas, as well as in the Todd polynomials, which appear in the Hirzebruch-Riemann-Roch formula.

This latter is briefly discussed at the end of Section 3 but is not proved in the book. One reason is that there are by now an abundance of proofs from many differing viewpoints, and we have nothing to add. A second reason is that our applications of the Riemann-Roch formula to specific geometric problems occur only for curves and surfaces, and we have given a direct argument establishing the result in these cases.

The final section of this chapter is about spectral sequences, together with a few of their applications to algebraic geometry, which we hope will give at least an idea of how they are utilized. Again the motif is differential forms, especially those with singularities. In our discussion of hypercohomology, the algebraic de Rham theorem, and differentials of the second kind it will be seen that the spectral sequence formalism distills out general patterns and yields sometimes deceptive derivations of classical results whose original proofs were responsible for introducing many of the techniques that have become second nature in the subject.

1. DISTRIBUTIONS AND CURRENTS

Let M be a compact, oriented n-manifold. We know from Poincaré duality and de Rham's theorem that if Γ is a p-cycle on M—for example, an oriented submanifold—then there exists a closed C^∞ $(n-p)$-form ω that is dual to Γ in the sense that for all closed p-forms φ

$$\int_\Gamma \varphi = \int_M \omega \wedge \varphi.$$

We also know that ω is unique up to an exact form.

A special case when all this has been made quite explicit is when M is complex manifold and Γ is the cycle carried by an analytic subvariety V of codimension 1. If V is given locally as the divisor of $f_\alpha \in \mathcal{O}(U_\alpha)$, and if we have chosen positive functions h_α in U_α with $h_\alpha/h_\beta = |f_\alpha/f_\beta|^2$ in $U_\alpha \cap U_\beta$, then $\omega = dd^c \log h_\alpha$ is the Chern class of the line bundle $[V]$. Especially noteworthy is the case when $[V]$ is positive in the sense that, with a suitable choice of the metric $\{h_\alpha\}$ in $[V]$, the real $(1,1)$-form ω is positive.

We shall introduce a formalism that includes both cycles and smooth forms. This will lead to a cohomology theory to which both the ordinary singular and de Rham's theories map, and both maps will be isomorphisms.

Definitions; Residue Formulas

We make our definitions first on $\mathbb{R}^n$. Let $C_c^\infty(\mathbb{R}^n)$ be the vector space of compactly supported smooth functions on $\mathbb{R}^n$. If $x = (x_1, \ldots, x_n)$ are coordinates on $\mathbb{R}^n$, we let $D_i = \partial/\partial x_i$ and $D^\alpha = D_1^{\alpha_1} \ldots D_n^{\alpha_n}$ for $\alpha = (\alpha_1, \ldots, \alpha_n) \in (\mathbb{Z}^+)^n$. The C^p-topology is defined on $C_c^\infty(\mathbb{R}^n)$ by saying that a sequence $\varphi_n \to 0$ in case there is a compact set K with all $\operatorname{supp} \varphi_n \subset K$ and with

$$D^\alpha \varphi_n(x) \longrightarrow 0$$

uniformly for $x \in K$ and all α satisfying $[\alpha] = \alpha_1 + \ldots + \alpha_n \leqslant p$. The C^∞ topology is defined by saying that $\varphi_n \to 0$ in case all $\operatorname{supp} \varphi_n \subset K$ and $\varphi_n \to 0$ in the C^p topology for each p.

DEFINITION.   A *distribution* on $\mathbb{R}^n$ is a linear map $T: C_c^\infty(\mathbb{R}^n) \to \mathbb{C}$ that is continuous in the C^∞ topology. The vector space of distributions on $\mathbb{R}^n$ is denoted $\mathcal{D}(\mathbb{R}^n)$.

We say that a distribution is *of order p* if it is continuous in the C^p-topology. Now any linear map from a topological vector space V to $\mathbb{C}$ is continuous $\Leftrightarrow$ the inverse of the unit ball in $\mathbb{C}$ is open in the topology of V. Since for the space $C_c^\infty(K)$ of functions supported in a compact set K the C^∞ topology is the union of the C^p topologies, we see that any distribution is locally of finite order.

Examples

1. If $\psi(x)$ is a locally L^1 function on $\mathbb{R}^n$, then we may define a distribution T_ψ of order zero by

$$T_\psi(\varphi) = \int_{\mathbb{R}^n} \varphi(x)\psi(x)\,dx.$$

Here $dx = dx_1 \wedge \ldots \wedge dx_n$, and we always assume that $\mathbb{R}^n$ is oriented by this form.

2. The δ-*function* is the distribution defined by

$$\delta(\varphi) = \varphi(0).$$

Next we extend the operators D_i to the space of distributions by setting

$$(D_i T)(\varphi) = -T(D_i\varphi).$$

If $T = T_\psi$ is the distribution associated to a function ψ of class C^1, then for $\varphi \in C_c^\infty(\mathbb{R}^n)$

$$\begin{aligned} (D_i T_\psi)(\varphi) &= -T_\psi(D_i\varphi) \\ &= -\int_{\mathbb{R}^n} \psi(x)\big[(\partial\varphi/\partial x_i(x))\big]\,dx \\ &= \int_{\mathbb{R}^n} \frac{\partial\psi(x)}{\partial s_i}\varphi(x)\,dx \end{aligned}$$

(by Stokes' theorem)

$$= (T_{D_i\psi})(\varphi),$$

so that our extended notion of differentiating distributions makes sense.

An example that illustrates the principle underlying the various residue theorems we shall discuss is obtained by considering the locally L^1 function $\psi(x)$ on $\mathbb{R}$ defined by

$$\begin{cases} \psi(x) = 0, & x < 0, \\ \psi(x) = 1, & x \geqslant 1. \end{cases}$$

Formally—i.e., ignoring the singularity—$\psi'(x) = 0$. However, the distributional derivative is given by

$$\begin{aligned} (DT_\psi)(\varphi) &= -\int_{-\infty}^{+\infty} \varphi'(x)\psi(x)\,dx \\ &= -\int_0^\infty \varphi'(x)\,dx \\ &= \varphi(0), \end{aligned}$$

i.e.,

$$DT_\psi = \delta.$$

The general principle will be

$$DT_\psi - T_{D\psi} = \text{``residue,''}$$

where $D\psi$ is the derivative of ψ computed formally. We will expound this in greater detail in a little while.

Another picture of distributions is obtained by looking at the torus $T = \mathbb{R}^n/(2\pi\mathbb{Z})^n$. In Section 6 of Chapter 0 on the proof of the Hodge theorem we defined the space $\mathcal{D}(T)$ of distributions on the torus and showed that

$$\mathcal{D}(T) = \bigcup_s H_s,$$

where H_s is the Sobolev space of formal Fourier series $T = \Sigma \, u_\xi e^{i(\xi, x)}$ satisfying $\Sigma(1 + \|\xi\|^2)^s |u_\xi|^2 < \infty$. By the Sobolev lemma proved there

$$C^\infty(T) = \bigcap_s H_s,$$

and for $\varphi = \Sigma \varphi_\xi e^{i(\xi, x)} \in C^\infty(T)$

$$T(\varphi) = \sum_\xi u_\xi \varphi_\xi.$$

The δ-function is given by

$$\delta = \sum_\xi e^{i(\xi, x)}.$$

As usual, the torus will provide an excellent illustration of our general remarks.

Now let $A_c^q(\mathbb{R}^n)$ be the space of C^∞ q-forms on $\mathbb{R}^n$ with compact support. In the obvious way the topology on $C_c^\infty(\mathbb{R}^n)$ may be used componentwise to make $A_c^q(\mathbb{R}^n)$ into a complete topological vector space.

DEFINITION.   The topological dual of $A_c^{n-q}(\mathbb{R}^n)$ is the space of *currents* of degree q, and is denoted by $\mathcal{D}^q(\mathbb{R}^n)$.

Examples

1.   In the following examples we will denote by $L^q(\mathbb{R}^n, \text{loc})$ the q-forms $\psi = \Sigma \psi_I(x)\,dx_I$ whose coefficient functions are locally L^1 functions on $\mathbb{R}^n$. For such a ψ there is an associated current $T_\psi \in \mathcal{D}^q(\mathbb{R}^n)$ defined by

$$T_\psi(\varphi) = \int_{\mathbb{R}^n} \psi \wedge \varphi, \qquad \varphi \in A_c^{n-q}(\mathbb{R}^n).$$

2. If Γ is a piecewise smooth, oriented $(n-q)$ chain in $\mathbb{R}^n$, then Γ defines a current $T_\Gamma \in \mathcal{D}^q(\mathbb{R}^n)$ by

$$T_\Gamma(\varphi) = \int_\Gamma \varphi, \qquad \varphi \in A_c^{n-q}(\mathbb{R}^n).$$

In general if we call the *support* of the current T the smallest closed set S such that $T(\varphi)=0$ for all $\varphi \in A_c^{n-q}(\mathbb{R}^n - S)$, then clearly $\mathrm{supp}(T_\Gamma)=\Gamma$.

The exterior derivative on smooth forms induces

$$d: \mathcal{D}^q(\mathbb{R}^n) \longrightarrow \mathcal{D}^{q+1}(\mathbb{R}^n)$$

defined by

$$(dT)(\varphi) = (-1)^{q+1} T(d\varphi), \qquad \varphi \in A_c^{n-q-1}(\mathbb{R}^n).$$

Then $d^2=0$. If $T=T_\psi$ for some smooth form $\psi \in A^q(\mathbb{R}^n)$, by Stokes' theorem

$$dT_\psi(\varphi) = (-1)^{q+1} \int_{\mathbb{R}^n} \psi \wedge d\varphi$$

$$= -\int_{\mathbb{R}^n} d(\psi \wedge \varphi) + \int_{\mathbb{R}^n} d\psi \wedge \varphi$$

$$= T_{d\psi}(\varphi).$$

Similarly, for T_Γ as in the second example,

$$dT_\Gamma(\varphi) = (-1)^{q+1} \int_\Gamma d\varphi$$

$$= (-1)^{q+1} \int_{\partial\Gamma} \varphi$$

$$= (-1)^{q+1} T_{\partial\Gamma}(\varphi).$$

Thus, d on the currents induces the usual exterior derivative on the smooth forms and $\pm\partial$ on the piecewise smooth chains.

Here is an example that interpolates between these two.

3. Suppose that $\psi \in L^q(\mathbb{R}^n, \mathrm{loc})$ is C^∞ outside a closed set S, and assume moreover that $d\psi$ on $\mathbb{R}^n - S$ extends to a locally L^1 form on $\mathbb{R}^n$. We define the *residue* $R(\psi)$ by the equation of currents

$$dT_\psi = T_{d\psi} + R(\psi). \tag{$*$}$$

It is clear that the support $\mathrm{supp}\, R(\psi) \subset S$.

For example, suppose that we consider the Cauchy kernel

$$\kappa = \frac{1}{2\pi\sqrt{-1}} \frac{dz}{z}$$

on $\mathbb{C}$. Then $\kappa \in L^{1,0}(\mathbb{C}, \mathrm{loc})$ and is C^∞ on $\mathbb{C} - \{0\}$; moreover, $d\kappa = \bar\partial\kappa = 0$

there. The general version of Cauchy's formula

$$\varphi(0) = \frac{1}{2\pi\sqrt{-1}} \int_{\mathbb{C}} \frac{\partial\varphi(z)}{\partial\bar{z}} \frac{dz \wedge d\bar{z}}{z}, \qquad \varphi \in C_c^\infty(\mathbb{C}),$$

given in Section 1 of Chapter 0 translates into the equation of currents

$$\bar{\partial}(T_\kappa) = \delta_{\{0\}}.$$

Equivalently, the residue

$$R\left(\frac{1}{2\pi\sqrt{-1}} \frac{dz}{z}\right) = \delta_{\{0\}}$$

of the Cauchy kernel is the δ-function at the origin.

We will generalize this, first to $\mathbb{R}^n$ and then to $\mathbb{C}^n$. The notations

$$r^2 = \sum_i x_i^2 = \|x\|^2,$$

$$r\,dr = \sum_i x_i\,dx_i,$$

$$\Phi(x) = dx_1 \wedge \cdots \wedge dx_n,$$

$$\Phi_i(x) = (-1)^{i-1} x_i\,dx_1 \wedge \cdots \wedge \widehat{dx_i} \wedge \cdots \wedge dx_n$$

will be used. We will also let C_n stand for a generic constant depending only on n. Finally, the operators such as $*$ that depend on a metric will refer to $ds^2 = \sum_i (dx_i)^2$.

We note that the function r^{-s} is locally integrable for $s < n$ but not for $s = n$. Define

$$\sigma = C_n \frac{\sum \Phi_i(x)}{\|x\|^n}$$

$$= C_n \frac{*r\,dr}{r^n}.$$

This form σ belongs to $L^{n-1}(\mathbb{R}^n, \text{loc})$, is invariant under the proper orthogonal group, and is smooth on $\mathbb{R}^n - \{0\}$. Since $d\Phi_i(x) = \Phi(x)$, it follows that in $\mathbb{R}^n - \{0\}$

$$d\sigma = C_n\left(\frac{n\Phi(x)}{r^n} - \frac{nr\,dr \wedge *(r\,dr)}{r^{n+2}}\right)$$

$$= 0.$$

By Stokes' theorem, then, the integral

$$\int_{\|x\|=\varepsilon} \sigma$$

of σ over a sphere is independent of the radius $\varepsilon > 0$. Consequently, choosing C_n properly, σ is the unique form on $\mathbb{R}^n - \{0\}$ that is invariant under proper rotations, orthogonal to the normal dr to spheres, and that has integral 1 over a sphere of any radius. In $\mathbb{R}^2$ with coordinates $(x,y) = (r\cos\theta, r\sin\theta)$,

$$\sigma = \frac{1}{2\pi} \frac{x\,dy - y\,dx}{x^2 + y^2} = \frac{1}{2\pi} d\theta.$$

In general if

$$x = r\omega,$$

where $r = \|x\|$ and $\omega \in S^{n-1}$ are polar coordinates in $\mathbb{R}^n$, then we may write

$$\sigma = C_n\, d\omega.$$

For $\varphi \in C_c^\infty(\mathbb{R}^n)$, by Stokes' theorem,

$$-\int_{\mathbb{R}^n} d\varphi \wedge \sigma = \lim_{\varepsilon \to 0} -\int_{\mathbb{R}^n - \{\|x\| \leqslant \varepsilon\}} d\varphi \wedge \sigma$$

$$= \lim_{\varepsilon \to 0} \int_{\|x\| = \varepsilon} \varphi\sigma$$

$$= \varphi(0).$$

Thus, the equation of currents

$$dT_\sigma = \delta_{\{0\}}$$

is valid, as is the residue relation

$$R(\sigma) = \delta_{\{0\}}.$$

On $\mathbb{C}^n \cong \mathbb{R}^{2n}$ the form σ decomposes into type, each component of which is invariant under the unitary group. Up to a constant to be specified in a moment, the component of type $(n, n-1)$ is

$$\beta = C_n \frac{\left(\sum \overline{\Phi_i(z)} \wedge \Phi(z) \right)}{\|z\|^{2n}}$$

$$= C_n \frac{*(r\bar\partial r)}{r^{2n}}.$$

Clearly $\beta \in L^{n,n-1}(\mathbb{C}^n, \text{loc})$, and since $\bar\partial \Phi_i(z) = \Phi(z)$, the same computation as for σ shows that

$$\bar\partial\beta = 0 \qquad \text{on } \mathbb{C}^n - \{0\}.$$

Since $d = \bar\partial$ on forms of type (n,q), we may repeat the previous argument to conclude that for a suitable choice of constant,

$$\bar\partial T_\beta = \delta_{\{0\}},$$

and therefore the residue

$$R(\beta) = \delta_{\{0\}}.$$

Explicitly, for $\varphi \in C_c^\infty(\mathbb{C}^n)$,

$$\varphi(0) = \int_{\mathbb{C}^n} \bar{\partial}\varphi \wedge \beta,$$

and just as in the one-variable case this formula may be extended to noncompactly supported forms to obtain

$$\varphi(0) = \int_{B[r]} \bar{\partial}\varphi \wedge \beta + \int_{\partial B[r]} \varphi\beta,$$

where $B[r] = \{z \in \mathbb{C}^n : \|z\| \leqslant r\}$ is the ball of radius r in $\mathbb{C}^n$. In case $\varphi \in \mathcal{O}(\mathbb{C}^n)$ is holomorphic, this reduces to the *Bochner–Martinelli formula*

$$\varphi(0) = \int_{\|z\|=r} \varphi(z)\beta(z,\bar{z}).$$

It is possible to prove these formulas by reducing to the one-variable case in a manner that sheds some additional light on the expression for β. First, we shall show that

$$\beta = C_n(\partial \log\|z\|^2) \wedge (\partial\bar{\partial}\log\|z\|^2)^{n-1}.$$

Proof. Denote by γ the form on the right-hand side of this equation. Since

$$\partial\log\|z\|^2 = \frac{(dz,z)}{(z,z)},$$

$$\partial\bar{\partial}\log\|z\|^2 = \partial\left(\frac{(z,dz)}{(z,z)}\right)$$

$$= \frac{(dz,dz)}{(z,z)} - \frac{(dz,z)\wedge(z,dz)}{(z,z)^2},$$

and since $(dz,z)\wedge(dz,z)=0$,

$$\gamma = C_n' \frac{(dz,z)\wedge(dz,dz)^{n-1}}{\|z\|^{2n}}.$$

The numerator is

$$C_n'\left(\sum_j \bar{z}_i\, dz_i\right) \wedge \left(\sum_j dz_j \wedge d\bar{z}_j\right)^{n-1}$$

$$= C_n''\left(\sum (-1)^{i-1}\bar{z}_i\, d\bar{z}_1 \wedge \cdots \wedge \widehat{d\bar{z}_i} \wedge \cdots \wedge d\bar{z}_n \wedge dz_1 \wedge \cdots \wedge dz_n\right),$$

which implies the result.

Now we recall that under the projection

$$\mathbb{C}^n - \{0\} \to \mathbb{P}^{n-1}$$

the Kähler form of the Fubini-Study metric pulls back to

$$\Omega = dd^c \log\|z\|^2$$
$$= \frac{\sqrt{-1}}{4\pi} \partial\bar{\partial} \log\|z\|^2.$$

Let $\tilde{\mathbb{C}}^n$ be the blow-up of $\mathbb{C}^n$ at the origin and

$$\pi: \tilde{\mathbb{C}}^n \to \mathbb{P}^{n-1}$$

the extension to $\tilde{\mathbb{C}}^n$ of the projection. $\tilde{\mathbb{C}}^n$ is the total space of the universal line bundle over projective space, and $\pi^*\Omega$ is smooth up on $\tilde{\mathbb{C}}^n$. Thus, on $\tilde{\mathbb{C}}^n$

$$\pi^*\beta = C_n \theta \wedge (\pi^*\Omega)^{n-1},$$

where $\theta = \partial \log\|z\|^2$ is a $(1,0)$-form that on each fiber $\{\lambda z\}_{\lambda \in \mathbb{C}}$ of $\tilde{\mathbb{C}}^n \to \mathbb{P}^{n-1}$ reduces to $d\lambda/\lambda$. Summarizing, $\pi^*\beta$ on $\tilde{\mathbb{C}}^n$ is the pullback of the standard volume form on $\mathbb{P}^{n-1}$ times a form θ that reduces to the Cauchy kernel in each fiber of $\tilde{\mathbb{C}}^n \to \mathbb{P}^{n-1}$. Using this interpretation, the n-variable Bochner-Martinelli formulas may, by pulling forms back to $\tilde{\mathbb{C}}^n$ and making an obvious iteration of the integrals, be reduced to the one-variable Cauchy formula.

A final remark is that the definition of distributions and currents may be localized. Thus, for U open in $\mathbb{R}^n$ the space $\mathcal{D}(U)$ of distributions on U is the dual of $C_c^\infty(U)$ with the obvious topology. Since a diffeomorphism $f: U \to V$ (U, V open in $\mathbb{R}^n$) induces a topological isomorphism $f^*: C_c^\infty(V) \to C_c^\infty(U)$, we may define the spaces $\mathcal{D}(M)$ and currents $\mathcal{D}^*(M)$ on a manifold M.

Smoothing and Regularity

A distribution $T \in \mathcal{D}(\mathbb{R}^n)$ is said to be *smooth* in case $T = T_\psi$ for a C^∞ function $\psi(x)$ on $\mathbb{R}^n$. We shall now make precise the sense in which the smooth distributions are dense among all distributions.

Let $\chi(x) \in C_c^\infty(\mathbb{R}^n)$ be a nonnegative function supported in a neighborhood of the origin, with

$$\int_{\mathbb{R}^n} \chi(x)\,dx = 1.$$

In a little while we shall assume that χ is *radially symmetric*, i.e., in polar coordinates $x = r\omega$

$$\chi(x) = \chi(r).$$

We set

$$\chi_\varepsilon(x) = \frac{1}{\varepsilon^n}\chi\left(\frac{x}{\varepsilon}\right).$$

If $\operatorname{supp}\chi = K$, then $\operatorname{supp}\chi_\varepsilon = \varepsilon K$ and

$$\int_{\mathbb{R}^n}\chi_\varepsilon(x)\,dx = 1.$$

We remark that

$$T_{\chi_\varepsilon} \to \delta \qquad \text{as } \varepsilon \to 0$$

in the sense that for any test function $\varphi \in C_c^\infty(\mathbb{R}^n)$

$$\lim_{\varepsilon \to 0}\int_{\mathbb{R}^n}\chi_\varepsilon(x)\varphi(x)\,dx = \varphi(0).$$

To see this, simply note that

$$\min_{x\in\varepsilon K}\varphi(x) \leqslant \int_{\mathbb{R}^n}\chi_\varepsilon(x)\varphi(x)\,dx \leqslant \max_{x\in\varepsilon K}\varphi(x),$$

which tends to $\varphi(0)$ as $\varepsilon \to 0$.

Having "smoothed" the δ-function, for a general distribution $T \in \mathcal{D}(\mathbb{R}^n)$ we consider the function

$$T_\varepsilon(x) = T_y\big(\chi_\varepsilon(x-y)\big),$$

where we use the subscript y on T to indicate that we consider $\chi_\varepsilon(x-y)$ as a function of y and apply T accordingly. $T_\varepsilon(x)$ is a C^∞ function on $\mathbb{R}^n$ with derivatives

$$D^\alpha T_\varepsilon(x) = \pm T_y(D_x^\alpha\chi_\varepsilon(x-y)).$$

By an abuse of notation, we denote by T_ε the distribution on $\mathbb{R}^n$ defined by the function $T_\varepsilon(x)$.

The following formal properties of the T_ε's will be proved:

1. $(T_\varphi)_\varepsilon = T_{\varphi_\varepsilon}$ for $\varphi(x) \in C^\infty(\mathbb{R}^n)$.
2. $T_\varepsilon(\psi) = T(\psi_\varepsilon)$ for $\psi(x) \in C_c^\infty(\mathbb{R}^n)$.
3. $(DT)_\varepsilon = D(T_\varepsilon)$ for $D = \partial^\alpha/\partial x^\alpha$.

Proof of 1.   For $\psi \in C_c^\infty(\mathbb{R}^n)$,

$$(T_\varphi)_\varepsilon(\psi) = \int_{\mathbb{R}^n}T_{\varphi_y}(\chi_\varepsilon(x-y)\psi(x)\,dx)$$

$$= \int\int\varphi(y)\chi_\varepsilon(x-y)\psi(x)\,dx\,dy$$

$$= T_{\varphi_\varepsilon}(\psi)$$

by interchanging the order of integration.

Proof of 2. Since T is linear,

$$T(\psi_\varepsilon) = T_y\left(\int \psi(x)\chi_\varepsilon(x-y)\,dx\right)$$
$$= \int \psi(x)T_y\chi_\varepsilon(x-y)\,dx$$
$$= \int \psi(x)T_\varepsilon(x)\,dx$$
$$= T_\varepsilon(\psi).$$

Proof of 3. We may suppose that $D = \partial/\partial x_i$. If $T = T_\psi$ for $\psi \in C^\infty(\mathbb{R}^n)$ and $\psi \in C_c^\infty(\mathbb{R}^n)$,

$$DT_\varepsilon(\varphi) = T_\varepsilon(-D\varphi)$$
$$= \int\int -\frac{\partial\varphi}{\partial x_i}(x)\chi_\varepsilon(x-y)\psi(y)\,dx\,dy$$
$$= \int \chi_\varepsilon(u)\left(\int -\frac{\partial\varphi}{\partial x_i}(x)\psi(x-u)\,dx\right)du$$
$$= \int \chi_\varepsilon(u)\left(\int \varphi(x)\frac{\partial\psi}{\partial x_i}(x-u)\,dx\right)du$$
$$= \int\int \frac{\partial\psi}{\partial y_i}(y)\varphi(x)\chi_\varepsilon(x-y)\,dx\,dy$$
$$= (DT)_\varepsilon(\varphi).$$

For a general $T \in \mathcal{D}(\mathbb{R}^n)$ and $\varphi \in C_c^\infty(\mathbb{R}^n)$,

$$(DT)_\varepsilon(\varphi) = (DT)(\varphi_\varepsilon)$$
$$= T(-D\varphi_\varepsilon)$$
$$= T(-D\varphi)_\varepsilon \qquad \text{(by the previous step)}$$
$$= T_\varepsilon(-D\varphi)$$
$$= DT_\varepsilon(\varphi),$$

which proves assertion 3.

In particular, we conclude that for any $\psi \in C_c^\infty(\mathbb{R}^n)$

$$D\psi_\varepsilon \to D\psi$$

uniformly, and consequently

$$T_\varepsilon(\psi) \to T(\psi) \qquad \text{as } \varepsilon \to 0.$$

There are, of course, many subtle questions about the convergence of the smoothing process in particular norms, but we need not get into these here.

A current $T \in \mathcal{D}^q(\mathbb{R}^n)$ may be considered as a differential form

$$T = \sum_{\#I=q} T_I \, dx_I$$

with distribution coefficients T_I defined by

$$T_I(\varphi) = \pm T(\varphi \, dx_{I^0})$$

for $\varphi \in C_c^\infty(\mathbb{R}^n)$. Here I^0 is the index set defined by $*dx_I = \pm dx_{I^0}$. The smoothing

$$T_\varepsilon = \sum_I (T_I)_\varepsilon \, dx_I$$

satisfies

$$T_\varepsilon(\varphi) \to T(\varphi) \qquad \text{as } \varepsilon \to 0, \qquad \varphi \in A_c^{n-q}(\mathbb{R}^n),$$

and

$$dT_\varepsilon = d(T_\varepsilon).$$

We will now use smoothing to prove some regularity results concerning the Laplace equation on distributions

$$\Delta T = S,$$

where

$$\Delta = -\sum_i \frac{\partial^2}{\partial x_i^2}.$$

Lemma. *If* $T \in \mathcal{D}(\mathbb{R}^n)$ *satisfies* $\Delta T = 0$, *then* $T = T_\varphi$ *for some* $\varphi \in C^\infty(\mathbb{R}^n)$ *with* $\Delta \varphi = 0$.

Proof. Smooth functions φ satisfying $\Delta \varphi = 0$ are said to be *harmonic*. We shall first prove that harmonic functions obey the *mean-value property*

$$\varphi(y) = \int_{\|x-y\|=\varepsilon} \varphi(x) \sigma_y(x),$$

where, if

$$\sigma = C_n \frac{*(r \, dr)}{r^n}$$

is the form encountered in the preceding section, then

$$\sigma_y(x) = \sigma(x-y)$$

is the invariant volume form on the sphere $\|x-y\| = \varepsilon$ having total area 1. Since the Laplacian is invariant under translations and proper rotations, it will suffice to prove the mean value property when $y = 0$.

We shall apply Stokes' theorem twice to spherical shells $B[\delta, \varepsilon] = \{\delta \leqslant \|x\| \leqslant \varepsilon\}$. The first time we take the $(n-1)$-form

$$\eta = \varphi \sigma.$$

Since $d\sigma = 0$,

$$d\eta = C_n \, d\varphi \wedge \frac{*(r\,dr)}{r^n} = \pm C_n * d\varphi \wedge \frac{dr}{r^{n-1}},$$

and Stokes' theorem gives

$$(*) \qquad \pm C_n \int_{B[\delta,\varepsilon]} *d\varphi \wedge \frac{dr}{r^{n-1}} = \int_{\|x\|=\varepsilon} \varphi\sigma - \int_{\|x\|=\delta} \varphi\sigma.$$

We write

$$*d\varphi \wedge \frac{dr}{r^{n-1}} = *d\varphi \wedge d\gamma,$$

where

$$\gamma = \begin{cases} \log r & \text{in case } n=2, \\ \left(-\dfrac{1}{n-2}\right)\dfrac{1}{r^{n-2}} & \text{in case } n \geqslant 3. \end{cases}$$

Now

$$d*d\varphi = \pm \Delta\varphi \, dx = 0,$$

so that

$$*d\varphi \wedge d\gamma = d(\gamma * d\varphi).$$

Applying Stokes' theorem once again, we may express the integral on the left of $(*)$ as a difference of integrals

$$C_n \int_{\|x\|=\rho} \gamma * d\varphi.$$

For fixed ρ, this integral is a constant times

$$\int_{\|x\|=\rho} *d\varphi = \int_{\|x\|\leqslant\rho} d*d\varphi = 0.$$

Thus, for a harmonic function φ,

$$\int_{\|x\|=\delta} \varphi\sigma = \int_{\|x\|=\varepsilon} \varphi\sigma.$$

If we let $\delta \to 0$, the left-hand side tends to $\varphi(0)$, and the mean-value property is established.

Now we assume that $\chi(x)$ is radically symmetric. Then a harmonic function φ satisfies $\varphi_\varepsilon = \varphi$ for $\varepsilon > 0$. By the formal properties 1–3 of smoothing, a harmonic distribution T satisfies $T_\delta = T$ for $\delta > 0$. More precisely, by property 3,

$$\Delta T_\varepsilon = (\Delta T)_\varepsilon = 0,$$

so that $T_\varepsilon = T_{\psi_\varepsilon}$ for a harmonic function ψ_ε. Then

$$(T_\varepsilon)_\delta = T_{(\psi_\varepsilon)_\delta} = T_{\psi_\varepsilon} = T_\varepsilon,$$

and for $\varphi \in C_c^\infty(\mathbb{R}^n)$,

$$
\begin{aligned}
T(\varphi) &= \lim_{\varepsilon \to 0} T_\varepsilon(\varphi) \\
&= \lim_{\varepsilon \to 0} (T_\varepsilon)_\delta(\varphi) \\
&= \lim_{\varepsilon \to 0} T_\varepsilon(\varphi_\delta) \\
&= T(\varphi_\delta) \qquad \text{(by property 2)} \\
&= T_\delta(\varphi);
\end{aligned}
$$

i.e.,

$$
T = T_\delta
$$

is a smooth distribution as desired. $\hfill$ Q.E.D.

We now extend regularity to the inhomogeneous equation.

Lemma. *If* $T \in \mathcal{D}(\mathbb{R}^n)$ *satisfies*

$$
\Delta T = \eta \in C_c^\infty(\mathbb{R}^n),
$$

then $T = T_\psi$ *for some* $\psi \in C^\infty(\mathbb{R}^n)$ *such that* $\Delta \psi = \eta$.

Proof. We will write down an explicit solution $\rho \in C^\infty(\mathbb{R}^n)$ to the equation

$$
\Delta \rho = \eta,
$$

using the classical *Green's function*

$$
G(x,y) = \begin{cases} \dfrac{1}{\|x-y\|^{n-2}}, & n \geqslant 3, \\[2mm] \log\|x-y\|, & n = 2. \end{cases}
$$

Then

$$
\Delta(T - T_\rho) = 0,
$$

and this lemma follows from the preceding one.

We shall assume that $n \geqslant 3$, the case $n = 2$ being essentially the same. Define

$$
\begin{aligned}
\rho(x) &= C_n \int_{y \in \mathbb{R}^n} \frac{\eta(y)\,dy}{\|x-y\|^{n-2}} \\
&= \pm C_n \int_{u \in \mathbb{R}^n} \frac{\eta(x-u)\,du}{\|u\|^{n-2}},
\end{aligned}
$$

where the equality follows from the change of variables $y = x - u$. The second expression shows that $\rho(x)$ is smooth and

$$
\Delta\rho(x) = \pm C_n \int_{u \in \mathbb{R}^n} \frac{\Delta\eta(x-u)\,du}{\|u\|^{n-2}}.
$$

We will prove that this integral is $\eta(x)$. By translating x to the origin, what must be verified is the *Poisson formula*

$$\eta(0) = C_n \int_{\mathbb{R}^n} \frac{\Delta \eta(x)\,dx}{\|x\|^{n-2}}.$$

In polar coordinates $x = r\omega$, where $r = \|x\|$ and $\omega \in S^{n-1}$,

$$\frac{\Delta\eta(x)\,dx}{\|x\|^{n-2}} = \frac{d * d\eta}{r^{n-2}}$$

$$= d\left(\frac{*d\eta}{r^{n-2}}\right) \pm \left(\frac{1}{n-2}\right)\frac{dr \wedge *d\eta}{r^{n-1}}$$

$$= d\left(\frac{*d\eta}{r^{n-2}}\right) \pm \left(\frac{1}{n-2}\right)\frac{d\eta \wedge *(r\,dr)}{r^n}$$

$$= d\left(\frac{*d\eta}{r^{n-2}}\right) \pm \left(\frac{1}{n-2}\right)d(\eta\sigma).$$

We apply Stokes' theorem to the region $\mathbb{R}^n - \{\|x\| \leqslant \varepsilon\}$ and to each of the forms on the right-hand side. Thus

$$\int_{\mathbb{R}^n} \frac{\Delta\eta(x)\,dx}{\|x\|^{n-2}} = \lim_{\varepsilon \to 0} \int_{\mathbb{R}^n - \{\|x\| \leqslant \varepsilon\}} \frac{\Delta\eta(x)\,dx}{\|x\|^{n-2}}$$

$$= A_\varepsilon + B_\varepsilon,$$

where

$$A_\varepsilon = \pm \int_{\|x\| = \varepsilon} \frac{*d\eta}{\varepsilon^{n-2}} = \frac{1}{\varepsilon^{n-2}} \int_{\|x\| \leqslant \varepsilon} \Delta\eta\,dx$$

$$\to 0 \qquad \text{as } \varepsilon \to 0,$$

since $\Delta\eta$ is C^∞, and so

$$\int_{\|x\| \leqslant \varepsilon} \Delta\eta = O(\varepsilon^n);$$

and where

$$B_\varepsilon = \text{constant} \int_{\|x\| = \varepsilon} \eta\sigma$$

$$\to \eta(0) \qquad \text{as } \varepsilon \to 0$$

for a suitable choice of the constant C_n. This proves the Poisson formula, and hence the lemma.

Regularity also works locally:

Lemma. *Given an open set* $U \subset \mathbb{R}^n$ *and* $T \in \mathcal{D}(U)$ *with* $\Delta T = 0$, *then* $T = T_\psi$ *for a function* ψ *harmonic in* U.

Proof. Given $V \subset U$ a relatively compact open subset, then for $\varphi \in C_c^\infty(V)$ and ε sufficiently small, $\operatorname{supp}\varphi_\varepsilon \subset U$. We can then define T_ε by

$$T_\varepsilon(\varphi) = T(\varphi_\varepsilon),$$

and repeat the previous argument to conclude that $T_\varepsilon = T_{\psi_V}$ for some ψ_V harmonic in V. Since ψ_V is the same for all ε, if $V \subset W \subset U$ we have $\psi_W|_V = \psi_V$. Consequently there is a harmonic function ψ in U such that $T = T_\psi$.   Q.E.D.

As an application we have the

Regularity for the $\bar\partial$-operator. *If* $U \subset \mathbb{C}^n$ *is an open set and* $T \in \mathcal{D}(U)$ *satisfies* $\bar\partial T = 0$, *then* $T = T_f$ *for some* $f \in \mathcal{O}(U)$.

Proof. By one of our Hodge identities from Section 6 of Chapter 0,

$$\Delta = \sqrt{-1}\, \Lambda \partial \bar\partial$$

on $\mathbb{C}^n$. Thus, $\bar\partial T = 0 \Rightarrow \Delta T = 0$, and so $T = T_f$ for some $f \in C^\infty(U)$ by the preceding lemma. But then $0 = \bar\partial T_f = T_{\bar\partial f} \Rightarrow \bar\partial f = 0$ and $f \in \mathcal{O}(U)$.   Q.E.D.

Finally, we will tie up the remaining loose end in Section 6 of Chapter 0 on the proof of the Hodge theorem. Namely, referring to Regularity Lemma I in the subsection entitled "Proof of the Hodge Theorem II: Global Theory" we want to prove that if φ lies in the Sobolev space $\mathcal{H}_s^{p,q}(M)$ and $\psi \in \mathcal{H}_0^{p,q}(M)$ is a weak solution of the equation

$$\Delta\psi = \varphi,$$

then $\psi \in \mathcal{H}_{s+2}^{p,q}(M)$. Writing $P = \bar\partial + \bar\partial^*$, $P^2 = \Delta$. Therefore, we consider the weak equation

$$(*) \qquad\qquad\qquad P\theta = \eta$$

and show that if $\eta \in \mathcal{H}_s^{p,q}(M)$, then $\theta \in \mathcal{H}_{s+1}^{p,q}(M)$. If $\rho \in C^\infty(M)$,   then

$$\begin{aligned} P(\rho\theta) &= P(\rho) \wedge \theta + \rho P(\theta) \\ &= P(\rho) \wedge \theta + \rho\eta. \end{aligned}$$

It will consequently suffice to prove the regularity assertion about weak solutions of the equation $(*)$ for forms compactly supported in a fixed coordinate patch on M. This coordinate patch may be taken to be diffeomorphic to $\mathbb{R}^n$, so that what we must show is the following

Regularity Lemma II. *Let* $Pu = Qu + Ru$, *where*

$$(Qu)_i = \sum_{k,j} a_{ij}^k(x) \frac{\partial u_j(x)}{\partial x_k},$$

$$(Ru)_i = \sum_j b_{ij}(x) u_j(x),$$

be a first-order differential operator with C^∞ *coefficients satisfying the Gårding inequality*

$$\|Pu\|_0 + \|u\|_0 \geqslant \|u\|_1$$

for compactly supported u. *If the distribution equation*

$$Pu = v$$

holds for some compactly supported v *in the Sobolev space* $\mathfrak{K}_s$, *then* u∈ $\mathfrak{K}_{s+1}$.

Proof. We define the smoothing

$$u_\varepsilon(x) = \int_{\mathbb{R}^n} u_\varepsilon(y)\chi_\varepsilon(x-y)\,dy$$

as above. The L^2 norm

$$\|u_\varepsilon - u\|_0^2 \to 0 \qquad \text{as } \varepsilon \to 0,$$

since the convergence $u_\varepsilon \to u$ is uniform. If we can prove that the Sobolev norms

$$\|u_\varepsilon\|_{s+1}$$

are uniformly bounded for $0 < \varepsilon \leqslant \varepsilon_0$, then, taking a sequence $\varepsilon_k \downarrow 0$, a subsequence of u_{ε_k} will converge weakly to an element u' of $\mathfrak{K}_{s+1}$, and u' must be equal to u.

By the Gårding inequality in our assumption, we can bound the $\mathfrak{K}_{s+1}$-norm of u_ε in terms of the $\mathfrak{K}_s$-norms of Qu_ε and u_ε. Inductively, we may assume that $u \in \mathfrak{K}_s$, and then the s-norm of u_ε is bounded by the s-norm of u.

It remains to bound the s-norm of Qu_ε. We know how to bound the s-norm of $(Qu)_\varepsilon = -(Ru)_\varepsilon + v_\varepsilon$, and so we must bound the s-norm of the difference

$$(**) \qquad\qquad (Qu)_\varepsilon - Q(u_\varepsilon).$$

For constant-coefficient operators this is zero, and so in general we may expect a bound in terms of the s-norm of u and 1-norm of the $a_{ij}^k(x)$'s. For simplicity we do the case $s=0$, the general argument being the same. The ith component of $(**)$ is

$$\frac{\partial}{\partial x^k}\left(\sum_{j,k} a_{ij}^k u_j\right) - \sum_{j,k} a_{ij}^k \frac{\partial}{\partial x^k}(u_j)_\varepsilon - \left[\sum_{j,k} \frac{\partial a_{ij}^k}{\partial x^k} u_j\right]_\varepsilon.$$

The last term is bounded by a constant times the L^2-norm of u. The other term is

$$\frac{1}{\varepsilon^{n+1}}\sum_{j,k}\int_{\mathbb{R}^n}(D_k\chi)\left(\frac{y}{\varepsilon}\right)\left(a_{ij}^k(x-y)-a_{ij}^k(x)\right)u_j(x-y)\,dy,$$

and the Minkowski inequality implies that its L_2-norm is less than

$$\left(\frac{C}{\varepsilon^{n+1}} \int_{\|y\| \leqslant \varepsilon K} \left|(D_k \chi)\left(\frac{y}{\varepsilon}\right)\right| |y| \, dy\right) \|u\|_0 \leqslant C' \|u\|_0$$

for suitable constants C, C'. 　　　　　　　　　　　　　　　　　　　　　　Q.E.D.

Cohomology of Currents

On a manifold M we have defined the *complex of currents* $(\mathcal{D}^*(M), d)$. The inclusion of smooth forms into the currents gives a natural map

$$H^*_{\mathrm{DR}}(M) \to H^*(\mathcal{D}^*(M), d)$$

from de Rham cohomology into the cohomology computed from currents. We will prove that this mapping is an isomorphism. By de Rham's theorem the same is true of the mapping

$$H^*(M, \mathrm{sing}) \to H^*(\mathcal{D}^*(M), d)$$

from the cohomology of piecewise smooth singular chains into the cohomology of currents. If Γ is a piecewise smooth $(n-p)$-cycle, then there will be a smooth, closed p-form ψ such that the equation of currents

$$T_\Gamma = T_\psi + dR$$

will be satisfied. Although we will not prove it, one may think of R as the current defined by a $(p-1)$-form η that is integrable on M, C^∞ on $M - \Gamma$, and where $d\eta = -\psi$ on $M - \Gamma$. Then the equation above becomes

$$dT_\eta - T_{d\eta} = T_\Gamma,$$

which is a residue formula of the sort discussed above.

Before doing this, we note that if M is a complex manifold, then we also have the complex $(\mathcal{D}^{p,*}(M), \bar{\partial})$ of currents of type (p, q). We will also prove that the map

$$H^{p,*}_{\bar{\partial}}(M) \to H^*(\mathcal{D}^{p,*}(M), \bar{\partial})$$

is an isomorphism. Since both proofs are essentially the same, we will do the complex case.

Let $\mathcal{D}^{p,q}$ be the sheaf of currents of type (p, q). Then there is a *complex of sheaves*

$(*)$ 　　　　　　$0 \to \Omega^p \to \mathcal{D}^{p,0} \xrightarrow{\bar{\partial}} \mathcal{D}^{p,1} \to \cdots \xrightarrow{\bar{\partial}} \mathcal{D}^{p,n} \to 0.$

Since distributions may be multiplied by C^∞ functions, the sheaves $\mathcal{D}^{p,q}$ admit partitions of unity. Consequently, $H^k(M, \mathcal{D}^{p,q}) = 0$ for $k > 0$, and the sheaf-theoretic proof of the de Rham and Dolbeault theorems from Section 3 of Chapter 0 will apply verbatim if we can prove that $(*)$ is exact. In other words, we must establish the $\bar{\partial}$-Poincaré lemma for currents.

The first step is just the regularity theorem for the $\bar{\partial}$-operator. Note that this step is trivial for the full exterior derivative d.

To prove the $\bar{\partial}$-Poincaré lemma for higher-degree currents, we shall give another proof for the C^∞ case that can be adapted to currents. This proof will be based on finding a homotopy operator

$$K: A_c^{0,q}(\mathbb{C}^n) \to A^{0,q-1}(\mathbb{C}^n).$$

The construction of K is based on the Bochner-Martinelli formula above, and the explicit expression will turn out to be useful in proving the holomorphic Lefschetz fixed-point formula.

Some notation will be helpful in defining K. Given complex manifolds M and N with local holomorphic coordinates z and w, the forms on the product $M \times N$ decompose into *bitype*, where, e.g.,

$$A^{(p,q)(r,s)}(M \times N)$$

denotes the C^∞ forms having type (p,q) in dz's and (r,s) in dw's, and therefore type $(p+r, q+s)$ on $M \times N$. We set

$$\Phi(\zeta) = d\bar{\zeta}_1 \wedge \cdots \wedge d\bar{\zeta}_n,$$

$$\Phi_i(\zeta) = (-1)^{i-1} \bar{\zeta}_i \, d\bar{\zeta}_1 \wedge \cdots \wedge \widehat{d\bar{\zeta}_i} \wedge \cdots \wedge d\bar{\zeta}_n,$$

and define the *Bochner-Martinelli kernel* on $\mathbb{C}^n \times \mathbb{C}^n$ by

$$k(z,w) = C_n \frac{\sum \overline{\Phi_i(z-w)} \wedge \Phi(w)}{\|z-w\|^{2n}}.$$

This form has singularities along the diagonal $z = w$ and is integrable on $\mathbb{C}^n \times \mathbb{C}^n$. Its decomposition into bitype is

$$k(z,w) \in \bigoplus_{q=1}^n L^{(0,q-1)(n,n-q)}(\mathbb{C}^n \times \mathbb{C}^n, \text{loc}).$$

We then define

$$K: A_c^{0,q}(\mathbb{C}^n) \to A^{0,q-1}(\mathbb{C}^n)$$

by

$$(K\varphi)(z) = \int_{w \in \mathbb{C}^n} k(z,w) \wedge \varphi(w).$$

This integral makes sense, since k is integrable and φ has compact support. With the usual change of variables $u = z - w$,

$$(K\varphi)(z) = \int_{u \in \mathbb{C}^n} k(z, z-u) \wedge \varphi(z-u)$$

is C^∞ in z since only $\|u\|^{2n}$ will appear in the denominator of the integrand.

We note that $K\varphi$ does not have compact support. There are analogues of $K\varphi$ for forms $\varphi \in A_c^{p,q}(\mathbb{C}^n)$ $(p \neq 0)$, but we shall leave it to the reader to write these out.

What we need to know about K is the *homotopy formula*

$$\bar\partial K + K\bar\partial = \text{identity}.$$

Proof. Since

$$\bar\partial \left(\frac{\sum \overline{\Phi_i(\zeta)}}{\|\zeta\|^{2n}} \right) = \frac{n\,\overline{\Phi(\zeta)}}{\|\zeta\|^{2n}} - \frac{n\bar\partial(\zeta,\zeta) \wedge \sum \overline{\Phi_i(\zeta)}}{\|\zeta\|^{2n+2}}$$

$$= \frac{n}{\|\zeta\|^{2n}} \left[\overline{\Phi(\zeta)} - \frac{\left(\sum \zeta_i\, \overline{d\zeta_i} \right) \wedge \left(\sum \overline{\Phi_i(\zeta)} \right)}{\|\zeta\|^2} \right]$$

$$= 0,$$

we see that *formally* $\bar\partial k(z,w)=0$. Ignoring for a moment the singularities, for a test form $\psi \in A_c^{n,n-q+1}(\mathbb{C}^n)$ Stokes' theorem gives

$$0 = \int_{\mathbb{C}^n \times \mathbb{C}^n} d(\psi(z) \wedge k(z,w) \wedge \varphi(w))$$

$$= \int_{\mathbb{C}^n \times \mathbb{C}^n} \bar\partial(\psi(z) \wedge k(z,w) \wedge \varphi(w))$$

$$= \int_{\mathbb{C}^n \times \mathbb{C}^n} \bar\partial\psi(z) \wedge k(z,w) \wedge \varphi(w) \pm \int_{\mathbb{C}^n \times \mathbb{C}^n} \psi(z) \wedge k(z,w) \wedge \bar\partial\varphi(w).$$

This equation says that, considering $K_\varphi = K\varphi \in A^{0,q-1}(\mathbb{C}^n)$ as a current operating on $A_c^{n,n-q+1}(\mathbb{C}^n)$,

$(*)$ $\bar\partial K_\varphi + K_\varphi \bar\partial = 0.$

Of course this formal computation is not correct, because in applying Stokes' theorem the singularities of the kernel along the diagonal come into the picture. Referring to the previously established Bochner-Martinelli formula,

$$\eta(0) = C_n \int_{\mathbb{C}^n} \bar\partial\eta(\zeta) \wedge \frac{\sum \overline{\Phi_i(\zeta)} \wedge \Phi(\zeta)}{\|\zeta\|^{2n}}$$

for $\eta \in C_c^\infty(\mathbb{C}^n)$, it seems pretty clear that the correction term that must be added to the right-hand side of $(*)$ is just the identity. This may be proved by writing everything out and using the Bochner-Martinelli formula, but since it is completely straightforward to carry out the computation, we will not do it here.

A first application of the homotopy formula is another proof of the $\bar{\partial}$-Poincaré lemma for smooth forms. Given a $\bar{\partial}$-closed form $\varphi \in A^{0,q}(U)$, where $U \subset \mathbb{C}^n$ is an open set, we may find a relatively compact open subset $V \subset U$ and bump function $\rho \in C_c^{\infty}(U)$ with $\rho \equiv 1$ on V. Then $\rho \varphi \in A_c^{0,q}(\mathbb{C}^n)$, and

$$(\rho\varphi)(z) = \bar{\partial}(K\rho\varphi)(z) + K\big(\bar{\partial}(\rho\varphi)\big)(z).$$

Restricting to V,

$$\varphi(z) = \bar{\partial}(K\rho\varphi)(z) \qquad (z \in V).$$

Now, suppose we say that a current $T \in \mathscr{D}^{0,q}(\mathbb{C}^n)$ is *compactly supported* if, for some relatively compact open set $U \subset\subset \mathbb{C}^n$, $T(\varphi) = 0$ whenever $\operatorname{supp}\varphi \subset\subset \mathbb{C}^n - U$. Such a current may then be defined on all of $A^{n,n-q}(\mathbb{C}^n)$, not just on the forms with compact support. Using this device, we may define KT for a compactly supported current T by

$$KT(\varphi) = T(K\varphi), \qquad \varphi \in A_c^{n,n-q+1}(\mathbb{C}^n).$$

Then $KT \in \mathscr{D}^{0,q-1}(\mathbb{C}^n)$, and for a test form $\psi \in A_c^{n,n-q}(\mathbb{C}^n)$,

$$\begin{aligned}
\big(\bar{\partial}(KT)\big)(\psi) + \big(K(\bar{\partial}T)\big)(\psi) &= (KT)(\bar{\partial}\psi) + (\bar{\partial}T)(K\psi) \\
&= T(K\bar{\partial}\psi + \bar{\partial}K\psi) \\
&= T_\psi,
\end{aligned}$$

so that, with this interpretation, the homotopy formula makes sense for compactly supported currents. In particular, the proof of the $\bar{\partial}$-Poincaré lemma for smooth forms may be extended verbatim to prove the result for currents.

This completes the argument establishing the isomorphisms

$$H_{\bar{\partial}}^{p,*}(M) \longrightarrow H^{p,*}\big(\mathscr{D}^{p,*}(M), \bar{\partial}\big),$$

$$H_{\mathrm{DR}}^*(M) \longrightarrow H^*\big(\mathscr{D}^*(M), d\big),$$

which we shall refer to as *smoothing of cohomology*.

2. APPLICATIONS OF CURRENTS TO COMPLEX ANALYSIS

Currents Associated to Analytic Varieties

Let M be a complex manifold. The currents $\mathscr{D}^{p,p}(M)$ of type (p,p) are the continuous linear functionals on the compactly supported forms $A_c^{n-p,n-p}(M)$. A (p,p) current T is *real* in case $T = \bar{T}$ in the sense that

$\overline{T(\varphi)} = T(\bar{\varphi})$ for all $\varphi \in A_c^{n-p,n-p}(M)$, and a real current is *positive* in case

$$(\sqrt{-1})^{p(p-1)/2} T(\eta \wedge \bar{\eta}) \geqslant 0, \qquad \eta \in A_c^{n-p,0}(M).$$

Especially noteworthy are the *closed, positive currents*. Note that for real $T \in \mathcal{D}^{p,p}(M)$,

$$dT = 0 \Leftrightarrow \partial T = \bar{\partial} T = 0.$$

The positivity of a current implies that it is order zero in the sense of distributions. For example, a current $T \in \mathcal{D}^{1,1}(M)$ is locally written as

$$T = \frac{\sqrt{-1}}{2} \sum_{i,j} t_{ij} \, dz_i \wedge d\bar{z}_j,$$

a differential form with distribution coefficients defined by

$$t_{ij}(\alpha) = (-1)^{n+i+j} (\alpha \, dz_1 \wedge \cdots \wedge \widehat{dz_i} \wedge \cdots \wedge dz_n \wedge d\bar{z}_1 \wedge \cdots \wedge \widehat{d\bar{z}_j} \wedge \cdots \wedge d\bar{z}_n).$$

The current is real if $\bar{t}_{ij} = t_{ji}$, and positive if for any $\lambda_1, \ldots, \lambda_n$ the distribution

$$\alpha \to T(\lambda)(\alpha) = \left(\sum_{i,j} t_{ij} \lambda_i \bar{\lambda}_j \right)(\alpha)$$

is nonnegative on positive functions. In this case, by taking monotone limits we may extend the domain of definition of $T(\lambda)$ to a suitable class of functions—including all the continuous functions—in $L^1(M, \text{loc})$ that are integrable for the positive measure $T(\lambda)$. A similar discussion applies to positive (p,p) currents.

Examples

1. Let $Z \subset M$ be a codimension-p analytic subvariety with $Z^* = Z - Z_s$ the set of smooth points. In the subsection on calculus on complex manifolds in Section 2 of Chapter 0 we proved what, in the language of currents, amounts to the assertion that the map

$$\varphi \to \int_{Z^*} \varphi, \qquad \varphi \in A_c^{n-p,n-p}(M),$$

defines a closed, positive current T_Z. This example is of fundamental importance.

The cohomology class defined by T_Z together with the isomorphism

$$H_{\text{DR}}^*(M) \cong H^*(\mathcal{D}^*(M), d)$$

is the fundamental class of Z.

2. A smooth $(1,1)$ form

$$\omega = \frac{\sqrt{-1}}{2} \left(\sum_{i,j} h_{ij} \, dz_i \wedge d\bar{z}_j \right)$$

is real if $\bar{h}_{ij} = h_{ji}$, strictly positive if the matrix h_{ij} is positive definite, and closed exactly when the corresponding hermitian metric

$$ds^2 = \sum_{i,j} h_{ij} \, dz_i \, d\bar{z}_j$$

is Kähler. The powers ω^p of a Kähler form define closed, positive (p,p) currents.

3. A real function $\varphi \in L^1(M, \text{loc})$ is said to be *plurisubharmonic* in case $\sqrt{-1} \, \partial\bar{\partial}\varphi$ is a positive $(1,1)$ current. Here the derivatives are taken in the sense of distributions. Plurisubharmonic functions define potentials especially suitable for complex function theory.

Lemma ($\partial\bar{\partial}$-Poincaré Lemma). *Let T be a closed, positive $(1,1)$ current. Then locally*

$$T = \sqrt{-1} \, \partial\bar{\partial}\varphi$$

for a real plurisubharmonic function φ, which is unique up to adding the real part of a holomorphic function.

Proof. By the $\bar{\partial}$-Poincaré lemma, locally

$$T = -\sqrt{-1} \, \bar{\partial}\eta$$

for some current η of type $(1,0)$. The current $\partial\eta$ is of type $(2,0)$, and $\bar{\partial}(\partial\eta) = -\partial\bar{\partial}\eta = (1/\sqrt{-1})\partial T = 0$. By the regularity theorem for the $\bar{\partial}$-operator, $\partial\eta$ is a closed holomorphic 2-form, and so by the d-Poincaré lemma for holomorphic forms $\partial\eta = d\xi$ for a holomorphic 1-form ξ. Then $T = -\sqrt{-1} \, \bar{\partial}\eta'$, where $\eta' = \eta - \xi$ satisfies $\partial\eta' = 0$. Now, by the ∂-Poincaré lemma, $\eta' = \partial\gamma$ for some distribution γ; $\varphi = \frac{1}{2}(\gamma + \bar{\gamma})$ is then a real distribution satisfying $\sqrt{-1} \, \partial\bar{\partial}\varphi = T$.

Using the fact that $\sqrt{-1} \, \partial\bar{\partial}\varphi$ is a distribution of order zero, it may be proved that φ is a locally L^1 function, but we will not completely prove this, since we do not need it. Intuitively, the argument is that

$$\Delta\varphi = \sqrt{-1} \, \Lambda\partial\bar{\partial}\varphi$$

is a distribution of order zero, hence it is (more or less) in the Sobolev space H_0. By the regularity theorem, then, φ is (more or less) in the Sobolev space H_2.

The function φ is called a *potential* for T, and it is unique up to adding a real function γ with $\partial\bar{\partial}\gamma = 0$. If γ is any such function then $\partial\gamma$ is a $\bar{\partial}$-closed current of type $(1,0)$, and so again by regularity is a closed holomorphic 1-form. Setting $f(z) = \int_{z_0}^{z} \partial\gamma$, then, we have $\gamma = \text{Re} \, f$.   Q.E.D.

If $T = T_\omega$ is the current associated to a Kähler metric, then its potential function φ is smooth. For instance, $\varphi(z) = \|z\|^2$ is a global potential function for the Euclidean metric on $\mathbb{C}^n$.

At the other extreme we have the

Lemma (Poincaré-Lelong Equation). *If the holomorphic function $f \in \mathcal{O}(M)$ has divisor the analytic hypersurface Z, then the equation of currents*

$$T_Z = \frac{\sqrt{-1}}{\pi} \, \partial\bar{\partial} \log|f|$$

is valid.

Proof. Around a smooth point we may choose coordinates $(z_1, \ldots, z_n)$ such that $f(z) = z_n$. Then

$$\frac{\sqrt{-1}}{\pi} \, \partial\bar{\partial} \log|f| = \bar{\partial}\left(\frac{1}{2\pi\sqrt{-1}} \, \partial \log f \right)$$

$$= \bar{\partial}\left(\frac{1}{2\pi\sqrt{-1}} \, \frac{dz_n}{z_n} \right)$$

$$= T_{\{z_n = 0\}}$$

by an obvious extension of the 1-variable Cauchy formula (in distributional form)

$$\bar{\partial}\left(\frac{1}{2\pi\sqrt{-1}} \, \frac{dz}{z} \right) = \delta_{\{0\}}$$

allowing dependence on parameters.

Next, suppose that $p(w) = w^n + a_1 w^{n-1} + \cdots + a_0$ is a polynomial in one complex variable, possibly with repeated roots. Then we have the distribution equation

$$\bar{\partial}\left(\frac{1}{2\pi\sqrt{-1}} \, \frac{p'(w)\,dw}{p(w)} \right) = \sum_{p(w_\nu)=0} \delta_{w_\nu}.$$

This means that the 1-form $\partial \log p(w)$ is integrable, and moreover for $\alpha \in C_c^\infty(\mathbb{C})$,

$$\frac{1}{2\pi\sqrt{-1}} \int\!\!\int \frac{\partial\alpha(w)}{\partial\bar{w}} \, \frac{p'(w)}{p(w)} \, dw \wedge d\bar{w} = \sum_{p(w_\nu)=0} \alpha(w_\nu).$$

The formula follows by writing $p(w) = \prod_{\nu=1}^n (w - w_\nu)$ and using the Cauchy formula on each factor.

Returning to the general Poincaré-Lelong formula, we must show that $\log|f|$ is integrable and

$$\frac{\sqrt{-1}}{\pi} \int_M \log|f| \, \bar{\partial}\partial\varphi = \int_{Z^*} \varphi$$

for $\varphi \in A_c^{n-1,n-1}(M)$. The problem is local around a point $p \in Z$ with local coordinates $(z_1,\ldots,z_n)$. We may assume that $f(z_1,\ldots,z_n)$ is a Weierstrass polynomial in z_n and that

$$\varphi = \alpha(z)\,dz_1 \wedge \cdots \wedge dz_{n-1} \wedge d\bar{z}_1 \wedge \cdots \wedge d\bar{z}_{n-1},$$

since these forms generate all forms under coordinate stretchings,

$$z_1' = z_1, \ \ldots, \ z_{n-1}' = z_{n-1}, \qquad z_n' = \beta_1 z_1 + \cdots + \beta_{n-1}z_{n-1} + z_n.$$

Effectively, then, we are reduced to 2-variables (z,w), where

$$\varphi = \alpha(z,w)\,dz \wedge \overline{dz}$$

and

$$f(z,w) = w^n + a_1(z)w^{n-1} + \cdots + a_0(z) = \prod_{\nu=1}^{n} (w - w_\nu(z))$$

is a Weierstrass polynomial. By iteration, the integral in question is a constant times

$$\int_{|z| \leqslant 1} \left(\int_{|w| < 1} \log|f(z,w)| \frac{\partial^2 \alpha(z,w)}{\partial w\, \partial \bar{w}}\, dw \wedge d\bar{w} \right) dz \wedge \overline{dz}\ .$$

Applying first Stokes' theorem and then the polynomial result to the inner integral gives

$$\int_{|z| \leqslant 1} \left(\sum_\nu \alpha(z, w_\nu(z)) \right) dz \wedge d\bar{z} = \int_Z \varphi. \qquad \text{Q.E.D.}$$

One may suspect that a general closed, positive current should be somewhere between the smooth currents and those supported by analytic varieties. This turns out to be basically true, and in order to describe what is known, we show how a closed, positive current $T \in \mathcal{D}^{p,p}(U)$ an open set U in $\mathbb{C}^n$ has associated to each point p a Lelong number

$$\Theta(T,p) \geqslant 0,$$

which is identically zero for smooth currents, and where at the other extreme

$$\Theta(T_Z,p) = \text{mult}_p(Z)$$

gives the multiplicity of an analytic variety Z at a point.

For simplicity we assume $U = \mathbb{C}^n$, p is the origin, and we use the notations

$$B[r] = \{z \in \mathbb{C}^n : \|z\| \leqslant r\},$$
$$\chi(r) = \text{characteristic function of } B[r],$$
$$B[r,R] = \{z \in \mathbb{C}^n : r \leqslant \|z\| \leqslant R\} \qquad (r < R),$$
$$\omega = \frac{\sqrt{-1}}{2}\left(\sum_i dz_i \wedge d\bar{z}_i \right).$$

As mentioned above, by taking monotone limits the current T may be defined on suitable L^1-forms, such as $\chi(r)\omega^{n-p}$. In case $T = T_Z$,

$$T_Z(\chi(r)\omega^{n-p}) = \int_{Z \cap B[r]} \omega^{n-p}$$
$$= \text{volume of } (Z \cap B[r])$$

by the Wirtinger theorem from Section 2 of Chapter 0. In general we set

$$\Theta(T,p,r) = \frac{1}{r^{2n-2p}} T(\chi(r)\omega^{n-p})$$

and shall prove the

Lemma. $\Theta(T,p,r)$ *is an increasing function of* r.

Proof. The smoothing T_ε of a closed, positive current is again a closed, positive current. Using this it will suffice to prove the lemma when $T = T_\psi$ for a smooth, closed (p,p) form ψ. Then

$$\Theta(T,p,r) = \frac{1}{r^{2n-2p}} \int_{B[r]} \psi \wedge \omega^{n-p}$$

$$= \left(\frac{\sqrt{-1}}{2}\right)^{n-p} \frac{1}{r^{2n-2p}} \int_{B[r]} \psi \wedge (\partial\bar{\partial}\|z\|^2)^{n-p}$$

$$= \left(\frac{\sqrt{-1}}{2}\right)^{n-p} \frac{1}{r^{2n-2p}} \int_{B[r]} d(\psi \wedge \bar{\partial}\|z\|^2 \wedge (\partial\bar{\partial}\|z\|^2)^{n-p-1},$$

since ψ is closed,

$$= \left(\frac{\sqrt{-1}}{2}\right)^{n-p} \frac{1}{r^{2n-2p}} \int_{\partial B[r]} \psi \wedge \bar{\partial}\|z\|^2 \wedge (\partial\bar{\partial}\|z\|^2)^{n-p-1}$$

by Stokes' theorem.

Now on the sphere $\|z\| = r$,

$$0 = d(z,z) = (dz,z) + (z,dz)$$

$$\Rightarrow \partial\bar{\partial}\log(z,z) = \partial\left(\frac{(z,dz)}{(z,z)}\right) = \frac{(dz,dz)}{(z,z)},$$

since $(dz,z) \wedge (z,dz) = -(dz,z) \wedge (dz,z) = 0$. The last integral is therefore equal to

$$\left(\frac{\sqrt{-1}}{2}\right)^{n-p} \int_{\|z\|=r} \psi \wedge \bar{\partial}\log\|z\|^2 \wedge (\partial\bar{\partial}\log\|z\|^2)^{n-p-1}.$$

By Stokes' theorem, for $r < R$ (remembering that p is the origin)

$$\Theta(T_\psi, p, R) - \Theta(T_\psi, p, r)$$

$$= \int_{\partial B[r,R]} \psi \wedge \left\{ \left(\frac{\sqrt{-1}}{2} \right)^{n-p} \bar\partial \log \|z\|^2 \wedge (\partial\bar\partial \log \|z\|^2)^{n-p-1} \right\}$$

$$= \pi^{n-p} \int_{B[r,R]} \psi \wedge \Omega^{n-p},$$

where

$$\Omega = \frac{\sqrt{-1}}{2\pi} \partial\bar\partial \log \|z\|^2$$

is the pullback to $\mathbb{C}^n$ of the Fubini-Study metric on $\mathbb{P}^{n-1}$. Since $\psi \wedge \Omega^{n-p} \geqslant 0$, we have proved the lemma. $\qquad$ Q.E.D.

DEFINITION. The *Lelong number* is

$$\Theta(T, p) = \frac{1}{\pi^{n-p}} \lim_{r \to 0} \Theta(T, p, r).$$

It is clear that $\Theta(T, p) \geqslant 0$ and is identically equal to zero in case T is a smooth current. As indicated above

$$\Theta(T_Z, p) = \operatorname{mult}_p(Z)$$

for currents defined by analytic varieties.

Sketch of proof. By the proof of the previous lemma,

$$\Theta(T_Z, 0) = \lim_{r \to 0} \int_{Z[r]} \Omega^{n-1},$$

where $Z[r] \subset \mathbb{P}^{n-1}$ is the set of lines $\overrightarrow{0q}$ for $q \in Z \cap B[r]$ and Ω is the standard Kähler form on $\mathbb{P}^{n-1}$. The limiting position of $Z[r]$ as $r \downarrow 0$ is the tangent cone $C(Z)$ to Z at the origin, and by the Wirtinger theorem applied this time to the projective space $\mathbb{P}^{n-1}$,

$$\int_{C(Z)} \Omega^{n-p} = \operatorname{degree}(C(Z))$$

$$= \operatorname{mult}_{\{0\}}(Z). \qquad \text{Q.E.D.}$$

This proof is not too difficult to make precise, and it is essentially obvious in case the origin is a smooth point of Z, which is all we shall use. Since the Lelong number is semicontinuous, it follows that

$$\Theta(T_Z, p) \geqslant 1$$

for $p \in Z$.

Building upon previous work by several authors, Siu has recently proved that for a general closed, positive current T the set of points where

$$\Theta(T,p) \geqslant \varepsilon > 0$$

is supported in a codimension-p analytic subvariety.* We shall not use this result, but it is worthwhile to keep in mind when we discuss the proper mapping theorem in the section after next, where in fact a special case of Siu's theorem will be proved.

Intersection Numbers of Analytic Varieties

Suppose that M is a compact, oriented manifold of real dimension n. Two closed currents T, S of complementary degrees have an *intersection number* defined by

$$T \cdot S = \int_M T_\varepsilon \wedge S_\delta,$$

where T_ε, S_δ are smooth forms in the cohomology classes defined by T and S using the isomorphism

$$H^*(\mathcal{D}^*(M), d) \cong H^*_{DR}(M).$$

This intersection number coincides with the usual topological one on piecewise smooth singular cycles, with the cup product on the smooth forms considered as currents, and with the usual pairing

$$\int_\Gamma \psi$$

of forms on cycles when $T = T_\psi$ for a smooth form ψ and $S = T_\Gamma$ for a piecewise smooth chain Γ.

In case M is a complex manifold of complex dimension n, the pairing

$$H^{p,q}_{\bar{\partial}}(M) \otimes H^{n-p,n-q}_{\bar{\partial}}(M) \to \mathbb{C}$$

induces an intersection number on $\bar{\partial}$-closed currents of complementary type (p,q) and $(n-p,n-q)$. In case $p = q$ and T is a real (p,p) current and S a real $(n-p,n-p)$ current, then

$$dT = 0 \Leftrightarrow \bar{\partial}T = 0,$$
$$dS = 0 \Leftrightarrow \bar{\partial}S = 0,$$

and the intersection number of closed currents is the same in either the d or $\bar{\partial}$ sense.

---

*Y. T. Siu, Analyticity of sets associated to Lelong numbers and the extension of closed positive currents, *Bull. Amer. Math. Soc.*, Vol. 79 (1973), pp. 1200–1205.

Now suppose that T is a closed, positive (p,p) current. Then by the smoothing of cohomology there is a closed, real smooth (p,p) form T_ε in the same cohomology class at T. With some care we could insure that

$$\lim_{\varepsilon \to 0} T_\varepsilon = T.$$

However, we *cannot* say that the T_ε are positive forms. For example, suppose that $M = \tilde{N}_p$ is the blow-up of a two-dimensional complex manifold N at a point p. The fiber over p in $M \to N$ is a curve $E \cong \mathbb{P}^1$ with normal bundle H^*, where $H \to \mathbb{P}^1$ has Chern class $+1$. Thus the self-intersection number $E \cdot E = -1$. If T_ε is a smoothing of T_E, then

$$E \cdot E = \int_E T_\varepsilon$$

shows that we cannot take T_ε to be a positive $(1,1)$ form.

The intuitive reason for this is that T_ε is a smooth form supported in ε-tubular neighborhood of E, and so T_ε has to do with the shape of the normal bundle of E. To say that T_ε is positive would be something like saying that the normal bundle has positive curvature, which is not the case in this example.

Using the theory of currents, we now will reprove the fundamental result from Section 4 of Chapter 0 about positivity of intersection numbers of analytic varieties meeting in isolated points.

Theorem. *Suppose that* Z *and* W *are analytic subvarieties of complementary dimensions* p *and* n−p *in* M *that meet at a finite number of points of* M. *Then the intersection number*

$$Z \cdot W = \sum_{p \in Z \cap W} m_p(Z, W),$$

where $(Z, W)_p$ *depends only on* Z *and* W *in a neighborhood of* p *and satisfies*

$$m_p(Z, W) \geq \mathrm{mult}_p(Z)\,\mathrm{mult}_p(W).$$

Proof. We first argue that we may assume W to be smooth. For this we consider the product $M \times M$. By the formal properties of the Künneth formula and Poincaré duality,

$$Z \cdot W = (Z \times W) \cdot \Delta,$$

where the right-hand side is the intersection number in $M \times M$ of $Z \times W$ with the diagonal Δ. Set-theoretically,

$$(Z \times W) \cap \Delta = \{(p,p) : p \in Z \cap W\}.$$

Also, it has been established in Section 1 of Chapter 0 that

$$\mathrm{mult}_{p \times q}(Z \times W) = \mathrm{mult}_p(Z)\,\mathrm{mult}_q(W).$$

Since the diagonal is smooth, the general case is therefore reduced to the situation when W is smooth.

Next, we may for simplicity assume that Z and W meet in a single point p_0. We may choose a holomorphic coordinate system $(z, w) = (z_1, \ldots, z_p; w_1, \ldots, w_{n-p})$ around p_0 such that W is given by $z = 0$ and the projection $(z, w) \to z$ is a finitely sheeted branched covering mapping on Z. Set $U_\varepsilon = \{(z, w) : \|z\| < \varepsilon, \|w\| < \varepsilon\}$ and let $U = U_1$. The picture is shown by Figure 1.

Suppose now that we have a current $S \in \mathcal{D}^{p,p-1}(U)$ such that

$$T_W | U = \bar{\partial} S.$$

Let ρ be a bump function that is 1 in U_{ε_0} and has compact support in U. Then

$$T'_W = T_W - \bar{\partial}(\rho S)$$

is a globally defined current on M in the same cohomology class as T_W. Moreover, $T'_W = (T_W - \rho \bar{\partial} S) - \bar{\partial}\rho \wedge S$ is smooth near $Z \cap W$, and so the integral

$$\int_Z T'_W$$

is defined and computes the intersection number $Z \cdot W$. If $Z_\varepsilon = Z \cap U_\varepsilon$, then since $T'_W = 0$ near p_0,

$$\int_Z T'_W = \lim_{\varepsilon \to 0} \int_{Z - Z_\varepsilon} T'_W$$

$$= \lim_{\varepsilon \to 0} - \int_{Z - Z_\varepsilon} \bar{\partial}(\rho S)$$

$$= \lim_{\varepsilon \to 0} \int_{\partial Z_\varepsilon} S$$

by Stokes' theorem. The formula

$$Z \cdot W = \lim_{\varepsilon \to 0} \int_{\partial Z_\varepsilon} S$$

reduces us to a purely local question.

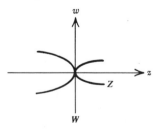

Figure 1

We take for S the current T_β defined by the Bochner-Martinelli form

$$\beta(z) = C_n\left(\partial \log\|z\|^2 \wedge (\partial\bar\partial \log\|z\|^2)^{p-1}\right)$$

discussed in Section 1 of this chapter. The equation

$$\bar\partial T_\beta = T_{\{z=0\}}$$

is just the Bochner-Martinelli formula with trivial dependence on the parameters w. Let $B_\varepsilon \subset \mathbb{C}^p$ be the ball $\{\|z\| < \varepsilon\}$. The projection

$$Z_\varepsilon \xrightarrow{\pi} B_\varepsilon$$

is a $d \geqslant \mathrm{mult}_p(Z)$ sheeted branched covering, and consequently

$$\int_{\partial Z_\varepsilon} S = d\int_{\partial B_\varepsilon} \beta = d. \qquad\qquad \text{Q.E.D.}$$

The local intersection numbers $m_p(Z, W)$ will be discussed once again and in greater detail in case Z and W are locally complete intersections in Section 2 of Chapter 5.

In case W is smooth of dimension 1, so that Z is an analytic hypersurface locally defined by a single holomorphic function f, the above proof gives the formula

$$Z \cdot W = \sum_{p \in Z \cap W} \mathrm{ord}_p\left(f|_W\right).$$

The Levi Extension and Proper Mapping Theorems

We first recall the statement of Remmert's

Proper Mapping Theorem. *Let* U *and* N *be complex manifolds,* M $\subset$ U *an analytic subvariety, and* f : U $\to$ N *a holomorphic mapping whose restriction to* M *is proper. Then the image* f(M) *is an analytic subvariety of* N.

We shall give a proof of this result under one additional technical assumption, which will be trivially satisfied in all of our applications. This is:

For each smooth point p $\in$ M *and each* k-*plane* Λ_p *in the tangent space to* M *at* p(k $\leqslant$ n = dim M), *there is a* k-*dimensional analytic subvariety* Z *of* M *having* Λ_p *as tangent plane at* p.

In practice U will be an open subset of an algebraic variety V, and we may take Z to be a linear section of M.

Our proof of the proper mapping theorem will use the discussion about currents from the preceding sections, together with the following

Levi Extension Theorem (I). *Let* f *be a meromorphic function defined outside an analytic variety* V *of codimension* $\geqslant 2$ *on a complex manifold* M. *Then* f *extends to a meromorphic function on* M.

Proof. Let $(f)_\infty$ be the polar divisor of f in $M - V$, and let $\overline{(f)}_\infty$ be its closure in M. If we make the assumption that $\overline{(f)}_\infty$ is an analytic subvariety of M, then we can argue as follows: for any $p \in M$, let $\overline{(f)}_\infty = (g)$ in a neighborhood U of p. Then $g \cdot f = \tilde{h}$ is holomorphic in $U \cap (M - V)$, and hence by Hartogs' theorem extends to a holomorphic function h in U. So h/g gives a meromorphic extension of f to U.

Since the question of whether $\overline{(f)}_\infty$ is an analytic variety is local around a point of M, the theorem is reduced to

Levi Extension Theorem (II). *In the polycylinder* Δ^n *in* $\mathbb{C}^n$ *let* V *be a codimension* $\geqslant 2$ *analytic subvariety, and* D *a subvariety of codimension* 1 *in* $\Delta^n - V$. *Then the closure* $\overline{D}$ *of* D *in* Δ^n *is analytic.*

Proof. This is a geometric variant of Hartogs' theorem. The analogous general result, where

$$\text{codim} D \leqslant (\text{codim} V) - 1,$$

has been proved by Remmert and Stein.

We begin by making some reductions. If we prove the result when V is nonsingular, then this will imply the general case by the following stratification device: Let V' be the variety of singular points of V, V'' the variety of singular points of V', etc. Applying the nonsingular case to sufficiently small neighborhoods of points $p \in V - V'$, we conclude that D extends to $\Delta^n - V'$. Repeating the argument, D will extend to $\Delta^n - V''$, and so forth.

Next, by localizing around a point of V and choosing coordinates properly, we may assume that V is a linear subspace of $\mathbb{C}^n$. The essential case is thus when $n = 2$ and $V = \{z_1 = z_2 = 0\}$ is the origin. We shall prove the result in this situation, from which the general conclusion may be drawn by analogy.

Let $\Delta' = \{|z_1| < 1, |z_2| < 1, z_1 \neq 0\} \cong \Delta^* \times \Delta$. Then we have proved in Section 3 of Chapter 0 that

$$H^1(\Delta', \mathcal{O}) = H^2(\Delta', \mathbb{Z}) = 0.$$

From the exact cohomology sequence of the exponential sheaf sequence this implies that $H^1(\Delta', \mathcal{O}^*) = 0$. Consequently, if $D^* = D \cap \Delta'$, then the line bundle $[D^*] \rightarrow \Delta'$ is trivial and we conclude that the analytic curve D^* is the divisor of some $h \in \mathcal{O}(\Delta')$.

We may assume that D does not contain the line $\{z_1 = 0\}$, and therefore $D \cap \{z_1 = 0\}$ consists of a finite number of points in the punctured disc

$0<|z_2|<1$. We may find a circle $|z_2|=\varepsilon$ that does not meet these points. It follows by continuity that, for δ sufficiently small, the locus

$$\{|z_1|\leqslant\delta,\ |z_2|=\varepsilon\}$$

will not meet D (Figure 2). For fixed z with $0<|z_1|\leqslant\delta$ the integral

$$\frac{1}{2\pi\sqrt{-1}}\int_{|z_2|=\varepsilon}\frac{dh}{h}$$

is well-defined, continuous, and integer-valued. It follows that D meets each vertical disc $\{z_1=C, |z_2|\leqslant\varepsilon, 0<|C|\leqslant\delta\}$ the same number d of times. Thus, projecting $\bar{D}$ on the z_1-axis gives a proper mapping $\pi:\bar{D}\to\Delta$ that restricts to a d-sheeted covering $\pi:D^*\to\Delta^*$ over the punctured disc. If $d=1$, we have the graph of a bounded holomorphic function, and our result follows from the Riemann extension theorem. In general we use the by-now-familiar argument involving the elementary symmetric functions: set

$$\varphi_i(z) = \frac{1}{2\pi\sqrt{-1}}\int_{|z_2|=\varepsilon}z_2^i\frac{dh(z_1,z_2)}{h(z_1,z_2)}$$

$$= \sum_{\nu=1}^{d}z_{2,\nu}(z_1)^i,$$

where $\pi^{-1}(z_1)=\{(z_1,z_{2,\nu}(z_1)\}_\nu$. The $\varphi_i(z_1)$ are holomorphic and bounded in $0<|z_1|\leqslant\delta$, and hence they extend to holomorphic functions on the full disc. We may then set

$$F(z_1,z_2) = z_2^d + p_1(\varphi_1(z_1),\dots,\varphi_d(z_1))z_2^{d-1}+\cdots+p_d(\varphi_1(z_1),\dots,\varphi_d(z_1))$$

a polynomial in z_1 whose roots are for fixed $z_1\neq0$ just the points $(z_1,z_{2,\nu}(z_1))$, and which is holomorphic in the bicylinder. The divisor of F is D, and we are done.   Q.E.D.

Note: The general principle is this: Let $W\subset\Delta^n$ be a closed subset such that (1) the projection $W\xrightarrow{\pi}\Delta^k$ is proper, and (2) outside an analytic subvariety $Z\subset\Delta^k$ this projection $W^*\xrightarrow{\pi}\Delta^k-Z$ $(W^*=W-\pi^{-1}(Z))$ is an

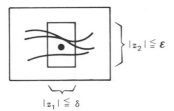

$$|z_1|\leqq\delta \qquad\qquad \textbf{Figure 2}$$

analytic branched covering. Then W is a k-dimensional analytic subvariety of Δ^n.

Now we come to the proof of the proper mapping theorem. We shall give several preliminary reductions before coming to the essential point.

1.   Since $f(M)$ is a closed subset of N, the question is local around a point $p \in f(M)$ in N. So we may assume that N is a polycylinder $\Delta^N = \Delta$ in $\mathbb{C}^N$.

Also, we may assume that M is irreducible, since only a finite number of components of M will have images meeting a given compact set in N.

2.   The proof is by induction on $n = \dim M$. Let $M^* = M - M_s$ be the complex manifold of smooth points of M, and choose a point $p_0 \in M^*$ where the Jacobian matrix of $f : M^* \to \mathbb{C}^N$ has maximum rank $k \leqslant n$. If $k < n$, by our assumption we may choose a k-dimensional analytic subvariety S in M passing through p_0 and such that $f \mid S$ has maximum rank k. We call such an S a *horizontal slice* for $f : M \to \mathbb{C}^N$. It is clear from the implicit function theorem that there is a neighborhood W of p_0 such that $f(W) = f(S \cap W)$. It follows that $f(M) = f(S)$, since M is irreducible.

This reduces us to proving the theorem when f has maximum rank $n = \dim M$ at some point $p_0 \in M^*$. We will then prove that $f(M)$ is an n-dimensional analytic subvariety of the polycylinder.

3.   At this juncture we may define the current $S \in \mathcal{D}^{p,p}(\Delta)$ $(p = N - n)$, which will turn out to be $T_{f(M)}$ once the theorem is proven. The definition is

$$S(\varphi) = \int_{M^*} f^*(\varphi), \qquad \varphi \in A_c^{n,n}(\Delta).$$

Since f is proper and holomorphic, S is a closed, positive current. What we must prove is that it is the current given by integration over an analytic variety, which must then be $f(M)$.

Note that at each point $q \in f(M)$ the Lelong number

$$\Theta(S, q) \geqslant 1.$$

This is true at points $q = f(p)$, where $p \in M^*$ and f has maximum rank, since then one piece of $f(M)$ passing through q will be a complex manifold, and it is therefore true on all of S by semicontinuity.

4.   We next argue that we may assume $N = n + 1$, so that $f(M)$ is to be analytic hypersurface. Precisely, we shall show that for a generic choice of coordinate system, the composition g in

$$
\begin{array}{ccc}
 & \xrightarrow{\;f\;} & \\
M & \longrightarrow & \Delta^N \\
 & {\scriptstyle g} \searrow & \downarrow \pi = \text{projections} \\
 & & \Delta^{n+1}
\end{array}
$$

are proper, at least if we allow ourselves to shrink the polycylinder Δ^N. If this has been established, and if we have proved the result in case $N = n + 1$, then a finite number of analytic functions of the form $h \cdot \pi$, where $h \in \mathcal{O}(\Delta^{n+1})$ has divisor $g(M)$, will define $f(M)$.

To prove the existence of these good projections, we let λ be a generic linear form on $\mathbb{C}^N$ and set $\lambda_f = \lambda \circ f$. Then $\lambda_f = 0$ defines

$$M_\lambda = f^{-1}\text{ (hyperplane section of } f(M)).$$

By the induction assumption, the image of

$$f \colon M_\lambda \to \Delta^{N-1}$$

is an analytic variety of dimension $\leqslant n - 1$. For a generic choice of coordinate system, the coordinate projections

$$f(M_\lambda) \to \Delta^n$$

are all proper mappings.

To complete the argument we make an observation: in $\mathbb{C} \times \mathbb{C}^p \times \mathbb{C}^q$ with coordinates $(u, v_1, \ldots, v_p, w_1, \ldots, w_q) - (u, v, w)$ we suppose given a closed subset S of the polycylinder $\Delta \times \Delta^p \times \Delta^q$ defined by $|u| < \varepsilon$, $|v_i| < \varepsilon$, $|u_\alpha| < \varepsilon$. Suppose that we let $S_0 = S \cap \{u = 0\}$, and assume that the projection $S_0 \to \Delta^p$ induced by $(0, v, w) \to v$ is proper. Then, taking a smaller ε if necessary, the projection $S \to \Delta \times \Delta^p$ induced by $(u, v, w) \to (u, v)$ will again be proper.

Following these reductions we come to the essential point.

Completion of the Proof. The idea is this. We are given a proper holomorphic mapping

$$f \colon M \to \Delta^{n+1}$$

that has maximal rank n at some point $p_0 \in M^*$. We let $W \subset M$ be the union of the singular set of M and subvariety where the Jacobian of f has rank $< n$. By the induction assumption $f(W)$ is an analytic subvariety of codimension $\geqslant 2$ in Δ^{n+1}. The image of a sufficiently small neighborhood of a point $p \in M - W$ is a piece of smooth analytic hypersurface in Δ^{n+1}, and the closure

$$\overline{f(M - W)} = f(M - W) \cup f(W).$$

The problem is therefore to show that the two pieces $f(M - W)$ and $f(W)$ fit together nicely.

What we do know is that

$$\varphi \to \int_{M^*} f^*(\varphi), \qquad \varphi \in A_c^{n,n}(\Delta^{n+1})$$

defines a closed, positive current $S \in \mathcal{D}^{1,1}(\Delta^{n+1})$. By the $\partial\bar{\partial}$-Poincaré lemma we may write

$$S = \frac{\pi}{\sqrt{-1}} \, \partial\bar\partial\varphi,$$

where φ is a real distribution on Δ^{n+1}. Around a point $q \in f(M - W)$ lying outside the codimension $\geqslant 2$ subvariety $f(W)$, the image $f(M)$ is locally the divisor of a holomorphic function h. By the Poincaré-Lelong formula

$$\partial\bar\partial(\varphi - \log|h|) = 0$$

near q, so that $\varphi - \log|h|$ is the real part of a holomorphic function j. This proves that the current

$$\theta = \partial\varphi = d\log h + dj \qquad \text{(locally)}$$

is a closed meromorphic 1-form on $\Delta^{n+1} - f(W)$. By the Levi extension theorem, θ extends to a meromorphic 1-form on all of Δ^{n+1}. The polar divisor of θ contains $f(M - W)$ and therefore is equal to $f(M)$. Equivalently, $f(M)$ is the divisor of the holomorphic function

$$e^{2\pi\sqrt{-1}\int_\theta}.$$

This completes the proof of the proper mapping theorem.

3. CHERN CLASSES

Definitions

In this section we will give the definition and some properties of the basic topological invariants of complex vector bundles, the Chern classes. We will not be concerned with holomorphic bundles until later; for the present, all our manifolds and vector bundles will be simply C^∞.

We begin by recalling some of the definitions of Section 5 of Chapter 0. Let M be a manifold, $E \xrightarrow{\pi} M$ a complex vector bundle, and $\mathcal{C}^p(E)$ the sheaf of E-valued p-forms, that is, the sheaf of C^∞ sections of the bundle $\Lambda^p T^*(M) \otimes E$. We define a *connection* D on E to be an operator

$$D: \mathcal{C}^0(E) \to \mathcal{C}^1(E)$$

satisfying Leibniz' rule

$$D(f \cdot \xi) = df \otimes \xi + f \cdot D\xi$$

for $f \in C^\infty(U)$, $\xi \in \mathcal{C}^0(E)(U)$. If $\varphi_\alpha : E|U_\alpha \to U_\alpha \times \mathbb{C}^n$ is a trivialization of E over $U_\alpha \subset M$, then we can identify sections ξ of E over U_α with n-vectors $\xi_\alpha = {}^t(\xi_{\alpha,1}, \ldots, \xi_{\alpha,n})$ of functions on U_α. If $\{e_{\alpha,i}\}$ is the frame for E over U_α given by the constant vectors $(0, \ldots, 1, \ldots, 0)$, we can write

$$De_{\alpha,i} = \sum \theta_{\alpha_{ij}} \otimes e_{\alpha,j}.$$

The matrix $\theta_\alpha = (\theta_{\alpha_{ij}})$ of 1-forms is called the *connection matrix* for D; we have for a general section $\xi \in \mathcal{C}^0(E)(U_\alpha)$

$$D\xi_\alpha = d\xi_\alpha + {}^t\theta_\alpha \cdot \xi_\alpha.$$

If $\varphi_\beta : E|U_\beta \to U_\beta \times \mathbb{C}^n$ is another trivialization of E over $U_\beta \subset M$ with $\varphi_\alpha = g_{\alpha\beta} \cdot \varphi_\beta$ and θ_β is the connection matrix for D in terms of φ_β, then

$$\theta_\alpha = g_{\alpha\beta} \cdot \theta_\beta \cdot g_{\alpha\beta}^{-1} + dg_{\alpha\beta} \cdot g_{\alpha\beta}^{-1}.$$

Note that the dependence of θ on the choice of frame is nonlinear—i.e., θ is not a tensor field of E. Indeed, by solving the equations $g_{\alpha\beta}(x_0) =$ identity and $dg_{\alpha\beta}(x_0) = -\theta_\alpha(x_0)$, we can find a trivialization of E in a neighborhood of any point $x_0 \in M$ in terms of which the connection matrix $\theta_\beta(x_0)$ of D vanishes at x_0.

We extend the connection D to an operator $D : \mathcal{C}^q(E) \to \mathcal{C}^{q+1}(E)$ by forcing Leibnitz' rule; that is, by setting, for $\xi \in \mathcal{C}^0(E)$ and η a q-form,

$$D(\eta \otimes \xi) = d\eta \otimes \xi + (-1)^q \eta \wedge D\xi \in \mathcal{C}^{q+1}(E).$$

We then define the *curvature operator* Θ by

$$\Theta = D^2 : \mathcal{C}^q(E) \to \mathcal{C}^{q+2}(E).$$

In terms of a trivialization φ_α, we have

$$(\Theta\xi)_\alpha = \Theta_\alpha \xi_\alpha,$$

where Θ_α is the matrix of 2-forms

$$\Theta_\alpha = d\theta_\alpha - \theta_\alpha \wedge \theta_\alpha;$$

Θ_α is called the *curvature matrix* of D in terms of φ_α. If φ_β is another trivialization with $\varphi_\alpha = g_{\alpha\beta}\varphi_\beta$,

$$\Theta_\alpha = g_{\alpha\beta} \Theta_\beta \cdot g_{\alpha\beta}^{-1}.$$

This transition rule just expresses the directly verifiable fact that Θ is linear over $C^\infty(M)$, i.e., that $\Theta \in A^2(\text{Hom}(E, E))$.

In the case of E a line bundle the curvature matrix is, according to the transition rule above, a global 2-form, and we have seen that the cohomology class $[(\sqrt{-1}/2\pi)\Theta]$, the Chern class of E, reflects the topological structure of E. In order to define the general Chern classes of a vector bundle, we digress for a moment to consider those functions of a variable matrix which are invariant under conjugation.

Let $\mathfrak{M}_n \cong \mathbb{C}^{n^2}$ denote the vector space of $n \times n$ matrices. A polynomial function $P : \mathfrak{M}_n \to \mathbb{C}$, homogeneous of degree k in the entries, is said to be *invariant* if

$$P(A) = P(gAg^{-1})$$

for all $A \in \mathfrak{M}_n$, $g \in \text{GL}_n$. The basic examples of such polynomials $P(A)$ are the elementary symmetric polynomials of the eigenvalues of A, i.e., the polynomials $P^i(A)$ defined by the relation

$$\det(A + t \cdot I) = \sum_{k=0}^{n} P^{n-k}(A) \cdot t^k.$$

In particular, $P^n(A) = \det(A)$ and $P^1(A) = \text{trace}(A)$; in general, if for any multiindexes I, $J \subset \{1,\dots,n\}$ we let $A_{I,J}$ denote the (I,J)th minor $(A_{ij})_{i \in I, j \in J}$ of A, we can write

$$P^k(A) = \sum_{\#I = k} \det(A_{I,I})$$

$$= \text{trace}(\wedge^k A).$$

The polynomials P^i are called the *elementary invariant polynomials*. In fact, any holomorphic function f on $\mathfrak{M}_n$ invariant under conjugation is expressible as a power series in the P^i: If we set

$$F(\lambda_1,\dots,\lambda_n) = f \begin{bmatrix} \lambda_1 & & 0 \\ & \ddots & \\ 0 & & \lambda_n \end{bmatrix},$$

then F is a symmetric holomorphic function in $\lambda_1,\dots,\lambda_n$. Write

$$F(\lambda_1,\dots,\lambda_n) = G(\sigma_1,\dots,\sigma_n),$$

where $\sigma_1,\dots,\sigma_n$ are the elementary symmetric polynomials in the λ_i; the equality

$$f(A) = G(P^1(A),\dots,P^n(A))$$

then holds throughout the connected and dense open set of semisimple (i.e., diagonalizable) matrices in GL_n, hence in all of $\mathfrak{M}_n$.

Now, a k-linear form

$$\tilde{P} : \mathfrak{M}_n \times \cdots \times \mathfrak{M}_n \to \mathbb{C}$$

is called *invariant* if for any $A_1,\dots,A_k \in \mathfrak{M}_n$, $g \in \text{GL}_n$,

$$\tilde{P}(A_1,\dots,A_k) = \tilde{P}(gA_1 g^{-1},\dots,gA_k g^{-1}).$$

An invariant form $\tilde{P}$ clearly gives an invariant polynomial P by

$$P(A) = \tilde{P}(A,\dots,A).$$

In fact, the converse is also true: any invariant polynomial P of degree k can be realized as the restriction of a symmetric invariant k-linear form $\tilde{P}$ on $\mathfrak{M}_n \times \cdots \times \mathfrak{M}_n$ to the diagonal. The form $\tilde{P}$, called the *polarization* of P, is uniquely determined by P. For example, for $k = 2$ we have

$$\tilde{P}(A,B) = \tfrac{1}{2}(P(A+B) - P(A) - P(B)).$$

In general, to polarize P^k, if for $(A^1,\dots,A^k) \in (\mathfrak{M}_n)^k$, $\tau \in S_k$ a permutation and $I \subset \{1,\ldots,n\}$ a multiindex of order k, we let A_I^τ be the $k \times k$ matrix whose ith column is the ith column of $A_{I,I}^{\tau(i)}$, then

$$\tilde{P}^k(A_1,\ldots,A_k) = \frac{1}{k!} \sum_{\tau \in S^k} \sum_{\#I=k} \det(A_I^\tau);$$

and the polarizations of a general invariant polynomial—expressed as a polynomial in the elementary invariant polynomials P^i—can be written out in a similarly unenlightening way.

We return now to our complex vector bundle $E \xrightarrow{\pi} M$ of rank n. Let $\{U_\alpha\}$ be an open cover of M with φ_α a trivialization of E over U_α and θ_α and Θ_α the connection and curvature matrices of the connection D on E in terms of φ_α. Then, since the wedge product is commutative on forms of even degree, for any invariant polynomial P of degree k on $\mathfrak{M}_n$ the expression

$$P(\Theta_\alpha)$$

is a well-defined form of degree $2k$ on U_α; since

$$\Theta_\alpha = g_{\alpha\beta} \cdot \Theta_\beta \cdot g_{\alpha\beta}^{-1},$$

we see that

$$P(\Theta_\alpha) = P(\Theta_\beta)$$

in $U_\alpha \cap U_\beta$, so that $P(\Theta) = P(\Theta_\alpha)$ *is a well-defined global* 2k-*form on* M, *independent of the trivializations chosen.* The basic fact is

Lemma. *For* P *any invariant polynomial of degree* k,

1. $dP(\Theta_\alpha) = 0$,
2. *The cohomology class* $[P(\Theta_\alpha)] \in H_{DR}^{2k}(M)$ *is independent of the connection chosen for* E.

Proof. Writing $P(\Theta_\alpha) = \tilde{P}(\Theta_\alpha,\ldots,\Theta_\alpha)$ for $\tilde{P}$ a polarization of P, by linearity

$$dP(\Theta_\alpha) = \sum \tilde{P}(\Theta_\alpha,\ldots,d\Theta_\alpha,\ldots,\Theta_\alpha).$$

Now $\Theta_\alpha = d\theta_\alpha - \theta_\alpha \wedge \theta_\alpha$, so $d\Theta_\alpha = d\theta_\alpha \wedge \theta_\alpha - \theta_\alpha \wedge d\theta_\alpha$. But $P(\Theta_\alpha)$ is invariant under change of frame for E, and as we saw for any $x_0 \in M$, we can find a frame for E in terms of which the connection matrix θ_β vanishes at x_0. Thus

$$dP(\Theta_\alpha) = dP(\Theta_\beta)$$

$$= \sum \pm \tilde{P}(\Theta_\beta,\ldots,d\theta_\beta \wedge \theta_\beta - \theta_\beta \wedge d\theta_\beta,\ldots,\Theta_\beta)$$

$$\Rightarrow dP(\Theta_\beta)(x_0) = 0$$

$$\Rightarrow dP(\Theta) \equiv 0.$$

In order to prove part 2, we need to establish an identity for invariant forms. We consider the holomorphic function on GL_n given by

$$f(g) = P(gA_1g^{-1},\ldots,gA_kg^{-1})$$

for any choice of $A_1,\ldots,A_k \in \mathfrak{M}_n$. Using as coordinates on GL_n the entries of $g' = g - I$, we compute the linear term f_1 of the power series expansion for f around I. First,

$$(I+g')^{-1} = I - g' + [2].$$

Thus

$$\begin{aligned}
f(g) &= P(gA_1g^{-1},\ldots,gA_kg^{-1})\\
&= P((I+g')A_1(I-g'),\ldots,(I+g')A_k(I-g')) + [2]\\
&= P(A_1,\ldots,A_k) + \sum_i P(A_1,\ldots,g'A_i - A_ig',\ldots,A_k) + [2].
\end{aligned}$$

But if P is invariant,

$$f = P(A_1,\ldots,A_k);$$

thus all higher-order terms in the power series for f vanish, and in particular

$$\sum_i P(A_1,\ldots,g'A_i - A_ig',\ldots,A_k) = 0.$$

Now if φ is a 1-form, g a matrix of functions, and A_i a matrix of forms of degree d_i, by multilinearity

$$\begin{aligned}
\sum_i (-1)^{d_1+\cdots+d_{i-1}} P(A_1,\ldots,\varphi\wedge gA_i,\ldots,A_k)\\
&= \sum_i \varphi\wedge P(A_1,\ldots,gA_i,\ldots,A_k)\\
&= \sum_i \varphi\wedge P(A_1,\ldots,A_ig,\ldots,A_k)\\
&= \sum_i (-1)^{d_1+\cdots+d_i} P(A_1,\ldots,A_i\wedge\varphi g,\ldots,A_k).
\end{aligned}$$

In general, if θ is any matrix of 1-forms, θ can be written $\sum \theta_\alpha g_\alpha$, where θ_α is a 1-form and g_α is a matrix of functions; by linearity again,

$$\begin{aligned}
(*) \quad \sum_i (-1)^{d_1+\cdots+d_{i-1}} P(A_1,\ldots,\theta\wedge A_i,\ldots,A_k)\\
&= \sum_i (-1)^{d_1+\cdots+d_i} P(A_1,\ldots,A_i\wedge\theta,\ldots,A_k).
\end{aligned}$$

Now we can prove Part 2. Let $D,\tilde{D}$ be two connections on E, with local connection and curvature matrices θ_α and $\tilde{\theta}_\alpha$, Θ_α and $\tilde{\Theta}_\alpha$. In terms of the trivialization φ_α, we have

$$D\xi_\alpha = d\xi_\alpha + {}'\theta_\alpha\xi_\alpha, \qquad \tilde{D}\xi_\alpha = d\xi_\alpha + {}'\tilde{\theta}_\alpha\xi_\alpha;$$

consequently the operator $\eta = D - \tilde{D}$ is linear over $C^\infty(M)$, and so it is given in terms of the trivialization φ_α as multiplication by the transpose of the matrix $\eta_\alpha = \theta_\alpha - \tilde{\theta}_\alpha$, which transforms by the rule

$$\eta_\alpha = g_{\alpha\beta} \eta_\beta g_{\alpha\beta}^{-1},$$

where $g_{\alpha\beta} = \varphi_\alpha \cdot \varphi_\beta^{-1}$. Consider the homotopy

$$D_t = \tilde{D} + t\eta, \qquad 0 \leqslant t \leqslant 1,$$

between $D_0 = \tilde{D}$ and $D_1 = D$. D_t has connection matrix $\theta_t = \tilde{\theta} + t\eta$, hence curvature matrix

$$\Theta_t = d(\tilde{\theta} + t\eta) - (\tilde{\theta} + t\eta) \wedge (\tilde{\theta} + t\eta).$$

Let P be an invariant polynomial of degree k. We claim that

$$[P(\Theta)] = [P(\tilde{\Theta})] \in H^{2k}_{DR}(M).$$

To prove this, we will consider the arc in $A^{2k}(M)$ given by

$$t \mapsto P(\Theta_t)$$

and show that its tangent vector $(\partial/\partial t) P(\Theta_t)$ lies in the subspace $dA^{2k-1}(M) \subset A^{2k}(M)$; this will show that the image curve $t \mapsto [P(\Theta_t)] \in H^{2k}_{DR}(M)$ is constant. The calculation goes as follows:

$$\frac{\partial}{\partial t} \Theta_t = d\eta - (\tilde{\theta} \wedge \eta + \eta \wedge \tilde{\theta}) - 2t\eta \wedge \eta,$$

hence

$$\frac{\partial}{\partial t} P(\Theta_t) = \frac{\partial}{\partial t} \tilde{P}(\Theta_t, \dots, \Theta_t)$$

$$= k \cdot \tilde{P}\left(\frac{\partial}{\partial t} \Theta_t, \Theta_t, \dots, \Theta_t\right)$$

$$= k\tilde{P}(d\eta, \Theta_t, \dots, \Theta_t) - k\tilde{P}(\tilde{\theta} \wedge \eta + \eta \wedge \tilde{\theta}, \Theta_t, \dots, \Theta_t)$$
$$\quad - 2kt\tilde{P}(\eta \wedge \eta, \Theta_t, \dots, \Theta_t).$$

Applying the identity (∗) with $\theta = \eta$,

$$\tilde{P}(\eta \wedge \eta, \Theta_t, \dots, \Theta_t) - (k-1)\tilde{P}(\eta, \eta \wedge \Theta_t, \Theta_t, \dots, \Theta_t)$$
$$= -\tilde{P}(\eta \wedge \eta, \Theta_t, \dots, \Theta_t) - (k-1)\tilde{P}(\eta, \Theta_t \wedge \eta, \Theta_t, \dots, \Theta_t),$$

so that

$$2kt\tilde{P}(\eta \wedge \eta, \Theta_t, \dots, \Theta_t) = tk(k-1)\tilde{P}(\eta, \eta \wedge \Theta_t - \Theta_t \wedge \eta, \dots, \Theta_t, \dots).$$

Similarly, by (∗),

$$\tilde{P}(\tilde{\theta} \wedge \eta, \Theta_t, \dots, \Theta_t) - (k-1)\tilde{P}(\eta, \tilde{\theta} \wedge \Theta_t, \dots, \Theta_t, \dots)$$
$$= -\tilde{P}(\eta \wedge \tilde{\theta}, \Theta_t, \dots, \Theta_t) - (k-1)\tilde{P}(\eta, \Theta_t \wedge \tilde{\theta}, \dots, \Theta_t, \dots),$$

and so

$$-k\tilde{P}(\tilde{\theta} \wedge \eta + \eta \wedge \tilde{\theta}, \dots, \Theta_t, \dots) = k(k-1)\tilde{P}(\eta, \Theta_t \wedge \tilde{\theta} - \tilde{\theta} \wedge \Theta_t, \dots, \Theta_t, \dots).$$

Thus we have

$$\frac{\partial}{\partial t} P(\Theta_t) = k\tilde{P}(d\eta, \Theta_t, \dots, \Theta_t)$$

$$+ k(k-1)\tilde{P}\big(\eta, \Theta_t \wedge (\tilde{\theta} + t\eta) - (\tilde{\theta} + t\eta) \wedge \Theta_t, \dots, \Theta_t, \dots, \big).$$

But for any connection θ with curvature Θ, $d\Theta = \theta \wedge \Theta - \Theta \wedge \theta$ and consequently

$$d\Theta_t = (\tilde{\theta} + t\eta) \wedge \Theta_t - \Theta_t \wedge (\tilde{\theta} + t\eta);$$

so we can write, finally,

$$\frac{\partial}{\partial t} P(\Theta_t) = k\tilde{P}(d\eta, \Theta_t, \dots, \Theta_t) - k(k-1)\tilde{P}(\eta, d\Theta_t, \dots, \Theta_t)$$

$$= k \cdot d\tilde{P}(\eta, \Theta_t, \dots, \Theta_t). \qquad\qquad \text{Q.E.D.}$$

Note: For those accustomed to the general formalism of differential geometry, we can sketch the above calculation in more intrinsic terms as follows: First, the operator $D: A^q(E) \to A^{q+1}(E)$ may be extended to an operator on all tensor bundles of E. Then, since the connection matrix of D can be made to vanish at any point, we obtain the *Bianchi identity*

$$D\Theta = 0,$$

and applying P to the algebra $A^*(\mathrm{Hom}(E, E))$,

$$d\tilde{P}(A_1, \dots, A_q) = \sum_i (-1)^{d_1 + \dots + d_{i-1}} \tilde{P}(A_1, \dots, DA_i, \dots, A_q),$$

where $A_i \in A^{d_i}(\mathrm{Hom}(E, E))$; thus $dP(\Theta) \equiv 0$. Finally, with D_t, θ_t, Θ_t, and η as above we see that $(\partial/\partial t)\Theta_t = D_t\eta$, and so

$$d(k\tilde{P}(\eta, \Theta_t, \dots, \Theta_t)) = k\tilde{P}(D_t\eta, \Theta_t, \dots, \Theta_t)$$

$$= k\tilde{P}\left(\frac{\partial}{\partial t}\Theta_t, \Theta_t, \dots, \Theta_t\right)$$

$$= \frac{\partial}{\partial t} P(\Theta_t).$$

To restate the lemma: If we let Φ denote the graded algebra of invariant polynomials, then for any vector bundle $E \to M$, we obtain a well-defined homomorphism of algebras

$$\Phi \overset{w}{\to} H_{\mathrm{DR}}^{2*}(M)$$

given by

$$P \overset{w}{\mapsto} [P(\Theta)],$$

where Θ is the curvature matrix of any connection in E; w is called the *Weil homomorphism*.

In particular, let P^i denote again the elementary invariant polynomials. We define the *Chern forms* $c_i(\Theta)$ of the curvature Θ in E by

$$c_i(\Theta) = P^i\left(\frac{\sqrt{-1}}{2\pi}\Theta\right),$$

and we define the *Chern classes* $c_i(E)$ by

$$c_i(E) = \left[P^i\left(\frac{\sqrt{-1}}{2\pi}\Theta\right)\right] \in H^{2i}_{DR}(M).$$

The *total Chern class* $c(E)$ is the sum of the Chern classes:

$$c(E) = \sum_{i>0} c_i(E) \in H^{2*}_{DR}(M),$$

where we set $c_0(E) = 1 \in H^0_{DR}(M)$. Also, for M a complex manifold, we take the Chern classes $c_i(M)$ of M to be the Chern classes of its holomorphic tangent bundle $T'(M)$.

Note that the definition of $c_1(E)$ here agrees with our former definition of the Chern class of a holomorphic line bundle. In general—as will be clear by the end of this section—the Chern classes of a vector bundle are likewise purely topological invariants. The basic properties of the Chern classes are these:

1. First, if $f: M \to N$ is any C^∞ map, $E \to N$ a complex vector bundle, then

$$c_r(f^*E) = f^*c_r(E).$$

To see this, note that if D is a connection on E, $U = \{U_\alpha\}$ an open cover of N with $e_{1,\alpha}, \ldots, e_{k,\alpha}$ a frame for E over U_α and θ_α the connection matrix for D relative to $\{e_{i,\alpha}\}$, then the matrices

$$f^*(\theta_\alpha) \quad \text{in } f^{-1}(U_\alpha)$$

define a connection D^* on $f^*E \to M$ with curvature

$$\Theta(D^*) = f^*(\Theta(D)).$$

2. Next, let $E \to M$, $F \to M$ be two vector bundles with connections D, D' and curvature matrices Θ, Θ', respectively. Then the operator

$$D'' = D \oplus D': \mathcal{C}^0(E \oplus F) \to \mathcal{C}^1(E \oplus F)$$

is a connection for the bundle $E \oplus F$, with curvature matrix

$$\Theta'' = \begin{pmatrix} \Theta & 0 \\ 0 & \Theta' \end{pmatrix}.$$

Then we have

$$\det(\Theta'' + tI) = \det(\Theta + tI) \cdot \det(\Theta' + tI)$$

as polynomials in t; i.e.,

$$c(E \oplus F) = c(E) \cdot c(F).$$

This is the *Whitney product formula*.

3. Similarly, if E is a vector bundle of rank r and L is a line bundle, we have seen that for appropriate connections on E, L, and $E \otimes L$,

$$\Theta_{E \otimes L} = \Theta_E \otimes 1 + I_r \otimes \Theta_L,$$

so that

$$c_1(E \otimes L) = \left[\text{trace} \, \frac{\sqrt{-1}}{2\pi} \Theta_{E \otimes L} \right] = c_1(E) + r \cdot c_1(L).$$

4. Finally for now, if Θ is the curvature matrix of a connection in a complex vector bundle E, then the dual connection in E^* has curvature matrix $-\Theta$; thus

$$c_r(E^*) = (-1)^r c_r(E).$$

We can use the Whitney product formula to evaluate the Chern classes $c_i(\mathbb{P}^n)$ of projective space, as follows. Let

$$\pi: \ \mathbb{C}^{n+1} - \{0\} \to \mathbb{P}^n$$

be the standard projection map; let $X_0, \ldots, X_n$ be linear coordinates on $\mathbb{C}^{n+1}$ and

$$x_i = X_i / X_0, \qquad i = 1, \ldots, n$$

corresponding affine coordinates on $\mathbb{P}^n$. Then we have

$$\pi^* \, dx_i = \frac{X_0 \cdot dX_i - X_i \cdot dX_0}{X_0^2},$$

and so, at a point $X \in \mathbb{C}^{n+1}$, the image under π of the tangent vector $\partial / \partial X_i$ is given by

$$\pi_* \frac{\partial}{\partial X_i} = \frac{1}{X_0} \cdot \frac{\partial}{\partial x_i}, \qquad i = 1, \ldots, n,$$

$$\pi_* \frac{\partial}{\partial X_0} = - \sum \frac{X_i}{X_0^2} \cdot \frac{\partial}{\partial x_i}.$$

It follows from this calculation that:

1. If $l(X)$ is any linear functional on $\mathbb{C}^{n+1}$, the vector field

$$v(X) = l(X) \frac{\partial}{\partial X_i}$$

descends to $\mathbb{P}^n$—that is, $\pi_* v(X) = \pi_* v(\lambda X)$ for any $X \in \mathbb{C}^{n+1}$, $\lambda \in \mathbb{C}$. We will denote by $\pi_* v$ the induced vector field on $\mathbb{P}^n$.

2. The tangent space $T'_x(\mathbb{P}^n)$ to $\mathbb{P}^n$ at a point $x = \pi(X)$ is spanned by the vectors

$$\left\{ \pi_* \frac{\partial}{\partial X_i} \right\}_{i=0,\ldots,n}$$

with the single relation

$$\sum X_i \frac{\partial}{\partial X_i} = 0.$$

Now, recalling that the fiber of the hyperplane line bundle $H \to \mathbb{P}^n$ over a point $x = \pi(X) \in \mathbb{P}^n$ corresponds to linear functionals on the line $\mathbb{C}\{X\} \subset \mathbb{C}^{n+1}$, we can define a bundle map

$$H^{\oplus(n+1)} = \underbrace{H \oplus \cdots \oplus H}_{n+1} \xrightarrow{\mathscr{E}} T'(\mathbb{P}^n)$$

by setting, for $\sigma = (\sigma_0, \ldots, \sigma_n)$ a section of $H^{\oplus(n+1)}$,

$$\mathscr{E}(\sigma) = \pi_* \left(\sum \sigma_i(X) \frac{\partial}{\partial X_i} \right).$$

By the second observation the map $\mathscr{E}$ is surjective, with kernel the trivial line bundle spanned by the section

$$\tau = (X_0, \ldots, X_n).$$

Thus we have an exact sequence of bundles on $\mathbb{P}^n$:

$$0 \longrightarrow \mathbb{C} \longrightarrow H^{\oplus(n+1)} \xrightarrow{\mathscr{E}} T'(\mathbb{P}^n) \longrightarrow 0,$$

called the *Euler sequence*. Now, from the C^∞ decomposition

$$H^{\oplus(n+1)} = T'(\mathbb{P}^n) \oplus \mathbb{C}$$

and the Whitney product formula, we find

$$c(T'(\mathbb{P}^n)) = c(H^{\oplus(n+1)}) = c(H)^{n+1} = (1+\omega)^{n+1},$$

where $\omega = \eta_H \in H^2(\mathbb{P}^n, \mathbb{Z})$ is the class of a hyperplane.

The Gauss-Bonnet Formulas

As we have seen, the first Chern class of a holomorphic line bundle is Poincaré dual to the cycle represented by the zero-locus of a global holomorphic section. A similar geometric description of the general Chern classes—or rather their Poincaré duals in homology—is available, and the remainder of this section will be spent in deriving it. The computation will not be made directly; instead, we will first compute the Chern classes of the universal bundles on the Grassmannians, and then by the functoriality of the Chern classes draw conclusions for general vector bundles.

Recall from Section 6 of Chapter 1 that for any strictly increasing flag

$$0 = V_0 \subset V_1 \subset \cdots \subset V_{n-1} \subset V_n = \mathbb{C}^n$$

of linear subspaces of $\mathbb{C}^n$, and for any nonincreasing sequence of k integers $a_i : 0 \leqslant a_i \leqslant n - k$, we define the *Schubert cycle* $\sigma_a(V) \subset G(k,n)$ in the Grassmannian of k-planes in $\mathbb{C}^n$ by

$$\sigma_a(V) = \{\Lambda : \dim(\Lambda \cap V_{n-k+i-a_i}) \geqslant i\}.$$

$\sigma_a(V)$ is an analytic subvariety of $G(k,n)$ of codimension Σa_i, with fundamental class σ_a independent of the flag V; as we saw, the integral homology of the Grassmannian is freely generated by the classes σ_a.

Recall also that the *universal subbundle* $S \to G(k,n)$ is defined to be the subbundle of the trivial bundle $\mathbb{C}^n \times G(k,n)$ whose fiber over a point $\Lambda \in G(k,n)$ is just the k-plane $\Lambda \subset \mathbb{C}^n$. Letting σ_a^* denote the Poincaré dual of the cycle σ_a, our fundamental result is the

Gauss-Bonnet Theorem I

$$c_r(S) = (-1)^r \cdot \sigma_{1,\ldots,1}^*.$$

Proof. By our computation of the intersection pairing in $H_*(G(k,n),\mathbb{Z})$, we must show that for any Schubert cycle σ_a of dimension r,

$$c_r(S)(\sigma_a) = (-1)^{r\#}(\sigma_{1,\ldots,1}\cdot\sigma_a)$$
$$= \begin{cases} (-1)^r, & \text{if } a = n-k,\ldots,n-k,n-k-1,\ldots,n-k-1, \\ 0, & \text{otherwise.} \end{cases}$$

We first note that if $\sigma_a(V)$ is any Schubert cycle of dimension r, and $a \neq n-k,\ldots,n-k,n-k-1,\ldots,n-k-1$, then a_{k-r+1} *must necessarily be* $n-k$, i.e., $\sigma_a(V) \subset \{\Lambda \in G(k,n) : \Lambda \supset V_{k-r+1}\}$. Thus if we take $e_1,\ldots,e_{k-r+1}$ any basis for $V_{k-r+1} \subset \mathbb{C}^n$, the corresponding sections e_i of the trivial bundle $\mathbb{C}^n \times G(k,n)$ all lie in S over $\sigma_a(V)$. The sections e_i of $S|_{\sigma_a(V)}$ then extend to give $k-r+1$ everywhere linearly independent sections $\tilde{e}_i$ of S over an open set $U \subset G(k,n)$ containing $\sigma_a(V)$. Let $S' \to U$ be the trivial subbundle of $S|_U$ spanned by $\tilde{e}_1,\ldots,\tilde{e}_{k-r+1}$, and let $S'' \to U$ be the quotient of $S|_U$ by S'. Since S' is trivial, we have $c(S')=1$; by the Whitney formula,

$$c(S|_U) = c(S''),$$

and hence

$$c_r(S)(\sigma_a(V)) = c_r(S'')((\sigma_a(V))=0,$$

since S'' has rank $r-1$.

Now set

$$Z_r = \sigma_{n-k,\ldots,n-k,n-k-1,\ldots,n-k-1}(V) = \{\Lambda : V_{k-r} \subset \Lambda \subset V_{k+1}\}.$$

It remains to check that

$$c_r(S)(Z_r) = (-1)^r.$$

To see this, let

$$Z_k = \sigma_{n-k-1,\ldots,n-k-1}(V)$$
$$= \{\Lambda: \Lambda \subset V_{k+1}\} \subset G(k,n).$$

$Z_k \cong \mathbb{P}(V_{k+1})^*$ is just the dual projective space of hyperplanes in V_{k+1}, and $Z_r \subset Z_k$ the linear subspace of hyperplanes containing V_{k-r}. The bundle $S|_{Z_k}$, moreover, is just the subbundle of the trivial bundle $V_{k+1} \times Z_k$ whose fiber over any $\Lambda \in Z_k$ is the hyperplane $\Lambda \subset V_{k+1}$. The quotient Q of $V_{k+1} \times Z_k$ by S is thus the universal quotient bundle on $Z_k \cong \mathbb{P}^k$, that is, the hyperplane line bundle. Letting ω denote the class of a hyperplane in $Z_k \cong \mathbb{P}^k$, we have then

$$c(Q) = 1 + \omega,$$

and since as C^∞ bundles

$$V_{k+1} \times Z_k = S|_{Z_k} \oplus Q,$$
$$1 = c(S|_{Z_k}) \cdot (1 + \omega),$$

hence

$$c(S|_{Z_k}) = 1 - \omega + \omega^2 - \omega^3 + \cdots,$$

i.e.,

$$c_r(S|_{Z_k}) = (-1)^r \omega^r.$$

Thus

$$c_r(S)(Z_r) = c_r(S|_{Z_r}) \cdot (Z_r)$$
$$= (-1)^r \omega^r (\mathbb{P}^r)$$
$$= (-1)^r,$$

and the theorem is proved.   Q.E.D.

Note that by the relation giving the Chern classes of a dual bundle

$$c_r(S^*) = (-1)^r c_r(S) = \sigma^*_{1,\ldots,1}$$

and via the isomorphism $(S^* \to G(n-k,n)) \cong (Q \to G(k,n))$, we see that

$$c_r(Q) = \sigma^*_r,$$

where Q is the universal quotient bundle.

The Gauss-Bonnet formula gives us a relatively concrete interpretation of Chern classes in general as follows. Let M be a compact, oriented manifold, $E \to M$ a complex vector bundle of rank k, and $\sigma = (\sigma_1, \ldots, \sigma_k)$ k global C^∞ sections of E. We define the *degeneracy set* $D_i(\sigma)$ to be the set of points $x \in M$, where $\sigma_1, \ldots, \sigma_i$ are linearly dependent, i.e.,

$$D_i(\sigma) = \{x: \sigma_1(x) \wedge \cdots \wedge \sigma_i(x) = 0\}.$$

We say that the collection σ of sections is *generic* if, for each i, σ_{i+1} intersects the subspace of E spanned by $\sigma_1,\ldots,\sigma_i$ transversely—so that $D_{i+1}(\sigma)$ is, away from $D_i(\sigma)$, a submanifold of codimension $2(k-i)$—and if, moreover, integration over $D_{i+1}(\sigma)-D_i(\sigma)$ defines a closed current as discussed in Section 1 of this chapter. (By the results of Section 2 this will occur if everything is complex analytic and the dimensions are correct.) In this case, we can give the smooth locus D_i-D_{i-1} an orientation: In a neighborhood of a point $x_0 \in D_i-D_{i-1}$, complete the sections $e_1 = \sigma_1,\ldots,e_{i-1}=\sigma_{i-1}$ to a frame for E, and write

$$\sigma_i(x) = \sum_j f_j(x)\cdot e_j(x).$$

D_i is then given near x_0 as the locus $(f_i = \cdots = f_k = 0)$; let Φ_i be the orientation on D_i near x_0 such that the form

$$\Phi_i \wedge \frac{\sqrt{-1}}{2}\left(df_{i+1} \wedge d\bar{f}_{i+1}\right) \wedge \cdots \wedge \frac{\sqrt{-1}}{2}\left(df_k \wedge d\bar{f}_k\right)$$

is positive for the given orientation on M. By the theorem on smoothing of cohomology given in Section 1 of this chapter, the locus D_i together with the orientation Φ_i on D_i-D_{i-1} represents a cycle in homology, called the *degeneracy cycle* of the sections σ.

Now suppose $\sigma_1,\ldots,\sigma_k$ are generic sections of E. Using a partition of unity on M, we can then construct additional sections $\sigma_{k+1},\ldots,\sigma_n$ of E such that together $\sigma_1(x),\ldots,\sigma_n(x)$ span the fiber E_x of E over each point $x \in M$. By the construction of Section 6 of Chapter 1, then, the sections $\sigma_1,\ldots,\sigma_n$ give us a map

$$\iota\colon M \to G(k,n).$$

In terms of a trivialization of E, we can express $\sigma_1,\ldots,\sigma_n$ as k-vectors $V_1,\ldots,V_n$ of C^∞ functions; the map ι is given by

$$x \xrightarrow{\iota} \left[(V_1(x),\ldots,V_n(x))\right] \in G(k,n).$$

Since the subspace $\iota(x) = \Lambda \subset \mathbb{C}^n$ corresponds to linear functionals on the fiber E_x of E over x, moreover, we see as before that $\iota^*(S) = E^*$, i.e.,

$$\iota^*(S^*) = E.$$

Now for each $r = 1,\ldots,k$ let $V_{n-k+r-1} = \{e_{k-r+2},\ldots,e_n\} \subset \mathbb{C}^n$. Then for any $x \in M$, the k-plane $\Lambda = \iota(x) \in G(k,n)$ will intersect $V_{n-k+r-1}$ in a space of dimension r or greater if and only if the sections $\sigma_1,\ldots,\sigma_{k-r+1}$ are linearly dependent at x—i.e., $\iota(M)$ meets the Schubert cycle $\sigma_{1,\ldots,1}(V) \subset G(k,n)$ exactly in the degeneracy set D_{k-r+1} of the sections $\sigma_1,\ldots,\sigma_k$. Moreover the condition that $\sigma_1,\ldots,\sigma_k$ be generic assures that $\iota(M)$ meets $\sigma_{1,\ldots,1}(V)$ transversely. If α is any cycle of real dimension $2r$ on M meeting

D_{k-r+1} transversely at points p_i, then, $\iota_*\alpha$ will meet $\sigma_{1,\dots,1}(V)$ transversely at the points $\iota(p_i)$, and by our choice of orientation for D_{k-r+1} the intersection number of $\iota_*\alpha$ with $\sigma_{1,\dots,1}(V)$ at $\iota(p_i)$ will be that of α with D_{k-r+1} at p_i. Thus

$$^\#\left(\iota_*\alpha\cdot\sigma_{1,\dots,1}\right) = {}^\#(\alpha\cdot D_{k-r+1}),$$

and we see that

$$\begin{aligned}
c_r(E)(\alpha) &= \iota^*(c_r(S^*))(\alpha)\\
&= c_r(S^*)(\iota_*\alpha)\\
&= {}^\#\left(\iota_*\alpha\cdot\sigma_{1,\dots,1}\right)\\
&= {}^\#(\alpha\cdot D_{k-r+1}).
\end{aligned}$$

We thus have the

Gauss-Bonnet Formula II. *The rth Chern class $c_r(E)$ is Poincaré dual to the degeneracy cycle D_{k-r+1}.*

Example. We can now make a second computation for the Chern classes of projective space. Let $X_0,\dots,X_n$ be linear coordinates on $\mathbb{C}^{n+1}$, and let $\mathcal{E}$ and π_* be as in the Euler sequence above. Let $A=(\alpha_{ij})$ be an $(n+1)\times(n+1)$ matrix all of whose minors are distinct and nonzero, and consider the vector fields

$$\begin{aligned}
v_i &= \mathcal{E}(\alpha_{i,0}X_0,\dots,\alpha_{i,n}X_n)\\
&= \pi_*\sum_j \alpha_{ij}X_i\frac{\partial}{\partial X_j}.
\end{aligned}$$

We will leave it as an exercise to verify that, under the assumptions made about A, $v_1,\dots,v_n$ are generic sections of $T'(\mathbb{P}^n)$ (this is simply a matter of writing v_i out in terms of Euclidean coordinates on $\mathbb{P}^n$), and compute the degeneracy cycles D_i of $v_1,\dots,v_i$. First, we see that v_1 vanishes at $X\in\mathbb{P}^n$ exactly when

$$[\alpha_{1,0}X_0,\dots,\alpha_{1,n}X_n] = [X_0,\dots,X_n],$$

and since by assumption $\alpha_{1i}\neq 0$ for all i and $\alpha_{1i}\neq\alpha_{1j}$ for all $i\neq j$, this is the case only for $X=p_i$, where

$$p_i = [0,\dots,0,1,0,\dots,0], \qquad i = 0,\dots,n.$$

Thus $c_n(\mathbb{P}^n)=n+1$. Now v_1 and v_2 will be linearly dependent at $X\in\mathbb{P}^n$ when there exist $(\lambda_1,\lambda_2)\neq 0$ such that

$$[\lambda_1\alpha_{10}X_0+\lambda_2\alpha_{20}X_0,\dots,\lambda_1\alpha_{1n}X_n+\lambda_2\alpha_{2n}X_n] = [X_0,\dots,X_n],$$

and by the assumption that all 2×2 minor determinants of A are distinct and nonzero, this will be the case only when all but two of the homogeneous coordinates of X are zero, i.e., when X lies on a line $\overline{p_ip_j}$ for some

$0 \leqslant i \neq j \leqslant r$. D_2 thus consists of the union of the $\binom{n+1}{2}$ lines $\overline{p_i p_j}$; or in other words, if ω is the hyperplane class on $\mathbb{P}^n$,

$$c_{n-1}(\mathbb{P}^n) = \binom{n+1}{2} \cdot \omega^{n-1}.$$

In general, $v_1, \ldots, v_q$ will be linearly dependent at X exactly when all but q of the homogeneous coordinates of X vanish, i.e.,

$$D_q = \bigcup_{\#I = q} \overline{p_{i_1}, p_{i_2}, \ldots, p_{i_q}}$$

consists of the union of the coordinate $(q-1)$-planes spanned by the points p_i. Thus

$$c_q(\mathbb{P}^n) = \binom{n+1}{q} \cdot \omega^q,$$

as we computed before.

As an immediate application, we can add one more identity to those previously mentioned. If $E \to M$ is a complex vector bundle of rank k, then the first Chern class $c_1(E)$ is dual to the cycle $D_k \subset X$ given as the locus where k generic sections $\sigma_1, \ldots, \sigma_k$ of E are linearly dependent. But the k sections σ_i of E together give one section

$$\sigma = \sigma_1 \wedge \cdots \wedge \sigma_k$$

of the line bundle $\wedge^k E \to M$, and the degeneracy set D_1 of σ is equal to D_k. Checking that the orientations are in fact the same, we have

$$c_1(\wedge^k E) = c_1(E).$$

Finally, note that given generic sections $\sigma_1, \ldots, \sigma_i$ we can define degeneracy cycles

$$D_i^{(j)} = \left\{ x : \dim \overline{\sigma_1(x), \ldots, \sigma_i(x)} \leqslant i - j \right\}.$$

If, as before, we complete the sections $\sigma_1, \ldots, \sigma_i$ to a collection $\sigma_1, \ldots, \sigma_n$ spanning each fiber, then the degeneracy cycle $D_i^{(j)}$ will be the inverse image, under the corresponding map $\iota : M \to G(k, n)$, of the Schubert cycle

$$\underbrace{\sigma_{j, \ldots, j}}_{k-i+1} (V_{n-i-j+1}) = \left\{ \Lambda : \dim \Lambda \cap V_{n-i-j+1} \geqslant k - i + 1 \right\}.$$

Composing ι *with the isomorphism* $* : G(k, n) \to G(n - k, n)$, *we find that*

$$D_i^{(j)} = (*\iota)^{-1} \bigg(\underbrace{\sigma_{k-i+1, \ldots, k-i+1}}_{j} \bigg);$$

and since $c_r(E) = (*\iota)^* \sigma_r$, we may combine this with Giambelli's formula on p. 205 to obtain

Porteous' Formula. *For $\sigma_1,\ldots,\sigma_i$ suitably generic, the Poincaré dual of the degeneracy cycle* $\mathrm{D}_i^{(j)}$ *is*

$$D_i^{(j)*} = \det \begin{bmatrix} c_{k-i+1}(E) & \cdots & c_{k-i+j}(E) \\ \vdots & & \vdots \\ c_{k-i-j+2}(E) & \cdots & c_{k-i+1}(E) \end{bmatrix}$$

Finally, we will specialize our general Gauss-Bonnet formula to obtain a more classical form, and also to explain the terminology. Suppose that M is of real dimension $2n$, $E \to M$ of complex rank n, and σ a global C^∞ section of E having nondegenerate zeros at points $p_\nu \in M$. For each ν, let $e_1,\ldots,e_n$ be a frame for E around p_ν, $x=(x_1,\ldots,x_{2n})$ oriented real coordinates on X centered around p_ν, and write

$$\sigma(x) = \sum \left(a_{ak}^\nu + \sqrt{-1}\, b_{ak}^\nu \right) \cdot x_a \cdot e_k(x) + [2], \qquad a_{ak}^\nu, b_{ak}^\nu \in \mathbb{R}.$$

Let A_{p_ν} be the $2n \times 2n$ matrix (A^ν, B^ν), where $A^\nu = (a_{ak}^\nu)$ and $B^\nu = (b_{ak}^\nu)$. Then, if we write

$$\sigma(x) = \sum f_k(x) \cdot e_k(x)$$

as before, we have

$$\left(df_k \wedge d\bar{f}_k \right)(p_\nu) = \sum_a \left(a_{ak}^\nu + \sqrt{-1}\, b_{ak}^\nu \right) dx_a \wedge \sum_b \left(a_{bk}^\nu - \sqrt{-1}\, b_{bk}^\nu \right) dx_b$$

$$= -2\sqrt{-1}\, \sum a_{ak}^\nu \cdot b_{bk}^\nu \cdot dx_a \wedge dx_b,$$

and so by linear algebra the sign of the point p_ν in the degeneracy cycle D_1 of σ is

$$(-1)^{n(n-1)/2} \cdot \operatorname{sgn} \det \left(A_{p_\nu} \right).$$

Thus by Gauss-Bonnet II we have

$$c_n(E) = \sum (-1)^{n(n-1)/2} \operatorname{sgn} \det \left(A_{p_\nu} \right).$$

Specializing still further, let M be a complex manifold of dimension n, $E = T'(M) \to M$ its holomorphic tangent bundle and σ a C^∞ section of E having nondegenerate zeros at $p_\nu \in M$. Let $z = (z_1,\ldots,z_n)$ be local holomorphic coordinates centered around p_ν, and write

$$z_i = x_{2i-1} + \sqrt{-1}\, x_{2i}$$

so that $x = (x_1,\ldots,x_{2n})$ is an oriented real coordinate system for M near p_ν. Then, if

$$v(z) = \sum \left(a_{jk}^\nu + \sqrt{-1}\, b_{jk}^\nu \right) z_j \frac{\partial}{\partial z_k} + [2]$$

and if $A_{p_\nu} = (A'', B'')$ as above, we have

$$c_n(M) = \sum (-1)^{n(n-1)/2} \operatorname{sgn} \det (A_{p_\nu}).$$

Now let

$$v'(z) = \tfrac{1}{2}\left(v(z) + \overline{v(z)}\right)$$

be the real vector field obtained from v by the real projection $T'(M) \to T_{\mathbb{R}}(M)$. Then

$$v'(z) = \frac{1}{2} \sum \left(a_{jk}^\nu + \sqrt{-1}\, b_{jk}^\nu\right) z_j \cdot \left(\frac{\partial}{\partial x_{2k-1}} - \sqrt{-1}\, \frac{\partial}{\partial x_{2k}}\right)$$

$$+ \frac{1}{2} \sum \left(a_{jk}^\nu - \sqrt{-1}\, b_{jk}^\nu\right) \bar{z}_j \cdot \left(\frac{\partial}{\partial x_{2k-1}} + \sqrt{-1}\, \frac{\partial}{\partial x_{2k}}\right) + [2]$$

$$= \sum a_{jk}^\nu x_j \frac{\partial}{\partial x_{2k-1}} + \sum b_{jk}^\nu x_j \cdot \frac{\partial}{\partial x_{2k}} + [2],$$

so the index of v' at p_ν is $(-1)^{n(n-1)/2}$ times the sign of the determinant of A_{p_ν}. Thus by the Hopf index theorem (to be proved in the next section)

$$\chi(M) = \sum (-1)^{n(n-1)/2,} \operatorname{sgn} \det (A_{p_\nu}),$$

and so we have

Gauss-Bonnet Formula III. $c_n(M) = \chi(M)$.

We have, in this discussion, inverted the historical order of things. The Chern classes of complex vector bundles and the analogous Steifel-Whitney classes of real vector bundles were originally defined using obstruction theory; in terms of this definition, the classes were visibly the Poincaré duals of degeneracy cycles. Chern then discovered the remarkable fact that these global topological invariants of a vector bundle could in fact be computed from the local hermitian differential geometric structure of the vector bundle; Chern's theorem has since been frequently adopted as a definition.

Some Remarks—Not Indispensable—Concerning Chern Classes of Holomorphic Vector Bundles

Suppose that $E \to M$ is a holomorphic vector bundle with base space a complex manifold M. If we choose a hermitian connection as in Section 5 of Chapter 0, then the hermitian symmetry $\Theta + {}'\overline{\Theta} = 0$ of the curvature matrix in a unitary frame implies the relations

$$c_p(\Theta) \text{ has type } (p,p), \qquad c_p(\Theta) = \overline{c_p(\Theta)}$$

on the Chern forms. In case M is a compact Kähler manifold, these imply that

$$c_p(E) \in H^{p,p}(M) \cap H^{2p}(M, \mathbb{Z});$$

i.e., *the Chern classes are integral and of Hodge type* (p,p).

   In case M is a projective algebraic variety, which by the Kodaira embedding theorem is equivalent to the existence of a positive holomorphic line bundle $L \to M$, we can say more. We assume that L is the hyperplane bundle relative to a projective embedding. First, the Chern classes of $E \cong (E \otimes L^k) \otimes L^{-k}$ can be expressed as polynomials in the Chern classes of $E \otimes L^k$ and L^{-k}. The Chern class of L^{-k} is

$$c(L^{-k}) = 1 - k\eta_D,$$

where D is a hyperplane section of M, and by Theorem B in Section 5 of Chapter 1 we may find a holomorphic embedding

$$M \to G(r, N) \qquad (r = \text{rank } E)$$

inducing $E \otimes L^k$ from the universal bundle over the Grassmannian. According to the preceding discussion, the Chern classes of $E \otimes L^k$ are Poincaré dual to the intersection of M with suitable Schubert cycles. In summary, *the Chern classes of a holomorphic vector bundle over an algebraic variety are represented by fundamental classes of algebraic cycles.*

   There is also a notion of *positivity* for the Chern classes of holomorphic vector bundles. We shall not enter into this in detail, as it will not be used in the study of specific varieties, but will offer two observations. If $E \to M$ is generated by its global holomorphic sections, we have seen at the end of Section 5 in Chapter 0 that there is a hermitian connection whose curvature matrix has the local form

$$\Theta^\alpha_\beta = \sum_\mu A^\alpha_\mu \wedge \overline{A}^\beta_\mu,$$

where $A^\alpha_\mu = \sum A^\alpha_{\mu j} dz_j$ is a matrix of $(1,0)$ forms. The qth Chern polynomial is then

$$c_q(\Theta) = \left(\frac{\sqrt{-1}}{2\pi} \right)^q \left\{ \sum_{\alpha_1 < \cdots < \alpha_q} \left(\frac{1}{q!} \sum_\pi \text{sgn} \, \pi \, \Theta^{\alpha_1}_{\alpha_{\pi(1)}} \wedge \cdots \wedge \Theta^{\alpha_q}_{\alpha_{\pi(q)}} \right) \right\}$$

$$= \left(\frac{\sqrt{-1}}{2\pi} \right)^q (-1)^{q(q-1)/2} \sum_{\substack{\alpha_1 < \cdots < \alpha_q \\ \mu_1 < \cdots < \mu_q}} \frac{\text{sgn} \, \pi}{q!} A^{\alpha_1}_{\mu_1} \wedge \cdots \wedge A^{\alpha_q}_{\mu_q} \wedge \overline{A}^{\alpha_{\pi(1)}}_{\mu_1} \wedge \cdots \wedge \overline{A}^{\alpha_{\pi(q)}}_{\mu_q}$$

$$= \sqrt{-1}^{q^2} \sum_{\mu = (\mu_1, \dots, \mu_q)} \eta_\mu \wedge \overline{\eta}_\mu,$$

where

$$\eta_\mu = \left(\frac{1}{2\pi}\right)^q \frac{1}{q!} \sum_{\substack{\alpha_1 < \cdots < \alpha_q \\ \pi}} \operatorname{sgn}\pi \cdot A_{\mu_1}^{\alpha_{\pi(1)}} \bigwedge \cdots \bigwedge A_{\mu_q}^{\alpha_{\pi(q)}}$$

is a form of type $(q,0)$. It follows that

$$\int_Z c_q(\Theta) \geqslant 0$$

for any q-dimensional analytic subvariety Z in M.

Perhaps more interesting are the *Schwarz-type inequalities*. The simplest of these is

$$\int_Z c_1(\Theta)^2 \geqslant 2 \int_Z c_2(\Theta),$$

where Z is a two-dimensional analytic subvariety of M. For simplicity of notation we prove this when the rank is 2, omitting the exterior multiplication symbol and summing repeated indices. Then

$$c_1(\Theta)^2 = \left(\frac{\sqrt{-1}}{2\pi}\right)^2 \left(A_\mu^1 \overline{A}_\mu{}^1 + A_\mu^2 \overline{A}_\mu{}^2\right)\left(A_\lambda^1 \overline{A}_\lambda{}^1 + A_\lambda^2 \overline{A}_\lambda{}^2\right)$$

$$= \left(\frac{\sqrt{-1}}{2\pi}\right)^2 \left\{ -\left(A_\mu^1 A_\lambda^1 \overline{A}_\mu{}^1 \overline{A}_\lambda{}^1 + A_\mu^2 A_\lambda^2 \overline{A}_\mu{}^2 \overline{A}_\lambda{}^2\right) + 2 A_\mu^1 \overline{A}_\mu{}^1 A_\lambda^2 \overline{A}_\lambda{}^2 \right\}$$

$$2c_2(\Theta) = \left(\frac{\sqrt{-1}}{2\pi}\right)^2 \left\{ 2 A_\mu^1 \overline{A}_\mu{}^1 A_\lambda^2 \overline{A}_\lambda{}^2 - 2 A_\mu^1 \overline{A}_\mu{}^2 A_\lambda^2 \overline{A}_\lambda{}^1 \right\}.$$

Then

$$c_1(\Theta)^2 - 2c_2(\Theta) = \left(\frac{\sqrt{-1}}{2\pi}\right)^2 \left\{ A_\mu^1 \overline{A}_\mu{}^1 A_\lambda^1 \overline{A}_\lambda{}^1 + A_\mu^2 \overline{A}_\mu{}^2 A_\lambda^2 \overline{A}_\lambda{}^2 - 2 A_\mu^1 \overline{A}_\mu{}^2 A_\lambda^2 \overline{A}_\lambda{}^1 \right\},$$

and the inequality

$$\left\langle c_1(\Theta)^2 - 2c_2(\Theta), \left(\frac{2}{\sqrt{-1}}\right)^2 \tau_1 \wedge \overline{\tau}_1 \wedge \tau_2 \wedge \overline{\tau}_2 \right\rangle \geqslant 0$$

for $(1,0)$ vectors τ_1, τ_2 follows from the usual Cauchy-Schwarz inequality. The inequalities

$$\begin{cases} c_q(E) \geqslant 0, \\ c_1^2(E) \geqslant 2c_2(E), \text{ etc.}, \end{cases}$$

are valid for any holomorphic vector bundle that is positive in a suitable sense. We shall not give the proof here, but the reader may consult S.

Bloch and D. Gieseker, The positivity of the Chern classes of an ample vector bundle, *Invent. Math.*, Vol. 12 (1971), 112–117.

4. FIXED-POINT AND RESIDUE FORMULAS

The Lefschetz Fixed-Point Formula

We now derive Lefschetz's formula for the number of fixed points, properly counted, of an endomorphism $f: M \to M$ on a compact oriented manifold M of dimension n in terms of the action of f^* on the cohomology of M. That such a formula should exist is not hard to see: a fixed point of f corresponds to a point of intersection of the graph $\Gamma_f \subset M \times M$ of f with the diagonal $\Delta \subset M \times M$, and as we have seen the intersection number $^\#(\Gamma_f \cdot \Delta)_{M \times M}$ depends only on the homology classes of Γ_f and Δ in $M \times M$. Nor is the calculation itself difficult; it will come out readily once we have obtained an expression for the cohomology class $\eta_\Delta \in H^n(M \times M)$ of the diagonal $\Delta \subset M \times M$. We do this as follows: First, for each q, let $\{\psi_{\mu,q}\}$ be a collection of closed q-forms on M representing a basis for $H^q_{\mathrm{DR}}(M)$, and let $\{\psi^*_{\mu,n-q}\}$ be $(n-q)$-forms representing the dual basis for $H^{n-q}_{\mathrm{DR}}(M)$, i.e., such that

$$\int_M \psi_{\mu,q} \wedge \psi^*_{\nu,n-q} = \delta_{\mu,\nu}.$$

Let π_1 and π_2 denote the two projection maps $M \times M \to M$. By the Künneth formula, the forms

$$\{\varphi_{\mu,\nu,p,q} = \pi_1^* \psi_{\mu,p} \wedge \pi_2^* \psi^*_{\nu,q}\}_{p+q=k}$$

represent a basis for $H^k_{\mathrm{DR}}(M \times M)$. The dual basis for $H^{2n-k}_{\mathrm{DR}}(M \times M)$ is then represented by

$$\{\varphi^*_{\mu,\nu,n-p,n-q} = (-1)^{q(p+q)} \pi_1^* \psi^*_{\mu,n-p} \wedge \pi_2^* \psi_{\nu,n-q}\}_{p+q=k}$$

since by a direct computation using iteration of the integral

$$\int_{M \times M} \varphi_{\mu,\nu,p,q} \wedge \varphi^*_{\mu',\nu',n-p',n-q'} = \delta_{\mu,\mu'} \cdot \delta_{\nu,\nu'} \cdot \delta_{p,p'} \cdot \delta_{q,q'}.$$

The Poincaré dual η_Δ of the homology class of the diagonal $\Delta \subset M \times M$ is thus represented by the form

$$\varphi_\Delta = \sum_{p,\mu,\nu} c_{p,\mu,\nu} \varphi_{\mu,\nu,p,n-p},$$

where

$$c_{p,\mu,\nu} = \int_\Delta \varphi^*_{\mu,\nu,n-p,p} = (-1)^{n-p} \delta_{\mu,\nu},$$

i.e., η_Δ is represented by

$$\varphi_\Delta = \sum_{p,\mu} (-1)^{n-p} \varphi_{\mu,\mu,p,n-p}.$$

Now let $f: M \to M$ be a C^∞ map. We say that a fixed point $p \in M$ of f is *nondegenerate* if it is isolated and in terms of local coordinates $x_1, \ldots, x_n$ on M centered around p, the Jacobian matrix

$$\mathcal{J}_f(p): T_p(M) \to T_p(M)$$

satisfies

$$\det\left(\mathcal{J}_f(p) - I\right) \neq 0;$$

under these circumstances, we define the *index* $\iota_f(p)$ of f at p to be

$$\iota_f(p) = \operatorname{sgn} \det\left(\mathcal{J}_f(p) - I\right).$$

We can give another interpretation of the nondegeneracy condition and the index as follows: let $\Gamma_f = \{(p, f(p))\} \subset M \times M$ be the graph of f. Γ_f is a submanifold of $M \times M$; we give it the orientation induced by the map

$$\tilde{f}: p \mapsto (p, f(p)).$$

Let p be a fixed point of f, $x_1, \ldots, x_n$ an oriented coordinate system for M centered around p; take as coordinates around $(p,p) \in M \times M$ the functions

$$y_i = \pi_1^* x_i \quad \text{and} \quad z_i = \pi_2^* x_i.$$

An oriented basis for $T_{(p,p)}(\Delta) \subset T_{(p,p)}(M \times M)$ is then given by

$$\Delta_*\left(\frac{\partial}{\partial x_1}, \ldots, \frac{\partial}{\partial x_n}\right) = \left(\frac{\partial}{\partial y_1} + \frac{\partial}{\partial z_1}, \ldots, \frac{\partial}{\partial y_n} + \frac{\partial}{\partial z_n}\right),$$

where Δ is the diagonal map $x \mapsto (x, x)$, and an oriented basis for $T_{(p,p)}(\Gamma_f) \subset T_{(p,p)}(M \times M)$ is given by

$$\tilde{f}_*\left(\frac{\partial}{\partial x_1}, \ldots, \frac{\partial}{\partial x_n}\right) = \left(\frac{\partial}{\partial y_1} + \sum \frac{\partial f_i}{\partial x_1} \cdot \frac{\partial}{\partial z_i}, \ldots, \frac{\partial}{\partial y_n} + \sum \frac{\partial f_i}{\partial x_n} \cdot \frac{\partial}{\partial z_i}\right).$$

The combined collection

$$\left(\Delta_*\left(\frac{\partial}{\partial x_1}\right), \ldots, \Delta_*\left(\frac{\partial}{\partial x_n}\right), \tilde{f}_*\left(\frac{\partial}{\partial x_1}\right), \ldots, \tilde{f}_*\left(\frac{\partial}{\partial x_n}\right)\right)$$

is consequently obtained from the standard oriented basis $(\partial/\partial y_1, \ldots, \partial/\partial y_n, \partial/\partial z_1, \ldots, \partial/\partial z_n)$ for $T_{(p,p)}(M \times M)$ by the matrix

$$\begin{pmatrix} I_n & I_n \\ I_n & \mathcal{J}_f(p) \end{pmatrix};$$

we see accordingly that the cycles Γ_f and Δ intersect transversely at (p,p) exactly when

$$\det\begin{pmatrix} I & I \\ I & \mathcal{J}_f(p) \end{pmatrix} = \det\left(\mathcal{J}_f(p) - I\right)$$

is nonzero, i.e., when p is a nondegenerate fixed point of f; and in this case the index of f at p is just the intersection number of Δ with Γ_f at p. Thus if f has only nondegenerate fixed points,

$$\sum_{f(p)=p} \iota_f(p) = {}^{\#}(\Delta \cdot \Gamma_f)_{M \times M},$$

and we can evaluate this intersection number by

$$
{}^{\#}(\Delta \cdot \Gamma_f) = \int_{\Gamma_f} \varphi_\Delta
$$

$$
= \sum_p (-1)^{n-p} \int_{\Gamma_f} \sum_\mu \pi_1^* \psi_{\mu,p} \wedge \pi_2^* \psi_{\mu,n-p}^*;
$$

since $\tilde{f}^* \pi_2^* = f^*$, this is

$$
= \sum_p (-1)^{n-p} \int_M \sum_\mu \psi_{\mu,p} \wedge f^* \psi_{\mu,n-p}^*
$$

$$
= \sum_p (-1)^{n-p} \cdot \operatorname{trace}\left(f^* \big|_{H_{DR}^{n-p}(M)}\right)
$$

$$
= \sum_p (-1)^p \operatorname{trace}\left(f^* \big|_{H_{DR}^p(M)}\right).
$$

The number $\sum (-1)^p \operatorname{trace}(f^*|_{H_{DR}^p(M)})$ is called the *Lefschetz number* of the map f, and is usually denoted $L(f)$; we have proved the

Lefschetz Fixed-Point Formula.

$$
\sum_{f(p)=p} \iota_f(p) = L(f).
$$

Note that without computing signs the number of fixed points of f must be at least the absolute value of $L(f)$, i.e.,

$$
{}^{\#}\{p \in M : f(p) = p\} \geqslant |L(f)|,
$$

and in particular,

$$
L(f) \neq 0 \Rightarrow f \text{ has a fixed point.}
$$

As an immediate corollary to the Lefschetz fixed-point formula we will prove the Hopf index theorem. Let M be as above, and let v be a global C^∞ vector field on M. We say a zero p of v is *nondegenerate* if it is isolated and, in terms of local coordinates $x_1, \ldots, x_n$ centered around p,

$$v(x) = \sum a_{ij} x_i \frac{\partial}{\partial x_j} + [2]$$

with $\Delta = (a_{ij})$ nonsingular; in this case we define the *index* $\iota_v(p)$ of v at p to be the sign of the determinant of Δ. Now, integrating the vector field v to time t gives a flow

$$f_t : M \to M.$$

For t small, the fixed points of f_t will be exactly the zeros of v, and if v is given as above near a zero p, then in terms of the coordinates x,

$$\mathcal{J}_{f_t}(p) = e^{tA} + \text{higher-order terms.}$$

Thus

$$\mathcal{J}_{f_t}(p) - I = t\left(A + \frac{tA^2}{2} + \frac{t^2A^3}{6} + \cdots\right),$$

and for t positive and sufficiently small,

$$\iota_{f_t}(p) = \operatorname{sgn} \det(\mathcal{J}_{f_t}(p) - I) = \operatorname{sgn} \det A = \iota_v(p).$$

Since f_t is homotopic to the identity, f_t^* acts as the identity on the cohomology of M, so that

$$\operatorname{trace} f_t^* \big|_{H^p_{\mathrm{DR}}(M)} = \dim H^p_{\mathrm{DR}}(M),$$

i.e.,

$$L(f_t) = \chi(M);$$

and we have the

Hopf Index Theorem.

$$\sum_{v(p)=0} \iota_v(p) = \chi(M).$$

The Holomorphic Lefschetz Fixed-Point Formula

Suppose now that M is a compact complex manifold of dimension n and $f : M \to M$ a holomorphic map. Then f acts not only on the de Rham cohomology of M but on the Dolbeault cohomology groups as well, and we may hope, by analogy with the Lefschetz fixed-point formula, that the action of f on $H^{**}_{\bar{\partial}}(M)$ will be reflected in the local behavior of f around its fixed points. This is in fact the case, and we will spend the remainder of this section deriving the corresponding formula.

Our starting point, as before, is a computation of the Dolbeault cohomology class of the diagonal $\Delta \subset M \times M$. To this end, for each p and q

let

$$\{\psi_{p,q,\mu}\}$$

be a collection of $\bar{\partial}$-closed (p,q)-forms representing a basis for $H_{\bar{\partial}}^{p,q}(M)$, and let

$$\{\psi_{n-p,n-q,\mu}^*\}$$

be $\bar{\partial}$-closed forms representing the dual basis for $H_{\bar{\partial}}^{n-p,n-q}(M)$ under the pairing

$$H_{\bar{\partial}}^{p,q}(M) \otimes H_{\bar{\partial}}^{n-p,n-q}(M) \to \mathbb{C}$$

given by

$$\psi \otimes \varphi \mapsto \int_M \psi \wedge \varphi.$$

By the Künneth formula from Section 6 of Chapter 0 a basis for $H_{\bar{\partial}}^{n,n}(M \times M)$ is represented by the forms

$$\{\varphi_{p,q,\mu,\nu} = \pi_1^* \psi_{p,q,\mu} \wedge \pi_2^* \psi_{n-p,n-q,\nu}^*\},$$

and the dual basis for $H_{\bar{\partial}}^{n,n}(M \times M)$ is represented, as in the real case above, by

$$\{\varphi_{n-p,n-q,\mu,\nu}^* = \pi_1^* \psi_{n-p,n-q,\mu}^* \wedge \pi_2^* \psi_{p,q,\nu}\}.$$

The Dolbeault class η_Δ of the diagonal is

$$\varphi_\Delta = \sum_{p,q,\mu} (-1)^{p+q} \varphi_{p,q,\mu,\mu}.$$

Now let $f: M \to M$ be a holomorphic map with isolated nondegenerate zeros; let $\Gamma_f = \{(p,f(p))\} \subset M \times M$ be its graph. If we compute the intersection number of Δ and Γ_f in $M \times M$, we find only that

$$L(f) = \int_{\Gamma_f} \varphi_\Delta$$

$$= \sum_{p,q} (-1)^{p+q} \int_{\Gamma_f} \sum_\mu \pi_1^* \psi_{p,q,\mu} \wedge \pi_2^* \psi_{n-p,n-q,\mu}^*$$

$$= \sum (-1)^{p+q} \operatorname{trace} f^* |_{H_{\bar{\partial}}^{p,q}(M)}.$$

This tells us nothing essentially new: in case M is Kähler, this follows from the ordinary Lefschetz fixed-point formula and the Hodge decomposition; in general, it follows from the Lefschetz formula and the Fröhlicher spectral sequence relating Dolbeault and de Rham cohomology given in Section 5 of this chapter. To obtain finer information about the action of f on the Dolbeault groups of M, let $\eta_\Delta^{p,q}$ be the (p,q)th component of the class η_Δ under the decomposition into bitype

$$H_{\bar{\partial}}^{n,n}(M \times M) = \bigoplus_{p,q} \left(\pi_1^* H_{\bar{\partial}}^{p,q}(M) \otimes \pi_2^* H_{\bar{\partial}}^{n-p,n-q}(M) \right),$$

and set

$$\eta_\Delta^0 = \sum_q \eta_\Delta^{0,q}.$$

η_Δ^0 is then represented by the form

$$\varphi_\Delta^0 = \sum_{q,\mu} (-1)^q \varphi_{0,q,\mu,\mu},$$

and so the value of η_Δ^0 on the cycle Γ_f is given by

$$\eta_\Delta^0(\Gamma_f) = \int_{\Gamma_f} \varphi_\Delta^0$$
$$= \sum_q (-1)^q \int_M \sum_\mu \psi_{0,q,\mu} \wedge f^* \psi_{n,n-q,\mu}^*$$
$$= \sum_q (-1)^q \operatorname{trace} f^* |_{H_{\bar\partial}^{n,n-q}(M)}$$
$$= \sum_q (-1)^q \operatorname{trace} f^* |_{H_{\bar\partial}^{0,q}(M)}$$

by Kodaira-Serre duality. The number $\sum_q (-1)^q \operatorname{trace} f^* |_{H_{\bar\partial}^{0,q}(M)}$ is called the *holomorphic Lefschetz number* of the map f, and is denoted $L(f, \mathcal{O})$.

We ask accordingly whether we can evaluate the number $\eta_\Delta^0(\Gamma_f)$ in terms of the local behavior of f around its fixed points. What makes this possible is the fact that while the full decomposition of forms on $M \times M$ into bitype (cf. Section 2 in this chapter)

$$A^{p,q}(M \times M) = \bigoplus_{\substack{p_1 + p_2 = p \\ q_1 + q_2 = q}} A^{(p_1, q_1), (p_2, q_2)}(M \times M),$$

does *not* commute with the $\bar\partial$-operator, the coarser direct-sum decomposition

$$A^{p,q}(M \times M) = \bigoplus_{p_1} A^{(p_1, *), (p - p_1, q - *)}(M \times M)$$

does. Here $*$ represents an index running from zero to q. It follows that if T_Δ^0 is the component of the current T_Δ of bitype $(0,*),(n,n-*)$—i.e., the current defined by the linear function

$$T_\Delta^0(\varphi) = \int_\Delta \sum_q \varphi^{(n,n-q),(0,q)}$$

on test forms φ, then T_Δ^0 is $\bar\partial$-*closed and represents the Dolbeault cohomology class* η_Δ^0. To compute $\eta_\Delta^0(\Gamma_f)$, then, we need only smooth the current T_Δ^0—that is, solve the equation of currents

$$(*) \qquad\qquad\qquad T_\Delta^0 = \varphi + \bar\partial k$$

with k any $(n, n-1)$-current on $M \times M$ and φ a smooth form; we will then have

$$\eta_\Delta^0(\Gamma_f) = \int_{\Gamma_f} \varphi.$$

In fact, as we will see, it will suffice just to solve the equation (∗) locally around the fixed points. We proceed as follows.

Recall from the subsection "Definitions; Residue Formulas" in Section 1 of this chapter the Bochner-Martinelli kernel on $\mathbb{C}^n \times \mathbb{C}^n$ is given by

$$k(z,\zeta) = C_n \frac{\sum \overline{\Phi_i(z-\zeta)} \wedge \Phi(\zeta)}{\|z-\zeta\|^{2n}},$$

where

$$\begin{cases} \Phi_i(x) = (-1)^{i-1} x_i\, dx_1 \wedge \cdots \wedge \widehat{dx_i} \wedge \cdots \wedge dx_n, \\ \Phi(x) = dx_1 \wedge \cdots \wedge dx_n. \end{cases}$$

This form has bitype $(0, *-1), (n, n-*)$ in the variables $(dz, d\bar{z})(d\zeta, d\bar{\zeta})$. Also, from $\overline{\partial}\Phi_i(z-\zeta) = \Phi_i(z-\zeta)$ it follows that

$$\overline{\partial}k(z,\zeta) = 0 \qquad \text{on } \mathbb{C}^n \times \mathbb{C}^n - \Delta,$$

so that the current defined by $k(z,\zeta)$ has distributional derivative $\overline{\partial}k$ supported on the diagonal. In fact, the homotopy formula proved in the subsection "Cohomology of Currents" is equivalent to the distributional equation

$$\overline{\partial}k = T_\Delta^0,$$

giving the desired "smoothing" of T_Δ^0 in $\mathbb{C}^n \times \mathbb{C}^n$.

Now we return to our complex manifold M and map $f: M \to M$. Assume that f has isolated, nondegenerate fixed points $\{p_\alpha\}$ and, in terms of local coordinates $z_{\alpha i}$ around p_α, write

$$f(z_\alpha)_i = \sum b_{ij} z_{\alpha j} + [2],$$

i.e.,

$$f(z_\alpha) = B_\alpha z_\alpha + [2],$$

where $B_\alpha = (b_{ij})$; by nondegeneracy, $(I - B_\alpha)$ is nonsingular. Let $B_\varepsilon(p_\alpha; p_\alpha)$ be a ball of radius ε around (p_α, p_α) in $M \times M$, and let ρ_α be a bump function with

$$\begin{aligned} \rho_\alpha &\equiv 1 &&\text{in } B_\varepsilon(p_\alpha, p_\alpha) \\ \rho_\alpha &\equiv 0 &&\text{in } M \times M - B_{2\varepsilon}(p_\alpha, p_\alpha); \end{aligned}$$

let k be the current on $M \times M$ given by

$$k = \sum_\alpha \rho_\alpha \cdot k(z_\alpha, \xi_\alpha),$$

where $k(z_\alpha, \xi_\alpha)$ is the Bochner-Martinelli kernel. Then in $B_\varepsilon(p_\alpha, p_\alpha)$ we have

$$\bar\partial k = \bar\partial k(z_\alpha, \xi_\alpha) = T_\Delta^0.$$

Moreover, k is smooth on $M \times M - \Delta$, so that if we set

$$\varphi = T_\Delta^0 - \bar\partial k,$$

φ will be a $\bar\partial$-closed current representing η_Δ^0, *smooth in an open set containing* Γ_f, and equal to $-\bar\partial k$ away from Δ. Then

$$\eta_\Delta^0(\Gamma_f) = \int_{\Gamma_f} \varphi$$

$$= -\int_{\Gamma_f - \cup B_\varepsilon(p_\alpha, p_\alpha)} \bar\partial k$$

$$= \sum_\alpha \int_{\partial(\Gamma_f \cap B_\varepsilon(p_\alpha, p_\alpha))} k$$

$$= \lim_{\varepsilon \to 0} \sum_\alpha \int_{\|z_\alpha\| = \varepsilon} k(z_\alpha, f(z_\alpha)).$$

Now if we set $w_\alpha = z_\alpha - f(z_\alpha)$, then

$$dw_{\alpha_1} \wedge \cdots \wedge dw_{\alpha_n} = \det(I - \mathcal{J}(f)) \cdot dz_{\alpha_1} \wedge \cdots \wedge dz_{\alpha_n},$$

and we have

$$\int_{\|z\| = \varepsilon} k(z_\alpha, f(z_\alpha))$$

$$= C_n \int_{\|z\| = \varepsilon} \frac{\sum (-1)^{i-1} \bar w_{\alpha_i} d\bar w_{\alpha_1} \wedge \cdots \wedge \widehat{d\bar w_{\alpha_i}} \wedge \cdots \wedge d\bar w_{\alpha_n} \wedge dz_{\alpha_1} \wedge \cdots \wedge dz_{\alpha_n}}{\|w_\alpha\|^{2n}}$$

$$= C_n \int_{\|z\| = \varepsilon} \frac{\sum (-1)^{i-1} \bar w_{\alpha_i} d\bar w_{\alpha_1} \wedge \cdots \wedge \widehat{d\bar w_{\alpha_i}} \wedge \cdots \wedge d\bar w_{\alpha_n} \wedge dw_{\alpha_1} \wedge \cdots \wedge dw_{\alpha_n}}{\|w_\alpha\|^{2n} \det(I - \mathcal{J}(f))}$$

$$= \frac{1}{\det(I - \mathcal{J}(f)(0))} = \frac{1}{\det(I - B_\alpha)}$$

by the Bochner-Martinelli formula proved in Section 1 of this chapter. Putting this all together, we have the *holomorphic Lefschetz fixed-point formula*:

$$L(f, \mathcal{O}) = \sum_{f(p_\alpha) = p_\alpha} \frac{1}{\det(I - B_\alpha)}.$$

The Bott Residue Formula

We ask now whether there exist refinements of the Gauss-Bonnet formula for holomorphic vector bundles on complex manifolds. The answer, in general, is no, for the reason that a zero of a section σ of a holomorphic vector bundle E on a complex manifold carries no nonobvious local structure: since we can choose a frame $e = (e_1, \ldots, e_k)$ for E and a local holomorphic coordinate system $z = (z_1, \ldots, z_n)$ for M independently, the local expansion

$$\sigma(z) = \sum b_{ij} z_i \cdot e_j + \sum b_{ijl} z_i z_j \cdot e_l + \ldots$$

for σ can be given virtually arbitrary form. The exception to this occurs when E is a holomorphic tensor bundle, e.g., when $E = T'(M)$ is the holomorphic tangent bundle of M: in this case a local coordinate system (z_i) determines naturally a frame $\{\partial/\partial z_i\}$ for $T'(M)$. Thus, in the neighborhood of a zero of the holomorphic vector field v, we set $A_p = (a_{ij})$, where

$$v(z) = \sum a_{ij} z_i \frac{\partial}{\partial z_j} + [2].$$

If $w = f(z)$ is any other coordinate system around $z = 0$ and we let $A'_p = (a'_{ij})$ be given by

$$v(z) = \sum a'_{ij} \cdot w_i \cdot \frac{\partial}{\partial w_j} + [2],$$

then for $g = (g_{ij}) = \mathcal{J}(f)$ the Jacobian of the change of coordinates,

$$\frac{\partial}{\partial z_i} = \sum g_{ji} \frac{\partial}{\partial w_j},$$

and hence

$$v(z) = \sum_{i,j,k,l} a_{ij} \cdot g_{ik}^{-1} \cdot w_k \cdot g_{lj} \cdot \frac{\partial}{\partial w_l} + [2].$$

Thus

$$A'_p = {}^t g^{-1} \cdot A_p \cdot {}^t g,$$

i.e., A_p *is determined up to conjugation.* The value $P(A_p)$ of any invariant polynomial P on A is therefore an invariant of v and p, and we may hope that the numbers $P(A_p)$ carry some global information. This is in fact the case: if Θ is any curvature matrix in the holomorphic tangent bundle $T'(M)$ of the compact complex manifold M, P any invariant polynomial of degree $n = \dim M$, v a global holomorphic vector field and A_p as above, we have the

Bott Residue Formula

$$\sum_{v(p)=0} \frac{P(A_p)}{\det(A_p)} = \int_M P\left(\frac{\sqrt{-1}}{2\pi} \Theta\right),$$

i.e., if we write P *as a polynomial*

$$P = Q(P^1, \ldots, P^n)$$

in the elementary invariant polynomials P^i,

$$\sum_{v(p)=0} \frac{P(A_p)}{\det(A_p)} = Q(c_1(M), \ldots, c_n(M)).$$

Proof.* The outline of the proof is this: we choose a metric in $T'(M)$ that is Euclidean in a neighborhood of the zeros $\{p_\nu\}$ of v, and let Θ be the curvature matrix of the metric connection on $T'(M)$. Then

$$\Theta \equiv 0$$

in a ball $B_\varepsilon(p_\nu)$ around each p_ν. We will construct a $C^\infty(n, n-1)$ form Λ on $M^* = M - \{p_\nu\}$ such that

$$d\Lambda = \bar{\partial}\Lambda = P(\Theta);$$

we will then have

$$\int_M P\left(\frac{\sqrt{-1}}{2\pi}\Theta\right) = \int_{M - \cup B_\varepsilon(p_\nu)} P\left(\frac{\sqrt{-1}}{2\pi}\Theta\right)$$

$$= -\left(\frac{\sqrt{-1}}{2\pi}\right)^n \sum_i \int_{\partial B_\varepsilon(p_\nu)} \Lambda,$$

and since our construction of Λ is essentially a local process, we will be able to evaluate the last integrals in terms of the local behavior of v at p_ν.

So: let $\{p_\nu\}$ denote the zeros of v, and $z_1, \ldots, z_n$ local holomorphic coordinates in $B_{2\varepsilon}(p_\nu)$, and let h_ν be the Euclidean metric in $B_{2\varepsilon}(p_\nu)$ given by

$$\left(\frac{\partial}{\partial z_j}, \frac{\partial}{\partial z_k}\right) = \delta_{jk}.$$

Let h_0 be any metric on $M^* = M - \{p_\nu\}$, and $\{\rho_0, \rho_\nu\}$ a partition of unity for the covering of M by $U_0 = M - \cup B_\varepsilon(p_\nu)$ and $U_\nu = B_{2\varepsilon}(p_\nu)$; we take as our metric on M

$$h = \rho_0 \cdot h_0 + \sum \rho_\nu h_\nu.$$

Let Θ hereafter be the curvature matrix of the associated metric connection D; clearly $\Theta \equiv 0$ in $B_\varepsilon(p_\nu)$ for each ν.

This proof is due to S. S. Chern, "Meromorphic vector fields and characteristic numbers, Scripta Mathematica, Vol. XXIX, pp. 243–251.

Now consider the bundle map

$$\wedge^{p-1}T' \otimes \wedge^q T'' \xrightarrow{\wedge v} \wedge^p T' \otimes \wedge^q T''$$

given by wedge product with $v(z) \in T'_z$. We define the *contraction operator*

$$\iota(v): A^{p,q}(M) \to A^{p-1,q}(M)$$

to be the adjoint of $\wedge v$; i.e., such that for any $\varphi \in A^{p,q}(M)$ and $\eta \in C^\infty(\wedge^{p-1}T' \otimes \wedge^q(T''))$,

$$\langle \iota(v)\varphi, \eta \rangle = \langle \varphi, v \wedge \eta \rangle.$$

Thus, if in terms of local coordinates z_i

$$v(z) = \sum_j v^j(z) \cdot \frac{\partial}{\partial z_j},$$

we have

$$\iota(v)(dz_i) = v^i$$

and in general

$$\iota(v)(f(z) \cdot dz_I) = \sum_\alpha (-1)^{\alpha-1} v^{i_\alpha}(z) f(z) dz_{I \{i_\alpha\}}.$$

In particular, since the coefficient functions v^i are holomorphic it follows from sign considerations that

$$\bar{\partial} \cdot \iota(v) + \iota(v) \cdot \bar{\partial} = 0.$$

The essential step in our construction of Λ is to express the tensor

$$\iota(v)(\Theta) \in A^{0,1}(T' \otimes T'^*)$$

as $\bar{\partial}$ of a global section of $T' \otimes T'^*$. To do this, we recall from Section 5 of Chapter 0 the definition of the *torsion* associated to a metric on $T'(M)$. As we saw then, if $v_1, \ldots, v_n$ is a unitary frame for $T'(M)$, $\varphi_1, \ldots, \varphi_n$ the dual coframe for T'^*, θ the connection matrix of D in terms of $\{v_i\}$ and $\theta^* = -{}^t\theta$ the connection matrix of the dual connection D^* on T'^* in terms of $\{\varphi_i\}$, then

$$d\varphi_i = \sum \theta^*_{ij} \wedge \varphi_j + \tau_i$$

with τ_i of type $(2,0)$; the vector $\tau = (\tau_1, \ldots, \tau_n)$ of 2-forms is called the *torsion* of the metric in terms of $\{v_i\}$. Now if

$$\left\{ v'_i = \sum g_{ij} \cdot v_j \right\}$$

is another frame, $\{\varphi'_i\}$ the dual coframe, and θ' and θ'^* the connection and curvature matrices of D and D^* in terms of $\{v'_i\}$ and $\{\varphi'_i\}$, then in matrix notation and setting $g^* = {}^t g^{-1}$

$$\varphi' = g^* \cdot \varphi,$$
$$\theta'^* = g^* \cdot \theta^* \cdot {}^t g + d(g^*) \cdot {}^t g$$

and

$$\begin{aligned}
\tau' &= d\varphi' - \theta'^* \wedge \varphi' \\
&= d(g^*\varphi) - \theta'^* \wedge g^*\varphi \\
&= d(g^*) \cdot \varphi + g^*\varphi - g^* \cdot \theta^* \cdot {}'g \cdot g^* \cdot \varphi - d(g^*) \cdot {}'g \cdot g^* \cdot \varphi \\
&= g^*\varphi - g^* \cdot \theta^* \wedge \varphi \\
&= g^* \cdot \tau
\end{aligned}$$

i.e., *the quantity*

$$\tilde{\tau} = \sum \tau_i \otimes v_i \in A^{2,0}(T')$$

is a tensor invariant of the metric, called the *torsion tensor.* Note that by our calculation, if $v'_1, \ldots, v'_n$ is any other frame for T', not necessarily unitary but with φ, θ, and θ^* as before, we still have

$$\tilde{\tau} = \sum_i \left(d\varphi'_i - \sum \theta'^*_{ij} \wedge \varphi'_j \right) \otimes v'_i.$$

Now let $(z_1, \ldots, z_n)$ be local coordinates on M and $\theta = (\theta_{ij})$ the connection matrix of D in terms of the frame $\{\partial/\partial z_i\}$ for $T'(M)$. Write

$$\theta_{ij} = \sum_k \Gamma^j_{ik} dz_k,$$

so that

$$Dv = D\left(\sum_i v^i \frac{\partial}{\partial z_i} \right) = \sum_{j,k} \left(\frac{\partial v^j}{\partial z_k} + \sum_i \Gamma^j_{ik} v^i \right) \frac{\partial}{\partial z_j} \otimes dz_k.$$

The torsion tensor $\tilde{\tau}$ is given by

$$\begin{aligned}
\tilde{\tau} &= -\sum_{i,j} \theta^*_{ji} \wedge dz_i \otimes \frac{\partial}{\partial z_j} \\
&= \sum_{i,j} \theta_{ij} \wedge dz_i \otimes \frac{\partial}{\partial z_j} \\
&= \frac{1}{2} \sum_{i,j,k} \left(\Gamma^j_{ik} - \Gamma^j_{ki} \right) \frac{\partial}{\partial z_j} \otimes (dz_i \wedge dz_k),
\end{aligned}$$

and so the contraction $\iota(v) \cdot \tau \in C^\infty(T' \otimes T'^*)$ of τ by v is given by

$$\iota(v) \cdot \tau = \sum_{i,j,k} \left(\Gamma^j_{ik} - \Gamma^j_{ki} \right) v^i \cdot \frac{\partial}{\partial z_j} \otimes dz_k.$$

Thus the tensor

$$\begin{aligned}
E &= -Dv + \iota(v) \cdot \tau \\
&= -\sum_{j,k} \left\{ \frac{\partial v^j}{\partial z_k} + \sum_i \Gamma^j_{ki} v^i \right\} \frac{\partial}{\partial z_j} \otimes dz_k
\end{aligned}$$

is a well-defined global section of the holomorphic vector bundle $T' \otimes T'^*$, and

$$\bar{\partial} E = - \sum \left(\frac{\partial}{\partial \bar{z}_l} \left\{ \frac{\partial v^j}{\partial z_k} + \sum \Gamma^j_{ki} v^i \right\} \cdot \frac{\partial}{\partial z_j} \otimes dz_k \right) d\bar{z}_l$$

$$= - \sum \left(\frac{\partial \Gamma^j_{ki}}{\partial \bar{z}_l} \cdot v^i \cdot \frac{\partial}{\partial z_j} \otimes dz_k \right) d\bar{z}_l.$$

On the other hand, the curvature tensor $\Theta \in A^2(T \otimes T^*)$ is given by

$$\Theta = \sum \Theta_{ij} \frac{\partial}{\partial z_j} \otimes dz_i,$$

where

$$\Theta_{ij} = \bar{\partial} \theta_{ij} = - \sum \frac{\partial \Gamma^j_{ik}}{\partial \bar{z}_l} \cdot dz_k \wedge d\bar{z}_l,$$

so that from the formula

$$\iota(v) \cdot \Theta_r = - \sum_{i,j,k} \left(\frac{\partial \Gamma^j_{ik}}{\partial \bar{z}_l} \cdot v^k \cdot \frac{\partial}{\partial z_j} \otimes dz_i \right) d\bar{z}_l$$

we deduce the desired relation

$$\iota(v) \Theta = \bar{\partial} E.$$

Now, consider Θ, E, and $\bar{\partial} E = \iota(v) \Theta$ again as matrix-valued 2-, 0-, and 1-forms, respectively; if P is any invariant polynomial of degree n on $GL(n)$ and $\tilde{P}$ its polarization, set

$$P_r(E, \Theta) = \binom{n}{r} \tilde{P} (\underbrace{E, \ldots, E}_{n-r}, \underbrace{\Theta, \ldots, \Theta}_{r}) \in A^{r,r}(M).$$

Since $\bar{\partial} \Theta = 0$ and $\bar{\partial} E = \iota(v) \Theta$,

$$\bar{\partial} P_r(E, \Theta) = \binom{n}{r} \sum_{i=1}^{n-r} \tilde{P}(E, \ldots, \iota(v) \cdot \Theta, \ldots, E, \Theta, \ldots, \Theta)$$

$$= \iota(v) \cdot P_{r+1}(E, \Theta).$$

Let $\omega \in A^{1,0}(M^*)$ be the form dual to v under the metric on M; set

$$\Phi_r = \omega \wedge (\bar{\partial} \omega)^{n-r-1} \wedge P_r(E, \Theta) \in A^{n,n-1}(M^*).$$

We have, for $0 \leqslant r \leqslant n-1$,

$$\bar{\partial} \Phi_r = (\bar{\partial} \omega)^{n-r} \wedge P_r(E, \Theta) - \omega \wedge (\bar{\partial} \omega)^{n-r-1} \wedge \iota(v) P_{r+1}(E, \Theta);$$

since $\iota(v) \omega = 1$,

$$0 = \iota(\bar{\partial} v) \omega + \iota(v) \bar{\partial} \omega \Rightarrow \iota(v) \bar{\partial} \omega = 0,$$

and so

$$\iota(v)\bar{\partial}\Phi_r = (\bar{\partial}\omega)^{n-r} \wedge \iota(v)P_r(E,\Theta) - (\bar{\partial}\omega)^{n-r-1} \wedge \iota(v)P_{r+1}(E,\Theta).$$

$\iota(v)P_0(E,\Theta)$ is trivially zero, and so if we set

$$\Phi = \sum_{i=0}^{n-1} \Phi_i,$$

we see that

$$\iota(v)\bar{\partial}\Phi = \sum_{i=1}^{n-1} (\bar{\partial}\omega)^{n-r} \wedge \iota(v)P_i(E,\Theta) - \sum_{i=1}^{n} (\bar{\partial}\omega)^{n-i} \wedge \iota(v) \cdot P_i(E,\Theta)$$

$$= -\iota(v)P_n(\Theta)$$

$$= -\iota(v) \cdot P(\Theta).$$

Since $\bar{\partial}\Phi$ and $P(\Theta)$ are both forms of top degree,

$$\iota(v)\big(\bar{\partial}\Phi + P(\Theta)\big) = 0$$

implies that

$$\bar{\partial}\Phi + P(\Theta) = 0$$

and we have constructed our explicit solution to $\bar{\partial}\Lambda = P(\Theta)$.

It remains now to evaluate the integral of Φ over the boundary of $B_\varepsilon(p_\nu)$. First of all, recall that by our choice of metric, Θ—and hence $P_r(E,\Theta)$ for $r > 0$—vanishes identically in $B_\varepsilon(p_\nu)$; thus

$$\int_{\partial B_\varepsilon(p_\nu)} \Phi = \int_{\partial B_\varepsilon(p_\nu)} P_0(E,\Theta) = \int_{\partial B_\varepsilon(p_\nu)} \omega \wedge (\bar{\partial}\omega)^{n-1} P(E).$$

Let $z = (z_1,\dots,z_n)$ be as before local coordinates around p_i such that

$$\left(\frac{\partial}{\partial z_i}, \frac{\partial}{\partial z_j}\right) = \delta_{ij}$$

in $B_\varepsilon(p_\nu)$; write

$$v(z) = \sum v^j(z) \cdot \frac{\partial}{\partial z_j}.$$

Then since our metric is Euclidean in $B_\varepsilon(p_\nu)$, the connection D is zero and

$$E_{jk} = -\left(\frac{\partial v^j}{\partial z_k} + \sum_i \Gamma^j_{ki} v^i\right) = -\frac{\partial v^j}{\partial z_k},$$

i.e.,

$$P(E)(p_\nu) = -P(A_{p\nu}).$$

Moreover,

$$\omega = \frac{\sum \bar{v}^i dz_i}{\sum v^i \bar{v}^i}$$
$$= \frac{(dz, v)}{(v, v)},$$

so

$$\bar{\partial}\omega = -\frac{(dz, dv)}{(v, v)} + \frac{(dz, v) \wedge (v, dv)}{(v, v)^2}$$

Thus, since $(dz, v) \wedge (dz, v) = 0$,

$$\left(\frac{\sqrt{-1}}{2\pi}\right)^n \omega \wedge (\bar{\partial}\omega)^{n-1} = (-1)^{n-1} \left(\frac{\sqrt{-1}}{2\pi}\right)^n \frac{(dz, v) \wedge (dz, dv)^{n-1}}{(v, v)^n}$$

$$= -C_n \frac{\sum_i (-1)^{i-1} \bar{v}^i d\bar{v}^1 \wedge \cdots \wedge \widehat{d\bar{v}^i} \wedge \cdots \wedge d\bar{v}^n \wedge dz_1 \wedge \cdots \wedge dz_n}{(v, v)^n},$$

where C_n is the constant appearing in the Bochner-Martinelli formula from Section 1 of this chapter,

$$= -\frac{1}{\det A_p} \beta(v, \bar{v}),$$

where β is the form appearing in that formula. Putting everything together,

$$\int_M P\left(\frac{\sqrt{-1}}{2\pi}\Theta\right) = \int_{M - \cup B_\epsilon(p_\nu)} P\left(\frac{\sqrt{-1}}{2\pi}\Theta\right)$$

$$= -\sum_\nu \int_{\partial B_\epsilon(p_\nu)} \Phi$$

$$= \sum_\nu \int_{\partial B_\epsilon(p_\nu)} \frac{P(A_{p_\nu})}{\det A_{p_\nu}} \beta(v, v) \qquad \text{where } A = (\partial v_i / \partial z_j),$$

$$= \sum_\nu \frac{P(A_{p_\nu})}{\det A_{p_\nu}}$$

by the Bochner-Martinelli formula. Q.E.D.

As an example of a computation involving the Bott residue theorem, we calculate for the third (and last) time the Chern classes of projective space. Let $X = (X_0, \ldots, X_n)$ be linear coordinates on $\mathbb{C}^{n+1}$, π_* and $\mathcal{E}$ as in Section 3 of this chapter, and $(\alpha_0, \ldots, \alpha_n)$ any $(n+1)$-vector of distinct nonzero complex numbers. Consider the vector field on $\mathbb{P}^n$,

$$v(X) = \pi_* \sum_{i=0}^{n} \alpha_i X_i \frac{\partial}{\partial X_i}$$

(since $\pi_* \sum X_i (\partial / \partial X_i) \equiv 0$, we may as well take $\sum \alpha_i = 0$). As we have seen, v vanishes exactly at the points $p_i = [0, \ldots, 1_i, \ldots, 0]$; in terms of Euclidean coordinates

$$x_j = \frac{X_j}{X_i}, \qquad j \neq i,$$

on $\mathbb{P}^n$ around p_i, we have

$$\pi_* \left(X_j \frac{\partial}{\partial X_j} \right) = x_j \frac{\partial}{\partial x_j}, \qquad j \neq i,$$

and

$$\pi_* \left(X_i \frac{\partial}{\partial X_i} \right) = -\sum_{j \neq i} x_j \frac{\partial}{\partial x_j}.$$

Thus

$$v(x) = \sum_{j \neq i} (\alpha_j - \alpha_i) x_j \frac{\partial}{\partial x_j},$$

i.e., the matrix A_{p_i} for v near p_i is just the diagonal matrix with entries $(\alpha_j - \alpha_i)$, $j \neq i$. According to the Bott residue formula, then,

$$c_1(\mathbb{P}^n)^n = \sum_{i=0}^{n} \frac{\left(\text{trace}(A_{p_i}) \right)^n}{\det(A_{p_i})}$$

$$= \sum_i \frac{\left(\sum_{j \neq i} (\alpha_j - \alpha_i) \right)^n}{\prod_{j \neq i} (\alpha_j - \alpha_i)}$$

$$= \sum_i \frac{\left(-(n+1)\alpha_i \right)^n}{\prod_{j \neq i} (\alpha_j - \alpha_i)},$$

since $\sum \alpha_k = 0$. To evaluate this expression, consider the meromorphic functions f, g on the Riemann sphere given in terms of a Euclidean coordinate by

$$f(z) = \prod_{k=0}^{n} (\alpha_k - z), \qquad g(z) = z^n;$$

then $(g(z)/f(z))\, dz = \varphi$ is a meromorphic differential with simple poles at

$z = \alpha_k$ and $z = \infty$, and

$$\mathrm{Res}_{\alpha_i}(\varphi) = \frac{-\alpha_i^n}{\Pi_{j \neq i}(\alpha_j - \alpha_i)},$$

$$\mathrm{Res}_{\infty}(\varphi) = (-1)^n.$$

By the residue theorem

$$\sum_i \left(\frac{\alpha_i^n}{\Pi_{j \neq i}(\alpha_j - \alpha_i)} \right) = (-1)^n$$

and consequently

$$c_1(\mathbb{P}^n)^n = \sum_i \frac{(-1)^n (n+1)^n \alpha_i^n}{\Pi_{j \neq i}(\alpha_j - \alpha_i)} = (n+1)^n;$$

since the nth power of the hyperplane class ω in $\mathbb{P}^n$ is 1, this implies that

$$c_1(\mathbb{P}^n) = (n+1)\omega.$$

Now to compute the rest of the Chern classes of $\mathbb{P}^n$ we need only evaluate the Chern numbers $c_1(\mathbb{P}^n)^{n-r} \cdot c_r(\mathbb{P}^n)$. By Bott residue applied to v,

$$c_1(\mathbb{P}^n)^{n-r} \cdot c_r(\mathbb{P}^n) = \sum_{i=0}^{n} \frac{\left(\sum_{j \neq i}(\alpha_j - \alpha_i) \right)^{n-r} \cdot \left(\sum_{i \notin I}^{\#I=r} \Pi_{j \in I}(\alpha_j - \alpha_i) \right)}{\Pi_{j \neq i}(\alpha_j - \alpha_i)}$$

$$= \sum_{i=0}^{n} \frac{(-1)^{n-r}(n+1)^{n-r} \alpha_i^{n-r} \cdot \sum_{i \notin I}^{\#I=r} \Pi_{i \in I}(\alpha_j - \alpha_i)}{\Pi_{j \neq i}(\alpha_j - \alpha_i)}.$$

Again, for $f(z)$ as above, $g(z) = z^{n-r} \sum_{\#I=r} \Pi_{k \in I}(\alpha_k - z)$, and $\varphi = (g/f)dz$

$$\mathrm{Res}_{\alpha_i}(\varphi) = \frac{-\alpha_i^{n-r} \sum_{\#I=r} \Pi_{j \in I}(\alpha_j - \alpha_i)}{\Pi_{j \neq i}(\alpha_j - \alpha_i)}$$

$$\mathrm{Res}_{\infty}(\varphi) = (-1)^{n-r} \binom{n+1}{r}$$

and the residue theorem together with $c_1(\mathbb{P}^n) = (n+1)\omega$ imply

$$c_r(\mathbb{P}^n) = \binom{n+1}{r}\omega^r.$$

The General Hirzebruch-Riemann-Roch Formula

Consider now how we arrived at the identity

$$c_n(M) = \chi(M)$$

for a compact complex manifold M of dimension n: On the one hand, the general Gauss-Bonnet formula tells us that we can realize $c_n(M)$ as the number of zeros, properly counted, of a generic C^∞ vector field on M; on the other hand, the Lefschetz fixed-point formula tells us that the Euler characteristic of M is equal to the number of fixed points, properly counted, of the map $\varphi_v : M \to M$ obtained by integrating v—that is, again the number of zeros of v. Now we have obtained refinements of both the Gauss-Bonnet and the Lefschetz fixed-point formulas in the holomorphic case, and we may try to apply them in the same way to arrive at a formula for the holomorphic Euler characteristic of a complex manifold.

So, suppose again that M is a compact Kähler manifold of dimension n and let v be a holomorphic vector field on M having isolated nondegenerate zeros. Let

$$f_t = \exp(tv): \ M \to M$$

be the map obtained by integrating the corresponding real vector field to time t; f_t is readily seen to be holomorphic. Moreover, if $z_1, \ldots, z_n$ are local coordinates around a zero p of v and

$$v(z) = \sum a_{ij} z_i \frac{\partial}{\partial z_j} + [2],$$

then the Jacobian of $f_t(z)$ at p is given by

$$B_p = e^{t \cdot A_p},$$

where $A_p = (a_{ij})$. Now for t small, f_t will have a fixed point exactly where v has a zero, and by the holomorphic Lefschetz fixed-point formula,

$$L(f_t, \mathcal{O}) = \sum_{v(p)=0} \frac{1}{\det(I - B_p)} .$$

Since f_t is homotopic to the identity, f_t^* is the identity on $H_{\bar\partial}^{p,q}(M)$, and so this formula reads

$$\chi(\mathcal{O}_M) = \sum_{v(p)=0} \frac{1}{\det(I - e^{tA_p})}$$

$$= \sum_{v(p)=0} \frac{1}{\det A_p} \cdot \left(\frac{\det A_p}{\det(I - e^{tA_p})} \right).$$

Now, for each t the holomorphic function

$$F_t(A) = \det(A) \cdot \left(\det(I - e^{tA}) \right)^{-1}$$

on GL_n is invariant under conjugation, and hence uniquely expressible as a power series in the elementary invariant polynomials P^i on GL_n. Explicitly, for $A \in GL_n$ semisimple with eigenvalues $\lambda_1, \ldots, \lambda_n$,

$$F_t(A) = \frac{\det A}{\det(I - e^{tA})}$$

$$= \prod_{i=1}^{n} \left(\frac{\lambda_i}{1 - e^{t\lambda_i}} \right)$$

$$= (-1)^n t^{-n} \left\{ 1 - \left(\frac{\sum \lambda_i}{2} \right) t + \left(\frac{\sum \lambda_i^2}{12} + \frac{\sum \lambda_i \lambda_j}{4} \right) t^2 \right.$$

$$\left. - \left(\frac{\sum \lambda_i \lambda_j \lambda_k}{8} + \frac{\sum \lambda_i^2 \lambda_j + \sum \lambda_i \lambda_j^2}{24} \right) t^3 + \cdots \right\}$$

$$= (-1)^n t^{-n} \left\{ 1 - P^1(A) t + \left(\frac{P^1(A)^2 + P^2(A)}{12} \right) t^2 \right.$$

$$\left. - \frac{P^1(A) P^2(A)}{24} t^3 + \cdots \right\},$$

where the summations occur over increasing indices. In general the coefficient of t^i in the bracketed power series may be expressed as a polynomial in the elementary invariant polynomials. The *Todd polynomials* Td_i are then defined by

$$\frac{\det A}{\det(I - e^{-tA})} = (-1)^n t^{-n} \left\{ \sum_i Td_i(P^1(A), \ldots, P^i(A)) t^i \right\}$$

Now we may express the Lefschetz fixed-point formula as applied to v and f_t by

$$\chi(\mathcal{O}_M) = \sum_{v(p)=0} \frac{1}{\det A_p} \cdot \frac{\det A_p}{\det(I - e^{tA_p})}$$

$$= (-1)^n t^{-n} \sum_i \left[\sum_{v(p)=0} (-1)^i \frac{Td_i(P^1(A_p), \ldots, P^i(A_p))}{\det A_p} \right] \cdot t^i.$$

But $\chi(\mathcal{O}_M)$ is obviously independent of t, and so *all terms on the right involving nonzero powers of* t *are necessarily zero*; thus

$$\chi(\mathcal{O}_M) = \sum_{v(p)=0} \frac{Td_n(P^1(A_p), \ldots, P^n(A_p))}{\det A_p},$$

and finally, by the Bott residue formula, we can evaluate this last term to arrive, in this special case, at the famous

Hirzebruch-Riemann-Roch Formula

$$\chi(\mathcal{O}_M) = Td_n(c_1(M), \ldots, c_n(M)).$$

For a curve, the formula reads

$$\chi(\mathcal{O}_M) = \tfrac{1}{2}c_1(M),$$

which is equivalent to *Riemann's relation*

$$g = \tfrac{1}{2}b_1(M).$$

This we proved by harmonic theory. For a surface, we have *Noether's formula*

$$\chi(\mathcal{O}_M) = \frac{c_1(M)^2 + c_2(M)}{12},$$

which we will prove and use extensively in the next chapter.

Unfortunately, our analogy between the Gauss-Bonnet III and Riemann-Roch formulas fails in one crucial aspect: while any differentiable manifold has many C^∞ vector fields to use as props in the proof of Gauss-Bonnet III, relatively few compact manifolds have any global holomorphic vector fields. (Cf. the theorem of Carrell and Liebermann proved in Section 4 of Chapter 5.) Of course, since the Riemann-Roch formula itself has nothing to do with the vector field v used to obtain it, we may suspect that the role of v is only auxiliary. This is in fact the case—the formula holds for any compact complex manifold—but we do not have available here the techniques necessary to prove it. Our derivation of the formula thus remains only a suggestion, and not a proof; we will, however, give a geometric proof of the formula for algebraic surfaces in the next chapter.

5. SPECTRAL SEQUENCES AND APPLICATIONS

Spectral Sequences of Filtered and Bigraded Complexes

Spectral sequences are algebraic tools for working with cohomology; basically they form an array of long exact sequences fit into a systematic pattern and are to be applied in a similar fashion. To someone who works with cohomology, they are essential in the same way that the various integration techniques are essential to a student of calculus. We shall use spectral sequences in rather limited circumstances, but it seems worthwhile to give the general definitions.

A *complex* $(K^*, d) = \{K^0 \xrightarrow{d} K^1 \xrightarrow{d} K^2 \to \cdots\}$ is a sequence of Abelian groups with differentials

$$d: K^p \to K^{p+1}$$

satisfying $d \circ d = 0$. The *cohomology* of the complex is

$$H^*(K^*) = \bigoplus_{p \geqslant 0} H^p(K^*),$$

where

$$H^p(K^*) = \frac{Z^p}{dK^{p-1}}$$

with $Z^p = \ker\{d : K^p \to K^{p+1}\}$ the group of *cycles* and $dK^{p-1} = B^p \subset Z^p$ the subgroup of *boundaries*. A *subcomplex* (J^*, d) is given by subgroups $J^p \subset K^p$ with $dJ^* \subset J^*$. The *quotient complex* (L^*, d) is defined by $L^* = K^*/J^*$ with the obvious differential. We then have an *exact sequence of complexes*

$$0 \to J^* \to K^* \to L^* \to 0;$$

by an easy and well-known argument, this gives rise to a *long exact cohomology sequence*

$$\cdots \to H^p(J^*) \to H^p(K^*) \to H^p(L^*) \to H^{p+1}(J^*) \to \cdots .$$

Generalizing the notion of a subcomplex is that of a *filtered complex* $(F^p K^*, d)$, defined as a decreasing sequence of subcomplexes

$$K^* = F^0 K^* \supset F^1 K^* \supset \cdots \supset F^n K^* \supset F^{n+1} K^* = \{0\}.$$

The single subcomplex mentioned above corresponds to the filtration

$$K^* \supset J^* \supset \{0\},$$

and the spectral sequence of a filtered complex will generalize the long exact cohomology sequence. Before coming to this, we need a few more definitions.

The *associated graded complex* to a filtered complex $(F^p K^*, d)$ is the complex

$$\operatorname{Gr} K^* = \bigoplus_{p \geqslant 0} \operatorname{Gr}^p K^*$$

where

$$\operatorname{Gr}^p K^* = \frac{F^p K^*}{F^{p+1} K^*}$$

and the differential is the obvious one. The filtration $F^p K^*$ on K^* also induces a filtration $F^p H^*(K^*)$ on the cohomology by

$$F^p H^q(K^*) = \frac{F^p Z^q}{F^p B^q}.$$

The *associated graded cohomology* is

$$\operatorname{Gr} H^*(K^*) = \bigoplus_{p,q} \operatorname{Gr}^p H^q(K^*),$$

where

$$\mathrm{Gr}^p\, H^q(K^*) = \frac{F^p H^q(K^*)}{F^{p+1} H^q(K^*)}.$$

DEFINITION.   A *spectral sequence* is a sequence $\{E_r, d_r\}$ $(r \geqslant 0)$ of bigraded groups

$$E_r = \bigoplus_{p,q \geqslant 0} E_r^{p,q}$$

together with differentials

$$d_r \colon E_r^{p,q} \to E_r^{p+r,q-r+1}, \qquad d_r^2 = 0,$$

such that

$$H^*(E_r) = E_{r+1}.$$

When working with spectral sequences it is useful—even essential—to draw the "picture" (Figure 3).

In practice we will always have $E_r = E_{r+1} = \cdots$ for $r \geqslant r_0$; we call this limit group E_∞ and say that *the spectral sequence* $\{E_r\}$ *converges to* E_∞.

Proposition. *Let* K^* *be a filtered complex. Then there exists a spectral sequence* $\{E_r\}$ *with*

$$E_0^{p,q} = \frac{F^p K^{p+q}}{F^{p+1} K^{p+q}},$$

$$E_1^{p,q} = H^{p+q}(\mathrm{Gr}^p K^*),$$

$$E_\infty^{p,q} = \mathrm{Gr}^p(H^{p+q}(K^*)).$$

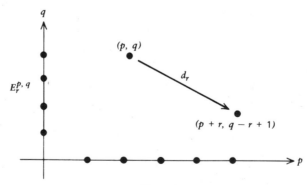

Figure 3

The last statement is usually written

$$E_r \Rightarrow H^*(K^*)$$

and we say that the spectral sequence abuts *to* H*(K*).

Proof. The initial term has been defined, and

$$d_0: E_0^{p,q} \longrightarrow E_0^{p,q+1}$$
$$\| \qquad\qquad\qquad \|$$
$$F^pK^{p+q}/F^{p+1}K^{p+q} \longrightarrow F^pK^{p+q+1}/F^{p+1}K^{p+q+1}$$

is obtained from the given differential d by passing to the quotient. The cohomology of $\{E_0, d_0\}$ is

$$E_1^{p,q} = \frac{\operatorname{Ker} d_0}{\operatorname{Im} d_0} = \frac{\{a \in F^pK^{p+q}: da \in F^{p+1}K^{p+q+1}\}}{d(F^pK^{p+q-1}) + F^{p+1}K^{p+q}}$$
$$= H^{p+q}\left(\frac{F^pK^*}{F^{p+1}K^*}\right)$$
$$= H^{p+q}(\operatorname{Gr}^p K^*)$$

as specified.

If $[a]$ is a class in $E_1^{p,q}$ as just above, then

$$da \in \frac{\{b \in F^{p+1}K^{p+q+1}: db \in F^{p+2}K^{p+q+2}\}}{d(F^{p+1}K^{p+q}) + F^{p+2}K^{p+q+1}}$$

defines a class in $E_1^{p+1,q}$, and this gives the differential

$$d_1: E_1^{p,q} \to E_1^{p+1,q}.$$

It follows that

$$\operatorname{Ker} d_1 = \frac{\{a \in F^pK^{p+q}: da \in F^{p+2}K^{p+q+1}\}}{d(F^pK^{p+q-1}) + F^{p+1}K^{p+q}},$$
$$\operatorname{Im} d_1 = \frac{d(F^{p-1}K^{p+q-1})}{d(F^pK^{p+q-1}) + F^{p+1}K^{p+q}},$$

so that

$$E_2^{p,q} = \frac{\{a \in F^pK^{p+q}: da \in F^{p+2}K^{p+q+1}\}}{d(F^{p-1}K^{p+q-1}) + F^{p+1}K^{p+q}}.$$

Here, the denominator is not a subgroup of the numerator; the meaning is that we take {denominator as written} ∩ {numerator}. A similar remark applies during the remainder of this proof.

Continuing in this way, we define in general

$$E_r^{p,q} = \frac{\{a \in F^pK^{p+q}: da \in F^{p+r}K^{p+q+1}\}}{d(F^{p-r+1}K^{p+q-1}) + F^{p+1}K^{p+q}},$$

and for $[a] \in E_r^{p,q}$ we define

$$d_r a = [da] \in \frac{\{b \in F^{p+r}K^{p+q+1}:\ db \in F^{p+2r+1}K^{p+q+2}\}}{d(F^pK^{p+q}) + F^{p+r+1}K^{p+q+1}} = E_r^{p+r,q-r+1}$$

A computation—straightforward but messy—gives

$$H^*(E_r) \cong E_{r+1}.$$

For r sufficiently large,

$$\begin{aligned}
E_r^{p,q} &= \frac{\{a \in F^pK^{p+q}:\ da=0\}}{dK^{p+q-1} + F^{p+1}K^{p+q}} \\
&\cong \frac{F^pH^{p+q}(K^*)}{F^{p+1}H^{p+q}(K^*)} \\
&= \mathrm{Gr}^p\, H^{p+q}(K^*).
\end{aligned}$$

This completes the proof of the proposition.   Q.E.D.

One of our main examples is the spectral sequence associated to a *double complex*. This latter is a bigraded group

$$K^{*,*} = \bigoplus_{p,q \geqslant 0} K^{p,q}$$

together with differentials

$$\begin{aligned}
d&:\ K^{p,q} \to K^{p+1,q}, \\
\delta&:\ K^{p,q} \to K^{p,q+1},
\end{aligned}$$

satisfying

$$d^2 = \delta^2 = 0, \qquad d\delta + \delta d = 0.$$

The double complex will be denoted $(K^{*,*}; d, \delta)$. The *associated single complex* (K^*, D) is defined by

$$\begin{aligned}
K^n &= \bigoplus_{p+q=n} K^{p,q} \\
D &= d + \delta.
\end{aligned}$$

There are two filtrations on (K^*, D) given by

$$'F^pK^n = \bigoplus_{\substack{p'+q=n \\ p' \geqslant p}} K^{p',q},$$

$$''F^qK^n = \bigoplus_{\substack{p+q''=n \\ q'' \geqslant q}} K^{p,q''}.$$

If, e.g., M is a complex manifold and

$$K^{p,q} = A^{p,q}(M), \qquad d = \partial, \qquad \delta = \bar{\partial},$$

then $'F^pA''(M)$ means "n-forms having at least p-dz's."

There are two spectral sequences, $\{'E_r\}$ and $\{''E_r\}$, both abutting to $H^*(K^*)$. By symmetry we may consider the first one. Then

$$'E_0^{p,q} = \frac{K^{p,q} + K^{p+1,q-1} + \cdots}{K^{p+1,q-1} + \cdots} \cong K^{p,q}.$$

The differential d_0 is induced from $D = d + \delta$ by passing to the quotient. Thus, under the above isomorphism $d_0 = \delta$ and

$$'E_1^{p,q} \cong H_\delta^q(K^{p,*}),$$

where the right-hand side denotes the qth cohomology group of the complex

$$\cdots \to K^{p,q-1} \overset{\delta}{\to} K^{p,q} \overset{\delta}{\to} K^{p,q+1} \to \cdots .$$

The differential d_1 is computed from $D = d + \delta$ on $'E_1$. Since $\delta = 0$ on $'E_1$, we see that $d_1 = d$ and

$$'E_2^{p,q} = H^*('E_1^{p,q}, d_1) \cong H_d^p(H_\delta^q(K^{*,*})).$$

The last expression denotes the cohomology of

$$\cdots \to H_\delta^q(K^{p-1,*}) \overset{d}{\to} H_\delta^q(K^{p,*}) \overset{d}{\to} H_\delta^q(K^{p+1,*}) \to \cdots,$$

which has meaning, since $d\delta + \delta d = 0$. Summarizing:

Associated to a bigraded complex $(K^{*,*}; d, \delta)$ *are two spectral sequences both abutting to the cohomology of the total complex and where*

$$\begin{cases} 'E_2^{p,q} \cong H_d^p(H_\delta^q(K^{*,*})) \\ ''E_2^{p,q} \cong H_\delta^q(H_d^p(K^{*,*})). \end{cases}$$

There is one point to be careful of here. A class $[a] \in 'E_1^{p,q}$ is given by $a \in K^{p,q}$ satisfying $\delta a = 0$ and taken modulo $\delta K^{p,q-1}$. Then a class $[a] \in 'E_2^{p,q}$ is given by $a \in K^{p,q}$ satisfying

$$\begin{cases} \delta a = 0, \\ da \in \delta K^{p+1,q-1} \end{cases}$$

and taken modulo

$$\delta K^{p,q-1} + dK^{p-1,q} \cap \operatorname{Ker} \delta;$$

we cannot assume $da = 0$, but only that $[da] = 0$ in $H_\delta^q(K^{p+1,*})$.

Examples

If M is a complex manifold and

$$\begin{cases} K^{p,q} = A^{p,q}(M), \\ d = d \quad \text{and} \quad \delta = \bar{\partial}, \end{cases}$$

then the associated single complex is the de Rham complex $(A^*(M), d)$. In general not much seems to be known about the resulting *Fröhlicher spectral sequences* $\{'E_r\}$ and $\{''E_r\}$, both of which abut to $H^*_{DR}(M)$.

If, however M is compact Kähler, then every class $[a] \in {}'E_1^{p,q} \cong H^{p,q}_{\bar{\partial}}(M)$ has a harmonic representative for the $\bar{\partial}$-Laplacian $\Delta_{\bar{\partial}}$. By the Kähler assumption, $2\Delta_{\bar{\partial}} = \Delta_d$, and consequently $da = 0$. Thus

$$'E_1 \cong {}'E_2 \cong \cdots \cong {}'E_\infty,$$

and the filtration on $H^*_{DR}(M)$ is the *Hodge filtration* defined by

$$F^p H^n_{DR}(M) \cong H^{n,0}(M) \oplus \cdots \oplus H^{p,n-p}(M).$$

If M is compact but not Kähler, it may happen that $'E_1 \neq {}'E_2$, but no example seems to be known where $'E_2 \neq {}'E_\infty$. An example of $'E_1 \neq {}'E_2$ is provided by the *Iwasawa manifold*

$$M = \frac{G}{\Gamma},$$

where G is the Lie group of all complex matrices

$$g = \begin{bmatrix} 1 & a & b \\ 0 & 1 & c \\ 0 & 0 & 1 \end{bmatrix}$$

and $\Gamma \subset G$ is the discrete subgroup all of whose entries are Gaussian integers $\alpha + i\beta (\alpha, \beta \in \mathbb{Z})$. Under the mapping $g \to (a, c)$ we may check that M is a holomorphic fiber bundle over a complex 2-torus with fiber a complex 1-torus. The entries in the Maurer-Cartan matrix $dg \cdot g^{-1}$ are right-invariant holomorphic forms on G and hence descend to M. These entries are

$$\omega_1 = da, \qquad \omega_2 = dc, \qquad \omega_3 = -cda + db.$$

In particular,

$$d\omega_3 = \omega_1 \wedge \omega_2,$$

so that ω_3 is a nonclosed holomorphic form on M. If we consider ω_3 as defining a class in $'E_1^{1,0} \cong H^{1,0}_{\bar{\partial}}(M) = H^0(\Omega^1_M)$, then

$$d_1[\omega_3] = [d\omega_3] = [\omega_1 \wedge \omega_2]$$

is nonzero in $'E_2^{2,0}$.

Since $\dim E_r \geq \dim E_{r+1}$ and the Euler characteristic is invariant under taking cohomology, we have the *Fröhlicher relations*

$$\sum_{p+q=r} h^{p,q} \geq b_r,$$

$$\sum_{p,q} (-1)^{p+q} h^{p,q} = \sum_r (-1)^r b_r = \chi(M),$$

where $h^{p,q} = \dim H^{p,q}_{\bar{\partial}}(M)$ and b_r is the rth Betti number.

At the other extreme, we suppose M is a noncompact complex manifold and that the Dolbeault cohomology

(*) $$H_{\bar{\partial}}^{p,q}(M) = 0, \qquad q > 0.$$

This happens if M is what is called a *Stein manifold*—e.g., in Section 3 of Chapter 0 we proved (*) when

$$M = \Delta^{*k} \times \Delta^{n-k}$$

is a *punctured polycylinder* defined by

$$\{z \in \mathbb{C}^n : |z_i| < 1, z_1 \cdots z_k \neq 0\}.$$

If (*) is satisfied, then $'E_1^{p,q} = 0$ for $q > 0$ and the first spectral sequence is trivial from E_2 onward; i.e., $'E_2 \simeq 'E_\infty$. What this implies is

$$H_{DR}^*(M) \simeq H_{DR}^*(M, \text{hol}),$$

where the right-hand side is the de Rham cohomology computed from the complex of holomorphic forms.

Hypercohomology

This is a useful generalization of ordinary sheaf cohomology. On a topological space X, a *complex of sheaves* $(\mathcal{K}^*, d)$ is given by sheaves of Abelian sheaves $\mathcal{K}^p$ together with sheaf maps

$$\mathcal{K}^0 \to \cdots \to \mathcal{K}^p \xrightarrow{d} \mathcal{K}^{p+1} \to \cdots$$

satisfying $d^2 = 0$. In this discussion the notation does *not* mean that the sheaf sequence is exact. We sometimes write

$$(\mathcal{K}^*, d) = \left\{ \mathcal{K}^0 \xrightarrow{d} \mathcal{K}^1 \xrightarrow{d} \mathcal{K}^2 \to \cdots \right\}.$$

Associated to a complex of sheaves $(\mathcal{K}^*, d)$ are the *cohomology sheaves* $\mathcal{H}^q = \mathcal{H}^q(\mathcal{K}^*)$: Setting $\mathcal{K}^q(U) = H^0(U, \mathcal{K}^q)$, the *presheaf*

$$U \mapsto \frac{\text{Ker}\{d: \mathcal{K}^q(U) \to \mathcal{K}^{q+1}(U)\}}{d\mathcal{K}^{q-1}(U)}$$

gives rise to a sheaf $\mathcal{H}^q$ whose stalk is

$$\mathcal{H}_x^q = \lim_{U \ni x} \frac{\text{Ker}\{d: \mathcal{K}^q(U) \to \mathcal{K}^{q+1}(U)\}}{d\mathcal{K}^{q-1}(U)}.$$

A section σ of $\mathcal{H}^q$ over an open set $U \subset X$ is given by a covering $\{U_\alpha\}$ of U and $\sigma_\alpha \in \mathcal{K}^q(U_\alpha)$ such that

$$d\sigma_\alpha = 0,$$

$$\sigma_\alpha - \sigma_\beta = d\eta_{\alpha\beta}, \qquad \eta_{\alpha\beta} \in \mathcal{K}^{q-1}(U_\alpha \cap U_\beta);$$

the section is zero in case

$$\sigma_\alpha = d\eta_\alpha, \qquad \eta_\alpha \in \mathcal{H}^{q-1}(U_\alpha),$$

after perhaps refining the given covering. We note that essentially by definition:

The cohomology sheaves $\mathcal{H}^q = 0$ for $q > 0 \Leftrightarrow$ the Poincaré lemma holds for the complex of sheaves $(\mathcal{H}^*, d)$.

Now let $\underline{U} = \{U_\alpha\}$ be a covering of X and $C^p(\underline{U}, \mathcal{H}^q)$ the Čech cochains of degree p with values in $\mathcal{H}^q$. The two operators

$$\delta: \ C^p(\underline{U}, \mathcal{H}^q) \to C^{p+1}(\underline{U}, \mathcal{H}^q),$$

$$d: \ C^p(\underline{U}, \mathcal{H}^q) \to C^p(\underline{U}, \mathcal{H}^{q+1}),$$

satisfy $\delta^2 = d^2 = 0, d\delta + \delta d = 0$; and hence gives rise to a double complex

$$\{\, C^{p,q} = C^p(\underline{U}, \mathcal{H}^q); \delta, d \,\}.$$

Let $(C^*(\underline{U}), D)$ be the associated single complex. A refinement $\underline{U}' < \underline{U}$ of coverings induces mappings

$$C^p(\underline{U}, \mathcal{H}^q) \to C^p(\underline{U}', \mathcal{H}^q),$$
$$H^*(C^*(\underline{U})) \to H^*(C^*(\underline{U}')),$$

and we define the *hypercohomology*

$$\mathbb{H}^*(X, \mathcal{H}^*) = \lim_{\underline{U}} H^*(C^*(\underline{U}), D).$$

Now the spectral sequences $'E, ''E$ associated to the double complex $(C^p(\underline{U}, \mathcal{H}^q), \delta, d)$ behave well with respect to refinements of the covering, and passing to the limit we obtain two spectral sequences abutting to $\mathbb{H}^*(X, \mathcal{H}^*)$ with

$$'E_2^{p,q} = H^p(X, \mathcal{H}^q(\mathcal{H}^*)),$$
$$''E_2^{p,q} = H_d^q(H^p(X, \mathcal{H}^*)).$$

Explanations. $H^*(X, \mathcal{H}^*(\mathcal{H}^*))$ is the Čech cohomology of the cohomology sheaves $\mathcal{H}^*(\mathcal{H}^*)$, and $H_d^*(H^*(X, \mathcal{H}^*))$ is the cohomology of the complex

$$H^*(X, \mathcal{H}^0) \xrightarrow{d} H^*(X, \mathcal{H}^1) \xrightarrow{d} \cdots.$$

Before giving some examples, we need one lemma. A map

$$j: \ \mathcal{L}^* \to \mathcal{H}^*$$

between complexes of sheaves is a *quasi-isomorphism* if it induces an isomorphism on cohomology sheaves:

$$j_*: \ \mathcal{H}^q(\mathcal{L}^*) \longrightarrow \mathcal{H}^q(\mathcal{H}^*), \qquad q \geqslant 0.$$

Lemma. *If* $j: \mathcal{L}^* \to \mathcal{K}^*$ *is a quasi-isomorphism, then the induced map on hypercohomology*

$$j_*: \mathbb{H}^*(X, \mathcal{L}^*) \to \mathbb{H}^*(X, \mathcal{K}^*)$$

is an isomorphism.

Proof. Clearly j induces mappings on the spectral sequences, and

$$j_*: H^p(X, \mathcal{K}^q(\mathcal{L}^*)) \longrightarrow H^p(X, \mathcal{K}^q(\mathcal{K}^*))$$

is an isomorphism by our assumption. It is a reasonably obvious general fact that a map between filtered complexes that induces an isomorphism on any term $\{E_r\}$ in the spectral sequences necessarily induces an isomorphism on the total cohomology.   Q.E.D.

Here are some examples.

1. *De Rham's theorem revisited.* Suppose M is a manifold and $(\mathcal{C}^*, d)$ the de Rham complex of sheaves of smooth forms

$$\mathcal{C}^0 \xrightarrow{d} \mathcal{C}^1 \xrightarrow{d} \mathcal{C}^2 \to \cdots.$$

We denote by $\mathbb{R}^*$ the trivial complex

$$\mathbb{R} \to 0 \to 0 \to \cdots$$

with $\mathbb{R}$ in degree zero and nothing elsewhere. By the d-Poincaré lemma,

$$\mathcal{K}^q(\mathcal{C}^*) = 0 \quad \text{for } q > 0, \qquad \mathcal{K}^0(\mathcal{C}^*) \cong \mathbb{R}.$$

Consequently, the inclusion

$$i: \mathbb{R}^* \to \mathcal{C}^*$$

is a quasi-isomorphism, and by the lemma

$$\mathbb{H}^*(M, \mathbb{R}^*) \cong \mathbb{H}^*(M, \mathcal{C}^*).$$

Evidently

$$('E_{\mathbb{R}^*})_2^{p,q} = \begin{cases} H^p(M, \mathbb{R}), & q=0, \\ 0, & q>0, \end{cases}$$

so the first spectral sequence for $\mathbb{R}^*$ is trivial and

$$H^*(M, \mathbb{R}) \cong \mathbb{H}^*(M, \mathbb{R}^*).$$

On the other hand, by the partition of unity argument $H^q(M, \mathcal{C}^*) = 0$ for $q > 0$, and so

$$(''E_{\mathcal{C}^*})_2^{p,q} = \begin{cases} H^p_{\mathrm{DR}}(M), & q=0, \\ 0, & q>0. \end{cases}$$

Combining the previous remarks yields again the de Rham isomorphism

$$H^*(M, \mathbb{R}) \cong H^*_{\mathrm{DR}}(M).$$

This is, of course, essentially the previous sheaf-theoretic proof of the theorem. However, it is cast in such a way that the essential aspects are more clearly isolated, thus leading naturally to the generalizations to appear shortly.

2. *Same for Dolbeault.* Suppose M is a complex manifold, and let $(\mathcal{O}^{p,*}, \bar{\partial})$ denote the Dolbeault complex of sheaves

$$\mathcal{O}^{p,0} \xrightarrow{\bar{\partial}} \mathcal{O}^{p,1} \xrightarrow{\bar{\partial}} \mathcal{O}^{p,2} \to \cdots,$$

and Ω^{p^*} the trivial complex

$$\Omega^p \to 0 \to 0.$$

Then, by the $\bar{\partial}$-Poincaré lemma the inclusion

$$\Omega^{p^*} \to \mathcal{O}^{p,*}$$

is a quasi-isomorphism. Repeating the argument just given for de Rham's theorem gives the Dolbeault isomorphism

$$H^q(M, \Omega^p) \cong H^{p,q}_{\bar{\partial}}(M).$$

3. *The complex of holomorphic forms.* We now show how to compute the ordinary cohomology $H^*(M, \mathbb{C})$ of a complex manifold M purely in terms of the holomorphic differentials. First, note that the Poincaré lemma holds for these forms: If φ is a closed holomorphic p-form ($p > 0$), then locally $\varphi = d\eta$ for a holomorphic $(p-1)$-form η. The proof may be done by the same method as the $\bar{\partial}$-Poincaré lemma—a much more sophisticated lemma will be proved when we discuss the log complex in the next example.

Now the holomorphic de Rham complex

$$\Omega^0 \xrightarrow{d} \Omega^1 \xrightarrow{d} \Omega^2 \to \cdots$$

and trivial complex

$$\mathbb{C} \to 0 \to 0 \to \cdots$$

are such that the inclusion

$$\mathbb{C}^* \to (\Omega^*, d)$$

is a quasi-isomorphism, and repeating the previous argument gives

$$(*) \qquad\qquad H^*(M, \mathbb{C}) \cong \mathbb{H}^*(M, \Omega^*),$$

expressing the complex Čech cohomology in terms of the holomorphic forms.

Concerning the right-hand side of $(*)$, the second spectral sequence has

$$''E_2^{p,q} = H_d^p(H^q(M, \Omega^p)).$$

Two cases are noteworthy: If M is compact Kähler, then $d = 0$ on $H^q(M, \Omega^p) \cong H^{p,q}_{\bar{\partial}}(M)$, since $2\Delta_{\bar{\partial}} = \Delta_d$; thus $''E_2 = E_\infty$ and

$$\mathbb{H}^n(M, \Omega^*) \cong \bigoplus_{p+q=n} H^q(M, \Omega^p),$$

which is the Hodge decomposition. In the Stein case, $H^q(M,\Omega^*)=0$ for $q>0$ and $(*)$ reduces to the previously noted isomorphism

$$H^*(M,\mathbb{C}) \cong H^*_{DR}(M,\text{hol}).$$

4. *The log complex.* We now come to an interesting situation. Suppose M is a complex manifold and D a divisor on M. We say that D has *normal crossings* in case $D=\Sigma_\nu D_\nu$, where the irreducible components D_ν of D are smooth and meet transversely. At a point p through which k of the D_ν pass, we may choose local holomorphic coordinates $(z_1,\ldots,z_n)$ in a neighborhood $U=\{|z_i|<1\}$ of $p=(0,\ldots,0)$ such that

$$D \cap U = \{z_1\cdots z_k=0\}$$

is the union of coordinate hyperplanes. The complement

$$U^* = U - U\cap D = (\Delta^*)^k \times \Delta^{n-k}$$

is a punctured polycylinder $P^*(k,n)$ given by

$$\{z: |z_i|<1, z_1\cdots z_k \neq 0\}.$$

Topologically, $P^*(k,n)$ is a product $\times^k S^1$ of k circles.

Denote by $\Omega^p(*D)= \bigcup_{k\geqslant 0} \Omega^p(kD)$ the sheaf on M of meromorphic p-forms that are holomorphic on $M^*=M-D$ and have poles of arbitrary (finite) order on D. Similarly, we define $\mathcal{Q}^p(*D)$ to be the sheaf on M coming from the presheaf

$$U \longrightarrow A^p(U-U\cap D).$$

Both of these fit into complexes of sheaves $(\Omega^*(*D),d)$ and $(\mathcal{Q}^*(*D),d)$ on M.

Next, we define $\Omega^p(\log D)$ to be the subsheaf of $\Omega^p(*D)$ generated by the holomorphic forms and the logarithmic differentials dz_i/z_i $(i=1,\ldots,k)$. Symbolically,

$$\Omega^p(\log D) = \Omega^p\left\{ \frac{dz_1}{z_1},\ldots,\frac{dz_k}{z_k} \right\}.$$

Clearly

$$d\Omega^p(\log D) \subset \Omega^{p+1}(\log D),$$

and the resulting complex $(\Omega^*(\log D),d)$ is called the *log complex*. An intrinsic characterization is given by the following

Lemma. *If f is a local defining equation for* D, *then* $\Omega^p(\log D)$ *is given by those meromorphic forms* φ *such that both*

$$f\varphi \quad \text{and} \quad fd\varphi$$

are holomorphic.

Proof. Obviously we may take $f=z_1\cdots z_k$, and then the necessary condition is clear.

Suppose, conversely, that $f\varphi$ and $fd\varphi$ are holomorphic. Using the notations

$$I = (1,\ldots,k), \qquad J,K,L \subset (1,\ldots,n) \text{ are index sets,}$$
$$z_J = z_{j_1}\cdots z_{j_q}, \qquad dz_J = dz_{j_1}\wedge\cdots\wedge dz_{j_q},$$

we may write

$$\varphi = \sum_{\left\{\begin{array}{c} J\subset I \\ K\cap I=\varnothing \end{array}\right.} \frac{\varphi_{JK}}{z_J}\frac{dz_{I-J}}{z_{I-J}}\wedge dz_K,$$

where φ_{JK} is holomorphic. Computing modulo terms T such that fT is holomorphic,

$$d\varphi \equiv -\sum_{J,K}\sum_{j\in J}\frac{\varphi_{JK}}{z_J}\frac{dz_j}{z_j}\wedge\frac{dz_{I-J}}{z_{I-J}}\wedge dz_K$$

$$= \sum_{L,K}\psi_{LK}\frac{dz_L}{z_L}\wedge dz_K,$$

where

$$z_{I-L}\psi_{LK} = \pm\sum_{i\in L}\frac{\varphi_{(I-L)\cup\{i\},K}}{z_i}$$

is holomorphic. It follows that φ_{JK}/z_J is holomorphic, as was to be proved.

Q.E.D.

Intuitively, if φ contains a term with $1/z_i$ but no dz_i in the numerator, then $d\varphi$ will contain dz_i/z_i^2—what we have verified is that no cancellation occurs.

The main local result, which as we will see plays the role of a Poincaré lemma in the present context, is the following

Lemma. *The two inclusions*

$$\left\{\begin{array}{l} \Omega^*(\log D)\subset \mathcal{C}^*(*D), \\ \Omega^*(*D)\subset \mathcal{C}^*(*D), \end{array}\right.$$

are both quasi-isomorphisms.

Proof. At a point $p\notin D$, the stalks are

$$\left\{\begin{array}{l} \Omega^*(\log D)_p = \Omega^*(*D)_p = \Omega^*_p, \\ \mathcal{C}^*(*D)_p = \mathcal{C}^*_p, \end{array}\right.$$

and the result follows from the usual holomorphic and C^∞ Poincaré lemmas, respectively.

Around $p\in D$ we consider neighborhoods U as above. By the de Rham theorem for the (open) manifold $P^*(k,n)$

$$H^q_{DR}(U - U \cap D) \cong H^q(\times^k S^1, \mathbb{C}) = \wedge^q H^1(\times^k S^1, \mathbb{C}),$$

and so the stalk

$$\mathcal{H}^q(\mathcal{Q}^*(*D))_p \cong H^q(\times^k S^1, \mathbb{C}).$$

Since the cohomology of $U^* = U - U \cap D$ has as basis the forms

$$\frac{dz_J}{z_J} \qquad (J \subset I),$$

the stalks $\mathcal{H}^q(\Omega^*(\log D))_p$ and $\mathcal{H}^q(\Omega^*(*D))_p$ both map *onto* $\mathcal{H}^q(\mathcal{Q}^*(*D))_p$. What must be verified is:

(*) *Let φ be a closed meromorphic p-form on the polycylinder such that φ has poles on* D *and $\varphi = 0$ in* $H^p_{DR}(P^*(k,n))$. *Then $\varphi = d\eta$, where η is meromorphic with poles on* D. *If φ is in the log complex and $\varphi = 0$ in* $H^p_{DR}(P^*(k,n))$, *then $\varphi = d\eta$ for a form η in the log complex.*

Before giving the proof, we remark that on two previous occasions we have proved the isomorphism

$$H^*(M, \mathbb{C}) \cong H^*_{DR}(M, \text{hol})$$

for a complex manifold M satisfying

$$H^q(M, \Omega^p) = 0, \qquad q > 0.$$

Since this latter is true for $M = P^*(k,n)$, we may write $\varphi = d\eta$ where η is holomorphic in $P^*(k,n)$ but may have an *essential singularity* on the divisor $(z_1 \cdots z_k) = 0$. By being careful we must show that η may be taken to be meromorphic.

Proof. The argument is not difficult but is a little long. We shall concentrate on writing $\varphi = d\eta$, where η has at most a pole on the divisor $(z_1 \cdots z_k) = 0$. The argument will also show that η is in the log complex in case this is true of φ.

Write $(z_1, \ldots, z_n) = (u_1, \ldots, u_k, v_1, \ldots, v_{n-k}) = (u, v)$, so that $P^*(k,n)$ is given by

$$\{(u,v): \ 0 < |u_i| < 1, |v_j| < 1\}$$

and the divisor D by $u_i \cdots u_k = 0$. We first eliminate the v's from the picture. Following the procedure in the proof of the $\bar{\partial}$-Poincaré lemma in Section 2 of Chapter 0, we suppose that $\varphi \equiv 0 (du, dv_1, \ldots, dv_l)$ and write

$$\varphi = \varphi' + \varphi'' \wedge dv_l,$$

where $\varphi', \varphi'' \equiv 0 (du, dv_1, \ldots, dv_{l-1})$. Then $d\varphi = 0 \Rightarrow (\partial \varphi'/\partial v_j) = (\partial \varphi''/\partial v_j) = 0$

for $j > l$, where if $\alpha = \Sigma \alpha_I dx_I$ is a differential form,

$$\frac{\partial \alpha}{\partial x_j} = \sum_I \frac{\partial \alpha_I}{\partial x_j} dx_I.$$

Since φ is holomorphic in v, we may use formal integration of power series to solve

$$\varphi'' = \frac{\partial \eta}{\partial v_l},$$

where η has the same order pole in u as φ'' and $\partial \eta / \partial v_j = 0$ for all $j > l$. Then $\varphi - d\eta \equiv 0(du, dv_1, \ldots, dv_{l-1})$. Continuing in this way, we may assume that $\varphi \equiv 0(du)$. Then $d\varphi = 0 \Rightarrow (\partial \varphi / \partial v_j) = 0$, and so the v's may effectively be ignored.

Inductively, we assume the theorem for $u' = (u_1, \ldots, u_{k-1})$ and write

$$\varphi = \psi' + \psi'' \wedge du_k,$$

where $\psi', \psi'' \equiv 0(du')$. Consider the Laurent series

$$\psi'' = \sum_{\nu = -N}^{\infty} \psi''(u')_\nu u_k^\nu.$$

Then, by formally integrating the series insofar as possible, we may write

$$\psi'' - \frac{\psi''(u')_{-1}}{u_k} = \frac{\partial \eta}{\partial u_k},$$

where η has the same order pole in u' and one less order pole in u_k. Clearly

$$\tilde{\varphi} = \varphi - d\eta = \xi' + \xi'' \wedge \frac{du_k}{u_k},$$

where $\xi'' \equiv 0(u', du')$ and $\xi' \equiv 0(du')$. Since $\tilde{\varphi}$ is closed, we deduce that $\xi' \equiv 0(u', du')$ and

$$d\xi' = 0 = d\xi''.$$

Now $\tilde{\varphi} = 0$ in $H_{\mathrm{DR}}^q((\Delta^*)^k)$, and thus the restriction of $\tilde{\varphi}$ to $H_{\mathrm{DR}}^q((\Delta^*)^{k-1})$ is zero, where $(\Delta^*)^{k-1} \subset (\Delta^*)^k$ is given by $u_k = \text{constant}$. This restriction is just ξ', and by induction $\xi' = d\gamma'$, where γ' has at most a pole in u'.

Finally we consider $\tilde{\tilde{\varphi}} = \tilde{\varphi} - d\gamma' = \xi'' \wedge du_k / u_k$. Writing $(\Delta^*)^k = (\Delta^*)^{k-1} \times \Delta^*$ and using Künneth, $\tilde{\tilde{\varphi}} = 0$ in $H_{\mathrm{DR}}^q((\Delta^*)^k) \Rightarrow \xi'' = 0$ in $H_{\mathrm{DR}}^{q-1}((\Delta^*)^{k-1})$. Then $\xi'' = d\gamma''$ where γ'' has at most a pole in u', and $\tilde{\tilde{\varphi}} = d(\gamma'' \wedge du_k / u_k)$.
                                                                                          Q.E.D.

We now draw some conclusions from the lemma. The sheaves $\mathcal{C}^*(*D)$ admit partitions of unity, and therefore $H^q(M, \mathcal{C}^*(*D)) = 0$ for $q > 0$ and, by the spectral sequence for hypercohomology,

$$\mathbb{H}^*(M, \mathcal{C}^*(*D)) \cong H_{\bar{d}}^*(H^0(M, \mathcal{C}^*(*D)))$$
$$= H_{DR}^*(M - D)$$
$$\cong H^*(M - D, \mathbb{C}).$$

Using this together with the lemma on quasi-isomorphisms, we deduce the isomorphisms

$$\mathbb{H}^*(M, \Omega^*(\log D)) \cong H^*(M - D, \mathbb{C})$$

(*) $\downarrow$ $\|$

$$\mathbb{H}^*(M, \Omega^*(*D)) \cong H^*(M - D, \mathbb{C}).$$

This gives a method for computing the cohomology of the complement of a divisor with normal crossing by using meromorphic forms that are holomorphic in $M - D$ and have poles along D.

Using the resolution of singularities theorem*, the second isomorphism

$$\mathbb{H}^*(M, \Omega^*(*D)) \cong H^*(M - D, \mathbb{C})$$

holds with no assumptions on the singularities of D.

Suppose now that the line bundle $[D] \to M$ is positive. By Theorem B,

$$H^q(M, \Omega^p(kD)) = 0 \qquad \text{for } q > 0, k \geqslant k_0.$$

If we set $U = M - D$ and denote by

$$H_{DR}^*(U, \text{alg})$$

the cohomology of the complex of meromorphic forms that are holomorphic in U and have poles on D, then by the degeneration of the second spectral sequence of hypercohomology we obtain

Grothendieck's Algebraic de Rham Theorem

$$H_{DR}^*(U, \text{alg}) \cong H^*(U, \mathbb{C}).$$

The reason for this description of the result is this. An *affine algebraic variety* U is a complex submanifold of $\mathbb{C}^N$ defined by polynomial equations. We denote by $\Omega^*(U, \text{alg})$ the complex of holomorphic forms on U that are the restrictions of rational differential forms in $\mathbb{C}^N$. This notation is consistent, since if we take the projective closure M_0 of $U \subset \mathbb{C}^N \subset \mathbb{P}^N$ and apply Hironaka's theorem to obtain a resolution of singularities

$$M \xrightarrow{\pi} M_0$$

that is an isomorphism on U, then $\Omega^*(U, \text{alg})$ are just the meromorphic forms on M that are holomorphic in U—cf. Section 4 of Chapter 1. The

---

*H. Hironaka, *On Resolution of Singularities*, Proc. Int. Congress Math., Stockholm (1962), pp. 507–525.

algebraic de Rham theorem then asserts that cohomology $H^*(U, \mathbb{C})$ may be computed from the complex $\Omega^*(U, \text{alg})$.

Differentials of the Second Kind*

Let M be a smooth algebraic variety. A *differential of the first kind* is the classical terminology for a holomorphic p-form on M. By Hodge theory these inject to give the part $H^{p,0}(M)$ of the cohomology $H^p(M, \mathbb{C})$ of M.

DEFINITION. A *differential of the second kind* is given by a closed meromorphic p-form φ on M such that, for some divisor D with complement $U = M - D$, φ is holomorphic in U and is in the image of

$$H^p_{\mathrm{DR}}(M) \to H^p_{\mathrm{DR}}(U).$$

Equivalently, a differential of the second kind is a closed meromorphic p-form on M, holomorphic on $M - D$, which can be extended, up to an exact form on $M - D$, to a C^∞ closed form on M. We let ρ_p be the dimension of the space

$$\frac{(p\text{-forms of the second kind})}{d \, (\text{meromorphic } (p-1)\text{-forms})}.$$

Historically, differentials of the second kind for $p = 1, 2$ played a pivotal role in the early development of the theory of algebraic surfaces. They furnished the technique for the first proof that the irregularity q of an algebraic surface was equal to $\frac{1}{2} b_1$—so that in particular b_1 is even—and the original proof that the Neron-Severi group defined below

$$\frac{\{\text{divisors on } S\}}{\{\text{divisors algebraically equivalent to zero}\}}$$

is finitely generated. For $p \geqslant 3$ the differentials of the second kind are only partially understood, and even that is fairly recent. Because of their historical importance and close tie-in with the algebraic de Rham theorem, we shall give a brief discussion of differentials of the second kind with special emphasis on the cases $p = 1, 2$.

We begin by amplifying the definition of second kind in two ways. Given a closed meromorphic p-form φ and divisor D such that φ is holomorphic in $U = M - D$, we define a *residue* to be an integral

$$\int_\gamma \varphi,$$

where $\gamma \in H_p(U, \mathbb{Z})$ is a p-cycle that is homologous to zero in M. It is clear

---

*This treatment is based on M. F. Atiyah and W. V. D. Hodge, Integrals of the second kind on an algebraic variety, *Annals of Math.*, Vol. 62 (1955), pp. 56–91.

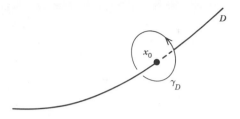

Figure 4

that φ *is of the second kind* $\Leftrightarrow$ *it has no residues in open sets* $U = M - D$ *for sufficiently large divisors* D.

For $p = 1$ we may obtain a clear picture of what the residues look like. Let D be an irreducible divisor and $x_0 \in D$ a simple point. The boundary γ_D of a normal disc to D in M at x_0 is then a 1-cycle in $H_1(M - D, \mathbb{Z})$ that bounds in M, and the class of γ_D is independent of x_0, since the smooth points of D form a connected manifold (Figure 4). Now suppose that $D = D_1 + \cdots + D_k$ is a divisor with irreducible components D_i. We may choose the γ_{D_i} to lie in $U = M - D$, and we claim that any cycle γ in

$$\mathrm{Ker}\{H_1(U, \mathbb{Z}) \longrightarrow H_1(M, \mathbb{Z})\}$$

is homologous to a linear combination of the γ_{D_i}. Indeed, by assumption $\gamma = \partial\Delta$, where Δ is a 2-chain in M. Since the singularities of D are in real codimension 4, we may assume that Δ meets D transversely at simple points. If $x_0 \in D_i$ is such an intersection point, then near x_0 we may picture the part Δ_ε of Δ lying within distance ε of D_i as a normal disc at x_0 (Figure 5), and so $\partial\Delta_\varepsilon = \gamma_{D_i}$. Consequently $\gamma - \gamma_{D_i}$ has one less intersection point with D, and repeating the argument gives a homology

$$\gamma \sim \sum m_i \gamma_{D_i}.$$

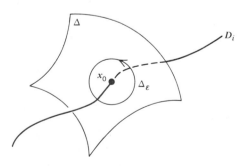

Figure 5

A consequence of this is:

> For p = 1, *a closed meromorphic* 1-*form* φ *is of the second kind* $\Leftrightarrow$ φ *has no residues in* any *open set of the form* $U = M - D$ *where it is holomorphic*.

The argument also makes it pretty clear that residues will be complicated when $p \geqslant 3$.

We shall now show that

> For a p-*form* φ *of the second kind, given any point* $x_0 \in M$ *there is a meromorphic* (p − 1)-*form* ψ *such that*
>
> $$\varphi - d\psi = \eta$$
>
> *is holomorphic near* x_0. *The converse is true when* p = 1.

Proof. Given $x_0 \in M$, we may find an ample divisor D not passing through x_0, and then for $U = M - D$ by the algebraic de Rham theorem,

$$H_{DR}^*(U) \cong H_{DR}^*(U, \text{alg}).$$

In fact, we may take U to be an affine neighborhood of x_0 as discussed at the end of the preceding section. Then for any divisor $D' \supset D$, $M - D' = U' \subset U$ will also be affine and consequently

$$H_{DR}^*(U') \cong H_{DR}^*(U', \text{alg}).$$

We may find a U' such that φ is holomorphic in U' and is the image of a class $\Phi \in H_{DR}^p(M)$. In the diagram

$$H_{DR}^p(M) \longrightarrow H_{DR}^p(U', \text{alg})$$
$$\searrow \qquad \nearrow$$
$$H_{DR}^p(U, \text{alg})$$

the restriction of Φ to U will be represented by a closed p-form η that is meromorphic on M and holomorphic in U. Restricting to U', we find the desired presentation

$$\varphi - \eta = d\psi,$$

where ψ is a meromorphic $(p - 1)$-form on M that is holomorphic in U'.

When $p = 1$, it is clear from our above description of residue cycles that a closed meromorphic 1-form that has local presentations

$$\varphi = d\psi + \eta$$

will have no residues, and consequently φ is of the second kind. Q.E.D.

To give the interpretations of ρ_1 and ρ_2, we define the *Picard number* ρ to be the rank of the image

$$H^1(M, \mathcal{O}^*) \xrightarrow{c_1} H^2(M, \mathbb{Z}).$$

Equivalently, according to the proof of the Lefschetz $(1,1)$ theorem from Section 2 of Chapter 1, ρ is the rank of $H^{1,1}(M) \cap H^2(M, \mathbb{Z})$, which is the rank of the quotient group

$$\frac{\text{divisors on } M}{\text{homological equivalence}}$$

of all divisors on M modulo those homologous to zero. We shall prove that

$$\begin{cases} \rho_1 = b_1, \\ \rho_2 = b_2 - \rho. \end{cases}$$

Proof. Recall that for a divisor D on M, $\Omega^p(*D)$ denotes the subsheaf of the sheaf $\mathcal{M}^p$ of all meromorphic p-forms consisting of those having poles only on D. We let

$$\Omega^p(*) = \bigcup_{D \in \mathrm{Div}(M)} \Omega^p(*D)$$

be the subsheaf of $\mathcal{M}^p$ of meromorphic p-forms whose polar loci are a part of a global divisor on M. Clearly

$$\Omega(*): \quad \Omega^0(*) \xrightarrow{d} \Omega^1(*) \to \cdots \xrightarrow{d} \Omega^n(*)$$

gives a complex of sheaves, and as usual $\mathcal{H}^p(\Omega(*))$ denotes the pth cohomology sheaf. Evidently

$$\mathcal{H}^0(\Omega(*)) \cong \mathbb{C},$$

and we shall prove the

Lemma. $\mathcal{H}^1(\Omega(*)) \cong \bigoplus_{D \in \mathrm{Div}\,M} \mathbb{C}_D$, where $\mathbb{C}_D$ is the constant sheaf concentrated on divisor D.

Proof. We let φ be a closed meromorphic 1-form given in a sufficiently small polycylindrical neighborhood W of a point $x_0 \in M$. The polar divisor of φ is $D = D_1 + \cdots + D_k$, where the D_i are irreducible and are divisors of holomorphic functions $f_i \in \mathcal{O}(W)$. By the same argument as above, if $W^* = W - D$, then $H_1(W^*, \mathbb{Z})$ is generated by 1-cycles γ_i consisting of circles turning once around D_i. If

$$\lambda_i = \frac{1}{2\pi\sqrt{-1}} \int_{\gamma_i} \varphi,$$

then

$$\varphi - \sum_i \lambda_i \frac{df_i}{f_i} = \psi$$

will have no periods, and consequently

$$g = \int \psi$$

will be a meromorphic function in W with

(*) $$\varphi = \sum_i \lambda_i \frac{df_i}{f_i} + dg.$$

We define the *residue map*

$$R: \mathcal{H}^1(\Omega(*)) \to \bigoplus_{D \in \text{Div } M} \mathbb{C}_D$$

by

$$R(\varphi) = \bigoplus_i \lambda_i \cdot 1_{D_i}.$$

The notation means that $R(\varphi)$ is the constant λ_i on the divisor D_i. The local presentation (*) shows that R is an isomorphism.   Q.E.D.

Now we write out the two spectral sequences abutting to $\mathbb{H}^*(\Omega(*))$. One of these has

$$''E_2^{p,q} = H_d^p(H^q(M, \Omega(*))).$$

Since the ample divisors are cofinal among all divisors,

$$H^q(M, \Omega(*)) = 0 \qquad \text{for } q > 0.$$

Consequently, $''E_2^{p,q} = 0$ for $q > 0$ and

$$\mathbb{H}^p(\Omega(*)) \cong \frac{\{\text{closed meromorphic } p\text{-forms}\}}{\{\text{exact forms}\}}.$$

We may therefore think of $\mathbb{H}^*(\Omega(*))$ as the de Rham cohomology of the function field of **M**.

For the other spectral sequence

(**) $$'E_2^{p,q} \cong H^p(M, \mathcal{H}^q(\Omega(*))).$$

Now any spectral sequence gives an exact sequence in low degrees, which in this case is

$$0 \to E_2'^{1,0} \to \mathbb{H}^1 \to 'E_2^{0,1} \xrightarrow{d_2} 'E_2^{2,0} \to \mathbb{H}^2 \to G \to 0,$$

where $G = \mathbb{H}^2/F^2\mathbb{H}^2$ has the subgroup $G' = \mathbb{H}^2/F^1\mathbb{H}^2$ with

$$G' \oplus G/G' \subset 'E_2^{1,1} \oplus 'E_2^{2,0}$$

a subgroup of $\ker d_2$. Substituting (**) in this exact sequence, we obtain

$$0 \to H^1(M, \mathbb{C}) \to \mathbb{H}^1(\Omega(*)) \xrightarrow{R} H^0\left(\bigoplus_{D \in \text{Div } M} \mathbb{C}_D\right) \xrightarrow{i} H^2(M, \mathbb{C}) \to \mathbb{H}^2(\Omega(*)) \to G.$$

The interpretations of the maps in this sequence are (we omit the proofs that diagrams commute):

1. Using the previously established isomorphism

$$(***) \qquad\qquad H^*(M,\mathbb{C}) \cong \mathbb{H}^*(\Omega^*),$$

the first map is the natural one

$$\mathbb{H}^1(\Omega^*) \to \mathbb{H}^1(\Omega(*))$$

induced from the inclusions $\Omega^p \to \Omega^p(*)$.

2. The second map assigns to a closed meromorphic 1-form its residue as in the proof of the lemma above.

3. The map i assigns to 1_D the fundamental class $\eta_D \in H^2(M,\mathbb{Z})$ of the divisor D.

4. The map $H^2(M,\mathbb{C}) \to \mathbb{H}^2(\Omega(*))$ is again induced by the isomorphism $(***)$ and inclusion $\Omega^p \hookrightarrow \Omega^p(*)$.

Now the isomorphism

$$H^1(M,\mathbb{C}) \cong \ker R$$
$$= \frac{\{1\text{-forms of the second kind}\}}{\{\text{exact forms}\}}$$

gives $\rho_1 = b_1$.

Next, we have

$$\frac{H^2(M,\mathbb{C})}{\left\{\begin{array}{c} \text{Chern classes} \\ \text{of holomorphic} \\ \text{line bundles} \end{array}\right\}} = \frac{H^2(M,\mathbb{C})}{iH^0(\oplus\mathbb{C}_D)}$$

$$\cong \text{image}\{H^2(M,\mathbb{C}) \to \mathbb{H}^2(\Omega(*))\}$$
$$= \frac{\{2\text{-forms of the second kind}\}}{\{\text{exact forms}\}},$$

and so $\rho_2 = b_2 - \rho$. \hfill Q.E.D.

It is clear that the identification

$$\text{image}\{'E^{0,p} \to \mathbb{H}^p(\Omega(*))\} \cong \frac{\{p\text{-forms of the second kind}\}}{\{\text{exact forms}\}}$$

allows the above proof to continue, but the subsequent interpretation of the numbers ρ_p has yet to yield much geometric information. So we shall conclude with some further remarks on the cases $p = 1, 2$.

For $p = 1$ perhaps the most interesting case is when M is an algebraic curve of genus g. Our definition of differentials of the second kind agrees with that given in Section 2 of Chapter 2 on Riemann surfaces. We will prove the result:

Let $D = p_1 + \cdots + p_g$ *be a nonspecial divisor of degree g. Then there is an isomorphism*

$$\left\{ \begin{array}{l} \text{1-forms } \varphi \text{ having} \\ \text{no residues and} \\ \text{polar divisor 2D} \end{array} \right\} \cong \frac{\{\text{1-forms of the second kind}\}}{\{\text{exact forms}\}}.$$

Proof.   By the Riemann-Roch theorem

$$h^0(D) = \deg D - g + 1 + i(D) = 1,$$

so the only meromorphic functions with polar divisor D are the constants. Again by Riemann-Roch applied to the line bundle $K_C + 2D$,

$$\begin{aligned} h^0(K_C + 2D) &= \deg(K_c + 2D) - g + 1 + i(K_C + 2D) \\ &= 2g - 2 + 2g - g + 1 \\ &= 3g - 1, \end{aligned}$$

so that the space of meromorphic differentials having polar divisor $2D$ has dimension $3g - 1$. The equations

$$\sum \text{Res}_{p_i}(\varphi) = 0$$

impose exactly $g - 1$ independent conditions on this space, due to the residue theorem

$$\sum_i \text{Res}_{p_i}(\varphi) = 0,$$

and observation that we may find $\varphi \in H^0(\mathcal{O}_C(K + 2D))$ with prescribed residues subject only to the residue theorem (cf. Section 2 in Chapter 2). So the space of 1-forms of the second kind with polar divisor $2D$ has dimension

$$3g - 1 - (g - 1) = 2g,$$

and none of these can be exact by our remark about meromorphic functions with polar divisor D.   Q.E.D.

We turn now to the case $p = 2$. To first explain how the relation

$$\rho_2 = b_2 - \rho$$

was used classically, we refer to the exact sequence

$$\mathbb{H}^1(\Omega(*)) \xrightarrow{R} H^0\left(\bigoplus_{D \in \text{Div } M} \mathbb{C}_D \right) \xrightarrow{i} H^2(M, \mathbb{C}),$$

which appeared in the proof above. We may interpret it in the following manner:

> If D *is a divisor on* M *with fundamental class* $\eta_D \in H^2(M, \mathbb{Z})$, *then* η_D *is a torsion element if and only if there exists a closed, meromorphic 1-form* φ *whose residue* $R(\varphi) = D$.

This was proved by Picard, and Severi showed that a multiple λD ($\lambda \in \mathbb{Z}$) is algebraically equivalent to zero (to be explained momentarily) if and only if there is a closed meromorphic 1-form whose residue is D. Combining these, it follows that the Neron-Severi group

$$NS(M) = \frac{\{\text{divisors on } M\}}{\left\{ \begin{array}{l} \text{divisors algebraically} \\ \text{equivalent to zero} \end{array} \right\}}$$

is finitely generated (*theorem of the base*). The structure of the group of divisors on M may be pictured by the diagram

$$H^{11}(M) \cap H^2(M, \mathbb{Z})$$

$$\underbrace{\text{Div} \supset \text{Div}_h}_{NS} \supset \underbrace{\text{Div}_a \supset \text{Div}_l}_{\text{Pic}^0}$$

$$\underbrace{\phantom{\text{Div} \supset \text{Div}_h \supset \text{Div}_a \supset \text{Div}_l}}_{\text{Pic}}$$

where Div_h, Div_a, Div_l are the divisors homologous, algebraically equivalent, and linearly equivalent to zero.

We shall give the precise difinitions and derive the finiteness theorem in a different way. Two effective divisors D_1, D_2 are *algebraically equivalent in the strong sense*, written

$$D_1 \overset{\equiv}{=} D_2,$$

if there is a connected parameter variety T with marked points $t_1, t_2 \in T$ and divisor D on $M \times T$ such that

$$D \cdot M \times \{t_i\} = D_i \qquad (i = 1, 2).$$

Intuitively, there is an algebraic family $D_t (t \in T)$ of divisors connecting D_1 and D_2.

Two divisors D_1, D_2 are *algebraically equivalent*, written $D_1 \equiv D_2$, if there is a divisor D such that both of $D + D_i$ are effective and $D + D_1 \overset{\equiv}{=} D + D_2$. We will see in a minute that this is an equivalence relation compatible with the group structure on $\text{Div}(M)$. The divisors algebraically equivalent to zero then form a subgroup "$\equiv$" of $\text{Div}(M)$, and the quotient

$$\text{Div}(M)/\text{“}\equiv\text{”} = NS(M)$$

is called the *Neron-Severi group*.

The basic result we need is the

Lemma. *Two divisors* D_1, D_2 *are algebraically equivalent if and only if they are homologous.*

Proof. It is clear that $D_1 \equiv D_2 \Rightarrow \eta_{D_1} = \eta_{D_2}$ in $H^2(M, \mathbb{Z})$. For the converse we assume that $\eta_{D_1} = \eta_{D_2}$, which is equivalent to $c_1([D_1]) = c_1([D_2])$ by the proposition in Section 1 of Chapter 1, and shall show that $D_1 \equiv D_2$. Let D_i^- be the part of D_i appearing with negative coefficients and add $E = D_1^- + D_2^-$ of each of D_1, D_2 to obtain effective divisors, thereby reducing us to proving that $D_1 \equiv D_2$ for effective divisors in the same homology class.

Now we come to the point. Recall that the Picard variety $\mathrm{Pic}^0(M) = H^1(M, \mathcal{O})/H^1(M, \mathbb{Z})$ parametrizes line bundles with first Chern class zero; we denote by $\{P_\xi \to M\}$ $(\xi \in H^1(M, \mathcal{O})/H^1(M, \mathbb{Z}))$ this family. Since $[D_1] \otimes [D_2]^*$ has zero Chern class,

$$[D_1] \otimes [D_2]^* = P_{\xi_0}$$

for some ξ_0. By the last result proved in the subsection "Intrinsic Formulations" in Section 6 of Chapter 2, we may find a line bundle $L \to M$ and sections $\theta_\xi \in H^0(M, \mathcal{O}(L \otimes P_\xi))$ such that $\theta_\xi \neq 0$ for generic ξ. In fact from the proof we may assume that $\theta_e, \theta_{\xi_0} \neq 0$. Setting $D_\xi = (\theta_\xi)$ from $[D_1 - D_2 + D_e] = [D_{\xi_0}]$, we deduce that the *linear* equivalence

$$D_1 + D_e \sim D_2 + D_{\xi_0}$$

holds. In particular

$$D_1 + D_e \equiv D_2 + D_{\xi_0},$$

and it is clear that

$$D_e \equiv D_{\xi_0}$$

via the family of divisors $\{D_\xi\}$ $(\xi \in \mathrm{Pic}^0(M))$. Thus $D_1 \equiv D_2$ and we are done.   Q.E.D.

As a corollary we deduce the theorem of the base: $\mathrm{NS}(M)$ *is a finitely generated group of rank* $\rho = b_2 - \rho_2$.

We have not dwelt on rational and algebraic equivalence of divisors or of general algebraic cycles, partly because we do not need these for our study of any specific varieties, and partly because the codimension-one theory is—at least as matters now stand—misleading as regards higher codimensional cycles.

The Leray Spectral Sequence

This is in many ways the most useful general spectral sequence, and so we want at least to say what it is and give an illustration. Suppose we are given topological spaces X, Y with a continuous mapping

$$f: X \to Y$$

and sheaf $\mathcal{F}$ over X. The qth *direct image sheaf* is the sheaf $R_f^q(\mathcal{F})$ on Y associated to the presheaf

$$U \to H^q(f^{-1}(U), \mathcal{F}).$$

The *Leray spectral sequence*, which exists under very mild restrictions (cf. the references at the end of this chapter) is a spectral sequence $\{E_r\}$ with

$$\begin{cases} E_\infty \Rightarrow H^*(X, \mathcal{F}), \\ E_2^{p,q} = H^p(Y, R_f^q(\mathcal{F})). \end{cases}$$

Suppose that $E \xrightarrow{\pi} B$ is a differentiable fiber bundle with compact fiber F. Then E, B, and F are manifolds, π is a C^∞ mapping, and

$$\pi^{-1}(U) \cong U \times F$$

for sufficiently small open sets $U \subset B$. For the constant sheaf $\mathbb{Q}$ on E, by the Künneth formula

$$H^q(\pi^{-1}(U), \mathbb{Q}) \cong H^q(F, \mathbb{Q}).$$

This suggests that as a first approximation

$$R_f^q(\mathbb{Q}) \cong H^q(F, \mathbb{Q})$$

is a constant sheaf on B. This is not quite correct, since account must be taken of how the fundamental group $\pi_1(B, x_0)$ acts on the cohomology $H^q(F_{x_0}, \mathbb{Q})(F_x = \pi^{-1}(x))$. More precisely, displacement of homology cycles in the fibers over a path γ from x_0 to x induces an isomorphism

$$H^q(F_x, \mathbb{Q}) \cong H^q(F_{x_0}, \mathbb{Q})$$

that depends only on the homotopy class of γ. This is reasonably intuitive and is proven in standard books on topology. The upshot is that first there is a representation

$$\rho: \pi_1(B, x_0) \to \text{Aut}(H^q(F_{x_0}, \mathbb{Q}))$$

that describes how cycles change when they are displaced around closed paths. Second, *any* representation of the fundamental group

$$\rho: \pi_1(B, x_0) \to \text{Aut}(V)$$

gives locally constant sheaf $\mathcal{V}_\rho$ on B. To construct $\mathcal{V}_\rho$, we take the vector bundle

$$V_\rho = \tilde{B} \times_{\pi_1} V$$

associated to the universal covering $\tilde{B} \to B$, and then the sections of $\mathcal{V}_\rho$ over an open set $U \subset B$ are just those which lift to constant sections of $\tilde{B} \times V$. Third, the qth direct image sheaf $R_\pi^q(\mathbb{Q})$ is the sheaf constructed in this way from the representation of $\pi_1(B, x_0)$ on $H^q(F_{x_0}, \mathbb{Q})$.

It is instructive to sketch the derivation of the Leray spectral sequence in de Rham cohomology. At any point $p \in E$ we let

$$T_p(F) = \ker\{\pi_*\colon T_p(E) \to T_{\pi(p)}(B)\}$$

be the tangent space to the fiber $F_{\pi(p)}$ passing through p. Setting

$$F^p(\wedge^n T_p(E)) = (\wedge^p T_p(F)) \wedge (\wedge^{n-p} T_p(E))$$

defines a filtration $\{F^p(\wedge^n T(E))\}$ on the exterior powers of the tangent bundle $T(E)$, and we let $\{F^p(\wedge^n T^*(E))\}$ be the dual filtration of the exterior powers of $T^*(E)$ given by

$$F^p(\wedge^n T^*(E)) = \operatorname{Ann}(F^{n-p+1}(\wedge^n T(E))).$$

This gives a filtration $F^p A^n(E)$ on the space of C^∞ differential forms of degree n on E, and, setting $A^n = A^n(E)$, we have

$$\begin{cases} A^n = F^0 A^n \supset F^1 A^n \supset \cdots \supset F^n A^n \supset F^{n+1} A^n = 0 \\ d\colon F^p A^n \to F^p A^{n+1}. \end{cases}$$

To picture this filtration, we choose local product coordinates (x,y) in E with $\pi(x,y) = x$. Then $T_p(F)$ is spanned by the vectors $\partial/\partial y_i$, and

$$F^p A^n = \left\{ \varphi = \sum_{\substack{\#I + \#J = n \\ \#I \geqslant p}} \varphi_{IJ}(x,y)\, dx_I \wedge dy_J \right\},$$

from which the two above properties of the filtration are apparent.

According to the general mechanism, once we have such a filtered complex $\{F^p A^*\}$, there is an associated spectral sequence $\{E_r\}$ with

$$E_\infty \Rightarrow H^*(A^*) = H^*_{\mathrm{DR}}(E).$$

We will calculate the terms E_1 and E_2.

Recall that

$$E_0^{p,q} = \frac{F^p A^{p+q}}{F^{p+1} A^{p+q}},$$

and d_0 is obtained from d by passing to the quotient. Taking a local product isomorphism

$$\pi^{-1}(U) \cong U \times F,$$

we may represent $E_0^{p,q}$ by forms

$$\varphi = \sum_{\#I = p} \eta_I(x,y,dy) \wedge dx_I,$$

where the η_I are q-forms on F. Computing modulo $F^{p+1} A^*$,

$$d_0 \varphi = \sum_{\#I = p} d_y \eta_I \wedge dx_I,$$

where d_y is the exterior derivative in the F-direction relative to the product decomposition. It follows that elements of $E_1^{p,q}$ are locally represented by

$$\bar\varphi = \sum_{\#I=p} \bar\eta_I \wedge dx_I,$$

where

$$\bar\eta_I(x,y,dy) \in H_{DR}^q(F_x).$$

Intuitively, we may think of $E_1^{p,q}$ as the p-forms on B with values in the bundle $H_{DR}^q(F)$ whose fibers are

$$H_{DR}^q(F)_x = H_{DR}^q(F_x).$$

We now compute $d_1\bar\varphi$. For φ as above with $d_0\varphi = d_y\varphi = 0$,

$$d_1\bar\varphi = \overline{d\varphi}.$$

Thus

$$d_1\bar\varphi = d_x\left(\sum_{\#I=p} \eta_I(x,y,dy) \wedge dx_I\right),$$

and so $E_2^{p,q}$ is given by

$$E_2^{p,q} = H_{DR}^p(B, H_{DR}^q(F)),$$

where the right-hand side may be defined by first interpreting $H_{DR}^q(F) \to B$ as a *flat vector bundle*—i.e., a vector bundle associated to a representation of the fundamental group—whose locally constant sections are just the sheaf $R_\pi^q(\mathbb{C})$, and then taking the de Rham cohomology of forms with values in this bundle. Granted that this interpretation needs some amplification, but once this is done we have derived the spectral sequence of a differentiable fibration.

These spectral sequences are generally nontrivial—i.e., $E_2 \neq E_\infty$—and may be extremely complicated. Even the simplest nontrivial fibration, the *Hopf fibration*,

$$\pi: S^{2n+1} \to \mathbb{P}^n,$$

has an interesting spectral sequence: The fiber is the circle S^1, and since $\mathbb{P}^n$ is simply connected,

$$E_2^{p,q} \cong H^q(S^1) \otimes H^p(\mathbb{P}^n).$$

Figure 6 pictures the E_2 term. If $\eta \in E_2^{0,1} \cong H^1(S^1)$ is a generator, then $d_2\eta \neq 0$, since $H^q(S^{2n+1}) = 0$ for $q \neq 0, 2n+1$. Thus

$$d_2\eta = \omega,$$

where $\omega \in E_2^{2,0} \cong H^2(\mathbb{P}^n)$ is a generator. If we represent S^{2n+1} as the unit sphere $\{z : \|z\| = 1\}$ in $\mathbb{C}^{n+1}$, then

$$\omega = dd^c \log\|z\|^2$$

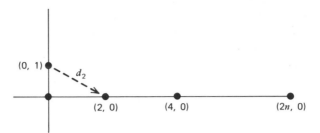

Figure 6

is the standard Kähler form on $\mathbb{P}^n$. Up on S^{2n+1},

$$\omega = d\eta,$$

where it is straightforward to check that

$$\eta = d^c \log\|z\|^2$$

restricts to the generator of $H^1(S^1)$ for each fiber. So, in this case the relation

$$d_2\eta = \omega$$

is quite visible. We also note that

$$d_2(\eta \wedge \omega^q) = \omega^{q+1} \qquad (0 \leqslant q \leqslant n).$$

By way of contrast, we suppose that E, B are compact Kähler manifolds and

$$\pi: E \to B$$

is a surjective, holomorphic mapping of maximal rank. This is a differentiable fiber bundle whose fiber F is a compact Kähler manifold, and we shall prove:*

The Leray spectral sequence degenerates at E_2; *i.e.,*

$$E_2 \cong E_\infty$$

so that

$$H^*(E, \mathbb{Q}) \cong H^*(B, R^*_\pi(\mathbb{Q})).$$

Before giving the proof, we wish to suggest two interpretations of this result. One is as another reflection of the extraordinary topological properties, such as those encountered in Sections 1 and 3 of Chapter 1, possessed

*Cf. P. Deligne, Théorème de Lefschetz et critéres de dégénérescence de suite spectrales, *Publ. Math. I.H.E.S.*, Vol. 35 (1968), pp. 107–126.

by an algebraic variety. The other interpretation is as focusing attention on the extremely important role played by the *monodromy group*, which is by definition the image of $\pi_1(B, x_0)$ in $\text{Aut}(H^*(G, \mathbb{Q})$ under the representation obtained by displacing cycles around closed paths.

Proof. We first remark that a closed k-form φ given on the total space E defines classes in $E_r^{p,k}$ for all r, and moreover that multiplication by φ induces

$$\varphi: E_r^{p,q} \to E_r^{p,q+k}$$

commuting with

$$d_r: E_r^{p,q} \to E_r^{p+r,q-r+1},$$

again for all r. These assertions are clear from our proof of the spectral sequence using differential forms and also were verified in the little example above.

Now let ω be a Kähler form on E, and denote by L the map induced by multiplication by ω. Then from the definition of the direct image sheaves, $L: R_\pi^q(\mathbb{C}) \to R_\pi^{q+2}(\mathbb{C})$ is defined and if $\dim F = n$ the hard Lefschetz theorem

$$L^k: R_\pi^{n-k}(\mathbb{C}) \to R_\pi^{n+k}(\mathbb{C})$$

is valid, simply because each stalk

$$R_\pi^q(\mathbb{C})_x \cong H^q(F_x, \mathbb{C})$$

and we may apply the usual hard Lefschetz theorem. Continuing this line of thought, if we define the *primitive Leray sheaf* by

$$P^{n-k} = \ker\{L^{k+1}: R^{n\ k} \to R^{n+k+2}\}, \qquad R^q = R_\pi^q(\mathbb{C}),$$

then for the same reasons the Lefschetz decomposition

$$R^q \cong \bigoplus_k L^k P^{q-2k} \qquad (q \leqslant n)$$

is valid.

We shall show that

$$d_2: E_2^{p,q} \to E_2^{p+2,q-1}$$

is zero, with the proof for the higher d_r's being the same. Since

$$E_2^{p,q} = H^p(B, R^q)$$

and

$$L^k: E_2^{p,n-k} \cong E_2^{p,n+k}$$

is an isomorphism commuting with d_2, it will suffice to show that $d_2 = 0$ on

$E_2^{p,n-k}$. Passing to the Lefschetz decomposition, we consider the commutative diagram

$$H^p(B, P^{n-k}) \overset{d_2}{\to} H^{p+2}(B, R^{n-k-1})$$
$$\downarrow L^{k+1} = 0 \qquad\qquad \downarrow L^{k+1}$$
$$H^p(B, R^{n+k+2}) \overset{d_2}{\to} H^{p+2}(B, R^{n+k+1}).$$

The right-hand vertical arrow is an isomorphism by hard Lefschetz, and the left-hand one is zero by definition of primitive. Thus $d_2 = 0$.   Q.E.D.

REFERENCES

This chapter gives a potpourri of general analytic, topological, and homological methods applied to complex manifolds and algebraic varieties. Some specific references were given in the text, and here we mention one or two sources for each topic that may assist the reader in amplifying the discussions in the book and serve as a guide to the literature.

Section 1

G. de Rham, *Variétès différentiables*, Hermann, Paris, 1954.

Section 2

P. Lelong, *Fonctionis plurisousharmoniques et formes différentielles positives*, Gordon and Breach, Paris-London-New York, 1968.

Section 3

S. S. Chern, Characteristic classes of hermitian manifolds, *Annals of Math.*, Vol. 57 (1946), pp. 85–121.

Section 4

M. F. Atiyah and R. Bott, A Lefschetz fixed point formula for elliptic complexes II, *Annals of Math.*, Vol. 88 (1968), pp. 451–491.

R. Bott, Vector fields and characteristic numbers, *Michigan Math. Jour.*, Vol. 14 (1967), pp. 231–244.

Section 5

R. Godement, *Theorie des Faisceaux*, Hermann, Paris, 1958.

P. Deligne, *Equations Différentielles à Points Singulers Réguliers*, Springer-Verlag, Berlin-Heidelberg-New York, 1970.

4
SURFACES

Perhaps the most striking aspect of the theory of algebraic surfaces, when first encountered, is how different it is in character from the theory of Riemann surfaces. Whereas curves, having the genus as their sole discrete invariant, fall into an orderly sequence of families, surfaces possess a variety of numerical invariants and are not so readily classified. Conversely, while curves have a natural continuous invariant—their periods, realized geometrically by the Jacobian—no fully satisfactory continuous invariant has been found for surfaces. As a result, the theory of algebraic surfaces does not possess the natural cohesiveness of the theory of curves; it tends to concentrate more on the study of special classes of surfaces. This is reflected in our treatment: with the exception of the basic tools presented in Sections 1 and 2 and the proof of Noether's formula, virtually all our results either describe or characterize specific families of surfaces.

Sections 1 and 2 contain all the techniques used in our study. For the most part, these results are special cases of general phenomena discussed before; the one new idea introduced here is the notion of a *rational map*. This is an important aspect of the theory of varieties in dimension two or more; in the case of surfaces we are able to give a complete description of birational maps.

In Section 3 we describe the general rational surface, and obtain in consequence the answer to some problems posed in curve theory. Section 4 is complementary to 3: its main result is a characterization of rational surfaces by numerical invariants.

Section 5 discusses the classification theorem for surfaces; this essentially amounts to a description, in varying detail, of all surfaces except those of general type.

It remains in Section 6 to prove Noether's formula. To do this, we introduce another technique of general interest: the blow-up of a complex manifold along any submanifold. Using this construction together with some remarks on singularities of surfaces in $\mathbb{P}^3$ we represent a general surface as a smooth divisor in a blow-up of $\mathbb{P}^3$, and obtain formulas for the numerical characters of a surface in terms of the projective invariants of a birational embedding in 3-space. Noether's formula is an immediate consequence of these.

1. PRELIMINARIES

Intersection Numbers, the Adjunction Formula, and Riemann-Roch

Let M be an algebraic surface, i.e., a compact complex manifold of dimension 2 that may be embedded in projective space. Since M is an oriented real 4-manifold, the intersection pairing

$$H_2(M, \mathbb{Z}) \times H_2(M, \mathbb{Z}) \to \mathbb{Z}$$

is symmetric and nondegenerate. For divisors D and D' on M we define the *intersection number $D \cdot D'$* of D and D' to be simply the intersection number of their fundamental classes (D), $(D') \in H_2(M, \mathbb{Z})$. Similarly, if $L \to M$ and $L' \to M$ are two line bundles, we take the *intersection number* $L \cdot L'$ of L and L' to be given by

$$L \cdot L' = (c_1(L) \cup c_1(L'))[M],$$

and likewise we define the intersection number $L \cdot D$ of a line bundle L with a divisor D to be just the value of the Chern class $c_1(L) \in H^2(M, \mathbb{Z})$ on the fundamental class $(D) \in H_2(M, \mathbb{Z})$ of D. Since intersection of cycles is Poincaré dual to cup product, all these definitions are consistent with the correspondence between divisors and line bundles; i.e., if $L = [D]$ and $L' = [D']$, then $D \cdot D' = L \cdot D' = L' \cdot D = L \cdot L'$.

There are a few points to be made about the intersection of divisors on an algebraic surface:

1. If L is a positive line bundle, then for any effective divisor D

$$L \cdot D = \int_D c_1(L) > 0.$$

2. Any two effective divisors D and D' intersecting in isolated points intersect positively; thus $D \cdot D' \geq 0$ unless D and D' have a component in common. In particular, if D is irreducible, then any effective divisor D' not containing D intersects D positively, and if in addition, $D \cdot D \geq 0$, then $D \cdot D' \geq 0$ for any effective divisor D'.

3. In a somewhat deeper vein, recall that by the Hodge-Riemann bilinear relations the intersection form is negative definite on the primitive cohomology $P^{1,1}(M) \subset H^{1,1}(M)$. By the Lefschetz decomposition, $P^{1,1}$ has codimension 1 in $H^{1,1}$; thus if D is any divisor on M with $D \cdot D > 0$, the

intersection pairing is negative definite on the orthogonal complement of η_D in $H^{1,1}(M)$. In particular, *if* $D \cdot D > 0$, *then for any divisor* D' *on M such that* $D' \cdot D = 0$, *either* $D' \cdot D' < 0$ *or* $(D') = 0$; this is commonly called the *index theorem*.

By way of terminology, we define a *curve* C on the surface M to be any effective divisor on M; a curve C is called *smooth* if it is the locus of a submanifold of M taken with multiplicity 1 and *irreducible* if it is not the sum of two nontrivial effective divisors.

Let C be a smooth, irreducible curve on M. By the adjunction formula from Section 2 of Chapter 1

$$K_C = (K_M + C)|_C,$$

where K_C and K_M denote, as usual, the canonical line bundles of C and M. If g is the genus of the curve C, it follows that

$$\begin{aligned} g &= \tfrac{1}{2}\deg K_C + 1 \\ &= \tfrac{1}{2}\deg(K_M + C)|_C + 1 \\ &= \frac{K_M \cdot C + C \cdot C}{2} + 1. \end{aligned}$$

This formula is also referred to as the adjunction formula. In general, we define the *virtual genus* $\pi(C)$ of an arbitrary curve C on M by

$$\pi(C) = \frac{K \cdot C + C \cdot C}{2} + 1.$$

Now let D be any smooth, irreducible curve on the surface M, and let $L = [D]$ be its associated line bundle. From the long exact cohomology sequence associated to the exact sheaf sequence

$$0 \to \mathcal{O}_M \to \mathcal{O}_M(L) \to \mathcal{O}_D(L) \to 0$$

we obtain

$$\chi(L) = \chi(\mathcal{O}_M) + \chi(\mathcal{O}_D(L)).$$

Now, by Riemann-Roch for D,

$$\begin{aligned} \chi(\mathcal{O}_D(L)) &= -\pi(D) + \deg(L|_D) + 1 \\ &= -\pi(D) + L \cdot L + 1. \end{aligned}$$

But by the adjunction formula,

$$\pi(D) = \frac{L \cdot L + L \cdot K}{2} + 1;$$

thus we have

$$\chi(L) = \chi(\mathcal{O}_M) + \frac{L \cdot L - L \cdot K}{2}.$$

This formula holds for an arbitrary line bundle L on M. We just choose a divisor D on M sufficiently positive so that both the linear series $|D|$ and $|L+D|$ contain smooth, irreducible divisors; setting

$$L' = L + D$$

the exact sequence

$$0 \to \mathcal{O}_M(L) \to \mathcal{O}_M(L') \to \mathcal{O}(L') \to 0$$

gives

$$\chi(L) = \chi(L') - \chi(L'|_D).$$

But

$$\chi(L'|_D) = -\pi(D) + \deg L'|_D + 1$$
$$= -\frac{D \cdot D + D \cdot K}{2} + L' \cdot D;$$

so

$$\chi(L) = \chi(\mathcal{O}_M) + \frac{L' \cdot L' - L' \cdot K}{2} + \frac{D \cdot D + D \cdot K - 2(L' \cdot D)}{2}$$

$$= \chi(\mathcal{O}_M) + \frac{(L' \cdot L' - 2L' \cdot D + D \cdot D) - (L' \cdot K - D \cdot K)}{2}$$

$$= \chi(\mathcal{O}_M) + \frac{L \cdot L - L \cdot K}{2};$$

this is the *Riemann-Roch formula* for line bundles on a surface.

As suggested in the last chapter, the holomorphic Euler characteristic $\chi(\mathcal{O}_M)$ of M is itself expressible as a polynomial in the Chern classes of M: the formula

$$\chi(\mathcal{O}_M) = \tfrac{1}{12}\big(c_1(M)^2 + c_2(M)\big)$$

$$= \tfrac{1}{12}(K \cdot K + \chi(M))$$

is called *Noether's formula*. We defer the proof until the last section of this chapter.

We observe that the Riemann-Roch theorem for line bundles gives a direct proof of the index theorem for divisors, as follows: let E be a positive divisor on S. We have seen (p.164) that the intersection pairing on the group $H^{1,1}(S) \cap H^2(S, \mathbb{Z})$ of divisors modulo homology is nondegenerate; if it had two positive eigenvalues, it would of course have at least one in the orthogonal complement of the class of E; i.e., we could find a divisor D with

$$D \cdot E = 0 \quad \text{and} \quad D \cdot D = d > 0.$$

We will show that such a divisor D cannot exist. First, since E has strictly positive intersection number with any effective divisor, neither mD nor

$-mD$ can be effective for any $m \neq 0$. Applying Riemann-Roch, we find

$$h^0(mD) - h^1(mD) + h^2(mD) = \frac{1}{2}m^2d - \frac{m}{2}K \cdot D + \chi(\mathcal{O}_S);$$

i.e.,

$$h^0(K - mD) = h^2(mD) \geq \frac{1}{2}m^2d - \frac{m}{2}K \cdot D + \chi(\mathcal{O}_S) + h^1(mD)$$

becomes arbitrarily large as m goes to either $-\infty$ or $+\infty$. In particular, $K + mD$ is linearly equivalent to an effective divisor E_m for all $m \gg 0$. But now the map

$$|K - mD| \longrightarrow |2K|$$

given by

$$G \mapsto G + E_m$$

is injective, and so the dimension of $|K - mD|$ is bounded—a contradiction.

Blowing Up and Down

We recall some definitions from Chapter 1, Section 5: let M be a complex manifold of dimension n, $z = (z_1, \ldots, z_n)$ holomorphic coordinates in an open set $U \subset M$ centered around the point $p \in M$. The *blow-up* $\tilde{M}$ of M at p is then taken to be the complex manifold obtained by adjoining to $M - \{p\}$ the manifold

$$\tilde{U} = \{(z,l): z \in l\} \subset U \times \mathbb{P}^{n-1}$$

via the isomorphism

$$\tilde{U} - (z = 0) \cong U - \{p\}$$

given by $(z,l) \mapsto z$. There is a natural projection map $\pi: \tilde{M} \to M$ extending the identity on $M - \{p\}$. The inverse image $E = \pi^{-1}(p)$ is naturally isomorphic to $\mathbb{P}(T_p(M)) \cong \mathbb{P}^{n-1}$ and is called the *exceptional divisor* of the blow-up $\tilde{M} \to M$.

When blow-ups were introduced in the course of the Kodaira embedding theorem, we were primarily concerned with the local geometry of M and $\tilde{M}$ near p and E, respectively. We would now like to relate the global geometry of $\tilde{M}$ to that of M. We begin by considering the topology of M and $\tilde{M}$: we set $M^* = M - \{p\}$, $\tilde{M}^* = \pi^{-1}M^* = \tilde{M} - E$, $U^* = U - \{p\}$ and $\tilde{U}^* = \pi^{-1}U^* = \tilde{U} - E$, and compare the Mayer-Victoris sequences of $M = M^* \cup U$ and $\tilde{M} = \tilde{M}^* \cup U$:

$$H_i(\tilde{U}^*) \to H_i(\tilde{U}) \oplus H_i(\tilde{M}^*) \to H_i(\tilde{M}) \to H_{i+1}(\tilde{U}^*)$$
$$\downarrow \pi_* \qquad\qquad \downarrow \pi_* \qquad\qquad \downarrow \pi_* \qquad\quad \downarrow \pi_*$$
$$H_i(U^*) \to H_i(U) \oplus H_i(M^*) \to H_i(M) \to H_{i+1}(U^*)$$

Now, π_* is an isomorphism between $H_*(\tilde{U}^*)$ and $H_*(U^*)$, and between $H_*(\tilde{M}^*)$ and $H_*(M^*)$. On the other hand, we may choose our open set U a ball around the point p; and the standard contraction $z \mapsto tz$ of U onto p induces, via π, a contraction of $\tilde{U}$ onto E. Thus we have

$$H_i(\tilde{M}) = H_i(M) \oplus H_i(E), \qquad i > 0,$$

Since all the cohomology of $E \cong \mathbb{P}^{n-1}$ is represented by analytic cycles,

$$h^{i,i}(\tilde{M}) = h^{i,i}(M) + 1, \qquad i > 0,$$

with all other Hodge numbers of $\tilde{M}$ equal to those of M.

We make here one new definition. Let p, M, $\tilde{M}$, and π be as above, and let $V \subset M$ be any analytic subvariety of M. Then we define the *proper transform* $\tilde{V} \subset \tilde{M}$ of V to be the closure in $\tilde{M}$ of the inverse image

$$\tilde{V} = \overline{\pi^{-1}(V - \{p\})} = \overline{\pi^{-1}(V) - E}$$

of V away from x. Clearly π maps $\tilde{V} - E = \pi^{-1}(V - \{p\})$ isomorphically onto $V - \{p\}$. To get a picture of $\tilde{V}$ near the exceptional divisor, let $z = (z_1, \ldots, z_n)$ be holomorphic coordinates around $p \in M$, $\tilde{U}_i$ the open set $(l_i \neq 0)$ in $\tilde{U} = \pi^{-1}(U)$, and

$$z(i)_j = \frac{z_j}{z_i} = \frac{l_j}{l_i}, \qquad j \neq i,$$
$$z_i = z_i$$

holomorphic coordinates on $\tilde{U}_i$ as on p. 184. Recall that the divisor E is given in $\tilde{U}_i$ as $(z_i = 0)$, and that the coordinates $\{z(i)_j\}_{j \neq i}$ restrict to Euclidean coordinates on $E \cong \mathbb{P}^{n-1}$. Now let f be any holomorphic function near $p \in M$, $V = (f)$ its divisor. Write

$$f(z) = \sum_{m \geq 0} f_m(z),$$

where

$$f_m(z) = \sum_{|a| = m} c_a \cdot z_1^{a_1} \cdots z_n^{a_n}$$

is the mth homogeneous component of f in terms of the coordinates z around p. Setting $\tilde{f} = \pi^* f$, $\tilde{f}_m = \pi^* f_m$, we have

$$\tilde{f}(z) = \sum \tilde{f}_m(z)$$

and

$$\tilde{f}_m(z) = \sum_{|a| = m} c_a \cdot (z_i \cdot z(i)_1)^{a_1} \cdots z_i^{a_i} \cdots (z_i \cdot z(i)_n)^{a_n}$$
$$= z_i^m \cdot \sum c_a \cdot z(i)_1^{a_1} \cdots \widehat{z_i^{a_i}} \cdots z(i)_n^{a_n}.$$

Consequently if f vanishes to order m_0 at x—i.e., if $f_0 = f_1 = \cdots = f_{m_0-1} = 0$

—then $\tilde{f}$ vanishes to order m_0 along E, and

$$\tilde{V} = \pi^* V - \text{mult}_p(V) \cdot E$$
$$= \pi^* V - \text{ord}_E(\pi^* V) \cdot E.$$

Moreover, we see that

$$\tilde{V} \cap E = (z_i^{-m_0} \cdot f_m)$$
$$= \left(\sum_{|a|=m_0} c_a \cdot l_1^{a_1} \cdots l_n^{a_n} \right),$$

i.e., *under the identification* $E \cong \mathbb{P}(T_p'(M))$, $\tilde{V} \cap E$ *is just the projective tangent cone to* V *at* p. Figure 1 illustrates the case of a surface M and a curve V in M with an ordinary double point at p.

Note finally that if p is a smooth point of the subvariety $V \subset M$, then the proper transform $\tilde{V}$ of V under the blow-up of M at p is just the blow-up of V at p. Accordingly, we sometimes refer to the proper transform $\tilde{V} \subset \tilde{M}$ of a subvariety $V \subset M$ as the blow-up of V at p, even when p is a singular point of V.

We now consider the case of a surface M and its blow-up $\tilde{M} \xrightarrow{\pi} M$ at $p \in M$. First, we see that if C is any curve on $\tilde{M}$ not containing the exceptional divisor E, then C is the proper transform of its image $\pi(C)$ in M; thus

$$(*) \qquad \text{Div}(\tilde{M}) = \pi^* \text{Div}(M) \oplus \mathbb{Z}\{E\}.$$

We can now compute intersection numbers readily. We have seen in Chapter 1 that the normal bundle to E in $\tilde{M}$ is just the dual of the hyperplane bundle on $E \cong \mathbb{P}^1$; thus

$$(E \cdot E) = \deg([E]|_E) = \deg(N_E) = -1.$$

Since the map π has degree 1—that is, the image under π_* of the fundamental class $[\tilde{M}] \in H_4(\tilde{M}, \mathbb{Z})$ of $\tilde{M}$ is just the fundamental class of M

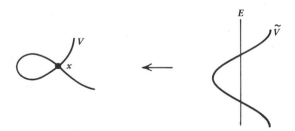

Figure 1

—we deduce that for any divisors D, D' on M,

$$\pi^* D \cdot \pi^* D' = D \cdot D',$$

and since the class (E) of the exceptional divisor of the blow-up is in the kernel of π_*,

$$\pi^* D \cdot E = {}^\#\left(D \cdot \left(\pi_*(E)\right)\right) = 0$$

for any divisor D on M. Summarizing, the isomorphism $(*)$ above is an isomorphism of inner product spaces.

Note in particular that if D, D' are two divisors on M intersecting transversely at p, $\tilde{D}$ and $\tilde{D}'$ their proper transforms in $\tilde{M}$, we have

$$\begin{aligned}
\tilde{D} \cdot \tilde{D}' &= (\pi^* D - E) \cdot (\pi^* D' - E) \\
&= \pi^* D \cdot \pi^* D' + E \cdot E \\
&= D \cdot D' - 1.
\end{aligned}$$

This is as we would expect from our picture of the proper transforms of curves: for every point p' of intersection of D and D' other than p, $\tilde{D}$ and $\tilde{D}'$ will meet at $\pi^{-1}(p')$; since D and D' have distinct tangents at p, however, $\tilde{D}$ and $\tilde{D}'$ will not meet at any point of $E = \pi^{-1}(p)$.

One point that should be brought out here is that if $\{D_\lambda\}$ is a linear system of curves on the surface M, the proper transforms $\{\tilde{D}_\lambda\}$ of the curves D_λ on $\tilde{M}$ *do not necessarily form a linear system on* $\tilde{M}$. Indeed, since

$$\tilde{D}_\lambda = \pi^* D_\lambda - \text{mult}_p(D_\lambda) \cdot E$$

and the curves $\{\pi^* D_\lambda\}$ do form a linear system, $\{\tilde{D}_\lambda\}$ will be a linear system if and only if all the curves D_λ have the same multiplicity at p. Thus when we speak of the *proper transform of a linear system* $\{D_\lambda\}$, we will mean the linear system of curves $\{\pi^* D_\lambda - mE\}$, where $m = \min\{\text{mult}_p(D_\lambda)\}_\lambda$ is the multiplicity of the generic curve D_λ at p.

We see from all the above that the blow-up $\tilde{M}$ of a surface M is very closely related to M. An important question to ask, then, is the converse: *Given a surface* M *and a curve* C *on* M, *when can we realize* M *as the blow-up* $\tilde{N}_{x_0}$ *of some surface* N, *with* $C = \pi^{-1}(\{x_0\})$? Clearly, necessary conditions are that C be rational and that $C \cdot C = -1$; in fact, the following result says that these are also sufficient.

Castelnuovo-Enriques Criterion. *Let* M *be an algebraic surface,* $C \subset M$ *a smooth rational curve on* M *of self-intersection* -1. *Then there exists a smooth algebraic surface* N *and a map* $\pi :: M \to N$ *such that* $M \xrightarrow{\pi} N$ *is the blow-up of* N *at* $p_0 \in N$, *and* $C = \pi^{-1}(p_0)$.

Proof. The proof here is along the lines of the Kodaira embedding theorem, but with a twist: we want to find a map $f : M \to \mathbb{P}^m$ that is one-to-one away from C, maps C to a point, and has smooth image. Accordingly, we look first for a line bundle $L \to M$ that is sufficiently positive away from C to have global sections, but whose restriction to C is trivial.

To find such a bundle, we start with a very ample line bundle L on M; choosing L sufficiently large, we may assume that

$$H^1(M, \mathcal{O}(L)) = 0.$$

Let $m = L \cdot C$ and consider, for each $k = 0, 1, \ldots, m$ the sequences

$$(*_k) \qquad 0 \to \mathcal{O}_M(L + (k+1)C) \to \mathcal{O}_M(L + kC) \to \mathcal{O}_C(L + kC) \to 0.$$

We note first that if $H \to C \cong \mathbb{P}^1$ is the point bundle on $\mathbb{P}^1$, $(L + kC)|_C = (m - k)H$, so that

$$H^1(C, \mathcal{O}(L + kC)) = 0 \qquad \text{for } k < m + 1.$$

It follows from the long exact cohomology sequence associated to $(*_k)$ that $H^1(M, \mathcal{O}(L + (k-1)C))$ surjects onto $H^1(M, \mathcal{O}(L + kC))$ for $k \leqslant m + 1$; and since by hypothesis $H^1(M, \mathcal{O}(L)) = 0$,

$$H^1(M, \mathcal{O}(L + kC)) = 0 \qquad \text{for } k \leqslant m + 1$$

so the restriction map $H^0(M, \mathcal{O}(L + kC)) \to H^0(C, \mathcal{O}((m - k)H))$ is surjective for $k \leqslant m + 1$. In particular, this tells us that the linear system $|L + kC|$ has no base points on C for $k \leqslant m$; since $|L|$ itself has no base points, it follows that $|L + kC|$ *has no base points for* $k \leqslant m$.

Consider now the map $\iota_{L'}$ given by the linear system $|L'| = |L + mC|$. Since $|L'|$ contains the subseries $|L| + mC$ and L is very ample, $\iota_{L'}$ embeds $M - C$ and separates points of C from points of $M - C$. On the other hand, since $L'|_C$ is trivial, any section $\sigma \in H^0(M, \mathcal{O}(L'))$ vanishing at a point of C vanishes identically along C; so $\iota_{L'}$ maps C to a point. To conclude the argument, we must show that $\iota_{L'}(C)$ is a smooth point of the image $\iota_{L'}(M)$; to see this, note that by the sequence $(*_{m-1})$ the restriction map

$$H^0(M, \mathcal{O}(L' - C)) \to H^0(C, \mathcal{O}(H))$$

is surjective. Let $p_1 \neq p_2 \in C$, and let ξ_1 be a section of L^1 vanishing on C that restricts, via the map above, to a section of H over C vanishing at p_1; let ξ_2 be a global section of L' restricting to a section of H vanishing at p_2. Let ξ_0 be any section of L' not vanishing identically on C (and hence nonzero on C), and set

$$z_1 = \frac{\xi_1}{\xi_0}, \qquad z_2 = \frac{\xi_2}{\xi_0}.$$

Let $U_1 = C - \{p_2\}$, $U_2 = C - \{p_1\}$. Then in some open set $\tilde{U}_1 \subset M$ containing U_1, z_1/z_2 is holomorphic; in fact, for $p \in U_1$ we have $d(z_1/z_2) \neq 0$ on $T'_p(C) \subset T'_p(M)$ and $dz_2 \neq 0$ on $T'_p(M)/T'_p(C)$, so that if we choose $\tilde{U}_1$ sufficiently small, we may take $z_2, z_1/z_2$ local coordinates on $\tilde{U}_1$. Similarly,

z_1 and z_2/z_1 furnish local coordinates on an open set $\tilde{U}_2 \subset M$ containing U_2. We see from this that the functions (z_1, z_2) map a neighborhood of C in M onto a neighborhood of the origin in $\mathbb{C}^2$, a mapping that is holomorphic outside C. This proves that $\iota_{L'}(C)$ is a smooth point of $\iota_{L'}(M)$, completing the proof of the Castelnuovo-Enriques criterion.   Q.E.D.

A smooth rational curve of self-intersection -1 on a surface is called an *exceptional divisor of the first kind*.

The Quadric Surface

We now consider a smooth surface of degree 2 in $\mathbb{P}^3$. Such a surface is given as the locus of

$$(x \cdot Qx) = \sum q_{ij} x_i x_j = 0$$

for $Q = (q_{ij})$ a symmetric matrix; since

$$\frac{\partial}{\partial x_i}(x \cdot Qx) = 2 \sum_j q_{ij} x_j,$$

we see that S is smooth exactly when the matrix Q is nonsingular. All nondegenerate symmetric quadratic forms on $\mathbb{C}^4$ are isomorphic, and it follows that *any two smooth quadric surfaces in $\mathbb{P}^3$ are projectively isomorphic*. Consider in particular the Segré map

$$\sigma: \mathbb{P}^1 \times \mathbb{P}^1 \to \mathbb{P}^3$$

given by

$$([s_0, s_1], [t_0, t_1]) \mapsto [s_0 t_0, s_0 t_1, s_1 t_0, s_1 t_1].$$

σ is clearly an embedding, and the image of σ is contained in—hence equal to—the smooth quadric

$$S_0 = (X_1 X_4 - X_2 X_3 = 0).$$

Thus *any quadric surface $S \subset \mathbb{P}^3$ is isomorphic to $\mathbb{P}^1 \times \mathbb{P}^1$*.

Of particular interest is the set of lines in $\mathbb{P}^3$ lying on a smooth quadric S. We see that under the Segré map σ, the curves $\{s\} \times \mathbb{P}^1$ and $\mathbb{P}^1 \times \{t\}$ on $\mathbb{P}^1 \times \mathbb{P}^1$ are sent into lines in $\mathbb{P}^3$. We will call these two families of lines on S the *A-lines* and the *B-lines*; clearly every A-line meets every B-line, and any two A-lines are disjoint, as are any two B-lines. These are, moreover, all the lines on S: if $L \subset S$ is any line, then obviously L must meet at least one A-line L_1 and one B-line L_2. But L_1 and L_2 meet, and the plane they span in $\mathbb{P}^3$ can meet S in at most two lines, so either $L = L_1$ or $L = L_2$.

We can describe the set of lines on a general smooth quadric S directly as follows: first, note that if Q is any point in the intersection of S with its tangent plane $T_p(S) \subset \mathbb{P}^3$ at P, the line $\overline{PQ}$ meets S three times—once at Q and twice at P—and so must lie in S. The locus $S \cap T_p(S)$ must therefore consist of a union of lines; since $S \cap T_p(S)$ has degree 2, it must consist of two lines. Conversely any line on S through P must lie in the locus $S \cap T_p(S)$, and so we see that *through every point* $P \in S$ *there pass exactly two lines on* S, *comprising the locus* $S \cap T_p(S)$. (Note that these two lines are necessarily distinct: if $T_p(S)$ met S in only one line L, $T_p(S)$ would have to be tangent to S everywhere along L, and so no other line on S could meet L. But the intersection of S with a general tangent plane $T_Q(S)$ not containing L will consist of a union of lines, and must meet L, so this cannot be the case.)

Now, pick one line $L_0 \subset S$ and call any line on S an A-line if it is either equal to or disjoint from L, a B-line if it meets L in one point. If two lines $L, L' \neq L_0$ on S meet in a point, the plane they span in $\mathbb{P}^3$ meets L_0 in a point, which must be a point of either L or L'; so one of the two is an A-line and the other a B-line. Conversely, if $L \neq L_0$ is an A-line and L' a B-line, the plane spanned by L' and L_0 must meet L in a point, which by definition cannot be a point of L_0; so L and L' intersect. Thus two lines on S meet if and only if they are of different type; since there will be a unique B-line passing through every point of L_0 and likewise a unique A-line passing through each point of a fixed B-line, we see that the families of A-lines and B-lines are each parametrized by $\mathbb{P}^1$ In sum, then, *the set of lines on* S *consists of two disjoint families, each parametrized by* $\mathbb{P}^1$, *with two lines meeting if and only if they are from different families*. It follows that $S \cong \mathbb{P}^1 \times \mathbb{P}^1$.

We can obtain another description of a quadric surface S by projecting from a point p of S onto a plane H in $\mathbb{P}^3$. Of course, the projection map $\pi_p : S - \{p\} \rightarrow H$ is not defined at, and does not extend over, the point p. If we let $\tilde{S}$ be the blow-up of S at p, however, we can extend the map π_p continuously over the exceptional divisor $E \subset \tilde{S}$, obtaining a holomorphic map $\tilde{\pi} : \tilde{S} \rightarrow H$: for a point $r \in E$ corresponding via the identification $E \cong \mathbb{P}(T'_p(S))$ to the line $\bar{r} \subset T_p(S)$, take $\tilde{\pi}(r)$ to be the point of intersection of H with the line $L_r \subset \mathbb{P}^3$ through p with tangent line $\bar{r}$.

Now let L_1, L_2 be the two lines on S passing through p, and let q_1 and q_2 be their points of intersection with H. Then for any point $q \in H$ other than q_1 and q_2, the line $\overline{pq}$ will either meet S in one point other than p, or be simply tangent to S at p; in either case q will be the image under $\tilde{\pi}$ of a single point of $\tilde{S}$. The inverse images of q_1 and q_2, on the other hand, will be the proper transforms $\tilde{L}_1$ and $\tilde{L}_2$ of L_1 and L_2 in $\tilde{S}$. (Note that the A-lines of S—i.e., lines meeting L_1—are mapped into the pencil of lines in H containing q_1, the B-lines into the pencil of lines through q_2, and the exceptional divisor E onto the line $\overline{q_1 q_2}$.) We see from this that $\tilde{\pi}$ is one-to-one on $\tilde{S} - \tilde{L}_1 - \tilde{L}_2$, and maps $\tilde{L}_1$ and $\tilde{L}_2$ onto q_1 and q_2—i.e., $\tilde{\pi} : \tilde{S} \rightarrow \mathbb{P}^2$ *is just the blow-up of* $\mathbb{P}^2$ *at* q_1 *and* q_2. Thus we may obtain $\mathbb{P}^2$ from a quadric surface S by blowing up one point p of S and blowing down the proper transforms of the two lines on S through p. In reverse: *we may obtain a quadric surface* $S \cong \mathbb{P}^1 \times \mathbb{P}^1$ *from* $\mathbb{P}^2$ *by blowing up two points* q_1, q_2 *on* $\mathbb{P}^2$ *and blowing down the proper transform of the line* $\overline{q_1 q_2} \subset \mathbb{P}^2$. We will see this operation more explicitly following our discussion of the cubic surface.

Note that since the only invariant of a symmetric quadratic form on $\mathbb{C}^n$ is its rank, there are all in all only three quadric surfaces without multiple components in $\mathbb{P}^3$: (1) those given as the locus of a nondegenerate form

$$X_0^2 + X_1^2 + X_2^2 + X_3^2$$

on $\mathbb{C}^4$—these are the smooth quadrics; (2) those given as the locus of a form

$$X_0^2 + X_1^2 + X_2^2;$$

such a quadric is the cone over a plane conic curve and singular at the vertex $[0,0,0,1]$ of the cone; and (3) those given as the locus of a form

$$X_0^2 + X_1^2;$$

these consist of the union of two planes.

The Cubic Surface

We now describe a smooth cubic surface in $\mathbb{P}^3$. We will first construct such a surface by blowing up six "general" points in $\mathbb{P}^2$ and embedding the blown-up surface in $\mathbb{P}^3$ as a cubic; we will then show that in fact every nonsingular cubic surface may be obtained in this way.

Choose six points $p_1, \dots, p_6 \in \mathbb{P}^2$ such that

1. $p_1, \dots, p_6$ do not all lie on a conic curve; and
2. no three of them lie on a line.

Let $\tilde{\mathbb{P}}^2 \xrightarrow{\pi} \mathbb{P}^2$ be the blow up of $\mathbb{P}^2$ at $p_1, \dots, p_6$, E_i the exceptional divisor over p_i, and consider the complete linear system $|\tilde{C}|$ where

$$\tilde{C} = \pi^* 3H - E_1 - \cdots - E_6.$$

If C is any cubic curve in the plane passing through all six points p_i, then the curve $\pi^{-1}(C) - E_1 - \cdots - E_6$ is certainly in the linear system $|\tilde{C}|$; conversely, if D is any curve in $|\tilde{C}|$, then

$$\pi(D) \cdot H = D \cdot \pi^* H = 3$$

so $\pi(D)$ is a cubic curve, and

$$D \cdot E_i = -E_i \cdot E_i = 1$$

so D meets every exceptional divisor E_i, i.e., $\pi(D)$ passes through all six points p_i. Thus the system $|\tilde{C}|$ consists exactly of curves

$$\pi^{-1}(C) - E_1 - \cdots - E_6,$$

where C is a cubic plane curve containing $p_1,\ldots,p_6$.

We claim now that *the linear system $|\tilde{C}|$ embeds $\tilde{\mathbb{P}}^2$ as a cubic surface in* $\mathbb{P}^3$. This involves quite a bit of checking: we have to show that

1. $\tilde{C}\cdot\tilde{C}=3$,
2. $\dim|\tilde{C}|=3$,
3. $\iota_{\tilde{C}}$ separates points $p \neq q \in \mathbb{P}^2$, for
   a. $p,q \in \tilde{\mathbb{P}}^2 - \cup E_i$,
   b. $p \in E_i,\ q \in \tilde{\mathbb{P}}^2 - \cup E_i$,
   c. $p \in E_i,\ q \in E_j$, and
   d. $p,q \in E_i$; and
4. $\iota_{\tilde{C}}$ has nonzero differential at p, for
   a. $p \in \tilde{\mathbb{P}}^2 - \cup E_i$, and
   b. $p \in E_i$.

Assertion 1 is immediate: we have

$$\tilde{C}\cdot\tilde{C} = \pi^*3H\cdot\pi^*3H + E_1\cdot E_1 + \cdots + E_6\cdot E_6 = 9 - 6 = 3.$$

The other assertions, however, are of a different character. For example, we know that the complete linear system of cubic curves in the plane has dimension 9, and that the requirement that a cubic pass through any one of the points p_i imposes one linear condition on the system $|3H|$; the statement $\dim|\tilde{C}|=3$ amounts to saying that the conditions imposed by the six points p_i are independent. This, and the last two assertions as well, will follow from the

Lemma. *Eight points* $p_1,\ldots,p_8 \in \mathbb{P}^2$ *fail to impose independent conditions on cubics only if either*

1. *All eight lie on a conic curve; or*
2. *Five of the points* p_i *are collinear.*

Proof. The first step in the proof is to show that *seven points* $p_1,\ldots,p_7 \in \mathbb{P}^2$ *fail to impose independent conditions on cubics only if five are collinear.* To see this, we argue as follows: Assume that $p_1,\ldots,p_7$ fail to impose independent conditions on cubics. Then for some point p_i, any cubic containing the other six will contain p_i; reordering, we may take p_i to be p_1. Let L_{ij} denote the line $\overline{p_i,p_j}$. The cubic curve

$$L_{23} + L_{45} + L_{67}$$

contains $p_2,\ldots,p_7$ and hence p_1 as well; thus p_1 is collinear with two other points p_i, which we may take to be p_2 and p_3.

Suppose now that the line $L = \overline{p_1 p_2 p_3}$ also contains one of the points $p_4, \ldots, p_7$, say p_4. Then since the cubic

$$L_{25} + L_{36} + L_{47}$$

contains p_1, we must have either p_5, p_6, or p_7 lying on L as well; thus we have five collinear points. If, on the other hand, none of the points $p_4, \ldots, p_7$ lies on the line L, then since the cubics

$$L_{24} + L_{35} + L_{67}, \qquad L_{24} + L_{36} + L_{57}, \quad \text{and} \quad L_{25} + L_{36} + L_{47}$$

all contain p_1 but the lines L_{24}, L_{25}, L_{35}, and L_{36} cannot, p_1 must lie on L_{47}, L_{57}, and L_{67}; thus p_4, p_5, and p_6 all lie on the line L_{17}, and again we have five collinear points.

The lemma follows readily from this first step. Suppose we have eight points $p_1, \ldots, p_8$ in the plane imposing only seven or fewer conditions on cubics, and assume that no five are collinear. By our first step, then, any seven of the eight points p_i do impose independent conditions, and it follows that any cubic passing through *any* seven of the points contains them all. Choose three noncollinear points; call them p_1, p_2, and p_3 and let C be a conic containing the remaining points $p_4, \ldots, p_8$. By hypothesis, the cubics

$$C + L_{12}, \qquad C + L_{13}, \quad \text{and} \quad C + L_{23}$$

each contain all eight points; since each of the points p_1, p_2, and p_3 lies outside one of the lines L_{12}, L_{13}, and L_{23}, it follows that the conic C contains all eight.   Q.E.D.

The statement of the lemma also holds in case p_1 is *infinitely near* p_2, that is, if p_1 is a point on the exceptional divisor E of the blow-up $\tilde{\mathbb{P}}^2 \overset{\pi}{\to} \mathbb{P}^2$ of $\mathbb{P}^2$ at p_2. In this case, we say that a curve C in the plane contains p_1 and p_2 if C passes through p_2 and the curve $\pi^{-1}(C) - E$ contains p_1, i.e., if either C is smooth at p_2 with tangent line corresponding to p_1, or C is singular at p_2. Thus, for example, we say that the points p_1, p_2, and p_3 are collinear if the proper transform in $\tilde{\mathbb{P}}^2$ of the line $\overline{p_2 p_3}$ contains p_1. Of course, the linear condition imposed by p_1 on the system of cubics is defined only on the subsystem of cubics passing through p_2, but the independence of the conditions imposed by $p_1, \ldots, p_8$ is still well-defined.

The argument for the lemma in case p_1 is infinitely near p_2 runs as follows: as before, we first want to show that any seven points $p_1, \ldots, p_7$, with p_1 infinitely near p_2, impose independent conditions on cubics unless five are collinear. Assuming that no five are collinear, we know from the first argument that the points $p_2, \ldots, p_7$ impose six conditions; if $p_1, \ldots, p_7$ fail to impose seven, every cubic passing through $p_2, \ldots, p_7$ will contain p_1. Now, if two of the points $p_3, \ldots, p_7$ lie on the line $L = L_{12}$—say p_3 and p_4—we are done: the cubic $L_{25} + L_{36} + L_{47}$ contains p_1, and so either p_5, p_6, or p_7 lies on L, giving us five collinear points. If exactly one of the points $p_3, \ldots, p_7$—say p_3—lies on L, then the cubics

$$L_{24} + L_{35} + L_{67}, \qquad L_{24} + L_{36} + L_{57}, \quad \text{and} \quad L_{25} + L_{36} + L_{47}$$

all contain p_1, and so must be singular at p_2; thus p_2 lies on L_{47}, L_{57}, and L_{67}, i.e., p_4, p_5, and p_6 all lie on the line L_{27}. If, finally, none of the points $p_3, \ldots, p_7$ lies on L, then since the cubic

$$L_{27} + L_{34} + L_{56}$$

contains p_1, either L_{34} or L_{56}—say L_{34}—must contain p_2. In this case, take L' any line through p_7 missing all the other points p_i; the cubic

$$L_{23} + L_{56} + L'$$

contains p_1; thus p_2 lies on L_{56}. But then since

$$L_{27} + L_{35} + L_{46}$$

contains p_1, either L_{35} or L_{46} must pass through p_2, and in either case it follows that p_2, p_3, p_4, p_5, and p_6 are collinear.

The lemma now follows just as in the original case: given eight points $p_1, \ldots, p_8$, with p_1 infinitely near p_2 and no five collinear, by the first step any conic containing all but any three noncollinear points p_i contains all eight.   Q.E.D.

We leave to the reader the proof of the lemma in three additional cases: when p_1 and p_2 are infinitely near p_3, when p_1 is infinitely near p_2 and p_3 is infinitely near p_4, and when p_1 is infinitely near p_2, which is itself infinitely near p_3.

A note: this lemma will reappear as a consequence of the general duality theory discussed in Section 4 of Chapter 5.

Let us return now to the blow-up $\pi \colon \tilde{\mathbb{P}}^2 \to \mathbb{P}^2$ of $\mathbb{P}^2$ at six points $p_1, \ldots, p_6$ as specified earlier, and the linear system $|\tilde{C}| = |\pi^*3H - E_1 - \cdots - E_6|$. As an immediate consequence of the lemma, we see that the points $p_1, \ldots, p_6$ impose independent conditions on cubics, so that $\dim |\tilde{C}| = 3$. The remaining assertions 3a–d and 4a and b likewise follow from the lemma: respectively, they may be restated as saying that the points $p_1, \ldots, p_6, p$ and q impose independent conditions on cubics in case

3a. $p \neq q \in \mathbb{P}^2 - \{p_1, \ldots, p_6\}$,
3b. p infinitely near p_i, $q \in \mathbb{P}^2 - \{p_1, \ldots, p_6\}$,
3c. p infinitely near p_i, q infinitely near p_j,
3d. $p \neq q$ infinitely near p_i,
4a. p infinitely near $q \in \mathbb{P}^2 - \{p_1, \ldots, p_6\}$,
4b. p infinitely near q infinitely near p_i.

In each of these cases, we see that since no three of the points p_i are collinear, no five of the points $p_1, \ldots, p_6, p, q$ are; and since the points p_i do not all lie on a conic, certainly $p_1, \ldots, p_6$, p and q do not. By the lemma, then, the points $p_1, \ldots, p_6$, q and p impose independent conditions on cubics, and the map $\iota_{\tilde{C}}$ embeds $\tilde{\mathbb{P}}^2$ as a cubic $S \subset \mathbb{P}^3$.

Before proceeding to study the geometry of S, we make one observation. Recall that a smooth quadric surface $S \subset \mathbb{P}^3$ may be obtained by blowing up two points q_1, q_2 on $\mathbb{P}^2$, and blowing down the proper transform in $\tilde{\mathbb{P}}^2_{q_1 q_2}$ of the line $\overline{q_1 q_2}$. The reader may wish to verify, by the techniques of the preceding argument, that the linear system $|\pi^*2H - E_1 - E_2|$ on $\tilde{\mathbb{P}}^2_{q_1 q_2}$ — corresponding to conic curves in $\mathbb{P}^2$ passing through q_1 and q_2 — does indeed give a map of $\tilde{\mathbb{P}}^2_{q_1 q_2}$ onto a quadric surface in $\mathbb{P}^3$, one-to-one except along the proper transform of $\overline{q_1 q_2}$.

Now return to our cubic surface $S \cong \tilde{\mathbb{P}}^2_{p_1, \ldots, p_6}$ in $\mathbb{P}^3$. Consider first the image of the exceptional divisors $E_1, \ldots, E_6$ in S. Since $\tilde{C} \cdot E_i = 1$, we see that each of the curves E_i has degree 1 in $\mathbb{P}^3$, hence must be a line. Likewise, if F_{ij} $(j > i)$ is the proper transform in $\tilde{\mathbb{P}}^2$ of the line $L_{ij} = \overline{p_i p_j}$ in $\mathbb{P}^2$, then

$$F_{ij} \cdot \tilde{C} = (\pi^* L_{ij} - E_i - E_j)(\pi^* 3H - \sum E_k)$$
$$= L_{ij} \cdot 3H - 2 = 3 - 2 = 1,$$

so that the image of F_{ij} in $S \subset \mathbb{P}^3$ is again a line; there are 15 such lines. Note that

$$F_{ij} \cdot F_{ij} = (\pi^* L_{ij} - E_i - E_j)(\pi^* L_{ij} - E_i - E_j)$$
$$= L_{ij} \cdot L_{ij} - 2 = -1$$

so that the lines F_{ij} are exceptional divisors of the first kind on S. Also, if G_i is the proper transform in $\tilde{\mathbb{P}}^2$ of the conic C_i in $\mathbb{P}^2$ through the five points $p_1, \ldots, \hat{p}_i, \ldots, p_6$,

$$G_i \cdot \tilde{C} = \left(\pi^* C_i - \sum_{j \neq i} E_j\right)\left(\pi^* 3H - \sum E_i\right)$$
$$= C_i \cdot 3H - 5 = 6 - 5 = 1.$$

Thus $G_i \subset S \subset \mathbb{P}^3$ is again a line, and

$$G_i \cdot G_i = \left(\pi^* C_i - \sum_{i \neq j} E_j\right)\left(\pi^* C_i - \sum_{i \neq j} E_j\right)$$
$$= C_i \cdot C_i - 5 = 4 - 5 = -1$$

so G_i is exceptional of the first kind.

Now if L is any line in S, we consider the locus $\pi(L) \subset \mathbb{P}^2$. Assuming L is not one of the exceptional divisors E_i, L can meet each line E_i at most once, and that transversely. Thus $\pi(L)$ will be a smooth rational curve in $\mathbb{P}^2$, hence by the genus formula either a line or a conic. Now

$$L = \pi^* \pi(L) - \sum_{p_i \in \pi(L)} E_i$$

and so

$$1 = \tilde{C} \cdot L = \left(\pi^* 3H - \sum E_i \right) \cdot \left(\pi^* \pi(L) - \sum_{p_i \in \pi(L)} E_i \right)$$

$$= 3H \cdot \pi(L) + \sum_{p_i \in \pi(L)} E_i \cdot E_i.$$

This tells us that $\pi(L)$ must contain exactly two of the points p_i in case $\pi(L)$ is a line, five of the points p_i if $\pi(L)$ is a conic, and hence that L must be one of the lines F_{ij}, G_i.

Thus there are exactly 27 *lines on the cubic surface we have constructed*: *six* E_i's, 15 F_{ij}'s, *and six* G_i's. The incidence relations among the lines are clearly seen from their description as curves in $\mathbb{P}^2$: the line E_i will meet all lines on S coming from plane curves passing through p_i, that is, F_{ij} for any j and G_j for any $j \neq i$. The line F_{ij} will meet, apart from E_i and E_j, any line coming from a curve in $\mathbb{P}^2$ having a point of intersection with $\overline{p_i p_j}$ other than p_i or p_j, that is, F_{kl} for $k, l \neq i, j$, G_i, and G_j. The line G_i will meet E_j for $j \neq i$, and F_{ij} for all j. Note in particular that *every line of* S *meets exactly ten other lines*; some other interesting aspects of this configuration of 27 lines are:

1. *There are exactly* 72 *sets of six disjoint lines on* S: these are

$$\{ E_i \} \tag{1},$$

$$\{ E_i, E_j, E_k, F_{lm}, F_{mn}, F_{ln} \} \tag{20},$$

$$\{ E_i, G_i, F_{jl}, F_{jk}, F_{jm}, F_{jn} \} \tag{30},$$

$$\{ G_i, G_j, G_k, F_{lm}, F_{mn}, F_{ln} \} \tag{20},$$

and

$$\{ G_i \} \tag{1}.$$

As the reader may verify, there is a unique automorphism of the configuration of 27 lines on S (not an automorphism of S) that carries any of these 72 into any other, in any assignment; thus *there are* $72 \cdot 6! = 51{,}840$ *symmetries of the configuration of lines on* S.

2. *If two of the lines* L, L' *on* S *intersect, then there is a unique other line on* S *that intersects them both*: the hyperplane in $\mathbb{P}^3$ containing L and L' must intersect S in a cubic curve including L and L', hence in a third line. In fact, the planes in $\mathbb{P}^3$ that meet S in a union of three lines are

$$H_{ij} = \overline{E_i G_j F_{ij}} \quad \text{and} \quad H_{ijklmn} = \overline{F_{ij} F_{kl} F_{mn}}.$$

3. Recall from our discussion of Grassmannians in Section 6 of Chapter 1 that if L_1, L_2, L_3, L_4 are four disjoint lines in $\mathbb{P}^3$, then there are exactly two lines $L, L' \subset \mathbb{P}^3$ meeting all four. Now if the lines L_i all lie on S,

then the lines L and L' meet S in four points, hence must also lie on S. Thus *for any four disjoint lines on a cubic surface S there will be exactly two other lines on S meeting all four.*

We now want to show that every smooth cubic surface S in $\mathbb{P}^3$ can be obtained by blowing up $\mathbb{P}^2$ in six points. We first locate six exceptional divisors on S to blow down; to find these we look for the cohomology classes they represent. Let $S_0 = \tilde{\mathbb{P}}^2_{p_1,\ldots,p_6}$ be the cubic surface constructed above, and let S be an arbitrary smooth cubic in $\mathbb{P}^3$. Let $W = |3H| \cong \mathbb{P}^{19}$ be the linear system of all cubic surfaces in $\mathbb{P}^3$, and consider the incidence correspondence

$$X = \{(S,p): p \in S\} \subset W \times \mathbb{P}^3.$$

The subset $V \subset W$ of singular cubics is a proper analytic subvariety of W, and so $W - V$ is connected; take $\gamma: I \to W - V$ a C^∞ embedding of the unit interval $I \subset \mathbb{R}$ in $W - V$ with $\gamma(0) = S_0$, $\gamma(1) = S$. Let $\pi: X \to W$ be the projection map on the first factor. The inverse image $X' = \pi^{-1}(\gamma(I)) \subset X$ is a smooth manifold, and the map $\gamma^{-1} \circ \pi: X' \to I$ is smooth. By standard manifold theory, then, X' is diffeomorphic to the product $I \times S_0$, and consequently S is diffeomorphic to S_0: since X' is compact and the map $\gamma^{-1} \circ \pi$ is smooth, we can by a partition of unity lift the vector field $-\partial/\partial t$ on I to a vector field v on X'; the flow $\varphi_t = \varphi_t(v)$ on X' will then map $\pi^{-1}(\gamma(t))$ diffeomorphically onto $\pi^{-1}(\gamma(0)) = S_0$. Note also that if $H \subset \mathbb{P}^3$ is any hyperplane meeting S and S_0 transversely, the set V' of cubic surfaces tangent to H is again an analytic subvariety of W. We may therefore choose our path γ to lie in $W - V - V'$, so that $Y' = X' \cap (W \times H)$ will be a submanifold of X' mapping smoothly onto I. Take v' a vector field on Y' lifting $-\partial/\partial t$ and choose v to extend v'; the diffeomorphism $\varphi = \varphi_1: S \to S_0$ will then carry the hyperplane section $H \cap S$ to $H \cap S_0$. This argument shows in general that *any two smooth hypersurfaces of degree d in $\mathbb{P}^n$ are diffeomorphic via a map carrying a hyperplane section of one to a hyperplane section of the other.*

Now by the adjunction formula applied to $S \subset \mathbb{P}^3$,

$$\begin{aligned} K_S &= (K_{\mathbb{P}^3} + S)|_S \\ &= -H|_S \end{aligned}$$

and similarly $K_{S_0} = -H|_{S_0}$. Since our diffeomorphism $\varphi: S \to S_0$ carries $S \cap H$ to $S_0 \cap H$, we deduce that

$$c_1(K_S) = \varphi^* c_1(K_{S_0}).$$

Let $\eta_{E_i} \in H^2(S_0, \mathbb{Z})$ be the cohomology class of the exceptional divisor $E_i \subset S_0 = \tilde{\mathbb{P}}^2_{p_1,\ldots,p_6}$, and set $\mu_i = \varphi^* \eta_{E_i}$. Since K_S is negative, it clearly cannot have any global sections, so $h^{2,0}(S) = h^{0,2}(S) = 0$ and the classes $\mu_i \in H^2(S, \mathbb{Z})$ are necessarily of type $(1,1)$. By the Lefschetz $(1,1)$ theorem, there exists a holomorphic line bundle $L_i \to S$ with $c_1(L_i) = \mu_i$. Since intersection numbers are topologically invariant,

$$L_i \cdot L_i = -1, \qquad L_i \cdot L_j = 0 \qquad (i \neq j)$$
$$L_i \cdot K_S = E_i \cdot K_{S_0} = -1.$$

Applying the Riemann-Roch

$$\chi(L_i) = \frac{L_i \cdot L_i - L_i \cdot K_S}{2} + \chi(\mathcal{O}_S) = \chi(\mathcal{O}_S).$$

Now, as remarked, $h^{2,0}(S) = 0$; by the Lefschetz hyperplane theorem

$$H^1(S, \mathbb{Z}) \cong H^1(\mathbb{P}^2, \mathbb{Z}) = 0,$$

so $h^{1,0}(S) = 0$ and consequently $\chi(\mathcal{O}_S) = 1$. Moreover, by Kodaira-Serre duality $h^2(L_i) = h^0(K_S - L_i)$; but

$$\deg(K_S - L_i)|_{S \cap H} = K_S \cdot H_S - L_i \cdot H_S = K_{S_0} \cdot H_{S_0} - E_i \cdot H_{S_0} = -3 - 1 = -4,$$

so $K_S - L_i$ cannot have any global sections. Thus

$$h^0(L_i) \geq 1,$$

so L_i has a nonzero global section, and μ_i is the cohomology class of an effective divisor D_i.

Since $D_i \cdot H_S = 1$, D_i is a line on S in $\mathbb{P}^3$. Thus D_i is a smooth rational curve on S with self-intersection -1 and so can be blown down. Moreover, since $D_i \cdot D_j = 0$, the lines D_i on S are disjoint, so that the image $\pi_i(D_j)$ of D_j under the blowing-down π_i of D_i is again a smooth rational curve of self-intersection -1. Thus we can blow down all six divisors D_i in turn; let $\tilde{S}$ be the surface obtained by blowing them down. We observe first that the Betti numbers of $\tilde{S}$ are

$$b^0(\tilde{S}) = b^4(\tilde{S}) = 1,$$
$$b^1(\tilde{S}) = b^3(\tilde{S}) = 0,$$
$$b^2(\tilde{S}) = b^2(S) - 6 = 7 - 6 = 1.$$

Note also that if $\pi : S \to \tilde{S}$ is the blowing-down map, then

$$K_S = \pi^* K_{\tilde{S}} + D_1 + \cdots + D_6,$$

and since K_S is negative, we deduce that for any curve $D \subset \tilde{S}$,

$$D \cdot K_{\tilde{S}} = \pi^* D \cdot (K_S - D_1 - \cdots - D_6)$$
$$\leq \pi^* D \cdot K_S < 0;$$

so the bundle $K_{\tilde{S}}$ is certainly not positive. Consequently our argument that S is $\mathbb{P}^2$ blown up six times will be complete once we prove the

Lemma. *If M is an algebraic surface with the same Betti numbers as* $\mathbb{P}^2$ *and* K_M *is not positive, then* $M \cong \mathbb{P}^2$.

Proof. Since $b_1(M)=0$, we have $\text{Pic}(M) \cong H^2(M,\mathbb{Z}) \cong \mathbb{Z}$. Since M is algebraic, there exists a positive line bundle L' on M; let L be the generator of $\text{Pic}(M)$ such that $L'=L^n$ for some $n>0$. (Note that L' positive implies that L is positive). By hypothesis, $H^2(M,\mathbb{C})=\mathbb{C}$ and since $H^{1,1}(M,\mathbb{C})=\mathbb{C}$, we have $h^{2,0}(M)=0$; $b^1(M)=0$ implies $h^{1,0}(M)=0$ and hence $\chi(\mathcal{O}_M)=1$. The topological Euler characteristic $\chi(M)=3$, and so by Noether's formula

$$1 = \chi(\mathcal{O}) = \frac{K_M \cdot K_M + \chi(M)}{12} \Rightarrow K_M \cdot K_M = 9.$$

Since $c_1(L)$ generates $H^2(M,\mathbb{Z})$, by Poincaré duality

$$L \cdot L = (c_1(L) \cup c_1(L))[M] = \pm 1,$$

and since L^k is effective for $k \gg 0$ and L is positive,

$$L \cdot L^k = k(L \cdot L) > 0 \Rightarrow L \cdot L = 1.$$

Thus, if we write $K_M = L^m$, m must be negative since K_M is not positive, and so

$$9 = K_M \cdot K_M = m^2(L \cdot L) \Rightarrow m = -3,$$

i.e., $K_M = L^{-3}$. Apply Riemann-Roch for L:

$$h^0(L) - h^1(L) + h^2(L) = 1 + \frac{L \cdot L - K \cdot L}{2} = 1 + \frac{1-(-3)}{2} = 3.$$

But $h^2(L) = h^0(K-L) = h^0(L^{-4}) = 0$ since L^{-4} is negative. Also, by the Kodaira vanishing theorem,

$$h^1(L) = h^1(K+4L) = 0,$$

since L^4 is positive. Consequently

$$h^0(L) = 3.$$

Now if $D \in |L|$ is any divisor in the linear system $|L|$, D must be irreducible: if $D = D_1 + D_2$ where $D_1, D_2 > 0$, we would obtain

$$1 = L \cdot L = L \cdot D_1 + L \cdot D_2$$

Moreover, D must be a smooth curve: if $p \in D$ is a singular point, since $\dim |L| = 2$ we can find $D' \neq D \in |L|$ such that $p \in D'$; we would then have

$$1 = L \cdot L = D \cdot D' > 1.$$

The genus of the curve D is given by the adjunction formula:

$$\pi(D) = \frac{D \cdot D + D \cdot K}{2} + 1 = \frac{1-3}{2} + 1 = 0,$$

i.e., $D \cong \mathbb{P}^1$. The restriction $L|_D$ is then the hyperplane (i.e., point) bundle $H_{\mathbb{P}^1}$; and from the cohomology of the exact sequence

$$0 \to \mathcal{O}_M \to \mathcal{O}_M(L) \to \mathcal{O}_{\mathbb{P}^1}(H_{\mathbb{P}^1}) \to 0$$

and the fact that $H^1(M, \mathcal{O}_M) = 0$, it follows that

$$H^0(M, \mathcal{O}_M(L)) \to H^0(\mathbb{P}^1, \mathcal{O}_{\mathbb{P}^1}(H_{\mathbb{P}^1})) \to 0.$$

$H_{\mathbb{P}^1}$ is very ample on $\mathbb{P}^1$ so the linear system $|L|$ separates points on each curve $D \in |L|$. But since $\dim |L| = 2$, we see that for every two points $p, q \in M$ we can find a curve $D \in |L|$ passing through p and q. Thus the linear system $|L|$ has no base points, and the map

$$\iota_L : M \to \mathbb{P}^2$$

separates points; it follows that ι_L is surjective, and hence is an isomorphism. Q.E.D.

We have now shown that every smooth cubic surface $S \subset \mathbb{P}^3$ is of the form $\tilde{\mathbb{P}}^2_{p_1,\ldots,p_6}$. Suppose that three of the points p_i lay on a line $L \subset \mathbb{P}^2$. Then the proper transform $\tilde{L}$ of L in S would be a smooth rational curve of self-intersection $1 \cdot 1 - 3 = -2$, and by the adjunction formula,

$$0 = \pi(\tilde{L}) = \frac{\tilde{L} \cdot \tilde{L} + K_S \cdot \tilde{L}}{2} + 1,$$

i.e., $K_S \cdot \tilde{L} = 0$. But the canonical bundle of S is negative, a contradiction. Similarly, suppose that the six points p_i lay on a conic curve $C \subset \mathbb{P}^2$. By the above C would have to be smooth, and so its proper transform $\tilde{C}$ in S would again be a smooth rational curve with self-intersection $2 \cdot 2 - 6 = -2$; the same argument shows this cannot happen. Thus if $S \cong \tilde{\mathbb{P}}^2_{p_1,\ldots,p_6}$, the points p_i necessarily satisfy the conditions 1 and 2 of p. 480; thus we see that

Every smooth cubic surface $S \subset \mathbb{P}^3$ may be obtained by blowing up $\mathbb{P}^2$ at six points $p_1, \ldots, p_6$, no three collinear and not all six on a conic, and embedding the blow-up in $\mathbb{P}^3$ by the proper transform of the linear system of cubics passing through the points p_i.

In particular, we see that our discussion of the lines on the surface constructed before applies to all smooth cubics.

As we will see in the following sections, the quadric and cubic surfaces are the only smooth hypersurfaces in $\mathbb{P}^3$ that may be obtained from $\mathbb{P}^2$ by a series of blow-ups and blow downs.

2. RATIONAL MAPS

Rational and Birational Maps

One of the basic geometric operations on algebraic varieties $V \subset \mathbb{P}^n$ is the projection

$$\pi_p : V \dashrightarrow \mathbb{P}^{n-1}$$

of a variety V from a point $p \in \mathbb{P}^n$ not lying on V to a hyperplane. In Chapter 2 we saw that, if V is a curve, the map π_p is well-defined even in case p lies on V: π_p, defined a priori only on $V - \{p\}$, may be extended by mapping p to the image in $\mathbb{P}^{n-1}$ of the tangent line to V at p. In general, however, if V has dimension greater than one and $p \in V$, the map π_p is not well-defined at, nor can it be extended over, the point p. This is not hard to see: for any point $q \in \mathbb{P}^{n-1} \cap T_p(V)$ in the image of the tangent plane to V at p there is a sequence $\{q_i\}$ of points on $V - \{p\}$ tending to p, such that $\pi_p(q_i)$ tends to q. Despite the fact that it is not everywhere defined, however, π_p is a natural geometric operation—as we have already had occasion to see in the previous section—and it is recognized as such in algebraic geometry. π_p is an example of a large class of transformations called *rational maps*, which we will now discuss.

   We begin with a definition.

DEFINITION.   A *rational* (or *meromorphic*) map of a complex manifold M to projective space $\mathbb{P}^n$ is a map

$$f: z \longrightarrow [1, f_1(z), \ldots, f_n(z)]$$

given by n global meromorphic functions on M. A rational map $f: M \to N$ to the algebraic variety $N \subset \mathbb{P}^n$ is a rational map $f: M \to \mathbb{P}^n$ whose image lies in N.

   One difficulty in understanding rational maps $f: M \to \mathbb{P}^n$ is the fact that they are not, strictly speaking, maps: they need not be defined on all of M. Let us first see how this occurs.

   As we saw in several contexts in the chapter on curves, any collection $f_1, \ldots, f_n$ of meromorphic functions on a Riemann surface S serves to define a holomorphic map

$$f: z \mapsto [1, f_1(z), \ldots, f_n(z)]$$

from S to $\mathbb{P}^n$: while f is defined a priori only away from the poles of the functions f_i, at any point $p = (z = 0) \in S$ we may set

$$m = \max\{-\operatorname{ord}_p(f_i)\}_i,$$

and the map

$$\tilde{f}: z \mapsto [z^m, z^m f_1(z), \ldots, z^m f_n(z)]$$

extends f over p. The fact that we are using here to extend f is simply that the point p is a divisor on the Riemann surface S; i.e., it is defined by a single function z, and any function vanishing at p must be divisible by z. This, of course, fails in higher codimension, and so we may expect that a general rational map will not be everywhere defined. The simplest case is the rational map

$$f: \mathbb{C}^2 \longrightarrow \mathbb{P}^1$$

given by the single meromorphic function $f(x,y)=y/x$, i.e., by

$$f(x,y) = \left[1, \frac{y}{x}\right] = [x,y]:$$

f is well-defined and holomorphic away from the origin $(0,0)\in\mathbb{C}^2$, but cannot be extended to a map on all of $\mathbb{C}^2$.

Another way to represent a rational map $f: M \to \mathbb{P}^n$ is by an $(n+1)$-tuple of holomorphic functions: if f is given by meromorphic functions $f_1,\ldots,f_n$, write each of the functions locally as

$$f_i = \frac{g_i}{h_i}$$

with h_i, g_i holomorphic and relatively prime; let h_0 be the least common multiple of the functions h_i. Then f may be given locally by

$$f: z \mapsto [1, f_1(z),\ldots,f_n(z)] = [h_0(z), f_1(z)h_0(z),\ldots,f_n(z)h_0(z)];$$

of course the functions $\tilde{f}_0 = h_0$ and $\tilde{f}_i = h_0 f_i$ are holomorphic, and f will be well-defined away from their common zero locus $\cap(\tilde{f}_i)$.

Note that the functions $\tilde{f}_i$ have no common factors: if k is any irreducible function dividing h_0 exactly m times, then k^m divides h_i for some i. Since k cannot then divide g_i, it follows that k cannot divide $f_i \cdot h_0 = g_i \cdot h_0/h_i$. Thus no function vanishing at p can divide all the functions $h_0, h_0 f_i$. It follows that the locus $\cap(\tilde{f}_i)$ contains no divisors, i.e., that *a rational map* f *is defined away from a subvariety of codimension 2 or more.* Conversely, if $V \subset M$ is any analytic subvariety of codimension at least 2, $f: M - V \to \mathbb{P}^n$ a holomorphic map, then by the Levi theorem from Section 2 of Chapter 3 the pullback to $M - V$ of the Euclidean coordinate functions $x_i = X_i/X_0$, $i=1,\ldots,n$, on $\mathbb{P}^n$ extend to meromorphic functions f_i on M; the map $f=[1, f_1(z),\ldots,f_n(z)]$ is thus rational. This affords a second point of view on rational maps, namely

A rational map

$$f: M \longrightarrow N$$

from the complex manifold M *to the algebraic variety* N *is given by a holomorphic map*

$$f: M - V \longrightarrow N$$

defined on the complement of a subvariety V *of codimension 2 or more in* M.

Next, we would like to relate rational maps to $\mathbb{P}^n$ to linear systems of divisors and sections of line bundles, as we have done with holomorphic maps. Let $L \to M$ be a line bundle and $\sigma_0,\ldots,\sigma_n \in H^0(M, \mathcal{O}(L))$ a collection of linearly independent global holomorphic sections of L. Then the meromorphic functions

$$f_i = \frac{\sigma_i}{\sigma_0}$$

determine a rational map

$$f: M \longrightarrow \mathbb{P}^{n^*}.$$

In terms of divisors, suppose $|D_\lambda|_{\lambda \in \mathbb{P}^n}$ is a linear system on M. Let E be the fixed component of $\{D_\lambda\}$—that is, the largest effective divisor such that $D_\lambda - E > 0$ for every λ—so that the divisors $\{D'_\lambda = D_\lambda - E\}$ form a linear system with base locus of codimension at least 2. Then we may define a rational map

$$f: M \longrightarrow \mathbb{P}^{n^*}$$

by setting

$$f(p) = \{\lambda : D'_\lambda \ni p\} \in \mathbb{P}^{n^*};$$

this is well-defined away from the base locus of $\{D'_\lambda\}$. Of course, if $\{D_\lambda\}$ is the linear system

$$D_\lambda = (\lambda_0 \sigma_0 + \cdots + \lambda_n \sigma_n)$$

associated to the vector space $\{\sigma_0, \ldots, \sigma_n\}$ of sections of the line bundle L above, then the maps f given by the system $\{D_\lambda\}$ and the meromorphic functions σ_i / σ_0 are the same.

Note that while any linear system gives in this way a rational map, we have an exact correspondence

$$\left\{ \begin{array}{l} \text{linear systems of divisors} \\ \text{on } M \text{ with base locus} \\ \text{of codimension } \geqslant 2 \end{array} \right\} \longleftrightarrow \left\{ \begin{array}{l} \text{rational maps} \\ f: M \to \mathbb{P}^n, \text{ up to} \\ \text{automorphisms of } \mathbb{P}^n \end{array} \right\}$$

From yet another viewpoint, we may consider a rational map $f: M \to \mathbb{P}^n$ as a subvariety of $M \times \mathbb{P}^n$. Explicitly, we define the *graph* $\Gamma_f \subset M \times \mathbb{P}^n$ of f to be the closure in $\mathbb{P}^n$ of the graph

$$\{(p, X) : f(p) = X\}$$

of f where defined. Note that this is an analytic subvariety: if f is given locally by

$$f: p \mapsto [g_0(p), \ldots, g_n(p)],$$

where $g_0, \ldots, g_n$ are holomorphic functions with no common factor, then Γ_f will be contained in the variety

$$\Gamma_0 = (g_i(p) \cdot X_j - g_j(p) X_i = 0)$$

and will agree with Γ_0 over the domain of definition M_0 of f in M. Γ_f is thus the irreducible component of Γ_0 containing $\Gamma_0 \cap M_0 \times \mathbb{P}^n$. Conversely, suppose $\Gamma \subset M \times \mathbb{P}^n$ is any k-dimensional analytic subvariety having intersection number

$$^{\#}(\Gamma, \{p\} \times \mathbb{P}^n) = 1$$

with the fibers of $M \times \mathbb{P}^n$ over M. For each $p \in M$, Γ will either meet the fiber $\{p\} \times \mathbb{P}^n$ transversely in a single point $(p, f(p))$—in which case by the implicit function theorem Γ is the graph of a holomorphic map near p —or have at least a curve in common with it. The former is clearly generically the case. Indeed, the locus V of points $p \in M$ where the latter case occurs must have codimension at least 2: if V were of dimension $k - 1$, the inverse image of V in Γ would have dimension k, and so would form a component of the irreducible variety Γ. Γ thus defines a rational map $f: M \to \mathbb{P}^n$. We have then:

A rational map $f: M \to \mathbb{P}^n$ *is given by an irreducible k-dimensional subvariety of* $M \times \mathbb{P}^n$ *having intersection number* 1 *with the fibers* $\{p\} \times \mathbb{P}^n$ *of* $M \times \mathbb{P}^n$ *over* M.

One point that emerges readily from this description is that for M compact, the image of M under a rational map $f: M \to \mathbb{P}^n$—that is, the closure of the image of f where defined—is an algebraic subvariety of $\mathbb{P}^n$. This follows from the proper mapping theorem, once we observe that the image of the closure of the graph Γ_f of f in $M \times \mathbb{P}^n$ is indeed just the closure of the image of f.

Birational Maps. We say that a rational map $f: M \to N$ is birational if there exists a rational map $g: N \to M$ such that $f \circ g$ is the identity as a rational map; two algebraic varieties are said to be *birationally isomorphic*, or simply *birational*, if there exists a birational map between them. In particular, a variety is called *rational* if it is birational to $\mathbb{P}^n$, i.e., if there exist n meromorphic functions on it providing local coordinates almost everywhere. Note that a rational map $f: M \to N$ is birational if and only if it is generically one-to-one: if, for generic $p \in N$, $f^{-1}(p)$ is a single point, then the graph $\Gamma_f \subset M \times N$ of f has intersection number 1 with the fibers $M \times \{p\}$, and so defines an inverse rational map.

Birational isomorphism represents an important intermediate notion of equivalence among varieties. Birational varieties are alike in more ways than they differ; to the classical geometers they were different manifestations of the same variety. This point of view is immediately clear to an algebraist, in whose terms the local rings of functions around points $p \in M$, $q \in N$ on two varieties M and N are isomorphic as local rings if and only if there is a birational map $f: M \to N$ taking p to q and biregular around p. It will take us somewhat longer to appreciate the close relationship between birational manifolds. To start, note the following:

Let $f: M \to N$ be a rational map, defined and holomorphic on the complement $M - V$ of a subvariety V of codimension $\geqslant 2$. If φ is any global holomorphic p-form on N, then by Hartogs' theorem the pullback $f^*\varphi$ on $M - V$ extends uniquely to a p-form on all of M; thus we have a map

$$f^*: \ H^0(N, \Omega_N^p) \longrightarrow H^0(M, \Omega_M^p)$$

for each p. More generally, if $E_M \to M$ is any contravariant tensor bundle, the natural map f^* from sections of E_N over N to sections of E_M over $M - V$ gives a map

$$f^*: \ H^0(N, \mathcal{O}(E_N)) \longrightarrow H^0(M, \mathcal{O}(E_M)).$$

If f is a birational map, of course, then all the functions f^* are isomorphisms; *thus the space of sections of any contravariant holomorphic tensor bundle is a birational invariant*; in particular, the Hodge numbers $h^{p,0}(M)$ are. Several of these invariants have been given names:

1. The number $h^{1,0}(S)$ of holomorphic 1-forms on a Riemann surface is its genus $g(S)$. In general, the number $h^{n,0}(M)$ of holomorphic forms of top degree on a compact complex n-manifold M is called the *geometric genus* of M and denoted $p_g(M)$.

2. An alternative generalization of the notion of genus is the number

$$p_a(M) = h^{n,0}(M) - h^{n-1,0}(M) + \cdots + (-1)^{n-1} h^{1,0}(M),$$

called the *arithmetic genus* of M. Using $h^{q,0}(M) = h^{0,q}(M)$ we can also write

$$p_a(M) = (-1)^n (\chi(\mathcal{O}_M) - 1).$$

3. The number $h^{1,0}(M)$ of holomorphic 1-forms on a compact complex manifold M is often denoted $q(M)$ and called the *irregularity* of M. If M is Kähler, of course, the irregularity is simply half the first Betti number.

4. Of interest also are the dimensions

$$P_n(M) = h^0(M, \mathcal{O}(K_M^n)),$$

of the spaces of sections of the nth powers of the canonical bundle, called collectively the *plurigenera* of M.

5. The fundamental group $\pi_1(M)$ of an algebraic variety is also a birational invariant: suppose

$$f: \ M \longrightarrow N$$

is a birational map, defined away from the subvariety $U \subset M$ and one-to-one away from the subvariety $V \subset M$. If γ is any loop on M, then we can find a loop γ' in M homotopic to γ and disjoint from U; and the class of $f(\gamma')$ on N will be independent of the choice of γ': since U has real codimension at least 4, if $\gamma' - \gamma''$ is the boundary of a disc in M, then it is the boundary of a disc in $M - U$. We thus obtain maps

$$f_* : \pi_1(M) \longrightarrow \pi_1(M)$$

and

$$f_*^{-1} : \pi_1(N) \longrightarrow \pi_1(M)$$

inverse to one another; and so $\pi_1(M) \cong \pi_1(N)$.

Another way in which a birational map carries structure is this: if $f : M \to N$ is a birational map, we may define two maps

$$f_* : \mathrm{Div}(M) \longrightarrow \mathrm{Div}(N),$$

called the *proper transform* and the *total transform*. The proper transform of a divisor D in M is defined to be the closure in N of the image of D under f where defined, while the total transform is defined to be the image in N of the inverse image of D in the graph $\Gamma \subset M \times N$ of f. The reader may verify that the total transform map preserves linear equivalence while the proper transform map does not.

Examples of Rational and Birational Maps

1. Any holomorphic map $M \to \mathbb{P}^n$ is trivially rational.
2. If $\tilde{M} \xrightarrow{\pi} M$ is the blow-up of an algebraic variety M at a collection of points $\{p_i\}$, then the inverse map

$$M - \{p_i\} \xrightarrow{\pi^{-1}} \tilde{M}$$

is clearly rational, so π is a birational isomorphism. A holomorphic map $f : \tilde{M} \to \mathbb{P}^n$ thus gives a rational map from M to $\mathbb{P}^n$; in fact—as we shall prove later in this section in case M is a surface—the converse is true: any rational map $f : M \to \mathbb{P}^n$ is induced by a holomorphic map on a (possibly multiple) blow-up $\tilde{M}$ of M.

3. As mentioned at the beginning of this section, the projection map

$$\pi_p : C - \{p\} \longrightarrow \mathbb{P}^{n-1}$$

of a curve $C \subset \mathbb{P}^n$ from a point p on C into a hyperplane in $\mathbb{P}^n$ extends to a holomorphic map on all of C. In general, if $V \subset \mathbb{P}^n$ is any variety, $p \in V$ any point, the projection map π_p of V from p to a hyperplane is a rational map. Indeed, π_p may always be extended to a holomorphic map on the blow-up $\tilde{V}$ of V at p by sending a point $r \in E$ in the exceptional divisor to the point of intersection of $\mathbb{P}^{n-1}$ with the tangent line to V at p corresponding to r.

Note that in case V is a quadric hypersurface the map π_p is a birational isomorphism. We have already seen this in the case of Q a quadric surface in $\mathbb{P}^3$, where the map π_p consists of the blow-up of the point p, followed by the blowing down of the two lines of Q through p.

4. If $\varphi: M \to \mathbb{P}^n$ is any holomorphic map of a k-dimensional manifold to $\mathbb{P}^n$, the associated *Gauss map*

$$\mathcal{G}: M^* \longrightarrow G(k+1, n+1),$$

sending any smooth point of the image to its tangent plane in $\mathbb{P}^n$, is a rational map: explicitly, if φ is given locally by

$$\varphi(z) = [\varphi_0(z), \ldots, \varphi_n(z)],$$

then the map $\mathcal{G}$ is given in terms of the Plücker embedding

$$G(k+1, n+1) \longrightarrow \mathbb{P}(\wedge^{k+1} \mathbb{C}^{n+1})$$

by the minors of the Jacobian matrix $\partial \varphi_i / \partial z_\alpha$ of φ.

5. If $V \subset \mathbb{P}^n$ is any variety, we may define a rational map

$$V^k \longrightarrow G(k, n+1),$$

from the k-fold product of V with itself to the Grassmannian of $(k-1)$-planes in $\mathbb{P}^n$, by

$$(v_1, \ldots, v_k) \longrightarrow \overline{v_1 \cdots v_k}.$$

The graph of this map is just the main irreducible component of incidence correspondence $I \subset V^k \times G(k, n+1)$ given by

$$I = \{(p_1, \ldots, p_k; \Lambda): p_i \in \Lambda \quad \text{for all } i\}.$$

6. We previously encountered the two birational maps

$$\mu^{(g)}: S^{(g)} \longrightarrow J(S)$$

and

$$\mu^{(g-1)}: S^{(g-1)} \longrightarrow \Theta$$

from the g-fold symmetric product of a Riemann surface S to its Jacobian $J(S)$, and from the $(g-1)$st symmetric product of S to the theta-divisor $\Theta \subset J(S)$. The latter map involves both of the two previous examples of rational maps: if $\mathcal{G}: \Theta \to \mathbb{P}^{g-1}$ is the Gauss map, as defined in Section 6 of Chapter 2, then the composition

$$S^{g-1} \overset{\pi}{\longrightarrow} S^{(g-1)} \overset{\mu^{(g-1)}}{\longrightarrow} \Theta \overset{\mathcal{G}}{\longrightarrow} \mathbb{P}^{g-1*}$$

(π the standard quotient map) is just the map defined in example 4 above, applied to the canonical curve $S \subset \mathbb{P}^{g-1}$.

7. A birational map of the projective plane $\mathbb{P}^2$ to itself is called a *Cremona transformation*. One basic example of a Cremona transformation may be given as follows: let a, b, c be noncollinear points of $\mathbb{P}^2$, and $\tilde{\mathbb{P}}^2$ the blow-up of $\mathbb{P}^2$ at these three points. The proper transforms $\tilde{L}_{ab}, \tilde{L}_{bc}$, and $\tilde{L}_{ac}$

of the lines $\overline{ab}$, $\overline{bc}$, and $\overline{ac}$ are then disjoint rational curves of self-intersection -1 in $\tilde{\mathbb{P}}^2$ and may all be blown down. (See Figure 2.) The resulting
surface S, by the last lemma of the previous section, is isomorphic to $\mathbb{P}^2$;
so we have given, up to an automorphism of $\mathbb{P}^2$, a birational map $\varphi_{a,b,c}$ of
$\mathbb{P}^2$ to itself. In terms of linear series, the map $\varphi_{a,b,c}$ is given by the linear
system $|2H|_{a+b+c}$ of conics in $\mathbb{P}^2$ passing through the three points a, b,
and c; in homogeneous coordinates, if

$$a = [1,0,0], \qquad b = [0,1,0], \qquad c = [0,0,1],$$

the map φ_{abc} is

$$\varphi_{abc} \colon \; [X_0, X_1, X_2] \longrightarrow [X_1 X_2, X_0 X_2, X_0 X_1].$$

Defined as it is by a linear system of conics, $\varphi_{a,b,c}$ is called a *quadratic
transformation* of the plane. Note that a general line L through the point a
is carried over into a line through the image point of L_{bc}, while a line L not
containing any of the points a,b,c is carried over into a conic passing
through all three image points $d = \varphi(L_{ab})$, $e = \varphi(L_{bc})$ and $f = \varphi(L_{ac})$. This
reflects the fact that $\varphi_{edf} \circ \varphi_{abc}$ is holomorphic.

Another Cremona transformation has been implicitly mentioned in the
last section. Let $a_1, \ldots, a_6$ be six points in $\mathbb{P}^2$ in general position with

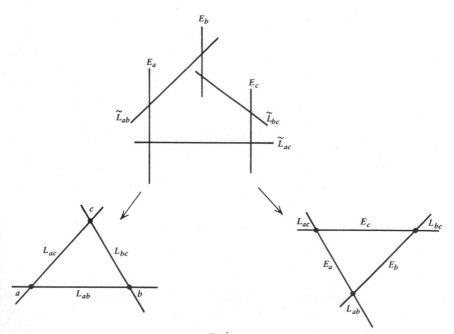

Figure 2

respect to lines and conics. Then in the blow-up $\tilde{\mathbb{P}}^2$ of $\mathbb{P}^2$ at the points a_i the proper transforms of the conics $G_i\{a_j\}_{j \neq i}$ in $\mathbb{P}^2$ passing through five of the six points a_i are disjoint rational curves of self-intersection -1, and so in turn may be blown down. The resulting surface is $\mathbb{P}^2$; thus we have another Cremona transformation ψ. The reader may verify that the birational map ψ is given by the linear system of quintic curves in $\mathbb{P}^2$ having double points at each of the points a_i. Of course, blowing down any of the 72 sets of six disjoint lines on the cubic $\tilde{\mathbb{P}}^2$ yields a Cremona transformation.

It is a classical result that the group of Cremona transformations is generated by the set of quadratic transformations φ_{abc}. An interesting exercise is to check this in the case of the map ψ above by expressing ψ as a composition of quadratic transformations; three will be needed.

We will return later in this section to prove a structure theorem for birational maps on surfaces; before we do that, however, we need to know some more about curves on surfaces.

Curves on an Algebraic Surface

We begin our discussion of curves on surfaces by proving a fact mentioned in Chapter 2: that *if* $C \subset S$ *is any irreducible curve on an algebraic surface, then there exists a compact Riemann surface* $\tilde{C}$ *and a holomorphic map*

$$\psi \colon \tilde{C} \longrightarrow C \subset S$$

that is one-to-one over smooth points of C. The Riemann surface $\tilde{C}$ together with the map ψ is called a *desingularization* of C.

To start, observe that the problem is a local one: we want to complete the (possibly) open Riemann surface $C^* = C - C_s$ to a compact one, and we may do this over one singular point at a time. Indeed, since the local irreducible components of C^* around a singular point $p \in C$ are all disjoint, we may proceed by completing one local component of C^* at a time. Explicitly, suppose $p_1, \ldots, p_m$ are the singular points of C, and $C_1^i, \ldots, C_{a_i}^i$ the irreducible components of C at p_i. If we can find maps

$$\psi_{i,\alpha} \colon \Delta_\varepsilon \longrightarrow C_\alpha^i$$

one-to-one away from $0 \in \Delta_\varepsilon$ and $p_i \in C_\alpha^i$, then we take our desingularization $\tilde{C}$ to be the union

$$C^* \bigcup_{\psi_{1,1}} \Delta \bigcup_{\psi_{1,2}} \Delta \bigcup \cdots \bigcup_{\psi_{1,a_1}} \Delta \bigcup_{\psi_{2,1}} \Delta \bigcup \cdots \bigcup_{\psi_{m,a_m}} \Delta$$

of the smooth locus C^* of C with the discs Δ via the maps $\{\psi_{i\alpha}\}$.

Now, let p be a singular point of C, and suppose C is irreducible in a small neighborhood Δ of p and smooth in $\Delta - \{p\}$. Let z, w be local holomorphic coordinates on S around $p=(0,0)$, and let C be given in Δ by the holomorphic function $f(z,w)$. After a holomorphic change of coordinates we may take f to be a Weierstrass polynomial in w and write

$$f(z,w) = w^k + p_1(z)w^{k-1} + \cdots + p_k(z)$$

with $p_i(0)=0$ for every i. Now for ε small and $0<|z|<\varepsilon$, the polynomial $f(z,w)$ will have k distinct roots $a_r(z)$; the functions $a_r(z)$ will be locally single-valued holomorphic functions of $z\neq0$, and

$$f(z,w) = \prod_{v=1}^{k} (w-a_r(z)).$$

Geometrically, this means that the projection map $\pi(z,w)\to z$ on the z-plane expresses the inverse image $\pi^{-1}(\Delta_\varepsilon^*)\subset C^*$ of the punctured disc $\Delta_\varepsilon^*=\Delta_\varepsilon-\{0\}$ as a topological covering space of Δ_ε^*.

Analytic continuation of the function $a_r(z)$ around the origin in the z-plane gives a new function element $a_{\sigma(r)}(z)$, where σ is a permutation of $(1,\ldots,k)$—that is, if we lift the path $t\mapsto z\cdot e^{2\pi it}$ from the z-plane to C, starting at the point $(z,a_r(z))\in C$, we end up at $(z,a_{\sigma(r)}(z))$. Since C is irreducible at p, the covering space $|\pi^{-1}(\Delta_\varepsilon^*)\to\Delta_\varepsilon^*$ is connected and the permutations $\{\sigma'\}$ act transitively; thus σ has order exactly k.

We now construct our local desingularization map

$$\psi: \Delta_{\varepsilon'} \longrightarrow C \qquad (\varepsilon'^k=\varepsilon)$$

as follows: Consider the function

$$b(\zeta) = a_1(\zeta^k),$$

defined a priori in a neighborhood of $\zeta=r$. Writing $\zeta=re^{i\theta}$, we see that as θ increases from 0 to $2\pi/k$, ζ^k turns once around the origin and, continuing b,

$$b(e^{2\pi i/k}\zeta) = a_{\sigma(1)}(\zeta^k).$$

Continuing further, we have

$$b(e^{2\pi i\mu/k}\zeta) = a_{\sigma^\mu(1)}(\zeta^k),$$

and so, since σ has order k, the analytic continuation of b around the circle $|\zeta|=r$ agrees with the original function b. Thus $b(\zeta)$ is well-defined in the punctured disc $\Delta_{\varepsilon'}^*$, and, being bounded, it extends to a holomorphic function on $\Delta_{\varepsilon'}$. Now let

$$\psi(\zeta) = (\zeta^k, b(\zeta)).$$

Clearly $f(\zeta^k, a_1(\zeta^k))\equiv0$, so ψ maps the disc $\Delta_{\varepsilon'}$ into C. Moreover, ψ must be one-to-one: if for some ζ,ζ', we had $\psi(\zeta)=\psi(\zeta')$, it would follow first that $\zeta^k = \zeta'^k$, hence

$$\zeta' = e^{2\pi i \mu/k}\zeta$$

for some $\mu = 1, \ldots, k$; then, since

$$b(\zeta') = a_{\sigma^\mu(1)}(\zeta^k) = a_1(\zeta^k) = b(\zeta),$$

we would have

$$\sigma^\mu(1) = 1.$$

But since σ acts transitively on $\{1, \ldots, k\}$, this implies that $\mu = k$, i.e., $\zeta = \zeta'$. Consequently the map

$$\psi: \Delta_{\varepsilon'} \longrightarrow C$$

restricts to an isomorphism

$$\psi^*: \Delta_{\varepsilon'}^* \longrightarrow C - \{p\},$$

and we have our desingularization. (Note that C, being the image of a disc Δ, has a uniquely determined tangent line at p.)

We see that the desingularization of C is unique: if $\pi: \tilde{C} \to C$, $\pi': \tilde{C}' \to C$ are two desingularizations, the isomorphism

$$\tilde{C} - \pi^{-1}(C_s) \longrightarrow C^* \longrightarrow C' - \pi'^{-1}(C_s)$$

extends continuously, hence holomorphically, to an isomorphism of $\tilde{C}$ and $\tilde{C}'$.

The desingularization of algebraic curves gives a second notion of the genus of a singular curve. Recall that for $C \subset S$ an irreducible curve on an algebraic surface S, the *virtual genus* $\pi(C)$ is defined by

$$\pi(C) = \frac{C \cdot C + K_S \cdot C}{2} + 1;$$

by the adjunction formula, $\pi(C)$ is the genus of any smooth curve homologous to C. On the other hand, we may define the *real genus* $g(C)$ of C to be the genus of its desingularization $\tilde{C}$. The focal point of this discussion is a comparison of the two notions of genus; to make this comparison we will use the explicit form of the adjunction formula: the Poincaré residue map.

Let S be a smooth surface, $C \subset S$ a smooth curve given locally in terms of holomorphic coordinates z, w on S by $f(z, w) = 0$. The Poincaré residue map

$$R: \Omega_S^2(C) \longrightarrow \Omega_C^1$$

is given locally by

$$g(z, w)\frac{dz \wedge dw}{f(z, w)} \longmapsto g(z, w)\frac{dz}{(\partial f/\partial w)(z, w)}\bigg|_{f(z, w) = 0};$$

as observed in Section 2 of Chapter 1, this is independent of the choice of coordinates z, w. We can extend R to a map from the space of meromorphic 2-forms in S having a pole of order at most one along C to the space of meromorphic 1-forms on C simply by letting $g(z, w)$ be meromorphic in the formula above. For a general meromorphic 2-form ω written as above, the Poincaré residue $R(\omega)$ on C will have the following zeros and poles:

1. At a point p of intersection of the divisor $D = (g) = (\omega) + (f) = K_S + C$ with C, $R(\omega)$ will have order exactly $m_p(D, C)$.

2. At a point where the restriction to C of the 1-form dz vanishes, $R(\omega)$ will have a zero.

3. At a point where the derivative $\partial f / \partial w$ vanishes, $R(\omega)$ will have a pole.

Now, as observed in the case of a curve in $\mathbb{P}^2$, the second and third factors exactly cancel each other out: at a point p with $(\partial f / \partial w)(p) = 0$, $(\partial f / \partial z)(p)$ must be nonzero since C is smooth and we have

$$df = \frac{\partial f}{\partial z} \, dz + \frac{\partial f}{\partial w} \, dw \equiv 0 \qquad \text{on } C,$$

hence

$$\text{ord}_p\left(\frac{\partial f}{\partial w}\right) = \text{ord}_p(dz)$$

on C. We see then that the canonical divisor $K = (R(\omega))$ on C is just the intersection of C with $K_S + C$, and consequently

$$2g - 2 = \deg K_C = C \cdot (K_S + C),$$

i.e.,

$$g = \frac{C \cdot C + K_S \cdot C}{2} + 1.$$

We would like to see how this goes over when C is singular. In this case, let $\tilde{C} \xrightarrow{\pi} C$ be the desingularization of C. As before, we let $\omega \in \Omega_S^2(C)$ be a meromorphic 2-form with

$$\text{ord}_C(\omega) = -1,$$

written locally as

$$\omega = g(z, w) \frac{dz \wedge dw}{f(z, w)}.$$

Then the pullback

$$\tilde{\omega} = \pi^* R(\omega) = \pi^*\left(g(z, w) \frac{dz}{(\partial f / \partial w)(z, w)}\right)$$

is a well-defined meromorphic 1-form on the inverse image $\pi^{-1}(C^*)$ of the smooth locus of C in $\tilde{C}$; we ask how $\tilde{\omega}$ behaves over the singular points of C. To facilitate the calculation, we first check that we can choose ω so that its divisor (ω) contains no components other than C passing through the singular points of C—that is, in the above expression for ω, g will be nonzero at all singular points of C. This is easy: if L is any positive line bundle on S, then for k sufficiently large, we can find $\sigma \in H^0(S, \Omega^2(L^k + C))$ and $\tau \in H^0(S, \mathcal{O}(L^k))$ nonzero on C_s; the quotient $\omega = \sigma/\tau$ will then be a meromorphic 2-form of the desired type.

First, we will consider the case of p a point of multiplicity $k > 1$ on C with C locally irreducible at p. Since C is irreducible at p the tangent cone to C at p consists of one line taken k times; let z, w be local coordinates on S centered around p such that the tangent line to C at p is given by $(w = 0)$. Let $f(z, w)$ be a defining function for C around p; we may take f to be a Weierstrass polynomial in w. Write

$$f(z, w) = \sum_i a_i \cdot z^i \cdot w^{k-i} + [k+1]$$

$$= \prod_i (\gamma_i z - \delta_i w) + [k+1]$$

with $(\gamma_i z - \delta_i w)$ the equations of the lines of the tangent cone to C at p; under the assumption that $(w = 0)$ is the only tangent line to C at p,

$$f(z, w) = w^k + [k+1],$$

i.e., the power series expansion of f in z and w contains no terms of degree $\leq k$ except w^k. Writing out f as a Weierstrass polynomial,

$$f(z, w) = w^k + p_1(z)w^{k-1} + \cdots + p_k(z),$$

then, *the function* $p_i(z)$ *must vanish to order at least* $i + 1$ *at* $z = 0$ *for each* i.

Let $\{a_r(z)\}$ be as before the function elements in a punctured disc in the z-plane such that

$$f(z, w) = \sum w^{k-i} p_i(z) = \prod_r (w - a_r(z));$$

set

$$b(\zeta) = a_1(\zeta^k)$$

and let $\pi : \Delta_\varepsilon \to C$ be the desingularization map

$$\pi(\zeta) = (\zeta^k, b(\zeta))$$

constructed above. Then

$$\pi^* dz = d(\zeta^k) = k \cdot \zeta^{k-1} d\zeta$$

and

$$\frac{\partial f}{\partial w} = \sum_r \left(\prod_{r' \neq r} (w - a_{r'}(z)) \right)$$

so

$$\pi^* \frac{\partial f}{\partial w}(\zeta) = \sum_r \left(\prod_{r' \neq r} (b(\zeta) - a_r(\zeta^k)) \right)$$

$$= \sum_r \left(\prod_{r' \neq r} (b(\zeta) - b(e^{2\pi i r'/k}\zeta)) \right)$$

$$= \prod_{r' \neq 1} (b(\zeta) - b(e^{2\pi i r'/k}\zeta)),$$

since $\{b(e^{2\pi i r/k}\zeta)\}_r = \{a_r(\zeta^k)\}_r$. We can write

$$\prod_r \left(\pi^* \frac{\partial f}{\partial w}(e^{2\pi i r/k}\zeta) \right) = \prod_r \prod_{r' \neq 1} (b(e^{2\pi i r}\zeta) - b(e^{2\pi i (r+r')/k}\zeta))$$

$$= \prod_{r \neq r'} (b(e^{2\pi i r/k}\zeta) - b(e^{2\pi i r'/k}\zeta)).$$

This last expression is a symmetric polynomial homogeneous of degree $k(k-1)$ in the functions $\{b(e^{2\pi i r/k}\zeta)\}_r = \{a_r(\zeta^k)\}_r$, and so is expressible as a polynomial in the elementary symmetric polynomials $p_i(\zeta^k)$ of $\{a_r(\zeta^k)\}_r$; we have

$$\prod_{r \neq r'} (b(e^{2\pi i r/k}\zeta) - b(e^{2\pi i r'/k}\zeta)) = \sum_e c_e p_1(\zeta^k)^{e_1} \cdot p_2(\zeta^k)^{e_2} \cdots p_k(\zeta^k)^{e_k}$$

with

$$\sum_i i \cdot e_i = k(k-1)$$

for each e such that $c_e \neq 0$. But the function p_i vanishes to order at least $i+1$ at 0, and therefore the function $p_i(\zeta^k)$ vanishes there to order $k(i+1)$. Thus the function $\prod_r (\pi^*(\partial f/\partial w)(e^{2\pi i r/k}\zeta))$ vanishes to order at least $k(k-1)(k+1)$ at $\zeta = 0$—and, since the functions $\{\pi^*(\partial f/\partial w)(e^{2\pi i r/k}\zeta)\}_r$ all vanish to the same order at $\zeta = 0$, it follows that $\pi^*(\partial f/\partial w)(\zeta)$ *vanishes to order at least* $(k-1)(k+1)$ *at* $\zeta = 0$.

Summarizing, with ω the 2-form above,

$$\tilde{\omega} = \pi^* R(\omega) = \pi^* g(z,w) \frac{\pi^* dz}{\pi^*(\partial f/\partial z)}$$

$$= \pi^* g(z,w) \frac{k \cdot \zeta^{k-1} d\zeta}{\pi^*(\partial f/\partial z)(\zeta)}$$

extends over $\pi^{-1}(p)$ to a meromorphic 1-form having a pole of order at least $(k-1)(k+1) - (k-1) = k(k-1)$ at $\pi^{-1}(p)$.

The computation in case C may be locally reducible around p is no more difficult. Let z, w, and f be as above, and write

$$f = \prod f_i$$

with f_i irreducible and zero at p; denote by

$$C_i = (f_i = 0)$$

the irreducible components of C around p, and let

$$\pi_i : \Delta \to C_i$$

be the corresponding desingularization maps, $\tilde{p}_i = \pi_i^{-1}(p_i)$. Observe that if

$$k_i = \text{mult}_p(C_i),$$

then

$$k = \text{mult}_p(C) = \sum k_i.$$

Consider again the Poincaré residue of ω on $\tilde{C}$ near p_i,

$$\tilde{\omega} = \pi_i^* g(z,w) \cdot \frac{\pi_i^* \, dz}{\pi_i^*(\partial f/\partial w)(z,w)}.$$

We have

$$\frac{\partial f}{\partial w} = \sum_i \left(\frac{\partial f_i}{\partial w} \cdot \prod_{j \neq i} f_j \right)$$

and, since f_i vanishes identically on C_i,

$$\pi_i^* \frac{\partial f}{\partial w} = \pi_i^* \frac{\partial f_i}{\partial w} \cdot \prod_{j \neq i} \pi_i^* f_j.$$

Thus

$$\tilde{\omega} = \pi_i^* g \cdot \frac{1}{\displaystyle\prod_{j \neq i} \pi_i^* f_j} \cdot \frac{\pi_i^* \, dz}{\pi_i^*(\partial f_i/\partial w)}.$$

By our previous computation, the form

$$\frac{\pi_i^* \, dz}{\pi_i^*(\partial f_i/\partial w)}$$

extends over $\tilde{p}_i$ to a meromorphic form having a pole of order at least $k_i(k_i - 1)$ at $\tilde{p}_i$. On the other hand, the function $\prod_{j \neq i} \pi_i^* f_j$ vanishes to order

$$\text{ord}_{\tilde{p}_i} \left(\prod_{j \neq i} \pi_i^* f_j \right) = m_p \left(C_i, \sum_{j \neq i} C_j \right)$$

$$= \sum_{j \neq i} m_p(C_i, C_j)$$

$$\geqslant \sum_{j \neq i} k_i k_j.$$

We see from this that $\tilde{\omega}$ extends over $\tilde{p}_i$ to a meromorphic 1-form having a pole of order at least

$$k_i(k_i - 1) + \sum_{j \neq i} k_i k_j = k_i \left(\sum k_j - 1 \right)$$

$$= k_i(k - 1)$$

at $\tilde{p}_i$. The form $\tilde{\omega}$ thus has a total of at least

$$\sum_i k_i(k-1) = k(k-1)$$

poles at the points $\{\tilde{p}_i\}$ lying over p. Summarizing, we have proved that

The form $\tilde{\omega}$ on $\tilde{C}^*$ extends to a meromorphic 1-form on all of $\tilde{C}$, having a total of at least k(k−1) *poles at the points of $\tilde{C}$ lying over a point of multiplicity* k *on* C.

Now we count the degree of the meromorphic form $\tilde{\omega}$ on $\tilde{C}$. Away from the inverse images in $\tilde{C}$ of the singular points of C, as in the smooth case $\tilde{\omega}$ will have poles and zeros exactly where $g(z, w)$ does; as before,

$$\deg(\tilde{\omega}|_{\tilde{C}^*}) = C(K_S + C).$$

Letting

$$\delta_p = \sum_{\pi(\tilde{p}_i)=p} -\operatorname{ord}_{\tilde{p}_i}(\tilde{\omega})$$

be the total order of $\tilde{\omega}$ at the points of $\tilde{C}$ lying over p, we have $\delta_p \geq k(k-1)$ for p a point of multiplicity k on C, and

$$2g(C) - 2 = \deg(\tilde{\omega})$$
$$= C \cdot C + C \cdot K_S - \sum_{p \in C_s} \delta_p,$$
$$g(C) = \frac{C \cdot C + C \cdot K_S}{2} + 1 - \frac{1}{2} \sum \delta_p.$$

This gives the basic

Lemma. *If the curve* C⊂S *has singular points* p_i *with multiplicities* k_i,

$$g(C) \leq \frac{C \cdot C + C \cdot K_S}{2} + 1 - \sum \frac{k_i(k_i - 1)}{2}.$$

In particular,

$$g(C) \leq \pi(C)$$

with equality holding if and only if C *is smooth.*

Note, as an important corollary, that

$\pi(C) \geq 0$ *for any irreducible curve* C *on a surface* S; *and if* $\pi(C)=0$, *then* C *is smooth.*

This in turn yields a stronger statement of the Castelnuovo-Enriques criterion for blowing down:

An irreducible curve C *on an algebraic surface* S *may be blown down if and only if* C·C *and* K·C *are both negative.*

Proof.

$$\pi(C) = \frac{C \cdot C + K \cdot C}{2} + 1 \geqslant 0,$$

and if $C \cdot C < 0$ and $K \cdot C < 0$, this implies that

$$C \cdot C = K \cdot C = -1.$$

Then

$$\pi(C) = 0;$$

hence C is smooth and the first version of the blowing-down criterion applies. Q.E.D.

Another important feature of the lemma is that it gives us a means of constructing the desingularization of a curve explicitly, as follows: Suppose C is an irreducible curve lying on the algebraic surface S, $p \in C$ a singular point of multiplicity k. Let $\tilde{S} \xrightarrow{\pi} S$ be the blow-up of S at p, $E = \pi^{-1}(p) \subset \tilde{S}$ the exceptional divisor of the blow-up, and $\tilde{C}$ the proper transform of C in $\tilde{S}$. Then

$$K_{\tilde{S}} \sim \pi^* K_S + E,$$
$$\tilde{C} \sim \pi^* C - kE,$$

so

$$\tilde{C} \cdot \tilde{C} = (\pi^* C \cdot \pi^* C) + k^2(E \cdot E)$$
$$= C \cdot C - k^2$$

and

$$K_{\tilde{S}} \cdot \tilde{C} = (\pi^* K_S \cdot \pi^* C) - k(E \cdot E)$$
$$= K_S \cdot C + k.$$

Combining, we have

$$\pi(\tilde{C}) = \frac{\tilde{C} \cdot \tilde{C} + K_{\tilde{S}} \cdot \tilde{C}}{2} + 1$$
$$= \frac{C \cdot C + K_S \cdot C}{2} + 1 - \frac{k(k-1)}{2}$$
$$= \pi(C) - \frac{k(k-1)}{2},$$

i.e., the virtual genus of $\tilde{C}$ will be strictly less than the virtual genus of C. This gives a recipe for the desingularization C. We define a sequence of curves and surfaces $C_i \subset S_i$ by letting C_1 be the proper transform of C in the blow-up $S_1 \xrightarrow{\pi_1} S$ of S at the singular points of C, C_2 the proper transform of C_1 in the blow-up $S_2 \xrightarrow{\pi_2} S_1$ of S_1 at the singular points of C_1, and so forth. If C_i were singular for all i, we would have

$$\pi(C) > \pi(C_1) > \pi(C_2) > \cdots.$$

The lemma tells us, however, that $\pi(C_i) \geqslant 0$ for every i, so this is impossible. Therefore for some i, the proper transform C_i must be smooth. By our construction, the map

$$\pi = \pi_1 \circ \pi_2 \circ \cdots \circ \pi_i : \; C_i \longrightarrow C$$

is one-to-one away from the singular locus of C, and so $C_i \to C$ is the desingularization of C.

Using this process we can, as promised in Section 5 of Chapter 1, evaluate the effect of any singular point on the genus of a curve. For example, suppose $C \subset S$ has a *tacnode*, that is, a double point whose branches are simply tangent at a point p. (See Figure 3.) If we let $\tilde{S} \to S$ be the blow-up of S at p, $\tilde{C}$ the the proper transform of C in $\tilde{S}$, then the proper transforms of the two branches of C will meet transversely at the point $r \in E$ in the exceptional divisor corresponding to their common tangent line at p. $\tilde{C}$ thus has an ordinary double point at r. If we let $\tilde{S}^{(2)} \to \tilde{S}$ be the blow-up of $\tilde{S}$ at r, then the proper transform $\tilde{C}^{(2)}$ of $\tilde{C}$ in $\tilde{S}^{(2)}$ will be smooth. Now

$$\tilde{C} \cdot \tilde{C} = C \cdot C - 4, \qquad K_{\tilde{S}} \cdot \tilde{C} = K_S \cdot C + 2,$$

$$\tilde{C}^{(2)} \cdot \tilde{C}^{(2)} = \tilde{C} \cdot \tilde{C} - 4, \qquad K_{\tilde{S}}^{(2)} \cdot \tilde{C}^{(2)} = K_{\tilde{S}} \cdot \tilde{C} + 2,$$

$\overset{\approx}{C}$

$\tilde{C}$

C

Figure 3

so that

$$\pi(\tilde{C}^{(2)}) = \frac{\tilde{C}^{(2)} \cdot \tilde{C}^{(2)} + K_{\tilde{S}}^{(2)} \cdot \tilde{C}^{(2)}}{2} + 1$$

$$= \frac{C \cdot C + K_S \cdot C}{2} + 1 - 2$$

$$= \pi(C) - 2,$$

i.e., *a tacnode drops the genus of a curve by* 2.

Similarly, if p is an ordinary triple point of C—that is, around p C consists of three arcs meeting transversely at p—then the proper transform $\tilde{C}$ of C in the blow-up $\tilde{S}$ of S at p will be smooth over p, and we have

$$\pi(\tilde{C}) = \pi(C) - 3,$$

i.e., *an ordinary triple point drops the genus of a curve by* 3.

One final note, which we will have occasion to use in what follows: if $C \subset S$ is a curve having singular points p_i with multiplicity k_i, C_0 a smooth curve homologous to C, and $f: \tilde{C} \to C$ the desingularization of C, then it has been proved that

$$g(C) \leqslant \pi(C) - \sum \frac{k_i(k_i - 1)}{2} = \pi(C_0) - \sum \frac{k_i(k_i - 1)}{2},$$

so

$$\chi(\tilde{C}) \geqslant \chi(C_0) + \sum k_i(k_i - 1).$$

On the other hand, taking a triangulation of $\tilde{C}$ having all the points $f^{-1}(p_i)$ as vertices, we deduce that

$$\chi(C) = \chi(\tilde{C}) - \sum_i {}^{\#}\{f^{-1}(p_i)\} - 1;$$

since the points of $f^{-1}(p_i)$ correspond exactly to the irreducible components of C around p_i, and there are less than k_i of these, this implies

$$\chi(C) \geqslant \chi(\tilde{C}) - \sum (k_i - 1).$$

Combining, we see that

$$\chi(C) \geqslant \chi(C_0) + \sum (k_i - 1)^2,$$

i.e., *the Euler characteristic of a singular curve on* S *is strictly greater than the Euler characteristic of a smooth curve homologous to it.*

In particular, if C has δ ordinary double points and no other singularities,

$$\chi(C) = \chi(C_0) + \delta.$$

We introduce here a classical formula relating the Euler characteristic of a surface to the structure of a pencil of curves on it. Suppose that M is any algebraic surface, $\{C_\lambda\}$ a pencil of generically irreducible curves on M. Assume in addition that all the curves C_λ are smooth at the base points of the pencil $\{C_\lambda\}$, so that if we blow M up $C_\lambda \cdot C_\lambda = n$ times at the base points of $\{C_\lambda\}$, the proper transforms $\tilde{C}_\lambda$ of the curves C_λ on $\tilde{M}$ form a pencil of disjoint, generically irreducible curves. Consider the map

$$\iota: \tilde{M} \to \mathbb{P}^1$$

given by the pencil $\{\tilde{C}_\lambda\}$. By Bertini's theorem, the generic curve $\tilde{C}_\lambda \cong C_\lambda$ is smooth; let $\tilde{C}_{\lambda_1}, \ldots, \tilde{C}_{\lambda_\mu}$ be the singular elements of the pencil. Then the restricted map

$$\iota: \tilde{M} - \bigcup_i C_{\lambda_i} \to \mathbb{P}^1 - \{\lambda_1, \ldots, \lambda_\mu\}$$

is proper and everywhere nonsingular, so that $M - \bigcup C_{\lambda_i}$ *is a* C^∞ *fiber bundle over* $\mathbb{P}^1 - \{\lambda_1, \ldots, \lambda_\mu\}$. Thus

$$\chi\left(\tilde{M} - \bigcup_i C_{\lambda_i}\right) = \chi(\mathbb{P}^1 - \{\lambda_1, \ldots, \lambda_\mu\}) \cdot \chi(C)$$
$$= (2 - \mu) \cdot \chi(C),$$

where $\chi(C)$ denotes the Euler characteristic of a generic curve C_λ. Taking a triangulation of $\tilde{M}$ in which the union of the singular fibers appears as a subcomplex, then, we see that

$$\chi(\tilde{M}) = (2 - \mu)\chi(C_2) + \sum_{i=1}^{\mu} \chi(C_{\lambda_i})$$

and so

$$\chi(M) = \chi(\tilde{M}) - n$$
$$= (2 - \mu)\chi(C_\lambda) + \sum \chi(C_{\lambda_i}) - n.$$
$$= 2\chi(C) + \sum_\lambda (\chi(C_\lambda) - \chi(C)) - n$$

If we make the additional assumption that each of the singular curves C_λ has one double point and no other singularities (a pencil satisfying these conditions is called a *Lefschetz pencil*), then we have

$$\chi(C_{\lambda_i}) = \chi(C) + 1,$$

i.e.,

Proposition. *If* $\{C_\lambda\}$ *is a Lefschetz pencil of curves on* M, *with self-intersection* n *and containing* μ *singular curves, then*

$$\chi(M) = 2\chi(C) + \mu - n,$$

where $\chi(C)$ *denotes the Euler characteristic of the generic element of the pencil.*

We remark that if $f: M \to B$ is any holomorphic map of a smooth surface S onto a curve B with singular fibers $C_{p_i} = f^{-1}(p_i)$, then the same argument

gives

$$\chi(M) = \chi(B - \{p_i\}) \cdot \chi(C) + \sum_i \chi(C_{p_i})$$

$$= \chi(B) \cdot \chi(C) + \sum_i \left(\chi(C_{p_i}) - \chi(C) \right),$$

where C is the generic fiber of f; combining this with the inequality $\chi(C_{p_i}) > \chi(C)$ noted above, we see that

If $f: M \to B$ *is any holomorphic map of* M *to a curve* B, C *the generic fiber of* f, *then*

$$\chi(M) \geqslant \chi(B) \cdot \chi(C).$$

The Structure of Birational Maps Between Surfaces

As we mentioned in the introduction to this chapter, we can give a comprehensive picture of birational maps on surfaces. This is the

Theorem. *Any birational map between surfaces may be obtained by a sequence of blow-ups followed by a sequence of blowing-downs; i.e., if* M *and* N *are algebraic surfaces and*

$$f: M \to N$$

a birational map, then there exists a surface $\tilde{M}$ *and maps* π_1, π_2

such that $f = \pi_2 \circ \pi_1^{-1}$, *and* π_1, π_2 *are blowing-up maps.*

Proof. The proof of this theorem consists of two parts: we will show that

1.   If $f: M \to N$ is any rational map on the surface M, then there exists a blow-up $\tilde{M} \overset{\pi_1}{\to} M$ such that $\pi_1 \circ f$ is holomorphic; and

2.   Any holomorphic birational map $\tilde{M} \overset{\pi_2}{\to} N$ is a sequence of blow-ups.

To prove part 1, we must prove that if $\{D_\lambda\}_{\lambda \mathbb{P}^n}$ is any linear system of divisors on M having only isolated base points, then there exists a blow-up $\tilde{M} \overset{\pi_1}{\to} M$ such that the proper transform in $\tilde{M}$ of the linear system $\{D_\lambda\}$ has no base points. This is fairly easy. Suppose that the point $p \in M$ is a base point of multiplicity k for the linear system $\{D_\lambda\}$ (i.e., p has multiplicity k in the generic D_λ). Let $\tilde{M} \overset{\pi}{\to} M$ be the blow-up of M at p, $E = \pi^{-1}(p)$ the exceptional divisor of the blow-up. Then

$$\tilde{D}_\lambda = \pi^* D_\lambda - kE,$$

and therefore $\tilde{D}_\lambda$ has self-intersection

$$\tilde{D}_\lambda \cdot \tilde{D}_\lambda = (\pi^* D_\lambda \cdot \pi^* D_\lambda) + k^2 (E \cdot E)$$
$$= D_\lambda \cdot D_\lambda - k^2 < D_\lambda \cdot D_\lambda.$$

Now define a sequence of blow-ups $M_i \xrightarrow{\pi_i} M_{i-1}$ and linear systems $\{D_\lambda^i\}$ as follows: let $M_1 \xrightarrow{\pi_1} M$ be the blow-up of M in the base points of $\{D_\lambda\}$ and $\{D_\lambda^1\}$ the proper transform in M_1 of the system $\{D_\lambda\}$, $M_2 \xrightarrow{\pi_2} M_1$ the blow-up of M_1 in the base points of $\{D_\lambda^1\}$ and $\{D_\lambda^2\}$ the proper transform of $\{D_\lambda^1\}$ in M^2, etc. If every series $\{D_\lambda^i\}$ had base points, we would have

$$D_\lambda \cdot D_\lambda > D_\lambda^1 \cdot D_\lambda^1 > D_\lambda^2 \cdot D_\lambda^2 > \cdots .$$

But for generic λ, λ', and any i, the divisors D_λ^i and D_λ^i have no common components, so

$$D_\lambda^i \cdot D_\lambda^i \geqslant 0$$

for all i. Thus the linear system $\{D_\lambda^i\}$ is base-point-free for some i, and we have proved part 1 of our theorem.

Part 2 is somewhat deeper. Suppose that $\pi: M \to N$ is a holomorphic birational map, that is, a holomorphic map one-to-one away from a finite collection of points in N. Note that for any point $p \in N$ the inverse image $f^{-1}(p) \subset M$ is connected: if it were not, we could find disjoint relatively compact open sets $U_1, U_2 \subset M$ each containing connected components of $f^{-1}(p)$; being open, they could not map to p nor to any curve through p, so by the proper mapping theorem the image of each would contain a neighborhood of p—contradicting the hypothesis that π is generically one-to-one. The inverse image of any point $p \in N$ is thus either a single point or a connected divisor. We claim now that

If the inverse image $\pi^{-1}(p)$ of a point $p \in N$ is a curve C, then C contains an exceptional curve of the first kind.

To prove this, we will use the index theorem. Let $C_1, \ldots, C_m$ be the irreducible components of C. We can certainly find a positive divisor E on N that does not pass through p; we have

$$(\pi^* E \cdot \pi^* E) = (E \cdot E) > 0$$

but

$$(\pi^* E \cdot C_i) = 0 \qquad \text{for every } i.$$

It follows from the index theorem that *the intersection pairing is negative definite on the subspace of* $H^2(M, \mathbb{Q})$ *spanned by the classes* $\{C_i\}$.

Let ω be any meromorphic 2-form on N, regular at p. The pullback $\pi^* \omega$ is a meromorphic 2-form on M, vanishing everywhere in C; we can thus write

$$K_M = (\pi^*\omega) = D + \sum a_i C_i$$

with D disjoint from C and $a_i > 0$ for every i. Now from the index theorem

$$\left(\sum a_i C_i \cdot \sum a_i C_i \right) < 0.$$

But since D is disjoint from C,

$$\left(\sum a_i C_i \cdot \sum a_i C_i \right) = \left(\sum a_i C_i \cdot K_M \right),$$

which implies that

$$C_i \cdot K < 0$$

for some i. But by the index theorem again,

$$C_i \cdot C_i < 0,$$

and so by the stronger version of the Castelnuovo-Enriques criterion, C_i is an exceptional curve of the first kind; we have thus proved the claim.

Assertion 2, and hence the main theorem, follow readily. If $f : M \to N$ is holomorphic and birational, but not biholomorphic, then for some $p \in N$, $f^{-1}(p)$ will be a curve and so contain an exceptional curve C_1 of the first kind. Let $M \xrightarrow{\pi_1} M_1$ be the blow-down of C_1; the map

$$f : M_1 - \pi_1(C) \longrightarrow M - C \to N$$

extends continuously, hence holomorphically, to a map

$$f_1 : M_1 \to N.$$

Again, if f_1 is not biholomorphic, we can find an exceptional curve of the first kind C_2 in M_1 lying over a point of N; let M_2 be the blow-down of C_2, and so define inductively a sequence of blow-downs $M_i \to M_{i+1}$ and holomorphic birational maps f_i

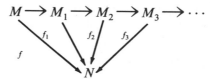

The Betti numbers satisfy

$$b_2(M) > b_2(M_1) > b_2(M_2) > \cdots$$

and, since $b_2(M)$ is finite, it follows that for some i, $M_i \xrightarrow{f_i} N$ is biholomorphic; the theorem is proved.

3. RATIONAL SURFACES I

Noether's Lemma

The next two sections will be devoted to a discussion of rational surfaces, that is, algebraic surfaces birationally isomorphic to $\mathbb{P}^2$. In this section our goal will be a description of all rational surfaces; as corollaries of the main theorem we will answer two questions left open in Chapter 2.

We start with

Noether's Lemma. *An algebraic surface S is rational if and only if it contains an irreducible rational curve C with* $\dim|C| \geq 1$.

Proof. One direction is clear: if $\pi : S \to \mathbb{P}^2$ is a birational map, then for the generic line $L \subset \mathbb{P}^2$, the pullback $C = \pi^* L$ on S will be such a curve. Conversely, suppose $C \subset S$ is an irreducible rational curve varying in a nontrivial linear system. Choose a pencil $\{C_\lambda\}_{\lambda \in \mathbb{P}^1}$ containing C in the complete linear system $|C|$. We have seen that if we blow up S sufficiently many times at the base points of the pencil $\{C_\lambda\}$, we obtain a surface $\tilde{S}$ on which the proper transforms $\{\tilde{C}_\lambda\}$ of the curves C_λ form a pencil without base points; clearly the curves $\tilde{C}_\lambda$ will again be rational. Thus we may as well assume from the start that S contains a pencil $\{C_\lambda\}$ of rational curves, not all reducible, having no base points.

Since any point of intersection of two distinct elements $C_\lambda, C_{\lambda'}$ of our pencil is a base point for the whole pencil,

$$C_\lambda \cdot C_\lambda = C_\lambda \cdot C_{\lambda'} = 0.$$

Now suppose a particular curve C_0 in the pencil is reducible; write

$$C_0 = \sum a_\nu C_\nu$$

with C_ν irreducible, $a_\nu > 0$. Since each C_ν is disjoint from $C_\lambda \sim C_0$ for $\lambda \neq 0$,

$$0 = C_0 \cdot C_\nu = \sum_{\nu'} a_{\nu'} (C_\nu \cdot C_{\nu'}).$$

But $C_\nu \cdot C_{\nu'} \geq 0$ for $\nu \neq \nu'$, and C_0, being the limiting position of irreducible curves C_λ, must be connected; we deduce that $C_\nu \cdot C_{\nu'} > 0$ for some $\nu' \neq \nu$. It follows that $C_\nu \cdot C_\nu < 0$ for all ν. By the adjunction formula,

$$\pi(C_0) = \frac{C_0 \cdot C_0 + C_0 \cdot K}{2} + 1 = 0$$

$$\Rightarrow C_0 \cdot K = \sum a_\nu C_\nu \cdot K = -2$$

$$\Rightarrow C_{\nu_0} \cdot K < 0 \qquad \text{for some } \nu_0.$$

Thus, by the strong version of the Castelnuovo-Enriques criterion, C_{ν_0} can be blown down. Let $S \xrightarrow{\pi} \tilde{S}'$ be the blowing-down of C_{ν_0}. Since every C_λ other than C_0 is disjoint from C_{ν_0}, the curves $\pi(C_\lambda)$ form a pencil of rational curves without base points on $\tilde{S}'$; by the same argument, if any curve $\pi(C_\lambda)$ is reducible, $\tilde{S}'$ can again be blown down. Since we can only blow down a surface a finite number of times, we see that after a finite number of steps we obtain a surface $\tilde{S}$ with map $\pi: S \to \tilde{S}$ such that the curves $\pi(C_\lambda)$ form a pencil of irreducible—hence smooth—disjoint rational curves. Such a surface is called a *rational ruled surface*; the proof of Noether's lemma will be completed in the following discussion.

Rational Ruled Surfaces

Let S be a rational ruled surface, $\{C_\lambda\}$ a pencil of disjoint smooth rational curves on S, and consider the map $\iota: S \to \mathbb{P}^1$ given by the pencil $\{C_\lambda\}$. We claim first that $\iota: S \to \mathbb{P}^1$ *is a holomorphic fiber bundle over* $\mathbb{P}^1$ *with fiber* $\mathbb{P}^1$, i.e., *for every* $\lambda_0 \in \mathbb{P}^1$, *there exists a neighborhood* $U \ni \lambda_0$ *in* $\mathbb{P}^1$ *and an isomorphism* $\varphi: \iota^{-1}(U) \cong U \times \mathbb{P}^1$ *fibering over* U. To see this, let $L \to S$ be a positive line bundle, sufficiently positive so that $H^1(S, \mathcal{O}(L-C)) = 0$. Then from the exact cohomology sequence associated to the sequence

$$0 \to \mathcal{O}S(L-C) \to \mathcal{O}S(L) \to \mathcal{O}C_\lambda(L) \to 0$$

we find

$$H^0(S, \mathcal{O}(L)) \to H^0(C_\lambda, \mathcal{O}(L)) \to 0$$

for each λ. Let $L \cdot C_\lambda = n$—so that $L|_{C_\lambda} \cong H^n$, where H is the hyperplane bundle on $C_\lambda \cong \mathbb{P}^1$—and let $\sigma_0, \ldots, \sigma_n$ be global sections of L whose restrictions to some fiber $C_0 = C_{\lambda_0}$ span $H^0(C_0, \mathcal{O}(L))$. Then for λ in some neighborhood U of λ_0 in $\mathbb{P}^1$, the restrictions of $\sigma_0, \ldots, \sigma_n$ to C_λ span $H^0(C_\lambda, \mathcal{O}(L))$, i.e., the map $\iota_\sigma: \iota^{-1}(U) \to \mathbb{P}^n$ given by $[\sigma_0, \ldots, \sigma_n]$ is well-defined and embeds each curve C_λ as a rational normal curve in $\mathbb{P}^n$.

Choose $n-1$ distinct points $p_1, \ldots, p_{n-1}$ on C_0. Since the fibers of the map $\iota: S \to \mathbb{P}^1$ are smooth, we can find holomorphic arcs $\gamma_1, \ldots, \gamma_{n-1}: \Delta \to S$ with γ_i meeting C_0 transversely at p_i; for λ in some open set U' around λ_0, then, the curve C_λ will likewise meet the arc γ_i transversely in a point $p_i(\lambda)$. For each $\lambda \in U'$, let $V(\lambda) \subset \mathbb{P}^n$ be the $(n-2)$-plane spanned by the points $\iota_\sigma(p_i(\lambda))$, $i = 1, \ldots, n-1$. Choose a line $L \subset \mathbb{P}^n$ disjoint from $V(\lambda)$ for all $\lambda \in U'$—restricting U' again if necessary—and let π_λ denote the projection map from $\mathbb{P}^n - V(\lambda)$ onto L. Note that since $p_i(\lambda)$—and hence $\iota_\sigma(p_i(\lambda))$—varies holomorphically with λ, the map π_λ likewise varies holomorphically with λ; in particular the map

$$\pi': \iota^{-1}(U') \to L \cong \mathbb{P}^1$$

given by

$$\pi'|_{C_\lambda} = \pi_\lambda \longrightarrow C_\lambda \overset{\sim}{\longrightarrow} L$$

is holomorphic. The map

$$\varphi = (\iota, \pi') : \iota^{-1}(U') \overset{\approx}{\longrightarrow} U' \times \mathbb{P}^1$$

then gives the bundle structure.

In general, if $E \to M$ is a holomorphic vector bundle on a complex manifold M, we define the *associated projective bundle* $\mathbb{P}(E) \to M$ to be the fiber bundle over M whose fiber over any point $x \in M$ is the projective space $\mathbb{P}(E_x)$. If $\{U_\alpha\}$ is an open cover of M, $\varphi_\alpha : E|_{U_\alpha} \to U_\alpha \times \mathbb{C}^r$ a trivialization of E over U_α for each α, the maps φ_α induce maps $\tilde\varphi_\alpha : \mathbb{P}(E)|_{U_\alpha} \to U_\alpha \times \mathbb{P}^{r-1}$, giving $\mathbb{P}(E)$ the structure of a holomorphic $\mathbb{P}^{r-1}$-bundle over M. Note that if $\{g_{\alpha\beta} : U_\alpha \cap U_\beta \to GL_r\}$ are the transition functions for the trivializations φ_α of E, then transition functions for $\mathbb{P}(E)$ relative to $\tilde\varphi_\alpha$ are given by the composition $\tilde g_{\alpha\beta}$ of $g_{\alpha\beta}$ with the standard projection map $GL_r \to PGL_r$. In particular, if L is any line bundle over M with transition functions $h_{\alpha\beta} : U_\alpha \cap U_\beta \to \mathbb{C}^*$, then $E \otimes L$ is given by transition functions $g'_{\alpha\beta} = h_{\alpha\beta} \cdot g_{\alpha\beta}$; since $\tilde g_{\alpha\beta} = \tilde g'_{\alpha\beta}$, we see that $\mathbb{P}(E) = \mathbb{P}(E \otimes L)$. Conversely, if E, E' are any two vector bundles over M with $\mathbb{P}(E) \cong \mathbb{P}(E')$, it follows that $E' = E \otimes L$ for some line bundle $L \to M$.

We claim now that any holomorphic $\mathbb{P}^{r-1}$ bundle P over $\mathbb{P}^1$ is of the form $\mathbb{P}(E)$ for some vector bundle $E \to \mathbb{P}^1$ of rank r. To see this, let $\tilde g_{\alpha\beta} : U_\alpha \cap U_\beta \to PGL_r$ be transition functions for P relative to some open cover $\{U_\alpha\}$ of $\mathbb{P}^1$. Assuming $\{U_\alpha\}$ is sufficiently fine, we can find liftings $g_{\alpha\beta} : U_\alpha \cap U_\beta \to GL_r$ of $\tilde g_{\alpha\beta}$ (the group $SL_r \subset GL_r$ of matrices with determinant 1 forms an unbranched r-sheeted cover of PGL_r); on $U_\alpha \cap U_\beta \cap U_\gamma$, set

$$h_{\alpha\beta\gamma} = g_{\alpha\beta} \times g_{\beta\gamma} \times g_{\gamma\alpha}.$$

Since $\tilde h_{\alpha\beta\gamma} = \tilde g_{\alpha\beta} \times \tilde g_{\beta\gamma} \times \tilde g_{\gamma\alpha} = I$, we see that $h_{\alpha\beta\gamma} : U_\alpha \cap U_\beta \cap U_\gamma \to \mathbb{C}^*$; i.e., $\{h_{\alpha\beta\gamma}\} \in Z^2(\underline{U}, \mathcal{O}^*)$. But from the exact cohomology sequence of $0 \to \mathbb{Z} \to \mathcal{O} \to \mathcal{O}^* \to 1$ and $H^2(\mathbb{P}^1, \mathcal{O}) = H^3(\mathbb{P}^1, \mathbb{Z}) = 0$, we deduce that $H^2(\mathbb{P}^1, \mathcal{O}^*) = 0$, so we can write

$$h_{\alpha\beta\gamma} = j_{\alpha\beta} \times j_{\beta\gamma} \times j_{\gamma\alpha}$$

for some Čech cochain $\{j_{\alpha\beta} : U_\alpha \cap U_\beta \to \mathbb{C}^*\}$. The functions $g_{\alpha\beta} \times j_{\alpha\beta}^{-1}$ then are the transition functions for a vector bundle $E \to \mathbb{P}^1$ with $P = \mathbb{P}(E)$. (Note that this argument works as well for a projective bundle over any Riemann surface.)

Summarizing, we have shown that *any rational ruled surface is of the form* $\mathbb{P}(E)$ *for some holomorphic vector bundle* E *of rank two over* $\mathbb{P}^1$. The following lemma gives a complete description of such vector bundles:

Lemma. *Any holomorphic vector bundle on* $\mathbb{P}^1$ *is decomposable—that is, a direct sum of line bundles.*

Proof. First note that a vector bundle E is decomposable if and only if $E \otimes H^k$ is decomposable for any k. From the exact sequence

$$0 \to \mathcal{O}(E \otimes H^{k-1}) \to \mathcal{O}(E \otimes H^k) E_x \otimes H_x^k \to 0,$$

we find that $H^1(\mathbb{P}^1, \mathcal{O}(E \otimes H^{k-1})) = 0 \Rightarrow H^0(\mathbb{P}^1, \mathcal{O}(E \otimes H^k)) \neq 0$; i.e., for $k \gg 0$, $E' = E \otimes H^k$ has a nontrivial global holomorphic section σ. Now suppose σ vanishes at n points on $\mathbb{P}^1$; then, multiplying σ by a meromorphic function on $\mathbb{P}^1$ with poles exactly at the zeros of σ, we obtain another section σ' of E' with σ and σ' everywhere linearly dependent and nowhere both zero. Together, they span a subline bundle L in E' of degree n. Note that by Riemann-Roch for $\mathbb{P}^1$, $h^0(L) = n+1$, and, since $H^0(\mathbb{P}^1, \mathcal{O}(L))$ injects into $H^0(\mathbb{P}^L, \mathcal{O}(E))$, we have $n \leq h^0(E)$; thus *no global section of* E *can have more than* $h^0(E) - 1$ *zeros*.

Assume now that rank $E = 2$. Let n be the greatest number of zeros of a global section of E, and let σ_0 be a global section of E with n zeros. Let L_1 be the corresponding subline bundle of E and $L_2 = E/L_1$ the quotient bundle, we have an exact sequence of bundles

$$0 \to L_1 \to E \to L_2 \to 0.$$

We claim now that $m = \deg L_2 \leq \deg L_1 = n$. Otherwise, let $\tilde{\tau}$ be a section of L_2 vanishing at $m > n$ points $p_1, \dots, p_m \in \mathbb{P}^1$. Since $H^1(\mathbb{P}^1, \mathcal{O}(L_1)) = 0$,

$$H^0(\mathbb{P}^1, \mathcal{O}(E)) \to H^0(\mathbb{P}^1, \mathcal{O}(L_2)) \to 0;$$

i.e., $\tilde{\tau}$ is the projection onto L_2 of a section τ of E; since $\tilde{\tau}(p_i) = 0, \tau(p_i) \in (L_1)_{p_i}$ for all i. For any collection $q_0, \dots, q_n$ of $n+1$ points in $\mathbb{P}^1$, $\deg(L_1 - q_0 - \cdots - q_n) = -1$, so

$$H^1(\mathbb{P}^1, \mathcal{O}(L_1 - (q_0 + \cdots + q_n))) = 0$$
$$\Rightarrow H^0(\mathbb{P}^1, \mathcal{O}(L_1 - (q_0 + \cdots + q_{n-1}))) \to \mathbb{C}_{q_n} \to 0.$$

Thus there exist sections of L_1 vanishing at $q_0, \dots, q_{n-1}$ and nonzero at q_n. Let τ_i be the section of L_1 vanishing at $p_1, \dots, \widehat{p_i}, \dots, p_{n+1}$ and taking the value $\tau(p_i)$ at p_i; then

$$\tau - \sum \tau_i$$

is a nonzero section of E vanishing at $n+1$ points, contradicting our assumption that no section of E vanishes at more than n points.

Next consider the sequence of bundles

$$0 \to \text{Hom}(L_2, L_1) \to \text{Hom}(L_2, E) \to \text{Hom}(L_2, L_2) \to 0.$$

Since $\deg L_1 \geqslant \deg L_2$, $\deg(\text{Hom}(L_2, L_1)) = \deg L_1 - \deg L_2 \geqslant 0$; so $H^1(\mathbb{P}^1, \mathcal{O}(\text{Hom}(L_2, L_1))) = 0$ and

$$H^0(\mathbb{P}^1, \mathcal{O}(\text{Hom}(L_2, E))) \to H^0(\mathbb{P}^1, \mathcal{O}(\text{Hom}(L_2, L_2))) \to 0.$$

Let $\iota: L_2 \to E$ be a section of $\text{Hom}(L_2, E)$ that maps onto the identity section of $\text{Hom}(L_2, L_2)$. Since ι composed with the projection map $E \to L_2$ is the identity, ι gives an inclusion of bundles $L_2 \to E$, with $\iota(L_2)_x$ disjoint from $(L_1)_x$ for all x; thus

$$E \cong L_1 \oplus L_2.$$

To prove the lemma for bundles of general rank, we use induction on the rank: if rank $E = r$ and the lemma is proved for all bundles of rank $< r$, take again a section σ and corresponding subline bundle L_1 of maximal degree; then

$$E' = \frac{E}{L_1} \cong \bigoplus_{i=2}^{r} L_i.$$

The same argument shows that $\deg L_i \leqslant \deg L_1$ for all i, hence

$$H^1(\mathbb{P}^1, \text{Hom}(E', L_1))) = \bigoplus_{i=2}^{n} H^1(\mathbb{P}^1, \text{Hom}(L_i, L_1))) = 0,$$

so that the exact sequence

$$0 \to L_1 \to E \to E' \to 0$$

again splits. Q.E.D.

By the lemma, any rational ruled surface is of the form

$$\mathbb{P}(E) = \mathbb{P}(L_1 \oplus L_2) = \mathbb{P}((L_1 \otimes L_2^*) \oplus \mathbb{C}_{\mathbb{P}^1}) = \mathbb{P}(H^n \oplus \mathbb{C}_{\mathbb{P}^1})$$

for some $n \geqslant 0$ (here $\mathbb{C}_{\mathbb{P}^1}$ stands for the trivial line bundle over $\mathbb{P}^1$); the bundle $\mathbb{P}(H^n \oplus \mathbb{C})$ is denoted S_n.

Let $E_0 \subset S_n$ be the image of the section $(0, 1)$ of $H^n \oplus \mathbb{C}_{\mathbb{P}^1}$; E_0 is called the *zero-section* of S_n. More generally, if σ is any holomorphic section of H^n, let E_σ be the image in S_n of the section $(\sigma, 1)$ of $H^n \oplus \mathbb{C}_{\mathbb{P}^1}$. Clearly E_σ is homologous to E_0, and since for σ a nontrivial section E_σ will meet E_0 exactly n times, the intersection number $E_0 \cdot E_0$ is n. (See Figure 4.)

Consider the section $(\sigma, 0)$ of $H^n \otimes \mathbb{C}_{\mathbb{P}^1}$ where σ is any section of H^n. Away from the zeros of σ, $(\sigma, 0)$ gives a curve in S_n; let E_∞ denote the closure of this curve. (Clearly E_∞ is independent of the choice of section σ, since $(\sigma, 0)$ and $(\sigma', 0)$ have the same image in S_n away from a finite number of points.) More generally, if σ is any meromorphic section of H^n,

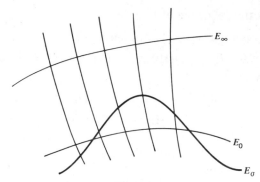

Figure 4

let E_σ denote the closure of the curve given by $(\sigma, 1)$ away from the poles of σ. Letting C be any fiber of the bundle map $S_n \to \mathbb{P}^1$, we have

$$E_0 \cdot E_0 = n$$
$$E_\sigma \cdot E_0 = \text{number of zeros of } \sigma,$$
$$E_\sigma \cdot E_\infty = \text{number of poles of } \sigma,$$
$$E_0 \cdot E_\infty = 0,$$
$$E_0 \cdot C = E_\sigma \cdot C = E_\infty \cdot C = 1.$$

$S_n - C_\lambda - E_0$ forms a $\mathbb{C}$-bundle over $\mathbb{P}^1 - \{\lambda\} \cong \mathbb{C}$, and therefore is contractible; thus

$$H_2(S_n, \mathbb{Z}) \cong H_2(C_\lambda \cup E_0, \mathbb{Z}) \cong \mathbb{Z}\{(C_\lambda), (E_0)\}$$

and

$$H_1(S_n, \mathbb{Z}) = H_1(C_\lambda \cup E_0, \mathbb{Z}) = 0.$$

Since $H^1(S_n, \mathbb{Z}) = 0$ and $H^2(S_n, \mathbb{Z})$ is spanned by $(1, 1)$-classes, we deduce that

$$H^1(S_n, \mathcal{O}) = H^2(S_n, \mathcal{O}) = 0.$$

In particular, the Chern class map

$$H^1(S_n, \mathcal{O}^*) \xrightarrow{c_1} H^2(S_n, \mathbb{Z})$$

is an isomorphism; i.e., two curves on S_n are linearly equivalent if and only if they are homologous. Consequently we can write

$$E_\infty \sim m_1 \cdot E_0 + m_2 \cdot C$$

for $m_1, m_2 \in \mathbb{Z}$. But then $E_\infty \cdot C = 1 \Rightarrow m_1 = 1$, and $E_\infty \cdot E_0 = 0 \Rightarrow m_2 = -n$; i.e.,

$$E_\infty \sim E_0 - n \cdot C,$$

and so

$$E_\infty \cdot E_\infty = E_0 \cdot E_0 - 2nC \cdot E_0 = -n.$$

Similarly, for σ a meromorphic section of H^n,

$$E_\sigma \sim E_0 + m \cdot C,$$

where m is the number of poles of the section σ.

Now suppose D is any irreducible curve on S_n. If $D \neq E_\infty$, then since D and E_∞ are irreducible, we have $D \cdot E_\infty \geq 0$; since D cannot contain every curve C_λ, and since C_λ is irreducible, $D \cdot C \geq 0$. If

$$D = m_1 \cdot E_0 + m_2 \cdot C,$$

we see that $D \cdot E_\infty \geq 0 \Rightarrow m_2 \geq 0$, and $D \cdot C \geq 0 \Rightarrow m_1 \geq 0$; consequently

$$D \cdot D = n \cdot m_1^2 + 2m_1 m_2 \geq 0.$$

From this it follows that E_∞ is the only irreducible curve on S_n with negative self-intersection: for $n \neq 0$, then, S_n *is the unique* $\mathbb{P}^1$-*bundle over* $\mathbb{P}^1$ *having an irreducible curve of self-intersection* $-n$. In particular, we see that the spaces $\{S_n\}_{n \geq 0}$ are all distinct as abstract compact complex manifolds.

Note that the blow-up $\tilde{\mathbb{P}}^2$ of $\mathbb{P}^2$ at a point $p \in \mathbb{P}^2$ is an S_n: the proper transforms $\tilde{L}_\lambda$ of the pencil of lines $L_\lambda \subset \mathbb{P}^2$ through p form a pencil of disjoint irreducible rational curves on $\tilde{\mathbb{P}}^2$. Since the exceptional divisor E of the blow-up has self-intersection -1,

$$\tilde{\mathbb{P}}^2 \cong S_1.$$

To determine the class of the canonical bundle K of S_n, note that by the adjunction formula,

$$0 = \pi(E_0) = \frac{E_0 \cdot E_0 + K \cdot E_0}{2} + 1$$

$$\Rightarrow K \cdot E_0 = -n - 2$$

and

$$0 = \pi(C) = \frac{C \cdot C + C \cdot K}{2} + 1$$

$$\Rightarrow K \cdot C = -2.$$

Thus if $K = m_1 E_0 + m_2 C$, $K \cdot C = -2$ implies that $m_1 = -2$, and $E_0 \cdot K = -n - 2$ implies that $m_2 = n - 2$; i.e.,

$$K = -2E_0 + (n-2)C.$$

Finally, we would like to relate the surfaces S_n to one another geometrically. To do this, let $x \in S_n$ be any point not on E_∞, say $x \in C_\lambda$. Blow up x to obtain a surface $\tilde{S}_n \xrightarrow{\pi_1} S_n$; the proper transform $\tilde{C}_\lambda$ of C_λ will then have self-intersection -1 and can be blown down. If $\tilde{S}_n \xrightarrow{\pi_2} S$ is the blowing-down map, we notice that the curves $\{\pi_2(\pi_1^*(C_\lambda))\}_\lambda$ form a pencil of irreducible rational curves on S with self-intersection 0, and hence S is again a ruled surface. Moreover, since $\pi_1^* E_\infty \cdot \tilde{C}_{\lambda_0} = 1$,

$$\pi_2 \pi_1^* E_\infty \cdot \pi_2 \pi_1^* E_\infty = E_\infty \cdot E_\infty + 1 = -n + 1,$$

i.e., S contains an irreducible curve of self-intersection $-n+1$, and hence S is biholomorphic to S_{n-1}. As Figure 5 attempts to show, the image $\pi_2(E_x) \subset S$ of the exceptional curve E_x of π_1 becomes an element of the pencil $\pi_2 \pi_1^* C_\lambda$, while $\tilde{E}_0^{(2)} = \pi_2 \pi_1^* E_0$ is the curve corresponding to a section τ of H^{n-1} with a single pole; the role of E_0 is taken over by $\pi_2 \pi_1^* E_\sigma$ for some E_σ passing through x. To obtain S_{n+1} from S_n, conversely, we blow up a point x on E_∞ and blow down the proper transform of the curve C_λ through x. We have seen this process once before, when we showed that $S_0 = \mathbb{P}^1 \times \mathbb{P}^1$ could be obtained by blowing up a point $q \notin E$ on the blow-up $\tilde{\mathbb{P}}^2 = S_1$ of $\mathbb{P}^2$ at a point p, and blowing down the proper transform of the line $\overline{pq}$.

The proof of Noether's lemma is at last complete: since the surfaces S_n are all obtained from one another by blowing up and down, and since $S_0 = \mathbb{P}^1 \times \mathbb{P}^1$ and S_1 are rational, it follows that *all the surfaces* S_n *are rational.*

The General Rational Surface

Having given a fairly thorough account of the rational ruled surfaces S_n, we may now complete our picture of rational surfaces in general with the

Theorem.   *Every rational surface is the blow-up of* $\mathbb{P}^2$ *or* S_n.

Proof.   We begin by making two observations. First, we claim that *any surface S with a pencil $|C|$ of irreducible rational curves is either* $\mathbb{P}^2$ *or* S_n. This is not hard: as we have seen, if we blow up the base points of the pencil $|C|$, we obtain a surface $\tilde{S} \to S$ with a pencil of disjoint irreducible

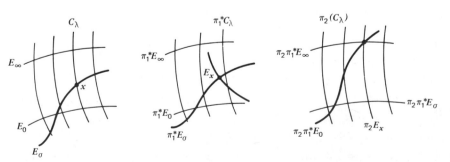

Figure 5

rational curves; $\tilde{S}$ must then be a rational ruled surface. But $b_2(S_n)=2$, and since the second Betti number increases by 1 every time we blow up, it follows that either S is rational ruled, or $b_2(S)=1$. In the latter case, since S is rational, we have

$$b_1(S) = b_3(S) = 0;$$

moreover, $P_n(S)=H^0(S,\mathcal{O}(K^n))=0$ for all n implies that K_S is not positive. By the lemma at the end of the discussion on cubic surfaces, then, we find that $S\cong\mathbb{P}^2$.

Our second point is more obvious. Suppose C is a curve on an algebraic surface S, L a positive line bundle, and $C\cdot L=n$. Then C *cannot be linearly equivalent to a sum of more than* n *effective divisors* D_i: if $C=\sum_{i=1}^{n+1}D_i$, we would have $L\cdot C=\sum L\cdot D_i\geqslant n+1$.

Now let S be any rational surface, $\{C_\lambda\}$ a pencil of rational curves on S, not all reducible. We want to show that either

1. S can be blown down; or
2. S is rational ruled or $\mathbb{P}^2$.

Since any surface can be blown down only finitely many times, this will suffice to prove the theroem.

If all the curves C_λ on S are irreducible, then by the above argument we are done. Suppose then that C_0 is reducible and write

$$C_0 = \sum_{\nu=1}^{k} a_\nu C_\nu, \qquad a_\nu > 0.$$

We note first that *all the curves* C_ν *must be rational*. This follows from writing

$$0 = \pi(C_\lambda) = \frac{\left(\sum a_\nu C_\nu\right)\cdot\left(\sum a_\nu C_\nu\right)+K_S\cdot\left(\sum a_\nu C_\nu\right)}{2}+1$$

$$= \frac{1}{2}\Big[\left(\sum(a_\nu-1)C_\nu\right)\cdot\left(\sum a_\nu C_\nu\right)$$

$$+ \sum_{\nu\neq\nu'} a_{\nu'}C_\nu\cdot C_{\nu'}+\sum_\nu a_\nu C_\nu\cdot C_\nu+\sum a_\nu\cdot K_S\cdot C_\nu+2\Big]$$

$$= \frac{1}{2}\left(\sum(a_\nu-1)C_\nu\right)\cdot\left(\sum a_\nu C_\nu\right)+\sum a_\nu\pi(C_\nu)+\sum_{\nu\neq\nu'} a_{\nu'}C_\nu\cdot C_{\nu'}-(k-1).$$

$C_\nu\cdot(\sum a_\nu C_\nu)=C_\nu\cdot C_\lambda\geqslant 0$, so the first term is nonnegative; since C_0 is connected, $\sum_{\nu\neq\nu'}C_\nu\cdot C_{\nu'}\geqslant k-1$ and so the third term is also nonnegative. It follows that $\sum a_\nu\pi(C_\nu)=0$, and hence $\pi(C_\nu)=0$. Since $C_\lambda\cdot C_\lambda\geqslant 0$, by the adjunction formula

$$0 = \pi(C_\lambda) = \frac{C_\lambda\cdot C_\lambda + K_S\cdot C_\lambda}{2}+1,$$

we see that $K_S \cdot C_\lambda < 0$, hence $K_S \cdot C_{\nu_0} < 0$ for some ν_0. Now if $C_{\nu_0} \cdot C_{\nu_0} < 0$, it follows that $C_{\nu_0} \cdot C_{\nu_0} = C_{\nu_0} \cdot K = -1$ and hence C_{ν_0} can be blown down; in this case we are done. Suppose on the other hand $C_{\nu_0} \cdot C_{\nu_0} \geqslant 0$; then, since S is rational, $\chi(\mathcal{O}_S) = 1$, and by Riemann Roch,

$$h^0(C_{\nu_0}) + h^0(K_S - C_{\nu_0}) \geqslant 1 + \frac{C_{\nu_0} \cdot C_{\nu_0} - C_{\nu_0} \cdot K_S}{2} > 1.$$

But $h^0(K_S) = 0$ implies $h^0(K_S - C_{\nu_0}) = 0$ and therefore $h^0(C_{\nu_0}) > 1$, i.e., C_{ν_0} is *itself an element of a pencil of rational curves*, which we will denote $\{C_\lambda^1\}$.

If all the curves C_λ^1 are irreducible, we are done; if not, let C_0^1 be a reducible element of $\{C_\lambda^1\}$ and write

$$C_0^1 = \sum a_\nu^1 \cdot C_\nu^1.$$

Again, $\pi(C_\lambda^1) = 0$ implies $K \cdot C_\lambda^1 < 0$, so $K \cdot C_{\nu_0}^1 < 0$ for some $C_{\nu_0}^1$, and either $C_{\nu_0}^1$ can be blown down or $C_{\nu_0}^1$ is itself an element of a pencil of rational curves $\{C_\lambda^2\}$. If S has no exceptional curves and is not $\mathbb{P}^2$ or S_n, we can continue to generate new pencils in this way. But after n steps we can write

$$C_\lambda = \sum_{\nu \neq \nu_0} C_\nu + \sum_{\nu \neq \nu_0} C_\nu^1 + \cdots + \sum C_\nu^n,$$

and so eventually either every element of the pencil we obtain will be irreducible or S will contain an exceptional curve.   Q.E.D.

Surfaces of Minimal Degree

In Section 3 of Chapter 1 we showed that the smallest possible degree of an irreducible, nondegenerate variety $M \subset \mathbb{P}^n$ of dimension m is $n - m + 1$. We can now describe exactly the surfaces that achieve this minimal degree. We will start by constructing some such surfaces, and then show that all surfaces of minimal degree may be obtained in this way.

Consider the linear system $|E_0 + kC|$ on the rational ruled surface $S_n = \mathbb{P}(H^n \oplus \mathbb{C})$. If σ is any meromorphic section of H^n having exactly k poles, then, as we have seen, the corresponding curve

$$E_\sigma = \sigma(\mathbb{P}^1) \subset S_n$$

is homologous, hence linearly equivalent, to $E_0 + kC$. Conversely, suppose D is any irreducible curve linearly equivalent to $E_0 + kC$. Then D meets each fiber C of the projection map $S_n \xrightarrow{\pi} \mathbb{P}^1$ exactly once, and away from the k points $\mu_1, \ldots, \mu_k \in \mathbb{P}^1$ over which D meets E_∞ we can define a section σ of H^n by

$$\overline{(\sigma(\mu), 1)} = D \cap C_\mu.$$

σ then extends to a global meromorphic section of H^n, having poles at $\mu_1, \ldots, \mu_k$, such that $D = E_\sigma$.

Note in particular that the linear system $|E_0 + kC|$ has no base points; we denote the corresponding map $\iota_{E_0 + kC}$ by $\varphi_{k,n}$.

To specify a global meromorphic section of σ having k poles, we have to specify first its polar divisor $(\sigma)_\infty = \mu_1 + \cdots + \mu_k$—involving k degrees of freedom—and then specify σ as an element of the vector space $H^0(\mathbb{P}^1, \mathcal{O}(H^n + \mu_1 + \cdots + \mu_k))$—involving $h^0(H^n + \mu_1 + \cdots + \mu_k) = n + k + 1$ degrees of freedom. Thus we may expect that the linear system $|E_0 + kC|$ is at least $k + (n + k + 1) = (n + 2k + 1)$-dimensional. The Riemann-Roch theorem confirms our guess: since $h^0(K_{S_n}) = 0$, $h^2(E_0 + kC) = h^0(K_{S_n} - E_0 - kC) = 0$, and we have

$$h^0(E_0 + kC) \geqslant 1 + \frac{(E_0 + kC) \cdot (E_0 + kC) - (E_0 + kC) \cdot (-2E_0 + (n-2)C)}{2}$$

$$= 1 + \frac{n + 2k + 2n + 2k - n + 2}{2}$$

$$= n + 2k + 2.$$

But now $\varphi_{k,n}$ maps S_n into projective space of dimension $h^0(E_0 + kC) - 1$ as a nondegenerate surface of degree

$$(E_0 + kC) \cdot (E_0 + kC) = n + 2k,$$

and so $h^0(E_0 + kC) - 1 \leqslant n + 2k + 1$. Thus equality must hold, and we see that *the image* $S_{k,n}$ *of* S_n *under* $\varphi_{k,n}$ *is a surface of minimal degree* $n + 2k$ *in* $\mathbb{P}^{n+2k+1}$.

We can give a nice description of the surfaces $S_{k,n}$ as follows: recall first that

$$E_0 \cdot (E_0 + kC) = n + k,$$
$$E_\infty \cdot (E_0 + kC) = k,$$
$$C \cdot (E_0 + kC) = 1.$$

In fact, we see from the correspondence between irreducible curves $E_\sigma \in |E_0 + kC|$ and meromorphic sections σ of H^n having k poles that the restrictions of $|E_0 + kC|$ to the curves E_0, E_∞, and $C \cong \mathbb{P}^1$ are the complete linear systems $|H_{\mathbb{P}^1}^{n+k}|$, $|H_{\mathbb{P}^1}^k|$, and $|H_{\mathbb{P}^1}|$, respectively: given any collection of points $\mu_1, \ldots, \mu_{n+k}, \nu_1, \ldots, \nu_k \in \mathbb{P}^1$ we can always find a meromorphic section σ of H^n with

$$(\sigma)_0 = \sum \mu_i, \qquad (\sigma)_\infty = \sum \nu_i;$$

likewise, given any point $\overline{(\xi, 1)} \in C_\lambda$, we can find σ with $\sigma(\lambda) = \xi$. Thus:

1. The image $\dot{D}_0$ of E_0 under $\varphi_{k,n}$ is a rational normal curve in some linear subspace $V_{n+k} \subset \mathbb{P}^{n+2k+1}$.

2. The image D_∞ of E_∞ under $\varphi_{k,n}$ is a rational normal curve in some linear subspace $V_k \subset \mathbb{P}^{n+2k+1}$.

3. The image L_λ of the curves C_λ under $\varphi_{k,n}$ are straight lines meeting D_0 and D_∞. Note that $S_{k,n}$ thus lies in the linear span of V_k and V_{n+k}, so

that these subspaces are necessarily complementary (i.e., disjoint) in $\mathbb{P}^{n+2k+1}$.

The surface $S_{k,n}$ consists of the union of the straight lines joining points p on the rational normal curve $D_0 \subset V_{n+k}$ with corresponding points $\psi(p)$ on the rational normal curve $D_\infty \subset V_k$.

Conversely, suppose that V_k, V_{n+k} are complementary linear subspaces in $\mathbb{P}^{n+2k+1}$, D_∞ and D_0 rational normal curves in V_k and V_{n+k}, respectively, and $\psi : D_0 \to D_\infty$ an isomorphism between the two curves. For each point $\mu \in D_0$, let L_μ be the line $\overline{\mu, \psi(\mu)}$ in $\mathbb{P}^{n+2k+1}$, and let

$$S = \bigcup_{\mu \in D_0} L_\mu$$

be the corresponding surface. To compute the degree of S, note that the generic hyperplane $H \subset \mathbb{P}^{n+2k+1}$ containing D_∞ meets D_0 transversely in $\deg D_0 = n + k$ points $\mu_1, \ldots, \mu_{n+k}$; we then have

$$H \cap S = D_\infty + L_{\mu_1} + \cdots + L_{\mu_{n+k}},$$

all components occurring with multiplicity 1. Therefore

$$\deg S = \deg H \cap S = n + 2k,$$

and S is a surface of minimal degree.

Now the lines $\{L_\mu\}$ are disjoint: If L_μ met $L_{\mu'}$, the 2-plane spanned by L_μ and $L_{\mu'}$ in $\mathbb{P}^{n+2k+1}$ would have to meet V_{n+k} in the line $\overline{\mu\mu'}$ and V_k in the line $\overline{\psi(\mu), \psi(\mu')}$, so that V_k and V_{n-k} would intersect. Thus *the map*

$$S \xrightarrow{\pi} D_0 \cong \mathbb{P}^1$$

sending L_μ to μ expresses S as a rational ruled surface. To determine which rational ruled surface S is, consider again a hyperplane section $D = H \cdot S = D_\infty + L_{\mu_1} + \cdots + L_{\mu_{n+k}}$ above. We have

$$n + 2k = D \cdot D$$
$$= D_\infty \cdot D_\infty + 2 D_\infty \cdot \left(\sum L_{\mu_i} \right).$$

But each line L_{μ_i} meets D_∞ transversely (otherwise it would lie in V_k), and so

$$D_\infty \cdot \left(\sum L_{\mu_i} \right) = n + k,$$

and hence

$$D_\infty \cdot D_\infty = -n,$$

so

$$S \cong S_n$$

with D_∞ corresponding to E_∞. Moreover, the hyperplane section of S is

$$D = D_\infty + L_{\mu_1} + \cdots + L_{\mu_{n+k}}$$

$$\sim E_\infty + (n+k)C$$

$$\sim E_0 + kC,$$

so that indeed $S = S_{k,n}$.

The surfaces $S_{k,n}$ are called *rational normal scrolls*. Note that in case $n > 0$ the curve $D_\infty \subset S_{k,n}$ is unique; it is called the *directrix* of $S_{k,n}$.

Now we can apply our theorem on rational surfaces to prove the

Proposition. *Every nondegenerate irreducible surface of degree* $m-1$ *in* $\mathbb{P}^m$ *is either a rational normal scroll or the Veronese surface* $\iota_{2H}(\mathbb{P}^2) \subset \mathbb{P}^5$.

Proof. Note first that if S is an irreducible surface of degree $m-1$ in $\mathbb{P}^m$, then any line L meeting S in three or more points must lie in S. To see this, suppose that L meets S in three points p_1, p_2, p_3 but does not lie in S. The points of intersection of S with a generic $(m-2)$-plane V_{m-2} containing L span V_{m-2}, and so $V_{m-2} \cap S$ must contain at least $m-3$ points $q_1, \ldots, q_{m-3}$ lying outside L—but $^\#(V_{m-2} \cdot S) = m-1$ and so it follows that V_{m-2} has a curve in common with S. The image $\pi_L(S)$ of S under projection from L into an $(m-2)$-plane W_{m-2} thus meets every $(m-4)$-plane in W_{m-2} in a curve, and so has dimension 3, an absurdity.

In particular, we see that if S has a singular point p, then for any point $q \in S$ the line $\overline{pq}$ must lie in S. S must therefore be the cone $\cup_{q \in C} \overline{pq}$ through p over any hyperplane section $C = S \cap H$ of S not containing p. Now C is nondegenerate and irreducible, since S is, and has degree $m-1$ in $II \cong \mathbb{P}^{m-1}$, hence is a rational normal curve. Thus $S = S_{0, m-1}$ *is the cone over a rational normal curve.*

The argument for S smooth is by induction. The result clearly holds for $m = 3$: as we have seen, the smooth quadric surface in $\mathbb{P}^3$ is just the image $S_{1,0}$ of $S_0 = \mathbb{P}^1 \times \mathbb{P}^1$. Suppose the result is proved for all $m \leqslant m_0$, $m_0 \geqslant 4$, and let S be a smooth irreducible nondegenerate surface of degree $m-1$ in $\mathbb{P}^m$. Assume first that S contains only finitely many lines. A generic point p of S will then lie on no lines on S, and since any line meeting S three times lies on S, it follows that no two points of S are collinear with p. This means that the projection map

$$\pi_p: S \to \mathbb{P}^{m-1}$$

gives an embedding of the blow-up $\tilde{S}$ of S at p as a surface of degree $m-2$ in $\mathbb{P}^{m-1}$. By induction hypothesis, then, we see that

1. S is rational; and
2. $\chi(S) = \chi(\tilde{S}) - 1 \leqslant 3$.

But we have seen that the only rational surface of Euler characteristic 3 is $\mathbb{P}^2$; so $S \cong \mathbb{P}^2$. Now, any base-point-free linear system on $\mathbb{P}^2$ has degree k^2 and dimension at most $((k+1)(k+2)/2) - 1$ for some k, and so the only embedding of $\mathbb{P}^2$ as a surface of minimal degree is that given by the complete linear system of conics; thus S must be the Veronese surface.

Suppose now that S does contain in irreducible one-parameter family $\{L_\mu\}_{\mu \in C}$ of lines. Note first that two generic lines in the family must be disjoint: if every two lines met, then every three lines would either lie in a plane—in which case every line in that plane would meet S three times and so lie in S—or meet in a point, with independent directions—impossible since S is assumed smooth. Set $b = [m/2]$ and choose b lines $L_1, \ldots, L_b$ of the family. $L_1, \ldots, L_b$ together span at most an $(m-1)$-plane; take H a hyperplane containing $L_1, \ldots, L_b$ and consider the intersection $H \cdot S$. Since H has intersection number 1 with a line, there must be a unique irreducible component of the divisor $H \cdot S$ having intersection number 1 with L_μ; call this curve D_∞. The remaining components of $H \cdot S$, having intersection number 0 with L_μ, must be themselves lines of the family; thus we can write

$$H \cdot S = D_\infty + L_1 + \cdots + L_b + L_{b+1} + \cdots + L_c.$$

Consider the curve D_∞. By the above, D_∞ has degree $k = m - c - 1$. On the other hand, the linear span of D_∞ must be a least a k-plane: otherwise, for any $m - k$ points $p_1, \ldots, p_{m-k}$ of $S - D_\infty$ we could find a hyperplane H' containing D_∞ and the points $p_1, \ldots, p_{m-k}$, and hence also the lines of the family passing through $p_1, \ldots, p_{m-k}$; the degree of $H' \cdot S$ would then be at least m, which is impossible. Thus D_∞ spans a k-plane, i.e., D_∞ *is a rational normal curve.*

Now let $L_1, \ldots, L_k$ be any lines of the family. $L_1, \ldots, L_k$ span at most a $(2k-1)$-plane in $\mathbb{P}^m$ (note that since $c \geqslant b = [m/2]$, $k = m - c - 1$ must be strictly less than $m/2$, so $L_1, \ldots, L_k$ all lie in a proper subspace of $\mathbb{P}^m$) which intersects the linear span $\overline{D_\infty}$ in at least the $(k-1)$-plane spanned by the points of intersection $L_1 \cdot D_\infty, \ldots, L_k \cdot D_\infty$. In fact, the span of the lines L_i cannot contain D_∞: if it did, for any $m - 2k$ points $p_1, \ldots, p_{m-2k} \in S - D_\infty - \cup L_i$, the lines L_i and the points p_i would all lie in a hyperplane, which would then contain the curve D_∞, the k lines L_i, and the $m - 2k$ lines of the family passing through the points p_i—altogether a curve of degree m. Thus we can find a hyperplane H in $\mathbb{P}^m$ containing the lines $L_1, \ldots, L_k$ but not D_∞.

Again, the hyperplane section $H \cdot S$ will contain one component having intersection number 1 with L_μ; call this curve D_0. Note that

$$D_0 \cdot D_\infty = (H \cdot S - L_1 - \cdots - L_k) \cdot D_\infty = 0$$

so D_0 and D_∞ will be disjoint. Since every line L_μ meets both D_0 and D_∞,

S lies in the linear span of D_0 and D_∞, so D_0 must span at least an $(m-k-1)$-plane; on the other hand,

$$\deg D_0 \leqslant \deg(H \cdot S - L_1 - \cdots - L_k) = m - k - 1$$

and it follows that D_0 *is a rational normal curve of degree* k, *in a* k-*plane complementary to the span of* D_∞. Thus S is the rational normal scroll $S_{k,m-2k-1}$, and the result is proved.　　　　　　　　　　　　Q.E.D.

The reader may find it amusing to verify directly what was in effect proved on p. 520: that the image of $S_{k,n}$ under projection from a point lying off the directrix $D_\infty \subset S_{k,n}$ is $S_{k,n-1}$, while the image of $S_{k,n}$ under projection from a point $q \in D_\infty$ is $S_{k-1,n+1}$.

Curves of Maximal Genus

We gave, in the section on linear systems on curves, Castelnuovo's upper bound on the genus of an irreducible nondegenerate curve B of degree d in $\mathbb{P}^n$. Briefly, we showed that if D was the hyperplane divisor of $B \subset \mathbb{P}^n$, then

$$h^0(kD) - h^0((k-1)D) \begin{cases} \geqslant k(n-1)+1, & k \leqslant m = \left[\dfrac{d-1}{n-1}\right], \\ = d, & k \geqslant m \end{cases}$$

leading directly to

$$(*) \quad \begin{cases} h^0(D) \geqslant n+1, \\ h^0(2D) \geqslant 3(n-1)+3, \\ \quad \vdots \\ h^0((m+j)D) \leqslant \dfrac{m(m+1)}{2}(n-1)+m+1+jd, \end{cases}$$

and the last equality, for $j \gg 0$, gives by Riemann-Roch

$$g(B) \leqslant m\left(d - \frac{m+1}{2}(n-2) - 1\right).$$
$$= \frac{m(m-1)}{2}(n-1) + m\varepsilon \quad \text{where} \quad d-1 = m(n-1) + \varepsilon.$$

We can now give a fairly complete description of those curves of degree $d > 2n$ that achieve this bound—called *Castelnuovo curves*—and, in so doing, verify that the bound is indeed sharp for all d and n.

To begin with, we note that if $C \subset \mathbb{P}^n$ is a Castelnuovo curve, equality must hold in all the inequalities above. In particular, we see that

$$h^0(C, \mathcal{O}(2H)) = 3n;$$

and since $h^0(\mathbb{P}^n, \mathcal{O}(2H)) = (n+1)(n+2)/2$, this implies that

> *The linear system* W *of quadrics in* $\mathbb{P}^n$ *containing* C *has dimension at least* $(n-1)(n-2)/2 - 1$.

Since, moreover, no quadric containing C can contain a hyperplane, the restriction of W to a hyperplane $\mathbb{P}^{n-1} \subset \mathbb{P}^n$ is injective; thus the linear system of quadrics in $n-1$ containing the points $\Gamma = C \cap \mathbb{P}^{n-1}$ likewise has dimension at least $(n-1)(n-2)/2 - 1$. Inasmuch as the linear system of all quadrics in $\mathbb{P}^{n-1}$ has dimension only $n(n+1)/2 - 1$, this means that

> *The points of a generic hyperplane section* $\Gamma = C \cap \mathbb{P}^{n-1}$ *of* C *impose only* $2n - 1$ *conditions on quadrics.*

Now this is certainly a very strong statement. As we saw in the original discussion of Castelnuovo's bound, *any* $2n - 1$ points in general position in $\mathbb{P}^{n-1}$ must impose independent conditions on quadrics; here we have an arbitrary number $d = \deg C$ of points imposing only this smallest possible number of conditions. Indeed, from our previous encounter with the phenomena of superabundance in the discussion of cubic surfaces, we may expect that the extreme failure of the points of Γ to impose independent conditions on quadrics should have strong geometric consequences. The problem is, it simply is not obvious how one should proceed from this hypothesis. To Castelnuovo, however, it must have been clear; after spending the first 30 pages of his original article arriving at this point, he draws the correct conclusion in a paragraph. The essential point seems to have been a familiarity with certain projective-geometric constructions called *Steiner constructions*, which we now describe.

Steiner Constructions

Let p_1 and p_2 be points in the plane. Parameterize the two pencils $\{L_1(\lambda)\}$ and $\{L_2(\lambda)\}$ of lines through p_1 and p_2 respectively by $\lambda \in \mathbb{P}^1$, choosing the parameterizations so that the one line $\overline{p_1 p_2}$ common to the two pencils corresponds to different values of λ—that is, so that $L_1(\lambda) \neq L_2(\lambda)$ for all λ. Then the curve

$$C = \bigcup_\lambda L_1(\lambda) \cap L_2(\lambda)$$

is clearly irreducible and nondegenerate, containing the points p_1 and p_2 but not lying in the line $\overline{p_1 p_2}$. Its intersection with a general line $L \subset \mathbb{P}^2$ consists of the fixed points of the automorphism of L sending the point

$L \cap L_1(\lambda)$ to $L \cap L_2(\lambda)$; since there can be at most two such fixed points it follows that *C is a conic curve.*

Note that given three additional points p_3, p_4, and p_5 in the plane, no two collinear with either p_1 or p_2, we may choose our parameterizations of the pencils L_1 and L_2 so that $L_1(0)$ and $L_2(0)$ both contain p_3, $L_1(1)$ and $L_2(1)$ contain p_4, and $L_1(\infty)$ and $L_2(\infty)$ contain p_5. If in addition we assume that p_3, p_4, and p_5 lie off the line $\overline{p_1 p_2}$ and are not all three collinear, then these parameterizations satisfy our requirement that the line $\overline{p_1 p_2}$ correspond to different λ in the two pencils. If indeed $\overline{p_1 p_2} = L_1(\lambda_0) = L_2(\lambda_0)$, then the automorphism of the line $L = \overline{p_3 p_4}$ taking $L \cap L_1(\lambda)$ to $L \cap L_2(\lambda)$ would fix the three points p_3, p_4, and $L \cap \overline{p_1 p_2}$, and so would be the identity; we would then have

$$p_5 = L_1(\infty) \cap L_2(\infty) = L_1(\infty) \cap L \in L.$$

We see, accordingly, that we may construct a smooth conic through any five points in the plane, no three collinear.

Classically, the common parameterization of the two pencils L_1 and L_2 was given geometrically by choosing two auxiliary lines M_1 and M_2 and an auxiliary point $q \notin M_1, M_2$, and for each line $M(\lambda)$ through q letting $L_1(\lambda)$ be the line joining p_1 and the point $M_1 \cap M(\lambda)$, $L_2(\lambda)$ the line joining p_2 and $M_2 \cap M(\lambda)$. Thus, for example, to construct the conic through $p_1, \ldots, p_5$ one could take

$$M_1 = \overline{p_3 p_4}, \qquad M_2 = \overline{p_3 p_5}, \qquad q = \overline{p_1 p_5} \cap \overline{p_2 p_4}.$$

This construction may be generalized to higher dimensional space in many ways, two of which are the following:

1. If V_1, V_2 are two $(n-2)$-planes in $\mathbb{P}^n$, we may choose any parameterization of the two pencils of hyperplanes $\{H_1(\lambda)\}$ and $\{H_2(\lambda)\}$ through V_1 and V_2 respectively such that $H_1(\lambda) \neq H_2(\lambda)$ for all λ, and consider the locus

$$Q = \bigcup_\lambda H_1(\lambda) \cap H_2(\lambda).$$

As in the previous construction, Q is readily seen to be an irreducible, nondegenerate hypersurface, and hence a quadric, intersecting a general line $L \subset \mathbb{P}^n$ in the fixed points of the automorphism of L sending $L \cap H_1(\lambda)$ to $L \cap H_2(\lambda)$. In the terminology of Section 1 of Chapter 6, Q is a quadric of rank either 3 or 4, with vertex $V_1 \cap V_2$.

2. Let $p_1, \ldots, p_n$ be linearly independent points in $\mathbb{P}^n$, and let $\{H_i(\lambda)\}$ be the pencil of hyperplanes containing the $(n-2)$-plane V_i spanned by $p_1, \ldots, \hat{p}_i, \ldots, p_n$; choose the parameterizations so the one hyperplane $V = \overline{p_1, \ldots, p_n}$ common to all the pencils corresponds to n different values of λ. Then for each λ, the planes $H_1(\lambda), \ldots, H_n(\lambda)$ meet only in a point: if none

of the planes $H_i(\lambda)$ are equal to V then the intersection $H_1(\lambda) \cap \ldots \cap H_n(\lambda)$ cannot meet V and so must be a point; while if $H_i(\lambda) = V$ then $H_j(\lambda) \cap H_i(\lambda)$ is just V_j, and the intersection $H_1(\lambda) \cap \ldots \cap H_n(\lambda) = p_i$. Thus the curve

$$C = \bigcup_{\lambda} H_1(\lambda) \cap \ldots \cap H_n(\lambda)$$

is irreducible; and as before it is nondegenerate, containing the points $p_1, \ldots, p_n$ but not lying in the hyperplane V they span. Its degree must therefore be at least n; and since its intersection with a general hyperplane $H \subset \mathbb{P}^n$ consists of the fixed points of the automorphism of H sending the point $H \cap H_1(\lambda) \cap \ldots \cap H_{n-1}(\lambda)$ to $H \cap H_2(\lambda) \cap \ldots \cap H_n(\lambda)$—that is, the eigenspaces of the corresponding linear transformation of H—we see that the degree of C must be exactly n, that is, C is a *rational normal curve*.

Note that if we set

$$Q_{ij} = \bigcup_{\lambda} H_i(\lambda) \cap H_j(\lambda)$$

then C will be the intersection of the quadrics Q_{ij}; thus we see that

A rational normal curve is cut out by quadrics.

Now, choose three additional points p_{n+1}, p_{n+2}, and p_{n+3} such that the points $p_1, \ldots, p_{n+3}$ are in general position. As in the construction of the plane conic, then, we can choose our parameterizations of the pencils H_i so that

$$p_{n+1} \in H_i(0), \qquad p_{n+2} \in H_i(1), \qquad p_{n+3} \in H_i(\infty)$$

for all i. This choice satisfies our requirement. If for some $\lambda \in \mathbb{P}^1$ we had $H_i(\lambda) = H_j(\lambda) = V$, the automorphism of the line $L = \overline{p_{n+1}p_{n+2}}$ sending $L \cap H_i(\lambda)$ to $L \cap H_j(\lambda)$ would fix the points p_{n+1}, p_{n+2} and $L \cap V$, and so would be the identity; $H_i(\infty) \cap H_j(\infty)$ would then meet L and so the $n+1$ points $p_1, \ldots, \hat{p}_i, \ldots, \hat{p}_j, \ldots, p_n, p_{n+1}, p_{n+2}$, and p_{n+3} would all lie in a hyperplane. Having chosen our parameterizations in this way, we then see that all the points $p_1, \ldots, p_{n+3}$ will lie on C; thus we can find a rational normal curve in $\mathbb{P}^n$ containing any $n+3$ points in general position. Indeed, such a curve is unique: if D is another rational normal curve containing $p_1, \ldots, p_{n+3}$, then each hyperplane $H_i(\lambda)$ will meet D in $p_1, \ldots, \hat{p}_i, \ldots, p_n$ and one more point, which we may denote $q_i(\lambda)$. But now the automorphism ϕ_{ij} of D sending $q_i(\lambda)$ to $q_j(\lambda)$ for each λ fixes p_{n+1}, p_{n+2}, and p_{n+3}, and so is the identity; thus $q_i(\lambda) = H_1(\lambda) \cap \ldots \cap H_n(\lambda)$ and correspondingly $D = C$. In sum, then,

Through any $n+3$ *points in general position in* $\mathbb{P}^n$ *there passes a unique rational normal curve.*

We note in passing some of the other variations on the theme of Steiner constructions. For example, we may take three nets of planes in $\mathbb{P}^3$ and parameterize each by $\lambda \in \mathbb{P}^2$; the union of the intersection of corresponding planes will then be a cubic surface. One can also take two pencils of planes in $\mathbb{P}^3$ parameterized by $\lambda \in \mathbb{P}^1$ and a correspondence $T: \mathbb{P}^1 \to \mathbb{P}^1$, and take the union of corresponding pairs of planes. If T has bidegree $(1,2)$ the resulting surface will be a cubic surface with a double line, while if T has bidegree $(2,2)$ the resulting surface is a quartic with two double lines; both of these surfaces will be discussed in Section 6 of this chapter.

Now we can without difficulty prove

Castelnuovo's Lemma. *A collection* $p_1, \ldots, p_d$ *of* $d \geq 2n+3$ *points in general position in* $\mathbb{P}^n$ *which impose only* $2n+1$ *conditions on quadrics lies on a rational normal curve.*

Proof. First note that, since any $2n+1$ points in general position in $\mathbb{P}^n$ impose independent conditions on quadrics, any quadric containing $2n+1$ of the points $p_1, \ldots, p_d$ will contain them all. Now let $\{H_i(\lambda)\}$ and $\{H(\lambda)\}$ be the pencils of hyperplanes in $\mathbb{P}^n$ through $p_1, \ldots, \hat{p}_i, \ldots, p_n$ and $p_{n+1}, \ldots, p_{2n-1}$, respectively, parameterized so that

$$p_{2n} \in H_i(0), H(0); \quad p_{2n+1} \in H_i(1), H(1); \quad p_{2n+2} \in H_i(\infty), H(\infty)$$

for all i. Then the quadrics

$$Q_i = \bigcup_\lambda H_i(\lambda) \cap H(\lambda),$$

containing the points $p_1, \ldots, \hat{p}_i, \ldots, p_{2n+2}$ must contain the points $p_{2n+3}, \ldots, p_d$ as well; that is, the remaining points $p_{2n+3}, \ldots, p_d$ also lie on corresponding hyperplanes of the pencils H_i, and hence lie on the rational normal curve

$$C = \bigcup_\lambda H_1(\lambda) \cap \ldots \cap H_n(\lambda).$$

We have shown then that $p_1, \ldots, p_n, p_{2n}, \ldots, p_d$ all lie on a rational normal curve, and hence after rearranging that any $d - n + 1 > n + 3$ of the points $p_1, \ldots, p_n$ do also; since a rational normal curve is determined by any $n+3$ points this implies that all the points $p_1, \ldots, p_n$ lie on a rational normal curve. Q.E.D.

Returning to our Castelnuovo curve $C \subset \mathbb{P}^n$, it is now straightforward to describe C explicitly. As we have seen, the linear system W of quadrics in $\mathbb{P}^n$ through C cuts out on a general hyperplane $\mathbb{P}^{n-1} \subset \mathbb{P}^n$ a linear system of quadrics through the hyperplane section $\Gamma = C \cap \mathbb{P}^{n-1}$ having codimension $2n-1$ in the system of all quadrics in $\mathbb{P}^{n-1}$; clearly these are all the quadrics containing Γ. Now, by Castelnuovo's lemma, Γ lies on a rational normal curve $D \subset \mathbb{P}^{n-1}$; since Γ consists of $d \geq 2n-1$ points, any quadric will contain Γ if and only if it contains D; and since a rational normal curve is cut out by quadrics it follows that the base locus of the linear system W intersects the hyperplane $\mathbb{P}^{n-1}$ in the rational normal curve D. But then the base locus of W must be a surface of degree $n-1$ in $\mathbb{P}^n$; so by our previous result,

> A Castelnuovo curve lies on either a rational normal scroll or the Veronese surface.

It is easily checked that any smooth plane curve, mapped to $\mathbb{P}^5$ via the Veronese map, is a Castelnuovo curve; in what follows we shall assume that C lies on a rational normal scroll $S = S_{k,1}$. We ask first for the homology class of the curve C on S; a priori we may write

$$C \sim aH + bL$$

where H and L are the classes of a hyperplane section of and line on S respectively. We have

$$d = \deg C = H \cdot C = a(n-1) + b$$

so $b = d - a(n-1)$; and applying the adjunction formula,

$$g(C) \leqslant (C) = \frac{C \cdot C + K_S \cdot C}{2} + 1$$

$$= \frac{(aH + (d - a(n-1))L) \cdot ((a-2)H + (d - (a-1)(n-1) - 2)L)}{2} + 1$$

$$= \tfrac{1}{2}(a(a-2)(n-1) + (a-2)(d - a(n-1)) + a(d - a(n-1) + n - 3))$$

$$= \frac{(a-1)(a-2)}{2}(n-1) + (a-1)(d - (a-1)(n-1) - 1)$$

This in fact achieves our bound exactly when $a = m + 1$, and, in case $\varepsilon = 0$, when $a = m$ as well. We see, then, that the curve C must be smooth, and have either class $(m+1)H - (n-2-\varepsilon)L$ in general or class $mH + L$ when $C = 0$. Another way to express this, since the linear series cut out on a rational normal scroll by hypersurfaces of degree m is complete for all m, is to say that C plus any $n - 2 - \varepsilon$ lines of S form the complete intersection of S with a hypersurface of degree $m + 1$ in $\mathbb{P}^n$, or, in the exceptional case, that C together with the directrix E_∞ of S and any $n - k - 2$ lines of S form the complete intersection of I with a hypersurface of degree $m + 1$.

Finally, to see that smooth irreducible curves with this homology class exist on the surface $S = S_{k,1}$ (at least for some k), we simply write

$$(m+1)H - (n-2-\varepsilon)L = (m+1)E_0 + (m(n-k-1) - k + 1 + \varepsilon)L.$$

Since the coefficient of L can, by a suitable choice of k, be made positive, we see that the linear system $|(m+1)H + (n-2-\varepsilon)L|$ on S has no base points and so the generic element is smooth; since any two components of a reducible curve homologous to $(m+1)H+(n-2-\varepsilon)L$ would meet, it follows that the generic element is irreducible as well.

Summing up, then, we can say that

The greatest possible genus of an irreducible nondegenerate curve C *of degree* d *in* $\mathbb{P}^n$ *is* $m(m-1)/2+m\varepsilon$, *where* $m=[(d-1)/(n-1)]$ *and* $d-1=m(n-1)+\varepsilon$. *Moreover, any curve achieving this bound is either*

1. *Residual to either* $n-2-\varepsilon$ *lines of* $n-k-2$ *lines plus the directrix in a complete intersection of a rational normal scroll* $S_{k,1}\subset\mathbb{P}^n$ *with a hypersurface of degree* $m+1$; *or*
2. *A smooth curve on the Veronese surface in* $\mathbb{P}^5$.

The Enriques-Petri Theorem

Recall from our initial discussion of curves of maximal genus that the curves of degree $d=2n$ in $\mathbb{P}^n$ having maximal genus are just the canonical curves of genus $g=n+1$. Much of the preceding analysis of extremal curves of degree greater than $2n$ applies as well in this case: for $C\subset\mathbb{P}^n$ a canonical curve, we have

$$h^0(L) = n+1, \qquad h^0(2L) = 3n,$$

and so the linear system $W\subset|2H|$ of quadrics in $\mathbb{P}^n$ containing C again has dimension

$$\dim W \geq \tfrac{1}{2}(n-1)(n-2)-1.$$

In addition, we see just as before that the restriction of W to a hyperplane is injective, and hence that the hyperplane section $\Gamma=C\cap\mathbb{P}^{n-1}$ imposes only $2n-1$ conditions on quadrics. At this point, our previous analysis breaks down: lacking $2n+1$ points, we cannot apply Castelnuovo's argument to prove that the hyperplane section of C lies on a rational normal curve. *If we hypothesize the existence of just one point of* S *not lying on* C, however, Castelnuovo's argument is again in force. To see this, we need only prove a slight strengthening of the basic general position lemma of Section 3, Chapter 2:

Basic Lemma II. *Let* $C\subset\mathbb{P}^n$ *be any nondegenerate curve,* $p\in\mathbb{P}^n$ *any point not lying on infinitely many chords of* C. *Then for* H *a generic hyperplane passing through* p, *the points*

$$\{p\}\cup(H\cap C)$$

are in general position.

Proof. We first show that for a generic hyperplane H containing p, the point p is linearly independent from any $n-1$ points of $H\cap C$. This is clear: by hypothesis, for generic H the projection map π_p of C from p onto a hyperplane $\mathbb{P}^{n-1}$ is one-to-one on $H \cap C$, and for any $n-1$ points $p_1,\ldots,p_{n-1} \in H \cap C$, p will lie in the linear span of $p_1,\ldots,p_{n-1}$ if and only if the points $\{\pi_p(p_i)\}$ are linearly dependent in $\mathbb{P}^{n-1}$. But by our original basic lemma, the generic hyperplane in $\mathbb{P}^{n-1}$ contains no such collection of points in $\pi_p(C)$.

To see that the generic H containing p will not contain n linearly dependent points of C, consider the incidence correspondence

$$I \subset C^n \times \mathbb{P}^{n*}$$

given by

$$I = \{(p_1,\ldots,p_n,H): p_i \in H\}$$

and let $J \subset I$ be given by

$$J = \{(p_1,\ldots,p_n,H): \dim \overline{p_1,\ldots,p_n} < n-1\}.$$

The projection map

$$\pi_1: J \to C^n$$

has fiber dimension at least 1. From the first half of our proof, moreover, we see that if every hyperplane through p contained n linearly dependent points $p_1,\ldots,p_n$ of C, then for a generic such hyperplane H the points $p_1,\ldots,p_n$ would uniquely determine H, so that the image $\pi_1(J) \subset C^n$ would have dimension at least $n-1$. But then J would have dimension at least n, and since the projection

$$\pi_2: J \to \mathbb{P}^{n*}$$

is finite-to-one, this would imply that $\pi_2(J) = \mathbb{P}^{n*}$, i.e., that every hyperplane section of C contained n linearly dependent points, contradicting our first basic lemma.   Q.E.D.

Now let $C \subset \mathbb{P}^n$ again be a canonical curve, $W \subset |2H|$ the linear system of quadrics through C, and suppose that the base locus S of W is not equal to C. If any point $p \in S - C$ lay on a chord $L = \overline{qr}$ of C the line L, meeting each quadric $Q \in W$ in the three points q, r and p, would lie in Q and hence in S; it follows that we may choose a point $p \in S - C$ not lying on infinitely many chords of C. By our basic lemma II, if H is a generic hyperplane through p the $2n+1$ points

$$\{p\} \cup (H \cap C)$$

are in general position. But now the restriction $W|_H$ to H of W is a linear system of quadrics of dimension at least $\frac{1}{2}(n-1)(n-2) - 1$ with base locus containing $2n+1$ points in general position, and so by Castelnuovo's argument, *the base locus* $S \cap H$ *of* $W|_H$ *must be a rational normal curve*, hence S *is a surface of minimal degree*.

If S is the Veronese surface $\iota_{2H}(\mathbb{P}^2) \subset \mathbb{P}^5$, then clearly C is just a quintic plane curve. On the other hand, if S is one of the ruled surfaces $S_{k,l}$, then by the computation of p. 532, the curve C—having maximal genus—must be linearly equivalent to

$$(m+1)H - (n-2-\varepsilon)C = 3H - (n-3)C$$

since

$$m = \left[\frac{d-1}{n-1}\right] = \left[\frac{2n-1}{n-1}\right] = 2.$$

In particular, we see that C has intersection number 3 with each of the lines of the surface $S_{k,l}$. C is thus expressible as a 3-sheeted cover of $\mathbb{P}^1$; such a curve is called *trigonal*.

Conversely, suppose the canonical curve $C \subset \mathbb{P}^n$ is trigonal, $\pi : C \to \mathbb{P}^1$ a threefold cover. Then the divisors $\{\pi^{-1}(\lambda) = p_1^\lambda + p_2^\lambda + p_3^\lambda\}_{\lambda \in \mathbb{P}^1}$ form a linear system of degree 3 and dimension 1 on C; by the geometric version of Riemann-Roch (p. 248), it follows that the points p_1^λ, p_2^λ, and p_3^λ are collinear for each λ. The line $L_\lambda = \overline{p_1^\lambda p_2^\lambda p_3^\lambda}$ then meets every quadric Q containing C in three points, and so lies on Q; the surface

$$S' = \bigcup_{\lambda \in \mathbb{P}^1} L_\lambda$$

is contained in—hence equal to—the intersection of all quadrics containing C.

Similarly, if C is a plane quintic curve, then by the adjunction formula

$$K_C = [2H_{\mathbb{P}^2}|_C],$$

so that the canonical map on C is just the restriction to C of the Veronese map $\iota_{2H} : \mathbb{P}^2 \to \mathbb{P}^5$. In particular, if L is any line in $\mathbb{P}^2$, $\iota_{2H}(L)$ is a conic curve in $\mathbb{P}^5$ meeting C in five points; as before, any quadric containing C will have to contain $\iota_{2H}(L)$. The intersection of the quadrics containing $C \subset \mathbb{P}^5$ thus contains—hence equals—the Veronese surface.

Summarizing, we have proved*

Theorem (Enriques; Petri). *For* $C \subset \mathbb{P}^n$ *any canonical curve, either*

1. C *is entirely cut out by quadric hypersurfaces; or*
2. C *is trigonal, in which case the intersection of all quadrics containing* C *is the rational normal scroll swept out by the trichords of* C; *or*
3. C *is a plane quintic, in which case the intersection of the quadrics containing* C *is the Veronese surface* $\iota_{2H}(\mathbb{P}^2) \subset \mathbb{P}^5$, *swept out by the conic curves through five coplanar points of* C.

*Cf. B. Saint-Donat, On Petri's Analysis of the linear system of quadrics through a canonical curve, *Math. Annalen*, Vol. 206 (1973), pp. 157–175.

Note that since the rational normal scrolls $S_{k,l}$ (other than $S_{0,1} \subset \mathbb{P}^3$) contain only one family of lines, a trigonal curve of genus $g \geqslant 5$ can contain only one linear system of degree 3 and dimension 1.

4. RATIONAL SURFACES II

The Castelnuovo-Enriques Theorem

Now that we have a fairly complete picture of rational surfaces, a natural question is whether we can characterize them by numerical birational invariants. Clearly, if S is rational, $q(S) = p_g(S) = P_n(S) = 0$; we now prove a converse.

Theorem of Castelnuovo-Enriques. *If S is an algebraic surface with* $q(S) = P_2(S) = 0$, *then S is rational.*

Proof. First of all, we can blow down S to obtain a surface birational to S that does not contain any exceptional curves of the first kind; thus we may assume from the start that S contains no such curves.

To apply Noether's lemma we must show that S contains an irreducible curve C with $\pi(C) = 0$ and $\dim|C| > 0$. To begin with, we transpose the problem slightly: since $P_2(S) = 0$, we have $p_g(S) = 0$—a nontrivial section σ of K_S yields a nontrivial section $\sigma \otimes \sigma$ of K_S^2—so

$$\chi(\mathcal{O}_S) = 1 - q(S) + p_g(S) = 1.$$

Moreover, for any curve C on S,

$$h^2(C) = h^0(K_S - C) = 0,$$

and the Riemann-Roch formula tells us that

$$h^0(C) \geqslant \frac{C \cdot C - K \cdot C}{2} + 1.$$

Now if C is a rational curve and $C \cdot C \geqslant 0$, then by the adjunction formula $K \cdot C \leqslant -2$; thus $h^0(C) \geqslant 2$ and $\dim|C| \geqslant 1$. It will suffice, then, to find an irreducible curve C on S such that

$$(*) \qquad\qquad\qquad \begin{cases} \pi(C) = 0, \\ C \cdot C \geqslant 0. \end{cases}$$

Before we proceed with the proof, we want to make explicit a special corollary to Bertini's theorem.

Lemma. *If* $\{D_\lambda\}$ *is a pencil of curves on a surface and the generic element of* $\{D_\lambda\}$ *is reducible—i.e.,*

$$D_\lambda = E + \sum C_{\nu_\lambda},$$

where E *is the fixed component of* $\{D_\lambda\}$, *then* $C_\nu \cdot C_\nu \geq 0$ *for each* ν.

Proof. Let $\{D'_\lambda\} = \{D_\lambda - E\}$ be the reduced pencil; $\{D_\lambda\}$ will have only isolated base points. Let $\tilde{S} \overset{\pi}{\to} S$ be the blow-up of S at the base points of $\{D'_\lambda\}$, so that the proper transforms

$$\tilde{D}'_\lambda = \sum \tilde{C}_{\nu_\lambda}$$

form a linear system $\{\tilde{D}'_\lambda\}$ without base points on $\tilde{S}$. Then, since a point of intersection of $\tilde{C}_{\nu_\lambda}$ with $\tilde{C}_{\nu'_\lambda}$ would be a singular point of $\tilde{D}'_\lambda$, we see that for generic λ, the curves $\tilde{C}_{\nu_\lambda}$ are disjoint. Thus,

$$\tilde{C}_\nu \cdot \tilde{C}_\nu = \tilde{C}_\nu \cdot \tilde{D}' = 0$$

and consequently $C_\nu \cdot C_\nu \geq 0$. $\hspace{4cm}$ Q.E.D.

The proof of the Castelnuovo-Enriques theorem is in three cases, $K \cdot K < 0$, $K \cdot K = 0$, and $K \cdot K > 0$, the last of which is the most difficult. We start with

Case 1. $K \cdot K = 0$

First, by Riemann-Roch applied to the divisor $-K$,

$$h^0(-K) + h^2(-K) = h^0(-K) + h^0(2K) \geq 1;$$

but $h^0(2K) = P_2(S) = 0$, and so $h^2(-K) \geq 1$; i.e., there exists an effective divisor D linearly equivalent to $-K$. Note that $D \neq 0$, since the bundle K is nontrivial.

Let $L = [E]$ be a very ample line bundle on S; we may assume that $h^0(L - D) \neq 0$. Since E is positive,

$$E \cdot K = -E \cdot D < 0;$$

hence

$$E \cdot (E + mK) < 0 \qquad \text{for } m \gg 0.$$

This implies that $h^0(E + mK) = 0$ for $m \gg 0$, since if $E + mK$ were linearly equivalent to an effective divisor, we would have $E \cdot (E + mK) > 0$. Choose n such that

$$h^0(E + nK) > 0,$$
$$h^0(E + (n+1)K) = 0.$$

Now let $D' \in |E + nK|$, and write $D' = \sum a_\nu C_\nu$. Then

$$K \cdot D' = K \cdot (E + nK) = K \cdot E < 0;$$

thus $K \cdot C_{\nu_0} < 0$ for some ν_0. By Riemann-Roch applied to the divisor $-C_{\nu_0}$,

$$h^0(-C_{\nu_0}) + h^0(K + C_{\nu_0}) \geq \frac{C_{\nu_0} \cdot C_{\nu_0} + C_{\nu_0} \cdot K}{2} + 1$$
$$= \pi(C_{\nu_0}).$$

But $h^0(-C_{\nu_0})=0$ clearly, and since $K+C_{\nu_0}<K+D'$,

$$h^0(K+C_{\nu_0}) \leqslant h^0(K+D') = h^0(E+(n+1)K) = 0;$$

thus we have

$$\pi(C_{\nu_0}) = 0.$$

By the adjunction formula $C_{\nu_0}\cdot K<0$ implies $C_{\nu_0}\cdot C_{\nu_0} \geqslant -1$; but if $C_{\nu_0}\cdot C_{\nu_0}= -1$, then C_{ν_0} is an exceptional curve of the first kind, and we assumed that S contains no such curve. Consequently C_{ν_0} satisfies the numerical conditions $(*)$, and we are done.

Case 2: $K\cdot K<0$

We claim first that, in this case, if E is any divisor on S,

$$h^0(E+nK) = 0 \qquad \text{for } n \gg 0.$$

To see this, first choose n_0 large enough that

$$K\cdot(E+n_0K) = K\cdot E + n_0K\cdot K < 0.$$

Now suppose $h^0(E+mK)\neq 0$ for some $m \geqslant n_0$; let $D \in |E+mK|$ and write $D=\sum_\nu a_\nu C_\nu$. $K\cdot D \leqslant K\cdot(E+n_0K)<0$, so $K\cdot C_{\nu_0}<0$ for some ν_0; then if $C_{\nu_0}\cdot C_{\nu_0}$ were negative, we would have $K\cdot C_{\nu_0}=C_{\nu_0}\cdot C_{\nu_0}= -1$, i.e., C_{ν_0} would be an exceptional curve of the first kind, contrary to assumption. Thus $C_{\nu_0}\cdot C_{\nu_0} \geqslant 0$ and hence, by the remark of p. 470, $C_{\nu_0}\cdot D' \geqslant 0$ for any effective divisor D'. Then, since $K\cdot C_{\nu_0}<0$, we have for $m'\gg 0$,

$$(E+m'K)\cdot C_{\nu_0} < 0 \Rightarrow h^0(E+m'K) = 0,$$

and our assertion is proved.

Let E be a very ample divisor with $h^0(E+K) \geqslant 2$; choose n such that

$$h^0(E+nK) \geqslant 2, \qquad h^0(E+(n+1)K) \leqslant 1.$$

Let D be a generic element of the system $|E+nK|$; by our corollary to Bertini's theorem, if we write

$$D = E + \sum C_\nu,$$

where E is the fixed component of D, then $C_\nu\cdot C_\nu \geqslant 0$ for all ν. Since $h^0(-C_{\nu_0})$ is clearly 0, we have by Riemann-Roch for $-C_\nu$,

$$h^0(K+C_\nu) \geqslant \frac{C_\nu\cdot C_\nu + C_\nu\cdot K}{2} + 1 = \pi(C_\nu).$$

But

$$h^0(K+C_\nu) \leqslant h^0(K+D) \leqslant 1,$$

and so $\pi(C_\nu)=0$ or $\pi(C_\nu)=1$ for all ν. If $\pi(C_\nu)=0$, we are done, since $C_\nu\cdot C_\nu \geqslant 0$; assume that $\pi(C_\nu)=1$. In this case $h^0(K+C_\nu)=h^0(K+D)=1$;

let $D' \in |K + C_\nu|$ and write

$$D' = \sum a_\mu E_\mu.$$

Note that $D' \neq 0$, since $D' = 0 \Rightarrow K \sim -C_\nu \Rightarrow K \cdot K = C_\nu \cdot C_\nu < 0$. By the adjunction formula,

$$\pi(C_\nu) = 1 \Rightarrow K \cdot C_\nu = -C_\nu \cdot C_\nu \Rightarrow D' \cdot C_\nu = (K + C_\nu) \cdot C_\nu = 0;$$

and since $C_\nu \cdot C_\nu \geqslant 0 \Rightarrow C_\nu \cdot E_\mu \geqslant 0$ for all μ, it follows that $E_\mu \cdot C_\nu = 0$ for all μ.

Since $K \cdot C_\nu < 0$ and $K \cdot K < 0$, we have $D' \cdot K < 0$; thus $E_{\mu_0} \cdot K < 0$ for some μ_0. But then

$$0 > E_{\mu_0} \cdot K = E_{\mu_0} \cdot (K + C_\nu)$$

$$= a_{\mu_0} E_{\mu_0} \cdot E_{\mu_0} + \sum_{\mu \neq \mu_0} E_{\mu_0} \cdot E_\mu$$

$$\geqslant a_{\mu_0} E_{\mu_0} \cdot E_{\mu_0}.$$

Thus $E_{\mu_0} \cdot K = E_{\mu_0} \cdot E_{\mu_0} = -1$, i.e., E_{μ_0} is an exceptional curve of the first kind, a contradiction.

Case 3: $K \cdot K > 0$

To begin with, since $h^0(2K) = 0$, we have by Riemann-Roch for $-K$,

$$h^0(-K) \geqslant 1 + \frac{K \cdot K - (K \cdot - K)}{2} > 1,$$

i.e., $|-K|$ contains a pencil of curves. Let D be a generic element of $|-K|$; by our lemma,

$$D = E + \sum a_\nu C_\nu$$

with E the fixed component of $|D|$ and $C_\nu \cdot C_\nu \geqslant 0$ for all ν. Now if D is reducible—i.e., $D \neq C_1$—we have

$$h^2(-C_1) = h^0(K + C_1) = h^0\left(-(a_1 - 1)C_1 - E - \sum_{\nu \neq 1} a_\nu C_\nu\right) = 0,$$

and of course

$$h^0(-C_1) = 0,$$

so that by Riemann-Roch for $-C_1$,

$$0 \geqslant \frac{C_1 \cdot C_1 + K \cdot C_1}{2} + 1 = \pi(C_1);$$

but then $\pi(C_1) = 0$ and $C_1 \cdot C_1 \geqslant 0$, so we are done. Thus we may assume $D = C_1$ is an irreducible curve on S; since $D \sim -K$, we have $D \cdot K = -D \cdot D$, and hence $\pi(D) = 1$.

Now if every very ample line bundle on S were a multiple of K, it would follow then that every bundle on S is a multiple of K; i.e.,

$$H^2(S, \mathbb{Z}) = H^{1,1}(S, \mathbb{Z}) \cong \mathbb{Z}$$

with $c_1(K)$ as a generator. But then by Poincaré duality, we would have $K \cdot K = 1$, and by Noether's formula

$$1 = \chi(\mathcal{O}_S) = \frac{K \cdot K + \chi(S)}{12} = \frac{1+3}{12},$$

a contradiction. Thus we can find a very ample line bundle $[E]$ on S that is not a multiple of K and such that $h^0(E + K) \geq 1$. Since $E \cdot K = -E \cdot D < 0$, we see that $E \cdot (E + nK) < 0$, and hence $h^0(E + nK) = 0$, for $n \gg 0$; let n_0 be the integer such that

$$h^0(E + n_0 K) \geq 1,$$
$$h^0(E + (n_0 + 1)K) = 0.$$

Let D' be a generic element of $|E + n_0 K|$ and write $D' = \sum a_\nu C_\nu$; we know that $D' \neq 0$ because $E \neq -n_0 K$. Now D is irreducible, and so $D \cdot D \geq 0 \Rightarrow K \cdot C_\nu = -D \cdot C_\nu \leq 0$ for all ν. Again, $h^0(K + C_\nu) \leq h^0(K + D') = 0$, and $h^0(-C_\nu) = 0$, so by Riemann-Roch

$$0 \geq \frac{C_\nu \cdot C_\nu + K \cdot C_\nu}{2} + 1 = \pi(C),$$

i.e., $\pi(C) = 0$. Now we know $K \cdot C_\nu \leq 0$; if $K \cdot C_\nu < -1$, then $C_\nu \cdot C_\nu \geq 0$ and we're done. On the other hand, if $K \cdot C_\nu = -1$, then C_ν is exceptional of the first kind. Thus we may assume

$$C_\nu \cdot C_\nu = -2, \qquad K \cdot C_\nu = 0.$$

Apply Riemann-Roch to the divisor $D - C_\nu = -C_\nu - K$; since

$$h^0(2K + C_\nu) \leq h^0(2K + D') = 0,$$
$$h^0(D - C_\nu) \geq \frac{(D - C_\nu) \cdot (D - C_\nu) - K \cdot (D - C_\nu)}{2} + 1$$
$$= \frac{D \cdot D + C_\nu \cdot C_\nu + D \cdot D}{2} + 1$$
$$= K \cdot K > 0;$$

Let $\Gamma \in |D - C_\nu|$ and write $\Gamma = \sum b_\nu \Gamma_\nu$; $\Gamma \neq 0$, since $\Gamma = 0 \Rightarrow C_\nu = D = -K \Rightarrow K \cdot K = C_\nu \cdot C_\nu = -2$. Applying Riemann-Roch to $-\Gamma_\nu$, we have

$$h^0(K + \Gamma_\nu) \leq h^0(K + \Gamma) = h^0(-C_\nu) = 0$$
$$\Rightarrow 0 = h^0(-\Gamma_\nu) \geq \frac{\Gamma_\nu \cdot \Gamma_\nu + \Gamma_\nu \cdot K}{2} + 1 = \pi(\Gamma_\nu),$$

i.e., $\pi(\Gamma_\nu) = 0$ for all ν. But now

$$\Gamma \cdot K = (-K - C_\nu) \cdot K < 0 \Rightarrow \Gamma_{\nu_0} \cdot K < 0 \qquad \text{for some } \nu_0.$$

Consequently, either $\Gamma_{\nu_0} \cdot \Gamma_{\nu_0} = -1$—in which case Γ_{ν_0} is exceptional of the first kind—or $\Gamma_{\nu_0} \cdot \Gamma_{\nu_0} \geq 0$, and we are done.   Q.E.D.

As an immediate corollary, we have

Luroth's Theorem. *If* M *is a rational surface,* $f : M \to N$ *a surjective holomorphic map, then* N *is rational.*

Proof. The proof is clear: if $P_2(N)$ were nonzero, then the vanishing of the pullback to M of a nonzero section of K_N^2 would imply that the Jacobian of f was everywhere zero, and hence that the image of f could not be all of N. Similarly, if N had a nonzero holomorphic 1-form, its pullback to M would have to vanish, so that again the Jacobian of f would be identically zero.   Q.E.D.

The Enriques Surface

We will now show that the hypotheses $q = P_2 = 0$ of the Castelnuovo-Enriques theorem cannot be weakened. The condition $q = 0$ clearly cannot be eliminated: if $S = \mathbb{P}^1 \times E$ is the product of $\mathbb{P}^1$ with a Riemann surface of genus 1, then $K_S = -2(\{p\} \times E)$ and hence $P_n(S) = 0$ for all n; but S cannot be rational, since $q(S) = 1$. To show that the requirement $P_2 = 0$ cannot be replaced by the weaker condition $p_g = 0$ is somewhat more difficult. Enriques did it by constructing a class of surfaces satisfying $q = p_g = 0$ and $P_2 \neq 0$, one of which we now describe.

Let $[X_0, X_1, X_2, X_3]$ be homogeneous coordinates on $\mathbb{P}^3$, and S the quartic Fermat surface, given as the locus of

$$F(X) = X_0^4 + X_1^4 - X_2^4 - X_3^4 = 0.$$

S is a smooth surface, and by the adjunction formula, the canonical bundle

$$K_S = (K_{\mathbb{P}^3} + S)|_S$$

is trivial. Let T be the automorphism of $\mathbb{P}^3$ given by

$$T: \; [X_0, X_1, X_2, X_3] \mapsto [X_0, \sqrt{-1}\, X_1, -X_2, -\sqrt{-1}\, X_3].$$

T preserves $S \subset \mathbb{P}^3$, and so generates a group $\{T^n\}$ of automorphisms of S, of order 4. T has four fixed points in $\mathbb{P}^3$, $[0,0,0,1]$, $[0,0,1,0]$, $[0,1,0,0]$, and $[1,0,0,0]$, none of which lies on S. On the other hand, T^2 has two fixed lines

$$l_1 = (X_0 = X_2 = 0) \quad \text{and} \quad l_2 = (X_1 = X_3 = 0),$$

each of which intersects S transversely in four points; thus T^2 has eight isolated fixed points $p_1, \ldots, p_8$ on S.

The quotient of S by the group of automorphisms $\{T''\}$ cannot be given the structure of a complex manifold—for one thing, a punctured neighborhood of the image of a fixed point p_i in $S/\{T''\}$ has fundamental group $\mathbb{Z}/2$. If we let $\tilde{S} = \tilde{S}_{p_1,\ldots,p_8} \xrightarrow{\pi} S$ be the blow-up of S at the points $p_1,\ldots,p_8$, however, the automorphisms T'' on $\tilde{S} - E_1 - \cdots - E_8 \cong S - \{p_i\}$ extend to automorphisms $\{\tilde{T}''\}$ of $\tilde{S}$, and the quotient $\tilde{S}/\{\tilde{T}''\}$ *is* a complex manifold. To see this, let

$$x = \frac{X_1}{X_0}, \qquad y = \frac{X_2}{X_0}, \qquad z = \frac{X_3}{X_0}$$

be Euclidean coordinates on $(X_0 \neq 0)$ in $\mathbb{P}^3$, so that S is given by

$$f(x,y,z) = 1 + x^4 - y^4 - z^4 = 0$$

and consider the fixed point $p = [1,0,1,0] = (0,1,0)$ of T^2 on S. In a neighborhood U of p in S (which we may take to be preserved by T^2) the functions x and z furnish local coordinates; if we let $\tilde{U}_1$ and $\tilde{U}_2$ be the complements in $\tilde{U} = \pi^{-1}U$ of the proper transforms of $(x=0)$ and $(z=0)$, respectively, then we may correspondingly take as local coordinates in U_1 the functions

$$x' = x, \qquad z' = \frac{z}{x},$$

and in U_2 the functions

$$x'' = \frac{x}{z}, \qquad z'' = z.$$

Now T^2 is given in U by

$$T^2 \colon (x,z) \to (-x,-z),$$

and so $\tilde{T}^2$ is given in U_1 and U_2 by

$$\tilde{T}^2(x',z') = (-x',z'), \qquad \tilde{T}^2(x'',z'') = (x'',-z'');$$

we see then that $\tilde{T}^2$ extends by the identity map on $E = \pi^{-1}(p)$ to an automorphism of $\tilde{U}$. On the image of U_1 in the quotient $\tilde{U}/\{\tilde{T}^2\}$, moreover, the functions $v = x'^2$ and z' provide local coordinates; on the image of U_2 in $\tilde{U}/\{\tilde{T}^2\}$, similarly, x'' and $u = z''^2$ provide local coordinates, giving the quotient the structure of a complex manifold. Since all the fixed points behave similarly, we see that *the quotient* $S'' = \tilde{S}/\{\tilde{T}^{2n}\}$ *has naturally the structure of a complex manifold; and the quotient map* $\iota \colon \tilde{S} \to S''$ *is a double cover simply branched at the divisors* $E_1,\ldots,E_8$.

Now the automorphism T likewise induces an automorphism $\tilde{T}$ on $\tilde{S}$, which then descends to S''. $\tilde{T}$ is fixed-point-free on S'', moreover, so that the quotient $S' = S''/\{\tilde{T}''\} = \tilde{S}/\{\tilde{T}''\}$ naturally inherits a complex structure; the quotient map $\iota' \colon S'' \to S'$ is, of course, an unbranched double cover.

Note that S'' (and hence S') is an algebraic variety: the reader may verify directly that the space of sections of H^4 on S invariant under T^2 (i.e., homogeneous polynomials of degree 4 involving only monomials $X_0^{\alpha_0} X_1^{\alpha_1} X_2^{\alpha_2} X_3^{\alpha_3}$ with $\alpha_1 + \alpha_3$ even) and vanishing to order 2 at the points p_i (or in other words, sections of $[\pi^*4H - 2E_1 - \cdots - 2E_8]$ on $\tilde{S}$ invariant under $\tilde{T}^2$) embeds S'' as a surface of degree 16 in $\mathbb{P}^9$. In fact, S'' has two linearly independent positive line bundles: the space of sections of H^6 on S invariant under T^2 and vanishing to order 4 at each p_i embeds S'' as a surface of degree 8 in $\mathbb{P}^5$.

First observe that $q(S') = 0$: if η were any holomorphic 1-form on S', $\iota'^*\eta$ would, of course, be a holomorphic 1-form on $\tilde{S}$, hence zero, since $q(\tilde{S}) = q(S_\cdot) = 0$. Similarly, if ω were a holomorphic 2-form on S', $\iota'^*\omega$ would be a holomorphic 2-form on $\tilde{S}$, and so would give a holomorphic 2-form on S *invariant under T*. But we know that $H^0(S, \Omega^2) \cong \mathbb{C}$, and we see from the Poincaré residue map that a generator of $H^0(S, \Omega^2)$ is

$$\varphi = \frac{dx \wedge dz}{\partial f / \partial y} = \frac{dx \wedge dz}{4y^3}.$$

Since

$$T^*\varphi = -\varphi,$$

it follows that S has no holomorphic 2-form invariant under T, and hence that $p_g(S') = 0$.

On the other hand, we have

$$T^{2*}\varphi = \varphi,$$

so φ descends to give a holomorphic 2-form ψ on S'' away from the branch locus $\iota(E_1 + \cdots + E_8)$ of the map ι. We claim that in fact ψ extends over $\iota(E_i)$; to see this, let x', z' and x'', z'' be the coordinates introduced above on the neighborhood $\tilde{U}$ of the exceptional divisor $E \subset \tilde{S}$. We can write

$$x = x', \qquad z = z'x',$$
$$dx = dx', \qquad dz = z'\,dx' + x'\,dz',$$

so

$$dx \wedge dz = x'\,dx' \wedge dz'.$$

Thus

$$\pi^*(\varphi) = \frac{x'}{(1 + x'^4 - z'^4 x'^4)^{3/4}}(dx' \wedge dz')$$
$$= \iota^* \frac{(dv \wedge dz')}{2(1 + v^2 - z'^4 v^2)^{3/4}},$$

so that indeed ψ extends over all of S''. Finally, since $\varphi \otimes \varphi$ is invariant under T, $\psi \otimes \psi$ must likewise be invariant under the induced involution $\tilde{T}$

of S''. Thus $\psi \otimes \psi$ descends to give a nonzero holomorphic section of $K_{S'} \otimes K_{S'}$, and we see that $P_2(S') \neq 0$; so S' cannot be rational.

The surface S' is called an *Enriques surface*. We can compute some of its invariants as follows: first, since $K_S = 0$,

$$K_{\tilde{S}} = E_1 + \cdots + E_8.$$

Now if ω is any meromorphic 2-form on S'', we see that

$$K_{\tilde{S}} = (\iota^* \omega) = \iota^* K_{S''} + E_1 + \cdots + E_8,$$

so the canonical bundle of S'' has Chern class 0. The holomorphic 2-form ψ on S'' is therefore nowhere zero, and $K_{S''}$ is trivial. Since

$$K_{S''} = \pi^* K_{S'},$$

moreover, we see that $K_{S'}$ has Chern class zero modulo torsion.

Since we know that $c_1(S)^2 = 0$, we can apply Noether's formula to obtain

$$\chi(S) = c_2(S) = 12\chi(\mathcal{O}_S) = 24,$$

and similarly, since $c_1(S'')^2 = c_1(S')^2 = 0$,

$$\chi(S'') = 24, \qquad \chi(S') = 12.$$

So $b_1(S') = b_3(S') = 0$, and $b_2(S') = h^{1,1}(S') = 10$. S' cannot be simply connected—otherwise it would not have a connected two-sheeted unbranched cover. In fact, by the Lefschetz theorem, S is simply connected, and hence so is $\tilde{S}$. Now any loop γ in S'' lifts to $\tilde{S}$—just take the base point of γ to be in the branch locus $\iota(E_1 + \cdots + E_8)$ of ι—so it follows that S'' is again simply connected, and hence

$$H_1(S', \mathbb{Z}) = \mathbb{Z}/2.$$

Another way to see that S'' is simply connected is as follows: we know that the fundamental group $\pi_1(S'')$ is torsion, since $q(S'') = 0$; if $\pi_1(S'')$ had a subgroup of index d, then there would exist a d-sheeted covering space $M \xrightarrow{j} S''$ of S''. M would be a compact complex manifold with

$$K_M = j^* K_{S''}$$

trivial, and

$$\chi(M) = d \cdot K_{S''} = 24 \cdot d.$$

Thus by Noether's formula

$$\chi(\mathcal{O}_M) = \frac{c_1^2 + c_2}{24} = 2d.$$

But since K_M is trivial, $p_g(M) = 1$, and $q(S'') = 0$ implies $q(M) = 0$, so we must have

$$\chi(\mathcal{O}_M) = 2, \qquad d = 1.$$

Cubic Surfaces Revisited

As an application of the techniques developed in the last two sections, we will now go back and give a shorter, if less ingenuous, analysis of a smooth cubic surface. We will then consider the correspondence between the lines on a cubic surface and the bitangents to a quartic curve in $\mathbb{P}^2$.

Let $S \subset \mathbb{P}^3$ be any smooth cubic surface. By the Lefschetz theorem, S is simply connected and so $q(S) = 0$; by the adjunction formula

$$K_S = (K_{\mathbb{P}^3} S)|_S = -H|_S,$$

the canonical bundle of S is negative, and so $P_n(S) = 0$ for all n. By the Castelnuovo-Enriques theorem, then, we see immediately that S is rational.

Now by Noether's formula,

$$1 = \chi(\mathcal{O}_S) = \frac{c_1(S)^2 + c_2(S)}{12},$$

and since $c_1(S) = -H$, $c_1(S)^2 = 3$ and it follows that

$$\chi(S) = c_2(S) = 9.$$

By our theorem on rational surfaces, S must be a ruled surface S_n blown up five times. But for any irreducible curve C on S we have

$$K \cdot C = -H \cdot C < 0,$$

and so by the adjunction formula $C \cdot C \geq -1$, i.e., S cannot contain an irreducible curve of self-intersection -2 or less. Thus S is S_0 or S_1 blown up five times, or, what is the same thing, $\mathbb{P}^2$ blown up six times. In fact, S must be $\mathbb{P}^2$ blown up in six distinct points $p_1, \ldots, p_6$: if at any stage in the sequence of blow-ups of $\mathbb{P}^2$ we blow up a point on the exceptional divisor of a previous blow-up, the proper transform of that exceptional divisor in S will have self-intersection < -1. Likewise, the points $p_1, \ldots, p_6$ must be "general" in the sense of p. 480: if three of the points p_i lay on a line $L \subset \mathbb{P}^2$, the proper transform $\tilde{L}$ of L in S would have self-intersection ≤ -2, and similarly if all six lay on a conic $C \subset \mathbb{P}^2$, the proper transform $\tilde{C}$ of C would have self-intersection -2. Finally, the embedding line bundle of $S \cong \tilde{\mathbb{P}}^2_{p_1, \ldots, p_6} \xrightarrow{\pi} \mathbb{P}^2$ is given by

$$H = -K_S = -(\pi^* K_{\mathbb{P}^2} + E_1 + \cdots + E_6)$$
$$= \pi^*(3H) - E_1 - \cdots - E_6.$$

Thus we can show as on p. 485 that S contains exactly 27 lines.

Now let S be, as above, a smooth cubic surface, $P \in S$ any point not lying on any of the 27 lines of S, and consider the projection map

$$\pi_P : S - \{P\} \to \mathbb{P}^2$$

of S from P onto a hyperplane $\mathbb{P}^2 \subset \mathbb{P}^3$. As we have seen, π_P extends to a holomorphic map

$$\tilde{\pi}_P : \tilde{S} \to \mathbb{P}^2$$

on the blow-up $\tilde{S}$ of S at P; $\tilde{\pi}_P$ expresses $\tilde{S}$ as a 2-sheeted branched cover of $\mathbb{P}^2$.

Let $B \subset \mathbb{P}^2$ be the branch locus of $\tilde{\pi}_P$. If $l \subset \mathbb{P}^2$ is a generic line, the plane $H_l = \overline{l, P} \subset \mathbb{P}^3$ spanned by l and P meets S in a smooth curve C_l: the generic hyperplane in $\mathbb{P}^3$ through P will not be tangent to S at P, and by Bertini's theorem will not be tangent to S anywhere else. The map $\tilde{\pi}_P$ then maps the proper transform $\tilde{C}_l \cong C_l$ onto $l \cong \mathbb{P}^1$ as a 2-sheeted cover; since C_l has genus 1, $\tilde{\pi}_P|_{\tilde{C}_l}$ must have four branch points, and since no branch point of a 2-sheeted cover can have multiplicity greater than 1, these points are all distinct. Thus the generic line l meets B in four points, and consequently B has degree 4. Note, moreover, that if $q \in \mathbb{P}^2$ is any point, then for the generic line $l \subset \mathbb{P}^2$ containing q the plane H_l meets S transversely: the generic plane in $\mathbb{P}^3$ containing $\overline{Pq}$ will not be tangent to S at any of the finite number of points of $\overline{Pq} \cap S$, and by Bertini's theorem will not be tangent to S elsewhere. Thus by the same argument the generic line through q in $\mathbb{P}^2$ meets B in four distinct points, so q cannot be a singular point of B; it follows that B is a smooth quartic curve.

We have argued that if the plane H_l meets S in a smooth curve, then l meets B in four distinct points, i.e., l is nowhere tangent to B. Conversely, let $Q \in S$ be any point of the branch locus $\tilde{B}$ of π_P, $q = \pi_P(Q) \in B$, and $l_0 = T_q(B)$ the tangent line to B at q. The line $\overline{PQ} \subset \mathbb{P}^3$ is clearly in the tangent plane $T_Q(S)$ to S at Q, and so is the tangent line $T_Q(\tilde{B})$ to $\tilde{B}$ at Q, hence so is the line $\pi_P(T_Q(B)) = l_0$; thus

$$T_Q(S) = H_{l_0}.$$

Summarizing, we see that for any line $l \subset \mathbb{P}^2$ through $q = \pi_P(Q) \in \tilde{B}$, l is tangent to B at Q if and only if H_l is tangent to S at Q, if and only if $C_l = H_l \cap S$ is singular at Q.

Now let $L_1, \ldots, L_{27}$ be the lines on S, and $l_1, \ldots, l_{27}$ their images in $\mathbb{P}^2$ under $\tilde{\pi}_P$. l_i is a line in $\mathbb{P}^2$ by our assumption that $P \notin L_i$. If $l_i = l_j$ for some $i \neq j$, moreover, the plane $H_{l_i} = H_{l_j}$ in $\mathbb{P}^3$ would contain both L_i and L_j and so meet S in the sum of three lines—but $P \in H_{l_i} \cap S$ does not lie on any line in S, so this cannot happen; thus the lines l_i are distinct. Note also that under the assumption that $P \notin L_i$, no line on S lies in the tangent plane T to S at P: if $L_i \subset T \cap S$, then we must have

$$T \cap S = L_i + C,$$

where C is a conic curve in T. But then C would be singular at P, hence would consist of two lines containing P.

Now consider the intersections of S with the planes H_{l_i}, $i = 1, \ldots, 27$. H_{l_i} meets S in a curve of degree 3 containing L_i and no other line; thus

$$H_{l_i} \cap S = L_i + C_i,$$

where C_i is a smooth conic curve in H_{l_i}. C_i then meets L_i in two points Q_i and R_i (not necessarily distinct), which are singular points of $H_{l_i} \cap S$. By what we said above, then, the points $q_i = \pi_P(Q_i)$ and $r_i = \pi_P(R_i)$ are points of tangency of l_i with B. Thus either

1. $q_i \neq r_i$—i.e., C_i meets L_i transversely—in which case l_i is a bitangent line to B, or
2. $q_i = r_i$—i.e., C_i is tangent to L_i at $Q_i = R_i$—in which case every line L through P in H_{l_i} other than $\overline{PQ_i}$ will meet C_i and L_i in two distinct points, so that l_i will meet B *only* at q_i—i.e., l_i will have contact or order 4 with B at q_i. Such a line is called a *hyperflex* of B.

Finally, let $l_{28} \subset \mathbb{P}^2$ be the image under π_P of the tangent plane T to S at p—or, in other words, the image under $\tilde{\pi}_P$ of the exceptional divisor $E \subset \tilde{S}$. T intersects S in a cubic curve $C \subset T$ with a singularity at P, either a node or a cusp. The tangent lines to C at P in T map via π_P to points of tangency of l_{28} with B, and no other line through P in T maps to a point of B, so that either

1. P is a node of C, i.e., l_{28} is bitangent to B, or
2. P is a cusp of C, i.e., l_{28} is a hyperflex of B.

Conversely, let $l \subset \mathbb{P}^2$ be any bitangent to B. If $H_l \neq T$, then C_l must have two singular points. Since C_l is a cubic curve in H_l, it must then contain the line joining these two points, i.e., $l = l_i$ for some i. Similarly, if $l \subset \mathbb{P}^2$ is a hyperflex of B and $l \neq l_{28}$, then C_l maps down to l via π_P as a double cover branched only over $l \cap B = \{q\}$. Since $l - \{q\}$ is simply connected, $C_l - \pi_P^{-1}(q)$ is disconnected. Thus C_l is reducible; since C_l is a cubic curve, one of its irreducible components must be a line, and again we have $l = l_i$, for some i.

Note that if we realize S as $\mathbb{P}^2$ blown up in six points $x_1, \ldots, x_6$ with $x_7 \in \mathbb{P}^2$ corresponding to $P \in S$, then the linear system giving the map $\tilde{\pi}_P : \tilde{S} \to \mathbb{P}^2$ is just the proper transform of the system of cubic curves $C \subset \mathbb{P}^2$ passing through $x_1, \ldots, x_7$. In particular if

1. $L_i = E_i$; then $C_{l_i} = H_i \cap S$ corresponds to the cubic curve $C \subset \mathbb{P}^2$ through $x_1, \ldots, x_7$ singular at x_i. l_i will be a bitangent if C has a node at x_i, a hyperflex if C has a cusp at x_i.
2. $L_i = G_{ij}$; then C_{l_i} corresponds to the line L through x_i and x_j in $\mathbb{P}^2$ plus the conic C through $\{x_k : k \neq i, j\}$. l_i will be a bitangent if C meets L transversely, a hyperflex is C is tangent to L.

3. $L_i = F_i$; then C_{l_i} is the line L through x_i and x_7 in $\mathbb{P}^2$ plus the conic $C \subset \mathbb{P}^2$ through $\{x_k : k \neq i, 7\}$; again, l_i will be a hyperflex or a bitangent according to whether these curves are tangent or not.

We see from the above discussion that every quartic curve in $\mathbb{P}^2$ obtained as the branch locus of the projection of a cubic surface from a point on the surface has exactly 28 bitangents and hyperflexes, and that the generic quartic curve of this form has no hyperflexes and 28 bitangents.

Now we show that in fact every nonsingular quartic curve $B \subset \mathbb{P}^2$ can be realized as the branch locus of the projection of a cubic surface $S \subset \mathbb{P}^2$ from a point $p \in S$. We first show that we can construct a surface $\tilde{S}$ that is a double cover of $\mathbb{P}^2$ branched at B. To do this, fix an isomorphism of line bundles on $\mathbb{P}^2$

$$H^2 \otimes H^2 \longrightarrow H^4.$$

and let $\sigma \in H^0(\mathbb{P}^2, \mathcal{O}(H^4))$ be a section defining B, i.e., such that $(\sigma) = B$. Then in the total space of the bundle $H^2 \overset{\pi}{\to} \mathbb{P}^2$, consider the locus

$$\tilde{S} = \{(p, \xi) : \xi \otimes \xi = \sigma(p)\}.$$

$\tilde{S}$ is readily seen to be a submanifold of H^2, and the projection map $\pi : H^2 \to \mathbb{P}^2$ expresses $\tilde{S}$ as a double cover of $\mathbb{P}^2$ branched exactly along B. (In general, a similar construction can be made of a double cover of $\mathbb{P}^2$ branched along any given curve of even degree; the singularities of the double cover will occur exactly over the singular points of the curve.)

Let $\tilde{B} \subset \tilde{S}$ be the branch locus of $\pi : \tilde{S} \to \mathbb{P}^2$ in $\tilde{S}$. If ω is any meromorphic 2-form on $\mathbb{P}^2$, we see that

$$K_{\tilde{S}} = (\pi^* \omega) = \pi^*(\omega) + \tilde{B} = \pi^*(-3H) + \tilde{B}.$$

But $2\tilde{B} = \pi^*(4H)$, and so

$$2K_{\tilde{S}} = \pi^*(-6H) + \pi^*(4H) = \pi^*(-2H).$$

Thus

$$\begin{aligned}
4K_{\tilde{S}} \cdot K_{\tilde{S}} &= \pi^*(-2H) \cdot \pi^*(-2H) \\
&= 2 \cdot (-2H) \cdot (-2H) \\
&= 8,
\end{aligned}$$

i.e., $K_{\tilde{S}} \cdot K_{\tilde{S}} = 2$.

Now, taking a triangulation of $\mathbb{P}^2$ extending a triangulation of B and lifting it to $\tilde{S}$, we see that

$$\begin{aligned}
\chi(\tilde{S}) &= 2 \cdot \chi(\mathbb{P}^2) - \chi(B) \\
&= 6 - (-4) \\
&= 10.
\end{aligned}$$

Thus by Noether's formula

$$\chi(\mathcal{O}_{\tilde{S}}) = \frac{10 + 2}{12} = 1.$$

But $2K_{\tilde{S}}$ is the inverse of an effective divisor, so

$$P_2(\tilde{S}) = p_g(\tilde{S}) = 0.$$

Hence $q(\tilde{S})=0$ as well, and by Castelnuovo-Enriques, $\tilde{S}$ is rational. Since $\chi(\tilde{S})=10$, $\tilde{S}$ must then be the blow-up six times of some ruled surface S_n. But now for any irreducible curve D on $\tilde{S}$,

$$K_{\tilde{S}}\cdot D = \tfrac{1}{2}\pi^*(-2H)\cdot D$$
$$= -H\cdot\pi(D) < 0,$$

since $\pi(D)$ must again be effective and nonzero. It follows from the adjunction formula that

$$D\cdot D \geqslant -1,$$

and hence, as on p. 545, $\tilde{S}$ must be either S_1 or S_0 blown up in six distinct points, or equivalently $\mathbb{P}^2$ blown up in seven distinct points $p_1,\ldots,p_7$. We see, moreover, that no three of the points p_i can lie on a line L: if they did, the proper transform $\tilde{L}$ of L in $\tilde{S}$ would have self-intersection $\leqslant -2$; similarly, no six of the points can lie on a conic curve $C\subset\mathbb{P}^2$: $\tilde{C}$ would have self-intersection $\leqslant -2$. Thus if we blow down any of the exceptional divisors E_i of $\tilde{S}=\tilde{\mathbb{P}}^2_{p_1,\ldots,p_7}$, the resulting surface $S=\tilde{\mathbb{P}}^2_{p_1,\ldots,\hat{p}_i,\ldots,p_7}$ may be embedded in $\mathbb{P}^3$ as a smooth cubic surface S.

To complete our argument, then, we claim that the map

$$\pi_p: \tilde{S}\to\mathbb{P}^2,$$

obtained by projecting S from the image point P of the exceptional divisor $E_i\subset\tilde{S}$, is the same as our original map $\pi:\tilde{S}\to\mathbb{P}^2$. But this is clear: on the one hand, the hyperplane section of $S\subset\mathbb{P}^3$ is just the dual $-K_S$ of the canonical bundle of S, and so the proper transforms in $\tilde{S}$ of hyperplane sections of S through P are elements of $|-K_{\tilde{S}}|$, i.e.,

$$\pi_p = \iota_{-K_{\tilde{S}}}.$$

On the other hand, we have seen that

$$2K_{\tilde{S}} = \pi^*(-2H);$$

since $\tilde{S}$ is rational and so has no torsion in $\mathrm{Pic}(S)=H^2(S,\mathbb{Z})$, it follows that $K_{\tilde{S}}=\pi^*(-H)$, i.e.,

$$\pi = \iota_{-K_{\tilde{S}}} = \pi_p.$$

Thus the branch locus of the projection of $S\subset\mathbb{P}^3$ from P is the quartic curve B we started with.

In conclusion, then, *every smooth quartic curve in $\mathbb{P}^2$ has exactly 28 bitangents and/or hyperflexes.*

The Intersection of Two Quadrics in $\mathbb{P}^4$

Recall that in the section on Grassmannians we saw that the set of lines lying on a quadric hypersurface $Q \subset \mathbb{P}^n$ represented the Schubert cycle $4 \cdot \sigma_{21}$ in the Grassmannian $G(2, n+1)$ of lines in $\mathbb{P}^n$. In particular, this suggested that the generic intersection of two quadrics $Q, Q' \subset \mathbb{P}^4$ contained

$$(4\sigma_{21} \cdot 4\sigma_{21})_{G(2,5)} = 16$$

lines. We can now show that this is indeed the case for any smooth intersection, $Q \cap Q'$.

Let Q and Q' be any two quadric hypersurfaces in $\mathbb{P}^4$ intersecting transversely in a surface S. First, by the adjunction formula,

$$K_Q = (K_{\mathbb{P}^4} + Q)|_Q = -3H|_Q$$

and

$$K_S = (K_Q + Q')|_S = -H|_S.$$

In particular,

$$c_1^2 = H \cdot H = \deg S = 4$$

and, since K_S is negative,

$$p_g(S) = P_2(S) = 0.$$

Now Q is a positive divisor on $\mathbb{P}^4$ and S a positive divisor on Q, so by the Lefschetz theorem,

$$H^1(S, \mathbb{Z}) = H^1(Q, \mathbb{Z}) = H^1(\mathbb{P}^4, \mathbb{Z}) = 0.$$

Hence

$$q(S) = 0,$$

and, by Castelnuovo-Enriques, S is rational. By Noether's formula,

$$1 = \chi(\mathcal{O}_S) = \frac{c_1^2 + c_2}{12} = \frac{4 + c_2}{12},$$

therefore $c_2(S) = \chi(S) = 8$. Then, since K_S is negative, for any irreducible curve D on S,

$$K_S \cdot D < 0,$$

which implies

$$D \cdot D \geqslant -1.$$

By our classification of rational surfaces, S *must be* $\mathbb{P}^2$ *blown up in five distinct points*. No three of these points may be collinear, moreover, since the proper transform in S of a line in $\mathbb{P}^2$ containing three of them would have self-intersection < -1.

Now let $E_1, \ldots, E_5$ be the five exceptional divisors of the blow-up, $\tilde{L}_{ij}$ the proper transform in S of the line $L_{ij} = \overline{p_i p_j} \subset \mathbb{P}^2$, and $\tilde{C}$ the proper transform in S of the conic $C \subset \mathbb{P}^2$ through all five points. Since the hyperplane section H of $S \subset \mathbb{P}^4$ is given by

$$H = -K_{\tilde{S}} = \pi^*(3H_{\mathbb{P}^2}) - E_1 - \cdots - E_5,$$

we see that

$$E_i \cdot H = -E_i \cdot E_i = 1,$$
$$\tilde{L}_{ij} \cdot H = 3(L_{ij} \cdot H_{\mathbb{P}^2}) - 2 = 1,$$
$$\tilde{C} \cdot H = 3(C \cdot H_{\mathbb{P}^2}) - 5 = 1,$$

i.e., E_i, $\tilde{L}_{ij}$, *and* $\tilde{C}$ *are all lines on* S. Conversely, if $D \neq E_i \subset S$ is any line, then since D can meet each line E_i in at most one point, its image $\pi(D) \subset \mathbb{P}^2$ is a smooth rational curve, hence either a line or a conic. If $\pi(D)$ is a line, then

$$1 = H \cdot D = \pi(D) \cdot H_{\mathbb{P}^2} - D \cdot \sum E_i$$
$$= 3 - D \cdot \sum E_i,$$

so D meets two of the exceptional divisors E_i; thus $\pi(D)$ contains two of the points p_i and so $D = \tilde{L}_{ij}$ for some i,j. Similarly, if $\pi(D)$ is a conic,

$$1 = H \cdot D = \pi(D) \cdot H_{\mathbb{P}^2} - D \cdot \sum E_i$$
$$= 6 - D \cdot \sum E_i$$

tells us that $\pi(D)$ contains all five points $p_1, \ldots, p_5$, i.e., $D = \tilde{C}$. Thus E_i, $\tilde{L}_{ij}$, and $\tilde{C}$ are all the lines on S, and consequently S contains exactly $5 + 10 + 1 = 16$ lines, as expected.

Note that any line on S will meet exactly five other lines on S: the line C will meet the five lines $\{E_i\}_i$, the line E_i will meet the line C and the four lines $\{L_{ij}\}_j$, and the line L_{ij} will meet the two lines E_i and E_j and the three lines $\{L_{kl}\}_{k \neq i,j; l \neq i,j}$.

We claim that conversely if $p_1, \ldots, p_5$ are any five points no three of which are collinear, and $S \xrightarrow{\pi} \mathbb{P}^2$ is the blow-up of $\mathbb{P}^2$ at these points, then the linear system $|-K_S| = |\pi^*(3H_{\mathbb{P}^2}) - E_1 - \cdots - E_5|$ embeds S in $\mathbb{P}^4$ as the intersection of two quadrics. First, note that if $p_6 \in S$ is any point lying off the inverse image $\pi^{-1}C$ of the conic $C \subset \mathbb{P}^2$ containing $p_1, \ldots, p_5$, our argument of p. 481 shows that the proper transform in the blow-up $\tilde{S}$ of S at p_6 of the linear system of curves $D \in |-K_{\tilde{S}}|$ passing through p_6 embeds $\tilde{S}$ as a cubic in $\mathbb{P}^3$; thus a fortiori the complete linear system $|-K_S|$ embeds S as a surface of degree 4 in $\mathbb{P}^4$. Now, since $-2K_S$ is positive, by the Kodaira vanishing theorem

$$H^1(S, \mathcal{O}(-2K_S)) = H^1(S, \Omega^2(-3K_S)) = 0,$$

and likewise

$$H^2(S, \mathcal{O}(-2K_S)) = H^2(S, \Omega^2(-3K_S)) = 0.$$

Thus by Riemann-Roch,

$$h^0(-2K_S) = 1 + \frac{(-2K_S \cdot -2K_S) - (-2K_S \cdot K_S)}{2}$$
$$= 1 + 3K_S \cdot K_S$$
$$= 13.$$

But the linear system $|2H|$ on $\mathbb{P}^4$ has dimension $\binom{6}{2} - 1 = 14$; since its restriction to S has dimension $13 - 1 = 12$, it follows that S must lie in—hence equal—the intersection of two quadric hypersurfaces in $\mathbb{P}^4$.

Note that we can also find the 16 lines on the intersection S of two quadrics Q, Q' by our knowledge of cubic surfaces in P^3. To see this, let $p \in S$ be any point not lying on a line of S; projection from p onto a hyperplane $\mathbb{P}^3$ then defines a holomorphic map

$$\pi_p : \tilde{S} \to \mathbb{P}^3$$

on the blow-up $\tilde{S}$ of S at p. This map is in fact an embedding: if any line L in $\mathbb{P}^4$ through p meet S twice away from p, it would have three points in common with each of the quadrics Q and Q', and so would lie on S—but we assumed to begin with that p lay on no line of S. The image $\pi_p(S)$ is a smooth cubic and so has 27 lines L_i on it, including the image of the exceptional divisor E of S. For each $L \neq \pi_p(E) \subset \pi_p(S)$, the inverse image $\tilde{L}$ of L in S will be either

1. a line on S, if L is disjoint from $\pi_p(E)$; or
2. a conic curve on S, if L meets $\pi_p(E)$.

Since, as we have seen, exactly 10 lines of $\pi_p(S)$ will meet $\pi_p(E)$, it follows that S contains $27 - 1 - 10 = 16$ lines.

5. SOME IRRATIONAL SURFACES

The Albanese Map

In this section we will discuss the overall classification of surfaces and briefly describe some basic types of surfaces other than the rational ones. We will classify surfaces by means of birational invariants, and will often assume that our surfaces are *minimal*; i.e., that they contain no exceptional curves of the first kind.

A basic new technique to be employed is the Albanese variety $\mathrm{Alb}(S)$ and Albanese mapping

$$\mu : S \to \mathrm{Alb}(S)$$

for a surface S. We recall (pp. 331–332) that $\text{Alb}(S) = V/\Lambda$ where $V = H^0(S, \Omega^1)^*$ and Λ are the linear functions obtained by integrating over cycles in $H_1(S, \mathbb{Z})$. Explicitly, if $\eta_1, \ldots, \eta_q$ are a basis for the holomorphic one-forms on S, then $V \cong \mathbb{C}^q$ and Λ is the lattice of vectors

$$\left(\int_\gamma \eta_1, \ldots, \int_\gamma \eta_q \right), \qquad \gamma \in H_1(S, \mathbb{Z}).$$

The mapping μ is given by choosing a base point p_0, and then for $p \in S$ setting

$$\mu(p) = \left(\int_{p_0}^p \eta_1, \ldots, \int_{p_0}^p \eta_q \right).$$

As in the curve case, the map μ induces isomorphisms

$$\mu_* : H_1(M, \mathbb{Z})/\text{torsion} \longrightarrow H_1(A, \mathbb{Z})$$

and

$$\mu^* : H^0(A, \Omega_A^1) \longrightarrow H^0(M, \Omega_M^1),$$

hence an isomorphism

$$\text{Pic}^0(A) = H^1(A, \mathcal{O}_A)/H^1(A, \mathbb{Z}) \underset{\mu^*}{\to} H^1(M, \mathcal{O}_M)/H^1(M, \mathbb{Z})$$

$$= \text{Pic}^0(M).$$

Irrational Ruled Surfaces

In Section 3 of this chapter we defined a *rational ruled surface* to be a holomorphic $\mathbb{P}^1$-bundle over $\mathbb{P}^1$. Similarly, we define an *irrational ruled surface* to be a holomorphic $\mathbb{P}^1$-bundle $S \overset{\Psi}{\to} E$ over an irrational curve E.

The first thing to notice about such a surface is that the pullback map Ψ^* on holomorphic 1-forms is injective. Conversely, since the fibers C of Ψ are rational, any holomorphic 1-form η on S restricts to zero on the fibers. It follows that η is the pullback of a 1-form on E: in a neighborhood of any fiber of Ψ we may choose a point p_0 and set

$$f(p) = \int_{p_0}^p \eta;$$

f, being constant along the (connected) fibers of Ψ, is the pullback of a function g on an open set in E, and we can write

$$\eta = \Psi^* \xi, \qquad \xi = dg.$$

Inasmuch as η determines ξ, ξ is globally defined on E. The pullback map

$$\Psi^* : H^0(E, \Omega_E^1) \to H^0(S, \Omega_S^1)$$

is thus an isomorphism; in particular, the irregularity $q(S)$ of S is the genus of E.

Second, the fibers C of Ψ have self-intersection 0 and so by adjunction

$$K \cdot C = -2.$$

But since $C \cdot C = 0$, any effective curve on S has nonnegative intersection number with C. Thus no multiple of K can be effective, i.e.,

$$P_m(S) = 0 \qquad \text{for all } m.$$

Also, since S is a $\mathbb{P}^1$-bundle over a curve of genus $q(S)$,

$$\chi(S) = 2 \cdot \chi(E) = 4 - 4q,$$

and it follows from Noether's formula

$$1 - q = \chi(\mathcal{O}_S) = \frac{c_1^2 + c_2}{12}$$

that

$$K \cdot K = 8 - 8q.$$

Finally, by either the Leray spectral sequence or the exact homotopy sequence of a fiber bundle, we see that the map

$$\Psi_* : H_1(S, \mathbb{Z}) \to H_1(E, \mathbb{Z})$$

is an isomorphism; it follows that the Albanese variety of S is just the Jacobian of E, and the Albanese map $S \to \mathrm{Alb}(S)$ the composition of Ψ with the natural map $\mu : E \to \mathcal{J}(E)$.

This is as far as we will go into the geometry of ruled surfaces. Our previous analysis of rational ruled surfaces applies to irrational ruled surfaces in one respect: any ruled surface $S \to E$ is, by the same argument as given earlier, the projective bundle associated to a vector bundle of rank 2 on E. Here the analogy ends: it is *not* the case that any vector bundle over an irrational curve is the direct sum of line bundles. To study ruled surfaces in any greater detail thus requires more knowledge of vector bundles on curves than we have. One point to bear in mind, however, is this: in large measure the geometry of a ruled surface is a reflection of the geometry of its base curve.

In the remainder of this discussion we will give two numerical criteria for a surface S to be ruled. The first is

The Castelnuovo-de Franchis Theorem. *If S is minimal, i.e., contains no exceptional curves of the first kind, and if $\chi(S) < 0$, then S is an irrational ruled surface.*

Proof. Before we begin, we prove the

Lemma. *If S is minimal, E a curve, and $\pi : S \to E$ any holomorphic map whose generic fiber is irreducible and rational, then S is a $\mathbb{P}^1$-bundle over E.*

Proof. We will show that $S \xrightarrow{\pi} E$ can contain no reducible fibers; since all fibers of π have the same virtual genus 0, this will imply that all fibers are smooth. From the argument used for rational ruled surfaces (p. 514) it will follow that S is a $\mathbb{P}^1$-bundle.

Suppose that π has a reducible fiber

$$C = \sum n_i C_i, \qquad n_i > 0, \quad C_i \text{ irreducible.}$$

We may then write

$$0 = C \cdot C_i = n_i C_i \cdot C_i + \sum_{j \neq i} n_j C_i \cdot C_j$$

and, since all fibers are connected, the latter term is strictly positive; thus

$$C_i \cdot C_i < 0$$

for all i. On the other hand,

$$\pi(C) = \frac{C \cdot C + K \cdot C}{2} + 1 = 0,$$

so

$$K \cdot C = -2$$

and hence $K \cdot C_{i_0} < 0$ for some i_0. C_{i_0} then has negative intersection both with itself and with the canonical bundle, and so is an exceptional curve of the first kind.   Q.E.D.

Thus, to prove the Castelnuovo-de Franchis theorem, we need only exhibit a map $\pi : S \to E$ whose generic fiber is irreducible and rational. We do this in two steps: we first find π under the assumption that S has two independent holomorphic 1-forms with wedge product identically zero; we then go back and show that every surface S with $\chi(S) < 0$ has two such forms. In following the proof of the former assertion, it is helpful to bear in mind the actual picture: for $S \xrightarrow{\pi} E$ ruled, any two 1-forms are pullbacks of forms η_1, η_2 on E. The quotient $f = \eta_1 / \eta_2$ then gives a map of E to $\mathbb{P}^1$ with the fibers of the composed map $\pi' : S \to E \to \mathbb{P}^1$ consisting of combinations of fibers of π, and we may reconstruct E as the set of connected components of fibers of π'.

Suppose that $\omega_1, \omega_2 \in H^0(S, \Omega^1)$ are linearly independent and that $\omega_1 \wedge \omega_2 \equiv 0$. Then the vectors

$$\omega_1(p), \omega_2(p) \in T_p^*(S)$$

are linearly dependent at every point $p \in S$, and therefore

$$\omega_1 = f \omega_2$$

for f some global meromorphic function on S; since ω_1 and ω_2 are linearly independent, f is nonconstant.

In a small polydisc Δ around any point $p_0 \in S$ we may set

$$\Psi(p) = \left(\int_{p_0}^{p} \omega_1, \int_{p_0}^{p} \omega_2 \right).$$

Then since $\omega_1 \wedge \omega_2 \equiv 0$ the Jacobian of Ψ has rank one at a generic p, and so the image is an analytic arc C in $\mathbb{C}^2$. Now, if the arc C is given in a neighborhood of the origin as the locus of the holomorphic function $g(z_1, z_2)$, then we have

$$f = \Psi^* \left(\frac{\partial g / \partial z_1}{\partial g / \partial z_2} \right).$$

Since f is locally the pullback of a meromorphic function *on the curve* C, then, it follows that *the zero and polar divisors of* f *are disjoint*, and hence that f gives a holomorphic—rather than rational—map

$$\pi': S \to \mathbb{P}^1$$

with fibers $C_\lambda = \pi'^{-1}(\lambda) = (f - \lambda)_0$. The fibers of π' may be (indeed will be) reducible; if so, by Bertini the irreducible components of the generic C_λ will be disjoint, and

$$C_\lambda = C_{\lambda, 1} + \cdots + C_{\lambda, n}$$

with $C_{\lambda, i}$ connected and generically irreducible, and

$$C_{\lambda, i} \cdot C_{\lambda, j} = 0 \qquad \text{for all } i \neq j;$$

since, of course, $C_\lambda \cdot C_{\lambda, i} = 0$, it follows that

$$C_{\lambda, i} \cdot C_{\lambda, i} = 0$$

as well.

Consider the set of connected components $E = \{C_{\lambda, i}\}_{\lambda, i}$ of curves in the pencil $\{C_\lambda\}$. E forms a branched cover of $\mathbb{P}^1$ via the map λ and so inherits the structure of an algebraic curve. This is intuitively clear; a formal proof of the fact is based on two observations: all the curves C_λ (taken with proper multiplicity) are homologous, and only finitely many pairs $C_{\lambda, i}$ and $C_{\mu, j}$ are linearly equivalent. The first follows from the fact that the curves $\{C_\lambda\}_{\lambda, i}$ must form a connected family: if instead the pairs (λ, i) broke up into two families A and B,

$$S = \left(\bigcup_{(\lambda, i) \in A} C_{\lambda, i} \right) \cup \left(\bigcup_{(\lambda, i) \in B} C_{\lambda, i} \right)$$

would itself be reducible. To see the second point, note that if two generic components $C_{\lambda, i}$ and $C_{\mu, j}$ are linearly equivalent, they span a pencil $\{D_\alpha\}$ of curves. Every curve $C_{\lambda, i}$ will then meet at least one D_α, and so lie in D_α; thus the pencil $\{D_\alpha\}$ is the pencil $\{C_\lambda\}$, and $C_{\lambda, i}$ and $C_{\mu, j}$ constitute the entire fibers C_λ, C_μ—but since the generic C_λ has two or more connected components, there can be only finitely many such fibers. We may thus choose λ_0, i_0 and define

$$E' \subset S \times \text{Pic}^0(S)$$

by

$$E' = \{(p, \delta): p \in C_{\lambda, i} \quad \text{and} \quad [C_{\lambda, i} - C_{\lambda_0, i_0}] = \delta \};$$

the desingularization E of E' is the curve we seek.

Now, the map

$$\pi': S \to \mathbb{P}^1$$

factors through E via the map

$$S \xrightarrow{\pi} E,$$

sending a point p to the pair (λ, i) such that $p \in C_{\lambda, i}$. The fibers $C_{\lambda, i}$ of π are irreducible, and both the forms ω_1 and ω_2 vanish identically on all fibers of π. It follows as on p. 553 that the forms ω_i are the pullbacks of 1-forms η_1, η_2 on the base E. Since E has at least the two one-forms η_1 and η_2, then,

$$g(E) \geqslant 2,$$

so

$$\chi(E) < 0.$$

Recalling from p. 510 the formula

$$\chi(S) \geqslant \chi(E) \cdot \chi(F)$$

for the Euler characteristic of a surface S mapped to a curve E with generic fiber F, it follows from $\chi(S) < 0$ that the fibers of π have positive Euler characteristic, and so must be rational; thus S is ruled.

To complete the proof of the Castelnuovo-de Franchis theorem, we now argue that any surface S with $\chi(S) < 0$ contains two independent 1-forms with wedge product identically zero. To see this, note that from the Hodge decomposition,

$$4q = 2 + 2p_g + h^{1,1} - \chi(S)$$
$$\geqslant 2p_g + 3 - \chi(S).$$

It follows that

$$2q \geqslant p_g + \left(\frac{3 - \chi(S)}{2} \right).$$

In particular, $q \geqslant 2$—if q were 1, the Albanese map would take S to an elliptic curve, and by the formula of p. 510 quoted above the Euler characteristic of S would be nonnegative—so S contains at least two 1-forms ω_1, ω_2.

Now, since $\pi_1(S)$ contains at least a $\mathbb{Z}$-factor, we may for any m construct an m-sheeted covering space $\tilde{S} \xrightarrow{\pi} S$; $\tilde{S}$ inherits from S the structure of an algebraic surface. We then have

$$\chi(\tilde{S}) = m \cdot \chi(S),$$

so by taking m large we may assume $\chi(\tilde{S}) \leqslant -5$. Now consider the map

$$\wedge^2\left(H^0\left(\tilde{S}, \Omega_{\tilde{S}}^1\right)\right) \xrightarrow{\rho} H^0\left(\tilde{S}, \Omega_{\tilde{S}}^2\right)$$

given by wedge product. The kernel of ρ has codimension at most

$$p_g(\tilde{S}) \leqslant 2q(\tilde{S}) - \left(\frac{3 - \chi(\tilde{S})}{2}\right) \leqslant 2q(\tilde{S}) - 4$$

in $\wedge^2 H^0(\tilde{S}, \Omega_{\tilde{S}}^1)$. On the other hand, the cone of decomposable vectors

$$\{\eta_1 \wedge \eta_2\} \subset \wedge^2 H^0\left(\tilde{S}, \Omega_{\tilde{S}}^1\right)$$

has dimension $2q(\tilde{S}) - 3$, and so must meet the kernel of ρ. $\tilde{S}$ thus contains two independent 1-forms with wedge product 0, and so by the first part of the argument is birational to a ruled surface. But as we have seen, on a ruled surface the wedge product of *any* two 1-forms is identically zero—in particular, the pullbacks $\pi^*\omega_1, \pi^*\omega_2$ of the two 1-forms ω_1, ω_2 on S have wedge product zero, and hence so do ω_1 and ω_2.   Q.E.D.

Note also that we can take any surface S with $\chi(S) < 0$ and, blowing down, arrive at a minimal surface S_0 with $\chi(S_0) \leqslant \chi(S) < 0$; thus

Any surface with $\chi(S) < 0$ is the blow-up of a ruled surface.

There is a second similar criterion for a surface to be ruled:

Theorem.   *If S is minimal and $c_1^2(S) < 0$, then S is irrational ruled.*

Proof.   We start by proving the

Lemma.   *If S is minimal and $P_m(S) \neq 0$ for any $m > 0$—that is, if any multiple mK of the canonical divisor on S is linearly equivalent to an effective divisor D—then $c_1^2(S) \geqslant 0$.*

Proof.   Write

$$mK \sim D = \sum n_i D_i,$$

with $n_i > 0$ and D_i irreducible. Suppose that $K \cdot K$ were negative; we would then have

$$K \cdot mK = K \cdot \sum n_i D_i < 0,$$
$$\Rightarrow K \cdot D_i < 0 \qquad \text{for some } i.$$

But then

$$0 > K \cdot n_i D_i = n_i D_i \cdot D_i + \sum_{j \neq i} n_j D_i \cdot D_j$$

$$\geqslant n_i^2 D_i \cdot D_i,$$

so $D_i \cdot D_i < 0$ and D_i is an exceptional curve of the first kind, contrary to the hypothesis that S is minimal.　　　　　　　　　　　　　　　Q.E.D.

From this we see that if S is minimal and $c_1^2(S) < 0$, then $P_m(S) = 0$ for all m; in particular, $P_2(S) = p_g(S) = 0$. If the irregularity q of S were zero, it would follow from Section 4 that S was rational, and from Section 3 that S was either rational ruled or $\mathbb{P}^2$; in either case $c_1^2(S)$ would be positive. Thus $q(S) > 0$; and since $p_g(S) = 0$, the Albanese map $\overline{\Psi} : S \to \mathrm{Alb}(S)$ maps S onto a curve $\overline{E} \subset \mathrm{Alb}(S)$. Now let

$$\pi : E \to \overline{E}$$

be the desingularization of $\overline{E}$. The map

$$\Psi = \pi^{-1} \circ \overline{\Psi} : S \to E$$

is defined outside the divisor $\overline{\Psi}^{-1}(\overline{E}_s)$ on S, and is given, in terms of a local coordinate z around a point $p \in \pi^{-1}(\overline{E}_s)$, by a bounded holomorphic function; by Riemann's extension theorem the map Ψ extends to all of S. Note that since all holomorphic 1-forms on S are induced via $\overline{\Psi}$ from $\mathrm{Alb}(S)$ (and hence via Ψ from E), E must have genus at least q; on the other hand, since the pullback map

$$\psi^* : H^0(E, \Omega_E^1) \to H^0(S, \Omega_S^1)$$

is injective, it follows that E must have genus exactly q.

The final point in setting up the proof is that the fibers of the map $\Psi : S \to E$ are generically irreducible. To see this, we first note that they are generically smooth (apply Bertini's theorem to the pullback $\{\Psi^*(D_\lambda)\}$ of any pencil $\{D_\lambda\}$ on E) and so, if the generic fiber were reducible, it would have more than one connected component. We could then make the construction used in the last argument (p. 557) to factor the map Ψ

through the curve F consisting of connected components of fibers of Ψ. If E were of genus $q \geqslant 2$ or if the map α were branched, then by the

Riemann-Hurwitz formula

$$g(F) = m(q-1) + 1 + b > q,$$

where b is the number of branch points of α and m its sheet number; since the pullback Ψ'^* on 1-forms is injective, this is a contradiction. On the other hand, if q were 1 and α unbranched, then the image

$$\alpha_*(H_1(F,\mathbb{Z})) \subset H_1(E,\mathbb{Z})$$

would have positive index—contradicting the fact that the composed map

$$\overline{\Psi}_*:\ H_1(S,\mathbb{Z})/\text{torsion} \xrightarrow{\ \Psi'_*\ } H_1(F,\mathbb{Z}) \xrightarrow{\ \alpha_*\ } H_1(E,\mathbb{Z}) \xrightarrow{\ \pi_*\ } H_1(\text{Alb}(S),\mathbb{Z})$$

$$\parallel \qquad\qquad\qquad \parallel \qquad\qquad\qquad \parallel$$

$$\mathbb{Z}^2 \qquad\qquad\qquad \mathbb{Z}^2 \qquad\qquad\qquad \mathbb{Z}^2$$

is an isomorphism. Thus α cannot have degree 2 or more, and the fibers of Ψ are generically irreducible.

This completes the setting up. Our object now is to show that the fibers of Ψ are rational; by the lemma used in the proof of the Castelnuovo-de Franchis theorem, this will establish that S is ruled. The first step is to prove the

Lemma.   If $c_1^2(S) < 0$, then S contains an irreducible curve D having non-negative self-intersection, and negative intersection number with K.

Proof.   First, since $K \cdot K < 0$, by the index theorem the intersection pairing has one positive eigenvalue on the orthogonal complement $K^\perp$ of the canonical class in $H^{1,1}(S,\mathbb{Z})$; i.e., we can find a divisor class D_1 on S with

$$D_1 \cdot K = 0, \qquad D_1 \cdot D_1 > 0.$$

By Riemann-Roch, for any m,

$$h^0(mD_1) + h^0(K - mD_1) \geqslant 1 - q + \frac{m^2 D_1 \cdot D_1}{2},$$

so for large m, either mD_1 or $K - mD_1$ will be effective. $K \cdot (K - mD_1) = K \cdot K$ is negative, so in the latter case we may take $D_2 = K - mD_1$. On the other hand, if mD_1 is effective, we apply Riemann-Roch to the divisor $mD_1 + K$ to obtain

$$h^0(mD_1 + K) + h^0(-mD_1) \geqslant 1 - q + \frac{m^2 D_1 \cdot D_1}{2}$$

—but since mD_1 is effective, $h^0(-mD_1) = 0$, and consequently $mD_1 + K$ is effective. $(mD_1 + K) \cdot K < 0$, so we may set $D_2 = mD_1 + K$. In either event we obtain an effective curve D_2 with $D_2 \cdot K < 0$, and of course some irreducible component D of D_2 will have negative intersection with K. Note that since $D \cdot K < 0$ and S is minimal, $D \cdot D \geqslant 0$.   Q.E.D.

Now, assume the fibers of Ψ are irrational of genus g. Let D be an irreducible curve on S with $D \cdot K < 0$, and consider the linear systems

$$|D + nK|, \qquad n = 0, 1, 2, \ldots .$$

These are eventually empty: for sufficiently large n

$$D \cdot (D + nK) < 0;$$

but D, being irreducible with nonnegative self-intersection, has nonnegative intersection number with every effective divisor on S. We can thus choose an integer n such that

$$h^0(D + nK) \geqslant 1,$$
$$h^0(D + (n+1)K) = 0.$$

Let G be a generic curve in the system $|D + nK|$; since

$$G \cdot K = D \cdot K + nK \cdot K < 0,$$

some irreducible component G_0 of G will have negative intersection number with K. Let us first see that G_0 cannot be contained in a fiber C of Ψ: if we write

$$C = \sum n_i C_i,$$

then

$$0 = C_i \cdot C = n_i C_i \cdot C_i + \sum_{j \neq i} n_j C_i \cdot C_j;$$

C being connected, the latter term is strictly positive, and so

$$C_i \cdot C_i < 0 \qquad \text{for all } i.$$

Since S contains no exceptional curves of the first kind, then,

$$C_i \cdot K \geqslant 0 \qquad \text{for all } i.$$

Thus, *no component of a fiber of Ψ has negative intersection number with* K; accordingly, our curve G_0 cannot lie in a fiber, and so it must have positive intersection number $k = G_0 \cdot C$ with C.

The argument now splits up into two cases:

Case 1: $q \geqslant 2$

Consider the representation

$$\Psi : G_0 \to E$$

of G_0 as a k-sheeted cover of E; if $\Psi : G_0 \to E$ has b branch points, by Riemann-Hurwitz

$$\pi(G_0) = k(q-1) + 1 + \frac{b}{2}$$

and in particular, if $k \geqslant 2$, then

$$\pi(G_0) > q.$$

In this case, from the Poincaré residue sequence

$$0 \to \Omega_S^2 \to \Omega_S^2(G_0) \to \Omega_{G_0}^1 \to 0$$

and

$$h^0(\Omega_{G_0}^1) = \pi(G_0) > h^1(\Omega_S^2)$$

we deduce that

$$h^0(\Omega_S^2(G_0)) \neq 0.$$

But

$$\begin{aligned} h^0(\Omega_S^2(G_0)) &= h^0(K + G_0) \leqslant h^0(K + G) \\ &= h^0(D + (n+1)K) \\ &= 0, \end{aligned}$$

so this is impossible. G_0 must thus have intersection number 1 with C and therefore is mapped biholomorphically onto E by Ψ. Note that since

$$\pi(G_0) = q \quad \text{and} \quad G_0 \cdot K < 0,$$

we have

$$G_0 \cdot G_0 > 2q - 2.$$

Now let C_λ and $C_{\lambda'}$ be two distinct generic fibers of $\Psi : S \to E$, and

$$G_1 = G_0 + C_{\lambda'} - C_\lambda.$$

G_1 being homologous to G_0, by Riemann-Roch

$$\begin{aligned} h^0(G_1) &\geqslant \chi(\mathcal{O}_S) + \frac{G_1 \cdot G_1 - G_1 \cdot K}{2} \\ &= 1 - q + \frac{G_0 \cdot G_0 - G_0 \cdot K}{2} \\ &\geqslant 1, \end{aligned}$$

so G_1 is effective. On the other hand, since G_0 and G_1 are homologous and not linearly equivalent, G_1 cannot contain G_0; thus G_1 and G_0 each meet the generic fiber C in a single point, and these points are distinct. But inasmuch as the line bundles $[C_\lambda]$ and $[C_{\lambda'}]$ on S both restrict to the trivial bundle on C,

$$[G_1]|_C = [G_0]|_C.$$

The single points $G_0 \cdot C$ and $G_1 \cdot C$ are thus linearly equivalent on C, contrary to the hypothesis that C is irrational.

Case 2: $q = 1$

Here our previous argument fails—a priori, G_0 could very well be a multisheeted unbranched cover of E— and so we must employ a somewhat subtler approach. Certainly, from the above we may conclude that

$$\pi(G_0) = q = 1.$$

Write

$$G_0 \cdot K = -d, \qquad d > 0;$$

then, by adjunction,

$$G_0 \cdot G_0 = d.$$

Now choose a fixed point $\lambda_0 \in E$, and for each $\lambda \in E$ set

$$G_\lambda = G_0 + C_\lambda - C_{\lambda_0}.$$

G_λ is once more homologous to G_0, and by Riemann-Roch

$$h^0(G_\lambda) \geq 1 - q + \frac{G_0 \cdot G_0 - G_0 \cdot K}{2}$$

$$\geq d;$$

in particular G_λ is effective. Note that in fact we must have $h^0(G_\lambda) = d$: since no curve in the system $|G_\lambda|$ can contain G_0, $|G_\lambda|$ cuts out on G_0 a linear system of degree d and dimension $h^0(G_\lambda) - 1$; if $h^0(G_\lambda)$ were $d + 1$ or greater, this would imply that G_λ was rational.

Now choose $d - 1$ generic points $p_1, \ldots, p_{d-1}$ on S. For generic $\lambda \in E$, there will be a unique curve in the system $|G_\lambda|$ passing through the points P_i; we will denote this curve by H_λ. For two generic points $\lambda, \lambda' \in E$, H_λ and $H_{\lambda'}$ will intersect in d points, consisting of $p_1, \ldots, p_{d-1}$ and an additional point, which we will call $Q(\lambda, \lambda')$. Note that the points $Q(\lambda, \lambda')$ fill up the surface S, since the curves $\{H_\lambda\}_\lambda$ do and on any H_λ the divisors

$$Q(\lambda, \lambda') - Q(\lambda, \lambda'') = (H_{\lambda'} - H_{\lambda''})|_{H_\lambda}$$

$$\cong (C_{\lambda'} - C_{\lambda''})|_{H_\lambda}$$

fill up $\mathrm{Pic}^0(H_\lambda)$. Now, considering the elliptic curve E as a group with origin λ_0, for any $\mu \in E$ set

$$F_\mu = \bigcup_{\lambda \in E} Q(\lambda, \mu - \lambda).$$

The points of F_μ are parametrized by the quotient of E by the involution $\lambda \mapsto \mu - \lambda$, and so F_μ is a priori either a point or a rational curve; since the points $\{Q(\lambda, \mu - \lambda)\}_{\mu, \lambda}$ fill up S, it follows that for generic $\mu \in E$, F_μ is a rational curve. S thus contains a one-parameter family of rational curves —but since any rational curve on S lies in a fiber of Ψ and the generic fiber is irreducible, this is impossible. Q.E.D.

Note that by the Riemann-Roch formula

$$\chi(\mathcal{O}_S) = 1 - q + p_g = \frac{c_1^2 + c_2}{12},$$

if the holomorphic Euler characteristic $\chi(\mathcal{O}_S)$ of S is negative, then either c_1^2 or c_2 is. We have, accordingly, a third

Theorem. *If* S *is minimal and* $\chi(\mathcal{O}_S) < 0$, *then* S *is ruled.*

A Brief Introduction to Elliptic Surfaces

An *elliptic surface* with base E is a surface S and a map $\Psi : S \to E$ to a curve E such that the generic fiber of Ψ is an irreducible elliptic curve. Elliptic surfaces form a far more varied class than ruled surfaces: for one thing, whereas all fibers of a ruled surface are irreducible and smooth, an elliptic surface may have singular, reducible, and/or multiple fibers; for another, while all fibers of a ruled surface are of necessity isomorphic to one another, the complex structure of the fibers of an elliptic surface will, in general, vary from fiber to fiber. The various questions arising from these considerations—what configurations of curves may occur as reducible fibers of elliptic surfaces and how they affect the global geometry of the surface; what variations of the complex structure of the fiber are possible, especially around singular fibers—are both fascinating and, to a large degree, tractable. We are not able, in the present context, to go into these questions fully; the interested reader is referred to the papers of Kodaira, "On compact complex analytic surfaces," I, II, III, and IV, listed at the end of this chapter. One phenomenon associated to elliptic surfaces, however, unlike anything we have dealt with previously and warranting some discussion is that of *multiple fibers*, which we now describe.

Let us first say what a multiple fiber is. If $\Psi : S \to E$ is any holomorphic map of a surface S onto a curve E, then for generic $p \in E$, the pullback $\Psi^* z$ of a local coordinate z on E centered around p will vanish simply to order 1 along the fiber $\Psi^{-1}(p)$ of Ψ over p. A fiber $C = \Psi^{-1}(p)$ of Ψ along which the pullback of a local defining function z for $p \in E$ vanishes to order $m \geq 2$ is called a *multiple fiber* of *multiplicity m*. (More properly, if $C = \Sigma C_i$ is reducible, and $\Psi^* z$ vanishes to order n_i along C_i, we say that C is multiple if the greatest common divisor of the n_i is $m \geq 2$.) We note first a few points about a multiple fiber C_p:

1. Since the divisors $C_\lambda = (\Psi^*(z - \lambda))$ on S are all homologous, including $(\Psi^* z) = m C_p$, we see that $m \cdot C_p$ *is homologous to a generic fiber* C *of* Ψ. In particular,

$$C_p \cdot C_p = 0 \quad \text{and} \quad C_p \cdot K = \frac{1}{m} C_\lambda \cdot K.$$

2. Similarly, if $\gamma : \Delta \to S$ is any holomorphic arc meeting the multiple fiber C_p transversely at $\gamma(0)$, the pullback $\gamma^* \Psi^* z$ vanishes to order m at 0; thus the map $\Psi \circ \gamma$ expresses Δ locally as an m-sheeted cover of its image in

E, with a branch point of multiplicity m at 0; in particular, $\gamma(\Delta)$ will meet every fiber near C_p not once but a total of m times. Likewise, if $\gamma(\Delta)$ meets C_p with multiplicity k, then $\Psi \circ \gamma$ expresses Δ as an mk-sheeted cover of its image, totally branched at 0, and $\gamma(\Delta)$ will meet fibers near C_p a total of mk times.

Now, it is easy to see that if the generic fiber of a map $\Psi : S \to E$ is rational, then no fiber C_p may be multiple: we would have

$$C_p \cdot C_p = 0 \quad \text{and} \quad C_p \cdot K = -\frac{2}{m},$$

contradicting at the very least the integrality of the virtual genus $\pi(C_p)$. If the generic fiber of Ψ is of genus $g \geqslant 2$, then we see in the same way that a multiple fiber C_p must have multiplicity m dividing $g-1$, and the genus of C_p will be $g' = (g-1)/m + 1 < g$. On the other hand, if $\Psi : S \to E$ is elliptic, Ψ may have multiple fibers of any multiplicity, all of the same genus 1.

We can construct a map $\Psi : S \to \Delta$ of an open surface S to the unit disc $\Delta \subset \mathbb{C}$ with a multiple fiber at 0 as follows. Let F be any elliptic curve, given as the complex plane with Euclidean coordinate w modulo the lattice $\Lambda = \{1, \tau\}$. Let z be the coordinate in the disc Δ, and consider the automorphism

$$\varphi : \Delta \times F \to \Delta \times F$$

given by

$$\varphi(z, w) = \left(e^{2\pi i / m} \cdot z, \, w + \frac{\tau}{m} \right).$$

φ has order m and all powers φ^i of φ are fixed-point-free; let S be the quotient of $\Delta \times F$ by the group $\{\varphi^i\}$ and $\Delta \times F \overset{\pi}{\to} S$ the quotient map. The map

$$\psi' : \Delta \times F \longrightarrow \Delta$$
$$(z, w) \mapsto z^m$$

factors through S to give a map

$$\Psi : S \to \Delta$$

whose fibers $C_\lambda = \Psi^{-1}(\lambda)$ are all elliptic curves. Now for $\lambda \neq 0 \in \Delta$ the divisor $\pi^* C_\lambda$ consists of the m elliptic curves $\{ \{\varepsilon\} \times F : \varepsilon^m = \lambda \}$ each taken singly, while the divisor $\pi^* C_0$ consists of the single curve $\{0\} \times F$, *taken with multiplicity 1 since the map π is unbranched.* C_0 is thus a multiple fiber of Ψ, of multiplicity m.

More generally, we can alter any elliptic surface $S_0 \overset{\Psi_0}{\to} E$ to create multiple fibers, as follows. Start with any point $p \in E$ with C_p smooth and nonmultiple. By way of preparation, let U be a small disc around p so that Ψ_0 has no singular fibers over U, let z be a local coordinate in U centered around p such that $U=\{|z|<1\}$, and let $\Sigma_0=\Psi_0^{-1}(U)$. Take a section α of Ψ_0—that is, a map $\alpha:U\to S_0$ such that $\Psi_0\circ\alpha=id$, and for each $z\in U$ consider the fiber C_z as a group with $\alpha(z)\in C_z$ as the origin. The points of order exactly m in the fibers C_z form an unbranched cover of U and so break up into disjoint arcs; choose one such arc and call it β. The elliptic curve C_z may be realized as $\mathbb{C}$ modulo the lattice $\{1,\tau(z)\}$, with $\alpha(z)$ corresponding to the origin and $\beta(z)$ the point $1/m$. For any complex number t, then, let $t\cdot\beta(z)$ denote the point of C_z corresponding to $(t/m)\in\mathbb{C}$; this is well-defined.

Now define

$$\Sigma\subset\Delta\times\Sigma_0$$

by

$$\Sigma=\{(w,r):\ z(r)=w^m\}.$$

Note that the projection $w:\Sigma\to\Delta$ expresses Σ as elliptic over Δ, and that the fibers over points w and $e^{2\pi i/m}w$ are naturally identified with the fiber C_{w^m} of Ψ_0; accordingly, we can define an automorphism φ on Σ by

$$\varphi(w,r)=\left(e^{2\pi i/m}w,\ r+\beta(w^m)\right).$$

The quotient Σ_1 of Σ by the finite group $\{\varphi^i\}$ is, as in the first example, an elliptic surface over Δ via the map $\Psi_1(w,r)=w^m=z$ with a fiber of multiplicity m over $w=0$. Moreover, the fiber $\tilde{C}_z$ of Σ_1 over z is isomorphic to the fiber of the original surface S over z; indeed, *the inverse image $\Psi_1^{-1}(\Delta-\{0\})$ of the punctured disc in Σ_1 and the inverse image $\Psi_0^{-1}(U-\{0\})$ are isomorphic as elliptic surfaces* via the map $\alpha:\Sigma\to S_0$ induced by

$$\bar{\alpha}:\ \Sigma\to S_0$$

$$:\ (w,r)\mapsto r+\left(\frac{1}{2\pi\sqrt{-1}}\log w\right)\cdot\beta(w^m)$$

away from the fibers over 0. We can thus glue the new surface Σ_1 into S_0 in place of the original Σ_0; i.e., we can set

$$S_1=S_0-\Psi_0^{-1}(0)\cup_\alpha\Sigma_1$$

to obtain an elliptic surface $S_1\to E$, isomorphic to S_0 away from $C_p=\Psi_0^{-1}(0)$ and having a fiber of multiplicity m over p.

This operation—replacing an ordinary fiber of an elliptic surface with a multiple one—is called a *logarithmic transformation*; it was invented by Kodaira. One warning: if S_1 is obtained from S_0 by a logarithmic transformation on the fiber C_p as above, then it is clear from the formulas that under the isomorphism

$$S_0-C_p\cong S_1-\tilde{C}_p,\qquad \tilde{C}_p=\Psi_1^{-1}(0),$$

a curve in S_0 transverse to the fiber C_p may be mapped to a curve in $S_1 - \tilde{C}_p$ having an essential singularity along $\tilde{C}_p$. There may be, accordingly, very little correlation between closed curves in S_0 and in S_1; indeed, S_0 may be algebraic and S_1 not, or vice versa.

One basic fact about multiple fibers is the

Lemma. *If B is a smooth multiple fiber of multiplicity* m *in the elliptic surface* $\Psi : S \to E$, *then the normal bundle* $N_{B/S} = [B]|_B$ *of B is torsion of order exactly* m *in* $\mathrm{Pic}^0(B)$.

Proof. It is easy to see that the normal bundle to B is m-torsion: the bundles $\{[\Psi^*(p)]|_B\}_{p \in E}$ form a continuous family, trivial for $p \neq q \in \Psi(B)$ and hence for all p, including $\Psi^*(q) = [mB]$. To see that $N_{B/S}$ is indeed of order m, choose a local coordinate w on E centered around $q = \Psi(B)$, and a covering $U = \{U_\alpha\}$ of a neighborhood U of B in S by small polydiscs. Since the function Ψ^*w vanishes to order m along B, we can in each U_α choose an mth root of Ψ^*w, i.e., a holomorphic function z_α on U_α with

$$z_\alpha^m = \Psi^*w;$$

write

$$z_\alpha = e^{2\pi i k_{\alpha\beta}/m} \cdot z_\beta \qquad \text{in } U_\alpha \cap U_\beta$$

for $k_{\alpha\beta} \in \{0, 1, \ldots, m-1\}$.

Since z_α vanishes to order 1 along B in U_α, the 1-form dz_α restricted to B gives a nonzero section of the conormal bundle $N_{B/S}^*$ in $B \cap U_\alpha$; transition functions for $N_{B/S}^*$ are thus given by the constant functions

$$\frac{dz_\alpha}{dz_\beta} = e^{2\pi i k_{\alpha\beta}/m}.$$

Suppose that the dth power $N_{B/S}^d$ (and hence the dth power $(N_{B/S}^*)^d$ is trivial. Then the cocycle

$$\left\{ g_{\alpha\beta} = e^{2\pi i d k_{\alpha\beta}/m} \right\} \in Z^1(B, \mathbb{C}^*)$$

is a coboundary, i.e., we can find constants $l_\alpha \in \mathbb{C}$ such that for all α, β,

$$e^{2\pi i d k_{\alpha\beta}/m} = \frac{l_\alpha}{l_\beta}.$$

We may normalize the l_α's by taking $l_1 = 1$; it then follows from the last equation that every l_α is a (d/m)th root of unity. Now let

$$z_\alpha' = l_\alpha \cdot z_\alpha^d.$$

The functions $z_\alpha' \in \mathcal{O}(U_\alpha)$ agree on the overlaps $U_\alpha \cap U_\beta$ and so define a single function $z' \in \mathcal{O}(U)$, with

$$z'^m = \Psi^* w^d.$$

Moreover, z', being constant along the fibers of Ψ, is in fact induced from a function w' on a neighborhood of q in E satisfying $w'^m = w^d$; but since w^d vanishes to order exactly d at q, $d = m \cdot \mathrm{ord}_q(w')$ is a multiple of m. We see, then, that $N_{B/S}^d$ is trivial if and only if m divides d.   Q.E.D.

The proof of this lemma suggests a way to invert the logarithmic transformation; we will sketch this construction, leaving the details as an exercise for the reader. Let B be a smooth fiber of multiplicity m on $S_1 \overset{\Psi_1}{\to} E$, $U = \{|w| < 1\} \subset E$ a neighborhood of $\Psi_1(B)$, and $\Sigma_1 = \Psi_1^{-1}(U)$. Consider the set Σ of pairs (p, z_α), where p is a point of $\Sigma_1 \subset S_1$ and z_α a function element around p satisfying $z_\alpha^m = \Psi_1^* w$. By the proof of the lemma, Σ forms a connected unbranched, m-sheeted cover of Σ_1, and the map

$$\Sigma \overset{z = z_\alpha}{\longrightarrow} \Delta$$

expresses Σ as an elliptic surface over the disc, with *no multiple fiber*: for $\lambda \neq 0$, the fiber $z^{-1}(\lambda)$ maps one-to-one onto the fiber $\Psi_1^{-1}(\lambda^m)$ of S_1, while $z^{-1}(0)$ forms an m-sheeted cover of the multiple fiber B of S_1. Now take an arc γ in S_1 transverse to B; γ then forms an m-sheeted cover of its image in E, branched totally over 0. The inverse image of γ in Σ then consists of m disjoint arcs, each transverse to the fibers of z_α. Choose one of these components and call it $\tilde{\gamma}$, and let φ_λ be the isomorphism

$$\varphi_\lambda = z^{-1}(\lambda) \longrightarrow z^{-1}(e^{2\pi i/m} \cdot \lambda)$$

consisting of the natural identification

$$z^{-1}(\lambda) \cong \Psi_1^{-1}(\lambda^m) \cong z^{-1}(e^{2\pi i/m} \cdot \lambda)$$

composed with a translation, and carrying $\tilde{\gamma} \cdot z^{-1}(\lambda)$ to $\tilde{\gamma} \cdot z^{-1}(e^{2\pi i/m} \cdot \lambda)$. The automorphism φ of Σ given by

$$\varphi(p, z_\alpha) = \left(\varphi_\lambda(p), e^{2\pi i/m} z_\alpha \right) \qquad (\lambda = z_\alpha(p))$$

then has order m and is fixed-point-free away from $z^{-1}(0)$, where it is the identity. The quotient Σ_0 of Σ by the group $\{\varphi^i\}$ is again elliptic via the map $w = z^m$ and is without multiple fibers; moreover, the complement of $w^{-1}(0)$ in Σ_0 is isomorphic to the complement of $\Psi_1^{-1}(0)$ in Σ_1, and so we may plug Σ_0 into $S_1 - \Psi_1^{-1}(0)$ to obtain a surface S_0, isomorphic to S_1 outside $\Psi_1^{-1}(0)$ and having a nonmultiple fiber over $q \in E$. The reader may verify that the operation is indeed inverse to the logarithmic transformation—i.e., that if we perform a logarithmic transformation to S_0 (making suitable choices of arcs α, β), we get S_1 back again—and so show that *every elliptic surface with smooth multiple fibers is obtained from an elliptic surface without multiple fibers by means of logarithmic transformations.*

We come now to the main point of our analysis of elliptic surfaces: the formula for the canonical divisor. We will consider here an elliptic surface $S \overset{\Psi}{\to} E$, all of whose multiple fibers are smooth—all of our formulas apply as well to the general case, but the proof is substantially harder.

To start, let $C_{\lambda_1}, \ldots, C_{\lambda_n}$ be n generic fibers of Ψ. Consider the Poincaré residue map

$$0 \to \Omega_S^2 \to \Omega_S^2(C_{\lambda_1} + \cdots + C_{\lambda_n}) \to \oplus \Omega_{C_{\lambda_i}}^1 \to 0.$$

The image in $H^0(\oplus \Omega_{C_{\lambda_i}}^1) = \oplus H^0(C_\lambda, \Omega_{C_{\lambda_i}}^1) \cong \mathbb{C}^n$ of $H^0(S, \Omega_S^2(\Sigma C_\lambda))$ has codimension at most $h^1(S, \Omega_S^2) = q(S)$; thus

$$h^0\left(K + \sum_{i=1}^n C_{\lambda_i}\right) \geqslant n + p_g - q.$$

In particular, for n large, we see that $K + \sum_{i=1}^n C_{\lambda_i}$ is linearly equivalent to an effective divisor D. Now any fiber C of S has self-intersection 0 and hence, by adjunction, intersection number 0 with K. D, accordingly, has intersection number

$$D \cdot C_\lambda = \left(K + \sum_{i=1}^n C_{\lambda_i}\right) \cdot C_\lambda = 0$$

with the fiber C_λ and so must consist of a linear combination of fibers and components of fibers. We claim that D cannot contain a component of a reducible fiber C unless it contains the entire fiber. To see this, decompose C into irreducible components

$$C = \sum n_i C_i$$

and write

$$D = D' + \sum m_i C_i.$$

with D' disjoint from C. By the standard argument (p. 555), every component C_i of C has strictly negative self-intersection, and so by the hypothesis that S contains no exceptional curves of the first kind, $K \cdot C_i \geqslant 0$ for all i. Writing

$$K = D - \sum C_{\lambda_i},$$

this implies that for any i

$$\sum_{j \neq i} m_j C_i \cdot C_j \geqslant -m_i C_i \cdot C_i.$$

Now,

$$0 = C \cdot C_i = n_i C_i \cdot C_i + \sum_{j \neq i} n_j C_j C_i,$$

and so we obtain the inequality

$$\frac{\sum\limits_{j\neq i} m_j C_i \cdot C_j}{\sum\limits_{j\neq i} n_j C_i \cdot C_j} \geqslant \frac{-m_i C_i \cdot C_i}{-n_i \cdot C_i \cdot C_i} = \frac{m_i}{n_i} \qquad \text{for any } i;$$

it follows that *all the ratios* m_i/n_i *are equal*. Thus, if C is nonmultiple (i.e., the coefficients n_i have no common divisor), D contains the entire fiber $C = \sum n_i C_i$ with some multiplicity.

From the above, we see that we can write the canonical divisor

$$K = \Psi^* D + \sum \rho_i B_i$$

as the pullback of a divisor D on E, plus a linear combination of the multiple fibers B_i of S. If B_i has multiplicity m_i, then we can incorporate any integral multiple of $m_i B_i$ into D; thus we may take

$$0 \leqslant \rho_i \leqslant m_i - 1.$$

This determines ρ_i: by the adjunction formula,

$$K_{B_i} = \left[K + B_i \right]\big|_{B_i} = \left[(\rho_i + 1) B_i \right]\big|_{B_i} \equiv 0;$$

since the bundle $[B_i]\big|_{B_i}$ is torsion of order exactly m_i, this implies

$$\rho_i = m_i - 1,$$

i.e.,

$$K = \Psi^* D + \sum (m_i - 1) B_i.$$

Finally, we ask for the degree d of D. We will find d by computing $h^0(K + \sum C_{\lambda_i})$ for n generic fibers $C_{\lambda_1}, \ldots, C_{\lambda_n}$ of S in two ways: by Riemann-Roch on E, and on S. First, note that since

$$\left[K + \sum C_{\lambda_i} \right]\big|_{B_i} = K\big|_{B_i} = \left[(m_i - 1) B_i \right]\big|_{B_i},$$

the divisor $\sum (m_i - 1) B_i$ *is a fixed component of the series* $|K + \sum C_{\lambda_i}|$. We have thus for n large

$$h^0\!\left(S, \mathcal{O}_S\!\left(K + \sum C_{\lambda_i}\right)\right) = h^0\!\left(E, \mathcal{O}\!\left(D + \sum \lambda_i\right)\right)$$
$$= \deg D + n - g(E) + 1$$

by Riemann-Roch on E. On the other hand, by Riemann-Roch on S,

$$h^0\!\left(K + \sum C_{\lambda_i}\right) - h^1\!\left(K + \sum C_{\lambda_i}\right) = \chi(\mathcal{O}_S),$$

inasmuch as $h^2(K + \sum C_{\lambda_i}) = h^0(-\sum C_{\lambda_i}) = 0$, and $K \cdot C_{\lambda_i} = C_{\lambda_i} \cdot C_{\lambda_i} = 0$. The problem hinges on determining $h^1(K + \sum C_{\lambda_i})$; to this end, consider the sequence

$$0 \to \mathcal{O}_S\left(-\sum C_{\lambda_i}\right) \to \mathcal{O}_S \to \oplus \mathcal{O}_{C_{\lambda_i}} \to 0.$$

From the long exact cohomology sequence

$$0 \to H^0\left(S, \mathcal{O}_S\left(-\sum C_{\lambda_i}\right)\right) \to H^0(S, \mathcal{O}_S) \to \oplus H^0(C_{\lambda_i}, \mathcal{O}_{C_{\lambda_i}})$$

$$\to H^1\left(S, \mathcal{O}_S\left(-\sum C_{\lambda_i}\right)\right) \to H^1(S, \mathcal{O}_S) \to \oplus H^1(C_{\lambda_i}, \mathcal{O}_{C_{\lambda_i}})$$

associated to this sequence, we see that

$$h^1\left(S, \mathcal{O}\left(K + \sum C_{\lambda_i}\right)\right) = h^1\left(S, \mathcal{O}\left(-\sum C_{\lambda_i}\right)\right)$$
$$= 0 - 1 + n + k,$$

where k is the dimension of the kernel of the map $H^1(S, \mathcal{O}_S) \to \oplus H^1(C_{\lambda_i}, \mathcal{O}_{C_{\lambda_i}})$ induced by restriction. To compute k, note that by the functoriality of the Dolbeault isomorphism—i.e., the commutativity of the diagram

$$H^1(S, \mathcal{O}_S) \longrightarrow \oplus H^1(C_{\lambda_i}, \mathcal{O}_{C_{\lambda_i}})$$

$$\| \qquad\qquad\qquad \|$$

$$H_{\bar\partial}^{0,1}(S) \longrightarrow \oplus H_{\bar\partial}^{0,1}(C_{\lambda_i})$$

$$\| \qquad\qquad\qquad \|$$

$$\overline{H_{\bar\partial}^{1,0}(S)} \longrightarrow \oplus \overline{H_{\bar\partial}^{1,0}(C_{\lambda_i})}$$

—this is just the number of holomorphic 1-forms on S whose restriction to each of the C_λ is identically zero.

If η is any 1-form on S with $\eta|_{C_{\lambda_i}} \equiv 0$, then the restriction of η to any smooth fiber C_λ of S is likewise zero in the de Rham cohomology of C_λ, and hence identically zero. Thus any 1-form vanishing on a single fiber of S vanishes on all fibers, and so by our previous argument (p. 553), is induced from a 1-form on the base E; conversely, of course, the pullback $\Psi^*\omega$ of any 1-form ω on E vanishes on every fiber of Ψ. The number of 1-forms on S vanishing on the curves C_λ is thus just the genus g of E; we have, accordingly,

$$h^1\left(K + \sum C_{\lambda_i}\right) = h^1\left(-\sum C_{\lambda_i}\right) = g + n - 1$$

and

$$h^0\left(K + \sum C_{\lambda_i}\right) = \chi(\mathcal{O}_S) + g + n - 1.$$

Combining this with the formula for $h^0(K + \sum C_\lambda)$ obtained from

Riemann-Roch on E, we see that

$$\chi(\mathcal{O}_S) + g + n - 1 = h^0(K + \Sigma C_{\lambda_i})$$
$$= \deg D + n - g + 1,$$

and hence $\qquad\qquad\qquad \deg D = 2g - 2 + \chi(\mathcal{O}_S).$

Summarizing, we have

The canonical bundle K *of an elliptic surface* S $\overset{\Psi}{\to}$ E *with multiple fibers* B$_i$ *of multiplicity* m$_i$ *is given by*

$$K = \psi^* D + \sum (m_i - 1) B_i,$$

where

$$\deg D = 2g(E) - 2 + \chi(\mathcal{O}_S).$$

Note that a suitable multiple mK of K will always be the pullback of a bundle on the base E, of degree

$$m\left(2g - 2 + \chi(\mathcal{O}_S) + \sum \frac{m_i - 1}{m_i}\right).$$

Kodaira Number and the Classification Theorem I

In terms of their gross characteristics, algebraic curves may be said to fall into three classes—genus 0, genus 1, and genus $g \geqslant 2$—according to whether the canonical bundle of the curve has negative, zero, or positive degree. Analogously, in trying to classify surfaces, we consider the behavior of their canonical bundles. Of course, we have for surfaces no notion completely analogous to the degree of a line bundle on a curve; nor does it suffice to consider only the dimension of the linear system $|K|$: as we have seen in our discussion of elliptic surfaces, there may exist surfaces on which a multiple of K is effective and nonzero, while $p_g = 0$. Indeed, taking the quotient of the Fermat quintic

$$S' = \left(X_0^5 + X_1^5 + X_2^5 + X_3^5 = 0\right) \subset \mathbb{P}^3$$

by the fixed-point-free group of automorphisms generated by

$$\varphi[X_0, X_1, X_2, X_3] = [X_0, e^{2\pi i/5} X_1, e^{4\pi i/5} X_2, e^{6\pi i/5} X_3],$$

we obtain a surface S (called a *Godeaux surface*) on which the canonical bundle is actually positive but has no sections. We therefore consider not just the dimension of the linear system $|K|$ but all the plurigenera $P_m(S) = H^0(S, \mathcal{O}(mK))$. There are, in broad terms, four possible types of behavior for the sequence $P_m(S)$:

1. It may be—as, for example, on a rational surface—that $P_m(S)=0$ for all m. Such a surface is said to have *Kodaira number* -1.

2. Assuming that $P_m(S)\neq0$ for some m, we may ask whether the integers $P_m(S)$ are bounded. If in fact they are, then $P_m(S)$ must be either 0 or 1 for all m: if for some m the bundle mK had two linearly independent global holomorphic sections σ and τ, then the bundle mnK would possess at least the $n+1$ independent sections

$$\sigma^n, \sigma^{n-1}\otimes\tau, \ldots, \sigma\otimes\tau^{n-1}, \tau^n.$$

A surface whose plurigenera are bounded but not all 0 is said to have *Kodaira number* 0.

3. If the sequence $P_m(S)$ is unbounded, but

$$P_m(S) \leqslant c\cdot m$$

for some constant c, then S is said to have *Kodaira number* 1.

4. Finally, if the sequence $P_m(S)/m$ is unbounded, S is said to have *Kodaira number* 2, and to be of *general type*.

The Kodaira number of a surface S, usually written $\kappa(S)$, can also be thought of as either one less than the transcendence degree over $\mathbb{C}$ of the quotient field of the *pluricanonical* (graded) *ring*

$$\bigoplus_{m=0}^{\infty} H^0(S, \mathcal{O}(mK))$$

or alternatively as the dimension of the image of S under the rational map given by the linear system $|mK|$ for m large (-1 if the map is not defined —i.e., if $|mK|$ is empty—for all m).

For example, any ruled surface $S \overset{\Psi}{\to} E$ has Kodaira number -1, as we have seen. An elliptic surface $S \overset{\Psi}{\to} E$, on the other hand, may have Kodaira number -1, 0, or 1. As we saw in the last discussion, if $\{B_i\}$ are the multiple fibers of Ψ, m_i the multiplicity of B_i, and m a common multiple of the m_i, then

$$mK_S = \Psi^*L$$

for some line bundle $L \to E$ of degree

$$\deg(L) = m\left(2g-2+\chi(\mathcal{O}_S)+\sum \frac{m_i-1}{m_i}\right),$$

where g is the genus of E. The Kodaira number of S is clearly -1 if

$$\sum \frac{m_i-1}{m_i} < 2-2g-\chi(\mathcal{O}_S)$$

and 1 if

$$\sum \frac{m_i - 1}{m_i} > 2 - 2g - \chi(\mathcal{O}_S),$$

while in case $\deg(L) = 0$, S will have Kodaira number either -1 or 0 depending on whether some power of L is trivial or not (we shall see later that in fact $\deg(L) = 0$ implies $L^n \equiv 0$ for some n). Note one point that emerges from our description of the canonical bundle of an elliptic surface S: if $K \cdot D > 0$ for any effective curve D on S (in particular if some multiple of K is effective and nonzero), then $\kappa(S) = 1$.

The version of the classification theorem for surfaces we shall prove here consists of describing in turn surfaces of Kodaira number -1, 0, and $+1$. The description of surfaces of general type is not yet in as complete a form. We begin with the relatively easy case $\kappa = +1$; we will prove that

Any surface S with Kodaira number 1 is elliptic.

The proof is fairly straightforward. We note first that if S is minimal with $\kappa(S) = 0$ or 1, then $c_1^2(S) = 0$: if $c_1^2(S)$ were negative, then S would be ruled, while if $c_1^2(S)$ were positive, we would have by Riemann-Roch

$$h^0(mK) + h^0(-(m-1)K) \geqslant \frac{mK \cdot mK - mK \cdot K}{2} + \chi(\mathcal{O}) > \frac{c_1^2}{4} m^2$$

for m large, so that either $h^0(-(m-1)K) \gg 0$—in which case $\kappa(S) = -1$—or $h^0(mK) \geqslant c_1^2 m^2 / 4$, i.e., $\kappa(S) = 2$.

Lemma. *If any multiple* $D = mK$ *of the canonical bundle on a minimal surface is effective, and* $D \cdot D = 0$, *then all irreducible components* D_i *of* D *satisfy*

$$K \cdot D_i = 0, \qquad D_i \cdot D_i = 0 \text{ or } -2.$$

Proof. Write

$$D = \sum n_i D_i, \qquad n_i > 0, \quad D_i \text{ irreducible;}$$

for each i we have

$$K \cdot D_i = \frac{1}{m} \left(n_i D_i \cdot D_i + \sum_{j \neq i} n_j D_j \cdot D_i \right) \geqslant \frac{n_i}{m} D_i \cdot D_i,$$

and it follows that $K \cdot D_i \geqslant 0$ for all i since otherwise D_i would be exceptional of the first kind. Now from the equation

$$0 = D \cdot D = m \sum n_i K \cdot D_i$$

we see that in fact $K \cdot D_i = 0$ for all i, and hence that $D_i \cdot D_i \leqslant (n_i / m) K \cdot D_i = 0$

must be either 0 or -2 for each i. Each component D_i is thus either rational or elliptic. Q.E.D.

Note that the lemma applies as well to curves D homologous to a multiple of K.

We may use this lemma to describe surfaces S with $\kappa(S) = 1$. For some m, the linear system $|mK|$ contains at least a pencil $\{D_\lambda\}$, and by the lemma all components of each curve D_λ are either elliptic or rational. Since the rational components all have negative self-intersection, moreover, they cannot vary; thus if F is the fixed component of the pencil $\{D_\lambda\}$, the generic element of the pencil

$$\{D_\lambda' = D_\lambda - F\}$$

will contain only elliptic compoments $D_{\lambda_1}', \ldots, D_{\lambda_n}'$. Inasmuch as all components of D_λ have intersection number 0 with K, and hence with D_λ, we have

$$
\begin{aligned}
D_\lambda' \cdot D_\lambda' &= D_\lambda \cdot D_\lambda - 2 D_\lambda \cdot F + F \cdot F \\
&\leqslant D_\lambda \cdot D_\lambda + F \cdot F \\
&\leqslant D_\lambda \cdot D_\lambda = 0.
\end{aligned}
$$

But since D_λ' moves in a pencil without fixed component, $D_\lambda' \cdot D_\lambda' \geqslant 0$; thus $D_\lambda' \cdot D_\lambda' = 0$. Finally, by the lemma $D_{\lambda_i}' \cdot D_{\lambda_i}' = 0$ and obviously $D_{\lambda_i}' \cdot D_{\lambda_j}' \geqslant 0$ for $i \neq j$, so it follows that $D_{\lambda_i}' \cdot D_{\lambda_j}' = 0$ for all i and j, i.e.,

The pencil $\{D_\lambda'\}$ has no base points, and its generic element D_λ' consists of a disjoint collection of elliptic curves.

By the construction introduced in the proof of the Castelnuovo-de Franchis theorem (p. 557), the map

$$\pi: S \to \mathbb{P}^1$$

given by the pencil $\{D_\lambda'\}$ factors

$$\pi: S \xrightarrow{\pi'} E \to \mathbb{P}^1$$

through the curve $E = \{D_{\lambda_i}'\}_{\lambda, i}$ consisting of connected components of curves in the pencil $\{D_\lambda'\}$, and the fibers of π' are generically irreducible elliptic curves; thus S is elliptic. Q.E.D.

Note, incidentally, that by this argument a minimal surface S with $K \cdot K = 0$ cannot have Kodaira number 2: if $P_m(S) > 1$ for any m, S will be elliptic and so $\kappa(S) \leqslant 1$.

We next consider surfaces of Kodaira number -1. We will prove that

A minimal surface S with $\kappa(S) = -1$ is either $\mathbb{P}^2$ or ruled.

A large part of the work involved in proving this has already been done: if $q(S)=0$, then by the Castelnuovo-Enriques theorem of Section 4 the vanishing of $P_2(S)$ implies that S is rational, and our discussion in Section 3 of minimal rational surfaces shows that S is either $\mathbb{P}^2$ or rational ruled. On the other hand, if either $c_1^2(S)$ or $c_2(S)$ is negative, then, as we have seen, S is ruled, so we may assume both are nonnegative; from this it follows that

$$0 \leqslant \frac{c_1^2 + c_2}{12} = \chi(\mathcal{O}_S) = 1 - q,$$

i.e.,

$$c_1^2 = c_2 = \chi(\mathcal{O}_S) = 0 \quad \text{and} \quad q(S) = 1.$$

Let S be a surface with these numerical characters, and assume that S is not ruled. We will describe the geometry of S; our principal object for the present will be to show that $P_m(S) \neq 0$ for some m.

We start with some generalities. First, the Albanese map $\Psi: S \to E$ maps S to an elliptic curve E; assuming S is not ruled, the fibers will have genus $g \geqslant 1$. Since, moreover, $\chi(S)=0$, by the formula of p. 510, all fibers of Ψ must be smooth irreducible curves of genus g. Note in particular that S *contains no rational curves*, since any such curve would necessarily lie in a fiber of the Albanese map. Also, since S is not ruled, by the argument of p. 561, S contains no effective curve having negative intersection number with the canonical bundle K; from this follows the basic

Lemma. *If D is any curve on S with*

$$K \cdot D = D \cdot D = 0,$$

then D consists of a disjoint collection of smooth elliptic curves D$_i$, each satisfying $D_i \cdot D_i = K \cdot D_i = 0$.

Proof. The proof is not difficult: writing

$$D = \sum n_i D_i,$$

we see first that, since no D_i can have negative intersection number with K, and

$$K \cdot D = \sum n_i K \cdot D_i = 0,$$

we must have

$$K \cdot D_i = 0 \qquad \text{for all } i.$$

Then, since S contains no rational curves,

$$D_i \cdot D_i \geqslant 0 \qquad \text{for all } i,$$

and the inequality

$$0 = D \cdot D = \sum n_i^2 D_i \cdot D_i + \sum_{i \neq j} n_i n_j D_i \cdot D_j$$

$$\geqslant \sum n_i^2 D_i \cdot D_i \geqslant 0$$

implies that

$$D_i \cdot D_j = 0 \qquad \text{for all } i, j,$$

so the curves D_i are disjoint. Finally, since S contains no rational curves, any irreducible curve of virtual genus $\pi = 1$ on S is smooth.   Q.E.D.

The main point of our study of S will be to show that S is elliptic *with rational base*. The argument for this proceeds in three steps: we show first that S must contain an elliptic curve transverse to the fibers C of Ψ, second that it must contain two disjoint such elliptic curves, and finally that it must contain an elliptic pencil transverse to the fibers of Ψ.

Step 1. *S contains an irreducible curve* F *with* $K \cdot F = F \cdot F = 0$, $F \cdot C > 0$, *transverse to the fibers of* Ψ.

This is the hardest of the three parts of the argument. We shall have to use two different approaches, depending on whether the genus g of the fibers of the Albanese map Ψ is 1, or more than 1.

Case 1: $g \geqslant 2$

In this case, we will show that S contains an effective curve homologous to $2K$; by the last lemma, every component of such a curve will be elliptic, and as we shall see, one must be transverse to the fibers.

Note first that since the fibers C_λ of Ψ have self-intersection 0, by the adjunction formula

$$K \cdot C_\lambda = 2g - 2.$$

For each $\lambda \in E$, consider the linear system

$$|2K + C_\lambda|.$$

Since

$$h^2(2K + C_\lambda) = h^0(-K - C_\lambda) \leqslant h^0(-K) = 0,$$

by Riemann-Roch we have

$$h^0(2K + C_\lambda) \geqslant \frac{(2K + C_\lambda)(K + C_\lambda)}{2} = 3g - 3.$$

On the other hand, the line bundle $[2K + C_\lambda]$ on S restricts to the bicanonical bundle $2K_{C_0}$ on any fiber C_0, and by Riemann-Roch for curves,

$$h^0\big(C_0, \mathcal{O}_{C_0}(2K_{C_0})\big) = 3g - 3.$$

Now, if for any λ the restriction map

$$r_\lambda: \ H^0(S, \mathcal{O}_S(2K + C_\lambda)) \to H^0\big(C_0, \mathcal{O}_{C_0}(2K_{C_0})\big)$$

failed to be injective, $2K + C_\lambda - C_0$ would be effective, and we would be done. Assume, on the other hand, that r_λ is injective (and hence an isomorphism) for all λ. In this case, if we choose any divisor $D = P_1 + \cdots + P_{4g-4}$ in the bicanonical series $|2K_{C_0}|$, then for every λ there will be a unique curve D_λ in the series $|2K + C_\lambda|$ cutting out D on C_0. Consider then the incidence correspondence

$$I \subset E \times S$$

defined by

$$I = \{(\lambda, p): \ p \in D_\lambda\}$$

Since the curves D_λ are distinct, the image of I under the projection π_2 onto S cannot be a curve; since I is compact, it follows that $\pi_2: I \to S$ is surjective. Thus, for any $Q \in C_0$, $Q \neq P_i$, there will be some curve D_λ containing Q—but then D_λ, containing the $4g - 3$ points $P_1, \ldots, P_{4g-4}$ and Q on C_0, will contain C_0. $F = D_\lambda - C_0 \in |2K + C_\lambda - C_0|$ is thus effective, and we are done.

Case 2:   The fibers of the Albanese map have genus $g = 1$

Note first that if the Albanese map $\Psi: S \to E$ had multiple fibers, then by the formula for the canonical class of an elliptic surface, S would have Kodaira number 1; assume therefore that Ψ has no multiple fibers. In particular, this means the canonical class of S is zero in homology. Let H be any curve on S having positive intersection number m with the fibers C_λ of Ψ. In each fiber C_λ of Ψ, consider the set of points

$$\big\{ p_i^\lambda \in C_\lambda: \ [mp_i^\lambda] = [H]|_{C_\lambda} \in \mathrm{Pic}(C_\lambda) \big\}.$$

Inasmuch as the map

$$E \to \mathrm{Pic}^0(E) \cong E$$

given by

$$p \mapsto [mp - mp_0]$$

is simply multiplication by m on the group E, there are exactly m^2 points $\{p_i^\lambda\}$ in each fiber C_λ, differing from one another by $1/m$ lattice points. The curve

$$F = \bigcup_{\lambda, i} \{p_i^\lambda\}$$

is thus an unbranched m^2-sheeted cover of E, and so every component F_i of F is elliptic. Since K is homologous to 0, $K \cdot F_i = 0$ and hence $F_i \cdot F_i = 0$, so we are done.

The remaining two steps apply equally in cases $g = 1$, $g \geqslant 2$.

Step 2. S *contains two disjoint irreducible elliptic curves* F *and* F' *satisfying* $K \cdot F = K \cdot F' = 0$, $F' \cdot C > 0$, $F \cdot C > 0$, *transverse to the fibers of* Ψ.

We have already located one such elliptic curve F in step 1. For any n,

$$[nK + nF]|_F = nK_F \equiv 0;$$

consider the sequences

$$0 \to \mathcal{O}_S(nK + (n-1)F) \to \mathcal{O}_S(nK + nF) \to \mathcal{O}_F \to 0.$$

We have, for $n \geqslant 2$

$$h^2(nK + (n-1)F) = h^0(-(n-1)K - (n-1)F) = 0$$

and likewise

$$h^2(nK + nF) = h^0(-(n-2)K - nF) = 0.$$

But

$$h^1(\mathcal{O}_F) = 1,$$

and so it follows that $h^1(nK + nF) \geqslant 1$. By Riemann-Roch, then,

$$h^0(nK + nF) = \frac{(nK + nF)((n-1)K + nF)}{2} + \chi(\mathcal{O}_S) + h^1(nK + nF)$$

$$= h^1(nK + nF) \geqslant 1,$$

so $nK + nF$ is equivalent to an effective curve G_n. We note that G_n cannot be simply a multiple of F for all n: if, for example, we had

$$G_n = nK + nF = mF$$

and

$$G_{n+1} = (n+1)K + (n+1)F = m'F,$$

we would have

$$K \sim (m' - m - 1)F,$$

and since $G_{n+1} \cdot C > G_n \cdot C, m' > m$, so this would imply $p_g \neq 0$. Thus, some G_n contains at least one component F' distinct from F, and by our lemma, F' is elliptic with $K \cdot F' = 0$. Finally, since $G_n \cdot F = F \cdot F = 0$, F' is disjoint from F, and since $F \cdot C > 0$ this in turn implies that F' is transverse to the fibers C of Ψ.

Step 3. S *is elliptic with rational base.*

Let F and F' be the two disjoint elliptic curves found above. We have

$$[2K + 2F + 2F']|_F = [2K + 2F]|_F = 2K_F \equiv 0$$

and likewise for F'; consider the sequence

$$0 \to \mathcal{O}_S(2K+F+F') \to \mathcal{O}_S(2K+2F+2F') \to \mathcal{O}_F \oplus \mathcal{O}_{F'} \to 0.$$

We have

$$h^2(2K+F+F') = h^0(-K-F-F') = 0$$

and likewise for $h^2(2K+2F+2F')$; since

$$h^1(\mathcal{O}_F \oplus \mathcal{O}_{F'}) = h^1(\mathcal{O}_F) \oplus h^1(\mathcal{O}_{F'}) = 2,$$

it follows that

$$h^1(2K+2F+2F') \geqslant 2.$$

By Riemann-Roch, then,

$$
\begin{aligned}
h^0(2K+2F+2F') &= \frac{(2K+2F+2F')(K+2F+2F')}{2} \\
&\quad + \chi(\mathcal{O}_S) + h^1(2K+2F+2F') \\
&= h^1(2K+2F+2F') \geqslant 2,
\end{aligned}
$$

i.e., the system $|2K+2F+2F'|$ contains at least a pencil $\{G_\lambda\}$. By the lemma of p. 576, every G_λ consists of a disjoint collection of elliptic curves; and we may apply once more the construction made in the proof of Castelnuovo's theorem to obtain a map

$$S \xrightarrow{\pi} B$$

of S onto a curve B, with fibers consisting of the variable components of the curves $\{G_\lambda\}$: thus S is elliptic. Finally, since $G_\lambda \cdot F = F \cdot F = 0$, every component of G_λ is either equal to or disjoint from F and so, as before, transverse to the fibers C of Ψ. The base B of an elliptic pencil on S must therefore be rational: if not, we could lift a holomorphic 1-form from B to S to obtain a 1-form on S not vanishing along the fibers of Ψ.

The assertion we set out to prove is easily seen, now that we have expressed S as an elliptic surface $\pi: S \to \mathbb{P}^1$ with rational base. If the fibers C of the Albanese map Ψ on S have genus $g \geqslant 2$, then the canonical bundle K_S has positive intersection with C, and we need only know that S is elliptic to conclude that $\kappa(S) = 1$. On the other hand, if the fibers of Ψ have genus 1, then we have seen that the canonical bundle of S is homologous to 0—but some multiple of K_S is the pullback π^*L of a line bundle L on $\mathbb{P}^1$ and L, having degree 0, is trivial; thus $\kappa(S) = 0$. This completes the proof that a minimal surface S with Kodaira number -1 is ruled.

In fact, however, we can prove a bit more: namely,

Enriques' Theorem. *A minimal surface* S *with* $P_4(S) = P_6(S) = 0$ *is ruled or* $\mathbb{P}^2$.

Proof. This is clear in case $q(S) = 0$ or $q(S) \geqslant 2$. If $q(S) = 1$, on the other hand, and S is not ruled, then we have seen that either

1. The Albanese map Ψ on S has elliptic fibers, with some multiple fibers; or

2. S is elliptic with rational base.

In case 1, applying the formula for the canonical bundle of an elliptic surface to $\Psi: S \to E$, we have

$$K_S = \Psi^* D + \sum (m_i - 1) B_i,$$

where $\deg D = 0$; so

$$2K_S = 2\Psi^* D + \sum (2m_i - 2) B_i$$
$$= \left(2\Psi^* D + \sum m_i B_i\right) + \sum (m_i - 2) B_i.$$

The first term in this expression is the pullback of a divisor of positive degree on E, and so effective; thus $2K_S$ is effective and $P_2(S) \neq 0$.

Assume then that case 2 holds, and let

$$\pi: S \to \mathbb{P}^1$$

be the map expressing S as an elliptic surface with rational base. Let B be the generic fiber of π, $B_1, \ldots, B_k$ the multiple fibers of π, and $m_1, \ldots, m_k$ their multiplicities. We have then

$$K_S = -2B + \sum_{i=1}^{k} (m_i - 1) B_i$$

and, since $\kappa(S) \geq 0$,

(*) $$\sum_{i=1}^{k} \frac{m_i - 1}{m_i} \geq 2$$

with equality holding when $\kappa(S) = 0$ (note that by (*), $k \geq 3$). Order the fibers B_i so that $m_1 \leq m_2 \leq \cdots \leq m_k$; we separate the possible values of $\{m_i\}$ into four cases:

1. $k \geq 4$,
2. $k = 3$, $m_1 = 2$, $m_2 = 3$; in this case by (*) we must have $m_3 \geq 6$,
3. $k = 3$, $m_1 = 2$, $m_3 \geq m_2 \geq 4$, and
4. $k = 3$, $m_3 \geq m_2 \geq m_1 \geq 3$.

In case 1,

$$2K_S = -4B + \sum_{i=1}^{k} (2m_i - 2) B_i$$

$$= -4B + \sum_{i=1}^{k} m_i B_i + \sum (m_i - 2) B_i$$

$$\geq \sum (m_i - 2) B_i \geq 0$$

is effective, so $P_2(S) \neq 0$. In case 4 we have

$$
\begin{aligned}
3K_S &= -6B + \sum (3m_i - 3)B_i \\
&= -6B + \sum 2m_i B_i + \sum (m_i - 3)B_i \\
&\geqslant \sum (m_i - 3)B_i \geqslant 0,
\end{aligned}
$$

so $P_3(S) \neq 0$. In case 3 we have

$$
\begin{aligned}
4K_S &= -8B + 4B_1 + (4m_2 - 4)B_2 + (4m_3 - 4)B_3 \\
&= -6B + 3m_2 B_2 + 3m_3 B_3 + (m_2 - 4)B_2 + (m_3 - 4)B_3 \\
&= (m_2 - 4)B_2 + (m_3 - 4)B_3 \geqslant 0,
\end{aligned}
$$

so $P_4(S) \neq 0$. Finally, in case 2 we see that

$$
\begin{aligned}
6K_S &= -12B + 6B_1 + 12B_2 + (6m_3 - 6)B_3 \\
&= -5B + 5m_3 B_3 + (m_3 - 6)B_3 \\
&= (m_3 - 6)B_3 \geqslant 0,
\end{aligned}
$$

so $P_6(S) \neq 0$.

Thus in every case either $P_4(S) \neq 0$ or $P_6(S) \neq 0$, and so Enriques' theorem is proved.   Q.E.D.

Note that there are exactly four collections of integers $m_i \geqslant 2$ that satisfy equality in (∗): they are

$$(2, 2, 2, 2), \quad (2, 3, 6), \quad (2, 4, 4), \quad (3, 3, 3).$$

We will see in the following discussion that each of these in fact represents the multiplicities of the multiple fibers of a nonruled elliptic surface with rational base, and so Enriques' theorem is sharp.

The Classification Theorem II

To complete the classification theorem, we discuss surfaces of Kodaira number 0; we will find four distinct types of such surfaces. We make two observations before starting: by the remarks of p. 574, a minimal surface S with $\kappa(S) = 0$ must have $c_1^2(S) = 0$; and inasmuch as $\chi(\mathcal{O}_S) \geqslant 0$ and $p_g(S) \leqslant 1$, the irregularity $q(S)$ must be 0, 1, or 2. We proceed now by cases:

Case 1: $q = 0$

There are two possibilities in this case: either $p_g = 0$ or $p_g = 1$. We consider these separately:

Case 1a: $p_g = 1$

Here we have $\chi(\mathcal{O}_S)=2$, and by Riemann-Roch for $2K$

$$h^0(2K) + h^0(-K) \geqslant \frac{2K \cdot 2K - 2K \cdot K}{2} + \chi(\mathcal{O}_S)$$
$$= 2.$$

But $h^0(2K)=1$, and consequently $-K$ must be effective; since K and $-K$ are both effective, it follows that *the canonical bundle* K *of S is trivial*. A surface with these invariants—$q=0$ and $K \equiv 0$—is called a *K-3 surface*; we will give a brief description of these surfaces later in this section.

Case 1b: $p_g = 0$

By the Castelnuovo-Enriques theorem, since $q(S)=0$ and S has Kodaira number 0, we must have $P_2(S)=1$. Now by Riemann-Roch applied to $3K$ we have

$$h^0(3K) + h^0(-2K) \geqslant \chi(\mathcal{O}_S) = 1.$$

But $h^0(3K)$ must be zero: We know that there exists a global section σ of $2K$ not identically zero; if we had as well a nontrivial section τ of $3K$, then since $P_6(S) \leqslant 1$ we would have

$$\sigma^3 = \lambda \cdot \tau^2$$

for some $\lambda \in \mathbb{C}$. But then if σ vanished to order k along any curve C in S, τ would vanish to order $3k/2$, and so τ/σ would be a global holomorphic section of K. Thus $h^0(3K)=0$, and so from Riemann-Roch $h^0(-2K) \neq 0$. As before, then, $h^0(2K)$, $h^0(-2K) \neq 0$ implies that $2K_S$ is trivial. A surface with these numerical characters—$q=p_g=0$ and $2K \equiv 0$—is called an *Enriques surface*; we have already seen one example of such a surface in Section 4 of this chapter, and we will discuss them in general at the end of this section.

Case 2: $q=2$

We will prove that

Any algebraic surface S *with* q=2 *and Kodaira number* 0 *is an Abelian variety*.

Note first that since $\chi(\mathcal{O}_S)$ is nonnegative, we must have $p_g=1$. Let η_1, η_2 be generators for the space of holomorphic 1-forms on S. If the wedge product $\eta_1 \wedge \eta_2$ were identically zero, the Albanese map Ψ on S would map S to a curve of genus 2; since $\chi(S)=0$ and S is not ruled, the fibers of Ψ would have genus 1. But we have seen that an elliptic surface over a base of genus $g \geqslant 2$ has Kodaira number 1; thus, under the assumption that $\kappa(S)=0$, the wedge product $\omega = \eta_1 \wedge \eta_2$ is a generator for $H^0(S, \Omega_S^2)$.

Consider now the Albanese map Ψ of S onto the two-dimensional Abelian variety $A = \text{Alb}(S)$. The Jacobian determinant of Ψ is, of course, zero exactly where the forms η_1 and η_2 are dependent, i.e., on the canonical divisor $D = (\omega = \eta_1 \wedge \eta_2)$; we consider what this locus may be.

We first dispense with the possibility that the image of D in A has dimension 0. If this were the case, then the map

$$S - D \xrightarrow{\Psi} A - \Psi(D)$$

would be an unbranched covering. But then, since

$$\pi_1(A - \Psi(D)) \cong \pi_1(A) \cong \mathbb{Z}^4$$

and $\pi_1(S - D)$ surjects onto $\pi_1(S)$, it would follow from the isomorphism

$$H_1(S, \mathbb{Z})/\text{torsion} \longrightarrow H_1(A, \mathbb{Z})$$

that Ψ was 1-sheeted—i.e., that Ψ was birational. By the structure theorem for birational maps (Section 2 of this chapter), then, Ψ would be a blowing-down map, contrary to the hypothesis that S is minimal.

We see then that if $D \neq 0$, its image in A must contain a curve. Suppose that this is the case. By the lemma of p. 574, every component of the divisor D is either elliptic or rational, and since the Abelian variety A contains no rational curves, it follows that D has an elliptic component D_i, with $E = \Psi(D_i) \subset A$ again elliptic. We may take the origin $0 \in A$ to lie on E, and consider the map

$$\mu: A \to \text{Pic}^0(A)$$

given by

$$\mu: \lambda \mapsto [t_\lambda(E) - E],$$

where t_λ is translation by λ in the group A. Since any map between Abelian varieties is, up to translation, a homomorphism, $E = \Psi(D_i)$ is a subgroup of A, so translation by any point $\lambda \in E$ fixes E; on the other hand the reader may check, either directly or via the set-up of pp. 315–317, that $[E]$ cannot be fixed by all of A. The fibers of μ are thus one-dimensional, and the image $B = \mu(A)$ a curve; indeed, since the fiber of μ over 0 is a subgroup of A and hence smooth, E constitutes one connected component of the fiber $\mu^{-1}(0)$. Making the construction used in the proof of Castelnuovo's theorem (p. 557), we obtain a map

$$\tilde{\mu}: A \longrightarrow \tilde{B}$$

of A onto a (a priori possibly) branched cover $\tilde{B}$ of B, with E the fiber over a point; composing $\tilde{\mu}$ with Ψ, we obtain a map of S onto $\tilde{B}$ with D_i a fiber. S is thus an elliptic surface—but we have seen that any elliptic surface with an effective, nonzero canonical divisor has Kodaira number 1. We conclude that the divisor D must be zero, i.e., the canonical bundle of S is trivial. The map Ψ is then an unbranched covering, and S is an Abelian variety.

Case 3: $q=1$

A surface S with these characters—$\kappa(S)=0$ and $q(S)=1$—is called *hyperelliptic*, and we can give a fairly complete account of such surfaces. We start by showing that the geometric genus $p_g(S)$ of S must be zero: to see this, note that since $\pi_1(S)$ contains a $\mathbf{Z}$-factor, we can construct for any m an unbranched m-sheeted cover $\tilde{S} \xrightarrow{\pi} S$. If $p_g(S)$ were 1, then, we would have $\chi(\mathcal{O}_S)=1$,

$$\chi(\mathcal{O}_{\tilde{S}}) = m \cdot \chi(\mathcal{O}_S) = m,$$

and so

$$p_g(\tilde{S}) \geqslant m.$$

But now a section $\sigma \in H^0(\tilde{S}, \Omega^2_{\tilde{S}})$ induces a section $\pi_* \sigma \in H^0(S, \mathcal{O}_S(K_S^m))$: since for any $p \in S$ and any $q \in \pi^{-1}(p)$ the fibers of K_S at p and $K_{\tilde{S}}$ at q are naturally identified via π, we may set

$$\pi_* \sigma(p) = \sigma(q_1) \otimes \cdots \otimes \sigma(q_m) \in K^{\otimes m}_{S,p},$$

where $\pi^{-1}(p)=\{q_1,\dots,q_m\}$. Clearly $\pi_* \sigma$ is not identically zero if σ is not. For $m \geqslant 2$, then, we could find a section σ of $K_{\tilde{S}}$ vanishing at some point $q \in \tilde{S}$ and another section τ of $K_{\tilde{S}}$ nonzero over $\pi(q)$; the images $\pi_* \tau$ and $\pi_* \sigma$ would then be two independent sections of $K_S^{\otimes m}$—so S would have Kodaira number $\geqslant 1$.

We conclude that a surface S with $\kappa(S)=0$ and $q=1$ must have $p_g=0$, and hence $c_1^2=c_2=0$. We have already discussed surfaces with these numerical invariants. Recall from our previous discussion that for such a surface S the fibers $\{C_\lambda\}$ of the Albanese map $\Psi: S \to E$ are elliptic, and none are multiple. S also contains a pencil $\{F_\lambda\}$ of curves, transverse to C_λ and having rational base. Let F be a nonmultiple element of the second pencil $\{F_\lambda\}$, and in the product $S \times F$ consider the surface

$$\tilde{S} = \{(p,q): \ \Psi(p)=\Psi(q)\}.$$

The projection $\pi_1: \tilde{S} \to S$ on the first factor expresses $\tilde{S}$ as an unbranched cover of S; the projection $\pi_2: \tilde{S} \to F$ expresses S as an elliptic surface with base F, again with no multiple or singular fibers. By our formula for the canonical bundle of an elliptic surface, we can write

$$K_{\tilde{S}} = \tilde{C}_\lambda - \tilde{C}_{\lambda'},$$

where $\tilde{C}_\lambda, \tilde{C}_{\lambda'}$ are fibers of $\pi_2 : \tilde{S} \to F$. Now let

$$\tilde{F} = \{(p,p) : p \in F\} \subset \tilde{S}.$$

$\tilde{F}$ maps via π_2 one-to-one onto F, and likewise one-to-one via π_1 onto $F \subset S$. But now we have

$$(C_\lambda - C_{\lambda'})|_{\tilde{F}} = K_{\tilde{S}}|_{\tilde{F}} = \pi_1^* K_S|_{\tilde{F}} = K_S|_F \equiv 0,$$

and hence

$$K_{\tilde{S}} \equiv 0.$$

Thus $p_g(\tilde{S}) = 1$, and since

$$\chi(\mathcal{O}_{\tilde{S}}) = m\chi(\mathcal{O}_S) = 0,$$
$$q(\tilde{S}) = 2.$$

Finally, $\tilde{S}$, like S, must have Kodaira number 0: if $K_{\tilde{S}}^{\otimes n}$ contained more than one linearly independent section, we could construct as above two independent sections of $K_S^{\otimes mn}$. Thus we see from our last argument that $\tilde{S}$ is an Abelian variety.

Indeed, we can be even more specific. Let C_0 be a fiber of the map π_2, and choose as the origin in $\tilde{S}$ the point of intersection of C_0 with $\tilde{F}$. Then we can define maps

$$\mu_1 : \tilde{S} \longrightarrow F \quad \text{and} \quad \mu_2 : \tilde{S} \longrightarrow C_0$$

by $\mu_1 = \pi_2$ and

$$\mu_2(\lambda) = t_\lambda(\tilde{F}) \cap C_0.$$

These maps give an isomorphism

$$\mu : \tilde{S} \longrightarrow C_0 \times F.$$

Thus, we see that *a surface S of Kodaira number 0 and irregularity 1 is the quotient, by a finite fixed-point-free group, of the product of two elliptic curves.*

We can construct these surfaces explicitly, as follows: let F and C be two arbitrary elliptic curves, with Euclidean coordinates z and w, and suppose C is given as $\mathbb{C}$ modulo the lattice $\Lambda = \{1, \tau\}$. Let $\zeta : C \to C$ be any automorphism on C of finite order m having fixed points (note that under this hypothesis the quotient of C by the group $\{\zeta^i\}$ is rational, because the quotient map $C \to C/\{\zeta^i\}$ is branched). Let φ be the automorphism of $F \times C$ defined by

$$\varphi(z,w) = \left(z + \frac{\tau}{m}, \zeta(w)\right).$$

φ is then fixed-point-free of order m, and the quotient S of $F \times C$ by the group $\{\varphi^i\}$ is a smooth algebraic surface. Since the 1-form dz on $F \times C$ is invariant under φ, it descends to give a 1-form on S. On the other hand,

$$\zeta^*(dw) = e^{2\pi i k/m} \cdot dw$$

for some $k \in \mathbb{Z}$, and since the quotient of C by $\{\zeta^i\}$—or any nonzero subgroup of $\{\zeta^i\}$—is rational, we see that k must be relatively prime to m. Thus neither of the forms dw nor $dz \wedge dw$ on S is invariant under φ. Since any holomorphic form on S lifts to a holomorphic form on $F \times C$ invariant under φ, it follows that

$$q(S) = 1, \qquad p_g(S) = 0;$$

more generally, since the generator $(dz \wedge dw)^{\otimes n}$ of $H^0(F \times C, \mathcal{O}(K^n))$ is invariant under φ if and only if m divides n,

$$nK_S \equiv 0, \quad \text{if } m | n,$$

$$nK_S \not\equiv 0, \quad \text{otherwise.}$$

Note that the Albanese map Ψ sends S to the curve $E = \mathbb{C}/\{1, \tau/m\}$, with fibers isomorphic to C, while the second pencil $\{F_p\}$ of elliptic curves on S consists of the images in S of the fibers $F \times \{p\}$ of $F \times C$. In particular, if $p \in C$ is not a fixed point of any multiple of ζ other than the identity, the curve F_p forms via Ψ an m-sheeted cover of E, meeting a fiber C of Ψ in the points $\{\zeta^i(p)\}_i$. On the other hand, if q is fixed under a subgroup of order k in $\{\zeta^i\}$, then $F \times \{q\}$ maps k-to-1 onto its image F_q; F_q will then be a multiple fiber of multiplicity k in the pencil $\{F_p\}$, meeting a fiber C of Ψ in the m/k points of the orbit $\{\zeta^i(q)\}$.

We have four examples of this construction:

1. If C is any elliptic curve, we may take $\zeta(w) = -w$ to obtain a surface S with $2K_S \equiv 0$, $K_S \not\equiv 0$. Note that the second elliptic pencil $\{F_p\}$ has four double fibers, corresponding to the four fixed points p_i of ζ shown in Figure 6. S in this case is said to be of type I_a.

2. If C is the elliptic curve given as $\mathbb{C}$ modulo the lattice $\Lambda = \{1, i\}$, we may take $\zeta(w) = iw$ to obtain a surface with $4K$ trivial, but $p_g = P_2 = 0$. The

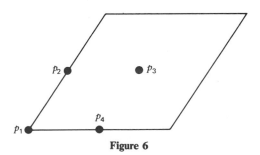

Figure 6

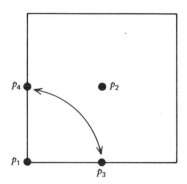

Figure 7

pencil $\{F_p\}$ on S has two quadruple fibers and one double, corresponding to the two fixed points p_1, p_2 of ζ and the fixed pair p_3, p_4 of ζ^2, as shown in Figure 7. S here is called type II_a.

3. If C is the elliptic curve $\mathbb{C}/\{1, e^{\pi i/3}\}$, we may take $\zeta(w) = e^{2\pi i/3}w$; S then has canonical bundle of order 3. The pencil $\{F_p\}$ then has three triple fibers, corresponding to the three fixed points p_i of ζ in Figure 8. S is said to be of type III_a.

4. With $C = \mathbb{C}/\{1, e^{\pi i/3}\}$ as above, we may set $\zeta(w) = e^{\pi i/3}w$; the canonical bundle of S then has order exactly 6. The pencil $\{F_p\}$ has one sextuple fiber, one triple fiber, and one double corresponding to the orbits $\{p_1\}$, $\{p_2, p_3\}$, and $\{p_4, p_5, p_6\}$ of ζ, respectively; see Figure 9. Note that S is the quotient of a surface of type III_a by an involution; S itself is said to be of type III_b.

Note that the multiplicities of the multiple fibers of the surfaces S expressed as elliptic surfaces with rational base—that is, $(2,2,2,2)$, $(2,4,4)$, $(2,3,6)$, and $(3,3,3)$ in cases 1 through 4, respectively—correspond to all four solutions of the equation (∗) of p. 581.

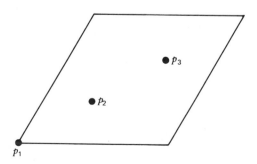

Figure 8

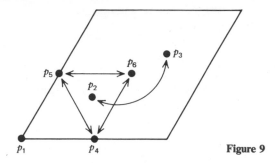

Figure 9

Finally, we can introduce one additional twist into our construction. Suppose that with C, F, ζ, and φ as above, we let

$$\zeta': C \to C$$

be a translation of order n on C that commutes with the automorphism ζ (i.e., translation by a fixed point of ζ). We may then define a second automorphism of $F \times C$ by

$$\varphi'(z,w) = \left(z + \frac{1}{n}, \zeta'(w)\right).$$

φ and φ' then generate a finite, fixed-point-free group of automorphisms of $F \times C$, and the quotient $\tilde{S} = F \times C/\{\varphi^i \varphi'^j\}$ is again hyperelliptic: since the automorphism $\bar{\varphi}'$ induced by φ' on the partial quotient $S = F \times C/\{\varphi^i\}$ described above preserves all the forms and multiforms on $\tilde{S}$, the numerical invariants of $\tilde{S}$ are the same as those of S. The Albanese map Ψ sends $\tilde{S}$ to the curve $E = \quad /\{1/n, \tau/m\}$ with fiber C, and the elements of the second pencil $\{F_p\}$ on S all form n-sheeted unbranched covers of their images $\tilde{F}_p$ in $\tilde{S}$, giving a second elliptic pencil on $\tilde{S}$ with multiple fibers corresponding exactly to those of $\{F_p\}$ on S. Explicitly, in each of the four cases above:

    1.   If $\zeta(w) = -w$ as in case 1 above, we may take ζ' to be translation by any of the points $\{p_i\}$ of order 2 on C, e.g.,

$$\varphi'(z,w) = \left(z + \tfrac{1}{2}, w + \tfrac{1}{2}\right).$$

The resulting surface $\tilde{S}$ is said to be of type I_b.

    2.   In case 2 above we must take ζ' to be translation by p_2, i.e.,

$$\varphi'(z,w) = \left(z + \frac{1}{2}, w + \frac{1+i}{2}\right);$$

$\tilde{S}$ is said to be of type II_b.

    3.   In case 3 we may take ζ to be translation by either of the points

p_2, p_3, e.g.,

$$\varphi'(z, w) = \left(z + \frac{1}{3}, w + \frac{3 + \sqrt{3}\, i}{6} \right).$$

$\tilde{S}$ is then called type III_c.

4. In the last case above no nontrivial translation commutes with ζ, and we cannot make this construction.

We have described now seven classes of hyperelliptic surfaces: namely, I_a, I_b, II_a, II_b, III_a, III_b, and III_c. The reader may, by examining in general finite commutative groups of automorphisms on elliptic curves C, see that we have constructed all hyperelliptic surfaces.

In sum we have the following version of the

Classification Theorem (Enriques; Kodaira)

1. *A minimal surface S with* $\kappa(S) = -1$ *is either* $\mathbb{P}^2$ *or ruled.*
2. *A minimal surface S with* $\kappa(S) = 0$ *is either*
   (a) *a K-3 surface, if* $q = 0$ *and* $p_g = 1$,
   (b) *an Enriques surface, if* $q = 0$ *and* $p_g = 0$,
   (c) *a hyperelliptic surface as constructed above, if* $q = 1$; *or*
   (d) *an Abelian variety, if* $q = 2$.
3. *A surface S with* $\kappa(S) = 1$ *is elliptic.*

K-3 Surfaces

To conclude this section, we wish to study in some more detail two types of surfaces encountered in the course of the classification theorem: K-3 surfaces and Enriques surfaces.

Let us first dispose of the numerical characters of a K-3 surface S. By definition,

$$q(S) = 0 \quad \text{and} \quad K_S \equiv 0,$$

so $p_g(S) = 1$ and $c_1^2(S) = 0$. By Riemann-Roch,

$$2 = \chi(\mathcal{O}_S) = \frac{c_2}{12},$$

so the topological Euler characteristic

$$\chi(S) = 24.$$

The Hodge diamond of S is

$$
\begin{array}{ccccc}
 & & 1 & & \\
 & 0 & & 0 & \\
1 & & 20 & & 1 \\
 & 0 & & 0 & \\
 & & 1 & &
\end{array}
$$

Suppose S is a K-3 surface embedded in $\mathbb{P}^n$, and suppose that S is normal—that is, the embedding is given by a complete linear system. Let $C = H \cdot S$ be a generic hyperplane section of S, and consider the standard sequence

$$0 \to \mathcal{O}_S \to \mathcal{O}_S(C) \to \mathcal{O}_C(C) \to 0.$$

Since $K_S \equiv 0$, we see by the adjunction formula that

$$\mathcal{O}_C(C) = \mathcal{O}_C(K_S + C) = \Omega^1_C,$$

i.e., the linear system cut out on C by hyperplane sections of $S \subset \mathbb{P}^n$ is a subsystem of the canonical series on C. Since, moreover, the linear system of hyperplane sections of S is the complete series $|H^0(S, \mathcal{O}_S(C))|$, and

$$h^1(S, \mathcal{O}_S) = q(S) = 0,$$

$H^0(\mathbb{P}^n, \mathcal{O}(H))$ surjects onto $H^0(S, \mathcal{O}(C))$ which surjects onto $H^0(C, \Omega^1_C)$. The hyperplanes in $\mathbb{P}^n$ thus cut out the complete canonical series on C, i.e., $C \subset \mathbb{P}^{n-1}$ is a *canonical curve*. Accordingly C has genus n and degree $2n - 2$; in particular,

A normal K-3 surface $S \subset \mathbb{P}^n$ *has degree* $2n - 2$.

We may also see this directly from Riemann-Roch: if $S \subset \mathbb{P}^n$ is a normal K-3 surface, C a hyperplane section of S, then since C is positive,

$$h^1(S, \mathcal{O}(C)) = h^1(S, \Omega^2_S(C)) = 0$$

and likewise

$$h^2(S, \mathcal{O}(C)) = 0$$

by the Kodaira vanishing theorem. Riemann-Roch then tells us

$$n + 1 = h^0(S, \mathcal{O}(C)) = \frac{C \cdot C}{2} + \chi(\mathcal{O}_S)$$
$$= \frac{\deg(S)}{2} + 2,$$

so $\deg(S) = 2n - 2$.

We will see, in the four cases $n = 2$, 3, 4, and 5, how we may realize such a surface. The easiest is $n = 3$, i.e., S a quartic surface in $\mathbb{P}^3$. By the Lefschetz hyperplane theorem, a smooth quartic in $\mathbb{P}^3$ has irregularity

$$q(S) = q(\mathbb{P}^3) = 0,$$

and by adjunction,

$$K_S = (K_{\mathbb{P}^3} + S)|_S = (-4H + 4H)|_S \equiv 0,$$

so S is a K-3 surface. Note that since the linear system of quartics in $\mathbb{P}^3$ has dimension 34 and PGL_4 dimension 15, *the family of quartic K-3's has dimension*

$$34 - 15 = 19.$$

The second case is that of a sextic K-3 surface S in $\mathbb{P}^4$. Observe that if C is the hyperplane section of S, then the system of quadrics in $\mathbb{P}^4$ cuts out on S a system of dimension at most

$$h^0(S, \mathcal{O}(2C)) - 1 = \frac{2C \cdot 2C}{2} + 2 - 1 = \frac{24}{2} + 1 = 13$$

—but the linear system of quadrics in $\mathbb{P}^4$ is 14-dimensional, and so S must lie on a quadric hypersurface $Q \subset \mathbb{P}^4$. Similarly, since

$$h^0(S, \mathcal{O}(3C)) = \frac{54}{2} + 2 = 29$$

and

$$h^0(\mathbb{P}^4, \mathcal{O}(3H)) = \frac{5 \cdot 6 \cdot 7}{6} = 35,$$

S must lie on a five-dimensional family of cubics in $\mathbb{P}^4$—but the system of cubics containing the quadric Q is only $h^0(\mathbb{P}^4, \mathcal{O}(H)) - 1 = 4$-dimensional, and so S must lie on a cubic Q' not containing Q. Because Q is irreducible, Q' must meet Q in a surface of degree 6 or less, and hence exactly in S. Thus, *a sextic K-3 in $\mathbb{P}^4$ is the complete intersection of a quadric and a cubic.* Conversely, if $S = Q \cap Q'$ is such a smooth complete intersection, then by the Lefschetz theorem on hyperplane sections applied twice, $q(S) = 0$, and by adjunction

$$\begin{aligned} K_S &= (K_{Q'} + Q)|_S \\ &= (K_{\mathbb{P}^4} + Q' + Q)|_S \\ &= (-5H + 3H + 2H)|_S \equiv 0, \end{aligned}$$

so S is K-3. Note, finally, that such a K-3 is determined by choosing a quadric Q out of the 14-dimensional family of quadrics in $\mathbb{P}^4$ and then a cubic Q' in the $35 - 5 - 1 = 29$-dimensional family of cubics in $\mathbb{P}^4$ modulo those containing Q. Since PGL_5 has dimension 24, we see that again *the family of sextic K-3's in $\mathbb{P}^4$ has dimension*

$$14 + 29 - 24 = 19.$$

Next, consider an octic K-3 surface $S \subset \mathbb{P}^5$. By Riemann-Roch

$$h^0(S, \mathcal{O}(2C)) = \frac{2C \cdot 2C}{2} + 2 = 18,$$

while $h^0(\mathbb{P}^5, \mathcal{O}(2H)) = 21$. S will thus always lie on three independent quadrics in $\mathbb{P}^5$; generically, S will be their complete intersection. Conversely, as in the last case, by the Lefschetz theorem and the adjunction formula any smooth complete intersection of three quadrics in $\mathbb{P}^5$ is a K-3 surface. Counting parameters, a generic octic K-3 is specified by a net of quadrics in $\mathbb{P}^5$—in other words, a point of the Grassmannian $G(3, H^0(\mathbb{P}^5, \mathcal{O}(2H)))$—and so the family of octic K-3's has dimension once again

$$\dim G(3, 21) - \dim \mathrm{PGL}_6 = 54 - 35 = 19.$$

The fourth case we shall look at is that of $n = 2$—that is, K-3 surfaces S expressed as double covers $S \xrightarrow{\pi} \mathbb{P}^2$ of the plane. The "hyperplane section" of S—i.e., the inverse image $\pi^{-1}(l)$ of a line $l \subset \mathbb{P}^2$—is a curve of genus 2, expressed by π as a double cover of $l \cong \mathbb{P}^1$. π is thus branched over six points in l; and the branch locus of π a sextic curve in $\mathbb{P}^2$. Conversely if $B \subset \mathbb{P}^2$ is any smooth sextic curve, we can construct a double cover $S \xrightarrow{\pi} \mathbb{P}^2$ of $\mathbb{P}^2$ branched along B by the construction of p. 548; and the surface S is a K-3 surface: as in Section 4, if $\tilde{B} = \pi^{-1}(B)$ is the branch locus of π in S, we have

$$K_S = \pi^* K_{\mathbb{P}^2} + \tilde{B},$$

and so

$$2K_S = 2\pi^* K_{\mathbb{P}^2} + 2\tilde{B}$$
$$= \pi^*(-6H) + \pi^* B \equiv 0.$$

(Note that this implies S is minimal.) Also, since B has genus 10,

$$\chi(B) = 2 - 2g(B) = -18,$$

and

$$\chi(S) = 2\chi(\mathbb{P}^2) - \chi(B) = 24,$$

so, by the classification theorem, S must be a K-3. We count parameters once again: the system of sextic curves in $\mathbb{P}^2$ has dimension 27, and is acted on by PGL_3, so the family of K-3 surfaces expressed as double covers of $\mathbb{P}^2$ is $27 - 8 = 19$-dimensional.

This is as much as we shall prove about K-3 surfaces. One comment, however, should be made: while the general statement which extrapolates our computations—that *for any* n, *there is a* 19-*dimensional irreducible family* Γ_n *of K-3 surfaces of degree* $2n - 2$ *in* $\mathbb{P}^n$—is true, it may give a false impression. In fact, if we drop the requirement of projectivity and simply define a K-3 surface to be a compact complex 2-manifold, simply connected and having trivial canonical bundle, then all K-3 surfaces will form an irreducible 20-dimensional family, the generic member of which is not algebraic; the families Γ_n form a countable union of subvarieties of this one moduli space. The picture is not unlike that for complex tori/Abelian varieties: in a family $\{S_\lambda\}$ of complex K-3 surfaces, parametrized by a polydisc, we may consider the cohomology group $H^2(S_\lambda, \mathbb{C})$ as a fixed vector space V and the subgroup $H^2(S_\lambda, \mathbb{Z})$ of integral classes likewise as a fixed lattice inside V. The subspace $H^{1,1}(S_\lambda) \subset V$, however, varies as the complex structure of S_λ varies; S_λ will belong to the family Γ_n only when $H^{1,1}(S_\lambda)$ meets a lattice point corresponding to an integral cohomology class of self-intersection $2n - 2$. (See Figure 10.) Note that more generally the group of divisors modulo homology on an algebraic S_λ is exactly the intersection of $H^{1,1}(S_\lambda)$ with $H^2(S_\lambda, \mathbb{Z})$, and indeed it turns out to be the case that

The family of K-3 surfaces having k *or more divisors independent in homology forms a dense countable union of subvarieties of dimension* $20 - k$ *in the family of all K-3's; in particular, on the generic algebraic K-3 surface all divisors are homologous to multiples of the hyperplane class.*

The reader may verify this in one particular case, by showing that a K-3 expressed as a double cover of $\mathbb{P}^2$ branched along a sextic curve B contains two or more independent curves if and only if there is in $\mathbb{P}^2$ a rational curve of degree d tangent to B at $3d$ points (i.e., a tritangent line, etc.).

Enriques Surfaces

We turn our attention now to Enriques surfaces. First, for the numerical invariants: by definition,

$$p_g = q = 0, \qquad \chi(\mathcal{O}_S) = 1,$$

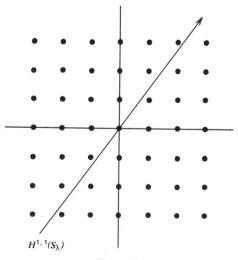

$H^{1,1}(S_\lambda)$

Figure 10

and, since $2K \equiv 0$,

$$c_1^2 = 0;$$

it follows from Riemann-Roch that

$$\chi(S) = 12$$

and the Hodge diamond of S is

$$
\begin{array}{ccccc}
 & & 1 & & \\
 & 0 & & 0 & \\
0 & & 10 & & 0 \\
 & 0 & & 0 & \\
 & & 1 & & \\
\end{array}
$$

Note in particular that since $H^{2,0}(S)=0$, all the second cohomology of S is represented by algebraic curves. The group of divisors modulo rational homology on any Enriques surface is thus $\mathbb{Z}^{10}$.

We have already constructed one Enriques surface in Section 4 of this chapter by letting S be the surface $(X_0^4 + X_1^4 - X_2^4 - X_3^4 = 0)$ and T the automorphism sending $[X_0, X_1, X_2, X_3]$ into $[X_0, iX_1, -X_2, -iX_3]$; we blew up the fixed points of T^2 on S and then took the quotient S'' of the blow-up by T^2; the Enriques surface S' was then the quotient of S'' by the involution T. S' was thus the quotient of the surface S''—which we can now identify as K-3—by a fixed-point-free involution. Indeed, it is not hard to see that any Enriques surface S arises as a quotient of a K-3 surface: simply let $\sigma \in H^0(S, \mathcal{O}(2K))$ be a nonzero section of the bundle $K \otimes K$, and consider, in the total space of the bundle K, the locus

$$X = \{(p, \zeta): \zeta \in K_p, \zeta \otimes \zeta = \sigma(p)\}.$$

Since σ is nowhere zero, X projects to S as an unbranched 2-sheeted covering space. We have, then,

$$q(X) = q(S) = 0,$$
$$\chi(X) = 2\chi(S) = 24,$$

and

$$\chi(\mathcal{O}_X) = 2\chi(\mathcal{O}_S) = 2.$$

In particular, we see from the first and third equality that $p_g(X)=1$, and indeed the section is visible: since $X \rightarrow S$ is unbranched, for any point $(p, \zeta) \in X$

$$K_X((p, \zeta)) = K_S(p),$$

and so we can define a section $\tilde{\sigma} \in H^0(X, \mathcal{O}(K_X))$ simply by

$$\tilde{\sigma}((p, \zeta)) = \zeta.$$

Clearly $\tilde{\sigma}$ never vanishes, and so K_X is trivial; consequently X is a K-3 surface:

Every Enriques surface is the quotient of a K-3 surface by a fixed-point-free involution.

A second way to represent an Enriques surfaces is as an elliptic surface S with rational base. To show that S has an elliptic pencil, we begin with the observation

If E is any smooth elliptic curve on S, *then* $h^0(2E) \geqslant 2$.

Since $h^0(2E) \geqslant h^0(E)$, if E moves in a pencil we are done, so we may suppose that E itself does not move, i.e., that $h^0(E) = 1$. Now, since

$$K \cdot E = 0,$$

it follows from adjunction that

$$E \cdot E = 0,$$

and hence, by Riemann-Roch, that

$$h^1(E) = h^0(E) - \frac{E \cdot E - K \cdot E}{2} + \chi(\mathcal{O}_S)$$
$$= 1 - 1 = 0,$$

since $h^2(E) = h^0(K - E) = 0$. Now we have

$$[2E]|_E = [2K + 2E]|_E = 2K_E \equiv 0,$$

and so from the long exact sequence associated to the sequence

$$0 \longrightarrow \mathcal{O}_S(E) \longrightarrow \mathcal{O}_S(2E) \longrightarrow \mathcal{O}_E \longrightarrow 0$$

we deduce that

$$h^0(S, \mathcal{O}(2E)) = h^0(S, \mathcal{O}(E)) + h^0(E, \mathcal{O}_E)$$
$$= 2,$$

and the assertion is proved.

Now $2E$, like E, has virtual genus 1; thus, to show that S is elliptic, we need only locate a smooth elliptic curve on S.

We start by locating an effective divisor of self-intersection 0 (and hence virtual genus 1) on S. By the index theorem the intersection pairing on $H^2(S, \mathbb{Z}) \cong \mathbb{Z}^{10}$ is unimodular with one positive and nine negative eigenvalues; so we can find a class $\alpha \neq 0 \in H^2(S, \mathbb{Z})$ with $\alpha \cdot \alpha = 0$.[*] Since $p_g(S) = 0$, α is of type $(1, 1)$, and consequently by the Lefschetz $(1, 1)$ theorem is the

---

[*]Cf. J.-P. Serre, *Cours d'Arithmétique*, Presses Universitaires de France, Paris, 1970, Chap. 5.

class of a divisor D' on S. By Riemann-Roch,

$$h^0(D') + h^0(K - D') \geqslant \frac{D' \cdot D' - K \cdot D'}{2} + \chi(\mathcal{O}_S) = 1,$$

so either D' or $K - D'$ is effective; call the effective one D. In either case, $D \cdot D = 0$.

Let $X \xrightarrow{\pi} S$ be the twofold covering of S by a K-3 surface X, and $\tilde{D} = \pi^* D$ the inverse image of D. We have

$$\tilde{D} \cdot \tilde{D} = 2D \cdot D = 0,$$

and so by Riemann-Roch on X,

$$h^0(\tilde{D}) \geqslant \frac{\tilde{D} \cdot \tilde{D} - K_X \cdot \tilde{D}}{2} + \chi(\mathcal{O}_X) = 2,$$

i.e., $\tilde{D}$ moves in a linear system on X. To separate out the fixed components of $|\tilde{D}|$ we write

$$|\tilde{D}| = |C| + \sum n_i E_i,$$

where the E_i's are irreducible, $n_i > 0$, and the linear system $|C|$ has no fixed components. E_i being fixed, we find

$$1 = h^0(E_i) \geqslant \frac{E_i \cdot E_i}{2} + 2,$$

while

$$0 \leqslant \pi(E_i) = \frac{E_i \cdot E_i}{2} + 1;$$

it follows that *the curves* E_i *are all rational of self-intersection* -2. If for each i we set

$$k_i = (\tilde{D} - n_i E_i) \cdot E_i = \left(C + \sum_{j \neq i} n_j E_j \right) \cdot E_i,$$

then,

$$
\begin{aligned}
0 = \tilde{D} \cdot \tilde{D} &= \tilde{D} \cdot \left(C + \sum n_i E_i \right) \\
&= \tilde{D} \cdot C + \sum n_i (\tilde{D} - n_i E_i) \cdot E_i + \sum n_i^2 E_i \cdot E_i \\
&= C \cdot C + \sum n_i C \cdot E_i + \sum n_i k_i - 2 \sum n_i^2.
\end{aligned}
$$

Now $C \cdot C \geqslant 0$, since C moves in a linear system without fixed components. If $C \cdot C = 0$, set $\tilde{D}_1 = C$; if $C \cdot C > 0$, then it follows that for some i_0,

$$k_{i_0} \leqslant 2n_{i_0}.$$

In this case, set

$$\tilde{D}_1 = \tilde{D} - (2n_{i_0} - k_{i_0}) E_{i_0}$$

We have then

$$\tilde{D}_1 \cdot \tilde{D}_1 = \tilde{D} \cdot \tilde{D} - 2(2n_{i_0} - k_{i_0})(\tilde{D} \cdot E_{i_0}) + (2n_{i_0} - k_{i_0})^2(E_{i_0} \cdot E_{i_0})$$
$$= -2(2n_{i_0} - k_{i_0})(k_{i_0} - 2n_{i_0}) - 2(2n_{i_0} - k_{i_0})^2$$
$$= 0.$$

Now once more by Riemann-Roch

$$h^0(\tilde{D}_1) + h^0(K - \tilde{D}_1) \geqslant \frac{\tilde{D}_1 \cdot \tilde{D}_1}{2} + 2 = 2,$$

and since

$$K - \tilde{D}_1 = K + (2n_{i_0} - k_{i_0})E_{i_0} - \tilde{D}$$

cannot be effective, $\tilde{D}_1$ must move in a linear system. Since $2n_{i_0} - k_{i_0} > 0$, we deduce that if the linear system $|\tilde{D}|$ has a rational fixed component, we may subtract an effective curve from $\tilde{D}$ to obtain a divisor $\tilde{D}_1$ moving in a linear series, again with self-intersection 0. If the system $|\tilde{D}_1|$ has rational fixed components, then, we may deduct an effective curve again to obtain a divisor $\tilde{D}_2 > 0$ with $\tilde{D}_2 \cdot \tilde{D}_2 \geqslant 0$, $h^0(\tilde{D}_2) \geqslant 2$, and so on. But, as was pointed out on p. 521, the divisor $\tilde{D}$ cannot be written as the sum of arbitrarily many effective curves, and so we arrive at a divisor $\tilde{D}_\alpha$ of self-intersection 0, moving in a linear system without fixed components. By the lemma of p. 576, every component of $\tilde{D}_\alpha$ is elliptic, with self-intersection 0.

Consider now the image $D_{\alpha,i}$ in S of a component $\tilde{D}_{\alpha,i}$ of $\tilde{D}_\alpha$. If $\tilde{D}_{\alpha,i}$ maps two-to-one to $D_{\alpha,i}$, then $D_{\alpha,i}$ is a smooth elliptic curve on S and by the lemma we are done. On the other hand, if $\pi: \tilde{D}_{\alpha,i} \to D_{\alpha,i}$ is generically one-to-one, then $D_{\alpha,i}$ will be singular exactly at those points $p \in S$ such that both points of $\pi^{-1}(p) \subset X$ lie in $\tilde{D}_{\alpha,i}$. In this case, let

$$\tilde{D}'_{\alpha,i} = \pi^* \pi_* \tilde{D}_{\alpha,i} - \tilde{D}_{\alpha,i}$$

be the remaining component of $\pi^* D_{\alpha,i}$. Since $\pi: \tilde{D}'_{\alpha,i} \to D_{\alpha,i}$ is again generically one-to-one,

$$\pi_*(\tilde{D}'_{\alpha,i}) = \pi_*(\tilde{D}_{\alpha,i})$$

and hence

$$\tilde{D}'_{\alpha,i} \cdot \tilde{D}'_{\alpha,i} = 0.$$

Since the self-intersection of $\pi^* \pi_* \tilde{D}_{\alpha,i} = \tilde{D}_{\alpha,i} + \tilde{D}'_{\alpha,i}$ is again 0, it follows that $\tilde{D}_{\alpha,i} \cdot \tilde{D}'_{\alpha,i} = 0$—i.e., $\tilde{D}_{\alpha,i}$ and $\tilde{D}'_{\alpha,i}$ are disjoint. But if $D_{\alpha,i}$ is singular at a point $p \in S$, then $\tilde{D}_{\alpha,i}$ must pass through both points of $\pi^{-1}(p)$ and $\tilde{D}'_{\alpha,i}$ likewise, so $\tilde{D}_{\alpha,i}$ and $\tilde{D}'_{\alpha,i}$ will meet over p. Thus $D_{\alpha,i}$ is a smooth elliptic curve, and we are done.

Consider now the Enriques surface S as an elliptic surface $\Psi: S \to \mathbb{P}^1$ with rational base. If S has multiple fibers B_i with multiplicity m_i, then since $\chi(\mathcal{O}_S) = 1$, we have by our formula for the canonical class

$$K_S = \Psi^*(-p) + \sum (m_i - 1) B_i,$$

and since

$$0 \equiv 2K_S = \Psi^*(-2p) + \sum 2(m_i - 1) B_i,$$

it follows that S has exactly two double fibers, B_1 and B_2. Finally, since $2B_1 = 2B_2 = \Psi^*(p)$, we may write

$$K_S = \Psi^*(-p) + B_1 + B_2 = B_1 - B_2 = B_2 - B_1,$$

i.e., *the canonical divisor of an Enriques surface S is just the difference of the two double fibers appearing in an elliptic pencil on S.*

Performing the inverse logarithmic transformation on the two double fibers of an Enriques surface $S \xrightarrow{\Psi} \mathbb{P}^1$, we obtain an elliptic surface $S' \xrightarrow{\Psi'} \mathbb{P}^1$ without multiple fibers. We see immediately that

$$c_1^2(S') = c_1^2(S) = 0$$

and

$$c_2(S') = c_2(S) = 12,$$

so by Riemann-Roch

$$\chi(\mathcal{O}_{S'}) = \chi(\mathcal{O}_S) = 1.$$

By our formula, then,

$$K_{S'} = \Psi^*(-p)$$

and so

$$\kappa(S') = -1;$$

in particular $p_g(S') = 0$, and from $\chi(\mathcal{O}_{S'}) = 1$ we deduce that $q(S') = 0$. By Castelnuovo's theorem, S' is rational; and by our classification of rational surfaces S' is some rational ruled surface blown up eight times, or $\mathbb{P}^2$ blown up nine times. In fact, since $-K_{S'}$ is effective and irreducible and has self-intersection 0, every curve on S' has nonpositive intersection number with $K_{S'}$ and hence self-intersection ≥ -2; by the standard argument, S' must be $\mathbb{P}^2$ blown up nine times. Finally, the images in $\mathbb{P}^2$ of the fibers C_λ of $S \xrightarrow{\Psi} \mathbb{P}^1$ under the blowing-down map $\pi : S' \to \mathbb{P}^2$ must represent sections of $|-K_{\mathbb{P}^2}|$, that is, cubic curves; since the C_λ are all disjoint, the nine points blown up are the base locus of the pencil $|\pi(C_\lambda)|$ of cubics. In sum

An Enriques surface may be obtained by blowing up $\mathbb{P}^2$ at the nine base points of pencil D_λ of cubic curves, and applying two logarithmic transformations of order 2 to the resulting elliptic surface $\tilde{\mathbb{P}}^2 \to \mathbb{P}^1$.

Conversely, performing logarithmic transforms in this case will always yield an algebraic surface, which the reader may easily verify is an Enriques surface. Note that this construction enables us to count parameters for Enriques surfaces: to construct an Enriques surface, we specify nine points in $\mathbb{P}^2$ forming the base locus of a pencil of cubics, blow them up, and then specify two fibers of the resulting elliptic surface (i.e., two cubics passing through the nine blown-up points) on which to perform logarithmic transformations. In short, then, the entire process is determined by the choice of two cubic curves in $\mathbb{P}^2$ meeting transversely; since there is a nine-dimensional family of cubics in $\mathbb{P}^2$, and dim $PGL_3 = 8$, the family of Enriques surfaces is irreducible of dimension

$$9 + 9 - 8 = 10.$$

6. NOETHER'S FORMULA

Noether's Formula for Smooth Hypersurfaces

A *Riemann-Roch formula* in general is a formula giving the holomorphic Euler characteristic of a vector bundle $E \to M$ on a compact complex manifold M in terms of the Chern classes of E and M. In practice this problem breaks up into two halves: first, expressing the holomorphic Euler characteristic $\chi(\mathcal{O}_M)$ of M in terms of the Chern classes of M—e.g., for curves and surfaces,

$$\chi(\mathcal{O}_M) = \tfrac{1}{2} c_1(M)$$

and

$$\chi(\mathcal{O}_M) = \tfrac{1}{12} \left(c_1^2(M) + c_2(M) \right)$$

—and second, expressing the holomorphic Euler characteristic $\chi(\mathcal{O}(E))$ in terms of the Chern classes of E and M and the holomorphic Euler characteristic $\chi(\mathcal{O}_M)$ of M, e.g., for line bundles L on curves and surfaces

$$\chi(\mathcal{O}(L)) = \chi(\mathcal{O}_M) + c_1(L)$$

and

$$\chi(\mathcal{O}(L)) = \chi(\mathcal{O}_M) + \tfrac{1}{2} \left(c_1^2(L) + c_1(L) c_1(M) \right).$$

Of the two halves of a Riemann-Roch formula, the second is usually much easier: once we know the formula for $(n-1)$-dimensional varieties, we can compute it for the line bundle $L \to M$ associated to a smooth divisor D on the n-dimensional manifold M simply by adding up the Euler characteristics of the sheaves in the sequence

$$0 \longrightarrow \mathcal{O}_M \longrightarrow \mathcal{O}_M(L) \longrightarrow \mathcal{O}_D(L) \longrightarrow 0;$$

the resulting formula holds for all line bundles $L \to M$. The first half —expressing $\chi(\mathcal{O}_M)$ in terms of the Chern classes of M—is in general harder. For curves, of course, the formula $\chi(\mathcal{O}_M) = \frac{1}{2}c_1(M)$ is an easy consequence of Hodge theory; it was originally proved, in form $h^0(\Omega_M^1) = b_1(M)/2$ or "the number of independent differentials of the first kind is equal to the number of handles," by Riemann. Our principal object in this section is to prove the analogous formula $\chi(\mathcal{O}_M) = \frac{1}{12}(c_1^2(M) + c_2(M))$ for surfaces, called *Noether's formula*.

To get a sense of the problem, we will first verify the formula for a smooth surface S in $\mathbb{P}^3$ of degree n. To begin with, we establish two general formulas: for $S \subset X$ a smooth surface on a threefold X, from the C^∞ decomposition

$$T_X|_S = T_S \oplus N_{S/X}$$
$$= T_S \oplus [S]|_S$$

and the Whitney product formula, we obtain the *adjunction formulas*

(∗) $\qquad\qquad c_1(X)|_S = c_1(S) + (S)|_S$

and

(∗∗) $\qquad\qquad c_2(X)|_S = c_2(S) + c_1(S) \cdot S|_S.$

The first of these is, of course, the standard adjunction formula applied to $c_1(S) = -K_S$.

Applying these formulas to our smooth surface $S \subset \mathbb{P}^3$ of degree n, and using the values

$$c_1(\mathbb{P}^3) = 4H, \qquad c_2(\mathbb{P}^3) = 6H^2,$$

we have

$$c_1(S)^2 = (n-4)^2 H^2$$
$$= n(n-4)^2$$
$$= n^3 - 8n^2 + 16n,$$

since $H \cdot H = n$ on S; and by (∗∗),

$$6H^2 = c_2(S) + c_1(S) \cdot c_1(N_S)$$
$$= c_2(S) + (4-n) \cdot n \cdot H^2,$$

i.e.,

$$\chi(S) = c_2(S) = (n(n-4)+6)H^2$$
$$= n(n(n-4)+6)$$
$$= n^3 - 4n^2 + 6n.$$

$\chi(\mathcal{O}_S)$ is likewise readily expressed in terms of n. By the Lefschetz theorem, $q(S) = 0$; to compute $p_g(S)$, consider the Poincaré residue map

$$0 \to \Omega_{\mathbb{P}^3}^3 \to \Omega_{\mathbb{P}^3}^3(S) \to \Omega_S^2 \to 0.$$

We have $h^0(\Omega^3_{\mathbb{P}^3}) = 0$ and $h^1(\Omega^3_{\mathbb{P}^3}) = h^{3,1}(\mathbb{P}^3) = 0$, so

$$p_g(S) = h^0(\Omega^2_S) = h^0(\Omega^3_{\mathbb{P}^3}(S))$$
$$= h^0(\mathbb{P}^3, \mathcal{O}((n-4)H))$$
$$= \binom{n-1}{3} = \frac{(n-1)(n-2)(n-3)}{6}.$$

Thus

$$\chi(\mathcal{O}_S) = \frac{(n-1)(n-2)(n-3)}{6} + 1$$
$$= \frac{n^3 - 6n^2 + 11n - 6}{6} + 1$$
$$= \frac{2n^3 - 12n^2 + 22n}{12}$$
$$= \frac{c_1(S)^2 + c_2(S)}{12},$$

and the Riemann-Roch formula is proved for S.

This computation illustrates the general principle that if we know the cohomology ring and Chern classes of a variety M, we can compute most of these invariants—and hence verify Riemann-Roch—for a smooth divisor on M. Of course, a general surface S cannot be realized as a smooth divisor in $\mathbb{P}^3$: while we can embed S in some large projective space and project to $\mathbb{P}^3$ to obtain a generically one-to-one map $\phi: S \to \mathbb{P}^3$, the image $S_0 = \phi(S)$ will in general be singular. To prove Noether's formula, then, we will extend the formulas obtained above for the numerical characters of a smooth surface S in $\mathbb{P}^3$ to the case of surfaces S_0 with standard singularities; we will do this by re-embedding S_0 as a smooth surface in a threefold X obtained by blowing up $\mathbb{P}^3$. This requires two preliminary steps: we have to describe those types of singularities which arise under a generic projection of a surface to $\mathbb{P}^3$; and, given a surface $S_0 \subset \mathbb{P}^3$ with these singularities, construct a blow-up $X \xrightarrow{\pi} \mathbb{P}^3$ in which the proper transform of S_0 is smooth. The first of these steps is simply a matter of dimension-theoretic case checking, and will be deferred for the moment. The second, on the other hand, involves an important extension of our notion of blowing up; we take this up in the following discussion.

Blowing Up Submanifolds

As previously, we start by constructing the blow-up of a disc along a coordinate plane. Let Δ be an n-dimensional disc with holomorphic coordinates $z_1, \ldots, z_n$, and let $V \subset \Delta$ be the locus $z_{k+1} = \cdots = z_n = 0$. Let $[l_{k+1}, \ldots, l_n]$ be homogeneous coordinates on $\mathbb{P}^{n-k-1}$, and let

$$\tilde{\Delta} \subset \Delta \times \mathbb{P}^{n-k-1}$$

be the smooth variety defined by the relations

$$\tilde{\Delta} = \{(z,l): z_i l_j = z_j l_i, \ k+1 \leqslant i,j \leqslant n\}.$$

The projection $\pi : \tilde{\Delta} \to \Delta$ on the first factor is clearly an isomorphism away from V, while the inverse image of a point $z \in V$ is a projective space $\mathbb{P}^{n-k-1}$. The manifold $\tilde{\Delta}$, together with the map $\pi : \tilde{\Delta} \to \Delta$, is called the *blow-up of* Δ *along* V; the inverse image $E = \pi^{-1}(V)$ is called the *exceptional divisor* of the blow-up.

$\tilde{\Delta}$ may be covered by coordinate patches

$$U_j = (l_j \neq 0), \qquad j = k+1, \ldots, n$$

with holomorphic coordinates

$$z_i = z_i, \qquad i = 1, \ldots, k,$$

$$z(j)_i = \frac{l_i}{l_j} = \frac{z_i}{z_j}, \qquad i = k+1, \ldots, \hat{j}, \ldots, n,$$

$$z_j = z_j$$

on U_j; the coordinates $\{z(j)_i\}$ are Euclidean coordinates on each fiber $\pi^{-1}(p) \cong \mathbb{P}^{n-k-1}$ of the exceptional divisor.

Note that the blow-up $\tilde{\Delta} \xrightarrow{\pi} \Delta$ is independent of the coordinates chosen in Δ: if $\{z_i' = f_i(z)\}$ is another coordinate system in Δ with V again given as $(z'_{k+1} = \cdots = z'_n = 0)$,

$$\tilde{\Delta}' = \{(z',l'): z_i' l_j' = z_j' l_i'\} \subset \Delta \times \mathbb{P}^{n-k-1}$$

the blow-up of Δ in this coordinate system, then the isomorphism

$$\tilde{f}: \tilde{\Delta} - E \longrightarrow \tilde{\Delta}' - E'$$

given by $z \mapsto f(z)$ may be extended over E by sending a point (z,l) with $z_{k+1} = \cdots = z_n = 0$ to the point $(f(z), l')$, where

$$l_j' = \sum_{i=k+1}^{n} \frac{\partial f_j}{\partial z_i}(z) \cdot l_i.$$

Indeed, we see from this that the identification of the fiber of $E \xrightarrow{\pi} V$ over a point $z = (z_1, \ldots, z_k, 0, \ldots, 0)$ with the projective normal space $\mathbb{P}(N_{V/\Delta}(z)) = \mathbb{P}(T_z'(\Delta)/T_z'(V))$ made via

$$(z,l) \mapsto \sum_{i=k+1}^{n} l_i \cdot \frac{\partial}{\partial z_i}$$

is natural, i.e., does not depend on the coordinate system used.

This last observation allows us to globalize our construction. Let M be a complex manifold of dimension n and $X \subset M$ a submanifold of dimension k. Let $\{U_\alpha\}$ be a collection of discs in M covering V such that in each disc

Δ_α the subvariety $X \cap \Delta_\alpha$ may be given as the locus $(z_{k+1} = \cdots = z_n = 0)$, and let $\tilde{\Delta}_\alpha \xrightarrow{\pi_\alpha} \Delta_\alpha$ be the blow-up of Δ_α along $X \cap \Delta_\alpha$. We have then isomorphisms

$$\pi_{\alpha\beta} : \pi_\alpha^{-1}(U_\alpha \cap U_\beta) \longrightarrow \pi_\beta^{-1}(U_\alpha \cap U_\beta)$$

and using them, we can patch together the local blow-ups $\tilde{\Delta}_\alpha$ to form a manifold

$$\tilde{\Delta} = \bigcup\nolimits_{\pi_{\alpha\beta}} \tilde{\Delta}_\alpha$$

with a map

$$\tilde{\Delta} \xrightarrow{\pi} \cup \Delta_\alpha.$$

Finally, since π is an isomorphism away from $X \cap (\cup \Delta_\alpha)$, we can take

$$\tilde{M} = \tilde{\Delta} \cup_\pi M - X;$$

$\tilde{M}$, together with the map $\pi : \tilde{M} \to M$ extending π on $\tilde{\Delta}$ and the identity on $M - X$, is called the *blow-up of* M *along* X. By the construction, the blow-up has the following properties

   1. π is an isomorphism away from $X \subset M$ and $E = \pi^{-1}(X) \subset \tilde{M}$.

   2.   The *exceptional divisor* E is a fiber bundle over X with fiber $\mathbb{P}^{n-k-1}$; indeed, $E \xrightarrow{\pi} X$ is naturally identified with the projectivization $\mathbb{P}(N_{X/M})$ of the normal bundle $N_{X/M}$ of X in M.

   3.   Locally the blow-up is isomorphic to the blow-up of a disc as given above.

   4.   As the reader may check by the same method as used in the case of blow-ups of a point, blow-ups of submanifolds are unique, in the sense that if

$$N \xrightarrow{\pi} M$$

is any map of complex manifolds that is an isomorphism away from a smooth subvariety X of dimension k in M, and such that the fiber of π over any point $z \in X$ is isomorphic to projective space $\mathbb{P}^{n-k-1}$, then $N \xrightarrow{\pi} M$ is the blow-up of M along X.

   5.   For any subvariety $Y \subset M$, we may define the *proper transform* $\tilde{Y} \subset \tilde{M}_X$ of Y in the blow-up $\tilde{M}_X$ to be the closure in $\tilde{M}_X$ of the inverse image

$$\pi^{-1}(Y - X) = \pi^{-1}(Y) - E$$

of Y away from the exceptional divisor E. As in the case of blowing up a point, we see that the intersection

$$\tilde{Y} \cap E \subset \mathbb{P}(N_{X/M})$$

corresponds to the image in $N_{X/M}$ of the tangent cones $T_p(Y) \subset T_p(M)$ to Y at points of $Y \cap X$. In particular, for $Y \subset M$ a divisor,

$$\tilde{Y} = \pi^{-1}Y - m \cdot E,$$

where

$$m = \text{mult}_X(Y)$$

is the multiplicity of Y at a generic point of X. Note also that blow-ups are functorial, in the sense that if Y meets X transversely everywhere, the proper transform $\tilde{Y}$ of Y in $\tilde{M}_X$ is just the blow-up of Y along $Y \cap X$.

The Cohomology of a Blow-up. We would like now to describe the relation between the cohomology ring of M and that of its blow-up $\tilde{M} = \tilde{M}_X$ along a submanifold. Cohomology is with $\mathbb{Z}$ coefficients throughout. As in our discussion of point blow-ups, we may take $U \subset M$ a tubular neighborhood of $X \subset M$, $\tilde{U} = \pi^{-1}U$, $U^* = U - X$, $\tilde{U}^* = \tilde{U} - E$, $M^* = M - X$, and $\tilde{M}^* = \tilde{M} - E$, and compare the Mayer-Vietoris sequences for $M = U \cup M^*$ and $\tilde{M} = \tilde{M}^* \cup \tilde{U}$. Since contractions yield, as before, isomorphisms

$$H^*(U) \longrightarrow H^*(X) \quad \text{and} \quad H^*(\tilde{U}) \longrightarrow H^*(E),$$

and clearly π^* gives isomorphisms

$$H^*(U^*) \longrightarrow H^*(\tilde{U}^*) \quad \text{and} \quad H^*(M^*) \longrightarrow H^*(\tilde{M}^*),$$

we obtain

$$H^{i-1}(U^*) \to H^i(\tilde{M}) \to H^i(M^*) \oplus H^i(E) \to H^i(U^*)$$

$$\| \qquad \uparrow \qquad \| \qquad \|$$

$$H^{i-1}(U^*) \to H^i(M) \to H^i(M^*) \oplus H^i(X) \to H^i(U^*).$$

Since the pullback map $\pi^*: H^*(M) \to H^*(\tilde{M})$ is injective (equivalently, and more visibly, the map $\pi_* H_*(\tilde{M}) \to H(_*(M)$ is surjective), we see from this that (additively)

$$H^*(\tilde{M}) = \pi^* H^*(M) \oplus H^*(E)/\pi^* H^*(X)$$

To describe the cohomology of $E \cong \mathbb{P}(N_{X/M})$, as well as the multiplicative structure of $H^*(\tilde{M})$, we need a general result on the cohomology of projective bundles. First a definition: for $E \to X$ a complex vector bundle of rank r and $\mathbb{P}(E) \overset{\pi}{\to} X$ its associated projective bundle, we define the *tautological line bundle* $T \to \mathbb{P}(E)$ to be the subbundle of the pullback bundle $\pi^* E \to \mathbb{P}(E)$ whose fiber at any point $(p, v) \in \mathbb{P}(E)$ is the line in E_p represented by v. Note that the bundle T is *not* determined by the abstract projective bundle $\mathbb{P}(E) \to X$ alone: if $L \to X$ is any line bundle, we have seen that

$$\mathbb{P}(E) \cong \mathbb{P}(E \otimes L);$$

but the tautological line bundles on $\mathbb{P}(E)$ and $\mathbb{P}(E \otimes L)$ will differ. One thing is always true: the restriction of T to each fiber $\mathbb{P}(E)_p \cong \mathbb{P}^{r-1}$ is the universal bundle.

Now, the cohomology ring $H^*(\mathbb{P}(E))$ is, via the pullback map,

$$H^*(X) \xrightarrow{\pi^*} H^*(\mathbb{P}(E)),$$

an algebra over the ring $H^*(X)$. A complete description of $H^*(\mathbb{P}(E))$ is given in these terms by the

Proposition. *For X any compact oriented C^∞ manifold, E→X any complex vector bundle of rank r, the cohomology ring $H^*(\mathbb{P}(E))$ is generated, as an $H^*(X)$-algebra, by the Chern class*

$$\zeta = c_1(T)$$

of the tautological bundle, with the single relation

$$\zeta^r - c_1(E)\zeta^{r-1} + c_2(E)\zeta^{r-2} + \cdots + (-1)^{r-1}c_{r-1}(E)\zeta + (-1)^r c_r(E) = 0.$$
(*)

Proof. We first establish the basic relation (*). To do this, let S be the quotient of the pullback π^*E by the tautological subbundle, and set $\eta_i = c_i(E)$. By Whitney; then,

$$(1 + \zeta)(1 + \eta_1 + \cdots + \eta_{r-1}) = \pi^*c(E)$$

and solving successively, we have

$$\eta_1 = c_1(E) - \zeta$$
$$\eta_2 = c_2(E) - \zeta \cdot c_1(E) + \zeta^2$$
$$\vdots$$
$$\eta_{r-1} = c_{r-1}(E) - \zeta \cdot c_{r-2}(E) + \cdots + (-1)^{r-1}\zeta^{r-1}.$$

The final equation

$$c_r(E) = \zeta \cdot \eta_{r-1}$$

is then our basic relation.

Now let $\{\psi_{i,\alpha}\}_\alpha$ be a basis for $H^i(X)$, with $\{\psi_{i,\alpha}\}$ and $\{\psi_{n-i,\alpha}\}$ orthogonal—i.e., such that

$$\psi_{i,\alpha} \cup \psi_{n-i,\beta} = \pm\delta_{\alpha,\beta}.$$

We claim that the classes

$$\{\pi^*\psi_{i,\alpha} \cup \zeta^j\}_{1 \leqslant i \leqslant n, 1 \leqslant j \leqslant r-1, \alpha}$$

are linearly independent in $H^*(\mathbb{P}(E))$. First, for any pair of classes $\psi_{i,\alpha}$ and $\psi_{n-i,\alpha}$, the cup product $\pi^*\psi_{i,\alpha} \cup \pi^*\psi_{n-i,\alpha}$ will be Poincaré dual to plus or minus the class of a fiber $\mathbb{P}(E)_p$ of $\mathbb{P}(E)$. But the restriction of ζ to $\mathbb{P}(E)_p$

is minus the class of a hyperplane in $\mathbb{P}(E)_p$, and consequently

$$\pi^*\psi_{i,\alpha} \cup \pi^*\psi_{n-i,\alpha} \cup \zeta^{r-1} = \pm 1,$$

or, in other words, for any j,

$$\left(\pi^*\psi_{i,\alpha} \cup \zeta^j\right) \cup \left(\pi^*\psi_{n-i,\alpha} \cup \zeta^{r-j-1}\right) = \pm 1.$$

On the other hand, for $\alpha \neq \beta$,

$$\pi^*\psi_{i,\alpha} \cup \pi^*\psi_{n-i,\beta} = 0;$$

likewise, for $i < k$ and any α, β, j,

$$\left(\pi^*\psi_{i,\alpha} \cup \zeta^j\right) \cup \left(\pi^*\psi_{n-k,\beta} \cup \zeta^{r-i-j+k-1}\right) = 0.$$

Therefore the intersection matrix for the classes $\{\psi_{i,\alpha} \cup \zeta^j\}_{i,j,\alpha}$ may be made upper triangular with ± 1's along the diagonal; in particular, we see that it is nonsingular, and so these elements are all linearly independent in $H^*(\mathbb{P}(E))$.

Finally, consider the Leray spectral sequence $(E_r^{p,q}, d_r)$ of the bundle $\mathbb{P}(E) \to X$. Since the cohomology of the fiber has rank at most 1 in each dimension, $\pi_1(X)$ acts trivially on $H^*(\mathbb{P}^{r-1})$, and so

$$E_2 \cong H^*(X) \otimes H^*(\mathbb{P}^{r-1}).$$

But since the classes $\{\psi_{i,\alpha} \cup \zeta^j\}$ are all independent in $H^*(\mathbb{P}(E))$,

$$\begin{aligned}
r \cdot \dim H^*(X) &\leqslant \dim H^*(\mathbb{P}(E)) \\
&= \dim E_\infty \\
&\leqslant \dim E_2 \\
&= r \cdot \dim H^*(X).
\end{aligned}$$

Equality must therefore hold everywhere, i.e., the classes $\{\psi_{i,\alpha} \cup \zeta^j\}$ span $H^*(\mathbb{P}(E))$ so that ζ generates $H^*(\mathbb{P}(E))$ as an $H^*(X)$-algebra, and there can be no relations on ζ other than $(*)$ above. Q.E.D.

One observation makes this result particularly applicable to blow-ups: if $\tilde{M} \to M$ is the blow-up of the manifold M along the submanifold X, $E = \mathbb{P}(N_{X/M})$ the exceptional divisor, then *the normal bundle to* E *in* $\tilde{M}$ *is just the tautological bundle on* $E \cong \mathbb{P}(N_{X/M})$. Indeed, for any point $(p, v) \in E$, we easily see that

$$\pi_* : T'_{(p,v)}(\tilde{M}) \to T'_p(M)$$

induces a map

$$\tilde{\pi}_* : N_{E/\tilde{M}}(p, v) \to N_{X/M}(p).$$

To see that the image of $\tilde{\pi}_*$ is just the line v in $N_{X/M}(p)$, it is sufficient to check it for the blow-up $\tilde{\mathbb{C}}_V^n \overset{\pi}{\to} \mathbb{C}^n$ of $\mathbb{C}^n$ along the subspace $V \cong \mathbb{C}^k$, and there it is clear. As a consequence, we see that the restriction to E of the cohomology class $e = c_1([E])$ is

$$e|_E = c_1(N_{E/\tilde{M}}) = c_1(T) = \zeta,$$

and correspondingly, with a knowledge of $H^*(E)$ and the restriction map $H^*(M) \to H^*(X)$, we may compute effectively in the cohomology ring of the blow-up $\tilde{M}_X$.

Chern Classes of Blow-ups. We have seen that if $\tilde{M} \xrightarrow{\pi} M$ is the blow-up of an n-dimensional complex manifold at a point, E the exceptional divisor, then

$$c_1(\tilde{M}) = -K_{\tilde{M}} = \pi^* c_1(M) - (n-1)E.$$

In a similar fashion, it is not hard to verify that for $\tilde{M} \xrightarrow{\pi} M$ the blow-up of M along a k-dimensional submanifold $X \subset M$, E again the exceptional divisor,

$$c_1(\tilde{M}) = \pi^* c_1(M) - (n-k-1)E.$$

This formula may be checked in general as it was in case $k=0$—that is, by writing out transition functions for the canonical bundle $K_{\tilde{M}}$. The computation is substantially easier, however, if we consider only algebraic varieties M. In this case we can find a meromorphic n-form ω on M, with X not contained in the zero or polar divisor of ω. The divisor of the pullback form $\pi^* \omega$ on $\tilde{M}$ is then, away from E, just the pullback of the divisor (ω). To see how $\pi^* \omega$ behaves around E, let p be a generic point of X and $z_1, \ldots, z_n$ local coordinates in a neighborhood U of p with

$$X \cap U = (z_{k+1}, \ldots, z_n = 0);$$

we may write

$$\omega = g(z) dz_1 \wedge \cdots \wedge dz_n$$

with g nonzero and holomorphic around p. In terms of coordinates

$$z_i = z_i, i = 1, \ldots, k, j,$$

and

$$z(j)_i = \frac{z_i}{z_j}, i = k+1, \ldots, \hat{j}, \ldots, n,$$

on the open set $U_j \subset \pi^{-1}(U)$ as described above, we have

$$\pi^* dz_i = dz_i, \qquad\qquad i = 1, \ldots, k, j,$$

$$\pi^* dz_i = d(z_j z(j)_i)$$

$$= z_j dz(j)_i + \tilde{z}(j)_i \cdot dz_j, \qquad i = k+1, \ldots, \hat{j}, \ldots, n.$$

Thus,

$$\pi^* \omega = \pi^* g(z) \cdot z_j^{n-k-1} \cdot dz_1 \wedge \cdots \wedge dz_k \wedge dz(j)_{k+1} \wedge \cdots \wedge dz(j)_n$$

vanishes to order $n - k - 1$ along $E = (\tilde{z}_j)$, and the formula is verified.

Computing the higher Chern classes of a general blow-up is substantially harder; in particular, one has to find the Chern classes of the exceptional divisor, and we do not have at present the requisite formalism of the *Chern character*. We may, however, determine the Chern classes of the blow-up of a threefold by essentially ad hoc methods; we will do this in the following two lemmas.

Lemma. *If $\tilde{M} \overset{\pi}{\to} M$ is the blow-up of the algebraic threefold M at a point,*

$$c_2(\tilde{M}) = \pi^* c_2(M).$$

Proof. We will prove this by applying the adjunction formulas $(*)$ and $(**)$ of p. 601 to surfaces in $\tilde{M}$ whose Chern classes we know. First, let E be the exceptional divisor of the blow-up, $l \in H^2(E)$ the class of a line in $E \cong \mathbb{P}^2$. We have seen that

$$E|_E = -l$$

while

$$c_1(E) = 3l \quad \text{and} \quad c_2(E) = 3.$$

By the formula $(**)$, then

$$
\begin{aligned}
c_2(M)|_E &= c_2(E) + c_1(E) \cdot E|_E \\
&= 3 + 3l \cdot (-l) \\
&= 0.
\end{aligned}
$$

Next, we do the same thing for a surface $S \subset M$ not containing p and its inverse image $S = \pi^{-1}(S) \subset \tilde{M}$. Inasmuch as $\tilde{S} \cong S$ and the fundamental class $\eta_{\tilde{S}} = \pi^* \eta_S$, we have

$$
\begin{aligned}
c_2(\tilde{M})|_{\tilde{S}} &= c_2(\tilde{S}) + c_1(\tilde{S}) \cdot \tilde{S}|_{\tilde{S}} \\
&= c_2(S) + c_1(S) \cdot S|_S \\
&= c_2(M)|_S \\
&= \pi^* c_2(M)|_{\tilde{S}}.
\end{aligned}
$$

We see from these two computations that the class $c_2(\tilde{M}) - \pi^* c_2(M)$ restricts to zero on—i.e., has intersection number 0 with—the exceptional divisor E and the inverse image of any surface $S \subset M$ not containing p. But any divisor on $\tilde{M}$ is homologous to a linear combination of such surfaces; and since the intersection form

$$H^{1,1}(\tilde{M}, \mathbb{Z}) \otimes H^{2,2}(\tilde{M}, \mathbb{Z}) \to \mathbb{Z}$$

is nondegenerate, this implies the lemma. Q.E.D.

Using the same approach, we can prove the slightly harder

Lemma. *If $\pi : \tilde{M} \to M$ is the blow-up of the algebraic threefold M along a smooth curve $X \subset M$, E the exceptional divisor of the blow-up, and $\eta_X \in$*

$H^4(M)$ *the class of* X, *then*

$$c_2(\tilde{M}) = \pi^*(c_2(M) + \eta_X) - \pi^* c_1(M) \cdot E.$$

Proof. Let $l \in H^2(E)$ denote the class of a fiber in $E \cong \mathbb{P}(N_{X/M}) \overset{\pi_E}{\to} X$; since the class $e = E|_E$ is the class of the tautological bundle on E, we have first

$$l \cdot e = -1.$$

From our basic relation

$$e \cdot e - e \cdot \pi_E^* c_1(N_{X/M}) = 0,$$

then, we have

$$e \cdot e = -c_1(N_{X/M}).$$

Now, by (∗),

$$\begin{aligned}
c_1(E) &= c_1(\tilde{M}) - E|_E \\
&= \pi^* c_1(M) - 2E|_E \\
&= (c_1(M) \cdot X) - 2e
\end{aligned}$$

and hence by (∗∗),

$$\begin{aligned}
c_2(\tilde{M})|_E &= c_2(E) + c_1(E) \cdot E \\
&= c_2(E) - c_1(M) \cdot X + 2c_1(N_{X/M}).
\end{aligned}$$

But

$$\begin{aligned}
c_2(E) &= \chi(E) \\
&= 2\chi(X) \\
&= 2c_1(X) \\
&= 2c_1(M) \cdot X - 2c_1(N_{X/M})
\end{aligned}$$

and so we have

$$\begin{aligned}
c_2(\tilde{M})|_E &= c_1(M) \cdot X \\
&= -\pi^* c_1(M) \cdot E|_E \\
&= (\pi^*(c_2(M) + \eta_X) - \pi^* c_1(M) \cdot E)|_E.
\end{aligned}$$

Next, let $S \subset M$ be a smooth surface meeting X transversely, and let $\tilde{S}$ be its inverse image in $\tilde{M}$. $\tilde{S}$ is just the blow-up of S at the points of $S \cap X$, and so

$$c_2(\tilde{S}) = c_2(S) + S \cdot X.$$

By (∗),

$$\begin{aligned}
c_1(\tilde{S}) &= (c_1(\tilde{M}) - \tilde{S})|_{\tilde{S}} \\
&= \pi^* c_1(S) - E|_S
\end{aligned}$$

and so from (**) we see that

$$c_2(\tilde{M})|_S = c_2(\tilde{S}) + c_1(\tilde{S}) \cdot \tilde{S}|_{\tilde{S}}$$
$$= c_2(S) + c_1(S) \cdot S|_S + S \cdot X - E \cdot \tilde{S}|_{\tilde{S}}$$
$$= \pi^* c_2(M)|_{\tilde{S}} + \pi^* \eta_X|_{\tilde{S}} - E \cdot \tilde{S}|_{\tilde{S}}$$
$$= \pi^*(c_2(M) + \eta_X)|_{\tilde{S}}$$

since $E \cdot \tilde{S} \cdot \tilde{S} = E \cdot \pi^*(S \cdot S) = 0$. Thus we see that the class $c_2(\tilde{M}) - \pi^*(c_2(M) + \eta_X) + \pi^* c_1(M) \cdot E$ has intersection number 0 with both E and $\tilde{S}$, and hence is zero.   Q.E.D.

Ordinary Singularities of Surfaces

Our task in this section is to describe the singularities of a *generic* projection of a surface $S \subset \mathbb{P}^N$ into $\mathbb{P}^3$. To begin with, we recall that for $N > 5$, the generic projection of $\tilde{S} \subset \mathbb{P}^N$ from a point is an embedding, so we may take $\tilde{S}$ smooth in $\mathbb{P}^5$ to start and consider the projection map

$$\pi_L : \tilde{S} \to \mathbb{P}^3$$

from a generic line $L \subset \mathbb{P}^5$. As we have seen, the map π_L will be 1-1 and smooth at a point $p \in \tilde{S}$ exactly when the 2-plane $\overline{pL}$ meets $\tilde{S}$ transversely at p and nowhere else; accordingly, we will try to determine, at least dimension-theoretically, the number of times a generic line $L \subset \mathbb{P}^5$ meets a chord of $\tilde{S}$, or a tangent plane to $\tilde{S}$, or lies in a 2-plane spanned by points of $\tilde{S}$, etc. One point before we proceed: while we shall argue that the generic projection of *any* surface $\tilde{S} \subset \mathbb{P}^5$ has only ordinary singularities as defined on p. 616, all we need to know for the purpose of proving Noether's formula is that any surface may be embedded in $\mathbb{P}^5$ in such a way that the generic projection has only ordinary singularities. Indeed, some of the subtler questions of "general position" that arise in the latter part of our argument may be decided immediately by taking the embedding $\tilde{S} \to \mathbb{P}^5$ to be of sufficiently high degree; accordingly we will leave the verification of these conditions to the reader, and merely show that they are satisfied for an appropriate embedding of $\tilde{S}$.

Now let $G(2,6)$ be the Grassmannian of lines in $\mathbb{P}^5$ and consider the incidence correspondence

$$I \subset \tilde{S} \times \tilde{S} \times G(2,6)$$

given by

$$I = \{(p,q,L) : p \neq q, \dim \overline{pqL} \leq 2\}.$$

Clearly for any two points $p \neq q \in \tilde{S}$, $\pi_L(p) = \pi_L(q)$ exactly when $(p,q,L) \in I$. But now if we let π_1, π_2, and π_3 be the projections of I onto the three factors of $\tilde{S} \times \tilde{S} \times G(2,6)$, we see that the fiber of the map

$$\pi_1 \times \pi_2 : I \to \tilde{S} \times \tilde{S}$$

over a point (p,q) corresponds to the set of lines $L \in G(2,6)$ meeting the line $\overline{pq} \subset \mathbb{P}^5$, i.e., to a Schubert cycle σ_3. Since σ_3 has codimension 3 in the eight-dimensional $G(2,6)$, the fibers of $\pi_1 \times \pi_2$ have dimension 5, and so

$$\dim I = 9.$$

Thus the fiber of the map $\pi_3 : I \to G(2,6)$ over a generic point $L \in G(2,6)$ has dimension at most 1. Indeed, as we shall see, $\pi_3^{-1}(L)$ cannot be empty or finite, so in fact $\pi_3^{-1}(L)$ must be one-dimensional for a generic L, and hence *the projection map* $\pi_L : \tilde{S} \to \mathbb{P}^3$ *is one-to-one outside the closure* $\tilde{C}$ *of the curve*

$$\pi_1\big(\pi_3^{-1}(L)\big) \subset \tilde{S}.$$

The curve $\tilde{C}$ is called the *double curve* of the map π_L; its image $C = \pi_L(\tilde{C})$ in the image surface $S = \pi_L(\tilde{S}) \subset \mathbb{P}^3$ is likewise called the *double curve* of S.

We claim now that π_L will be 3-1 only at a finite number of points, and nowhere 4-1 or more. To see this let

$$I' \subset \tilde{S} \times \tilde{S} \times \tilde{S} \times G(2,6)$$

be given by

$$I' = \big\{ (p,q,r,L) : p \neq q \neq r \neq p, \dim \overline{pqrL} \leqslant 2 \big\}$$

and let π_1, π_2, π_3, and π_4 be the projections of I' on the factors of $\tilde{S} \times \tilde{S} \times \tilde{S} \times G(2,6)$. Clearly the generic triple (p,q,r) of distinct points on $\tilde{S}$ span a 2-plane; thus the fiber of

$$\pi_1 \times \pi_2 \times \pi_3 : I' \to \tilde{S} \times \tilde{S} \times \tilde{S}$$

over any point *not* in the locus

$$J = \big\{ (p,q,r) : p \neq q \neq r \neq p \text{ collinear} \big\} \subset \tilde{S} \times \tilde{S} \times \tilde{S}$$

corresponds to lines L lying in $\overline{pqr}$ and so is two-dimensional. Thus

$$\dim(\pi_1 \times \pi_2 \times \pi_3)^{-1}(\tilde{S} \times \tilde{S} \times \tilde{S} - J) = 8.$$

On the other hand, since a generic 3-plane $V_3 \subset \mathbb{P}^5$ meets $\tilde{S}$ in a collection of points in general position, the generic chord $\overline{pq}$ to $\tilde{S}$ will meet $\tilde{S}$ only at p and q, so J is at most three-dimensional. The fiber of $\pi_1 \times \pi_2 \times \pi_3$ over a point of J being, as we have seen, five-dimensional, we have

$$\dim(\pi_1 \times \pi_2 \times \pi_3)^{-1} J \leqslant 8.$$

Thus I' is eight-dimensional, and so the generic fiber of the projection $\pi_4 : I' \to G(2,8)$ is finite; this proves the first part of our present claim. In fact, we can say a bit more: from the proof of our basic lemma (p. 249), we see that among those 3-planes V_3 meeting $\tilde{S}$ in a collection of points not in general position, the generic one contains four points of $\tilde{S}$ spanning a 2-plane, and *not three collinear points*. Thus if we define

$$K \subset \tilde{S} \times \tilde{S} \times \tilde{S} \times G(4,6)$$

by

$$K = \{(p,q,r,\Lambda): p \neq q \neq r \in \Lambda \text{ and } r \in \overline{pq}\},$$

we see that the image of K under projection on the factor $G(4,6)$ has codimension at least 2, i.e., dimension at most 6. Assuming that $\tilde{S}$ contains only finitely many lines, then, it follows that $\dim K \leqslant 6$, and since the fibers of the projection map $\pi_1 \times \pi_2 \times \pi_3 : K \rightarrow \tilde{S} \times \tilde{S} \times \tilde{S}$ are all four-dimensional, that the dimension of $J = \pi_1 \times \pi_2 \times \pi_3(K)$ is at most 2. If $\tilde{S}$ does contain a family of lines, of course, J will be three-dimensional; but as we will see, this causes no trouble.

Now to see that π_L is never 4-1 or worse, let

$$I'' \subset \tilde{S} \times \tilde{S} \times \tilde{S} \times \tilde{S} \times G(2,6)$$

be given by

$$I'' = \{(p,q,r,t,L): p,q,r,t \text{ distinct and } \dim \overline{pqrtL} \leqslant 2\},$$

and let $\pi_1, \ldots, \pi_5$ be the corresponding projection maps. First off, since the generic triple (p,q,r) of distinct points on $\tilde{S}$ are linearly independent and the 2-plane they span contains no other points of $\tilde{S}$, the map $\pi_1 \times \pi_2 \times \pi_3$ maps I'' into a proper subvariety of $\tilde{S} \times \tilde{S} \times \tilde{S}$ with fiber dimension 2 away from J; i.e.,

$$\dim(\pi_1 \times \pi_2 \times \pi_3)^{-1}(\tilde{S} \times \tilde{S} \times \tilde{S} - J) \leqslant 7.$$

On the other hand, $\pi_1 \times \pi_2 \times \pi_3$ has fiber dimension 5 over J, so if $\tilde{S}$ does not contain a family of lines,

$$\dim(\pi_1 \times \pi_2 \times \pi_3)^{-1} J \leqslant 7.$$

Thus $\dim I'' \leqslant 7$, and the projection $\pi_5 : I'' \rightarrow G(2,6)$ cannot be surjective. Finally, if S does contain a family of lines, then I'' may be 10-dimensional —but the generic point of I'' lies in a fiber of π_5 of dimension 4, and so again π_5 cannot be surjective.

In sum, then, we have seen that for generic L, $\pi_L : \tilde{S} \rightarrow S \subset \mathbb{P}^3$ is 1-1 outside of the double curve $\tilde{C} \subset \tilde{S}$, generically 2-1 on $\tilde{C}$, and 3-1 over a finite collection of points. We consider now the possible singularities of $\tilde{\pi}_L$. First, let

$$I_1 \subset \tilde{S} \times G(2,6)$$

be given by

$$I_1 = \left\{(q,L): \dim \overline{T_q(\tilde{S}),L} \leqslant 3\right\}$$

and let π_1, π_2 be the projection maps. For each $q \in \tilde{S}$, the fiber $\pi_1^{-1}(q)$ of π_1 over q is the Schubert cycle σ_2 of lines $L \subset \mathbb{P}^5$ meeting $T_q(\tilde{S})$, and so has dimension 6; thus $\dim I_1 = 8$. The generic fiber of π_2 on I_1 is thus finite, so that for generic L the set

$$\tilde{B} = \pi_1(\pi_2^{-1}(L)) \subset \tilde{S}$$

of points where π_L fails to be smooth is finite. (Note that if $(q,L) \in I_1$, then (q,q,L) lies in the closure of I above; thus we see that $\tilde{B}$ lies in $\tilde{C}$.) Moreover, since for generic $q \in \tilde{S}$ not every line tangent to $\tilde{S}$ at q meets $\tilde{S}$ in another point besides q, the locus

$$I_1' = \{(q,r,L): (q,L) \in I_1, (q,r,L) \in I\}$$

has dimension at most 7, so that π_L will be 1-1 at the points of $\tilde{B}$; and since the generic tangent line to S is simply tangent, the 2-plane $\overline{qL}$ will be simply tangent to $\tilde{S}$ at each point of $\tilde{B}$.

All that remains is to check that if $\pi_L(q) = \pi_L(r)$ for two points $q \neq r \in S$, then the images in $\mathbb{P}^3$ of neighborhoods of q and r meet transversely, and likewise for triple points. In the first case, neighborhoods of q and r will fail to meet transversely in $\mathbb{P}^3$ exactly when $\overline{T_q(\tilde{S}),L} = \overline{T_r(\tilde{S}),L}$; thus we consider the variety

$$I_2 \subset I \subset \tilde{S} \times \tilde{S} \times G(2,6)$$

given by

$$I_2 = \left\{(q,r,L): \overline{T_q(\tilde{S}),L} = \overline{T_r(\tilde{S}),L}\right\}.$$

Letting π_1, π_2, and π_3 denote the projection maps on I_2, we see that for $(q,r) \in \tilde{S} \times \tilde{S}$, $(\pi_1 \times \pi_2)^{-1}(\tilde{q}, \tilde{r})$ will be empty if $T_q(\tilde{S})$ is disjoint from $T_r(\tilde{S})$, the Schubert cycle $\sigma_{3,1} \subset G(2,6)$ of lines lying in $\overline{T_q(\tilde{S}),T_r(\tilde{S})}$ and meeting $\overline{qr}$ if $T_q(\tilde{S})$ and $T_r(\tilde{S})$ meet in a point, and the Schubert cycle σ_3 of lines meeting $\overline{qr}$ if $T_q(\tilde{S})$ and $T_r(\tilde{S})$ have a line or more in common. The reader may check that in fact the only nondegenerate surface $\tilde{S}$ in $\mathbb{P}^5$ every two of whose tangent planes meet is the Veronese surface, and any surface $\tilde{S} \subset \mathbb{P}^5$ such that $T_p(\tilde{S})$ meets $T_q(\tilde{S})$ in a line for all (p,q) in a three-dimensional subvariety of $\tilde{S} \times \tilde{S}$ must contain a family of lines. Except for these exceptional cases, then, the variety I_2 has dimension at most 7; if $\tilde{S}$ is the Veronese surface or contains a family of lines, on the other hand, we see that I_2 is at most eight-dimensional and the fiber of the map π_3 through the generic point of I_2 is positive dimensional. Thus in any case $\pi_3: I_2 \to G(2,6)$ cannot be surjective.

Alternatively, we can guarantee the condition $\dim I_2 \leq 7$ by rechoosing our embedding of $\tilde{S}$ in $\mathbb{P}^5$: if $L \to \tilde{S}$ is a positive line bundle, then for $k \gg 0$ we see by the proof of the Kodaira embedding theorem that L^k is very ample and for any two points $p, q \in \tilde{S}$,

$$H^1(\tilde{S}, \mathcal{I}_{p,q}(L^k)) = H^1(\tilde{S}, \mathcal{I}^2_{p,q}(L^k)) = 0.$$

It follows that

$$h^0(\tilde{S}, \mathcal{I}_{p,q}(L^k)) = h^0(\tilde{S}, \mathcal{O}(L^k)) - 2$$

and

$$h^0(\tilde{S}, \mathcal{I}^2_{p,q}(L^k)) = h^0(\tilde{S}, \mathcal{O}(L^k)) - 6,$$

i.e., the linear subspace of divisors $D \in |L^k|$ singular at two fixed points p_0 and q_0 is codimension 6. Thus the generic sublinear system of dimension 5 in $|L^k|$ contains no such divisor, or in other words no hyperplane section of the image of $\iota_{L^k}(\tilde{S})$ under a generic projection to $\mathbb{P}^5$ is singular at both p_0 and q_0. This implies that the tangent spaces to $\tilde{S} \subset \mathbb{P}^5$ at p_0 and q_0 do not both lie in any 4-plane, and so are disjoint. Likewise, we see that for fixed p_0 the locus of divisors $D \in |L^k|$ singular at p_0 and at some other point $q \in \tilde{S}$ as well has codimension 4. The generic five-dimensional sublinear system of $|L^k|$ will then contain at most a finite number of lines from this locus, that is, under a generic projection of $\iota_{L^k}(\tilde{S})$ to $\mathbb{P}^5$, there will be only finitely many $q \in \tilde{S}$ such that a pencil of hyperplane sections of $\tilde{S} \subset \mathbb{P}^5$ is singular at both p_0 and q. The locus of pairs $(p,q) \in \tilde{S} \times \tilde{S}$ with $T_p(\tilde{S})$ meeting $T_q(\tilde{S})$ in a line is thus at most two-dimensional, and so I_2 has dimension ≤ 7.

Lastly, if $\pi_L(p) = \pi_L(q) = \pi_L(r)$ for distinct points $p, q, r \in S$, the images of neighborhoods of the three points will fail to meet transversely at $\pi_L(p) \in \mathbb{P}^3$ exactly when the hyperplanes $\overline{T_p(\tilde{S})}, L, \overline{T_q(\tilde{S})}, L$ and $\overline{T_r(\tilde{S})}, L$ intersect in a 3-plane. Since we have seen that the generic $L \subset \mathbb{P}^5$ will not meet any line containing three points of $\tilde{S}$, we consider

$$I'_2 \subset \tilde{S} \times \tilde{S} \times \tilde{S} \times G(2,6)$$

given by

$$I'_2 = \Big\{ (p,q,r,L) : L \subset \overline{pqr},$$

$$\dim\left(\overline{T_p(\tilde{S}), q, r} \cap \overline{T_q(\tilde{S}), p, r} \cap \overline{T_r(\tilde{S}), p, q} \right) \geq 3 \Big\}.$$

Again, we leave to the reader the verification that the projection map $\pi_4 : I'_2 \to G(2,6)$ cannot be surjective, and argue that for an appropriate embedding of $\tilde{S}$, I'_2 will have dimension at most 7. This is not hard: as before, we take L a positive line bundle and choose k such that

$$H^1(\tilde{S}, \mathcal{I}_{p,q,r}(L^k)) = H^1(\tilde{S}, \mathcal{I}^2_{p,q,r}(L^k)) = 0.$$

It then follows that the space of divisors $D \in |L^k|$ singular at p, q, and r has codimension 9, and hence that the spaces E_p, E_q, and $E_r \subset |L^k|$ of divisors $D \in |L^k|$ containing all three points and singular at p, q, or r, respectively, have codimension 5 and are in general position in $|L^k|$. The generic five-dimensional sublinear system of $|L^k|$ will therefore intersect E_p, E_q, and E_r in three linearly independent points, or in other words under the generic projection of $\iota_{L^k}(\tilde{S})$ into $\mathbb{P}^T$, *no pencil of hyperplane sections of* S *through all three points can contain elements singular at* p, q, *and* r. But if $\overline{T_p(\tilde{S}),q,r}$, $\overline{T_q(\tilde{S}),p,r}$, and $\overline{T_r(\tilde{S}),q,p}$ met in a 3-plane, the set of hyperplane sections of $\tilde{S}$ containing that 3-plane would be just such a pencil. Thus the projection

$$(\pi_1 \times \pi_2 \times \pi_3): I'_2 \to \tilde{S} \times \tilde{S} \times \tilde{S}$$

maps onto a proper subvariety of $\tilde{S} \times \tilde{S} \times \tilde{S}$; since the fiber dimension of the map is clearly $\leqslant 2$, we see that $\dim I'_2 \leqslant 7$.

Putting this all together, then, we see that any singular point of the image $S \subset \mathbb{P}^3$ of $\tilde{S}$ under a generic projection π is one of the following three types:

1. A transverse *double point* of S, i.e., the image of two distinct points of $\tilde{S}$. A neighborhood of p in S then consists of two smooth polydiscs intersecting transversely in the double curve C of S (see Figure 11); in terms of an appropriate local holomorphic coordinate system (u,v,w) for $\mathbb{P}^3$ near p,

(∗) $S = (uv = 0)$

and

$$C = (u = 0, v = 0).$$

Around the two points p',p'' in the inverse image of p, the functions

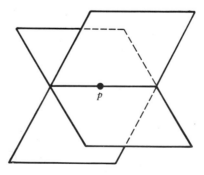

Figure 11

(π^*v, π^*w) and (π^*u, π^*w) furnish local holomorphic coordinates; $\tilde{C}$ is given near p' and p'' by $\pi^*v = 0$ and $\pi^*u = 0$, respectively. Note in particular that C and $\tilde{C}$ are smooth at p and $\pi^{-1}(p)$, as is the map $\pi : \tilde{C} \to C$.

2. A *triple point* of S, that is, the image of three distinct points of $\tilde{S}$. A neighborhood of p in S then consists of three smooth polydiscs intersecting transversely (see Figure 12); we can choose holomorphic coordinates (u, v, w) for $\mathbb{P}^3$ near p so that

$$(*) \qquad\qquad S = (uvw = 0),$$
$$C = (u = v = 0) \cup (u = w = 0) \cup (v = w = 0).$$

Around the three points p', p'', and p''' of $\tilde{S}$ lying over p we may take as local coordinates (π^*v, π^*w), (π^*u, π^*w) and (π^*u, π^*v); $\tilde{C}$ is then given in these coordinate systems by $(\pi^*v \cdot \pi^*w = 0)$, $(\pi^*u \cdot \pi^*w = 0)$, and $(\pi^*u \cdot \pi^*v = 0)$, respectively.

3. A *cuspidal* (or *flat*, or *pinch*) *point* of S, i.e., the image in S of a simple tangent line to $\tilde{S}$. Here the local character of the map π near p is not so plain. Choose Euclidean coordinates $u_1, \ldots, u_5$ in $\mathbb{P}^5$ so that the family of 2-planes containing the line of projection L is given by $(u_1, u_2, u_3) = (c_1, c_2, c_3)$, and so that the line $u_1 = u_2 = u_3 = u_4 = 0$ is tangent to $\tilde{S}$ at p, and choose local coordinates (s, t) on $\tilde{S}$ such that under the inclusion $T_{p'}(\tilde{S}) \subset T_{p'}(\mathbb{P}^5)$,

$$\frac{\partial}{\partial t} = \frac{\partial}{\partial u_5} \quad \text{and} \quad \frac{\partial}{\partial s} = \frac{\partial}{\partial u_3}.$$

Then the inclusion $\tilde{S} \subset \mathbb{P}^5$ will have the form

$$(s, t) \mapsto ([2], [2], s + [2], [2], t + [2])$$

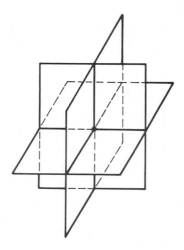

Figure 12

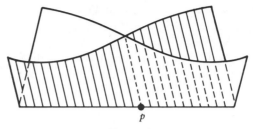

Figure 13

and in terms of Euclidean coordinates u_1, u_2, u_3 on $\mathbb{P}^3$,

$$\pi: (s,t) \mapsto ([2], [2], s + [2]).$$

We can then find Euclidean coordinates u, v, w on $\mathbb{P}^3$ such that (after a change in the coordinate s)

$$\pi: (s,t) \mapsto (st + [3], t^2 + [3], s + [3]).$$

A local defining equation for S will then have the form

(∗) $$f(u,v,w) = u^2 - vw^2 + [4].$$

C is thus given near p by

$$C = (u + [2] = w + [2] = 0);$$

we see that both C and $\tilde{C}$ are smooth near p and p', and that p' is a branch point of the map $\pi: \tilde{C} \to C$. The picture is this (Figure 13): at any point $q \neq p \in C$ near p, the two branches of S—corresponding to the two points of $\tilde{C}$ lying over q—meet transversely; at p, these two branches come together. (Although we shall not need the fact, we can find holomorphic coordinates (s,t) on $\tilde{S}$ and (u,v,w) on $\mathbb{P}^3$ near p such that

$$\pi(s,t) = (st, t^2, s)$$

and correspondingly

$$S = (u^2 - vw^2).)$$

The local defining equations (∗) for the surface S given above are called the *normal forms* of the various singular points. A surface in general is said to have *ordinary singularities* if every singular point of S is one of the above types, i.e., if S can be given in a neighborhood of any point by one of the normal forms above.

Noether's Formula for General Surfaces

We have now at our disposal all the tools necessary to prove Noether's formula along the lines suggested earlier. Given any algebraic surface S, embed S in $\mathbb{P}^5$ and choose a generic projection

$$\varphi : S \longrightarrow S_0 \subset \mathbb{P}^3$$

mapping S onto a surface $S_0 \subset \mathbb{P}^3$ of degree n having ordinary singularities. Let $p_1,\ldots,p_t$ be the triple points of S_0, $C_1,\ldots,C_u$ the irreducible components of the double curve C of S_0, and d_i and g_i the degree and genus of C_i, respectively; call $d = \sum d_i$ and $g = \sum g_i$ the degree and genus of C.

Our object is to compute both sides of Noether's formula for S in terms of the numbers n, d, g, u, and t. The first step is to describe a blow-up $X \xrightarrow{\pi} \mathbb{P}^3$ such that the proper transform of S_0 in X is smooth; because of the relatively simple nature of ordinary singularities, this is not difficult. To begin with, let

$$\pi_1 : Y \longrightarrow \mathbb{P}^3$$

be the blow-up of $\mathbb{P}^3$ at the triple points $p_1,\ldots,p_t$ of S_0, E_i the exceptional divisor over p_i. In a neighborhood of each exceptional divisor E_i, the proper transform S_1 of S will consist of three smooth sheets, intersecting pairwise in smooth arcs and intersecting $E_i \cong \mathbb{P}^2$ in three lines; the double curve of S_1 is the proper transform of C, that is, the three arcs comprising the pairwise intersections of the three components of S_1, as shown in Figure 14. Explicitly, suppose z_1, z_2, z_3 are local coordinates in an open set U around the triple point p such that S_0 is given in U as the locus $(z_1 z_2 z_3 = 0)$. $\pi^{-1}(U)$ is then covered by three open sets U_1, U_2, U_3, where U_i is the complement in $\pi_1^{-1}(U)$ of the proper transform of the coordinate hyperplane $(z_i = 0)$; and in terms of coordinates

$$z_i = z_i, \qquad z(i)_j = \frac{z_j}{z_i}, \qquad z(i)_k = \frac{z_k}{z_i}$$

on U_i, we see that

$$\pi_1^{-1}(S_0) = (z_i \cdot z_i z(i)_j z_i z(i)_k = 0) \quad \text{omit}$$
$$= 3E_i + (z(i)_j = 0) + (\bar{z}(i)_k = 0)$$

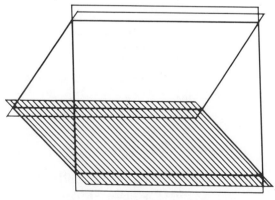

Figure 14

i.e., $S_1 \cap U_i$ consists of the proper transforms of the two coordinate hyperplanes $(z_j = 0)$ and $z_k = 0$. The double curve $\tilde{C}$ of S_1 is the union of the arcs $(z(i)_j = z(i)_k = 0) \subset U_i$; in particular, we note that $\tilde{C}$ is smooth, and hence that all the irreducible components $\tilde{C}_i$ of $\tilde{C}$ are disjoint.

Next, we let

$$\pi_2 \colon X \longrightarrow Y$$

be the blow-up of Y along the double curve $\tilde{C} = \cup \tilde{C}_i$ of S_1, $\pi = \pi_2 \circ \pi_1$ the combined blow-up. Let F_i denote the exceptional divisor over $\tilde{C}_i$, $\tilde{S}$ the proper transform of S_1 in X, and E_i the inverse image of the exceptional divisor $E_i \subset Y$. Our first observation is that $\tilde{S}$ *is smooth in* X. Clearly this has to be checked at the inverse image of a point $p \in \tilde{C}$. If p is not a pinch point of S_1, then we may take coordinates z_1, z_2, z_3 on a neighborhood U of p in Y such that in U,

$$S_1 = (z_2 z_3 = 0), \qquad C = (z_2 = z_3 = 0).$$

The inverse image of U in X is covered by the complements U_2 and U_3 of the proper transforms of the coordinate hyperplanes $(z_2 = 0)$ and $(z_3 = 0)$. In U_2 we have coordinates

$$z_1 = z_1, \qquad z_2 = z_2, \qquad z(2)_3 = \frac{z_3}{z_2}$$

in terms of which $F = (z_2 = 0)$ and

$$\pi_2^{-1}(S_1) = (z_2 \cdot z_2 z(2)_3 = 0)$$
$$= 2F + (z(2)_3 = 0)$$

so $\tilde{S}$ is smooth in U_2; similarly in terms of coordinates

$$z_1 = z_1, \qquad z(3)_2 = \frac{z_2}{z_3}, \qquad z_3 = z_3$$

on U_3, we have

$$\pi_2^{-1}(S_1) = (z_3 \cdot z_3 \cdot z(3)_2 = 0)$$
$$= 2F + (z(3)_2 = 0)$$

so $\tilde{S}$ is smooth in U_3. Thus $\tilde{S}$ is smooth around $\pi_2^{-1}(p)$; indeed, we see that near p the intersection $\tilde{S} \cap F$ is just the two sections of the bundle $F \xrightarrow{\pi_2} \tilde{C}$ corresponding to the normal directions to $\tilde{C}$ in the two branches of S_1 around p.

If p is a pinch point of S_1, then we may choose coordinates z_1, z_2, z_3 in a neighborhood U of p such that

$$S_1 = (z_2^2 - z_1 z_3^2 = 0),$$
$$C = (z_2 = z_3 = 0).$$

With U_i, $\tilde{z}_i$, and $\tilde{z}(j)_i$ as above, then, we see that in U_2,

$$\pi_2^{-1}(S_1) = (z_2 - z_1 \cdot z_2^2 z(2)_3^2 = 0)$$
$$= 2F + (1 - z_1 z(2)_3^2 = 0)$$

i.e., $\tilde{S}$ intersects each fiber $z_1 = c$ of F (except for $z=0$) in the two points $\tilde{z}(2)_3 = \pm \sqrt{1/c}$, and in particular $\tilde{S}$ is smooth. In U_3,

$$\pi_2^{-1}(S_1) = \left(z_3^2 z^1(3)_2^2 - z_1 z_3^2 = 0\right)$$
$$= 2F + \left(z(3)_2^2 - z_1\right)$$

so $\tilde{S}$ intersects the fiber $z_1 = c$ of F in the two points $z(3)_2 = \pm \sqrt{c}$, and the fiber $z_1 = 0$ tangentially at the point $z(3)_2 = 0$, i.e., $\pi_2^{-1}(p)$ is just a branch point of the twofold cover $\pi_2 : \tilde{S} \cap F \to \tilde{C}$. Again, we see immediately that $\tilde{S}$ is smooth at $\pi^{-1}(p)$, and thus $\tilde{S}$ is everywhere smooth.

We obtain in this fashion a desingularization of any surface $S_0 \subset \mathbb{P}^3$ having only ordinary singularities. Note that in case S_0 is the image under a generic projection of a smooth surface $S \subset \mathbb{P}^5$, the surface $\tilde{S}$ is not the surface S: the identity map

$$\tilde{S} - \pi^{-1}(C) \longrightarrow S - \varphi^{-1}(C)$$

extends to an isomorphism

$$\tilde{S} - \pi^{-1}(\{p_1,\ldots,p_t\}) \longrightarrow S - \varphi^{-1}(\{p_1,\ldots,p_t\})$$

and then to a holomorphic map $\tilde{S} \to S$ blowing down the curves $\tilde{S} \cap E$ lying over $p_1,\ldots,p_t$; i.e., $\tilde{S}$ is the blow-up of S at the $3t$ points $\varphi^{-1}(\{p_1,\ldots,p_t\})$. We will see later that if $S_0 \subset \mathbb{P}^3$ is any surface with ordinary singularities and $\tilde{S}$ is proper transform in the blow-up X of $\mathbb{P}^3$ as constructed above, then the curves of $\tilde{S} \cap E$ are all exceptional of the first kind. If we blow down these curves, we obtain a *minimal desingularization* of S_0, that is, a surface S mapping holomorphically to $S_0 \subset \mathbb{P}^3$ which cannot be blown down to another smooth surface mapping holomorphically to S_0.

One point to be made here is that while the particularly simple nature of ordinary singularities allows us to remove them by only two blow-ups, any singularity may be eventually resolved by this process, i.e.,

Theorem (Resolution of Singularities). *Given any variety* $V \subset \mathbb{P}^n$, *there exists a blow-up* $\tilde{\mathbb{P}}^n \to \mathbb{P}^n$ *such that the proper transform of* V *in* X *is smooth.*

The proof of this theorem, due to Hironaka (cf. p. 453 for the reference), is far beyond the scope of this book.

The next step is to compute the cohomology ring of X, at least in even dimensions. To start, the cohomology ring $H^*(Y)$ is easily expressed: if $E_1,\ldots,E_t$ are the exceptional divisors of $Y \xrightarrow{\pi} \mathbb{P}^3$, L_i a line in $E_i \cong \mathbb{P}^2$, then we have

$$H^2(Y) = \pi^* H^2(\mathbb{P}^3) \oplus \mathbb{C}\{E_1,\ldots,E_t\}$$
$$= \mathbb{C}\{H, E_1,\ldots,E_t\}$$

and likewise

$$H^4(Y) = \mathbb{C}\{H^2, L_1,\ldots,L_t\}.$$

Clearly $H \cdot E_i = E_j \cdot E_i = 0$ for $i \neq j$; and since the restriction $[E_i]|_{E_i} \cong [-L_i]$, $E_i \cdot E_i = -L_i$. In complementary dimensions, then,

$$H \cdot H^2 = 1, \qquad H \cdot L_i = 0,$$
$$E_i \cdot H^2 = 0, \qquad E_i \cdot L_j = -\delta_{ij}.$$

By our formulas,

$$c_1(Y) = \pi_1^* c_1(\mathbb{P}^3) - 2\sum E_i$$
$$= 4H - 2\sum E_i$$

and $c_2(Y) = \pi^* c_2(\mathbb{P}^3) = 6H^2$.

To find the class of $\tilde{C}_i$ in $H^4(Y)$, let τ_{ij} be the number of branches of C at p_j belonging to $\tilde{C}_i$. (Note that $\sum_i \tau_{ij} = 3$ for all j, and so $\sum_{i,j} \tau_{ij} = 3t$.) Then

$$\tilde{C}_i \cdot H = d_i, \qquad \tilde{C}_i \cdot E_j = \tau_{ij},$$

and accordingly

$$\tilde{C}_i \sim d_i \cdot H^2 - \sum \tau_{ij} L_j.$$

In particular, we have

$$c_1(N_{\tilde{C}_i/Y}) = c_1(T_Y)|_{\tilde{C}_i} - c_1(T_{\tilde{C}_i})$$
$$= 4d_i - 2\sum_j \tau_{ij} + 2g_i - 2.$$

We proceed now to X. Letting F_i denote as before the exceptional divisor of the blow-up $\pi_2 : X \to Y$ over $\tilde{C}_i$, M_i a fiber of the bundle $\pi_2 : F_i \to \tilde{C}_i$ and E_j and L_j the inverse images of E_j and L_j in Y, we see that

$$H^2(X) = \mathbb{C}\{H, E_1, \ldots, E_t, F_1, \ldots, F_u\}$$

and

$$H^4(X) = \mathbb{C}\{H^2, L_1, \ldots, L_t, M_1, \ldots, M_u\}.$$

The intersection pairing in complementary dimensions is readily determined; we note first that as before

$$H \cdot H^2 = 1, \quad H \cdot L_i = 0, \quad E_i \cdot L_j = -\delta_{ij}, \quad E_i \cdot H^2 = 0,$$

and similarly

$$H \cdot M_i = E_j \cdot M_i = H^2 \cdot F_i = F_i \cdot L_j = 0,$$

since in each case the cycles can clearly be made disjoint. Lastly, since $[F_i]|_{F_i}$ is just the tautological bundle on $F_i = \mathbb{P}(N_{\tilde{C}_i/Y})$

$$F_i \cdot M_j = -\delta_{ij}.$$

In the pairing $H^2(X) \times H^2(X) \to H^4(X)$, the relations

$$H \cdot E_i = 0, \qquad E_i \cdot E_j = -\delta_{ij} L_j$$

are immediate. Since a hyperplane in $\mathbb{P}^3$ will meet C_i in d_i points, its inverse image in X will intersect the exceptional divisor F_i in d_i fibers, i.e.,

$$H \cdot F_i = d_i M_i;$$

and likewise $\tilde{E}_j$ will intersect F_i in the fibers of F_i over the points of intersection $\tilde{C}_i \cap E_j$, so

$$E_j \cdot F_i = \tau_{ij} M_i.$$

Finally, since the class $[F_i]|_{F_i}$ is the class ξ of the tautological bundle on $F_i \cong \mathbb{P}(N_{\tilde{C}_i/Y}) \overset{\pi_2}{\to} \tilde{C}_i$ and by our relation

$$\begin{aligned}
0 &= \xi^2 - \xi \cdot \pi_2^* c_1(N_{\tilde{C}_i/Y}) \\
&= F_i^2|_{F_i} - F_i|_{F_i} \cdot c_1(N_{\tilde{C}_i/Y}) \cdot M_i \\
&= F_i^2|_{F_i} + 4d_i + 2g_i - 2 - 2\sum_j \tau_{ij}
\end{aligned}$$

we have

$$F_i^3 = -\left(4d_i + 2g_i - 2 - 2\sum_j \tau_{ij}\right).$$

This, together with the products

$$F_i^2 \cdot H = F_i \cdot (F_i \cdot H) = F_i \cdot d_i M_i = -d_i$$

and

$$F_i^2 \cdot E_j = F_i (F_i \cdot E_j) = F_i \cdot \tau_{ij} M_i = -\tau_{ij}$$

yield the formula

$$F_i^2 = -d_i H^2 + \left(4d_i + 2g_i - 2 - 2\sum_j \tau_{ij}\right) M_i + \sum_j \tau_{ij} L_j.$$

In sum, then, the intersection form on $H^{2*}(X)$ is given by the multiplication tables

	H	E_i	F_i
H^2	1	0	0
L_j	0	$-\delta_{ij}$	0
M_j	0	0	$-\delta_{ij}$

	H	E_j	F_i
H	H^2	0	$d_i M_i$
E_k		$-\delta_{jk} L_j$	$\tau_{ij} M_i$
F_k			$\delta_{ij}(-d_i H^2 + \sum_j \tau_{ij} L_j$ $+ (4d_i + 2g_i - 2 - 2\sum_j \tau_{ij}) M_i)$

Note that the class of $\tilde{S}$ is $nH - 3\sum E_j - 2\sum F_i$, so that

$$\tilde{S} \cdot H^2 = n, \qquad \tilde{S} \cdot L_j = 3, \quad \text{and} \quad \tilde{S} \cdot M_i = 2.$$

Now, to compute $c_1^2(S)$ and $c_2(S)$ we have only to apply the adjunction formulas (*) and (**) of p. 601. First,

$$c_1(X) = \pi_2^* c_1(Y) - \sum F_i$$
$$= 4H - 2\sum E_j - \sum F_i$$

so

$$c_1(\tilde{S}) = \left(c_1(T_X) - (\tilde{S})\right)\big|_{\tilde{S}}$$
$$= -(n-4)H + \sum E_j + \sum F_i$$

and

$$c_1^2(\tilde{S}) = \tilde{S}\Bigg[(n-4)^2 H^2 - 2(n-4)\sum d_i M_i - \sum L_i$$

$$+ 2\sum_{i,j} \tau_{ij} M_i - \sum d_i H^2$$

$$+ \sum_i \left(4d_i + 2g_i - 2 - 2\sum_j \tau_{ij}\right) M_i + \sum_{i,j} \tau_{ij} L_j\Bigg]$$

$$= n(n-4)^2 - 4(n-4)d - 3t + 12t - nd + 8d$$
$$\quad + 4g - 4u - 12t + 9t$$

$$= n(n-4)^2 - 5nd + 24d + 4g - 4u + 6t.$$

Since $\tilde{S}$ is the blow-up of S at $3t$ points, then,

$$c_1^2(S) = c_1(\tilde{S}) + 3t = n(n-4)^2 - 5nd + 24d + 4g - 4u + 9t.$$

Next, we have

$$c_2(X) = \pi_2^*\left(c_2(Y) + \sum \tilde{C}_i\right) - \pi_2^* c_1(Y)\cdot \sum F_i$$
$$= (d+6)H^2 - \sum_i \left(4d_i - 2\sum_j \tau_{ij}\right) M_i - 2\sum_{i,j} \tau_{ij} L_j,$$

hence

$$c_2(\tilde{S}) = \left(c_2(T_X) - c_1(\tilde{S})\cdot \tilde{S}\right)\big|_{\tilde{S}}$$

$$= \tilde{S}\cdot\Bigg[(d+6)H^2 - \sum_i \left(4d_i - 2\sum_j \tau_{ij}\right) M_i - 2\sum_{i,j} \tau_{ij} L_j$$

$$+ n(n-4)H^2 - n\sum d_i M_i - 3\sum_j L_j - 2(n-4)\sum d_i M_i$$

$$+ 5\sum_{i,j} \tau_{ij} M_i - 2\sum d_i H^2 + 2\sum_{i,j} \tau_{ij} L_j$$

$$+ 2\sum_i \left(4d_i + 2g_i - 2 - 2\sum_j \tau_{ij}\right) M_i\Bigg]$$

$$= n(d+6) - 8d + 12t - 9t - 4(n-4)d + n^2(n-4)$$
$$\quad - 2dn - 9t + 30t - 2nd + 18t + 16d + 8g - 8u - 24t$$

and

$$c_2(S) = c_2(\tilde{S}) - 3t$$
$$= n^2(n-4) + 6n + 24d - 7nd + 8g - 8u + 15t.$$

Thus, in sum,

$$\frac{c_1^2(S) + c_2(S)}{12} = \frac{(n-1)(n-2)(n-3)}{6} - (n-4)d + g - u + 2t + 1.$$

To prove Noether's formula we have now to express the holomorphic Euler characteristic $\chi(\mathcal{O}_S) = \chi(\mathcal{O}_{\tilde{S}})$ also in terms of n, d, g, u, and t. To begin with, by the Poincaré residue sequence for $\tilde{S} \subset X$

$$0 \longrightarrow \Omega_X^3 \longrightarrow \Omega_X^3(\tilde{S}) \longrightarrow \Omega_{\tilde{S}}^2 \longrightarrow 0$$

we see that

$$\chi(\mathcal{O}_{\tilde{S}}) = \chi(\Omega_{\tilde{S}}^2) = \chi(\Omega^3(\tilde{S})) - \chi(\Omega_X^3) = \chi(\Omega_X^3(\tilde{S})) + 1$$

since $\chi(\Omega_X^3) = \chi(\Omega_{\mathbb{P}^3}^3) = -1$. To evaluate the holomorphic Euler characteristic

$$\chi(\Omega_X^3(\tilde{S})) = \chi(\mathcal{O}_X(K_X + \tilde{S}))$$
$$= \chi\left(\mathcal{O}_X\left((n-4)H - \sum E_j - \sum F_i\right)\right)$$

we use a succession of restriction maps. First, we consider the sequence

$$0 \to \mathcal{O}_X\left((n-4)H - \sum E_j - \sum F_i\right) \to \mathcal{O}_X\left((n-4)H - \sum E_j\right)$$
$$\to \bigoplus_i \mathcal{O}_{F_i}\left(\left((n-4)H - \sum E_j\right)\right) \to 0.$$

To find the Euler characteristic of the last term, we use Riemann-Roch for line bundles on F_i: the divisor $((n-4)H - \sum E_j)|_{F_i}$ is just the sum of $d_i(n-4) - \sum_j \tau_{ij}$ fibers of the ruled surface $F_i \xrightarrow{\pi_2} \tilde{C}_i$; since the fibers have self-intersection 0 and intersection number -2 with K_{F_i},

$$\chi\left(\mathcal{O}_{F_i}\left((n-4)H - \sum E_j\right)\right) = \chi(\mathcal{O}_{F_i}) + d_i(n-4) - \sum_j \tau_{ij}$$
$$= 2 - 2g_i + d_i(n-4) - \sum_j \tau_{ij}.$$

Thus

$$\chi\left(\bigoplus_i \mathcal{O}_{F_i}\left((n-4)H - \sum E_j\right)\right) = u - g + d(n-4) + 3t$$

and

$$\chi(\mathcal{O}_S) = \chi\left(\mathcal{O}_X\left((n-4)H - \sum E_j\right)\right) - d(n-4) + g - u + 3t + 1.$$

Next, from the sequence

$$0 \to \mathcal{O}_X((n-4)H - \sum_j E_j(\to \mathcal{O}_X(n-4)H) \to \bigoplus_j \mathcal{O}_{E_j}((n-4)H) \to 0$$

$$\|$$

$$\bigoplus_j \mathcal{O}_{E_j}$$

we see that

$$\chi\big(\mathcal{O}_X\big((n-4)H - \sum E_j\big)\big) = \chi(\mathcal{O}_X((n-4)H)) - \chi(\oplus \mathcal{O}_{E_j})$$
$$= \chi(\mathcal{O}_X((n-4)H)) - t$$

and hence

$$\chi(\mathcal{O}_{\tilde{S}}) = \chi(\mathcal{O}_X((n-4)H)) - d(n-4) + g - u + 2t + 1.$$

Finally, to evaluate $\chi(\mathcal{O}_X((n-4)H))$, in case $n \geqslant 4$ we let $T \subset \mathbb{P}^3$ be a smooth surface of degree $n-4$ missing $p_1, \ldots, p_t$ and meeting each curve C_i transversely; we let $\tilde{T} \subset X$ be its inverse image and consider the sequence

$$0 \longrightarrow \mathcal{O}_X \longrightarrow \mathcal{O}_X((n-4)H) \longrightarrow \mathcal{O}_{\tilde{T}}((n-4)H) \longrightarrow 0.$$

On $\tilde{T}$, we have $((n-4)H)^2 = (n-4)H \cdot K_{\tilde{T}}$, and by Riemann-Roch,

$$\chi(\mathcal{O}_{\tilde{T}}((n-4)H)) = \chi(\mathcal{O}_{\tilde{T}}) = \chi(\mathcal{O}_T) = \frac{(n-1)(n-2)(n-3)}{6} + 1$$

so

$$\chi(\mathcal{O}_X((n-4)H)) = \frac{(n-1)(n-2)(n-3)}{6}.$$

In case $n = 1$, 2, or 3, we let T instead be a surface of degree $4-n$ in $\mathbb{P}^3$, and from the sequence

$$0 \longrightarrow \mathcal{O}_X((n-4)H) \longrightarrow \mathcal{O}_X \longrightarrow \mathcal{O}_{\tilde{T}} \longrightarrow 0$$

we deduce again that

$$\chi(\mathcal{O}_X((n-4)H)) = 1 - \chi(\mathcal{O}_{\tilde{T}})$$
$$= 0$$
$$= \frac{(n-1)(n-2)(n-3)}{6}.$$

Thus, in either case, we have

$$\chi(\mathcal{O}_{\tilde{S}}) = \chi(\mathcal{O}_{\tilde{S}})$$
$$= \frac{(n-1)(n-2)(n-3)}{6} - d(n-4) + g - u + 2t + 1$$

and Noether's formula is proved.

It should be noted that neither the geometric genus or the irregularity of the surface S appears by itself in the above formulas. The fact is that while, as we shall see, we can usually determine $p_g(S)$ and $q(S)$ for any given surface $S \subset \mathbb{P}^3$, these invariants are not determined by the numbers n, d_i, g_i, u, and t.

To find the geometric genus of a surface $S \to S_0 \subset \mathbb{P}^3$ as given above, we return to the Poincaré residue sequence on the desingularization $\tilde{S} \subset X$:

$$0 \longrightarrow \Omega_X^3 \longrightarrow \Omega_X^3(\tilde{S}) \longrightarrow \Omega_{\tilde{S}}^2 \longrightarrow 0.$$

Since X is rational,

$$h^0(X, \Omega_X^3) = 0 \quad \text{and} \quad h^1(X, \Omega_X^3) = h^0(X, \Omega_X^2) = 0$$

so

$$\begin{aligned}
p_g(S) &= h^0(X, \Omega_X^3(\tilde{S})) \\
&= h^0\left(X, \mathcal{O}_X\left((n-4)H - \sum E_j - \sum F_i\right)\right).
\end{aligned}$$

Now, any section of the line bundle $(n-4)H$ on $\mathbb{P}^3$ vanishing along the curve C gives a section of $(n-4)H - \sum E_j - \sum F_i$ on X, and conversely by Hartogs' theorem any section $\sigma \in H^0(X, \mathcal{O}_X((n-4)H - \sum E_j - \sum F_i))$ is the pullback of a section of $(n-4)H$ on $\mathbb{P}^3$ vanishing on C. Thus,

The canonical series $|K_S|$ of S is cut out by surfaces of degree n-4 in $\mathbb{P}^3$ containing the curve C;

and we may express $p_g(S)$ accordingly: setting $|E| = \pi^*|\mathcal{O}_{\mathbb{P}^3}((n-4)H)| \subset |\mathcal{O}_{\tilde{C}}(\pi^*(n-4)H)|$,

The geometric genus $p_g(S)$ is the number $\binom{n-1}{3}$ of surfaces of degree n-4 in $\mathbb{P}^3$, less the vector space dimension of the linear system $|E|$ they cut out on $\tilde{C}$.

Comparing this with our previous formula for the Euler characteristic $\chi(\mathcal{O}_S) = p_g(S) - q(S) + 1$, we obtain a particularly simple expression for $q(S)$: we have

$$\begin{aligned}
q(S) &= p_g(S) - \chi(\mathcal{O}_{\tilde{S}}) + 1 \\
&= \binom{n-1}{3} - \dim|E| - \binom{n-1}{3} \\
&\quad + d(n-4) - g + u - 2t \\
&= \sum_{i=1}^{u} (d_i(n-4) - g_i + 1) - \dim|E| \\
&= h^0(\tilde{C}, \mathcal{O}_{\tilde{C}}((n-4)H)) - \dim|E| \\
&\quad - h^1(\tilde{C}, \mathcal{O}_{\tilde{C}}((n-4)H)) - 2t.
\end{aligned}$$

The difference of the first two terms represents the failure of the linear system $|E|$ to be complete; it is called the *deficiency* of the system $|E|$. In these terms we have

The irregularity q(S) *is the deficiency minus the index of speciality of the linear system* $|E|$ *cut out on* $\tilde{C}$ *by surfaces of degree* $n-4$ *in* $\mathbb{P}^3$, *less twice the number of triple points.*

A final point to be made in this context is that the number b of pinch points of a surface $S_0 \subset \mathbb{P}^3$ as given above is determined by the data n, d, g, u, and t: if $D_i \subset S$ is the inverse image of the curve $\tilde{C}_i \subset S_1$, then the number b_i of pinch points of S_0 along C_i is just the number of branch points of the two-sheeted covering map $\pi_2 : D_i \to \tilde{C}_i$, and by Riemann-Hurwitz and adjunction this number is

$$b_i = (2g(D_i)-2) - (2g_i-2)$$
$$= D_i \cdot K_{\tilde{S}} + D_i \cdot D_i - 4g_i + 4.$$

But we have seen that

$$K_{\tilde{S}} = \left((n-4)H - \sum E_j - \sum F_i\right)\big|_{\tilde{S}}$$
$$= \left((n-4)H - \sum E_j\right)\big|_{\tilde{S}} - \sum D_i$$

so

$$D_i \cdot (K_{\tilde{S}} + D_i) = 2(n-4)d_i - 2\sum_j \tau_{ij}$$

and

$$b_i = 2(n-4)d_i - 2\sum_j \tau_{ij} - 4g_i + 4.$$

The total number of pinch points on S is thus

$$b = 2d(n-4) - 6t - 4g + 4u.$$

Some Examples

We consider now some examples of irreducible surfaces $S_0 \subset \mathbb{P}^3$ with ordinary singularities. In each case we will let $S \xrightarrow{\pi} S_0$ be the minimal desingularization of S_0, $C \subset S_0$ the double curve of S_0, and $D \subset S$ its inverse image in S, and take n, d, g, u, and t as above.

To begin with, suppose S_0 is a cubic surface. Inasmuch as the generic plane section $H \cdot S_0$ of S_0 is then an irreducible plane cubic curve singular at the d points of $H \cdot C$, we see that $d \leq 1$, i.e., C can be at most a line. Supposing that C is a line, it follows immediately that S is a rational ruled surface: the pencil $\{H_\lambda\}$ of planes in $\mathbb{P}^3$ containing C cuts out on S a pencil $\{L_\lambda\}$ of lines. In terms of the basis $\{E_0, L_\lambda\}$ for $S \cong S_n$, we can write the class of a hyperplane on S as

$$H = aE_0 + bL_\lambda;$$

since $H \cdot L_\lambda = 1$, $a = 1$ and then from

$$3 = H \cdot H = (E_0 + bL_\lambda)^2 = n + 2b$$

it follows that $n = 1$, $H = E_0 + L_\lambda$, and $D = H - L_\lambda = E_0$. Now, we have seen that the complete linear system $|E_0 + L_\lambda|$ embeds the ruled surface S_1 as the Steiner surface $S_{1,1} \subset \mathbb{P}^4$; thus

A cubic surface $S_0 \subset \mathbb{P}^3$ with a double line is the projection of the Steiner surface $S_{1,1} \subset \mathbb{P}^4$.

Conversely, any Steiner surface $S \cong S_{1,1} \subset \mathbb{P}^4$ may be realized as the union of lines joining points on a line $D_\infty \subset \mathbb{P}^4$ to corresponding points on a conic D_0 in a complementary 2-plane $W \subset \mathbb{P}^4$; and it is not hard to see that the projection π_p of $S_{1,1}$ from a point $p \in W - D_0$ is one-to-one away from D_0 and maps D_0 two-to-one onto a line. Since any irreducible curve in the two-dimensional system $|E_0|$ may be chosen as D_0 in this construction, any point $p \in \mathbb{P}^4 - S_{1,1}$ lies in the 2-plane spanned by such a curve, and hence

The image of a Steiner surface $S_{1,1} \subset \mathbb{P}^4$ under projection from any point $p \in \mathbb{P}^4 - S_{1,1}$ is a cubic surface with a double line.

We turn now to quartic surfaces S_0. Note first that since the generic plane section of S_0 is an irreducible quartic with $d = \deg(C)$ singularities, we must have $d \leqslant 3$. Also, any line meeting C three times meets S_0 six times and so lies in S_0; and we accordingly eliminate the possibility of C being the union of three disjoint lines—as the reader may easily verify, the locus of lines in $\mathbb{P}^3$ meeting each of three skew lines is a quadric surface. The remaining possibilities are:

1. C a line,
2. C a smooth plane conic,
3. C the union of two skew lines,
4. C a rational normal curve,
5. C the union of three lines meeting at a point.

Note that in all these cases

$$K_S = -D < 0$$

so that $P_m(S)=0$ for all m; in cases 1, 2, 4, and 5 we see as well that $q(S)=0$, and hence S is rational. By cases, then,

2.   C *is a smooth plane conic.* By our formula,

$$c_2(S) = n^2(n-4) + 24d - 7nd + 6n + 8g - 8u + 15t$$
$$= 0 + 48 - 56 + 24 + 0 - 8 + 0$$
$$= 8$$

so S must be a ruled surface blown up four times, or $\mathbb{P}^2$ blown up five times; since

$$K_S = -D = -H$$

is strictly negative, no curve can have self-intersection less than -1; it follows as usual that *S is* $\mathbb{P}^2$ *blown up in five general points,* no three collinear. We see in addition that each of the five exceptional divisors $E_1,\ldots,E_5$ must meet $D=-K_S$ once; thus if $\iota:S\to\mathbb{P}^2$ is the blowing-up map, the image $\iota(D)$ must be a curve of self-intersection

$$D\cdot D + 5 = 9,$$

containing all five blown-up points, i.e.,

$$H = \iota^*3H - E_1 - \cdots - E_5.$$

But we have seen that the linear system $|\iota^*3H - E_1 - \cdots - E_5|$ embeds S in $\mathbb{P}^4$ as the intersection of two quadrics; thus

a quartic S with a double conic is the projection into $\mathbb{P}^3$ *of the intersection of two quadrics in* $\mathbb{P}^4$.

3.   C *is two disjoint lines* C_1 *and* C_2. Since $H^0(\mathbb{P}^3, \mathcal{O}_{\mathbb{P}^3}((n-4)H)) = h^0(\mathbb{P}^3, \mathcal{O}_{\mathbb{P}^3})=1$ while $h^0(C,\mathcal{O})=h^0(C_1,\mathcal{O})+h^0(C_2,\mathcal{O})=2$, and neither $\mathcal{O}_{C_1}$ nor $\mathcal{O}_{C_2}$ is special, we see that $q(S)=1$; thus S is birationally ruled over an elliptic curve. Indeed, by our formula $c_2(S)=0$, so S is ruled. We can locate the ruling: the pencil $\{H_\lambda\}$ of hyperplanes through C_1 cuts out on S a pencil of conics $\{C_\lambda\}$ which, being singular at the points $H_\lambda \cap C_2$, must all consist of two lines L_λ, L_λ'. Since the pencil $\{C_\lambda\}$ has no base points on S, moreover, the lines L_λ, L_λ' are disjoint there—one passes through each of the points of S lying over the point $H_\lambda \cap C_2$. The curves D_1 and D_2 are thus sections of the ruled surface S.

The reader may find it an amusing exercise to show that the surface S_0 may be realized in two other ways: either as the union of the lines corresponding to the intersection of the Grassmannian $G(2,4)\subset\mathbb{P}^5$ of lines in $\mathbb{P}^3$ with a generic quadric surface $Q\subset\mathbb{P}^3\subset\mathbb{P}^5$; or as the union of the lines joining corresponding points on two skew lines C_1 and C_2 in $\mathbb{P}^3$, under a correspondence of bidegree $(2,2)$ between C_1 and C_2.

4.   C *is a rational normal curve.* S *is* now regular, hence rational; and since by the formula (∗)

$$c_2(S) = 4,$$

we see that S is a rational ruled surface. To see the ruling, let Q be a generic element of the net N of quadrics through C; Q intersects S in a curve of type $(4,4)$—that is, homologous to a sum of four lines from each family—and since a rational normal curve has type $(1,2)$ on Q, the residual intersection of Q with S is of type $(4,4) - 2(1,2) = (2,0)$—that is, the sum of two lines, L, L', each meeting C twice. Since any quadric $Q \in N$ containing a third point of L' contains L', we have a pencil of quadrics $\{Q_\lambda\}$ containing L'; the residual intersection of $\{Q_\lambda\}$ with S will then be a pencil $\{L_\lambda\}$ of lines.

Now, consider the divisor $D - H$ on S. By our formulas

$$D \cdot D = K \cdot K = 8$$

and since

$$H \cdot D = 6$$

we see that

$$
\begin{aligned}
h^0(D - H) &\geqslant \frac{(D - H)(D - H - K)}{2} + 1 \\
&= \frac{(D - h)(2D - h)}{2} + 1 \\
&= \frac{16 - 18 + 4}{2} + 1 \\
&= 2
\end{aligned}
$$

i.e., $D - H$ moves in at least a pencil. Since

$$(D - H)^2 = 8 - 12 + 4 = 0$$

and

$$(D \cdot H) \cdot L_\lambda = \tfrac{1}{2}(D - H)(2H - D) = 1,$$

we see that the curves in $|D - H|$ form a second ruling of S transverse to the first; thus $S \cong \mathbb{P}^1 \times \mathbb{P}^1$ with L_λ and $E = D - H$ the fibers. Finally, we have

$$
\begin{aligned}
H &= (D - H) + (2H - D) \\
&= E + 2L_\lambda,
\end{aligned}
$$

so we see that the complete linear system $|H|$ embeds $S \cong \mathbb{P}^1 \times \mathbb{P}^1$ as the rational normal scroll $S_{2,0} \subset \mathbb{P}^5$; so

a quartic surface S_0 *double along a rational normal curve is a projection of the surface* $S_{2,0} \subset \mathbb{P}^5$.

5.   C *consists of three lines* C_1, C_2, C_3 *meeting in a point* p. This is the easiest case: we have by our formulas

$$\chi(\mathcal{O}_S) = 1,$$

hence $q(S)=0$ and S is rational. But now

$$c_2(S) = 3$$

and so $S \cong \mathbb{P}^2$. Since the degree of S_0 is four, S_0 is a projection of the Veronese surface $S \subset \mathbb{P}^5$.

Conversely, we can see that the projection of the Veronese surface $S \subset \mathbb{P}^5$ from a generic line $L \subset \mathbb{P}^5$ is such a quartic: we have seen that the chordal variety of the Veronese is equal to the union of the 2-planes spanned by the conic curves (i.e., the images in S of lines in $\mathbb{P}^2$) on S, and that this is a cubic hypersurface in $\mathbb{P}^5$. L then meets this cubic hypersurface in three points; i.e., there are exactly three conics in S whose 2-planes intersect L and under the projection these three conics are mapped two-to-one onto double lines of the image S_0.

We leave it to the reader to show that a quartic surface with a double line is the image of $\mathbb{P}^2$ blown up at nine points under the map given by the system of quartics double at one point and passing through the other eight.

Our last example is perhaps the most interesting. We found, in the previous section, two ways of representing an Enriques surface: as the quotient of a K-3 surface by a fixed-point-free involution, or as an elliptic surface with rational base, having two double fibers. We can now give, in addition, a projective realization of an Enriques surface, as follows. (See Figure 15.) Let T be a tetrahedron in $\mathbb{P}^3$ with vertices p_1, p_2, p_3, p_4, edges $l_{ij} = \overline{p_i p_j}$, and faces $H_{ijk} = \overline{p_i p_j p_k}$, and let $S \subset \mathbb{P}^3$ be a surface of degree 6 with ordinary singularities whose double curve is exactly the sum of the six lines l_{ij}.

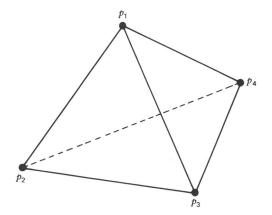

Figure 15

Now if $\tilde{S} \xrightarrow{\pi} S \subset \mathbb{P}^3$ is the desingularization of $\tilde{S}$, $\tilde{l}_{ij} = \pi^{-1}l_{ij}$, then we have

$$K_{\tilde{S}} = \pi^*(2H) - \sum \tilde{l}_{ij},$$

i.e., the canonical series on $\tilde{S}$ is cut out by surfaces of degree 2 in $\mathbb{P}^3$ passing simply through the edges of T. But any quadric containing the lines l_{ij}, l_{jk}, and l_{ik} contains the plane H_{ijk}, so there are no such quadrics; thus

$$p_g(\tilde{S}) = 0.$$

On the other hand, twice the canonical series

$$2K_{\tilde{S}} = \pi^*(4H) - 2\sum \tilde{l}_{ij}$$

is cut out by quartic surfaces in $\mathbb{P}^3$ passing doubly through the edges of T. There is one such quartic: namely the sum

$$Q = \sum H_{ijk}$$

of the four faces of T. Moreover, each plane H_{ijk} meets S in the sextic curve $2l_{ij} + 2l_{jk} + 2l_{ik}$ and nowhere else; thus Q meets S only along the lines l_{ij}, and so the bundle $2K_{\tilde{S}}$ is trivial.

Now, note that the desingularization $\tilde{C}$ of the double curve $C = \sum l_{ij}$ of S consists of six disjoint rational curves; so that the system $|E|$ of p. 627 is nonspecial and has deficiency

$$h^0(\tilde{C}, \mathcal{O}(2)) - 10 = 3 \cdot 6 - 10 = 8.$$

The irregularity of $\tilde{S}$ is thus

$$q(\tilde{S}) = 8 - 2t = 0$$

'and hence $\tilde{S}$ is an Enriques surface.

We can realize a canonical divisor of $\tilde{S}$ explicitly as follows: let Q be the quadric

$$H_{ijk} + H_{ijl}$$

consisting of two faces of T. Then Q passes doubly through the common line l_{ij} of the two faces, simply through the edges l_{ik}, l_{il}, l_{jk}, and l_{jl} and not at all through the edge l_{kl}. Since the canonical curve of $\tilde{S}$ is $\pi^*2H - \sum \tilde{l}_{ij}$, then, we see that

$$K_{\tilde{S}} = \tilde{l}_{ij} - \tilde{l}_{kl},$$

i.e., *the canonical divisor on $\tilde{S}$ is the difference of the inverse images of any two opposite edges of* T.

Now, in a previous discussion we showed that an Enriques surface $\tilde{S}$ can be represented as an elliptic surface with rational base, having two double fibers. Indeed, if $\tilde{S}$ is given as a sextic $S \to S$ in $\mathbb{P}^3$ double along the edges of a tetrahedron, we can find three elliptic pencils on S directly: take two disjoint edges l_{ij}, l_{kl} of T and consider the linear system of quadrics in $\mathbb{P}^3$ passing through the remaining four edges $l_{ik}, l_{il}, l_{jk}, l_{jl}$ of T. To see that there is at least a pencil $\{Q_\lambda\}$ of such quadrics, choose arbitrary points $q_1 \in l_{ik}$, $q_2 \in l_{il}$, $q_3 \in l_{jk}$, and $q_4 \in l_{jl}$ distinct from the vertices of T; any quadratic containing the four vertices $\{p_i\}$ of T and the four points $\{q_i\}$ will then have three points in common with each of the edges $l_{ik}, l_{il}, l_{jk}, l_{jl}$ and so will contain them. Since the linear system of quadrics in $\mathbb{P}^3$ is nine-dimensional, there will be at least a $9 - 8 = 1$-dimensional family $\{Q_\lambda\}$ of such quadrics. (Conversely, since the four lines comprise the complete intersection of any two quadrics containing them, there can be no more than a pencil of such quadrics.)

Note that the pencil $\{Q_\lambda\}$ will contain exactly two reducible quadrics: $Q_0 = H_{ilk} + H_{jlk}$ and $Q_1 = H_{ijk} + H_{ijl}$. Every other quadric in the pencil will be smooth, inasmuch as it contains, for example, the two disjoint lines l_{ik} and l_{jl}, whereas we have seen that every two lines on an irreducible singular quadric in $\mathbb{P}^3$ meet.

Now write

$$Q_\lambda \cdot S = 2l_{ik} + 2l_{il} + 2l_{jk} + 2l_{jl} + C_\lambda.$$

Consider the pencil $\{C_\lambda\}$ of curves on $\tilde{S}$ and their inverse images $\tilde{C}_\lambda = \pi^* C_\lambda$ in $\tilde{S}$. We note that

$$\tilde{C}_\lambda \cdot \tilde{C}_\lambda = 0,$$

since in particular

$$C_0 = 4l_{kl} \quad \text{and} \quad C_1 = 4l_{ij}$$

and their inverse images

$$\tilde{C}_0 = 2\tilde{l}_{kl} \quad \text{and} \quad \tilde{C}_1 = 2\tilde{l}_{ij}$$

are disjoint. Since $\tilde{S}$ is an Enriques surface, $K \cdot \tilde{C}_\lambda = 0$; so

$$\pi(\tilde{C}_\lambda) = \frac{\tilde{C}_\lambda \cdot \tilde{C}_\lambda}{2} + 1 = 1,$$

and by Bertini the generic $\tilde{C}_\lambda$ is smooth. *The surface $\tilde{S}$ is thus an elliptic surface via the map*

$$\Psi : \tilde{S} \longrightarrow \mathbb{P}^1$$

given by the pencil $\{C_\lambda\}$; *the two multiple fibers are* $2\tilde{l}_{ij}$ *and* $2\tilde{l}_{kl}$. Note that if $L = [p]$ is the line bundle associated to a point $p \in \mathbb{P}^1$, by our formula

$$K_{\tilde{S}} = -\Psi^* L + \tilde{l}_{ij} + \tilde{l}_{kl} = \tilde{l}_{ij} - \tilde{l}_{kl},$$

since $2\tilde{l}_{k,l} = \Psi^* L$; this agrees with our previous computation.

Finally, while we will not prove that every Enriques surface can be realized as a sextic in $\mathbb{P}^3$, we can suggest this fact by counting parameters for sextics in $\mathbb{P}^3$ double along the edges of a tetrahedron T. To begin with, we may take the vertices of T to be the coordinate points $p_1 = [1,0,0,0]$, $p_2 = [0,1,0,0]$, $p_3 = [0,0,1,0]$, and $p_4 = [0,0,0,1]$. The requirement that a sextic $S \subset \mathbb{P}^3$, given as the locus of a polynomial $f(X_0, \ldots, X_3)$, be double along the edges of T is simply that its intersection with each face $H_{jkl} = (X_i = 0)$ of T be the double triangle

$$2l_{jk} + 2l_{jl} + 2l_{kl};$$

e.g., that

$$f(0, X_1, X_2, X_3) = \lambda_0 \cdot X_1^2 X_2^2 X_3^2,$$

$$f(X_0, 0, X_2, X_3) = \lambda_1 \cdot X_0^2 X_2^2 X_3^2,$$

and so on. Every term in f other than the four terms $X_j^2 X_k^2 X_l^2$ must thus contain the factor $X_0 X_1 X_2 X_3$, and so we can write

$$f(X_0, X_1, X_2, X_3)$$

$$= \lambda_0 X_1^2 X_2^2 X_3^2 + \lambda_1 X_0^2 X_2^2 X_3^2 + \lambda_2 X_0^2 X_1^2 X_3^2 + \lambda_3 X_0^2 X_1^2 X_2^2 + Q(X) \cdot X_0 X_1 X_2 X_3,$$

where $\lambda_0, \ldots, \lambda_3 \in \mathbb{C}$ and $Q(X)$ is some homogeneous quadratic polynomial in $X_0, \ldots, X_3$. Conversely, since the sextics in $\mathbb{P}^3$ given by polynomials f of this type form a linear system without base locus except along the edges of T, for generic Q the locus of f is an Enriques surface.

Now the group of automorphisms of $\mathbb{P}^3$ fixing the tetrahedron T is generated by the permutations

$$[X_0, \ldots, X_3] \mapsto [X_{\sigma(0)}, \ldots, X_{\sigma(3)}]$$

of the coordinates, plus the diagonal maps

$$[X_0, \ldots, X_3] \mapsto [\mu_0 X_0, \ldots, \mu_3 X_3].$$

There is, thus, up to a permutation $\sigma \in \Sigma_4$, a unique automorphism of $\mathbb{P}^3$ carrying any sextic double along the edges of a tetrahedron into the locus of

$$g(X_0, X_1, X_2, X_3)$$

$$= X_1^2 X_2^2 X_3^2 + X_0^2 X_2^2 X_3^2 + X_0^2 X_1^2 X_3^2 + X_0^2 X_1^2 X_2^2 + Q(X) \cdot X_0 X_1 X_2 X_3.$$

We see from this that the family of such sextics, up to projective isomorphism, has dimension $H^0(\mathbb{P}^3, \mathcal{O}(2H)) = 10$. This is, of course, the dimension of the family of Enriques surfaces as we computed in the previous section; since the family of Enriques surfaces is irreducible and any Enriques surface—having irregularity 0—has only countably many divisor classes, hence at most countably many representations as a sextic in $\mathbb{P}^3$, this tells us that the generic Enriques surface may be realized as a sextic in $\mathbb{P}^3$, double along the edges of a tetrahedron.

Isolated Singularities of Surfaces

Thus far we have dealt only with surfaces in $\mathbb{P}^3$ having positive-dimensional singular locus, for the simple reason that these are the only singularities that necessarily arise from a projection of a smooth surface. Isolated singularities of surfaces are ubiquitous in other contexts, however, and we would be remiss if we did not mention them. Since the general theory is far too complex for our present purposes, we will give here a few examples of surfaces with ordinary isolated double points.

To begin with, if S is a surface lying on a smooth threefold X and $p \in S$ is an isolated point of multiplicity m on S, then the tangent cone to S at p will be a curve of degree m (counting multiplicity) in $\mathbb{P}(T_p(X)) \cong \mathbb{P}^2$; we say that p is an *ordinary* m-fold point of S if the tangent cone is smooth with multiplicity 1. We consider first the simplest possible case, that of an ordinary double point $p \in S$; to avoid complication, assume for the time being that S is smooth away from p. We construct the desingularization of S as follows: choose local coordinates x,y,z on a neighborhood U of p in X so that the defining function $f(x,y,z)$ of S has the form

$$f(x,y,z) = x^2 + y^2 + z^2 + [3].$$

Let $\tilde{X} \xrightarrow{\pi} X$ be the blow-up of X at p. As per Section 5 of Chapter 1, we may take as local coordinates on the complement U_1 in $\pi^{-1}(U)$ of the closure of $\pi^*(x=0, (y,z)\neq 0)$ the functions

$$x_1 = x, \qquad y_1 = \frac{y}{x}, \qquad z_1 = \frac{z}{x};$$

on $U_2 = \pi^{-1}(U) - \overline{\pi^{-1}(y=0, (x,z)\neq 0)}$ the functions

$$x_2 = \frac{x}{y}, \qquad y_2 = y, \qquad z_2 = \frac{z}{y}$$

and on $U_3 = \pi^{-1}(U) - \overline{\pi^{-1}(z=0, (x,y)\neq 0)}$,

$$x_3 = \frac{x}{z}, \qquad y_3 = \frac{y}{z}, \qquad z_3 = z.$$

We have, then,

$$\begin{aligned}
x &= x_1 = x_2 y_2 = x_3 z_3, \\
y &= x_1 y_1 = y_2 = y_3 z_3, \\
z &= x_1 z_1 = y_2 z_2 = z_3.
\end{aligned}$$

In U_1 we have

$$\begin{aligned}
\pi^{-1}(S) = (\pi^* f) &= x_1^2 + x_1^2 y_1^2 + x_1^2 z_1^2 + [x_1^3] \\
&= (x_1^2)(1 + y_1^2 + z_1^2 + [x_1]),
\end{aligned}$$

and so the proper transform $\tilde{S}$ of S is given by

$$\tilde{S} = \pi^{-1}(S) - 2E = \left(1 + y_1^2 + z_1^2 + [x_1]\right),$$

where $E = (x_1)$ is the exceptional divisor of the blow-up; clearly $\tilde{S}$ is smooth over p. Likewise, in U_2, $E = (y_2)$ and we have

$$\begin{aligned} \pi^{-1}(S) &= (\pi^*f) \\ &= x_2^2 y_2^2 + y_2^2 + y_2^2 z_2^2 + [y_2^3] \\ &= (y_2^2)(x_2^2 + 1 + z_2^2 + [y_2]), \end{aligned}$$

so $\tilde{S} = (x_2^2 + 1 + z_2^2 + [y_2])$, which is smooth in the locus $y_2 = 0$; and similarly we check that $\tilde{S}$ is smooth in $U_3 \cap E$. Since by hypothesis S is smooth away from p, $\tilde{S}$ is everywhere smooth, and the map $\pi: \tilde{S} \to S$ is the desingularization of S. Note that the inverse image of p in $\tilde{S}$ is the smooth conic curve C given, in terms of Euclidean coordinates y_1, z_1 on $E \cong \mathbb{P}^2$, by

$$1 + y_1^2 + z_1^2 = 0.$$

Now we can compute the canonical bundle of $\tilde{S}$ readily: recalling from Section 5 of Chapter 1 that

$$K_{\tilde{X}} = \pi^* K_X + 2E$$

and

$$\tilde{S} \sim \pi^* S - 2E,$$

we see that

$$\begin{aligned} K_{\tilde{S}} &= \left(K_{\tilde{X}} + \tilde{S}\right)\big|_{\tilde{S}} \\ &= \pi^*(K_X + S), \end{aligned}$$

i.e., the canonical divisor on $\tilde{S}$ is cut out by the linear system $|K_X + S|$ on X, just as for a smooth surface S' of the same class as S on X; in particular,

$$c_1^2(\tilde{S}) = c_1^2(S').$$

Indeed, writing out the Poincaré residue sequence

$$0 \longrightarrow \Omega_X^3 \longrightarrow \Omega_X^3(S) \longrightarrow \Omega_{\tilde{S}}^2 \longrightarrow 0,$$

we see that the codimension in $|K_S|$ of the series cut out by $|K_X + S|$ is the dimension of the kernel of the map $H^1(X, \Omega_X^3) \to H^1(X, \Omega_X^3(S))$, just as it is for S'; thus we have also

$$p_g(\tilde{S}) = p_g(S').$$

Now, since $K_{\tilde{S}} = \pi^*(K_X + S)$,

$$K_{\tilde{S}} \cdot C = 0.$$

By the adjunction formula, then,

$$C \cdot C = -2.$$

Alternatively, another way to find the self-intersection of C is to write

$$\begin{aligned}(C \cdot C)_{\tilde{S}} &= (E \cdot E \cdot \tilde{S})_X \\ &= (E \cdot E \cdot (\pi^* S - 2E))_{\tilde{X}} \\ &= -2(E \cdot E \cdot E)_{\tilde{X}};\end{aligned}$$

since $[E]|_E$ is the dual of the hyperplane bundle H on $E \cong \mathbb{P}^2$, we have

$$(E \cdot E \cdot E)_{\tilde{X}} = (-H \cdot -H)_E = 1,$$

and so $C \cdot C = -2$.

To find $\chi(\mathcal{O}_{\tilde{S}})$ we consider the exact sequence of sheaves

$$0 \longrightarrow \mathcal{O}_X(-S) \longrightarrow \mathcal{I}_{p,X} \xrightarrow{\pi^*} \mathcal{O}_{\tilde{S}}(-E) \longrightarrow 0;$$

we have

$$\chi(\mathcal{O}_{\tilde{S}}(-E)) = \chi(\mathcal{O}_{\tilde{S}}) + \frac{E \cdot E + K \cdot E}{2} = \chi(\mathcal{O}_{\tilde{S}}) - 1,$$

and from the exact sequence

$$0 \longrightarrow \mathcal{I}_{p,X} \longrightarrow \mathcal{O}_X \longrightarrow \mathbb{C}_p \longrightarrow 0$$

we see that

$$\chi(\mathcal{I}_{p,X}) = \chi(\mathcal{O}_X) - 1.$$

It follows that

$$\chi(\mathcal{O}_{\tilde{S}}) = \chi(\mathcal{O}_X) - \chi(\mathcal{O}_X(-S)),$$

which, we see from the analogous exact sequence

$$0 \longrightarrow \mathcal{O}_X(-S') \longrightarrow \mathcal{O}_X \longrightarrow \mathcal{O}_{S'} \longrightarrow 0,$$

is just the holomorphic Euler characteristic of a smooth surface $S' \subset X$ of the same class as S. Since $p_g(\tilde{S}) = p_g(S)$, it follows that $q(\tilde{S}) = q(S)$; from $c_1^2(\tilde{S}) = c_1^2(S)$ and Riemann-Roch, it follows that $c_2(\tilde{S}) = c_2(S)$. In sum, then,

> *The desingularization $\tilde{S}$ of a surface $S \subset X$ with an ordinary double point p is the proper transform of S in the blow-up of $\mathbb{P}^3$ at p; the inverse image of p in $\tilde{S}$ is a smooth rational curve of self-intersection -2, and all the invariants q, χ, and $|K|$ of $\tilde{S}$ are the same as those of a smooth surface of the same class on X.*

One generalization of this case is straightforward: if p is an ordinary singular point of multiplicity m on $S \subset X$, then the proper transform $\tilde{S}$ of S

in the blow-up of X at p will always be smooth. The invariants of $\tilde{S}$—while not in general equal to those of a smooth surface, equivalent to S as above —are then relatively easy to find. For example, since

$$\tilde{S} \sim \pi^* S - mE,$$

we see that

$$K_{\tilde{S}} = (\pi^* K_X - (m-2)E)|_{\tilde{S}},$$

i.e., the canonical divisor on $\tilde{S}$ is cut out by surfaces in the series $|K_X + S|$ on X containing p with multiplicity $m-2$. Likewise, we see that the inverse image $C = \tilde{S} \cap E \subset \tilde{S}$ of p is a smooth plane curve of degree m in $E \cong \mathbb{P}^2$, having self-intersection $-m$ in $\tilde{S}$, and so on.

Of course, in general the proper transform $\tilde{S}$ of a surface $S \subset X$ in the blow-up of X at a singular point p of S may still be singular at a point over p, necessitating further blow-ups. Consider, for example, a couple of nonordinary double points, both having as their tangent cone two distinct lines:

$$S_1 = (x^2 + y^2 + z^3 + [4] = 0)$$

and

$$S_2 = (x^2 + y^2 + z^4 + [5] = 0).$$

Taking $\tilde{X} \xrightarrow{\pi} X$ the blow-up of X at $p = (0,0,0)$ with open sets U_i and coordinate systems (x_i, y_i, z_i) as above, the proper transform $\tilde{S}_1$ of S_1 in $\tilde{X}$ is given as

$$\begin{aligned}
\left(1 + y_1^2 + [x_1]\right) && \text{in } U_1, \\
\left(1 + x_2^2 + [y_2]\right) && \text{in } U_2,
\end{aligned}$$

and

$$\left(x_3^2 + y_3^2 + [z_3]\right) \qquad \text{in } U_3.$$

We see than that $\tilde{S}_1$ is smooth, with $C = \pi^{-1}(p)$ the pair of rational curves C_1 and C_2, given in U_1, U_2, and U_3 by

$$C_1 = (y_1 = i, x_1 = 0) = (x_2 = -i, y_2 = 0) = (y_3 = ix_3, z_3 = 0)$$

and

$$C_2 = (y_1 = -i, x_1 = 0) = (x_2 = i, y_2 = 0) = (y_3 = -ix_3, z_3 = 0),$$

respectively, each having self-intersection -2 and meeting in the point $y_3 = x_3 = z_3 = 0$, as in Figure 16. The proper transform $\tilde{S}_2$ of S_2, however, is given by

$$\begin{aligned}
\left(1 + y_1^2 + x_1^2 z_1^4 + [x_1^3]\right) && \text{in } U_1, \\
\left(x_2^2 + 1 + y_2^2 z_2^4 + [y_2^3]\right) && \text{in } U_2,
\end{aligned}$$

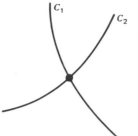

Figure 16

and

$$\left(x_3^2+y_3^2+z_3^2+\left[z_3^3\right]\right) \qquad \text{in } U_3.$$

Once again, the inverse image $\pi^{-1}(p)$ in $\tilde{S}_2$ is the two curves C_1 and C_2, but this time their point $p'=(x_3=y_3=z_3=0)$ of intersection is an ordinary double point of $\tilde{S}_2$. If we let $\tilde{\tilde{X}}\xrightarrow{\pi'}\tilde{X}$ be the blow-up of $\tilde{X}$ at p', then the proper transform $\tilde{\tilde{S}}_2$ of $\tilde{S}_2$ will be smooth, and $\tilde{\tilde{S}}_2\to S_2$ the desingularizationof S_2. The inverse image $(\pi\circ\pi')^{-1}(p)$ of p in $\tilde{S}_2$ will thus consist of three curves: the proper transforms $\tilde{C}_1$ and $\tilde{C}_2$ of C_1 and C_2 and the inverse image $C_3=\pi'^{-1}(p')$, forming the configuration shown in Figure 17.

To see how isolated singularities affect the geometry of surfaces in projective space, we consider a cubic surface S in $\mathbb{P}^3$ having δ isolated double points. By what we have said, the arguments of Section 4 of this chapter apply here to show that the desingularization $\tilde{S}$ of S is $\mathbb{P}^2$ blown up at six points $\{p_i\}$; since $\tilde{S}$ will contain δ rational curves of self-intersection -2, however, it is no longer true that the points p_i are necessarily distinct (i.e., some p_i may lie on the exceptional divisor of the blow-up of $\mathbb{P}^2$ at p_j), or that they are in general position.

Suppose first that S has exactly one ordinary double point p; let $\tilde{D}$ be its inverse image in $\tilde{S}$, and $D=\pi(\tilde{D})$ the image of $\tilde{D}$ under the blowing-down map $\pi:\tilde{S}\to\mathbb{P}^2$. There are then three possibilities:

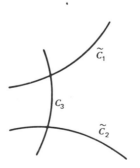

Figure 17

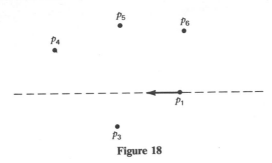

Figure 18

1. $\deg D = 0$, i.e., $\tilde{D}$ is an exceptional divisor. Since $\tilde{D}$ is the only curve of self-intersection < -1 on $\tilde{S}$, this can occur in only one way (see Figure 18): if the points $p_1, p_3, \ldots, p_6$ are all distinct, p_2 is a point on the exceptional divisor E_1 of the blow-up $\tilde{\mathbb{P}}^2$ of $\mathbb{P}^2$ at p_1, and $\tilde{D}$ is the proper transform of E_1 under the blow-up of $\tilde{\mathbb{P}}^2$ at p_2. Also no three of the points $p_1, p_3, \ldots, p_6$ may be collinear, as this would give rise to a second curve of self-intersection -2 on $\tilde{S}$; likewise, if v is the tangent direction to p_1 specified by p_2, then the line through p_1 in the direction v contains none of the points $p_3, \ldots, p_6$, and no conic containing $p_3, \ldots, p_6$ passes through p_1 with tangent v. We can count the number of lines on the surface $S \subset \mathbb{P}^3$: since the map $\tilde{S} \to \mathbb{P}^3$ is given by the inverse canonical series $|-K_S|$, the lines on S are, as before, the rational curves of self-intersection -1 on $\tilde{S}$: namely, the five exceptional divisors $E_2, E_3, \ldots, E_6$, the ten lines $\{L_{ij}\}_{i,j \neq 2}$ plus the line L_{12} through p_1 in the direction v specified by p_2, the four conics $\{C_i\}_{i \neq 1,2}$ passing through the points $p_1, p_3, \ldots, \hat{p}_i, \ldots, p_6$ and having tangent line v at p_1, and the conic C_2 passing through $p_1, p_3, \ldots, p_6$. We have thus a total of 21 lines.

2. $\deg D = 1$. In this case (Figure 19) exactly three of the points p_i—say p_1, p_2, and p_3—lie on the line D_1; apart from that, the points $\{p_i\}$ are in general position. Again, we have 21 lines on S: the six exceptional divisors $E_1, \ldots, E_6$, the 12 lines $\{L_{ij}\}$ for i,j not both in $\{1,2,3\}$, and the three conics $\{C_i\}_{i=1,2,3}$.

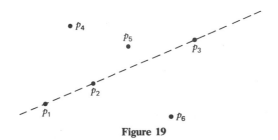

Figure 19

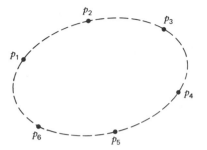

Figure 20

3. $\deg D = 2$. In this case (Figure 20) all the points p_i lie on the conic D and are otherwise in general position. Once more we have 21 lines on S: the six exceptional divisors E_i and the 15 lines L_{ij}.

The same argument as given for the smooth cubic surface shows that $\deg D \leqslant 2$, so these are the only possibilities.

Note, finally, that any S may be realized as any one of these types: in case 1, the six lines $\{L_{1j}\}_{j=2,\ldots,6}$, C_2, and E_2 are disjoint and may be blown down to obtain $\mathbb{P}^2$; the image of the exceptional divisor E_1 is then a conic curve containing all six image points (this blowing-down amounts to projection of S_q from the double point). Likewise, the exceptional divisors E_2, C_2, L_{13}, and $\{L_{3j}\}_{j=4,5,6}$ are all disjoint and may be blown down; under this map to $\mathbb{P}^2$ E_1 maps a line containing the image points of E_2, C_2, and L_{13}.

A cubic surface S with two double points may be obtained by blowing up a configuration as shown in Figure 21; the lines $\overline{p_2 p_3 p_4}$ and $\overline{p_2 p_5 p_6}$ become the double points. Such a surface will have 16 lines: the six exceptional divisors, the lines $\{L_{1j}\}_{j=2,\ldots,6}$ and $\{L_{35}, L_{36}, L_{45}, L_{46}\}$, and the conic C_2. Note that apart from the one line E_2 joining the two double points, there will be four lines on S through each of the double points: for example, through the image of $\overline{p_2 p_3 p_4}$ pass E_3, E_4, L_{15}, and L_{16}.

Of course, the desingularization $\tilde{S}$ of a cubic surface S with two double points may also be realized as the blow-up of $\mathbb{P}^2$ at other configurations of points (for example, projection of S from either of its two double points expresses $\tilde{S}$ as the blow-up of $\mathbb{P}^2$ at five points $p_1, \ldots, p_5$, blown up again at the point of the exceptional divisor E_5 corresponding to the tangent line at p_5 to the conic through $p_1, \ldots, p_5$). The reader may, as an exercise, find all such configurations and then show that they are all equivalent, i.e., that by blowing down a suitable collection of six disjoint lines every cubic with two double points may be realized as $\mathbb{P}^2$ blown up in any of these configurations. (For example, if the surface $\tilde{S}$ is a priori the blow-up described above, we may blow down the exceptional divisors E_1, E_2, $\tilde{L}_{34}$,

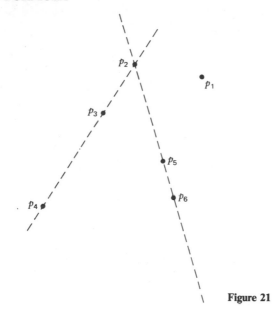

Figure 21

$\tilde{L}_{45}$, $\tilde{L}_{35}$, and E_6 to express $\tilde{S}$ as $\mathbb{P}^2$ blown up in the configuration of Figure 21, with p_1, p_2, $\overline{p_2 p_3 p_4}$, and $\overline{p_2 p_5 p_6}$ the images of $\tilde{L}_{34}$, E_6, C_6, and E_5, respectively.) Note one configuration that does not work: in the blow-up $\tilde{S}$ of $\mathbb{P}^2$ at the points $p_1, \ldots, p_6$ shown in Figure 22 the proper transforms of the lines $\overline{p_1 p_2 p_3}$ and $\overline{p_4 p_5 p_6}$ meet, and under the map of $\tilde{S}$ to $\mathbb{P}^3$ given by $|-K_{\tilde{S}}|$ they will blow down to form a single nonordinary double point, of the same type as S_1 in the example of p. 639.

A cubic with three double points may be obtained by blowing up the points $p_1, \ldots, p_6$ as shown in Figure 23; the proper transforms of the lines $\overline{L_{123}}$, $\overline{L_{345}}$, and $\overline{L_{156}}$ will map down to the double points. We have in this case 12 lines: $E_1, \ldots, E_6$, L_{24}, L_{25}', L_{26}, L_{41}, L_{46}, and L_{56}.

Note that, apart from the three lines E_1, E_3, E_5 forming the edges of the triangle with vertices at the double points of S, there will be just two lines through each of these double points (e.g., E_2 and L_{46} pass through the image of L_{123}).

To obtain a cubic with four double points, we specialize still further to the configuration of Figure 24. Here we have nine lines: again, the six E_i, plus the three lines L_{24}, L_{15}, and L_{36}. Note that the lines E_i form the edges of the tetrahedron whose vertices are the double points of $S \subset \mathbb{P}^3$, while the lines L_{24}, L_{15}, and L_{36} form a triangle of lines joining opposite edges of the tetrahedron, disjoint from the double points. (See Figure 25.)

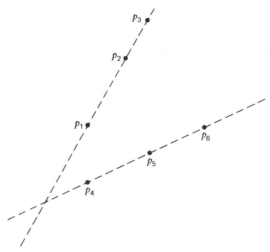

Figure 22

Finally, we note that a cubic surface S cannot contain more than four isolated singularities. To see this, suppose S had five double points $P_1, \ldots, P_5$. (See Figure 26.) Then all the lines $L_{ij} = \overline{P_i P_j}$ lie on S, from which it follows that no four of the points P_i are coplanar: if they were, the plane containing them would have six lines in common with the cubic S and so would necessarily lie in S. Now the points $P_1, \ldots, P_4$ form the vertices of a

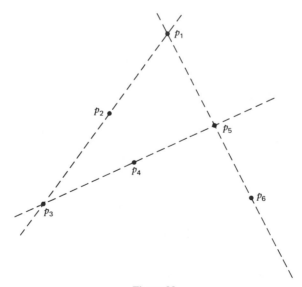

Figure 23

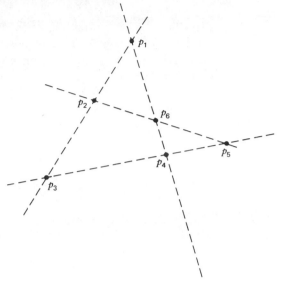

Figure 24

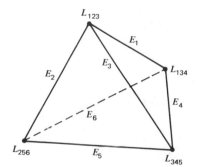

Figure 25

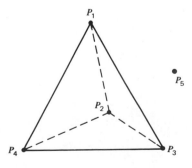

Figure 26

645

tetrahedron T all of whose edges lie on S, and each face of the tetrahedron will meet S in exactly the three edges lying on it. The line $\overline{P_4 P_5}$ must therefore meet the face $\overline{P_1 P_2 P_3}$ at a point on one of the lines $\overline{P_1 P_2}$, $\overline{P_2 P_3}$, or $\overline{P_1 P_3}$—this implies that P_5 lies on one of the faces of T containing P_4, a contradiction.

REFERENCES

General References

As in the case of curves, the literature is vast. Two sources are especially helpful:

O. Zariski, *Algebraic Surfaces*, 2nd ed., Springer-Verlag, Berlin-Heidelberg-New York. 1971. Contains a summary of the classical theory and an extensive bibliography that has recently been updated.

E. Bombieri and D. Husemuller, Classification and embeddings of surfaces, *Proc. Symposia in Pure Math.*, Vol. 29, American Math. Society, Providence, 1975, pp. 329–420. This paper provides a survey of, and bibliographical guide to, the recent literature.

Further general references are:

F. Enriques, *Le superficie algebriche*, Zanichelli, Bologna, 1949.

F. Conforto, *Le superficie razionali*, Zanichelli, Bologna, 1939.

And, as mentioned in the introduction,

S. Lefschetz, *L'analysis situs et la géométrie algébrique*, selected papers, Chelsea, N.Y., 1971.

5

RESIDUES

Thus far in this book most of the methods we have developed for studying algebraic varieties have centered around the divisors—especially the linear systems—that lie on the variety. Not only does this technique generally suffice for obtaining a deep understanding of curves and surfaces, but it also entails a minimal amount of analytic and algebraic machinery. On the other hand, many of the outstanding questions in algebraic geometry are concerned with higher-dimensional varieties. Because of the Lefschetz theorems from Chapters 0 and 1, the "new"—i.e., not coming from a lower-dimensional subvariety—cohomology of a smooth n-dimensional algebraic variety M lies in $H^{[n/2]}(M)$, so that going to dimension $n \geqslant 3$ or studying subvarieties of codimension $k \geqslant 2$ are closely related, while divisors pertain to cohomology in degrees 1 and 2. So in this chapter we shall present a modest introduction to some of the methods for dealing with general higher-codimensional problems, both local and global, and in the last chapter we shall investigate a three-dimensional variety.

As in the divisorial case we will develop the theory around the concept of residue. The local residue, given by a variant of the n-variable Cauchy formula, has been present since the early days of several complex variables. It has recently come into focus in an algebraic context in connection with Grothendieck's general duality theorem, which in fact isolated the functorial aspects of the local analytic residue. The subsequent global residue theorem expresses the duality characteristic of a closed variety and should yield many specific applications.

In Section 1 we give an analytic definition of the residue as an integral. It may be alternatively interpreted as a cohomology class, and many of the various integral formulas in several complex variables are manifestations of this same class in different cohomology theories. We then proceed to derive its two most important local properties, the behavior of the residue under a change of variables and local duality theorem. Once the local residue has been properly understood, the global residue theorem turns out, not surprisingly, to be Stokes' theorem.

Next in Section 2 we give some applications of residues. The first two are to intersection numbers and finite holomorphic mappings. These are topics in local analytic geometry, and the use of residues affords an elegant method for studying them. Then we turn to applications of the global residue theorem in projective space. Here it is a kind of Lagrange interpolation formula in several variables, and it provides an amusing technique for studying configurations of points in $\mathbb{P}^2$ leading to several classical results in the theory of plane algebraic curves, including a discussion of the converse to the Bezout theorem.

In Section 3 some of the recent algebraic techniques are introduced. The discussion here is minimal and develops only those methods that will be applied to concrete geometric problems. Following a discussion of Ext, Tor, and Koszul complexes, a synthesis occurs when our analytically defined local residue reappears in a final intrinsic form, one that opens the way for globalization. Other standard applications of computations based on the Koszul complex include Hilbert's syzygy and Noether's "$AF + BG$" theorems.

Next, in this same section, coherent sheaves are introduced. In essentially the only violation of our principle of always proving the "hard" theorems used in the book, we discuss but do not prove the two main facts —Oka's lemma and the finite dimensionality of cohomology. In fact, these are not used in our study of any specific questions, but we felt it would be misleading in a book on algebraic geometry to leave such an important topic unmentioned.

As hinted above, in Section 4 we reap one dividend of the intrinsic understanding of residues when we arrive at a global duality theorem in functorial form. We only prove a special case of the most general duality statement—one that is at the opposite extreme from the Kodaira-Serre duality previously encountered and that suffices for our applications. The methods used will adapt to a more general context.

Our first application is a recent theorem of Carrell and Liebermann concerning vector fields with isolated zeros on compact Kähler manifolds. Following this we derive two "reciprocity formulas" which give methods for calculating the superabundance—or equivalently the measure of the failure to impose independent conditions on a linear system—of a configuration of points on an algebraic surface. Indeed, the second reciprocity formula deals with 0-dimensional schemes and not just points, and uses in an essential way the local and global duality theorems.

Finally we turn to a question, initiated by Schwarzenberger, of understanding the relation between points on a surface and rank-two vector bundles. This illustrates both the global duality theorem and original definition of "Ext" in terms of extensions. The end result is a generalization of the residue theorem to sections of vector bundles and subsequent interpretation of this as imposing necessary and sufficient Abel-type conditions on a configuration of points on a surface to be the zeros of a section of a rank-two vector bundle, perhaps helping to clarify those aspects of the fundamental correspondence between divisors and line bundles that will and will not generalize.

We would like to specifically thank Maurizio Cornalba and David Mumford for extremely valuable help in preparing this chapter.

1. ELEMENTARY PROPERTIES OF RESIDUES

Definition and Cohomological Interpretation

Let U be the ball $\{z \in \mathbb{C}^n : \|z\| < \varepsilon\}$ and $f_1, \ldots, f_n \in \mathcal{O}(\overline{U})$ functions holomorphic in a neighborhood of the closure $\overline{U}$ of U. Since we are interested in the local theory around the origin, we shall allow ourselves to decrease the radius ε as necessary. We assume that the $f_i(z)$ have the origin as isolated common zero, or equivalently that set-theoretically $f^{-1}(0) = \{0\}$, where $f = (f_1, \ldots, f_n)$. We set

$$D_i = (f_i) = \text{divisor of } f_i,$$
$$D = D_1 + \cdots + D_n,$$
$$U_i = U - D_i,$$
$$U^* = U - \{0\} = \bigcup_{i=1}^{n} U_i.$$

Note that $\underline{U} = \{U_i\}$ gives an open cover of the punctured ball U^*.

We shall be interested in residues associated to a meromorphic n-form

$$\omega = \frac{g(z)\,dz_1 \wedge \cdots \wedge dz_n}{f_1(z) \cdots f_n(z)} \qquad (g \in \mathcal{O}(\overline{U}))$$

having polar divisor D. The residue is a variant of the Cauchy integral in several variables, and is defined as follows: Let Γ be the real n-cycle defined by

$$\Gamma = \{z : |f_i(z)| = \varepsilon\}$$

and oriented by

$$d(\arg f_1) \wedge \cdots \wedge d(\arg f_n) \geq 0.$$

Then the *residue* is given by

$$\text{Res}_{\{0\}} \omega = \left(\frac{1}{2\pi\sqrt{-1}}\right)^n \int_{\Gamma} \omega.$$

Here are some elementary properties of the residue.

First, since $\omega \in H^0(U-D,\Omega^n)$ is holomorphic in $U-D$, the exterior derivative $d\omega=0$. Consequently, *the residue depends only on the homology class of* $\Gamma \in H_n(U-D,\mathbb{Z})$ *and the cohomology class* $[\omega] \in H^n_{DR}(U-D)$ *of* ω.

Second, *the residue is linear in* g *and alternating in the* f_i, the latter being due to the manner in which the cycle Γ has been oriented.

Third, we shall say that $f=(f_1,\dots,f_n)$ is *nondegenerate* in case the Jacobian determinant

$$\mathcal{J}_f(0) = \left| \frac{\partial(f_1,\dots,f_n)}{\partial(z_1,\dots,z_n)}(0) \right| \neq 0$$

is nonzero at the origin. Later on we shall see that the Jacobian is not identically zero. In the nondegenerate case we find that

$$\text{Res}_{\{0\}} = \frac{g(0)}{\mathcal{J}_f(0)}.$$

To prove this, consider the mapping $w=f(z)$, which by the inverse function theorem is biholomorphic in a neighborhood of the origin. Set

$$G(w) = g(f^{-1}(w)),$$

$$K(w) = \frac{dw_1}{w_1} \wedge \cdots \wedge \frac{dw_n}{w_n} \quad \text{(Cauchy kernel)},$$

and

$$\mathcal{J}_f(w) = \mathcal{J}_f(f^{-1}(w)).$$

Then

$$\omega = f^* \left(\frac{GK}{\mathcal{J}} \right),$$

and by change of variables in the integral and the usual Cauchy integral formula from Section 1 of Chapter 0,

$$\int_\Gamma \omega = \int_{|w_i|=\varepsilon} \frac{G(w)K(w)}{\mathcal{J}_f(w)} = (2\pi\sqrt{-1})^n \frac{G(0)}{\mathcal{J}_f(0)}.$$

Finally, we denote by $I(f)=f_1,\dots,f_n$ the ideal generated by the f_i's in the ring of germs of holomorphic functions around 0. Then:

$$\text{Res}_{\{0\}} \omega = 0 \quad \text{in case } g \in I(f).$$

To prove this, it suffices by linearity to consider the case $g=hf_1$. But then

$$\omega = \frac{h(z)\,dz_1 \wedge \cdots \wedge dz_n}{f_2(z)\cdots f_n(z)}$$

is holomorphic in the larger open set $U_{\{i\}^0}=U-(D_1+\cdots+\hat{D}_i+\cdots+D_n)$.

If Γ_i is the chain

$$\Gamma_i = \{z: \ |f_j(z)| = \varepsilon \text{ for } j \neq i, \ |f_i(z)| \leqslant \varepsilon\},$$

then $\Gamma_i \subset U_{(i)^\circ}$ and $\partial \Gamma_i = \pm \Gamma$. Hence $\int_\Gamma \omega = \pm \int_{\Gamma_i} d\omega = 0$ by Stokes' theorem.

We now give a sheaf-cohomological interpretation of the residue. To motivate this we note that, even though the meromorphic form ω has polar divisor $D_1 + \cdots + D_n$, it is the origin $\{0\} = D_1 \cap \cdots \cap D_n$ with which we are most concerned. To express this, we consider $\omega \in H^0(U_1 \cap \cdots \cap U_n, \Omega^n)$ as a Čech $(n-1)$-cochain for the sheaf Ω^n and covering $\underline{U} = \{U_i\}$ of U^*. Thus $\omega \in C^{n-1}(\underline{U}, \Omega^n)$, and since trivially $\delta \omega = 0$, we obtain a class in $H^{n-1}(U^*, \Omega^n)$. Denote by η_ω the image of $(1/2\pi\sqrt{-1})^n \omega$ under the Dolbeault isomorphism

$$H^{n-1}(U^*, \Omega^n) \cong H_{\bar{\partial}}^{n,n-1}(U^*).$$

Now, since $d = \bar{\partial}$ on forms of type (n,q), there is a natural mapping

$$H_{\bar{\partial}}^{n,n-1}(U^*) \to H_{\mathrm{DR}}^{2n-1}(U^*).$$

The punctured ball U^* is homotopically just the $2n-1$ sphere, and so the right side is $\mathbb{C}$ with the isomorphism given by

$$\eta \to \int_{S^{2n-1}} \eta,$$

the orientation on the sphere being induced from that in $\mathbb{C}^n$. We shall prove that

Lemma. $\operatorname{Res}_{\{0\}} \omega = \eta_\omega$, or equivalently

$$\left(\frac{1}{2\pi\sqrt{-1}}\right)^n \int_\Gamma \omega = \int_{S^{2n-1}} \eta_\omega.$$

Proof. Recall that the $\bar{\partial}$-Poincaré lemma gives exact sheaf sequences

$$0 \to \mathcal{Z}_{\bar{\partial}}^{n,n-p-1} \to \mathcal{Q}^{n,n-p-1} \xrightarrow{\bar{\partial}} \mathcal{Z}_{\bar{\partial}}^{n,n-p} \to 0,$$

where $\mathcal{Q}^{p,q}$ is the sheaf of $C^\infty(p,q)$ forms and $\mathcal{Z}_{\bar{\partial}}^{p,q} \subset \mathcal{Q}^{p,q}$ is the subsheaf of $\bar{\partial}$-closed forms. Since the sheaves $\mathcal{Q}^{p,q}$ have no higher cohomology, the Dolbeault isomorphism is a composition of isomorphisms

$$i_p: H^p\big(U^*, \mathcal{Z}_{\bar{\partial}}^{n,n-p-1}\big) \xrightarrow{\sim} H^{p-1}\big(U^*, \mathcal{Z}_{\bar{\partial}}^{n,n-p}\big)$$

obtained from coboundary maps in the exact cohomology sequence of the above sheaf sequence. For $p = 1$, the right-hand side is to be replaced by

$$H^0\big(U^*, \mathcal{Z}_{\bar{\partial}}^{n,n-1}\big) / \bar{\partial} H^0(U^*, \mathcal{Q}^{n,n-1}) = H_{\bar{\partial}}^{n,n-1}(U^*).$$

Now we may follow our cocycle ω through this sequence of isomorphisms. Beginning with

$$\omega_{n-1} = \left(\frac{1}{2\pi\sqrt{-1}}\right)^n \omega \in H^{n-1}(U^*, \mathcal{Z}_{\bar{\partial}}^{n,0}),$$

we let $U_I = \cup_{i \in I} U_i$ and

$$\omega_p = \{\omega_{p,I} \in \mathcal{Z}_{\bar{\partial}}^{n,n-p-1}(U_I)\}_{\#I=p}$$

denote a representative of

$$i_{p+1} \circ \cdots \circ i_{n-1}(\omega_{n-1});$$

and then let

$$\xi_p = \{\xi_{p,I} \in \mathcal{Q}^{n,n-p-1}(U_I)\}_{\#I=p}$$

be cochains such that

$$\delta\xi_p = \omega_p, \qquad \bar{\partial}\xi_p = \omega_{p-1}.$$

Next, let Γ_I be the chain defined by

$$\Gamma_I = \{z : |f_i(z)| = \varepsilon \text{ for } i \in I, |f_j(z)| \leqslant \varepsilon \text{ for } j \notin I\}$$

and with orientation

$$d(\arg f_{i_1}) \wedge \cdots \wedge d(\arg f_{i_p}) \wedge \left(\bigwedge_{j \notin I} \frac{\sqrt{-1}}{2} df_j \wedge \overline{df_j}\right) \geqslant 0,$$

where $I = \{i_1 < \cdots < i_p\}$. Then the boundary

$$\partial\Gamma_I = \sum_{j \notin I} (-1)^{(j,I-\{j\})} \Gamma_{I \cup \{j\}},$$

where $(j, I - \{j\})$ is the position from the rear of the index j when $I \cup \{j\}$ is ordered in the usual manner. Now, since $d\xi_I = \bar{\partial}\xi_I$, we may apply Stokes' theorem to obtain

$$
\begin{aligned}
\sum_{\#I=p} \int_{\Gamma_I} \omega_{p-1,I} &= \sum_{\#I=p} \int_{\Gamma_I} d\xi_{p,I} \\
&= \sum_{\#I=p} \int_{\partial\Gamma_I} \xi_{p,I} \\
&= \sum_{\#I=p} \left(\sum_{j \notin I} \int_{\Gamma_{I \cup \{j\}}} (-1)^{(j,I \cup \{j\})} \xi_{p,I}\right) \\
&= \sum_{\#J=p+1} \int_{\Gamma_J} (-1)^{(j,J)} \xi_{p,J-\{j\}} \\
&= \sum_{\#J=p+1} \int_{\Gamma_J} (\delta\xi_p)_J \\
&= \sum_{\#J=p+1} \int_{\Gamma_J} \omega_{p,J}
\end{aligned}
$$

by the combinatorial definition of δ. In summary, *the total sum*

$$\sum_{\#I=p+1} \int_{\Gamma_I} \omega_{p,I}$$

is the same for all p. At the two extremes $p = n-1$ and $p = 0$ we obtain

$$\left(\frac{1}{2\pi\sqrt{-1}}\right)^n \int_\Gamma \omega = \sum_{i\in I} \int_{\Gamma_i} \omega_{0,i}$$

$$= \sum_{i\in I} \int_{\Gamma_i} \eta_\omega, \qquad \text{since } \eta_\omega = \omega_{0,i} \text{ in } U_i,$$

$$= \int_{\partial,\Gamma_0} \eta_\omega, \qquad \text{where } \Gamma_0 = \{z: |f_1(z)| \leqslant \varepsilon, \ldots, |f_n(z)| \leqslant \varepsilon\},$$

$$= \int_{S^{2n-1}} \eta_\omega. \qquad\qquad\qquad\qquad \text{Q.E.D.}$$

We observe that this lemma does not use the assumption that ω is meromorphic in U with polar divisor D. Only $\omega \in H^0(U-D,\Omega^n)$ is required, so that ω could have a higher order pole or even an essential singularity along D. In case ω is meromorphic with polar divisor D, we may find a distinguished representative for the Dolbeault class η_ω as follows. Set

$$\rho_i = \frac{|f_i|^2}{|f_1|^2 + \cdots + |f_n|^2}$$

and observe that

$$\rho_i \text{ is } C^\infty \text{ in } U^*,$$

$$\sum_i \rho_i \equiv 1,$$

and

$$\operatorname{supp}(\rho_i) \subset U_i.$$

Thus $\{\rho_i\}$ looks something like a partition of unity for the covering $\{U_i\}$ of U^* and may be used as such for any ω having first-order poles on the D_i. Indeed, given

$$\omega = \frac{g(z)\,dz_1\wedge\cdots\wedge dz_n}{f_1(z)\cdots f_n(z)}, \qquad g(z)\in \mathcal{O}(U),$$

we see that

$$\rho_i\omega = \frac{\bar{f}_i g}{\|f\|^2}\cdot \frac{dz_1\wedge\cdots\wedge dz_n}{f_1\cdots\widehat{f}_i\cdots f_n} \in A^{n,0}(U_{\{i\}^0}),$$

so we can set

$$\xi_{\{i\}^0} = \pm\rho_i\omega, \qquad \omega_{\{i\}^0} = \pm\bar{\partial}\rho_i\omega.$$

Proceeding to the next step, for $j \neq i$,

$$\rho_j \omega_{\{i\}^0} \in A^{n,1}(U_{\{i,j\}^0}),$$

so we can set

$$\xi_{\{i,j\}^0} = \pm (\rho_i \omega_{\{j\}^0} - \rho_j \omega_{\{i\}^0}),$$
$$\omega_{\{i,j\}^0} = \pm 2 \bar{\partial} \rho_i \wedge \bar{\partial} \rho_j \wedge \omega.$$

Continuing, we finally arrive at

$$\eta_\omega = \omega_{\{i\}} = n!(-1)^{i-1} \bar{\partial} \rho_1 \wedge \cdots \wedge \widehat{\bar{\partial} \rho_i} \wedge \cdots \wedge \bar{\partial} \rho_n \wedge \omega$$

$$= \frac{n!(-1)^{i-1} g \bar{\partial} \rho_1 \wedge \cdots \wedge \widehat{\bar{\partial} \rho_i} \wedge \cdots \wedge \bar{\partial} \rho_n \wedge dz_1 \wedge \cdots \wedge dz_n}{f_1 \cdots f_n}.$$

But, setting $f = (f_1, \ldots, f_n)$ and $\|f\|^2 = \Sigma_i |f_i|^2$,

$$\bar{\partial} \rho_i = \frac{f_i \, d\bar{f}_i}{\|f\|^2} - \frac{|f_i|^2 \Sigma_j f_j \, d\bar{f}_j}{\|f\|^4},$$

and so the wedge product

$$\bigwedge_{j \neq i} \bar{\partial} \rho_j = \frac{\left(\bigwedge_{j \neq i} f_j \, d\bar{f}_j \right)}{\|f\|^{2n-2}} - \frac{\sum_{k \neq i} (-1)^{(k,\{i\}^0)} \left(\bigwedge_{j \neq i,k} f_j \, d\bar{f}_j \right) \Sigma_l f_l \, d\bar{f}_l |f_k|^2}{\|f\|^{2n}}$$

$$= \frac{1}{\|f\|^{2n}} \left(\|f\|^2 \bigwedge_{j \neq i} f_j \, d\bar{f}_j - \sum_{k \neq i} |f_k|^2 \left(\bigwedge_{j \neq i} f_j \, d\bar{f}_j \right) \right.$$

$$\left. - |f_k|^2 \sum_{k \neq i} (-1)^{k-i-1} \bigwedge_{j \neq k} f_j \, d\bar{f}_j \right)$$

$$= \frac{1}{\|f\|^{2n}} \left(|f_i|^2 \bigwedge_{j \neq i} f_j \, d\bar{f}_j + \sum_{k \neq i} |f_k|^2 (-1)^{k-i} \bigwedge_{j \neq k} f_j \, d\bar{f}_j \right)$$

$$= \frac{f_1 \cdots f_n (-1)^i \left(\sum (-1)^k \bar{f}_k \bigwedge_{j \neq k} d\bar{f}_j \right)}{\|f\|^{2n}}.$$

Putting this all together, what we might call the *distinguished Dolbeault representative* of $(1/2\pi\sqrt{-1})^n \omega$ is

$$\eta_\omega = g(z) \left[\frac{C_n \sum (-1)^{i-1} \bar{f}_i \, \overline{df_1} \wedge \cdots \wedge \widehat{\overline{df_i}} \wedge \cdots \wedge \overline{df_n} \wedge dz_1 \wedge \cdots \wedge dz_n}{\|f\|^{2n}} \right],$$

where C_n is a constant depending only on n.

At this juncture, recall from Section 1 of Chapter 3 the *Bochner-Martinelli kernel*

$$k(z,\xi) = C_n \frac{\sum (-1)^{i-1}(\overline{z_i-\xi_i}) \bigwedge_{j\neq i} (\overline{dz}_j - \overline{d\xi}_j) \wedge d\xi_1 \wedge \cdots \wedge d\xi_n}{\|z-\xi\|^{2n}}$$

on $\mathbb{C}^n \times \mathbb{C}^n$. If $F: U \to \mathbb{C}^n \times \mathbb{C}^n$ is defined by

$$F(z) = (z+f(z),z),$$

then

$$\eta_\omega = gF^*k.$$

Taking $f_i(z) = z_i$ and applying our lemma, we obtain another proof of the Bochner-Martinelli formula,

$$\int_{\|z\|=\varepsilon} g(z)\beta(z,\bar{z}) = g(0).$$

Recall also from Section 2 of Chapter 3 on the holomorphic Lefschetz fixed-point formula that we proved that if the origin is an isolated nondegenerate fixed point of a map $f: U \to \mathbb{C}^n$, then

$$\int_{\|z\|=\varepsilon} F^*k = \mathscr{G}_f(0).$$

We now know that for any type of isolated fixed point,

$$\int_{\|z\|=\varepsilon} F^*k = \operatorname{Res}_{\{0\}} \left(\frac{dz_1 \wedge \cdots \wedge dz_n}{f_1(z) \cdots f_n(z)} \right).$$

This leads to a corresponding extension of the holomorphic Lefschetz theorem.

The Global Residue Theorem

Suppose that $M \subset M'$ are complex n-manifolds, where M is relatively compact with smooth boundary $\partial M = \overline{M} - M$. The case that $M = M'$ is itself compact will be in many respects the most interesting situation. Suppose that $D_1, \ldots, D_n$ are effective divisors defined in some neighborhood U of $\overline{M}$ in M' and whose intersection $D_1 \cap \cdots \cap D_n$ is a discrete— hence finite—set of points in M. By analogy with the previous notation, we set

$$D = D_1 + \cdots + D_n,$$
$$U^* = U - (D_1 \cap \cdots \cap D_n),$$
$$U_i = U - D_i,$$

so that $\underline{U} = \{U_i\}$ is an open covering of U^*. Suppose that

$$\omega \in H^0(U, \Omega^n(D))$$

is a meromorphic n-form on U with polar divisor D. For each point $P \in U_1 \cap \cdots \cap U_n$ we may restrict ω to a neighborhood U_P of P and define the residue

$$\operatorname{Res}_P \omega$$

as in the previous section. On the other hand,

$$\omega \in C^{n-1}(\underline{U}, \Omega^n)$$

defines a class $[\omega] \in H^{n-1}(U^*, \Omega^n)$ that has a Dolbeault representative

$$\eta_\omega \in H_{\bar{\partial}}^{n, n-1}(U^*) \cong H^{n-1}(U^*, \Omega^n),$$

and we have the

Residue Theorem

$$\sum_P \operatorname{Res}_P \omega = \int_{\partial M} \eta_\omega.$$

In particular, if M is compact, then

$$\sum_P \operatorname{Res}_P \omega = 0.$$

Proof.   As in the Riemann surface case, we let $U_P(\varepsilon)$ be an ε-ball around P and use $d\eta_\omega = 0$ and Stokes' theorem to write

$$\int_{\partial M} \eta_\omega = \sum_P \int_{\partial U_P(\varepsilon)} \eta_\omega$$

$$= \sum_P \operatorname{Res}_P \omega \qquad \text{by the above lemma,}$$

since $\eta_\omega | U_P^*$ is a Dolbeault representative of $[\omega|_{U_P}] \in H^{n-1}(U_P^*, \Omega^n)$.   Q.E.D.

Of course, the essential step here is to convert the original n-dimensional path of integration into one of dimension $2n - 1$ so that Stokes' theorem may be utilized.

The Transformation Law and Local Duality

We now explore what might be called the functorial aspects of the residue symbol. To begin with we shall use the residue theorem to derive one of our main techniques, the method of continuity. Suppose that $f_t = (f_{t,1}, \ldots, f_{t,n})$ are n-functions of (z, t), holomorphic for z in a neighborhood of $\bar{U}$ where U is a small ball around the origin in $\mathbb{C}^n$, and continuous in a parameter variable $0 \leqslant t \leqslant \delta$. We set $f = f_0$, and for a form

$$\omega = \frac{g(z) \, dz_1 \wedge \cdots \wedge dz_n}{f_1(z) \cdots f_n(z)} \qquad (g(z) \in \mathcal{O}(\bar{U}))$$

we let

$$\omega_t = \frac{g(z)\,dz_1 \wedge \cdots \wedge dz_n}{f_{t,1}(z)\cdots f_{t,n}(z)}$$

If we assume that $f^{-1}(0)$ is a finite set of points interior to U, then $\|f(z)\| \geqslant \varepsilon > 0$ on the boundary $\partial U = \overline{U} - U$, and so $\|f_t(z)\| \geqslant \varepsilon/2 > 0$ for t sufficiently close to 0. Consequently $f_t^{-1}(0)$ will again be a finite set of points interior to U. On the other hand, by the explicit formula

$$\eta_{\omega_t} = C_n g(z) \frac{\sum (-1)^{i-1} \bar{f}_{i,t}\, d\bar{f}_{t,1} \wedge \cdots \wedge \widehat{d\bar{f}_{t,i}} \wedge \cdots \wedge d\bar{f}_{t,n} \wedge dz_1 \wedge \cdots \wedge dz_n}{\|f_t(z)\|^2}$$

for the Dolbeault representative of $[\omega_t] \in H^{n-1}(U^*, \Omega^n)$, we see that the boundary integral

$$\int_{\partial U} \eta_{\omega_t}$$

is continuous in t. Going to the residue theorem, we find the *principle of continuity*:

$$(*) \qquad \lim_{t \to 0} \sum_{P_t \in f_t^{-1}(0)} \operatorname{Res}_{P_t} \omega_t = \sum_{P \in f^{-1}(0)} \operatorname{Res}_P \omega.$$

To apply this, we need to discuss perturbations of a given map $f: U \to \mathbb{C}^n$ having $f^{-1}(0) = \{0\}$. A family of maps $f_t: U \to \mathbb{C}^n$ defined and holomorphic in a neighborhood of $\overline{U}$, varying continuously with t and such that $f_0 = f$, is said to be a *good perturbation* of f in case f_t has only nondegenerate zeros for $t \neq 0$. We will be able to easily see the existence of good perturbations when we discuss finite holomorphic mappings below. For the moment they may be deduced from Sard's theorem as follows: Since the critical values of $f: U \to \mathbb{C}^n$ have measure zero in $\mathbb{C}^n$, we can find an arc $\gamma(t)$, $0 \leqslant t \leqslant \varepsilon$, with $\gamma(0) = \{0\}$ and $\gamma(t)$ not a critical value for $t \neq 0$. Then

$$f_t(z) = f(z) - \gamma(t)$$

is a good perturbation of f.

Now we use the existence of good perturbations and continuity method to prove the

Transformation Law. *Suppose* $f = (f_1, \ldots, f_n)$ *and* $g = (g_1, \ldots, g_n)$ *give holomorphic maps* $f, g: \overline{U} \to \mathbb{C}^n$ *with* $f^{-1}(0) = \{0\} = g^{-1}(0)$. *Suppose moreover that*

$$g_i(z) = \sum_j a_{ij}(z) f_j(z)$$

for some holomorphic matrix $A(z) = (a_{ij}(z))$. *Equivalently, the ideals should satisfy*

$$\{g_1, \ldots, g_n\} \subset \{f_1, \ldots, f_n\}.$$

Then, for $h(z) \in \mathcal{O}(\overline{U})$

$$\text{Res}_{\{0\}}\left(\frac{h\,dz_1 \wedge \cdots \wedge dz_n}{f_1 \cdots f_n}\right) = \text{Res}_{\{0\}}\left(\frac{h\det A\,dz_1 \wedge \cdots \wedge dz_n}{g_1 \cdots g_n}\right).$$

Proof.   We prove this in cases of increasing difficulty.

Case 1: $\mathcal{J}_f(0) \neq 0$ and $\det A(0) \neq 0$

Then $\mathcal{J}_g(0) = \mathcal{J}_f(0)\det A(0)$, and by the evaluation of the residue integral in the nondegenerate case

$$\text{Res}_{\{0\}}\left(\frac{h\,dz_1 \wedge \cdots \wedge dz_n}{f_1 \cdots f_n}\right) = (2\pi\sqrt{-1}\,)^n \frac{h(0)}{\mathcal{J}_f(0)}$$

$$= (2\pi\sqrt{-1}\,)^n \frac{h(0)\det A(0)}{\mathcal{J}_g(0)}$$

$$= \text{Res}_{\{0\}}\left(\frac{h\det A\,dz_1 \wedge \cdots \wedge dz_n}{g_1 \cdots g_n}\right).$$

Case 2: $\det A(0) \neq 0$ but f possibly degenerate

Since the result is local around the origin, we may shrink U and assume that $\det A(z) \neq 0$ in $\overline{U}$. If f_t is a good perturbation of $f = f_0$, then $g_t = A \cdot f_t$ is a good perturbation of $g = g_0$, and by continuity and case 1

$$\text{Res}_{\{0\}}\left(\frac{h\,dz_1 \wedge \cdots \wedge dz_n}{f_1 \cdots f_n}\right) = \lim_{t \to 0} \sum_{P_t \in f_t^{-1}(0) \cap U} \text{Res}_{P_t}\left(\frac{h\,dz_1 \wedge \cdots \wedge dz_n}{f_{t,1} \cdots f_{t,n}}\right)$$

$$= \lim_{t \to 0} \sum_{P_t \in g_t^{-1}(0) \cap U} \text{Res}_{P_t}\left(\frac{h\det A\,dz_1 \wedge \cdots \wedge dz_n}{g_{t,1} \cdots g_{t,n}}\right)$$

$$= \text{Res}_{\{0\}}\left(\frac{h\det A\,dz_1 \wedge \cdots \wedge dz_n}{g_1 \cdots g_n}\right).$$

Case 3: f, g, and A arbitrary

Now we let $A_t(z)$ be a continuous family of holomorphic matrices with $A_0(z) = A(z)$ and $\det A_t(0) \neq 0$ for $t \neq 0$. Set $g_t = A_t \cdot f$, and observe that since $g^{-1}(0) = \{0\}$, $g_t^{-1}(0) = \{P_t\}$ is an isolated set of points interior to U. For $P_t \neq 0, f(P_t) \neq 0$. Suppose $f_1(P_t) \neq 0$ and denote by $A_{i,j}$ the i,jth minor of A. Then by Laplace's expansion of the determinant, for z near P_t

$$\det A_t(z) = \sum_j (-1)^j A_{tj,1}(z) a_{tj,1}(z)$$

$$= \frac{1}{f_1(z)}\left(\sum_{i,j} (-1)^j A_{tj,1} a_{tj,i} f_i(z)\right), \quad \text{since } \sum_j A_{tj,1} a_{tj,i} = 0 \text{ for } i \neq 1,$$

$$= \frac{1}{f_1(z)}\left(\sum_j (-1)^j A_{tj,1} g_{t,j}(z)\right).$$

Thus $\det A_t(z)$ is in the ideal $\{g_{t,1},\ldots,g_{t,n}\}_{P_t}$, and by the second elementary property of the residue integral

$$\operatorname{Res}_{P_t}\left(\frac{h\det A_t\, dz_1\wedge\cdots\wedge dz_n}{g_{t,1}\cdots g_{t,n}}\right)=0 \qquad \text{for } P_t\neq 0.$$

Now then we use this together with case 2 to have:

$$\operatorname{Res}_{\{0\}}\left(\frac{h\det A\, dz_1\wedge\cdots\wedge dz_n}{g_1\cdots g_n}\right)=\lim_{t\to0}\left(\sum\operatorname{Res}_{P_t}\left(\frac{h\det A_t\, dz_1\wedge\cdots\wedge dz_n}{g_{t,1}\cdots g_{t,n}}\right)\right)$$

$$=\lim_{t\to0}\left(\operatorname{Res}_{\{0\}}\left(\frac{h\det A_t\, dz_1\wedge\cdots\wedge dz_n}{g_{t,1}\cdots g_{t,n}}\right)\right)$$

$$=\lim_{t\to0}\operatorname{Res}_{\{0\}}\left(\frac{h\, dz_1\wedge\cdots\wedge dz_n}{f_1\cdots f_n}\right)$$

$$=\operatorname{Res}_{\{0\}}\left(\frac{h\, dz_1\wedge\cdots\wedge dz_n}{f_1\cdots f_n}\right). \qquad \text{Q.E.D.}$$

Local Duality. We now come to the local duality theorem. Given U a sufficiently small neighborhood of the origin and $f: U\to\mathbb{C}^n$ with $f^{-1}(0)=\{0\}$, or equivalently given an ideal $I=I(f)=\{f_1,\ldots,f_n\}$ in the local ring $\mathcal{O}=\mathcal{O}_{\{0\}}$ at the origin and having $\{0\}$ as isolated common zero of the f_i's, we may use the property

$$\operatorname{Res}_{\{0\}}\left(\frac{g\, dz_1\wedge\cdots\wedge dz_n}{f_1\cdots f_n}\right)=0 \qquad \text{for } g\in I,$$

to define a symmetric pairing

$$\mathrm{res}_f:\ \mathcal{O}/I\otimes\mathcal{O}/I\to\mathbb{C}$$

by setting

$$\mathrm{res}_f(g,h)=\operatorname{Res}_{\{0\}}\left(\left(\frac{1}{2\pi\sqrt{-1}}\right)^n\frac{g(z)h(z)\, dz_1\wedge\cdots\wedge dz_n}{f_1(z)\cdots f_n(z)}\right).$$

The basic result is the

Local Duality Theorem I. *The pairing "res_f" is nondegenerate; i.e., if*

$$\left(\frac{1}{2\pi\sqrt{-1}}\right)^n\int_{|f_i(z)|=\varepsilon}\frac{g(z)h(z)\, dz_1\wedge\cdots\wedge dz_n}{f_1(z)\cdots f_n(z)}=0$$

for all h(z)$\in\mathcal{O}$, *then* g(z) *lies in the ideal* $\{f_1,\ldots,f_n\}$.

Proof. The proof is based on the transformation law and two further general results in local analytic geometry. The first of these is that $f_1,\ldots,f_n\in\mathcal{O}$ form a *regular sequence*, which by definition means that

f_i *is not a zero divisor in* $\mathcal{O}/\{f_1,\ldots,f_{i-1}\}$ $(1\leq i\leq n)$.

Intuitively, this amounts to saying that the analytic varieties $V_i = \{f_1(z) = \cdots = f_i(z) = 0\}$ have codimension exactly equal to i, which seems quite reasonable and may be rigorously proved in the case $n = 2$ as follows: We need to show that if $gf_2 = 0$ in $\mathcal{O}/\{f_1\}$, then $g = hf_1$ is a multiple of f_1. The problem is unchanged if we multiply the f_i's or g by units, and so we may choose coordinates (z, w) such that $f_1, f_2, g \in \mathcal{O}_z[w]$ are all Weierstrass polynomials. By the division theorem,

$$g = hf_1 + r,$$

where $r \in \mathcal{O}_z[w]$ is a polynomial of degree less than $d = \deg f_1$. For $|z| < \varepsilon$, we denote by $w_1(z), \ldots, w_d(z)$ the roots of

$$f_1(z, w) = 0,$$

where some roots may be repeated. Then, since the equations $f_1(z, w) = f_2(z, w) = 0$ have only $(0, 0)$ as common solution, for z^* close to zero all $f_2(z^*, w_\nu(z^*)) \neq 0$. But then, since by assumption $g(z, w_\nu(z)) f_2(z, w_\nu(z)) = 0$, the equation $r(z^*, w) = 0$ will have $d > \deg r$ roots. Hence $r \equiv 0$ and $g = hf_1$.
                                                                                                                 Q.E.D.

The general statement is:

For U *a sufficiently small neighborhood of the origin and* $f = (f_1, \ldots, f_n): U \to \mathbb{C}^n$ *a holomorphic mapping, the conditions*

1. $f^{-1}(0) = \{0\}$,
2. $\operatorname{codim}\{f_{i_1}(z) = \cdots = f_{i_k}(z) = 0\} = k$,
3. $f_1, \ldots, f_n$ *is a regular sequence,*

are all equivalent.

Since we shall be discussing regular sequences in detail in the section on Koszul complexes and shall give another proof of local duality there, we shall let our discussion in the case $n = 2$ suffice for the moment.

The second result in local analytic geometry is the *nullstellensatz* for the ideal $\{f_1, \ldots, f_n\}$:

There exists $k_i > 0$ *such that*

$$z_i^{k_i} \in \{f_1, \ldots, f_n\}.$$

We will prove this in the next section on finite holomorphic mappings.

Now to the proof of local duality. The idea is to directly verify the statement for ideals $\{z_1^{k_1}, \ldots, z_n^{k_n}\}$, and then to use the transformation law to deduce the result for the ideal $\{f_1, \ldots, f_n\} \supseteq \{z_1^{k_1}, \ldots, z_n^{k_n}\}$.

Step One. In case $f_i(z) = z_i^{k_i + 1}$, we take $h(z) = z_1^{l_1} \cdots z_n^{l_n}$ and write the power series

$$g(z) = \sum g_{i_1 \cdots i_n} z_1^{i_1} \cdots z_n^{i_n}.$$

Then, by iterating the usual Cauchy integral formula,

$$\mathrm{res}_f(g,h) = \sum_{i_1 \cdots i_n} g_{i_1 \cdots i_n} \left(\frac{1}{2\pi\sqrt{-1}} \right)^n \int_{|z_i| = \varepsilon} \frac{dz_1 \wedge \cdots \wedge dz_n}{z_1^{k_1 + 1 - l_1 - i_1} \cdots z_n^{k_n + 1 - l_n - i_n}}$$

$$= g_{k_1 - l_1, \ldots, k_n - l_n}.$$

Thus, $\mathrm{res}_f(g,h) = 0$ for all h is equivalent to $g_{i_1 \cdots i_n} = 0$ for $i_1 \leqslant k_1, \ldots, i_n \leqslant k_n$, in which case $g \in \{z_1^{k_1 + 1}, \ldots, z_n^{k_n + 1}\}$. This proves the local duality theorem in this case.

Step Two. We will use the transformation law to prove the

Lemma. *Let* $f_1', f_1, \ldots, f_n \in \mathcal{O}$ *and set* $f' = (f_1', f_2, \ldots, f_n)$, $f = (f_1, \ldots, f_n)$. *Assume that* $f^{-1}(0) = \{0\} = f'^{-1}\{0\}$ *and that* $f_1' \in \{f_1, f_2, \ldots, f_n\}$; *i.e.,* $I(f') \subseteq I(f)$. *Then, if the residue pairing is nondegenerate for* f', *it is nondegenerate for* f.

Proof. Let $\pi: \mathcal{O}/I(f') \to \mathcal{O}/I(f)$ be the natural projection, and write

$$f_1' = \sum_i b_i f_i,$$

so that $f' = Af$, where

$$A = \begin{bmatrix} b_1 & b_2 & \cdots & b_n \\ 0 & 1 & \cdots & 0 \\ \vdots & \vdots & \ddots & \\ 0 & 0 & & 1 \end{bmatrix}.$$

If $g = \sum_i c_i f_i$ is in the ideal $I(f)$, then

$$b_1 g = c_1 \left(\sum_i b_i f_i \right) + \sum_{i \geqslant 2} (b_1 c_i - c_1 b_i) f_i$$

is in the ideal $I(f')$. Thus multiplication by b_1 gives a map

$$\alpha: \mathcal{O}/I(f) \to \mathcal{O}/I(f')$$

going in the opposite direction to π. Since $\det A = b_1$, the transformation law states exactly that the diagram

$$\begin{array}{ccc} \mathcal{O}/I(f) \otimes \mathcal{O}/I(f) & \xrightarrow{\ \mathrm{res}_f\ } & \mathbb{C} \\ \alpha \downarrow & \uparrow \pi & \| \\ \mathcal{O}/I(f') \otimes \mathcal{O}/I(f') & \xrightarrow{\ \mathrm{res}_{f'}\ } & \mathbb{C} \end{array}$$

is commutative; i.e.,

$$\text{res}_f(g,h) = \text{res}_{f'}(b_1 g, h)$$

for all $g, h \in \mathcal{O}$. If $\text{res}_f(g, h) = 0$ for all h, then by the assumed nondegeneracy of $\text{res}_{f'}$ it follows that $b_1 g \in I(f')$. Thus

$$b_1 g = c_1 f_1' + \sum_{i \geq 2} c_i f_i$$
$$= c_1 b_1 f_1 + \sum_{i \geq 2} (b_1 c_i - b_i c_1) f_i,$$

so that

$$b_1 g = c_1 b_1 f_1 \qquad \text{in } \mathcal{O}/\{f_2, \ldots, f_n\}.$$

This implies that either

$$g = c_1 f_1 \qquad \text{in } \mathcal{O}/\{f_2, \ldots, f_n\}$$

or

$$b_1 \text{ is a zero-divisor} \qquad \text{in } \mathcal{O}/\{f_2, \ldots, f_n\}.$$

In the first case, $g \in \{f_1, f_2, \ldots, f_n\}$ as desired. In the second case, $b_1 f_1$ is a zero-divisor in $\mathcal{O}/\{f_2, \ldots, f_n\}$, and hence so is $f_1' = b_1 f_1 + (b_2 f_2 + \cdots + b_n f_n)$. But this contradicts the regular sequence property of $\{f_1', f_2, \ldots, f_n\}$. Q.E.D.

Step Three. The theorem now follows easily. Given $f = (f_1, \ldots, f_n)$, we inductively choose a coordinate system so that

$$F_i = (z_1, \ldots, z_i, f_{i+1}, \ldots, f_n)$$

has an isolated zero at the origin. Appealing to the nullstellensatz, we may take k_i sufficiently large so that $z_i^{k_i} \in I(F_{i-1})$. Then res_{F_n} is nondegenerate by step one, and by the lemma

$$\text{res}_{F_n} \text{ nondegenerate} \Rightarrow \text{res}_{F_{n-1}} \text{ nondegenerate}$$

$$\vdots$$

$$\Rightarrow \text{res}_{F_1} \text{ nondegenerate}$$

$$\Rightarrow \text{res}_{F_0} = \text{res}_f \text{ nondegenerate}. \qquad \text{Q.E.D.}$$

2. APPLICATIONS OF RESIDUES

Intersection Numbers

Recall that our discussion of the local structure of those analytic varieties defined by a single function—i.e., analytic hypersurfaces—was based on the one-variable Cauchy formula and subsequent residue theorem. It is similarly possible to use the n-variable residue theorem to derive the local properties of analytic varieties of codimension n defined by n holomorphic functions in $U \subset \mathbb{C}^N$. We shall now carry this out in case the variety is zero-dimensional—i.e., $N = n$. By allowing dependence on parameters, it is possible to adapt the method to the more general situation just mentioned.

We begin by discussing intersection numbers, thereby complementing our previous definitions, which were either topological or used the theory of currents—cf. Section 4 of Chapter 0 and Section 2 of Chapter 3.

Consider an ideal $I(f) = \{f_1, \ldots, f_n\}$ of holomorphic functions $f_i \in \mathcal{O}(\bar{U})$ whose divisors D_i have the origin as set-theoretic intersection—i.e., $f^{-1}(0) = \{0\}$, where $f = (f_1, \ldots, f_n)$. As usual, we allow ourselves to shrink U when necessary. Doing this, we may assume that $f^{-1}(w)$ is a discrete set of points in U for $\|w\| < \varepsilon$, since we will have $|f(z)| \geq C > 0$ for $z \in \partial U$.

We write $w = f(z)$, denote by $K = dw_1/w_1 \wedge \cdots \wedge dw_n/w_n$ the *Cauchy kernel*, and set

$$\omega(f_1, \ldots, f_n) = f^* K = \frac{df_1}{f_1} \wedge \cdots \wedge \frac{df_n}{f_n}.$$

The *local intersection number* is defined by

$$(D_1, \ldots, D_n)_{\{0\}} = \mathrm{Res}_{\{0\}} \omega(f_1, \ldots, f_n).$$

We shall give a list of its properties:

(a) $(D_1, \ldots, D_n)_{\{0\}}$ *is an integer that depends only on the ideal* $I(f)$ *and not the choice of generators* f_i. *In particular, it depends only on the divisors* D_i *and not on their defining functions.*

Proof. $(1/2\pi\sqrt{-1})^n \omega(f_1, \ldots, f_n)$ represents an integral cohomology class in $H^n_{DR}(U - D)$, and so the intersection number is an integer. If

$$f_i' = \sum_j a_{ij} f_j$$

where $\Delta = \det(a_{ij}) \neq 0$, then

$$\frac{df_1' \wedge \cdots \wedge df_n'}{f_1' \cdots f_n'} = \Delta \frac{df_1 \wedge \cdots \wedge df_n}{f_1' \cdots f_n'} + g \frac{dz_1 \wedge \cdots \wedge dz_n}{f_1' \cdots f_n'},$$

where g is in the ideal. By the transformation law

$$\mathrm{Res}_{\{0\}}\left(\frac{\Delta df_1 \wedge \cdots \wedge df_n}{f_1' \cdots f_n'} \right) = \mathrm{Res}_{\{0\}}\left(\frac{df_1 \wedge \cdots \wedge df_n}{f_1 \cdots f_n} \right),$$

while

$$\mathrm{Res}_{\{0\}}\left(g \frac{dz_1 \wedge \cdots \wedge dz_n}{f_1' \cdots f_n'} \right) = 0,$$

since g is in the ideal.

(b) *The intersection number is linear in each divisor* D_i.

Proof. If $D_1 = D_1' + D_1''$ corresponds to the factorization $f_1 = f_1' f_1''$, then clearly

$$(*) \qquad \omega(f_1, f_2, \ldots, f_n) = \omega(f_1', f_2, \ldots, f_n) + \omega(f_1'', f_2, \ldots, f_n).$$

This is not yet enough to prove linearity, owing to the complicated nature of the path of integration $\Gamma = \{|f_i| = \varepsilon\}$ in the definition of the residue. What is suggested is that we use the Dolbeault isomorphism to convert Γ into the sphere $\|z\| = \varepsilon$.

Thus, we consider $\omega(f_1', f_2, \ldots, f_n)$ as defining a class in $H^{n-1}(U', \Omega^n)$, where $U' = \{U_1', U_2, \ldots, U_n\}$ is the corresponding covering of $U^* = \bar{U} - \{0\}$. Since $U_1 \subset U_1'$, there is a restriction mapping ρ' leading to a commutative diagram

$$H^{n-1}(\underline{U}', \Omega^n) \xrightarrow{\rho'} H^{n-1}(\underline{U}, \Omega^n)$$

$$\searrow \eta \qquad\qquad \nearrow \eta'$$

$$H_{\bar{\partial}}^{n,n-1}(U^*)$$

where η and η' are Dolbeault maps. Setting $\eta(f_1, \ldots, f_n) = \eta(\omega(f_1, \ldots, f_n))$ and so forth, it follows from $(*)$ that

$$\eta(f_1, f_2, \ldots, f_n) = \eta(f_1', f_2, \ldots, f_n) + \eta(f_1'', f_2, \ldots, f_n)$$

in $H_{\bar{\partial}}^{n,n-1}(U^*)$. (It is *not* the case that $\eta = \eta' + \eta''$ as differential forms, since the Bochner-Martinelli kernel is nonlinear. What the commutativity of the diagram proves is that $\eta = \eta' + \eta'' + \bar{\partial}\xi$.) By the lemma on p. 651 above,

$$(D_1, \ldots, D_n)_{\{0\}} = \int_{\|z\| = \varepsilon} \eta(f_1, f_2, \ldots, f_n),$$

from which the linearity of the intersection number follows.

(c) Suppose now that the divisors $D_i = (f_i)$ meet at a finite number of points P_ν interior to U. The total number of intersections of the D_i in U is defined by

$$(D_1, \ldots, D_n)_U = \sum_\nu (D_1, \ldots, D_n)_{P_\nu}.$$

We shall prove:

The total intersection number is invariant under continuous deformation of the D_i.

Proof. We assume that $f_{t,i}(z) \in \mathcal{O}(\bar{U})$ is continuous in t and has divisor $D_i(t)$ with $f_{0,i} = f_i$ and $D_i(0) = D_i$. Since $\sum_i |f_i(z, t)|^2 \geqslant C > 0$ for $z \in \partial U$ and $|t| < \varepsilon$, the divisors $D_i(t)$ will meet at isolated points interior to U. The total intersection number

$$(D_1(t), \ldots, D_n(t))_U$$

is on the one hand an integer and on the other hand, by the continuity principle, continuous in t. Consequently, it is constant.   Q.E.D.

Given divisors D_i having the origin as isolated point of intersection, we may perturb them slightly to smooth divisors D_i' having a finite number of transverse intersections near the origin (Figure 1). Each of these transverse intersections has local intersection number $+1$, and $(D_1,\ldots,D_n)_{\{0\}}$ is the total number of such intersections.

(d)   We now assume that the D_i meet at the origin and that D_1 is nonsingular. Set $D_i' = D_1 \cap D_i$ for $i \geqslant 2$. Then we claim that

$$(D_1,\ldots,D_n)_{\{0\}} = (D_2',\ldots,D_n')_{\{0\}}.$$

Proof.   We may choose coordinates so that $f_1(z)=z_1$. Set $z=(z_1,z')$ and $f_i'(z')=f_i(0,z')=f_i|_{D_1}$. Then if $\Gamma=\{|f_1(z)|=\cdots=|f_n(z)|=\varepsilon\}$ and $\Gamma'=\{|f_2'(z')|=\cdots=|f_n'(z')|=\varepsilon\}$, we may iterate the Cauchy integral formula to obtain

$$(D_1,\ldots,D_n)_{\{0\}} = \left(\frac{1}{2\pi\sqrt{-1}}\right)^n \int_\Gamma \frac{dz_1}{z_1} \wedge \frac{df_2}{f_2} \wedge \cdots \wedge \frac{df_n}{f_n}$$

$$= \left(\frac{1}{2\pi\sqrt{-1}}\right)^{n-1} \int_{\Gamma'} \frac{df_2'}{f_2'} \wedge \cdots \wedge \frac{df_n'}{f_n'}$$

$$= (D_2',\ldots,D_n')_{\{0\}}.$$

Using this, we shall prove:

The Jacobian $\partial(f_1,\ldots,f_n)/\partial(z_1,\ldots,z_n) \not\equiv 0$ and the local intersection number $(D_1,\ldots,D_n)_{\{0\}} > 0$.

Proof.   The proof is by induction on n, with the case $n=1$ being clear.
Choose a point z_0 that is a smooth point on D_1 and is very close to the origin. If we assume that $df_1 \wedge df_2 \wedge \cdots \wedge df_n \equiv 0$ and set $f_i' = f_i|D_1$, then $df_2' \wedge \cdots \wedge df_n' \equiv 0$ near z_0. Indeed, we may choose local coordinates

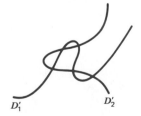

D_1 D_2 D_1' D_2'

Figure 1

$(u_1, u_2, \ldots, u_n)$ around z_0 such that $f_1 = u_1^m$, where $m > 0$. Then $df_1 \wedge df_2 \wedge \cdots \wedge df_n \equiv 0 \Rightarrow u_1^{m-1} du_1 \wedge df_2 \wedge \cdots \wedge df_n \equiv 0 \Rightarrow df_2 \wedge \cdots \wedge df_n \equiv 0$ modulo $du_1 \Rightarrow df_2' \wedge \cdots \wedge df_n' \equiv 0$. On the other hand, if we let $f_i'(z_0) = w_i'$, then the equations $f_i'(z') = w_i'$ have z_0 as an isolated solution on D_1 near z_0. Setting $D_i' = (f_i' - w_i')$, the local intersection number $(D_2', \ldots, D_n')_{\{z_0\}} > 0$ by induction hypothesis. This is in contradiction to $df_2' \wedge \cdots \wedge df_n' \equiv 0$.

Now, assuming that $df_1 \wedge \cdots \wedge df_n \not\equiv 0$, we shall prove that $(D_1, \ldots, D_n)_{\{0\}} > 0$. The Dolbeault representative is

$$\eta(f_1, \ldots, f_n) = C_n \frac{\sum (-1)^{i-1} \bar{f}_i \, d\bar{f}_1 \wedge \cdots \wedge \widehat{d\bar{f}_i} \wedge \cdots \wedge d\bar{f}_n \wedge df_1 \wedge \cdots \wedge df_n}{\|f\|^{2n}}$$

$$= f^*(\beta),$$

where, according to the Bochner-Martinelli formula in Section 1 of Chapter 3,

$$\beta = C_n \frac{\sum (-1)^{i-1} \bar{w}_i \, d\bar{w}_1 \wedge \cdots \wedge \widehat{d\bar{w}_i} \wedge \cdots \wedge d\bar{w}_n \wedge dw_1 \wedge \cdots \wedge dw_n}{\|w\|^{2n}}$$

is a closed $(n, n-1)$-form in $\mathbb{C}^n - \{0\}$ whose restriction to every sphere $\|w\| = \varepsilon$ is a $(2n-1)$-form with total integral one. On every sphere $\|z\| = \varepsilon$ the form $f^*(\beta)$ is $\geqslant 0$, and it is strictly positive at a point z_0 where $(df_1 \wedge \cdots \wedge df_n)(z_0) \neq 0$. For a sphere passing through such a point,

$$\int_{\|z\| = \|z_0\|} f^*\beta > 0.$$

This proves the positivity of the local intersection number.

(e) In fact it proves more. If we consider $f = (f_1, \ldots, f_n)$ as a mapping

$$f: U^* \to \mathbb{C}^n - \{0\},$$

then we have essentially shown that

The local intersection number is the topological degree deg(f) *of f.*

Proof. The form β gives an integral generator of $H_{\mathrm{DR}}^{2n-1}(S^{2n-1}(\varepsilon))$ for any sphere $\|w\| = \varepsilon$. By definition of the degree,

$$\deg(f) = \int_{\|z\| = \varepsilon} f^*\beta$$

$$= \int_{\|z\| = \varepsilon} \eta(f_1, \ldots, f_n)$$

$$= (D_1, \ldots, D_n)_{\{0\}}$$

by our basic integral formula.

Finite Holomorphic Mappings

We now want to tie in the local intersection number with the properties of f viewed as a holomorphic mapping $f: U \to \mathbb{C}^n$. For this, the following standard terminology will be useful: On a complex manifold M a *zero cycle* is a formal finite sum

$$\Gamma = \sum_\nu m_\nu P_\nu$$

of points $P_\nu \in M$ with multiplicities $m_\nu \in \mathbb{Z}$. We set

$$\underbrace{P + \cdots + P}_{k} = k \cdot P.$$

The zero cycle is *effective* in case all $m_\nu \geqslant 0$. The *degree* of a zero cycle is given by

$$\deg(\Gamma) = \sum_\nu m_\nu.$$

Suppose now that $f: U \to \mathbb{C}^n$ is a holomorphic mapping with $f^{-1}(0) = \{0\}$. We define the *multiplicity of* f *at the origin* to be the topological degree d of $f: U^* \to \mathbb{C}^n - \{0\}$. We then say that *the equation*

$$f(z) = 0$$

has the origin as a solution of multiplicity d.

Now, according to the continuity property (c) of the local intersection numbers, for $\|w\| < \varepsilon$ the equation

$$f(z) = w$$

will have exactly d solutions $z_\nu(w)$ close to the origin. Of course, some of the $z_\nu(w)$ may be repeated. Using the zero-cycle notation, we write

$$f^{-1}(w) = \sum_\nu z_\nu(w).$$

Let $W = \{\|w\| < \varepsilon\}$ and redefine $U = f^{-1}(W)$. Then we claim that the holomorphic mapping

$$f: U \to W$$

has the following properties: It is *surjective*, *open*, and *finite*. The first of these is by definition. The second means that open sets map onto open sets, which is clear, as is the third property. These finite mappings behave quite differently from, for example, blowing-down mappings such as

$$(u, v) \to (u, uv),$$

which are not open. In general, they share most of the properties of maps in one variable, as we shall now prove. For this we need the following:

Lemma. *For* $h(z) \in \mathcal{O}(U)$, *the* trace

$$\sigma_h(w) = \sum_{\nu=1}^{d} h(z_\nu(w))$$

is a holomorphic function of $w \in W$.

Proof. We consider σ_h as a distribution operating on the compactly supported (n,n) forms $A_c^{n,n}(W)$ by the rule

$$\sigma_h(\varphi) = \int_W \sigma_h(w)\varphi(w)$$

$$= \int_U h(z)(f^*\varphi)(z),$$

where $\varphi \in A_c^{n,n}(W)$. By the regularity theorem from Section 1 of Chapter 3 it will suffice to show that $\bar\partial \sigma_h = 0$ in the sense of currents. Now, for $\psi \in A_c^{n,n-1}(W)$, $f^*\psi$ is compactly supported and

$$\bar\partial \sigma_h(\psi) = \int_W \sigma_h(w)\bar\partial \psi(w)$$

$$= \int_U h(z)\bar\partial(f^*\psi)(z)$$

$$= -\int_U \bar\partial h(z)f^*\psi(z)$$

$$= 0,$$

since $h \in \mathcal{O}(U)$.   Q.E.D.

If we apply the lemma to the power sums $\sum_\nu h(z_\nu(w))^k$, then we deduce that any symmetric function—such as

$$h(z_1(w)) \cdot \cdots \cdot h(z_d(w))$$

—is holomorphic in w.

One application is a proof of the *proper mapping theorem* for $f: U \xrightarrow{\cdot} W$, and hence for general finite surjective mappings: If $V \subset U$ is an analytic variety defined by equations $\{h_\alpha(z)=0\}$, then $f(V) \subset W$ is defined by $\{H_\alpha(w)=0\}$, where $H_\alpha(w) = h_\alpha(z_1(w)) \cdots h_\alpha(z_d(w))$.

Note in particular that the *discriminant*, or *branch locus*, $D \subset W$, defined as the image $f(R)$ of the *ramification divisor*

$$\left\{ \frac{\partial(f_1,\ldots,f_n)}{\partial(z_1,\ldots,z_n)}(z) = 0 \right\},$$

is an analytic hypersurface. For $w \in W - D$, $h^{-1}(w) = \sum_\nu z_\nu(w)$, where the $z_\nu(w)$ are distinct. Choosing a path $w(t)$ with $w(0)=0$ and $w(t) \in W - D$ for $t \neq 0$, we find the explicit good perturbation $f_t(z) = f(z) - w(t)$ of $f(z)$.

As another application of the lemma, we suppose that $h(z) \in \mathcal{O}(U)$ and consider the expression

$$H(z) = \prod_{\nu=1}^{d} \left(h(z) - h(z_\nu(f(z))) \right).$$

On the one hand, $H(z) \equiv 0$, since $z = z_\nu(f(z))$ for some ν. On the other hand, H is a polynomial of the form

$$h(z)^d + a_1(w)h(z)^{d-1} + \cdots + a_d(w) \qquad (w = f(z)),$$

whose coefficients are holomorphic functions of $w = f(z)$. Now, via the mapping $f: U \to W$ the local ring $\mathcal{O}_w = \{$germs of holomorphic functions $h(w)$ defined in some neighborhood of $w = 0\}$ injects into $\mathcal{O}_z$, and we have proved

The degree of the extension $[\mathcal{O}_z : \mathcal{O}_w] = d$; *i.e., every* $h \in \mathcal{O}_z$ *satisfies a polynomial equation of degree* $\leqslant d$ *with coefficients in* $f^*\mathcal{O}_w \subset \mathcal{O}_z$, *and moreover* d *is the least such integer.*

As a corollary we have the following special case of the nullstellensatz:

If $h(z) \in \mathcal{O}_z$ *vanishes at* $z = 0$, *then*

$$h(z)^d \in \{ f_1(z), \ldots, f_n(z) \}.$$

Proof. As $z \to 0$, both $f(z)$ and $z_\nu(f(z)) \to 0$. Consequently, the coefficients $a_\nu(w)$ in the polynomial H vanish at $w = 0$. This implies that $h^d = 0$ modulo $\{ f_1, \ldots, f_n \}$.

(f) Finally, we can give one more interpretation of the local intersection number $(D_1, \ldots, D_n)_{\{0\}}$, where $D_i = (f_i)$. Let $\mathcal{O} = \mathcal{O}_z$ and $I \subset \mathcal{O}$ be the ideal $\{ f_1, \ldots, f_m \}$ defined by $f^*(m_w)$ where $m_w \subset \mathcal{O}_w$ is the maximal ideal of functions $h(w)$ with $h(0) = 0$. Then we have:

$\mathcal{O}/I$ *is a finite-dimensional complex vector space, and*

$$\dim_{\mathbb{C}}(\mathcal{O}/I) = (D_1, \ldots, D_n)_{\{0\}}.$$

Summarizing: Let $D_i = (f_i)$ be n divisors given in some small neighborhood U of the origin in $\mathbb{C}^n$ with $\cap_i D_i = \{0\}$. Then the local intersection number has the following interpretations:

(1) *Analytic*: The formula

$$(D_1, \ldots, D_n)_{\{0\}} = \mathrm{Res}_{\{0\}} \left(\frac{df_1}{f_1} \wedge \cdots \wedge \frac{df_n}{f_n} \right)$$

was taken as our definition.

(2)   *Topological*: Setting $f = (f_1, \ldots, f_n) : U^* \to \mathbb{C}^n - \{0\}$,

$$(D_1, \ldots, D_n)_{\{0\}} = \text{degree}(f).$$

Equivalently, $f : U \to W$ is a finite open surjective holomorphic mapping for some neighborhood W of the origin in $\mathbb{C}^n$. Since f is orientation preserving, $(D_1, \ldots, D_n)_{\{0\}}$ is the sheet number of f.

(3)   *Algebraic*: If $\mathcal{O}$ is the local ring at the origin and $I \subset \mathcal{O}$ the ideal generated by the f_i, then

$$(D_1, \ldots, D_n)_{\{0\}} = \dim_{\mathbb{C}}(\mathcal{O}/I).$$

In general, if D_i are divisors on a complex manifold M meeting at a finite number of isolated points P_ν, we define the effective zero cycle

$$D_1 \cdots \cdot D_n = \sum_\nu m_\nu P_\nu,$$

where

$$m_\nu = (D_1, \ldots, D_n)_{P_\nu}.$$

The degree

$$\deg(D_1 \cdots \cdot D_n) = \sum_\nu m_\nu$$

is the total intersection number of the D_i.

Applications to Plane Projective Geometry

We shall apply the residue theorem to the simplest global case $M = \mathbb{P}^n$, with special attention to the case $n = 2$. Suppose then that $D_1, \ldots, D_n$ are hypersurfaces of respective degrees $d_1, \ldots, d_n$ and meeting in isolated points P_ν. According to the discussion in the preceding section, we may write the intersection as a zero cycle

$$D_1 \cdots \cdot D_n = \sum_\nu m_\nu P_\nu,$$

where the local intersection numbers $m_\nu = (D_1, \ldots, D_n)_{P_\nu}$ are given by a residue, and the global *Bezout theorem*

$$\deg(D_1 \cdots \cdot D_n) = \sum_\nu m_\nu = d_1 \cdots d_n$$

is valid. In a suitable Euclidean coordinate system $(x_1, \ldots, x_n)$, we may assume that all P_ν lie in $\mathbb{C}^n \subset \mathbb{P}^n$ and that D_i is the divisor of a polynomial $f_i(x_1, \ldots, x_n)$ of degree d_i. The most general meromorphic n-form on $\mathbb{P}^n$ with polar divisor $D = D_1 + \cdots + D_n$ has in $\mathbb{C}^n$ an expression

$$\omega = \frac{g(x)\, dx_1 \wedge \cdots \wedge dx_n}{f_1(x) \cdots f_n(x)}$$

where $g(x)$ is a polynomial. Under a typical change of coordinates in $\mathbb{P}^n$

$$x_1 = \frac{1}{x_1'}, \quad x_2 = \frac{x_2'}{x_1'}, \quad \ldots, \quad x_n = \frac{x_n'}{x_1'},$$

we have

$$dx_1 \wedge \cdots \wedge dx_n = \frac{1}{(x_1')^{n+1}} dx_1' \wedge dx_2' \wedge \cdots \wedge dx_n',$$

$$f_i(x_1, \ldots, x_n) = \frac{1}{(x_1')^{d_i}} f_i'(x_1', x_2', \ldots, x_n').$$

It follows that ω does not have the hyperplane at infinity as a component of its polar divisor exactly when the degree restriction

$$\deg(g) \leqslant (d_1 + \cdots + d_n) - (n+1)$$

is satisfied. The global residue theorem then gives

(∗) $$\sum_\nu \text{Res}_{P_\nu} \left\{ \frac{g(x) dx_1 \wedge \cdots \wedge dx_n}{f_1(x) \cdots f_n(x)} \right\} = 0.$$

In the case where the D_i meet transversely at $d_1 \cdots d_n$ distinct points, (∗) reduces to the *Jacobi relation*

$$\sum_\nu \frac{g(P_\nu)}{(\partial(f_1, \ldots, f_n)/\partial(x_1, \ldots, x_n))(P_\nu)} = 0, \quad \deg(g) \leqslant \sum d_i - (n+1)$$

proved by him in 1834. For $n=1$ we obtain the *Lagrange interpolation formula*

$$\sum_\nu \frac{g(P_\nu)}{f'(P_\nu)} = 0, \quad \deg(g) \leqslant \deg(f) - 2;$$

it was in this context that Jacobi was led to his formula.

In the case $n=2$ the Jacobi relation immediately implies the

Cayley-Bacharach Theorem. *If* C *and* D *are curves in* $\mathbb{P}^2$ *of respective degrees* m *and* n *and meeting at* mn *distinct points, then any curve* E *of degree* m + n − 3 *that passes through all but one point of* C∩D *necessarily passes through that remaining point also.*

It is clear that the stronger relation (∗) gives a more general statement than the Cayley-Bacharach theorem when C and D may not have transverse intersections. Rather than attempt to formalize this, we shall usually go ahead and use the Cayley-Bacharach theorem in degenerate cases where the proof will be an immediate consequence of (∗).

To illustrate, we give an example of a degenerate case:

Suppose that the curves C *and* D *above have intersection*

$$C \cdot D = \sum_{\nu} m_{\nu} P_{\nu},$$

where all the points P_{ν} *are smooth points of* C. *If* E *is a curve of degree* m + n − 3 *such that for some* ν_0,

$$(C \cdot E)_{P_{\nu}} \geqslant m_{\nu}, \qquad \nu \neq \nu_0,$$
$$(C \cdot E)_{P_{\nu_0}} \geqslant m_{\nu_0} - 1,$$

then

$$(C \cdot E)_{P_{\nu_0}} \geqslant m_{\nu_0}.$$

Proof. By hypothesis, we may choose local holomorphic coordinates (z, w) around P_{ν_0} and defining functions $f(z, w)$, $g(z, w)$ for C, D, respectively, such that

$$\begin{cases} f(z, w) = z, \\ g(0, w) = w^{m_{\nu_0}} + \cdots. \end{cases}$$

The defining function $h(z, w)$ for E will then satisfy

$$h(0, w) = \alpha w^{m_{\nu_0} - 1} + \cdots$$

and

$$(E, C)_{P_{\nu_0}} \geqslant m_{\nu_0} \Leftrightarrow \alpha = 0.$$

Consequently, if we can show that

$$\mathrm{Res}_{\{0\}}\left(\frac{b(z, w)\, dz \wedge dw}{f(z, w) g(z, w)} \right) = 0 \Leftrightarrow \alpha = 0,$$

our assertion will follow from (*). By iterating the integral in the definition of the residue,

$$\mathrm{Res}_{\{0\}}\left(\frac{h(z, w)\, dz \wedge dw}{f(z, w) g(z, w)} \right) = \left(\frac{1}{2\pi\sqrt{-1}} \right)^2 \int_{|g(z, w)| = \varepsilon} \left(\int_{|z| = \varepsilon} \frac{h(z, w)\, dz}{g(z, w) z} \right) dw$$

$$= \frac{1}{2\pi\sqrt{-1}} \int_{|w| = \varepsilon} \frac{h(0, w)\, dw}{g(0, w)}$$

$$= \frac{1}{2\pi\sqrt{-1}} \int_{|w| = \varepsilon} (\alpha + \cdots) \frac{dw}{w}$$

$$= \alpha. \qquad\qquad \text{Q.E.D.}$$

The first nontrivial case is when $m = n = 3$; then we obtain the classical statement:

Suppose that C *and* D *are cubic curves meeting in nine points that are not necessarily distinct but that are simple points of* C. *Then any cubic* E *passing through eight of these points must contain the remaining one also.*

This fact was known in 1748 to Euler, who remarked that as a consequence polynomial functions in two or more variables would necessarily be much more complicated than in one variable, since then it is not generally the case that a set of mn points in plane is the common zero locus of a pair of polynomials.

As another application, we can prove

Pascal's Theorem. *The pairs of opposite sides of a hexagon inscribed in a smooth conic* Q *meet in three collinear points.*

Proof. Suppose that $L_1 L_2 L_3 L_4 L_5 L_6$ is the inscribed hexagon. Take $C = L_1 + L_3 + L_5$, $D = L_2 + L_4 + L_6$, and $E = Q + \overline{P_{12}P_{34}}$, where $P_{ij} = L_i \cap L_j$. Then E passes through the remaining point P_{56} of $C \cap D$. Q.E.D.

There is also a

Converse to Pascal's Theorem. *If* $H = L_1 L_2 L_3 L_4 L_5 L_6$ *is a hexagon such that the opposite sides meet in three collinear points, then the vertices of* H *are on a conic.*

Proof. Set $P_{ij} = L_i \cap L_j$ and let L be the line through P_{14}, P_{25}, and P_{36}. Then if Q is a conic passing through the five vertices $P_{12}, P_{23}, P_{34}, P_{45}, P_{56}$ of H, we may take $C = L_1 + L_3 + L_5$, $D = L_2 + L_4 + L_6$, and $E = Q + L$ to conclude that Q passes through P_{61}. Q.E.D.

Along similar lines but at a deeper level we shall prove a converse to the Cayley-Bacharach theorem. Suppose that

$$\Gamma = P_1 + \cdots + P_{n^2}$$

is a zero-cycle consisting of n^2 distinct points. *We say that* Γ *satisfies the Cayley-Bacharach property if every curve* E *of degree* $2n - 3$ *that passes through all but one point of* Γ *necessarily contains* Γ. Since the dimension of the linear system of curves of degree $2n - 3$ is

$$n(2n - 3) = 2n^2 - 3n,$$

there are plenty of such "test curves" E. The result is the following.

Proposition. *Suppose that* $\Gamma = P_1 + \cdots + P_{n^2}$ *satisfies the Cayley-Bacharach property. Then* Γ *lies on a pencil of curves of degree* n.

Proof. We consider the *Veronese embedding*

$$i_n : \mathbb{P}^2 \hookrightarrow \mathbb{P}^N, \qquad N = \frac{n(n+3)}{2},$$

given by the complete linear system of curves of degree n—i.e., by $H^0(\mathbb{P}^2, \mathcal{O}(nH))$. Since the hyperplane sections of $i_n(\mathbb{P}^2)$ are just the curves of degree n, we must show that:

$(**)$ *The points* $i_n(P_\nu)$ *lie on a* $\mathbb{P}^{N-2}$ *in* $\mathbb{P}^N$.

This in turn will be the case if any N of the points $i_n(P_\nu)$ are linearly dependent in $\mathbb{P}^N$.

Suppose we select N of the points P_ν, say $P_1, \ldots, P_{n(n+3)/2}$ for simplicity of notation, and let $A \subset \mathbb{P}^N$ be any hyperplane containing $N-1$ of them, say $P_2, \ldots, P_{n(n+3)/2}$. Since

$$n^2 = \frac{n(n+3)}{2} + \frac{n(n-3)}{2}$$

and $\dim H^0(\mathbb{P}^2, \mathcal{O}((n-3)H)) = n(n-3)/2 + 1$, we may find a curve B of degree $n-3$ passing through $P_{(n(n+3)/2)+1}, \ldots, P_{n^2}$. Then $A + B$ is a curve of degree $2n-3$ passing through $P_2, \ldots, P_{n^2}$, and consequently $A + B$ contains P_1. Now in general no $n(n-3)/2 + 1$ of the points P_ν will lie on a curve of degree $n-3$. In this case P_1 lies on A, and we have proved:

> *Given* N *of the points* P_ν, *any hyperplane containing* N -1 *of* $i_n(P_\nu)$ *contains the* N*th point also.*

This clearly implies $(**)$.

In the exceptional case we label our points $P_1, \ldots, P_{n(n+3)/2}$ so that the curve B of degree $n-3$ passes through exactly

$$P_k, \ldots, P_{n^2}, \qquad k \leqslant \frac{n(n+3)}{2}.$$

Given any curve A_i of degree n passing through $P_1, \ldots, \hat{P}_i, \ldots, P_k$, $A_i + B$ will contain Γ and so P_i lies on A_i. *Consequently, the points* $i_n(P_1), \ldots, i_n(P_k)$ *are linearly dependent in* $\mathbb{P}^N$.

This again implies $(**)$.   Q.E.D.

We have now illustrated the application of the residue theorem to points arising as intersections of plane algebraic curves having no multiple components. Multiple components arise naturally when we wish to know not only about the position in $\mathbb{P}^2$ of the points of intersection, but also about higher-order infinitesimal behavior.

For example, let $L \subset \mathbb{P}^2$ be a line. If we mark points $P_1, \ldots, P_n$ on L, then it is trivially possible to find an algebraic curve C of degree n passing through the P_ν—just take C to be a union of lines. It is equally easy to prescribe the tangent lines T_ν that C is to have at P_ν. However, if we assign second-order elements of arc C_ν passing through P_ν and with tangent T_ν, then it is not always possible to find an algebraic curve C having the prescribed second-order behavior C_ν around P_ν. There is one condition here, the *Reiss relation*, which we proceed to derive.

Suppose that C has affine equation $f(x,y)=0$, that L is the line $\{x=0\}$, and that the n points of intersection of C with L are distinct finite points on the y-axis. We shall prove the

Reiss Relation. *With the notations* $f_y = (\partial f / \partial y)(x, y)$, *etc.*

$$\sum \frac{\left(f_{xx}f_y^2 - 2f_{xy}f_xf_y + f_{yy}f_x^2\right)}{f_y^3} = 0,$$

the terms in the sum being evaluated at the points $L \cdot C$.

Proof. In a general vein, the mth-order behavior of C near the points of intersection $C \cap L$ will be reflected in the residues of

$$\omega = \frac{p(x,y)\,dx \wedge dy}{xf(x,y)^m}.$$

If $f(x,y)$ has degree n, then ω will not have the line at infinity as a component of its polar divisor provided that $\deg(p) \leqslant mn - 2$. In case $m = 2$, the restriction $\deg(p) \leqslant 2n - 2$ suggests taking p to be of the form $p(x,y) = \alpha f_{xx}f + \beta f_{xy}f + \gamma f_{yy}f + \delta f_x^2 + \varepsilon f_x f_y + \kappa f_y^2$. To see what p to choose, we assume that the origin is one of the points of intersection and will prove the

Lemma.

$$\operatorname{Res}_{\{0\}}\left(\frac{p(x,y)\,dx \wedge dy}{xf(x,y)^2}\right) = \frac{p_y}{f_y^2} - \frac{pf_{yy}}{f_y^3}.$$

Proof of Lemma. This is an application of the transformation formula from Section 2. We may assume that $f(x,y)$ has a Taylor series

$$f(x,y) = ax + by + \frac{cx^2}{2} + dxy + \frac{ey^2}{2} + \cdots, \qquad b \neq 0.$$

Consider the ideals

$$I = \{x,y^2\}, \qquad I' = \{x,f(x,y)^2\}.$$

For a suitable function $g(x,y)$ holomorphic in a neighborhood of the origin,

$$f(x,y)^2 = g(x,y)x + (b^2 + bey + \cdots)y^2.$$

Consequently, $I' \subset I$ with transformation matrix

$$A = \begin{pmatrix} 1 & g(x,y) \\ 0 & b^2 + bey + \cdots \end{pmatrix}.$$

Note that the determinant $\Delta = b^2 + bey + \cdots$ is nonzero at the origin. For $h(x,y)$ holomorphic, the transformation law gives

$$\operatorname{Res}_{\{0\}} \left(\frac{h(x,y)\,dx \wedge dy}{xy^2} \right) = \operatorname{Res}_{\{0\}} \left(\frac{\Delta(x,y)h(x,y)\,dx \wedge dy}{xf(x,y)^2} \right)$$

By the Cauchy formula the left-hand side is $h_y(0,0)$. Taking $h = p/\Delta$, we obtain

$$\operatorname{Res}_{\{0\}} \left(\frac{p(x,y)\,dx \wedge dy}{xf(x,y)^2} \right) = \frac{p_y(0)}{f_y(0)^2} - \frac{p(0)f_{yy}(0)}{f_y(0)^3},$$

since $f_y(0) = b$ and $f_{yy}(0) = e$. Q.E.D. for Lemma.

On the basis of the lemma and elementary fiddling around, if we take

$$p = f_x^2 - f f_{xx},$$

then

$$\operatorname{Res}_{\{0\}} \left(\frac{p(x,y)\,dx \wedge dy}{xf(x,y)^2} \right) = -\frac{\left(f_{xx}f_y^2 - 2f_{xy}f_x f_y + f_{yy}f_x^2 \right)}{f_y^3}.$$

Applying the residue theorem in the form $(*)$ gives the Reiss relation.
Q.E.D.

The expression in the Reiss relation has an interpretation encountered in the differential geometry of plane curves—in the calculus sense. Namely, suppose that $(x, y(x))$ is a parametric representation of C near the origin. Differentiating $f(x, y(x)) \equiv 0$ at the origin gives the equations

$$\begin{cases} f_x + f_y y' = 0, \\ f_{xx} + 2f_{xy}y' + f_{yy}y'^2 + f_y y'' = 0, \end{cases}$$

and eliminating y' yields

$$y'' = -\frac{\left(f_{xx}f_y^2 - 2f_{xy}f_x f_y + f_{yy}f_x^2 \right)}{f_y^3}.$$

On the other hand, it is elementary calculus that

$$y''(0) = \frac{\kappa}{\sin^3 \theta},$$

where κ is the curvature of C at the origin and θ is the angle that the tangent to C makes with the y-axis. Consequently, the Reiss relation may be expressed in the very pretty metric form

$$\sum_{\nu} \frac{\kappa_{\nu}}{\sin^3 \theta_{\nu}} = 0,$$

where κ_{ν} is the curvature of C at P_{ν} and θ_{ν} is the angle that the tangent T_{ν} makes with the line L.

We shall now show that the Reiss relation is sufficient. The polynomials $f(x,y)$ of degree n form a vector space of dimmension $(n+1)(n+2)/2$. Those of the form $g(x,y)x^3$ $(\deg(g)=n-3)$ form a vector space of dimension $(n-2)(n-1)/2$. The quotient space V has dimension

$$\frac{n^2+3n+2}{2} - \frac{n^2-3n+2}{2} = 3n.$$

Finding a curve C of degree n and with prescribed second-order behavior at points P_{ν} on the line $\{x=0\}$ is equivalent to finding a suitable point in the projective space $\mathbb{P}(V) \cong \mathbb{P}^{3n-1}$. Each second-order arc element imposes three linear conditions, and so there are $3n$ conditions in all. It follows that the Reiss relation is both necessary and sufficient.

Finally, we wish to point out that the residue theorem from Section 1 applies to configurations of points on general algebraic surfaces, not just $\mathbb{P}^2$. More precisely, suppose that L, L' are holomorphic line bundles over a surface S and $C \in |L|, C' \in |L'|$ are curves meeting transversely at $d = L \cdot L'$ points. Then we have the

Proposition. *Any curve* $D \in |K+L+L'|$ *that passes through all but one point of* $C \cdot C'$ *necessarily contains that remaining point.*

Proof. If $\sigma \in H^0(S, \mathcal{O}(L))$ and $\sigma' \in H^0(S, \mathcal{O}(L'))$ define C and C', and if $\psi \in H^0(S, \mathcal{O}(K+L+L')) = H^0(S, \Omega^2(L+L'))$, then

$$\omega = \frac{\psi}{\sigma \cdot \sigma'}$$

is a meromorphic 2-form on S with polar curve $C+C'$ to which the general residue theorem

$$\sum_{P_{\nu} \in C \cap C'} \text{Res}_{P_{\nu}}(\omega) = 0$$

clearly implies the result.   Q.E.D.

An extension to general vector bundles will be given in Section 4 at the end of this chapter.

3. RUDIMENTS OF COMMUTATIVE AND HOMOLOGICAL ALGEBRA WITH APPLICATIONS

Commutative Algebra

As the reader is no doubt aware, laying the proper algebraic foundations for the subject of algebraic geometry is an all-consuming task. On the other hand, just as sheaf cohomology greatly facilitates the study of divisors on a variety—a case where the local theory is relatively simple—the introduction of some algebraic machinery will clarify some of the preceding discussion concerning the local properties of a set of analytic equations $f_1(z_1,\ldots,z_n) = \cdots = f_n(z_1,\ldots,z_n) = 0$ having the origin as isolated common zero. This will be especially true of the transformation law and local duality theorem associated to our analytically defined residues; these two results will eventually achieve a very symmetric form.

We use the notation

$$\mathcal{O} = \lim_{\{0\} \in U} \mathcal{O}(U)$$

for the germs of analytic functions defined in some neighborhood U of the origin in $\mathbb{C}^n$. Clearly, $\mathcal{O} = \mathbb{C}\{z_1,\ldots,z_n\}$ is the ring of convergent power series. When involved in inductive arguments we shall write $\mathcal{O}_n$ for $\mathcal{O}$. Recall that a *local ring* is a ring having a unique maximal ideal. $\mathcal{O}$ is such a local ring with maximal ideal $m = \{z_1,\ldots,z_n\}$ the ideal of functions $f \in \mathcal{O}$ with $f(0) = 0$. The units are just $\mathcal{O}^* = \mathcal{O} - m$.

In Section 1 of Chapter 0 we proved that, given $f \neq 0$ in $\mathcal{O}_n$, there is a linear coordinate system $(z_1, z_2, \ldots, z_n) = (z', z_n)$ and unique Weierstrass polynomial

$$w(z) = z_n^d + a_1(z')z_n^{d-1} + \cdots + a_d(z') \in \mathcal{O}_{n-1}[z_n],$$

where $a_i(z') \in \mathcal{O}_{n-1}$ are nonunits such that

$$f(z) = u(z)w(z)$$

with $u \in \mathcal{O}^*$. In addition to the Weierstrass preparation theorem, we also proved the division theorem: For $g \in \mathcal{O}_n$,

$$g = hf + r,$$

where $r \in \mathcal{O}_{n-1}[z_n]$ has degree less than that of w. These two results provide the basic tools for studying the local ring $\mathcal{O}$ —especially the ideals in $\mathcal{O}$.

The method is frequently by induction on n. For example, the inductive hypothesis and Gauss lemma imply that $\mathcal{O}_{n-1}[z_n]$ is a unique factorization domain, and using the preparation theorem we deduced that

$\mathcal{O}_n$ *is a unique factorization domain.*

Similarly, we shall prove:

$\mathcal{O}_n$ *is a Noetherian ring,*

Proof. We must show that any ideal $I \subset \mathcal{O}$ has a finite number of generators. Let $0 \neq f \in I$. We may assume that $f \in \mathcal{O}_{n-1}[z_n]$ is a Weierstrass polynomial. Set $I' = I \cap \mathcal{O}_{n-1}[z_n]$. By induction hypothesis $\mathcal{O}_{n-1}$ is Noetherian, and then the Hilbert basis theorem implies that I' has a finite set $f_1, \ldots, f_k \in \mathcal{O}_{n-1}[z_n]$ of $\mathcal{O}_{n-1}$ generators. We claim that

$$I = \{ f, f_1, \ldots, f_k \}.$$

To see this, let $g \in I$ and apply the division theorem to obtain

$$g = hf + r.$$

Then $r \in I \cap \mathcal{O}_{n-1}[z_n] = I'$ and may be expressed in terms of $f_1, \ldots, f_k$.
$$\text{Q.E.D.}$$

Our discussion of commutative algebra will center around $\mathcal{O}$-*modules,* usually denoted by $M, N, R, \ldots$ *and which we always assume to be finitely generated.* Choosing generators $m_1, \ldots, m_k$ for an $\mathcal{O}$-module M, there is an exact sequence

$$0 \to R \to \mathcal{O}^{(k)} \overset{\pi}{\to} M \to 0$$

of $\mathcal{O}$-modules, where

$$\mathcal{O}^{(k)} = \underbrace{\mathcal{O} \oplus \cdots \oplus \mathcal{O}}_{k}$$

is the *free $\mathcal{O}$-module of rank* k,

$$\pi(g_1, \ldots, g_k) = g_1 m_1 + \cdots + g_k m_k,$$

and

$$R = \{ (g_1, \ldots, g_k) : g_1 m_1 + \cdots + g_k m_k = 0 \}$$

is the *module of relations* among the m_i's. We claim that R is again finitely generated. The proof is by induction on k, with the case $k = 1$ being that of an ideal in $\mathcal{O}$ just discussed. Setting $R' = R \cap \mathcal{O}^{(k-1)}$, in the exact sequence

$$0 \to R' \to R \to R/R' \to 0$$

both R' and $R/R' \subset \mathcal{O}$ are finitely generated, and hence so is R.

As examples of $\mathcal{O}$-modules, in addition to the free $\mathcal{O}$-modules mentioned above, the most important ones are

$$\begin{cases} I = \{ f_1, \ldots, f_k \} & \text{an } ideal \text{ in } \mathcal{O}, \\ M = \mathcal{O} / \{ f_1, \ldots, f_k \}. \end{cases}$$

Very roughly speaking, the second of these is the local ring at the origin of the variety $f_1(z) = \cdots = f_k(z) = 0$. We shall say more about this later. Given an ideal $\{f_1, \ldots, f_k\}$, where the $f_i \in \mathcal{O}_{n-1}[z_n]$ are Weierstrass polynomials, it is natural to consider $I' = I \cap \mathcal{O}_{n-1}[z_n]$ as a quotient-module of $\mathcal{O}_{n-1}^{(k)}$ over $\mathcal{O}_{n-1}$. Consequently, even though ideals in $\mathcal{O}_n$ may be our primary interest, more general modules arise naturally in inductive arguments.

$\mathcal{O}$-modules admit the operations of linear algebra, such as

$$M \oplus N, \qquad M \otimes_{\mathcal{O}} N, \qquad \mathrm{Hom}_{\mathcal{O}}(M, N).$$

Given an exact sequence of $\mathcal{O}$-modules

$$0 \to P \to Q \to R \to 0,$$

the resulting sequences

$$\begin{cases} P \otimes_{\mathcal{O}} M \to Q \otimes_{\mathcal{O}} M \to R \otimes_{\mathcal{O}} M \to 0, \\ 0 \to \mathrm{Hom}_{\mathcal{O}}(M, P) \to \mathrm{Hom}_{\mathcal{O}}(M, Q) \to \mathrm{Hom}_{\mathcal{O}}(M, R), \end{cases}$$

are exact. We express this by saying that $\otimes$ *is right-exact* and Hom *is left-exact*. Much of our discussion will be centered around the kernel of $P \otimes_{\mathcal{O}} M \to Q \otimes_{\mathcal{O}} M$ and cokernel of $\mathrm{Hom}_{\mathcal{O}}(M, Q) \to \mathrm{Hom}_{\mathcal{O}}(M, R)$.

Associated to an $\mathcal{O}$-module M is its *fiber* $M_0 = M/mM$—the motivation for this terminology will emerge when we discuss coherent sheaves. This is a module over $\mathcal{O}/m = \mathbb{C}$ and is therefore a finite-dimensional vector space. Our main technical tool is the

Nakayama Lemma. *If* $M = mM$, *then* $M = (0)$.

Proof. We define the ideal $I = \{f \in \mathcal{O} : f \cdot M = 0\}$ and shall prove that $I = \mathcal{O}$. Suppose $m_1, \ldots, m_k$ generate M and write

$$m_i = \sum_j a_{ij} m_j$$

or equivalently

$$\sum_j (\delta_{ij} - a_{ij}) m_j = 0,$$

where $a_{ij} \in m$. By Cramer's rule this implies

$$\Delta \cdot m_j = 0,$$

where

$$\Delta = \det(\delta_{ij} - a_{ij}) \in 1 + m.$$

Thus Δ is a unit, and so $I = \mathcal{O}$.   Q.E.D.

The Nakayama lemma is most useful in the following form:

$m_1, \ldots, m_k$ *generate* $M \Leftrightarrow$ *they generate* M_0.

Proof. The implication $\Rightarrow$ is obvious. Conversely, assume that $m_1,\ldots,m_k$ generate M_0 and let $S \subset M$ be the submodule of M that they generate. To show that $S = M$ we set $Q = M/S$ and consider the exact sequence

$$0 \to S \to M \overset{\pi}{\to} Q \to 0.$$

If $m \in M$, then $m - s \in mM$ for some $s \in S$. Consequently, $\pi(m) = \pi(m - s) \in mQ$ and $Q = mQ$. Then $Q = (0)$ as desired.   Q.E.D.

We note one final version:

> If $\varphi : M \to N$ is a homomorphism of $\mathcal{O}$-modules such that $\varphi_0 : M_0 \to N_0$ is surjective, then φ is surjective.

Now we come to a main standard definition. An $\mathcal{O}$-module M is *projective* if the following diagram holds:

$$
\begin{array}{ccc}
& M & \\
\gamma \Big\downarrow & & \searrow{\scriptstyle \beta} \\
K \underset{\alpha}{\to} & L & \to 0
\end{array}
$$

This diagram is to be interpreted as follows: K and L are given $\mathcal{O}$-modules, and α and β are given $\mathcal{O}$-module homomorphisms with α being surjective. Then there exists γ such that the diagram is commutative. Briefly, *the solid arrows are given and the dotted arrows can be filled in*. This notation will be consistently used.

Lemma. M *is projective* $\Leftrightarrow$ *it is free.*

Proof. Assume M is free—we may as well take $M = \mathcal{O}$—and let $l_i \in L$ be generators and $k_i \in K$ with $\alpha(k_i) = l_i$. If $\beta(1) = \Sigma_i f_i l_i$, then we may set $\gamma(1) = \Sigma_i f_i k_i$ to fill in the dotted arrow.

Conversely, assume M is projective. Taking $M = L$ and K to be free, we have

$$\mathcal{O}^{(k)} \overset{\alpha}{\dashrightarrow} M \to 0$$

$$\underset{\gamma}{}$$

We may assume that k is the minimal number of generators of M, or equivalently that the map $\mathbb{C}^k \overset{\alpha_0}{\to} M_0$ on fibers is an isomorphism. Then $\gamma \circ \alpha$ is surjective and γ is surjective on the fibers. By Nakayama's lemma (third form) γ is surjective and α is an isomorphism.   Q.E.D.

Note that the definition of projective may be rephrased as follows:

$$K \to L \to 0$$

$$\Downarrow$$

$$\mathrm{Hom}_{\mathcal{O}}(M, K) \to \mathrm{Hom}_{\mathcal{O}}(M, L) \to 0.$$

On the other hand, since projective modules are free, for M projective we have

$$0 \to P \to Q$$

$$\Downarrow$$

$$0 \to M \otimes_{\mathcal{O}} P \to M \otimes_{\mathcal{O}} Q.$$

Consequently, *both the functors* $\mathrm{Hom}_{\mathcal{O}}(M, \cdot)$ *and* $M \otimes_{\mathcal{O}} \cdot$ *are exact for* M *projective*. We shall explore this systematically in the next discussion.

Homological Algebra

We begin by remembering a series of definitions, most of which are probably familiar from algebraic topology.

(a)   A *complex* is given by either

$$(K.) \qquad \to K_n \xrightarrow{\partial} K_{n-1} \xrightarrow{\alpha} \ldots, \qquad \partial^2 = 0,$$

or

$$(K\cdot) \qquad \to K^n \xrightarrow{\delta} K^{n+1} \xrightarrow{\delta} \ldots, \qquad \delta^2 = 0.$$

Here the K's will always be finitely generated $\mathcal{O}$-modules and maps $\mathcal{O}$-module homomorphisms, although most of the present discussion goes over to modules over general rings. Taking cycles/boundaries gives respectively $H_*(K.) = \oplus H_n(K.)$ (*homology*) and $H^*(K\cdot) = \oplus H^n(K\cdot)$ (*cohomology*). We shall give the remaining discussion in homology, leaving the dual considerations to the reader.

(b)   A *mapping* or *homomorphism of complexes* $\varphi : K. \to L.$ is given by a commutative diagram

$$\to K_n \xrightarrow{\partial} K_{n-1} \to \cdots$$
$$\downarrow \varphi \qquad \downarrow \varphi$$
$$\to L_n \xrightarrow{\partial} L_{n-1} \to \cdots$$

It induces a map $\varphi_* : H_*(K.) \to H_*(L.)$ on homology. When necessary we shall write $\varphi_n : K_n \to L_n$ and ∂_K, ∂_L for the boundary maps. The set $\text{Hom}(K., L.)$ of homomorphisms of complexes is a group with $(\varphi + \psi)_* = \varphi_* + \psi_*$.

(c)   A homomorphism of complexes $\varphi : K. \to L.$ is *homotopic to zero*, denoted $\varphi \sim 0$, if there is a chain homotopy

$$\varphi = \partial_L \alpha_n + \alpha_{n-1} \partial_K$$

as indicated by the diagram

$$
\begin{array}{ccccc}
K_{n+1} & \xrightarrow{} & K_n & \xrightarrow{\partial_K} & K_{n-1} \\
 & \alpha_n \swarrow & \downarrow \varphi & \swarrow \alpha_{n-1} & \\
L_{n+1} & \xrightarrow{\partial_L} & L_n & \xrightarrow{} & L_{n-1}
\end{array}
$$

In this case $\varphi_* = 0$. Two maps φ and ψ are homotopic if $\varphi - \psi \sim 0$; then $\varphi_* = \psi_*$.

(d)   Most importantly, an exact sequence of complexes

$$0 \to K. \to L. \to M. \to 0$$

is defined in the obvious way. It gives rise to a long exact homology sequence

$$\cdots \to H_n(K.) \to H_n(L.) \to H_n(M.) \xrightarrow{\partial_*} H_{n-1}(K.) \to \cdots .$$

The following definition and proposition are our primary technical tools:

DEFINITION.   A *projective resolution* $E.(M)$ of an $\mathcal{O}$-module M is given by an exact sequence

$$E.(M): \quad \cdots \to E_m \xrightarrow{\partial} E_{m-1} \xrightarrow{\partial} \cdots \xrightarrow{\partial} E_0 \to M \to 0,$$

where the E_m are projective (=free) $\mathcal{O}$-modules.

Note that $H_n(E.(M)) = 0$ for $n > 0$ and $H_0(E.(M)) \cong M$. Given a projective resolution $E.(M)$ and an exact sequence

$$\to F_m \to F_{m-1} \to \cdots \to F_0 \to 0,$$

where the F_m are free, we obtain a new projective resolution $E'.(M)$ by setting $E'_m = E_m \oplus F_m$. We shall prove later that any projective resolution may be so modified as to have $E'_m = 0$ for $m > n$ (Syzygy theorem).

Proposition.   1.   *Projective resolutions exist*;

2.   *Given* $\varphi : M \to N$ *and projective resolutions* $E.(M)$ *and* $E.(N)$, *we may find a mapping of complexes* $\Phi : E.(M) \to E.(N)$ *inducing* φ *in the sense of the*

commutative diagram

$$H_0(E_{\cdot}(M)) \xrightarrow{\Phi_*} H_0(E_{\cdot}(N))$$
$$\| \wr \qquad\qquad\qquad \| \wr$$
$$M \xrightarrow{\varphi} N$$

3. Φ *is unique up to homotopy*; *and*

4. *If* $0 \to M' \to M \to M'' \to 0$ *is exact, then we may choose projective resolutions and mappings of complexes so that* $E_{\cdot}(M') \to E_{\cdot}(M) \to E_{\cdot}(M'') \to 0$ *is an exact sequence of complexes.*

Proofs. Since we have proved that the kernel of any surjective map $\mathcal{O}^{(k)} \to M \to 0$ is a finitely generated $\mathcal{O}$-module, assertion 1 follows.

The proofs of assertions 2–4 are all similar, but with increasing complexity of notation. We shall therefore only prove assertion 2, leaving 3 and 4 for the reader to carry out or look up in the references.

Given the solid arrow in the diagram

$$\begin{array}{ccc} E_0 \to M \to 0 \\ \Big\downarrow {\Phi_0} \quad \Big\downarrow {\varphi} \\ F_0 \to N \to 0 \end{array}$$

the dotted arrow Φ_0 exists by the definition of projective. Proceeding to the next step, if R_0 and S_0 are defined by

$$0 \to R_0 \to E_0 \to M \to 0$$
$$\Big\downarrow {\Phi_0} \quad \Big\downarrow {\varphi}$$
$$0 \to S_0 \to F_0 \to N \to 0$$

then what we have is the solid arrows in the diagram

$$\begin{array}{ccc} E_1 \to R_0 \to 0 \\ \Big\downarrow {\Phi_1} \quad \Big\downarrow {\Phi_0} \\ F_1 \to S_0 \to 0 \end{array}$$

and the dotted arrow fills in by projectivity. Continuing in this manner gives assertion 2.   Q.E.D.

DEFINITION.   Given finitely generated $\mathcal{O}$-modules M and N,

$$\begin{cases} \operatorname{Ext}^n_{\mathcal{O}}(M,N) = H^n(\operatorname{Hom}_{\mathcal{O}}(E_{\cdot}(M),N)), \\ \operatorname{Tor}^{\mathcal{O}}_n(M,N) = H_n(E_{\cdot}(M) \otimes_{\mathcal{O}} N). \end{cases}$$

We shall derive the main properties of Ext, for the most part leaving the analogous properties of Tor to the reader. We first note that by 2 and 3 Ext is well-defined independently of the projective resolution $E_.(M)$. More generally, maps

$$\varphi: M \to M', \qquad \psi: N \to N'$$

induce

$$\Phi^*: \operatorname{Ext}_\Theta(M',N) \to \operatorname{Ext}_\Theta(M,N),$$
$$\Psi_*: \operatorname{Ext}_{\ddot{\Theta}}^*(M,N) \to \operatorname{Ext}_\Theta(M,N'),$$

with functoriality properties such as

$$\overset{\lambda}{\overbrace{M'' \underset{\gamma}{\to} M' \underset{\varphi}{\to} M}}$$

$$\Downarrow$$

$$\Lambda^* = \Phi^* \circ \Gamma^*.$$

Thus, $\operatorname{Ext}_{\ddot{\Theta}}^*(M,N)$ *is a functor contravariant in* M *and covariant in* N.

Next, we note that the definitions of Ext and Tor are not symmetric in M and N. For Tor this may be rectified as follows: Take projective resolutions $E_.(M)$ and $F_.(N)$ for M and N and consider the double complex

$$(E_.(M) \otimes F_.(N), \partial_M \otimes 1 \pm 1 \otimes \partial_N).$$

Recall from Chapter 3 that there are two spectral sequences with

$$'E_1 = H_*(E_.(M) \otimes_\Theta F_.(N), 1 \otimes \partial_N),$$
$$''E_1 = H_*(E_.(M) \otimes_\Theta F_.(N), \partial_M \otimes 1),$$

both of which abut to the hypercohomology

$$H_*(E_.(M) \otimes_\Theta F_.(N), \partial_M \otimes 1 \pm 1 \otimes \partial_N).$$

Since tensoring with a free module preserves exact sequences, $'E_1^{p,q} = 0$ for $q > 0$ and $''E_1^{p,q} = 0$ for $p > 0$. Thus both spectral sequences are trivial, and we deduce that

$$H_*(E_.(M) \otimes_\Theta N) \cong \operatorname{Tor}_*^\Theta(M,N) \cong H_*(M \otimes_\Theta F_.(N)).$$

For Ext the situation is more complicated and necessitates discussing injective resolutions for the second factor. Since this will not be required for our discussion, we won't get into these matters.

Next, we observe that

$$(*) \qquad\qquad \operatorname{Ext}_\Theta^0(M,N) \cong \operatorname{Hom}_\Theta(M,N).$$

Proof.   If $E_1 \to E_0 \to M \to 0$ is exact, then so is

$$0 \to \mathrm{Hom}_\mathcal{O}(M, N) \to \mathrm{Hom}_\mathcal{O}(E_0, N) \to \mathrm{Hom}_\mathcal{O}(E_1, N).\qquad \text{Q.E.D.}$$

The main property of the Ext functor is:

Short exact sequences of $\mathcal{O}$-modules

$$\begin{cases} 0 \to M' \to M \to M'' \to 0, \\ 0 \to N' \to N \to N'' \to 0, \end{cases}$$

induce long exact sequences

$$\begin{cases} \cdots \to \mathrm{Ext}^n_\mathcal{O}(M, N) \to \mathrm{Ext}^n_\mathcal{O}(M', N) \to \mathrm{Ext}^{n+1}_\mathcal{O}(M'', N) \to \cdots, \\ \cdots \to \mathrm{Ext}^n_\mathcal{O}(M, N) \to \mathrm{Ext}^n_\mathcal{O}(M, N'') \to \mathrm{Ext}^{n+1}_\mathcal{O}(M, N') \to \cdots, \end{cases}$$

of Ext's.

Proof.   First we note that a short exact sequence of free $\mathcal{O}$-modules splits, as indicated by the dotted arrow in the diagram

$$0 \to E' \to E \to E'' \to 0.$$

Thus $E \cong E' \oplus E''$, and consequently

$$0 \to \mathrm{Hom}_\mathcal{O}(E'', N) \to \mathrm{Hom}_\mathcal{O}(E, N) \to \mathrm{Hom}_\mathcal{O}(E', N) \to 0$$

is exact for any $\mathcal{O}$-module N. Choosing projective resolutions so that

$$0 \to E_.(M') \to E_.(M) \to E_.(M'') \to 0$$

is exact, it follows that

$$0 \to \mathrm{Hom}_\mathcal{O}(E_.(M''), N) \to \mathrm{Hom}_\mathcal{O}(E_.(M), N) \to \mathrm{Hom}_\mathcal{O}(E_.(M'), N) \to 0$$

is an exact sequence of complexes, and this gives the first long exact sequence. The second one is even simpler.   Q.E.D.

For example, given $0 \to N' \to N \to N'' \to 0$, we obtain

$$(\ast\ast)\; 0 \to \mathrm{Hom}_\mathcal{O}(M, N') \to \mathrm{Hom}_\mathcal{O}(M, N) \to \mathrm{Hom}_\mathcal{O}(M, N'') \to \mathrm{Ext}^1_\mathcal{O}(M, N'),$$

so that $\mathrm{Ext}^1_\mathcal{O}(M, \cdot)$ measures the extent to which $\mathrm{Hom}_\mathcal{O}(M, \cdot)$ fails to be right-exact.

We next shall prove:

$\mathrm{Ext}^q_\mathcal{O}(M, N) = 0$ *for* $q > 0$ *and every* $\mathcal{O}$-*module* $N \Leftrightarrow M$ *is projective.*

Proof.   Clearly if M is projective, the higher Ext's are zero.
Conversely, suppose that $\mathrm{Ext}^1_\mathcal{O}(M, N) = 0$ for all N, and consider a

diagram

$$M$$
$$\beta \nearrow \quad \searrow \alpha$$
$$0 \to N \to P \to Q \to 0$$

in which the solid arrows are given. Applying (**) above and $\mathrm{Ext}^1_{\mathcal{O}}(M,N) = 0$ gives

$$\mathrm{Hom}_{\mathcal{O}}(M,P) \to \mathrm{Hom}_{\mathcal{O}}(M,Q) \to 0,$$

so that the dotted arrow β can be filled in. Consequently M is projective.

Q.E.D.

Finally we shall refine this to:

$\mathrm{Ext}^1_{\mathcal{O}}(M,E) = 0$ *for all projective modules* $E \Leftrightarrow M$ *is projective*.

Proof. Suppose that $\mathrm{Ext}^1_{\mathcal{O}}(M,E)$ for all projective (=free) modules E. Choosing generators for M, we obtain a short exact sequence

$$0 \to R \to E \to M \to 0$$

with E free. Applying the other long exact sequence of Ext's gives

$$\mathrm{Hom}_{\mathcal{O}}(E,E) \to \mathrm{Hom}_{\mathcal{O}}(R,E) \to \mathrm{Ext}^1_{\mathcal{O}}(M,E) = 0.$$

Consequently the dotted arrow π exists, and $M \cong \ker \pi$, $E \cong R \oplus M$. Since a direct summand of a projective module is again projective, we are done.

Q.E.D.

In closing we should like to comment that the name "Ext" suggests extensions, and it was in this context that Ext^1 was first defined. We shall discuss this in Section 4, where it will arise quite naturally in context.

Another possible interpretation of Ext is pertaining to some sort of duality, since it reflects the properties of passing from an $\mathcal{O}$-module M to the "dual" $\mathcal{O}$-module $\mathrm{Hom}_{\mathcal{O}}(M, \cdot)$. This will be made precise in the next section, where in particular the local duality theorem will be put in intrinsic form.

Thus Ext has two quite different faces, each interesting in its own right.

The Koszul Complex and Applications

Koszul Complex. We continue using the notation $\mathcal{O}$ for the local ring of germs of analytic functions defined in some neighborhood of the origin in $\mathbb{C}^n$. Suppose $f_1, \ldots, f_r \in \mathcal{O}$; denote by $I_k = \{f_1, \ldots, f_k\}$ the ideal generated by the first k functions, and set $I = I_r$.

DEFINITION. $(f_1, \ldots, f_r)$ is a *regular sequence* if f_k is not a zero divisor in $\mathcal{O}/I_{k-1}$ for $k = 1, \ldots, r$.

We recall the geometric interpretation, mentioned above and proved in the case $n = 2$, that this is equivalent to $\mathrm{codim}\, V_k = k$, where $V_k = \{f_1(z) = \cdots = f_k(z) = 0\}$.

Given a regular sequence, the Koszul complex will give a particularly nice projective resolution of the $\mathcal{O}$-module I. It is modeled on the well-known fact from linear algebra that, for an n-dimensional vector space V and nonzero vector $v^* \in V^*$, the *contraction operator*

$$i(v^*): \wedge^k V \to \wedge^{k-1} V$$

induces an exact sequence of vector spaces

$$0 \to \wedge^n V \to \wedge^{n-1} V \to \cdots \to \wedge^2 V \to V \to \mathbb{C} \to 0$$

($\mathbb{C} = \wedge^0 V$). The basis for our intrinsic formulation of local duality is that, under the identifications

$$\mathrm{Hom}(\wedge^k V, \mathbb{C}) \cong \wedge^k V^* \cong \wedge^n V^* \otimes \wedge^{n-k} V,$$

the above sequence is *self-dual* in the sense that the diagram

$$
\begin{array}{ccc}
\mathrm{Hom}(\wedge^k V, \mathbb{C}) & \xrightarrow{\sim} & \wedge^n V^* \otimes \wedge^{n-k} V \\
\downarrow{\scriptstyle i(v^*)^*} & & \downarrow{\scriptstyle 1 \otimes i(v^*)} \\
\mathrm{Hom}(\wedge^{k+1} V, \mathbb{C}) & \xrightarrow{\sim} & \wedge^n V^* \otimes \wedge^{n-(k+1)} V
\end{array}
$$

is commutative.

Now to construct the Koszul complex let $e_1, \ldots, e_k$ be the standard basis for $\mathbb{C}^r$ and set

$$
\begin{cases}
E_k = \mathcal{O} \otimes_{\mathbb{C}} \wedge^k \mathbb{C}^r, \\
e_J = e_{j_1} \wedge \cdots \wedge e_{j_k}, \quad J = (j_1, \ldots, j_k) \subset (1, \ldots, r).
\end{cases}
$$

Then E_k is a free $\mathcal{O}$-module with basis $\{e_J\}$, and we define

$$E_k \xrightarrow{\partial} E_{k-1}$$

by $\mathcal{O}$-linearity and the usual boundary formula

$$\partial(e_J) = \sum_{\nu=1}^{k} (-1)^{\nu-1} f_{j_\nu} e_{j_1} \wedge \cdots \wedge \hat{e}_{j_\nu} \wedge \cdots \wedge e_{j_k}.$$

For $k = 1$ we set $E_0 = \mathcal{O}$ and $\partial(e_i) = f_i$. This defines the *Koszul complex* $E_\cdot(f)$ for any set of functions $f = (f_1, \ldots, f_r)$, and we have the

Lemma. *In case* $(f_1, \ldots, f_r)$ *is a regular sequence*,

$$H_q(E_\cdot(f)) = 0 \quad \text{for } q > 0$$

and

$$H_0(E_.(f)) \cong \mathcal{O}/I.$$

Consequently, $E_.(f)$ *gives a projective resolution of* $\mathcal{O}/I$.

Proof. It is clear that the image of $E_1 \xrightarrow{\partial} E_0 = \mathcal{O}$ is just the ideal I, so that $H_0(E_.(f)) \cong \mathcal{O}/I$. We shall prove by induction on r that the higher homology is zero.

In case $r = 1$ the Koszul complex is $0 \to \mathcal{O} \xrightarrow{f_1} \mathcal{O}$ since $f_1 \neq 0$, and the result is clear.

Now we assume the result for $r-1$, and let $F_k \subset E_k$ be induced by the inclusion $\wedge^k \mathbb{C}^{r-1} \subset \wedge^k \mathbb{C}^r$, where $\mathbb{C}^{r-1}$ is spanned by $e_1, \ldots, e_{r-1}$. There results a big commutative diagram:

$$
\begin{array}{ccccccccc}
& & 0 & & 0 & & 0 & & 0 \\
& & \downarrow & & \downarrow & & \downarrow & & \downarrow \\
F_. : & 0 \to & F_{r-1} \to & F_{r-2} \to & \cdots \to & F_1 \to & I_{r-1} & \to 0 \\
& & \downarrow & & \downarrow & & \downarrow & & \downarrow \\
E_. : & 0 \to E_r \to & E_{r-1} \to & E_{r-2} \to & \cdots \to & E_1 \to & I_r & \to 0 \\
& & \downarrow & & \downarrow & & \downarrow & & \downarrow \\
Q_. : & 0 \to Q_r \to & Q_{r-1} \to & Q_{r-2} \to & \cdots \to & Q_1 \xrightarrow{\alpha} & I_r/I_{r-1} \to 0 \\
& & \downarrow & & \downarrow & & \downarrow & & \downarrow \\
& & 0 & & 0 & & 0 & & 0 \\
\end{array}
$$

We make the identification

$$Q_k \cong \mathcal{O}(e_r \otimes \wedge^{k-1}\mathbb{C}^{r-1}).$$

This being done, for $J = (j_1, \ldots, j_{k-1}) \subset (1, \ldots, r-1)$.

$$\partial(e_r \otimes e_J) = f_r e_J \pm e_r \otimes \partial e_J$$
$$\equiv e_r \otimes \partial e_J \text{ modulo } F_k.$$

Thus $Q_.$ is again a Koszul complex, to which the induction assumption applies.

We now examine the lower right-hand corner

$$
\begin{array}{ccc}
E_1 \to & I_r & \to 0 \\
\downarrow & \downarrow & \\
Q_2 \xrightarrow{\partial} Q_1 \xrightarrow{\alpha} & I_r/I_{r-1} \to 0 \\
\downarrow & \downarrow & \\
0 & 0 & \\
\end{array}
$$

Under the identifications

$$Q_2 \cong \mathcal{O}(e_r \otimes \mathbb{C}^{r-1}), \qquad \partial(e_r \otimes e_j) = f_j e_r,$$
$$Q_1 \cong \mathcal{O} \cdot e_r, \qquad \alpha(g e_r) = g f_r,$$

the diagram is commutative. If $\alpha(ge_r) = 0$, then $gf_r \in \{f_1, \ldots, f_{r-1}\}$, and so $g \in \{f_1, \ldots, f_{r-1}\}$ by the regular sequence assumption. Thus $ge_r \in \partial Q_2$, and so the big diagram is commutative and exact. Since $H_*(F_.) = 0 = H_*(Q_.)$, we deduce that $H_*(E_.) = 0$ as desired.   Q.E.D.

Intrinsic Form of Local Duality. We shall use the Koszul complex to compute $\text{Ext}_\mathcal{O}^* (\mathcal{O}/I, \mathcal{O})$, and then interpret the result as an intrinsic form of the duality theorem from Section 2 above. In fact, we shall reprove the duality theorem in this new form.

The following plays an analogous role to the $*$-operator in Hodge theory:

Lemma. *There are isomorphisms $\text{Hom}_\mathcal{O}(E_k, \mathcal{O}) \cong E_{r-k}$ such that the diagram*

$$
\begin{array}{ccc}
\text{Hom}_\mathcal{O}(E_k, \mathcal{O}) & \xrightarrow{\sim} & E_{r-k} \\
\downarrow{\scriptstyle \partial^*} & \sim & \downarrow{\scriptstyle \partial} \\
\text{Hom}_\mathcal{O}(E_{k+1}, \mathcal{O}) & \xrightarrow{\sim} & E_{r-k-1}
\end{array}
$$

is commutative.

Proof. For an index set $J \subset (1, \ldots, r)$, we let $J^0 = (1, \ldots, r) - J$ be the complementary index set and define

$$
e_{J*} = \pm e_{J^0} \in E_{r-k}.
$$

The sign is chosen to make $e_J \wedge e_{J*} = e_1 \wedge \cdots \wedge e_r$. Then we define $\hat{e}_J \in \text{Hom}_\mathcal{O}(E_k, \mathcal{O})$ by

$$
\hat{e}_J(e_{J'}) = \begin{cases} 0, & J \neq J', \\ 1, & J = J'. \end{cases}
$$

The isomorphism in the lemma is given by

$$
\hat{e}_J \to e_{J*}.
$$

It is a direct computation that the diagram is commutative.   Q.E.D.

Applying this lemma gives the first part of the

Proposition. *Suppose that $f = (f_1, \ldots, f_r)$ is a regular sequence generating an ideal $I = I(f)$. Then*

$$
(*) \qquad \text{Ext}^k_\mathcal{O}(\mathcal{O}/I, \mathcal{O}) = 0, \quad k < r; \qquad \text{Ext}^r_\mathcal{O}(\mathcal{O}/I, \mathcal{O}) \cong \mathcal{O}/I.
$$

The second isomorphism has the following functoriality property: Suppose that $I' = I(f')$ is a regular ideal contained in I, so that

$$
f'_i = \sum_j a_{ij} f_j.
$$

Denote by $\Delta = det\,(a_{ij})$ *the determinant of the matrix* (a_{ij}). *Then the diagram*

(**)
$$\begin{array}{ccc} \mathrm{Ext}_{\mathcal{O}}^{r}(\mathcal{O}/I,\mathcal{O}) & \xrightarrow{\sim} & \mathcal{O}/I \\ \downarrow & & \downarrow{\scriptstyle\Delta} \\ \mathrm{Ext}_{\mathcal{O}}^{r}(\mathcal{O}/I',\mathcal{O}) & \xrightarrow{\sim} & \mathcal{O}/I' \end{array}$$

is commutative. Moreover, the vertical map is injective.

Proof. The computation of the $\mathrm{Ext}_{\mathcal{O}}^{k}(\mathcal{O}/I,\mathcal{O})$ follows from the previous lemma. To prove the transformation formula (**), we shall define mappings

$$E_{\cdot}(f): 0 \to E_r \to E_{r-1} \to \cdots \to E_k \to \cdots \to E_1 \to E_0 \to \mathcal{O}/I \to 0$$
$$\uparrow{\scriptstyle A_r} \quad \uparrow{\scriptstyle A_{r-1}} \qquad \uparrow{\scriptstyle A_k} \qquad \uparrow{\scriptstyle A_1} \quad \uparrow{\scriptstyle A_0} \quad \uparrow$$
$$E_{\cdot}(f'): 0 \to E_r' \to E_{r-1}' \to \cdots \to E_k' \to \cdots \to E_1' \to E_0' \to \mathcal{O}/I' \to 0$$

between the Koszul complexes as follows: The map $\mathcal{O}/I' \to \mathcal{O}/I$ is the natural map induced by the inclusion $I' \subset I$, and A_0 is the identity under the identifications $E_0 \cong \mathcal{O} \cong E_0'$. $A_1 : E_1' \to E_1$ is defined by

$$A_1(e_i') = \sum_j a_{ij} e_j,$$

so that

$$\partial A_1(e_i') = \sum a_{ij} f_j = f_i' = A_0(\partial e_i').$$

The remaining maps $A_k : E_k' \to E_k$ are the kth exterior powers of A_1. The diagram is then commutative. Under the identifications

$$E_r \cong \mathcal{O}, \qquad E_r' \cong \mathcal{O},$$

A_r is just the determinant Δ.

It remains to prove the injectivity. Before doing this, it might be instructive to verify directly that

$$\Delta \cdot I \subset I',$$

so that multiplication by Δ induces a map $\mathcal{O}/I \xrightarrow{\Delta} \mathcal{O}/I'$ going in the nonobvious direction. By Cramer's rule

$$\Delta \delta_{ij} = \sum_k a_{kj} A_{ik},$$

where A_{ik} is $\pm$ the (i,k)th cofactor of (a_{ij}). Then

$$\Delta f_i = \sum_j \Delta \delta_{ij} f_j = \sum_{j,k} a_{kj} f_j A_{ik} = \sum_k A_{ik} f_k',$$

so that $\Delta I \subset I'$ as desired.

Consider now the exact sequence

$$0 \to I/I' \to \mathcal{O}/I' \to \mathcal{O}/I \to 0.$$

The long exact sequence of Ext's gives

$$\to \operatorname{Ext}_{\mathcal{O}}^{k}(\mathcal{O}/I', \mathcal{O}) \to \operatorname{Ext}_{\mathcal{O}}^{k}(I/I', \mathcal{O}) \to \operatorname{Ext}^{k+1}(\mathcal{O}/I, \mathcal{O}) \to \cdots .$$

Our desired injectivity thus follows from

$$\operatorname{Ext}_{\mathcal{O}}^{r-1}(I/I', \mathcal{O}) = 0,$$

which we now prove.

Set $I_k' = \{f_1', \ldots, f_k'\}$ and consider the following array of sequences of $\mathcal{O}$-modules, which are exact by the regular sequence property of the f_i':

$$0 \xrightarrow{\quad} \mathcal{O} \xrightarrow{f_1'} \mathcal{O} \xrightarrow{\quad} \mathcal{O}/I_1' \to 0$$

$$0 \xrightarrow{\quad} \mathcal{O}/I_1' \xrightarrow{f_2'} \mathcal{O}/I_1' \xrightarrow{\quad} \mathcal{O}/I_2' \to 0$$

$$\vdots \qquad\qquad \vdots \qquad\qquad \vdots$$

$$0 \xrightarrow{\quad} \mathcal{O}/I_{r-1}' \xrightarrow{f_r'} \mathcal{O}/I_{r-1}' \xrightarrow{\quad} \mathcal{O}/I' \to 0$$

Applying the exact sequences of Ext in the second variable gives

$$\operatorname{Ext}_{\mathcal{O}}^{r-2}(I/I', \mathcal{O}/I_1') \to \operatorname{Ext}_{\mathcal{O}}^{r-1}(I/I', \mathcal{O}) \xrightarrow{f_1'} \operatorname{Ext}_{\mathcal{O}}^{r-1}(I/I', \mathcal{O})$$

$$\operatorname{Ext}_{\mathcal{O}}^{r-3}(I/I', \mathcal{O}/I_2') \to \operatorname{Ext}_{\mathcal{O}}^{r-2}(I/I', \mathcal{O}/I_1') \xrightarrow{f_2'} \operatorname{Ext}_{\mathcal{O}}^{r-2}(I/I', \mathcal{O}/I_1')$$

$$\vdots \qquad\qquad\qquad \vdots \qquad\qquad\qquad \vdots$$

$$\operatorname{Ext}_{\mathcal{O}}^{0}(I/I', \mathcal{O}/I_{r-1}') \to \operatorname{Ext}_{\mathcal{O}}^{1}(I/I', \mathcal{O}/I_{r-2}') \xrightarrow{f_{r-1}'} \operatorname{Ext}_{\mathcal{O}}^{1}(I/I', \mathcal{O}/I_{r-2}')$$

Now, and this is the point, the maps

$$\operatorname{Ext}_{\mathcal{O}}^{r-k}(I/I', \mathcal{O}/I_{k-1}') \xrightarrow{f_k'} \operatorname{Ext}_{\mathcal{O}}^{r-k}(I/I', \mathcal{O}/I_{k-1}')$$

are all zero, since these maps are $\mathcal{O}$-linear, and therefore the multiplication by f_k' can be moved from the factor $\mathcal{O}/I_{k-1}'$ to I/I', where it is zero. Putting this all together, we obtain a surjective map

$$\operatorname{Hom}_{\mathcal{O}}(I/I', \mathcal{O}/I_{r-1}') \to \operatorname{Ext}_{\mathcal{O}}^{r-1}(I/I', \mathcal{O}) \to 0.$$

If $\varphi \in \operatorname{Hom}_{\mathcal{O}}(I/I', \mathcal{O}/I_{r-1}')$, then for any $g \in I/I'$

$$f_r' \varphi(g) = \varphi(f_r' g) = 0 \Rightarrow \varphi(g) = 0$$

$$\Rightarrow \operatorname{Ext}_{\mathcal{O}}^{r-1}(I/I', \mathcal{O}) = 0. \qquad \text{Q.E.D.}$$

We now return to the local duality theorem. Let $I = \{f_1, \ldots, f_n\}$ and $I' = \{f'_1, \ldots, f'_n\}$ be regular ideals with $I' \subset I$, and denote by Ω^n the stalk at the origin of the sheaf of holomorphic n-forms. A choice of coordinates $z_1, \ldots, z_n$ near the origin induces an isomorphism

$$\mathcal{O} \cong \Omega^n$$

given by

$$g(z) \to g(z) \, dz_1 \wedge \cdots \wedge dz_n.$$

We recall that the pairing

$$\mathrm{res}_f : \ \mathcal{O}/I \otimes \mathcal{O}/I \to \mathbb{C}$$

defined by

$$\mathrm{res}_f(h, g) = \mathrm{Res}_{\{0\}} \left(\frac{g(z) h(z) \, dz_1 \wedge \cdots \wedge dz_n}{f_1(z) \cdots f_n(z)} \right)$$

depends on the choice of generators f_i for I and local coordinates $z_1, \ldots, z_n$. The behavior of res_f under changing generators for I or changing local coordinates is given by the transformation formula. This brings us to the

Local Duality Theorem II. *For regular ideals* $\mathrm{I} = \{f_1, \ldots, f_n\}$ *the pairing*

$$\mathrm{res}: \ \mathcal{O}/I \otimes \mathrm{Ext}^n_{\mathcal{O}}(\mathcal{O}/I, \Omega^n) \to \mathbb{C}$$

defined by the isomorphism $(*)$ *in the previous proposition and residue* res_f *is nondegenerate, independent of the choice of local coordinates and generators of* I, *and functorial in the sense that the diagram*

$$\begin{array}{ccc}
\mathcal{O}/I \otimes \mathrm{Ext}^n_{\mathcal{O}}(\mathcal{O}/I, \Omega^n) & \overset{\mathrm{res}}{\to} & \mathbb{C} \\
\uparrow_{\pi} \qquad \downarrow_{\pi^*} & & \| \\
\mathcal{O}/I' \otimes \mathrm{Ext}^n_{\mathcal{O}}(\mathcal{O}/I', \Omega^n) & \overset{\mathrm{res}}{\to} & \mathbb{C}
\end{array}$$

is commutative for regular ideals $I' \subset I$.

Proof. The independence of the pairing "res" from choice of local coordinates and generators for I, together with the functoriality, all follow from the commutative diagram $(**)$ and transformation formula. To show that the pairing $\mathcal{O}/I \otimes \mathrm{Ext}^n_{\mathcal{O}}(\mathcal{O}/I, \Omega^n) \overset{\mathrm{res}}{\longrightarrow} \mathbb{C}$ is nondegenerate, it will suffice to find a regular ideal $I' \subset I$ for which the pairing is nondegenerate, and then use the functoriality together with the facts that $\mathcal{O}/I' \overset{\pi}{\to} \mathcal{O}/I$ is surjective (obvious) and $\mathrm{Ext}^n_{\mathcal{O}}(\mathcal{O}/I, \Omega^n) \overset{\pi^*}{\to} \mathrm{Ext}^n_{\mathcal{O}}(\mathcal{O}/I', \Omega^n)$ is injective, which was proved in the previous proposition. Appealing to nullstellensatz in Section 1, we may take $I' = \{z_1^d, \ldots, z_n^d\}$, where $d = \dim_{\mathbb{C}}(\mathcal{O}/I)$. Q.E.D.

Tor and the Syzygy Theorem. Having used Ext to put the local duality theorem in final form, we shall use Tor to prove the

Syzygy Theorem. *Let* M *be a finitely generated $\mathcal{O}$-module and*

$$0 \to F \to E_{n-1} \to \cdots \to E_1 \to E_0 \to M \to 0$$

an exact sequence of $\mathcal{O}$-modules where the E_k are projective ($=$free). Then F *is also projective.*

Let $m = (z_1, \ldots, z_n)$ be the maximal ideal and $\mathbb{C} = \mathcal{O}/m$ considered as an $\mathcal{O}$-module. We begin by proving:

Lemma. $\mathrm{Tor}_1^{\mathcal{O}}(\mathbb{C}, N) = 0 \Rightarrow N$ *is a free $\mathcal{O}$-module.*

Proof. We first remark that

$$\mathrm{Tor}_0^{\mathcal{O}}(M, N) \cong M \otimes_{\mathcal{O}} N.$$

This is because $\otimes$ is right-exact, so that $E_1 \to E_0 \to M$ gives $E_1 \otimes_{\mathcal{O}} N \to E_0 \otimes_{\mathcal{O}} N \to M \otimes_{\mathcal{O}} N \to 0$.

Next, we note that short exact sequences

$$\begin{cases} 0 \to M' \to M \to M'' \to 0 \\ 0 \to N' \to N \to N'' \to 0 \end{cases}$$

give rise to long exact sequences of Tor's

$$\begin{cases} \cdots \to \mathrm{Tor}_k^{\mathcal{O}}(M, N) \to \mathrm{Tor}_k^{\mathcal{O}}(M'', N) \to \mathrm{Tor}_{k-1}^{\mathcal{O}}(M', N) \to \cdots \\ \cdots \to \mathrm{Tor}_k^{\mathcal{O}}(M, N) \to \mathrm{Tor}_k^{\mathcal{O}}(M, N'') \to \mathrm{Tor}_{k-1}^{\mathcal{O}}(M, N') \to \cdots \end{cases}$$

for the same reason as for Ext.

Now to prove the lemma. Observe that

$$M \otimes_{\mathcal{O}} \mathbb{C} \cong M/mM = M_0$$

is the fiber of M. Choose a free $\mathcal{O}$-module E such that $E_0 \cong M_0$. By the Nakayama lemma, we may extend this isomorphism to a surjective map $E \to M \to 0$. Let R be the module of relations defined by

$$0 \to R \to E \to M \to 0.$$

By the exact sequence of $\mathrm{Tor}_k^{\mathcal{O}}(\mathbb{C}, \cdot)$,

$$\mathrm{Tor}_1^{\mathcal{O}}(\mathbb{C}, M) \to \mathbb{C} \otimes_{\mathcal{O}} R \to \mathbb{C} \otimes_{\mathcal{O}} E \to \mathbb{C} \otimes_{\mathcal{O}} M \to 0$$

$$\| \qquad\qquad \| \qquad\quad \| \qquad\qquad \|$$

$$0 \qquad \to \quad R_0 \quad \to \quad E_0 \quad \overset{\sim}{\to} \quad M_0$$

$$\Rightarrow R_0 = 0$$

$$\Rightarrow R = 0$$

by Nakayama again. Thus $E \cong M$ and the lemma is proved.

Now we can prove the syzygy theorem. For $0 \leqslant k \leqslant n$, we define R_k by

$$\begin{cases} R_0 = M, \\ R_k = \text{image } E_k \to E_{k-1} \quad (0 < k < n), \\ R_n = F. \end{cases}$$

Then we have short exact sequences

$$\begin{cases} 0 \to \quad R_1 \quad \to \quad E_0 \quad \to \quad R_0 \quad \to 0, \\ 0 \to R_{k+1} \quad \to \quad E_k \quad \to \quad R_k \quad \to 0 \quad (0 < k < n), \\ 0 \to \quad R_n \quad \to E_{n-1} \to R_{n-1} \to 0. \end{cases}$$

Since higher Tor's are zero if one of the modules is free, the long exact sequence in the second factor gives

$$\text{Tor}_{q+1}^{0}(\mathbb{C}, R_{k-1}) \cong \text{Tor}_q^0(\mathbb{C}, R_k), \quad q \geqslant 1.$$

In particular

$$\text{Tor}_1^0(\mathbb{C}, R_n) \cong \text{Tor}_{n+1}^0(\mathbb{C}, M).$$

To show that the right-hand side is zero, we let

$$K_{\cdot} : \quad 0 \to K_n \to K_{n-1} \to \cdots \to K_0 \to \mathcal{O}/m = \mathbb{C} \to 0$$

be the Koszul complex associated to the maximal ideal $m = \{z_1, \ldots, z_n\}$. Since

$$\text{Tor}_*^0(\mathbb{C}, M) = H_*(K_{\cdot} \otimes_0 M),$$

it follows that $\text{Tor}_{n+k}^0(\mathbb{C}, M) = 0$ for $k \geqslant 1$.   Q.E.D.

A Brief Tour Through Coherent Sheaves

Definitions and Elementary Properties. On an open set $U \subset \mathbb{C}^n$ we now denote by $\mathcal{O}$ the sheaf of holomorphic functions and by $\mathcal{O}_z = \lim_{z \in V} \mathcal{O}(V)$ the stalk of $\mathcal{O}$ at a point $z \in U$. A sheaf mapping $\mathcal{O}^{(p)} \xrightarrow{F} \mathcal{O}^{(q)}$ is given by a $(p \times q)$ matrix of holomorphic functions defined on U. We define the sheaf of $\mathcal{O}$-modules $\mathcal{R}$ by

$$0 \to \mathcal{R} \to \mathcal{O}^{(p)} \xrightarrow{F} \mathcal{O}^{(q)}.$$

In the discussion of local rings, we pointed out that, because of the Noetherian property of $\mathcal{O}_{z_0}$, $\mathcal{R}_{z_0}$ was a finitely generated $\mathcal{O}_{z_0}$-module. The following fundamental lemma is due to Oka:

Oka's Lemma. *The sheaf $\mathcal{R}$ is locally finitely generated as a sheaf of $\mathcal{O}$-modules. More precisely, if $r_1, \ldots, r_m$ are sections of $\mathcal{R}$ in a neighborhood* *of z_0 that generate the $\mathcal{O}_{z_0}$-module $\mathcal{R}_{z_0}$, then they generate the $\mathcal{O}_z$-modules $\mathcal{R}_z$ for $\|z - z_0\| < \varepsilon$.*

We shall not give here the proof of this lemma, which is found in the references given at the end of this chapter.

Taking $q = 1$, $F = (f_1, \ldots, f_p)$ generates an ideal sheaf $I \subset \mathcal{O}$, and $\mathcal{R}$ is the sheaf of relations $\sum r_i f_i = 0$ among the generators. Oka's lemma is therefore a sort of Noetherian property of $\mathcal{O}$, not just in each stalk but, so to speak, spread out over sufficiently small open sets. We note the similarity to the following, which was proved in Section 1 of Chapter 0:

If f and g are holomorphic in U and are relatively prime in the local ring $\mathcal{O}_{z_0}$, then they are relatively prime in $\mathcal{O}_z$ for $\|z - z_0\| < \varepsilon$.

The proof of this result used the Weierstrass division theorem, and the same is true of the proof of Oka's lemma.

Here is the basic

DEFINITION. Let M be a complex manifold with structure sheaf $\mathcal{O}$ and $\mathcal{F}$ a sheaf of $\mathcal{O}$-modules. Then $\mathcal{F}$ is *coherent* if locally it has a presentation

$$\mathcal{O}^{(p)} \to \mathcal{O}^{(q)} \to \mathcal{F} \to 0.$$

In other words, $\mathcal{F}$ is coherent if, given any point $z_0 \in M$, there is a neighborhood U of z_0 and finitely many sections of $\mathcal{F}|U$ that generate each $\mathcal{O}_z$-module $\mathcal{F}_z$ ($z \in U$), and if moreover the relations among these generators are finitely generated over U.

Here are some remarks and examples. The gist throughout is that Oka's lemma allows properties in the local ring $\mathcal{O}_{z_0}$ to propagate to the same properties in nearby local rings $\mathcal{O}_z$. We shall refer to this as the *propagation principle*; it gives rise to the name *coherent*.

We begin by noting that:

Coherent sheaves admit local syzygies

$$0 \to \mathcal{O}^{(k_n)} \to \mathcal{O}^{(k_{n-1})} \to \cdots \to \mathcal{O}^{(k_0)} \to \mathcal{F} \to 0.$$

Proof. By definition we have

$$\mathcal{O}^{(p)} \to \mathcal{O}^{(q)} \to \mathcal{F} \to 0$$

in a neighborhood U of z_0. Applying Oka's lemma, we find

$$\mathcal{O}^{(r)} \to \mathcal{O}^{(p)} \to \mathcal{O}^{(q)} \to \mathcal{F} \to 0$$

in a possibly smaller neighborhood U' of z_0. Applying it again, we obtain

$$\mathcal{O}^{(s)} \to \mathcal{O}^{(r)} \to \mathcal{O}^{(p)} \to \mathcal{O}^{(q)} \to \mathcal{F} \to 0$$

in $U'' \subset U'$. After at most n steps, the syzygy theorem assures us that the kernel on the left will have as stalk at z_0 a free $\mathcal{O}_{z_0}$-module, and this then gives our local syzygy. Q.E.D.

As an application we have:

For a coherent sheaf $\mathcal{F}$, the cohomology sheaves

$$\mathcal{H}^q(\mathcal{F}) = 0 \quad \text{for } q > 0.$$

Proof. By the $\bar{\partial}$-Poincaré lemma, $\mathcal{H}^q(\mathcal{O}) = 0$ for $q > 0$. Arguing by induction on the length of a local syzygy, we may assume that we have

$$0 \to \mathcal{R} \to \mathcal{O}^{(k)} \to \mathcal{F} \to 0,$$

where $\mathcal{H}^q(\mathcal{R}) = 0$ for $q > 0$. Our result then follows by the exact sequence of cohomology. Q.E.D.

A further property of coherent sheaves we shall repeatedly use is:

Given an exact sequence

$$0 \to \mathcal{F}' \to \mathcal{F} \to \mathcal{F}'' \to 0$$

of sheaves of $\mathcal{O}$-modules in which two of the three are coherent, then the remaining one is also.

The proof is just tedious checking of details and will be omitted.

Now we come to some examples. The simplest are those $\mathcal{F}$ such that locally $\mathcal{F} \cong \mathcal{O}^{(r)}$. Then $\mathcal{F}$ is said to be *locally free of rank* r, and such $\mathcal{F}$ are exactly the sheaves $\mathcal{O}(E)$, where $E \to M$ is a holomorphic vector bundle with fiber $\mathbb{C}^r$.

A subsheaf $I \subset \mathcal{O}$ that is locally finitely generated is called an *ideal sheaf* or *sheaf of ideals*. By Oka's lemma, these are always coherent, and because of the exact sequence

$$0 \to I \to \mathcal{O} \to \mathcal{O}/I \to 0$$

the same is true for $\mathcal{O}/I$. If locally $I = \{f_1, \ldots, f_m\}$ is generated by holomorphic functions $f_1, \ldots, f_m$, then the *support* of $\mathcal{O}/I$ is defined as

$$\begin{aligned} Z &= \operatorname{supp}(\mathcal{O}/I) \\ &= \{z \in M : I_z \neq \mathcal{O}_z\} \\ &= \{z \in M : f_1(z) = \cdots = f_m(z) = 0\}. \end{aligned}$$

As a point set Z is an analytic variety. However, this should be refined, and the pair $(Z, \mathcal{O}_Z)$ should be thought of as a space whose support is an analytic variety but whose *structure sheaf* $\mathcal{O}_Z = \mathcal{O}/I$ is a sheaf of rings possibly with nilpotent elements.

An ideal sheaf I that locally has a single generator f is locally free of rank one, and hence is of the form

$$I \cong \mathcal{O}(L^*)$$

for some holomorphic line bundle $L^* \to M$. Denoting by $D = (f)$ the divisor of f, we have previously used the notations $L^* = [-D]$ and $L = [D]$ for this line bundle and its dual. The sheaf $\mathcal{O}(D)$ is then the sheaf of meromorphic functions g with $(g) + D \geqslant 0$. In general, sheaves $\mathcal{O}(D)$ for a not necessarily effective divisor D are said to be *invertible*. The multiplicative group of invertible sheaves on an algebraic variety M is just $H^1(M, \mathcal{O}^*) = \mathrm{Pic}(M)$.

An ideal sheaf I is a *sheaf of regular ideals* if locally $I = \{f_1, \ldots, f_r\}$, where the f_i define a regular sequence in the local rings $\mathcal{O}_z$. For sheaves of regular ideals the Koszul complex from the preceding section provides an especially nice local syzygy. Later on we shall be especially concerned with the codimension-2 case. If locally $I = \{f_1, f_2\}$, then the Koszul complex gives the local syzygy

$$0 \to \mathcal{O} \xrightarrow{\lambda} \mathcal{O} \oplus \mathcal{O} \xrightarrow{\eta} \mathcal{O} \to \mathcal{O}/I \to 0,$$

where

$$\lambda(g) = (-f_2 g) \oplus (f_1 g),$$
$$\eta(g_1 \oplus g_2) = f_1 g_1 + f_2 g_2.$$

To illustrate how nilpotents arise geometrically, suppose that $Z \subset M$ is an irreducible subvariety defined by a sheaf of prime ideals $I \subset \mathcal{O}$. Then the ideal sheaves $I^{\mu+1}$ define spaces $Z_\mu = (Z, \mathcal{O}/I^{\mu+1})$, which may be thought of as the *μth infinitesimal neighborhood* of Z.

In this context let us reexamine the Reiss relation discussed in Section 2. Here $M = \mathbb{P}^2$ and $Z = L$ is a line. We denote by $\mathcal{O}_{(\mu)} = \mathcal{O}/I^{\mu+1}$ the structure sheaf of the μth infinitesimal neighborhood. The data of a second-order element of arc crossing L is equivalent to locally giving a section of $\mathcal{O}_{(2)}$ defined up to multiplication by units in $\mathcal{O}_{(2)}^*$.

Explicitly, let $\{U_\alpha\}$ be an open covering of a neighborhood of L in $\mathbb{P}^2$ such that in U_α we have holomorphic coordinates (z_α, w_α) with $L \cap U_\alpha$ defined by $w_\alpha = 0$. In $U_\alpha \cap U_\beta$, $z_\alpha = z_\alpha(z_\beta, w_\beta)$ and $w_\alpha = w_\alpha(z_\beta, w_\beta)$, where $w_\beta(z_\beta, 0) = 0$. In U_α the sections of the sheaf $\mathcal{O}_{(\mu)}$ are just the holomorphic functions $f_\alpha(z_\alpha, w_\alpha) = f_0(z_\alpha) + f_1(z_\alpha) w_\alpha + \cdots + f_\mu(z_\alpha) w_\alpha^\mu$ taken modulo $w_\alpha^{\mu+1}$. The data in the Reiss relation are given by $f_\alpha \in \mathcal{O}_{(2)}(U_\alpha)$ with $f_\alpha/f_\beta = f_{\alpha\beta} \in \mathcal{O}_{(2)}^*(U_\alpha \cap U_\beta)$. *Thus, giving the second-order elements of arc is the same as giving an invertible sheaf* $\mathcal{L}_{(2)} \in H^1(L_{(2)}) \mathcal{O}_{(2)}^*)$ *and section* $\sigma_{(2)} \in H^0(\mathcal{L}_{(2)})$.

We now ask when there is an invertible sheaf $\mathcal{L} \in H^1(\mathcal{O}_{\mathbb{P}^2}^*)$ that restricts to $\mathcal{L}_{(2)}$. For this we consider the exact sequence

$$0 \to 1 + I^3 \to \mathcal{O}_{\mathbb{P}^2}^* \to \mathcal{O}_{(2)}^* \to 0,$$

where $I \cong \mathcal{O}_{\mathbb{P}^2}(-L)$ is the ideal sheaf of the line $L \subset \mathbb{P}^2$ and $1 + I^3$ denotes the multiplicative sheaf of functions $1 + f$, where f vanishes to third order along L. Clearly $1 + I^3 \cong I^3$, and since $I^3 \cong \mathcal{O}_{\mathbb{P}^2}(-3)$,

$$H^1(\mathcal{O}_{\mathbb{P}^2}(-3L)) = 0 \qquad \text{by Kodaira vanishing,}$$

$$H^2(\mathcal{O}_{\mathbb{P}^2}(-3L)) \cong H^0(\mathcal{O}_{\mathbb{P}^2}) \cong \mathbb{C} \qquad \text{by Kodaira-Serre duality,}$$

$$H^2(\mathcal{O}_{\mathbb{P}^2}^*) = 0,$$

where the last step follows from the cohomology sequence of $0 \to \mathbb{Z} \to \mathcal{O}_{\mathbb{P}^2} \to \mathcal{O}_{\mathbb{P}^2}^* \to 1$. Thus we obtain

$$0 \to H^1(\mathcal{O}_{\mathbb{P}^2}^*) \to H^1(\mathcal{O}_{(2)}^*) \to \mathbb{C} \to 0,$$

and consequently: *There is one condition on $\mathcal{L}_{(2)} \in H^1(\mathcal{O}_{(2)}^*)$ to be the restriction of some $\mathcal{L} \in H^1(\mathcal{O}_{\mathbb{P}^2}^*)$.*

Assuming now this to be the case, we have $\mathcal{L} \cong \mathcal{O}_{\mathbb{P}^2}(n)$ $(n > 0)$, and the exact sheaf sequence

$$0 \to \mathcal{O}_{\mathbb{P}^2}(n-3) \to \mathcal{O}_{\mathbb{P}^2}(n) \to \mathcal{O}(\mathcal{L}_{(2)}) \to 0$$

together with $H^1(\mathcal{O}_{\mathbb{P}^2}(n-3)) \cong H^1(\mathcal{O}_{\mathbb{P}^2}(-n)) = 0$ gives in cohomology

$$0 \to H^0(\mathcal{O}_{\mathbb{P}^2}(n-3)) \to H^0(\mathcal{O}_{\mathbb{P}^2}(n)) \to H^0(\mathcal{O}(\mathcal{L}_{(2)})) \to 0.$$

Combining this with the previous paragraph, we conclude: *There is exactly one condition that the second-order arcs C_i ($i = 1, \ldots, n$) be cut out by an algebraic curve C in $\mathbb{P}^2$.* The Reiss relation gives this condition explicitly; this alternate approach illustrates the use of nilpotents.

As another example of nilpotents, we assume that $I \subset \mathcal{O}$ is a sheaf of regular ideals whose support Z consists of a finite set of points. Thus, locally $I = \{f_1, \ldots, f_n\}$, where $n = \dim_\mathbb{C} M$. Setting $\mathcal{O}_Z = \mathcal{O}/I$ the ringed space $(Z, \mathcal{O}_Z)$ consists of the points $P \in Z$ together with a finite-dimensional $\mathbb{C}$-algebra $\mathcal{O}_{Z,P} = \mathcal{O}_P/I_P$. The associated zero-cycle is $\sum_{P \in Z} \dim_\mathbb{C}(\mathcal{O}_{Z,P})P$. The space $(Z, \mathcal{O}_Z)$ contains more information than just the set of points $P \in Z$, even if we include the multiplicities $\dim_\mathbb{C}(\mathcal{O}_{Z,P})$.

Now we come to the question of *sheafifying* Ext and Tor. Recall from the section on homological algebra that we proved a proposition giving four properties of projective resolutions of $\mathcal{O}_z$-modules. The definition and basic properties of Ext and Tor for modules over local rings were formal consequences of this proposition. The point we wish to make here is this: *By the propagation principle, the same four properties in that proposition are valid locally for coherent sheaves.* For example, the first one, that projective resolutions exist, becomes that local syzygies exist, which we have already checked.

As a consequence, if one thinks matters through, the following conclusion emerges: *Given coherent sheaves $\mathcal{F}$ and $\mathcal{G}$, we may define sheaves*

$\underline{\mathrm{Ext}}_{\mathcal{O}}^{k}(\mathcal{F},\mathcal{G})$ *and* $\underline{\mathrm{Tor}}_{k}^{\mathcal{O}}(\mathcal{F},\mathcal{G})$ *with the properties*:

1. $\begin{cases} \underline{\mathrm{Ext}}_{\mathcal{O}}^{k}(\mathcal{F},\mathcal{G})_{x} \cong \underline{\mathrm{Ext}}_{\mathcal{O}_{x}}^{k}(\mathcal{F}_{x},\mathcal{G}_{x}), \\ \underline{\mathrm{Tor}}_{k}^{\mathcal{O}}(\mathcal{F},\mathcal{G})_{x} \cong \underline{\mathrm{Tor}}_{k}^{\mathcal{O}_{x}}(\mathcal{F}_{x},\mathcal{G}_{x}); \end{cases}$

2. $\begin{cases} \underline{\mathrm{Ext}}_{\mathcal{O}}^{0}(\mathcal{F},\mathcal{G}) \cong \underline{\mathrm{Hom}}_{\mathcal{O}}(\mathcal{F},\mathcal{G}), \\ \underline{\mathrm{Tor}}_{0}^{\mathcal{O}}(\mathcal{F},\mathcal{G}) \cong \mathcal{F} \otimes_{\mathcal{O}} \mathcal{G}; \end{cases}$

3. *The exact sequences of* Ext *and* Tor *are valid*; *and*

4. $\underline{\mathrm{Ext}}_{\mathcal{O}}^{*}(\mathcal{F},\mathcal{G})$ *and* $\underline{\mathrm{Tor}}_{*}^{\mathcal{O}}(\mathcal{F},\mathcal{G})$ *are coherent sheaves.*

The last property is because $\underline{\mathrm{Ext}}$ and $\underline{\mathrm{Tor}}$ fit into exact sequences where two out of three terms are coherent.

As an illustration of property 3, given an exact sequence $0 \to \mathcal{G}' \to \mathcal{G} \to \mathcal{G}'' \to 0$ of coherent sheaves, application of $\otimes_{\mathcal{O}} \mathcal{F}$ gives

$$\cdots \to \underline{\mathrm{Tor}}_{1}^{\mathcal{O}}(\mathcal{G},\mathcal{F}) \to \underline{\mathrm{Tor}}_{1}^{\mathcal{O}}(\mathcal{G}'',\mathcal{F}) \to \mathcal{G}' \otimes_{\mathcal{O}} \mathcal{F} \to \mathcal{G} \otimes_{\mathcal{O}} \mathcal{F} \to \mathcal{G}'' \otimes_{\mathcal{O}} \mathcal{F} \to 0.$$

This sequence will prove useful in a little while.

Cohomology of Coherent Sheaves. Suppose now that M is a compact complex manifold and $\mathcal{F}$ is a coherent sheaf on M. The fundamental global fact is: *The cohomology* $H^{*}(M,\mathcal{F})$ *is a finite-dimensional vector space.*

Again, this is proved in the references listed at the end of this chapter. We shall not prove it here but will show how the finite dimensionality may be used to draw consequences in case M is a smooth algebraic variety.

Suppose then that $L \to M$ is a positive line bundle, which we may as well take to be the hyperplane bundle relative to a smooth projective embedding $M \subset \mathbb{P}^{N}$. We let $\mathcal{L} = \mathcal{O}(L)$ and set $\mathcal{F}(k) = \mathcal{F} \otimes_{\mathcal{O}} \mathcal{L}^{k}$. The sections of $\mathcal{F}(k)$ may be thought of as sections of $\mathcal{F}$ having poles of order k along a hyperplane. Consider the following two assertions:

Theorem A. *The global sections* $H^{0}(M,\mathcal{F}(k))$ *generate each* $\mathcal{O}_{x}$-*module* $\mathcal{F}(k)_{x}$ *for* $k \geqslant k_{0}$; *i.e.*,

$$H^{0}(M,\mathcal{F}(k)) \to \mathcal{F}(k)_{x}/m_{x}\mathcal{F}(k) \to 0,$$

where $m_{x} \subset \mathcal{O}_{x}$ *is the maximal ideal.*

(The equivalence of the two statements in this theorem is the Nakayama lemma. In general, $\mathcal{F}_{x}/m_{x}\mathcal{F}_{x}$ may be called the *fiber* of the coherent sheaf $\mathcal{F}$ at $x \in M$.)

Theorem B. $H^{q}(M,\mathcal{F}(k)) = 0$ *for* $q > 0$, $k \geqslant k_{0}$.

We have proved the finite dimensionality and also Theorems A and B in case $\mathcal{F} = \mathcal{O}(E)$ is locally free so that potential-theoretic methods may be used. Now we prove the assertions:

1. *Theorem A $\Rightarrow$ Theorem B.*
2. *Theorem B $\Rightarrow$ Theorem A.*
3. *dim $H^1(M, \mathcal{F}) < \infty$ for all coherent sheaves $\mathcal{F} \Rightarrow$ Theorem A.*

Proof of 1. Assuming Theorem A, we have

$$0 \to \mathcal{G}' \to \mathcal{O}^{(p)} \to \mathcal{F}(k) \to 0$$

for some large k. Applying $\otimes \mathcal{L}^{-k}$ to this exact sequence and setting $\mathcal{G} = \mathcal{G}'(-k)$, we obtain

$$0 \to \mathcal{G} \to \mathcal{E}_0 \to \mathcal{F} \to 0.$$

Now apply the same procedure to $\mathcal{G}$, and keep on going. After at most $n = \dim_{\mathbb{C}} M$ steps we arrive at a global syzygy

$$(*) \qquad 0 \to \mathcal{E}_n \to \mathcal{E}_{n-1} \to \cdots \to \mathcal{E}_0 \to \mathcal{F} \to 0,$$

where each $\mathcal{E}_l$ is locally free. Note that for $0 \leqslant l \leqslant n-1$, $\mathcal{E}_k$ is a direct sum of copies of $\mathcal{L}^{m_k}$, but all we can say about the last term is that $\mathcal{E}_n = \mathcal{O}(E)$ for some holomorphic vector bundle $E \to M$. The existence of such global syzygies for coherent sheaves is of fundamental importance.

Returning to the proof of 1, we have proved in Section 4 of Chapter 1 that $H^q(M, \mathcal{E}(k)) = 0$ for $\mathcal{E}$ locally free, $q > 0$, and $k \geqslant k_0$. Applying this inductively on the length of a global syzygy gives Theorem B.

Proof of 2. For each $x_0 \in M$, we have

$$0 \to m_{x_0} \mathcal{F}(k) \to \mathcal{F}(k) \to \mathcal{F}(k)_{x_0} / m_{x_0} \mathcal{F}(k) \to 0,$$

where $m_{x_0} \subset \mathcal{O}$ is the sheaf of ideals given by the maximal ideal m_{x_0} at x_0. The fiber $\mathcal{F}(k)_{x_0} / m_{x_0} \mathcal{F}(k)$ is an example of a coherent sheaf supported at a point—these are sometimes called *skyscraper sheaves*. Now $m_{x_0} \mathcal{F}(k) = (m_{x_0} \mathcal{F})(k) = \mathcal{G}(k)$, where $\mathcal{G} = m_{x_0} \mathcal{F}$ is a coherent sheaf. Using $H^1(M, \mathcal{G}(k)) = 0$ for $k \geqslant k_0$, we deduce that the global sections $H^0(M, \mathcal{F}(k))$ generate the fiber of $\mathcal{F}(k)$ at x_0 for $k \geqslant k_0$. By the Nakayama lemma, these global sections generate the $\mathcal{O}_{x_0}$-module $\mathcal{F}(k)_{x_0}$ for $k \geqslant k_0$. By Oka's lemma they generate the $\mathcal{O}_x$-modules $\mathcal{F}(k)_x$ for x near to x_0. The result now follows by the compactness of M.

Proof of 3. The proof is by induction on $n = \dim_{\mathbb{C}} M$. Given a point $x \in M$ and hyperplane ξ in the tangent space $T'_x(M)$, we may find a nonsingular hypersurface passing through x and with tangent plane ξ. Replacing $\mathcal{L}$ by $\mathcal{L}^k$, we may assume that this hypersurface is a hyperplane H. Then we have an exact sequence

$$0 \to \mathcal{O}_M(-1) \xrightarrow{\sigma} \mathcal{O}_M \to \mathcal{O}_H \to 0,$$

where $\sigma \in H^0(M, \mathcal{O}(1))$ defines H and $\mathcal{O}_H$ is the usual structure sheaf on the complex manifold H. Applying $\otimes \mathcal{F}$ to this sequence gives $(\mathcal{O} = \mathcal{O}_M)$

$$0 \to \underline{\text{Tor}}_1^0(\mathcal{O}_H, \mathcal{F}) \to \mathcal{F}(-1) \to \mathcal{F} \to \mathcal{F}_H \to 0,$$

where $\mathcal{F}_H = \mathcal{F} \otimes_{\mathcal{O}_M} \mathcal{O}_H$ is a coherent sheaf of $\mathcal{O}_H$-modules, and where we used that $\underline{\text{Tor}}_1^0(\mathcal{O}_M, \mathcal{F}) = 0$. The sheaf $\mathcal{G} = \text{Tor}_1^0(\mathcal{O}_H, \mathcal{F})$ is a coherent sheaf of $\mathcal{O}_M$-modules. Multiplying a section of $\mathcal{G}$ by σ gives zero, since $\sigma \cdot \mathcal{O}_H = 0$, and so $\mathcal{G} = \mathcal{G}_H$ is a coherent sheaf of $\mathcal{O}_H$-modules.

Now apply $\otimes^k \mathcal{L}$ to this sequence. Since locally $\mathcal{L} \cong \mathcal{O}$, exactness is preserved and we obtain

$$(**) \qquad 0 \to \mathcal{G}_H(k) \to \mathcal{F}(k-1) \to \mathcal{F}(k) \to \mathcal{F}_H(k) \to 0.$$

The induction hypothesis applies to give Theorem A, and hence Theorem B, for $\mathcal{G}_H(k)$ and $\mathcal{F}_H(k)$. Thus $H^q(\mathcal{G}_H(k)) = H^q(\mathcal{F}_H(k)) = 0$ for $q > 0$ and $k \geqslant k_0$. From the exact cohomology sequence of $(**)$ we obtain *surjective* maps

$$H^1(\mathcal{F}(k)) \twoheadrightarrow H^1(\mathcal{F}(k+1)) \twoheadrightarrow H^1(\mathcal{F}(k+2)) \twoheadrightarrow \cdots$$

for $k \geqslant k_0$. Since $H^1(\mathcal{F}(k))$ is finite dimensional, we must have isomorphisms

$$H^1(\mathcal{F}(k)) \xrightarrow{\hspace{1em}} H^1(\mathcal{F}(k+1)) \xrightarrow{\hspace{1em}} H^1(\mathcal{F}(k+2))$$

for $k \geqslant k_1$. But then the cohomology sequence of $(**)$ gives

$$H^0(\mathcal{F}(k)) \to H^0(\mathcal{F}_H(k)) \to 0$$

for $k \geqslant k_1$. Now $H^0(\mathcal{F}_H(k))$ generates $\mathcal{F}_H(k)_x$ as an $\mathcal{O}_{H,x}$-module for $k \geqslant k_2$ and any $x \in H$. Since the tangent space to H at x was assigned arbitrarily, it follows easily that $H^0(\mathcal{F}(k))$ generates $\mathcal{F}(k)_x$ as an $\mathcal{O}_{M,x}$-module.   Q.E.D.

Noether's "$AF + BG$" Theorem. As an illustration of a particular global syzygy and application of the local residue theorem, we shall discuss a classical result of Max Noether, which is traditionally used as a cornerstone in the algebraic treatment of plane curves.

In $\mathbb{P}^2$ with homogeneous coordinates $X = [X_0, X_1, X_2]$ let $F(X)$ and $G(X)$ be homogeneous polynomials of respective degrees m and n whose divisors are plane curves C and D, which we assume to have no common component. Given a homogeneous polynomial $H(X)$ of degree $d = m + k = n + l$ with $k, l \geqslant 0$, we ask when there is a relation

$$(*) \qquad\qquad H = AF + BG.$$

An obvious necessary condition is that $(*)$ should hold locally. This has the following meaning: Let $P \in C \cap D$ and suppose that P is contained in the affine coordinate system $(x, y) = [1, x, y]$. Then $f(x, y) = F(1, x, y)$ and $g(x, y) = G(1, x, y)$ generate an ideal I_P in the local ring $\mathcal{O}_P$ of germs of holomorphic functions defined in a neighborhood of P. The obvious necessary local condition is that, setting $h(x,y) = H(1,x,y)$,

$$(**) \qquad\qquad h(x,y) \in I_P \subset \mathcal{O}_P$$

for each $P \in C \cap D$. Conversely, we shall prove

Noether's AF + BG Theorem. *If the local conditions* (**) *are satisfied, then there is a global relation* (*).

Proof. We let $I \subset \mathcal{O}$ be the sheaf of ideals generated by the various localizations f and g as above. Then I is coherent and $\mathrm{supp}(\mathcal{O}/I) = C \cap D$. Setting $d = m + k = n + l$ and $r = k - n = l - m$, the Koszul complex gives the global syzygy (cf. p. 698)

$$0 \to \mathcal{O}(r) \to \mathcal{O}(m) \oplus \mathcal{O}(n) \to I(d) \to 0,$$

where $I(d) = I \otimes_{\mathcal{O}} \mathcal{O}(d)$ and the maps in this sequence are

$$\eta \to \eta G \oplus -\eta F, \qquad \eta \in \mathcal{O}(r),$$

$$\xi \oplus \psi \to F\xi + G\psi, \qquad \xi \in \mathcal{O}(k), \quad \psi \in \mathcal{O}(l),$$

where F, G are considered as global sections of $\mathcal{O}(m), \mathcal{O}(n)$, respectively.

Next we recall that $H^1(\mathbb{P}^2, \mathcal{O}(r)) = 0$ for all r, since first $H^1(\mathbb{P}^2, \mathcal{O}(r)) = 0$ for $r < 0$ by the Kodaira vanishing theorem, and second

$$H^1(\mathbb{P}^2, \mathcal{O}(r)) \cong H^1(\mathbb{P}^2, \mathcal{O}(-r-3)) = 0$$

for $r \geqslant 0$ by Kodaira-Serre duality. The exact cohomology sequence then gives

$$H^0(\mathbb{P}^2, \mathcal{O}(m)) \oplus H^0(\mathbb{P}^2, \mathcal{O}(n)) \to H^0(\mathbb{P}^2, I(d)) \to 0.$$

Our local assumptions (**) exactly mean that

$$H \in H^0(\mathbb{P}^2, I(d)) \subset H^0(\mathbb{P}^2, \mathcal{O}(d)),$$

and this proves the theorem. Q.E.D.

In order to apply Noether's theorem, it is useful to have numerical criteria for when the local conditions (**) are satisfied. It is pretty clear that the local duality theorem is relevant to this question, and we shall pursue this lead in one rather simple case here.

Suppose that $f(z,w)$ is holomorphic in a neighborhood of the origin and has divisor a nonsingular curve C passing through the origin. If $g(z,w)$ is holomorphic near the origin, then we define $\mathrm{Ord}_C(g)$ to be the order of vanishing of $g|_C$ at the origin. Suppose now that $g(z,w)$ has divisor D and that the set-theoretic intersection $C \cap D = \{0\}$. Denote by $I \subset \mathcal{O}$ the ideal $\{f,g\}$ in the local ring at the origin.

Lemma.   *Given* $h(z,w) \in \mathcal{O}$, *if* $\operatorname{Ord}_C(h) \geqslant \operatorname{Ord}_C(g)$, *then* $h \in I$.

Proof.   According to the local duality theorem we must prove that

$$\operatorname{Res}_{\{0\}} \left(\frac{hk\,dz \wedge dw}{fg} \right) = 0$$

for all $k \in \mathcal{O}$. Since $\operatorname{Ord}_C(hk) \geqslant \operatorname{Ord}_C(h)$ this will follow from showing that

$$\operatorname{Res}_{\{0\}} \left(\frac{h\,dz \wedge dw}{fg} \right) = 0$$

whenever $\operatorname{Ord}_C(h) \geqslant \operatorname{Ord}(g)$. We may choose local coordinates so that $f(z,w) = z$. Then, by iteration of the residue integral

$$\operatorname{Res}_{\{0\}} \left(\frac{h\,dz \wedge dw}{fg} \right) = \left(\frac{1}{2\pi\sqrt{-1}} \right) \int_{|g| = \varepsilon} \left(\int_{|z| = \varepsilon} \frac{h(z,w)\,dz}{g(z,w)z} \right) dw$$

$$= \frac{1}{2\pi\sqrt{-1}} \int_{|g(0,w)| = \varepsilon} \frac{h(0,w)\,dw}{g(0,w)}$$

$$= 0,$$

since $\operatorname{Ord}_C(h) \geqslant \operatorname{Ord}_C(g)$.   Q.E.D.

Of course this particular lemma may be proved directly, but the method of using residues and local duality will work in a variety of circumstances. Using the Max Noether theorem and this lemma, we shall reprove the result on cubics encountered in Section 4:

> *Suppose that* C, D, E *are cubics in* $\mathbb{P}^2$ *and that each point* $P \in C \cap D$ *is a simple point on* C. *Suppose that for all but one such point* $\operatorname{Ord}_C(E)_P \geqslant \operatorname{Ord}_C(D)_P$, *and at the remaining one, say* Q, *we have* $\operatorname{Ord}_C(E)_Q \geqslant \operatorname{Ord}_C(D)_Q - 1$. *Then* $\operatorname{Ord}_C(E)_Q \geqslant \operatorname{Ord}_C(D)_Q$. *Briefly stated: any cubic* E *passing through eight of the nine points of* $C \cap D$ *passes through the remaining point also.*

Proof.   Let F, G, H be homogeneous cubic polynomials defining C, D, E, respectively. Suppose L is a linear form vanishing at Q and at two points R_1, R_2 on C but not on D. Applying the lemma and Max Noether theorem to HL, we have

$$HL = AF + BG.$$

The linear form B vanishes at R_1 and R_2, and so $B = \beta L$. It follows that L divides AF, and since the line $L = 0$ is not a component of C, it follows that $A = \alpha L$. Then $H = \alpha F + \beta G$, and so $\operatorname{Ord}_C(H)_Q \geqslant \operatorname{Ord}_C(G)_Q$.   Q.E.D.

These methods may be generalized to prove the Cayley-Bacharach theorem from Section 4.

4. GLOBAL DUALITY

Global Ext

Let M be a compact, complex manifold and $\mathcal{L}$ the invertible sheaf associated to a positive line bundle $L \to M$. Given coherent sheaves $\mathcal{F}, \mathcal{G}$ on M, and using Theorem A discussed in the previous section, we may find a *global syzygy*

$$0 \to \mathcal{E}_n \to \mathcal{E}_{n-1} \to \cdots \to \mathcal{E}_1 \to \mathcal{E}_0 \to \mathcal{F} \to 0$$

for $\mathcal{F}$. This gives rise to a complex of sheaves $\mathrm{Hom}_{\mathcal{O}}(\mathcal{E}_{\cdot}(\mathcal{F}), \mathcal{G})$, whose associated hypercohomology we take as the definition of global Ext, written

$$\mathrm{Ext}(M; \mathcal{F}, \mathcal{G}) = \mathbb{H}^*(M, \mathrm{Hom}_{\mathcal{O}}(E_{\cdot}(\mathcal{F}), \mathcal{G})).$$

Of course, we must prove that the right-hand side is independent of the choice of global syzygy. Moreover, we would like global Ext to have functorial properties analogous to those enjoyed by Ext for local rings and the sheaf Ext.

As was the case for the sheaf Ext, these matters will fall into place if we have at hand some global analogue of the four properties of projective resolutions given in the section on homological algebra. To achieve this, we recall the notation $\mathcal{F}(k) = \mathcal{F} \otimes_{\mathcal{O}} \mathcal{L}^k$ and note that since $\mathrm{Hom}_{\mathcal{O}}(\mathcal{F}(k), \mathcal{G}(k)) \cong \mathrm{Hom}_{\mathcal{O}}(\mathcal{F}, \mathcal{G})$, we may replace $\mathcal{F}$ by $\mathcal{F}(k)$ when convenient. Thus, suppose we are given a commutative diagram

$$\mathcal{E}'$$
$$\swarrow \quad \downarrow$$
$$0 \to \mathcal{R} \to \mathcal{E} \to \mathcal{F} \to 0$$

of coherent sheaves on M where $\mathcal{E}$ and $\mathcal{E}'$ are locally free. It may not be possible to fill in the dotted arrow as it stands, but we can do the following: A section $s \in H^0(M, \mathcal{L}^k)$ gives an inclusion $\mathcal{E}'(-k) \subset \mathcal{E}'$, and we claim that, for $k \geqslant k_0$, the dotted arrow in the diagram

$$\mathcal{E}'(-k)$$
$$\swarrow \quad \downarrow$$
$$0 \to \mathcal{R} \to \mathcal{E} \to \mathcal{F} \to 0$$

may be filled in.

Proof. Since $\mathcal{E}'(-k)$ is locally free, $\underline{\mathrm{Ext}}^1_{\mathcal{O}}(\mathcal{E}'(-k), \cdot) = 0$, and so the exact sequence of Ext's gives

$$0 \to \mathrm{Hom}_{\mathcal{O}}(\mathcal{E}'(-k), \mathcal{R}) \to \mathrm{Hom}_{\mathcal{O}}(\mathcal{E}'(-k), \mathcal{E}) \to \mathrm{Hom}_{\mathcal{O}}(\mathcal{E}'(-k), \mathcal{F}) \to 0.$$

By Theorem B,

$$H^1(M, \mathrm{Hom}_{\mathcal{O}}(\mathcal{E}'(-k), \mathcal{R})) = H^1(M, \mathrm{Hom}_{\mathcal{O}}(\mathcal{E}', \mathcal{R})(k)) = 0$$

for $k \geqslant k_0$. Consequently, we obtain a surjection

$$H^0(M, \mathrm{Hom}_{\mathcal{O}}(\mathcal{E}'(-k), \mathcal{E})) \to H^0(M, \mathrm{Hom}(\mathcal{E}'(-k), \mathcal{F})) \to 0. \qquad \text{Q.E.D.}$$

From this we may draw the following conclusion: *When working globally with coherent sheaves on* M, *the four properties of projective resolutions of* $\mathcal{O}$-*modules carry over to global syzygies, at least provided we allow ourselves to twist with* $\mathcal{O}^k$. As a consequence, $\mathrm{Ext}(M; \mathcal{F}, \mathcal{G})$ is well-defined and has functorial properties analogous to those of local Ext. The most important of these are the two long exact sequences.

In order to calculate global Ext, a main tool are the two spectral sequences of hypercohomology. The first of these is a spectral sequence $\{'E_r\}$ with

$$'E_2^{p,q} = H^p(M, \underline{\mathrm{Ext}}_{\mathcal{O}}^q(\mathcal{F}, \mathcal{G})),$$
$$'E_\infty^{p,q} \Rightarrow \mathrm{Ext}^{p+q}(M; \mathcal{F}, \mathcal{G}).$$

Two applications of this spectral sequence will be useful. The first one is: *For* $\mathcal{E}$ *a locally free sheaf on* M,

$$\mathrm{Ext}^q(M; \mathcal{E}, \mathcal{G}) \cong H^q(M, \mathcal{E}^* \otimes_{\mathcal{O}} \mathcal{G}).$$

In particular, for any coherent sheaf $\mathcal{F}$,

$$\mathrm{Ext}^q(M, \mathcal{O}, \mathcal{F}) \cong H^q(M, \mathcal{F}).$$

This is clear, since for $\mathcal{E}$ locally free, $\underline{\mathrm{Ext}}_{\mathcal{O}}^q(\mathcal{E}, \mathcal{G}) = 0$ for $q > 0$ and $\underline{\mathrm{Ext}}_{\mathcal{O}}^0(\mathcal{E}, \mathcal{G}) \cong \mathrm{Hom}_{\mathcal{O}}(\mathcal{E}, \mathcal{G}) \cong \mathcal{E}^* \otimes_{\mathcal{O}} \mathcal{G}$.

The second property is: *Suppose* $\underline{\mathrm{Ext}}_{\mathcal{O}}^q(\mathcal{F}, \mathcal{G}) = 0$ *for* $0 \leqslant q < k$. *Then*

$$\mathrm{Ext}^k(M; \mathcal{F}, \mathcal{G}) \cong H^0\big(M, \underline{\mathrm{Ext}}_{\mathcal{O}}^k(\mathcal{F}, \mathcal{G})\big).$$

Proof. The E_2 term of the spectral sequence has only zeros below the horizontal line passing through $(0, k)$, and this gives the result.   Q.E.D.

We now are in a position to globalize the local duality theorem. Suppose that $I \subset \mathcal{O}$ is a sheaf of regular ideals such that the support $Z = \mathrm{supp}(\mathcal{O}/I)$ has dimension zero. Equivalently, locally $I = \{f_1, \ldots, f_n\}$, where the f_i form a regular sequence and $n = \dim_{\mathbb{C}} M$. We consider Z as a ringed space with structure sheaf $\mathcal{O}_Z = \mathcal{O}/I$.

We now refer to the intrinsic form of the local duality theorem in Section 3 above. According to the proposition in that section, the sheaves $\underline{\mathrm{Ext}}_{\mathcal{O}}^q(\mathcal{O}_Z, \Omega^n) = 0$ for $q < n$. Moreover, since the sheaves $\mathcal{O}_Z$ and

$\underline{\operatorname{Ext}^n_{\mathcal{O}}}(\mathcal{O}_Z, \Omega^n)$ are skyscraper sheaves,

$$\left\{ \begin{array}{c} H^0(M, \mathcal{O}_Z) \cong \bigoplus_{P \in Z} \mathcal{O}_{Z,P}, \\ H^0(M, \underline{\operatorname{Ext}^n_{\mathcal{O}}}(\mathcal{O}_Z, \Omega^n)) \cong \bigoplus_{P \in Z} \underline{\operatorname{Ext}^n_{\mathcal{O}_P}}(\mathcal{O}_{Z,P}, \Omega^n_P), \\ H^q(M, \mathcal{O}_Z) = H^q(M, \underline{\operatorname{Ext}^n_{\mathcal{O}}}(\mathcal{O}_Z, \Omega^n)) = 0 \qquad \text{for } q > 0 \end{array} \right.$$

Adding up the local duality theorems in each point $P \in Z$ gives the

Global Duality Theorem I. *Let* $I \subset \mathcal{O}$ *be a sheaf of regular ideals such that* $Z = \operatorname{supp}(\mathcal{O}/I)$ *has dimension zero. Then there is a nondegenerate pairing*

$$H^q(M, \mathcal{O}_Z) \otimes \operatorname{Ext}^{n-q}(M; \mathcal{O}_Z, \Omega^n) \to \mathbb{C}$$

that is functorial in the sheaf of ideals I.

Explanation of the General Global Duality Theorem

We have now found duality theorems for the coherent sheaf cohomology $H^q(M, \mathcal{F})$ in the two cases where $\mathcal{F} \cong \mathcal{O}(F)$ is locally free and $\mathcal{F} = \mathcal{O}_Z$ with $\dim Z = 0$ and $\mathcal{O}_Z = \mathcal{O}/I$ with I a sheaf of regular ideals. These represent the two extremes of a general duality theorem for $H^q(M, \mathcal{F})$, which will now be explained.

The steps are the following:

1. Given modules L, M, N over the local ring $\mathcal{O} = \mathcal{O}_n$, the pairing

$$\operatorname{Hom}_{\mathcal{O}}(L, M) \otimes_{\mathcal{O}} \operatorname{Hom}_{\mathcal{O}}(M, N) \to \operatorname{Hom}_{\mathcal{O}}(L, N)$$

induces a pairing, called the *Yoneda pairing*

$$\operatorname{Ext}^p_{\mathcal{O}}(L, M) \otimes_{\mathcal{O}} \operatorname{Ext}^q_{\mathcal{O}}(M, N) \to \operatorname{Ext}^{p+q}_{\mathcal{O}}(L, N)$$

having associativity and graded commutativity properties analogous to the usual cup product. This is a formal exercise using the four-part proposition.

2. Applying the propogation principle, if $\mathcal{F}, \mathcal{G}, \mathcal{H}$ are coherent sheaves on M, then there is

$$\underline{\operatorname{Ext}^p_{\mathcal{O}}}(\mathcal{F}, \mathcal{G}) \otimes_{\mathcal{O}} \underline{\operatorname{Ext}^q_{\mathcal{O}}}(\mathcal{G}, \mathcal{H}) \to \underline{\operatorname{Ext}^{p+q}_{\mathcal{O}}}(\mathcal{F}, \mathcal{H})$$

inducing the previous pairing in each stalk.

3. This procedure globalizes to give a pairing

$$\operatorname{Ext}^p(M; \mathcal{F}, \mathcal{G}) \otimes \operatorname{Ext}^q(M; \mathcal{G}, \mathcal{H}) \to \operatorname{Ext}^{p+q}(M; \mathcal{F}, \mathcal{H}).$$

Taking

$$q = n - p,$$
$$\mathcal{F} = \mathcal{O}, \quad \mathcal{G} = \mathcal{F}, \quad \mathcal{H} = \Omega^n,$$

this pairing is

$$(*) \qquad H^p(M, \mathcal{F}) \otimes \mathrm{Ext}^{n-p}(M; \mathcal{F}, \Omega^n) \to H^n(M, \Omega^n),$$

since $\mathrm{Ext}^*(M; \mathcal{O}, \mathcal{F}) \cong H^*(M, \mathcal{F})$.

All this can be defined for any complex manifold M. For M an algebraic variety the proofs have essentially been given. In case M is compact and connected, $H^n(M, \Omega^n) \cong \mathbb{C}$ and $(*)$ becomes

$$H^p(M, \mathcal{F}) \otimes \mathrm{Ext}^{n-p}(M; \mathcal{F}, \Omega^n) \to \mathbb{C}.$$

Global Duality Theorem II. *The above pairing is nondegenerate and is functorial in the following sense : A sheaf mapping $\rho : \mathcal{F} \to \mathcal{G}$ induces $\rho_* : H^*(M, \mathcal{F}) \to H^*(M, \mathcal{G})$ and $\rho^* : \mathrm{Ext}^*(M; \mathcal{G}, \Omega^n) \to \mathrm{Ext}^*(M; \mathcal{F}, \Omega^n)$ such that the diagram*

$$\begin{array}{ccc}
H^p(M, \mathcal{F}) \otimes \mathrm{Ext}^{n-p}(M; \mathcal{F}, \Omega^n) \to \mathbb{C} \\
\rho_* \downarrow \qquad\qquad \uparrow \rho^* \qquad\qquad \| \\
H^p(M, \mathcal{G}) \otimes \mathrm{Ext}^{n-p}(M; \mathcal{G}, \Omega^n) \to \mathbb{C}
\end{array}$$

is commutative.

As mentioned before, we have proved this in the two extreme cases $\mathcal{F} \cong \mathcal{O}(E)$ and $\mathcal{F} = \mathcal{O}_Z$, which is all that we shall have geometric applications for. The general result can also be proved without too much additional effort—and most of this in the nature of formalism—from our local duality theorem.

Finally, there is an even more general duality theorem dealing with a map—cf. the reference to Hartshorne's notes at the end of this chapter.

Global Ext and Vector Fields with Isolated Zeros

We shall prove a recent theorem, due to Carrell and Liebermann,[*] which will illustrate several of the techniques developed above, and which also will tie in with several previous results in the book.

Let M be a compact Kähler manifold and v a holomorphic vector field having a set Z of isolated zeros.

Theorem. *If Z is nonempty, then*

$$H^{p,q}(M) = 0 \qquad \text{for } p \neq q.$$

---

[*]J. Carrell and D. Liebermann, Holomorphic vector fields and Kähler manifolds, *Inventiones Math.*, Vol. 21 (1973), pp. 303–309.

Actually, Carrell and Lieberman proved the more general statement

$$H^{p,q}(M) = 0 \qquad for \ |p - q| > \dim_{\mathbb{C}} Z,$$

where Z is the zero set of any holomorphic vector field on M. Granted the general duality theorem, the proof of this stronger assertion runs about the same as the one we shall now give, which proceeds in two steps.

Step One in the Proof. We denote by $\iota(v)$ the operation of contraction of a differential form with the vector field v. This operator was already encountered in the proof of the Bott residue theorem. If locally

$$\begin{cases} v = \sum_i v_i(z) \dfrac{\partial}{\partial z_i} & \text{and} \\[2ex] \varphi = \dfrac{1}{p!q!} \sum_{I,J} \varphi_{I,J} dz_I \wedge d\bar{z}_J \end{cases}$$

is a (p,q) form, then

$$\iota(v)\varphi = \frac{1}{(p-1)!q!} \sum_{I,J} \left(\sum_{i \in I} \pm v_i \varphi_{IJ} dz_{I - \{i\}} \wedge d\bar{z}_J \right).$$

From this the formal rules

$$\begin{cases} \iota(v): A^{p,q}(M) \to A^{p-1,q}(M), \\ \iota(v)^2 = 0, \\ \iota(v)\bar{\partial} + \bar{\partial}\iota(v) = 0, \\ \iota(v)(\varphi \wedge \psi) = \iota(v)\varphi \wedge \psi + (-1)^{\deg \varphi} \varphi \wedge \iota(v)\psi, \end{cases}$$

are easily verified.

In particular, contraction with v gives the complex of sheaves

$$\Omega^n \xrightarrow{\iota(v)} \Omega^{n-1} \to \cdots \to \Omega^1 \xrightarrow{\iota(v)} \mathcal{O}.$$

We note that the image of $\Omega^1 \xrightarrow{\iota(v)} \mathcal{O}$ is the ideal sheaf I of Z; in fact, near a zero of v the above sequence is the Koszul complex associated to regular ideal $\{v_1(z), \ldots, v_n(z)\}$. Consequently we have a very natural global syzygy for $\mathcal{O}_Z = \mathcal{O}/I$, one which will be used to calculate global Ext.

For this we observe the commutative diagram

$$\begin{array}{ccc} \underline{\operatorname{Hom}}_{\mathcal{O}}(\Omega^p, \Omega^n) & \xrightarrow{\sim} & \Omega^{n-p} \\[1ex] \iota(v)^* \downarrow & & \downarrow \iota(v) \\[2ex] \underline{\operatorname{Hom}}_{\mathcal{O}}(\Omega^{p+1}, \Omega^n) & \xrightarrow{\sim} & \Omega^{n-p-1} \end{array}$$

similar to the one encountered in the lemma in the discussion concerning the intrinsic form of local duality in Section 3 above. Recall that $\text{Ext}^*(M; \mathcal{O}_Z, \Omega^n)$ is the hypercohomology of the complex of sheaves

$$\underline{\text{Hom}}_{\mathcal{O}}(\mathcal{O}, \Omega^n) \to \underline{\text{Hom}}_{\mathcal{O}}(\Omega^1, \Omega^n) \to \cdots.$$

Using the identifications provided by the commutative diagram, we write this complex of sheaves as $\Omega^{n-\cdot}$. Thus

$$\text{Ext}^*(M; \mathcal{O}_Z, \Omega^n) \cong \mathbb{H}^*(M, \Omega^{n-\cdot})$$

We note that the differential used to calculate the hypercohomology on the right is $\delta \pm \iota(v)$, where δ is the Čech coboundary mapping.

Now, according to the general discussion of hypercohomology there are two spectral sequences $\{''E_r\}$ and $\{'E_r\}$ abutting to $\mathbb{H}^*(M, \Omega^{n-\cdot})$. One of them has

$$''E_2^{p,q} = H^p\big(M, \underline{\text{Ext}}_{\mathcal{O}}^q(\mathcal{O}_Z, \Omega^n)\big)$$
$$= 0, \qquad \text{unless } p = 0 \text{ and } q = n.$$

The other spectral sequence has

$$'E_1^{p,q} = H^q(M, \Omega^{n-p}).$$

The differentials $d_1', d_2', \cdots$ are induced from $\iota(v)$. If we can show that $d_1' = d_2' = \cdots = 0$, then

$$'E_1^{p,q} \cong {}'E_2^{p,q} \cong \cdots \cong {}'E_\infty^{p,q}$$
$$= 0, \qquad \text{unless } p + q = n$$

by the previous spectral sequence. This proves the theorem.

Step Two. Let $L \in H^{1,1}(M)$ be the cohomology class of a Kähler metric ω. The proof that $d_1' = d_2' = \cdots = 0$ will use the hard Lefschetz isomorphism

$$L^k: H^{n-k}(M) \overset{\sim}{\to} H^{n+k}(M)$$

and primitive decomposition

$$\left\{ \begin{array}{l} H^l(M) = \bigoplus_{j \leqslant [l/2]} L^j P^{l-2j}(M), \qquad \text{where} \\ P^{n-k}(M) = \ker\{L^{k+1}: H^{n-k}(M) \to H^{n+k+2}(M)\} \end{array} \right\},$$

both of which were proved in Section 6 of Chapter 0. We recall also that the primitive decomposition is compatible with the Hodge (p,q) decomposition.

Now, as noted above, the diagram

$$\begin{array}{ccc} 'E_1^{p,q} & \overset{d_1}{\longrightarrow} & 'E_1^{p+1,q} \\ \| & & \| \\ H^{n-p,q}(M) & \overset{\iota(v)}{\longrightarrow} & H^{n-p-1,q}(M) \end{array}$$

is commutative, at least up to ± 1. Thus, we must prove that $\iota(v)$ induces zero as a map on cohomology. For a holomorphic 1-form $\varphi \in H^{1,0}(M)$, $\iota(v)\varphi$ is a holomorphic function on M that vanishes on $Z \neq \varphi$. Thus $\iota(v)\varphi = 0$. Using this, we shall prove

Lichnerowicz' Lemma. $\iota(\mathrm{v})\omega = 0$ in $H^{0,1}(M)$.

Proof. By hard Lefschetz and Kodaira-Serre duality, the pairing

$$H^{1,0}(M) \otimes H^{0,1}(M) \to \mathbb{C}$$

given by

$$\varphi \otimes \psi \to \int_M \omega^{n-1} \wedge \varphi \wedge \psi$$

is nondegenerate. According to the formal rules for $\iota(v)$ listed above, for all $\varphi \in H^{1,0}(M)$

$$0 = \iota(v)(\omega^n \wedge \varphi) \qquad \text{(since } \omega^n \wedge \varphi \equiv 0 \text{ for trivial reasons)}$$

$$= n\omega^{n-1} \wedge \iota(v)\omega \wedge \varphi \qquad \text{(since as observed above } \iota(v)\varphi \equiv 0)$$

$$\Rightarrow \int_M \omega^{n-1} \wedge \iota(v)\omega \wedge \varphi = 0$$

$$\Rightarrow \iota(v)\omega = 0 \text{ in } H^{0,1}(M)$$

by the nondegeneracy of the pairing. Q.E.D. for lemma.

In particular, $d_1' L = 0$, so that L defines a class in $'E_2^{n-1,1}$. Since

$$d_r': \ 'E_r^{n-1,1} \to \ 'E_r^{n-1+r, 2-r} = 0$$

for $r \geq 2$, it follows that L defines a class in $'E_r^{n-1,1}$ for all r. Moreover, multiplication by L^k commutes with the differentials in the spectral sequence, as follows by the formal rules for calculating with $\iota(v)$. Therefore, to prove that $d_1' = 0$, by using the primitive decomposition and hard Lefschetz it will suffice to prove that this is the case on primitive cohomology. Let

$$\psi \in P^{n-q-k,q}(M) \subset \ 'E^{q+k,q}.$$

Then, essentially repeating the argument from the degeneration of the Leray spectral sequence in Section 6 of Chapter 3,

$$0 = \iota(v)(\omega^{k+1}\psi) = \omega^{k+1}\iota(v)\psi$$

in cohomology. But $\iota(v)\psi \in H^{n-k-1}(M)$, and so $L^{k+1}\iota(v)\psi = 0 \Rightarrow \iota(v)\psi = 0$ by hard Lefschetz. Thus $d_1' = 0$.

The argument for $d_2' = d_3' = \cdots = 0$ is the same. Q.E.D.

We note that this proof has not used the full strength of duality. For example, the equality

$$\dim \mathrm{Ext}^*(M; \mathcal{O}_Z, \Omega^n) = \deg(Z) = \dim H^0(M, \mathcal{O}_Z)$$

gives

$$\sum_p h^{p,p}(M) = \deg(Z).$$

Since the left-hand side is just the topological Euler characteristic, what we have is just a special case of the Hopf index theorem. More substantial applications, including a proof of Bott's residue formula, arise by keeping track of the filtrations induced by the spectral sequences. These are given in the paper of Carrell and Liebermann.

Global Duality and Superabundance of Points on a Surface

Let $L \to S$ be a holomorphic line bundle over an algebraic surface. In the Riemann-Roch theorem for surfaces

$$\chi(\mathcal{O}_S(L)) = \tfrac{1}{2}(L \cdot L - K \cdot L) + \chi(\mathcal{O}_S)$$

the terms

$$h^0(L), \quad h^2(L) = h^0(K-L), \quad p_g, \quad q, \quad L \cdot L, \quad K \cdot L$$

all have immediate geometric interpretations, at least in case $L=[D]$ for some effective divisor D on S. The Italian algebraic geometers first wrote this formula as

$$\dim|L| + h^0(K-L) = \tfrac{1}{2}(L \cdot L - K \cdot L) + p_g - q + \omega,$$

and then proved directly that the quantity ω defined by this equation was nonnegative, which they then called the *superabundance*. The reader should keep in mind that the dual of $H^1(\mathcal{O}_S(L))$ is $H^1(\mathcal{O}_S(K-L))$, and sheaf cohomology was 50 years in the future. Working backward historically, we shall use our global duality theorem for coherent sheaves to geometrically interpret the superabundance in some cases. We begin with an example; the final result is the Reciprocity Formula II on page 716.

Suppose that Γ_0 is a set of distinct points in $\mathbb{P}^2$ and $|C_0|=|\mathcal{I}_{\Gamma_0}(n)|$ is the linear system of curves of degree n passing through Γ_0. Let S be the quadratic transform of $\mathbb{P}^2$ along Γ_0 and $|C|$ the linear system on S of proper transforms of curves $C \in |\mathcal{I}_{\Gamma_0}(n)|$. Denote by $\pi: S \to \mathbb{P}^2$ the projection map and $E = \pi^{-1}(\Gamma_0)$ the exceptional curve. Then $|C|$ is the complete linear system $|L|$ where

$$L = \pi^* H^n - E$$

for $H \to \mathbb{P}^2$ the hyperplane bundle. The canonical bundle of S is

$$K_S = \pi^*(K_{\mathbb{P}^2}) + E$$

$$= \pi^* H^{-3} + E,$$

and the numerical characters for $L \to S$ in the Riemann-Roch formula are

$$h^2(L) = h^0(K_S - L) = 0, \qquad\qquad p_g = q = 0,$$

$$C \cdot C = C_0 C_0 - d = n^2 - d, \qquad \text{where } d = \deg \Gamma_0,$$

$$C \cdot K_S = C \cdot (\pi^* H^{-3} + E) = -3n + d.$$

Consequently, by the Riemann-Roch formula,

$$r = \dim|L| = \tfrac{1}{2}(C \cdot C - C \cdot K_S) + \omega$$

$$= \frac{n(n+3)}{2} - d + \omega.$$

On the other hand from the exact cohomology sequence of

$$0 \to \mathcal{I}_{\Gamma_0}(n) \to \mathcal{O}_{\mathbf{P}^2}(n) \to \mathcal{O}_{\Gamma_0}(n) \to 0$$

and $h^1(\mathcal{O}_{\mathbf{P}^2}(n)) = 0$, we obtain

$$r = \dim|\mathcal{I}_{\Gamma_0}(n)|$$

$$= \frac{n(n+3)}{2} - d + h^1(\mathcal{O}_{\mathbf{P}^2}(n)),$$

so that the superabundance

$$\omega = h^1(\mathcal{O}_S(L)) = h^1(\mathcal{I}_{\Gamma_0}(n)).$$

It is now clear that $\omega = 0$ *if and only if the points in* Γ_0 *impose independent conditions on the linear system* $|\mathcal{O}_{\mathbf{P}^2}(n)|$. As was seen in the Cayley-Bacharach theorem in Section 2 of this chapter, it may well happen that $h^1(\mathcal{I}_{\Gamma_0}(n)) > 0$—indeed, this is frequently the interesting case.

Returning now to a general surface S with line bundle $L \to S$, we will show: *Suppose that* $\dim|L| > 0$ *and that the complete linear system* $|L|$ *has no base curves. Assume moreover that the irregularity* $q = 0$. *Then the superabundance* $\omega \doteq h^1(L)$ *is given by*

$$\omega = \dim|\mathcal{I}_\Gamma(K_S + L)| - 2p_g + \dim|K_S - L| + 2,$$

where $\Gamma = C \cdot C'$ *for general curves* $C, C' \in |L|$.

Proof. Let $s, s' \in H^0(\mathcal{O}_S(L))$ define C, C', respectively, and consider the Koszul complex

$$0 \to \mathcal{O}(K_S - L) \to \mathcal{O}(K_S) \oplus \mathcal{O}(K_S) \to \mathcal{I}_\Gamma(K_S + L) \to 0.$$

By our assumption

$$h^1(\mathcal{O}(K_S)) = h^{2,1}(S) = h^{0,1}(S) = 0,$$

so we find

$$h^1(\mathcal{O}(L)) = h^1(\mathcal{O}(K_S - L)) \qquad \text{(by duality)}$$

$$= h^0(\mathcal{I}_\Gamma(K_S + L)) - 2h^0(\mathcal{O}(K_S)) + h^0(\mathcal{O}(K_S - L)),$$

which gives our assertion. Q.E.D.

In case $p_g = 0$, $\dim|K_S - L| = -1$, and the formula simplifies to

$$\omega = \dim|\mathcal{I}_\Gamma(K_S + L)| + 1.$$

As an application, suppose that Γ_0 is a set of $d < n(n+3)/2$ points in $\mathbb{P}^2$. Then the linear system $|\mathcal{I}_{\Gamma_0}(n)|$ of curves of degree n passing through Γ_0 contains at least a pencil, and either

1. this linear system has a fixed curve of degree less than n; or
2. general curves $C, C' \in |\mathcal{I}_{\Gamma_0}(n)|$ will have intersection

$$C \cdot C' = \Gamma_0 + \Gamma,$$

where Γ is a set of $n^2 - d$ points that we call a *residue* of Γ_0 with respect to curves of degree n. We shall prove the

Reciprocity Formula, I

$$\dim|\mathcal{I}_{\Gamma_0}(n)| = \left\{ \frac{n(n+3)}{2} - d \right\} + h^0(\mathcal{I}_\Gamma(n-3)).$$

Thus, the superabundance of Γ_0 relative to the linear system $|\mathcal{O}_{\mathbb{P}^2}(n)|$ is given by

$$\omega = h^0(\mathcal{I}_\Gamma(n-3)).$$

Proof. Let S be the blow-up of $\mathbb{P}^2$ along Γ_0 considered above and $L = \pi^* H^n - E$. Then $K_S + L = \pi^* H^{n-3}$ and by the result of p. 713

$$\dim|\mathcal{I}_{\Gamma_0}(n)| = \dim|L|$$
$$= \left\{ \frac{n(n+3)}{2} - d \right\} + \omega,$$

where $\omega = h^0(\mathcal{I}_\Gamma(K_S + L)) = \dim|\mathcal{I}_\Gamma(n-3)| + 1$.   Q.E.D.

As a first illustration we shall show how the reciprocity formula may be used to derive the properties of linear systems of cubics that arose in Section 1 of Chapter 4 in our study of the cubic surface. We begin with:

A set Γ_0 of seven points imposes independent conditions on $|\mathcal{O}_{\mathbb{P}^2}(3)|$, unless five of the seven are collinear.

Proof. If there are two cubics $C, C' \in |\mathcal{I}_{\Gamma_0}(3)|$ without a common component, then for the residual set Γ we have $h^0(\mathcal{I}_\Gamma) = 0$, and by (the most trivial case of) the reciprocity formula the points Γ_0 impose independent conditions on $|\mathcal{O}_{\mathbb{P}^2}(3)|$.

So we may assume that $\dim|\mathcal{I}_{\Gamma_0}(3)| \geqslant 3$ and that any two cubics in this linear system have a common component C_0, which must be a line or a conic. Since the linear system of lines has dimension 2, C_0 cannot be a conic and so must be a line. If C_0 contains $\leqslant 4$ points from Γ_0, then there will be a set Γ_0' of $\geqslant 3$ points left over. These will impose independent conditions on the linear system $|\mathcal{O}_{\mathbb{P}^2}(2)|$ of plane conics, and consequently

$$\dim|\mathcal{I}_{\Gamma_0}(3)| = \dim|\mathcal{I}_{\Gamma_0}(2)| \leqslant 5 - 3 = 2,$$

which is a contradiction. Q.E.D.

A set Γ_0 of eight points imposes independent conditions on $|\mathcal{O}_{\mathbb{P}^2}(3)|$, unless five are on a line or all eight are on a conic.

Proof. If we assume that Γ_0 fails to impose independent conditions, then $\dim|\mathcal{I}_{\Gamma_0}(3)| \geqslant 2$ and, as before, we conclude that any two cubics from this linear system have a common component C_0. If C_0 is a conic, then since $\dim|\mathcal{I}_{\Gamma_0}(3)| \geqslant 2$, all the points of Γ_0 must lie on C_0. If C_0 is a line, then the previous argument shows that at most three points of Γ_0 can fail to lie on C_0. Q.E.D.

The result we needed in the section on cubic surfaces now follows easily:

Let Δ be six points in $\mathbb{P}^2$, no three of which are on a line and which are not on a conic. Then $\Gamma_0 = \Delta + p + q$ imposes independent conditions on $|\mathcal{O}_{\mathbb{P}^2}(3)|$ for any $p, q \in \mathbb{P}^2$.

Proof. If not, then either five points from Γ_0 must be collinear or all eight must be on a conic—this contradicts the assumption on Δ. Q.E.D.

Here is one more illustration of the reciprocity formula.

Let Γ_0 be a set of 12 points in $\mathbb{P}^2$ that fails to impose independent conditions on $|\mathcal{O}_{\mathbb{P}^2}(4)|$. Then either

$$\begin{cases} \Gamma_0 = C_4 \cdot C_3 \text{ is a complete intersection, or} \\ 10 \text{ points from } \Gamma_0 \text{ are on a conic, or} \\ \text{six points from } \Gamma_0 \text{ are collinear.} \end{cases}$$

Proof. We assume that $\dim|\mathcal{I}_{\Gamma_0}(4)| \geqslant 3$. Recalling that $\dim|\mathcal{O}_{\mathbb{P}^2}(4)| = 14$, if there are two curves C, C' from this linear system having no common component, then

$$C \cdot C' = \Gamma_0 + \Gamma.$$

By the reciprocity formula, Γ consists of four collinear points, and this implies that $\Gamma_0 = C_4 \cdot C_3$.

Now assume that any two curves from $|\mathcal{I}_{\Gamma_0}(4)| = |C|$ have a common component C_0. It is not possible that C_0 is a cubic, since otherwise the residual system $|C - C_0|$ would consist of lines and have dimension $\geqslant 3$. Suppose next that C_0 is a conic containing $\leqslant 9$ points from Γ_0. Then the linear system of conics $|C - C_0|$ will pass through $\geqslant 3$ points and have dimension at least 3, which is a contradiction. So 10 or more points from Γ_0 lie on a conic.

If, finally, C_0 is a line containing $\leqslant 5$ points from Γ_0, then $|C - C_0|$ will be a linear system of $\infty^{3+\rho}(\rho \geqslant 0)$ cubics passing through $\geqslant 7$ points. By our previous result, either five will be on a line—in which case 10 points from Γ_0 are on a (degenerate) conic—or eight will be on a conic. But then this conic must be a fixed component of the $\infty^{3+\rho}$ cubics $C - C_0$, which is a contradiction. Q.E.D.

Now the Reciprocity Formula I was proved for $\mathbb{P}^2$ under the assumption that $C \cdot C' = \Gamma_0' + \Gamma$ where the 0-cycle $\Gamma_0 + \Gamma$ consists of distinct points of transverse intersection. It is easy to extend the formula to a general surface, but relaxing the restriction on $\Gamma_0 + \Gamma$ is more difficult by the previous method, which was to convert the ideal sheaf of Γ_0 into a locally free one by a blowing up. In practice it is desirable to have a more general reciprocity formula, and as an application of global duality we shall give this extension.

Suppose that S is a regular algebraic surface—thus $h^{1,0}(S) = h^{2,1}(S) = 0$ —and $L \to S$ is a holomorphic line bundle with two sections s, s' such that the simultaneous equations $s = 0, s' = 0$ define a zero-dimensional sub-scheme Z of S. There is an ideal sheaf $\mathcal{I} \subset \mathcal{O}$ with $\mathcal{O}_Z = \mathcal{O}/\mathcal{I}$; in fact, $\mathcal{I}$ is the image under the mapping

$$\mathcal{O}(L^*) \oplus \mathcal{O}(L^*) \to \mathcal{O}$$

given by $(f, f') \to fs + f's'$. Suppose that we decompose Z into two disjoint sets Γ_0 and Γ; we may think of Γ_0 as part of the base of the pencil $|s + \lambda s'| \subset |L|$, and shall refer to Γ as the *residue* of Γ_0.

Reciprocity Formula (II). *With the above notations,*

$$h^1(\mathcal{I}_{\Gamma_0}(L)) = h^0(\mathcal{I}_\Gamma(K + L)) - 2p_g + h^0(\mathcal{O}(K - L)).$$

In particular, if both $q = p_g = 0$, *then*

$$h^1(\mathcal{I}_{\Gamma_0}(L)) = h^0(\mathcal{I}_\Gamma(K + L)).$$

Proof. We consider the two exact sheaf sequences

$$\begin{cases} 0 \to \mathcal{I}(L) \to \mathcal{I}_{\Gamma_0}(L) \to \mathcal{O}_\Gamma(L) \to 0, \\ 0 \to \mathcal{O}(L^*) \to \mathcal{O} \oplus \mathcal{O} \to \mathcal{I}(L) \to 0, \end{cases}$$

where $\mathcal{O}_\Gamma = \mathcal{O}/\mathcal{I}_\Gamma$ in the first, and the second is the Koszul resolution. By the duality theorem, $H^1(\mathcal{I}_{\Gamma_0}(L))$ and $\text{Ext}^1(S; \mathcal{I}_{\Gamma_0}(L), \Omega^2)$ are cononically dual vector spaces. We shall calculate the latter by applying the exact sequence of global Ext and interpreting the maps.

First we observe from $\underline{\text{Ext}}^0_\mathcal{O}(\mathcal{O}_\Gamma(L), \Omega^2) = \underline{\text{Ext}}^1_\mathcal{O}(\mathcal{O}_\Gamma(L), \Omega^2) = 0$ and the spectral sequence

$$E_2^{p,q} \Rightarrow \text{Ext}^*\big(S; \mathcal{O}_\Gamma(L), \Omega^2\big)$$

$$\|$$

$$H^p\big(S, \,\underline{\text{Ext}}_\mathcal{O}^q(\mathcal{O}_\Gamma(L), \Omega^2)\big)$$

for global Ext that $\text{Ext}^1(S; \mathcal{O}_\Gamma(L), \Omega^2) = 0$. Thus we have

$$(*) \quad 0 \to \text{Ext}^1\big(S; \mathcal{I}_{\Gamma_0}(L), \Omega^2\big) \to \text{Ext}^1\big(S; \mathcal{I}(L), \Omega^2\big) \overset{\rho}{\to} \text{Ext}^2\big(S; \mathcal{O}_\Gamma(L), \Omega^2\big).$$

For the middle term we use the second exact sheaf sequence, noting that $\text{Ext}^1(S; \mathcal{O} \oplus \mathcal{O}, \Omega^2) \cong H^1(S; \Omega^2 \oplus \Omega^2) = 0$ since S is regular, and also that

$$\begin{cases} \text{Ext}^0\big(S; \mathcal{O}(L^*), \Omega^2\big) \cong H^0(\mathcal{O}(K+L)), \\ \text{Ext}^0\big(S; \mathcal{O} \oplus \mathcal{O}, \Omega^2\big) \cong H^0(\mathcal{O}(K)) \oplus H^0(\mathcal{O}(K)), \\ \text{Ext}^0\big(S; \mathcal{I}(L), \Omega^2\big) \cong H^0\big(\underline{\text{Hom}}(\mathcal{I}(L), \Omega^2)\big) \cong H^0(\mathcal{O}(K-L)) \end{cases}$$

to obtain

$$0 \to H^0(\mathcal{O}(K-L)) \to H^0(\mathcal{O}(K)) \oplus H^0(\mathcal{O}(K))$$
$$\to H^0(\mathcal{O}(K+L)) \to \text{Ext}^1(S; \mathcal{I}(L), \Omega^2) \to 0.$$

This gives the interpretation

$$(**) \quad \text{Ext}^1(S; \mathcal{I}(L), \Omega^2) \cong \left\{ \begin{array}{l} H^0(\mathcal{O}(K+L))/\{s\omega + s'\omega'\}, \quad \text{where} \\ \omega, \omega' \in H^0(\mathcal{O}(K)). \end{array} \right\}.$$

Now since $\underline{\text{Ext}}_\mathcal{O}^0(\mathcal{O}_\Gamma(L), \Omega^2) = \underline{\text{Ext}}_\mathcal{O}^1(\mathcal{O}_\Gamma(L), \Omega^2) = 0$ and $\underline{\text{Ext}}_\mathcal{O}^2(\mathcal{O}_\Gamma(L), \Omega^2)$ is a skyscraper sheaf concentrated at points $p \in \Gamma$ and with stalks *canonically* isomorphic to $(\mathcal{O}_\Gamma(L)_p)^*$,

$$\text{Ext}^2\big(S; \mathcal{O}_\Gamma(L), \Omega^2\big) \cong \bigoplus_{p \in \Gamma} (\mathcal{O}_\Gamma(L)_p)^*.$$

Combining this with $(*)$ and $(**)$ yields

$$0 \to \text{Ext}^1\big(S; \mathcal{I}_{\Gamma_0}(L), \Omega^2\big) \to \{H^0(\mathcal{O}(K+L))/\{s\omega + s'\omega'\}\} \overset{\rho}{\to} \bigoplus_{p \in \Gamma} (\mathcal{O}_\Gamma(L)_p)^*.$$

To interpret the mapping ρ, we suppose that $\psi \in H^0(\mathcal{O}(K+L))$ and $\eta \in \mathcal{O}_\Gamma(L)_p$. Then

$$\text{Res}_p\left(\frac{\eta\psi}{s \cdot s'}\right)$$

has intrinsic meaning since $\eta\psi \in \mathcal{O}(K+2L)_p$ and $s \cdot s' \in \mathcal{O}(2L)_p$. Because duality is functorial, we deduce that

$$\rho(\psi)(\eta) = \text{Res}_p\left(\frac{\eta\psi}{s \cdot s'}\right).$$

From the local duality theorem it follows that

$$\ker \rho \cong H^0(\mathcal{I}_\Gamma(K+L))/\{s\omega + s'\omega'\}.$$

We conclude from (∗) and (∗∗) that

$$
\begin{aligned}
h^1(\mathcal{I}_{\Gamma_0}(L)) &= \dim \operatorname{Ext}^1\!\left(S; \mathcal{I}_{\Gamma_0}(L), \Omega^2\right) \\
&= \dim(\ker \rho) \\
&= h^0(\mathcal{I}_\Gamma(K+L)) - 2p_g + h^0(\mathcal{O}(K-L)),
\end{aligned}
$$

which establishes the reciprocity formula.   Q.E.D.

We now illustrate how the singularities enter in a special case. Suppose that C and C' are two irreducible plane quartic curves having three ordinary double points p_i ($i = 1, 2, 3$) in common. We assume that at each of these points the four tangent lines to the two curves are distinct. These curves then define an ideal $\mathcal{I}_{p_i} \subset \mathcal{O}_{p_i}$, which is contained in but not equal to the square m_i^2 of the maximal ideal, and which we now shall describe: Choose local coordinates (x, y) relative to which C and C' have respective equations

$$
\begin{cases}
xy = 0, \\
(x - y)(x - \gamma y) = 0.
\end{cases}
$$

This is possible by identifying the directions through p_i with $\mathbb{P}^1$ and noting that any four points of $\mathbb{P}^1$ may be projectively transformed to $\{0, 1, \gamma, \infty\}$. So in fact γ is the *cross-ratio* associated to these four tangent lines in some order. Functions $f(x, y)$ in the ideal have the form

$$f(x, y) = \alpha xy + \beta(x - y)(x - \gamma y).$$

In general β will be a unit; then we may assume $\beta = 1$ and

$$f(x, y) = (x - \mu y)(x - \lambda y) + (\text{higher-order terms})$$

where

$$\mu\lambda = \gamma, \quad \lambda + \mu = 1 + \gamma - \alpha.$$

Having fixed the tangent directions to C to correspond to the points $0, \infty \in \mathbb{P}^1$, the tangent directions to the curve C_f defined by f will be μ, λ and the condition $\mu\lambda = \gamma$ has intrinsic meaning and defines the ideal $\mathcal{I}_{p_i} \subset \mathcal{O}_{p_i}$. *Geometrically, the curve C_f must have an ordinary double point at p_i and the cross-ratio of its tangents together with those of C is prescribed.*

We now write

$$C \cdot C' = \Gamma_0 + \Gamma,$$

where Γ_0 and Γ are zero-dimensional schemes with $\mathcal{I}_{\Gamma_0} = \mathcal{I}_{p_1} \cap \mathcal{I}_{p_2} \cap \mathcal{I}_{p_3}$ and Γ is the residue of Γ_0 relative to the pencil $|C + \lambda C'|$. We note that

$\deg \Gamma_0 = 12$ and consequently $\deg \Gamma = 4$. The Reciprocity Formula II gives

$$h^1(\mathcal{I}_{\Gamma_0}(4)) = h^0(\mathcal{I}_\Gamma(1)) \leqslant 1,$$

where $\mathcal{I}_{\Gamma_0}(4) = \mathcal{I}_{\Gamma_0} \otimes \mathcal{O}_{\mathbb{P}^2}(4)$, and where equality holds on the right if and only if the points of Γ are distinct and collinear. Since $h^0(\mathcal{O}_{\mathbb{P}^2}(4)) = 15$ and $h^1(\mathcal{O}_{\mathbb{P}^2}(4)) = 0$, it follows that: *The linear system of plane quartics through Γ_0 has dimension given by*

$$\dim |\mathcal{I}_{\Gamma_0}(4)| = 2 \text{ or } 3$$

where the second possibility holds exactly when the points of Γ are distinct and collinear.

To see when this happens we consider the triangle Δ with vertices p_1, p_2, p_3. This is a plane cubic with double points at the p_i, and we shall say that our configuration is in *special position* in case the defining equation of Δ is in the ideal $\mathcal{I}_{p_i}$ at each vertex. We now prove that: *The configuration is in special position if, and only if, the points of Γ are distinct and collinear.*

Proof. If the points of Γ are distinct and collinear, then some member E of the pencil $|C + \lambda C'|$ will have this line L_0 as tangent, from which it follows that

$$E = \Delta + L_0,$$

and so $\Delta \in |\mathcal{I}_{\Gamma_0}(3)|$ and the configuration is in special position. If, conversely, $\Delta \in |\mathcal{I}_{\Gamma_0}(3)|$, then the curves $\Delta + L$, L a line in $\mathbb{P}^2$, give a $\mathbb{P}^2$ in the projective space $|\mathcal{I}_{\Gamma_0}(4)|$. Since not all curves in this linear system are reducible, we deduce that $\dim |\mathcal{I}_{\Gamma_0}(4)| = 3$, which gives our conclusion.

                                             Q.E.D.

It is interesting to investigate the rational map

$$f: \mathbb{P}^2 \to \mathbb{P}^3$$

defined by the linear system $|\mathcal{I}_{\Gamma_0}(4)|$ when the configuration is in special position. The image is a surface S of degree four with the property that there are ∞^2 reducible hyperplane sections.

To see what the image S of f is, we observe first that f is well-defined on the blow-up $\tilde{\mathbb{P}}^2$ of $\mathbb{P}^2$ at the points p_1, p_2, p_3 of Γ_0. (See Figures 2 and 3.) If E_i is the exceptional divisor in $\tilde{\mathbb{P}}^2$ over p_i, then the proper transform $\tilde{D}$ of a generic element $D \in |\mathcal{I}_{\Gamma_0}(4)|$ is given by

$$\tilde{D} \sim \pi^* D - 2E_1 - 2E_2 - 2E_3.$$

The degree of the image $S = f(\tilde{\mathbb{P}}^2)$ in $\mathbb{P}^3$ is thus

$$\begin{aligned}
\tilde{D} \cdot \tilde{D} &= D \cdot D - 4E_1 \cdot E_1 - 4E_2 \cdot E_2 - 4E_3 \cdot E_3 \\
&= 16 - 4 - 4 - 4 \\
&= 4.
\end{aligned}$$

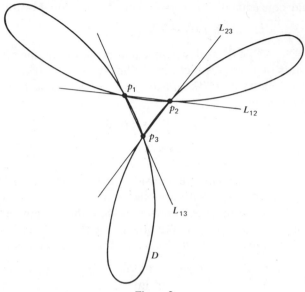

Figure 2

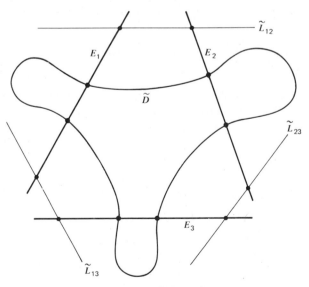

Figure 3

Now consider the map $f: \mathbb{P}^2 \to \mathbb{P}^3$. Since the linear system $|\mathcal{I}_{\Gamma_0}(4)|$ contains, as a subsystem, the triangle Δ plus the linear system of lines, f will be one-to-one and smooth away from the inverse image in $\tilde{\mathbb{P}}^2$ of the triangle. The proper transforms $\tilde{L}_{ij}$ of the lines $L_{ij} = \overline{p_i p_j}$, on the other hand, are blown down to points: any curve $D \in |\mathcal{I}_{\Gamma_0}(4)|$ containing a point $q \in L_{ij}$ other than p_i and p_j has two double points and one single point of intersection with L_{ij}, and so contains L_{ij}. Also, while the proper transform of the linear system $|\mathcal{I}_{\Gamma_0}(4)|$ in $\tilde{\mathbb{P}}^2$ has intersection number 2 with each E_i, it does not cut out a complete linear system in E_i: fixing one tangent line to a curve $D \in |\mathcal{I}_{\Gamma_0}(4)|$ at p_i determines the other, and so f maps E_i two-to-one onto a line in $\mathbb{P}^3$. These lines are double lines of the image S. Finally, since the triangle Δ is in the ideal $\mathcal{I}_{\Gamma_0}$, the points of intersection of the proper transforms $\tilde{L}_{ij}$ and $\tilde{L}_{ik}$ with E_i, while distinct on $\tilde{\mathbb{P}}^2$, are identified under the map $\tilde{f}$. In other words, after blowing down the lines $\tilde{L}_{ij}$ on $\tilde{\mathbb{P}}^2$ the divisors E_i form a triangular configuration. (See Figure 4.) The map f then folds each side of this triangle over so that the vertices are identified; the resulting configuration is shown in Figure 5. *The surface $S \subset \mathbb{P}^3$ is thus a quartic with three double lines meeting in a point.*

In fact, we have already encountered this surface, in Section 5 of Chapter 4; we saw there that S is the image under projection to $\mathbb{P}^3$ of the Veronese surface in $\mathbb{P}^5$. Indeed, we can see this directly in the present context: Since the transformation φ of $\mathbb{P}^2$ which blows up p_1, p_2, p_3 and blows down the lines $\tilde{L}_{ij}$ is given by the linear system $|\mathcal{I}_{p_1} \otimes \mathcal{I}_{p_2} \otimes \mathcal{I}_{p_3}(2)|$ of conics through the points p_i, the composition $i_{|\mathcal{O}(2)|} \circ \varphi: \mathbb{P}^2 \to \mathbb{P}^5$ of φ with the map is given by the linear system $|\mathcal{I}_{p_1}^2 \otimes \mathcal{I}_{p_2}^2 \otimes \mathcal{I}_{p_3}^2(4)|$ of quartics with double points at the points p_i; the map f, given by the sublinear system $|\mathcal{I}_{\Gamma_0}(4)| \subset |\mathcal{I}_{p_1}^2 \otimes \mathcal{I}_{p_2}^2 \otimes \mathcal{I}_{p_3}^2(4)|$, is just the composition of $i_{|\mathcal{O}(2)|} \circ \varphi$ with a projection to $\mathbb{P}^3$.

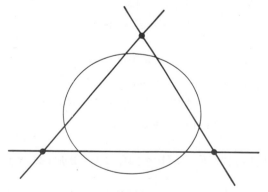

Figure 4

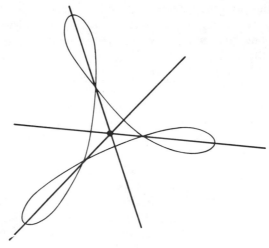

Figure 5

Extensions of Modules

Ext[1] and Extensions—Local Case. We consider again the local ring $\mathcal{O} = \mathbb{C}\{z_1,\ldots,z_n\}$ and finitely generated modules over $\mathcal{O}$. An *extension* of M by N is given by a short exact sequence

$$(E) \qquad\qquad 0 \to N \to E \to M \to 0.$$

The *trivial* or *split extension* is $M \oplus N$, and two extensions are *equivalent* in case there is a commutative diagram

$$
\begin{array}{ccccccccc}
0 & \to & N & \to & E & \to & M & \to & 0 \\
  &   & \| &   & \downarrow & & \| & & \\
0 & \to & N & \to & E' & \to & M & \to & 0
\end{array}
$$

The name "Ext" is derived from the following

Lemma. *There is a bijective correspondence between equivalence classes of extensions and* $\mathrm{Ext}^1_{\mathcal{O}}(M,N)$, *with zero corresponding to the trivial extension.*

Proof. Given an extension (E), we have

$$\mathrm{Hom}_{\mathcal{O}}(M,E) \to \mathrm{Hom}(M,M) \xrightarrow{\partial} \mathrm{Ext}^1_{\mathcal{O}}(M,N).$$

The obstruction to splitting the sequence (E) is $\partial(1_M) \in \mathrm{Ext}^1_{\mathcal{O}}(M,N)$, where

1_M is the identity map from M to itself. This gives the map from extensions to $\text{Ext}^1_{\mathcal{O}}(M,N)$.

Before giving the inverse map, we need one remark. Given the data

$$\left\{ \begin{array}{l} 0 \to R \xrightarrow{i} S \xrightarrow{\pi} M \to 0, \\ R \xrightarrow{j} N, \end{array} \right.$$

we may construct an extension

(F) $\qquad\qquad\qquad 0 \to N \to F \to M \to 0$

as follows: Define $\mu = j \oplus i : R \to N \oplus S$ and $F = N \oplus S/\mu(R)$. Then $n \oplus s \to \pi(s)$ and $n \to n \oplus (0)$ gives the exact sequence (F).

To construct $\text{Ext}^1_{\mathcal{O}}(M,N)$, we start with part of a projective resolution

$$E_2 \to E_1 \to E_0 \to M \to 0$$

and take kernel/image in

$$\text{Hom}_{\mathcal{O}}(E_0,N) \to \text{Hom}_{\mathcal{O}}(E_1,N) \to \text{Hom}_{\mathcal{O}}(E_2,N).$$

Thus a cycle gives a map $E_1/E_2 \to N$, and so a class in $\text{Ext}^1_{\mathcal{O}}(M,N)$ gives the data

$$\left\{ \begin{array}{l} 0 \to E_1/E_2 \to E_0 \to M \to 0, \\ E_1/E_2 \to N \end{array} \right. .$$

Applying the discussion of the previous paragraph gives an extension.

We leave it as an exercise to check that the two mappings

$$\left\{ \begin{array}{l} \text{equivalent classes} \\ \text{of extensions} \end{array} \right\} \quad \underset{\longleftarrow}{\overset{\longrightarrow}{\rightleftarrows}} \quad \text{Ext}^1_{\mathcal{O}}(M,\mathcal{O})$$

arc well-defined and inverse to one another. $\qquad\qquad$ Q.E.D.

Now suppose that $\mathcal{O} = \mathbb{C}\{z_1,z_2\}$ is the local ring in *two* variables and $I = \{f_1,f_2\}$ is a regular ideal. From the exact sequence

$$0 \to I \to \mathcal{O} \to \mathcal{O}/I \to 0$$

and computation of Ext's in the section on Koszul complexes we have

$$\text{Ext}^1_{\mathcal{O}}(I,\mathcal{O}) \cong \text{Ext}^2_{\mathcal{O}}(\mathcal{O}/I,\mathcal{O}) \cong \mathcal{O}/I.$$

The second isomorphism depends on the choice of generators for I, but the assertion:

$e \in \text{Ext}^1_{\mathcal{O}}(I,\mathcal{O}) \cong \mathcal{O}/I$ *is a unit—i.e.*, $e(0) \neq 0$,

has intrinsic meaning, since if also $I = \{f'_1,f'_2\}$, then

$$f'_i = \sum_j a_{ij} f_j \quad \text{and} \quad e = \Delta e',$$

where $\Delta = \det(a_{ij})$ is a unit. For our construction of rank-two vector bundles on a surface, we will use the

Lemma. *Suppose that* $e \in \mathrm{Ext}^1_\mathcal{O}(I, \mathcal{O})$ *gives an extension*

$$0 \to \mathcal{O} \to E \to I \to 0.$$

Then E *is projective* $\Leftrightarrow$ e *is a unit.*

Proof. The exact sequence of Ext gives

$$\mathrm{Hom}_\mathcal{O}(\mathcal{O}, \mathcal{O}) \xrightarrow{\partial} \mathrm{Ext}^1_\mathcal{O}(I, \mathcal{O}) \to \mathrm{Ext}^1_\mathcal{O}(E, \mathcal{O}) \to 0.$$

By definition, $\partial(1) = e$, where 1 means the constant function "one" under the identification $\mathrm{Hom}_\mathcal{O}(\mathcal{O}, \mathcal{O}) \cong \mathcal{O}$. Identifying $\mathrm{Ext}^1_\mathcal{O}(I, \mathcal{O})$ with $\mathcal{O}/I$ and using that ∂ is $\mathcal{O}$-linear, if e is a unit,

$$\partial(e^{-1}) = 1 \in \frac{\mathcal{O}}{I}.$$

It follows that ∂ is surjective, and so $\mathrm{Ext}^1_\mathcal{O}(E, \mathcal{O}) = 0$. It is trivially the case that $\mathrm{Ext}^q_\mathcal{O}(E, \mathcal{O}) = 0$ for $q \geqslant 2$.

We use this to prove that $\mathrm{Ext}^q_\mathcal{O}(M, N) = 0$ for any $\mathcal{O}$-module N and $q \geqslant 1$. The argument is by induction on the length of a projective resolution of N. Thus we may assume given

$$0 \to R \to F \to N \to 0,$$

where F is free and $\mathrm{Ext}^q_\mathcal{O}(M, R) = 0$ for $q \geqslant 1$. The exact sequence of $\mathrm{Ext}^*_\mathcal{O}(M, \cdot)$ then gives the result.

From our original discussion of Ext, it follows from the vanishing of $\mathrm{Ext}^1_\mathcal{O}(E, N)$ for all N that E is projective ($=$ free); this happens if e is a unit. If e is not a unit, then $\mathrm{Ext}^1_\mathcal{O}(E, \mathcal{O}) \neq 0$ and E is not projective.   Q.E.D.

Ext^1 *and Extensions—Global Case.* Let M be an algebraic variety and $\mathcal{F}, \mathcal{G}$ coherent sheaves on M. We may speak of *global extensions*

$$(\mathcal{E}) \qquad\qquad 0 \to \mathcal{F} \to \mathcal{E} \to \mathcal{G} \to 0,$$

by which we mean an exact sequence of sheaves of $\mathcal{O}$-modules—then $\mathcal{E}$ is necessarily coherent—and with the equivalence relation and notion of trivial extension as in the local case. One's first guess might be that such $(\mathcal{E})$'s are in bijective correspondence with $H^0(M, \underline{\mathrm{Ext}}^1_\mathcal{O}(\mathcal{F}, \mathcal{G}))$. This is not quite correct for the following reason:

Given a global section of $H^0(M, \underline{\mathrm{Ext}}^1_\mathcal{O}(\mathcal{G}, \mathcal{F}))$, choose a sufficiently fine covering $\underline{\mathcal{U}} = \{\mathcal{U}_\alpha\}$ and corresponding local extensions

$$(\mathcal{E}_\alpha) \qquad\qquad 0 \to \mathcal{F}|\mathcal{U}_\alpha \to \mathcal{E}_\alpha \to \mathcal{G}|\mathcal{U}_\alpha \to 0.$$

In $\mathcal{U}_\alpha \cap \mathcal{U}_\beta$ there will be a commutative diagram

$$
\begin{array}{ccccccccc}
0 & \to & \mathcal{F}|\mathcal{U}_\alpha \cap \mathcal{U}_\beta & \to & \mathcal{E}_\alpha|\mathcal{U}_\beta \cap \mathcal{U}_\alpha & \to & \mathcal{G}|\mathcal{U}_\alpha \cap \mathcal{U}_\beta & \to & 0 \\
 & & \| & & \downarrow{\varphi_{\alpha\beta}} & & \| & & \\
0 & \to & \mathcal{F}|\mathcal{U}_\alpha \cap \mathcal{U}_\beta & \to & \mathcal{E}_\beta|\mathcal{U}_\alpha \cap \mathcal{U}_\beta & \to & \mathcal{G}|\mathcal{U}_\alpha \cap \mathcal{U}_\beta & \to & 0,
\end{array}
$$

but it need *not* be the case that in $\mathcal{U}_\alpha \cap \mathcal{U}_\beta \cap \mathcal{U}_\gamma$ the triangle

$$\begin{array}{ccc} & \mathcal{E}_\alpha & \\ {\scriptstyle\varphi_{\alpha\beta}}\swarrow & & \searrow{\scriptstyle\varphi_{\gamma\beta}} \\ \mathcal{E}_\beta & \xrightarrow[\varphi_{\beta\gamma}]{} & \mathcal{E}_\gamma \end{array}$$

is commutative—i.e., the "transition functions" for gluing the local extensions $(\mathcal{E}_\alpha)$ may not satisfy the cocycle rule, and thus may not patch together to give a global extension. What is true is the

Lemma. *The equivalence classes of global extensions $(\mathcal{E})$ are in bijective correspondence with* $\mathrm{Ext}^1(M; \mathcal{G}, \mathcal{F})$.

Proof. Given $(\mathcal{E})$, the exact sequence of global Ext's gives

$$\mathrm{Ext}^0(M; \mathcal{G}, \mathcal{E}) \to \mathrm{Ext}^0(M; \mathcal{G}, \mathcal{G}) \xrightarrow{\partial} \mathrm{Ext}^1(M; \mathcal{G}, \mathcal{F}) \to \cdots$$
$$\| \qquad\qquad\qquad \|$$
$$H^0(M, \underline{\mathrm{Hom}}_{\mathcal{O}}(\mathcal{G}, \mathcal{E})) \to H^0(M, \underline{\mathrm{Hom}}_{\mathcal{O}}(\mathcal{G}, \mathcal{G}))$$

and the obstruction to splitting the sequence $(\mathcal{E})$ is just $\partial(1_\mathcal{G})$ as in the local case.

The converse is more interesting. Let $\mathcal{E}_\bullet(\mathcal{G}): \cdots \to \mathcal{E}_2 \xrightarrow{\partial} \mathcal{E}_1 \xrightarrow{\partial} \mathcal{E}_0 \to \mathcal{G} \to 0$ be the global syzygy for $\mathcal{G}$, and $\mathcal{U} = \{\mathcal{U}_\alpha\}$ a sufficiently fine covering of M so that a class $e \in \mathrm{Ext}^1(M; \mathcal{G}, \mathcal{F})$ is given by a cocycle in the hypercohomology group

$$\mathbb{H}^1(\underline{\mathcal{U}}, \underline{\mathrm{Hom}}_{\mathcal{O}}(\mathcal{E}_\bullet(\mathcal{G}), \mathcal{F})).$$

In the diagram

$$C^0(\underline{\mathcal{U}}, \underline{\mathrm{Hom}}_{\mathcal{O}}(\mathcal{E}_1, \mathcal{F})) \oplus C^1(\underline{\mathcal{U}}, \underline{\mathrm{Hom}}_{\mathcal{O}}(\mathcal{E}_0, \mathcal{F}))$$

$$\partial^*\swarrow \qquad \searrow{\scriptstyle\delta} \qquad \partial^*\swarrow \qquad\qquad \searrow{\scriptstyle\delta}$$

$$C^0(\underline{\mathcal{U}}, \underline{\mathrm{Hom}}_{\mathcal{O}}(\mathcal{E}_2, \mathcal{F})) \oplus C^1(\underline{\mathcal{U}}, \underline{\mathrm{Hom}}_{\mathcal{O}}(\mathcal{E}_1, \mathcal{F})) \oplus C^2(\underline{\mathcal{U}}, \underline{\mathrm{Hom}}_{\mathcal{O}}(\mathcal{E}_0, \mathcal{F})),$$

The cocycle e is given by $\varphi \oplus \eta$, where

$$\varphi = \{\varphi_\alpha\} \quad \text{with } \varphi_\alpha \in H^0(\mathcal{U}_\alpha, \underline{\mathrm{Hom}}_{\mathcal{O}}(\mathcal{E}_1, \mathcal{F})),$$
$$\eta = \{\eta_{\alpha\beta}\} \quad \text{with } \eta_{\alpha\beta} \in H^0(\mathcal{U}_\alpha \cap \mathcal{U}_\beta, \underline{\mathrm{Hom}}_{\mathcal{O}}(\mathcal{E}_0, \mathcal{F})).$$

Writing out the conditions that e be a cocycle gives the relations:

(1) $\qquad \partial^*\varphi = 0 \Rightarrow \varphi_\alpha \in H^0(\mathcal{U}_\alpha, \underline{\mathrm{Hom}}_{\mathcal{O}}(\mathcal{E}_1/\mathcal{E}_2, \mathcal{F}))$
$$\Rightarrow \varphi_\alpha \text{ defines an extension}$$
$(\mathcal{E}_\alpha) \qquad\qquad 0 \to \mathcal{F}|\mathcal{U}_\alpha \to \mathcal{E}_\alpha \to \mathcal{G}|\mathcal{U}_\alpha \to 0$

by the same argument as in the proof of the first lemma in the preceding section,

(2) $\delta\varphi = \partial^* \eta \Rightarrow \varphi_\alpha - \varphi_\beta = \partial^* \eta_{\alpha\beta}$

> $\Rightarrow$ the local extensions $(\mathcal{E}_\alpha)$ given above patch together in double intersections $\mathcal{U}_\alpha \cap \mathcal{U}_\beta$; and

(3) $\delta\eta = 0$ $\Rightarrow$ the cocycle rule for the patchings of the local extensions in double intersections.

Admittedly, step 3 needs some amplification, but the details to be checked are straightforward enough.   Q.E.D.

Points on a Surface and Rank-Two Vector Bundles

As an application of the global duality theorem (I), we shall discuss the following question:* *Given an algebraic surface* S *and sheaf of regular ideals* $I \subset \mathcal{O}$ *with* $\mathrm{supp}(\mathcal{O}/I)$ *a set of points* Z, *we define* $\mathcal{O}_Z = \mathcal{O}/I$ *and ask whether there exists a rank-two holomorphic vector bundle* $E \to S$ *with given first Chern class* $c_1(E)$ *and section* $s \in H^0(S, \mathcal{O}(E))$ *whose divisor* (s) *is* Z *ideal-theoretically?*

To answer this question, suppose first that $E \to S$ is the rank-two bundle and $s \in H^0(S, \mathcal{O}(E))$ the holomorphic section with divisor $(s) = Z$ that we are trying to construct. We may consider s as a sheaf mapping $\mathcal{E}^* \xrightarrow{s} \mathcal{O}$, $\mathcal{E}^* = \mathcal{O}(E^*)$, and what we are asking for is a short exact sequence

(*) $0 \to \mathcal{L} \xrightarrow{i} \mathcal{E}^* \xrightarrow{s} I \to 0$

where $\mathcal{L}$ is locally free of rank one.

Proof.   Locally, $\mathcal{E} \cong \mathcal{O} \oplus \mathcal{O}$ and $s = (f_1, f_2)$. The map $\mathcal{E}^* \xrightarrow{s} I$ is given by

$$(g_1, g_2) \to f_1 g_1 + f_2 g_2,$$

and by comparison with the Koszul complex—of which this is the first step—$\mathcal{L}$ is locally isomorphic to $\mathcal{O}$ in such a way that $i(h) = (-f_2 h, f_1 h)$.
                                                                                          Q.E.D.

The relation between the line bundle $\mathcal{L}$ and vector bundle $\mathcal{E}$ is

$$c_1(\mathcal{L}) = -c_1(\mathcal{E}).$$

---

*This was first considered by R. L. E. Schwarzenberger, Vector bundles on algebraic surfaces, *Proc. London Math. Soc.*, Vol. 11 (1961), pp. 601–622, and Vector bundles on the projective plane, *loc. cit.*, Vol. 11 (1961), pp. 623–640.

Proof. On $S^* = S - Z$ we have

$$0 \to \mathcal{L}|S^* \to \mathcal{E}^*|S^* \to \mathcal{O}_{S^*} \to 0$$

$$\Rightarrow c_1(\mathcal{L}) = c_1(\mathcal{E}^*) \quad \text{in } H^2(S^*, \mathbb{Z})$$

$$\Rightarrow c_1(\mathcal{L}) = c_1(\mathcal{E}^*) \quad \text{in } H^2(S, \mathbb{Z}),$$

since in the exact cohomology sequence

$$H^2(S, S^*; \mathbb{Z}) \to H^2(S, \mathbb{Z}) \to H^2(S^*, \mathbb{Z})$$

we have by excision

$$H^2(S, S^*, \mathbb{Z}) \cong \sum_{p \in Z} H^2(B_p, B_p^*; \mathbb{Z})$$

$$= 0,$$

where B_p is a ball around p. Q.E.D.

Actually this makes sense, since, very roughly speaking, giving $\mathcal{E}$ is the same as giving its Chern classes $c_1(E)$ and $c_2(E)$, and $c_2(E)$ is just Z. The assertion $c_1(\mathcal{L}) = - c_1(\mathcal{E})$ may be refined to

$$\mathcal{L} = \wedge^2 \mathcal{E}^* \quad \text{in} \quad \text{Pic}(S) = H^1(S, \mathcal{O}^*),$$

which follows from the Levi Extension Theorem given in Section 2 of Chapter 3.

Referring to (∗), we may rephrase the problem as follows: *Given* $(Z, \mathcal{O}_Z)$ *and* $\mathcal{L} \in \text{Pic}(S)$, *we seek*

$$(**) \quad \begin{cases} e \in \text{Ext}^1(S; I, \mathcal{L}), & \text{such that } e_p \text{ is a unit in} \\ \text{Ext}^1(I, \mathcal{L})_p \cong \mathcal{O}_{Z,p} \text{ for each point } p \in Z. \end{cases}$$

Explanation. For any open set $U \subset S$, there is a restriction mapping

$$\text{Ext}^*(S; \mathcal{F}, \mathcal{G}) \to \text{Ext}^*(U; \mathcal{F}, \mathcal{G})$$

of global Ext's. For U sufficiently small so that $H^q(U, \underline{\text{Ext}}_{\mathcal{O}}^*(\mathcal{F}, \mathcal{G})) = 0$ for $q > 0$,

$$\text{Ext}^*(U; \mathcal{F}, \mathcal{G}) \cong H^0(U, \text{Ext}_{\mathcal{O}}^*(\mathcal{F}, \mathcal{G}))$$

by the spectral sequence relating local and global Ext's. Thus $e \in \text{Ext}^1(S; I, \mathcal{L})$ induces e_p in each stalk $\underline{\text{Ext}}_{\mathcal{O}}^1(I, \mathcal{L})_p$ for any point $p \in S$.

By the discussion in the preceding section, a class $e \in \text{Ext}^1(S; I, \mathcal{L})$ defines a global extension

$$0 \to \mathcal{L} \to \mathcal{E}^* \to I \to 0$$

over S, and by the lemma on p. 724 the coherent sheaf $\mathcal{E}^*$ will be locally free if each e_p is a unit for $p \in Z$. Thus, *solving* (∗∗) *and finding* (∗) *are entirely equivalent*.

The first approximation to understanding (∗∗) is to look into the spectral sequence relating local and global Ext's.

Using that $E_2^{p,q} = H^p(S, \underline{\text{Ext}}_0^q(I, \mathcal{L}))$, the picture of E_2 is

$E_2^{0,1}$

$\parallel$

$H^0(\underline{\text{Ext}}_0^1(I, \mathcal{L}))$ $\qquad\qquad$ $E_2^{2,0} = H^0(\underline{\text{Ext}}_0^0(I, \mathcal{L})) \cong H^0(\mathcal{L})$

where the isomorphism results from

$$\begin{cases} 0 \to I \to \mathcal{O} \to \mathcal{O}_Z \to 0, & \text{and} \\ \underline{\text{Ext}}_0^0(\mathcal{O}_Z, \mathcal{L}) = 0 \end{cases}$$
$$\Rightarrow \mathcal{L} \cong \underline{\text{Ext}}_0^0(\mathcal{O}, \mathcal{L}) \cong \underline{\text{Ext}}_0^0(I, \mathcal{L}),$$

using the exact sequence of Ext.

In particular, if $E_2^{2,0} = 0$, then $\overline{\text{Ext}}^1(S; I, \mathcal{L}) \cong H^0(S, \underline{\text{Ext}}_0^1(I, \mathcal{L}))$, and $(**)$ may be solved. Thus: *If* $H^2(S, \mathcal{L}) = 0$, *then we may find a rank-two holomorphic vector bundle* $E \to S$ *and section* $s \in H^0(S, \mathcal{E})$ *such that* $c_1(\mathcal{L}) = -c_1(\mathcal{E})$ *and* s *defines* Z *ideal-theoretically. In particular, we may take* $\mathcal{L} = \mathcal{O}$ *in case* $p_g(S) = 0$. *Taking* $\mathcal{L}$ *to be sufficiently ample, we may always arrange that* $H^2(S, \mathcal{L}) = 0$, *so that our original problem will have at least one solution.*

Example

Take $S = \mathbb{P}^2$, so that the $p_g = 0$ condition is satisfied. Then there exists a rank-two holomorphic vector bundle $E \to \mathbb{P}^2$ and section $s \in H^0(\mathbb{P}^2, \mathcal{O}(E))$ that defines any given Z. If Z is nonempty, then we claim that s is unique up to a constant, and the vector bundle E is *not* a global extension

$$0 \to L \to E \to L' \to 0$$

of line bundles on $\mathbb{P}^2$. Thus, in this manner we have found a whole collection of "new" vector bundles over $\mathbb{P}^2$.

Proof. If $s' \in H^0(\mathbb{P}^2, \mathcal{O}(E))$ also defines Z, then $s \wedge s' \in H^0(\mathbb{P}^2, \mathcal{O}(\wedge^2 E)) = H^0(\mathbb{P}^2, \mathcal{O}) = \mathbb{C}$, since $\wedge^2 E$ is a trivial line bundle because $c_1(E) = 0$. Thus either $s \wedge s' \equiv 0$, in which case s' is a constant multiple of s, or else $s \wedge s'$ is nowhere zero, which is excluded by the assumption that Z is nonempty.

If E is a global extension of line bundles, then $\mathcal{L} \cong \mathcal{O}(n)$ and $\mathcal{L}' \cong \mathcal{O}(n')$, since $\text{Pic}(\mathbb{P}^2) \cong \mathbb{Z}$. Now $\text{Ext}^1(\mathbb{P}^2, \mathcal{L}', \mathcal{L}) \cong H^1(\mathbb{P}^2, \mathcal{O}(n - n')) = 0$. Also, $n + n' = 0$, since $c_1(E) = 0$. Thus

$$\mathcal{E} \cong \mathcal{O}(n) \oplus \mathcal{O}(-n),$$

where $n \geqslant 0$, and this is a contradiction, since any section of $\mathcal{E}$ is either nowhere zero ($n = 0$) or else vanishes on a curve ($n > 0$). $\qquad$ Q.E.D.

We still have not found necessary and sufficient conditions that $(**)$ may be solved. To do this, we assume for simplicity that

$$\begin{cases} \mathcal{L} = \mathcal{O}, & \text{and} \\ I_p = m_p & \text{is the maximal ideal for each point } p \in Z. \end{cases}$$

The exact sequence of global Ext applied to

$$0 \to I \to \mathcal{O} \to \mathcal{O}_Z \to 0$$

gives

$$\cdots \to H^1(S,\mathcal{O}) \to \mathrm{Ext}^1(S;I,\mathcal{O}) \to \mathrm{Ext}^2(S;\mathcal{O}_Z,\mathcal{O}) \to H^2(S,\mathcal{O}) \to \cdots.$$

Since $\underline{\mathrm{Ext}}^q_{\mathcal{O}}(\mathcal{O}_Z,\mathcal{O})=0$ for $q \neq 2$ while $\underline{\mathrm{Ext}}^2_{\mathcal{O}}(\mathcal{O}_Z,\mathcal{O})$ is a skyscraper sheaf concentrated on Z with stalks

$$\underline{\mathrm{Ext}}^2_{\mathcal{O}}(\mathcal{O}_Z,\mathcal{O})_p \cong \wedge^2 T'_p(S),$$

the above exact sequence is the top row in the diagram

$$\mathrm{Ext}^1(S;I,\mathcal{O}) \to \bigoplus_{p \in Z} \wedge^2 T'_p(S) \to H^2(S,\mathcal{O})$$

(∗∗∗)
$$\updownarrow \qquad\qquad \updownarrow \qquad\qquad \updownarrow$$

$$\mathrm{Ext}^1(S;I,\mathcal{O})^* \leftarrow \bigoplus_{p \in Z} \wedge^2 T'_p{}^*(S) \overset{\rho}{\leftarrow} H^0(S,\Omega^2)$$

The bottom row are the dual vector spaces, where the dual of $\mathrm{Ext}^2(S,\mathcal{O}_Z,\mathcal{O})$ is $H^0(S,\mathcal{O}_Z \otimes \Omega^2)$ by the duality theorem (I). By functorality, the mapping ρ is simply the restriction of a global holomorphic 2-form on S to each point $p \in Z$.

Now what we are seeking is

$$e \in \mathrm{Ext}^1(S;I,\mathcal{O}) \qquad \text{with } e_p \neq 0 \text{ in each } \wedge^2 T'_p(S) \quad (p \in Z).$$

Applying the duality in (∗∗∗), we have the following result:

Given a set of points $Z \subset S$, there is a rank-two holomorphic vector bundle $E \to S$ with $\wedge^2 \mathcal{E} \cong \mathcal{O}$ and section $s \in H^0(S,\mathcal{O}(\mathcal{E}))$ that defines Z ⇔ there are bivectors $0 \neq \tau_p \in \wedge^2 T'_p(S)$ $(p \in Z)$ such that

$$\sum_{P \in Z} \langle \psi, \tau_p \rangle = 0$$

for all $\psi \in H^0(S,\Omega^2)$. In particular, if $\deg Z > p_g(S)$, then (E,s) always exists.

It remains to intrinsically interpret this relation, which we shall do in the next section.

Residues and Vector Bundles

We will interpret the relation at the end of the preceding section as a residue theorem for general vector bundles and will then put our conclusions in a more geometric form.

Suppose that M is a compact, complex manifold of dimension n and

$$\mathbb{C}^n \to E \to M$$

is a rank-n vector bundle having a holomophic section $s \in H^0(M, \mathcal{O}(E))$ with a set Z of isolated zeros. Using the notations

$$\begin{cases} \wedge^q \mathcal{E}^* = \mathcal{O}(\wedge^q E^*), \\ \mathcal{I}_Z = \text{ideal sheaf of } Z \text{ and } \mathcal{O}_Z = \mathcal{O} / I_Z, \end{cases}$$

the sequence

(*) $0 \to \wedge^n \mathcal{E}^* \xrightarrow{s} \cdots \to \wedge^2 \mathcal{E}^* \xrightarrow{s} \mathcal{E}^* \to \mathcal{I}_Z \to 0$

localizes to the Koszul complex, and therefore gives a global projective resolution of both $\mathcal{O}_Z$ and $\mathcal{I}_Z$. In particular (*) gives an element

$$e \in \text{Ext}^{n-1}(M, \mathcal{I}_Z, \wedge^n \mathcal{E}^*).$$

In the spectral sequence relating global and local Ext's we consider

$$d_{n-1} \colon H^0\big(M; \underline{\text{Ext}}_{\mathcal{O}}^{n-1}(\mathcal{I}_Z, \wedge^n \mathcal{E}^*)\big) \to H^n(M, \wedge^n \mathcal{E}^*),$$

where we have used the isomorphism

$$\underline{\text{Ext}}_{\mathcal{O}}^0(\mathcal{I}_Z, \wedge^n \mathcal{E}^*) \cong \wedge^n \mathcal{E}^*$$

from the section on Koszul complexes. For each $p \in Z$ there is an induced local extension class

$$e_p \in \underline{\text{Ext}}_{\mathcal{O}}^{n-1}(\mathcal{I}_Z, \wedge^n \mathcal{E}^*)_p,$$

where $\bigoplus_{p \in Z} e_p \in H^0(M, \underline{\text{Ext}}_{\mathcal{O}}^{n-1}(\mathcal{I}_Z, \wedge^n \mathcal{E}^*))$ is the image of e, and therefore satisfies

$$d_{n-1}\Big(\bigoplus_{p \in Z} e_p \Big) = 0 \qquad \text{in } H^n(M, \wedge^n \mathcal{E}^*).$$

We will interpret this relation as a residue theorem.

For this we consider the vector space $H^0(M, \mathcal{O}(K \otimes \det E))$ dual to $H^n(M, \wedge^n \mathcal{E}^*)$. In terms of a local holomorphic frame $e_1, \ldots, e_n$ for E and local holomorphic coordinates $z_1, \ldots, z_n$ on M, a section

$$\psi \in H^0(M, \mathcal{O}(K \otimes \det E))$$

is

$$\psi = h(z)(dz_1 \wedge \cdots \wedge dz_n) \otimes (e_1 \wedge \cdots \wedge e_n).$$

Writing

$$s = s_1(z)e_1 + \cdots + s_n(z)e_n,$$

we consider the form

$$\frac{\psi}{s} = \frac{h(z)dz_1 \wedge \cdots \wedge dz_n}{s_1(z) \cdots s_n(z)}.$$

Of course the right-hand side is not well-defined, but by the transformation formula the *residue* at a point $p \in Z$

(**) $$\text{Res}_p\left(\frac{\psi}{s}\right) = \text{Res}_p\left\{\frac{h(z)dz_1 \wedge \cdots \wedge dz_n}{s_1(z) \cdots s_n(z)}\right\}$$

is independent of choices. Because of the functorial property of duality we have

$$0 = \left\langle d_{n-1}\left(\bigoplus_{p \in Z} e_p\right), \psi \right\rangle$$
$$= \sum_{p \in Z} \text{Res}_p\left(\frac{\psi}{s}\right),$$

which we may state formally as the

Residue Theorem for Vector Bundles. *Given a rank-n holomorphic vector bundle* E→M *over a compact, complex n-manifold and holomorphic section* $s \in H^0(M, \mathcal{O}(E))$ *having a set* Z *of isolated zeros, if for each* $\psi \in H^0(M, \mathcal{O}(K \otimes \det E))$ *and* $p \in Z$ *we define the residue*

$$\text{Res}_p\left(\frac{\psi}{s}\right)$$

by (**) *above, then*

$$\sum_{p \in Z} \text{Res}_p\left(\frac{\psi}{s}\right) = 0.$$

Corollary (Cayley-Bacharach for Vector Bundles). *If* Z *consists of distinct simple points, then each* $D \in |K \otimes \det E|$ *that passes through all but one point of* Z *necessarily contains that remaining point.*

The result at the end of the preceding section may be rephrased as:

Corollary. *On an algebraic surface* S *given a set* Z *of isolated points and holomorphic line bundle* L, *there exists a rank-two holomorphic vector bundle* $\mathbb{C}^2 \to E \to S$ *with* $\det E = L$ *and having a section* $s \in H^0(S, \mathcal{O}(E))$ *with* $(s) = Z$ *if, and only if,* Z *has the Cayley-Bacharach property relative to the linear system* $|K \otimes L|$.

Finally, the Cayley-Bacharach property may be given a nice geometric interpretation in case the linear system $|K \otimes L|$ gives a base-point-free mapping

$$S \to \mathbb{P}^r.$$

We denote by $\overline{Z}$ the linear span in $\mathbb{P}^r$ of a set Z of d distinct points on S. For generic Z, $\dim \overline{Z} = d - 1$; the Cayley-Bacharach property implies that

$$\dim \overline{Z} = d - 2 - \rho \qquad (\rho \geqslant 0),$$

so that configurations Z satisfying that property may be roughly thought of as "multisecant planes" such as trichords, etc.

REFERENCES

We give a few sources to assist the reader in amplifying the discussion in this chapter. These will also serve as a guide to the literature.

Section 1

R. Harvey, *Integral Formulas Connected by Dolbeault's Isomorphism*, Rice University Studies, Vol. 56 (1969), pp. 77–97.

Section 2

R. Gunning, *Lectures in Complex Analytic Varieties—Finite Analytic Mappings*, Princeton University Press, Princeton, N.J., 1974.

Section 3

M. F. Atiyah and I. G. MacDonald, *Introduction to Commutative Algebra*, Addison-Wesley, Reading, Mass., 1969.

Section 4

R. Gunning and H. Rossi, *Analytic Functions of Several Complex Variables*, Prentice-Hall, Englewood Cliffs, N.J., 1965. Gives a complete treatment of coherent sheaf theory.

Section 5

A. Grothendieck, Théorems de dualité pour les faisceaux algebriques coherents, *Séminaire Bourbaki*, No. 49 (1957).

R. Hartshorne, *Residues and Duality*, Springer-Verlag, Berlin-Heidelberg-New York, 1966.

R. Hartshorne, Varieties of small codimension in projective space, *Bull. Amer. Math. Soc.*, Vol. 80 (1974), pp. 1017–1032 (especially Section 6 and the bibliography).

6
THE QUADRIC
LINE COMPLEX

This chapter occupies a somewhat anomalous position in the book: it falls, in fact, somewhere between a chapter and a protracted exercise. No new ground is broken: even the discussion of quadrics in Section 1 represents a gap in the previous material rather than further development. There are three reasons for its inclusion:

First of all in Chapters 2 and 4 we have discussed in some detail the theory of curves and surfaces; it is natural now to look at varieties of higher dimension, such as threefolds. Unfortunately, there is for threefolds no systematic body of knowledge comparable to what we have for curves and surfaces. Whatever the reason, the fact is that the only wholly successful treatment of threefolds has been in special cases; this is one such.

Second, while we have tried to provide applications of the theory and techniques developed in this book, we have not yet encountered a problem broad enough to bring to bear the full range of our techniques. The quadric line complex is just such a problem: in the course of our analysis of it we will have occasion to call upon results from Hodge theory, curves, Abelian varieties, surfaces, Chern classes, and the Schubert calculus.

The third and final reason for the inclusion of this chapter is simply the subject itself. The quadric line complex is an object of long-standing attraction: much of the material that follows was developed in the mid-nineteenth century and is still of interest today. It is a subject full of intricate symmetries and surprises; we hope the reader will find it as delightful to study as we did.

1. PRELIMINARIES: QUADRICS

Rank of a Quadric

A quadric hypersurface $F \subset \mathbb{P}^n$ may be represented as the locus of a quadratic form

$$Q(X,X) = \sum_{i,j=0}^{n} q_{ij} X_i X_j$$

with the matrix $Q = (q_{ij})$ symmetric. The *rank* of the quadric F is defined to be the rank of the matrix Q; since the only invariant of a symmetric quadratic form over $\mathbb{C}$ is its rank, two quadrics $F, F' \subset \mathbb{P}^n$ will be projectively isomorphic if and only if they have the same rank. Now, taking partials,

$$\frac{\partial}{\partial X_i} Q(X,X) = 2 \sum_j q_{ij} X_j,$$

we deduce that the singular locus of F is just the linear subspace of $\mathbb{P}^n$ corresponding to the kernel of the matrix Q on $\mathbb{C}^{n+1}$; thus

   A quadric $F \subset \mathbb{P}^n$ *is smooth if and only if it has maximal rank* $n+1$,

and more generally,

   A quadric $F \subset \mathbb{P}^n$ *of rank* $n-k$ *is singular along a* k-*plane* $\Lambda \subset F \subset \mathbb{P}^n$.

   Indeed, we can be more explicit in our description: suppose $F \subset \mathbb{P}^n$ is a quadric of rank k with singular set $\Lambda \cong \mathbb{P}^{n-k}$, and take V_{k-1} a generic $(k-1)$-plane complementary to, i.e., disjoint from, Λ; $\tilde{F} = F \cap V_{k-1}$ is then a smooth quadric of dimension $k-2$. Now if L is any line in $\mathbb{P}^n$ meeting both Λ and $\tilde{F}$, L meets F three times and so is contained in F. Conversely, if $p \in F$ is any point lying off Λ, the $(n-k+1)$-plane spanned by p and Λ must meet V_{k-1} in a point q. The line $L = \overline{pq}$ then meets F at p and twice again in Λ, and so lies in F; in particular $q \in \tilde{F}$, so p lies on a line joining Λ and $\tilde{F}$. Consequently

   A quadric $F \subset \mathbb{P}^n$ *of rank* k *is the cone through an* $(n-k)$-*plane* $\Lambda \subset F \subset \mathbb{P}^n$ *over a quadric of rank* k *in* $\mathbb{P}^{k-1}$.

   Note, incidentally, that since F contains all lines joining any point $p \in F$ to Λ, the tangent plane to F at any point contains Λ. Thus, any plane in $\mathbb{P}^n$ disjoint from Λ intersects F smoothly.

We can see most of this in terms of the Gauss map

$$\mathcal{G} : F \to \mathbb{P}^{n*}$$

defined by sending a point $p \in F$ to its tangent plane $T_p(F) \in \mathbb{P}^{n*}$. Since the tangent plane to the quadric given by Q above at a point $p = [a_0, \ldots, a_n]$ is

$$T_p(F) = \left(\sum_{i,j} q_{ij} a_j X_i = 0 \right),$$

we see that the Gauss map on F is just the restriction to F of the rational map $\mathbb{P}^n \to \mathbb{P}^{n*}$ given by the matrix Q. If F is smooth, $\mathcal{G}$ is an isomorphism, and the dual variety $F^* = \mathcal{G}(F) \subset \mathbb{P}^{n*}$ is again a smooth quadric. Note that in this case no hyperplane in $\mathbb{P}^n$ will be tangent to F more than once; so every tangent hyperplane section $T_p(F) \cap F$ of a smooth quadric in $\mathbb{P}^n$ has rank $n - 1$, i.e., is the cone through p over a smooth quadric in $\mathbb{P}^{n-2}$. In general, if F has rank k and singular set Λ_{n-k}, then every tangent hyperplane to F contains Λ, and $\mathcal{G}$ maps F to a smooth quadric in the subspace $\mathbb{P}^{k-1*} \subset \mathbb{P}^{n*}$ of hyperplanes containing Λ.

Linear Spaces on Quadrics

One fascinating aspect of quadrics is the behavior of the linear spaces lying on them. This is described in the

Proposition. *A smooth quadric* F *of dimension* m *contains no linear spaces of dimension strictly greater than* m/2; *on the other hand*

    1. *If* m = 2n + 1 *is odd, then* F *contains an irreducible* (n + 1)(n + 2)/2-*dimensional family of* n-*planes; while*
    2. *If* m = 2n *is even, then* F *contains two irreducible,* n(n + 1)/2-*dimensional families of* n-*planes and moreover for any two* n-*planes* $\Lambda, \Lambda' \subset$ F,

$$\dim(\Lambda \cap \Lambda') \equiv n \ (2)$$

if and only if Λ *and* Λ' *belong to the same family.*

Before we prove this, note that we have already observed this phenomenon in the case $m = 2$: on a quadric surface in $\mathbb{P}^3$ there are two one-dimensional families of lines; and two lines of opposite families always meet in a point, while lines of the same family are either disjoint or meet in a line. The reader is also referred to the discussion in Section 2 of the geometry of the Grassmannian $G(2,4)$ to see in detail the behavior of 2-planes on a quadric in $\mathbb{P}^5$.

The first statement of the proposition is readily verified: since the Gauss map $\mathcal{G}$ on a smooth quadric $F \subset \mathbb{P}^{m+1}$ is the restriction of a linear isomorphism $\mathbb{P}^{m+1} \to \mathbb{P}^{m+1*}$, the family of tangent planes to F along a linear subspace $\Lambda_k \subset F$ forms a k-dimensional linear subspace of $\mathbb{P}^{m*}$. Since the tangent space to F at any point of Λ contains Λ, moreover, the image $\mathcal{G}(\Lambda)$ lies entirely in the $(m-k)$-dimensional subspace of $\mathbb{P}^{m+1*}$ of planes through Λ; thus

$$k \leqslant m - k$$

i.e., $k \leqslant m/2$.

To prove the remainder of the proposition we use an induction on n. Let $\Sigma'_n \subset G(n+1, 2n+3)$ be the set of n-planes Λ lying on a smooth quadric F of odd dimension $2n+1$ in $\mathbb{P}^{2n+2}$, and $\Sigma_n \subset G(n+1, 2n+2)$ the family of n-planes on a smooth $F_{2n} \subset \mathbb{P}^{2n+1}$. Assume the statement of the proposition for $m < n$ (it is trivially true for $n=0$), and for $F \subset \mathbb{P}^{2n+2}$ a smooth quadric consider the incidence correspondence

$$I \subset F \times G(n+1, 2n+3)$$

defined by

$$I = \{(p, \Lambda_n) : p \in \Lambda \subset F\}.$$

The projection map $\pi_2 : I \to G(n+1, 2n+3)$ maps I onto Σ'_n, with fibers isomorphic to $\mathbb{P}^n$. On the other hand, consider the fibers of the projection $\pi_1 : I \to F$, that is, the n-planes on F passing through a point p. Clearly, any such n-plane Λ lies in the tangent plane to F at p, and hence in the intersection $F \cap T_p(F)$. But we have seen that $F \cap T_p(F)$ is just the cone through p over a smooth quadric $\tilde{F}_{2n-1} \subset \mathbb{P}^{2n}$, and so the n-planes in F through p are exactly the n-planes spanned by p together with $(n-1)$-planes in $\tilde{F}$. The fibers of π_1 are therefore isomorphic to Σ'_{n-1}, which by hypothesis is irreducible of dimension $n(n+1)/2$; it follows that I itself is irreducible of dimension $n(n+1)/2 + 2n + 1$. Finally, since the map $\pi_2 : I \to \Sigma'_n$ has fiber dimension n, we see that Σ'_n is irreducible of dimension

$$\frac{n(n+1)}{2} + 2n + 1 - n = \frac{(n+1)(n+2)}{2},$$

and part 1 of our proposition is proved.

Now let $F_{2n} \subset \mathbb{P}^{2n+1}$ be a smooth quadric; again, we set

$$I = \{(p, \Lambda_n) : P \in \Lambda \subset F\} \subset F \times G(n+1, 2n+2).$$

As before, the fibers of the projection map $\pi_2 : I \to \Sigma_n \subset G(n+1, 2n+2)$ are isomorphic to $\mathbb{P}^n$, and the fibers of $\pi_1 : I \to F$ isomorphic to Σ_{n-1}. In this case, however, by induction Σ_{n-1} is the disjoint union of two irreducible varieties of dimension $n(n-1)/2$. The connected components of the fibers of π_1 thus constitute an unbranched 2-sheeted cover of F, which, since F is rational *and hence simply connected*, must be disconnected. It follows that I has two connected components, each mapping via π_1 onto F with fibers isomorphic to one irreducible component of Σ_{n-1}; as in the last argument, each of the connected components of I is irreducible of dimension $n(n-1)/2+2n$. Since the fibers of the projection map $\pi_2:I\to\Sigma_n$ are irreducible of dimension n, we see that Σ_n has two connected components Σ_n^1 and Σ_n^2, each irreducible of dimension

$$\frac{n(n-1)}{2}+2n-n=\frac{n(n+1)}{2}.$$

Finally, it remains to show that for any two n-planes $\Lambda,\Lambda'\subset F$, the dimension of their intersection is congruent to n mod 2 if and only if they belong to the same family. Again, we proceed by induction: the statement is trivially true for $n=0$ (and more visibly for $n=1$); assume it for all $m<n$. Suppose first that Λ and Λ' intersect, and let p by any point of $\Lambda\cap\Lambda'$. Let $\mathbb{P}^{2n}$ be any hyperplane in $\mathbb{P}^{2n+1}$ not containing p; by what we have seen, the intersection $F\cap T_p(F)$ of F with its tangent plane at p is just the cone through p over the smooth, $(2n-2)$-dimensional quadric $\tilde{F}=F\cap T_p(F)\cap\mathbb{P}^{2n}$. Set

$$\tilde{\Lambda}=\Lambda\cap\mathbb{P}^{2n}\quad\text{and}\quad\tilde{\Lambda}'=\Lambda'\cap\mathbb{P}^{2n};$$

$\tilde{\Lambda}$ and $\tilde{\Lambda}'$ are then $(n-1)$-planes in $\tilde{F}$, and by our previous argument Λ and Λ' belong to the same family on F if and only if $\tilde{\Lambda}$ and $\tilde{\Lambda}'$ belong to the same family on $\tilde{F}$. But the intersection $\Lambda\cap\Lambda'$ is just the plane spanned by the intersection $\tilde{\Lambda}\cap\tilde{\Lambda}'$ together with p. By the induction hypothesis we have

Λ,Λ' belong to the same family of n-planes on F

$\Leftrightarrow\tilde{\Lambda},\tilde{\Lambda}$ belong to the same family of $(n-1)$-planes on $\tilde{F}$

$\Leftrightarrow\dim(\tilde{\Lambda}\cap\tilde{\Lambda}')\equiv n-1\,(2)$

$\Leftrightarrow\dim(\Lambda\cap\Lambda')=\dim(\tilde{\Lambda}\cap\tilde{\Lambda}')+1\equiv n\,(2),$

and we are done. Suppose on the other hand that Λ and Λ' are disjoint. In this case, take any point $p\in\Lambda$ and set

$$\Lambda''=\overline{\Lambda'\cap T_p(F),p}\,.$$

Now $T_p(F)$ cannot contain Λ'—all n-planes in $T_p(F)\cap F$ contain p and hence meet Λ—so Λ'' is an n-plane and

$$\dim(\Lambda'\cap\Lambda'')=n-1,$$

and we deduce from our first argument that Λ' and Λ'' belong to opposite families. We also see that Λ meets Λ'' only in the point p—if $\Lambda\cap\Lambda''$ contained a line, Λ would necessarily meet the hyperplane $\Lambda'\cap T_p(F)\subset\Lambda''$. Thus, by our first argument, Λ and Λ'' belong to the same family on F if and only if $n\equiv 0\,(2)$; it follows that

Λ and Λ' belong to the same family

$\Leftrightarrow n\equiv-1=\dim(\Lambda\cap\Lambda')\,(2).$

This completes the proof of the proposition.

We can write down explicitly the two families of n-planes on the smooth $2n$-dimensional quadric $F \subset \mathbb{P}^{2n+1}$ given by

$$Q(X) = \sum_{i=0}^{n} X_i X_{n+i+1}.$$

In this case for B any $(n+1) \times (n+1)$ matrix the n-plane Λ_B spanned by the row vectors $e_i = (0, \ldots, 1, 0, \ldots, 0, b_{i,0}, \ldots, b_{i,n})$ of the $2n \times n$ matrix (I, B) lies in F if and only if

$$Q(e_i, e_j) = b_{ij} + b_{ji} = 0$$

for all i and j, i.e., if and only if B is skew-symmetric. The n-planes $\{\Lambda_B\}$ form an open set Γ_0 in one of the two families of n-planes on F. (Note that

$$\dim(\Lambda_B \cap \Lambda_{B'}) = n - \operatorname{rank}(B - B') \equiv n \quad (2)$$

for any B, B' skew-symmetric.) More generally, if $I = \{i_1, \ldots, i_m\}$ is any subset of $\{0, \ldots, n\}$, then the automorphism φ_I of F defined by

$$\varphi_I[X] = [X'], \quad X_i' = \begin{cases} X_{n+i+1}, & i \in I, \\ X_i, & i \notin I, \end{cases}$$

$$X_{n+1+i}' = \begin{cases} X_i, & i \in I, \\ X_{n+1+i}, & i \notin I, \end{cases}$$

carries the set $\Gamma_0 = \{\Lambda_B\}$ of n-planes into another set Γ_I; Γ_I will be of the same family as Γ_0 if and only if $m = {}^\#I$ is even. In this way, we represent all n-planes on F.

We consider now the family of k-planes on a smooth quadric F in $\mathbb{P}^{n+1}$. The dimension of this family is easy to compute: we let $|F| \cong \mathbb{P}^{(n+2)(n+3)/2-1}$ denote the linear system of all quadrics in $\mathbb{P}^{n+1}$ and consider the incidence correspondence

$$I \subset |F| \times G(k+1, n+2)$$

given by

$$I = \{(F, \Lambda): \Lambda \subset F\}.$$

The linear system $|F|$ cuts out on any k-plane Λ the complete $(k+1)(k+2)/2 - 1$-dimensional linear series of quadrics in Λ, so the fibers of the projection map $\pi_2 : I \to G(k+1, n+2)$ have dimension

$$\frac{(n+2)(n+3)}{2} - \frac{(k+1)(k+2)}{2} - 1,$$

and I has dimension

$$(k+1)(n-k+1) + \frac{(n+2)(n+3)}{2} - \frac{(k+1)(k+2)}{2} - 1;$$

it follows that a fiber of $\pi_1 : I \to |F|$—the family of k-planes on a quadric F

— has dimension

$$(k+1)(n-k+1) - \frac{(k+1)(k+2)}{2}$$

or, alternatively, codimension $(k+1)(k+2)/2$ in the Grassmannian $G(k+1, n+2)$.

Let us now determine the class on $G(k+1, n+2)$ of the cycle $\Sigma_{k,n}$ of k-planes on a smooth quadric $F \subset \mathbb{P}^{n+1}$. Recall from Section 6 of Chapter 1 that for any flag $V_0 \subset V_1 \subset \cdots \subset V_{n+1} \subset \mathbb{C}^{n+2}$ the cohomology group $H^{(k+1)(k+2)}(G(k+1, n+2))$ is generated by the classes of the Schubert cycles

$$\sigma_{a_1, \ldots, a_{k+1}} = \left\{ \Lambda_{k+1} : \dim(\Lambda \cap V_{n-k-1+i-a_i}) \geq i \right\}$$

for all sequences

$$n - k + 1 \geq a_1 \geq \cdots \geq a_{k+1} \geq 0$$

with $\Sigma a_i = (k+1)(k+2)/2$. The cohomology in complementary dimension is likewise generated by Schubert cycles σ_b with $\Sigma b_i = (k+1)(n-k+1) - (k+1)(k+2)/2$; the intersection pairing is

$$\#(\sigma_{a_1, \ldots, a_{k+1}} \cdot \sigma_{b_1, \ldots, b_{k+1}}) = \begin{cases} 1, & \text{if } a_i + b_{k+2-i} = n-k+1 \text{ for all } i, \\ 0, & \text{otherwise.} \end{cases}$$

To find the class of $\Sigma_{k,n}$, accordingly, we have to evaluate the intersection numbers $\#(\Sigma_{k,n} \cdot \sigma_b)$ for all such $b = (b_1, \ldots, b_{k+1})$ with $\Sigma b_i = (k+1)(n-k-1) - (k+1)(k+2)/2$. We start by noting that if the flag $\{V_\alpha\}$ is generically chosen, each subspace $\overline{V}_\alpha \subset \mathbb{P}^{n+1}$ will intersect F in a smooth $(\alpha-2)$-dimensional quadric $F_{\alpha-2}$. Now, as we have seen, $F_{\alpha-2}$ cannot contain any linear subspaces of projective dimension greater than $(\alpha-2)/2$; thus, no k-plane Λ_k lying on F can meet $\overline{V}_\alpha$ in a space of projective dimension $> (\alpha-2)/2$. If $\#(\Sigma_{k,n} \cdot \sigma_b)$ is to be nonzero, then we must have

$$n - k + 1 + i - b_i \geq 2i \qquad \text{for all } i;$$

i.e.,

$$b_i \leq n - k - i + 1.$$

But from

$$(n-k+1)(k+1) - \frac{(k+1)(k+2)}{2}$$

$$= \sum_{i=1}^{k+1} b_i$$

$$\leq \sum_{i=1}^{k+1} n-k-i+1$$

$$= (n-k+1)(k+1) - \sum_{i=1}^{k+1} i$$

$$= (n-k+1)(k+1) - \frac{(k+1)(k+2)}{2}$$

we deduce that $b_i = n - k - i + 1$, i.e.,

> *The cycle* $\Sigma_{k,n} \subset G(k+1, n+2)$ *has intersection number 0 with all Schubert cycles of complementary dimension except* $\sigma_{n-k, n-k-1, n-k-2, \ldots}$.

To compute the intersection number of $\Sigma_{k,n}$ with

$$\sigma_{n-k, n-k-1, \ldots} = \{\Lambda_k : \dim(\Lambda_k \cap V_{2i}) \geqslant i\}$$

we read off the defining conditions for $\sigma_{n-k, n-k-1, \ldots}$ one by one. The first condition says that any $\Lambda \in \Sigma_{k,n} \cap \sigma_{n-k, n-k-1, \ldots}$ must meet a line $\overline{V}_2 \subset \mathbb{P}^{n+1}$ in a point; since $\Lambda \subset F$, this point must be one of the two points p_1, p_2 of intersection of $\overline{V}_2$ with F. For each $i = 1, 2$, let $\mathbb{P}_i^{n-1}$ be an $(n-1)$-plane contained in the tangent plane $T_{p_i}(F)$ to F at p_i and not containing p_i; $\mathbb{P}_i^{n-1}$ then intersects F in a smooth quadric F_i, with $F \cap T_{p_i}(F)$ the cone through p_i over F_i. Now the second condition on $\sigma_{n-k, n-k-1, \ldots}$ says that any $\Lambda \in \Sigma_{k,n} \cap \sigma_{n-k, n-k-1, \ldots}$ must meet the 3-plane $\overline{V}_4$ in a line. But $\overline{V}_4$ will meet $\mathbb{P}_i^{n-1}$ in a line, and F_i in a pair of points p_{i1}, p_{i2}; and writing any k-plane $\Lambda \subset F$ through p_i as

$$\Lambda = \overline{p_i, \Lambda \cap \mathbb{P}_i^{n-1}},$$

we see that any $\Lambda \in p_i$ meets $\overline{V}_3$ in a line if and only if Λ contains either of the points p_{i1} or p_{i2}.

Consider now the set of k-planes on F passing through the points p_i and p_{ij}. Take $\mathbb{P}_{ij}^{n-3}$ an $(n-3)$-plane lying in the intersection $T_{p_i}(F) \cap T_{p_{ij}}(F)$ and missing the line $\overline{p_i p_{ij}}$; $\mathbb{P}_{ij}^{n-3}$ intersects F in a smooth quadric F_{ij}, with $F \cap T_{p_i}(F) \cap T_{p_{ij}}(F)$ the cone through the line $\overline{p_i p_{ij}}$ over F_{ij}. The third condition on $\sigma_{n-k, n-k-1, \ldots}$ says that any $\Lambda \in \Sigma_{k,n} \cap \sigma_{n-k, n-k-1, \ldots}$ meets the 5-plane $\overline{V}_6$ in a 2-plane. But $\overline{V}_6$ meets $\mathbb{P}_{ij}^{n-3}$ in a line, and F_{ij} in a pair of points p_{ij1} and p_{ij2}; and writing any k-plane $\Lambda \subset F$ through p_i and p_{ij} as

$$\Lambda = \overline{p_i, p_{ij}, \Lambda \cap \mathbb{P}_{ij}^{n-3}},$$

we see that Λ satisfies this condition if and only if it contains either p_{ij1} or p_{ij2}.

The process is now clear. Defining inductively a collection of points $p_{i_1}, p_{i_1 i_2}, \ldots, p_{i_1, \ldots, i_k}$ by letting $p_{i_1, \ldots, i_{m-1}, 1}$ and $p_{i_1, \ldots, i_{m-1}, 2}$ be the two points of intersection of $\overline{V}_{2m}$ with a chosen $(n - 2m + 1)$-plane in the intersection of the tangent spaces to F at $p_{i_1}, p_{i_1, i_2}, \ldots, p_{i_2, \ldots, i_{m-1}}$, we find that the k-planes $\Lambda \subset F$ lying in $\sigma_{n-k, n-k-1, \ldots}$ are exactly the planes

$$\overline{p_{i_1}, p_{i_1, i_2}, p_{i_1, i_2, i_3}, \ldots, p_{i_1, i_2, \ldots, i_{k+1}}},$$

and there are 2^{k+1} of these. Consequently

$$^{\#}(\Sigma_{k,n} \cdot \sigma_{n-k, n-k-1, \ldots}) = 2^{k+1},$$

and we have

$$\Sigma_{k,n} \sim 2^{k+1} \cdot \sigma_{k+1,k,k-1,\ldots,1}$$

in the cohomology of $G(k+1, n+2)$.

Note that since the two families of n-planes on a $2n$-dimensional quadric in $\mathbb{P}^{2n+1}$ may be taken into one another by an automorphism of $\mathbb{P}^{2n+1}$, they represent the same class on $G(n+1, 2n+1)$, and hence each represents the class $2^n \cdot \sigma_{n+1,n,\ldots,1}$. Also, in case the quadric has odd dimension $n = 2m+1$ and $k = m$, the codimension $(m+1)(m+2)/2$ of the cycle $\Sigma_{m,2m+1}$ is exactly half the dimension of the Grassmannian $G(m+1, 2m+3)$, and so we may expect there to be a finite number of m-planes in the generic intersection of two quadrics in $\mathbb{P}^{2m+2}$; indeed, by our calculation this number is

$$^{\#}(\Sigma_{m,2m+1} \cdot \Sigma_{m,2m+1}) = 2^{2m+2} \cdot (\sigma_{m+1,m,\ldots,1} \cdot \sigma_{m+1,\ldots,1})$$
$$= 2^{2m+2}.$$

We have already verified this in case $n = 3$.

Linear Systems of Quadrics

Thus far, we have examined the geometry of a single quadric hypersurface in $\mathbb{P}^n$. We would now like to consider linear systems of quadrics; specifically we will study linear systems of quadrics in $\mathbb{P}^2$ and $\mathbb{P}^3$.

We begin with $\mathbb{P}^2$. In the complete system $W \cong \mathbb{P}^5$ of conic plane curves, let $W_1 \subset W$ be the subvariety of conics of rank two or less and $W_2 \subset W_1$ the set of conics of rank one. W_1 is a hypersurface in W; we first ask for its degree. This question may be answered in four ways:

1. Suppose $L = \{F_\lambda\}$ is a generic line in W, that is, a generic pencil of quadrics in $\mathbb{P}^2$. The conics F of the pencil L may be given as the zero loci of the quadratic forms

$$Q^\lambda(X) = \sum q_{ij}^\lambda X_i X_j,$$

where

$$Q^\lambda = (q_{ij}^\lambda) = Q^0 + \lambda Q^\infty$$

for suitable choice of nonsingular symmetric matrices Q^0 and Q^∞. F_λ will then be singular exactly when the determinant $|Q^0 + \lambda Q^\infty|$ vanishes; since this determinant is a cubic polynomial in λ, this will occur for three values of λ. L thus intersects W_1 three times, so $\deg(W_1) = 3$. Note that in general by this argument the singular quadrics in $\mathbb{P}^n$ form a hypersurface of degree $n+1$ in the system of all quadrics.

2. Letting L be, as above, a generic pencil of conics, we have by the

formula of p. 509

$$\chi(\mathbb{P}^2) = 2\chi(F_\lambda) + \mu - n,$$

where F_λ is a generic element of L, $n = F_\lambda \cdot F_\lambda$ the number of base points of L, and μ the number of singular conics in L. Since $\chi(F_\lambda) = 2$ and $n = 4$, this yields

$$3 = 2 \cdot 2 + \mu - 4,$$

i.e., $\mu = 3$, and W_1 is cubic.

3. Letting L again be a generic pencil of W, L will have four base points p_1, p_2, p_3, p_4 and will consist of all conics in $\mathbb{P}^2$ passing through the points $\{p_i\}$. (See Figure 1.) But since no three of the points p_i are collinear, if F is a conic consisting of two lines l, l' and containing $\{p_i\}$, then l and l' must each contain two of the points $\{p_i\}$. The singular conics passing through $\{p_i\}$ are therefore

$$\overline{p_1 p_2} + \overline{p_3 p_4}, \qquad \overline{p_1 p_3} + \overline{p_2 p_4} \quad \text{and} \quad \overline{p_1 p_4} + \overline{p_2 p_3}.$$

So we see again that L contains three singular conics.

4. Alternatively, note that $W_1 \subset W$ is the image of $\mathbb{P}^{2*} \times \mathbb{P}^{2*}$ under the map f sending a pair of lines (l_1, l_2) to the conic $l_1 + l_2 \in W$. Now the cohomology ring of $\mathbb{P}^{2*} \times \mathbb{P}^{2*}$ is generated by the classes ω_1 and ω_2, where

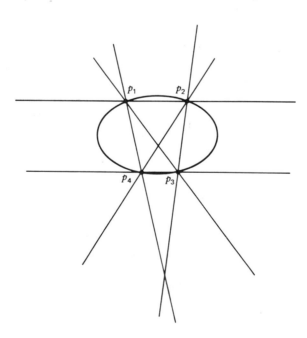

Figure 1

ω_1 and ω_2 are the pullbacks of the hyperplane class in $\mathbb{P}^{2*}$ via the two projection maps, with the relations $\omega_1^3 = \omega_2^3 = 0$, $\omega_1^2\omega_2^2 = 1$. If $H \subset W$ is the hyperplane in W consisting of conics containing a point $p \in \mathbb{P}^2$, then the pullback f^*H is the divisor of pairs (l_1, l_2) with either $p \in l_1$ or $p \in l_2$, and so it represents the class $\omega_1 + \omega_2$. Consequently, since f is two-to-one,

$$\begin{aligned}
\deg W_1 &= (H)_{W_1}^4 \\
&= \tfrac{1}{2}(\omega_1 + \omega_2)_{\mathbb{P}^{2*} \times \mathbb{P}^{2*}}^4 \\
&= \tfrac{1}{2} \cdot 6 = 3.
\end{aligned}$$

Note that the subvariety $W_2 \subset W_1 \subset W$ is just the image under f of the diagonal $\Delta \cong \mathbb{P}^{2*}$ in $\mathbb{P}^{2*} \times \mathbb{P}^{2*}$, which is the branch locus of f. Since the series $|\omega_1 + \omega_2|$ cuts out the complete series $|\mathcal{O}_{\mathbb{P}^2}(2H)|$ on Δ, W_2 is the *Veronese surface* $\iota_{2H}(\mathbb{P}^2)$ *in* $W \cong \mathbb{P}^5$.

We note that W_1 is smooth away from W_2: if $F \in W_1$ is a conic consisting of two distinct lines, we can find another conic G meeting F transversely so that the pencil L generated by F and G will have four distinct base points. By argument 3, L will meet W_1 in three distinct points, so that $m_F(L, W_1) = 1$ and F is a smooth point of W_1. On the other hand, if F is a double line and L a generic line through F, we see (Figure 2) that the pencil L will consist of all conics passing through the points p, p' of intersection of F with a second conic G of L, and tangent to (i.e., having intersection multiplicity > 1 with) G at those points. The only singular conic of L other than F is thus the sum of the tangent lines to C at p and p'; so $m_F(L, W_1) = 2$ and F is a double point of W_1. The reader may check that the tangent space to W_1 at a smooth point $F = l_1 + l_2$ is just the plane $H \subset W$ of conics passing through the point $p = l_1 \cap l_2 \in \mathbb{P}^2$, while the tangent cone to W_1 at a double point $F = 2l$ is the locus of conics tangent

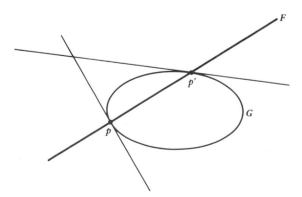

Figure 2

to l. (Note that since W_2 is the double locus of the cubic W_1, any line meeting W_2 twice must lie in W_1; this provides another proof that the chordal variety of the Veronese surface is a cubic hypersurface.)

Finally, it is interesting to observe that there are two distinct four-dimensional families of lines on the variety W_1—that is, two kinds of pencils of singular conics. First, there are the pencils formed by a fixed line l_0 plus a pencil l_λ of lines; for example,

$$L = \{(\lambda X_0 X_1 + X_0 X_2)\}_\lambda \qquad (l_0 = (X_0 = 0)).$$

(See Figure 3.) Such a pencil will either miss W_2 altogether or meet it in a single point, depending on whether the base point of the pencil l_λ lies on l_0. Second, there are the chords to W_2 in W_1; such a pencil, containing two distinct double lines, will have only a single point p as its base locus and so will be just the pullback, via the rational projection $\pi_p : \mathbb{P}^2 \to \mathbb{P}^1$, of a pencil on $\mathbb{P}^1$. (See Figure 4.) For example,

$$L = \{(\lambda X_0^2 + X_1^2)\}$$

is such a pencil.

We now turn to quadrics in $\mathbb{P}^3$. Let $W \cong \mathbb{P}^9$ be the complete linear system of all quadrics, $W_1 \subset W$ the locus of quadrics of rank three or less, $W_2 \subset W_1 \subset W$ the locus of quadrics of rank two or less and W_3 the set of rank-one quadrics. By the first of our previous arguments, W_1 is a hypersurface of degree 4 in W. Again, W_1 is smooth away from W_2: if F is

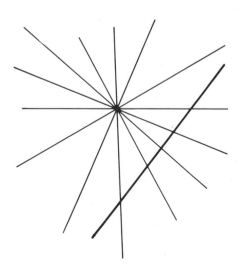

Figure 3

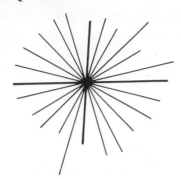

Figure 4

any quadric of rank three—which we may take to be given by the matrix

$$Q = \begin{bmatrix} 0 & 0 & 0 & 0 \\ 0 & 1 & 0 & 0 \\ 0 & 0 & 1 & 0 \\ 0 & 0 & 0 & 1 \end{bmatrix},$$

and L is the pencil generated by F and a generic quadric G, given by the matrix Q', then the polynomial

$$|\lambda Q + Q'|$$

has degree 3 in λ—i.e., L will contain three singular quadrics other than F, so $m_F(L \cdot W_1) = 1$ and F is a smooth point of W_1. Note that the polynomial $|\lambda Q + Q'|$ will fail to have degree 3 exactly when the upper left-hand entry of Q' is zero, i.e., when the quadric G contains the point $[1,0,0,0]$. The tangent plane to W_1 at F is thus the space of quadrics containing the singular point of F.

Similarly, a quadric $F \in W_2 - W_3$ of rank two may be represented by the matrix

$$Q = \begin{bmatrix} 0 & 0 & 0 & 0 \\ 0 & 0 & 0 & 0 \\ 0 & 0 & 1 & 0 \\ 0 & 0 & 0 & 1 \end{bmatrix};$$

for generic Q', then, the polynomial $|\lambda Q + Q'|$ will have degree 2; that is, a generic pencil L in W containing F will meet W_1 in only two other points. Thus F is a double point of W_1; indeed, since the polynomial $|\lambda Q + Q'|$ will have degree <2 exactly when the determinant of the upper left-hand 2×2 minor of Q' is zero, we deduce that the tangent cone to W_1 at a point $F \in W_2$ is just the locus of quadrics tangent to the singular line of F.

To find the degree of W_2, we proceed as in 4 above: W_2 is the image in W of $\mathbb{P}^{3*} \times \mathbb{P}^{3*}$ by the map f sending a pair (H_1, H_2) of hyperplanes in $\mathbb{P}^{3*}$

to the quadric $H_1 + H_2$. The cohomology of $\mathbb{P}^{3*} \times \mathbb{P}^{3*}$ is generated by the pullbacks ω_1 and ω_2 of the hyperplane class in $\mathbb{P}^{3*}$ via the two projection maps; as before, since f is 2-sheeted, we obtain

$$\deg W_2 = \tfrac{1}{2}(\omega_1 + \omega_2)^6$$
$$= \tfrac{1}{2} \cdot 20\omega_1^3\omega_2^3 = 10.$$

Lines on Linear Systems of Quadrics

Earlier in this section, we found the class on the Grassmannian of the cycle of k-planes lying on a smooth quadric in $\mathbb{P}^n$. It is interesting to try and answer the same question for the cycle of k-planes lying on a linear system of quadrics; we will discuss here the case of lines on quadrics in $\mathbb{P}^3$.

To begin with, recall that the integral homology of the Grassmannian $G(2,4)$ is generated by the Schubert cycles

$$\sigma_1(l_0) = \{x \in G: \ l_x \cap l_0 \neq \varnothing\},$$
$$\sigma_2(p_0) = \{x \in G: \ l_x \ni p_0\},$$
$$\sigma_{1,1}(h_0) = \{x \in G: \ l_x \subset h_0\},$$

and

$$\sigma_{2,1}(p_0, h_0) = \{x \in G: \ p_0 \in l_x \subset h_0\}$$

for $p_0 \in l_0 \subset h_0$ any choice of point, line, and hyperplane in $\mathbb{P}^3$. The intersections of these Schubert cycles are

$$\sigma_1 \cdot \sigma_1 = \sigma_2 + \sigma_{1,1},$$
$$\sigma_1 \cdot \sigma_2 = \sigma_1 \cdot \sigma_{1,1} = \sigma_{2,1},$$
$$\sigma_2 \cdot \sigma_2 = \sigma_{1,1} \cdot \sigma_{1,1} = \sigma_1 \cdot \sigma_{2,1} = 1,$$
$$\sigma_2 \cdot \sigma_{1,1} = 0.$$

We have seen in the preceding discussion that the variety $V(F)$ of lines lying on a smooth quadric $F \subset \mathbb{P}^3$ is homologous to $4\sigma_{2,1}$: consider now the variety $V_0(L)$ of lines in $\mathbb{P}^3$ lying on *some* quadric of a generic pencil $L = \{F_\lambda\}$ of quadrics.

The base locus of the pencil L, being a smooth intersection of two quadrics, is an elliptic curve C of degree 4, and in fact it is not hard to see that $V_0(L)$ is just the set of chords to C: on the one hand, if $l \subset F_\lambda$ for some λ, then $C \cap l = F_\lambda \cap F_{\lambda'} \cap l = F_{\lambda'} \cap l$ consists of two points; on the other hand, if l meets C in two points p and q, then for any third point $r \in l$ some quadric $F_\lambda \in L$ contains r, and so contains l.

This being established, it is easy to compute the class of $V_0(L) \subset G(2,4)$: First, since a generic hyperplane $H \subset \mathbb{P}^3$ meets C in four points, $\binom{4}{2} = 6$

chords of C will lie in H, so

$$^{\#}(V_0(L)\cdot\sigma_{1,1}) = 6.$$

Second, projection of C from a generic point $p \in \mathbb{P}^3$ to a plane maps C to a plane quartic, which by the genus formula will have two double points; consequently p lies on two chords of C and

$$^{\#}(V_0(L)\cdot\sigma_2) = 2.$$

In sum,

$$V_0(L) \sim 2\sigma_2 + 6\sigma_{1,1}.$$

We proceed to a generic net $N = \{F_{\lambda,\mu}\}_{(\lambda,\mu)\in\mathbb{P}^2}$ of quadrics. In this case we may associate to N two varieties of lines: the set $V_0(N) = \cup_{\mu,\lambda} V(F_{\mu,\lambda})$ of all lines contained in some quadric of N, and the set $V_1(N)$ of lines that lie on a pencil of quadrics in N. The latter is readily described: if $l \subset \mathbb{P}^3$ lies on a pencil $\overline{F_{\mu,\lambda}, F_{\mu',\lambda'}}$ of quadrics in N, then the intersection of l with the base locus of N consists of two points:

$$l \cap F_{\mu,\lambda} \cap F_{\mu',\lambda'} \cap F_{\mu'',\lambda''} = l \cap F_{\mu'',\lambda''}$$

for any third quadric $F_{\mu'',\lambda''}$ in N. Conversely, if l contains two base points p, q, of N, choose a third point $r \in l$; r will lie on a pencil of quadrics from N that, containing p, q, and $r \in l$, contain l. Since N has eight base points, no three collinear, $V_1(N)$ will consist of the $\binom{8}{2} = 28$ lines joining these points.

The class of $V_0(N) \subset G(2,4)$ may be determined as follows: let p be a generic point of $\mathbb{P}^3$, H a generic plane containing p. Then the restriction to H of the set of quadrics in N containing p is a pencil L of conics with p as one base point, and by argument 3 above, p will lie on exactly three lines of L. Thus

$$^{\#}(V_0(N)\cdot\sigma_{2,1}) = 3$$

and hence

$$V_0(N) \sim 3\sigma_1.$$

Finally let W be a generic web of quadrics. Since in this case the set $V_0(W)$ of all lines on W is all of $G(2,4)$, we will be concerned with the variety $V_1(W) \subset G(2,4)$ of lines lying on a pencil of quadrics from W. To begin with, if $p \in \mathbb{P}^3$ is a generic point, then the set of quadrics in W through p forms a generic net N_p, with p as a base point. By the argument given in the count for $V_1(N)$, the lines through p lying on a pencil of quadrics from W will just be the lines joining p to the other seven base points of N_p. Consequently

$$^{\#}(V_1(W)\cdot\sigma_2) = 7.$$

There is another way to make the count, based on the fact that a smooth point p on a quadric F will lie on two lines of F if F is smooth, but only one if F is singular. Let $\mathbb{P}^2 \subset \mathbb{P}^3$ be a plane not containing p_1 and $I \subset \mathbb{P}^2 \times N_p$ the incidence correspondence defined by

$$I = \{(q,F): \ \overline{pq} \subset F\}.$$

The projection of I on the second factor expresses I as a double cover of $N_p \cong \mathbb{P}^2$, branched over the locus of singular quadrics in N_p. But by our analysis of the linear system of quadrics in $\mathbb{P}^3$, the locus of singular quadrics in N_p is a smooth quartic curve. Using the discussion of Section 4 of Chapter 4, I has Euler characteristic 10. On the other hand, the map $I \to \mathbb{P}^2$ expresses I as the blow-up of $\mathbb{P}^2$ at the points of intersection of $\mathbb{P}^2$ with the lines $l \in V_1(W)$ through p; there are thus $\chi(I) - \chi(\mathbb{P}^2) = 10 - 3 = 7$ such lines.

The calculation for $^\#(V_1(W) \cdot \sigma_{1,1})$ is somewhat more difficult. Let H be a generic plane in $\mathbb{P}^3$, and let X be the restriction to H of the web W. If $l \subset H \subset \mathbb{P}^3$ lies on a pencil $\{F_\lambda\}$ of quadrics in W, then the conics $\{C_\lambda = F_\lambda \cap H\}$ in X are all singular; thus we may ask for the number of pencils of singular conics in X having a fixed line. Now, by our discussion of the system of conics, the locus of singular conics in X is a cubic surface with four double points, these corresponding to the double lines in X. Such a surface has, we have seen in Section 6 of Chapter 4, nine lines on it—but of these nine, six comprise the edges of the tetrahedron whose vertices are the double points of the surface, and the pencils corresponding to these lines are of the second type (p. 744). Of the nine pencils of singular conics in X, then, only three have fixed lines. Thus

$$^\#(V_1(W) \cdot \sigma_{1,1}) = 3$$

and finally

$$V_1(W) \sim 7\sigma_2 + 3\sigma_{1,1}.$$

We may check this calculation as follows: let N_1, N_2 be two generic nets in the web W, $L = N_1 \cap N_2$ their common pencil, and consider the intersection $V_0(N_1) \cap V_0(N_2)$. If a line l lies on a quadric $F_1 \in N_1$ and a quadric $F_2 \in N_2$, then either

(1) $F_1 \neq F_2$, so l lies on the pencil $\overline{F_1 F_2} \subset W$, and hence $l \in V_1(W)$; or
(2) $F_1 = F_2 \in L$, i.e., $l \in V_0(L)$.

Since, conversely, both $V_0(L)$ and $V_1(W)$ are contained in $V_0(N_1) \cap V_0(N_2)$,

$$V_0(N_1) \cap V_0(N_2) = V_1(W) \cup V_0(L).$$

Now $V_0(N_1) \sim V_0(N_2) \sim 3\sigma_1$, so the intersection $V_0(N_1) \cap V_0(N_2)$ has class

$$(3\sigma_1)^2 = 9\sigma_{1,1} + 9\sigma_2;$$

on the other hand, $V_0(L) \sim 2\sigma_2 + 6\sigma_{1,1}$, so we find again that

$$V_1(W) \sim 7\sigma_2 + 3\sigma_{1,1}.$$

The reader may find it an interesting exercise to prove that, for a generic web W, the surface $V_1(W)$ is an Enriques surface.

The Problem of Five Conics

To conclude this section, we will use the computation of Section 6, Chapter 4, for the cohomology ring of a blow-up to solve a classical problem in enumerative geometry:

Given $C_1, \ldots, C_5 \subset \mathbb{P}^2$ five smooth conic curves chosen generically, how many smooth conic curves in $\mathbb{P}^2$ are tangent to all five?

To answer this question, consider first the linear system

$$W = |2H| \cong \mathbb{P}^5$$

of all conic curves in $\mathbb{P}^2$. For any smooth conic curve C, let $V_C \subset W$ be the set of conic curves tangent to C (that is, having a point of intersection multiplicity $\geqslant 2$ with C); V_C is a hypersurface of some degree d in $\mathbb{P}^5$. If we could show that for a generic choice of five conics the hypersurfaces $V_{C_1}, \ldots, V_{C_5} \subset W$

1. met transversely away from the subvariety of singular conics, and
2. contained no singular conics in common,

the answer to our question would be easy: it would just be the fivefold self-intersection $(\deg V_C)^5$ of V_C in $W \cong \mathbb{P}^5$. Unfortunately, matters are not so simple: while assertion 1 above is the case, and half of assertion 2, namely

2′. for $C_1, \ldots, C_5$ generically chosen, no conic consisting of two distinct lines will be tangent to all five

holds, the problem is that all the hypersurfaces $V_C \subset W$ will contain the subvariety

$$W_2 = \{2L\}_{L \subset \mathbb{P}^2}$$

of double lines.

We can overcome this difficulty by blowing up. Precisely, let

$$\pi: \tilde{W} \longrightarrow W$$

be the blow-up of W along the variety W_2 of double lines; for C any smooth conic, denote by $\tilde{V}_C$ the proper transform of the subvariety

$V_C \subset \mathbb{P}^5$. Then, once we verify assertions 1 and 2 above and the additional assertion that for $C_1, \ldots, C_5$ generically chosen,

3. the proper transforms $\tilde{V}_{C_1}, \ldots, \tilde{V}_{C_5}$ have no common points in the exceptional divisor of $\tilde{W}$,

the answer to our original question will be simply the fivefold self-intersection of the divisor $\tilde{V}_C$ on $\tilde{W}$, and readily calculable. We will proceed with the computation, leaving the proof of assertions 1, 2, and 3 until later.

We first compute the degree of the hypersurface $V_C \subset \mathbb{P}^5$ for smooth C; to do this, let $L \subset W$ be a generic line and $\{C_\lambda\}_{\lambda \in \mathbb{P}^1}$ the pencil of conics it represents. The curves $\{C_\lambda\}$ then cut out on C a linear system of degree 4 without base points. The corresponding map expresses C as a 4-sheeted cover of $\mathbb{P}^1$; and by the Riemann-Hurwitz formula, the number of branch points of this map is

$$b = 2g(C) - 2 - 4(2g(\mathbb{P}^1) - 2)$$
$$= 6.$$

The pencil $\{C_\lambda\}$ therefore contains six conics tangent to C, and consequently

$$\deg V_C = 6.$$

In fact, this argument tells us a bit more. Suppose that C' is a smooth point of V_C and that C' is simply tangent to C at a single point $p \in C$. If $L \subset W$ is a generic line through C' lying in the hyperplane $H_p \subset W$ of conics containing p, the corresponding pencil $\{C'_\lambda\}_{\lambda \in \mathbb{P}^1}$ will cut out on C a linear system of degree 4, *with p as a base point*. The corresponding map then expresses C as a 3-sheeted cover of $\mathbb{P}^1$, and so has only

$$b = 2(g(c) - 2) - 3(2g(\mathbb{P}^1) - 2)$$
$$= 4$$

branch points—i.e., the pencil $\{C'_\lambda\}$ can contain at most four conics tangent to C other than C'. It follows that H_p *is the tangent plane to* V_C *at* C', and conversely if C' is simply tangent to C at only one point, then C' is a smooth point of V_C.

Next, we compute the multiplicity of the locus W_2 of double lines in the generic divisor V_C. This is not hard: for C a conic, $2L$ a generic double line, and $\{C_\lambda\}$ a generic pencil of conics containing the double line $2L$ as an element, $\{C_\lambda\}$ again cuts out on C a pencil of degree 4, without base points. The corresponding map then has six branch points as before—but two of these are just the points of intersection of L with C. $\{C_\lambda\}$ thus has four points of intersection with V_C other than $2L$; it follows that

$$\mathrm{mult}_{2L}(\{C_\lambda\}, V_C) = 2,$$

and so, for generic C,

$$\mathrm{mult}_{W_2}(V_C) = 2.$$

We can thus write

$$\tilde{V}_C \sim 6\tilde{\omega} - 2e \in H^2(\tilde{W}, \mathbb{Z}),$$

where $\tilde{\omega} = \pi^*\omega$ is the pullback to $\tilde{W}$ of the class ω of the hyperplane in W, and e the class of the exceptional divisor E.

Now, to determine the fivefold self-intersection

$$(6\tilde{\omega} - 2e)^5$$

of V_C in $\tilde{W}$, recall from our discussion in Section 1 that the surface W_2 is the Veronese surface $\iota_{2H}(\mathbb{P}^2)$. Let l and $p = l^2$ denote the classes of a point and a line in $W_2 \cong \mathbb{P}^2$; let $\tilde{p} = \pi^*p$ and $\tilde{l} = \pi^*l$ be the pullback classes in $E \subset \tilde{W}$. We have

$$\omega|_{W_2} = 2l,$$

and so

$$\omega^2|_{W_2} = (2l)^2 = 4p.$$

Now by the computation for the Chern classes of projective space,

$$c(T(W)|_{W_2}) = (1 + 6\omega + 15\omega^2)|_{W_2}$$
$$= 1 + 12l + 60l^2$$

and

$$c(T(W_2)) = 1 + 3l + 3l^2.$$

From the C^∞ decomposition of vector bundles

$$T(W)_{W_2} = T(W_2) \oplus N_{W_2/W}$$

we obtain

$$c(N_{W_2/W}) = \frac{c(T(W))}{c(T(W_2))},$$

and performing the divison

$$
\begin{array}{r}
1 + 9l + 30l^2 \\
1 + 3l + 3l^2 \overline{)\, 1 + 12l + 60l^2} \\
1 + 3l + 3l^2 \\
\hline
9l + 57l^2 \\
9l + 27l^2 \\
\hline
30l^2 \\
30l^2 \\
\hline
\end{array}
$$

we find that

$$c(N_{W_2/W}) = 1 + 9l + 30l^2.$$

Thus if $\zeta \in H^2(E, \mathbb{Z})$ denotes the Chern class of the tautological bundle on $E \cong \mathbb{P}(N_{W_2/W})$, our general relation (p. 606) reads

$$(*) \qquad\qquad \zeta^3 - 9\tilde{l}\cdot\zeta^2 + 30\tilde{l}^2\cdot\zeta = 0.$$

Now we have seen that the tautological bundle restricts to the universal bundle $[-H]$ on each fiber E_p of $E \to W_2$, and so

$$\zeta^2\cdot\tilde{l}^2 = c_1\big(T|_{E_p}\big)^2 = 1.$$

Multiplying the basic relation $(*)$ by $\tilde{l}$—and recalling that $\tilde{l}^3 = 0$—we have

$$\tilde{l}\cdot\zeta^3 - 9\tilde{l}^2\cdot\zeta^2 = 0$$

and hence

$$\tilde{l}\cdot\zeta^3 = 9.$$

Finally, multiplying $(*)$ by ζ,

$$\zeta^4 - 9\tilde{l}\,\zeta^3 + 30\tilde{l}^2\zeta^2 = 0$$

$$\Rightarrow \zeta^4 \;= 9\tilde{l}\,\zeta^3 - 30\tilde{l}^2\zeta^2$$

$$= 51.$$

It is now possible to calculate $(6\tilde{\omega} - 2e)^5$. First, since the class ω of a hyperplane in $\mathbb{P}^5$ restricts to the class $2l$ on W_2

$$\tilde{\omega}|_E = 2\tilde{l},$$

and the tautological bundle

$$T = N_{E/\mathbb{P}^5},$$

we obtain

$$e|_E = c_1(T) = \zeta.$$

Also,

$$(\tilde{\omega}^5)_{\tilde{W}} = (\omega^5)_W = 1.$$
$$\tilde{\omega}^5 = 1,$$
$$\tilde{\omega}^4\cdot e = \big((2\tilde{l}\,)^4\big)_E = 0,$$
$$\tilde{\omega}^3\cdot e^2 = \big((2\tilde{l}\,)^3\cdot\zeta\,\big)_E = 0,$$
$$\tilde{\omega}^2\cdot e^3 = \big((2\tilde{l}\,)^2\cdot\zeta^2\big)_E = 4\big(\tilde{l}^2\zeta^2\big)_E = 4,$$
$$\tilde{\omega}\cdot e^4 = \big(2\tilde{l}\cdot\zeta^3\big)_E = 18,$$
$$e^5 = \zeta^4 = 51,$$

and so

$$(6\tilde{\omega} - 2e)^5 = 6^5\tilde{\omega}^5 - 5 \cdot 6^4 \cdot 2 \cdot \tilde{\omega}^4 \cdot e + 10 \cdot 6^3 \cdot 2^2 \cdot \tilde{\omega}^3 \cdot e^2 - 10 \cdot 6^2 \cdot 2^3 \cdot \tilde{\omega}^2 \cdot e^3$$
$$+ 5 \cdot 6 \cdot 2^4 \cdot \tilde{\omega} \cdot e^4 - 2^5 \cdot e^5$$
$$= 6^5 - 10 \cdot 6^2 \cdot 2^3 \cdot 4 + 5 \cdot 6 \cdot 2^4 \cdot 18 - 2^5 \cdot 51$$
$$= 7776 - 11520 + 8640 - 1632$$
$$= 3264.$$

The answer, then, is that

For a generic choice of five conic curves in $\mathbb{P}^2$, there will be exactly 3264 smooth conics tangent to all five.

We now go back and verify the transversality assertions 1, 2, and 3. For assertion 1, note that for C smooth, the divisor V_C is irreducible: to see this, let

$$I' \subset V_C \times C$$

be the incidence correspondence given by

$$I' = \{(C_0, p): C_0 \text{ is tangent to } C \text{ at } p\}.$$

Since C is irreducible and the fibers of the projection map

$$\pi_2: I' \to C$$

are linear subspaces of W, I' is irreducible. This implies that V_C is irreducible. Now let $U \subset W$ be the open set of smooth conics and denote by I the incidence correspondence

$$I \subset (W)^5 \times U$$

defined by

$$I = \{(C_1, \ldots, C_5; C'): C' \in V_{C_i} \text{ for all } i\};$$

let $J \subset I$ be the closed subvariety of I consisting of $(C_1, \ldots, C_5; C')$ such that C' is a nontransverse point of intersection of $V_{C_1}, \ldots, V_{C_5}$. The fibers of the projection

$$\pi_2: I \to U$$

on the last factor are isomorphic to $(V_{C'})^5$, and so irreducible; consequently I is irreducible. Since the map $\pi_1: I \to (W)^5$ is generically finite-to-one, then, we see that assertion 1 can fail to hold—i.e., J can map surjectively onto $(W)^5$—only if $J = I$. To verify this assertion it will suffice to exhibit a point of $I - J$; that is, six conics $C_1, \ldots, C_5$ and C' such that $V_{C_1}, \ldots, V_{C_5}$ meet transversely at C'. But this is clear: if C' is any smooth conic, $C_1, \ldots, C_5$ conics simply tangent to C' at distinct points $p_1, \ldots, p_5$, then the tangent hyperplanes $T_{C'}(V_{C'}) = H_{p_i}$ are independent.

Assertions 2′ and 3 are easier. Note first that in general *if* $\{D_\mu\}$ *is any family of divisors without base points on an* n-*dimensional variety* V, *the generic choice of* n + 1 *divisors* $D_{\mu_1}, \ldots, D_{\mu_{n+1}}$ *of the family have no points in common*. This follows by an induction argument: if we assume the result for varieties of dimension $n - 1$, then by restricting the divisors $\{D_\mu\}$ to a hyperplane section of V the generic choice of n divisors $D_{\mu_1}, \ldots, D_{\mu_n}$ will have only finitely many points in common. Since the family $\{D_\mu\}$ has no base points, for generic $D_{\mu_{n+1}}$

$$D_{\mu_1} \cap \cdots \cap D_{\mu_n} \cap D_{\mu_{n+1}} = \varnothing.$$

Now since the locus $W_1 \subset W$ of conics of rank two has dimension 4, to prove assertion 2′ we need only check that the family $\{V_C\}_{C \in W}$ has no base points on this locus. This is immediate: for any conic of rank two, we can obviously find a conic not tangent to it.

Assertion 3 remains. We must prove that the family $\{\tilde{V}_C\}$ has no base points in E. To do this, note that for any point $2L \in W_2$ and a normal vector v to W_2 at $2L$ represented by a line $\{C_\lambda\}$ in W, the proper transform $\tilde{V}_C$ will contain the point of E corresponding to v if and only if the line $\{C_\lambda\}$ has intersection multiplicity 3 or more with V_C at $2L$; it will thus suffice to show that for any point $2L \in W_2$ and any line $\{C_\lambda\}$ through $2L$ but not tangent to W_2 at $2L$, there exists a conic C such that

$$\text{mult}_{2L}(V_C, \{C_\lambda\}) = 2.$$

Now, if any pencil of conics contains two double lines $2L$ and $2L'$, it has a single base point of order 4, and so must consist entirely of singular conics. In the limiting case, then, we see that any pencil tangent to W_2 at $2L$ consists entirely of singular conics; the tangent plane $T_{2L}(W_2)$ to W_2 at a point $2L$ is therefore contained in—hence equal to—the 2-plane

$$\{L + L'\}_{L' \in \mathbb{P}^{2*}} \subset W.$$

If $\{C_\lambda\}$ *is any pencil through* 2L *but not in the tangent space* $T_{2L}(W_2)$, *then, it can have only finitely many base points*. Choosing the conic C to miss these base points, the same argument as before shows that $\{C_\lambda\}$ meets V_C with multiplicity 2 at $2L$.

A note: The problem of determining the number of conics tangent to five conics is of some historical importance, being one of the first problems requiring nontrivial intersection theory; it is interesting to see how it may be solved without explicit reference to abstract blow-ups or cohomology. One argument proceeds as follows: let I_p and $I_l \subset W$ be, respectively, the variety of conics passing through the point p, and tangent to the line l; let $\tilde{I}_p$ and $\tilde{I}_l$ be their proper transforms in the blow-up $\tilde{W}$ of W along W_2. Then it is easy to see that, in the cohomology ring of $\tilde{W}$,

$$\tilde{I}_p \sim \tilde{\omega} \quad \text{and} \quad \tilde{I}_l \sim 2\tilde{\omega} - e,$$

so

$$\tilde{V}_C \sim 2\tilde{I}_p + 2\tilde{I}_l.$$

Without reference to blow-ups or cohomology, then, one could make the statement: "the condition that a conic be tangent to a conic C is equivalent to the condition that it contain either of two points, or be tangent to either of two lines"; this can be seen by noting that, as the conic C degenerates into a pair of lines $l_1 + l_2$, the variety V_C degenerates into the variety $I_{l_1} + I_{l_2} + I_{l_1 \cdot l_2}$, the latter component occurring with multiplicity 2. (In fact, the blow-up W may be constructed geometrically as follows: let W^* denote the linear system of conics in $\mathbb{P}^{2^*}$, W_1^* W^* the locus of singular conics, and take the closure in $W \times W^*$ of the locus

$$\{(C, D): \ D = C^*\} \quad (W - W_1) \times (W^* - W_1^*).$$

A pair (C, D) in this closure was classically called a *complete conic*). Now, the product

$$\tilde{V}_C^5 = 32\left(\tilde{I}_p + \tilde{I}_l\right)^5$$
$$= 32\left(\tilde{I}_p^5 + 5\tilde{I}_p^4\tilde{I}_l + 10\tilde{I}_p^3\tilde{I}_l^2 + 10\tilde{I}_p^2\tilde{I}_l^3 + 5\tilde{I}_p\tilde{I}_l^4 + \tilde{I}_l^5\right)$$

can be evaluated by elementary geometry: since there is a unique conic in the plane through five generically chosen points,

$$\tilde{I}_p^5 = 1.$$

Likewise, the conics through four generic points cut out on a generic line l a pencil of degree 2, which then has two branch points; so

$$\tilde{I}_p^4\tilde{I}_l = 2.$$

Next, the quadratic transformation of $\mathbb{P}^2$ based at three points p_1, p_2, p_3 transforms the net of conics through p_1, p_2, p_3 into the complete series of lines in $\mathbb{P}^2$, and the generic lines in $\mathbb{P}^2$ into conics; the number of conics through p_1, p_2, p_3 tangent to two lines is just the number of lines in $\mathbb{P}^2$ tangent to two conics. Since the tangent lines to a conic in $\mathbb{P}^2$ form a conic curve in $\mathbb{P}^{2^*}$, this number is

$$\tilde{I}_p^3 \cdot \tilde{I}_l^3 = 4.$$

The remaining three products of $\tilde{I}_p$ and $\tilde{I}_l$ are dual to the ones above—e.g., a conic $C \subset \mathbb{P}^2$ will be tangent to five lines $l_1, \ldots, l_5 \subset \mathbb{P}^2$ if the dual conic $C^* \subset \mathbb{P}^{2^*}$ of tangent lines to C contains the five points $l_1, \ldots, l_5 \in \mathbb{P}^{2^*}$—so we have

$$\tilde{I}_p^2\tilde{I}_l^3 = \tilde{I}_p^3\tilde{I}_l^2 = 4, \quad \tilde{I}_p\tilde{I}_l^4 = \tilde{I}_p^4\tilde{I}_l = 2, \quad \tilde{I}_l^5 = \tilde{I}_p^5 = 1.$$

The answer to the problem—modulo the checking of transversality assumptions—is then

$$\tilde{V}_C^5 = 32(1 + 5 \cdot 2 + 10 \cdot 4 + 10 \cdot 4 + 5 \cdot 2 + 1)$$
$$= 32 \cdot 102 = 3264.$$

2. THE QUADRIC LINE COMPLEX: INTRODUCTION

Geometry of the Grassmannian $G(2,4)$

First we will discuss the geometry of the Grassmannian $G(2,4)$ of 2-planes in $\mathbb{C}^4$, viewed primarily as the set of lines in $\mathbb{P}^3$. Recall from Section 5 of Chapter 1 that the Plücker embedding

$$G(2,4) \longrightarrow \mathbb{P}(\Lambda^2 \mathbb{C}^4) = \mathbb{P}^5$$

is given by mapping the 2-plane Λ spanned by vectors $v_1, v_2 \in \mathbb{C}^4$ into the wedge product $v_1 \wedge v_2 \in \Lambda^2 \mathbb{C}^4$. As was proved there, a general multivector ω will be decomposable—that is, of the form $v_1 \wedge v_2$—exactly when

$$\omega \wedge \omega = 0.$$

This is a quadratic relation; the image of $G(2,4)$ under the Plücker embedding is therefore a quadric hypersurface in $\mathbb{P}^5$, which we will henceforth denote by G. The reader is referred to p. 746 for the definition and intersection numbers of the Schubert cycles $\sigma_1(l_0)$, $\sigma_2(p_0)$, $\sigma_{1,1}(h_0)$, and $\sigma_{2,1}(p_0, h_0)$ on G.

Now, since the wedge product

$$\wedge : \Lambda^2 \mathbb{C}^4 \times \Lambda^2 \mathbb{C}^4 \to \Lambda^4 \mathbb{C}^4 \cong \mathbb{C}$$

is a nondegenerate pairing, every hyperplane in $\mathbb{P}(\Lambda^2 \mathbb{C}^4)$ is of the form

$$H_{\omega_0} = \{\omega : \omega \wedge \omega_0 = 0\}.$$

In particular, if $\omega_0 = v_1 \wedge v_2$ the hyperplane section $H_{\omega_0} \cap G$ of G consists of the Schubert cycle $\sigma_1(l_0)$ of lines in $\mathbb{P}^3$ meeting the line $l_0 = \overline{v_1, v_2}$ spanned by v_1 and v_2. Thus

Every Schubert cycle $\sigma_1(l_0) \subset G$ is a hyperplane section of G.

Since the Schubert cycle $\sigma_{2,1}(p,h) \subset G$ has intersection number 1 with the hyperplane class σ_1, it follows that

Every Schubert cycle $\sigma_{2,1}(p,h) \subset G$ is a line in $\mathbb{P}^5$.

Similarly, since

$$\sigma_1^2 \cdot \sigma_{1,1} = \sigma_1^2 \cdot \sigma_2 = 1,$$

Every Schubert cycle $\sigma_2(p)$ or $\sigma_{1,1}(h) \subset G$ is a 2-plane in $\mathbb{P}^5$.

To prove the converse of the last two statements, let $x \in G$ be any point. Since $G \subset \mathbb{P}^5$ is a quadric, by what we have seen the intersection $T_x(G) \cap G$ is just the locus of lines in G through x. But if $x' \in G$ is any point whose corresponding line in $\mathbb{P}^3$ $l_{x'}$ meets l_x, then x and x' both lie on the Schubert cycle $\sigma_{2,1}(p,h)$ of lines in $\mathbb{P}^3$ through the point $p = l_x \cap l_{x'}$ and contained in the hyperplane $h = \overline{l_x, l_{x'}}$. Since $\sigma_{2,1}(p,h)$ is a line, it follows that $\sigma_{2,1}(p,h)$—and hence x'—lies in the locus $T_x(G) \cap G$. The hyperplane section $T_x(G) \cap G$ thus contains the Schubert cycle $\sigma_1(l_x)$ of lines meeting l_x—but $\sigma_1(l_x)$ is itself a hyperplane section of G, and so we have:

For any $x \in G$

$$T_x(G) \cap G = \sigma_1(l_x).$$

It follows that for any $x, x' \in G$,

$$l_x \cap l_{x'} \neq \phi \Leftrightarrow x' \in T_x(G)$$
$$\Leftrightarrow \overline{x, x'} \subset G.$$

We see from this that

Any line L *lying on the Grassmannian is a Schubert cycle* $\sigma_{2,1}(p, h)$.

For any two points $x \neq x' \in L$, let $p = l_x \cap l_{x'}$ be the point of intersection of the corresponding lines and $h = \overline{l_x, l_{x'}}$ the plane they span; the line $\sigma_{2,1}(p,h)$ in G then contains x and x', and so equals L.

Finally, to see that

Every 2-plane $V_2 \subset \mathbb{P}^5$ *contained in* G *is a Schubert cycle* $\sigma_2(p)$ *or* $\sigma_{1,1}(h)$.

Observe that for any point $x \in V_2$ the tangent plane section $T_x(G) \cap G$ contains V_2; thus for x_1, x_2, x_3 any three noncollinear points of V_2,

$$V_2 \subset G \cap T_{x_1}(G) \cap T_{x_2}(G) \cap T_{x_3}(G) = \{x \in G: \ l_x \cap l_{x_i} \neq \emptyset, i = 1,2,3\}.$$

But the line $\overline{x_i x_j}$ lies in $V_2 \subset G$, and so the corresponding lines l_{x_i} and l_{x_j} must have a point p_{ij} in common. Since by hypothesis x_1, x_2, and x_3 do not all lie on a Schubert cycle $\sigma_{2,1}(p,h)$, we must have either

1. $p_{12}, p_{23},$ and p_{13} are distinct, in which case a line $l \subset \mathbb{P}^3$ will meet l_{x_1}, l_{x_2}, and l_{x_3} if and only if l lies in the hyperplane $h = \overline{p_{12}, p_{23}, p_{13}} = \overline{l_{x_1}, l_{x_2}, l_{x_3}}$; or

2. $p_{12} = p_{23} = p_{13}$, in which case, since l_{x_1}, l_{x_2}, and l_{x_3} cannot be coplanar, a line $l \subset \mathbb{P}^3$ will meet l_{x_1}, l_{x_2}, and l_{x_3} if and only if it passes through the point $p = p_{12}$.

In the first case, V_2 is contained in—hence equal to—the Schubert cycle $\sigma_{1,1}(h)$ of lines lying in h; in the second case V_2 is contained in, and so equal to, the Schubert cycle $\sigma_2(p)$ of lines through p.

We will henceforth write the Schubert cycles on G simply as $\sigma(p)$, $\sigma(h)$, $\sigma(l)$, and $\sigma(p,h)$. In particular, the Schubert cycle $L = \sigma(p,h)$ of lines through a point p and lying in a hyperplane $h \subset \mathbb{P}^3$ is called a *pencil* of lines. The common point $p = \bigcap_{x \in L} l_x$ of a pencil L is called its *focus* and will be denoted p_L; the plane $h = \bigcup_{x \in L} l_x$ swept out by the lines of the pencil is called simply its *plane* and will be denoted h_L.

Note that we can write, for any $x \in G$,

$$T_x(G) \cap G = \sigma(l_x) = \bigcup_{p \in l_x} \sigma(p) = \bigcup_{h \supset l_x} \sigma(h),$$

and conversely, for any line $L \subset G$,

$$G \cap \bigcap_{x \in L} T_x(G) = \sigma(p_L) \cup \sigma(h_L).$$

We can get a nice picture of the relations among the Schubert cycles on G by considering again the locus $T_x(G) \cap G$. As we have seen, if $V_3 \subset T_x(G)$ is any 3-plane not containing x

$$G \cap T_x(G) = \bigcup_{y \in V_3 \cap G} \overline{xy},$$

i.e., $G \cap T_x(G)$ is the cone over the smooth quadric surface $Q = V_3 \cap G$. (See Figure 5.) Now, Q has two families $\{L_\lambda\}_{\lambda \in \mathbb{P}^1}$ and $\{L_\lambda'\}_{\lambda \in \mathbb{P}^1}$ of lines on it, with two lines meeting if and only if they are of different families. Let L be any line of the first family. Then the 2-plane $\overline{x,L}$ spanned by x and L lies in G, and so must be of the form

$$\sigma(p), \qquad \text{for some } p \in l_x,$$

or

$$\sigma(h), \qquad \text{for some } h \supset l_x.$$

Indeed, since two Schubert cycles $\sigma(p), \sigma(p')$ intersect only in one point, while for $p \in l_x \subset h$ the Schubert cycles $\sigma(p)$ and $\sigma(h)$ intersect in a line, we see that the 2-planes $\{\overline{x,L_\lambda}\}_{\lambda \in \mathbb{P}^1}$ spanned by x and the lines of one ruling

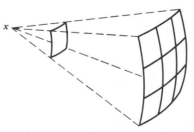

Figure 5. $T_x(G) \cap G$.

must be all the Schubert cycles $\{\sigma(p)\}_{p \in l_x}$, while the planes $\{\overline{x, L'_\lambda}\}_{\lambda \in \mathbb{P}^1}$ associated to lines of the second ruling must be the Schubert cycles $\{\sigma(h)\}_{h \supset l_x}$. Note that since the tangent plane $T_y(Q)$ to Q at any point $y \in Q$ meets Q in the sum of two lines, one from each family, the 3-plane $\overline{x, T_y(Q)}$ meets G in the sum of a $\sigma(p)$ and a $\sigma(h)$, showing directly that

$$\sigma_1^2 = \sigma_{1,1} + \sigma_2.$$

Line Complexes

We have given, above and in Section 1 of this chapter, accounts of various cycles in the Grassmannian $G(2,4)$ arising from the geometry of $\mathbb{P}^3$. Of interest classically was the converse problem: to describe the geometry of the family of lines in $\mathbb{P}^3$ cut out in $G(2,4) \subset \mathbb{P}^5$ by hypersurfaces in $\mathbb{P}^5$. In particular, we define

DEFINITION.   A *line complex* of degree d in $\mathbb{P}^3$ is the three-parameter family of lines in $\mathbb{P}^3$ corresponding to the intersection of the Grassmannian $G(2,4) \subset \mathbb{P}^5$ with a hypersurface of degree d in $\mathbb{P}^5$.

We consider first *linear line complexes*, that is, line complexes $X = G \cap H$ given as the intersection of G with a hyperplane $H \subset \mathbb{P}^5$. If X is singular— —i.e., if $H = T_x(G)$ is the tangent plane to G at some point x—then, as we have seen, the complex X is the Schubert cycle $\sigma(l_x)$ of lines in $\mathbb{P}^3$ meeting l_x. Suppose on the other hand that X is smooth. For each $p \in \mathbb{P}^3$, then, the set

$$X_p = \sigma(p) \cap H$$

of lines of the complex X passing through p is either all of $\sigma(p)$, or a line in $\sigma(p)$. But the set of tangent planes

$$\{T_x(G)\}_{x \in \sigma(p)}$$

to G at points of $\sigma(p)$ form the linear system of all hyperplanes containing $\sigma(p)$, i.e., any hyperplane containing $\sigma(p)$ is tangent to G. Thus X_p must be a line, that is,

For each $p \in \mathbb{P}^3$, *the lines of* X *through* p *form a pencil* $\sigma(p, h)$.

Likewise, H cannot contain the 2-plane $\sigma(h)$ for any hyperplane $h \subset \mathbb{P}^3$, and so

For each hyperplane $h \subset \mathbb{P}^3$, *the lines of* X *lying in* h *form a pencil* $\sigma(p, h)$.

Here is another way to view this: any element ω of $\Lambda^2 \mathbb{C}^4$ corresponds to a skew-symmetric quadratic form

$$\Gamma_\omega(v,v') = \omega \wedge v \wedge v' \in \Lambda^4 \mathbb{C}^4 \cong \mathbb{C};$$

the corresponding linear line complex $X = H_\omega \cap G$ is then given by

$$X = \left\{ l = \overline{v,v'} : \Gamma_\omega(v,v') = 0 \right\}.$$

If $\omega = v \wedge v'$ is decomposable, then H_ω is tangent to G at $l = \overline{v,v'}$, and $X = H_\omega \cap G$ is the Schubert cycle $\sigma(l)$; if, on the other hand, ω is indecomposable, then the form Γ_ω is nondegenerate and for any $p = [v] \in \mathbb{P}^3$

$$X_p = \sigma(p,h),$$

where the hyperplane $h \subset \mathbb{P}^3$ is the kernel of the linear functional $\Gamma_\omega(v, \cdot)$ on $\mathbb{C}^4$.

An amusing construction associated to a nonsingular linear complex $X = G \cap H$ is the *configuration of Möbius*, defined as follows: Let T be any tetrahedron in $\mathbb{P}^3$, with sides h_1, h_2, h_3, h_4 and vertices

$$p_i = \bigcap_{j \neq i} h_j.$$

For each i, let h_i' be the plane of the pencil $X_{p_i} = \sigma(p_i) \cap H$ of lines of X through p_i and p_i' the focus of the pencil $X_{h_i} = \sigma(h_i) \cap H$ of lines of X lying in h_i. Note first that the planes h_i' are linearly independent: if all four contained a point q, then all four points p_i would have to lie in the plane swept out by the pencil X_q of lines of X through q; dually, the points $\{p_i'\}$ are independent. Next, we observe that for any $i \neq j$ the line $h_i \cap h_j'$ is a line of the complex X, lying in h_j' and passing through the point p_i'. Thus

$$p_i' = \bigcap_{j \neq i} h_j',$$

i.e., *the points $\{p_i'\}$ are the vertices of the tetrahedron T' having sides $\{h_i'\}$.* (See Figure 6.)

The line complex X thus associates to any tetrahedron T in $\mathbb{P}^3$ a "dual" tetrahedron T^* both inscribed in and circumscribed about T.

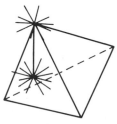

Figure 6

This process, moreover, is self-dual: the tetrahedron associated to T^* is T again.

We now claim that conversely any such configuration of two tetrahedrons T and T' inscribed in and circumscribed about each other determines uniquely a smooth linear line complex in $\mathbb{P}^3$: if T has sides $\{h_i\}$ and vertices $\{p_i\}$, T' sides $\{h_i'\}$ and vertices $\{p_i'\}$ as above, then T' will be the dual tetrahedron of T with respect to the complex X exactly when the lines

$$L_i = \sigma(p_i, h_i'), \qquad i = 1,2,3,4,$$

and

$$L_i' = \sigma(p_i', h_i), \qquad i = 1,2,3,4,$$

in G all lie in X. But we have

$$L_i \cap L_j' \neq \varnothing \qquad \text{for } i \neq j;$$

and

$$L_i \cap L_i' = \varnothing.$$

The lines $\{L_i\}, \{L_i'\}$ in $\mathbb{P}^5$ thus form the configuration shown in Figure 7, and so all lie in the 4-plane spanned by the points $L_1' \cap L_3$, $L_1' \cap L_4$, $L_2' \cap L_3$, $L_2' \cap L_4$, and $L_3' \cap L_2$. On the other hand, no quadric surface $Q = G \cap V_3$ in $\mathbb{P}^3$ can contain such a configuration of lines: if Q were smooth, then clearly the lines $\{L_i\}$ and $\{L_i'\}$ would belong to opposite families—but in that case L_1 and L_1' would meet; if Q had rank three, all lines on Q would meet, and if Q were the union of two planes, any hyperplane containing V_3 would be tangent to G. Consequently the lines $\{L_i, L_i'\}$ lie in a unique 4-plane. In sum, we have proved the rather amusing result:

The set of nondegenerate skew-symmetric quadratic forms on $\mathbb{C}^4$, up to multiplication by scalars, is in one-to-one correspondence with the set of tetrahedra inscribed in and circumscribed about a given tetrahedron T_0 in $\mathbb{P}^3$.

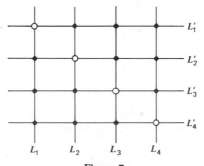

Figure 7

The Quadric Line Complex and Associated Kummer Surface I

We come now to the main object of study in this chapter: the *quadric line complex*, defined to be the family of lines in $\mathbb{P}^3$ corresponding to the smooth intersection $X = G \cap F$ of the Grassmannian $G \subset \mathbb{P}^5$ with a quadric hypersurface F. As in the case of the linear complex, our initial problem in regard to the quadric line complex is to identify the pencils of lines in X and to determine, for any point p and any hyperplane h in $\mathbb{P}^3$, the locus of lines in our complex passing through p or contained in h. We first check that

Lemma. *No 2-plane $\sigma(p)$ or $\sigma(h)$ lies in the quadric line complex* $X = F \cap G$.

Proof. We will give two proofs of this fact. First, in an elementary but rather special vein, we can argue as follows: if the quadrics F and G contained a 2-plane $V_2 \subset \mathbb{P}^5$ in common, then the Gauss maps

$$\mathcal{G}_F : F \to \mathbb{P}^{5*} \quad \text{and} \quad \mathcal{G}_G : G \to \mathbb{P}^{5*}$$

would each map V_2 isomorphically onto the set V_2^* of hyperplanes containing V_2. But then the isomorphism

$$\mathcal{G}_F^{-1} \circ \mathcal{G}_G : V_2 \to V_2$$

would have a fixed point—i.e., for some $x \in V_2$ we would have $T_x(F) = T_x(G)$, contradicting the assumption that F and G meet transversely.

Alternatively, we see by the Lefschetz theorem on hyperplane sections that the generator of

$$H^2(X, \mathbb{Z}) \cong H^2(G, \mathbb{Z}) \cong H^2(\mathbb{P}^5, \mathbb{Z})$$

is the restriction to X of the hyperplane class ω in $\mathbb{P}^5$; in particular, that every surface on X has even degree. Note that this argument may be used in general to show that a smooth nondegenerate complete intersection of dimension n in $\mathbb{P}^N$ cannot contain a linear subspace of dimension $> n/2$.

Now, we deduce from the lemma that for each $p \in \mathbb{P}^3$ the set

$$X_p = X \cap \sigma(p)$$

of lines in the complex X passing through p forms a conic curve in $\sigma(p)$. There are three possible cases:

1. F meets $\sigma(p)$ transversely, i.e., X_p is a smooth conic curve. The locus of lines in X through p will then be a cone through p over a smooth conic curve (Figure 8). As we shall see, this is the generic case.

2. F is tangent to $\sigma(p)$ at a point, i.e., X_p consists of two pencils with focus p. In this case the locus of the lines in X_p will be two hyperplanes (Figure 9).

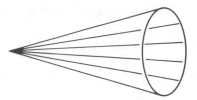

Figure 8

3. F is tangent to $\sigma(p)$ along a line, i.e., X_p consists of one double line. In this case, the locus of X_p will be a single hyperplane (Figure 10).

Dually, for every hyperplane $h \subset \mathbb{P}^3$ the set $X_h = X \cap \sigma(h)$ of lines of X lying in h is a conic curve; again, there are three possible cases:

1'. F meets $\sigma(h)$ transversely, so that $X_h \subset \sigma(h)$ is a smooth conic curve. The lines of X lying in h are thus the set of tangent lines to a smooth conic curve in h (Figure 11).

2'. F is tangent to $\sigma(h)$ at one point, so that X_h consists of two pencils with plane h (Figure 12).

3'. F is tangent to $\sigma(h)$ along a line. In this case, X_h will consist of one pencil in h (Figure 13).

Let $S \subset \mathbb{P}^3$ be the locus of points $p \in \mathbb{P}^3$ such that X_p is singular, i.e., such that case 2 or 3 above occurs. S is called the *associated Kummer surface* of the quadric line complex X; it may be thought of, in slightly different terms, as the set of foci of pencils of lines in the complex X. We denote by $R \subset S$ the locus of points $p \in S$ such that case 3 occurs. We define the *dual Kummer surface* $S^* \subset \mathbb{P}^{3*}$ to be the locus of hyperplanes $h \in \mathbb{P}^{3*}$ such that X_h is singular, i.e., the set of planes in $\mathbb{P}^3$ swept out by the pencils of X; let $R^* \subset S^*$ be the set of hyperplanes $h \in \mathbb{P}^{3*}$ such that case 3' above occurs. Inasmuch as the set of singular plane conic curves has codimension 1 in the linear system of all conics, and the set of double lines codimension 3, we would expect the varieties S and R to be a surface and a finite collection of points, respectively. That S is indeed a surface will be apparent from the following computations; that R is finite will emerge later.

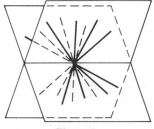

Figure 9

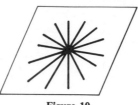

Figure 10

Our first task will be to determine the degree of S. To this end, we offer a computation and a proof, as follows.

1.   Let $l_x \subset \mathbb{P}^3$ be a generic line of the complex X—which we will assume is not tangent to S—and consider the locus $l_x \cap S$. For every point $p \in l_x \cap S$, the line l_x will be an element of one or both of the two pencils in our complex with focus p; in other words, x will lie on one or both of the lines of $F \cap \sigma(p)$. Conversely, of course, any pencil of lines in X containing l_x has its focus on l_x, and hence in $l_x \cap S$. Thus, if we make the assumption that the generic line l_x does not lie on two confocal pencils of X, the points of intersection of l_x with S correspond exactly to the lines L on X through x. But we have seen that the locus of lines in G (resp. F) through any point x is just the intersection $T_x(G) \cap G$ (resp. $T_x(F) \cap F$), so the locus of lines in $X = F \cap G$ through x is

$$T_x(X) \cap X = T_x(F) \cap F \cap T_x(G) \cap G.$$

$T_x(X) \cap X$ has degree 4, and—making the final assumption that it contains no multiple components—it must consist of four lines. We thus have

$$\deg S = {}^{\#}(l_x \cap S) = 4.$$

Now, all the assumptions made about the generic line l_x of our complex are in fact the case, but their verifications are best left until we know more about the complex. There is one point worth mentioning now, which will emerge from this computation once we have established that S is quartic: Since $T_x(X) \cap X$ can never contain more than four lines, for any point $p \in S - R$ the line l_x held in common by the two pencils in X through p—that is, the line of intersection of the two hyperplanes comprising the

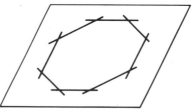

Figure 11

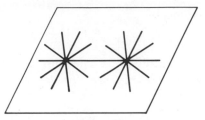

Figure 12

locus of X_p—can lie on at most two lines in X not on $\sigma(p)$. Thus l_x meets S in at most three points and so must be a tangent line to S.

2. A more conclusive argument for the degree of S goes as follows: we first claim that for a generic $x \in G$, the surface

$$U = T_x(G) \cap X \subset \mathbb{P}^5$$

is smooth—this fact will emerge in a moment. Granting this, we recall

$$G \cap T_x(G) = \bigcup_{p \in l_x} \sigma(p)$$

so that the curves

$$X_p = \sigma(p) \cap F \subset U$$

form a linear system on U without base point. In fact, we see that

$$\deg S = {}^\#(l_x \cap S) = {}^\#\{p : X_p \text{ is singular}\}$$

is just the number μ of singular curves in this pencil. Now the generic curve X_p is a smooth conic, with Euler characteristic 2, and if we take l_x disjoint from R, all the singular curves X_p in our pencil will consist of two distinct lines, i.e., the pencil will be Lefschetz. By the general formula

$$\chi(S) = 2\chi(C_\lambda) - n + \mu$$

of Section 2, Chapter 4, we have

$$\chi(U) = 4 + \mu.$$

But U, being the smooth intersection of two quadrics in $\mathbb{P}^4$, is biholomorphic to $\mathbb{P}^2$ blown up five times (Section 4, Chapter 4) and so has Euler

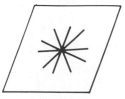

Figure 13

characteristic 8. Consequently

$$\deg S = \mu = 4.$$

In fact, this last argument gives us something more: it tells us that S *is smooth away from the locus* R. To see this, let q be any point of $S - R$. Then the hyperplane sections

$$\{T_x(G) \cap X\}_{x \in \sigma(q)}$$

form a linear system on X; by Bertini's theorem, for generic $x \in \sigma(q)$ the surface $U_x = T_x(G) \cap X$ will be smooth away from the base locus $X_q = \sigma(q) \cap X$ of the linear system. If $q \notin R$, moreover, then each U_x can be singular only at the singular point of X_q—but the hyperplanes $\{T_x(G)\}_{x \in \sigma(q)}$ are exactly all the hyperplanes in $\mathbb{P}^5$ containing $\sigma(q)$, and so the generic one will not contain the tangent space to X at the singular point of X_q. We have thus shown that for l_x a generic line in $\mathbb{P}^3$ through $q \in S - R$, the surface U_x is smooth. The argument above then shows that l_x meets S in four distinct points, and hence meets S transversely; a fortiori, it shows that q is a smooth point of S.

Note that all three of these arguments apply as well to show that the dual Kummer surface S^* is a quartic surface smooth away from the locus R^*. In the first argument, we observe that the points of intersection of S^* with the pencil $l_x^* \subset \mathbb{P}^{3*}$ of hyperplanes in $\mathbb{P}^3$ containing a line l_x of our complex again correspond to the pencils in X containing l_x, and hence to the lines L on X containing x. Likewise, the second argument goes over, and indeed establishes an important point: given any line $l_x \subset \mathbb{P}^3$ not passing through any points of R or lying in any hyperplanes of R^*, we have two pencils on the surface $U = T_x(G) \cap X$:

$$\{X_p = \sigma(p) \cap U\}_{p \in l_x} \quad \text{and} \quad \{X_h = \sigma(h) \cap U\}_{h \supset l_x}.$$

Both are Lefschetz, and so the number of singular fibers in each is $\chi(U) - 4$. But while the singular fibers of the pencil $\{X_p\}$ correspond to points of intersection of l_x with S, singular fibers of $\{X_h\}$ correspond to points of intersection of the dual line $l_x^* \subset \mathbb{P}^{3*}$ of hyperplanes containing l_x with S^*. In particular, $^\#(l_x \cap S) < 4 \Leftrightarrow {}^\#(l_x^* \cap S^*) < 4$, i.e., l_x *is tangent to* S *if and only if* l_x^* *is tangent to* S*. Now suppose $p \in S$ is any point, $h = T_p(S)$ its tangent plane, and let p^* and h^* be the hyperplane and point in $\mathbb{P}^3$ dual to p and h, respectively. The dual lines $\{l_x^*\}$ to the pencil of lines $\{l_x\}$ in $\mathbb{P}^3$ through p and lying in h form the pencil of lines in $\mathbb{P}^{3*}$ containing h^* and lying in p^*, and they are all tangent to S^*. Every element of the pencil $\{l_x^* \cdot S^*\}$ they cut out on the curve $p^* \cap S^*$ is therefore singular, and so by Bertini they are all singular at the base locus h^* of $\{l_x^*\}$, i.e., $h^* \in S^*$ and

$p^* = T_{h^*}(S^*)$. We see, then, that

S *and* S* *are dual surfaces,*

that is, S^* is the locus of tangent planes to S and vice versa.

Singular Lines of the Quadric Line Complex

The next step in our study of X is to introduce a subvariety $\Sigma \subset X$ closely related to the Kummer surface S.

DEFINITION. For any $x \in X$, the line l_x is called a *singular line* of the complex X if it is an element of two confocal pencils of X— in other words, if $\sigma(p)$ is tangent to F at x for some point $p \in l_x$.

For $p \in S - R$, of course, there is a unique singular line through p: the line of intersection of the two hyperplanes comprising the locus of X_p; for $p \in R$, any line l_x of X through p is singular. We denote by $\Sigma \subset X$ the set of $x \in X$ such that l_x is singular.

We first check that no line l_x is singular at more than one point, i.e., that if $\sigma(p)$ is tangent to F at x, then for $q \neq p \in l_x$, $\sigma(q)$ cannot also be tangent to F at x. But $\sigma(p) \cap \sigma(q) = \{x\}$, so the linear span of $\sigma(p)$ and $\sigma(q)$ in $\mathbb{P}^5$ is all of $T_x(G)$; thus $\sigma(p)$ and $\sigma(q)$ cannot both be contained in $T_x(F) \neq T_x(G)$. We can therefore define a map

$$\pi : \Sigma \to S$$

sending each $x \in \Sigma$ to the unique $p \in l_x$ for which $\sigma(p)$ is tangent to F at x. By what was said above, π is one-to-one and surjective over $S - R$, with $\pi^{-1}(p) = X_p \cong \mathbb{P}^1$ for $p \in R$.

Σ is easy to describe, once we have the following characterization.

Lemma. *For* $x \in X$,

$$x \in \Sigma \Leftrightarrow T_x(F) \text{ is tangent to } G.$$

Proof. Say $T_x(F)$ is tangent to G at x'. Then $x \in T_{x'}(G)$, and so l_x meets $l_{x'}$ at a point $p \in \mathbb{P}^3$. The plane $\sigma(p)$ is then contained in $T_{x'}(G) = T_x(F)$, i.e., is tangent to F at x; thus $x \in \Sigma$.

Conversely, if $\sigma(p) \subset T_x(F)$, then the quadric threefold $T_x(F) \cap G$ contains a 2-plane and so by our earlier argument must be singular; thus $T_x(F)$ must be tangent to G somewhere.   Q.E.D.

This argument will become clearer if we refer back to our picture of the locus $T_x(G) \cap G$ as the cone over a quadric $Q = T_x(G) \cap G \cap H$, H a hyperplane disjoint from x. (See Figure 14.) Recall that the 2-planes

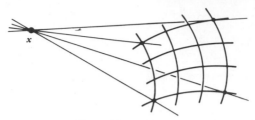

Figure 14. $T_x(G) \cap G$.

$\{\sigma(p)\}_{p \in l_x}$ lying in $T_x(G) \cap G$ are spanned by x together with the lines of one of the rulings of Q, while the planes $\{\sigma(h)\}_{h \supset l_x}$ are spanned by x and the lines of the other ruling of Q. Now if $T_x(F)$ is tangent to G at some point y, we may take $y \in H$, so that the locus $T_x(F) \cap T_x(G) \cap G$ consists of the two 2-planes $\sigma(p)$ and $\sigma(h)$ spanned by x and the two lines of intersection $Q \cap T_x(F)$. (See Figure 15.) Of the four lines of $T_x(X) \cap X = T_x(F) \cap T_x(G) \cap G \cap F$, then, two will lie on the 2-plane $\sigma(p)$ and two on $\sigma(h)$. Conversely, if $T_x(F)$ is nowhere tangent to G, then the locus $T_x(F) \cap T_x(G) \cap G$ will just be the cone over the smooth conic $T_x(F) \cap Q$, and no two of the lines of $T_x(X) \cap X$ will lie on the same 2-plane $\sigma(p)$—unless, of course, F is tangent to $T_x(F) \cap Q$, i.e., $T_x(X) \cap X$ contains a multiple line. (See Figure 16.)

One corollary of our lemma implied by this picture is that the locus $T_x(X) \cap X$ will contain two lines from the same $\sigma(p)$ if and only if it contains two lines from the same $\sigma(h)$: in other words,

A line l_x of our complex is singular—i.e., lies on two confocal pencils—if and only if it lies on two coplanar pencils.

We can now give an explicit description of $\Sigma \subset X$. Let $X = [x_0, \dots, x_5]$ be homogeneous coordinates on $\mathbb{P}^5$, and suppose that G and F are given as the loci

$$(Qx, x) = 0 \quad \text{and} \quad (Q'x, x) = 0,$$

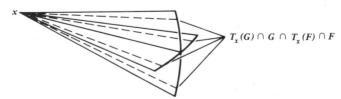

Figure 15. $T_x(G) \cap G \cap T_x(F)$ if $x \in \Sigma$.

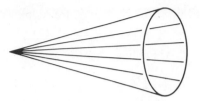

Figure 16. $T_x(G) \cap G \cap T_x(F)$ if $x \notin \Sigma$.

respectively. Then, in terms of dual coordinates x^* on $\mathbb{P}^{5*}$, the Gauss maps of G and F are given by

$$x^* = Qx \quad \text{and} \quad x^* = Q'x;$$

the dual hypersurfaces G^* and $F^* \subset \mathbb{P}^{5*}$ of tangent hyperplanes to G and F are thus

$$G^* = ((x^*, Q^{-1}x^*)=0)$$

and

$$F^* = ((x^*, Q'^{-1}x^*)=0.)$$

We see from this that for $x \in F$, $T_x(F)$ will be tangent to G if and only if

$$\mathcal{G}_F(x) \in G^*,$$

i.e., when

$$(Q'x, Q^{-1}Q'x) = (Q'Q^{-1}Q'x, x) = 0.$$

The surface $\Sigma \subset X$ is thus cut out by the quadric hypersurface

$$H = ((Q'Q^{-1}Q'x, x)=0).$$

We claim now that in fact the intersection

$$\Sigma = F \cap G \cap H$$

is everywhere transverse. To see this, suppose that for some $x \in F \cap G \cap H$ the hyperplanes $T_x(F), T_x(G)$, and $T_x(H)$ were linearly dependent, i.e., that the points

$$\mathcal{G}_G(x) = Qx, \qquad \mathcal{G}_F(x) = Q'x, \quad \text{and} \quad \mathcal{G}_H(x) = Q'Q^{-1}Q'x$$

in $\mathbb{P}^{5*}$ lay on a line. The three points

$$x, \qquad x' = Q^{-1}Q'x, \quad \text{and} \quad x'' = (Q^{-1}Q')^2 x$$

would then likewise be collinear in $\mathbb{P}^5$; since all three lie on G, the line L they span would lie on G. But now the linear transformation

$$M: x \mapsto Q^{-1}Q'x$$

taking G into G takes x and x' (distinct, since by hypothesis $Qx \neq Q'x$ for any $x \in F \cap G$) into L, and so takes L into itself; thus $L \subset F \cap G$. M must have a fixed point y somewhere on L, i.e., for some $y \in L$,

$$Qy = Q'y.$$

But since $L \subset F \cap G$, this implies that F and G are tangent at y, a contradiction.

Now that we have described Σ as the smooth intersection of three quadrics in $\mathbb{P}^5$, the reader will recognize Σ as a K-3 surface (Section 5, Chapter 4); in particular, Σ has numerical invariants

$$K_\Sigma \equiv 0, \quad q(\Sigma) = 0, \quad p_g(\Sigma) = 1, \quad c_1^2(\Sigma) = 0, \quad c_2(\Sigma) = 24.$$

Inasmuch as Σ is minimal and smooth, moreover, the map

$$\Sigma \xrightarrow{\pi} S$$

is the minimal desingularization os S; and since the inverse images $\pi^{-1}(p) = X_p$ of the singular points $p \in S$ in Σ are all smooth rational curves, having by adjunction self-intersection -2 on Σ, we see from our discussion of isolated singularities of surfaces that *the points of R are all ordinary double points of* S.

It remains to determine the number $^\#R$ of double points on S. We will do this first by an Euler characteristic argument, as follows: Let $\{h_\lambda\}$ be a generic pencil of hyperplanes in $\mathbb{P}^3$—specifically, one such that for each $p \in R$, p lies on a unique H_λ and H_λ is generic among hyperplanes containing p; and such that the pencil $\{H_\lambda \cap S\}$ is Lefschetz on $S - R$. Let

$$\{C_\lambda = \pi^{-1}(H_\lambda)\}$$

be the corresponding pencil of curves on Σ. The generic curve C_λ is isomorphic to a smooth plane quartic, hence has genus 3 and Euler characteristic -4; C_λ will be singular if H_λ either contains a point $p \in R$ or is tangent to S. (See Figure 17.) In the first case, we can write

$$C_\lambda = \tilde{C}_\lambda + X_p$$

with—by taking H_λ generic—$\tilde{C}_\lambda$ a smooth curve meeting X_p in two distinct points. Now $\tilde{C}_\lambda$ is the disingularization of the plane quartic $H_\lambda \cap S$ having one double point at p, and so has genus 2; since X_p is a line and meets $\tilde{C}_\lambda$ in two points,

$$\chi(C_\lambda) = \chi(\tilde{C}_\lambda) = -2.$$

In the latter case—when H_λ is simply tangent to S—C_λ is isomorphic to a plane quartic with one ordinary double point and

$$\chi(C_\lambda) = -3.$$

Thus if ν is the number of tangent hyperplanes to S in a pencil, the pencil

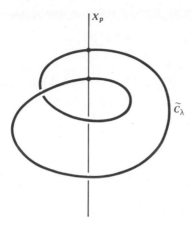

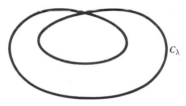

Figure 17

$\{C_\lambda\}$ on Σ has exactly

$$\mu = \nu + {}^{\#}R$$

singular elements. By the formula of p. 509, then, we see that

$$\chi(\Sigma) = 2 \cdot -4 + \nu + 2 {}^{\#}R$$

But as we have seen the dual Kummer surface S^* is the dual surface to S, so that

$$\nu = \deg S^* = 4,$$

and, since $\chi(\Sigma) = 24$, this yields

$${}^{\#}R = \tfrac{1}{2}(24 + 8) = 16.$$

Another way to compute the number of double points of S is by Schubert calculus, inasmuch as ${}^{\#}R$ will be just the number of points of intersection of the three- and six-dimensional cycles

$$\tau = \{\sigma(p)\}_{p \in \mathbb{P}^3}$$

and

$$\omega_F = \{\Lambda_2 \subset \mathbb{P}^5 : V_2 \cdot F \text{ is a double line}\}$$

in the Grassmannian $G(3,6)$ of 2-planes in $\mathbb{P}^5$. We have seen that

$$\tau \sim 4\sigma_{3,2,1},$$

where

$$\sigma_{3,2,1} = \{\Lambda_2 \subset \mathbb{P}^5 : \Lambda \ni p, \dim(\Lambda \cap V_2) \geqslant 1, \Lambda \subset V_4\}$$

for any point, 2-plane, and hyperplane $p \in V_2 \subset V_4$. To compute

$$^{\#}(\tau \cdot \omega_F) = 4 \cdot {}^{\#}(\sigma_{3,2,1} \cdot \omega_F)$$

let p, V_2, and V_4 be generic, so that $p \not\in F$, V_2 intersects F in a smooth conic curve C, and V_4 intersects F in a smooth quadric threefold Q. Say $\Lambda \in \omega_F \cap \sigma_{3,2,1}$, i.e., Λ is a 2-plane containing p, having a line in common with V_2, lying in V_4, and meeting F in a line. (See Figure 18.) Then the line $\Lambda \cap V_2$ can meet C in only one point, hence must be one of the two tangent lines L_1, L_2 to C through p in V_2. Let x_1, x_2 denote the points of tangency of L_1, L_2 with C; the locus of lines on $Q = F \cap V_4$ through x_i is

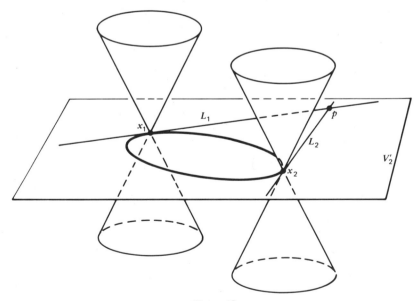

Figure 18

just $T_{x_i}(Q) \cap Q$. Let U_i be a 2-plane in $T_{x_i}(Q)$ containing p and not containing x_i; then $F \cap U_i$ is a smooth conic curve C_i and $T_{x_i}(Q) \cap Q$ is just the locus of lines through x_i meeting C_i. Λ must therefore intersect U_i, $i = 1$ or 2, in one of the two tangent lines L_{i_1}, L_{i_2} to C_i through p; i.e., Λ must be one of the four 2-planes Λ_{ij} spanned by L_i and L_{ij}. Clearly all four 2-planes Λ_{ij} lie in $\omega_F \cap \sigma_{3,2,1}$, so we see that

$$(\omega_F \cdot \sigma_{3,2,1}) = 4$$

and finally

$$(\tau \cdot \omega_F) = 16.$$

Note that, since any line of the complex X lies in two confocal pencils of X if and only if it lies in two coplanar pencils, we can also define a map

$$\pi' : \Sigma \longrightarrow S^*$$

by sending any point $x \in \Sigma$ to the common plane $h \in S^*$ of the two coplanar pencils containing l_x, or equivalently to the unique plane $h \supset l_x$ for which $\sigma(h)$ is tangent to F at x. The map π' is, by virtue of the same arguments, the desingularization of S^*; note, however, that the lines $\{X_h = \pi'^{-1}(h)\}_{h \in R^*}$ of Σ lying over the double points of S^* are not the lines X_p of Σ lying over the double points of S.

For later use, we compute the Euler characteristic $\chi(S)$, as follows. Take a triangulation of Σ that extends a triangulation of $\pi^{-1}(R) = \cup X_p$. Then the images of the simplices in Σ not in $\pi^{-1}(R)$, together with the points $p \in R$ as vertices, form a cell decomposition of S. Since, in the course of passing from Σ to S, we lose all the simplices in $\cup X_p$ and gain one new vertex for each p, we have

$$\chi(S) = \chi(\Sigma) - \sum_{p \in R} (\chi(X_p) - 1)$$
$$= \chi(\Sigma) - 16 = 8.$$

Two Configurations

There are two classical configurations associated to the Kümmer surface $S \subset \mathbb{P}^3$ and its desingularization $\Sigma \subset \mathbb{P}^5$. The first has to do with the 16 double points of S and may be described as follows. Let $p_0 \in R$ be any of the double points of S, let $\tilde{S}$ be the blow-up of S at p_0, and consider the map

$$r : \tilde{S} \longrightarrow \mathbb{P}^2$$

obtained by projection from p_0 onto a hyperplane. The generic hyperplane section C_h of S through p_0 is a plane quartic curve with one double point at

p_0, its proper transform $\tilde{C}_h \subset \tilde{S}$ its desingularization. $\tilde{C}_h$ thus has genus 2, and since r expresses $\tilde{C}_h$ as a 2-sheeted cover of its image $L = h \cap \mathbb{P}^2 \cong \mathbb{P}^1$, r must be branched at exactly six points over L. The branch locus $F \subset \mathbb{P}^2$ of r is thus a sextic plane curve without multiple components. On the other hand, if h is a generic hyperplane passing through p_0 and another double point p_i of S, then the curve C_h, having two double points, is elliptic, and the map $r : \tilde{C}_h \rightarrow \mathbb{P}^1$, expressing $\tilde{C}_h$ as a 2-sheeted cover of $\mathbb{P}^1$, can be branched at at most four points other than $r(p_i)$. The generic line $L \subset \mathbb{P}^2$ through $r(p_i)$ thus meets F at most four times away from $r(p_i)$, and so we see that the images $\overline{p}_i = r(p_i)$ of the double points of S are double points of F.

Now, suppose the curve F has irreducible components F_i of degree d_i. Singular points of F then arise in two ways: either as points of intersection of components F_i, F_j or as singular points of a component F_i. There are, of course, at most $\sum_{i \neq j} d_i d_j$ singular points of F of the former kind and, by the result of Section 2, Chapter 4, at most $\sum_i ((d_i - 1)(d_i - 2)/2)$ of the latter. But we know that $\sum d_i = \deg F = 6$, and we have seen that F has at least the 15 singular points $r(p_i)$, $i = 1, \ldots, 15$. From the chain of inequalities

$$15 \leqslant \sum_{i \neq j} d_i d_j + \sum \frac{(d_i - 1)(d_i - 2)}{2}$$

$$= \tfrac{1}{2} \left(\sum d_i \right)^2 - \sum \frac{d_i}{2} - \sum (d_i - 1)$$

$$= 18 - 3 - \sum (d_i - 1)$$

we conclude that $d_i = 1$ for all i, i.e., that F consists of the sum of six distinct lines L_i. F then has exactly the 15 double points $L_i \cdot L_j$; these must, of course, be the images $r(p_i)$. It follows that each of the lines L_i contains exactly five of the points $r(p_i)$, and correspondingly that the plane $\overline{p_0, L_i} \subset \mathbb{P}^3$ contains exactly six of the double points p_i of S. Our first observation, then, is that

Through each double point p *of* S *there pass six hyperplanes, each containing six of the points* p_i.

Let us consider in more detail one of the hyperplanes $h = \overline{p_0, L}$ found in the last argument. We note first that, inasmuch as L is part of the branch locus of the map r, every line through p_0 in the plane h meets S in exactly one more point and is tangent to S there. It follows from Bertini's theorem that h *is tangent to* S *at every point* $p \in S \cap h$, since otherwise the pencil cut out on C_h by the lines in h through p would be generically singular away from its base locus p. The curve C_h is thus a plane conic, counted with multiplicity 2 in the intersection $S \cdot h$. We see from this that the hyperplane h is a double point of the dual Kummer surface $S^* \subset \mathbb{P}^{3^*}$: clearly $h \in S^*$, so that if h were not in R^*, then X would contain two pencils lying in h, and through a generic point $p \in C_h$ there would pass two distinct lines of the complex. But the common line of the two pencils of X through each $p \in C_h$, we have seen, is tangent to S at p and so lies in h; if X contained a secant line through p in h, it would follow that X contained the pencil $\sigma(p,h)$, hence all of $\sigma(h)$. Thus, X can contain a priori only one pencil in $\sigma(h)$, and so $h \in R^*$.

Finally, applying the same arguments to the dual Kummer surface $S^* \subset \mathbb{P}^{3^*}$, we see that every point $h^* \in R^*$ lies on six of the hyperplanes $p^* \in R$, or in other words every hyperplane h in $\mathbb{P}^3$ corresponding to a point of R^* contains six of the points p_i; in sum, then, we have that:

Every hyperplane $h \in R^*$ *contains exactly six of the* 16 *double points of* S *and every double point of* S *lies on exactly six of the* 16 *hyperplanes* $h \in R^*$.

This configuration of 16 points and 16 hyperplanes is called the (16_6) configuration.

Now consider the K-3 surface $\Sigma \subset \mathbb{P}^5$. Σ contains 32 lines: the 16 lines $\{X_p\}_{p \in R}$ forming the inverse image $\pi^{-1}(R)$ of the double points of S, and likewise the 16 lines $\{X_h\}_{h \in R^*}$; the latter may be thought of either as the exceptional divisors of the desingularization $\pi' : \Sigma \to S^*$ or as the inverse images $\{\pi^{-1}(C_h)\}_{h \in R^*}$ of the 16 double hyperplane sections of S. The lines $\{X_p\}$ are, of course, all disjoint, as are the lines $\{X_h\}$; and from our last argument we see that each line X_p on Σ meets exactly six of the lines $\{X_h\}$, and vice versa.

Note that these are all the lines on Σ: if $L \subset \Sigma$ is any line, $\sigma(p,h)$ the corresponding pencil, then by definition every line $l \in \sigma(p,h)$ belongs to two confocal pencils of X. If the common focus of these two pencils is p for every l, then clearly $\sigma(p,h) = X_p$, while if for generic $l \in \sigma(p,h)$ the common focus of the pencils containing l is a point $q \neq p \in C_h$, then clearly h cannot contain two pencils, and so $\sigma(p,h) = X_h$.

We wish now to describe a set of special hyperplane sections of Σ. To do this, we go back to the picture of the (16_6) configuration obtained by projection from a point $p_0 \in R$. We saw that under such a projection, the 15 remaining points of R were mapped to the points of intersection of six lines $L_1, \ldots, L_6 \subset \mathbb{P}^2$; let $\overline{p_{ij}} = L_i \cdot L_j$ and let p_{ij} be the point of R lying over $\overline{p_{ij}}$. Choose three of the lines L_i, L_j, and L_k, and consider the lines on Σ corresponding to the points p_0, p_{ij}, p_{jk}, and $p_{ik} \in R$, and the hyperplanes $h_i = \overline{p_0 L_i}$, $h_j = \overline{p_0 L_j}$, and $h_k = \overline{p_0 L_k} \in R^*$; these form on Σ a configuration as

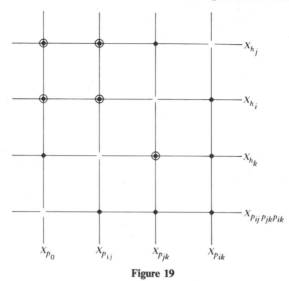

Figure 19

shown in Figure 19. Note that these seven lines lie in the hyperplane in $\mathbb{P}^5$ spanned by the points that are circled. Now in that hyperplane, $X_{p_{ik}}$ and $X_{p_{jk}}$ span a 3-plane, which must then meet $X_{p_{ij}}$ in a point; thus there is a line $L \subset \mathbb{P}^5$ meeting $X_{p_{ij}}$, $X_{p_{ik}}$, and $X_{p_{jk}}$. But since $\Sigma \subset \mathbb{P}^5$ is cut out by quadrics, the line L, meeting Σ in three points, must lie in Σ; since L meets lines of the form X_p on Σ, we must have $L = X_h$ for some $h \in R^*$; and since L meets $X_{p_{ij}}$, $X_{p_{ik}}$, and $X_{p_{jk}}$, we must have $h = \overline{p_{ij} p_{jk} p_{ik}}$. Thus all four faces of the tetrahedron in $\mathbb{P}^3$ with vertices p_0, p_{ij}, p_{jk}, and p_{ik} are hyperplanes $h \in R^*$. Such a tetrahedron will be called *special*; corresponding to a special tetrahedron we have a hyperplane section of Σ consisting of eight lines forming the configuration of Figure 19. Indeed, since we have one special tetrahedron passing through p_0 for every choice of three lines L_i, L_j, L_k out of the six $\{L_i\}$, every line X_p (and likewise every line X_h) on Σ lies on 20 such hyperplanes. Finally, since we have 16 points $p \in R$, 20 special tetrahedra containing each p as a vertex, and four vertices on each tetrahedron, we see that there are exactly 80 such hyperplane sections of Σ. In sum, then,

The surface $\Sigma \subset \mathbb{P}^5$ contains 32 lines, forming two families of 16 disjoint lines, with each line meeting exactly six members of the opposite family. There are 80 hyperplanes in $\mathbb{P}^5$ intersecting Σ in the sum of eight lines—four from each family—forming the configuration of Figure 19; and every line in Σ lies on 20 such hyperplane sections of Σ.

This configuration of 32 lines and 80 hyperplanes in $\mathbb{P}^5$ we will call the $(32_{20}80_8)$ configuration.

This last discussion sheds some additional light on the (16_6) configuration. In terms of our description of the 16 points of R above, we could a priori identify only six of the 16 hyperplanes of R^*: the planes $h_i = \overline{p_0, L_i}$, containing the points p_0 and $\{p_{ij}\}_j$. We can now describe the remaining 10: as we saw, for each triple L_i, L_j, L_k of lines, the hyperplane $h_{ijk} = \overline{p_{ij}p_{ik}p_{jk}} \in R^*$; we want now to identify the remaining three points q_1, q_2, q_3 of R lying on h_{ijk}. (See Figure 20.) To do this, we recall that the points $p_{ij}, p_{jk}, p_{ik}, q_1, q_2,$ and q_3 all lie on a conic curve, and hence so do their images $\overline{p}_{ij}, \overline{p}_{jk}, \overline{p}_{ik}, \overline{q}_1, \overline{q}_2,$ and $\overline{q}_3$. In particular, this means that no three of these points are collinear, i.e., that $\overline{q}_1, \overline{q}_2,$ and $\overline{q}_3$ must lie off the lines $L_i, L_j,$ and L_k. These three lines, however, account for 12 of the 15 points $\{p_{ij}\}$; consequently the points $q_1, q_2,$ and q_3 can only be the points $p_{lm}, p_{mn},$ and p_{ln}. Thus, if we label the 16 double points of S by $\{p_0, p_{ij}\}$ and the 16 double points of S^* as $\{h_i, h_{ijk} = h_{lmn}\}$, the incidence relationships are

$$h_i \supset \{p_0, p_{ij}\}, \qquad j \neq i,$$
$$h_{ijk} \supset \{p_{ij}, p_{ik}, p_{jk}, p_{lm}, p_{mn}, p_{nl}\},$$
$$p_0 \in h_i, \qquad i = 1, \ldots, 6,$$

and

$$p_{ij} \in h_i, h_j, h_{ijk}, \qquad k \neq i, j.$$

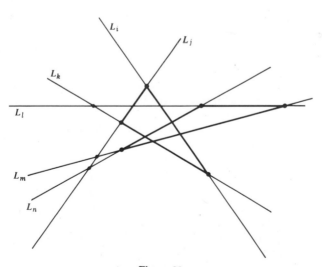

Figure 20

3. LINES ON THE QUADRIC LINE COMPLEX

The Variety of Lines on the Quadric Line Complex

We now introduce a central variety in our study: the variety $A = \{L \subset \mathbb{P}^5 : L \subset X\} \subset G(2,6)$ of lines lying on the quadric line complex X. To show that A is smooth, we first compute its cohomology class in $G(2,6)$. Recalling from Section 1 of Chapter 6 that the cycle $\tau(F) \subset G(2,6)$ of lines in $\mathbb{P}^5$ lying on a quadric hypersurface is homologous to the Schubert cycle

$$\tau(F) \sim 4 \cdot \sigma_{2,1},$$

we see that the variety $A = \tau(F) \cdot \tau(G)$ represents the cycle

$$A \sim 16(\sigma_{2,1} \cdot \sigma_{2,1});$$

in particular, the intersection number of A with the Schubert cycles

$$\sigma_{1,1}(V_4) = \{L \subset \mathbb{P}^5 : L \subset V_4\}$$

and

$$\sigma_2(V_2) = \{L \subset \mathbb{P}^5 : L \cap V_2 \neq \varnothing\}$$

in $G(2,6)$ is given, according to our reduction formulas, by

$$\begin{aligned}
{}^{\#}(A \cdot \sigma_{1,1}) &= 16(\sigma_{2,1} \cdot \sigma_{2,1} \cdot \sigma_{1,1})_{G(2,6)} \\
&= 16(\sigma_1 \cdot \sigma_1)_{G(2,3)} \\
&= 16
\end{aligned}$$

and

$$\begin{aligned}
{}^{\#}(A \cdot \sigma_2) &= 16 \cdot (\sigma_{2,1} \cdot \sigma_{2,1} \cdot \sigma_2)_{G(2,6)} \\
&= 16 \cdot (\sigma_1 \cdot \sigma_1 \cdot \sigma_2)_{G(2,4)} \\
&= 16.
\end{aligned}$$

Thus we can write

$$A \sim 16 \cdot \sigma_{4,2} + 16 \cdot_{3,3}.$$

Now, for any point $a \in A$, we can find a hyperplane $V_4 \subset \mathbb{P}^5$ containing the corresponding line $L_a \subset X$ and intersecting X transversely (by Bertini, the generic V_4 containing L_a meets $X - L_a$ transversely, and by direct examination we see that $V_4 \cap X$ is smooth along L_a for a generic such 4-plane). But we have seen in Section 4 of Chapter 4 that any smooth intersection of two quadrics in $\mathbb{P}^4$ contains exactly 16 lines, so that the Schubert cycle $\sigma_{1,1}(V_4) \subset G(2,6)$ will meet A in 16 distinct points, including a. Since ${}^{\#}(A \cdot \sigma_{1,1}) = 16$, it follows that A has intersection multiplicity 1 with $\sigma_{1,1}(V_4)$ at every point of $\sigma_{1,1}(V_4) \cap A$, and hence that a is a smooth point of A.

For every pencil $L \subset X$ in the complex X, the focus p_L of L is by definition a point of the Kummer surface S and the plane h_L of L likewise a point of the dual Kummer surface S^*; thus we have natural maps

$$j: A \to S \quad \text{and} \quad j': A \to S^*$$

defined by

$$j: L \mapsto p_L \quad \text{and} \quad j': L \mapsto h_L.$$

For $p \in S - R$, X contains two pencils with focus p, while for $p \in R$, X contains a single such pencil p; thus j expresses A as a double cover of S branched in the 16 points of R. Similarly, a hyperplane $h \in S^* - R^*$ contains two pencils of X while a hyperplane $h \in R^*$ contains only one; thus $j': A \to S^*$ is a double cover of S^* branched at R^*. Let

$$\iota: A \to A$$

be the involution of A that exchanges the sheets of $j: A \to S$, sending each pencil $L \subset X$ to the unique other pencil of X confocal with L; let

$$\iota': A \to A$$

similarly be the involution exchanging sheets of $j': A \to S^*$, sending each $L \subset X$ to the other pencil of X coplanar with L.

We can now describe A intrinsically. First, from the expression of A as a double cover of S branched in the 16 points of R, we see that

$$\chi(A) = 2\chi(S) - 16 = 2 \cdot 8 - 16 = 0.$$

We have seen that $K_\Sigma = 0$; let ω be a holomorphic nonzero 2-form on Σ. Let $\pi^{-1}(\omega)$ denote the corresponding 2-form on $(S - R) \cong \Sigma - \cup_{p \in R} X_p$. Then $j^* \pi^{-1}(\omega)$ is a holomorphic nonzero 2-form on $A - j^{-1} R$ and by Hartogs' theorem it extends to a global nonzero holomorphic 2-form on A; so

$$K_A = 0.$$

By Riemann-Roch,

$$\chi(\mathcal{O}_A) = \frac{c_1^2 + c_2}{12} = 0,$$

so $q(A) = 2$; and from the classification theorem of Section 5, Chapter 4, we recognize that

A *is an Abelian variety.*

The involutions ι and ι' are readily identified: Let z_1, z_2 be Euclidean coordinates on $\mathbb{C}^2$, and consider the holomorphic 1-forms dz_1, dz_2 on A: the forms

$$\omega_i = dz_i + \iota^* dz_i$$

are invariant under ι^*, and so we can write

$$\omega_i = j^*\tilde{\omega}_i$$

for $\tilde{\omega}_1, \tilde{\omega}_2$ holomorphic 1-forms on $S - R$. $\{\pi^*\tilde{\omega}_i\}_{i=1,2}$ are then bounded holomorphic 1-forms on $\Sigma - \cup_{p \in R} X_p$; by Riemann's theorem they extend to all of Σ, and, since Σ is simply connected, it follows that $\omega_i \equiv 0$. Thus $\iota^* dz_i = - dz_i$, i.e., ι *is the standard involution of the Abelian variety* $A = \mathbb{C}^2/\Lambda$ *induced by the map* $(z_1, z_2) \mapsto (-z_1, -z_2)$ *on* $\mathbb{C}^2$; precisely the same argument shows that the involution ι' is likewise induced by the involution $z \mapsto -z$ on $\mathbb{C}^2$, but with a different choice of base point.

Curves on the Variety of Lines

We wish now to consider curves on the Abelian variety A. To start with, recall that the Schubert cycle σ_1 on $G(2,6)$ is given by

$$\sigma_1(V_3) = \{L \subset \mathbb{P}^5 : L \cap V_3 \neq \varnothing\},$$

and that σ_1 is the hyperplane section of $G(2,6)$ under the Plücker embedding $G(2,6) \to \mathbb{P}(\Lambda^2 \mathbb{C}^6)$. For any 3-plane $V_3 \subset \mathbb{P}^5$ we set

$$\begin{aligned} D_V &= A \cap \sigma_1(V_3) \\ &= \{L \subset X : L \cap V_3 \neq \varnothing\} \subset A. \end{aligned}$$

The self-intersection of D_V on A is given by

$$\begin{aligned} (D_V \cdot D_V)_A &= (A \cdot \sigma_1 \cdot \sigma_1)_{G(2,6)} \\ &= (A \cdot (\sigma_{1,1} + \sigma_2))_{G(2,6)} \\ &= 16 + 16 = 32. \end{aligned}$$

We claim now that for a generic 3-plane V, the curve $D_V \subset A$ is smooth. Note that this does not follow immediately from Bertini's theorem: the divisors $\{D_V\}_{V \subset \mathbb{P}^5}$ are all linearly equivalent, but they do not form a linear system. Indeed, the complete linear system $|\sigma_1|$ of hyperplane sections of the Grassmannian $G(2,6) \subset \mathbb{P}(\Lambda^2 \mathbb{C}^6)$ corresponds naturally to the projective space

$$\mathbb{P}(\Lambda^2 \mathbb{C}^6)^* = \mathbb{P}(\Lambda^4 \mathbb{C}^6);$$

and the map

$$G(4,6) \to \mathbb{P}(\Lambda^4 \mathbb{C}^6)$$

given by

$$V_3 \mapsto \sigma_1(V_3) \in |\sigma_1|$$

is just the Plücker embedding of the dual Grassmannian $G(4,6)$ of 3-planes in $\mathbb{P}^5$. However, since the Schubert cycle

$$\sigma_{2,2,2,1}(V_2, V_4) = \{V_3 \subset \mathbb{P}^5 : V_2 \subset V_3 \subset V_4\}$$

in $G(4,6)$ has degree

$$^{\#}\left(\sigma_{2,2,2,1}\cdot\sigma_1\right)_{G(4,6)} = 1$$

under the dual Plücker embedding, the family

$$\{D_V\}_{V\in\sigma_{2,2,1}(V_2,V_4)}$$

of divisors on A is in fact a pencil. Now, as we have seen, through a generic $x\in X$ there pass four lines in X, comprising the locus $X\cap T_x(X)$. Let V_2 be a generic 2-plane, meeting X in four distinct such points, and let V_4 be a generic hyperplane containing V_2, not containing any line on X meeting V_2; consider the pencil $\{D_V\}_{V:V_2\subset V\subset V_4}$ on A. By Bertini, the generic element of this pencil is smooth away from the base locus. But the base locus of this pencil consists of the 16 lines of X passing through the four points of $V_2\cap X$, and the 16 lines lying in the hyperplane section $V_4\cap X$ of X—32 distinct lines in all. The base points of our pencil are therefore all simple points and hence smooth points of every curve D_V in our pencil. Thus the generic divisor D_V is smooth. Note that the genus of a smooth D_V is then given by

$$\pi(D_V) = \frac{D_V\cdot D_V}{2} + 1 = 17.$$

A second family of curves on A, more fundamental than the curves D_V, are the *incidence divisors* $B_L\subset A$, defined to be the set of lines on X meeting a given line L. More precisely—since it is not a priori clear when L itself is to be counted among the lines meeting L—we will define B_L to be the closure in A of the set of lines $L'\in A-\{L\}$ meeting L; the Lévi theorem assures us that B_L is analytic, and we will see later under what circumstances $L_0\in B_{L_0}$. The curves $\{B_L\}_{L\in A}$ form a continuous, connected family, and so all represent the same homology class on A. Since we can find 3-planes $V_3\subset\mathbb{P}^5$ intersecting X in the sum of four lines L_1, L_2, L_3, L_4—for example, $T_x(X)$—we see from this that

$$D_V = B_{L_1} + B_{L_2} + B_{L_3} + B_{L_4}$$
$$\sim 4B_L.$$

We have then

$$B_L\cdot B_L = \tfrac{1}{16}D_V\cdot D_V = 2$$

and hence the virtual genus

$$\pi(B_L) = \frac{B_L\cdot B_L}{2} + 1 = 2.$$

Note also that since D_V is positive, so is B_L.

We claim now that for any $L\subset X$, the curve $B_L\subset A$ is smooth. To see this, we observe that if two lines L and L' in X meet—i.e., if the corresponding pencils have a line l in common—then the focus $p_{L'}$ of the second pencil must lie on the line l, and hence on the plane h_L of the first pencil. The map

$$j: A \to S$$

sending each line $L \subset X$ to its focus p_L *thus maps the curve* B_L

$$j: B_L \to h_L \cap S$$

onto the hyperplane section $h_L \cap S$ *of* S; $j|_{B_L}$ is clearly generically one-to-one. By the duality of S and S^*, h_L is tangent to S, so that for generic L the curve $C_L = h_L \cap S$ is a plane quartic with one ordinary double point. By the genus formula, then,

$$g(B_L) = g(C_L) = 2,$$

so B_L is smooth. (Note that since $\pi(B_L) = 2$ implies a priori that $g(C_L) = g(B_L)$ is less than or equal to 2, this affords another proof that h_L is tangent to S, i.e., that S and S^* are dual.)

Now, since B_L is a positive divisor on A by the Lefschetz theorem the inclusion map on integral homology

$$i_*: H_1(B_L, \mathbb{Z}) \twoheadrightarrow H_1(A, \mathbb{Z})$$

is surjective. But since B_L has genus 2,

$$H_1(B_L, \mathbb{Z}) \cong H_1(A, \mathbb{Z}) \cong \mathbb{Z} \oplus \mathbb{Z} \oplus \mathbb{Z} \oplus \mathbb{Z};$$

so the kernel of i_* must have rank zero; since $H_1(B_L, \mathbb{Z})$ has no torsion, this implies that *the map* i_* *is an isomorphism.* Likewise, by Lefschetz the restriction map

$$H^{1,0}(A) \to H^{1,0}(B_L)$$

is an isomorphism, and so we have

$$A \cong \frac{(H^{1,0}(A))^*}{H_1(A, \mathbb{Z})} = \frac{(H^{1,0}(B_L))^*}{H_1(B_L, \mathbb{Z})} = \mathcal{J}(B_L),$$

i.e.,

The Abelian variety A *is the Jacobian of the curve* B_L.

Note that since the analytic representative B_L of the cohomology class $[B_L] \in H^2(A, \mathbb{Z})$ is unique up to translations, *all the curves* $B_L \subset A$ *are translates of one another.* Hence all the curves B_L are smooth, and $A = \mathcal{J}(B_L)$ for any $L \in A$.

To relate the various curves B_L on A, let L_0 be one of the 16 lines in $j'^{-1}(R^*)$ and take L_0 to be the origin in A. Since clearly

$$\iota'(L) \in B_L \qquad \text{for } L \neq \iota'(L),$$

by continuity,

$$L_0 \in B_{L_0};$$

so we can also take L_0 as base point on the curve B_{L_0}. Now, we saw in Section 6 of Chapter 2 that the theta-divisor of a principally polarized Abelian variety cannot be carried into itself by a translation other than the identity. Thus we may define a map

$$\kappa \colon A \to A$$

by setting, for each L,

$$B_L = B_{L_0} + \kappa(L);$$

our first problem is to identify κ. This is not hard: since $\kappa(0)=0$, by the result of Section 6 of Chapter 2, κ is a group homomorphism. We have

$$\iota'(L) \in B_L = B_{L_0} + \kappa(L)$$

for each L, and hence

$$\kappa(L) + L \in - B_{L_0} = B_{L_0}$$

for each L. But the map $L \mapsto \kappa(L) + L$ is again a group homomorphism, and since $B_{L_0} + B_{L_0} = A$, this implies that $\kappa(L) + L$ is constant, i.e.,

$$\kappa(L) = - L$$

or in other words

$$B_L = B_{L_0} - L \qquad \text{for all } L.$$

We can now identify the line bundles j^*H and j'^*H associated to the maps j and j'. To begin with, we note that for any hyperplane $h \subset \mathbb{P}^3$, the inverse image j^*h in A is just the set of pencils $L \in A$ with focus lying on the hyperplane section $h \cap S$ of S. In particular, if we take $h \in S^*$—so that h contains two pencils L and $\iota'(L)$ from X—then j^*h will consist simply of the set of pencils having a line in common with either L or $\iota'(L)$—i.e.,

$$j^*h = B_L \cup B_{\iota'(L)}.$$

(To avoid confusion, we will here use the union symbol $\cup$ to denote addition of divisors.) Similarly, for any point $p \in S$, the pullback $j'^*(p^*)$ of the dual hyperplane $p^* \subset \mathbb{P}^{3*}$ of hyperplanes containing p will consist of pencils whose plane contains p—that is, of pencils having a line in common with either of the pencils L' and $\iota(L')$ with focus p. Thus

$$j'^*P^* = B_L \cup B_{\iota(L)}.$$

Now in general, for any two lines L and L' and any element $\lambda \in A$, the divisors

$$B_L \cup B_{L'} \quad \text{and} \quad (B_L + \lambda) \cup (B_{L'} - \lambda)$$

are linearly equivalent: the map

$$A \to \hat{A} = \text{Pic}^0(A)$$

defined by

$$\lambda \mapsto [(B_L + \lambda) \cup (B_{L'} - \lambda)] - [B_L \cup B_{L'}]$$

sends the points λ and $\lambda' = L - L' - \lambda$ into the same point—but being a group homomorphism, this implies it is constant. Thus we can write

$$\begin{aligned}
j^* h &= B_L \cup B_{\iota'(L)} \\
&= (B_{L_0} - L) \cup (B_{L_0} + L) \\
&= 2B_{L_0}
\end{aligned}$$

and

$$\begin{aligned}
j'^* H &= B_L \cup B_{\iota'(L)} \\
&= (B_{L_0} - L) \cup (B_{L_0} + L + \mu) \\
&= 2B_{L_0} + \tfrac{1}{2}\mu,
\end{aligned}$$

for some $\mu \in A$, i.e., *the line bundles* j*H' *and* j'*H *differ by translation.* Since by the theorem of p. 317,

$$h^0(2B_{L_0}) = h^0(2B_{L_0} + \tfrac{1}{2}\mu) = 4,$$

we see that both j and j' are given by complete linear systems, it follows that

The Kummer surfaces S *and* S* *are projectively isomorphic.*

Combined with the fact that $S^* \subset \mathbb{P}^{3*}$ is the dual variety of $S \subset \mathbb{P}^3$, this proves that

The Kummer surface S *is self-dual.*

Two Configurations Revisited

We may, by considering the Kummer surface $S \subset \mathbb{P}^3$ and its desingularization $\Sigma \subset \mathbb{P}^5$ as the images of the Abelian variety A, get a new slant on the configurations associated to these varieties. To see this, think of A as the Jacobian of the curve $B = B_L$, and realize B as the locus of

$$y^2 = \prod_{i=0}^{5} (x - \lambda_i),$$

with $p_i = (\lambda_i, 0)$ the Weierstrass points of B. Then, since the hyperelliptic series on B contains the divisors $2p_i$, the points

$$\mu_i = (p_i - p_0) \in \text{Pic}^0(B) = A, \qquad i = 0, \dots, 5,$$

are points of order 2 on A, as are the points

$$\mu_{ij} = (p_i + p_j - 2p_0) \in A, \qquad 1 \leqslant i < j \leqslant 5.$$

Inasmuch as the hyperelliptic series on B is unique, no pair $p_i + p_j$ is linearly equivalent to another pair $p_k + p_l$, so the points μ_i, μ_{ij} are all distinct; these, then, are the 16 half-lattice points of A. The group law on the points μ_i, μ_{ij} is easily written down: clearly

$$\mu_i + \mu_j = \mu_{ij},$$

and since the meromorphic function

$$f(x,y) = \frac{y}{(x - \lambda_0)^3}$$

on B has divisor

$$(f) = \sum_{i=0}^{5} p_i - 6p_0,$$

we see that

$$\mu_i + \mu_{jk} \sim (p_i + p_j + p_k - 3p_0)$$
$$\sim (-p_l - p_m + 2p_0) \sim -\mu_{lm} = \mu_{lm}$$

for i, j, k, l, m distinct; and

$$\mu_{ij} + \mu_{kl} \sim (p_i + p_j + p_k + p_l - 4p_0)$$
$$\sim (-p_m + p_0) \sim -\mu_m = \mu_m.$$

Note that the standard theta-divisor

$$\Theta = \{ (p - p_0) : p \in B \} \subset A$$

of course contains the six half-lattice points $\{ \mu_i \}$; likewise its translate

$$\Theta_i = \Theta + \mu_i = \{ (p + p_i - 2p_0) \}$$

contains the six points $\mu_0 = 0$, μ_i and $\{ \mu_{ij} \}_{j \neq 0, i}$ and

$$\Theta_{ij} = \Theta + \mu_{ij} = \{ (p + p_i + p_j - 3p_0) \}$$

contains the six points μ_i, μ_j, μ_{ij}, and $\{ \mu_{lm} \}_{l,m \neq i,j}$. Conversely, each of the half-lattice points $\mu_i \mu_{ij}$ lies on exactly six of the divisors Θ_i, Θ_{ij}:

$$\mu_i \in \Theta, \ \Theta_i, \ \text{and} \ \Theta_{ij} \ \text{for} \ j \neq 0, i$$

and

$$\mu_{ij} \in \Theta_i, \ \Theta_j, \ \Theta_{ij}, \ \text{and} \ \Theta_{kl} \ \text{for} \ k, l \neq i, j.$$

Now, we have seen that the map $j : A \to S$ from A to the Kummer surface $S \subset \mathbb{P}^3$ is given by some translate $|2\Theta + \lambda|$ of the linear system $|2\Theta|$ on A;

since $|2\Theta + \lambda|$ is invariant under the involution $\mu \mapsto -\mu$ fixing the 16 points μ_i, μ_{ij}, we must have $\lambda = 0$. In particular, then, the divisors $2\Theta_i, 2\Theta_{ij}$ are all elements of the linear series $|2\Theta|$; and being invariant under the involution $\mu \mapsto -\mu$ they are mapped 2-1 onto hyperplane sections of S, consisting of double conic curves. Each divisor Θ_i, Θ_{ij} contains exactly six of the half-lattice points of A; consequently each of the corresponding hyperplane sections of S will pass through exactly six of the double points of S, and every double point of S is contained in exactly six of these hyperplanes, giving us the (16_6) configuration.

Now consider the map ρ from A to the K-3 surface $\Sigma \subset \mathbb{P}^5$. ρ is given, as the reader may check, by the linear series of curves in the system $|4\Theta|$ passing through the 16 half-lattice points of A, or more properly by the linear system

$$|4\pi^*\Theta - \sum E_i|$$

on the blow-up $\tilde{A}$ of A at the half-lattice points of A. The map is 2-sheeted, branched exactly at the 16 exceptional divisors E_i of the blow-up.

We first locate the 32 lines of Σ. Sixteen are obvious: there are the images X_p of the 16 exceptional divisors E_i, each of which has intersection number 1 with the system $|\pi^*4\Theta - \sum E_i|$ and maps 1-1 onto a line in $\mathbb{P}^5$. The other 16 are the images in $\mathbb{P}^5$ of the proper transforms of the theta-divisors Θ_i, Θ_{ij} on A. Each of these has intersection number 8 with $\pi^*4\Theta$, and, meeting six of the exceptional divisors E_i, intersection number 2 with $\pi^*4\Theta - \sum E_i$; being invariant under the involution fixing the half-lattice points, it maps 2-1 onto a line in $\mathbb{P}^5$.

Now, by the same argument as before, for any $\lambda_1, \lambda_2, \lambda_3$, and $\lambda_4 \in A$ the divisor

$$(\Theta + \lambda_1) \cup (\Theta + \lambda_2) \cup (\Theta + \lambda_3) \cup (\Theta + \lambda_4)$$

will be in the linear system $|4\Theta|$ if and only if $\sum \lambda_i = 0$. In particular, we see that the system $|4\Theta|$ contains the 80 divisors

$$\alpha_{ij} = \Theta \cup \Theta_i \cup \Theta_j \cup \Theta_{ij} \qquad (1 \leqslant i < j \leqslant 5),$$

$$\beta_{ijk} = \alpha_{jk} + \mu_i = \Theta_i \cup \Theta_{ij} \cup \Theta_{ik} \cup \Theta_{lm} \qquad (1 \leqslant i \leqslant 5; 1 \leqslant j < k \leqslant 5),$$

$$\gamma_{ij} = \Theta_{ij} \cup \Theta_k \cup \Theta_l \cup \Theta_m \qquad (1 \leqslant i < j \leqslant 5),$$

$$\delta_{ij} = \gamma_{ij} + \mu_j = \Theta_i \cup \Theta_{jk} \cup \Theta_{jl} \cup \Theta_m \qquad (1 \leqslant i \leqslant 5, 1 \leqslant j \leqslant 5),$$

$$\varepsilon_{ijk} = \gamma_{lm} + \mu_k = \Theta \cup \Theta_{ij} \cup \Theta_{ik} \cup \Theta_{jk} \qquad (1 \leqslant i < j < k \leqslant 5).$$

Each of these divisors contains all 16 half-lattice points, and each contains exactly four of them with multiplicity 3: three of the four components of α_{ij}, for example, pass through each of μ_0, μ_i, μ_j, and μ_{ij}, while three components of γ_{ij} pass through each of μ_{kl}, μ_{lm}, μ_{km}, and μ_0; the

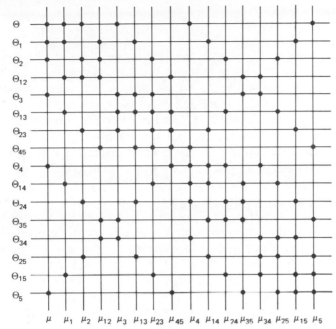

Figure 21

remaining divisors β_{ijk}, δ_{ij}, and ε_{ijk} are all translates of these two types. The corresponding elements of the linear series $|\pi^*4\Theta - \Sigma E_i|$ on $\tilde{A}$ thus all consist of four of the curves $\tilde{\Theta}_i, \tilde{\Theta}_{ij}$ and four of the exceptional divisors E_i taken with multiplicity 2; and the corresponding hyperplane sections of $\Sigma \subset \mathbb{P}^5$ consist of eight lines forming the configuration of Figure 19. These, then, are the 32 lines and 80 hyperplanes of the $(32_{20}\,80_8)$ configuration on Σ.

The incidence relations among the 16 theta-divisors $\Theta_0, \Theta_i, \Theta_{ij}$ and the 16 points μ_0, μ_i, μ_{ij} (that is, among the points and planes of the 16_6 configuration, or among the 32 lines on Σ) are diagramed in Figure 21.

The Group Law

We will now give an abstract representation of the curves B_L, which will allow us both to identify B_L (and hence $A = \mathcal{J}(B_L)$) and to describe geometrically the group law on the variety A of lines of X.

First, we consider not just the two quadrics F and G in $\mathbb{P}^5$, but the entire pencil $\{F_\lambda\}$ spanned by F and G, that is, the pencil of all quadrics in $\mathbb{P}^5$ containing X.

We define a map

$$\pi : B_L \to \mathbb{P}^1$$

as follows: for any line $L' \subset X$ meeting L, let $\Lambda = \overline{L, L'}$ be the 2-plane spanned by L and L'. There is then a unique quadric $F_{\lambda(L')}$ in the pencil $\{F_\lambda\}$ containing the 2-plane Λ. To see this, let $q \in \Lambda$ be any point of Λ lying off L and L'. (See Figure 22.) q is then contained in some quadric $F_{\lambda(L')}$—but $F_{\lambda(L')}$, containing L, L', and q, has three points of intersection with any line L'' in Λ through q, and so contains L''; thus $F_{\lambda(L')}$ contains Λ. $F_{\lambda(L')}$ is clearly unique; if Λ lay on two quadrics of the pencil F_λ, it would be contained in X; but X, as we saw, contains no 2-planes. We may thus define the map π by sending any line $L' \in B_L$ to $\lambda(L')$.

Now let F_λ be any quadric in our pencil, and consider the inverse image $\pi^{-1}(\lambda)$. If Λ is any 2-plane in F_λ containing L, then the intersection of Λ with X—that is, the intersection of Λ with any second element F_μ of the pencil—will consist of L plus a second line L'; the inverse image $\pi^{-1}(\lambda)$ thus corresponds to the 2-planes in F_λ containing L. There are two possibilities: first, if F_λ is smooth, then, as we have seen, the 2-planes on F_λ fall into two connected three-dimensional components. Now if $p \in L \subset F_\lambda$ is any point of L, the intersection $T_p(F_\lambda) \cap F_\lambda$ will be a cone over the smooth quadric surface $\tilde{F}_\lambda$ cut out on F_λ by any 3-plane in $T_p(F_\lambda)$ missing p, and the 2-planes on F_λ through the point p will be spanned by the lines on $\tilde{F}_\lambda$ together with p. Since there are two lines on $\tilde{F}_\lambda$ containing the point $L \cap \tilde{F}_\lambda$, there will be two 2-planes on F_λ containing L, one from each family. Suppose, on the other hand, that F_λ is singular. Inasmuch as $X = F_\lambda \cap F_\mu$ is smooth, the singular locus of F_λ must lie outside F_μ; in particular, it follows that the singular locus of F_λ is only a point q, and that F_λ is the cone through q over a smooth quadric $\tilde{F}_\lambda$ in a $\mathbb{P}^4 \subset \mathbb{P}^5$. In this

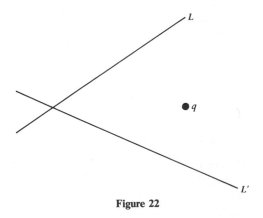

Figure 22

case, the 2-planes on F_λ will form a single irreducible three-dimensional family: namely, the 2-planes spanned by q together with the lines on $\tilde{F}_\lambda$; and the 2-plane $\overline{q,L}$ will clearly be the only 2-plane in F_λ containing L.

We see then that *the map* $\pi : B_L \to \mathbb{P}^1$ *expresses* B_L *as a 2-sheeted cover of* $\mathbb{P}^1$, *branched at the points of* $\mathbb{P}^1$ *corresponding to the singular quadrics in the pencil* $\{F_\lambda\}$; indeed, all the curves B_L may be naturally identified with the abstract curve B of irreducible families of 2-planes in the quadrics of the pencil $\{F_\lambda\}$.

To be explicit, suppose that our original pair of quadrics G and F are given as the locus of two symmetric quadric forms Q and Q'. We can, of course, take Q to be given by the identity matrix, and by standard linear algebra we may at the same time diagonalize Q'; i.e., we may take

$$G = \left(\sum X_i^2 = 0 \right) \quad \text{and} \quad F = \left(\sum \lambda_i X_i^2 = 0 \right).$$

The singular elements of the pencil

$$F_\lambda = \left(\sum_{i=0}^{5} (\lambda - \lambda_i) X_i^2 = 0 \right)$$

are then the six quadrics $F_{\lambda_0}, \ldots, F_{\lambda_5}$. The map π is thus branched at the six points $\lambda_0, \ldots, \lambda_5$; and consequently

The variety A *of lines on the quadric line complex* X *given as the intersection of the two quadrics*

$$G = \left(\sum X_i^2 = 0 \right) \quad \text{and} \quad F = \left(\sum \lambda_i X_i^2 = 0 \right)$$

is the Jacobian of the curve expressible as a double cover of $\mathbb{P}^1$ *branched at the six points* $\lambda_0, \ldots, \lambda_5$.

As promised, we can now describe geometrically the group law on A. There are basically two ingredients in this construction. The first is to note that *the sum on* A *of four lines comprising the intersection of* X *with a 3-plane* V *is constant.* This is because if $V \cdot X = L_1 + L_2 + L_3 + L_4$, then by the argument of p. 784 we may write

$$D_V = B_{L_1} \cup B_{L_2} \cup B_{L_3} \cup B_{L_4}$$
$$= \left(B_{L_0} - L_1 \right) \cup \left(B_{L_0} - L_2 \right) \cup \left(B_{L_0} - L_3 \right) \cup \left(B_{L_0} - L_4 \right)$$
$$= 3 B_{L_0} \cup \left(B_{L_0} - L_1 - L_2 - L_3 - L_4 \right).$$

Since all divisors D_V are linearly equivalent, and since no translation of A fixes B_{L_0}, it follows that the sum $L_1 + L_2 + L_3 + L_4$ does not depend on V. Choose as the origin in A a line L_0 with $4L_0 \sim D_V$, so that the sum of any four lines on S lying in a 3-plane is zero on A.

The second point is to identify the isomorphism

$$t_{L_0 - L} : B_{L_0} \to B_L$$

of B_{L_0} and B_L given by translation on A. To do this, consider the set of all isomorphisms

$$\varphi_L : B_{L_0} \to B_L;$$

since B_L can have only finitely many automorphisms, the set $\{\varphi_L\}_L$ forms an unbranched covering of A, of which the isomorphisms $\{t_{L_0 - L}\}$ form one sheet. But we can also define for each L an isomorphism $\varphi_2 : B_{L_0} \to B_L$ via the natural identification of both B_{L_0} and B_L with the abstract curve B introduced above; since $\varphi_{L_0} = t_0 = \mathrm{id}$., it follows that $\varphi_2 = t_{L_0 - L}$ for all L.

Now suppose we are given two lines L_1 and L_2 in X, and we want to find their sum $L_1 + L_2$ in A.

The first step is to express L_1 as the sum of two points on the curve B_{L_0}. This is easy: L_1 and L_0 together span a 3-plane V in $\mathbb{P}^5$, which will intersect X in L_0 and L_1 plus two additional lines M_1 and M_2 meeting L_0 and L_1; we have

$$L_1 = -M_1 - M_2$$

in A. (See Figure 23.) The second step is to translate the points $M_1, M_2 \in A$ by L_2; this is done by identifying the curves B_{L_0} and B_{L_2} via the abstract curve B, as follows: each of the lines M_1 and M_2 determines, together with L_0, a unique quadric F_λ in the pencil spanned by F and G, and an irreducible family of 2-planes in F_λ. In that family of 2-planes, moreover,

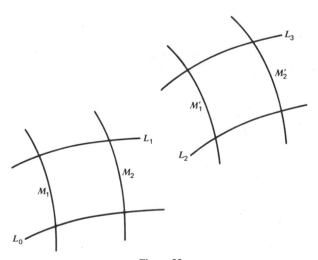

Figure 23

there will be a unique element Λ_i containing L_2; if we let M_i' be the remaining line of intersection of A_i with X, then as we have seen,

$$M_i' = M_i - L_2.$$

Finally, the lines L_2, M_1', and M_2' span a 3-plane $V' \subset \mathbb{P}^5$ that will intersect S in L_2, M_1', M_2', and a fourth line L_3. We have then

$$
\begin{aligned}
L_3 &= -M_1' - M_2' - L_2 \\
&= -M_1 - M_2 + L_2 \\
&= L_1 + L_2
\end{aligned}
$$

in A; this is the group law.

4. THE QUADRIC LINE COMPLEX: REPRISE

The Quadric Line Complex and the Associated Kummer Surface II

We return now to the geometry of the complex X of lines in $\mathbb{P}^3$. Our starting point this time around is the question: which lines l_x of our complex are tangent lines to the Kummer surface S? To answer this, we go back to our initial computation of the degree of the Kummer surface:

Let $l_x, x \in X$, be any line of the complex. Then for any point $p \in l_x \cap S$ of intersection of l_x with S, l_x will be an element of one or both of the pencils of lines in the complex through the point p—that is, the point $x \in X$ will lie on one or both of the lines of $X_p = \sigma(p) \cap F$; and conversely, for any line $L \subset X$ containing x, the focus p_L of the corresponding pencil of lines in $\mathbb{P}^3$ must by definition lie in $l_x \cap S$. Now the locus

$$T_x(X) \cap X = T_x(G) \cap G \cap T_x(F) \cap F$$

of lines on X passing through the point x has degree 4. We concluded, then, if l_x did not lie on any pair of confocal pencils, and if $T_x(X) \cap X$ contained no multiple components, that l_x met S in four distinct points. We have since seen that the degree of S is indeed four, and so we can now invert our argument to obtain the characterization:

For any x∈X, *the line* l$_x$ *will be tangent to* S *if and only if either*

    1. l$_x$ *is a singular line, i.e., it is held in common by two confocal pencils; or*
    2. *the intersection* T$_x$(X)∩X *contains a multiple component.*

We have already seen that the locus $\Sigma \subset X$ of singular lines is the smooth intersection of X with a quadric hypersurface in $\mathbb{P}^5$; we turn our attention now to the second possibility. Now we notice something unexpected: the intersection of $T_x(X)$ with X will fail to be transverse—that is, fail to consist of four distinct lines—everywhere along a line $L \subset X$ if the intersection

$$T_x(X) \cap T_y(X) = T_x(F) \cap T_y(F) \cap T_x(G) \cap T_y(G)$$

is two-dimensional for all $y \in L$. But the family of hyperplanes

$$\{T_x(F)\}_{x \in L}$$

forms a pencil, as does the family $\{T_x(G)\}_{x \in L}$; thus for any $x \neq x' \in L$,

$$T_x(G) \cap T_{x'}(G) = \bigcap_{y \in L} T_y(G)$$

and

$$T_x(F) \cap T_{x'}(F) = \bigcap_{y \in L} T_y(F).$$

This says that the intersection

$$T_x(X) \cap T_y(X) = \bigcap_{x \in L} T_x(X)$$

will be two-dimensional for *any* pair of distinct points $x, y \in L$ if and only if it is two-dimensional for *all* pairs $x, y \in L$; in other words, the line L will be a multiple component of the intersection $T_x(X) \cap X$ for some $x \in L$ if and only if it is for all $x \in L$, if and only if the locus

$$\bigcap_{x \in L} T_x(X)$$

contains a 2-plane. In this case, all the lines $\{l_x\}_{x \in L}$ of the corresponding pencil will be tangent to S; thus we see that

A line $\mathrm{l_x}$ *of the complex* X, *other than a singular line, is tangent to* S *if and only if it lies on a pencil of lines of* X *all tangent to* S.

Note that if $L \subset X$ is any pencil of lines, all tangent to S, then by Bertini they must all be tangent at the focus p_L of the pencil, i.e., the plane h_L of the pencil must be the tangent plane to S at p_L. We may thus make the following definition:

DEFINITION. A line $L \subset X$ is called *special* if, equivalently,

1. $\dim(\bigcap_{x \in L} T_x(X)) = 2$; or
2. the locus $T_x(X) \cap X$ of lines in X through a generic point $x \in L$ consists of fewer than four lines;

3. $h_L = T_{p_L}(S)$, i.e., all the lines $\{l_x\}_{x \in L}$ are tangent to S at p_L.

Let $\tilde{D} \subset A$ be the set of special lines of X, and

$$\Delta = \bigcup_{L \in \tilde{D}} L \subset X$$

the locus of all special lines. We can also write

$$\Delta = \{x \in X : T_x(X) \cap X \text{ contains fewer than four lines}\}$$

and

$$\{x \in X : l_x \text{ is tangent to } S\} = \Sigma \cup \Delta.$$

To find the degree of Δ, we make a second computation for the genus of the curve

$$D_V = \{L \subset X : L \cap V_3 \neq \varnothing\} \subset A.$$

Note that the generic $V_3 \subset \mathbb{P}^5$ meets X in a curve $E \subset V_3$ that is the smooth intersection of two quadrics on $V_3 \cong \mathbb{P}^3$. By the adjunction formula, E is an elliptic curve. Since E contains no lines, every line $L \subset X$ meeting E meets E in only one point, and so we may define a map

$$\tau : D = \{L \subset X : L \cap V_3 \neq \varnothing\} \to E = V_3 \cap X$$

expressing D as a fourfold branched cover of E. Now

$$K_E = 0$$

and, as we have seen, the generic curve D_V is smooth, so

$$\deg K_D = 32;$$

thus the map τ must have 32 branch points. But the branch locus of τ in E is just the set of points $x \in E$ having fewer than four lines through them; thus

$$\deg \Delta = {}^{\#}(\Delta \cdot V_3)_{\mathbb{P}^5} = 32.$$

Similarly, this argument yields

$${}^{\#}(D_V \cdot \tilde{D})_A = 32,$$

hence

$${}^{\#}(B_L \cdot \tilde{D})_A = \tfrac{1}{4} {}^{\#}(D_V \cdot \tilde{D})_A = 8$$

and likewise

$${}^{\#}(\Delta \cdot L)_X = 8.$$

We are now in a position to sketch a picture of the generic pencil L of the complex X in relation to the Kummer surface S. Assume that neither L

nor its coplanar pencil $L' = \iota'(L)$ is special, and let

$h_L = h_{L'}$ be the plane of the pencil $\{l_x\}_{x \in L}$,
$p_L, p_{L'}$ be the foci of the pencils L and L',
$C_L = h_L \cap S$,

$$j|_{B_L} : B_L \to C_L$$

the map sending a line $M \subset X$ meeting L to the focus p_M of the corresponding pencil, and

$$\gamma : B_L \to L$$

the extension of the map from $B_L - \{L\}$ to L sending each line $M \neq L \in B_L$ to its point of intersection with L. Note that γ can be realized as the composition of $j|_{B_L}$ with the projection map of C_L from the point p_L.

To start, we note that the pencil $\{l_x\}_{x \in L}$ contains 10 tangent lines to S: two singular lines corresponding to points of intersection of L with $\Sigma = X \cap H$, and eight nonsingular tangents, corresponding to the eight points of intersection of L with Δ. (In fact only eight of these lines—namely the eight nonsingular tangent lines—correspond to honest branch points of the map $\gamma : B_L \to L$.) We can locate the two singular lines in the pencil L readily enough: first, the common line of the pencil L and its confocal pencil $\iota(L)$, i.e., the tangent line to C_L at p_L. Second, we have seen that a line l_x of the complex lies in two confocal pencils if and only if it lies on two other coplanar pencils, so the line $\overline{p_L p_{L'}}$ held in common by L and its coplanar pencil L' must be the second singular line of the pencil L. (See Figure 24.) In particular, we see that the line $\overline{p_L p_{L'}}$ meets S in just one point q other than p_L and $p_{L'}$.

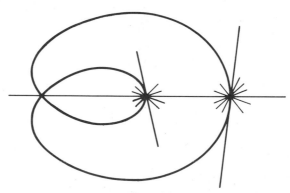

Figure 24

We can now identify the singular point $q' \in C_L$. Clearly, the lines $\overline{p_L, q'}$ and $\overline{p_{L'}, q'}$ are both tangent lines to S; we claim that in fact

$$\overline{p_L, q'} = \overline{p_{L'}, q'},$$

i.e.,

$$q = q'$$

is the singular point of C_L. This is clear: if $\overline{p_L, q'}$ and $\overline{p_{L'}, q'}$ were distinct and nonsingular, then they would necessarily lie in one special pencil, which could only be the pencil of lines through q' in h_L—but L and L' are the only pencils of X in h_L. On the other hand, through a point $q' \notin R$ in S there is only one singular line of X, and so we must have $\overline{p_L, q'} = \overline{p_{L'}, q}$. Thus in general, if $h \in S^*$ is any hyperplane and L, L' the two pencils of X in h, h *is tangent to S at the focus of the two confocal pencils of* X *containing the singular line* $\overline{p_L, p_{L'}}$.

Dually, of course, for $p \in S$ any point, L and $L' = \iota(L)$ the two pencils of X confocal at p,

The tangent plane to S at p is swept out by the two coplanar pencils of X containing the singular line $h_L \cap h_{L'}$.

Note in particular that the map

$$j: B_L \to C_L$$

is one-to-one at p_L, and that

$$j(\iota(L)) = p_L.$$

It follows from this that $B_L - \{L\}$ is closed, and hence that

$$L \notin B_L$$

for L a nonspecial line. This, finally, gives us the means to describe the divisor $\tilde{D} \subset A$ of special lines on X. Let

$$\tilde{D}' = \{L \in A : L \in B_L\}.$$

Then we have

$$\begin{aligned}
\tilde{D}' &= \{L : L \in B_{L_0} - L\} \\
&= \{L : 2L \in B_{L_0}\} \\
&= m_2^* B_{L_0},
\end{aligned}$$

where $m_2 : A \to A$ is the map multiplication by two. In particular,

$$\#\left(\tilde{D}' \cdot B_{L_0}\right) = 4 \cdot \left(B_{L_0} \cdot B_{L_0}\right) = 8.$$

Now, since no nonspecial line L is an element of $\tilde{D}'$,

$$\tilde{D}' \subset \tilde{D},$$

i.e., $\tilde{D} - \tilde{D}'$ is an effective divisor on A. But we have seen that

$$(\tilde{D} \cdot B_L) = 8,$$

and so

$$((\tilde{D} - \tilde{D}') \cdot B_L) = 0;$$

since B_L is positive and $\tilde{D} - \tilde{D}'$ effective, this implies that

$$\tilde{D} - \tilde{D}' = 0.$$

In sum, then,

A line $L \subset X$ is special if and only if $L \in B_L$; the divisor $\tilde{D} \subset A$ of special lines is the pullback $m_2^* B_{L_0}$ of B_{L_0} under multiplication by two.

Rationality of the Quadric Line Complex

We now shift our focus to consideration of the quadric line complex $X = F \cap G$ as an abstract variety. In particular, we want to consider, for any line $L \cup X$, the rational map

$$f_L : X - L \to \mathbb{P}^3$$

obtained by projection from L onto a complementary 3-plane $V_3 \subset \mathbb{P}^5$. We claim first that f_L is a birational isomorphism of X with $\mathbb{P}^3$. To see this, simply note that if any 2-plane $V_2 \subset \mathbb{P}^5$ containing L contains two points $p \neq q$ of X not on L, then the line $\overline{pq} \subset V_2$ must meet X in at least three points—p, q, and the point of intersection $\overline{pq} \cup L$—and so must lie in X. (See Figure 25.) Thus the map f_L is one-to-one away from the locus of lines in X meeting L; this is sufficient to establish that f_L is birational.

A closer examination of f_L, in fact, tells us a good deal more about X. To begin with, note that if

$$\pi : \tilde{X}_L \to X$$

is the blow-up of X along L and $F = \pi^{-1}(L) \subset \tilde{X}_L$ the exceptional divisor of the blow-up, then f_L may be extended to a holomorphic map

$$\tilde{f}_L : \tilde{X}_L \to \mathbb{P}^3$$

by sending a point $(p, \eta) \in F$, corresponding to the normal vector η to L at p, to the point of intersection of V_3 with the 2-plane spanned by L and any line through p representing the vector η—since η is defined as a tangent vector to X at p modulo tangent vectors to L at p, this is well-defined.

Now let $E_L \subset \mathbb{P}^3$ be the image under f_L of the locus $\cup_{L' \in B_L} L'$ of lines in X meeting L, and let $Q \subset \mathbb{P}^3$ be the image $\tilde{f}_L(F)$ of the exceptional divisor

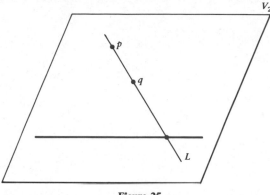

Figure 25

of $\tilde{X}_L$. E_L is a curve naturally isomorphic to B_L, and we can compute its degree as follows: for any hyperplane $V_2 \subset V_3$, the points of intersection $V_2 \cap E_L$ will correspond to the lines in X meeting L and lying in the hyperplane $\overline{L, V_2} \subset \mathbb{P}^5$. But for generic V_2, the hyperplane section $\overline{L, V_2} \cap X$ is the smooth intersection of two quadrics in 4-space, and we have seen that each of the 16 lines on such a surface meets exactly five other lines on the surface. Thus E_L is a quintic space curve. The image Q of F, on the other hand, is readily seen to be a quadric surface—in fact, it is just the intersection of $V_3 \subset \mathbb{P}^5$ with the quadric hypersurface

$$\bigcup_{x \in L} T_x(S).$$

The map $\tilde{f}_L$ is best understood by cases: for each point $r \in V_3$, let $V_2(r)$ be the 2-plane spanned by r and L, and write

$$G \cdot V_2(r) = L + L_1, \qquad F \cdot V_2(r) = L + L_2.$$

There are then a number of possibilities:

1.   Generically, L, L_1, and L_2 are all distinct, and L_1 meets L_2 at a point $p \in X$ not on L. (See Figure 26.) In this case $V_2(r)$ will not be tangent to X anywhere along L, so

$$\tilde{f}_L^{-1}(r) = \{p\}.$$

2.   In case L_1, L_2, and L are again distinct, but have a point $p \in L$ in common—i.e., $V_2(r) \cap X = L$—we see that $V_2(r)$ is tangent to X exactly at p. (See Figure 27.) The point r is thus the image of the point $r(p) \in F$ on the exceptional divisor of $\tilde{X}_L$ corresponding to the normal vector to $L \subset X$ at p lying in $V_2(r)$.

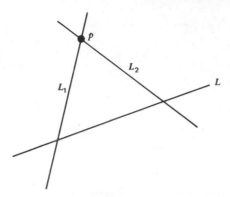

Figure 26

3. In case $L_1 = L \neq L_2$—or similarly $L_2 = L \neq L_1$—we see as in the least case that $V_2(r)$ is tangent to X at the point p of intersection of L with L_2 (resp. L_1). (See Figure 28.) r is thus the image of the normal vectors to $L \subset X$ at p lying in $V_2(r)$.

4. If $L_1 = L_2 \neq L$, then clearly r is the image of the proper transform in $\tilde{X}_L$ of the line $L_1 = L_2 \subset X$. (See Figure 29.)

5. The final possibility is $L_1 = L_2 = L$. This can occur only when L is a special line and

$$V_2(r) = \bigcap_{x \in L} T_x(X).$$

In this case, $V_2(r)$ contains a normal vector to $L \subset X$ at each point of L, and the map $\tilde{f}_L$ sends the curve consisting of these normal vectors to the point r.

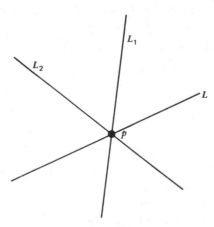

Figure 27

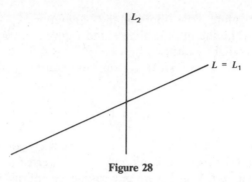

Figure 28

Suppose now that the line L of projection is not a special line. Then by the above, the map $\tilde{f}_L$ is one-to-one away from the proper transforms in $\tilde{X}_L$ of the lines on X meeting L, and maps each of these proper transforms onto the corresponding point of E_L, i.e., that

$$\tilde{f}_L : \tilde{X}_L \to \mathbb{P}^3$$

is the blow-up of the quintic curve $E_L \subset \mathbb{P}^3$. We can identify one of the rulings on the quadric $Q = \tilde{f}_L(F)$: first, for every $x \in L$, the image under $\tilde{f}_L$ of $\pi^{-1}(x) \subset \tilde{X}_L$ is just the line $V_3 \cap T_x(X)$ lying on Q. Note that since L is nonspecial, for $x \neq x' \in L$, $T_x(X)$ meets $T_{x'}(X)$ only in L, so that the corresponding lines $\tilde{f}_L(\pi^{-1}x)$ and $\tilde{f}_L(\pi^{-1}x')$ are disjoint; thus Q is a smooth quadric. Two of the lines in the second ruling are also visible: at each point $p \in L$, one normal vector to $L \subset X$ will lie in the 3-plane $\cap_{x \in L} T_x(G)$, and the images of the points of $F \subset X_L$ corresponding to these normal vectors will be the line $(\cap_{x \in L} T_x(G)) \cap V_3$ in Q; similarly the intersection of V_3 with $\cap_{x \in L} T_x(F)$ will be a line of the second ruling in Q. Note that the

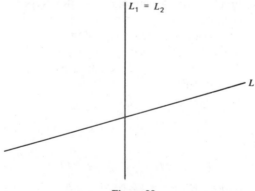

Figure 29

lines of the first ruling—the fibers of the blow-up $\pi : \tilde{X}_L \to X$—each meet E_L three times, while the lines in the second ruling meet E_L twice.

The situation is slightly different in case L is a special line of X. Now all the lines $\{ \tilde{f}_L(\pi^{-1}x) = V_3 \cap T_x(X) \}_{x \in L}$ on the quadric Q have in common the point

$$p = V_3 \cap \bigcap_{x \in L} T_x(X)$$

corresponding to the 2-plane tangent to X everywhere along L. Thus Q is singular—it is the cone over a conic curve, with vertex p. Away from the inverse image $\tilde{f}_L^{-1}(p)$, $\tilde{f}_L$ is as before one-to-one except on the locus of lines in X meeting L and as we shall see later, the vertex p of Q lies in the closure E_L of the image of this locus. Thus $\tilde{f}_L : \tilde{X}_L \to \mathbb{P}^3$ is again the blow-up of the curve E_L. (Recalling that a special line $L \subset X$ is to be counted among the lines meeting L, we may think of the line $\tilde{f}_L^{-1}(p)$ of points corresponding to normal vectors to $L \subset X$ in $\cap_{x \in L} T_x(X)$ as the "proper transform of L" itself in the blow-up $\tilde{X}_L$ of X).

In either case, then, we have seen that the birational map $f_L : X \to \mathbb{P}^3$ consists of the blow-up of the line $L \subset X$, followed by the blowing-down of the proper transforms in $\tilde{X}_L$ of the lines in X meeting L. In reverse, then, *the quadric line complex X is obtained by blowing up the quintic curve* $E_L \subset \mathbb{P}^3$ *and blowing down the proper transform of the quadric Q containing it* (*more precisely, the proper transforms of the family of trichords to* E_L) *to a curve.*

One question that arises in this context is: what is the hyperplane bundle on the curve E_L? Explicitly, we have seen that for every line $L \in A$ on the quadric line complex, we obtain an embedding $E_L \subset \mathbb{P}^3$ of the curve B. Accordingly, we may define a map

$$\rho : A = \mathcal{J}(B) \to \mathcal{J}(B)$$

by sending each line $L \in A$ to the class of the hyperplane bundle on $B \cong E_L \subset \mathbb{P}^3$; we ask now for a description of the map ρ.

To answer this question, we argue as follows. First, we note that the linear system associated to any divisor D of degree 5 on the curve B gives an embedding of B in $\mathbb{P}^3$ $\mathbb{P}^3$ as a quintic curve E_D (Section 1, Chapter 2). Second, since by Riemann-Roch

$$h^0(2D) = 10 - 2 + 1 = 9$$

and the vector space $H^0(\mathbb{P}^3, \mathcal{O}(2H))$ of quadrics on $\mathbb{P}^3$ has dimension 10, the restriction map

$$H^0(\mathbb{P}^3, \mathcal{O}(2H)) \to H^0(B, \mathcal{O}(2D))$$

must have a kernel—i.e., E_D must lie on a quadric surface Q in $\mathbb{P}^3$. Since

E_D is nondegenerate of degree 5, moreover, we see that the quadric Q is uniquely determined by E_D.

Suppose first that Q is a singular quadric, i.e., Q is the cone pC over a smooth conic curve C. Q then contains a single family of lines $\{L_q = \overline{pq}\}_{q \in C}$; since any two of these lines comprise a hyperplane section of Q, it follows that E_D contains the vertex p of Q and every line $L_q \subset Q$ meets E_D in two points other than p. But now the divisors

$$D_q = L_q \cdot E_D - p$$

form a linear system of degree 2, and so D_q must be the standard hyperelliptic divisor D_0 on B. Thus the divisor $D = H \cdot E_D$ on B is of the form

$$D = 2D_0 + p.$$

Conversely, suppose that D is of the form $2D_0 + p$ for some $p \in C$. Then the divisors

$$\{p + D_0 + D_\lambda\}_{D_\lambda \sim D_0}$$

are all hyperplane sections of $E_D \subset \mathbb{P}^3$, and so p must be collinear with the points of D_0. The lines $L_\lambda = \{\overline{pD_\lambda}\}_{D_\lambda \sim D_0}$, containing three points of E_D, must lie on the quadric Q; it follows that

$$Q = \cup L_\lambda$$

is a singular quadric with singular point p.

We have seen then that among all divisors D of degree 5 on B, the divisors for which $E_D = \iota_D(B)$ lies on a singular quadric are exactly those of the form $2D_0 + p$. Now the set of such divisors forms a translate of the theta-divisor Θ on $\mathcal{J}(B)$. But by what we have said, the inverse image $\rho'\Theta$ of lines $L \in A$ such that E_L lies on a singular quadric is just the divisor $\tilde{D} \subset A \cong \mathcal{J}(B)$, i.e., up to translation

$$\rho^*\Theta = \tilde{D} = m_2^*\Theta$$

it follows—at least in case B has no automorphisms other than the hyperelliptic—that, up to translation, *the map ρ is simply multiplication by two.*

One point that emerges from this discussion is this: since ρ is surjective, the quadric line complex X is determined by the curve B. Indeed, we can give an explicit recipe for the reconstruction of X from B: first embed B in $\mathbb{P}^3$ as a quintic E_D—by the above, it will not matter what divisor D we employ for the embedding. Then blow up $\mathbb{P}^3$ along the curve E_D, and blow down the family of proper transforms in $\tilde{\mathbb{P}}^3_{E_D}$ of the trichords of E_D into a curve. (Note that if D and D' are two divisors of degree 5 on B, not linearly equivalent, then $\tilde{\mathbb{P}}^3_{E_D}$ will not in general be isomorphic to $\tilde{\mathbb{P}}^3_{E_{D'}}$; they become isomorphic only after we blow down the trichords to E_D and $E_{D'}$, respectively). In particular, since B is itself determined by the Abelian variety A,

The quadric line complex X *is determined up to isomorphism by the abstract variety* A *of lines lying on it.*

Note, incidentally, that the preceding gives us another characterization of the special lines on X: for any line $L \subset X$ we have a C^∞ decomposition of vector bundles on L:

$$T(\mathbb{P}^5)|_L = N_{X/\mathbb{P}^5|_L} \oplus N_{L/X} \oplus T(L).$$

Now we have

$$c_1(T(\mathbb{P}^5))|_L = 6,$$
$$c_1(N_{X/\mathbb{P}^5|_L}) = c_1(N_{F/\mathbb{P}^5|_L}) + c_1(N_{G/\mathbb{P}^5|_L})$$
$$= 2 + 2 = 4,$$

and of course

$$c_1(T(L)) = 2;$$

it follows that

$$c_1(N_{L/S}) = 0.$$

Thus, by our classification (Section 3, Chapter 4) of vector bundles on $\mathbb{P}^1$, we can write

$$N_{L/X} = H^n \oplus H^{-n}, \qquad n \geqslant 0,$$

where H is the hyperplane bundle on $L \cong \mathbb{P}^1$. If L is nonspecial, then we have seen that

$$\mathbb{P}(N_{L/X}) = \mathbb{P}^1 \times \mathbb{P}^1$$

and it follows that $n = 0$, i.e., *the normal bundle of* L *in* X *is trivial.* On the other hand, if L is special, then $\mathbb{P}(N_{L/X})$ is the ruled surface $S_{0,2} = \mathbb{P}(H^m \oplus H^{m+2})$, and so

$$N_{L/X} = H \oplus H^{-1}.$$

Thus we see that *the special lines* L $\subset$ X *are exactly the lines in* X *having normal bundle* H $\oplus$ H^{-1} *in* X; *the nonspecial lines in* X *are exactly the lines having trivial normal bundle.*

If we use the intermediate Jacobian $J(X) = H^3(X, \mathbb{R}H^3(X, \mathbb{Z})$ defined on p. 331, then many of the results of this chapter may be summarized as follows:

The intermediate Jacobian J(X), *together with its principal polarization determined by the intersection form on* H^3(X, $\mathbb{Z}$), *is biholomorphic to the surface* A *of lines in* X *with the corresponding polarization on* A *being given by the incidence curve* B.

In general, if X is the transverse intersection of two smooth quadrics in $\mathbb{P}^{2n+1}$, then the set A of $\mathbb{P}^{n-1}$'s contain in X has the structure of an Abelian variety which may be identified with the middle intermediate Jacobian of X; a proof of this may be found in Ran Donagi, The variety of linear spaces on the intersection of two quadrics, to appear. The principally polarized Abelian variety determines the variety X so that we have a Torelli theorem—i.e., the Hodge structure of X determines the variety X.

Particular to the case $n=2$ is the Kummer surface S defined by taking the quotient of A by the involution $z \rightarrow -z$, and which we have identified geometrically as the surface in $\mathbb{P}^3$ defined by the condition that the conic $X_i p$ of lines in the quadric line complex passing through p should be singular. The Kummer surface S uniquely determines A and hence X: If we desingularize S to obtain a K-3 surface $\tilde{S}$ having a divisor $E = \sum_{i=1}^{16} E_i$ lying over the double points of S, then the class of E in $H^2(\tilde{S}, \mathbb{Z})$ is even so that we may construct a two-sheeted covering $\pi: \tilde{A} \rightarrow \tilde{S}$ branched over E. The curves $\tilde{C}_i = \pi^{-1}(C_i)$ are rational curves with $\tilde{C}_i^2 = -1$; blowing them down gives the Abelian surface A.

REFERENCES

The quadric line complex and its associated Kummer surface were extensively studied in the last century; a classic source is

F. Klein, Zur Theorie der Linencomplexe des ersten und zweiten Grades, *Math. Ann.*, Vol. 2 (1970), pp. 198–226.

It has reappeared in connection with the moduli of stable vector bundles over curves; the reference here is

M. S. Narasimhan and S. Ramanan, Moduli of vector bundles on a compact Riemann surface, *Ann. of Math.*, Vol. 89 (1969), pp. 14–51.

This paper contains the result that the Kummer surface associated to the quadric line is obtained from the Jacobian of the hyperelliptic curve defined by the pencil of quadrics.

Finally, an interesting general reference for threefolds and their intermediate Jacobians is

A. N. Turin, Five lectures on three-dimensional varieties, *Uspeki Math. Nauk.*, Vol. 27 (1972), pp. 4–50 (English translation: *Russian Math. Surveys*, Vol. 27 (1972), 1–53).

INDEX